Small Business Sourcebook

ISSN 0883-3397

Small Business Sourcebook

The Entrepreneur's Resource

THIRTIETH EDITION

Volume 6

General Small Business Resources
(Includes State and Federal Sections)

(Entries 55540-62191)

Sonya D. Hill
Project Editor

GALE
CENGAGE Learning

Detroit • New York • San Francisco • New Haven, Conn • Waterville, Maine • London

Small Business Sourcebook, 30th edition

Project Editor: Sonya D. Hill

Editorial Support Services: Charles Beaumont

Composition and Electronic Prepress: Gary Leach

Manufacturing: Rita Wimberley

© 2013 Gale, Cengage Learning

For product information and technology assistance, contact us at
Gale Customer Support, 1-800-877-4253.
For permission to use material from this text or product,
submit all requests online at **www.cengage.com/permissions.**
Further permissions questions can be emailed to
permissionrequest@cengage.com

Gale
27500 Drake Rd.
Farmington Hills, MI, 48331-3535

ISBN-13: 978-1-4144-7957-6 (set)
ISBN-10: 1-4144-7957-3 (set)
ISBN-13: 978-1-4144-7958-3 (vol. 1)
ISBN-10: 1-4144-7958-1 (vol. 1)
ISBN-13: 978-1-4144-7959-0 (vol. 2)
ISBN-10: 1-4144-7959-X (vol. 2)
ISBN-13: 978-1-4144-7960-6 (vol. 3)
ISBN-10: 1-4144-7960-3 (vol. 3)
ISBN-13: 978-1-4144-7961-3 (vol. 4)
ISBN-10: 1-4144-7961-1 (vol. 4)
ISBN-13: 978-1-4144-7962-0 (vol. 5)
ISBN-10: 1-4144-7962-X (vol. 5)
ISBN-13: 978-1-4144-7963-7 (vol. 6)
ISBN-10: 1-4144-7963-8 (vol. 6)

ISSN 0883-3397

Printed in the United States of America
1 2 3 4 5   17 16 15 14 13

Contents

The appeal of small business ownership remains perpetually entrenched in American culture as one of the most viable avenues for achieving the American Dream. To many entrepreneurs going into business for themselves represents financial independence, an increased sense of identity and self-worth, and the fulfillment of personal goals. Small business owners strive to make their mark in today's competitive marketplace by establishing healthy businesses that can, over time, become legacies handed down from one generation to the next. Entrepreneurs from each generation tackle the obstacles and adversities of the current business and economic climate to test their business savvy and generate opportunities. Today's entrepreneurs face many of the problems of their predecessors, as well as some distinctly new challenges.

With the rightsizing, downsizing, and reorganization of corporate America, many individuals have decided to confront the risks of developing and operating their own businesses. Small business ownership is rapidly becoming a viable alternative to what is perceived as an equally unstable corporate environment. These entrepreneurs, many of whom have firsthand experience with the problems and inefficiencies inherent in today's large corporations, seek to improve upon an archaic business model and to capitalize on their own ingenuity and strengths. Led by their zeal, many would-be entrepreneurs let their desire, drive, and determination overshadow the need for business knowledge and skill. Ironically, aids in obtaining these components of entrepreneurial success are widely available, easily accessible, and often free of charge.

Small Business Sourcebook (*SBS*) is a six-volume annotated guide to more than 21,310 listings of live and print sources of information designed to facilitate the start-up, development, and growth of specific small businesses, as well as over 26,280 similar listings on general small business topics. An additional 12,367 state-specific listings and over 2,220 U.S. federal government agencies and offices specializing in small business issues, programs, and assistance are also included. *SBS* covers 340 specific small business profiles and 99 general small business topics.

Features of This Edition

This edition of *Small Business Sourcebook* has been revised and updated, incorporating thousand of changes to names, addresses, contacts, and descriptions of listings from the previous edition.

Contents and Arrangement

The geographical scope of *SBS* encompasses the United States and Canada, with expanded coverage for resources pertaining to international trade and for resources that have a U.S. or Canadian distributor or contact. Internet sites that are maintained outside of the U.S. and Canada are also included if they contain relevant information for North American small businesses. Resources that do not relate specifically to small businesses are generally not included.

The information presented in *SBS* is grouped within four sections: Specific Small Business Profiles, General Small Business Topics, State Listings, and Federal Government Assistance. Detailed outlines of these sections may be found in the Users' Guide following this Introduction. Also included is a Master Index to Volumes 1 through 6.

Specific Small Business Profiles This section includes the following types of resources: start-up information, associations and other organizations, educational programs, directories of educational programs, reference works, sources of supply, statistical sources, trade periodicals, videocassettes/audiocassettes, trade shows and conventions, consultants, franchises and business opportunities, computerized databases, computer systems/software, Internet databases, libraries, and research centers-all arranged by business type. Entries range from Accounting Service to Word Processing Service, and include such businesses as Airbag Replacement Service Centers, Computer Consulting, Damage Restoration Service, and Web Site Design.

General Small Business Topics This section offers such resources as associations, books, periodicals, articles, pamphlets, educational programs, directories of educational programs, videocassettes/audiocassettes, trade shows and conventions, consultants, computerized databases, Internet databases, software, libraries, and research centers, arranged alphabetically by business topic.

State Listings Entries include government, academic, and commercial agencies and organizations, as well as select coverage of relevant state-specific publications; listings are arranged alphabetically by state, territory, and Canadian province. Some examples include small business development consultants, educational programs, financing and loan programs, better business bureaus, and chambers of commerce.

Federal Government Assistance Listings specializing in small business issues, programs, assistance, and policyare arranged alphabetically by U.S. government agency or office; regional or branch offices are listed alphabetically by state.

Master Index All entries in Volumes 1 through 6 are arranged in one alphabetic index for convenience.

Entries in *SBS* include (as appropriate andavailable):

- Organization, institution, or product name
- Contact information, including contact name, address and phone, toll-free, and fax numbers
- Author/editor, date(s), and frequency
- Availability, including price
- Brief description of purpose, services, or content
- Company and/or personal E-mail addresses
- Web site addresses

SBS also features the following:

Guide to Publishers—An alphabetic listing of 2,470 companies, associations, institutions, and individuals that publish the periodicals, directories, guidebooks, and other publications noted in the Small Business Profiles and General Topics sections. Users are provided with full contact information, including address, phone, fax,and e-mail and URL when available. The Guide to Publishers facilitates contact with publishers and provides a one- stop resource for valuable information.

Method of Compilation

SBS was compiled by consulting small business experts and entrepreneurs, as well as a variety of resources, including direct contact with the associations, organizations, and agencies through telephone surveys, Internet research, or through materials provided by those listees; government resources; and data obtained from other relevant Gale directories. *SBS* was reviewed by a team of small business advisors, all of whom have numerous years of expertise in small business counseling and identification of small business information resources. The last and perhaps most important resource we utilize is direct contact with our readers, who provide valuable comments and suggestions to improve our publication. *SBS* relies on these comprehensive market contacts to provide today's entrepreneurs with relevant, current, and accurate informationon all aspects of small business.

Available in Electronic Formats

Licensing. Small Business Sourcebook is available for licensing. The complete database is provided in a fielded format and is deliverable on such media as disk or CD-ROM. For more information, contact Gale's Business Development Group at1-800-877-GALE, or visit our website at www.gale.com/bizdev.

Comments and Suggestions Welcome

Associations, agencies, business firms, publishers, and other organizations that provide assistance and information to the small business community are encouraged to submit material about their programs, activities, services, or products. Comments and suggestions from users of this directory are also welcomed and appreciated. Please contact:

Project Editor
Small Business Sourcebook
Gale, Cengage Learning
27500 Drake Rd.
Farmington Hills, MI 48331-3535
Phone: (248) 699-4253
Fax: (248) 699-8070
E-mail: BusinessProductsgale.com
URL: www.gale.com

Small Business Sourcebook (*SBS*) provides information in a variety of forms and presentations for comprehensive coverage and ease of use. The directory contains four parts within two volumes:

- Specific Small Business Profiles
- General Small Business Topics
- State Listings
- Federal Government Assistance

Information on specific businesses is arranged by type of business; the many general topics that are of interest to the owners, operators, or managers of all small businesses are grouped in a separate section for added convenience. Users should consult the various sections to benefit fully from the information *SBS* offers. For example, an entrepreneur with a talent or interest in the culinary arts could peruse a number of specific small business profiles, such as Restaurant, Catering, Cooking School, Specialty Food/Wine Shop, Bakery/Doughnut Shop, Healthy Restaurant, or Candy/Chocolate Store. Secondly, the General Small Business Topics section could be consulted for any applicable subjects, such as Service Industry, Retailing, Franchising, and other relevant topics. Then, the appropriate state within the State Listings section would offer area programs and offices providing information and support to small businesses, including venture capital firms and small business development consultants. Finally, the Federal Government Assistance section could supply relevant government offices, such as procurement contacts.

Features Included in Volumes 1 through 3

List of Small Business Profiles. This list provides an alphabetic outline of the small businesses profiled, with cross-references for related profiles and for alternate names by which businesses may be identified. The page number for each profile is indicated.

Standard Industrial Classification (SIC) Codes for Profiled Small Businesses. This section lists four-digit SIC codes and corresponding classification descriptions for the small businesses profiled in this edition. The SIC system,

which organizes businesses by type, is a product of the Statistical Policy Division of the U.S. Office of Management and Budget. Statistical data produced by government, public, and private organizations is usually categorized according to SIC codes, thereby facilitating the collection, comparison, and analysis of data as well as providing a uniform method for presenting statistical information. Hence, knowing the SIC code for a particular small business increases access and the use of a variety of statistical data from many sources.

Guide to Publishers. This resource lists alphabetically the companies, associations, institutions, and individuals that publish the periodicals, directories, guidebooks, and other publications noted in the "Small Business Profiles" and "General Topics" sections. Users are provided with full contact information, including address, phone, fax, and e-mail and URL when available. The "Guide" facilitates contact with publishers and provides a one-stop resource for valuable information.

Glossary of Small Business Terms. This glossary defines nearly 400 small business terms, including financial, governmental, insurance, procurement, technical, and general business definitions. Cross-references and acronyms are also provided.

Small Business Profiles A-Z. A total of 340 small businesses is represented in volumes 1 through 3. Profiles are listed alphabetically by business name. Entries within each profile are arranged alphabetically by resource type, within up to 17 subheadings.These subheadings are detailed below:

- *Start-up Information*—Includes periodical articles, books, manuals, book excerpts, kits, and other sources of information. Entries offer title; publisher; address; phone, fax, toll-free numbers; company e-mail and URL addresses; and a description. Bibliographic data is provided for cited periodical articles whenever possible.

- *Associations and Other Oganizations*—Includes trade and professional associations whose members gather and disseminate information of interest to small business owners. Entries offer the association's name; address; phone, toll-free and fax numbers; company e-mail address; contact name; purpose and objective; a description of membership; telecommunication services; and a listing of its publications, including publishing frequency.

- *Educational Programs*—Includes university and college programs, schools, training opportunities, association seminars, correspondence courses, and other educational programs.Entries offer name of program or institution, sponsor name, address, phone, toll-free and fax numbers, e-mail and URL addresses; and description of program.

- *Directories of Educational Programs*—Includes directories and other publications that list educational programs. Entries offer name of publication; publisher name, address, and phone, toll-free and fax numbers; editor; frequency or date of publication; price; and description of contents, including directory arrangement and indexes.

- *Reference Works*—Includes handbooks, manuals, textbooks, guides, directories, dictionaries, encyclopedias, and other published reference materials. Entries offer name of publication; publisher name, address, and phone, toll-free and fax numbers; e-mail and URL addresses; and, when available, name of author or editor, publication year or frequency, and price. A brief description is often featured.

- *Sources of Supply*—Includes buyer's guides,directories, special issues of periodicals, and other publications that list sources of equipment, supplies, and services related to the operation of the profiled small business. Entries offer publication name; publisher name, address, and phone, toll-free and fax numbers; e-mail and URL addresses; and, when available, editor's name, frequency or publication year, and price. A brief description of the publication, including directory arrangement and indexes, is often provided.

- *Statistical Sources*—Includes books, reports, pamphlets, and other sources of statistical data of interest to an owner, operator or manager of the profiled small business, such as wage, salary, and compensation data; financial and operating ratios; prices and costs; demographics; and other statistical information. Entries offer publication/data source name; publisher (if applicable); address; phone, toll-free and fax numbers of data source; publication date or frequency; and price. A brief description of the publication/data source is often provided.

- *Trade Periodicals*—Includes trade journals, newsletters, magazines, and other serials that offer information about the management and operation of the profiled small business. Such periodicals often contain industry news; trends and developments; reviews; articles about new equipment and supplies;

and other information related to business operations. Entries offer publication name; publisher name, address, phone, toll-free and fax numbers, and e-mail and URL addresses; editor name; publication frequency; andprice. A brief description of the publication's content is also included, when known.

- *Videocassettes/Audiocassettes*—Includes videocassettes, audiocassettes, and other audiovisual media offering information on the profiled small business. Entries offer program title; distributor name, address, phone, toll-free and fax numbers, and e-mail and URL addresses; description of program; release date; price; and format(s).

- *Trade Shows and Conventions*—Includes tradeshows, exhibitions, expositions, conventions, and other industry meetings that provide prospective and existing business owners with the opportunity to meet and exchange information with their peers, review commercial exhibits, establish business or sales contacts, and attend educational programs. Entries offer event name; sponsor or management company name, address, phone, toll-free and fax numbers, and e-mail and URL addresses; a description of the event, including audience, frequency, principal exhibits, and dates and locations of event for as many years ahead as provided by the event's sponsor.

- *Consultants*—Includes consultants and consulting organizations that provide services specifically related to the profiled small business. Entries offer individual consultant or consulting organization name, address, and phone, toll-free and fax numbers; company and individual e-mail addresses; and a brief description of consulting services. (For e-mail and URL addresses, see the Small Business Development Consultants subheadings in the State Listings section in Volume 2.)

- *Franchises and Business Opportunities*—Includes companies granting franchise licenses for enterprises falling within the scope of the profiled small business, as well as other non-franchised business opportunities that operate within a given network or system. Entries offer franchise name, address, phone, toll-free and fax numbers, and e-mail and URL addresses, as well as a description of the franchise or business opportunity, which has been expanded whenever possible to include the number of existing franchises, the founding date of the franchise, franchise fees, equity capital requirements, royalty fees, any managerial assistance offered, and available training.

- *Computerized Databases*—Includes diskettes, magnetic tapes, CD-ROMs, online systems, and other computer-readable databases. Entries offer database name; producer name, address, phone, toll-free and fax numbers, e-mail and URL addresses; description; and available format(s), including vendor name.

(Many university and public libraries offer online information retrieval services that provide searches of databases, including those listed in this category.)

- **Computer Systems/Software**—Includes softwareand computerized business systems designed to assist in the operation of the profiled small business. Entries offer name of the software or system; publisher name, address, phone, toll-free and fax-numbers; price; and description.

- **Libraries**—Includes libraries and special collections that contain material especially applicable to the profiled small business. Entries offer library or collection name; parent organization (where applicable); address; phone, toll-free and fax numbers; e-mail and URL addresses; contact name and title; scope of collection; and description of holdings, subscriptions, and services.

- **Research Centers**—Includes university-related and independently operated research institutes and information centers that generate, through their research programs, data related to the operation of the profiled small business. Also listed are associations and other business-related organizations that conduct research programs. Entries offer name of organization; address; phone, toll-free and fax numbers; company web site address; contact name and personale-mail; a description of principal fields of research or services; publications, including title and frequency; and related conferences.

Features Included in Volumes 2 through 6

General Small Business Topics. This section offers chapters on different topics in the operation of any small business, for example, venture capital and other funding, or compensation. Chapters are listed alphabetically by small business topic; entries within each chapter are arranged alphabetically, within up to 14 subheadings, by resource type:

- **Associations and Other Organizations**—Includes trade and professional associations that gather and disseminate information of interest to small business owners. Entries offer the association's name; address; phone, toll-free and fax numbers; organization e-mail and URL addresses; contact name;purpose and objectives; a description of membership; telecommunication services; and a listing of its publications, including publishing frequency.

- **Educational Programs**—Includes university and college programs, schools, training opportunities, association seminars, correspondence courses, and other educational programs. Entries offer name of program or institution, sponsor name, address, phone, toll-free and fax numbers, e-mail and URL addresses, and description of program.

- **Directories of Educational Programs**—Includes directories and other publications that list educational programs. Entries offer name of publication; publisher name, address, phone, toll-free and fax numbers, and e-mail and URL addresses; editor; frequency or date of publication; price; and description of contents, including arrangement and indexes.

- **Reference Works**—Includes articles, handbooks, manuals, textbooks, guides, directories, dictionaries, encyclopedias, and other published reference materials. Entries offertitle of article, including bibliographic information; name of publication; publisher name, address, phone, toll-free and fax numbers, and e-mail and URL addresses; and, when available, name of author oreditor, publication year or frequency, and price. A brief descriptionis often featured.

- **Sources of Supply**—Includes buyer's guides,directories, special issues of periodicals, and other publications that list sources of equipment, supplies, and services. Entries offer publication name; publisher name, address, phone, toll-free and fax numbers, and e-mail and URL addresses; editor's name, frequency or publication year, price, and a brief description of the publication, when available.

- **Statistical Sources**—Includes books, reports, pamphlets, and other sources of statistical data of interest to an owner, operator, or manager of a small business, such as wage, salary, and compensation data; financial and operating ratios; prices and costs; demographics; and other statistical information. Entries offer publication/data source name; publisher (if applicable); address; phone, toll-free and fax numbers of data source; publication date or frequency; and price. A brief description is often provided.

- **Trade Periodicals**—Includes journals, newsletters, magazines, and other serials. Entries offer name of publication; publisher name, address, phone, toll-free and fax numbers, and e-mail and URL addresses; and name of editor, frequency, and price.A brief description of the periodical's content is included when known.

- **Videocassettes/Audiocassettes**—Includes videocassettes, audiocassettes, and other audiovisual media. Entries offer program title; distributor name, address, phone, toll-free and fax numbers, and e-mail and URL addresses; price; description of program; release date; and format(s).

- **Trade Shows and Conventions**—Includes tradeshows, exhibitions, expositions, seminars, and conventions. Entries offer event name; sponsor or management company name, address, phone, toll-free and fax numbers, and e-mail and URL addresses; frequency of event; and dates and locations of the event for as many years ahead as known.

- **Consultants**—Includes consultants and consulting organizations. Entries offer individual consultant or-consulting organization name, address, and phone, toll-free and fax numbers; company and individual e-mail addresses; and a brief description of consulting services. (See also Consultants in the State Listings section.)

- **Computerized Databases**—Includes diskettes, CD-ROMs, magnetic tape, online systems and other computer-readable databases. Entries offer database name; producer, address, phone, toll-free and fax numbers, and e-mail and URL addresses; description; and available format(s), including vendor name. (Many university and public libraries offer online information retrieval services that provide searches of databases, including those listed in this category.)

- **Computer Systems/Software**—Includes software and computerized business systems. Entries offer name of the software or system; publisher name, address, phone, toll-free and fax numbers, and e-mail and URL addresses; price; and description.

- **Libraries**—Includes libraries and special collections that contain material applicable to the small business topic. Entries offer library or collection name, parent organization (where applicable), address, phone and fax numbers, e-mail and URL addresses, scope of collection, and description of holdings and services.

- **Research Centers**— Includes university-related and independently operated research institutes and information centers that generate, through their research programs, data related to specific small business topics. Entries offer name of organization, address, phone, toll-free and fax numbers, e-mail and URL addresses, a description of principal fields of research or services, and related conferences.

State Listings. This section lists various sources of information and assistance available within given states, territories, and Canadian provinces; entries include governmental, academic, and commercial agencies, and are arranged alphabetically within up to 15 subheadings by resource type:

- **Small Business Development Center Lead Office**— Includes the lead small business development center (SBDC) for each state.

- **Small Business Development Centers**—Includes any additional small business development centers (SBDC) in the state, territory, or province. SBDCs provide support services to small businesses, including individual counseling, seminars, conferences, and learning center activities.

- **Small Business Assistance Programs**—Includes state small business development offices and other programs offering assistance to small businesses.

- **SCORE Offices**—Includes SCORE office(s) for each state. The Service Corps of Retired Executives Association (SCORE), a volunteer program sponsored by the Small Business Administration, offers counseling, workshops, and seminars across the U.S. for small business entrepreneurs.

- **Better Business Bureaus**—Includes various better business bureaus within each state. By becoming a member of the local Better Business Bureau, a small business owner can increase the prestige and credibility of his or her business within the community, as well as make valuable business contacts.

- **Chambers of Commerce**—Includes various chambers of commerce within each state. Chambers of Commerce are valuable sources of small business advice and information; often, local chambers sponsor SCORE counseling several times per month for a small fee, seminars, conferences, and other workshops to its members. Also, by becoming a member of the local Chamber of Commerce, a small business owner can increase the prestige and credibility of his or herbusiness within the community, as well as make valuable business contacts.

- **Minority Business Assistance Programs**—Includes minority business development centers and other sources of assistance for minority-owned business.

- **Financing and Loan Programs**—Includes venture capital firms, small business investment companies (SBIC), minority enterprise small business investment companies (MESBIC), and other programs that provide funding to qualified small businesses.

- **Procurement Assistance Programs**—Includes state services such as counseling, set-asides, and sheltered-market bidding, which are designed to aid small businesses in bidding on government contracts.

- **Incubators/Research and Technology Parks**—Includes small business incubators, which provide newly established small business owners with work sites, business services, training, and consultation; also includes research and technology parks, which sponsor research and facilitate commercialization of new technologies.

- **Educational Programs**—Includes university and college programs, as well as those sponsored by other organizations that offer degree, nondegree, certificate, and correspondence programs in entrepreneurship and in small business development.

- **Legislative Assistance**—Includes committees, subcommittees, and joint committees of each state's senate and house of representatives that are concerned with small business issues and regulations.

- **Consultants**—Includes consultants and consulting firms offering expertise in small business development.

- **Publications**—Includes publications related to small business operations within the profiled state.

- **Publishers**—Includes publishers operating in or for the small business arena within the profiled state.

Federal Government Assistance. This section lists federal government agencies and offices, many with additional listings for specific offices, as well as regional or district branches. Main agencies or offices are listed alphabetically; regional, branch, ordistrict offices are listed after each main office or agency.

Master Index. This index provides an alphabetic listing of all entries contained in Volumes 1 throgh 6. Citations are referenced by their entry numbers. Publication titles are rendered in italics.

Acknowledgements

The editors would like to extend sincere thanks to the following members of the Small Business Sourcebook advisory board for their expert guidance, recommendations, and suggestions for the ongoing development of this title:

Susan C. Awe
Assistant Director,
William J. Parish Memorial Business Library

Jill Clever
Business Technology Specialist,
Toledo-Lucas County Public Library

Jules Matsoff
District Manager,
Service Corps of Retired Executives (SCORE) Milwaukee
* Chapter*

Ken MacKenzie
President,
Southeast Business Appraisal

The editors would also like to thank the individuals from associations and other organizations who provided information for the compilation of this directory.

SMALL BUSINESS ASSISTANCE PROGRAMS

55540 ■ Council for Entrepreneurial Development
Alexandria Technology Center
100 Capitola Dr., Ste. 101
Durham, NC 27713
Ph: (919)549-7500
Fax: (919)549-7405
Co. E-mail: info@cednc.org
URL: http://www.cednc.org
Contact: Joan Siefert Rose, President
Description: Council of entrepreneurs, business and financial service providers, public policy makers, and university faculty, united to promote the enhancement of entrepreneurial development in North Carolina through monthly programs, newsletters, consultation programs, membership directories, seminars and workshops, and an annual venture capital conference.

55541 ■ East Carolina University - Center for Applied Technology
Technology Enterprise Center
Greenville, NC 27858-4353
Ph: (252)328-6708
Fax: (252)328-1545
Co. E-mail: gaulandd@mail.ecu.edu
URL: http://www.ecu.edu/rds/CAT/
Description: Provides technical and scientific assistance through contract research for industries, businesses, and municipalities.

55542 ■ Frank Hawkins Kenan Institute of Private Enterprise
Campus Box 3440
The Kenan Center
Chapel Hill, NC 27599-3440
Ph: (919)962-8201
Fax: (919)962-8202
Co. E-mail: kenan_institute@unc.edu
URL: http://www.kenan-flagler.unc.edu/KI/
Contact: John D. Kasarda, Director
Description: National center for private enterprise research focusing on entrepreneurial development, new venture management, and coursework development.

55543 ■ North Carolina Community College System - Small Business Center Network
Caswell Bldg.
200 W Jones St.
Raleigh, NC 27603-5003
Ph: (919)807-7100
Fax: (919)807-7164
Co. E-mail: sbcndirector@nccommunitycolleges.edu
URL: http://www.ncccs.cc.nc.us/Business_and_Industry
Contact: George Millsaps, Director
Description: Offers consultations and referrals, including business planning. Operates a resource and information center containing printed and electronic resources. Sponsors business and computer

expos in cooperation with business and community organizations. Offers workshops to potential and existing small businesses on business topics, including business plans, basics of business, motivation, management, financial planning, computer and software applications, customer relations, farm recordkeeping, and franchising.

55544 ■ North Carolina Department of Agriculture and Consumers Services, Marketing Division
2 W Edenton St., Rm.402
Raleigh, NC 27601
Ph: (919)733-7887
Fax: (919)733-0999
URL: http://www.ncagr.com/markets/
Contact: Tom Slade, Director
Description: Provides small businesses with information on doing business internationally.

55545 ■ North Carolina Department of Commerce - Business/Industry Development Division
4301 Mail Service Ctr.
Raleigh, NC 27699-4301
Ph: (919)733-4151
Fax: (919)733-9265
URL: http://www.nccommerce.com/en
Contact: Roger J. Shackleford, Executive Director
Description: Assists international, national, and state firms in locating new or expanded facilities in North Carolina.

55546 ■ North Carolina Rural Economic Development Center
4021 Carya Dr.
Raleigh, NC 27610
Ph: (919)250-4314
Fax: (919)250-4325
Co. E-mail: info@ncruralcenter.org
URL: http://www.ncruralcenter.org
Contact: Valerie Lee
Description: Provides and is involved in research and demonstration efforts to identify new ideas, strategies, or programs that will generate economic development in rural North Carolina.

55547 ■ North Carolina Small Business Partnership
5003 Mail Service Ctr.
Raleigh, NC 27699-5003
Ph: (919)807-7100
Fax: (919)807-7164
Co. E-mail: dickens@ncccs.cc.nc.us
URL: http://www.nccs.cc.nc.us
Contact: Willa Dickens, Director
Description: Consists of eleven state and state-supported organizations united to promote cooperation and collaboration in meeting economic concerns. Purposes include serving as an advocate for smaller business interests, and informing public policy makers of small business assistance resources and services.

55548 ■ North Carolina Small Business and Technology Development Center
5 W. Hargett St., Ste. 600
Raleigh, NC 27601-1348
Ph: (919)715-7272
Free: 800-621-0008
Fax: (915)715-7777
Co. E-mail: info@sbtdc.org
URL: http://www.sbtdc.org
Contact: Scott Daugherty, Executive Director
Description: Goals are to increase job opportunities and capital investments; to assist in the creation or retention of jobs; to expand economic opportunities; to reduce the incidence of business failure; to assist in community development efforts; and to assist in the development, growth, and expansion of commercial, industrial, and business activities.

55549 ■ North Carolina State University - Industrial Extension Service
Campus Box 7902
Raleigh, NC 27695-7902
Ph: (919)515-2358
Fax: (919)515-6159
Co. E-mail: ies_services@ncsu.edu
URL: http://www.ies.ncsu.edu
Description: Provides assistance to North Carolina industries to help them have a competitive advantage through better utilization of engineering technologies.

SCORE OFFICES

55550 ■ Coastal Carolina SCORE
3615 Arendell St.
Morehead City, NC 28557
Ph: (252)222-6126
Fax: (252)222-6124
URL: http://coastalcarolina.score.org
Description: Promotes business and community development in Morehead City, NC. Conducts business education seminars and workshops to those wanting to start a business. **Founded:** 1964.

55551 ■ Durham SCORE
Co. E-mail: alnabb@aol.com

55552 ■ East Carolina SCORE
Co. E-mail: score@mideastcom.org

55553 ■ Outer Banks SCORE
Co. E-mail: mail@score497.org

55554 ■ SCORE Asheboro/Randolph
c/o Asheboro/Randolph Chamber of Commerce
317 E Dixie Dr.
Asheboro, NC 27203
Ph: (336)626-2626
Fax: (336)626-7077
URL: http://asheboro.score.org
URL(s): chamber.asheboro.com. **Description:** Provides public service to America by offering small business advice and training.

55555 ■ SCORE Asheville
Federal Bldg., Rm. 259
151 Patton Ave.
Asheville, NC 28801
Ph: (828)271-4786
Fax: (828)271-4786
Co. E-mail: info@ashevillescore.org
URL: http://www.ashevillescore.org
Description: Serves as volunteer program in which working and retired business management professionals provide free business counseling to men and women who are considering starting a small business, encountering problems with their business, or expanding their business. Offers free one-on-one counseling, online counseling and low cost workshops on a variety of business topics. **Founded:** 1966.

55556 ■ SCORE Chapel Hill
Chapel Hill - Carrboro Chamber of Commerce Bldg.
104 S Estes Dr.
Chapel Hill, NC 27514
Ph: (919)968-6894
Fax: (919)967-7000
Co. E-mail: info@scorechapelhill.org
URL: http://www.scorechapelhill.org
Description: Provides in-depth, industry-specific business assistance to evaluate a business idea or plan, stimulates business growth and ensure long-term stability. **Founded:** 1981.

55557 ■ SCORE Charlotte
One Fairview Center
6302 Fairview Rd., Ste. 300
Charlotte, NC 28210
Ph: (704)344-6576
Fax: (704)344-6769
Co. E-mail: charlottescore47@carolina.rr.com
URL: http://www.charlottescore.org
Contact: Mr. James Mortimer, Chairman
URL(s): charlotte.score.org. **Description:** Serves as volunteer program in which working and retired business management professionals provide free business counseling to men and women who are considering starting a small business, encountering problems with their business, or expanding their business. Offers free one-on-one counseling, online counseling and low cost workshops on a variety of business topics.

55558 ■ SCORE Down East
233 Middle St.
New Bern, NC 28560
Ph: (252)633-6688
Fax: (252)633-9608
URL: http://downeast.score.org
Description: Provides entrepreneur education for the formation, growth and success of small businesses in the area. **Founded:** 1988.

55559 ■ SCORE Greensboro
1451 S Elm Eugene St., Ste. 2306
Greensboro, NC 27406
Ph: (336)333-5399
Co. E-mail: greens025score@scoregso.org
URL: http://www.scoregso.org
Contact: Dan Lyons, Chairman
Description: Serves as volunteer program in which working and retired business management professionals provide free business counseling to men and women who are considering starting a small business, encountering problems with their business, or expanding their business. Offers free one-on-one counseling, online counseling and low cost workshops on a variety of business topics.

55560 ■ SCORE Hendersonville
140 4th Ave. W
Hendersonville, NC 28792
Ph: (828)693-8702
Co. E-mail: hcounselors@scorewnc.org
Description: Serves as volunteer program in which working and retired business management professionals provide free business counseling to men and women who are considering starting a small business, encountering problems with their business, or expanding their business. Offers free one-on-one counseling, online counseling and low cost workshops on a variety of business topics.

55561 ■ SCORE High Point
c/o High Point Chamber of Commerce
1634 N Main St.
High Point, NC 27262
Ph: (336)882-8625
Fax: (336)889-9499
Co. E-mail: contact@highpointscore.org
URL: http://www.highpointscore.org
Description: Serves as volunteer program in which working and retired business management professionals provide free business counseling to men and women who are considering starting a small business, encountering problems with their business, or expanding their business. Offers free one-on-one counseling, online counseling and low cost workshops on a variety of business topics.

55562 ■ SCORE Raleigh
300 Fayetteville St.
Mall Century PO Bldg., Ste. 306
Raleigh, NC 27602
Ph: (919)856-4739
Fax: (919)856-4466
Co. E-mail: contact.raleigh@scorevolunteer.org
URL: http://raleigh.score.org
Contact: William C. Zinno, Co-Chairperson
Description: Serves as volunteer program in which working and retired business management professionals provide free business counseling to men and women who are considering starting a small business, encountering problems with their business, or expanding their business. Offers free one-on-one counseling, online counseling and low cost workshops on a variety of business topics.

55563 ■ SCORE Sandhills Area - No. 364
c/o Chamber of Commerce
10677 US 15-501 Hwy.
Southern Pines, NC 28387
Ph: (910)692-3926
Co. E-mail: contact@sandhillsscore.org
URL: http://sandhillsscore.org
Description: Serves as volunteer program in which working and retired business management professionals provide free business counseling to men and women who are considering starting a small business, encountering problems with their business, or expanding their business. Offers free one-on-one counseling, online counseling and low cost workshops on a variety of business topics.

55564 ■ SCORE Wilmington
4010 Oleander Dr.
Browning Plz. 2
Wilmington, NC 28403
Ph: (910)452-5395
Fax: (910)452-5369
Co. E-mail: counselor@wilmingtonscore.org
URL: http://www.wilmingtonscore.org
Description: Serves as volunteer program in which working and retired business management professionals provide free business counseling to men and women who are considering starting a small business, encountering problems with their business, or expanding their business. Offers free one-on-one counseling, online counseling and low cost workshops on a variety of business topics.

BETTER BUSINESS BUREAUS

55565 ■ Better Business Bureau of Asheville/ Western North Carolina
112 Executive Park
Asheville, NC 28801
Ph: (828)253-2392
Fax: (828)252-5039
URL: http://www.asheville.bbb.org
Contact: Ms. Norma Messer, President
Description: Seeks to promote and foster the highest ethical relationship between businesses and the public through voluntary self-regulation, consumer and business education, and service excellence. Provides information to help consumers and businesses make informed purchasing decisions and avoid costly scams and frauds; settles consumer complaints through arbitration and other means.

55566 ■ Better Business Bureau of Eastern North Carolina
5540 Munford Rd., Ste. 130
Raleigh, NC 27612
Ph: (919)277-4222
Free: 800-222-0950
Fax: (919)277-4221
Co. E-mail: info@raleigh.bbb.org
URL: http://easternnc.bbb.org
Contact: David G. Mallen, Deputy Director
Description: Promotes ethics in the business community. Provides information to consumers regarding the reliability of area businesses. Assists in resolving disputes between businesses and consumers. Encourages adherence to the Code of Advertising. Conducts educational programs. **Founded:** 1971. **Publications:** *BusinessLine* (Monthly).

55567 ■ Better Business Bureau of Northwest North Carolina
500 W 5th St., Ste. 202
Winston-Salem, NC 27101-2728
Ph: (336)725-8348
Free: 800-777-8348
Fax: (336)777-3727
Co. E-mail: info@nwncbbb.com
URL: http://nwnc.bbb.org
Contact: David W. Dalrymple, President
Description: Seeks to promote and foster the highest ethical relationship between businesses and the public through voluntary self-regulation, consumer and business education, and service excellence. Provides information to help consumers and businesses make informed purchasing decisions and avoid costly scams and frauds; settles consumer complaints through arbitration and other means. **Founded:** 1960.

55568 ■ Better Business Bureau of Southern Piedmont
13860 Ballantyne Corporate Pl., Ste. 225
Charlotte, NC 28277
Ph: (704)927-8611
Free: 877-317-7236
Fax: (704)927-8615
Co. E-mail: info@charlotte.bbb.org
URL: http://charlotte.bbb.org
Contact: Tom Bartholomy, President
Description: Seeks to promote and foster the highest ethical relationship between businesses and the public through voluntary self-regulation, consumer and business education, and service excellence. Provides information to help consumers and businesses make informed purchasing decisions and avoid costly scams and frauds; settles consumer complaints through arbitration and other means.

55569 ■ *BusinessLine*
5540 Munford Rd., Ste. 130
Raleigh, NC 27612
Ph: (919)277-4222
Free: 800-222-0950
Fax: (919)277-4221
Co. E-mail: info@raleigh.bbb.org
URL: http://easternnc.bbb.org
Contact: David G. Mallen, Deputy Director
Released: Monthly **Price:** $15.

CHAMBERS OF COMMERCE

55570 ■ *Action*
PO Box 3829
Durham, NC 27702-3829
Ph: (919)328-8700
Fax: (919)688-8351
Co. E-mail: info@durhamchamber.org
URL: http://www.durhamchamber.org
Contact: Casey Steinbacher, President
Released: Monthly

55571 ■ Alamance County Area Chamber of Commerce
PO Box 450
Burlington, NC 27216-0450
Ph: (336)228-1338

Fax: (336)228-1330
Co. E-mail: info@alamancechamber.com
URL: http://www.alamancechamber.com
Contact: Mac Williams, President
Description: Promotes business and community development in Alamance County, NC. **Publications:** *Industrial Profile/Directory* (Annual); *Membership Directory and Buyer's Guide* (Annual).

55572 ■ Alexander County Chamber of Commerce (ACCC)
16 W Main Ave.
Taylorsville, NC 28681
Ph: (828)632-8141
Fax: (828)632-1096
Co. E-mail: chamberasst@alexandercountychamber. com
URL: http://www.alexandercountychamber.com
Contact: Renee Meade, President
Description: Promotes business and community development in Alexander County, NC. **Founded:** 1960. **Publications:** *The Informer* (Monthly).

55573 ■ Alleghany Business Directory
58 S Main St.
Sparta, NC 28675
Ph: (336)372-5473
Free: 800-372-5473
Fax: (336)245-9601
Co. E-mail: info@sparta-nc.com
URL: http://www.sparta-nc.com
Contact: Vickie Scott, President
Released: Periodic

55574 ■ Alleghany County Chamber of Commerce (ACCC)
58 S Main St.
Sparta, NC 28675
Ph: (336)372-5473
Free: 800-372-5473
Fax: (336)245-9601
Co. E-mail: info@sparta-nc.com
URL: http://www.sparta-nc.com
Contact: Vickie Scott, President
Description: Promotes business and community development in Alleghany County, NC and operates visitor center. Sponsors Choose and Cut Christmas Tree Day and Mountain Heritage Festival. **Founded:** 1983. **Publications:** *Alleghany Business Directory* (Periodic); *Chamber Views* (Monthly).

55575 ■ Andrews Chamber of Commerce
PO Box 800
Andrews, NC 28901
Ph: (828)321-3584
Co. E-mail: info@andrewschamber.com
URL: http://www.andrewschambercommerce.com
Contact: Bob Ferreira, Executive Director
Description: Strives to advance the general welfare and prosperity of the Town of Andrews. Works toward the betterment of the community and endeavors to improve the economic, civic, environmental, cultural, industrial, educational, agricultural, commercial, professional, recreational, and travel and tourism interest of the area. **Founded:** 1985.

55576 ■ Angier Chamber of Commerce (ACC)
24 E Depot St.
Angier, NC 27501
Ph: (919)639-2500
Fax: (919)639-8826
Co. E-mail: angiercc@angierchamber.org
URL: http://www.angierchamber.org
Contact: Cindy P. Hunter, Executive Director
Description: Promotes business and community development in Angier, NC. **Founded:** 1956. **Publications:** *Chamber Update* (Monthly).

55577 ■ Annual Directory and Economic Data Book
260 Town Hall Dr., Ste. A
Morrisville, NC 27560
Ph: (919)463-7150
Fax: (919)439-0212
Co. E-mail: chamber@morrisvillenc.com
URL: http://morrisvillechamber.org
Contact: Carlotta Ungaro, President
Released: Annual

55578 ■ Anson County
107-A E Wade St.
Wadesboro, NC 28170
Ph: (704)694-4181
Fax: (704)694-3830
Co. E-mail: ansonchamber@windstream.net
URL: http://www.ansoncounty.org
Contact: Ashlie Jones, Chairperson
Released: Biennial

55579 ■ Anson County Chamber of Commerce (ACCC)
107-A E Wade St.
Wadesboro, NC 28170
Ph: (704)694-4181
Fax: (704)694-3830
Co. E-mail: ansonchamber@windstream.net
URL: http://www.ansoncounty.org
Contact: Ashlie Jones, Chairperson
Description: Seeks to promote and preserve the business climate and quality of life for the general welfare of all citizens of Anson County and members through diverse leadership and a shared vision of excellence. **Founded:** 1963. **Publications:** *Anson County* (Biennial); *Chamberlines* (Monthly). **Educational Activities:** Anson County Chamber of Commerce Board meeting (Monthly). **Awards:** W. Dunlop Covington Award for Community Service (Annual).

55580 ■ Apex Chamber of Commerce
220 N Salem St.
Apex, NC 27502
Ph: (919)362-6456
Free: 800-345-4504
Fax: (919)362-9050
Co. E-mail: info@apexchamber.com
URL: http://www.apexchamber.com
Contact: Graham Wilson, Executive Director
Description: Promotes business and community development in the Apex, NC area. **Founded:** 1958. **Publications:** *The Chamber Express* (Monthly). **Awards:** Business Appreciation Award (Annual); Citizen of the Year (Annual).

55581 ■ Archdale-Trinity Chamber of Commerce (ATCC)
213 Balfour Dr.
Archdale, NC 27263
Ph: (336)434-2073
Fax: (336)431-5845
Co. E-mail: info@archdaletrinitychamber.com
URL: http://www.archdaletrinitychamber.com
Contact: Beverly M. Nelson, President
Description: Promotes business and community development in Archdale and Trinity, NC. Conducts seminars and training programs. **Founded:** 1982. **Publications:** *Chamber Voice*; *Membership Resources Guide*. **Educational Activities:** Bush Hill Heritage Festival (Annual); Members Golf Tournament (Annual). **Telecommunication Services:** beverly@archdaletrinitychamber.com.

55582 ■ The Architect
123 N Center St.
Mount Olive, NC 28365
Ph: (919)658-3113
Fax: (919)658-3125
Co. E-mail: president@mountolivechamber.com
URL: http://www.moachamber.com
Contact: Lynn Williams, Chairperson
Released: Quarterly **Price:** free.

55583 ■ Ashe
303 E Second St.
West Jefferson, NC 28694
Ph: (336)846-9550
Free: 888-343-2743
Fax: (336)246-8671
Co. E-mail: tourism@ashechamber.com
URL: http://www.ashechamber.com
Contact: Cabot Hamilton, Executive Director
Released: Annual

55584 ■ Ashe County Chamber of Commerce and Visitors Center
303 E Second St.
West Jefferson, NC 28694
Ph: (336)846-9550
Free: 888-343-2743

Fax: (336)246-8671
Co. E-mail: tourism@ashechamber.com
URL: http://www.ashechamber.com
Contact: Cabot Hamilton, Executive Director
Description: Strives to ensure the economic health of the local community by nurturing business growth and encouraging economic development. **Publications:** *Ashe* (Annual); *Ashe* (Annual). **Telecommunication Services:** info@ashechamber.com.

55585 ■ Asheboro/Randolph Chamber of Commerce
317 E Dixie Dr.
Asheboro, NC 27203
Ph: (336)626-2626
Fax: (336)626-7077
Co. E-mail: chamber@asheboro.com
URL: http://chamber.asheboro.com
Contact: Kim Markham, Chairman
Description: Aims to preserve the competitive enterprise system of business and to promote business and community growth and development. **Publications:** *Images of Asheboro/Randolph* (Annual); *Update* (Monthly); *Images of Asheboro/Randolph*. **Educational Activities:** Business After Hours (Monthly). **Telecommunication Services:** gusler@asheboro.com.

55586 ■ Asheville Area Chamber of Commerce
PO Box 1010
Asheville, NC 28802-1010
Ph: (828)258-6114
Fax: (828)251-0926
Co. E-mail: member@ashevillechamber.org
URL: http://www.ashevillechamber.org
Contact: Kit Cramer, President
E-mail: kcramer@ashevillechamber.org
Description: Promotes business and community development in the Asheville, NC area. Conducts local festivals. **Founded:** 1898. **Publications:** *Asheville Report* (Monthly); *Industrial Directory* (Periodic); *Major Employers' Directory* (Annual); *Membership Directory*; *Buncombe County Major Employers Directory*; *Western North Carolina Industrial Directory*. **Awards:** Manufacturing Leadership Award (Annual); Sky High Growth Award (Monthly); Small Business Leader of the Year (Annual); Small Business of the Month (Monthly). **Telecommunication Services:** contactus@exploreasheville.com.

55587 ■ Asheville Report
PO Box 1010
Asheville, NC 28802-1010
Ph: (828)258-6114
Fax: (828)251-0926
Co. E-mail: member@ashevillechamber.org
URL: http://www.ashevillechamber.org
Contact: Kit Cramer, President
E-mail: kcramer@ashevillechamber.org
Released: Monthly

55588 ■ At Work
204 E Innes St.
Salisbury, NC 28145-0559
Ph: (704)633-4221
Fax: (704)639-1200
Co. E-mail: info@rowanchamber.com
URL: http://www.rowanchamber.com
Released: Monthly

55589 ■ Ayden Chamber of Commerce
PO Box 31
Ayden, NC 28513
Ph: (252)746-2266
Co. E-mail: chamber@ayden.com
URL: http://www.aydenchamber.com
Contact: Stacy Gaskins, Executive Director
Description: Promotes business and community development in Ayden, NC. **Founded:** 1981. **Publications:** *Chamber News* (Bimonthly). **Awards:** Best Christmas Decoration (Annual); Business of the Year (Annual); Citizen of the Year (Annual); Volunteer of the Year (Annual).

55590 ■ Beech Mountain Area Chamber of Commerce
403-A Beech Mountain Pkwy.
Beech Mountain, NC 28604

Ph: (828)387-9283
Free: 800-468-5506
Co. E-mail: chamber@beechmtn.com
URL: http://beechmountainchamber.com
Contact: Peggy Coscia, Executive Director
Description: Promotes business and community development in Beech Mountain, NC area.

55591 ■ Belhaven Community Chamber of Commerce
125 W Main St.
Belhaven, NC 27810-0147
Ph: (252)943-3770
Fax: (252)943-3769
Co. E-mail: belhaveninfo@gotricounty.com
URL: http://www.belhavenchamber.com
Contact: Mr. Lloyd Ballance, Executive Director
Description: Promotes business and community development in Bath, Belhaven, and Pantego, NC. Conducts annual 4th of July celebration. **Founded:** 1952. **Publications:** Chamber News.

55592 ■ Benson Area Chamber of Commerce (BACC)
303 E Church St.
Benson, NC 27504-0246
Ph: (919)894-3825
Fax: (919)894-1052
Co. E-mail: loretta@benson-chamber.com
URL: http://www.benson-chamber.com
Contact: Scott Tart, President
Description: Promotes the Benson area through different activities for the family. Encourages area businesses to prosper.

55593 ■ Black Mountain-Swannanoa Chamber of Commerce
201 E State St.
Black Mountain, NC 28711
Ph: (828)669-2300
Free: 800-669-2301
Fax: (828)669-1407
Co. E-mail: info@blackmountain.org
URL: http://www.blackmountain.org
Contact: Bob McMurray, Executive Director
Description: Promotes business and community development in the Black Mountain, NC area. Sponsors Sourwood Festival. Publications: none. **Founded:** 1923.

55594 ■ Blowing Rock Chamber of Commerce (BRCC)
PO Box 406
Blowing Rock, NC 28605
Ph: (828)295-7851
Free: 800-295-7851
Fax: (828)295-7651
Co. E-mail: info@blowingrock.com
URL: http://www.blowingrock.com/chamber.php
Contact: Charles Hardin, Executive Director
Description: Promotes business and community development in Blowing Rock, NC. Sponsors Art in the Park which occurs monthly in the summer. **Founded:** 1936. **Publications:** Chamber Businesses (Annual). **Educational Activities:** Art in the Park (Annual).

55595 ■ Boone Area Chamber of Commerce
870 W King St., Ste. A
Boone, NC 28607-3457
Ph: (828)264-2225
Fax: (828)264-6644
Co. E-mail: info@boonechamber.com
URL: http://www.boonechamber.com
Contact: Daniel F. Meyer, President
Description: Promotes business and community development in the Boone, NC area. **Founded:** 1949.

55596 ■ Brevard - Transylvania Chamber of Commerce
175 E Main St.
Brevard, NC 28712
Ph: (828)883-3700

Fax: (828)883-8550
Co. E-mail: libby@brevardncchamber.org
URL: http://www.brevardncchamber.org
Contact: Mary Lynn Manley, President
Description: Promotes business and community development in the Brevard, NC area. **Scope:** how to start and maintain a small business. **Founded:** 1923. **Subscriptions:** 100. **Publications:** E News Brief (Weekly). **Telecommunication Services:** brevchamber@citcom.net.

55597 ■ Bright Leaf
PO Box 820
Oxford, NC 27565
Ph: (919)693-6125
Fax: (919)693-6126
Co. E-mail: wanda@granville-chamber.com
URL: http://www.granville-chamber.com
Contact: George Ritchie, President

55598 ■ Brunswick Bulletin
PO Box 1185
Shallotte, NC 28459
Ph: (910)754-6644
Free: 800-426-6644
Fax: (910)754-6539
Co. E-mail: info@brunswickcountychamber.org
URL: http://www.brunswickcountychamber.org
Contact: Shannon Viera, President
Released: Monthly **Price:** free for members.

55599 ■ Brunswick County Chamber of Commerce
PO Box 1185
Shallotte, NC 28459
Ph: (910)754-6644
Free: 800-426-6644
Fax: (910)754-6539
Co. E-mail: info@brunswickcountychamber.org
URL: http://www.brunswickcountychamber.org
Contact: Shannon Viera, President
Description: Promotes business and community development in the South Brunswick Islands, NC coastal area. **Founded:** 1976. **Publications:** Brunswick Bulletin (Monthly); Visitors and Business Guide (Annual). **Educational Activities:** King Classic Fishing Tournament (Annual); North Carolina Oyster Festival (Annual).

55600 ■ Burke County Chamber of Commerce
110 E Meeting St.
Morganton, NC 28655
Ph: (828)437-3021
Fax: (828)437-1613
Co. E-mail: mmcnally@burkecounty.org
URL: http://www.burkecounty.org
Contact: Mr. Michael McNally, President
Description: Promotes business and community development in Burke County, GA. **Founded:** 1945. **Publications:** The Rock (Monthly); Burke County Chamber of Commerce--Membership Directory. **Telecommunication Services:** info@burkecounty.org.

55601 ■ Business
102 N Church St.
Hillsborough, NC 27278
Ph: (919)732-8156
Fax: (919)732-4566
Co. E-mail: info@hillsboroughchamber.com
URL: http://www.hillsboroughchamber.com
Contact: Margaret Wood Cannell, Executive Director
Released: Annual

55602 ■ Business Advocate
1634 N Main St.
High Point, NC 27262
Ph: (336)882-5000
Fax: (336)889-9499
Co. E-mail: info@highpointchamber.org
URL: http://www.highpointchamber.org
Contact: Tom Dayvault, President
Released: Monthly

55603 ■ Business Connection
401 Circle Dr.
Garner, NC 27529
Ph: (919)772-6440

Fax: (919)772-6443
Co. E-mail: npadgett@garnerchamber.com
URL: http://www.garnerchamber.com
Contact: Neal Padgett, President
Released: Periodic

55604 ■ The Business Connection
401 Circle Dr.
Garner, NC 27529
Ph: (919)772-6440
Fax: (919)772-6443
Co. E-mail: npadgett@garnerchamber.com
URL: http://www.garnerchamber.com
Contact: Neal Padgett, President
Released: Monthly

55605 ■ Business Directory
104 S Estes Dr.
Chapel Hill, NC 27515-2897
Ph: (919)967-7075
Fax: (919)968-6874
Co. E-mail: info@carolinachamber.org
URL: http://www.carolinachamber.org
Contact: Aaron Nelson, President
E-mail: anelson@carolinachamber.org
Released: Annual

55606 ■ Business Directory
PO Box 392
Rocky Mount, NC 27802-0392
Ph: (252)446-0323
Fax: (252)446-5103
Co. E-mail: rmacc@rockymountchamber.org
URL: http://www.rockymountchamber.org/cwt/external/wcpages/index.aspx
Contact: Theresa Pinto, President
Released: Annual **Price:** $25.

55607 ■ Business Directory
1482 Russ Ave.
PO Drawer 600
Waynesville, NC 28786-0600
Ph: (828)456-3021
Free: 877-456-7265
Fax: (828)452-7265
Co. E-mail: info@haywood-nc.com
URL: http://www.haywood-nc.com
Contact: CeCe Hipps, Executive Director
Released: Annual **Price:** $5.

55608 ■ The Business Directory
678 S Van Buren Rd.
Eden, NC 27288
Ph: (336)623-3336
Fax: (336)623-8800
Co. E-mail: info@edenchamber.com
URL: http://www.edenchamber.com
Contact: Michael Dougherty, Chairman of the Board
Released: Annual

55609 ■ The Business Link
903 Skyway Dr.
Monroe, NC 28110
Ph: (704)289-4567
Fax: (704)282-0122
Co. E-mail: info@unioncountycoc.com
URL: http://www.unioncountycoc.com
Contact: Sharon Rosche, President
Released: Monthly

55610 ■ Business Matters
104 S Estes Dr.
Chapel Hill, NC 27515-2897
Ph: (919)967-7075
Fax: (919)968-6874
Co. E-mail: info@carolinachamber.org
URL: http://www.carolinachamber.org
Contact: Aaron Nelson, President
E-mail: anelson@carolinachamber.org
Released: Bimonthly **Price:** free for members.

55611 ■ Business Review
307 N Academy St.
Cary, NC 27513
Ph: (919)467-1016
Free: 800-919-2279

Fax: (919)469-2375
Co. E-mail: info@carychamber.com
URL: http://www.carychamber.com
Contact: Howard S. Johnson, President
E-mail: hjohnson@carychamber.com
Released: Monthly

55612 ■ *Business Today*
104 S Estes Dr.
Chapel Hill, NC 27515-2897
Ph: (919)967-7075
Fax: (919)968-6874
Co. E-mail: info@carolinachamber.org
URL: http://www.carolinachamber.org
Contact: Aaron Nelson, President
E-mail: anelson@carolinachamber.org
Released: Monthly

55613 ■ *Business Update*
301 N Queen St.
Kinston, NC 28502-0157
Ph: (252)527-1131
Fax: (252)527-1914
Co. E-mail: info@kinstonchamber.com
URL: http://kinstonchamber.com
Contact: Armistead Mauck, Chairperson
Released: Monthly

55614 ■ *Business Wise*
316 S Front St.
New Bern, NC 28560
Ph: (252)637-3111
Fax: (252)637-7451
Co. E-mail: nbchamber@newbernchamber.com
URL: http://www.newbernchamber.com
Contact: Tom Braaten, Chairman
Released: Monthly; every second Thursday.

55615 ■ *Buyer's Guide*
307 N Academy St.
Cary, NC 27513
Ph: (919)467-1016
Free: 800-919-2279
Fax: (919)469-2375
Co. E-mail: info@carychamber.com
URL: http://www.carychamber.com
Contact: Howard S. Johnson, President
E-mail: hjohnson@carychamber.com

55616 ■ Caldwell County Chamber of Commerce (CCCC)
1909 Hickory Blvd. SE
Lenoir, NC 28645
Ph: (828)726-0616
Fax: (828)726-0385
Co. E-mail: visitors@caldwellcochamber.org
URL: http://www.caldwellcochamber.org
Contact: Ralph Prestwood, Chairman of the Board
Description: Promotes business and community development in Caldwell County, NC. **Founded:** 1920. **Publications:** *Chamber Action* (Monthly). **Telecommunication Services:** deborah@caldwellcochamber.org.

55617 ■ Carteret County Chamber of Commerce (CCCC)
801 Arendell St., Ste. 1
Morehead City, NC 28557
Ph: (252)726-6350
Free: 800-622-6278
Fax: (252)726-3505
Co. E-mail: cart.coc@nccoastchamber.com
URL: http://www.nccoastchamber.com
Contact: Tom Kies, Chairman
Description: Promotes business and community development in Carteret County, NC. **Founded:** 1962. **Publications:** *Vacation Guide/Membership Directory* (Annual); *Carteret County Chamber of Commerce--Directory and Visitors Guide* (Annual).

55618 ■ Cary Chamber of Commerce
307 N Academy St.
Cary, NC 27513
Ph: (919)467-1016
Free: 800-919-2279

Fax: (919)469-2375
Co. E-mail: info@carychamber.com
URL: http://www.carychamber.com
Contact: Howard S. Johnson, President
E-mail: hjohnson@carychamber.com
Description: Promotes business and community development in Cary, NC. Conducts seminars and Business After Hours parties. **Founded:** 1962. **Publications:** *Business Review* (Monthly); *Buyer's Guide*; *Community Profile*; *Program of Work*; *Cary Chamber of Commerce Directory of Major Business*; *Cary Chamber of Commerce Member Directory*; *Relocation Guide: Town of Cary Overview & Demographics*; *Cary Chamber of Commerce Membership Directory & Buyers Guide*; *Wake County Directory of Manufacturing Firms*; *Wake County Directory of Major Employers*. **Educational Activities:** Leadership Conference (Annual). **Awards:** Community Service Award (Annual); Innovation Award (Annual). **Telecommunication Services:** hjohnson@carychamber.com.

55619 ■ Cashiers Area Chamber of Commerce
PO Box 238
Cashiers, NC 28717-0238
Ph: (828)743-5191
Fax: (828)743-9446
Co. E-mail: sue@cashiers.org
URL: http://www.cashiersnorthcarolina.com
Contact: Sue Bumgarner, Executive Director
Description: Promotes business and community development in Cashiers, NC area. **Founded:** 1982.

55620 ■ Caswell County Chamber of Commerce
PO Box 29
Yanceyville, NC 27379
Ph: (336)694-6106
Co. E-mail: sharon@caswellchamber.com
URL: http://www.caswellnc.com
Contact: Sharon Sexton, Director
Description: Promotes business and community development in Caswell County, NC.

55621 ■ Catawba County Chamber of Commerce (CCCC)
PO Box 1828
Hickory, NC 28603-1828
Ph: (828)328-6111
Fax: (828)328-1175
Co. E-mail: pmanfredi@catawbachamber.org
URL: http://www.catawbachamber.org
Contact: Danny Hearn, President
E-mail: dhearn@catawbachamber.org
Description: Promotes business and community development in Catawba County, NC. Sponsors Winterfest and Busch Grand National Race Fan Appreciation. **Founded:** 1971. **Publications:** *Catawba County Manufacturing Directory*; *e-Views* (Monthly); *Economic Profile* (Periodic); *Catawba County Chamber of Commerce--Membership Directory/Relocation Guide*. **Telecommunication Services:** dhearn@catawbachamber.org; info@catawbachamber.org.

55622 ■ *Chamber Action*
1909 Hickory Blvd. SE
Lenoir, NC 28645
Ph: (828)726-0616
Fax: (828)726-0385
Co. E-mail: visitors@caldwellcochamber.org
URL: http://www.caldwellcochamber.org
Contact: Ralph Prestwood, Chairman of the Board
Released: Monthly **Price:** free.

55623 ■ *Chamber Business Update*
302 S Greene St.
Greenville, NC 27834-1564
Ph: (252)752-4101
Fax: (252)752-5934
Co. E-mail: chamber@greenvillenc.org
URL: http://www.greenvillenc.org
Contact: Susanne D. Sartelle, President
Released: Monthly

55624 ■ *Chamber Businesses*
PO Box 406
Blowing Rock, NC 28605
Ph: (828)295-7851
Free: 800-295-7851

Fax: (828)295-7651
Co. E-mail: info@blowingrock.com
URL: http://www.blowingrock.com/chamber.php
Contact: Charles Hardin, Executive Director
Released: Annual **Price:** free.

55625 ■ *Chamber Chats*
1115 Industrial Park Dr.
Smithfield, NC 27577-0467
Ph: (919)934-9166
Fax: (919)934-1337
Co. E-mail: rchildrey@smithfieldselma.com
URL: http://www.smithfieldselma.com
Contact: Richard Childrey, President
Released: 8/year

55626 ■ *Chamber Chatter*
301 E Main St.
Clayton, NC 27520
Ph: (919)553-6352
Fax: (919)553-1758
Co. E-mail: jim@claytonchamber.com
URL: http://www.claytonchamber.com
Contact: James Lipscomb, President
Released: Monthly

55627 ■ *Chamber Clips*
115 N Pine St.
Wendell, NC 27591-0562
Ph: (919)365-6318
Fax: (919)366-2010
Co. E-mail: wendellcc@bellsouth.net
URL: http://www.wendellcc.com
Contact: Bruce Lynch, President
Released: Semiannual

55628 ■ *Chamber Comments*
150 W Mountain St.
Kings Mountain, NC 28086-0794
Ph: (704)739-4755
Fax: (704)739-8149
Co. E-mail: shirley@clevelandchamber.org
URL: http://www.clevelandchamber.org
Contact: Michael Chrisawn, President
Released: Monthly

55629 ■ *The Chamber Communicator*
207 Main St.
Knightdale, NC 27545-0601
Ph: (919)266-4603
Fax: (919)266-8010
Co. E-mail: knightdalechamber@knightdalechamber.com
URL: http://www.knightdalechamber.com
Contact: Jun Lee, President
Released: Monthly **Price:** included in membership dues.

55630 ■ *Chamber Communique*
308 N William St.
Goldsboro, NC 27530
Ph: (919)734-2241
Fax: (919)734-2247
Co. E-mail: bonnieg@waynecountychamber.com
URL: http://www.waynecountychamber.com
Contact: Bonnie Grady, President
Released: Monthly

55631 ■ *Chamber Connection*
121 N Main St.
Fuquay Varina, NC 27526
Ph: (919)552-4947
Fax: (919)552-1029
Co. E-mail: barb@fuquay-varina.com
URL: http://www.fuquay-varina.com
Contact: Ron Tropcich, Executive Director
Released: Monthly

55632 ■ *Chamber E-News*
1170 W Tate St.
Marion, NC 28752
Ph: (828)652-4240
Fax: (828)659-9620
Co. E-mail: mountains@mcdowellchamber.com
URL: http://www.mcdowellchamber.com
Contact: Harold Walker, President
E-mail: harold.walker@firstcitizens.com
Released: Bimonthly

55633 ■ *The Chamber Express*
220 N Salem St.
Apex, NC 27502
Ph: (919)362-6456
Free: 800-345-4504
Fax: (919)362-9050
Co. E-mail: info@apexchamber.com
URL: http://www.apexchamber.com
Contact: Graham Wilson, Executive Director
Released: Monthly **Price:** free.

55634 ■ *The Chamber Focus*
200 W Nash St.
Wilson, NC 27894-1146
Ph: (252)237-0165
Fax: (252)243-7931
Co. E-mail: Isoprun@wilsonncchamber.com
URL: http://www.wilsonncchamber.com
Contact: Bruce Beasley, President
Released: Monthly

55635 ■ *Chamber Focus*
101 W Broad Ave.
Rockingham, NC 28379
Ph: (910)895-9058
Fax: (910)895-9056
Co. E-mail: info@richmondcountychamber.com
URL: http://www.richmondcountychamber.com
Contact: Terry Greene, Chairman
Released: Monthly **Price:** free for members.

55636 ■ *Chamber at a Glance*
PO Box 3829
Durham, NC 27702-3829
Ph: (919)328-8700
Fax: (919)688-8351
Co. E-mail: info@durhamchamber.org
URL: http://www.durhamchamber.org
Contact: Casey Steinbacher, President
Released: Weekly **Price:** free.

55637 ■ *Chamber News*
125 W Main St.
Belhaven, NC 27810-0147
Ph: (252)943-3770
Fax: (252)943-3769
Co. E-mail: belhaveninfo@gotricounty.com
URL: http://www.belhavenchamber.com
Contact: Mr. Lloyd Ballance, Executive Director
Released: published if necessary. **Price:** free.

55638 ■ *Chamber News*
425 Porter St.
Franklin, NC 28734
Ph: (828)524-3161
Free: 866-372-5546
Fax: (828)369-7516
Co. E-mail: facc@franklin-chamber.com
URL: http://www.franklin-chamber.com
Contact: Linda Harbuck, Executive Director
Released: Bimonthly

55639 ■ *Chamber News*
101 Town Hall Dr.
Kill Devil Hills, NC 27948-1757
Ph: (252)441-8144
Fax: (252)441-0338
Co. E-mail: info@outerbankschamber.com
URL: http://www.outerbankschamber.com
Contact: Karen S. Brown, President
Released: Monthly **Price:** $25, /year.

55640 ■ *Chamber News*
101 N Main St.
Raeford, NC 28376
Ph: (910)875-5929
Fax: (910)875-1010
Co. E-mail: rae-hokchamber@embarqmail.com
URL: http://www.raefordhokechamber.com
Contact: Jackie Lynch, Executive Director
Released: Monthly

55641 ■ *Chamber News*
4841 Long Beach Rd. SE
Southport, NC 28461-8712
Ph: (910)457-6964
Free: 800-457-6964

Fax: (910)457-0598
Co. E-mail: info@southport-oakisland.com
URL: http://www.southport-oakisland.com
Contact: Sam Keziah, President
Released: Bimonthly

55642 ■ *Chamber News*
102 N York St.
Windsor, NC 27983-0572
Ph: (252)794-4277
Fax: (252)794-5070
Co. E-mail: windsorchamber@gate811.net
URL: http://windsorbertiechamber.com
Contact: Ron Wesson, President
Released: Monthly **Price:** free.

55643 ■ *Chamber News*
PO Box 31
Ayden, NC 28513
Ph: (252)746-2266
Co. E-mail: chamber@ayden.com
URL: http://www.aydenchamber.com
Contact: Stacy Gaskins, Executive Director
Released: Bimonthly

55644 ■ *Chamber News*
350 S White St.
Wake Forest, NC 27587
Ph: (919)556-1519
Fax: (919)556-8570
Co. E-mail: info@wakeforestchamber.org
URL: http://www.wakeforestchamber.org
Contact: Marla Akridge, President
Released: Monthly

55645 ■ *Chamber Notes*
106 W Main St.
Burnsville, NC 28714
Ph: (828)682-7413
Free: 800-948-1632
Fax: (828)682-6599
Co. E-mail: info@yanceychamber.com
URL: http://www.yanceychamber.com
Contact: Barbara Tester, President
Released: Bimonthly

55646 ■ *Chamber Notes*
2753 Lynn Rd., Ste. A
Tryon, NC 28782
Ph: (828)859-6236
Fax: (828)859-2301
Co. E-mail: info@polkchamber.org
URL: http://www.polkchamber.org
Contact: Janet Wooley, Executive Director
Released: Monthly

55647 ■ *Chamber Report*
211 N Main St.
Roxboro, NC 27573
Ph: (336)599-8333
Fax: (336)599-8335
Co. E-mail: chamber@roxboronc.com
URL: http://www.roxboronc.com
Contact: Ernie Wood, Chairman
Released: Monthly

55648 ■ *Chamber Update*
24 E Depot St.
Angier, NC 27501
Ph: (919)639-2500
Fax: (919)639-8826
Co. E-mail: angiercc@angierchamber.org
URL: http://www.angierchamber.org
Contact: Cindy P. Hunter, Executive Director
Released: Monthly **Price:** free.

55649 ■ *Chamber Update*
PO Box 62
Louisburg, NC 27549
Ph: (919)496-3056
Fax: (919)496-0422
Co. E-mail: mail@franklin-chamber.org
URL: http://www.franklin-chamber.org
Contact: Laureen Jones, Chairperson
Released: Monthly

55650 ■ *Chamber Views*
58 S Main St.
Sparta, NC 28675

Ph: (336)372-5473
Free: 800-372-5473
Fax: (336)245-9601
Co. E-mail: info@sparta-nc.com
URL: http://www.sparta-nc.com
Contact: Vickie Scott, President
Released: Monthly

55651 ■ *Chamber Voice*
213 Balfour Dr.
Archdale, NC 27263
Ph: (336)434-2073
Fax: (336)431-5845
Co. E-mail: info@archdaletrinitychamber.com
URL: http://www.archdaletrinitychamber.com
Contact: Beverly M. Nelson, President

55652 ■ *Chamber Voice*
1099 Gum Branch Rd.
Jacksonville, NC 28540
Ph: (910)347-3141
Fax: (910)347-4705
Co. E-mail: mpadrick@jacksonvilleonline.org
URL: http://www.jacksonvilleonline.org
Contact: Mona Padrick, President
Released: Monthly; newspaper insert every first
Monday. **Price:** free with newspaper.

55653 ■ *Chamberlines*
107-A E Wade St.
Wadesboro, NC 28170
Ph: (704)694-4181
Fax: (704)694-3830
Co. E-mail: ansonchamber@windstream.net
URL: http://www.ansoncounty.org
Contact: Ashlie Jones, Chairperson
Released: Monthly

55654 ■ *Chamberlink*
135 S Salisbury St.
Mocksville, NC 27028-2331
Ph: (336)751-3304
Fax: (336)751-5697
Co. E-mail: chamber@daviecounty.com
URL: http://www.daviechamber.com
Contact: Kyle Swicegood, Chairman of the Board
Released: Monthly

**55655 ■ Chapel Hill - Carrboro Chamber of
Commerce (CHCCC)**
104 S Estes Dr.
Chapel Hill, NC 27515-2897
Ph: (919)967-7075
Fax: (919)968-6874
Co. E-mail: info@carolinachamber.org
URL: http://www.carolinachamber.org
Contact: Aaron Nelson, President
E-mail: anelson@carolinachamber.com
Description: Promotes business and community
development in Chapel Hill, NC. **Publications:** *Business
Directory* (Annual); *Business Matters* (Bi-
monthly); *Business Today* (Monthly); *Perspectives*;
Images (Annual); *Community Profile*. **Awards:** Busi-
ness Newcomer of the Year (Annual); Business of
the Year (Annual); Duke Power Citizenship and
Service Award (Annual). **Telecommunication Ser-
vices:** anelson@carolinachamber.org.

55656 ■ *Chapel Hill Herald/Herald Sun*
102 N Church St.
Hillsborough, NC 27278
Ph: (919)732-8156
Fax: (919)732-4566
Co. E-mail: info@hillsboroughchamber.com
URL: http://www.hillsboroughchamber.com
Contact: Margaret Wood Cannell, Executive Director

**55657 ■ Charlotte Chamber of Commerce
(CCC)**
330 S Tryon St.
Charlotte, NC 28232
Ph: (704)378-1300
URL: http://www.charlottechamber.com
Contact: Mr. Bob Morgan, President
Description: Promotes business and community
development in Charlotte, NC.

55658 ■ Chatham County United Chamber of Commerce (CCUCC)
1609 E 11th St.
Siler City, NC 27344-2823
Ph: (919)742-3333
Fax: (919)742-1333
Co. E-mail: info@ccucc.net
URL: http://www.ccucc.net
Contact: Kim Nelson, President
Description: Promotes business and community development in Chatham County. Holds Business After Hours mixers. Sponsors Chicken Festival. Conducts seminars. **Founded:** 1947. **Publications:** *Concerning Chatham County* (Monthly); *Membership Directory and Buyer's Guide* (Biennial).

55659 ■ Cherokee Chamber of Commerce (CCC)
PO Box 460
Cherokee, NC 28719-0460
Free: 800-438-1601
Fax: (828)497-2505
Co. E-mail: travel@nc-cherokee.com
URL: http://www.cherokee-nc.com/index.php-?page=290
Contact: Mary Jane Ferguson, Director
Description: Promotes business and community development in the Cherokee Indian Reservation in Cherokee, NC. Operates Cherokee Visitor Center. **Founded:** 1976. **Publications:** *Cherokee Group Tour Manual* (Annual); *Cherokee Official Vacation Map and Directory* (Annual); *Cherokee Visitor Center Newsletter* (Quarterly).

55660 ■ Cherokee County Chamber of Commerce (CCCC)
805 U.S. 64 W
Murphy, NC 28906
Ph: (828)837-2242
Fax: (828)837-6012
Co. E-mail: info@cherokeecountychamber.com
URL: http://www.cherokeecountychamber.com
Contact: Phylis Blackmon, Executive Director
Description: Promotes business and community development in Cherokee County, NC. **Publications:** *Cherokee County Directory.* **Educational Activities:** Chautatuqua Andrews Valley Experience (Annual).

55661 ■ *Cherokee County Directory*
805 U.S. 64 W
Murphy, NC 28906
Ph: (828)837-2242
Fax: (828)837-6012
Co. E-mail: info@cherokeecountychamber.com
URL: http://www.cherokeecountychamber.com
Contact: Phylis Blackmon, Executive Director

55662 ■ *Cherokee Group Tour Manual*
PO Box 460
Cherokee, NC 28719-0460
Free: 800-438-1601
Fax: (828)497-2505
Co. E-mail: travel@nc-cherokee.com
URL: http://www.cherokee-nc.com/index.php-?page=290
Contact: Mary Jane Ferguson, Director
Released: Annual

55663 ■ *Cherokee Official Vacation Map and Directory*
PO Box 460
Cherokee, NC 28719-0460
Free: 800-438-1601
Fax: (828)497-2505
Co. E-mail: travel@nc-cherokee.com
URL: http://www.cherokee-nc.com/index.php-?page=290
Contact: Mary Jane Ferguson, Director
Released: Annual

55664 ■ *Cherokee Visitor Center Newsletter*
PO Box 460
Cherokee, NC 28719-0460
Free: 800-438-1601

Fax: (828)497-2505
Co. E-mail: travel@nc-cherokee.com
URL: http://www.cherokee-nc.com/index.php-?page=290
Contact: Mary Jane Ferguson, Director
Released: Quarterly

55665 ■ Cherryville Chamber of Commerce EDC
220 E Main St.
Cherryville, NC 28021
Ph: (704)435-3451
Fax: (704)435-4200
Co. E-mail: chamber@cityofcherryville.com
URL: http://www.cherryvillechamber.com
Contact: Mr. Richard Randall, President
Description: Promotes business and community development in Cherryville, NC.

55666 ■ Clay County Chamber of Commerce
388 Business Hwy. 64
Hayesville, NC 28904
Ph: (828)389-3704
Free: 877-389-3704
Fax: (828)389-1033
Co. E-mail: info@ncmtnchamber.com
URL: http://www.ncmtnchamber.com
Contact: Pam Roman, Executive Director
Description: Serves the business community by providing leadership and educational support for its members in an effort to preserve the quality of life in Clay County through responsible growth.

55667 ■ Clayton Chamber of Commerce (CCC)
301 E Main St.
Clayton, NC 27520
Ph: (919)553-6352
Fax: (919)553-1758
Co. E-mail: jim@claytonchamber.com
URL: http://www.claytonchamber.com
Contact: James Lipscomb, President
Description: Promotes business and community development in Clayton, NC. Sponsors annual Harvest Festival in October. **Founded:** 1952. **Publications:** *Chamber Chatter* (Monthly); *Membership Directory and Buyers' Guide* (Annual); *Clayton Chamber of Commerce--Membership Directory & Buyers Guide* (Annual). **Telecommunication Services:** chamber@claytonchamber.com.

55668 ■ Cleveland County Chamber of Commerce
PO Box 879
Shelby, NC 28150
Ph: (704)487-8521
Fax: (704)487-7458
Co. E-mail: info@clevelandchamber.org
URL: http://www.clevelandchamber.org
Contact: Michael Chrisawn, President
Description: Promotes business and community development in Cleveland County, NC. **Publications:** *Come Closer* (Bimonthly); *InterAction* (Monthly). **Educational Activities:** Business After Hours (Monthly).

55669 ■ Cleveland County Chamber of Commerce (Kings Mountain, North Carolina)
150 W Mountain St.
Kings Mountain, NC 28086-0794
Ph: (704)739-4755
Fax: (704)739-8149
Co. E-mail: shirley@clevelandchamber.org
URL: http://www.clevelandchamber.org
Contact: Michael Chrisawn, President
Description: Seeks to provide proactive leadership, to foster economic opportunity, and enhance community's quality of life. **Founded:** 1950. **Publications:** *Chamber Comments* (Monthly); *Membership Listing.* **Educational Activities:** King's Mountain Advisory Board (Monthly).

55670 ■ *Clinton Area Chamber of Commerce*
PO Box 467
Clinton, NC 28329-0467
Ph: (910)592-6177

Fax: (910)592-5770
Co. E-mail: clintonareacoc@intrstar.net
URL: http://www.clintonsampsonchamber.com
Contact: Ms. Lauren Balkcum, Executive Director
Released: Quarterly **Price:** free for members.

55671 ■ Clinton-Sampson Chamber of Commerce (CACC)
PO Box 467
Clinton, NC 28329-0467
Ph: (910)592-6177
Fax: (910)592-5770
Co. E-mail: clintonareacoc@intrstar.net
URL: http://www.clintonsampsonchamber.com
Contact: Ms. Lauren Balkcum, Executive Director
Description: Promotes business and community development in Clinton, NC area. **Publications:** *Clinton Area Chamber of Commerce* (Quarterly). **Telecommunication Services:** info@clintonsampsonchamber.org.

55672 ■ *Club and Organizations Directory*
302 S Greene St.
Greenville, NC 27834-1564
Ph: (252)752-4101
Fax: (252)752-5934
Co. E-mail: chamber@greenvillenc.org
URL: http://www.greenvillenc.org
Contact: Susanne D. Sartelle, President
Released: Annual **Price:** $5.

55673 ■ *Clubs and Associations*
PO Box 3829
Durham, NC 27702-3829
Ph: (919)328-8700
Fax: (919)688-8351
Co. E-mail: info@durhamchamber.org
URL: http://www.durhamchamber.org
Contact: Casey Steinbacher, President
Released: Annual **Price:** $3, for members; $6, for nonmembers.

55674 ■ *Come Closer*
PO Box 879
Shelby, NC 28150
Ph: (704)487-8521
Fax: (704)487-7458
Co. E-mail: info@clevelandchamber.org
URL: http://www.clevelandchamber.org
Contact: Michael Chrisawn, President
Released: Bimonthly

55675 ■ *Community Profile*
307 N Academy St.
Cary, NC 27513
Ph: (919)467-1016
Free: 800-919-2279
Fax: (919)469-2375
Co. E-mail: info@carychamber.com
URL: http://www.carychamber.com
Contact: Howard S. Johnson, President
E-mail: hjohnson@carychamber.com

55676 ■ *Concerning Chatham County*
1609 E 11th St.
Siler City, NC 27344-2823
Ph: (919)742-3333
Fax: (919)742-1333
Co. E-mail: info@ccucc.net
URL: http://www.ccucc.net
Contact: Kim Nelson, President
Released: Monthly

55677 ■ Davie County Chamber of Commerce
135 S Salisbury St.
Mocksville, NC 27028-2331
Ph: (336)751-3304
Fax: (336)751-5697
Co. E-mail: chamber@daviecounty.com
URL: http://www.daviechamber.com
Contact: Kyle Swicegood, Chairman of the Board
Description: Promotes business and community development in Davie County, NC. **Publications:** *Chamberlink* (Monthly).

55678 ■ *Directory of Businesses and Services*
PO Box 1008
Lumberton, NC 28359-1008
Ph: (910)739-4750
Fax: (910)671-9722
Co. E-mail: lumbertonchamber@bellsouth.net
URL: http://lumbertonchamber.com
Contact: Abe Marshal, Chairman
Released: Annual

55679 ■ Dunn Area Chamber of Commerce (DACC)
209 W Divine St.
Dunn, NC 28335
Ph: (910)892-4113
Fax: (910)892-4071
Co. E-mail: office@dunnchamber.com
URL: http://www.dunnchamber.com
Contact: Clint Stanley, President
Description: Represents business and industry. Seeks to work together to advance the economic growth, well-being and quality of life of its members and the community. **Founded:** 1921. **Publications:** *It's All Right Here!* (Monthly).

55680 ■ *E News Brief*
175 E Main St.
Brevard, NC 28712
Ph: (828)883-3700
Fax: (828)883-8550
Co. E-mail: libby@brevardncchamber.org
URL: http://www.brevardncchamber.org
Contact: Mary Lynn Manley, President
Released: Weekly **Price:** free.

55681 ■ *e-Views*
PO Box 1828
Hickory, NC 28603-1828
Ph: (828)328-6111
Fax: (828)328-1175
Co. E-mail: pmanfredi@catawbachamber.org
URL: http://www.catawbachamber.org
Contact: Danny Hearn, President
E-mail: dhearn@catawbachamber.org
Released: Monthly

55682 ■ *Economic Profile*
PO Box 1828
Hickory, NC 28603-1828
Ph: (828)328-6111
Fax: (828)328-1175
Co. E-mail: pmanfredi@catawbachamber.org
URL: http://www.catawbachamber.org
Contact: Danny Hearn, President
E-mail: dhearn@catawbachamber.org
Released: Periodic

55683 ■ Eden Chamber of Commerce
678 S Van Buren Rd.
Eden, NC 27288
Ph: (336)623-3336
Fax: (336)623-8800
Co. E-mail: info@edenchamber.com
URL: http://www.edenchamber.com
Contact: Michael Dougherty, Chairman of the Board
Description: Promotes, supports and enhances the business interest of its members. **Founded:** 1955. **Publications:** *The Business Directory* (Annual); *The Voice of Business* (Monthly). **Educational Activities:** Coffee's (Monthly). **Awards:** Distinguished Citizen of the Year (Annual).

55684 ■ Edenton-Chowan Chamber of Commerce (ECCC)
116 E King St.
Edenton, NC 27932-0245
Ph: (252)482-3400
Free: 800-775-0111
URL: http://www.edenton.com/chamber
Contact: Kathleen Miller, Director
URL(s): www.ncarts.org/county.cfm?county=Chowan.
Description: Promotes business and community development in Chowan County, NC. **Founded:** 1957. **Publications:** *Membership Journal* (Quarterly).

55685 ■ *Elected Officials Directory*
204 E Innes St.
Salisbury, NC 28145-0559

Ph: (704)633-4221
Fax: (704)639-1200
Co. E-mail: info@rowanchamber.com
URL: http://www.rowanchamber.com

55686 ■ Elizabeth City Area Chamber of Commerce
502 E Ehringhaus St.
Elizabeth City, NC 27909
Ph: (252)335-4365
Fax: (252)335-5732
Co. E-mail: info@elizabethcitychamber.org
URL: http://www.elizabethcitychamber.org
Contact: Kelly Thorsby, President
Description: Works for the business community's growth and well-being. Offers networking opportunities throughout the year.

55687 ■ Elizabethtown-White Lake Area Chamber of Commerce
103 E Broad St.
Elizabethtown, NC 28337-0306
Ph: (910)862-4368
Fax: (910)862-4368
Co. E-mail: tourism28337@embarqmail.com
URL: http://www.elizabethtownwhitelake.com
Contact: Allen Johnson, President
Description: Promotes business and community development in the Elizabethtown, NC area.

55688 ■ *Enterprise*
PO Box 392
Rocky Mount, NC 27802-0392
Ph: (252)446-0323
Fax: (252)446-5103
Co. E-mail: rmacc@rockymountchamber.org
URL: http://www.rockymountchamber.org/cwt/external/wcpages/index.aspx
Contact: Theresa Pinto, President
Released: Quarterly

55689 ■ *Enterprise and Endeavor*
200 N Main St.
Mount Airy, NC 27030-0913
Ph: (336)786-6116
Free: 800-948-0949
Fax: (336)786-1488
Co. E-mail: president1@mtairyncchamber.org
URL: http://www.mtairyncchamber.org
Contact: Dennis Lowe, Chairman of the Board
Released: Bimonthly **Price:** included in membership dues; $3, for nonmembers.

55690 ■ *Fayetteville Business*
1019 Hay St.
Fayetteville, NC 28305
Ph: (910)483-8133
Fax: (910)483-0263
Co. E-mail: info@fayettevillencchamber.org
URL: http://business.fayettevillencchamber.org
Contact: Douglas S. Peters, President
Released: Monthly

55691 ■ Fayetteville-Cumberland County Chamber of Commerce
1019 Hay St.
Fayetteville, NC 28305
Ph: (910)483-8133
Fax: (910)483-0263
Co. E-mail: info@fayettevillencchamber.org
URL: http://business.fayettevillencchamber.org
Contact: Douglas S. Peters, President
Description: Promotes business and community development in the Fayetteville, NC area. **Founded:** 1899. **Publications:** *Fayetteville Business* (Monthly). **Educational Activities:** Business After Hours (Monthly). **Awards:** Athena Award (Annual); Realtors Cup Award (Annual).

55692 ■ *For Members Only*
316 S Front St.
New Bern, NC 28560
Ph: (252)637-3111
Fax: (252)637-7451
Co. E-mail: nbchamber@newbernchamber.com
URL: http://www.newbernchamber.com
Contact: Tom Braaten, Chairman
Released: Monthly **Price:** free for members.

55693 ■ Franklin Area Chamber of Commerce (FACC)
425 Porter St.
Franklin, NC 28734
Ph: (828)524-3161
Free: 866-372-5546
Fax: (828)369-7516
Co. E-mail: facc@franklin-chamber.com
URL: http://www.franklin-chamber.com
Contact: Linda Harbuck, Executive Director
Description: Promotes business and community development in the Franklin, NC area. Promotes tourism. Conducts Town Fest, Gemboree, and Clogging festival. **Publications:** *Images of the Franklin Area*; *Chamber News* (Bimonthly); *Images of the Franklin Area*. **Educational Activities:** Business After Hours (Monthly).

55694 ■ Franklin County Chamber of Commerce (FCCC)
PO Box 62
Louisburg, NC 27549
Ph: (919)496-3056
Fax: (919)496-0422
Co. E-mail: mail@franklin-chamber.org
URL: http://www.franklin-chamber.org
Contact: Laureen Jones, Chairperson
Description: Promotes business and community development in Franklin County, NC. Sponsors Tar River Festival. **Founded:** 1977. **Publications:** *Chamber Update* (Monthly).

55695 ■ Fuquay-Varina Area Chamber of Commerce (FVACC)
121 N Main St.
Fuquay Varina, NC 27526
Ph: (919)552-4947
Fax: (919)552-1029
Co. E-mail: barb@fuquay-varina.com
URL: http://www.fuquay-varina.com
Contact: Ron Tropcich, Executive Director
Description: Promotes business and community development in Fuquay-Varina, NC. **Publications:** *Chamber Connection* (Monthly).

55696 ■ Garner Chamber of Commerce (GCC)
401 Circle Dr.
Garner, NC 27529
Ph: (919)772-6440
Fax: (919)772-6443
Co. E-mail: npadgett@garnerchamber.com
URL: http://www.garnerchamber.com
Contact: Neal Padgett, President
Description: Promotes business and community development in southeastern Wake County, NC. Conducts lobbying activities. Participates in charitable programs; sponsors Garner Celebration and golf outings. **Founded:** 1964. **Publications:** *Business Connection* (Periodic); *The Business Connection* (Monthly); *Newcomer's Guide* (Annual).

55697 ■ Gaston Regional Chamber
601 W Franklin Blvd.
Gastonia, NC 28052
Ph: (704)864-2621
Fax: (704)854-8723
Co. E-mail: enews@gastonchamber.com
URL: http://www.gastonchamber.com
Contact: John Kimbrell, President
Description: Promotes business and community development in Gaston County, NC. **Scope:** business, community, education, state. **Founded:** 1913. **Subscriptions:** 175. **Awards:** Business of the Month; Small Business Awards (Annual).

55698 ■ *The Gateway*
PO Box 279
Maggie Valley, NC 28751
Ph: (828)926-1686
Free: 800-624-4431
Fax: (828)926-9398
Co. E-mail: cmaggie@maggievalley.org
URL: http://www.maggievalley.org
Contact: Ms. Lynn Collins, Executive Director
Released: Periodic

55699 ■ *Gorge-US*
PO Box 32
Chimney Rock, NC 28720
Ph: (828)625-2725
Free: 877-625-2725
Fax: (828)625-9601
URL: http://www.hickorynut.org
Contact: Cheryl Sondak, Coordinator, Member Services
Released: Monthly

55700 ■ Granville County Chamber of Commerce (GCCC)
PO Box 820
Oxford, NC 27565
Ph: (919)693-6125
Fax: (919)693-6126
Co. E-mail: wanda@granville-chamber.com
URL: http://www.granville-chamber.com
Contact: George Ritchie, President
Description: Promotes business and community development in Granville County, NC. Convention/Meeting: none. **Founded:** 1942. **Publications:** *Bright Leaf.*

55701 ■ Greater Durham Chamber of Commerce (DCC)
PO Box 3829
Durham, NC 27702-3829
Ph: (919)328-8700
Fax: (919)688-8351
Co. E-mail: info@durhamchamber.org
URL: http://www.durhamchamber.org
Contact: Casey Steinbacher, President
Description: Promotes business and community development in the Durham, NC area. **Publications:** *Action* (Monthly); *Chamber at a Glance* (Weekly); *Clubs and Associations* (Annual).

55702 ■ Greater Hampstead Chamber of Commerce
PO Box 151
Hampstead, NC 28443
Ph: (910)270-9642
Free: 800-833-2483
Fax: (910)270-4000
Co. E-mail: hampsteadcoc1@bellsouth.net
URL: http://hampsteadchamber.com
Contact: Alissa Combs, President
Description: Promotes business and community development in Greater Hampstead, NC. **Founded:** 1993.

55703 ■ Greater Hendersonville Chamber of Commerce
204 Kanuga Rd.
Hendersonville, NC 28739
Ph: (828)692-1413
Fax: (828)693-8802
Co. E-mail: chamber@hendersonvillechamber.org
URL: http://www.hendersonvillechamber.org
Contact: Robert R. Williford, President
Description: Promotes business and community development in the greater Hendersonville, NC area. **Publications:** *The Hendersonville Information Guide* (Annual); *Membership Directory and Buyers' Guide* (Annual). **Educational Activities:** Chamber Business Showcase (Annual); Healthy Lifestyles Expo (Annual). **Awards:** The G. Ray Cantrell Award (Annual); Industrialist of the Year (Annual); Small Business Leader of the Year (Annual).

55704 ■ Greater Mount Airy Chamber of Commerce
200 N Main St.
Mount Airy, NC 27030-0913
Ph: (336)786-6116
Free: 800-948-0949
Fax: (336)786-1488
Co. E-mail: president1@mtairyncchamber.org
URL: http://www.mtairyncchamber.org
Contact: Dennis Lowe, Chairman of the Board
Description: Promotes business and community development in the greater Mt. Airy, NC area. Sponsors annual Autumn Leaves Festival. **Founded:** 1959. **Publications:** *Enterprise and Endeavor* (Bimonthly). **Awards:** Citizen of the Year (Annual).

55705 ■ Greater Raleigh Chamber of Commerce (GRCC)
PO Box 2978
Raleigh, NC 27602-2978
Ph: (919)664-7000
Fax: (919)664-7097
Co. E-mail: mail@raleighchamber.org
URL: http://www.raleighchamber.org
Contact: Harvey A. Schmitt, President
Description: Promotes business and community development in Raleigh and Wake County, NC. **Founded:** 1888. **Publications:** *Major Employers Directory* (Periodic); *Manufacturers Directory* (Periodic); *Greater Raleigh Chamber of Commerce--Manufacturers Directory*; *Greater Raleigh Chamber of Commerce--Major Employers Directory*; *Greater Raleigh Chamber of Commerce--Membership Directory and Buyer's Guide*; *Greater Raleigh Chamber of Commerce--International Firms Directory*; *Triangle Business Journal's Book of Lists.* **Telecommunication Services:** hschmitt@the-chamber.org.

55706 ■ Greater Smithfield-Selma Area Chamber of Commerce
1115 Industrial Park Dr.
Smithfield, NC 27577-0467
Ph: (919)934-9166
Fax: (919)934-1337
Co. E-mail: rchildrey@smithfieldselma.com
URL: http://www.smithfieldselma.com
Contact: Richard Childrey, President
Description: Promotes business and community development in the Greater Smithfield-Selma and Johnston County, NC area. **Founded:** 1970. **Publications:** *Chamber Chats* (8/year). **Educational Activities:** Brightleaf Golf Tournament (Annual). **Telecommunication Services:** chamber@smithfieldselma.com.

55707 ■ Greater Topsail Area Chamber of Commerce and Tourism
PO Box 2486
Surf City, NC 28445
Ph: (910)329-4446
Free: 800-626-2780
Fax: (910)329-4432
Co. E-mail: info@topsailcoc.com
URL: http://www.topsailcoc.com
Contact: Scott Wheeler, Chairman
Description: Promotes business and community development in Greater Topsail, NC area. **Publications:** *Topsail Area Guide*; *Membership Directory and Quality of Life Guide*; *Topsail Area Guide.*

55708 ■ Greater Whiteville Chamber of Commerce (GWCC)
601 S Madison St.
Whiteville, NC 28472
Ph: (910)642-3171
Free: 888-533-7196
Fax: (910)642-6047
Co. E-mail: chambercow@weblnk.net
URL: http://www.whitevillechamber.org
Contact: Janice Young, Executive Vice President
Description: Promotes business and community development in the greater Whiteville, NC area. **Founded:** 1937.

55709 ■ Greater Wilmington Chamber of Commerce
1 Estell Lee Pl.
Wilmington, NC 28401-3360
Ph: (910)762-2611
Fax: (910)762-9765
Co. E-mail: info@wilmingtonchamber.org
URL: http://www.wilmingtonchamber.org
Contact: Connie Majure-Rhett, President
Description: Promotes business and community development in Wilmington, NC. Sponsors the Greater Wilmington Chamber Foundation. **Publications:** *Greater Wilmington's Best* (Annual); *Return On Investment* (Bimonthly); *Greater Wilmington's Best* (Annual).

55710 ■ *Greater Wilmington's Best*
1 Estell Lee Pl.
Wilmington, NC 28401-3360
Ph: (910)762-2611

Fax: (910)762-9765
Co. E-mail: info@wilmingtonchamber.org
URL: http://www.wilmingtonchamber.org
Contact: Connie Majure-Rhett, President
Released: Annual

55711 ■ Greater Winston-Salem Chamber of Commerce
601 W 4th St., Ste. 101
Winston-Salem, NC 27101
Ph: (336)728-9200
Fax: (336)721-2209
Co. E-mail: anderson@winstonsalem.com
URL: http://www.winstonsalem.com
Contact: Dr. John McConnell, Chairman
Description: Promotes business and community development in Winston-Salem, NC area.

55712 ■ *Greensboro*
342 N Elm St.
Greensboro, NC 27401
Ph: (336)387-8300
Fax: (336)275-9299
Co. E-mail: dhooper@greensboro.org
URL: http://www.greensborochamber.com
Contact: Deborah Hooper, President
Released: Annual

55713 ■ Greensboro Area Chamber of Commerce
342 N Elm St.
Greensboro, NC 27401
Ph: (336)387-8300
Fax: (336)275-9299
Co. E-mail: dhooper@greensboro.org
URL: http://www.greensborochamber.com
Contact: Deborah Hooper, President
Description: Promotes business and community development in Greensboro, NC. **Founded:** 1877. **Publications:** *Greensboro* (Annual). **Educational Activities:** Business After Hours (Monthly).

55714 ■ Greenville - Pitt County Chamber of Commerce
302 S Greene St.
Greenville, NC 27834-1564
Ph: (252)752-4101
Fax: (252)752-5934
Co. E-mail: chamber@greenvillenc.org
URL: http://www.greenvillenc.org
Contact: Susanne D. Sartelle, President
Description: Promotes business and community development in Greenville, NC. **Founded:** 1907. **Publications:** *Chamber Business Update* (Monthly); *Manufacturer's Directory* (Annual); *Greenville-Pitt County Chamber of Commerce--Clubs & Organizations Directory*; *Images of Greenville - Pitt County, NC*; *Club and Organizations Directory* (Annual); *Images of Greenville Pitt County, NC*; *Greenville-Pitt County Chamber of Commerce--Membership Directory*; *Greenville-Pitt County Chamber of Commerce--Manufacturers Directory.* **Telecommunication Services:** susanne@greenvillenc.org.

55715 ■ Havelock Chamber of Commerce
201 Tourist Center Dr.
Havelock, NC 28532
Ph: (252)447-1101
Fax: (252)447-0241
Co. E-mail: info1@havelockchamber.org
URL: http://www.havelockchamber.org
Contact: Stephanie Duncan, Executive Director
Description: Promotes business and community development in the Greater Havelock, NC area. **Founded:** 1971.

55716 ■ Haywood County Chamber of Commerce
1482 Russ Ave.
PO Drawer 600
Waynesville, NC 28786-0600
Ph: (828)456-3021
Free: 877-456-7265

Fax: (828)452-7265
Co. E-mail: info@haywood-nc.com
URL: http://www.haywood-nc.com
Contact: CeCe Hipps, Executive Director
Description: Promotes business and community development in Western North Carolina. Sponsors Elected Officials Reception, Melange of the Mountains-A Culinary Gala, Dust Off the Rust Golf Tournament, Home Business Expo, and Haywood County Apple Festival. Hold Issues & Eggs, Business After Hours, Annual Dinner and Holiday Cheer. **Publications:** *Business Directory* (Annual); *Vantage Point* (Monthly). **Awards:** Small Business of the Month (Monthly); Special Project Awards (Annual); Teacher of the Month (Monthly).

55717 ■ *Heartbeat*
136 E Mountain St.
Kernersville, NC 27284-2939
Ph: (336)993-4521
Fax: (336)993-3756
Co. E-mail: kchamber@kernersvillenc.com
URL: http://www.kernersvillenc.com
Contact: Danny Jefferson, Chairman of the Board
Released: Periodic

55718 ■ Henderson-Vance County Chamber of Commerce
414 S Garnett St.
Henderson, NC 27536
Ph: (252)438-8414
Fax: (252)492-8989
Co. E-mail: info@hendersonvance.org
URL: http://www.hendersonvance.org
Contact: John Barnes, President
Description: Promotes business and community development in Henderson and Vance County, NC.

55719 ■ *The Hendersonville Information Guide*
204 Kanuga Rd.
Hendersonville, NC 28739
Ph: (828)692-1413
Fax: (828)693-8802
Co. E-mail: chamber@hendersonvillechamber.org
URL: http://www.hendersonvillechamber.org
Contact: Robert R. Williford, President
Released: Annual **Price:** free.

55720 ■ Hickory Nut Gorge Chamber of Commerce
PO Box 32
Chimney Rock, NC 28720
Ph: (828)625-2725
Free: 877-625-2725
Fax: (828)625-9601
URL: http://www.hickorynut.org
Contact: Cheryl Sondak, Coordinator, Member Services
Description: Promotes business and community development in western Rutherford County, NC. Sponsors fundraising activities. **Founded:** 1984. **Publications:** *Gorge-US* (Monthly).

55721 ■ High Point Chamber of Commerce (HPCC)
1634 N Main St.
High Point, NC 27262
Ph: (336)882-5000
Fax: (336)889-9499
Co. E-mail: info@highpointchamber.org
URL: http://www.highpointchamber.org
Contact: Tom Dayvault, President
Description: Promotes business and community development in High Point, NC. **Founded:** 1918. **Publications:** *Business Advocate* (Monthly). **Educational Activities:** Robert McInnis Golf Classic (Annual). **Awards:** Business of the Year (Annual); Small Business of the Year (Annual); Small Business Advocate of the Year (Annual). **Telecommunication Services:** tom@highpointchamber.org.

55722 ■ Highlands Area Chamber of Commerce (HACC)
PO Box 62
Highlands, NC 28741
Ph: (828)526-5841
Free: 866-526-5841

Fax: (828)526-5803
Co. E-mail: president@highlandschamber.org
URL: http://www.highlandschamber.org
Contact: Eric NeSmith, Chairman
Description: Promotes business and community development in Highlands, NC. **Founded:** 1940. **Publications:** *Highlands Happenings* (Monthly).

55723 ■ *Highlands Happenings*
PO Box 62
Highlands, NC 28741
Ph: (828)526-5841
Free: 866-526-5841
Fax: (828)526-5803
Co. E-mail: president@highlandschamber.org
URL: http://www.highlandschamber.org
Contact: Eric NeSmith, Chairman
Released: Monthly

55724 ■ Hillsborough/Orange County Chamber of Commerce—Hillsborough Area Chamber of Commerce
102 N Church St.
Hillsborough, NC 27278
Ph: (919)732-8156
Fax: (919)732-4566
Co. E-mail: info@hillsboroughchamber.com
URL: http://www.hillsboroughchamber.com
Contact: Margaret Wood Cannell, Executive Director
Description: Works to represent the business community in Hillsborough and Northern Orange County. Provides local access to information about members, businesses, and government agencies. **Founded:** 1759. **Publications:** *Business* (Annual); *Chapel Hill Herald/Herald Sun*. **Telecommunication Services:** margaret@hillsboroughchamber.com.

55725 ■ *Images of Asheboro/Randolph*
317 E Dixie Dr.
Asheboro, NC 27203
Ph: (336)626-2626
Fax: (336)626-7077
Co. E-mail: chamber@asheboro.com
URL: http://chamber.asheboro.com
Contact: Kim Markham, Chairman
Released: Annual **Price:** free.

55726 ■ *Images of the Franklin Area*
425 Porter St.
Franklin, NC 28734
Ph: (828)524-3161
Free: 866-372-5546
Fax: (828)369-7516
Co. E-mail: facc@franklin-chamber.com
URL: http://www.franklin-chamber.com
Contact: Linda Harbuck, Executive Director

55727 ■ *Images of Greenville Pitt County, NC*
302 S Greene St.
Greenville, NC 27834-1564
Ph: (252)752-4101
Fax: (252)752-5934
Co. E-mail: chamber@greenvillenc.org
URL: http://www.greenvillenc.org
Contact: Susanne D. Sartelle, President

55728 ■ *Images of Jackson County*
773 W Main St.
Sylva, NC 28779-8211
Ph: (828)586-2155
Free: 800-962-1911
Fax: (828)586-4887
Co. E-mail: info@mountainlovers.com
URL: http://www.mountainlovers.com
Contact: Julie H. Spiro, Director
Released: Annual

55729 ■ *Images of Jacksonville-Onslow*
1099 Gum Branch Rd.
Jacksonville, NC 28540
Ph: (910)347-3141
Fax: (910)347-4705
Co. E-mail: mpadrick@jacksonvilleonline.org
URL: http://www.jacksonvilleonline.org
Contact: Mona Padrick, President
Released: Annual

55730 ■ *Images of Richmond County*
101 W Broad Ave.
Rockingham, NC 28379
Ph: (910)895-9058
Fax: (910)895-9056
Co. E-mail: info@richmondcountychamber.com
URL: http://www.richmondcountychamber.com
Contact: Terry Greene, Chairman
Released: Annual

55731 ■ *Images of Stanley County*
116 E North St.
Albemarle, NC 28002-4048
Ph: (704)982-8116
Fax: (704)983-5000
Co. E-mail: tramseur@stanlychamber.org
URL: http://www.stanlychamber.org
Contact: Tom Ramseur, President

55732 ■ *Images of Wilkes*
PO Box 727
North Wilkesboro, NC 28659
Ph: (336)838-8662
Fax: (336)838-3728
Co. E-mail: info@wilkesnc.org
URL: http://www.wilkesnc.org
Contact: Chuck Smithey, Chairman

55733 ■ *Impact*
260 Premier Blvd.
Roanoke Rapids, NC 27870
Ph: (252)537-3513
Fax: (252)535-5767
Co. E-mail: apurser@rvchamber.com
URL: http://www.rvchamber.com
Contact: Allan Purser, President

55734 ■ *Industrial Directory*
PO Box 1010
Asheville, NC 28802-1010
Ph: (828)258-6114
Fax: (828)251-0926
Co. E-mail: member@ashevillechamber.org
URL: http://www.ashevillechamber.org
Contact: Kit Cramer, President
E-mail: kcramer@ashevillechamber.org
Released: Periodic

55735 ■ *Industrial Directory*
PO Box 392
Rocky Mount, NC 27802-0392
Ph: (252)446-0323
Fax: (252)446-5103
Co. E-mail: rmacc@rockymountchamber.org
URL: http://www.rockymountchamber.org/cwt/external/wcpages/index.aspx
Contact: Theresa Pinto, President
Released: Periodic

55736 ■ *Industrial Profile/Directory*
PO Box 450
Burlington, NC 27216-0450
Ph: (336)228-1338
Fax: (336)228-1330
Co. E-mail: info@alamancechamber.com
URL: http://www.alamancechamber.com
Contact: Mac Williams, President
Released: Annual **Price:** $6, for nonmembers.

55737 ■ *The Informer*
16 W Main Ave.
Taylorsville, NC 28681
Ph: (828)632-8141
Fax: (828)632-1096
Co. E-mail: chamberasst@alexandercountychamber.com
URL: http://www.alexandercountychamber.com
Contact: Renee Meade, President
Released: Monthly

55738 ■ *InterAction*
PO Box 879
Shelby, NC 28150
Ph: (704)487-8521
Fax: (704)487-7458
Co. E-mail: info@clevelandchamber.org
URL: http://www.clevelandchamber.org
Contact: Michael Chrisawn, President
Released: Monthly

55739 ■ *It's All Right Here!*
209 W Divine St.
Dunn, NC 28335
Ph: (910)892-4113
Fax: (910)892-4071
Co. E-mail: office@dunnchamber.com
URL: http://www.dunnchamber.com
Contact: Clint Stanley, President
Released: Monthly

**55740 ■ Jackson County Chamber of
Commerce (JCCC)**
773 W Main St.
Sylva, NC 28779-8211
Ph: (828)586-2155
Free: 800-962-1911
Fax: (828)586-4887
Co. E-mail: info@mountainlovers.com
URL: http://www.mountainlovers.com
Contact: Julie H. Spiro, Director
Description: Promotes business and community
development in Jackson County, NC. Sponsors fund-
raisers. **Founded:** 1905. **Publications:** *Images of
Jackson County* (Annual); *Jackson County Report*
(Monthly).

55741 ■ *Jackson County Report*
773 W Main St.
Sylva, NC 28779-8211
Ph: (828)586-2155
Free: 800-962-1911
Fax: (828)586-4887
Co. E-mail: info@mountainlovers.com
URL: http://www.mountainlovers.com
Contact: Julie H. Spiro, Director
Released: Monthly

**55742 ■ Jacksonville - Onslow Chamber of
Commerce**
1099 Gum Branch Rd.
Jacksonville, NC 28540
Ph: (910)347-3141
Fax: (910)347-4705
Co. E-mail: mpadrick@jacksonvilleonline.org
URL: http://www.jacksonvilleonline.org
Contact: Mona Padrick, President
Description: Promotes business and community
development in Jacksonville and Onslow County, NC.
Sponsors annual Heritage Festival in May, Holiday
Parade in November, and Business Expo in March.
Founded: 1944. **Publications:** *Chamber Voice*
(Monthly); *Images of Jacksonville-Onslow* (Annual);
Welcome Guide (Annual).

55743 ■ Kernersville Chamber of Commerce
136 E Mountain St.
Kernersville, NC 27284-2939
Ph: (336)993-4521
Fax: (336)993-3756
Co. E-mail: kchamber@kernersvillenc.com
URL: http://www.kernersvillenc.com
Contact: Danny Jefferson, Chairman of the Board
Description: Promotes business and community
development in Kernersville, NC. Sponsors Spring
Folly Festival, Music at Twilight, Golf Tournament,
Christmas Parade, and other events. **Founded:**
1968. **Publications:** *Heartbeat* (Periodic).

55744 ■ King Chamber of Commerce (KCC)
PO Box 863
King, NC 27021
Ph: (336)983-9308
Fax: (336)983-9526
Co. E-mail: kcoc@windstream.net
URL: http://www.kingnc.com
Contact: Derek Edwards, President
Description: Promotes business and community
development in King, NC. Sponsors KingFest Com-
munity Festival in May. **Founded:** 1988. **Publica-
tions:** *King Chamber of Commerce Newsletter*
(Bimonthly).

55745 ■ *King Chamber of Commerce
Newsletter*
PO Box 863
King, NC 27021
Ph: (336)983-9308

Fax: (336)983-9526
Co. E-mail: kcoc@windstream.net
URL: http://www.kingnc.com
Contact: Derek Edwards, President
Released: Bimonthly

**55746 ■ Kinston-Lenoir County Chamber of
Commerce (KLCCC)**
301 N Queen St.
Kinston, NC 28502-0157
Ph: (252)527-1131
Fax: (252)527-1914
Co. E-mail: info@kinstonchamber.com
URL: http://kinstonchamber.com
Contact: Armistead Mauck, Chairperson
Description: Promotes business and community
development in Lenoir County, NC. **Founded:** 1910.
Publications: *Business Update* (Monthly).

55747 ■ Knightdale Chamber of Commerce
207 Main St.
Knightdale, NC 27545-0601
Ph: (919)266-4603
Fax: (919)266-8010
Co. E-mail: knightdalechamber@knightdalechamber.
com
URL: http://www.knightdalechamber.com
Contact: Jun Lee, President
Description: Committed to advancing civic, com-
mercial, industrial, economic, and general welfare to
the businesses and citizens of Knightdale, NC.
Founded: 1972. **Publications:** *The Chamber Com-
municator* (Monthly); *Knightdale Chamber of Com-
merce Map of Knightdale*; *Knightdale Chamber of
Commerce Membership Directory/Economic Data
Booklet.* **Telecommunication Services:** jennifer.
bryan@knightdalechamber.org.

55748 ■ *Knightdale Chamber of Commerce
Map of Knightdale*
207 Main St.
Knightdale, NC 27545-0601
Ph: (919)266-4603
Fax: (919)266-8010
Co. E-mail: knightdalechamber@knightdalechamber.
com
URL: http://www.knightdalechamber.com
Contact: Jun Lee, President
Released: every 1-2 years.

55749 ■ *Knightdale Chamber of Commerce
Membership Directory/Economic Data
Booklet*
207 Main St.
Knightdale, NC 27545-0601
Ph: (919)266-4603
Fax: (919)266-8010
Co. E-mail: knightdalechamber@knightdalechamber.
com
URL: http://www.knightdalechamber.com
Contact: Jun Lee, President
Released: every 1-2 years.

**55750 ■ Lake Gaston Chamber of Commerce
(LGCC)**
2475 Eaton Ferry Rd.
Littleton, NC 27850
Ph: (252)586-5711
Free: 866-730-5711
Fax: (252)586-3152
Co. E-mail: lgcc@earthlink.net
URL: http://www.lakegastonchamber.com
Contact: Brady Martin, President
Description: Serves the citizens and the community
of the Lake Gaston area.

55751 ■ *The Lake Link*
19900 W Catawba Ave., Ste. 101
Cornelius, NC 28031
Ph: (704)892-1922
Fax: (704)892-5313
Co. E-mail: chamber@lakenorman.org
URL: http://www.lakenormanchamber.org
Contact: William E. Russell, President
Released: Monthly

**55752 ■ Lake Norman Chamber and
Convention and Visitors Bureau**
19900 W Catawba Ave., Ste. 101
Cornelius, NC 28031
Ph: (704)892-1922
Fax: (704)892-5313
Co. E-mail: chamber@lakenorman.org
URL: http://www.lakenormanchamber.org
Contact: William E. Russell, President
Description: Provides programs, information, and
outreach opportunities that enhance the community
and support economic development. **Publications:**
The Lake Link (Monthly). **Educational Activities:**
Business After Hours (Monthly). **Telecommunication
Services:** russell@lakenorman.org.

**55753 ■ Laurinburg/Scotland County Area
Chamber of Commerce (LSCC)**
606 Atkinson St.
Laurinburg, NC 28353-1025
Ph: (910)276-7420
Fax: (910)277-8785
Co. E-mail: info@laurinburgchamber.com
URL: http://www.laurinburgchamber.com
Contact: Theresa M. Pinto Lamson, President
Description: Promotes business and community
development in Laurinburg and Scotland County, NC.
Founded: 1938. **Publications:** *The Scots Piper.*
Educational Activities: Laurinburg After Five Con-
cert. **Awards:** Dunbar/McCoy Award (Annual); Com-
munity Youth Service Award (Annual).

**55754 ■ Lillington Area Chamber of
Commerce (LACC)**
PO Box 967
Lillington, NC 27546
Ph: (910)893-3751
Co. E-mail: contact@lillingtonchamber.org
URL: http://www.lillingtonchamber.org
Contact: Brian Honeycutt, President
Description: Promotes business and community
development in Lillington, NC. Conducts Lillington
Fall Festival and other activities; bestows community
service awards.

55755 ■ *The Linc*
PO Box 1617
Lincolnton, NC 28093-1617
Ph: (704)735-3096
Fax: (704)735-5449
Co. E-mail: lincolnchambernc@bellsouth.net
URL: http://www.lincolnchambernc.org
Contact: Ken Kindley, President
Released: Periodic **Price:** included in membership
dues.

**55756 ■ Lincolnton-Lincoln County Chamber
of Commerce**
PO Box 1617
Lincolnton, NC 28093-1617
Ph: (704)735-3096
Fax: (704)735-5449
Co. E-mail: lincolnchambernc@bellsouth.net
URL: http://www.lincolnchambernc.org
Contact: Ken Kindley, President
Description: Promotes business and community
development in Lincolnton and Lincoln County, NC.
Publications: *The Linc* (Periodic). **Awards:** Chamber
Scholarship (Annual); New Member of the Year (An-
nual); Volunteer of the Year (Annual); Small Business
Person of the Year (Annual).

55757 ■ *Linked*
116 E North St.
Albemarle, NC 28002-4048
Ph: (704)982-8116
Fax: (704)983-5000
Co. E-mail: tramseur@stanlychamber.org
URL: http://www.stanlychamber.org
Contact: Tom Ramseur, President
Released: Monthly

**55758 ■ Lumberton Area Chamber of
Commerce**
PO Box 1008
Lumberton, NC 28359-1008
Ph: (910)739-4750

Fax: (910)671-9722
Co. E-mail: lumbertonchamber@bellsouth.net
URL: http://lumbertonchamber.com
Contact: Abe Marshal, Chairman
Description: Promotes business and community development in Lumberton and Robeson County, NC. **Founded:** 1937. **Publications:** *Directory of Businesses and Services* (Annual).

55759 ■ Maggie Musings
PO Box 279
Maggie Valley, NC 28751
Ph: (828)926-1686
Free: 800-624-4431
Fax: (828)926-9398
Co. E-mail: cmaggie@maggievalley.org
URL: http://www.maggievalley.org
Contact: Ms. Lynn Collins, Executive Director
Released: Monthly

55760 ■ Maggie Valley Area Chamber of Commerce and Visitors' Bureau (MVCC/VB)
PO Box 279
Maggie Valley, NC 28751
Ph: (828)926-1686
Free: 800-624-4431
Fax: (828)926-9398
Co. E-mail: cmaggie@maggievalley.org
URL: http://www.maggievalley.org
Contact: Ms. Lynn Collins, Executive Director
Description: Promotes tourism and business and community development in the Maggie Valley, NC area. Sponsors hospitality seminar and competitions. Operates the Maggie Valley Chamber of Commerce and Visitors Bureau. **Founded:** 1963. **Publications:** *The Gateway* (Periodic); *Maggie Musings* (Monthly); *Visitors Guide* (Annual). **Educational Activities:** Maggie Valley Arts and Crafts (Semiannual); Mountaineer Antique Auto Club (Annual).

55761 ■ Major Employers Directory
PO Box 2978
Raleigh, NC 27602-2978
Ph: (919)664-7000
Fax: (919)664-7097
Co. E-mail: mail@raleighchamber.org
URL: http://www.raleighchamber.org
Contact: Harvey A. Schmitt, President
Released: Periodic **Price:** $15, for members; $20, for nonmembers.

55762 ■ Major Employers' Directory
PO Box 1010
Asheville, NC 28802-1010
Ph: (828)258-6114
Fax: (828)251-0926
Co. E-mail: member@ashevillechamber.org
URL: http://www.ashevillechamber.org
Contact: Kit Cramer, President
E-mail: kcramer@ashevillechamber.org
Released: Annual

55763 ■ Manufacturers Directory
PO Box 2978
Raleigh, NC 27602-2978
Ph: (919)664-7000
Fax: (919)664-7097
Co. E-mail: mail@raleighchamber.org
URL: http://www.raleighchamber.org
Contact: Harvey A. Schmitt, President
Released: Periodic **Price:** $15, for members; $20, for nonmembers.

55764 ■ Manufacturers Directory
204 E Innes St.
Salisbury, NC 28145-0559
Ph: (704)633-4221
Fax: (704)639-1200
Co. E-mail: info@rowanchamber.com
URL: http://www.rowanchamber.com

55765 ■ Martin County Chamber of Commerce (MCCC)
419 E Blvd.
Williamston, NC 27892
Ph: (252)792-4131

Fax: (252)792-1013
Co. E-mail: info@martincountync.com
URL: http://www.martincountync.com
Contact: David Whitley, Executive Director
Description: Promotes business and community development in Martin County, NC. **Founded:** 1951.

55766 ■ Matthews Business
PO Box 601
Matthews, NC 28106-0601
Ph: (704)847-3649
Fax: (704)847-3364
Co. E-mail: info@matthewschamber.com
URL: http://www.matthewschamber.com
Contact: Mike Simons, President
Released: Monthly

55767 ■ Matthews Chamber of Commerce (MCC)
PO Box 601
Matthews, NC 28106-0601
Ph: (704)847-3649
Fax: (704)847-3364
Co. E-mail: info@matthewschamber.com
URL: http://www.matthewschamber.com
Contact: Mike Simons, President
Description: Promotes business and community development in the greater Matthews, North Carolina area. **Founded:** 1980. **Subscriptions:** archival material articles maps papers photographs. **Publications:** *Matthews Business* (Monthly); *Newcomer's Guide and Business Directory* (Annual).

55768 ■ McDowell Chamber of Commerce
1170 W Tate St.
Marion, NC 28752
Ph: (828)652-4240
Fax: (828)659-9620
Co. E-mail: mountains@mcdowellchamber.com
URL: http://www.mcdowellchamber.com
Contact: Harold Walker, President
E-mail: harold.walker@firstcitizens.com
Description: Promotes business and community development in McDowell County, NC. **Founded:** 1957. **Publications:** *Business Directory*; *Manufacturing Directory*; *Chamber E-News* (Bimonthly); *McDowell Community Viewbook* (Biennial). **Educational Activities:** Chamber Dinner/Dance/Auction (Annual); Chamber Golf Tournament (Annual).

55769 ■ McDowell Community Viewbook
1170 W Tate St.
Marion, NC 28752
Ph: (828)652-4240
Fax: (828)659-9620
Co. E-mail: mountains@mcdowellchamber.com
URL: http://www.mcdowellchamber.com
Contact: Harold Walker, President
E-mail: harold.walker@firstcitizens.com
Released: Biennial

55770 ■ Membership Directory and Buyer's Guide
PO Box 450
Burlington, NC 27216-0450
Ph: (336)228-1338
Fax: (336)228-1330
Co. E-mail: info@alamancechamber.com
URL: http://www.alamancechamber.com
Contact: Mac Williams, President
Released: Annual **Price:** $10, for nonmembers.

55771 ■ Membership Directory and Buyers' Guide
301 E Main St.
Clayton, NC 27520
Ph: (919)553-6352
Fax: (919)553-1758
Co. E-mail: jim@claytonchamber.com
URL: http://www.claytonchamber.com
Contact: James Lipscomb, President
Released: Annual

55772 ■ Membership Directory and Buyers' Guide
204 Kanuga Rd.
Hendersonville, NC 28739
Ph: (828)692-1413

Fax: (828)693-8802
Co. E-mail: chamber@hendersonvillechamber.org
URL: http://www.hendersonvillechamber.org
Contact: Robert R. Williford, President
Released: Annual **Price:** $5, for members; $10, includes shipping and handling.

55773 ■ Membership Directory and Buyer's Guide
1609 E 11th St.
Siler City, NC 27344-2823
Ph: (919)742-3333
Fax: (919)742-1333
Co. E-mail: info@ccucc.net
URL: http://www.ccucc.net
Contact: Kim Nelson, President
Released: Biennial

55774 ■ Membership Directory and Quality of Life Guide
PO Box 2486
Surf City, NC 28445
Ph: (910)329-4446
Free: 800-626-2780
Fax: (910)329-4432
Co. E-mail: info@topsailcoc.com
URL: http://www.topsailcoc.com
Contact: Scott Wheeler, Chairman

55775 ■ Membership Journal
116 E King St.
Edenton, NC 27932-0245
Ph: (252)482-3400
Free: 800-775-0111
URL: http://www.edenton.com/chamber
Contact: Kathleen Miller, Director
Released: Quarterly **Price:** free.

55776 ■ Membership Listing
150 W Mountain St.
Kings Mountain, NC 28086-0794
Ph: (704)739-4755
Fax: (704)739-8149
Co. E-mail: shirley@clevelandchamber.org
URL: http://www.clevelandchamber.org
Contact: Michael Chrisawn, President

55777 ■ Membership Resources Guide
213 Balfour Dr.
Archdale, NC 27263
Ph: (336)434-2073
Fax: (336)431-5845
Co. E-mail: info@archdaletrinitychamber.com
URL: http://www.archdaletrinitychamber.com
Contact: Beverly M. Nelson, President

55778 ■ Mitchell County
PO Box 858
Spruce Pine, NC 28777
Ph: (828)765-9483
Free: 800-227-3912
Fax: (828)765-9034
URL: http://www.mitchell-county.com
Contact: Bob Hensley, President
Released: Periodic

55779 ■ Mitchell County Chamber of Commerce
PO Box 858
Spruce Pine, NC 28777
Ph: (828)765-9483
Free: 800-227-3912
Fax: (828)765-9034
URL: http://www.mitchell-county.com
Contact: Bob Hensley, President
Description: Promotes business and community development in Mitchell County and western North Carolina. Sponsors festival. **Publications:** *Mitchell County* (Periodic).

55780 ■ Montgomery County Chamber of Commerce
444 N Main St.
Troy, NC 27371-0637
Ph: (910)572-2575

Fax: (910)572-5193
Co. E-mail: chamber@montgomery-county.com
URL: http://www.montgomery-county.com
Contact: Judy Stevens, Executive Director
Description: Works with other community resources to promote local tourism, create jobs, and recruit new businesses in Montgomery County, NC area.

55781 ■ Moore County Chamber of Commerce
10677 Hwy. 15-501
Southern Pines, NC 28387
Ph: (910)692-3926
Fax: (910)692-0619
Co. E-mail: info@moorecountychamber.com
URL: http://www.moorecountychamber.com
Contact: Richard Higginbotham, Chairman
Description: Promotes business and community development in Moore County. **Founded:** 1967.

55782 ■ Mooresville-South Iredell Chamber of Commerce
149 E Iredell Ave.
Mooresville, NC 28115
Ph: (704)664-3898
Free: 800-338-8443
Fax: (704)664-2549
Co. E-mail: info@mooresvillenc.org
URL: http://www.mooresvillenc.org
Contact: Kirk Ballard, President
Description: Promotes business and community development in Mooresville and South Iredell County, NC. **Founded:** 1916. **Telecommunication Services:** msi@mooresvillenc.org.

55783 ■ Morrisville Chamber of Commerce
260 Town Hall Dr., Ste. A
Morrisville, NC 27560
Ph: (919)463-7150
Fax: (919)439-0212
Co. E-mail: chamber@morrisvillenc.com
URL: http://morrisvillechamber.org
Contact: Carlotta Ungaro, President
Description: Promotes business and community development in Morrisville, NC. **Scope:** local area and trade info. **Founded:** 1990. **Publications:** *Morrisville Chamber Communicator* (Monthly); *Annual Directory and Economic Data Book* (Annual).

55784 ■ *Morrisville Chamber Communicator*
260 Town Hall Dr., Ste. A
Morrisville, NC 27560
Ph: (919)463-7150
Fax: (919)439-0212
Co. E-mail: chamber@morrisvillenc.com
URL: http://morrisvillechamber.org
Contact: Carlotta Ungaro, President
Released: Monthly

55785 ■ Mount Olive Area Chamber of Commerce
123 N Center St.
Mount Olive, NC 28365
Ph: (919)658-3113
Fax: (919)658-3125
Co. E-mail: president@mountolivechamber.com
URL: http://www.moachamber.com
Contact: Lynn Williams, Chairperson
Description: Promotes economic development in the Mt. Olive, NC area. Sponsors Annual North Carolina Pickle Festival. Conducts educational seminar. **Founded:** 1930. **Publications:** *The Architect* (Quarterly); *Mt. Olive Area Chamber of Commerce Membership Directory and Resource Magazine* (Annual). **Telecommunication Services:** moacc@bellsouth.net.

55786 ■ *Mt. Olive Area Chamber of Commerce Membership Directory and Resource Magazine*
123 N Center St.
Mount Olive, NC 28365
Ph: (919)658-3113
Fax: (919)658-3125
Co. E-mail: president@mountolivechamber.com
URL: http://www.moachamber.com
Contact: Lynn Williams, Chairperson
Released: Annual

55787 ■ New Bern Area Chamber of Commerce
316 S Front St.
New Bern, NC 28560
Ph: (252)637-3111
Fax: (252)637-7451
Co. E-mail: nbchamber@newbernchamber.com
URL: http://www.newbernchamber.com
Contact: Tom Braaten, Chairman
Description: Promotes business and community development in Craven County, NC. **Founded:** 1899. **Publications:** *Business Wise* (Monthly); *For Members Only* (Monthly); *Business Wise* (Monthly); *New Bern Area Guide and Business* (Annual); *New Bern Area Guide and Business* (Annual). **Educational Activities:** Administrative Professionals Day (Annual); New Bern Area Chamber of Commerce Banquet (Annual); Business Expo (Annual). **Awards:** Entrepreneur of the Year (Annual); Small Business Person of the Year (Annual). **Telecommunication Services:** kroberts@newbernchamber.com.

55788 ■ *New Bern Area Guide and Business*
316 S Front St.
New Bern, NC 28560
Ph: (252)637-3111
Fax: (252)637-7451
Co. E-mail: nbchamber@newbernchamber.com
URL: http://www.newbernchamber.com
Contact: Tom Braaten, Chairman
Released: Annual

55789 ■ *Newcomer's Guide*
401 Circle Dr.
Garner, NC 27529
Ph: (919)772-6440
Fax: (919)772-6443
Co. E-mail: npadgett@garnerchamber.com
URL: http://www.garnerchamber.com
Contact: Neal Padgett, President
Released: Annual

55790 ■ *Newcomers Guide*
903 Skyway Dr.
Monroe, NC 28110
Ph: (704)289-4567
Fax: (704)282-0122
Co. E-mail: info@unioncountycoc.com
URL: http://www.unioncountycoc.com
Contact: Sharon Rosche, President

55791 ■ *Newcomer's Guide and Business Directory*
PO Box 601
Matthews, NC 28106-0601
Ph: (704)847-3649
Fax: (704)847-3364
Co. E-mail: info@matthewschamber.com
URL: http://www.matthewschamber.com
Contact: Mike Simons, President
Released: Annual **Price:** $20, /issue.

55792 ■ Outer Banks Chamber of Commerce (OBCC)
101 Town Hall Dr.
Kill Devil Hills, NC 27948-1757
Ph: (252)441-8144
Fax: (252)441-0338
Co. E-mail: info@outerbankschamber.com
URL: http://www.outerbankschamber.com
Contact: Karen S. Brown, President
Description: Promotes business and community development in Currituck, Dare, and Hyde counties, NC. Sponsors seminars. **Founded:** 1949. **Publications:** *Chamber News* (Monthly); *Outer Banks Relocation & Investors Guide* (Annual); *Outer Banks Relocation and Investors Guide*; *Outer Banks Vacation Guide* (Annual). **Educational Activities:** Health and Fitness Expo (Annual); Legislative Breakfast (Periodic). **Telecommunication Services:** chamber@outer-banks.com.

55793 ■ Perquimans County Chamber of Commerce (PCCC)
118 W Market St.
Hertford, NC 27944
Ph: (252)426-5657

Fax: (252)426-7542
Co. E-mail: chamber@perquimans.com
URL: http://www.visitperquimans.com
Contact: Susan Cox, President
Description: Promotes business and community development in Perquimans County, NC. Sponsors Indian Summer Festival. **Founded:** 1961. **Publications:** *Promoting Perquimans*. **Awards:** Policeman/Fireman of the Year (Annual); Small Business of the Year (Annual).

55794 ■ *Perspectives*
104 S Estes Dr.
Chapel Hill, NC 27515-2897
Ph: (919)967-7075
Fax: (919)968-6874
Co. E-mail: info@carolinachamber.org
URL: http://www.carolinachamber.org
Contact: Aaron Nelson, President
E-mail: anelson@carolinachamber.org
Price: free.

55795 ■ Pleasure Island, Carolina Beach, and Kure Beach Chamber of Commerce (PICBKBCC)
1121 N Lake Park Blvd.
Carolina Beach, NC 28428
Ph: (910)458-8434
Fax: (910)458-7969
Co. E-mail: visitor@pleasureislandnc.org
URL: http://www.pleasureislandnc.org
Contact: Gail McCloskey, President
Description: Promotes business and community development in Carolina Beach and Kure Beach, NC. **Founded:** 1978. **Publications:** *Pleasure Island Newsletter*.

55796 ■ Polk County Chamber of Commerce
2753 Lynn Rd., Ste. A
Tryon, NC 28782
Ph: (828)859-6236
Fax: (828)859-2301
Co. E-mail: info@polkchamber.org
URL: http://www.polkchamber.org
Contact: Janet Wooley, Executive Director
Description: Promotes business and community development in Polk County, NC and surrounding areas. **Founded:** 1927. **Publications:** *Chamber Notes* (Monthly); *Visitors Guide* (Annual); *A Sense of Heritage: The Tryon Chamber of Commerce, 1991*. **Awards:** Hall of Fame (Annual); Volunteer of the Year (Annual).

55797 ■ *Program of Work*
307 N Academy St.
Cary, NC 27513
Ph: (919)467-1016
Free: 800-919-2279
Fax: (919)469-2375
Co. E-mail: info@carychamber.com
URL: http://www.carychamber.com
Contact: Howard S. Johnson, President
E-mail: hjohnson@carychamber.com

55798 ■ *Promoting Perquimans*
118 W Market St.
Hertford, NC 27944
Ph: (252)426-5657
Fax: (252)426-7542
Co. E-mail: chamber@perquimans.com
URL: http://www.visitperquimans.com
Contact: Susan Cox, President

55799 ■ Raeford - Hoke Chamber of Commerce (RHCC)
101 N Main St.
Raeford, NC 28376
Ph: (910)875-5929
Fax: (910)875-1010
Co. E-mail: rae-hokchamber@embarqmail.com
URL: http://www.raefordhokechamber.com
Contact: Jackie Lynch, Executive Director
Description: Promotes business and community development in Raeford, NC. **Publications:** *Chamber News* (Monthly). **Awards:** Citizen of the Year (Annual); Director of the Year (Annual); Golden Apple (Annual).

55800 ■ Randleman Chamber of Commerce
PO Box 207
Randleman, NC 27317
Ph: (336)495-1100
Fax: (336)495-1133
Co. E-mail: info@randlemanchamber.com
URL: http://randlemanchamber.com
Contact: Carla Burrow, Executive Director
Description: Promotes business and community development in Randleman, NC.

55801 ■ *Return On Investment*
1 Estell Lee Pl.
Wilmington, NC 28401-3360
Ph: (910)762-2611
Fax: (910)762-9765
Co. E-mail: info@wilmingtonchamber.org
URL: http://www.wilmingtonchamber.org
Contact: Connie Majure-Rhett, President
Released: Bimonthly

55802 ■ Richmond County Chamber of Commerce (RCCC)
101 W Broad Ave.
Rockingham, NC 28379
Ph: (910)895-9058
Fax: (910)895-9056
Co. E-mail: info@richmondcountychamber.com
URL: http://www.richmondcountychamber.com
Contact: Terry Greene, Chairman
Description: Promotes business and community development in Richmond County, NC. **Founded:** 1983. **Publications:** *Images of Richmond County* (Annual); *Chamber Focus* (Monthly); *Images of Richmond County* (Annual).

55803 ■ Roanoke Valley Chamber of Commerce
260 Premier Blvd.
Roanoke Rapids, NC 27870
Ph: (252)537-3513
Fax: (252)535-5767
Co. E-mail: apurser@rvchamber.com
URL: http://www.rvchamber.com
Contact: Allan Purser, President
Description: Promotes business and community development in Roanoke Rapids, NC. **Publications:** *Impact.* **Educational Activities:** Car (Annual).

55804 ■ *The Rock*
110 E Meeting St.
Morganton, NC 28655
Ph: (828)437-3021
Fax: (828)437-1613
Co. E-mail: mmcnally@burkecounty.org
URL: http://www.burkecounty.org
Contact: Mr. Michael McNally, President
Released: Monthly **Price:** free to members.

55805 ■ Rocky Mount Area Chamber of Commerce
PO Box 392
Rocky Mount, NC 27802-0392
Ph: (252)446-0323
Fax: (252)446-5103
Co. E-mail: rmacc@rockymountchamber.org
URL: http://www.rockymountchamber.org/cwt/
    external/wcpages/index.aspx
Contact: Theresa Pinto, President
Description: Seeks to improve the overall business climate for its members through sponsorship of programs which stimulate economic growth, promote civic development and enhance political action. **Founded:** 1904. **Publications:** *Business Directory* (Annual); *Enterprise* (Quarterly); *Industrial Directory* (Periodic); *Rocky Mount View Book* (Annual). **Awards:** Woody Brown Award (Annual).

55806 ■ Rowan County Chamber of Commerce
204 E Innes St.
Salisbury, NC 28145-0559
Ph: (704)633-4221

Fax: (704)639-1200
Co. E-mail: info@rowanchamber.com
URL: http://www.rowanchamber.com
Description: Promotes business and community development in Salisbury and Rowan County, NC. **Founded:** 1925. **Publications:** *At Work* (Monthly); *Elected Officials Directory*; *Manufacturers Directory*.

55807 ■ Roxboro Area Chamber of Commerce (RACC)
211 N Main St.
Roxboro, NC 27573
Ph: (336)599-8333
Fax: (336)599-8335
Co. E-mail: chamber@roxboronc.com
URL: http://www.roxboronc.com
Contact: Ernie Wood, Chairman
Description: Promotes business and community development in Person County, NC. Sponsors September Personality Festival. Maintains Business After Hours programs and numerous other programs. **Founded:** 1935. **Publications:** *Chamber Report* (Monthly). **Educational Activities:** Roxboro Area Chamber of Commerce Banquet (Annual).

55808 ■ Rutherford County Chamber of Commerce
162 N Main St.
Rutherfordton, NC 28139-2502
Ph: (828)287-3090
Fax: (828)287-0799
Co. E-mail: info@rutherfordcoc.com
URL: http://www.rutherfordcoc.org
Contact: Clark Poole, Executive Director
Description: Strives to advance the commercial, industrial, civic, and cultural interests of the citizens of Rutherford County. **Telecommunication Services:** chamberdude@bellsouth.net.

55809 ■ *The Scots Piper*
606 Atkinson St.
Laurinburg, NC 28353-1025
Ph: (910)276-7420
Fax: (910)277-8785
Co. E-mail: info@laurinburgchamber.com
URL: http://www.laurinburgchamber.com
Contact: Theresa M. Pinto Lamson, President

55810 ■ *A Sense of Heritage: The Tryon Chamber of Commerce, 1991*
2753 Lynn Rd., Ste. A
Tryon, NC 28782
Ph: (828)859-6236
Fax: (828)859-2301
Co. E-mail: info@polkchamber.org
URL: http://www.polkchamber.org
Contact: Janet Wooley, Executive Director

55811 ■ *Sources*
200 W Nash St.
Wilson, NC 27894-1146
Ph: (252)237-0165
Fax: (252)243-7931
Co. E-mail: lsoprun@wilsonncchamber.com
URL: http://www.wilsonncchamber.com
Contact: Bruce Beasley, President
Released: Annual

55812 ■ Southport-Oak Island Chamber of Commerce
4841 Long Beach Rd. SE
Southport, NC 28461-8712
Ph: (910)457-6964
Free: 800-457-6964
Fax: (910)457-0598
Co. E-mail: info@southport-oakisland.com
URL: http://www.southport-oakisland.com
Contact: Sam Keziah, President
Description: Promotes business and community development in the Southport and Oak Island, NC area. **Founded:** 1978. **Publications:** *Chamber News* (Bimonthly); *Visitors and Residents Guide*. **Awards:** Small Business Person of the Year (Annual).

55813 ■ Spring Lake Area Chamber of Commerce (SLACC)
300 Ruth St.
Spring Lake, NC 28390
Ph: (910)497-8821

Fax: (910)497-1897
URL: http://www.springlakechamber.com
Contact: Jonn Thomas, President
Description: Promotes business and community development in Spring Lake, NC. **Founded:** 1962.

55814 ■ Stanly County Chamber of Commerce (SCCC)
116 E North St.
Albemarle, NC 28002-4048
Ph: (704)982-8116
Fax: (704)983-5000
Co. E-mail: tramseur@stanlychamber.org
URL: http://www.stanlychamber.org
Contact: Tom Ramseur, President
Description: Promotes business and community development in Stanly County, NC. **Founded:** 1936. **Publications:** *Images of Stanley County*; *Linked* (Monthly).

55815 ■ Swain County Chamber of Commerce
210 Main St.
Bryson City, NC 28713
Ph: (828)488-3681
Free: 800-867-9246
Fax: (828)488-6858
Co. E-mail: chamber@greatsmokies.com
URL: http://www.greatsmokies.com
Contact: Karen Proctor Wilmot, Executive Director
Description: Promotes business and community development in Swain County, NC. Encourages tourism. Sponsors event in the 4th of July. **Publications:** *Swain County Chamber News* (Quarterly). **Educational Activities:** Chili Cook Off (Annual).

55816 ■ *Swain County Chamber News*
210 Main St.
Bryson City, NC 28713
Ph: (828)488-3681
Free: 800-867-9246
Fax: (828)488-6858
Co. E-mail: chamber@greatsmokies.com
URL: http://www.greatsmokies.com
Contact: Karen Proctor Wilmot, Executive Director
Released: Quarterly

55817 ■ Tarboro - Edgecombe Chamber of Commerce
PO Drawer F
Tarboro, NC 27886
Ph: (252)823-7241
Fax: (252)823-1499
Co. E-mail: bmartin@tarborochamber.com
URL: http://www.tarborochamber.com
Contact: Bobbie Martin, President
Description: Promotes business and community development in Tarboro, NC. **Founded:** 1933. **Publications:** *TECC Update* (Monthly). **Awards:** Distinguished Citizen (Annual).

55818 ■ *TECC Update*
PO Drawer F
Tarboro, NC 27886
Ph: (252)823-7241
Fax: (252)823-1499
Co. E-mail: bmartin@tarborochamber.com
URL: http://www.tarborochamber.com
Contact: Bobbie Martin, President
Released: Monthly

55819 ■ *Topsail Area Guide*
PO Box 2486
Surf City, NC 28445
Ph: (910)329-4446
Free: 800-626-2780
Fax: (910)329-4432
Co. E-mail: info@topsailcoc.com
URL: http://www.topsailcoc.com
Contact: Scott Wheeler, Chairman

55820 ■ Union County Chamber of Commerce
903 Skyway Dr.
Monroe, NC 28110
Ph: (704)289-4567

Fax: (704)282-0122
Co. E-mail: info@unioncountycoc.com
URL: http://www.unioncountycoc.com
Contact: Sharon Rosche, President
Description: Leads in the promotion and advancement of Union County, NC's economic interests and improvement of the quality of life for its citizens. **Publications:** *Newcomers Guide* (Annual); *Union County Industrial Directory*; *The Business Link* (Monthly); *Newcomers Guide*; *Union County Economic Development Resource Directory*. **Educational Activities:** Human Resources (Monthly). **Awards:** Business Hall of Fame (Annual); Entrepreneur of the Year (Annual); Minority Entrepreneur of the Year (Annual); Volunteer of the Year (Annual); 21st Century Award for Telecommunications Technology (Annual). **Telecommunication Services:** jim@unioncountycoc.com.

55821 ■ *Union County Economic Development Resource Directory*
903 Skyway Dr.
Monroe, NC 28110
Ph: (704)289-4567
Fax: (704)282-0122
Co. E-mail: info@unioncountycoc.com
URL: http://www.unioncountycoc.com
Contact: Sharon Rosche, President
Price: $5, for nonmembers; $7, for members.

55822 ■ *Update*
317 E Dixie Dr.
Asheboro, NC 27203
Ph: (336)626-2626
Fax: (336)626-7077
Co. E-mail: chamber@asheboro.com
URL: http://chamber.asheboro.com
Contact: Kim Markham, Chairman
Released: Monthly; last Thursday.

55823 ■ *Vacation Guide/Membership Directory*
801 Arendell St., Ste. 1
Morehead City, NC 28557
Ph: (252)726-6350
Free: 800-622-6278
Fax: (252)726-3505
Co. E-mail: cart.coc@nccoastchamber.com
URL: http://www.nccoastchamber.com
Contact: Tom Kies, Chairman
Released: Annual

55824 ■ *Vantage Point*
1482 Russ Ave.
PO Drawer 600
Waynesville, NC 28786-0600
Ph: (828)456-3021
Free: 877-456-7265
Fax: (828)452-7265
Co. E-mail: info@haywood-nc.com
URL: http://www.haywood-nc.com
Contact: CeCe Hipps, Executive Director
Released: Monthly

55825 ■ *Visions*
308 N William St.
Goldsboro, NC 27530
Ph: (919)734-2241
Fax: (919)734-2247
Co. E-mail: bonnieg@waynecountychamber.com
URL: http://www.waynecountychamber.com
Contact: Bonnie Grady, President
Released: Annual

55826 ■ *Visitors and Business Guide*
PO Box 1185
Shallotte, NC 28459
Ph: (910)754-6644
Free: 800-426-6644
Fax: (910)754-6539
Co. E-mail: info@brunswickcountychamber.org
URL: http://www.brunswickcountychamber.org
Contact: Shannon Viera, President
Released: Annual

55827 ■ *Visitors Guide*
PO Box 279
Maggie Valley, NC 28751
Ph: (828)926-1686

Free: 800-624-4431
Fax: (828)926-9398
Co. E-mail: cmaggie@maggievalley.org
URL: http://www.maggievalley.org
Contact: Ms. Lynn Collins, Executive Director
Released: Annual

55828 ■ *Visitors Guide*
2753 Lynn Rd., Ste. A
Tryon, NC 28782
Ph: (828)859-6236
Fax: (828)859-2301
Co. E-mail: info@polkchamber.org
URL: http://www.polkchamber.org
Contact: Janet Wooley, Executive Director
Released: Annual **Price:** free.

55829 ■ *Visitors and Residents Guide*
4841 Long Beach Rd. SE
Southport, NC 28461-8712
Ph: (910)457-6964
Free: 800-457-6964
Fax: (910)457-0598
Co. E-mail: info@southport-oakisland.com
URL: http://www.southport-oakisland.com
Contact: Sam Keziah, President

55830 ■ *The Voice of Business*
678 S Van Buren Rd.
Eden, NC 27288
Ph: (336)623-3336
Fax: (336)623-8800
Co. E-mail: info@edenchamber.com
URL: http://www.edenchamber.com
Contact: Michael Dougherty, Chairman of the Board
Released: Annual **Price:** free for members.

55831 ■ Wake Forest Chamber of Commerce
350 S White St.
Wake Forest, NC 27587
Ph: (919)556-1519
Fax: (919)556-8570
Co. E-mail: info@wakeforestchamber.org
URL: http://www.wakeforestchamber.org
Contact: Marla Akridge, President
Description: Serves as the voice of business in the Wake Forest Area. Encourages profitable enterprise and social progress for the benefit of the community. **Founded:** 1948. **Publications:** *Chamber News* (Monthly). **Telecommunication Services:** jodi@wakeforestchamber.org.

55832 ■ Wallace Chamber of Commerce (WCC)
PO Box 427
Wallace, NC 28466
Ph: (910)285-4044
Fax: (910)285-3310
Co. E-mail: lou@wallacechamber.com
URL: http://www.wallacechamberofcommerce.com
Contact: Lou Powell, Executive Director
Description: Promotes business and community development in Wallace, NC. Sponsors Christmas parade. Holds monthly board meeting. Publications: none.

55833 ■ Warsaw Chamber of Commerce (WCC)
PO Box 585
Warsaw, NC 28398
Ph: (910)293-7804
Fax: (910)293-6773
Co. E-mail: warsawchamber@embarqmail.com
URL: http://www.townofwarsawnc.com
Description: Promotes business and community development in Warsaw, NC. **Founded:** 1921.

55834 ■ Washington - Beaufort County Chamber of Commerce (WBCCC)
PO Box 665
Washington, NC 27889
Ph: (252)946-9168
Co. E-mail: info@wbcchamber.com
URL: http://www.wbcchamber.com
Contact: Catherine Glover, Executive Director
Description: Promotes business and community development in Washington, NC. **Founded:** 1904. **Telecommunication Services:** cglover@wbcchamber.com.

55835 ■ Wayne County Chamber of Commerce
308 N William St.
Goldsboro, NC 27530
Ph: (919)734-2241
Fax: (919)734-2247
Co. E-mail: bonnieg@waynecountychamber.com
URL: http://www.waynecountychamber.com
Contact: Bonnie Grady, President
Description: Promotes business and community development in Wayne County, NC. **Founded:** 1918. **Publications:** *Visions* (Annual); *Chamber Communique* (Monthly); *Visions* (Annual). **Educational Activities:** Farm City (Annual). **Telecommunication Services:** steveh@waynecountychamber.com.

55836 ■ *Welcome Guide*
1099 Gum Branch Rd.
Jacksonville, NC 28540
Ph: (910)347-3141
Fax: (910)347-4705
Co. E-mail: mpadrick@jacksonvilleonline.org
URL: http://www.jacksonvilleonline.org
Contact: Mona Padrick, President
Released: Annual

55837 ■ Wendell Chamber of Commerce (WCC)
115 N Pine St.
Wendell, NC 27591-0562
Ph: (919)365-6318
Fax: (919)366-2010
Co. E-mail: wendellcc@bellsouth.net
URL: http://www.wendellchamber.com
Contact: Bruce Lynch, President
Description: Promotes business and community development in Wendell, NC. **Founded:** 1903. **Publications:** *Chamber Clips* (Semiannual). **Awards:** Business of the Month (Monthly).

55838 ■ *The Western Flyer*
112 W Murphy St.
Madison, NC 27025-1924
Ph: (336)548-6248
Fax: (336)548-4466
Co. E-mail: info@westernrockinghamchamber.com
URL: http://www.westernrockinghamchamber.com
Contact: Anne Griffin, Executive Director
Released: Monthly

55839 ■ Western Rockingham Chamber of Commerce (WRCC)
112 W Murphy St.
Madison, NC 27025-1924
Ph: (336)548-6248
Fax: (336)548-4466
Co. E-mail: info@westernrockinghamchamber.com
URL: http://www.westernrockinghamchamber.com
Contact: Anne Griffin, Executive Director
Description: Promotes business and community development in Madison, NC. **Publications:** *The Western Flyer* (Monthly).

55840 ■ Wilkes Chamber of Commerce
PO Box 727
North Wilkesboro, NC 28659
Ph: (336)838-8662
Fax: (336)838-3728
Co. E-mail: info@wilkesnc.org
URL: http://www.wilkesnc.org
Contact: Chuck Smithey, Chairman
Description: Strives to promote economic development and to enhance the quality of life in Wilkes County. **Founded:** 1946. **Publications:** *Images of Wilkes*. **Educational Activities:** Brushy Mountain Apple Festival (Annual).

55841 ■ Wilson Chamber of Commerce (WCC)
200 W Nash St.
Wilson, NC 27894-1146
Ph: (252)237-0165

Fax: (252)243-7931
Co. E-mail: lsoprun@wilsonncchamber.com
URL: http://www.wilsonncchamber.com
Contact: Bruce Beasley, President
Description: Promotes business and community development in Wilson and Wilson County, NC. **Publications:** *The Chamber Focus* (Monthly); *Sources* (Annual). **Awards:** Visual Improvement Award (Bimonthly).

55842 ■ Windsor/Bertie County Chamber of Commerce
102 N York St.
Windsor, NC 27983-0572
Ph: (252)794-4277
Fax: (252)794-5070
Co. E-mail: windsorchamber@gate811.net
URL: http://windsorbertiechamber.com
Contact: Ron Wesson, President
Description: Membership is made up of area businesses, nonprofits, service and healthcare industries, manufacturers and individuals. Promotes business, tourism and community development. **Founded:** 1946. **Publications:** *Chamber News* (Monthly). **Awards:** Merchants Award (Semiannual).

55843 ■ Yadkin County Chamber of Commerce
PO Box 1840
Yadkinville, NC 27055-1840
Ph: (336)679-2200
Free: 877-492-3546
Fax: (336)679-3034
Co. E-mail: btodd@yadkinchamber.org
URL: http://www.yadkinchamber.org
Contact: Marty Driver, Chairman
Description: Advocates for the business community and supports pro-business policies on the local, state, and federal level. Sponsors business seminars throughout the year. **Telecommunication Services:** jamie@yadkinchamber.org.

55844 ■ Yadkin Valley Chamber of Commerce
116 E Market St.
Elkin, NC 28621
Ph: (336)526-1111
Fax: (336)526-1879
Co. E-mail: lauretteleagon@yadkinvalley.org
URL: http://www.yadkinvalley.org
Contact: Randy Bledsoe, Chairman of the Board
Description: Promotes business and community development in the Yadkin Valley Elkin, NC area.

55845 ■ Yancey County/Burnsville Chamber of Commerce
106 W Main St.
Burnsville, NC 28714
Ph: (828)682-7413
Free: 800-948-1632
Fax: (828)682-6599
Co. E-mail: info@yanceychamber.com
URL: http://www.yanceychamber.com
Contact: Barbara Tester, President
Description: Promotes business and community development in Yancey County, NC. Conducts public forums and seminars. Sponsors annual crafts fair. **Founded:** 1962. **Publications:** *Chamber Notes* (Bimonthly); *Yancey County Business Directory* (Periodic). **Educational Activities:** Old Timey Fall (Annual).

55846 ■ *Yancey County Business Directory*
106 W Main St.
Burnsville, NC 28714
Ph: (828)682-7413
Free: 800-948-1632
Fax: (828)682-6599
Co. E-mail: info@yanceychamber.com
URL: http://www.yanceychamber.com
Contact: Barbara Tester, President
Released: Periodic

55847 ■ Zebulon Chamber of Commerce
PO Box 546
Zebulon, NC 27597
Ph: (919)269-6320

Fax: (919)269-6350
Co. E-mail: zebcoc@zebulonchamber.org
URL: http://www.zebulonchamber.org/home.asp
Contact: Kim Valentine, Executive Director
Description: Business members and individual members of the community that join together for the common good of promoting businesses and the general welfare and prosperity of the Zebulon community. Provides benefits, programs, services, and a voice to the community and fellow member businesses. **Awards:** Citizen of the Year (Annual).

MINORITY BUSINESS ASSISTANCE PROGRAMS

55848 ■ Center for Economic Empowerment & Development - Women's Business Center of Fayetteville
230 Hay St.
Fayetteville, NC 28301
Ph: (910)323-3377
Fax: (910)323-8828
Co. E-mail: ceedinfo@ncceed.org
URL: http://www.ncceed.org
Contact: S. Ray, Executive Director
Description: Works to promote the economic empowerment of women in North Carolina. Provides a variety of business ownership services.

55849 ■ North Carolina Cherokee Satellite Office - Native American Business Development Center
70 Woodfin Pl., Ste. 305
Park Place Offices
Asheville, NC 28801
Ph: (828)252-2516
Fax: (828)497-9009
Co. E-mail: ashevillebdc@yahoo.com
URL: http://www.mbda.gov Center

55850 ■ North Carolina Institute of Minority Economic Development - NC Minority Business Enterprise Center
114 W Parrish St.
Durham, NC 27701
Ph: (919)956-8889
Fax: (919)688-7668
Co. E-mail: info@ncimed.com
URL: http://www.ncimed.com
Contact: Farad Ali
Description: Provides finance management, access to capital, consulting, and procurement services to minority businesses in North Carolina.

FINANCING AND LOAN PROGRAMS

55851 ■ Academy Funds / Longleaf Venture Fund LLC
PO Box 99748
Raleigh, NC 27624
Ph: (919)991-5425
Fax: (919)991-5421
Co. E-mail: info@academyfunds.com
URL: http://www.academyfunds.com
Contact: Glenn Kline, Managing Partner
Investment Policies: Seed, start-up, early and first stage, and research and development. **Industry Preferences:** Communications and media, computer software and hardware, Internet specific, semiconductors and other electronics, biotechnology, medical and health, consumer related, industrial and energy, and transportation. **Geographic Preference:** North Carolina.

55852 ■ A.M. Pappas & Associates, LLC
PO Box 110287
Research Triangle Park, NC 27709
Ph: (919)998-3300
Fax: (919)998-3301
Co. E-mail: info@pappasventures.com
URL: http://www.pappasventures.com
Contact: Arthur M. Pappas, Managing Partner
E-mail: apappas@pappasventures.com
Preferred Investment Size: $100,000 to $6,000,000. **Investment Policies:** Balanced, first, early, later, and second stage, and mezzanine. **Industry Prefer-**

ences: Medical and health, biotechnology, computer software and services, and Internet specific. **Geographic Preference:** Mid Atlantic, Northeast, Northern California, Southeast, and West Coast U.S.; Ontario and Quebec, Canada.

55853 ■ Aurora Funds, Inc.
3100 Tower Blvd., Ste. 1600
Durham, NC 27707
Ph: (919)484-0400
Fax: (919)484-0444
URL: http://www.aurorafunds.com
Contact: Scott Albert, Partner
Preferred Investment Size: $50,000 to $2,500,000. **Industry Preferences:** Medical and health, Internet specific, computer software and services, biotechnology, semiconductors and other electronics, communications and other media, industrial and energy. **Geographic Preference:** Mid Atlantic and Southeast.

55854 ■ Frontier Capital, LLC
1111 Metropolitan Ave., Ste. 1050
Charlotte, NC 28204
Ph: (704)414-2880
Fax: (704)414-2881
URL: http://www.frontierfunds.com
Contact: Richard Maclean, Managing Partner
E-mail: richard@frontiercapital.com
Preferred Investment Size: $5,000,000 to $15,000,000. **Industry Preferences:** Internet specific, Communications, computer software, medical and health, financial services, and business service. **Geographic Preference:** Mid Atlantic, South, and Southeast.

55855 ■ Intersouth Partners
406 Blackwell St., Ste. 200
Durham, NC 27701
Ph: (919)493-6640
Fax: (919)493-6649
Co. E-mail: contact@intersouth.com
URL: http://www.intersouth.com
Contact: Dennis Dougherty, Partner
Preferred Investment Size: $500,000 to $6,000,000. **Industry Preferences:** Medical and health, biotechnology, Internet specific, computer software and services, industrial and energy, semiconductors and other electronics, other products, computer hardware, communications and media, and consumer related. **Geographic Preference:** Southeast.

55856 ■ MCNC Ventures LLC
3021 Cornwallis Rd.
Research Triangle Park, NC 27709-2889
Ph: (919)248-1900
Fax: (919)248-1101
URL: http://www.mcnc.org
Contact: Joe Freddoso, Chief Executive Officer
E-mail: joe@mcnc.org
Investment Policies: Seed and early stage. **Industry Preferences:** Communications. **Geographic Preference:** North Carolina.

55857 ■ The North Carolina Enterprise Fund, L.P.
3600 Glenwood Ave., Ste. 107
Raleigh, NC 27612
Ph: (919)781-2691
Fax: (919)783-9195
Co. E-mail: info@ncef.com
URL: http://www.ncef.com
Preferred Investment Size: $2,000,000 minimum. **Industry Preferences:** Medical and health, communications and media, computer software and services, biotechnology, computer hardware, other products, Internet specific, semiconductors and other electronics, and consumer related. **Geographic Preference:** North Carolina and Southeast.

55858 ■ Southern Capitol Ventures
21 Glenwood Ave., Ste. 105
Raleigh, NC 27603
Ph: (919)858-7580

Fax: (919)863-2394
Co. E-mail: info@southerncapitalventures.com
URL: http://www.southerncapitolventures.com
Contact: Benjamin Brooks, Founder

Preferred Investment Size: $500,000 to $1,500,000.
Industry Preferences: Semiconductors and other electronics, computer software and services, Internet specific, communications and media. **Geographic Preference:** Southeast and Mid Atlantic.

55859 ■ The Sustainable Jobs Fund / SJF Ventures
200 N. Mangum St., Ste. 203
Durham, NC 27701
Ph: (919)530-1177
Fax: (919)530-1178
URL: http://www.sjfund.com
Contact: David Griest, Managing Director
E-mail: dgriest@sjfund.com

Preferred Investment Size: $1,000,000 to $2,000,000. **Industry Preferences:** Computer software, semiconductors and other electronics, medical and health, consumer related, industrial and energy, business service, manufacturing, and utilities. **Geographic Preference:** U.S.

55860 ■ Truepilot, LLC
2505 Meridian Pky., Ste. 250
Durham, NC 27713
Ph: (919)433-3705
Fax: (919)433-3719
Co. E-mail: foundation@b-a.org
URL: http://www.b-a.org
Contact: Michael Brader-Araje, Chief Executive Officer

Preferred Investment Size: $50,000 to $500,000.
Industry Preferences: Internet specific. **Geographic Preference:** North Carolina.

PROCUREMENT ASSISTANCE PROGRAMS

55861 ■ North Carolina Department of Administration - Purchase and Contract Division - State Purchasing Office
1305 Mail Service Center
Raleigh, NC 27699-1305
Ph: (919)807-4500
Fax: (919)807-4502
Co. E-mail: doa.pchelpdesk@ncmail.net
URL: http://www.doa.state.nc.us/PandC/
Contact: James D. Staton, Director

55862 ■ North Carolina Small Business and Technology Development Center - SBTDC Regional Office
300 E First St.
ECU Willis Bldg.
Greenville, NC 27858-4353
Ph: (252)737-1385
Co. E-mail: info@sbtdc.org
URL: http://www.sbtdc.org
Contact: Carolyn Wilburn, Regional Director

Description: Helps businesses obtain contracts by providing comprehensive assistance in selling products and services to local, state and federal government entities.

55863 ■ North Carolina Small Business and Technology Development Center - SBTDC Regional Office
1612 Military Cutoff Rd., Ste. 208
Wilmington, NC 28403-5977
Ph: (910)962-3744
Co. E-mail: uncw@sbtdc.org
URL: http://www.sbtdc.org
Contact: Fran Scarlett, Regional Director

Description: Helps businesses obtain contracts by providing comprehensive assistance in selling products and services to local, state and federal government entities.

INCUBATORS/RESEARCH AND TECHNOLOGY PARKS

55864 ■ Babcock Demon Incubator
Wake Forest University
3455 University Pky.
Winston-Salem, NC 27106
Ph: (336)758-5422
Free: 866-925-3622
Fax: (336)758-5830
Co. E-mail: email-bdi@wfubdi.org
URL: http://www.wfubdi.org/

Description: A small business incubator whose mission is to foster entrepreneurial education at Wake Forest and an entrepreneurial spirit in the Triad by providing personalized services and relationships to growth-oriented, early stage ventures. It offers office space, Internet access, and business resources for growing companies.

55865 ■ Ben Craig Center Incubator & Accelerator
8701 Mallard Creek Rd.
Charlotte, NC 28262
Ph: (704)548-9113
Fax: (704)602-2179
Co. E-mail: contact@bencraigcenter.com
URL: http://bencraigcenter.com/site/index.cfm
Contact: Paul Wetenhall, President

Description: A small business incubator providing state-of-the-art office space to the region's most promising companies in order to accelerate their growth by offering them advisory services, mentoring relationships, sales and marketing expertise and access to capital.

55866 ■ Fayetteville Business Center
2520 Murchison Rd.
Fayetteville, NC 28301
Ph: (910)222-8900
Fax: (910)222-8910
Co. E-mail: fshorter@uncfsu.edu
URL: http://www.fayettevillebusinesscenter.com/
Contact: Floyd Shorter, Director

Description: A small business incubator promoting economic development in the City of Fayetteville and the Murchison Road corridor by providing nurturing to entrepreneurs and business assistance in the growth and development of small business concerns and promoting a healthy entrepreneurial spirit for the growth and economic renewal of the community.

55867 ■ First Flight Venture Center
2 Davis Dr.
Research Triangle Park, NC 27709-3169
Ph: (919)990-8558
Fax: (919)558-0156
Co. E-mail: jdraper@nctda.org
URL: http://www.ffvcn.org
Contact: John Draper, Chief Executive Officer

Description: A technology incubator serving entrepreneurs and early-stage businesses in the Research Triangle Park area.

55868 ■ MCNC Research and Development
3021 Cornwallis Rd.
Durham, NC 27709
Ph: (919)248-1900
Fax: (919)248-1101
URL: http://www.mcnc.org
Contact: John Crites, Chief Executive Officer

Description: Promotes the use and development of electronic and information technologies by providing advanced research facilities in North Carolina's universities.

55869 ■ Nussbaum Center for Entrepreneurship
2007 Yanceyville St.
Greensboro, NC 27405
Ph: (336)379-5001
Fax: (336)379-5020
Co. E-mail: director@nussbaumcfe.com
URL: http://www.nussbaumcfe.com/

Description: A small business incubator designed to support non-retail, new or emerging businesses by providing modestly-priced office and light manufactur-

ing space, along with shared support services such as business counseling, a receptionist, copier, fax, mail boxes, and data entry.

EDUCATIONAL PROGRAMS

55870 ■ Caldwell Community College and Technical Institute - Small Business Center
2855 Hickory Blvd.
Hudson, NC 28638
Ph: (828)726-2200
Fax: (828)726-2472
Co. E-mail: easher@cccti.edu
URL: http://www.cccti.edu

Description: Seminars, workshops, and management consultation are available for small business owners.

55871 ■ Sandhills Community College
3395 Airport Rd.
Pinehurst, NC 28374
Ph: (910)692-6185
Free: 800-338-3944
Fax: (910)695-1823
Co. E-mail: neelym@sandhills.edu
URL: http://www.sandhills.edu

Description: Offers many business-related and personal enrichment classes, both at the college and at various off-campus sites. A Small Business Center has been established to attract, train, counsel, and provide educational services to small business owners or individuals interested in establishing small businesses in the area.

55872 ■ South College
140 Sweeten Creek Rd.
Asheville, NC 28803
Ph: (828)398-2500
Fax: (828)398-1491
Co. E-mail: support@southcollegecollegenc.edu
URL: http://www.southcollegenc.edu

Description: Offers a program in small business administration.

55873 ■ Wilson Community College - Small Business Center
902 Herring Ave.
Wilson, NC 27893
Ph: (252)291-1195
Fax: (252)243-7148
URL: http://www.wilsoncc.edu

Description: Provides consultative services, resource information, and a variety of seminars, workshops, and courses to assist in the development of new businesses and the success of existing businesses.

PUBLICATIONS

55874 ■ *Smart Start your North Carolina Business*
PSI Research
300 N. Valley Dr.
Grants Pass, OR 97526
Ph: (503)479-9464
Free: 800-228-2275
Fax: (503)476-1479
Co. E-mail: info@psi-research.com
URL: http://www.psi-research.com

Ed: Michael D. Jenkins. **Released:** Revised edition, 1992. **Price:** $29.95 (looseleaf binder); $24.95 (paper). **Description:** Part of the Successful Business Library series.

PUBLISHERS

55875 ■ International Puzzle Features
4507 Panther Pl.
Charlotte, NC 28269
Ph: (704)921-1818

Fax: (704)597-1331
Co. E-mail: drfun@cleverpuzzles.com
URL: http://www.cleverpuzzles.com
Contact: Pat Battaglia, Publisher
E-mail: drfun@cleverpuzzles.com
Description: Description: Publishes books of clever word games with surprising answers and amusing features for readers of all ages. Also provides a weekly variety puzzle/game column to newspapers. Accepts submissions of individual puzzles/games, not columns. Send for Writers Guidelines with SASE. Refer to web site for samples. Reaches market through reviews, listings, and distributors and wholesalers. **Founded:** 1990.

SMALL BUSINESS DEVELOPMENT CENTERS

55876 ■ North Dakota Small Business Development Center - Belcourt
c/o Betty Hamley, Consultant
Box 900, Hwy. 5 W
Belcourt, ND 58316
Ph: (701)477-3561
Co. E-mail: belcourt@ndsbdc.org
URL: http://www.ndsbdc.org
Contact: Betty Hamley, Consultant
Description: Represents and promotes the small business sector. Provides management assistance to current and prospective small business owners. Helps to improve management skills and expand the products and services of members.

55877 ■ North Dakota Small Business Development Center - Bismarck
c/o Nancy Krogen-Abel, Regional Dir.
1120 College Dr., Ste. 105
Bismarck, ND 58501
Ph: (701)328-5865
Co. E-mail: bismarck@ndsbdc.org
URL: http://www.ndsbdc.org
Contact: Nancy Krogen-Abel, Regional Director
Description: Represents and promotes the small business sector. Provides management assistance to current and prospective small business owners. Helps to improve management skills and expand the products and services of members.

55878 ■ North Dakota Small Business Development Center - Devils Lake
c/o Sandy Shively, Consultant
PO Box 651
Devils Lake, ND 58301
Ph: (701)662-8131
Fax: (701)662-8132
Co. E-mail: sandyncpc@gondtc.com
URL: http://www.ndsbdc.org
Contact: Sandy Shively, Consultant
Description: Represents and promotes the small business sector. Provides management assistance to current and prospective small business owners. Helps to improve management skills and expand the products and services of members.

55879 ■ North Dakota Small Business Development Center - Dickinson
c/o Ray Ann Kilen, Regional Dir.
Strom Center for Entrepreneurship & Innovation
1679 6th Ave. W
Dickinson, ND 58601
Ph: (701)483-2470
Co. E-mail: rayann.kilen@dsu.nodak.edu
URL: http://www.ndsbdc.org
Contact: Ray Ann Kilen, Regional Director
Description: Represents and promotes the small business sector. Provides management assistance to current and prospective small business owners. Helps to improve management skills and expand the products and services of members.

55880 ■ North Dakota Small Business Development Center - Fargo
c/o Donovan Wadholm, Regional Dir.
51 N Broadway, Ste. 505
Fargo, ND 58102
Ph: (701)235-1495
Co. E-mail: donovan.wadholm@und.edu
URL: http://www.ndsbdc.org
Contact: Donovan Wadholm, Regional Director
Description: Represents and promotes the small business sector. Provides management assistance to current and prospective small business owners. Helps to improve management skills and expand the products and services of members.

55881 ■ North Dakota Small Business Development Center - Fort Yates
c/o Jonathan Anderson, Mgr.
1341 92nd St.
Fort Yates, ND 58538
Ph: (701)854-8122
Co. E-mail: jonathana@sbci.edu
URL: http://www.ndsbdc.org
Contact: Jonathan Anderson, Manager
Description: Represents and promotes the small business sector. Provides management assistance to current and prospective small business owners. Helps to improve management skills and expand the products and services of members.

55882 ■ North Dakota Small Business Development Center - Grand Forks
c/o Josh Klug, Consultant
4200 James Ray Dr.
Grand Forks, ND 58203
Ph: (701)738-4851
Co. E-mail: josh@ndsbdc.org
URL: http://www.ndsbdc.org
Contact: Josh Klug, Consultant
Description: Represents and promotes the small business sector. Provides management assistance to current and prospective small business owners. Helps to improve management skills and expand the products and services of members.

55883 ■ North Dakota Small Business Development Center - Jamestown
c/o Deb Kantrud, Regional Dir.
120 2nd St. SE
Jamestown, ND 58402
Ph: (701)952-8060
Co. E-mail: jamestown@ndsbdc.org
URL: http://www.ndsbdc.org
Contact: Deb Kantrud, Regional Director
Description: Represents and promotes the small business sector. Provides management assistance to current and prospective small business owners. Helps to improve management skills and expand the products and services of members.

55884 ■ North Dakota Small Business Development Center - Minot
c/o Mary Beth Votava, Regional Dir.
1925 S Broadway, Ste. 2
Minot, ND 58703
Ph: (701)857-8211
Co. E-mail: minot@ndsbdc.org
URL: http://www.ndsbdc.org
Contact: Mary Beth Votava, Regional Director
Description: Represents and promotes the small business sector. Provides management assistance to current and prospective small business owners. Helps to improve management skills and expand the products and services of members.

SMALL BUSINESS ASSISTANCE PROGRAMS

55885 ■ North Dakota Department of Commerce - Division of Economic Development and Finance
PO Box 2057
Bismarck, ND 58502-2057
Ph: (701)328-5300
Fax: (701)328-5320
Co. E-mail: plucy@nd.gov
URL: http://www.growingnd.com
Contact: Paul Lucy, Director
Description: Encourages the establishment of new businesses and industries and assists new and expanding businesses with information and location decisions.

55886 ■ University of North Dakota (CI)
Ina Mae Rude Entrepreneur Center
Grand Forks, ND 58203
Ph: (701)777-3132
Fax: (701)777-2339
Co. E-mail: info@innovators.net
URL: http://www.innovators.net
Contact: Jordan T. Schuetzle, Director
E-mail: jordan@innovators.net
Description: Provides technical and business support services to entrepreneurs, inventors, and small manufacturers. Assists specifically with the product evaluation process, the patenting process, and technology transfer. **Scope:** Offers market and demographical research, business plan development, financial forecasts and manufacturing services to entrepreneurs, particularly manufacturing technology start up enterprises. Provides assistance to innovators, entrepreneurs, and researchers to launch new ventures, commercialize new technologies, and secure access to capital from private and public sources. **Services:** Commercial Evaluations for Emerging Technologies (11/year). **Founded:** 1984. **Publications:** "The Business Plan: A State-Of-The-Art Guide"; "The Marketing Plan: Step-By-Step"; "The Ultimate Business Planner"; "Campus Entrepreneurship: A Changing Curriculum for Changing Times"; "Financing Startup Ventures"; "The Business Plan: A State-of-the-Art Guide"; "The Marketing Plan: Step-by-Step". **Educational Activities:** Center for Innovation Conferences and workshops (Monthly), Seed and Angel Capital, Entrepreneur Startups, Business Planning, Market Feasibility. **Telecommunication Services:** celia@innovators.net; bruce@innovators.net; askme@innovators.net.

SCORE OFFICES

55887 ■ SCORE Bismarck-Mandan
700 E Main Ave., 2nd Fl.
Bismarck, ND 58506-5509
Ph: (701)328-5861
Fax: (701)250-4304
Co. E-mail: score365@btinet.net
URL: http://bismarckmandan.score.org
Description: Provides entrepreneur education for the formation, growth and success of small businesses in the area.

55888 ■ SCORE Fargo
51 Broadway N, Ste. 505
Fargo, ND 58108
Ph: (701)239-5677
Fax: (701)237-9734
Co. E-mail: info@fargoscore.org
URL: http://fargo.score.org
Contact: Joel Simons, President
Description: Provides entrepreneur education for the formation, growth and success of small businesses in the area.

55889 ■ SCORE Minot
1925 S Broadway, Ste. 2
Minot, ND 58701
Ph: (701)852-6883
Fax: (701)852-6905
Co. E-mail: scoreminot1@srt.com
URL: http://minot.score.org/chapters/minot-score
Description: Provides entrepreneur education for the formation, growth and success of small businesses in the area.

55890 ■ SCORE Upper Red River
1501 28th Ave. S
Grand Forks, ND 58201-6727
Ph: (701)746-5851
Fax: (701)746-5748
Co. E-mail: score@gra.midco.net
URL: http://upperredriver.score.org/chapters/upper-red-river-score
Description: Provides entrepreneur education for the formation, growth and success of small businesses in the area.

CHAMBERS OF COMMERCE

55891 ■ *At Work*
120 W 8th St., Ste. 3
Harvey, ND 58341
Ph: (701)324-2604
Fax: (701)324-2674
Co. E-mail: chamber@harveynd.com
URL: http://www.harveynd.com
Contact: Ms. Sara Balfour, Executive Vice President
Released: Monthly

55892 ■ Beulah Chamber of Commerce (BCC)
120 Central Ave. N
Beulah, ND 58523-0730
Ph: (701)873-4585
Free: 800-441-2649
Fax: (701)873-5361
Co. E-mail: chamber@westriv.com
URL: http://www.beulahnd.org
Description: Promotes business and community development in Beulah, ND. **Founded:** 1952. **Publications:** *Chamber Chatter* (Monthly).

55893 ■ Bismarck-Mandan Chamber of Commerce (BMCC)
PO Box 1675
Bismarck, ND 58502-1675
Ph: (701)223-5660
Fax: (701)255-6125
Co. E-mail: info@bismarckmandan.com
URL: http://www.bismarckmandan.com
Contact: Kelvin Hullet, President
Description: Promotes business and community development in the Bismarck, ND Area. Participates in area Folkfest and Band Days Parade. **Founded:** 1990. **Publications:** *Chamber Connection* (Monthly).

55894 ■ Bowman Area Chamber of Commerce
PO Box 1143
Bowman, ND 58623
Ph: (701)523-5880
Free: 866-752-2691
Fax: (701)523-3322
Co. E-mail: chamber@bowmannd.com
URL: http://www.bowmannd.com
Contact: Jeanine Clendenen, President
Description: Helps in the development of employment, industry, tourism and economic attributes within Bowman County.

55895 ■ *The Bridge*
PO Box 2443
Fargo, ND 58108-2443
Ph: (218)233-1100
Fax: (218)233-1200
Co. E-mail: info@fmchamber.com
URL: http://fmwfchamber.com
Contact: Craig Whitney, President
Released: Monthly

55896 ■ *Building Bridges*
PO Box 2443
Fargo, ND 58108-2443
Ph: (218)233-1100
Fax: (218)233-1200
Co. E-mail: info@fmchamber.com
URL: http://fmwfchamber.com
Contact: Craig Whitney, President
Released: Annual

55897 ■ Carrington Area Chamber of Commerce
871 Main St.
Carrington, ND 58421
Ph: (701)652-2524
Free: 800-641-9668
Fax: (701)652-2391
Co. E-mail: cgtncham@daktel.com
URL: http://www.cgtn-nd.com
Contact: Laurie Dietz, Executive Director
Description: Promotes business and community development in the city of Carrington, ND and surrounding area. Conducts charitable activities and competitions; sponsors Harvest Fest and Fourth of July celebration. **Founded:** 1962. **Publications:** *The Carrington Connection* (Monthly).

55898 ■ *The Carrington Connection*
871 Main St.
Carrington, ND 58421
Ph: (701)652-2524
Free: 800-641-9668
Fax: (701)652-2391
Co. E-mail: cgtncham@daktel.com
URL: http://www.cgtn-nd.com
Contact: Laurie Dietz, Executive Director
Released: Monthly

55899 ■ Cavalier Area Chamber of Commerce
301 Division Ave. N
Cavalier, ND 58220-0271
Ph: (701)265-8188
Fax: (701)265-8720
Co. E-mail: cacc@polarcomm.com
URL: http://www.caviernd.com
Description: Promotes economic and community development in Cavalier and the surrounding area. **Founded:** 1878.

55900 ■ *Chamber Chatter*
120 Central Ave. N
Beulah, ND 58523-0730
Ph: (701)873-4585
Free: 800-441-2649
Fax: (701)873-5361
Co. E-mail: chamber@westriv.com
URL: http://www.beulahnd.org
Released: Monthly **Price:** free for members.

55901 ■ *Chamber of Commerce of Fargo Moorhead*
PO Box 2443
Fargo, ND 58108-2443
Ph: (218)233-1100

Fax: (218)233-1200
Co. E-mail: info@fmchamber.com
URL: http://fmwfchamber.com
Contact: Craig Whitney, President
Description: Unifies and advances business and community interests in a bi-state, metropolitan community and the surrounding region. **Founded:** 1879. **Publications:** *The Bridge* (Monthly); *Building Bridges* (Annual); *Community Profile* (Annual). **Educational Activities:** Business After Hours (Bimonthly). **Awards:** Business of the Year (Annual); Small Business of the Year (Annual); Not-for-Profit of the Year (Annual).

55902 ■ *Chamber Connection*
PO Box 1675
Bismarck, ND 58502-1675
Ph: (701)223-5660
Fax: (701)255-6125
Co. E-mail: info@bismarckmandan.com
URL: http://www.bismarckmandan.com
Contact: Kelvin Hullet, President
Released: Monthly

55903 ■ *Chamber News*
120 2nd St. SE
Jamestown, ND 58402
Ph: (701)252-4830
Fax: (701)252-4837
Co. E-mail: chamber@jamestownchamber.com
URL: http://www.jamestownchamber.com
Contact: JoDee Rasmusson, Executive Director
Released: Monthly

55904 ■ *Chamber Newsletter*
PO Box 458
Watford City, ND 58854-0458
Ph: (701)580-1493
Free: 800-701-2804
Co. E-mail: wcchamber@ruggedwest.com
URL: http://www.watfordcitychamber.com
Released: Monthly **Price:** free.

55905 ■ *Chamber Pride*
PO Box 724
Valley City, ND 58072-0724
Ph: (701)845-1891
Fax: (701)845-1892
Co. E-mail: chamber@hellovalley.com
URL: http://www.valleycitynd.com
Contact: Briana Schlosser, Office Manager
Released: Monthly

55906 ■ *Chamber Profile*
10 Main St.
Williston, ND 58802
Ph: (701)577-6000
Fax: (701)577-8591
Co. E-mail: wchamber@willistonchamber.net
URL: http://www.willistonchamber.net/default.aspx-?AspxAutoDetectCookieSupport=1
Contact: Marci Seamples, Executive Director
Released: 8/year

55907 ■ *Chamberline*
314 3rd Ave. W
Dickinson, ND 58601
Ph: (701)225-5115
Fax: (701)225-5116
URL: http://www.dickinsonchamber.org
Contact: Lexi Sebastian, Executive Director
Released: Monthly **Price:** free for members.

55908 ■ *Community Profile*
PO Box 2443
Fargo, ND 58108-2443
Ph: (218)233-1100
Fax: (218)233-1200
Co. E-mail: info@fmchamber.com
URL: http://fmwfchamber.com
Contact: Craig Whitney, President
Released: Annual

55909 ■ Devils Lake Area Chamber of Commerce (DLACC)
208 Hwy. 2 W
Devils Lake, ND 58301-0879
Ph: (701)662-4903
Free: 800-233-8048

Fax: (701)662-2147
Co. E-mail: chamber@gondtc.com
URL: http://www.devilslakend.com
Contact: Suzie Kenner, Executive Director
Description: Promotes business and community development and tourism in the Devils Lake, ND area. Sponsors Fishing Tournament and Old Settlers Weekend. **Publications:** *News-N-Views* (Monthly).

55910 ■ Dickinson Area Chamber of Commerce (DACC)
314 3rd Ave. W
Dickinson, ND 58601
Ph: (701)225-5115
Fax: (701)225-5116
URL: http://www.dickinsonchamber.org
Contact: Lexi Sebastian, Executive Director
Description: Promotes business, economic, and community development in Dickinson and Southwest North Dakota. **Publications:** *Chamberline* (Monthly); *Quarterly Activities Report* (Quarterly). **Awards:** Business Persons of the Year (Annual); Parochial Schools Teacher of the Year (Annual); Public Schools Teacher of the Year (Annual); University Schools Teacher of the Year (Annual).

55911 ■ Geographical Center of North America Chamber of Commerce (GCNACC)
224 Hwy. 2 SW
Rugby, ND 58368-2426
Ph: (701)776-5846
Fax: (701)776-6390
Co. E-mail: rugbychamber@stellarnet.com
URL: http://www.rugbynorthdakota.com
Contact: Sonia Mullally, President
Description: Promotes agricultural, business, and community development in the Rugby, ND area. **Founded:** 1909. **Telecommunication Services:** pc-trugby@gondtc.com.

55912 ■ Grafton Area Chamber of Commerce (GCC)
432 Hill Ave.
Grafton, ND 58237
Ph: (701)352-0781
Fax: (701)352-3043
Co. E-mail: gracha@polarcomm.com
URL: http://www.graftonchamber.com
Contact: Jean Jiskra, President
Description: Promotes business and community development in Grafton, ND. Sponsors SummerFest, Charity Ball, and other events. Convention/Meeting: none. **Publications:** *Membership List* (Periodic).

55913 ■ Grand Forks Chamber of Commerce (GFCC)
202 N 3rd St.
Grand Forks, ND 58203-3733
Ph: (701)772-7271
Fax: (701)772-9238
Co. E-mail: info@gochamber.org
URL: http://www.gochamber.org
Contact: Barry Wilfahrt, President
Description: Promotes business and community development in the Grand Forks, ND area. **Founded:** 1912. **Publications:** *The Voice* (Monthly).

55914 ■ Greater Bottineau Area Chamber of Commerce (GBACC)
519 Main St.
Bottineau, ND 58318-1202
Ph: (701)228-3849
Free: 800-735-6932
Fax: (701)228-5130
Co. E-mail: bcc@utma.com
URL: http://bottineau.org
Contact: Clint M. Reinoehl, Executive Director
Description: Promotes business and community development in Bottineau, ND.

55915 ■ Harvey Area Chamber of Commerce
120 W 8th St., Ste. 3
Harvey, ND 58341
Ph: (701)324-2604

Fax: (701)324-2674
Co. E-mail: chamber@harveynd.com
URL: http://www.harveynd.com
Contact: Ms. Sara Balfour, Executive Vice President
Description: Promotes business and community development in the Harvey, ND area. **Publications:** *At Work* (Monthly).

55916 ■ Hazen Chamber of Commerce
PO Box 423
Hazen, ND 58545
Ph: (701)748-6848
Free: 888-464-2936
Co. E-mail: hazenchamber@westriv.com
URL: http://www.hazennd.org
Contact: Kolie Kadrmas, Executive Director
Description: Promotes business and community development in Hazen, ND area.

55917 ■ Hettinger Area Chamber of Commerce
PO Box 1031
Hettinger, ND 58639-1031
Ph: (701)567-2531
Fax: (701)567-2690
Co. E-mail: adamschmbr@ndsupernet.com
URL: http://www.hettingernd.com
Contact: Earleen Friez, Executive Secretary Treasurer
Description: Promotes business and community development in the Hettinger, ND area. **Awards:** Business Person of the Year (Annual); Community Volunteer of the Year (Annual).

55918 ■ Jamestown Area Chamber of Commerce
120 2nd St. SE
Jamestown, ND 58402
Ph: (701)252-4830
Fax: (701)252-4837
Co. E-mail: chamber@jamestownchamber.com
URL: http://www.jamestownchamber.com
Contact: JoDee Rasmusson, Executive Director
Description: Promotes business and community development in Jamestown, ND. Sponsors Water and Buffalo Days. **Founded:** 1930. **Publications:** *Chamber News* (Monthly).

55919 ■ Kenmare Association of Commerce
PO Box 896
Kenmare, ND 58746
Ph: (701)385-4275
Fax: (701)385-4395
Co. E-mail: news@kenmarend.com
URL: http://www.kenmarend.com
Contact: Jamie Livingston, President
Description: Serves businesses, professionals and individuals to help advance the economic status of Kenmare, North Dakota.

55920 ■ Linton Industrial Development Corporation (LIDC)
c/o Sharon Jangula
101 NE 1st St.
Linton, ND 58552
Ph: (701)254-4460
Fax: (701)254-4382
Co. E-mail: lidcbek@bektel.com
URL: http://lintonnd.org
Contact: Sharon Jangula, Coordinator
Description: Aims to promote and assist existing businesses to prosper and expand. Assists clients in developing business ideas and business plans, in obtaining financing from local, state and federal agencies. Gives positive direction to the development of commerce in the City of Linton, the County of Emmons and the state of North Dakota. Carries out activities that will enhance the image and reputation of Linton as a place to live and invest.

55921 ■ *Membership List*
432 Hill Ave.
Grafton, ND 58237
Ph: (701)352-0781
Fax: (701)352-3043
Co. E-mail: gracha@polarcomm.com
URL: http://www.graftonchamber.com
Contact: Jean Jiskra, President
Released: Periodic

55922 ■ *News-N-Views*
208 Hwy. 2 W
Devils Lake, ND 58301-0879
Ph: (701)662-4903
Free: 800-233-8048
Fax: (701)662-2147
Co. E-mail: chamber@gondtc.com
URL: http://www.devilslakend.com
Contact: Suzie Kenner, Executive Director
Released: Monthly

55923 ■ North Dakota Chamber of Commerce (NDCC)
2000 Schafer St.
Bismarck, ND 58502-1204
Ph: (701)222-0929
Free: 800-382-1405
Fax: (701)222-1611
Co. E-mail: ndchamber@ndchamber.com
URL: http://www.ndchamber.com
Contact: Valerie Frohlich, Administrative Assistant
Description: Strives to enhance North Dakota's business climate through efforts like the New Economy Initiative. Creates and fights for public policy initiatives and state and federal legislation that is pro-business. Supports and develops programs and services that help improve and strengthen North Dakota businesses. Creates economic development initiatives to create new jobs and new wealth in North Dakota. Promotes North Dakota's image as an outstanding place to live, work and do business. Unites the North Dakota business community on vital business issues. **Founded:** 1924. **Awards:** Agricultural Award (Annual); Business and Industrial Development Award (Annual); Community Leadership Award (Annual); Education & Business Partnership Award (Annual); Entrepreneurial Spirit Award (Annual); Greater North Dakotan Award (Annual); Natural Resources Award (Annual); Tourism and Recreational Development Award (Annual); Vision Award (Annual).

55924 ■ Oakes Area Chamber of Commerce
c/o Audrey O'Brien
412 Main Ave.
Oakes, ND 58474
Ph: (701)742-3508
Co. E-mail: oakesnd@drtel.net
URL: http://www.oakesnd.com/chamberofcommerce.php
Contact: Jean Schmaltz, President
Description: Advances the commercial, industrial, professional, agricultural, educational and civic interests of the Oakes area. Stimulates and supports business creation and expansion.

55925 ■ *Quarterly Activities Report*
314 3rd Ave. W
Dickinson, ND 58601
Ph: (701)225-5115
Fax: (701)225-5116
URL: http://www.dickinsonchamber.org
Contact: Lexi Sebastian, Executive Director
Released: Quarterly

55926 ■ Valley City Area Chamber of Commerce/CVB
PO Box 724
Valley City, ND 58072-0724
Ph: (701)845-1891
Fax: (701)845-1892
Co. E-mail: chamber@hellovalley.com
URL: http://www.valleycitynd.com
Contact: Briana Schlosser, Office Manager
URL(s): www.hellovalley.com. **Description:** Promotes business and community development in the Valley City, ND area. Conducts Annual Chili Cook-Off, Community Days Festival, Ag Appreciation Days, Christmas Promotion and Parade, Crazy Day and Sheyenne Valley Fall Festival. **Founded:** 1904. **Publications:** *Chamber Pride* (Monthly); *Weekly E-zine Newsletter* (Weekly).

55927 ■ *The Voice*
202 N 3rd St.
Grand Forks, ND 58203-3733
Ph: (701)772-7271

Fax: (701)772-9238
Co. E-mail: info@gochamber.org
URL: http://www.gochamber.org
Contact: Barry Wilfahrt, President
Released: Monthly

55928 ■ Wahpeton Breckenridge Area Chamber of Commerce and Visitors Center
118 6th St. N
Wahpeton, ND 58075-4327
Ph: (701)642-8744
Free: 800-892-6673
Fax: (701)642-8745
URL: http://www.wahpetonbreckenridgechamber.com
Contact: Jim Oliver, Executive Vice President
Description: Promotes the businesses and community of Wahpeton, ND. **Founded:** 1937. **Awards:** Extra Mile Award (Quarterly).

55929 ■ Walhalla Area Chamber of Commerce
PO Box 34
Walhalla, ND 58282
Ph: (701)549-3939
Fax: (701)549-2410
Co. E-mail: walchmbr@utma.com
URL: http://walhalland.org
Description: Promotes the region's natural resources, scenic overlooks, historic sites, Red River oxcart trails, Native American culture, and Paleo-Indian traditions. Conducts recreational activities and events.

55930 ■ Watford City Area Chamber of Commerce
PO Box 458
Watford City, ND 58854-0458
Ph: (701)580-1493
Free: 800-701-2804
Co. E-mail: wcchamber@ruggedwest.com
URL: http://www.watfordcitychamber.com
Description: Promotes business and community development in the Watford City, ND area. **Publications:** *Chamber Newsletter* (Monthly).

55931 ■ *Weekly E-zine Newsletter*
PO Box 724
Valley City, ND 58072-0724
Ph: (701)845-1891
Fax: (701)845-1892
Co. E-mail: chamber@hellovalley.com
URL: http://www.valleycitynd.com
Contact: Briana Schlosser, Office Manager
Released: Weekly **Price:** free for members.

55932 ■ West Fargo Chamber of Commerce (WFCC)
PO Box 753
West Fargo, ND 58078-0753
Ph: (701)282-4444
Fax: (701)282-3665
Co. E-mail: chamber@westfargochamber.com
URL: http://www.westfargochamber.com
Contact: Kent P. Campbell, Executive Director
Description: Promotes business and community development in West Fargo, ND. **Founded:** 1958. **Awards:** Yard of the Month (Monthly).

55933 ■ Williston Area Chamber of Commerce (WACC)
10 Main St.
Williston, ND 58802
Ph: (701)577-6000
Fax: (701)577-8591
Co. E-mail: wchamber@willistonchamber.net
URL: http://www.willistonchamber.net/default.aspx-?AspxAutoDetectCookieSupport=1
Contact: Marci Seamples, Executive Director
Description: Seeks to promote the trade area and income potential of businesses, facilitate positive and proactive activities and encourage public/private partnerships that benefit members and citizens. **Founded:** 1907. **Publications:** *Chamber Profile* (8/year).

MINORITY BUSINESS ASSISTANCE PROGRAMS

55934 ■ North Dakota/South Dakota Native American Business Enterprise Center
3315 University Dr., Bldg. 61
Bismarck, ND 58504
Ph: (701)530-0608
Fax: (701)530-0607
Co. E-mail: bmaxon@uttc.edu
URL: http://www.ndsd-nabec.com
Contact: Brek Maxon
Description: Offers management and technical assistance services to Native American businesses.

PROCUREMENT ASSISTANCE PROGRAMS

55935 ■ Fargo Small Business Development Center - University of North Dakota
51 N Broadway, Ste. 505
Fargo, ND 58102
Ph: (701)235-1495
Free: 800-698-5726
Fax: (701)235-9734
Co. E-mail: djwadholm@dakotamep.com
URL: http://www.ndsbdc.org
Contact: Donovan Wadholm, Director

55936 ■ North Dakota Economic Development and Finance Department - Procurement Division
State Capital Tower, 14th Fl.
600 E Boulevard Ave., Dept. 012
Bismarck, ND 58505-0310
Ph: (701)328-2683
Fax: (701)328-1615
Co. E-mail: infospo@nd.gov
URL: http://www.nd.gov/spo/
Contact: Nancy Abfalter, Director, Procurement
Description: Helps businesses obtain federal, state, and local government contracts.

INCUBATORS/RESEARCH AND TECHNOLOGY PARKS

55937 ■ NDSU Research & Technology Park
1854 NDSU Research Cir. N
Fargo, ND 58102
Ph: (701)499-3600
Fax: (701)499-3610
Co. E-mail: tony@ndsuresearchpark.com
URL: http://www.ndsuresearchpark.com/Pages/default.aspx
Contact: Tony S, Grindberg, Director
Description: A small business incubator whose mission is to be a hub of technology entrepreneurship in Fargo-Moorhead and the region by providing proactive, value-added support to startup companies.

55938 ■ North Dakota State University - Upper Great Plains Transportation Institute - North Dakota Local Technical Assistance Program
515 1/2 E Broadway, Ste. 101
Bismarck, ND 58501
Ph: (701)328-9855
Free: 800-726-4143
Fax: (701)328-9866
Co. E-mail: ndsu.ndltap@ndsu.edu
URL: http://www.ndltap.org/
Contact: Dr. Donald Anderson, Director
E-mail: theusch@planis.nodak.edu
Description: Enables North Dakota businesses to use the most advanced technologies available.

55939 ■ Regional Small Business Center
417 Main Ave.
Fargo, ND 58103
Ph: (701)235-7885

Fax: (701)235-6706
Co. E-mail: don@lakeagassiz.com
URL: http://www.lakeagassiz.com/rsbc/rsbcmain.html
Contact: Don Litch, Manager, Operations
Description: A non-profit business incubator operated by the Lake Agassiz Regional Development Corporation, Fargo, North Dakota whose purpose is to assist new and existing smaller businesses in critical areas such as management, marketing, manufacturing and finance. The Center provides attractive, cost-effective space and administrative support services to its tenants.

55940 ■ University of North Dakota Center for Innovation
Ina Mae Rude Entrepreneur Center
4200 James Ray Dr.
Grand Forks, ND 58203
Ph: (701)7773132
Fax: (701)777-2339
Co. E-mail: info@innovators.net
URL: http://www.innovators.net/
Description: A small business incubator providing assistance to innovators, entrepreneurs, and researchers to launch new ventures, commercialize new technologies, and secure access to capital from private and public sources.

EDUCATIONAL PROGRAMS

55941 ■ Lake Region State College
1801 N College Dr.
Devils Lake, ND 58301-1598
Ph: (701)662-1600
Free: 800-443-1313
Fax: (701)662-1570
URL: http://www.lrsc.nodak.edu
Description: Two-year college offering a accounting and business management.

55942 ■ University of North Dakota - Workforce Development
PO Box 7131
Grand Forks, ND 58202-7131
Ph: (701)777-2663
Free: 800-225-5863
Fax: (701)777-2140
Co. E-mail: UND.pst@UND.edu
URL: http://www.und.nodak.edu
URL(s): professionaservices.UND.edu. **Description:** Offers a variety of business-related and professional enrichment courses, institutes, seminars, and workshops. The Department of Conferences and Institutes coordinates a large number of business skills and management development seminars and workshops geared for particular audiences, including small business owners/managers.

PUBLISHERS

55943 ■ Gateway Publishing Company Ltd. (Pembina, North Dakota)
276 Cavalier St.
Pembina, ND 58271-0559
Free: 800-665-4878
Co. E-mail: cookbooks@gatebook.com
URL: http://www.gatebook.com
Contact: Sherry Phaneuf, Director
Description: Description: Publishes books about child safety and also cookbooks. **Founded:** 1965.

55944 ■ University of North Dakota (CI)
Ina Mae Rude Entrepreneur Center
Grand Forks, ND 58203
Ph: (701)777-3132
Fax: (701)777-2339
Co. E-mail: info@innovators.net
URL: http://www.innovators.net
Contact: Jordan T. Schuetzle, Director
E-mail: jordan@innovators.net
Description: Provides technical and business support services to entrepreneurs, inventors, and small manufacturers. Assists specifically with the product evaluation process, the patenting process, and technology transfer. **Scope:** Offers market and demographical research, business plan development, financial forecasts and manufacturing services to

entrepreneurs, particularly manufacturing technology start up enterprises. Provides assistance to innovators, entrepreneurs, and researchers to launch new ventures, commercialize new technologies, and secure access to capital from private and public sources. **Services:** Commercial Evaluations for Emerging Technologies (11/year). **Founded:** 1984.

Publications: "The Business Plan: A State-Of-The-Art Guide"; "The Marketing Plan: Step-By-Step"; "The Ultimate Business Planner"; "Campus Entrepreneurship: A Changing Curriculum for Changing Times"; "Financing Startup Ventures"; "The Business Plan: A State-of-the-Art Guide"; "The Marketing Plan: Step-by-Step". **Educational Activities:** Center for Innova-

tion Conferences and workshops (Monthly), Seed and Angel Capital, Entrepreneur Startups, Business Planning, Market Feasibility. **Telecommunication Services:** celia@innovators.net; bruce@innovators. net; askme@innovators.net.

SMALL BUSINESS DEVELOPMENT CENTERS

55945 ■ Akron Small Business Development Center
526 S Main St., Ste. 813
Akron, OH 44311-4403
Ph: (330)375-2111
Co. E-mail: info@akronsbdc.org
URL: http://www.akronsbdc.org
Contact: Mary Ann Jasionowski, Advisor

Description: Represents and promotes the small business sector. Provides management assistance to current and prospective small business owners. Helps to improve management skills and expand the products and services of members.

55946 ■ Kent/Portage Small Business Development Center
Kent State University
Kent Regional Business Alliance
211 E Summit St.
Kent, OH 44242
Ph: (330)474-3595
URL: http://www.krba.biz/sbdc.php

Description: Represents and promotes the small business sector. Provides management assistance to current and prospective small business owners. Helps to improve management skills and expand the products and services of members.

55947 ■ Ohio Small Business Development Center at Ashland University
201 E 5th St.
Mansfield, OH 44902
Ph: (419)207-5568
Free: 877-289-1468
Fax: (419)289-5910
Co. E-mail: tmoore@braintreepartners.org
Contact: Timothy Moore, Director

Description: Represents and promotes the small business sector. Provides management assistance to current and prospective small business owners. Helps to improve management skills and expand the products and services of members.

55948 ■ Ohio Small Business Development Center at the Clermont Chamber of Commerce
4355 Ferguson Dr., Ste. 150
Cincinnati, OH 45245
Ph: (513)576-5000
Fax: (513)576-5001
Co. E-mail: john.melvin@clermontchamber.com
URL: http://www.clermontchamber.com/Small-Business-Development-Center.29.0.html
Contact: John Melvin, Director

Description: Represents and promotes the small business sector. Provides management assistance to current and prospective small business owners. Helps to improve management skills and expand the products and services of members.

55949 ■ Ohio Small Business Development Center at Terra Community College
2830 Napoleon Rd.
Fremont, OH 43420-9670
Ph: (419)559-2210
Free: 800-826-2431
Co. E-mail: bauxter@terra.edu

Description: Represents and promotes the small business sector. Provides management assistance to current and prospective small business owners. Helps to improve management skills and expand the products and services of members.

55950 ■ Small Business Development Center at Columbus State Community College
315 Cleveland Ave., Ste. 317
Columbus, OH 43215
Ph: (614)287-5294
Co. E-mail: sbdc@cscc.edu
URL: http://www.entrepreneurohio.org/center.aspx?center=17018&subloc=0
Contact: Papa Omar Diop, Director

Description: Represents and promotes the small business sector. Provides management assistance to current and prospective small business owners. Helps to improve management skills and expand the products and services of members.

55951 ■ Small Business Development Center at Edison Community College
1973 Edison Ave.
Piqua, OH 45356
Ph: (937)381-1516
Co. E-mail: jerry.alexander@edisonohio.edu
URL: http://www.entrepreneurohio.org
Contact: Jerry Alexander, Director

Description: Represents and promotes the small business sector. Provides management assistance to current and prospective small business owners. Helps to improve management skills and expand the products and services of members.

55952 ■ Small Business Development Center at James A. Rhodes State College
Keese Hall
4240 Campus Dr.
Lima, OH 45804
Ph: (419)995-8184
Co. E-mail: keller.k@rhodesstate.edu
URL: http://www.entrepreneurohio.org
Contact: Kathleen Keller, Director

Description: Represents and promotes the small business sector. Provides management assistance to current and prospective small business owners. Helps to improve management skills and expand the products and services of members.

55953 ■ Small Business Development Center at Kent State University Stark Campus
Professional Education and Conference Ctr.
6000 Frank Ave. NW
Canton, OH 44720

Ph: (330)244-3290
Co. E-mail: vpavona@kent.edu
URL: http://www.entrepreneurohio.org/center.aspx?center=17093&subloc=0
Contact: Victor Pavona, Director
URL(s): www.cantonsbdc.org. **Description:** Represents and promotes the small business sector. Provides management assistance to current and prospective small business owners. Helps to improve management skills and expand the products and services of members.

55954 ■ Small Business Development Center at Kent State University Tuscarawas Campus
Science & Advance Technology Bldg.
330 University Dr. NE
New Philadelphia, OH 44663
Ph: (330)308-7479
Co. E-mail: sschill10@kent.edu
URL: http://www.ohiosbdc.org/center.aspx?center=17103&subloc=0
Contact: Steve Schillig, Director

Description: Represents and promotes the small business sector. Provides management assistance to current and prospective small business owners. Helps to improve management skills and expand the products and services of members.

55955 ■ Small Business Development Center at Lake County Economic Development Center
One Victoria Pl., Ste. 265A
Painesville, OH 44077
Ph: (440)357-2290
Co. E-mail: gdisanto@lakelandcc.edu
URL: http://www.entrepreneurohio.org/center.aspx?center=17082&subloc=0
Contact: Cathy Walsh, Director

Description: Represents and promotes the small business sector. Provides management assistance to current and prospective small business owners. Helps to improve management skills and expand the products and services of members.

55956 ■ Small Business Development Center at Marietta
308 Front St.
Marietta, OH 45750
Ph: (740)373-5150
Co. E-mail: plankford@wscc.edu
URL: http://www.entrepreneurohio.org
Contact: Pamela Lankford, Director
URL(s): mariettachamber.com/index.php?pg=166.
Description: Represents and promotes the small business sector. Provides management assistance to current and prospective small business owners. Helps to improve management skills and expand the products and services of members.

55957 ■ Small Business Development Center at Maumee Valley Planning Organization
Defiance County East Bldg.
1300 E 2nd St., Ste. 201
Defiance, OH 43512

Ph: (419)782-6270
Co. E-mail: nwsbdc@defiance-county.com
URL: http://www.entrepreneurohio.org/center.
  aspx?center=17024&subloc=0
Contact: Merry Beavers, Director
Description: Represents and promotes the small business sector. Provides management assistance to current and prospective small business owners. Helps to improve management skills and expand the products and services of members.

55958 ■ Small Business Development Center at Ohio University
The Ridges, Bldg. 20
20 E Circle Dr.
Athens, OH 45701
Ph: (740)593-1797
Fax: (740)593-1795
Co. E-mail: mallett@ohio.edu
URL: http://www.entrepreneurohio.org
Contact: Shawn Mallett, Director
URL(s): sbdc.voinovichschool.ohio.edu. **Description:** Represents and promotes the small business sector. Provides management assistance to current and prospective small business owners. Helps to improve management skills and expand the products and services of members.

55959 ■ Small Business Development Center at The Lorain County Chamber of Commerce
151 Innovation Dr.
Elyria, OH 44035
Ph: (440)366-4314
Co. E-mail: melanie@glideit.org
URL: http://www.entrepreneurohio.org/center.
  aspx?center=17083&subloc=0
Contact: Jim Kraft, Director
Description: Represents and promotes the small business sector. Provides management assistance to current and prospective small business owners. Helps to improve management skills and expand the products and services of members.

55960 ■ Small Business Development Center at The OSU South Centers
Endeavor Center
1864 Shyville Rd.
Piketon, OH 45661
Ph: (740)289-3727
Free: 800-860-7232
Co. E-mail: mapes.281@cfaes.osu.edu
URL: http://www.entrepreneurohio.org
Contact: Ryan Mapes, Director
URL(s): sbdc.osu.edu. **Description:** Represents and promotes the small business sector. Provides management assistance to current and prospective small business owners. Helps to improve management skills and expand the products and services of members.

55961 ■ Small Business Development Center at The Urban League of Greater Cleveland
2930 Prospect Ave.
Cleveland, OH 44115
Ph: (216)622-0999
Fax: (216)622-0997
Co. E-mail: melran@clevelandsbdc.com
Description: Represents and promotes the small business sector. Provides management assistance to current and prospective small business owners. Helps to improve management skills and expand the products and services of members.

55962 ■ Small Business Development Center at Toledo Regional Chamber of Commerce
Toledo Edison Bldg.
300 Madison Ave., Ste. 200
Toledo, OH 43604
Ph: (419)243-8191
Co. E-mail: charlene.page@toledochamber.com
URL: http://www.entrepreneurohio.org/center.
  aspx?center=17021&subloc=0
Contact: Bill Wersell, Regional Director
Description: Represents and promotes the small business sector. Provides management assistance to current and prospective small business owners. Helps to improve management skills and expand the products and services of members.

55963 ■ Small Business Development Center at University of Cincinnati
3458 Reading Rd.
Cincinnati, OH 45237
Ph: (513)487-6517
Co. E-mail: smixon@gcul.org
Contact: Sheilah Mixon, Regional Director
Description: Represents and promotes the small business sector. Provides management assistance to current and prospective small business owners. Helps to improve management skills and expand the products and services of members.

55964 ■ Small Business Development Center at Wright State University
Rike Hall, Rm. 120
3640 Colonel Glenn Hwy.
Dayton, OH 45435
Ph: (937)775-3487
Fax: (937)775-3545
Co. E-mail: carol.baumhauer@wright.edu
URL: http://www.entrepreneurohio.org
Contact: Earl Gregorich, Director
Description: Represents and promotes the small business sector. Provides management assistance to current and prospective small business owners. Helps to improve management skills and expand the products and services of members.

55965 ■ Small Business Development Center at Youngstown State University
1 University Plaza
Youngstown, OH 44502
Ph: (330)941-2140
Co. E-mail: pkveisz@ysu.edu
URL: http://www.entrepreneurohio.org/center.
  aspx?center=17121&subloc=0
Contact: Patricia Veisz, Regional Director
Description: Represents and promotes the small business sector. Provides management assistance to current and prospective small business owners. Helps to improve management skills and expand the products and services of members.

55966 ■ Small Business Development Center at Zane State College
Willett-Pratt Training Ctr.
9900 Brick Church Rd.
Cambridge, OH 43725
Ph: (740)432-6568
Co. E-mail: cvoorhies@zanestate.edu
URL: http://www.entrepreneurohio.org/center.
  aspx?center=17105&subloc=0
Contact: Cindy Voorhies, Director
Description: Represents and promotes the small business sector. Provides management assistance to current and prospective small business owners. Helps to improve management skills and expand the products and services of members.

SMALL BUSINESS ASSISTANCE PROGRAMS

55967 ■ Ohio Department of Development - Entrepreneurship and Small Business Division
77 S High St.
Columbus, OH 43216-1001
Ph: (614)466-2711
Free: 800-848-1300
Fax: (614)466-0829
Co. E-mail: hskick@odod.state.oh.us
URL: http://www.odod.state.oh.us
Description: Provides assistance to small businesses.

55968 ■ Ohio Department of Development - Technology and Innovation Division
77 S High St., 25th Fl.
Columbus, OH 43215-6108
Ph: (614)466-3887
Free: 800-848-1300
Fax: (614)644-5758
URL: http://www.odod.state.oh.us/tech
Description: Stimulates working partnerships between business and academia in an effort to generate new technological ideas, new products and

processes, and new companies. The three major components are: Edison Technology Centers, Edison Seed Development Fund, and Edison Incubators.

SCORE OFFICES

55969 ■ Canton Regional SCORE
Co. E-mail: cantonscore@gmail.com

55970 ■ Columbus SCORE
401 N Front St., Ste. 200
Columbus, OH 43215
Ph: (614)469-2357
Fax: (614)469-5848
Co. E-mail: info@scorecolumbus.org
URL: http://www.scorecolumbus.org
Description: Assists individuals with their decisions to begin or to operate small businesses. Provides educational seminars and business counseling. **Founded:** 1965.

55971 ■ East Central Ohio SCORE
Co. E-mail: score@eastcentralohioscore.org

55972 ■ North Central Ohio SCORE
Co. E-mail: ncoscore@ncoscore.org

55973 ■ Northwest Ohio SCORE
Co. E-mail: scoretoledo@hotmail.com

55974 ■ SCORE Akron
175 S Main St.
Akron, OH 44308
Ph: (330)379-3163
Free: 877-AKS-CORE
Fax: (330)379-3164
Co. E-mail: akronsscore81@aol.com
URL: http://www.akronscore.org/texis/SCORE/pilot/
  main.html
Contact: Diana Bennett, Chairman
Description: Provides professional guidance and information to maximize the success of existing and emerging small businesses. Promotes entrepreneur education in Akron area, Ohio. **Founded:** 1965.

55975 ■ SCORE Butler County

55976 ■ SCORE Chapter 107
200 W 2nd St., Ste. 104
Dayton, OH 45402
Ph: (937)225-2887
Co. E-mail: score@daytonscore.org
URL: http://www.daytonscore.org
Contact: Rodney Childs, Chairman
Description: Represents volunteer businessmen and women. Provides free small business management assistance to individuals in Dayton, OH, and surrounding counties. **Scope:** starting a business. **Founded:** 1970. **Subscriptions:** 500.

55977 ■ SCORE Cincinnati
Co. E-mail: score@scoreworks.org

55978 ■ SCORE Cleveland
Co. E-mail: admin@scorecleveland.org

55979 ■ SCORE Geauga County

55980 ■ SCORE Huron County (Norwalk)

55981 ■ SCORE Lake County

55982 ■ SCORE South Central Ohio
Co. E-mail: mjones@chillicotheohio.com

55983 ■ SCORE Warren County

55984 ■ SCORE West Chester

55985 ■ Youngstown SCORE
Youngstown State University
Williamson College of Business
31 Lincoln Ave., Rm. 306
Youngstown, OH 44555
Ph: (330)746-2687
Co. E-mail: ysuscore@yahoo.com
Description: Promotes business and community development in Youngstown, OH area. Conducts business education seminars and workshops to those wanting to start a business. **Founded:** 1966.

BETTER BUSINESS BUREAUS

55986 ■ Better Business Bureau of Akron
222 W Market St.
Akron, OH 44303-2111
Ph: (330)253-4590
Fax: (330)253-6249
Co. E-mail: vwlaszyn@akronbbb.org
URL: http://akron.bbb.org
Contact: Victor J. Wlaszyn, President

Description: Provides business reliability reports and complaint handling, including informal mediation, arbitration and alternative dispute resolution, business/consumer education resources and materials, national and local charitable information and the promotion of ethical business standards and voluntary self-regulation. **Founded:** 1920. **Publications:** *Facts* (Bimonthly). **Telecommunication Services:** info@akron.bbb.org.

55987 ■ Better Business Bureau of Central Ohio—Better Business Bureau serving Columbus and Central Ohio
1169 Dublin Rd.
Columbus, OH 43215
Ph: (614)486-6336
Free: 800-759-2400
Fax: (614)486-6631
Co. E-mail: info@columbus-ohbbb.org
URL: http://www.centralohio.bbb.org
Contact: Kip Morse, President

Description: Seeks to promote and foster ethical relationship between businesses and the public through voluntary self-regulation, consumer and business education, and service excellence. Provides information to help consumers and businesses make informed purchasing decisions and avoid costly scams and frauds; settles consumer complaints through arbitration and other means.

55988 ■ Better Business Bureau, Cleveland
2800 Euclid Ave., 4th Fl.
Cleveland, OH 44115
Ph: (216)241-7678
Free: 800-233-0361
Fax: (216)861-6365
Co. E-mail: info@cleveland.bbb.org
URL: http://cleveland.bbb.org
Contact: David Weiss, President

Description: Seeks to promote and foster ethical relationship between businesses and the public through voluntary self-regulation, consumer and business education, and service excellence. Provides information to help consumers and businesses make informed purchasing decisions and avoid costly scams and frauds; settles consumer complaints through arbitration and other means.

55989 ■ Better Business Bureau of Dayton/ Miami Valley
15 W 4th St., Ste. 300
Dayton, OH 45402
Ph: (937)222-5825
Free: 800-776-5301
Fax: (937)222-3338
Co. E-mail: info@dayton.bbb.org
URL: http://dayton.bbb.org
Contact: John North, President

Description: Seeks to promote and foster ethical relationship between businesses and the public through voluntary self-regulation, consumer and business education, and service excellence. Provides information to help consumers and businesses make informed purchasing decisions and avoid costly scams and frauds; settles consumer complaints through arbitration and other means.

55990 ■ Better Business Bureau of Mahoning Valley
PO Box 1495
Youngstown, OH 44501-1495
Ph: (330)744-3111

Fax: (330)744-7336
Co. E-mail: pat@youngstown.bbb.org
URL: http://youngstown.bbb.org
Contact: Patricia B. Rose, President
Description: Seeks to promote and foster ethical relationship between businesses and the public through voluntary self-regulation, consumer and business education, and service excellence. Provides information to help consumers and businesses make informed purchasing decisions and avoid costly scams and frauds; settles consumer complaints through arbitration and other means.

55991 ■ Better Business Bureau, Northwest Ohio and Southeastern Michigan
Integrity Pl.
7668 King's Pointe Rd.
Toledo, OH 43617
Ph: (419)531-3116
Free: 800-743-4222
Fax: (419)578-6001
Co. E-mail: info@toledobbb.org
URL: http://toledo.bbb.org
Contact: Richard T. Eppstein, President
Description: Businesses in the Toledo, OH area. Seeks to promote and foster ethical relationship between businesses and the public through voluntary self-regulation, consumer and business education, and service excellence. Provides information to help consumers and businesses make informed purchasing decisions and avoid costly scams and frauds; settles consumer complaints through arbitration and other means. **Founded:** 1919.

55992 ■ Better Business Bureau of West Central Ohio
219 N McDonel St.
Lima, OH 45801
Ph: (419)223-7010
Fax: (419)229-2029
Co. E-mail: info@limabbb.org
URL: http://lima.bbb.org
Contact: Neil Winget, President
Description: Seeks to promote and foster ethical relationship between businesses and the public through voluntary self-regulation, consumer and business education, and service excellence. Provides information to help consumers and businesses make informed purchasing decisions and avoid costly scams and frauds; settles consumer complaints through arbitration and other means.

55993 ■ Cincinnati Better Business Bureau
7 W 7th St., Ste. 1600
Cincinnati, OH 45202-2097
Ph: (513)421-3015
Fax: (513)621-0907
Co. E-mail: info@cincinnati.bbb.org
URL: http://cincinnati.bbb.org
Contact: Jocile Ehrlich, President
Description: Seeks to promote and foster the highest ethical relationship between businesses and the public through voluntary self-regulation, consumer and business education, and service excellence. Provides information to help consumers and businesses make informed purchasing decisions and avoid costly scams and frauds; settles consumer complaints through arbitration and other means.

55994 ■ *Facts*
222 W Market St.
Akron, OH 44303-2111
Ph: (330)253-4590
Fax: (330)253-6249
Co. E-mail: vwlaszyn@akronbbb.org
URL: http://akron.bbb.org
Contact: Victor J. Wlaszyn, President
Released: Bimonthly

CHAMBERS OF COMMERCE

55995 ■ *Accent*
12455 State Rte. 104
Waverly, OH 45690
Ph: (740)947-7715

Fax: (740)947-7716
Co. E-mail: mail@pikechamber.org
URL: http://www.pikechamber.org
Contact: Tom Adkins, President
Released: Monthly

55996 ■ *ACTION*
222 Market Ave. N
Canton, OH 44702-1418
Ph: (330)456-7253
Free: 800-533-4302
Fax: (330)452-7786
Co. E-mail: info@cantonchamber.org
URL: http://www.cantonchamber.org
Contact: Dennis P. Saunier, President
Price: $25, for nonmembers.

55997 ■ Adams County Chamber of Commerce
111 W Main St.
West Union, OH 45693
Ph: (937)544-5454
Fax: (937)544-5555
Co. E-mail: deana@adamscountychamber.org
URL: http://adamscountychamber.org
Contact: Deana Swayne, Executive Director
Description: Seeks to improve and preserve the physical and economic development of the county. **Founded:** 1989.

55998 ■ *Allen County Business Directory*
144 N Main St.
Lima, OH 45801
Ph: (419)222-6045
Fax: (419)229-0266
Co. E-mail: chamber@limachamber.com
URL: http://www.limachamber.com
Contact: Jed E. Metzger, President
Price: $75.

55999 ■ *Alliance*
225 S Detroit St.
Kenton, OH 43326
Ph: (419)673-4131
Free: 888-642-7346
Fax: (419)674-4876
Co. E-mail: alliance@hardinohio.org
URL: http://www.hardinohio.org
Released: Bimonthly

56000 ■ Alliance Area Chamber of Commerce (AACC)
210 E Main St.
Alliance, OH 44601
Ph: (330)823-6260
Fax: (330)823-4434
Co. E-mail: info@allianceohiochamber.org
URL: http://www.allianceohiochamber.org
Contact: R. Mark Locke, President
Description: Promotes business and community development in the Alliance, OH area. Sponsors Carnation City Festival. **Founded:** 1915. **Publications:** *Image Booklet* (Triennial); *Update* (Quarterly); *Alliance for your Future.*

56001 ■ Anderson Area Chamber of Commerce
8072B Beechmont Ave.
Cincinnati, OH 45255-3177
Ph: (513)474-4802
Fax: (513)474-4857
Co. E-mail: info@andersonareachamber.org
URL: http://andersonareachamber.org
Contact: Eric Miller, Executive Director
Description: Supports the area business community, develops programs to assure their success, and creates partnerships with government and residents for the overall benefit of the Anderson Area. Provides outstanding programs in the areas of business assistance, government affairs, community development, and membership services. **Publications:** *Chamber Notes.* **Educational Activities:** After Hours (Periodic). **Awards:** Citizen of the Year (Annual).

56002 ■ Archbold Area Chamber of Commerce
300 N Defiance St.
Archbold, OH 43502
Ph: (419)445-2222

Fax: (419)445-0205
Co. E-mail: aacc@rtcexpress.net
URL: http://www.archbold.com
Contact: Julie Brink, Director
Description: Promotes business and community development in Archbold, OH area.

56003 ■ Ashland Area Chamber of Commerce (AACC)
211 Claremont Ave.
Ashland, OH 44805
Ph: (419)281-4584
Fax: (419)281-4585
Co. E-mail: chamber@ashlandoh.com
URL: http://www.ashlandohio.com
Contact: Barbie Lange, President
Description: Promotes and enhances the economic well-being of the Ashland area.

56004 ■ Ashtabula Area Chamber of Commerce (AACC)
4536 Main Ave.
Ashtabula, OH 44004
Ph: (440)998-6998
Fax: (440)992-8216
Co. E-mail: jessica@ashtabulachamber.net
URL: http://www.ashtabulachamber.net
Contact: Jessica Forsythe, President
Description: Promotes business and community development in the Ashtabula, OH area. **Founded:** 1887. **Publications:** *News and Views* (Monthly).

56005 ■ Aurora Chamber of Commerce
9 E Garfield Rd., No. 101
Aurora, OH 44202
Ph: (330)562-3355
Fax: (330)995-9052
Co. E-mail: mary@allaboutaurora.com
URL: http://www.allaboutaurora.com
Contact: Mary Sullivan, Executive Director
Description: Promotes business and community development in Aurora, OH. **Founded:** 1976. **Publications:** *Community Profile and Map.* **Awards:** Adult (Annual); Business (Annual); Citizen of the Year (Annual); Matching (Annual); Youth (Annual). **Telecommunication Services:** director@allaboutaurora.com.

56006 ■ *Bandstand*
16 State St.
Gallipolis, OH 45631
Ph: (740)446-0596
Fax: (740)446-7031
Co. E-mail: lneal@galliacounty.org
URL: http://www.galliacounty.org
Contact: Jimmy Wiseman, President
Released: Monthly **Price:** included in membership dues.

56007 ■ Barnesville Area Chamber of Commerce
130 W Main St.
Barnesville, OH 43713
Ph: (740)425-4300
Fax: (740)425-1048
Co. E-mail: bacc@sbcglobal.net
URL: http://www.barnesvilleohio.com
Contact: John Rataiczak, President
Description: Promotes business and community development in Barnesville, OH. **Founded:** 1939. **Subscriptions:** 25000. **Awards:** Citizen of the Year (Annual).

56008 ■ Beachwood Chamber of Commerce (BCC)
Three Commerce Park Sq.
2550 Chagrin Blvd., Ste. 201
Beachwood, OH 44122
Ph: (216)831-0003
Fax: (216)831-1209
Co. E-mail: mail@beachwood.org
URL: http://www.beachwood.org
Contact: Bill Mann, President
Description: Promotes business and community development in Beachwood, OH. **Founded:** 1991. **Publications:** *The Business Link* (Monthly); *Purchase Directory.*

56009 ■ Bedford Chamber of Commerce (BCC)
33 S Park St.
Bedford, OH 44146
Ph: (440)232-0115
Fax: (440)232-0521
Co. E-mail: bedfordchamberoh@sbcglobal.net
URL: http://www.bedfordchamberoh.org
Contact: Mike Romito, President
Description: Promotes business and community development in Bedford, OH. Sponsors annual town picnic. **Publications:** *Business Directory of Bedford* (Biennial); *Chamber Chatter* (Monthly).

56010 ■ Bedford Heights Chamber of Commerce (BHCC)
24816 Aurora Rd., Ste. C
Bedford Heights, OH 44146
Ph: (440)232-3369
Fax: (440)232-4868
URL: http://bedfordheightschamber.com
Contact: Mark DeLaney, President
Description: Represents the interests of businessmen and women associated together in a joint effort to preserve and protect the American free enterprise system.

56011 ■ Bellaire Area Chamber of Commerce
PO Box 205
Bellaire, MI 49615
Ph: (231)533-6023
Fax: (231)533-8764
Co. E-mail: info@bellairechamber.org
URL: http://www.bellairechamber.org
Contact: Patricia Savant, Executive Director
Description: Promotes the economic viability, cultural richness, environmental sensitivity, and the social needs of Bellaire, MI.

56012 ■ Bellbrook - Sugarcreek Area Chamber of Commerce (BSACoC)
64 W Franklin St.
Bellbrook, OH 45305-1903
Ph: (937)848-4930
Fax: (937)848-4930
Co. E-mail: info@bellbrooksugarcreekchamber.com
URL: http://bellbrooksugarcreekchamber.com
Contact: Chris Ewing, Executive Director
Description: Promotes business and community development in Bellbrook-Sugarcreek area of Ohio. **Publications:** *Newsgram* (Semiannual); *Community Business Directory* (Annual). **Educational Activities:** Business Meeting (Monthly). **Awards:** Carl Valentine Scholarship (Annual); The Chamber Pot (Annual).

56013 ■ Belpre Area Chamber of Commerce (BACC)
713 Park Dr.
Belpre, OH 45714
Ph: (740)423-8934
Fax: (740)423-6616
Co. E-mail: info@belprechamber.com
URL: http://www.belprechamber.com
Contact: Jonathan Neff, President
Description: Promotes business and community development in the Belpre, OH area. Conducts community social and promotional activities. **Founded:** 1929. **Publications:** *Chamberletter* (Bimonthly). **Educational Activities:** Business After Hours (Monthly).

56014 ■ Berea Chamber of Commerce
173 Front St.
Berea, OH 44017
Ph: (440)243-8415
Fax: (440)243-8470
Co. E-mail: bereachamber@sbcglobal.net
URL: http://www.bereaohio.com/home.cfm
Contact: Judy Groty, Executive Director
Description: Advances and develops the commercial, industrial, civic and general interest for the residents and the City of Berea. **Founded:** 1939. **Awards:** Grindstone Award (Annual).

56015 ■ Bexley Area Chamber of Commerce (BACC)
2770 E Main St., Ste. 5
Bexley, OH 43209

Ph: (614)470-4500
Co. E-mail: info@bexleyareachamber.org
URL: http://www.bexleyareachamber.org
Contact: Mary Greenman, President
Description: Promotes business and community development in the Bexley area.

56016 ■ Brecksville Chamber of Commerce (BCC)
49 Public Sq.
Brecksville, OH 44141
Ph: (440)526-7350
Fax: (440)526-7889
Co. E-mail: chambe@brecksvillechamber.com
URL: http://www.brecksvillechamber.com
Contact: Debra Branske, President
Description: Promotes business and community development in Brecksville, OH. **Founded:** 1968. **Publications:** *The Voice* (Bimonthly).

56017 ■ Bremen Chamber of Commerce
PO Box 45
Bremen, OH 43107
Ph: (740)569-9150
Co. E-mail: bremencoc@gmail.com
URL: http://www.bremenvillage.com
Contact: Natalie Nutter, President
Description: Promotes business and community development in Bremen, OH.

56018 ■ *Bridge Tour*
227 E 5th St.
Marysville, OH 43040
Ph: (937)642-6279
Free: 800-642-0087
Fax: (937)644-0422
Co. E-mail: dschaner@unioncounty.org
URL: http://www.unioncounty.org
Contact: Debra Schaner, Office Manager
Released: Annual

56019 ■ Brimfield Area Chamber of Commerce
PO Box 3414
Kent, OH 44240-3414
Ph: (330)677-6439
Co. E-mail: ddarlas2000@yahoo.com
URL: http://www.brimfieldchamber.com
Contact: Scott Mikula, President
Description: Promotes business and community development in the Brimfield, OH area. Organizes community donations for schools and police. **Founded:** 1960. **Publications:** *Monthly Minutes* (Monthly). **Educational Activities:** Brimfield Sausage Fest (Annual).

56020 ■ Broadview Heights Chamber of Commerce (BHCC)
PO Box 470201
Broadview Heights, OH 44147
Ph: (440)838-4510
Co. E-mail: office@broadviewhts.org
URL: http://www.broadviewhts.org
Contact: Thomas H. Craft, President
Description: Businesses, professionals, and government officials dedicated to advancing the prosperity of the Broadview Heights area, its residents, and business. Offers many free and low-cost promotional opportunities for members along with group benefits and discounts on products and services. **Founded:** 1979.

56021 ■ Brunswick Area Chamber of Commerce (BACC)
1434 Towne Center Blvd., Ste. C50
Brunswick, OH 44212
Ph: (330)225-8411
Fax: (330)273-8172
Co. E-mail: admin@brunswickareachamber.org
URL: http://www.brunswickareachamber.org
Contact: Melissa Krebs, President
Description: Businesses, organizations, and individuals interested in promoting the Brunswick, OH area. Holds seminars and social functions. **Founded:** 1931. **Publications:** *Connections* (Monthly). **Educational Activities:** Brunswick Area Chamber of Commerce Breakfast (Monthly).

56022 ■ Bryan Area Chamber of Commerce
c/o Daniel S. Yahraus, Exec. Dir.
Bryan, OH 43506
Ph: (419)636-2247
Fax: (419)636-5556
Co. E-mail: info@bryanchamber.org
URL: http://www.bryanchamber.org
Contact: Daniel S. Yahraus, Executive Director
Description: Promotes Bryan and enhance the quality of life and economic stability of the community.
Founded: 1947. **Publications:** *Top of Ohio Topics* (Monthly). **Telecommunication Services:** bryancc@cityofbryan.net.

56023 ■ Bucyrus Area Chamber of Commerce (BACC)
122 W Rensselaer St.
Bucyrus, OH 44820-2214
Ph: (419)562-4811
Fax: (419)562-9966
Co. E-mail: bacc@bucyrusohio.com
URL: http://www.bucyrusohio.com
Contact: Debra J. Pinion, Executive Director
Description: Promotes business and community development in Crawford County, OH. Convention/Meeting: none. **Founded:** 1925. **Publications:** *Chamber of Commerce News* (Bimonthly); *Quality of Life Book.*

56024 ■ Bulletin
245 N Main St., Ste. 100
Hudson, OH 44236
Ph: (330)650-0621
Fax: (330)656-1646
Co. E-mail: info@hudsoncoc.org
URL: http://www.explorehudson.com
Contact: Carolyn Konefal, President
Released: Monthly

56025 ■ The Business Advisor
7887 Washington Village Dr., Ste. 265
Dayton, OH 45459
Ph: (937)433-2032
Fax: (937)433-6881
Co. E-mail: deanna.lang@smrcoc.org
URL: http://www.smrcoc.org
Contact: Deanna Lang, Office Manager
Released: Monthly

56026 ■ Business Barometer
PO Box 39007
Cleveland, OH 44139-0007
Ph: (216)965-4474
Fax: (440)248-4888
Co. E-mail: ohioisraelchamber@ameritech.net
URL: http://ohioisraelchamber.com
Contact: Howard Gudell, President
Released: Quarterly **Price:** free.

56027 ■ Business Broadcast
400 S Gay St.
Mount Vernon, OH 43050
Ph: (740)393-1111
Fax: (740)393-1590
Co. E-mail: chamber@knoxchamber.com
URL: http://www.knoxchamber.com
Contact: Carol Grubaugh, Executive Director
Released: Monthly

56028 ■ Business and Community Directory
PO Box 74
Waterville, OH 43566
Ph: (419)878-5188
Fax: (419)878-5199
Co. E-mail: admin@watervillechamber.com
URL: http://www.watervillechamber.com
Contact: Dave Boothe, President
Released: Quarterly **Price:** included in membership dues.

56029 ■ Business Directory of Bedford
33 S Park St.
Bedford, OH 44146
Ph: (440)232-0115
Fax: (440)232-0521
Co. E-mail: bedfordchamberoh@sbcglobal.net
URL: http://www.bedfordchamberoh.org
Contact: Mike Romito, President
Released: Biennial

56030 ■ Business and Industry Directory
20 N Broadway
Lebanon, OH 45036
Ph: (513)932-1100
Fax: (513)932-9050
Co. E-mail: info@lebanonchamber.org
URL: http://www.lebanonchamber.org
Contact: Sara Arseneau, Executive Director
Released: Periodic

56031 ■ The Business Link
Three Commerce Park Sq.
2550 Chagrin Blvd., Ste. 201
Beachwood, OH 44122
Ph: (216)831-0003
Fax: (216)831-1209
Co. E-mail: mail@beachwood.org
URL: http://www.beachwood.org
Contact: Bill Mann, President
Released: Monthly

56032 ■ Business Network
144 N Main St.
Lima, OH 45801
Ph: (419)222-6045
Fax: (419)229-0266
Co. E-mail: chamber@limachamber.com
URL: http://www.limachamber.com
Contact: Jed E. Metzger, President
Released: Monthly

56033 ■ Business Notes
c/o Barb Hornyak, Admin. Asst.
80 Community Rd.
Tallmadge, OH 44278
Ph: (330)633-5417
Fax: (330)633-5415
Co. E-mail: tallmadgechamber@onecommail.com
URL: http://www.tallmadge-chamber.com
Contact: Mary Cea, Executive Director
Released: Monthly

56034 ■ Business and Professional Directory
20 S Limestone St., Ste. 100
Springfield, OH 45502
Ph: (937)325-7621
Free: 800-803-1553
Fax: (937)325-8765
Co. E-mail: info@greaterspringfield.com
URL: http://chamber.greaterspringfield.com
Contact: Michael J. McDorman, President
Released: Annual **Price:** $30, for nonmembers; $15, for members (one copy free).

56035 ■ Business Update
325 S Main St.
Springboro, OH 45066
Ph: (937)748-0074
Fax: (937)748-0525
Co. E-mail: chamber@springboroohio.org
URL: http://www.springboroohio.org
Contact: Anne Stremanos, Executive Director
Released: Monthly **Price:** free for members.

56036 ■ Businews
13 W Columbus St.
Pickerington, OH 43147
Ph: (614)837-1958
Fax: (614)837-6420
Co. E-mail: president@pickeringtonchamber.com
URL: http://www.pickeringtonchamber.com
Contact: Brett A. Miller, Chairman
Released: Monthly

56037 ■ Buyers Guide
137 Lincoln Way E
Massillon, OH 44646
Ph: (330)833-3146
Co. E-mail: info@massillonohchamber.com
URL: http://www.massillonohchamber.com
Contact: Robert A. Sanderson, President
Released: Annual

56038 ■ Buyer's Guide
40 N South St.
Wilmington, OH 45177
Ph: (937)382-2737
Free: 888-922-2250

Fax: (937)383-2316
Co. E-mail: karenhaley@wccchamber.com
URL: http://www.wccchamber.com
Contact: Karen M. Haley, President
Released: Annual

56039 ■ Buyer's Guide and Membership Directory
226 N Main St.
Celina, OH 45822-1663
Ph: (419)586-2219
Fax: (419)586-8645
Co. E-mail: info@celinamercer.com
URL: http://www.celinamercer.com
Contact: Pam Buschur, Executive Director
Released: Annual

56040 ■ Buyer's Guide and Membership Directory
713 E State St.
Salem, OH 44460-2911
Ph: (330)337-3473
Fax: (330)337-3474
Co. E-mail: dave.nestic@jumpstartinc.org
URL: http://www.salemohiochamber.org
Contact: Dave Nestic, President
Released: Periodic

56041 ■ Calcutta Area Chamber of Commerce
15442 Pugh Rd.
Calcutta, OH 43920
Ph: (330)386-6060
Fax: (330)386-6060
Co. E-mail: calcuttaareachamber@stclairtwp.com
URL: http://www.calcuttaohiochamber.com
Contact: Lori Kline, Executive Director
Description: Promotes business and community development in Calcutta, OH.

56042 ■ Cambridge Area Chamber of Commerce (CCC)
607 Wheeling Ave.
Cambridge, OH 43725
Ph: (740)439-6688
Fax: (740)439-6689
Co. E-mail: info@cambridgeohiochamber.com
URL: http://www.cambridgeohiochamber.com
Contact: Joanne Sexton, President
Description: Promotes business and community development in the Cambridge, OH area. **Publications:** *Crossroads* (Quarterly). **Educational Activities:** Swing into Spring Homeshow (Annual).

56043 ■ Canal Winchester Area Chamber of Commerce (CWACC)
20 N High St.
Canal Winchester, OH 43110
Ph: (614)837-1556
Fax: (614)837-9901
Co. E-mail: chamber@canalwinchester.com
URL: http://www.canalwinchester.com
Contact: Amanda Lemke, Executive Director
Description: Represents businesses, individuals and organizations dedicated to the promotion of business and the community. Promotes and fosters the free enterprise system through economic development. Advocates for local business interests, and provides investor benefits. **Founded:** 1985. **Publications:** *The Reporter* (Monthly). **Educational Activities:** Membership (Monthly).

56044 ■ Canton Regional Chamber of Commerce
222 Market Ave. N
Canton, OH 44702-1418
Ph: (330)456-7253
Free: 800-533-4302
Fax: (330)452-7786
Co. E-mail: info@cantonchamber.org
URL: http://www.cantonchamber.org
Contact: Dennis P. Saunier, President
Description: Provides services to members and helps advance the economic growth of Canton and the Stark County region. **Founded:** 1917. **Publications:** *ACTION.*

56045 ■ Carey Area Chamber of Commerce
PO Box 94
Carey, OH 43316-0094
Ph: (419)396-7856
Fax: (419)396-7856
Co. E-mail: director@careychamber.com
URL: http://www.careychamber.com
Contact: Ron Dunn, Executive Director
Description: Promotes business and community development in Carey, OH. **Scope:** current local and county business, industry lists, phone directory distribution, brochures, social and civic lists, membership directories. **Founded:** 1993. **Subscriptions:** books business records maps papers reports.

56046 ■ Celina-Mercer County Chamber of Commerce
226 N Main St.
Celina, OH 45822-1663
Ph: (419)586-2219
Fax: (419)586-8645
Co. E-mail: info@celinamercer.com
URL: http://www.celinamercer.com
Contact: Pam Buschur, Executive Director
Description: Promotes business and community development in the Mercer County, OH area. Sponsors area festival and operates Small Business Development Center. **Founded:** 1935. **Publications:** *Buyer's Guide and Membership Directory* (Annual). **Educational Activities:** Ambassador Committee Meeting (Monthly).

56047 ■ Chagrin Valley
88 N Main St.
Chagrin Falls, OH 44022
Ph: (440)247-6607
Co. E-mail: info@cvcc.org
URL: http://www.cvcc.org
Contact: Darci Spilman, Executive Director
Released: Annual

56048 ■ Chagrin Valley Chamber of Commerce (CVCC)
88 N Main St.
Chagrin Falls, OH 44022
Ph: (440)247-6607
Co. E-mail: info@cvcc.org
URL: http://www.cvcc.org
Contact: Darci Spilman, Executive Director
Description: Serves as a powerful regional force, encouraging business to relocate to the Chagrin Valley. Presents the interests of business and industry before local and state governments. Supports the cultural and civic life of the communities and works to make the Valley a better place to live and do business. **Founded:** 1943. **Publications:** *Chagrin Valley* (Annual); *The Reporter* (Monthly).

56049 ■ *The Chamber Bulletin*
234 Broadway St.
Jackson, OH 45640-1702
Ph: (740)286-2722
Fax: (740)286-8443
Co. E-mail: info@jacksonohio.org
URL: http://www.jacksonohio.org
Contact: Randy R. Heath, Executive Director
Released: Monthly **Price:** free.

56050 ■ *Chamber Chat*
111 South St.
Chardon, OH 44024
Ph: (440)285-9050
Fax: (440)286-8964
Co. E-mail: emabel@chardonchamber.com
URL: http://www.chardonchamber.com
Contact: Matt Moormeier, President
Released: 3/year

56051 ■ *Chamber Chat*
30 E Auglaize St.
Wapakoneta, OH 45895
Ph: (419)738-2911
Fax: (419)738-2977
Co. E-mail: wapcofc@bright.net
URL: http://www.wapakoneta.com
Contact: Dan Graf, Director
Released: Monthly

56052 ■ *Chamber Chatter*
33 S Park St.
Bedford, OH 44146
Ph: (440)232-0115
Fax: (440)232-0521
Co. E-mail: bedfordchamberoh@sbcglobal.net
URL: http://www.bedfordchamberoh.org
Contact: Mike Romito, President
Released: Monthly **Price:** free.

56053 ■ *Chamber Chatter*
401 Main St.
Coshocton, OH 43812
Ph: (740)622-5411
Fax: (740)622-9902
Co. E-mail: chamberofcommerce@coshoctoncounty.net
URL: http://www.coshoctoncounty.net/agency/chamber
Contact: Amy Stockdale, Executive Director
Released: 10/year

56054 ■ *Chamber Chatter*
161 W Water St.
Oak Harbor, OH 43449
Ph: (419)898-0479
Fax: (419)898-2429
Co. E-mail: chamber@oakharborohio.net
URL: http://www.oakharborohio.com
Contact: Valerie Winterfield, Executive Director
Released: Periodic

56055 ■ *Chamber Chronicle*
PO Box 13607
Whitehall, OH 43213
Ph: (614)237-7792
Fax: (614)235-8646
Co. E-mail: info@whitehallchamber.org
URL: http://www.whitehallchamber.org
Contact: Jennifer Moeller, President

56056 ■ *Chamber of Commerce News*
122 W Rensselaer St.
Bucyrus, OH 44820-2214
Ph: (419)562-4811
Fax: (419)562-9966
Co. E-mail: bacc@bucyrusohio.com
URL: http://www.bucyrusohio.com
Contact: Debra J. Pinion, Executive Director
Released: Bimonthly **Price:** free for members.

56057 ■ *Chamber of Commerce Newsletter*
120 N Market St.
Lisbon, OH 44432
Ph: (330)424-1803
Fax: (330)424-9003
Co. E-mail: lacoc2@sbcglobal.net
URL: http://www.lisbonareachamber.com
Contact: Marilyn McCullough, Executive Director
Released: Quarterly

56058 ■ *Chamber Communicator*
235 Main St.
Conneaut, OH 44030
Ph: (440)593-2402
Fax: (440)593-1514
URL: http://www.conneautchamber.org
Contact: Wendy DuBey, Executive Director
Released: Periodic

56059 ■ *Chamber Connect*
441 Vine St., Ste. 300, Carew Twr.
Cincinnati, OH 45202-2812
Ph: (513)579-3100
Fax: (513)579-3101
Co. E-mail: info@cincinnatichamber.com
URL: http://www.gccc.com
Contact: Ellen van der Horst, President
Released: Monthly

56060 ■ *Chamber Connection*
328 N Main St.
Columbiana, OH 44408
Ph: (330)482-3822
Co. E-mail: info@columbianachamber.com
URL: http://www.columbianachamber.com
Contact: Deann Davis, Director
Released: Monthly **Price:** included in membership dues.

56061 ■ *Chamber Connection*
377 W Liberty St.
Wooster, OH 44691
Ph: (330)262-5735
Fax: (330)262-5745
Co. E-mail: wchamber@bright.net
URL: http://www.woosterchamber.com
Contact: Sue Peeples, Vice President
Released: Monthly

56062 ■ *Chamber Connection*
105 W Indiana Ave.
Perrysburg, OH 43551
Ph: (419)874-9147
Fax: (419)872-9347
Co. E-mail: director@perrysburgchamber.com
URL: http://www.perrysburgchamber.com
Contact: Sandy Latchem, Executive Director
Released: Monthly

56063 ■ *Chamber Directory*
9 W National Rd.
Englewood, OH 45322
Ph: (937)836-2550
Fax: (937)836-2485
URL: http://www.northmont-area-coc.org
Contact: Cathy Hutton, Chief Executive Officer
Price: included in membership dues.

56064 ■ *Chamber Hi-Lites*
2460 Navarre Ave.
Oregon, OH 43616
Ph: (419)693-5580
Fax: (419)693-9990
Co. E-mail: director@embchamber.org
URL: http://www.embchamber.org
Contact: Angela Crosby, President
Released: Monthly

56065 ■ *Chamber Insider*
28938 Lorain Rd., Ste. 204
North Olmsted, OH 44070
Ph: (440)777-3368
Fax: (440)777-9361
Co. E-mail: rlgarno@aol.com
URL: http://www.nolmstedchamber.com
Contact: John Sobolewski, Executive Director
Released: Monthly

56066 ■ *The Chamber Link*
145 N Court St.
Medina, OH 44256
Ph: (330)723-8773
Fax: (330)722-6844
Co. E-mail: info@medinaohchamber.com
URL: http://www.medinaohchamber.com
Contact: Valerie Rapp, Chairperson
Released: Bimonthly **Price:** included in membership dues.

56067 ■ *The Chamber Network*
325 Clinton St.
Defiance, OH 43512
Ph: (419)782-7946
Fax: (419)782-0111
Co. E-mail: isaaclee@defiancechamber.com
URL: http://www.defiancechamber.com
Contact: Isaac Lee, President
Released: Monthly

56068 ■ *Chamber News*
PO Box 32611
Euclid, OH 44132
Ph: (216)731-9322
Fax: (216)865-4925
Co. E-mail: sheila@euclidchamber.com
URL: http://www.euclidchamber.com/home.aspx
Contact: Brian Moore, Chairman
Released: Monthly

56069 ■ *Chamber News*
6972 Spinach Dr.
Mentor, OH 44060
Ph: (440)255-1616
Fax: (440)255-1717
Co. E-mail: info@mentorchamber.org
URL: http://www.mentorchamber.org
Contact: Marie S. Pucak, Executive Director
Released: Monthly

56070 ■ *Chamber News*
2250 E Enterprise Pkwy.
Twinsburg, OH 44087
Ph: (330)963-6249
Fax: (330)963-6995
Co. E-mail: djohnson@twinsburgchamber.com
URL: http://www.twinsburgchamber.com
Contact: Mr. Douglas H. Johnson, Executive Director
Released: Monthly **Price:** free for members.

56071 ■ *Chamber News*
113 Miami St.
Urbana, OH 43078
Ph: (937)653-5764
Free: 877-873-5764
Fax: (937)652-1599
Co. E-mail: info@champaignohio.com
URL: http://www.champaigncoc.com
Contact: Tina Knotts, Executive Director
Released: Bimonthly

56072 ■ *Chamber News*
334 W Market St.
Xenia, OH 45385-2843
Ph: (937)372-3591
Fax: (937)372-2192
Co. E-mail: xacc@xacc.com
URL: http://www.xacc.com
Contact: Alan Liming, President
Released: Monthly

56073 ■ *Chamber News*
405 SW Public Sq., Ste. 330
Troy, OH 45373
Ph: (937)339-8769
Fax: (937)339-4944
Co. E-mail: tacc@troyohiochamber.com
URL: http://www.troyohiochamber.com
Contact: J.C. Wallace, President
Released: Monthly

56074 ■ *Chamber News*
101 Dayton St.
Yellow Springs, OH 45387-1817
Ph: (937)767-2686
Fax: (937)767-7876
Co. E-mail: info@yellowspringsohio.org
URL: http://www.yellowspringsohio.org
Contact: Karen Wintrow, Executive Director
Released: Monthly

56075 ■ *Chamber Notes*
8072B Beechmont Ave.
Cincinnati, OH 45255-3177
Ph: (513)474-4802
Fax: (513)474-4857
Co. E-mail: info@andersonareachamber.org
URL: http://andersonareachamber.org
Contact: Eric Miller, Executive Director

56076 ■ *Chamber Report*
109 N Broad St.
Lancaster, OH 43130
Ph: (740)653-8251
Fax: (740)653-7074
Co. E-mail: info@lancoc.org
URL: http://www.lancoc.org
Contact: Travis Markwood, President
Released: Monthly **Price:** included in membership dues.

56077 ■ *Chamber Update*
12 N Central Ave.
Fairborn, OH 45324-5002
Ph: (937)878-3191
Fax: (937)878-3197
Co. E-mail: chamber@fairborn.com
URL: http://www.fairborn.com
Contact: Paul Newman, Executive Director
Released: Monthly **Price:** free for members.

56078 ■ *Chamber Viewpoint*
1199 Professional Dr.
Van Wert, OH 45891
Ph: (419)238-4390
Free: 877-770-4438

Fax: (419)238-4589
Co. E-mail: chamber@vanwertchamber.com
URL: http://www.vanwertchamber.com
Contact: Kate Gribble, President
Released: Monthly **Price:** included in membership dues.

56079 ■ *Chamber Vision*
62 S Washington St.
Tiffin, OH 44883
Ph: (419)447-4141
Fax: (419)447-5141
Co. E-mail: info@tiffinchamber.com
URL: http://tiffinchamber.com
Contact: Anne Lange DeVine, Chairman
Released: Periodic

56080 ■ *Chamberletter*
713 Park Dr.
Belpre, OH 45714
Ph: (740)423-8934
Fax: (740)423-6616
Co. E-mail: info@belprechamber.com
URL: http://www.belprechamber.com
Contact: Jonathan Neff, President
Released: Bimonthly **Price:** free for members.

56081 ■ *ChamberLetter*
201 Dayton St.
Hamilton, OH 45011-1633
Ph: (513)844-1500
Fax: (513)844-1999
Co. E-mail: kenny@hamilton-ohio.com
URL: http://www.hamilton-ohio.com
Contact: Kenny Craig, President
Released: Monthly

56082 ■ *ChamberNotes*
32 S Sandusky St.
Delaware, OH 43015
Ph: (740)369-6221
Fax: (740)369-4817
Co. E-mail: dachamber@delawareohiochamber.com
URL: http://www.delawareareachamber.com
Contact: Holly Quaine, President

56083 ■ *Chambervision*
441 Vine St., Ste. 300, Carew Twr.
Cincinnati, OH 45202-2812
Ph: (513)579-3100
Fax: (513)579-3101
Co. E-mail: info@cincinnatichamber.com
URL: http://www.gccc.com
Contact: Ellen van der Horst, President
Released: Monthly

56084 ■ *ChamberWatch*
1 Chamber Plz.
Dayton, OH 45402-2400
Ph: (937)226-1444
Fax: (937)226-8254
Co. E-mail: info@dacc.org
URL: http://www.daytonchamber.org
Contact: Phillip L. Parker, President
Released: Bimonthly

56085 ■ Champaign County Chamber of Commerce
113 Miami St.
Urbana, OH 43078
Ph: (937)653-5764
Free: 877-873-5764
Fax: (937)652-1599
Co. E-mail: info@champaignohio.com
URL: http://www.champaigncoc.com
Contact: Tina Knotts, Executive Director
Description: Promotes business and community development in Champaign County, OH. Holds monthly board meeting. **Founded:** 1950. **Publications:** *Chamber News* (Bimonthly).

56086 ■ Chardon Area Chamber of Commerce (CACC)
111 South St.
Chardon, OH 44024
Ph: (440)285-9050

Fax: (440)286-8964
Co. E-mail: emabel@chardonchamber.com
URL: http://www.chardonchamber.com
Contact: Matt Moormeier, President
Description: Promotes business and community development in the Chardon, OH area. **Founded:** 1927. **Publications:** *Chamber Chat* (3/year). **Educational Activities:** Community Business Seminar (Annual). **Awards:** Business Person of the Year (Annual).

56087 ■ Chesterland Chamber of Commerce (CCC)
8228 Mayfield Rd., Ste. 4B
Chesterland, OH 44026
Ph: (440)729-7297
Fax: (440)729-2690
Co. E-mail: ccoc@chesterlandchamber.com
URL: http://www.chesterlandchamber.com
Description: Promotes business and community development in Chester Township, Ohio and surrounding areas, including Geauga County and adjacent Cuyahoga and Lake counties. Publishes the Chester telephone directory annually. **Founded:** 1962. **Publications:** *The Communicator* (Monthly); *Telephone Directory* (Annual). **Educational Activities:** Community Appreciation Dinner (Annual); Chesterland Chamber of Commerce Meeting (Monthly).

56088 ■ Chillicothe Ross Chamber of Commerce (CRCC)
45 E Main St.
Chillicothe, OH 45601
Ph: (740)702-2722
Fax: (740)702-2727
Co. E-mail: eschmidt@chillicotheohio.com
URL: http://www.chillicotheohio.com
Contact: Marvin E. Jones, President
Description: Promotes business and community development in Ross County, OH. **Founded:** 1912. **Publications:** *Chillicothe Ross Chamber of Commerce--Membership Directory & Buyer's Guide* (Annual); *Membership Directory and Buyer's Guide* (Annual). **Awards:** Entrepreneur of the Year (Annual); Volunteer of the Year (Annual). **Telecommunication Services:** ccinfo@chillicotheohio.com.

56089 ■ Cincinnati U.S.A. Business Connections Directory
441 Vine St., Ste. 300, Carew Twr.
Cincinnati, OH 45202-2812
Ph: (513)579-3100
Fax: (513)579-3101
Co. E-mail: info@cincinnatichamber.com
URL: http://www.gccc.com
Contact: Ellen van der Horst, President
Released: Annual

56090 ■ Circleville - Pickaway Chamber of Commerce
325 W Main St.
Circleville, OH 43113
Ph: (740)474-4923
Fax: (740)477-6800
Co. E-mail: chamber@pickaway.com
URL: http://pickawaychamber.camp7.org
Contact: Amy Elsea, President
Description: Represents the interests of the business industry in Pickaway County.

56091 ■ Clermont County Chamber of Commerce (CCC)
4355 Ferguson Dr., Ste. 150
Cincinnati, OH 45245
Ph: (513)576-5000
Fax: (513)576-5001
Co. E-mail: chamber@clermontchamber.com
URL: http://www.clermontchamber.com
Contact: Matthew D. Van Sant, President
Description: Encourages businesses to relocate to Clermont, existing businesses to stay in Clermont, and new and growing businesses to establish their operations in the county. Provides economic development assistance to companies interested in Clermont County, including assistance with financing, expansion, relocation, site identification, and labor force development. **Founded:** 1969. **Publications:** *Images of Clermont County* (Annual); *Intercom* (Monthly); *Im-*

ages of Clermont County (Annual). **Awards:** Business Advocate Award (Annual); Customer Focus (Annual); Emerging Small Business Award (Annual); Innovative Business Practice (Annual); New Member of the Year (Annual).

56092 ■ *Club List*
PO Box 32611
Euclid, OH 44132
Ph: (216)731-9322
Fax: (216)865-4925
Co. E-mail: sheila@euclidchamber.com
URL: http://www.euclidchamber.com/home.aspx
Contact: Brian Moore, Chairman
Released: Monthly

56093 ■ Columbiana Area Chamber of Commerce (CACC)
328 N Main St.
Columbiana, OH 44408
Ph: (330)482-3822
Co. E-mail: info@columbianachamber.com
URL: http://www.columbianachamber.com
Contact: Deann Davis, Director
Description: Represents business and community leaders committed to integrity and fair trade. Strives to promote business and commerce in the Columbiana area. Serves members by providing networking opportunities and promoting area businesses, industry and the community as a whole. Offers business involvement in: Safety Council; Human Resource Seminars; Quarterly Networking Opportunities; and Quarterly Educational Opportunities. **Scope:** business. **Publications:** *Chamber Connection* (Monthly). **Awards:** Community Awards (Annual).

56094 ■ Columbus Chamber
150 S Front St., Ste. 200
Columbus, OH 43215
Ph: (614)225-6923
Fax: (614)221-1408
Co. E-mail: ty_marsh@columbus.org
Contact: Ty D. Marsh, President
Description: Fosters economic growth and business development in Greater Columbus community. **Publications:** *Member Connection* (Monthly); *Columbus Employment Resource Directory* (Biennial).

56095 ■ *Commerce*
205 N 5th St.
Zanesville, OH 43701
Ph: (740)455-8282
Free: 800-743-2303
Fax: (740)454-2963
Co. E-mail: dmatz@zmchamber.com
URL: http://www.zmchamber.com
Contact: Thomas C. Poorman, President
Released: Annual

56096 ■ *The Communicator*
99 Commerce Park Dr.
Westerville, OH 43082
Ph: (614)882-8917
Fax: (614)882-2085
Co. E-mail: info@westervillechamber.com
URL: http://www.westervillechamber.com
Contact: Janet Davis, President
Released: Monthly **Price:** free for members.

56097 ■ *The Communicator*
8228 Mayfield Rd., Ste. 4B
Chesterland, OH 44026
Ph: (440)729-7297
Fax: (440)729-2690
Co. E-mail: ccoc@chesterlandchamber.com
URL: http://www.chesterlandchamber.com
Released: Monthly

56098 ■ *Communique*
5706 Turney Rd., Ste. 101
Garfield Heights, OH 44125
Ph: (216)475-7775
Fax: (216)475-2237
Co. E-mail: gabriellah@garfieldchamber.com
URL: http://www.garfieldchamber.com
Contact: Gabriella Huszarik, Executive Director
Released: Periodic

56099 ■ *Community Business Directory*
64 W Franklin St.
Bellbrook, OH 45305-1903
Ph: (937)848-4930
Fax: (937)848-4930
Co. E-mail: info@bellbrooksugarcreekchamber.com
URL: http://bellbrooksugarcreekchamber.com
Contact: Chris Ewing, Executive Director
Released: Annual **Price:** free.

56100 ■ *Community Guide and Profile*
13 W Columbus St.
Pickerington, OH 43147
Ph: (614)837-1958
Fax: (614)837-6420
Co. E-mail: president@pickeringtonchamber.com
URL: http://www.pickeringtonchamber.com
Contact: Brett A. Miller, Chairman

56101 ■ *Community Profile Book*
334 W Market St.
Xenia, OH 45385-2843
Ph: (937)372-3591
Fax: (937)372-2192
Co. E-mail: xacc@xacc.com
URL: http://www.xacc.com
Contact: Alan Liming, President
Released: Biennial

56102 ■ *Community Profile and Map*
9 E Garfield Rd., No. 101
Aurora, OH 44202
Ph: (330)562-3355
Fax: (330)995-9052
Co. E-mail: mary@allaboutaurora.com
URL: http://www.allaboutaurora.com
Contact: Mary Sullivan, Executive Director

56103 ■ *Compass*
108 E Wyandot Ave.
Upper Sandusky, OH 43351
Ph: (419)294-3349
Free: 800-686-1261
Fax: (419)294-3531
Co. E-mail: upperchamber@udata.com
URL: http://www.uppersanduskychamber.com
Contact: Aaron Korte, Executive Director
Released: Bimonthly

56104 ■ *The Complete Wage and Hour Manual*
230 E Town St.
Columbus, OH 43215-0159
Ph: (614)228-4201
Free: 800-622-1893
Fax: (614)228-6403
Co. E-mail: occ@ohiochamber.com
URL: http://www.ohiochamber.com
Contact: Andrew E. Doehrel, President

56105 ■ *Comprehensive Guide to Members*
7887 Washington Village Dr., Ste. 265
Dayton, OH 45459
Ph: (937)433-2032
Fax: (937)433-6881
Co. E-mail: deanna.lang@smrcoc.org
URL: http://www.smrcoc.org
Contact: Deanna Lang, Office Manager
Released: Annual

56106 ■ Conneaut Area Chamber of Commerce (CACC)
235 Main St.
Conneaut, OH 44030
Ph: (440)593-2402
Fax: (440)593-1514
URL: http://www.conneautchamber.org
Contact: Wendy DuBey, Executive Director
Description: Promotes business and community development in the Conneaut, OH area. Sponsors annual Community Appreciation Week in August, flag program in downtown area and harbor area, lights of love tree in November and December. **Founded:** 1906. **Publications:** *Chamber Communicator* (Periodic).

56107 ■ *Connections*
1434 Towne Center Blvd., Ste. C50
Brunswick, OH 44212

Ph: (330)225-8411
Fax: (330)273-8172
Co. E-mail: admin@brunswickareachamber.org
URL: http://www.brunswickareachamber.org
Contact: Melissa Krebs, President
Released: Monthly

56108 ■ *Convention & Visitors Bureau*
227 E 5th St.
Marysville, OH 43040
Ph: (937)642-6279
Free: 800-642-0087
Fax: (937)644-0422
Co. E-mail: dschaner@unioncounty.org
URL: http://www.unioncounty.org
Contact: Debra Schaner, Office Manager
Released: Monthly

56109 ■ Coshocton County Chamber of Commerce—Coshocton Area Chamber of CommerceCoshocton Chamber of Commerce;
401 Main St.
Coshocton, OH 43812
Ph: (740)622-5411
Fax: (740)622-9902
Co. E-mail: chamberofcommerce@coshoctoncounty. net
URL: http://www.coshoctoncounty.net/agency/ chamber
Contact: Amy Stockdale, Executive Director
Description: Promotes business and community development in Coshocton County, OH. Sponsors annual Coshocton Canal Festival, Coshocton Hot Air Balloon Race, and T.V. Auction. **Publications:** *Chamber Chatter* (10/year). **Awards:** Community Improvement Award of the Year (Annual); Richard Rea Small Business of the Year Award (Annual); Rotary Club Employee of the Year Award (Annual).

56110 ■ *County Directory*
37840 Cadiz-Dennison Rd.
Cadiz, OH 43907
Ph: (740)942-3350
Fax: (740)942-0009
Co. E-mail: hrcctour@eohio.net
URL: http://pages.eohio.net/harrisonchamber
Contact: Ed Coultrap, Executive Director

56111 ■ *Crossroads*
607 Wheeling Ave.
Cambridge, OH 43725
Ph: (740)439-6688
Fax: (740)439-6689
Co. E-mail: info@cambridgeohiochamber.com
URL: http://www.cambridgeohiochamber.com
Contact: Joanne Sexton, President
Released: Quarterly

56112 ■ Cuyahoga Falls Chamber of Commerce (CFCC)
151 Portage Trail, Ste. 1
Cuyahoga Falls, OH 44221
Ph: (330)929-6756
Fax: (330)929-4278
Co. E-mail: info@cfchamber.com
URL: http://www.cfchamber.com
Contact: Laura Petrella, Chief Executive Officer
URL(s): cfchamber.com. **Description:** Promotes economic growth and development by encouraging programs designed to support, strengthen and expand the local businesses in Cuyahoga Falls. Supports activities of a civic, social and cultural nature which are designed to increase the functional and aesthetic values of the community. **Founded:** 1926. **Publications:** *Cuyahoga Falls Chamber of Commerce--Membership Directory.*

56113 ■ Darke County Chamber of Commerce
622 S Broadway
Greenville, OH 45331

Ph: (937)548-2102
Co. E-mail: info@darkecountyohio.com
URL: http://www.darkecountyohio.com/cwt/external/
  wcpages/index.aspx
Contact: Sharon Deschambeau, President
Description: Promotes business and community development in the Greenville, OH area. **Founded:** 1927. **Publications:** *Industrial Directory*; *Business Start-up Guide*; *Darke County Image Book*.

56114 ■ **Dayton Area Chamber of Commerce**
1 Chamber Plz.
Dayton, OH 45402-2400
Ph: (937)226-1444
Fax: (937)226-8254
Co. E-mail: info@dacc.org
URL: http://www.daytonchamber.org
Contact: Phillip L. Parker, President
Description: Promotes business and community development in Dayton, OH area. **Founded:** 1907. **Publications:** *ChamberWatch* (Bimonthly); *Focus* (Quarterly); *Dayton Area Chamber of Commerce-- Membership Directory and Community Guide* (Annual); *International Trade Directory for Dayton, Ohio* (Biennial). **Educational Activities:** Membership Meeting (Annual).

56115 ■ **Defiance Area Chamber of Commerce**
325 Clinton St.
Defiance, OH 43512
Ph: (419)782-7946
Fax: (419)782-0111
Co. E-mail: isaaclee@defiancechamber.com
URL: http://www.defiancechamber.com
Contact: Isaac Lee, President
Description: Office holders, business leaders, educators, youth professionals and small business owners. Acts as a respected voice of advocacy for business and education in Defiance County. **Publications:** *The Chamber Network* (Monthly).

56116 ■ **Delaware Area Chamber of Commerce (DACC)**
32 S Sandusky St.
Delaware, OH 43015
Ph: (740)369-6221
Fax: (740)369-4817
Co. E-mail: dachamber@delawareohiochamber.com
URL: http://www.delawareareachamber.com
Contact: Holly Quaine, President
Description: Promotes business and community development in Delaware County, OH. **Founded:** 1907. **Publications:** *ChamberNotes*; *Manufacturer Directory* (Annual); *Welcome Book* (Quadrennial).

56117 ■ **Delphos Area Chamber of Commerce (DACC)**
310 N Main St.
Delphos, OH 45833
Ph: (419)695-1771
Fax: (419)692-1751
Co. E-mail: info@delphoschamber.com
URL: http://www.delphoschamber.com
Description: Promotes business and community development in the Delphos, OH area. Sponsors annual Canal Days Festival. **Founded:** 1929.

56118 ■ **Delta Chamber of Commerce**
PO Box 96
Delta, OH 43515-0096
Ph: (419)822-3089
URL: http://deltaohio.com/chamber/index.htm
Description: Promotes business and community development in Delta, OH.

56119 ■ **Deshler Chamber of Commerce**
PO Box 123
Deshler, OH 43516
Ph: (419)278-8129
Co. E-mail: inforequest@deshlerohiochamber.com
URL: http://www.deshlerohiochamber.com
Contact: Jackie Arps, Secretary Treasurer
Description: Promotes business and community development in Deshler, OH.

56120 ■ *Directions*
1 Cascade Plz., 17th Fl.
Akron, OH 44308

Ph: (330)376-5550
Fax: (330)379-3164
Co. E-mail: info@greaterakronchamber.org
URL: http://www.greaterakronchamber.org
Contact: Daniel C. Colantone, President
Released: Bimonthly

56121 ■ *Directions*
2152 Tremont Ctr.
Upper Arlington, OH 43221
Ph: (614)481-5710
Fax: (614)481-5711
Co. E-mail: becky@uachamber.org
URL: http://www.uachamber.org
Contact: Becky Hajost, President
Released: Monthly

56122 ■ *Directory of Members*
410 W Main St.
Montpelier, OH 43543
Ph: (419)485-4416
Fax: (419)495-4416
Co. E-mail: macofc@verizon.net
URL: http://www.montpelierchamber.com
Contact: Ms. Terry L. Buntain, Executive Director

56123 ■ **Eastern Maumee Bay Chamber of Commerce**
2460 Navarre Ave.
Oregon, OH 43616
Ph: (419)693-5580
Fax: (419)693-9990
Co. E-mail: director@embchamber.org
URL: http://www.embchamber.org
Contact: Angela Crosby, President
Description: Strives to improve the quality of life, general welfare and prosperity of Eastern Maumee Bay community. **Publications:** *Chamber Hi-Lites* (Monthly).

56124 ■ **Eaton - Preble County Chamber of Commerce**
PO Box 303
Eaton, OH 45320-0303
Ph: (937)456-4949
Co. E-mail: chamberoffices@preblecountyohio.com
URL: http://www.preblecountyohio.com
Contact: Virginia Lindsey, Secretary
Description: Promotes free enterprise and advances the business community in the Eaton and Preble County area. **Founded:** 1952.

56125 ■ *Economic and Demographics of Tuscarawas County*
1323 4th St. NW
New Philadelphia, OH 44663
Ph: (330)343-4474
Fax: (330)343-6526
Co. E-mail: info@tuschamber.com
URL: http://www.tuschamber.com
Contact: Jill R. McCartney, President

56126 ■ *The Entrepreneur*
The Riverview Bldg.
Marietta, OH 45750
Ph: (740)373-5176
Fax: (740)373-7808
Co. E-mail: info@mariettachamber.com
URL: http://www.mariettachamber.com
Contact: Charlotte Keim, President
Released: Monthly

56127 ■ *Environmental and Safety Directory*
230 E Town St.
Columbus, OH 43215-0159
Ph: (614)228-4201
Free: 800-622-1893
Fax: (614)228-6403
Co. E-mail: occ@ohiochamber.com
URL: http://www.ohiochamber.com
Contact: Andrew E. Doehrel, President
Released: Annual

56128 ■ **Euclid Chamber of Commerce (ECC)**
PO Box 32611
Euclid, OH 44132
Ph: (216)731-9322

Fax: (216)865-4925
Co. E-mail: sheila@euclidchamber.com
URL: http://www.euclidchamber.com/home.aspx
Contact: Brian Moore, Chairman
Description: Individuals from business, industry, the professions, and the public sector interested in promoting business and community development in Euclid, OH. **Founded:** 1930. **Publications:** *Chamber News* (Monthly); *Club List* (Monthly); *Membership Directory and Buyer's Guide* (Annual). **Educational Activities:** Awards Dinner (Annual); Business After Hours (Periodic); Small Business Breakfasts (Periodic).

56129 ■ **Fairborn Area Chamber of Commerce (FACC)**
12 N Central Ave.
Fairborn, OH 45324-5002
Ph: (937)878-3191
Fax: (937)878-3197
Co. E-mail: chamber@fairborn.com
URL: http://www.fairborn.com
Contact: Paul Newman, Executive Director
Description: Promotes business and community development in the Fairborn, OH area. Participates in the annual Sweet Corn Festival and 4th of July parade. **Founded:** 1944. **Publications:** *Chamber Update* (Monthly); *Membership Directory and Buyers' Guide* (Annual). **Educational Activities:** Chamber Chat (Annual); Christmas Open House (Monthly); Fairborn Area Chamber of Commerce Meeting (Annual). **Awards:** Outstanding AFJROTC; President's Award (Annual); W. Ed Duncan Distinguished Citizen Award (Annual).

56130 ■ *The Fairfield Advantage*
670 Wessel Dr.
Fairfield, OH 45014
Ph: (513)881-5500
Co. E-mail: president@fairfieldchamber.com
URL: http://www.fairfieldchamber.com
Contact: Denise Rawls, Office Manager
Released: Monthly

56131 ■ **Fairfield Chamber of Commerce**
670 Wessel Dr.
Fairfield, OH 45014
Ph: (513)881-5500
Co. E-mail: president@fairfieldchamber.com
URL: http://www.fairfieldchamber.com
Contact: Denise Rawls, Office Manager
Description: Promotes business and community development in the Fairfield, OH area. Sponsors Indian Summer Days Festival. **Founded:** 1956. **Publications:** *The Fairfield Advantage* (Monthly).

56132 ■ **Fayette County Chamber of Commerce**
101 E East St.
Washington Court House, OH 43160
Ph: (740)335-0761
Fax: (740)335-0762
Co. E-mail: fayettechamber@yahoo.com
URL: http://www.fayettecountyohio.com
Contact: Roger D. Blackburn, President
Description: Seeks to promote and enhance the business environment within the area.

56133 ■ **Findlay-Hancock County Chamber of Commerce**
123 E Main Cross St.
Findlay, OH 45840
Ph: (419)422-3313
Fax: (419)422-9508
Co. E-mail: info@findlayhancockalliance.com
URL: http://www.findlayhancockalliance.com/default.
  aspx
Contact: Dionne K. Neubauer, Director
Description: Promotes the growth of the community by concentrating on the needs of businesses. Provides medical and business opportunities for the members and interested individuals. **Publications:** *Investor Report* (Bimonthly).

56134 ■ *Focus*
1 Chamber Plz.
Dayton, OH 45402-2400
Ph: (937)226-1444

Fax: (937)226-8254
Co. E-mail: info@dacc.org
URL: http://www.daytonchamber.org
Contact: Phillip L. Parker, President
Released: Quarterly

56135 ■ Fostoria Area Chamber of Commerce (FACC)
121 N Main St.
Fostoria, OH 44830-2215
Ph: (419)435-0486
Fax: (419)435-0936
Co. E-mail: chamberfost@aol.com
URL: http://www.fostoriachamber.org
Contact: Sheri L. Fleegle, Executive Director
Description: Promotes business and community development in the Fostoria, OH area. **Founded:** 1951.

56136 ■ Gahanna Area Chamber of Commerce
1000 Creekside Plz.
Gahanna, OH 43230
Ph: (614)471-0451
Fax: (614)471-5122
Co. E-mail: info@gahannaareachamber.com
URL: http://www.gahannaareachamber.com
Contact: Mrs. Leslee Blake, President
Description: Promotes business and community development in Gahanna, OH. **Founded:** 1981.

56137 ■ Galion Area Chamber of Commerce (GACC)
106 Harding Way E
Galion, OH 44833-1901
Ph: (419)468-7737
Fax: (419)462-5487
Co. E-mail: galionchamber@galionchamber.org
URL: http://www.galionchamber.org
Contact: Susan VanderMaas, Chairperson
Description: Promotes business and community development in the Galion, OH area. **Publications:** *Galion Today* (Bimonthly).

56138 ■ *Galion Today*
106 Harding Way E
Galion, OH 44833-1901
Ph: (419)468-7737
Fax: (419)462-5487
Co. E-mail: galionchamber@galionchamber.org
URL: http://www.galionchamber.org
Contact: Susan VanderMaas, Chairperson
Released: Bimonthly

56139 ■ Gallia County Chamber of Commerce
16 State St.
Gallipolis, OH 45631
Ph: (740)446-0596
Fax: (740)446-7031
Co. E-mail: lneal@galliacounty.org
URL: http://www.galliacounty.org
Contact: Jimmy Wiseman, President
Description: Promotes, supports and strengthens business and economic development throughout the county, and provides leadership through networking and education, to improve the overall business environment for Chamber members. **Publications:** *Bandstand* (Monthly); *Gallia County Chamber of Commerce Membership Directory & Community Profile* (Biennial). **Awards:** The Bud & Donna McGhee Community Service Award (Annual).

56140 ■ *Gallia County Chamber of Commerce Membership Directory & Community Profile*
16 State St.
Gallipolis, OH 45631
Ph: (740)446-0596
Fax: (740)446-7031
Co. E-mail: lneal@galliacounty.org
URL: http://www.galliacounty.org
Contact: Jimmy Wiseman, President
Released: Biennial **Price:** $10.

56141 ■ Garfield Heights Chamber of Commerce (GHCC)
5706 Turney Rd., Ste. 101
Garfield Heights, OH 44125

Ph: (216)475-7775
Fax: (216)475-2237
Co. E-mail: gabriellah@garfieldchamber.com
URL: http://www.garfieldchamber.com
Contact: Gabriella Huszarik, Executive Director
Description: Works to promote and serve the local business, civic and social interests in the Garfield Heights, OH area. **Publications:** *Communique* (Periodic).

56142 ■ Garrettsville - Hiram Area Chamber of Commerce (GHACC)
PO Box 1
Garrettsville, OH 44231
Ph: (330)527-2411
Co. E-mail: patricks@apk.net
URL: http://garrettsvillehiramarea.com
Contact: Gretchen Cram, President
Description: Promotes business and community development in Portage County, OH. Helps operate People Tree for the needy. Sponsors Silver Crik Turkey Daze Festival. **Publications:** *Garrettsville: New England Charm Today - We Have it All.*

56143 ■ *Garrettsville: New England Charm Today - We Have it All*
PO Box 1
Garrettsville, OH 44231
Ph: (330)527-2411
Co. E-mail: patricks@apk.net
URL: http://garrettsvillehiramarea.com
Contact: Gretchen Cram, President

56144 ■ Geneva Area Chamber of Commerce (GACC)
PO Box 84
Geneva, OH 44041
Ph: (440)466-8694
Fax: (440)466-0823
Co. E-mail: info@genevachamber.org
URL: http://www.genevachamber.org
Description: Promotes business and community development in the Geneva, OH area.

56145 ■ Geneva on the Lake Chamber of Commerce
5536 Lake Rd.
Geneva, OH 44041
Ph: (440)466-8600
Free: 800-862-9948
Co. E-mail: gotl@roadrunner.com
URL: http://www.visitgenevaonthelake.com

56146 ■ *Getting It Right The First Time: A Pocket Guide For New Business*
PO Box 281
Waynesville, OH 45068-0281
Ph: (513)897-8855
Fax: (513)897-9833
Co. E-mail: waynsville@aol.com
URL: http://www.waynesvilleohio.com
Contact: Dawn Schroeder, Executive Director

56147 ■ Greater Akron Chamber of Commerce
1 Cascade Plz., 17th Fl.
Akron, OH 44308
Ph: (330)376-5550
Fax: (330)379-3164
Co. E-mail: info@greaterakronchamber.org
URL: http://www.greaterakronchamber.org
Contact: Daniel C. Colantone, President
Description: Serves business organizations to improve the economic and social status of Greater Akron. **Publications:** *Directions* (Bimonthly). **Telecommunication Services:** colantone@greaterakronchamber.org.

56148 ■ Greater Buckeye Lake Chamber of Commerce
PO Box 5
Buckeye Lake, OH 43008
Ph: (740)929-2529
Co. E-mail: jmiller@buckeyelakecc.com
URL: http://www.buckeyelakecc.com
Contact: Tim Ryan, President
Description: Promotes business and community development in Buckeye Lake, OH area.

56149 ■ Greater Cincinnati Chamber of Commerce
441 Vine St., Ste. 300, Carew Twr.
Cincinnati, OH 45202-2812
Ph: (513)579-3100
Fax: (513)579-3101
Co. E-mail: info@cincinnatichamber.com
URL: http://www.gcc.com
Contact: Ellen van der Horst, President
URL(s): www.cincinnatijas.com. **Description:** Promotes business and community development in the Cincinnati, OH area. **Founded:** 1839. **Publications:** *Greater Cincinnati Chamber of Commerce--Cincinnati USA Business Connections Directory*; *Chamber Connect* (Monthly); *Chambervision* (Monthly); *Japanese Investment in the Midwest*; *Foreign Consulates*; *Building and Sites Guide*; *Major Employers* (Annual); *Fortune Firms Headquartered in Cincinnati and Ohio*; *Major Manufacturers*; *Headquartered Companies*; *Medium-Sized Companies*; *Foreign Firms* (Annual); *Industrial PinPointer: Cincinnati* (Biennial); *Greater Cincinnati International Trade Directory* (Biennial); *Greater Cincinnati Chamber of Commerce--Cincinnati USA Business Connections Directory: Membership Directory and Resource Guide* (Annual); *Greater Cincinnati Chamber of Commerce--Clubs and Organizations Directory* (Annual); *Cincinnati U.S.A. Business Connections Directory* (Annual); *Greater Cincinnati Chamber of Commerce International Trade Directory* (Biennial). **Awards:** Great Living Cincinnatians Award (Annual); Outstanding Community Service Award (Annual). **Telecommunication Services:** jasgc@gccc.com.

56150 ■ Greater Cincinnati and Northern Kentucky African American Chamber of Commerce (GCNKAACC)
2945 Gilbert Ave.
Cincinnati, OH 45206
Ph: (513)751-9900
Fax: (513)751-9100
Co. E-mail: info@african-americanchamber.com
URL: http://african-americanchamber.com
Contact: Sean Rugless, President
Description: Works to identify new market opportunities. Improves access to capital and economic growth for established and emerging African American businesses. **Founded:** 1996.

56151 ■ Greater Columbus Area Chamber of Commerce
150 S Front St., Ste. 200
Columbus, OH 43215
Ph: (614)221-1321
Fax: (614)221-1408
Co. E-mail: michael_dalby@columbus.org
URL: http://www.columbus.org
Contact: Michael Dalby, President
Description: Promotes business and community development in Columbus, OH area. **Founded:** 1884.

56152 ■ Greater Hamilton Chamber of Commerce (GHCC)
201 Dayton St.
Hamilton, OH 45011-1633
Ph: (513)844-1500
Fax: (513)844-1999
Co. E-mail: kenny@hamilton-ohio.com
URL: http://www.hamilton-ohio.com
Contact: Kenny Craig, President
Description: Promotes business and community development in the Hamilton, OH area. **Founded:** 1910. **Publications:** *ChamberLetter* (Monthly). **Awards:** Citizen of Year (Annual).

56153 ■ Greater Lawrence County Area Chamber of Commerce (GLCACC)
216 Collins Ave.
South Point, OH 45680
Ph: (740)377-4550
Free: 800-408-1334
Fax: (740)377-2091
Co. E-mail: bobsmith@lawrencecountyohio.org
URL: http://www.lawrencecountyohio.org
Contact: Bob Smith, Director
Description: Promotes business and community development in Lawrence County, OH. Conducts seminars and workshops. **Founded:** 1983.

56154 ■ Greater Medina Chamber of Commerce
145 N Court St.
Medina, OH 44256
Ph: (330)723-8773
Fax: (330)722-6844
Co. E-mail: info@medinaohchamber.com
URL: http://www.medinaohchamber.com
Contact: Valerie Rapp, Chairperson
Description: Unites hundreds of businesses and professional firms and serves as the central agency that works to improve business and build a better community. **Founded:** 1938. **Publications:** *The Chamber Link* (Bimonthly).

56155 ■ *Greater Powell Area Chamber of Commerce Directory and Community Guide*
50 S Liberty St., Ste. 170
Powell, OH 43065
Ph: (614)888-1090
Fax: (614)888-4803
Co. E-mail: admin@powellchamber.com
URL: http://www.powellchamber.com
Contact: Craig Sedoris, President
Released: Annual **Price:** free.

56156 ■ Green Chamber of Commerce
3700 Massillon Rd., Ste. 115
Uniontown, OH 44685
Ph: (330)896-3023
Fax: (330)899-9052
Co. E-mail: info@greencoc.org
URL: http://www.greencoc.org
Contact: Lori Howerton, Chief Executive Officer
Description: Works to advance the interest of business and professional firms in the City of Green, Ohio and the surrounding communities. **Founded:** 2000.

56157 ■ Grove City Area Chamber of Commerce (GCACC)
4069 Broadway
Grove City, OH 43123
Ph: (614)875-9762
Fax: (614)875-1510
Co. E-mail: e.dir@gcchamber.org
URL: http://www.gcchamber.org
Contact: William H. Diehl, Executive Director
Description: Business, industry, and professional persons interested in promoting business and community development in the southwestern Franklin County, OH area. Sponsors flea and farmer's markets. **Founded:** 1978. **Awards:** Community Service Award; School and Business Awards; Ohio Business Week Scholarships.

56158 ■ Hardin County Chamber of Commerce
225 S Detroit St.
Kenton, OH 43326
Ph: (419)673-4131
Free: 888-642-7346
Fax: (419)674-4876
Co. E-mail: alliance@hardinohio.org
URL: http://www.hardinohio.org
Description: Business, industry, and professional persons dedicated to business and community development in the Hardin County, OH area. **Founded:** 1921. **Publications:** *Alliance* (Bimonthly). **Awards:** Citizen of the Year (Annual); Community Service Awards.

56159 ■ Harrison Regional Chamber of Commerce (HRCC)
37840 Cadiz-Dennison Rd.
Cadiz, OH 43907
Ph: (740)942-3350
Fax: (740)942-0009
Co. E-mail: hrcctour@eohio.net
URL: http://pages.eohio.net/harrisonchamber
Contact: Ed Coultrap, Executive Director
Description: Promotes business and community development in Harrison County, OH. Sponsors Ohio Business Week. Promotes tourism. Operates welcome station. **Founded:** 1975. **Publications:** *County Directory*; *HRCC Communicator* (Bimonthly); *Plat Books*. **Educational Activities:** Harrison Regional Chamber of Commerce Banquet (Annual); Business

After Hours (Periodic); Business Expo (Semiannual); Harrison Regional Chamber of Commerce Seminar (Semiannual); Tourism/Beautification Awards (Annual).

56160 ■ Heights-Hillcrest Regional Chamber of Commerce (HRCC)
3109 Mayfield Rd., Ste. 202
Cleveland Heights, OH 44118
Ph: (216)397-7322
Fax: (216)397-7353
Co. E-mail: info@hrcc.org
URL: http://www.hrcc.org
Contact: Angie Pohlman, Executive Director
Description: Represents the interests of businesses and professionals in the cities of Cleveland Heights, Lyndhurst, Richmond Heights, Shaker Heights, South Euclid and University Heights. **Founded:** 1948.

56161 ■ Hilliard Area Chamber of Commerce (HACC)
4081 Main St.
Hilliard, OH 43026-1501
Ph: (614)876-7666
Fax: (614)876-3113
Co. E-mail: info@hilliardchamber.org
URL: http://www.hilliardchamber.org
Contact: Libby Gierach, President
Description: Businesses, organizations, and government officials organized to promote business and community development in northwestern Franklin County, OH. Sponsors seminars; holds luncheons and Business After Hours parties. Awards scholarships. Sponsors Hollyfest auction and art fair. **Founded:** 1973. **Publications:** *Hilliard Area Chamber of Commerce Professional Directory* (Annual); *News and Views* (Monthly). **Awards:** Business/Business Person of the Year (Annual); Galbreath Award; Hollyfest Scholarship Foundation (Annual).

56162 ■ *Hilliard Area Chamber of Commerce Professional Directory*
4081 Main St.
Hilliard, OH 43026-1501
Ph: (614)876-7666
Fax: (614)876-3113
Co. E-mail: info@hilliardchamber.org
URL: http://www.hilliardchamber.org
Contact: Libby Gierach, President
Released: Annual

56163 ■ Holland - Springfield Chamber of Commerce
c/o Pat Hicks, Pres., CEO
7350 Airport Hwy.
Holland, OH 43528
Ph: (419)865-2110
Fax: (419)865-3740
Co. E-mail: info@hollandspringfieldcoc.org
URL: http://www.hollandspringfieldcoc.org
Contact: Pat Hicks, President
Description: Represents businesses. Provides business endorsements and referrals to members. **Founded:** 1990.

56164 ■ Holmes County Chamber of Commerce
6 W Jackson St., Ste. A
Millersburg, OH 44654
Ph: (330)674-3975
Fax: (330)674-3976
Co. E-mail: info@holmescountychamber.com
URL: http://www.holmescountychamber.com
Contact: Shasta Mast, Executive Director
Description: Promotes business and community development in the Millersburg, OH area.

56165 ■ *HRCC Communicator*
37840 Cadiz-Dennison Rd.
Cadiz, OH 43907
Ph: (740)942-3350
Fax: (740)942-0009
Co. E-mail: hrcctour@eohio.net
URL: http://pages.eohio.net/harrisonchamber
Contact: Ed Coultrap, Executive Director
Released: Bimonthly **Price:** free.

56166 ■ Huber Heights Chamber of Commerce
Shaw Commercial Center
4756 Fishburg Rd.
Huber Heights, OH 45424
Ph: (937)233-5700
Fax: (937)233-5769
Co. E-mail: joshsullenberger@daytonymca.org
URL: http://huberheightschamber.com
Contact: Josh Sullenberger, President
Description: Promotes business and community development in Huber Heights, OH. **Founded:** 1980.

56167 ■ Hudson Area Chamber of Commerce (HACC)
245 N Main St., Ste. 100
Hudson, OH 44236
Ph: (330)650-0621
Fax: (330)656-1646
Co. E-mail: info@hudsoncoc.org
URL: http://www.explorehudson.com
Contact: Carolyn Konefal, President
Description: Promotes business and community development in the Hudson, OH area. Holds annual dinner. **Founded:** 1983. **Publications:** *Bulletin* (Monthly).

56168 ■ Huron Chamber of Commerce (HCC)
509 Huron St.
Huron, OH 44839
Ph: (419)433-5700
URL: http://www.huron.net
Contact: Sheila Ehrhardt, Director
Description: Promotes business and community development in Huron, OH. **Publications:** *The Wave* (Monthly).

56169 ■ *Image Booklet*
210 E Main St.
Alliance, OH 44601
Ph: (330)823-6260
Fax: (330)823-4434
Co. E-mail: info@allianceohiochamber.org
URL: http://www.allianceohiochamber.org
Contact: R. Mark Locke, President
Released: Triennial

56170 ■ *Images of Clermont County*
4355 Ferguson Dr., Ste. 150
Cincinnati, OH 45245
Ph: (513)576-5000
Fax: (513)576-5001
Co. E-mail: chamber@clermontchamber.com
URL: http://www.clermontchamber.com
Contact: Matthew D. Van Sant, President
Released: Annual

56171 ■ *Images of Fairfield County*
109 N Broad St.
Lancaster, OH 43130
Ph: (740)653-8251
Fax: (740)653-7074
Co. E-mail: info@lancoc.org
URL: http://www.lancoc.org
Contact: Travis Markwood, President

56172 ■ *Images of Tuscarawas County*
1323 4th St. NW
New Philadelphia, OH 44663
Ph: (330)343-4474
Fax: (330)343-6526
Co. E-mail: info@tuschamber.com
URL: http://www.tuschamber.com
Contact: Jill R. McCartney, President
Released: Annual

56173 ■ Indian Lake Area Chamber of Commerce (ILACoC)
PO Box 717
Russells Point, OH 43348
Ph: (937)843-5392

Fax: (937)843-9051
Co. E-mail: office@indianlakechamber.org
URL: http://www.indianlakechamber.org
Contact: Rick Fuller, President
Description: Individuals, businesses, churches, and organizations united to promote business and community development in the Russells Point, OH area. **Founded:** 1957. **Publications:** *The Soundings* (Monthly). **Awards:** Citizen of the Year (Annual).

56174 ■ Industrial Directory
622 S Broadway
Greenville, OH 45331
Ph: (937)548-2102
Co. E-mail: info@darkecountyohio.com
URL: http://www.darkecountyohio.com/cwt/external/wcpages/index.aspx
Contact: Sharon Deschambeau, President

56175 ■ Industrial Guide
The Riverview Bldg.
Marietta, OH 45750
Ph: (740)373-5176
Fax: (740)373-7808
Co. E-mail: info@mariettachamber.com
URL: http://www.mariettachamber.com
Contact: Charlotte Keim, President
Price: included in membership dues.

56176 ■ Industry Business
108 E Wyandot Ave.
Upper Sandusky, OH 43351
Ph: (419)294-3349
Free: 800-686-1261
Fax: (419)294-3531
Co. E-mail: upperchamber@udata.com
URL: http://www.uppersanduskychamber.com
Contact: Aaron Korte, Executive Director
Released: Periodic

56177 ■ The Informer
9 W National Rd.
Englewood, OH 45322
Ph: (937)836-2550
Fax: (937)836-2485
URL: http://www.northmont-area-coc.org
Contact: Cathy Hutton, Chief Executive Officer
Released: Monthly **Price:** included in membership dues.

56178 ■ Insider
Enterprise, Ste. 200
300 Madison Ave.
Toledo, OH 43604-1575
Ph: (419)243-8191
Fax: (419)241-8302
Co. E-mail: joinus@toledochamber.com
URL: http://www.toledochamber.com/cwt/external/wcpages/index.aspx
Contact: Mark A. V'Soske, President
Released: Monthly **Price:** free for members.

56179 ■ Insight
7908 Day Dr.
Parma, OH 44129
Ph: (440)886-1700
Fax: (440)886-1770
Co. E-mail: chamber@parmaareachamber.org
URL: http://parmaareachamber.org
Contact: Dave Nedrich, Chief Executive Officer
Released: Monthly

56180 ■ Intercom
4355 Ferguson Dr., Ste. 150
Cincinnati, OH 45245
Ph: (513)576-5000
Fax: (513)576-5001
Co. E-mail: chamber@clermontchamber.com
URL: http://www.clermontchamber.com
Contact: Matthew D. Van Sant, President
Released: Monthly

56181 ■ Investor Report
123 E Main Cross St.
Findlay, OH 45840
Ph: (419)422-3313

Fax: (419)422-9508
Co. E-mail: info@findlayhancockalliance.com
URL: http://www.findlayhancockalliance.com/default.aspx
Contact: Dionne K. Neubauer, Director
Released: Bimonthly

56182 ■ Island Guide
148 Delaware Ave.
Put-in-Bay, OH 43456
Ph: (419)285-2832
URL: http://visitputinbay.com/visitus
Contact: Maggie Beckford, Executive Director
Released: Annual **Price:** included in membership dues.

56183 ■ Jackson Area Chamber of Commerce (JACC)
234 Broadway St.
Jackson, OH 45640-1702
Ph: (740)286-2722
Fax: (740)286-8443
Co. E-mail: info@jacksonohio.org
URL: http://www.jacksonohio.org
Contact: Randy R. Heath, Executive Director
Description: Promotes business and community development in Jackson, OH. **Founded:** 1911. **Publications:** *The Chamber Bulletin* (Monthly). **Awards:** Entrepreneur of the Year (Annual); Person of the Year (Annual). **Telecommunication Services:** rheath@zoomnet.net.

56184 ■ Jackson - Beldon Chamber of Commerce (JBCC)
5735 Wales Ave. NW
Massillon, OH 44646-9097
Ph: (330)833-4400
Fax: (330)833-4456
URL: http://www.jbcc.org
Contact: Steven M. Meeks, President
Description: Works to promote integrity, good faith, just, and equitable principles in business and to foster, protect, and advance the commercial, mercantile, industrial, professional, social and civic interests of Jackson Township and its citizens. Strives to be an advocate of business in Jackson and Stark County. Helps in servicing the needs of businesses and develops program that benefit the members.

56185 ■ Jefferson Area Chamber of Commerce
PO Box 100
Jefferson, OH 44047-0100
Ph: (440)576-0133
Co. E-mail: membership@jeffersonchamber.com
URL: http://www.jeffersonchamber.com
Contact: Peggy Stadler, Treasurer
Description: Aims to advance the commercial, industrial, professional, civic and general interests of the Jefferson trades areas. **Awards:** Citizen of the Year (Annual).

56186 ■ Jefferson County Chamber of Commerce
630 Market St.
Steubenville, OH 43952
Ph: (740)282-6226
Co. E-mail: info@jeffersoncountychamber.com
URL: http://www.jeffersoncountychamber.com
Contact: Susan Hershey, President

56187 ■ KACC Member Newsletter
c/o Lori Wemhoff, Exec. Dir.
138 E Main St., Ste. 102
Kent, OH 44240
Ph: (330)673-9855
Fax: (330)673-9860
Co. E-mail: lwemhoff@kentbiz.com
URL: http://www.kentbiz.com
Contact: Lori Wemhoff, Executive Director
Released: Monthly **Price:** included in membership dues; $15, for additional subscription.

56188 ■ Kelleys Island Chamber of Commerce (KICC)
PO Box 783-F
Kelleys Island, OH 43438-0783

Ph: (419)746-2360
URL: http://www.kelleysislandchamber.com
Contact: Kelly Bradford, President
Description: Promotes tourism on Kelleys Island. Develops increased cooperation between the Kelleys Island Village Council and the business community.

56189 ■ Kent Area Chamber of Commerce (KACC)
c/o Lori Wemhoff, Exec. Dir.
138 E Main St., Ste. 102
Kent, OH 44240
Ph: (330)673-9855
Fax: (330)673-9860
Co. E-mail: lwemhoff@kentbiz.com
URL: http://www.kentbiz.com
Contact: Lori Wemhoff, Executive Director
Description: Promotes business and community development in the Kent, OH area. **Publications:** *KACC Member Newsletter* (Monthly). **Awards:** Kent Medal for Public Service (Annual); Small Business Award (Annual).

56190 ■ Kettering - Moraine - Oakwood Chamber of Commerce (KMOCC)
2977 Far Hills Ave.
Kettering, OH 45419
Ph: (937)299-3852
Fax: (937)299-3851
Co. E-mail: info@kmo-coc.org
URL: http://www.kmo-coc.org
Contact: Ann-Lisa Rucker, Executive Director
Description: Promotes business and community development in Kettering, Moraine, and Oakwood, OH. **Founded:** 1957. **Awards:** Enterprise Spirit Award (Annual).

56191 ■ Lake Township Chamber of Commerce (LTCC)
PO Box 1207
Hartville, OH 44632
Ph: (330)877-5500
Fax: (330)877-2149
Co. E-mail: president@lakechamber.com
URL: http://www.lakechamber.com
Contact: Christa Kozy, President
Description: Promotes business and community development in the Hartville, OH area.

56192 ■ Lakewood Chamber of Commerce (LCC)
16017 Detroit Ave.
Lakewood, OH 44107-3712
Ph: (216)226-2900
Fax: (216)226-1340
Co. E-mail: info@lakewoodchamber.org
URL: http://www.lakewoodchamber.org/site
Contact: Patty Ryan, President
Description: Promotes business and community development in Lakewood, OH. **Founded:** 1911.

56193 ■ Lancaster Fairfield County Chamber of Commerce
109 N Broad St.
Lancaster, OH 43130
Ph: (740)653-8251
Fax: (740)653-7074
Co. E-mail: info@lancoc.org
URL: http://www.lancoc.org
Contact: Travis Markwood, President
Description: Promotes business and community development in the Lancaster, OH area. **Publications:** *Chamber Report* (Monthly); *Images of Fairfield County*. **Educational Activities:** Info Tech Meeting (Monthly); Legislative Action Council Meeting (Monthly). **Telecommunication Services:** travis@lancoc.org.

56194 ■ Lebanon Area Chamber of Commerce (LACC)
20 N Broadway
Lebanon, OH 45036
Ph: (513)932-1100

Fax: (513)932-9050
Co. E-mail: info@lebanonchamber.org
URL: http://www.lebanonchamber.org
Contact: Sara Arseneau, Executive Director
Description: Promotes business and community development in the Lebanon, OH area. Sponsors Christmas Festival and Artstreet. **Founded:** 1924. **Publications:** *Business and Industry Directory* (Periodic).

56195 ■ Leetonia-Washingtonville Area Chamber of Commerce
c/o Kristen Figg, Treas.
712 Columbia St.
Leetonia, OH 44431
Ph: (330)427-1600
URL: http://www.leetonia.org
Contact: Heather MacNaughton, President
Description: Promotes business and community development in Leetonia, OH. **Founded:** 1998.

56196 ■ *Legislative Directory*
205 N 5th St.
Zanesville, OH 43701
Ph: (740)455-8282
Free: 800-743-2303
Fax: (740)454-2963
Co. E-mail: dmatz@zmchamber.com
URL: http://www.zmchamber.com
Contact: Thomas C. Poorman, President
Released: Annual

56197 ■ Leipsic Area Chamber of Commerce
142 E Main St.
Leipsic, OH 45856
Ph: (419)943-2009
Co. E-mail: info@leipsic.com
URL: http://www.leipsic.com
Contact: Kevin Lammon, Administrator
Description: Represents businesses in Leipsic, OH.

56198 ■ Lima/Allen County Chamber of Commerce
144 N Main St.
Lima, OH 45801
Ph: (419)222-6045
Fax: (419)229-0266
Co. E-mail: chamber@limachamber.com
URL: http://www.limachamber.com
Contact: Jed E. Metzger, President
Description: Promotes business and community development in the Lima, OH area. **Founded:** 1887. **Publications:** *Allen County Business Directory*; *Business Network* (Monthly); *Minority Business/Professional Directory*; *Minority Business/Professional Directory*; *Allen County Interactive CD-ROM*. **Educational Activities:** Safety Council Meeting (Monthly); Wake, Rattle and Roll (Monthly). **Telecommunication Services:** jmetzger@limachamber.com.

56199 ■ Lisbon Area Chamber of Commerce (LACC)
120 N Market St.
Lisbon, OH 44432
Ph: (330)424-1803
Fax: (330)424-9003
Co. E-mail: lacoc2@sbcglobal.net
URL: http://www.lisbonareachamber.com
Contact: Marilyn McCullough, Executive Director
Description: Promotes business and community development in the Lisbon, OH area. Sponsors annual Johnny Appleseed Festival. **Founded:** 1964. **Publications:** *Chamber of Commerce Newsletter* (Quarterly).

56200 ■ Lodi Area Chamber of Commerce
PO Box 6
Lodi, OH 44254
Ph: (330)948-8047
Co. E-mail: info@lodiohiochamber.com
URL: http://www.lodiohiochamber.com
Contact: Cecelia Sivard, President
Description: Promotes businesses in Lodi, OH. Provides networking and information services to members. **Founded:** 1949. **Awards:** Business/Community Person of the Year (Annual).

56201 ■ Logan County Area Chamber of Commerce (LCCC)
100 S Main St.
Bellefontaine, OH 43311-2083
Ph: (937)599-5121
Co. E-mail: info@logancountyohio.com
URL: http://www.logancountyohio.com
Contact: Fred Burkhardt, President
Description: Promotes business and community development in the Logan County, OH area. **Founded:** 1928. **Telecommunication Services:** fburkhardt@logancountyohio.com.

56202 ■ Logan - Hocking Chamber of Commerce
4 E Hunter St.
Logan, OH 43138
Ph: (740)385-6836
Fax: (740)385-7259
Co. E-mail: lo-hockchamber@hocking.net
URL: http://www.logan-hockingchamber.com
Contact: Bill Rienhart, Executive Director
Description: Aims to keep Logan area's economic condition at a level where businesses will risk their resources in the hope of making a profit.

56203 ■ Lorain County Chamber of Commerce
226 Middle Ave., 5th Fl.
Elyria, OH 44035
Ph: (440)328-2550
Fax: (440)328-2557
Co. E-mail: info@loraincountychamber.com
URL: http://www.loraincountychamber.com
Contact: Frank P. DeTillio, President
Description: Businesses and individuals promoting economic and community development and social programs in Lorain County, OH. **Founded:** 1883. **Publications:** *Take Action* (Periodic); *Vista*.

56204 ■ Loudonville - Mohican Area Convention and Visitor's Bureau
131 W Main St.
Loudonville, OH 44842
Ph: (419)994-2519
Free: 877-2-MOHICAN
Co. E-mail: info@loudoville-mohican.com
URL: http://www.loudonville-mohican.com
Description: Promotes business and community development in the Loudonville, OH area. **Founded:** 1957.

56205 ■ Louisville Area Chamber of Commerce
PO Box 67
Louisville, OH 44641
Ph: (330)875-7371
Fax: (330)875-3839
Co. E-mail: info@louisvilleohchamber.com
URL: http://www.louisvilleohchamber.com
Contact: Kelly Chaney, Chairperson
Description: Strives to develop and enhance the economic and business environment in the Louisville area through leadership, advocacy, and investor benefits. **Founded:** 1991. **Telecommunication Services:** lcoc@neo.rr.com.

56206 ■ Loveland Area Chamber of Commerce
442 W Loveland Ave.
Loveland, OH 45140
Ph: (513)683-1544
Fax: (513)683-5449
Co. E-mail: info@lovelandchamber.org
URL: http://www.lovelandchamber.org
Contact: Paulette Leeper, Executive Director
Description: Promotes business and community development in the Loveland, OH area. Sponsors Music in the Park concerts, valentine stamping program, and golf outing. **Founded:** 1965. **Telecommunication Services:** paulette@lovelandchamber.org.

56207 ■ Madison County Chamber of Commerce
730 Keny Blvd.
London, OH 43140
Ph: (740)852-2250

Fax: (740)852-5133
Co. E-mail: sean@madisoncountychamber.org
URL: http://www.madisoncountychamber.org
Contact: Sean K. Hughes, Executive Director
Description: Promotes business and community development in the London, OH area. **Founded:** 1959.

56208 ■ Madison - Perry Area Chamber of Commerce
5965 N Ridge Rd.
Madison, OH 44057
Ph: (440)428-3760
Fax: (440)428-6668
Co. E-mail: exec@mpacc.org
URL: http://www.mpacc.org
Contact: Cindy Girdler, President
Description: Represents businesses in Madison and Perry, OH. Stimulates community leadership and economic development.

56209 ■ Mansfield-Richland Area Chamber of Commerce (MRACC)
55 N Mulberry St.
Mansfield, OH 44902
Ph: (419)522-3211
Fax: (419)526-6853
Co. E-mail: info@mrachamber.com
URL: http://www.mrachamber.com/cwt/external/ wcpages/index.aspx
Contact: Kevin Nestor, President
Description: Promotes business and community development in the Richland County, OH area. **Founded:** 1899.

56210 ■ *Manufacturer Directory*
32 S Sandusky St.
Delaware, OH 43015
Ph: (740)369-6221
Fax: (740)369-4817
Co. E-mail: dachamber@delawareohiochamber.com
URL: http://www.delawareareachamber.com
Contact: Holly Quaine, President
Released: Annual

56211 ■ Marblehead Peninsula Chamber of Commerce
5681 E Harbor Rd., Ste. C
Marblehead, OH 43440
Ph: (419)734-9777
Fax: (419)960-7206
URL: http://themarbleheadpeninsula.com
Contact: Al Stoss, President
Description: Promotes business and community development in the Marblehead, OH area.

56212 ■ Marietta Area Chamber of Commerce
The Riverview Bldg.
Marietta, OH 45750
Ph: (740)373-5176
Fax: (740)373-7808
Co. E-mail: info@mariettachamber.com
URL: http://www.mariettachamber.com
Contact: Charlotte Keim, President
Description: Promotes business and community development in the Marietta, OH area. **Founded:** 1887. **Publications:** *The Entrepreneur* (Monthly); *Industrial Guide*.

56213 ■ Marion Area Chamber of Commerce
205 W Center St., Ste.100
Marion, OH 43302
Ph: (740)382-2181
Fax: (740)387-7722
Co. E-mail: phall@marionareachamber.org
URL: http://www.marionareachamber.org
Contact: Pamela S. Hall, President
Description: Represents businesses in Marion, OH. Provides leadership for improvement of the economic prosperity and quality of life in the local community. **Publications:** *Progressing Together* (Monthly).

56214 ■ Massillon Area Chamber of Commerce (MACC)
137 Lincoln Way E
Massillon, OH 44646

Ph: (330)833-3146
Co. E-mail: info@massillonohchamber.com
URL: http://www.massillonohchamber.com
Contact: Robert A. Sanderson, President
Description: Promotes business and community development in the Massillon, OH area. **Founded:** 1915. **Publications:** *Buyers Guide* (Annual).

56215 ■ Maumee Chamber of Commerce
605 Conant St.
Maumee, OH 43537-3356
Ph: (419)893-5805
Fax: (419)893-8699
Co. E-mail: info@maumeechamber.com
URL: http://www.maumeechamber.com
Contact: Brenda Clixby, Executive Director
Description: Promotes business and community development in Maumee, OH. **Founded:** 1955. **Publications:** *Members Bulletin* (8/year). **Awards:** College Scholarships (Annual).

56216 ■ Meigs County Chamber of Commerce (MCCC)
238 W Main St.
Pomeroy, OH 45769
Ph: (740)992-5005
Co. E-mail: michelle@meigscountychamber.com
URL: http://www.meigscountychamber.com
Contact: Steve Story, President
Description: Promotes business and community development in Meigs County, OH. **Founded:** 1980.

56217 ■ *Member Connection*
150 S Front St., Ste. 200
Columbus, OH 43215
Ph: (614)225-6923
Fax: (614)221-1408
Co. E-mail: ty_marsh@columbus.org
Contact: Ty D. Marsh, President
Released: Monthly

56218 ■ *Members Bulletin*
605 Conant St.
Maumee, OH 43537-3356
Ph: (419)893-5805
Fax: (419)893-8699
Co. E-mail: info@maumeechamber.com
URL: http://www.maumeechamber.com
Contact: Brenda Clixby, Executive Director
Released: 8/year

56219 ■ *Membership Directory and Buyer's Guide*
45 E Main St.
Chillicothe, OH 45601
Ph: (740)702-2722
Fax: (740)702-2727
Co. E-mail: eschmidt@chillicotheohio.com
URL: http://www.chillicotheohio.com
Contact: Marvin E. Jones, President
Released: Annual

56220 ■ *Membership Directory and Buyer's Guide*
PO Box 32611
Euclid, OH 44132
Ph: (216)731-9322
Fax: (216)865-4925
Co. E-mail: sheila@euclidchamber.com
URL: http://www.euclidchamber.com/home.aspx
Contact: Brian Moore, Chairman
Released: Annual

56221 ■ *Membership Directory and Buyers' Guide*
12 N Central Ave.
Fairborn, OH 45324-5002
Ph: (937)878-3191
Fax: (937)878-3197
Co. E-mail: chamber@fairborn.com
URL: http://www.fairborn.com
Contact: Paul Newman, Executive Director
Released: Annual

56222 ■ *Membership Directory and Buyer's Guide*
1199 Professional Dr.
Van Wert, OH 45891
Ph: (419)238-4390

Free: 877-770-4438
Fax: (419)238-4589
Co. E-mail: chamber@vanwertchamber.com
URL: http://www.vanwertchamber.com
Contact: Kate Gribble, President
Released: Biennial

56223 ■ *Membership Directory and Buyer's Guide*
28 Public Sq.
Willoughby, OH 44094
Ph: (440)942-1632
Fax: (440)942-0586
Co. E-mail: info@willoughbyareachamber.com
URL: http://www.willoughbyareachamber.com
Contact: Nikki Matala, Executive Director
Released: Annual

56224 ■ *Membership Notes*
230 E Town St.
Columbus, OH 43215-0159
Ph: (614)228-4201
Free: 800-622-1893
Fax: (614)228-6403
Co. E-mail: occ@ohiochamber.com
URL: http://www.ohiochamber.com
Contact: Andrew E. Doehrel, President
Released: Bimonthly

56225 ■ *Membership Reference Guide*
Enterprise, Ste. 200
300 Madison Ave.
Toledo, OH 43604-1575
Ph: (419)243-8191
Fax: (419)241-8302
Co. E-mail: joinus@toledochamber.com
URL: http://www.toledochamber.com/cwt/external/wcpages/index.aspx
Contact: Mark A. V'Soske, President
Released: Annual **Price:** $35, /issue.

56226 ■ Mentor Area Chamber of Commerce (MACC)
6972 Spinach Dr.
Mentor, OH 44060
Ph: (440)255-1616
Fax: (440)255-1717
Co. E-mail: info@mentorchamber.org
URL: http://www.mentorchamber.org
Contact: Marie S. Pucak, Executive Director
Description: Promotes business and community development in the Mentor, OH area. **Founded:** 1960. **Publications:** *Chamber News* (Monthly). **Educational Activities:** Golf Outing (Annual).

56227 ■ Middlefield Chamber of Commerce
PO Box 801
Middlefield, OH 44062
Ph: (440)632-5705
Co. E-mail: mccinfo@middlefieldcc.com
URL: http://www.geaugalink.com/extlinks/mfdccfrm.html
Contact: Geri Watson, President
Description: Promotes business and community development in Middlefield Township, OH.

56228 ■ Milford Miami Township Chamber of Commerce
983 Lila Ave.
Milford, OH 45150-5708
Ph: (513)831-2411
Fax: (513)831-3547
Co. E-mail: director@milfordmiamitownship.com
URL: http://www.milfordmiamitownship.com
Contact: Charles Evans, President

56229 ■ Minerva Area Chamber of Commerce (MACOC)
203 N Market St.
Minerva, OH 44657
Ph: (330)868-7979
Co. E-mail: denise.freeland@minervachamber.org
URL: http://www.minervachamber.org
Contact: Denise Freeland, Executive Director
Description: Promotes the advancement of the industrial, retail, commercial, and professional environment in Minerva Area, OH.

56230 ■ *Minority Business/Professional Directory*
144 N Main St.
Lima, OH 45801
Ph: (419)222-6045
Fax: (419)229-0266
Co. E-mail: chamber@limachamber.com
URL: http://www.limachamber.com
Contact: Jed E. Metzger, President
Price: included in membership dues; $5, for nonmembers.

56231 ■ Monroe County Chamber of Commerce (SOCC)
PO Box 643
Woodsfield, OH 43793
Ph: (740)472-5499
Fax: (740)472-5499
Co. E-mail: monroechamber@gmn4u.com
URL: http://www.monroechamber.com
Contact: Rusty Atkinson, President
Description: Promotes business and community development in Monroe County, OH. Sponsors festival. **Founded:** 1974.

56232 ■ *Monthly Minutes*
PO Box 3414
Kent, OH 44240-3414
Ph: (330)677-6439
Co. E-mail: ddarlas2000@yahoo.com
URL: http://www.brimfieldchamber.com
Contact: Scott Mikula, President
Released: Monthly

56233 ■ Montpelier Area Chamber of Commerce (MACC)
410 W Main St.
Montpelier, OH 43543
Ph: (419)485-4416
Fax: (419)495-4416
Co. E-mail: macofc@verizon.net
URL: http://www.montpelierchamber.com
Contact: Ms. Terry L. Buntain, Executive Director
Description: Promotes business and community development in the Montpelier, OH area. Sponsors annual Bean Days Festival and Blue Water train excursion. Maintains retail division. Holds bimonthly board meeting. Sponsors Bean Days Festival. **Founded:** 1845. **Publications:** *Directory of Members.*

56234 ■ Morrow County Chamber of Commerce and Visitors' Bureau (MCCCVB)
17-1/2 W High St.
Mount Gilead, OH 43338
Ph: (419)946-2821
Fax: (419)946-3861
Co. E-mail: chamuway@bright.net
URL: http://www.morrowchamber.org
Contact: Rosemary Levings, Executive Director
Description: Promotes economic growth and community development in Morrow County, OH. **Founded:** 1960. **Awards:** Career Passport Award (Annual); Citizen of the Year (Annual); Student of the Month (Bimonthly).

56235 ■ Mount Vernon - Knox County Chamber of Commerce
400 S Gay St.
Mount Vernon, OH 43050
Ph: (740)393-1111
Fax: (740)393-1590
Co. E-mail: chamber@knoxchamber.com
URL: http://www.knoxchamber.com
Contact: Carol Grubaugh, Executive Director
Description: Represents businesses in Mount Vernon, OH. **Publications:** *Business Broadcast* (Monthly). **Awards:** Heart Award (Annual); Investor in the Future (Annual); Paul Slaughter Volunteer of the Year Award (Annual); Quality of Life Award (Annual); Small Business of the Year Award (Annual); Women in Business Leadership Award (Annual).

56236 ■ *Moving a Business to Stow*
4381 Hudson Dr., Ste. K2
Stow, OH 44224
Ph: (330)688-1579

Fax: (330)688-6234
Co. E-mail: smfcc@smfcc.com
URL: http://www.smfcc.com
Contact: Cindy Smith Lewis, Executive Director
Price: free.

56237 ■ Muskingum Valley Area Chamber of Commerce (MVACC)
PO Box 837
Beverly, OH 45715
Ph: (740)984-8259
Co. E-mail: jawagner@aep.com
URL: http://www.mvacc.com
Contact: Glen O. Miller, Chairman
Description: Advances the general welfare and prosperity of Muskingum Valley area.

56238 ■ Napoleon - Henry County Chamber of Commerce
611 N Perry St.
Napoleon, OH 43545
Ph: (419)592-1786
Fax: (419)592-4945
Co. E-mail: hcncoc@ohiohenrycounty.com
URL: http://www.naphcchamber.com
Contact: Andy Anderson, Director
Description: Promotes business and community development in Napoleon, OH. Sponsors new teacher breakfast, tourism activities, and business after hours. **Founded:** 1952.

56239 ■ *The Navigator*
316 W Main St.
Mason, OH 45040
Ph: (513)336-0125
Fax: (513)398-6371
Co. E-mail: info@necchamber.org
URL: http://www.necchamber.org/home
Contact: Chet Mastalerz, President
Released: Monthly

56240 ■ *News and Notes*
45 S Columbus St.
Sunbury, OH 43074
Ph: (740)965-2860
Fax: (740)965-2860
Co. E-mail: info@sunburybigwalnutchamber.com
URL: http://www.sunburybigwalnutchamber.com
Contact: Chad Brownfield, President
Released: Quarterly

56241 ■ *News and Views*
4536 Main Ave.
Ashtabula, OH 44004
Ph: (440)998-6998
Fax: (440)992-8216
Co. E-mail: jessica@ashtabulachamber.net
URL: http://www.ashtabulachamber.net
Contact: Jessica Forsythe, President
Released: Monthly

56242 ■ *News and Views*
4081 Main St.
Hilliard, OH 43026-1501
Ph: (614)876-7666
Fax: (614)876-3113
Co. E-mail: info@hilliardchamber.org
URL: http://www.hilliardchamber.org
Contact: Libby Gierach, President
Released: Monthly

56243 ■ *News and Views*
33595 Bainbridge Rd., Ste. 101
Solon, OH 44139-2942
Ph: (440)248-5080
Fax: (440)248-9121
Co. E-mail: staff@solonchamber.com
URL: http://www.solonchamber.com
Contact: Nancy Traum, President
Released: Monthly

56244 ■ *Newsgram*
64 W Franklin St.
Bellbrook, OH 45305-1903
Ph: (937)848-4930

Fax: (937)848-4930
Co. E-mail: info@bellbrooksugarcreekchamber.com
URL: http://bellbrooksugarcreekchamber.com
Contact: Chris Ewing, Executive Director
Released: Semiannual

56245 ■ Nordonia Hills Chamber of Commerce
PO Box 34
Northfield, OH 44067-0034
Ph: (330)467-8956
Fax: (330)468-4901
Co. E-mail: laura@nordoniahillschamber.org
URL: http://www.nordoniahillschamber.org
Contact: Laura Sparano, Executive Director
Description: Promotes business and community development in the Northfield, OH area.

56246 ■ North Canton Area Chamber of Commerce (NCACC)
121 S Main St.
North Canton, OH 44720-3021
Ph: (330)499-5100
Fax: (330)499-7181
Co. E-mail: cathy@northcantonchamber.org
URL: http://www.northcantonchamber.org
Contact: Randall Smith, Chairman
Description: Businesses, schools, churches, and individuals united to promote business in the North Canton, OH area. **Founded:** 1959.

56247 ■ North Coast Chamber of Commerce
PO Box 275
Avon Lake, OH 44012-0275
Ph: (440)933-9311
Co. E-mail: contact@northcoastchamber.com
URL: http://www.northcoastchamber.com
Contact: Linda Hamann, President
Description: Strives to improve the quality of life in and around the local community. **Founded:** 1989.

56248 ■ North Olmsted Chamber of Commerce (NOCC)
28938 Lorain Rd., Ste. 204
North Olmsted, OH 44070
Ph: (440)777-3368
Fax: (440)777-9361
Co. E-mail: rlgarno@aol.com
URL: http://www.nolmstedchamber.org
Contact: John Sobolewski, Executive Director
Description: Businesses, industries, and individuals. Promotes business and community development in North Olmsted, OH. **Founded:** 1954. **Publications:** *Chamber Insider* (Monthly). **Awards:** Scholarship Award (Annual). **Telecommunication Services:** nocc@nolmstedchamber.org.

56249 ■ Northeast Cincinnati Chamber of Commerce
316 W Main St.
Mason, OH 45040
Ph: (513)336-0125
Fax: (513)398-6371
Co. E-mail: info@necchamber.org
URL: http://www.necchamber.org/home
Contact: Chet Mastalerz, President
Description: Provides valuable services to its members, advocates for a positive business environment, and stimulates economic development. Works closely with township, city, and county officials to help attract new business and assist with planned growth and development. **Publications:** *The Navigator* (Monthly).

56250 ■ Northmont Area Chamber of Commerce (ENCC)
9 W National Rd.
Englewood, OH 45322
Ph: (937)836-2550
Fax: (937)836-2485
URL: http://www.northmont-area-coc.org
Contact: Cathy Hutton, Chief Executive Officer
Description: Promotes business and economic growth in northern Montgomery County, OH. **Founded:** 1977. **Publications:** *Chamber Directory*; *The Informer* (Monthly); *The Outlook* (Monthly).

56251 ■ Norwalk Area Chamber of Commerce (NACC)
10 W Main St.
Norwalk, OH 44857
Ph: (419)668-4155
Fax: (419)663-6173
Co. E-mail: chamber@accnorwalk.com
URL: http://www.norwalkareachamber.com
Contact: Melissa James, Executive Director
Description: Promotes the general welfare and prosperity of the citizens, businesses, and industries of the Norwalk, OH area. **Founded:** 1938.

56252 ■ Oak Harbor Area Chamber of Commerce (OHACC)
161 W Water St.
Oak Harbor, OH 43449
Ph: (419)898-0479
Fax: (419)898-2429
Co. E-mail: chamber@oakharborohio.net
URL: http://www.oakharborohio.net
Contact: Valerie Winterfield, Executive Director
Description: Promotes business and community development in the Oak Harbor, OH area. **Founded:** 1970. **Publications:** *Chamber Chatter* (Periodic).

56253 ■ Oberlin Area Chamber of Commerce
13 S Main St., 2nd Fl.
Oberlin, OH 44074
Ph: (440)774-6262
Fax: (440)775-2423
Co. E-mail: oberlinchamber@oberlin.net
URL: http://www.oberlinchamber.org
Contact: Jennifer McCoy, President
Description: Aims to advance the general welfare and prosperity of Oberlin area.

56254 ■ Ohio Chamber of Commerce (OCC)
230 E Town St.
Columbus, OH 43215-0159
Ph: (614)228-4201
Free: 800-622-1893
Fax: (614)228-6403
Co. E-mail: occ@ohiochamber.com
URL: http://www.ohiochamber.com
Contact: Andrew E. Doehrel, President
Description: Businesses organized to foster economic and industrial growth in Ohio. Serves as liaison between government and business. Keeps members informed of employment conditions, economic developments, and pertinent regulations. Conducts lobbying activities. **Founded:** 1893. **Publications:** *Environmental and Safety Directory* (Annual); *Membership Notes* (Bimonthly); *Ohio Matters* (Bimonthly); *The Complete Wage and Hour Manual.* **Telecommunication Services:** adoehrel@ohiochamber.com.

56255 ■ Ohio-Israel Chamber of Commerce (OICC)
PO Box 39007
Cleveland, OH 44139-0007
Ph: (216)965-4474
Fax: (440)248-4888
Co. E-mail: ohioisraelchamber@ameritech.net
URL: http://ohioisraelchamber.com
Contact: Howard Gudell, President
Description: Promotes business between Ohio and Israeli companies by programming, matchmaking, and government contacts. **Founded:** 1996. **Publications:** *Business Barometer* (Quarterly).

56256 ■ *Ohio Matters*
230 E Town St.
Columbus, OH 43215-0159
Ph: (614)228-4201
Free: 800-622-1893
Fax: (614)228-6403
Co. E-mail: occ@ohiochamber.com
URL: http://www.ohiochamber.com
Contact: Andrew E. Doehrel, President
Released: Bimonthly

56257 ■ Ohio Small Business Development Center at the Clermont Chamber of Commerce
4355 Ferguson Dr., Ste. 150
Cincinnati, OH 45245
Ph: (513)576-5000

Fax: (513)576-5001
Co. E-mail: john.melvin@clermontchamber.com
URL: http://www.clermontchamber.com/Small-Business-Development-Center.29.0.html
Contact: John Melvin, Director
Description: Represents and promotes the small business sector. Provides management assistance to current and prospective small business owners. Helps to improve management skills and expand the products and services of members.

56258 ■ *Opening a Business in Stow*
4381 Hudson Dr., Ste. K2
Stow, OH 44224
Ph: (330)688-1579
Fax: (330)688-6234
Co. E-mail: smfcc@smfcc.com
URL: http://www.smfcc.com
Contact: Cindy Smith Lewis, Executive Director

56259 ■ Ottawa Area Chamber of Commerce
129 Court St.
Ottawa, OH 45875
Ph: (419)523-3141
Fax: (419)523-5860
Co. E-mail: ottawachamber@earthlink.net
URL: http://ottawachamber.org
Contact: Mary Jo Bockrath, Executive Director
Description: Promotes businesses in Ottawa, OH. Provides resources, referrals and promotional opportunities to members. **Founded:** 1950.

56260 ■ *The Outlook*
9 W National Rd.
Englewood, OH 45322
Ph: (937)836-2550
Fax: (937)836-2485
URL: http://www.northmont-area-coc.org
Contact: Cathy Hutton, Chief Executive Officer
Released: Monthly

56261 ■ Over-The-Rhine Chamber of Commerce (OTRCC)
111 E 13th St.
Cincinnati, OH 45202
Ph: (513)241-2690
Fax: (513)241-6770
Co. E-mail: otrchamber@zoomtown.com
URL: http://www.otrchamber.com
Contact: Russell Wilson, Chairman
Description: Promotes business and community development in Over-the-Rhine, OH area. **Founded:** 1985. **Awards:** Architecture Award (Annual); Arts Organization of the Year (Annual); Business of the Year (Annual); Chairman's Award (Annual); Entrepreneur of the Year (Annual); Individual Contribution Award (Annual); New Business of the Year (Annual); President's Award (Annual).

56262 ■ Oxford Chamber of Commerce (OCC)
30 W Park Pl.
Oxford, OH 45056
Ph: (513)523-5200
Fax: (513)523-2308
Co. E-mail: jonell@oxfordchamber.org
URL: http://www.oxfordchamber.org
Contact: Jonell Rowan, President
Description: Businesspersons and professionals interested in promoting business and community development in Oxford, OH. **Founded:** 1979.

56263 ■ Painesville Area Chamber of Commerce
1 Victoria Sq., Ste. 265a
Painesville, OH 44077
Ph: (440)357-7572
Fax: (440)357-8752
Co. E-mail: office@painesvilleohchamber.org
URL: http://www.painesvilleohchamber.org
Description: Promotes business and community development to enrich the economic, civic, social, cultural and environmental well being of Painesville area. **Awards:** Citizen of the Year (Annual).

56264 ■ Parma Area Chamber of Commerce (PACC)
7908 Day Dr.
Parma, OH 44129

Ph: (440)886-1700
Fax: (440)886-1770
Co. E-mail: chamber@parmaareachamber.org
URL: http://parmaareachamber.org
Contact: Dave Nedrich, Chief Executive Officer
Description: Provides benefits and opportunities to over 500 business and organization members including networking referrals, sponsorships, advertising, direct marketing, discounts on insurance, payroll, timekeeping and credit card processing, workers' compensation group programs, member to member discounts and more. Supports community and member events, regional and local partnerships, legislative impact, leadership, and volunteer roles. **Founded:** 1955. **Publications:** *Insight* (Monthly).

56265 ■ Perrysburg Area Chamber of Commerce
105 W Indiana Ave.
Perrysburg, OH 43551
Ph: (419)874-9147
Fax: (419)872-9347
Co. E-mail: director@perrysburgchamber.com
URL: http://www.perrysburgchamber.com
Contact: Sandy Latchem, Executive Director
Description: Promotes business, community development and free enterprise system in the Perrysburg, OH area. **Publications:** *Chamber Connection* (Monthly).

56266 ■ Pickerington Area Chamber of Commerce (PACC)
13 W Columbus St.
Pickerington, OH 43147
Ph: (614)837-1958
Fax: (614)837-6420
Co. E-mail: president@pickeringtonchamber.com
URL: http://www.pickeringtonchamber.com
Contact: Brett A. Miller, Chairman
Description: Promotes business and community development in Pickerington, OH. **Founded:** 1978. **Publications:** *Businews* (Monthly); *Community Guide and Profile*; *Pickerington Area Map*. **Awards:** Community Service Award; Safety Award; PACC Scholarship (Annual); Business of the Quarter/Business of the Year.

56267 ■ *Pickerington Area Map*
13 W Columbus St.
Pickerington, OH 43147
Ph: (614)837-1958
Fax: (614)837-6420
Co. E-mail: president@pickeringtonchamber.com
URL: http://www.pickeringtonchamber.com
Contact: Brett A. Miller, Chairman

56268 ■ Pike County Chamber of Commerce (PCCC)
12455 State Rte. 104
Waverly, OH 45690
Ph: (740)947-7715
Fax: (740)947-7716
Co. E-mail: mail@pikechamber.org
URL: http://www.pikechamber.org
Contact: Tom Adkins, President
Description: Promotes business and community development in Pike County, OH. **Founded:** 1960. **Publications:** *Accent* (Monthly).

56269 ■ Piqua Area Chamber of Commerce (PACC)
326 N Main St.
Piqua, OH 45356
Ph: (937)773-2765
Fax: (937)773-8553
Co. E-mail: info@piquaareachamber.com
URL: http://www.piquaareachamber.com/cwt/external/wcpages/index.aspx
Contact: Lisa K. Whitaker, President
Description: Promotes business and community development in the Piqua, OH area.

56270 ■ *Plat Books*
37840 Cadiz-Dennison Rd.
Cadiz, OH 43907
Ph: (740)942-3350

Fax: (740)942-0009
Co. E-mail: hrcctour@eohio.net
URL: http://pages.eohio.net/harrisonchamber
Contact: Ed Coultrap, Executive Director

56271 ■ Powell Area Chamber of Commerce
50 S Liberty St., Ste. 170
Powell, OH 43065
Ph: (614)888-1090
Fax: (614)888-4803
Co. E-mail: admin@powellchamber.com
URL: http://www.powellchamber.com
Contact: Craig Sedoris, President
Description: Promotes business and community development in the greater Powell, OH area. **Founded:** 1991. **Publications:** *Greater Powell Area Chamber of Commerce Directory and Community Guide* (Annual). **Awards:** Business Person of the Year (Annual); Citizen of the Year (Annual); Restoration of the Year (Annual).

56272 ■ *Progressing Together*
205 W Center St., Ste.100
Marion, OH 43302
Ph: (740)382-2181
Fax: (740)387-7722
Co. E-mail: phall@marionareachamber.org
URL: http://www.marionareachamber.org
Contact: Pamela S. Hall, President
Released: Monthly **Price:** included in membership dues.

56273 ■ *Purchase Directory*
Three Commerce Park Sq.
2550 Chagrin Blvd., Ste. 201
Beachwood, OH 44122
Ph: (216)831-0003
Fax: (216)831-1209
Co. E-mail: mail@beachwood.org
URL: http://www.beachwood.org
Contact: Bill Mann, President

56274 ■ Put-in-Bay Chamber of Commerce (PBCC)
148 Delaware Ave.
Put-in-Bay, OH 43456
Ph: (419)285-2832
URL: http://visitputinbay.com/visitus
Contact: Maggie Beckford, Executive Director
Description: Seeks to attract business and tourism to the Put-in-Bay, OH area. **Publications:** *Island Guide* (Annual).

56275 ■ *Quality of Life Book & Membership Directory*
227 E 5th St.
Marysville, OH 43040
Ph: (937)642-6279
Free: 800-642-0087
Fax: (937)644-0422
Co. E-mail: dschaner@unioncounty.org
URL: http://www.unioncounty.org
Contact: Debra Schaner, Office Manager
Released: Annual

56276 ■ Ravenna Area Chamber of Commerce (RACC)
135 E Main St.
Ravenna, OH 44266
Ph: (330)296-3886
Fax: (330)296-6986
Co. E-mail: ravennachamber@att.net
URL: http://www.ravennaareachamber.com
Contact: Jack Ferguson, Executive Director
Description: Promotes business and community development in the Ravenna, OH area. **Founded:** 1907. **Awards:** Raven Awards (Annual).

56277 ■ Reading Chamber of Commerce
PO Box 15164
Reading, OH 45215
Ph: (513)741-7951
Fax: (513)741-8778
Co. E-mail: drflege@hotmail.com
URL: http://www.readingohiochamber.org
Contact: Dave Flege, President
Description: Promotes business and community development in Reading, OH area.

56278 ■ *The Reporter*
20 N High St.
Canal Winchester, OH 43110
Ph: (614)837-1556
Fax: (614)837-9901
Co. E-mail: chamber@canalwinchester.com
URL: http://www.canalwinchester.com
Contact: Amanda Lemke, Executive Director
Released: Monthly

56279 ■ *The Reporter*
88 N Main St.
Chagrin Falls, OH 44022
Ph: (440)247-6607
Co. E-mail: info@cvcc.org
URL: http://www.cvcc.org
Contact: Darci Spilman, Executive Director
Released: Monthly

56280 ■ Reynoldsburg Area Chamber of Commerce (RACC)
1580 Brice Rd.
Reynoldsburg, OH 43068
Ph: (614)866-4753
Fax: (614)866-7313
Co. E-mail: jan@reynoldsburgchamber.com
URL: http://www.reynoldsburgchamber.com
Contact: Jan Hills, President
Description: Promotes a strong business environment by being the collective voice in the Reynoldsburg area, enhances the general welfare of the community through economic prosperity. **Awards:** Wingrove Award (Annual).

56281 ■ Rittman Area Chamber of Commerce
12 N Main St., Ste. 2
Rittman, OH 44270
Ph: (330)925-4828
Co. E-mail: rittmanchamber@ohio.net
URL: http://www.rittmanchamber.com
Contact: Kimberly Field-Springer, Executive Director
Description: Promotes businesses in Rittman, OH.

56282 ■ *River Biz*
20220 Center Ridge Rd., Ste. 130
Rocky River, OH 44116
Ph: (440)331-1140
Fax: (440)331-3485
Co. E-mail: info@rockyriverchamber.com
URL: http://www.rockyriverchamber.com
Contact: Liz Manning, Executive Director
Released: Monthly

56283 ■ Rocky River Chamber of Commerce (RRCC)
20220 Center Ridge Rd., Ste. 130
Rocky River, OH 44116
Ph: (440)331-1140
Fax: (440)331-3485
Co. E-mail: info@rockyriverchamber.com
URL: http://www.rockyriverchamber.com
Contact: Liz Manning, Executive Director
Description: Promotes business and community development in Rocky River, OH. Holds annual Christmas party to benefit Rocky River Assistance Program. **Founded:** 1938. **Publications:** *River Biz* (Monthly); *Rocky River Residence Reference Guide* (Annual). **Educational Activities:** Business Mixers; Business to Business Expo (Annual).

56284 ■ *Rocky River Residence Reference Guide*
20220 Center Ridge Rd., Ste. 130
Rocky River, OH 44116
Ph: (440)331-1140
Fax: (440)331-3485
Co. E-mail: info@rockyriverchamber.com
URL: http://www.rockyriverchamber.com
Contact: Liz Manning, Executive Director
Released: Annual

56285 ■ Rootstown Area Chamber of Commerce
PO Box 254
Rootstown, OH 44272
Co. E-mail: alohacomputer@att.net
URL: http://www.rootstownchamber.org
Contact: Joe Paulus, President
Description: Promotes interest of its members and of business in general.

56286 ■ Salem Area Chamber of Commerce (SACC)
713 E State St.
Salem, OH 44460-2911
Ph: (330)337-3473
Fax: (330)337-3474
Co. E-mail: dave.nestic@jumpstartinc.org
URL: http://www.salemohiochamber.org
Contact: Dave Nestic, President
Description: Promotes business and community development in the Salem, OH area. Sponsors Salem Jubilee festival. **Founded:** 1956. **Publications:** *Salem Industrial Directory* (Biennial); *Salem Update* (Monthly); *Buyer's Guide and Membership Directory* (Periodic).

56287 ■ *Salem Industrial Directory*
713 E State St.
Salem, OH 44460-2911
Ph: (330)337-3473
Fax: (330)337-3474
Co. E-mail: dave.nestic@jumpstartinc.org
URL: http://www.salemohiochamber.org
Contact: Dave Nestic, President
Released: Biennial

56288 ■ *Salem Update*
713 E State St.
Salem, OH 44460-2911
Ph: (330)337-3473
Fax: (330)337-3474
Co. E-mail: dave.nestic@jumpstartinc.org
URL: http://www.salemohiochamber.org
Contact: Dave Nestic, President
Released: Monthly

56289 ■ Sharonville Chamber of Commerce
4015 Executive Park Dr., Ste. 302
Sharonville, OH 45241
Ph: (513)554-1722
Fax: (513)554-1307
Co. E-mail: info@sharonvillechamber.com
URL: http://www.sharonvillechamber.com
Contact: Rich Arnold, President
Description: Promotes member businesses by providing value through networking, benefits, education and marketing opportunities.

56290 ■ Shelby Chamber of Commerce
142 N Gamble St., Ste. A
Shelby, OH 44875
Ph: (419)342-2426
Fax: (419)342-2189
Co. E-mail: carol.knapp@shelbyoh.com
URL: http://www.shelbyoh.com
Contact: Carol A. Knapp, President
Description: Promotes a positive business environment for economic growth and development within and for the community.

56291 ■ Small Business Development Center at The Lorain County Chamber of Commerce
151 Innovation Dr.
Elyria, OH 44035
Ph: (440)366-4314
Co. E-mail: melanie@glideit.org
URL: http://www.entrepreneurohio.org/center.
   aspx?center=17083&subloc=0
Contact: Jim Kraft, Director
Description: Represents and promotes the small business sector. Provides management assistance to current and prospective small business owners. Helps to improve management skills and expand the products and services of members.

56292 ■ Small Business Development Center at Toledo Regional Chamber of Commerce
Toledo Edison Bldg.
300 Madison Ave., Ste. 200
Toledo, OH 43604
Ph: (419)243-8191
Co. E-mail: charlene.page@toledochamber.com
URL: http://www.entrepreneurohio.org/center.
   aspx?center=17021&subloc=0
Contact: Bill Wersell, Regional Director
Description: Represents and promotes the small business sector. Provides management assistance to current and prospective small business owners. Helps to improve management skills and expand the products and services of members.

56293 ■ Solon Chamber of Commerce (SCC)
33595 Bainbridge Rd., Ste. 101
Solon, OH 44139-2942
Ph: (440)248-5080
Fax: (440)248-9121
Co. E-mail: staff@solonchamber.com
URL: http://www.solonchamber.com
Contact: Nancy Traum, President
Description: Promotes business and community development in Solon, OH. **Founded:** 1927. **Publications:** *News and Views* (Monthly); *The Solon Community Directory*; *The Solon Industrial Directory*; *The Solon Industrial Guide*. **Educational Activities:** Coffee Connection (Monthly). **Telecommunication Services:** ntraum@solonchamber.com.

56294 ■ *The Solon Community Directory*
33595 Bainbridge Rd., Ste. 101
Solon, OH 44139-2942
Ph: (440)248-5080
Fax: (440)248-9121
Co. E-mail: staff@solonchamber.com
URL: http://www.solonchamber.com
Contact: Nancy Traum, President
Price: $5, additional copy.

56295 ■ *The Solon Industrial Directory*
33595 Bainbridge Rd., Ste. 101
Solon, OH 44139-2942
Ph: (440)248-5080
Fax: (440)248-9121
Co. E-mail: staff@solonchamber.com
URL: http://www.solonchamber.com
Contact: Nancy Traum, President
Price: free for members; $30, for nonmembers.

56296 ■ *The Soundings*
PO Box 717
Russells Point, OH 43348
Ph: (937)843-5392
Fax: (937)843-9051
Co. E-mail: office@indianlakechamber.org
URL: http://www.indianlakechamber.org
Contact: Rick Fuller, President
Released: Monthly

56297 ■ *South Metro Monthly Magazine*
7887 Washington Village Dr., Ste. 265
Dayton, OH 45459
Ph: (937)433-2032
Fax: (937)433-6881
Co. E-mail: deanna.lang@smrcoc.org
URL: http://www.smrcoc.org
Contact: Deanna Lang, Office Manager
Released: Monthly

56298 ■ South Metro Regional Chamber of Commerce
7887 Washington Village Dr., Ste. 265
Dayton, OH 45459
Ph: (937)433-2032
Fax: (937)433-6881
Co. E-mail: deanna.lang@smrcoc.org
URL: http://www.smrcoc.org
Contact: Deanna Lang, Office Manager
Description: Promotes business and community development in the Southern Dayton, OH metropolitan area. Holds Business After Hours parties and monthly board of directors meeting. **Founded:** 1969. **Publications:** *The Business Advisor* (Monthly); *Comprehensive Guide to Members* (Annual); *South Metro Monthly Magazine* (Monthly).

56299 ■ Southeastern Franklin County Chamber of Commerce
6198 Meriden Ct.
Canal Winchester, OH 43110
Ph: (614)834-7700
Fax: (614)834-9185
Co. E-mail: chambersefc@gmail.com
URL: http://www.chambersefc.com
Contact: Terri Christensen, Executive Director
Description: Promotes business and community development in Southeastern Franklin County, OH.

56300 ■ Southwestern Auglaize County Chamber of Commerce
22 S Water St.
New Bremen, OH 45869
Ph: (419)629-0313
Fax: (419)629-0411
Co. E-mail: info@auglaize.org
URL: http://www.auglaize.org
Contact: Ben Baumer, President
Description: Works to improve the economy and quality of life in Southwest Auglaize and the surrounding areas. **Founded:** 1998.

56301 ■ Spring Valley Area Chamber of Commerce (SVACC)
PO Box 396
Spring Valley, OH 45370
Ph: (937)862-4110
URL: http://springvalleyoh.com/springvalley/svcc/svcc.htm
Contact: Judy Madden, President
Description: Promotes business and community development in Spring Valley, OH.

56302 ■ Springboro Chamber of Commerce
325 S Main St.
Springboro, OH 45066
Ph: (937)748-0074
Fax: (937)748-0525
Co. E-mail: chamber@springboroohio.org
URL: http://www.springboroohio.org
Contact: Anne Stremanos, Executive Director
Description: Promotes and supports local business and community. **Founded:** 1975. **Subscriptions:** 4. **Publications:** *Business Update* (Monthly).

56303 ■ Springfield-Clark County Chamber of Commerce (SACC)
20 S Limestone St., Ste. 100
Springfield, OH 45502
Ph: (937)325-7621
Free: 800-803-1553
Fax: (937)325-8765
Co. E-mail: info@greaterspringfield.com
URL: http://chamber.greaterspringfield.com
Contact: Michael J. McDorman, President
Description: Promotes business and community development in the Springfield, OH area. **Founded:** 1894. **Publications:** *Business and Professional Directory* (Annual).

56304 ■ Stow-Munroe Falls Chamber of Commerce (SMFCC)
4381 Hudson Dr., Ste. K2
Stow, OH 44224
Ph: (330)688-1579
Fax: (330)688-6234
Co. E-mail: smfcc@smfcc.com
URL: http://www.smfcc.com
Contact: Cindy Smith Lewis, Executive Director
Description: Promotes business and community development in the Stow-Munroe Falls area. Sponsors annual Pride Week, golf outing and Community Showcase, Candidates and Issues Night, Public Officials Reception and more. Conducts charitable activities. **Founded:** 1965. **Publications:** *Moving a Business to Stow; Opening a Business in Stow; Stow-Munroe Falls Chamber of Commerce Member Business Directory.* **Awards:** Business Person of Year (Annual); Friend of the Community Award (Annual); Lifetime Membership (Annual); 25 Year Members (Annual).

56305 ■ *Stow-Munroe Falls Chamber of Commerce Member Business Directory*
4381 Hudson Dr., Ste. K2
Stow, OH 44224
Ph: (330)688-1579
Fax: (330)688-6234
Co. E-mail: smfcc@smfcc.com
URL: http://www.smfcc.com
Contact: Cindy Smith Lewis, Executive Director

56306 ■ Streetsboro Area of Chamber of Commerce (SACC)
9205 State Rte. 43, Ste. 106
Streetsboro, OH 44241
Ph: (330)626-4769
Fax: (330)422-1118
Co. E-mail: sacc@streetsborochamber.org
URL: http://www.streetsborochamber.org
Contact: Meghan Urbon, Executive Director

56307 ■ *Strictly Business*
1323 4th St. NW
New Philadelphia, OH 44663
Ph: (330)343-4474
Fax: (330)343-6526
Co. E-mail: info@tuschamber.com
URL: http://www.tuschamber.com
Contact: Jill R. McCartney, President
Released: Quarterly **Price:** $5.

56308 ■ Strongsville Chamber of Commerce (SCC)
18829 Royalton Rd.
Strongsville, OH 44136-5130
Ph: (440)238-3366
Free: 800-551-3119
Fax: (440)238-7010
Co. E-mail: info@strongsvillechamber.com
URL: http://www.strongsvillechamber.com
Contact: Ms. Rea Cantwell, Executive Director
Description: Promotes business and community development in Strongsville, OH. Monitors legislation. Sponsors annual homecoming festival. **Founded:** 1941. **Publications:** *Strongsville Chamber of Commerce News* (Periodic).

56309 ■ *Strongsville Chamber of Commerce News*
18829 Royalton Rd.
Strongsville, OH 44136-5130
Ph: (440)238-3366
Free: 800-551-3119
Fax: (440)238-7010
Co. E-mail: info@strongsvillechamber.com
URL: http://www.strongsvillechamber.com
Contact: Ms. Rea Cantwell, Executive Director
Released: Periodic

56310 ■ Sunbury - Big Walnut Area Chamber of Commerce
45 S Columbus St.
Sunbury, OH 43074
Ph: (740)965-2860
Fax: (740)965-2860
Co. E-mail: info@sunburybigwalnutchamber.com
URL: http://www.sunburybigwalnutchamber.com
Contact: Chad Brownfield, President
Description: Encourages the development of a local infrastructure that will support existing and new businesses; organizes and supports civic activities for the benefit of community residents and enhances the relationship between the Sunbury/Big Walnut Area residents and business community. **Publications:** *News and Notes* (Quarterly).

56311 ■ Swanton Area Chamber of Commerce (SACC)
100 Broadway
Swanton, OH 43558
Ph: (419)826-1941
Fax: (419)826-3242
Co. E-mail: swantoncc@aol.com
URL: http://www.swantonareacoc.com/page/page/5184460.htm
Contact: Neil Toeppe, Executive Director
Description: Businesses, factories, retail stores, wholesalers, professional and fraternal organizations, and individuals interested in promoting business and

community development in eastern Fulton and western Lucas counties, OH. Conducts workshops. **Founded:** 1975.

56312 ■ Swedish-American Chamber of Commerce, Ohio
PO Box 81242
Cleveland, OH 44181
Ph: (216)496-0873
Co. E-mail: lars.eriksson@sacc-ohio.org
URL: http://www.sacc-ohio.org
Contact: Lars Eriksson, President

56313 ■ Sylvania Area Chamber of Commerce (SACC)
5632 N Main St.
Sylvania, OH 43560
Ph: (419)882-2135
Fax: (419)885-7740
Co. E-mail: info@sylvaniachamber.org
URL: http://www.sylvaniachamber.org
Contact: Ms. Pat Nowak, Executive Director
Description: Promotes business and community development in the Sylvania, OH area. Sponsors annual Arts and Crafts Festival. **Founded:** 1954.

56314 ■ *Take Action*
226 Middle Ave., 5th Fl.
Elyria, OH 44035
Ph: (440)328-2550
Fax: (440)328-2557
Co. E-mail: info@loraincountychamber.com
URL: http://www.loraincountychamber.com
Contact: Frank P. DeTillio, President
Released: Periodic

56315 ■ Tallmadge Chamber of Commerce
c/o Barb Hornyak, Admin. Asst.
80 Community Rd.
Tallmadge, OH 44278
Ph: (330)633-5417
Fax: (330)633-5415
Co. E-mail: tallmadgechamber@onecommail.com
URL: http://www.tallmadge-chamber.com
Contact: Mary Cea, Executive Director
Description: Promotes business and community development in Tallmadge, OH. Sponsors arts and crafts festival. Conducts charitable activities. **Founded:** 1955. **Publications:** *Business Notes* (Monthly). **Educational Activities:** Tallmadge Chamber of Commerce Banquet (Annual).

56316 ■ *Telephone Directory*
8228 Mayfield Rd., Ste. 4B
Chesterland, OH 44026
Ph: (440)729-7297
Fax: (440)729-2690
Co. E-mail: ccoc@chesterlandchamber.com
URL: http://www.chesterlandchamber.com
Released: Annual

56317 ■ Tiffin Area Chamber of Commerce (TACC)
62 S Washington St.
Tiffin, OH 44883
Ph: (419)447-4141
Fax: (419)447-5141
Co. E-mail: info@tiffinchamber.com
URL: http://tiffinchamber.com
Contact: Anne Lange DeVine, Chairman
Description: Seeks to promote and support community enhancement activities that are beneficial to Tiffin area. **Publications:** *Chamber Vision* (Periodic).

56318 ■ *Toledo Profile Series*
Enterprise, Ste. 200
300 Madison Ave.
Toledo, OH 43604-1575
Ph: (419)243-8191
Fax: (419)241-8302
Co. E-mail: joinus@toledochamber.com
URL: http://www.toledochamber.com/cwt/external/wcpages/index.aspx
Contact: Mark A. V'Soske, President

56319 ■ Toledo Regional Chamber of Commerce (TRCC)
Enterprise, Ste. 200
300 Madison Ave.
Toledo, OH 43604-1575
Ph: (419)243-8191
Fax: (419)241-8302
Co. E-mail: joinus@toledochamber.com
URL: http://www.toledochamber.com/cwt/external/wcpages/index.aspx
Contact: Mark A. V'Soske, President
Description: Businesses. Promotes business and community development in the Toledo, OH area. Offers cost-saving benefits and networking opportunities to members. **Publications:** *Insider* (Monthly); *Membership Reference Guide* (Annual); *Toledo Profile Series.* **Educational Activities:** Business After Hours (Periodic). **Awards:** ATHENA Award (Annual).

56320 ■ *Top of Ohio Topics*
c/o Daniel S. Yahraus, Exec. Dir.
Bryan, OH 43506
Ph: (419)636-2247
Fax: (419)636-5556
Co. E-mail: info@bryanchamber.org
URL: http://www.bryanchamber.org
Contact: Daniel S. Yahraus, Executive Director
Released: Monthly

56321 ■ Troy Area Chamber of Commerce
405 SW Public Sq., Ste. 330
Troy, OH 45373
Ph: (937)339-8769
Fax: (937)339-4944
Co. E-mail: tacc@troyohiochamber.com
URL: http://www.troyohiochamber.com
Contact: J.C. Wallace, President
Description: Seeks to enhance the quality of life of Troy community through promotion of economic vitality and growth, stimulation of business environment and advancement of free enterprise system. **Publications:** *Chamber News* (Monthly). **Awards:** Community Service Award (Annual); Distinguished Citizen (Annual); Educator of the Year (Annual); Young Man/Woman of the Year (Annual). **Telecommunication Services:** ccochran@troyohiochamber.com.

56322 ■ Tuscarawas County Chamber of Commerce (TCCC)
1323 4th St. NW
New Philadelphia, OH 44663
Ph: (330)343-4474
Fax: (330)343-6526
Co. E-mail: info@tuschamber.com
URL: http://www.tuschamber.com
Contact: Jill R. McCartney, President
Description: Promotes business and community development in Tuscarawas County, OH. Operates safety council and export resource center. **Founded:** 1959. **Publications:** *Economic and Demographics of Tuscarawas County*; *Images of Tuscarawas County* (Annual); *Strictly Business* (Quarterly).

56323 ■ Twin City Chamber of Commerce (TCCC)
210 E 3rd St.
Uhrichsville, OH 44683
Ph: (740)922-5623
Fax: (740)922-1371
Co. E-mail: twincityinfo@sbcglobal.net
URL: http://www.twincitychamber.org
Contact: Teri Edwards, Executive Director
Description: Manufacturers, retail store owners, and interested individuals organized to promote business and community development in the Dennison and Uhrichsville, OH area. Sponsors various community activities. **Founded:** 1913.

56324 ■ Twinsburg Chamber of Commerce (TCC)
2250 E Enterprise Pkwy.
Twinsburg, OH 44087
Ph: (330)963-6249

Fax: (330)963-6995
Co. E-mail: djohnson@twinsburgchamber.com
URL: http://www.twinsburgchamber.com
Contact: Mr. Douglas H. Johnson, Executive Director
Description: Provides advocacy, education, cost savings benefits, and business promotion opportunities to businesses in the local area. **Founded:** 1921. **Publications:** *Chamber News* (Monthly); *Twinsburg Industrial and Commercial Directory* (Annual); *Twinsburg Quick Facts*; *Twinsburg Industrial and Commercial Directory* (Annual). **Educational Activities:** Golf Outing (Annual).

56325 ■ *Twinsburg Industrial and Commercial Directory*
2250 E Enterprise Pkwy.
Twinsburg, OH 44087
Ph: (330)963-6249
Fax: (330)963-6995
Co. E-mail: djohnson@twinsburgchamber.com
URL: http://www.twinsburgchamber.com
Contact: Mr. Douglas H. Johnson, Executive Director
Released: Annual **Price:** free for members.

56326 ■ *Twinsburg Quick Facts*
2250 E Enterprise Pkwy.
Twinsburg, OH 44087
Ph: (330)963-6249
Fax: (330)963-6995
Co. E-mail: djohnson@twinsburgchamber.com
URL: http://www.twinsburgchamber.com
Contact: Mr. Douglas H. Johnson, Executive Director
Price: free.

56327 ■ Union County Chamber of Commerce
227 E 5th St.
Marysville, OH 43040
Ph: (937)642-6279
Free: 800-642-0087
Fax: (937)644-0422
Co. E-mail: dschaner@unioncounty.org
URL: http://www.unioncounty.org
Contact: Debra Schaner, Office Manager
Description: Promotes business and community development in the Union County, Marysville, OH area. **Publications:** *Bridge Tour* (Annual); *Convention & Visitors Bureau* (Monthly); *Quality of Life Book & Membership Directory* (Annual).

56328 ■ *Update*
210 E Main St.
Alliance, OH 44601
Ph: (330)823-6260
Fax: (330)823-4434
Co. E-mail: info@allianceohiochamber.org
URL: http://www.allianceohiochamber.org
Contact: R. Mark Locke, President
Released: Quarterly

56329 ■ Upper Arlington Area Chamber of Commerce
2152 Tremont Ctr.
Upper Arlington, OH 43221
Ph: (614)481-5710
Fax: (614)481-5711
Co. E-mail: becky@uachamber.org
URL: http://www.uachamber.org
Contact: Becky Hajost, President
Description: Promotes business and community development in Upper Arlington, OH. **Founded:** 1977. **Publications:** *Directions* (Monthly).

56330 ■ Upper Sandusky Area Chamber of Commerce (USACC)
108 E Wyandot Ave.
Upper Sandusky, OH 43351
Ph: (419)294-3349
Free: 800-686-1261
Fax: (419)294-3531
Co. E-mail: upperchamber@udata.com
URL: http://www.uppersanduskychamber.com
Contact: Aaron Korte, Executive Director
Description: Promotes business and community development in Wyandot County, OH. **Founded:** 1947. **Publications:** *Compass* (Bimonthly); *Industry Business* (Periodic).

56331 ■ Valley City Chamber of Commerce
PO Box 304
Valley City, OH 44280
Ph: (330)483-1111
Co. E-mail: chamberofcommerce@valleycity.org
URL: http://www.valleycity.org
Contact: Cindy Kintop, President
Description: Aims to advance the commercial, industrial, civic and general welfare of Liverpool Township and the surrounding community. Promotes economic opportunity by providing leadership and ongoing communication with its members, government and the public.

56332 ■ Van Wert Area County Chamber of Commerce (VWCCC)
1199 Professional Dr.
Van Wert, OH 45891
Ph: (419)238-4390
Free: 877-770-4438
Fax: (419)238-4589
Co. E-mail: chamber@vanwertchamber.com
URL: http://www.vanwertchamber.com
Contact: Kate Gribble, President
Description: Promotes business and community development in the Van Wert, OH area. Sponsors annual Home Show. **Founded:** 1926. **Publications:** *Chamber Viewpoint* (Monthly); *Van Wert Community Guide* (Semiannual); *Membership Directory and Buyer's Guide* (Biennial); *Van Wert Community Guide* (Semiannual). **Educational Activities:** Business After Hours (Periodic); Van Wert Home and Garden Show (Annual). **Telecommunication Services:** kgribble@vanwertchamber.com.

56333 ■ *Van Wert Community Guide*
1199 Professional Dr.
Van Wert, OH 45891
Ph: (419)238-4390
Free: 877-770-4438
Fax: (419)238-4589
Co. E-mail: chamber@vanwertchamber.com
URL: http://www.vanwertchamber.com
Contact: Kate Gribble, President
Released: Semiannual

56334 ■ Vermilion Chamber of Commerce (VCC)
5495 Liberty Ave.
Vermilion, OH 44089
Ph: (440)967-4477
Fax: (440)967-2877
Co. E-mail: vermilionchamber@centurytel.net
URL: http://www.vermilionohio.com
Contact: Pam Cooper, President
Description: Promotes business and community development in Vermilion, OH. Sponsors annual dinner, Festival of Fish, Woollybear Festival, and awards luncheon. **Founded:** 1962.

56335 ■ Vinton County Chamber of Commerce
104 W Main St.
McArthur, OH 45651
Ph: (740)596-5033
Free: 800-596-4459
Fax: (740)596-9262
Co. E-mail: info@vintoncounty.com
URL: http://www.vintoncounty.com
Contact: Jerry Zinn, President
Description: Promotes business and community development in the McArthur, OH area. **Awards:** Student of the Year (Annual).

56336 ■ *Vista*
226 Middle Ave., 5th Fl.
Elyria, OH 44035
Ph: (440)328-2550
Fax: (440)328-2557
Co. E-mail: info@loraincountychamber.com
URL: http://www.loraincountychamber.com
Contact: Frank P. DeTillio, President

56337 ■ *The Voice*
49 Public Sq.
Brecksville, OH 44141
Ph: (440)526-7350

Fax: (440)526-7889
Co. E-mail: chambe@brecksvillechamber.com
URL: http://www.brecksvillechamber.com
Contact: Debra Branske, President
Released: Bimonthly

56338 ■ *Voice*
205 N 5th St.
Zanesville, OH 43701
Ph: (740)455-8282
Free: 800-743-2303
Fax: (740)454-2963
Co. E-mail: dmatz@zmchamber.com
URL: http://www.zmchamber.com
Contact: Thomas C. Poorman, President
Released: Monthly

56339 ■ Wadsworth Area Chamber of Commerce (WACC)
123 Broad St., Ste. C
Wadsworth, OH 44281
Ph: (330)336-6150
Fax: (330)336-2672
Co. E-mail: business@wadsworthchamber.com
URL: http://www.wadsworthchamber.com
Contact: Michelle Masica, Chief Executive Officer
Description: Promotes business and community development in the Wadsworth, OH area. Evaluates and responds to the needs of local businesses; provides programs and services to members.
Founded: 1954. **Telecommunication Services:** beth@wadsworthchamber.com.

56340 ■ Wapakoneta Area Chamber of Commerce (WACC)
30 E Auglaize St.
Wapakoneta, OH 45895
Ph: (419)738-2911
Fax: (419)738-2977
Co. E-mail: wapcofc@bright.net
URL: http://www.wapakoneta.com
Contact: Dan Graf, Director
Description: Promotes business and community development in the Wapakoneta, OH area. Sponsors the Indian Summer Festival. **Publications:** *Chamber Chat* (Monthly).

56341 ■ Waterville Area Chamber of Commerce (WACC)
PO Box 74
Waterville, OH 43566
Ph: (419)878-5188
Fax: (419)878-5199
Co. E-mail: admin@watervillechamber.com
URL: http://www.watervillechamber.com
Contact: Dave Boothe, President
Description: Businesspersons, professionals, retail and service merchants, manufacturer's representatives, and industry interested in promoting business and community development in the Waterville, OH area. Assists new business; provides input for economic development. Sponsors Riverfest and annual Roche de Boeuf Festival. **Founded:** 1970. **Publications:** *Business and Community Directory* (Quarterly).

56342 ■ Wauseon Chamber of Commerce (WCC)
115 N Fulton St.
Wauseon, OH 43567
Ph: (419)335-9966
Fax: (419)335-7693
Co. E-mail: debbie@wauseonchamber.com
URL: http://www.wauseonchamber.com
Contact: Debbie Nelson, Executive Director
Description: Promotes business and community development in the Wauseon, OH area. **Founded:** 1937.

56343 ■ *The Wave*
509 Huron St.
Huron, OH 44839
Ph: (419)433-5700
URL: http://www.huron.net
Contact: Sheila Ehrhardt, Director
Released: Monthly

56344 ■ *Wayne County Industrial*
377 W Liberty St.
Wooster, OH 44691
Ph: (330)262-5735
Fax: (330)262-5745
Co. E-mail: wchamber@bright.net
URL: http://www.woosterchamber.com
Contact: Sue Peeples, Vice President
Released: Annual **Price:** free for members; $10, for nonmembers.

56345 ■ Waynesville Area Chamber of Commerce
PO Box 281
Waynesville, OH 45068-0281
Ph: (513)897-8855
Fax: (513)897-9833
Co. E-mail: waynsville@aol.com
URL: http://www.waynesvilleohio.com
Contact: Dawn Schroeder, Executive Director
Description: Works to advance, protect, and preserve the civic, economic, business, and individual interest of the Waynesville area. **Founded:** 1969. **Publications:** *Getting It Right The First Time: A Pocket Guide For New Business.*

56346 ■ Wellington Chamber of Commerce
226 Wenner St.
Wellington, OH 44090
Ph: (440)647-2222
URL: http://www.wellingtonohio.net
Contact: Virginia Haynes, President

56347 ■ West Shore Chamber of Commerce
1100 Crocker Rd.
Westlake, OH 44145
Ph: (440)835-8787
Fax: (440)835-8798
Co. E-mail: sandy@wetshorechamber.org
URL: http://www.westshorechamber.org
Contact: John Sobolewski, Executive Director
Description: Works as a voluntary organization of the business community. Unites hundreds of business and professional firms, thus creating a unique central agency working to improve business and build a better community. **Founded:** 1979.

56348 ■ Westerville Area Chamber of Commerce
99 Commerce Park Dr.
Westerville, OH 43082
Ph: (614)882-8917
Fax: (614)882-2085
Co. E-mail: info@westervillechamber.com
URL: http://www.westervillechamber.com
Contact: Janet Davis, President
Description: Promotes business and community development in the Westerville, OH area. **Founded:** 1968. **Publications:** *The Communicator* (Monthly). **Educational Activities:** Westerville Music and Arts Festival (Annual). **Awards:** Outstanding Business Person of the Year (Annual).

56349 ■ Whitehall Area Chamber of Commerce
PO Box 13607
Whitehall, OH 43213
Ph: (614)237-7792
Fax: (614)235-8646
Co. E-mail: info@whitehallchamber.org
URL: http://www.whitehallchamber.org
Contact: Jennifer Moeller, President
Description: Seeks to preserve and enhance the positive image of Whitehall community. **Publications:** *Chamber Chronicle.* **Awards:** Beautification Award (Annual).

56350 ■ Willard Area Chamber of Commerce
16 S Myrtle Ave.
Willard, OH 44890
Ph: (419)935-1888
Co. E-mail: willardchamber@yahoo.com
URL: http://www.willardchamber.com
Contact: Ricky Branham, Executive Director
Description: Promotes business and community development in Willard, OH.

56351 ■ Willoughby Area Chamber of Commerce (WACC)
28 Public Sq.
Willoughby, OH 44094
Ph: (440)942-1632
Fax: (440)942-0586
Co. E-mail: info@willoughbyareachamber.com
URL: http://www.willoughbyareachamber.com
Contact: Nikki Matala, Executive Director
Description: Promotes business and community development in the Willoughby, Willoughby Hills, and Kirtland, OH area. Offers Workers' Compensation and Health Insurance at greatly reduced premiums. **Founded:** 1903. **Publications:** *Membership Directory and Buyer's Guide* (Annual). **Awards:** Distinguished Civic Organization (Annual).

56352 ■ Wilmington - Clinton County Chamber of Commerce (WCCCC)
40 N South St.
Wilmington, OH 45177
Ph: (937)382-2737
Free: 888-922-2250
Fax: (937)383-2316
Co. E-mail: karenhaley@wcccchamber.com
URL: http://www.wcccchamber.com
Contact: Karen M. Haley, President
Description: Promotes business and community development in the Clinton County, OH area. Convention/Meeting: none. **Founded:** 1957. **Publications:** *Buyer's Guide* (Annual).

56353 ■ Wooster Area Chamber of Commerce (WACC)
377 W Liberty St.
Wooster, OH 44691
Ph: (330)262-5735
Fax: (330)262-5745
Co. E-mail: wchamber@bright.net
URL: http://www.woosterchamber.com
Contact: Sue Peeples, Vice President
Description: Promotes business and community development in Wayne County, OH. **Founded:** 1900. **Publications:** *Chamber Connection* (Monthly); *Wayne County Industrial* (Annual); *Wayne County Industrial* (Annual); *Wayne County Plat Book.* **Educational Activities:** Wooster Area Chamber of Commerce Dinner (Annual); Wayne County Home and Garden (Annual). **Awards:** Business of the Year (Annual); New Business of the Year (Annual); Small Business Person of the Year (Annual); Wall of Fame (Annual). **Telecommunication Services:** peeples@neo-bright.net.

56354 ■ Xenia Area Chamber of Commerce (XACC)
334 W Market St.
Xenia, OH 45385-2843
Ph: (937)372-3591
Fax: (937)372-2192
Co. E-mail: xacc@xacc.com
URL: http://www.xacc.com
Contact: Alan Liming, President
Description: Promotes business and community development in the Xenia, OH area. **Founded:** 1949. **Publications:** *Chamber News* (Monthly); *Community Profile Book* (Biennial).

56355 ■ Yellow Springs Chamber of Commerce
101 Dayton St.
Yellow Springs, OH 45387-1817
Ph: (937)767-2686
Fax: (937)767-7876
Co. E-mail: info@yellowspringsohio.org
URL: http://www.yellowspringsohio.org
Contact: Karen Wintrow, Executive Director
Description: Promotes business and community development in Yellow Springs, OH area. **Publications:** *Chamber News* (Monthly).

56356 ■ Youngstown/Warren Regional Chamber of Commerce
11 Central Sq., Ste. 1600
Youngstown, OH 44503
Ph: (330)744-2131

Fax: (330)746-0330
Co. E-mail: tom@regionalchamber.com
URL: http://www.regionalchamber.com
Contact: Thomas M. Humphries, President
Description: Promotes business and community development in Youngstown/Warren Region, OH area.

56357 ■ Zanesville - Muskingum County Chamber of Commerce
205 N 5th St.
Zanesville, OH 43701
Ph: (740)455-8282
Free: 800-743-2303
Fax: (740)454-2963
Co. E-mail: dmatz@zmchamber.com
URL: http://www.zmchamber.com
Contact: Thomas C. Poorman, President
Description: Promotes business and community development in the Muskingum County, OH area. **Founded:** 1905. **Publications:** *Commerce* (Annual); *Legislative Directory* (Annual); *Voice* (Monthly); *Legislative Directory* (Annual). **Telecommunication Services:** tpoorman@zmchamber.com

MINORITY BUSINESS ASSISTANCE PROGRAMS

56358 ■ City of Cleveland - Office of Equal Opportunities
City Hall
601 Lake Side Ave.
Cleveland, OH 44114
Ph: (216)664-4152
Fax: (216)664-3870
URL: http://www.cleveland-oh.gov
Contact: Debra Linn Talley, Director
Description: Managerial and technical assistance is provided to develop, support and promote business development for program participants in Cleveland.

56359 ■ Women's Entrepreneurial Network
PO Box 514
Maumee, OH 43537
Ph: (419)536-6732
URL: http://www.wen-usa.com
Contact: Linda Everhardt-Kardux, President
Description: Provides business development for female entrepreneurs.

FINANCING AND LOAN PROGRAMS

56360 ■ Athenian Ventures / Ohio Valley Venture Fund
20 E. Circle Dr., Ste. 229
Athens, OH 45701-3751
Ph: (614)360-1155
Fax: (740)593-9311
URL: http://www.athenianvp.com
Contact: Karl O. Elderkin, Managing Partner
Preferred Investment Size: $2,000,000 to $6,000,000. **Industry Preferences:** Computer software and services, medical and health, biotechnology, computer hardware, semiconductors and other electronics, Internet specific, communications and media, consumer related, and other products. **Geographic Preference:** Midwestern, Eastern, and Western U.S.

56361 ■ Blue Chip Venture Company
1100 Chiquita Ctr.
250 E. 5th St.
Cincinnati, OH 45202
Ph: (513)723-2300
Fax: (513)723-2306
URL: http://www.bcvp.com
Contact: John H. Wyant, Managing Director
Preferred Investment Size: $4,000,000 to $6,000,000. **Industry Preferences:** Internet specific, computer software and services, medical and health, communications and media, semiconductors and other electronics, other products, consumer related, industrial and energy, biotechnology, and computer hardware. **Geographic Preference:** Midwest, Mid Atlantic, Northeast, and West Coast.

56362 ■ Brantley Partners
3550 Lander Rd., Ste. 300
Pepper Pike, OH 44124
Ph: (216)464-8400
Fax: (216)464-8405
Co. E-mail: info@brantleypartners.com
URL: http://www.brantleypartners.com
Contact: Robert P. Pinkas, Partner
Preferred Investment Size: $3,000,000 to $10,000,000. **Industry Preferences:** Other products, industrial and energy, medical and health, biotechnology, computer software and services, consumer related, semiconductors and other electronics, communications and media, and Internet specific. **Geographic Preference:** U.S and Canada.

56363 ■ Clarion Capital Corp.
Ohio Savings Plz.
1801 E. 9th St., Ste. 1120
Cleveland, OH 44114
Ph: (216)687-1096
Fax: (216)694-3545
URL: http://www.clarioncap.com
Contact: Tom Niehaus, Chief Financial Officer
Industry Preferences: Consumer related, biotechnology, other products, medical and health, industrial and energy, computer hardware, software and services, Internet specific, communications and media, semiconductors and other electronics. **Geographic Preference:** Northeast, Midwest, and West Coast.

56364 ■ Crystal Internet Venture Fund, L.P.
c/o CIVF Management, Ltd.
1120 Chester Ave., Ste. 418
Cleveland, OH 44114
Ph: (216)263-5515
Fax: (216)263-5518
Co. E-mail: crystal@crystalventures.com
URL: http://www.crystalventures.com
Contact: Daniel Kellogg, Managing Director
Preferred Investment Size: $1,000,000 to $5,000,000. **Investment Policies:** Equity. **Industry Preferences:** Internet specific, computer software and services, communications and media, semiconductors and other electronics, and computer hardware. **Geographic Preference:** Silicon Valley.

56365 ■ Early Stage Partners, L.P.
1801 E. 9th St., Ste., 1700
Cleveland, OH 44114
Ph: (216)781-4600
Fax: (216)781-0158
Co. E-mail: inbox@esplp.com
URL: http://www.esplp.com
Contact: Charles C. MacMillan, Chief Financial Officer
Investment Policies: Early stage. **Industry Preferences:** Computer software, industrial and energy, and manufacturing. **Geographic Preference:** Midwest and Ohio.

56366 ■ Morgenthaler Ventures (Cleveland)
Terminal Tower
50 Public Sq., Ste. 2700
Cleveland, OH 44113
Ph: (216)416-7500
Fax: (216)416-7501
URL: http://www.morgenthaler.com
Contact: Joe Machado, Principal
Preferred Investment Size: $5,000,000 to $20,000,000. **Industry Preferences:** Semiconductors and other electronics, communications and media, medical and health, Internet specific, computer software and services, biotechnology, industrial and energy, other products, computer hardware, and consumer related. **Geographic Preference:** U.S.

56367 ■ National City Equity Partners, LLC
1900 E. 9th St., 17th Fl.
Cleveland, OH 44114
Ph: (216)222-3763
Fax: (216)222-9965
URL: http://www.ncepi.com
Contact: William Schecter, President
Preferred Investment Size: $5,000,000 to $35,000,000. **Industry Preferences:** Semiconductors and other electronics, other products, consumer related, communications and media, industrial and energy, Internet specific, medical and health, and computer hardware. **Geographic Preference:** U.S.

56368 ■ Primus Venture Partners, Inc.
5900 Landerbrook Dr., Ste. 200
Cleveland, OH 44124-4020
Ph: (440)684-7300
Fax: (440)684-7342
Co. E-mail: info@primuscapital.com
URL: http://www.primusventure.com
Contact: Loyal W. Wilson, Managing Director
E-mail: lwilson@primuscapital.com
Preferred Investment Size: $15,000,000 to $40,000,000. **Industry Preferences:** Communications and media, other products, Internet specific, consumer related, medical and health, biotechnology, business services, computer software and services, computer hardware, semiconductors and other electronics. **Geographic Preference:** U.S. and Canada.

56369 ■ Reservoir Venture Partners
400 W. Wilson Bridge Rd., Ste. 130
Columbus, OH 43085
Ph: (614)846-7241
Fax: (614)846-7267
Co. E-mail: info@reservoirvp.com
URL: http://www.reservoirvp.com
Contact: Curtis D. Crocker, Managing Director
E-mail: ccrocker@reservoirvp.com
Preferred Investment Size: $500,000 to $1,000,000. **Investment Policies:** Seed and early stage. **Industry Preferences:** Communications, computer software, biotechnology, medical and health, and industrial and energy. **Geographic Preference:** Midwest.

56370 ■ The Walnut Group
312 Walnut St., Ste. 1151
Cincinnati, OH 45202
Ph: (513)651-3300
Fax: (513)651-1084
URL: http://www.thewalnutgroup.com
Contact: James M. Gould, Partner
E-mail: James.Gould@TheWalnutGroup.com
Preferred Investment Size: $2,000,000 to $6,000,000. **Industry Preferences:** Medical and health, consumer related, financial services, business service, and other. **Geographic Preference:** U.S.

PROCUREMENT ASSISTANCE PROGRAMS

56371 ■ Eastgate Regional Council of Government - Mahoning Valley Technical Procurement Center - EDATA
City Centre One Bldg.
100 E Federal St., Ste. 1000
Youngstown, OH 44503
Ph: (330)779-3800
Fax: (330)779-3838
Co. E-mail: moreinfo@eastgatecog.org
URL: http://www.eastgatecog.org
Contact: Norma Webb, Program Manager
E-mail: npickens@edata.org

56372 ■ Kent Procurement Technical Assistance Center - Kent Regional Business Alliance - Kent State University
College of Business, Rm. 300-B
Kent, OH 44242-0001
Ph: (330)672-9448
Fax: (330)672-9338
Co. E-mail: ptac@krbz.biz
URL: http://www.krba.biz/ptac
Description: Offers assistance in all areas of government contracting and is designed to increase Ohio's share of the government marketplace. All services are free of charge and available to businesses in Medina, Portage, Stark, Summit, and Wayne counties.

56373 ■ Northeast Ohio Procurement Technical Assistance Center - Lake County Economic Development Center
Lake Erie College
3991 W Washington St.
Painesville, OH 44077-5198

Ph: (440)357-2292
Fax: (440)357-2296
Co. E-mail: bobfenn@lcedc.org
URL: http://www.lcedc.org
Contact: Robert Fenn, Director
Description: Helping to small and mid-size businesses interested in selling their products and services to federal, state, and local government agencies.

56374 ▪ Northeast Ohio Procurement Technical Assistance Center - Lake Erie College Campus
3991 W Washington St.
Painesville, OH 44077
Ph: (440)357-2294
Fax: (440)357-2296
Co. E-mail: bobfenn@lcedc.org
URL: http://www.lcedc.org/PTAC/ptac.htm
Contact: Robert Fenn, Director
E-mail: bobfenn@lcedc.org
Description: Provides education, training, and consultation services as needed depending on the experience of the business.

56375 ▪ Ohio Procurement Technical Assistance Center
300 Madison Ave., Ste. 200
Toledo, OH 43604-1575
Ph: (419)243-8191
Fax: (419)241-8302
Co. E-mail: megan.reichart@toledochamber.com
URL: http://www.toledochamber.com
Contact: Avery Sledge, Director
Description: Offers many business development resources to help entrepreneurs start a new venture or expand their existing one.

56376 ▪ Ohio Procurement Technical Assistance Center - Cincinnati Procurement Outreach Center - Toledo Chamber of Commerce
300 Madison Ave., Ste. 200
Toledo, OH 43604-1575
Ph: (419)243-8191
Fax: (419)241-8302
Co. E-mail: megan.reichart@toledochamber.com
URL: http://www.toledochamber.com
Contact: Avery Sledge, Director
E-mail: nancy.rogers@uc.edu
Description: Offers many business development resources to help entrepreneurs start a new venture or expand their existing one.

56377 ▪ Ohio Procurement Technical Assistance Center - Kent Regional Business Alliance - Kent State University
College of Business, Rm. 300-B
Kent, OH 44242
Ph: (330)672-9448
Fax: (330)672-9338
Co. E-mail: ptac@krbz.biz
URL: http://www.krba.biz/ptac
Description: Offers assistance in all areas of government contracting and is designed to increase Ohio's share of the government marketplace serving Medina, Portage, Stark, Summit, and Wayne counties.

56378 ▪ Ohio Procurement Technical Assistance Center - Lawrence Economic Development Corporation - Procurement Outreach Center
216 Collins Ave.
South Point, OH 45680-0488
Ph: (740)377-4550
Free: 800-408-1334
Fax: (740)377-2091
Co. E-mail: jordan@sopoc.org
URL: http://www.lawrencecountyohio.org
Contact: Jordan Lucas, Program Manager
Description: Identifies business firms that are qualified to sell their goods and services to the Department of Defense (DoD), other federal agencies, and state government programs serving Adams, Brown, Gallia, Highland, Jackson, Lawrence, Pike, Ross, Scioto and Vinton counties.

56379 ▪ Ohio Procurement Technical Assistance Center - Mahoning Valley Technical Procurement Center - MVEDC
4319 Belmont Ave.
Youngstown, OH 44505
Ph: (330)759-3668
Fax: (330)759-3686
Co. E-mail: info@mvedc.com
URL: http://www.mvedc.com
Contact: Steve Danyi, Director
Description: Offers many business development resources to help entrepreneurs start a new venture or expand their existing one.

56380 ▪ Ohio Procurement Technical Assistance Center - Ohio University - Procurement Technical Assistance Program
The Ridges, Bldg. 20
Athens, OH 45701
Ph: (740)597-1868
Fax: (740)593-1795
Co. E-mail: ptac@arei.org
URL: http://www.voinovichcenter.ohio.edu/
Contact: Sharon Hopkins, Director
E-mail: williams@mcnet.marietta.edu
Description: Helps companies sell their products or service to local, state, or federal government agencies.

56381 ▪ Ohio Procurement Technical Assistance Center - Procurement Technical Assistance Program
1275 Kinnear Rd.
Columbus, OH 43212
Ph: (614)466-5700
Free: 800-848-1300
Fax: (614)466-4172
Co. E-mail: fatou.ndiaye@development.ohio.gov
URL: http://www.development.ohio.gov
Contact: N. Fatou Ndiaye, Program Manager
Description: Provides counseling, technical resources, historical contracting data, military specifications, financial guidance, and advocacy for federal procurement opportunities.

56382 ▪ Ohio Procurement Technical Assistance Center - Toledo Regional Chamber of Commerce
300 Madison St., Ste. 200
Toledo, OH 43604-1575
Ph: (419)243-8191
Fax: (419)241-8002
Co. E-mail: JoinUs@toledochamber.com
URL: http://www.toledochamber.com
Contact: David Wood, Director
E-mail: avery.sledge@toledochamber.com
Description: Offers many business development resources to help entrepreneurs start a new venture or expand their existing one.

56383 ▪ Ohio University Procurement Technical Assistance Center - Ohio University Voinovich Center for Leadership and Public Affairs
The Ridges, Bldg. 20
Athens, OH 45701
Ph: (740)597-1868
Fax: (740)593-1795
URL: http://www.ohio.edu/ptac
Contact: Sharon Hopkins, Director
E-mail: hopkins1@ohio.edu
Description: Provides training, information, and technical assistance to businesses in Appalachia Ohio seeking government contracts.

56384 ▪ Procurement Technical Assistance Center - Lawrence Economic Development Corporation
c/o Greater Lawrence County Area Chamber of Commerce
216 Collins Ave.
South Point, OH 45680-0488
Ph: (740)377-4550
Free: 800-408-1334

Fax: (740)377-2091
Co. E-mail: bill@ledcorp.org
URL: http://www.lawrencecountyohio.org
Contact: Bill Dingus, Executive Director
E-mail: cfreeman@zoomnet.net

56385 ▪ South Central Ohio Small Business Development Center Consortium - Procurement Outreach Center
Marietta College SBDC
213 Fourth St., 2nd Fl.
Marietta, OH 45750
Ph: (740)376-4832
Fax: (740)376-4901
Co. E-mail: sppoc@zoominternet.net
URL: http://www.lawrencecountyohio.org
Contact: Emerson Shrimp, Director
Description: Serves Adams, Brown, Gallia, Highland, Jackson, Lawrence, Pike, Ross, Scioto and Vinton counties.

56386 ▪ Southwest Central Ohio Procurement Technical Assistance Center - SWCO PTAC Cincinnati Center
1776 Mentor Ave., Ste. 420
Cincinnati, OH 45212
Ph: (513)489-2528
Co. E-mail: bwirth@emtec.org
URL: http://swcoptac.org
Contact: Brian Worth, Counselor
E-mail: ccharlton@emtec.org
Description: Assists small businesses throughout southwest central Ohio cut through the red tape and successfully promote their goods and services to the federal, state, and local governments. Serves Butler, Clermont, Clinton, Hamilton, and Warren.

56387 ▪ Southwest Central Ohio Procurement Technical Assistance Center - SWCO PTAC Pickerington Satellite Office
c/o Pickerington Area Chamber of Commerce
13 W Columbus St.
Pickerington, OH 43147
Ph: (937)253-0038
Co. E-mail: mthreatt@emtec.org
URL: http://swcoptac.org
Description: Assists small businesses throughout southwest central Ohio cut through the red tape and successfully promote their goods and services to the federal, state, and local governments. Serves Pickerington and Fairfield county area.

56388 ▪ Southwest Central Ohio Procurement Technical Assistance Center - SWCO PTAC Satellite Office
3155 Research Blvd., Ste. 202
Dayton, OH 45420
Ph: (937)259-1368
Co. E-mail: mthreatt@emtec.org
URL: http://swcoptac.org
Contact: Meredith Threatt, Director
E-mail: mthreatt@emtec.org
Description: Assists small businesses throughout southwest central Ohio cut through the red tape and successfully promote their goods and services to the federal, state, and local governments. Serves the Hamilton and Butler County area.

56389 ▪ Southwest Central Ohio Procurement Technical Assistance Center - SWCO PTAC Satellite Office
c/o Lancaster Chamber of Commerce
109 N Broad St.
Lancaster, OH 43130
Ph: (937)253-0038
URL: http://swcoptac.org
Contact: Meredith Threatt, Director
E-mail: mthreatt@emtec.org
Description: Assists small businesses throughout southwest central Ohio cut through the red tape and successfully promote their goods and services to the federal, state, and local governments. Serves the Lancaster and Fairfield County area.

INCUBATORS/RESEARCH AND TECHNOLOGY PARKS

56390 ■ Akron Global Business Accelerator
526 S. Main St.
Akron, OH 44311
Ph: (330)375-2173
Fax: (330)762-3657
Co. E-mail: asabo@akronincubator.com
URL: http://www.ci.akron.oh.us/aii/
Contact: Terry Martell, Director
Description: A small business incubator that assists in the business start-up process and gives aid to new businesses to help ensure their survival.

56391 ■ Allen Economic Development Group
147 S Main St., Ste. 200
Lima, OH 45801
Ph: (419)222-7706
Fax: (419)222-7916
Co. E-mail: info@aedg.org
URL: http://www.aedg.org
Contact: Marcel Wagner, Chief Executive Officer
Description: A small business incubator dedicated to supporting emerging firms through shared resources and other services.

56392 ■ Appalachian Center for Economic Networks (ACEnet)
94 Columbus Rd.
Athens, OH 45701
Ph: (740)592-3854
Fax: (740)593-5451
Co. E-mail: info@acenetworks.org
URL: http://www.acenetworks.org/
Contact: June Holley, President
Description: The ACEnet, located in rural, southeastern Ohio, is an incubator dedicated to improving the economy of the region. Offers business incubation, e-commerce, specialty food production, and venture loans.

56393 ■ Barberton Community Development Corp.
542 W Tuscarawas Ave.
Barberton, OH 44203
Ph: (330)745-3070
Fax: (330)745-1070
Co. E-mail: info@bcdc.org
URL: http://www.bcdc.org
Contact: Larry Lallo, Executive Director
Description: Provides business development services for the area.

56394 ■ Beachwood Business Development Center
25325 Fairmount Blvd.
23230 Chagrin Blvd., Ste. 900
Beachwood, OH 44122
Ph: (216)292-1915
Fax: (216)292-1989
Co. E-mail: Vince.Adamus@beachwoodohio.com
URL: http://www.beachwoodbusiness.com/econdev.html
Description: Works to assist local businesses and improve the economic base.

56395 ■ BIOSTART
3130 Highland Ave., No. 2
Cincinnati, OH 45219-2374
Ph: (513)-475-6610
Fax: (513)-221-1980
Co. E-mail: dfranken@biostart.org
URL: http://www.biostart.org/
Contact: Carl J. Frankenstein, President
Description: A small business incubator providing newly-formed life science companies with the perfect mix of low cost, state-of-the-art lab and office space and services, readily available business and scientific expertise, and a supportive entrepreneurial culture to enable and accelerate growth during their critical early years.

56396 ■ BizTech Center
20 High St.
Hamilton, OH 45011
Ph: (513)737-6543
Fax: (513)737-6755
Co. E-mail: mcollmer@biztechcenter.com
URL: http://www.biztechcenter.com/
Contact: Marilyn Collmer, Manager
Description: A small business incubator providing everything a young or start-up business needs, from professional mentoring and networking to office space in a convenient location.

56397 ■ Braintree Business Development Center
201 E. Fifth St.
Mansfield, OH 44902
Ph: (419)525-1614
Fax: (419)525-3492
Co. E-mail: info@braintreepartners.org
URL: http://www.braintreepartners.org/
Description: A non-profit business incubator which assists business startups and emerging companies in North Central Ohio, offering counseling, customer referral, access to capital, and training opportunities.

56398 ■ Endeavor Center
1862 Shyville Rd.
Piketon, OH 45661
Ph: (740)289-1605
Co. E-mail: brackman@ag.osu.edu
URL: http://endeavor.osu.edu/
Description: A small business incubator that provides flexible lease space, management guidance, networking, and shared services to entrepreneurs in south central Ohio.

56399 ■ Entrepreneurs Center
714 E Monument Ave.
Dayton, OH 45402
Ph: (937)281-0168
Fax: (937)281-0099
Co. E-mail: info@TECdayton.com
URL: http://www.tecdayton.com/
Contact: Barbara Hayde, President
Description: A small business incubator dedicated to the care and nurturing of individuals who are willing to take the risk to foster economic development and invest in the region by starting up technology enterprises.

56400 ■ Hamilton County Business Center
1776 Mentor Ave.
Box 110
Cincinnati, OH 45212
Ph: (513)458-2211
Fax: (513)351-0610
Co. E-mail: longo@hcdc.com
URL: http://www.hcdc.com/incubation
Contact: David K. Main, President
Description: A nationally-recognized business incubation program helping Greater Cincinnati entrepreneurs launch and build successful companies. It is a mixed-use, technology-focused incubation program catering to those entrepreneurs who are starting up an innovative and growing business.

56401 ■ Kent Business Incubator
211 E Summit St.
Kent, OH 44240
Ph: (330)474-3595
Fax: (330)672-9338
URL: http://www.krba.biz/incubator/
Description: A small business incubator providing a nurturing environment where businesses can develop and grow.

56402 ■ Muskingum County Business Incubator
56 N Fifth St.
Zanesville, OH 43701
Ph: (740)453-3649
Co. E-mail: chumphreys@mcbi.info
URL: http://www.mcbi.info/
Contact: Carol Humphreys, Director
Description: A small business incubator providing an intensive set of services by professional staff, personnel from other agencies, and mentors to help businesses start, grow and become successful companies.

56403 ■ Ohio University Innovation Center - Ohio University
340 W State St., Unit 7
Athens, OH 45701
Ph: (740)593-1818
Fax: (740)593-0186
Co. E-mail: innovation@ohio.edu
URL: http://www.innovationcenter.ohiou.edu
Contact: Linda Clark, Director
Description: Provides incubation resources to the local area.

56404 ■ River East Corp.
615 Front St.
Toledo, OH 43605
Ph: (419)698-2310
Fax: (419)698-3640
Co. E-mail: reerc-rea@kmbs.com
URL: http://www.toledorivereast.com
Contact: Donald Monroe, Executive Director

56405 ■ TechColumbus
1275 Kinnear Rd.
Columbus, OH 43212
Ph: (614)487-3700
URL: http://www.techcolumbus.org/
Description: A small business incubator whose mission is to accelerate and support the growth of Central Ohio's tech economy - to make the most of its technology assets.

56406 ■ Toledo Business and Technology Center
1946 N 13th St.
Toledo, OH 43624
Ph: (419)255-6700
Fax: (419)255-6264
Co. E-mail: toledobtc@aol.com
Contact: Christi Abner, Manager

56407 ■ Youngstown Business Incubator
241 W Federal St.
Youngstown, OH 44503
Ph: (330)746-5003
Fax: (330)746-6863
Co. E-mail: jcossler@ybi.org
URL: http://www.ybi.org/
Contact: James Cossler, Director
Description: The YBI was established to nurture emerging technology and light manufacturing companies through shared resources, business assistance, and other services.

EDUCATIONAL PROGRAMS

56408 ■ Bryant and Stratton Business Institute - Parma Campus
12955 Snow Rd.
Parma, OH 44130-1005
Ph: (216)265-3151
Fax: (216)265-0325
URL: http://www.bryantstratton.edu
Description: Business college offering programs in business management and business operations.

56409 ■ Cuyahoga Community College
700 Carnegie Ave.
Cleveland, OH 44115
Ph: (216)987-4000
Free: 800-954-8742
URL: http://www.tri-c.edu/
Description: Two-year college offering a small business management program. **Publications:** The High Point (Monthly); The Mosaic (Biweekly).

56410 ■ Kent State University - Graduate School of Management
Kent State University
Kent, OH 44242
Ph: (330)672-2282
Fax: (330)672-7303
Co. E-mail: gradbus@kent.edu
URL: http://www.business.kent.edu
Description: Offers an Executive MBA Program for professional growth. The concentrated seven semester program allows degree candidates to participate

in foreign study trips and in elective courses including entrepreneurship and small business financial management.

56411 ■ Southeastern Business College
3879 Rhodes Ave.
New Boston, OH 45662
Ph: (740)456-4124
Free: 877-258-7796
Fax: (740)456-5163
URL: http://www.daymarcollege.edu
Description: Business college offering classes in small business management.

56412 ■ University of Akron
302 Buchtel Common
Akron, OH 44325-6501
Ph: (330)972-7111
Fax: (330)972-6952
URL: http://www.uakron.edu
Description: Two-year college offering a small business management program.

LEGISLATIVE ASSISTANCE

56413 ■ Ohio House Economic Development and Small Business Committee
77 S High St., 13th Fl.
Columbus, OH 43215-0011
Ph: (614)466-6111
Free: 800-848-1300
Fax: (614)719-0011
URL: http://www.odod.state.oh.us
Contact: Sandra Williams, Chairperson

TRADE PERIODICALS

56414 ■ Ohio United Way Legislative Bulletin
Pub: Ohio United Way
Released: Weekly. **Price:** $55, individuals includes OUW's Administrative Report; $125, institutions;. **Description:** Reports on human service legislation in Ohio.

PUBLICATIONS

56415 ■ Business First: The Greater Columbus Business Authority
471 E. Broad St., Ste. 1500
Columbus, OH 43215
Ph: (614)461-4040
Fax: (614)365-2980
Co. E-mail: businessfirst@amcity.com
URL: http://www.bizjournals.com/columbus/

56416 ■ The Clevelander-Growth Association
1240 Huron Road E
Ste. 300
Cleveland, OH 44115
Ph: (216)621-3300
Fax: (216)621-6013
URL: http://www.gcpartnership.com

56417 ■ Crain's Cleveland Business
700 W. St. Clair Ave., Ste 310
Cleveland, OH 44113-1230
Ph: (216)522-1383
Fax: (216)522-0625
Co. E-mail: cle.crains@mail.multiverse.com
URL: http://crainscleveland.com

56418 ■ How to Form Your Own Ohio Corporation Before the Inc. Dries!: A Step by Step Guide, With Forms
333 S. Taylor Ave.
Oak Park, IL 60302
Ph: (708)524-9033
Fax: (708)524-9038
Ed: Phillip Williams. **Released:** Second edition, 1994. **Price:** $24.95. **Description:** Volume 2 of the Small Business Incorporation series. Explains the advantages and disadvantages of incorporation and shows, step-by-step, how the small business owners can incorporate at low cost. Covers Ohio profit and nonprofit corporations, Ohio professional service corporations, subchapter S corporations, and Delaware corporations. Includes forms necessary for incorporation.

56419 ■ Smart Start your Ohio Business
PSI Research
300 N. Valley Dr.
Grants Pass, OR 97526
Ph: (503)479-9464
Free: 800-228-2275
Fax: (503)476-1479
Co. E-mail: info@psi-research.com
URL: http://www.psi-research.com
Ed: Michael D. Jenkins. **Released:** Revised edition, 1992. **Price:** $29.95 (looseleaf binder); $24.95 (paper). **Description:** Part of the Successful Business Library series.

56420 ■ Toledo Business Journal
27 Broadway at the River
Toledo, OH 43602
Ph: (419)244-8200
Fax: (419)244-5773
URL: http://www.toledobiz.com

PUBLISHERS

56421 ■ Betterway Books
4700 E Galbraith Rd.
Cincinnati, OH 45236-2726
Ph: (513)531-2690
Free: 800-666-0963
Fax: (513)891-7185
Co. E-mail: sberger@fwpubs.com
URL: http://www.betterwaybooks.com
Contact: David Aussbaum, President
E-mail: david.aussbaum@fwmedia.com
Description: Description: Publishes resource guides and handbooks on home building and remodeling, small business and finance, theater, woodworking, home decorating, parenting and genealogy. Accepts unsolicited manuscripts. Reaches market through commission representatives and wholesalers. **Founded:** 1980. **Publications:** The Internet for Genealogists: A Beginner's Guide; The Crafts Supply Sourcebook: A Comprehensive Shop-by-Mail Guide (Biennial); Complete Guide & Resource to In-Line Skating; The Doll Sourcebook.

56422 ■ Home Business News
12221 Beaver Pke.
Jackson, OH 45640
Ph: (614)988-2331
Fax: (614)988-2331
Contact: Edwin L. Simpson, Owner
E-mail: esimpson@zoomnet.net
Description: Description: Publishes books and computer software for home-based business owners. offers magazine and mailing lists. Reaches market through direct mail. Does not accept unsolicited manuscripts. **Founded:** 1982.

56423 ■ McGraw-Hill Inc.
PO Box 182604
Columbus, OH 43272
Ph: (614)430-4000
Free: 877-833-5524
Fax: (614)759-3749
Co. E-mail: customer.service@mcgraw-hill.com
URL: http://www.mcgraw-hill.com
Contact: Henry Hirschberg, President
Description: Description: Publishes about education, financial sectors, information and media. **Founded:** 1888. **Publications:** Modern Plastics Encyclopedia (Annual); Architectural Record (Monthly); Standard Corporation Records (Quarterly); NetWare Technical Journal; Defense Technology International (Bi-monthly); My House in the Mountain States (Bi-monthly); Business Week--1,000 Issue (Annual); ENR Directory of Contractors (Biennial); Online Broker and Trading Directory; Business Week--R&D Scoreboard (Annual); Metals Week (Weekly); ENR--Top 400 Construction Contractors Issue (Annual); Chemical Engineering Buyers Guide (Annual); ENR--Top Owners Issue (Annual); New York Construction News (Monthly); Aviation Week & Space Technology (Weekly); Business Week--Corporate Scoreboard Issue (Quarterly); The Online Broker and Trading Directory; Ultimate Start-Up Directory; Online Broker and Trading Directory; Data Communications--Product Selection Guide (Annual); Nursing Experience: Trends, Challenges and Transitions; Computer Support Directory; Business Week (Weekly); Power (Monthly); Electronics Engineers' Handbook; ENR--Top 500 Design Firms Issue (Annual); Career Training Sourcebook: Where to Get Free, Low-Cost, and Salaried Job Training; CPI Equipment Reporter (Bimonthly); Business Week--Survey of Executive Compensation Issue (Weekly); A/C FLYER: Best Read Resale Magazine Worldwide (Monthly); Independent Power Report's Avoided-Cost Quarterly (Quarterly); Electronics Buyers' Guide; ENR Directory of Design Firms (Biennial); Military/Space Electronic Design (Semimonthly); ENR--Top International Contractors Issue (Annual); ENR--Top 600 Specialty Contractors Issue (Annual); Business Week--Survey of Labor Union Leaders Compensation Issue; Aerospace and Defense International Product News (Bimonthly); Business Week International--Top 200 Banking Institutions Issue (Annual); ENR--Top International Design Firms Issue (Annual); ENR--Top 100 Construction Management Firms Issue (Annual); Aviation Internet Directory: A Guide to the 500 Best Aviation Web Sites; Industrial Chemical News (Monthly); ENR: Engineering News-Record: The Construction Weekly (Weekly); The African American Resource Guide to the Internet and Online Services; Modern Plastics Encyclopedia--Directory of Trade Names (Annual).

56424 ■ Opportunity Hot-Line
Business Network, 5420 Mayfield Rd., Ste. 205
Cleveland, OH 44121
Ph: (440)442-5600
Fax: (440)449-3227
Contact: Irwin Friedman, Chairman of the Board
Description: Description: Publishes business books. Conducts research and development studies on a negotiated basis. Reports and documents occasionally copyrighted. Also finance, buy, sell, and find businesses. As well as finding investing partners. Reaches market through reviews and listings. **Founded:** 1975. **Publications:** Opportunity Hot-Line.

56425 ■ York Publishing Co.
16781 Chagrin Blvd., Ste. 112
Cleveland, OH 44120
Fax: (216)491-0251
Contact: Rachal Rapoport, President
Description: Description: Publishes books on business with a concentration on business consulting. **Founded:** 1993.

SMALL BUSINESS DEVELOPMENT CENTERS

56426 ■ Carl Albert College Small Business Development Center
FL Holton Business Ctr., 3rd Fl.
1507 S McKenna St.
Poteau, OK 74953
Ph: (918)449-6280
Co. E-mail: bluejr@nsuok.edu
URL: http://www.osbdc.org/center.
aspx?center=64040&subloc=1
Contact: Amy Lomon, Specialist
Description: Represents and promotes the small business sector. Provides management assistance to current and prospective small business owners. Helps to improve management skills and expand the products and services of members.

56427 ■ East Central University Small Business Development Center
Administration Bldg., Rm. 251
E 12th St. & S Francis St.
Ada, OK 74820
Ph: (580)436-3190
Co. E-mail: aritter@ecok.edu
URL: http://www.osbdc.org/center.
aspx?center=64040&subloc=0
Contact: Ann Ritter, Director
Description: Represents and promotes the small business sector. Provides management assistance to current and prospective small business owners. Helps to improve management skills and expand the products and services of members.

56428 ■ Langston University Small Business Development Center
Oklahoma City Campus, Rm. 112
4205 N Lincoln Blvd.
Oklahoma City, OK 73105
Ph: (405)530-7519
Co. E-mail: dmdean@langston.edu
URL: http://www.osbdc.org
Contact: Della Dean, Director
Description: Represents and promotes the small business sector. Provides management assistance to current and prospective small business owners. Helps to improve management skills and expand the products and services of members.

56429 ■ Northeastern State University Small Business Development Center (Broken Arrow, Oklahoma)
Bldg. A, Ste. 325
3100 E New Orleans St.
Broken Arrow, OK 74014
Ph: (918)449-6280
Fax: (918)449-6284
Co. E-mail: bluejr@nsuok.edu
URL: http://www.osbdc.org
Contact: John Blue, Director
URL(s): navajo.nsuok.edu/osbdc/index.html. **Description:** Represents and promotes the small business sector. Provides management assistance to cur-

rent and prospective small business owners. Helps to improve management skills and expand the products and services of members.

56430 ■ Northeastern State University Small Business Development Center (Muskogee, Oklahoma)
2400 E Shawnee Rd., Rm. 146
Muskogee, OK 74401
Ph: (918)444-5412
Co. E-mail: bluejr@nsuok.edu
URL: http://www.osbdc.org
Contact: John Blue, Regional Director
Description: Represents and promotes the small business sector. Provides management assistance to current and prospective small business owners. Helps to improve management skills and expand the products and services of members.

56431 ■ Northeastern State University Small Business Development Center (Tahlequah, Oklahoma)
309 N Muskogee Ave.
Tahlequah, OK 74464
Ph: (918)456-5511
Co. E-mail: livesaaj@nsuok.edu
URL: http://navajo.nsuok.edu/osbdc/index.html
Contact: Andy Livesay, Specialist
Description: Represents and promotes the small business sector. Provides management assistance to current and prospective small business owners. Helps to improve management skills and expand the products and services of members.

56432 ■ Northwestern Oklahoma State University Small Business Development Center (Alva, Oklahoma)
Shockley Hall, Rm. 107
1038 8th St.
Alva, OK 73717
Ph: (580)327-8608
Co. E-mail: jmcole@nwosu.edu
URL: http://www.osbdc.org/center.
aspx?center=64050&subloc=1
Contact: Jeanne Cole, Specialist
Description: Represents and promotes the small business sector. Provides management assistance to current and prospective small business owners. Helps to improve management skills and expand the products and services of members.

56433 ■ Northwestern Oklahoma State University Small Business Development Center (Enid, Oklahoma)
2929 E Randolph Ave.
Enid, OK 73701
Ph: (580)213-3197
Co. E-mail: micole@nwosu.edu
URL: http://www.osbdc.org/center.
aspx?center=64050&subloc=0
Contact: Missy Cole, Specialist
Description: Represents and promotes the small business sector. Provides management assistance to current and prospective small business owners. Helps to improve management skills and expand the products and services of members.

56434 ■ Rose State College Small Business Development Center
Professional Training and Education Center
1720 Hudiburg Dr.
Midwest City, OK 73110
Ph: (405)733-7348
Co. E-mail: varmstrong@rose.edu
URL: http://www.osbdc.org
Contact: Victoria Armstrong, Director
URL(s): www.rose.edu/small-business-development-center. **Description:** Represents and promotes the small business sector. Provides management assistance to current and prospective small business owners. Helps to improve management skills and expand the products and services of members.

56435 ■ Southeastern Oklahoma State University Small Business Development Center
301 W University Blvd.
Durant, OK 74701
Ph: (580)745-2954
Co. E-mail: wcarter@se.edu
URL: http://www.osbdc.org
Contact: Bill Carter, Director, Business Development
Description: Represents and promotes the small business sector. Provides management assistance to current and prospective small business owners. Helps to improve management skills and expand the products and services of members.

56436 ■ Southwestern Oklahoma State University Small Business Development Center - Weatherford
301 E Davis St.
Weatherford, OK 73096
Ph: (580)774-7095
Co. E-mail: lisa.thiessen@swosu.edu
URL: http://www.osbdc.org
Contact: Lisa Thiessen, Specialist
Description: Represents and promotes the small business sector. Provides management assistance to current and prospective small business owners. Helps to improve management skills and expand the products and services of members.

SMALL BUSINESS ASSISTANCE PROGRAMS

56437 ■ Oklahoma Center for the Advancement of Science Technology - Oklahoma Inventor's Assistance Service
755 Research Parkway, Ste. 110
395 Cordell S
Stillwater, OK 73104-3612
Ph: (405)319-8400
Fax: (405)319-8426
Co. E-mail: invent@okstate.edu
URL: http://ias.okstate.edu
Contact: Dr. Ranji Vaidyanathan, Director
Description: Helps inventors navigate the invention process with information, educational and referrals.

56438 ■ Oklahoma Department of Agriculture, Food and Forestry - Market Development Division
2800 N Lincoln Blvd.
Oklahoma City, OK 73105-4298
Ph: (405)521-3864
Fax: (405)522-4912
URL: http://www.state.ok.us/
Contact: Terry L. Peach, Commissioner
Description: Develops direct marketing outlets for farmers, including the promotion of direct retail sales, and the promotion of direct wholesaling through commercial systems. Offers the Made in Oklahoma/ Grown in Oklahoma marketing program, featuring trademarked logos.

56439 ■ Oklahoma Department of Career and Technology Education - Oklahoma State Department of Vocational and Technical Education (TIP) - Training for Industry Program
1500 W 7th Ave.
Stillwater, OK 74074-4364
Ph: (405)377-2000
Fax: (405)743-5541
Co. E-mail: pbowl@okcareertech.org
URL: http://www.okcareertech.org
Contact: Phil Berkenbile, Director
Description: Provides customized needs assessment, pre-employment training, curriculum development, training facilities, equipment, and instructors at no cost to new or expanding companies. Other services include customized retraining, upgraded training, a bid assistance network, management and business development training programs, and a business development program for small and growing companies.

56440 ■ Oklahoma Department of Commerce - Administration and Central Services
900 N Stiles Ave.
Oklahoma City, OK 73104-3234
Ph: (405)815-6552
Free: 800-TRY-OKLA
Fax: (405)815-5199
Co. E-mail: info@okcommerce.gov
URL: http://www.okcommerce.gov
Contact: Beth Schmidt, Director, Communications
Description: Provides assistance in developing business plans, financial packages, industry customized training, domestic and foreign market services, and small and minority business programs.

56441 ■ Oklahoma Department of Commerce - Business Development Division
900 N Stiles Ave.
Oklahoma City, OK 73104-3234
Ph: (405)815-6552
Free: 800-TRY-OKLA
Co. E-mail: bddinfo@odoc.state.ok.us
URL: http://www.okcommerce.gov/
Contact: Shelli Todd, Director
Description: Develops industrial prospects and assists local communities in their industrial development efforts. Community profiles provide information to new industries on building and industrial sites, industrial foundations and trusts, local financing, and utility and rail services. Offers one-stop service to businesses on tax information, required permits, and available industrial revenue bonds.

56442 ■ Oklahoma Department of Commerce - Export Assistance Program
301 NW 63rd, Ste. 330
Oklahoma City, OK 73116
Ph: (405)608-5302
Free: 800-879-6552
Fax: (405)608-4211
URL: http://www.buyusa.gov/oklahomacity/
Contact: Ronald Wilson, Director
Description: Specializes in export programs to assist small Oklahoma companies.

56443 ■ Oklahoma Department of Commerce - Global Business Solutions
700 N. Greenwood Ave., Ste 1400
Tulsa, OK 74106-0703
Ph: (918)594-8412

Free: 800-879-6552
Fax: (918)605-2988
URL: http://www.okcommerce.gov/
Contact: Dessie Apostolova, Director
Description: Encourages foreign investment by working with Oklahoma companies to increase their exports. Works closely with the governor's International and Waterways teams to promote the use and development of the Arkansas River navigation system.

56444 ■ University of Oklahoma - Center for Business and Economic Development
1666 Cross Center Dr., Rm. 302
Norman, OK 73072
Ph: (405)325-3136
Fax: (405)325-7329
Co. E-mail: bettyk@ou.edu
URL: http://cbed.occe.ou.edu/
Contact: Betty Kettman, Director
Description: Assists small businesses throughout the state.

SCORE OFFICES

56445 ■ Ardmore SCORE
Co. E-mail: score633@brightok.net

56446 ■ Enid/Northwest Oklahoma SCORE
Co. E-mail: score@nwosu.edu

56447 ■ Lawton SCORE
Co. E-mail: score304@gptech.org

56448 ■ Oklahoma City SCORE
Co. E-mail: info@okcscore.org

56449 ■ SCORE Chapter 194—Tulsa SCORE
907 S Detroit St., Ste. 1012
Tulsa, OK 74120
Ph: (918)581-7462
Free: 800-634-0245
Fax: (918)581-6908
Co. E-mail: consult@tulsascore.org
URL: http://www.tulsascore.org
Contact: John Bryant, Officer, Recruiting
Description: Volunteer program through which active and retired business people provide free management assistance to people who are considering starting a small business, encountering problems with their business, or expanding their business. **Scope:** small business. **Founded:** 1964.

BETTER BUSINESS BUREAUS

56450 ■ Better Business Bureau of Central Oklahoma
17 S Dewey Ave.
Oklahoma City, OK 73102-2421
Ph: (405)239-6081
Fax: (405)235-5891
Co. E-mail: info@oklahomacity.bbb.org
URL: http://oklahomacity.bbb.org
Contact: Bob Manista, President
Description: Seeks to promote and foster ethical relationship between businesses and the public through voluntary self-regulation, consumer and business education, and service excellence. Provides information to help consumers and businesses make informed purchasing decisions and avoid costly scams and frauds; settles consumer complaints through arbitration and other means.

56451 ■ *The Member*
1722 S Carson Ave., Ste. 3200
Tulsa, OK 74119
Ph: (918)492-1266
Fax: (918)492-1276
Co. E-mail: info@tulsabbb.org
URL: http://tulsa.bbb.org
Contact: Rick Brinkley, Chief Operating Officer
Released: Bimonthly

56452 ■ Tulsa Better Business Bureau
1722 S Carson Ave., Ste. 3200
Tulsa, OK 74119
Ph: (918)492-1266

Fax: (918)492-1276
Co. E-mail: info@tulsabbb.org
URL: http://tulsa.bbb.org
Contact: Rick Brinkley, Chief Operating Officer
Description: Members of the business community in eastern Oklahoma. Promotes the self-regulation of businesses. **Founded:** 1930. **Publications:** *The Member* (Bimonthly); *Consumer Tips*.

CHAMBERS OF COMMERCE

56453 ■ *Achiever*
701 SW 74th St.
Oklahoma City, OK 73139-4599
Ph: (405)634-1436
Fax: (405)634-1462
Co. E-mail: info@southokc.com
URL: http://www.southokc.com
Contact: Elaine Lyons, President
Released: Bimonthly **Price:** free for members.

56454 ■ *Action News*
302 W Gore Blvd.
Lawton, OK 73501-3709
Ph: (580)355-3541
Free: 800-872-4540
Fax: (580)357-3642
Co. E-mail: dburch@lawtonfortsillchamber.com
URL: http://www.lawtonfortsillchamber.com
Contact: Debra Burch, President
Released: Periodic

56455 ■ Ada Area Chamber of Commerce
c/o Jeff Warmuth, Pres./CEO
209 W Main St.
Ada, OK 74821
Ph: (580)332-2506
Fax: (580)332-3265
Co. E-mail: adachamber@adachamber.com
URL: http://www.adachamber.com
Contact: Jeff Warmuth, President
Description: Promotes business and community development in Ada, OK.

56456 ■ *The Advocate*
330 NE 10th St.
Oklahoma City, OK 73104-3220
Ph: (405)235-3669
Fax: (405)235-3670
Co. E-mail: info@okstatechamber.com
URL: http://www.okstatechamber.com
Contact: Fred S. Morgan, President
Released: Periodic

56457 ■ Altus Chamber of Commerce (ACC)
301 W Commerce St.
Altus, OK 73522-0518
Ph: (580)482-0210
Fax: (580)482-0223
Co. E-mail: altuschamber@altuschamber.com
URL: http://www.altuschamber.com
Contact: Holley Urbanski, President
Description: Promotes business and community development in Altus, OK. **Founded:** 1908. **Publications:** *Infogram* (Monthly).

56458 ■ Alva Area Chamber of Commerce
410 College Ave.
Alva, OK 73717
Ph: (580)327-1647
Free: 888-854-2262
Fax: (580)327-1648
Co. E-mail: chamber@alvaok.net
URL: http://www.alvaok.net
Contact: Lance Harzman, President
Description: Promotes business and community development in the Alva, OK area. **Publications:** *Chamber Newsletter* (Monthly).

56459 ■ Anadarko Chamber of Commerce
516 W Kentucky Ave.
Anadarko, OK 73005
Ph: (405)247-6651

Fax: (405)247-6652
Co. E-mail: info@anadarko.org
URL: http://www.anadarko.org
Contact: Carla Hall, Executive Director
Description: Promotes business and community development in Anadarko, OK. **Founded:** 1937. **Publications:** *Positively Anadarko* (Monthly).

56460 ■ Ardmore Chamber of Commerce (ACOC)
410 W Main St.
Ardmore, OK 73401
Ph: (580)223-7765
Fax: (580)223-7825
Co. E-mail: wstucky@ardmore.org
URL: http://chamber.ardmore.org
Contact: Wes Stucky, President
Description: Promotes business and community development in Ardmore, OK. **Subscriptions:** reports. **Publications:** *Ardmoreport* (Monthly); *Membership Directory and Information Guide* (Annual).

56461 ■ *Ardmoreport*
410 W Main St.
Ardmore, OK 73401
Ph: (580)223-7765
Fax: (580)223-7825
Co. E-mail: wstucky@ardmore.org
URL: http://chamber.ardmore.org
Contact: Wes Stucky, President
Released: Monthly

56462 ■ Arnett Chamber of Commerce
PO Box 415
Arnett, OK 73832
Ph: (580)885-7535
Co. E-mail: arnettchamber@pldi.net
URL: http://www.arnettchamber.com
Contact: Bill Mitchell, President
Description: Promotes business and community development in the Arnett, OK area.

56463 ■ Atoka County Chamber of Commerce
415 E Court St.
Atoka, OK 74525-0778
Ph: (580)889-2410
Fax: (580)889-2410
Co. E-mail: chamber1atoka@sbcglobal.net
URL: http://www.atokachamber.com
Contact: Brian Kathy, President
Description: Promotes business and community development in Atoka County, OK.

56464 ■ Bartlesville Regional Chamber of Commerce (BRCC)
201 SW Keeler Ave.
Bartlesville, OK 74003-2631
Ph: (918)336-8708
Fax: (918)337-0216
Co. E-mail: byronboles@att.net
URL: http://www.bartlesville.com
Contact: Byron Boles, Chairman
Description: Promotes business and community development in the Bartlesville, OK area. **Founded:** 1903. **Publications:** *Business Voice* (Monthly).

56465 ■ Bixby Metro Chamber of Commerce
10441 S Regal Blvd., Ste. 104
Bixby, OK 74008
Ph: (918)366-9445
Fax: (918)366-9443
Co. E-mail: info@bixbychamber.com
URL: http://www.bixbychamber.com
Contact: Russ Smith, Chairman
Description: Promotes business and community development in Bixby, OK. **Publications:** *Business Insurance Guide*; *Chamber Newsline* (Monthly); *Who's Who in Business* (Annual). **Educational Activities:** Bixby Chamber of Commerce Luncheon (Monthly).

56466 ■ Blackwell Area Chamber of Commerce
120 S Main St.
Blackwell, OK 74631
Ph: (580)363-4195

Fax: (580)363-1704
Co. E-mail: info@blackwellchamber.com
URL: http://www.blackwellchamber.org
Contact: Jeff Seymour, Executive Director
Description: Promotes business and community development in Blackwell, OK. **Founded:** 1911.

56467 ■ Broken Arrow Chamber of Commerce
210 N Main, Ste. C
Broken Arrow, OK 74013
Ph: (918)251-1518
Fax: (918)251-1777
Co. E-mail: wes.smithwick@bachamber.com
URL: http://www.brokenarrow.org
Contact: Wes Smithwick, President
Description: Promotes business and community development in Broken Arrow, OK. **Founded:** 1903. **Publications:** *Directions* (Monthly).

56468 ■ Broken Bow Chamber of Commerce
113 W Martin Luther King Dr.
Broken Bow, OK 74728
Ph: (580)584-3393
Free: 800-528-7337
Fax: (580)584-7665
Co. E-mail: bchamber@pine-net.com
URL: http://www.brokenbowchamber.com
Contact: Charity O'Donnell, Executive Director
Description: Promotes business and community development in Broken Bow, OK. **Founded:** 1954.

56469 ■ Buffalo Chamber of Commerce
PO Box 521
Buffalo, OK 73834
Ph: (580)735-2521
Free: 800-642-1883
Co. E-mail: buffalo@pldi.net
URL: http://www.buffalook.net/chamber.html
Description: Promotes business and community development in Buffalo, OK.

56470 ■ *Business Insurance Guide*
10441 S Regal Blvd., Ste. 104
Bixby, OK 74008
Ph: (918)366-9445
Fax: (918)366-9443
Co. E-mail: info@bixbychamber.com
URL: http://www.bixbychamber.com
Contact: Russ Smith, Chairman

56471 ■ *Business Voice*
201 SW Keeler Ave.
Bartlesville, OK 74003-2631
Ph: (918)336-8708
Fax: (918)337-0216
Co. E-mail: byronboles@att.net
URL: http://www.bartlesville.com
Contact: Byron Boles, Chairman
Released: Monthly

56472 ■ *Chamber Challenger*
1301 E Main St.
Cushing, OK 74023-3049
Ph: (918)225-2400
Fax: (918)225-2903
Co. E-mail: manager@cushingchamber.org
URL: http://www.cushingchamber.org
Contact: Mr. Brent Thompson, Executive Director

56473 ■ *Chamber Chatter*
112 E Paul St.
Drawer 638
Pauls Valley, OK 73075
Ph: (405)238-6491
Fax: (405)238-2335
Co. E-mail: pvchamber@sbcglobal.net
URL: http://www.paulsvalley.com/chamber.html
Released: Monthly

56474 ■ *Chamber Chatter*
PO Box 502
Perkins, OK 74059
Ph: (405)747-6809
Co. E-mail: perkinschamber@gmail.com
URL: http://www.perkinscc.com
Contact: David Massey, President

56475 ■ *Chamber Chimes*
114 N Broadway St.
Tecumseh, OK 74873
Ph: (405)598-8666
Fax: (405)598-6760
Co. E-mail: chamber@tecumsehok.org
URL: http://www.tecumsehok.com
Contact: Sharon Pattillo, President
Released: Monthly

56476 ■ *Chamber Comments*
121 N Main St.
Sand Springs, OK 74063
Ph: (918)245-3221
Fax: (918)245-2530
Co. E-mail: chamber@sandspringschamber.com
URL: http://www.sandspringschamber.com
Contact: Mr. J.C. Kinder, Jr., President

56477 ■ *Chamber Communicant*
107 N Main St.
Lindsay, OK 73052
Ph: (405)756-4312
Co. E-mail: lchamber@telepath.com
URL: http://www.angelfire.com/biz/lindsayok
Contact: Danny Siebel, President
Released: Monthly

56478 ■ *Chamber Directory*
310 W Broadway St.
Muskogee, OK 74401-6610
Ph: (918)682-2401
Free: 866-381-6543
Fax: (918)682-2403
Co. E-mail: info@muskogeechamber.org
URL: http://www.muskogeechamber.org
Contact: Treasure McKenzie, President
Released: Biennial **Price:** included in membership dues.

56479 ■ *The Chamber e-Voice*
825 E 2nd St., Ste. 100
Edmond, OK 73034
Ph: (405)341-2808
Fax: (405)340-5512
Co. E-mail: info@edmondchamber.com
URL: http://www.edmondchamber.com
Contact: Ken Moore, President

56480 ■ *Chamber News*
624 N Main St.
Fairview, OK 73737-1216
Ph: (580)227-2527
Co. E-mail: fairviewchamber@att.net
URL: http://www.fairviewokchamber.net
Contact: Jeannie Marlin, Executive Director
Released: Monthly **Price:** free for members.

56481 ■ *Chamber News*
105 W Delaware St.
Vinita, OK 74301
Ph: (918)256-7133
Fax: (918)256-8261
Co. E-mail: chamber@vinita.com
URL: http://www.vinita.com
Contact: J.C. Kinder, Executive Director
Released: Semimonthly

56482 ■ *Chamber Newsletter*
410 College Ave.
Alva, OK 73717
Ph: (580)327-1647
Free: 888-854-2262
Fax: (580)327-1648
Co. E-mail: chamber@alvaok.net
URL: http://www.alvaok.net
Contact: Lance Harzman, President
Released: Monthly **Price:** free for members.

56483 ■ *Chamber Newsline*
10441 S Regal Blvd., Ste. 104
Bixby, OK 74008
Ph: (918)366-9445
Fax: (918)366-9443
Co. E-mail: info@bixbychamber.com
URL: http://www.bixbychamber.com
Contact: Russ Smith, Chairman
Released: Monthly

56484 ■ *Chamber Voice*
123 E Delaware St.
Tahlequah, OK 74464
Ph: (918)456-3742
Fax: (918)456-3751
Co. E-mail: david@tahlequahchamber.com
URL: http://tahlequahchamber.com
Contact: David Moore, Executive Director
Released: Monthly **Price:** free.

56485 ■ *ChamberNews*
304 E Rogers Blvd.
Skiatook, OK 74070-1206
Ph: (918)396-3702
URL: http://www.skiatookchamber.com
Contact: Stephanie Upton, Executive Director
Released: Monthly

56486 ■ Chandler Chamber of Commerce
804 Manvel Ave.
Chandler, OK 74834
Ph: (405)258-0673
Fax: (405)258-0377
Co. E-mail: chandlerchamber@sbcglobal.net
URL: http://chandlerok
Description: Promotes business and community development in Chandler, OK.

56487 ■ Checotah Chamber of Commerce
c/o Lloyd Jernigan, Exec. Dir.
201 N Broadway St.
Checotah, OK 74426-2431
Ph: (918)473-2070
Fax: (918)473-1453
Co. E-mail: checotahchamber@windstream.net
URL: http://www.checotah.com
Contact: Lloyd Jernigan, Executive Director
Description: Promotes business and community development in Checotah, OK. Sponsors Old Settlers Day. **Founded:** 1946. **Publications:** *Courier* (Periodic).

56488 ■ Cheyenne - Roger Mills Chamber of Commerce and Tourism
PO Box 57
Cheyenne, OK 73628
Ph: (580)497-3318
Free: 877-497-3318
Co. E-mail: cheyennecoc@yahoo.com
URL: http://www.cheyenneokcoc.com
Contact: Mrs. Rhonda Robertson, President
Description: Promotes business and community development in Cheyenne, OK and Roger Mills County. Sponsors arts and crafts show and Christmas Jubilee. Makes charitable donations for New Year Baby, food baskets, Harvest Queen, turkey giveaway, and Christmas treat giveaway. **Founded:** 1961. **Publications:** *Visit Roger Mills County and Cheyenne, Oklahoma.* **Awards:** Father of the Year (Annual); Mother of the Year (Annual); Volunteer of the Year (Annual).

56489 ■ Chickasha Chamber of Commerce
221 W Chickasha Ave.
Chickasha, OK 73018-2604
Ph: (405)224-0787
Fax: (405)222-3730
Co. E-mail: info@chickashachamber.com
URL: http://www.chickashachamber.com
Contact: Susan Routh, Chairperson
Description: Promotes business and community development in Chickasha, OK. Convention/Meeting availabilities. **Founded:** 1927.

56490 ■ Choctaw Chamber of Commerce
PO Box 1000
Choctaw, OK 73020
Ph: (405)390-3303
Fax: (405)390-3330
Co. E-mail: tmosleychoctawchamber@tds.net
URL: http://www.choctawchamber.com
Contact: Ms. Tracy Mosley, Executive Vice President
Description: Works to promote business growth and development in Choctaw, OK. **Founded:** 1977.

56491 ■ Chouteau Chamber of Commerce
PO Box 332
Chouteau, OK 74337

Ph: (918)476-8222
URL: http://chouteauok.net
Description: Promotes business and community development in Chouteau, OK.

56492 ■ Cimarron County Chamber of Commerce (CCCC)
PO Box 1027
Boise City, OK 73933
Ph: (580)544-3344
Free: 800-821-7204
Fax: (580)544-3344
Co. E-mail: cccc@ptsi.net
URL: http://www.ccccok.org
Description: Promotes business and community development in the Boise City and Cimarron County, OK areas. Sponsors Santa Fe Trail Daze Festival. Publications: none. **Founded:** 1927.

56493 ■ City of Oilton Council
PO Box 400
Oilton, OK 74052
Ph: (918)862-3202
Fax: (918)862-3203
URL: http://cityofoilton.com
Contact: Mr. Jerry Green, Mayor

56494 ■ Claremore Chamber of Commerce
419 W Will Rogers Blvd.
Claremore, OK 74017-6820
Ph: (918)341-2818
Fax: (918)342-0663
Co. E-mail: chamber@claremore.org
URL: http://www.claremore.org
Contact: Dell Davis, President
Description: Promotes business and community development in Claremore, OK area. **Founded:** 1942. **Publications:** *Weekly Memo* (Weekly).

56495 ■ Cleveland Area Chamber of Commerce
113 N Broadway St.
Cleveland, OK 74020
Ph: (918)358-2131
Fax: (918)358-5710
Co. E-mail: info@chamberofcleveland.com
URL: http://www.chamberofcleveland.com
Contact: Diana Tilley-Esparza, Executive Director
Description: Works to advance the general welfare and prosperity of the Cleveland area so that its citizens and all areas of its business community shall prosper. Provides all necessary means of promotion and gives particular attention and emphasis to economic, civic, commercial, cultural, industrial and educational interests of the area. **Scope:** Cleveland area. **Subscriptions:** 50 business records maps periodicals.

56496 ■ Clinton Chamber of Commerce
101 S 4th St.
Clinton, OK 73601-3423
Ph: (580)323-2222
Fax: (580)323-2931
Co. E-mail: office@clintonok.org
URL: http://www.clintonok.org
Contact: Julie Menge, President
Description: Promotes business and community development in Clinton, OK. Sponsors activities including pageants, art festivals, and parades. Conducts charitable activities. **Publications:** *Clinton Connection* (Monthly). **Telecommunication Services:** juliemenge@clintonok.org.

56497 ■ *Clinton Connection*
101 S 4th St.
Clinton, OK 73601-3423
Ph: (580)323-2222
Fax: (580)323-2931
Co. E-mail: office@clintonok.org
URL: http://www.clintonok.org
Contact: Julie Menge, President
Released: Monthly

56498 ■ Collinsville Chamber of Commerce
1126 W Main St.
Collinsville, OK 74021-3113

Ph: (918)371-4703
Co. E-mail: cvillechamber3477@gmail.com
URL: http://www.collinsvillechamber.net
Contact: Bill Johnston, President
Description: Promotes business and community development in Collinsville, OK. **Publications:** *Quest* (Monthly).

56499 ■ *Communicator*
327 N 7th St.
Perry, OK 73077-6405
Ph: (580)336-4684
Fax: (580)336-3522
Co. E-mail: information@perrychamber.net
URL: http://www.perryokchamber.com/ourChamber.htm
Contact: Brett Powers, President
Released: Quarterly

56500 ■ *Courier*
c/o Lloyd Jernigan, Exec. Dir.
201 N Broadway St.
Checotah, OK 74426-2431
Ph: (918)473-2070
Fax: (918)473-1453
Co. E-mail: checotahchamber@windstream.net
URL: http://www.checotah.com
Contact: Lloyd Jernigan, Executive Director
Released: Periodic

56501 ■ Coweta Chamber of Commerce
107 S Broadway
Coweta, OK 74429
Ph: (918)486-2513
Fax: (918)279-0829
Co. E-mail: info@cowetachamber.com
URL: http://www.cowetachamber.com
Contact: Heather Davis, Director
Description: Promotes business and community development in Coweta, OK area.

56502 ■ Cushing Chamber of Commerce and Industry
1301 E Main St.
Cushing, OK 74023-3049
Ph: (918)225-2400
Fax: (918)225-2903
Co. E-mail: manager@cushingchamber.org
URL: http://www.cushingchamber.org
Contact: Mr. Brent Thompson, Executive Director
Description: Promotes business and community development in Cushing, OK. **Publications:** *Chamber Challenger.*

56503 ■ Davenport Chamber of Commerce
PO Box 66
Davenport, OK 74026
Ph: (918)377-2241
Fax: (918)377-2506
Co. E-mail: davenportcoc@brightok.net
URL: http://www.davenportok.org
Description: Promotes business and community development in Davenport, OK.

56504 ■ Davis Chamber of Commerce
100 E Main St.
Davis, OK 73030-1902
Ph: (580)369-2402
Fax: (580)369-3719
Co. E-mail: davischamber@sbcglobal.net
URL: http://www.davisok.org
Contact: Michael Summers, President
Description: Promotes business and community development in Davis, OK.

56505 ■ *Directions*
210 N Main, Ste. C
Broken Arrow, OK 74013
Ph: (918)251-1518
Fax: (918)251-1777
Co. E-mail: wes.smithwick@bachamber.com
URL: http://www.brokenarrow.org
Contact: Wes Smithwick, President
Released: Monthly

56506 ■ *Directory and Buyer's Guide*
825 E 2nd St., Ste. 100
Edmond, OK 73034
Ph: (405)341-2808

Fax: (405)340-5512
Co. E-mail: info@edmondchamber.com
URL: http://www.edmondchamber.com
Contact: Ken Moore, President
Released: Annual

56507 ■ Drumright Chamber of Commerce
PO Box 828
Drumright, OK 74030
Ph: (918)352-2204
URL: http://www.drumright.net/chamber.htm
Contact: Darrel Morris, President
Description: Promotes business and community development in Drumright, OK.

56508 ■ Duncan Chamber of Commerce and Industry
PO Box 699
Duncan, OK 73534
Ph: (580)255-3644
Fax: (580)255-6482
Co. E-mail: duncancc@duncanchamber.com
URL: http://www.duncanchamber.com
Contact: Chris Deal, President
Description: Promotes business and community development in Duncan, OK.

56509 ■ Edmond Area Chamber of Commerce
825 E 2nd St., Ste. 100
Edmond, OK 73034
Ph: (405)341-2808
Fax: (405)340-5512
Co. E-mail: info@edmondchamber.com
URL: http://www.edmondchamber.com
Contact: Ken Moore, President
Description: Promotes business and community development in the Edmond, OK area. **Founded:** 1954. **Publications:** Edmond Living Magazine; The Chamber e-Voice; Directory and Buyer's Guide (Annual); Edmond Living Magazine. **Educational Activities:** Business After Hours (Monthly).

56510 ■ Edmond Living Magazine
825 E 2nd St., Ste. 100
Edmond, OK 73034
Ph: (405)341-2808
Fax: (405)340-5512
Co. E-mail: info@edmondchamber.com
URL: http://www.edmondchamber.com
Contact: Ken Moore, President

56511 ■ El Reno Chamber of Commerce and Development Corporation (ERCC)
206 N Bickford Ave.
El Reno, OK 73036
Ph: (405)262-1188
Fax: (405)262-1189
Co. E-mail: elrenochamber@swbell.net
URL: http://www.elrenochamber.com
Contact: Carlee Nicklos, Executive Director
Description: Promotes business and community development in El Reno, OK. **Founded:** 1911.

56512 ■ Elk City Chamber of Commerce
PO Box 972
Elk City, OK 73648
Ph: (580)225-0207
Free: 800-280-0207
Fax: (580)225-1008
Co. E-mail: elkcitychamber@itlnet.net
URL: http://www.elkcitychamber.com
Contact: Sandi Odom, President
Description: Promotes business and community development in Elk City, OK.

56513 ■ Erick Chamber of Commerce
PO Box 1232
Erick, OK 73645-1232
Ph: (580)526-3505
Fax: (580)526-3332
Co. E-mail: erickchamber@yahoo.com
URL: http://www.erickchamber.com
Description: Promotes business and community development in Erick, OK.

56514 ■ Eufaula Area Chamber of Commerce
c/o Jimmie J. Phelan, Exec. Dir.
321 N Main St.
Eufaula, OK 74432-1630
Ph: (918)689-2791
Fax: (918)689-7746
Co. E-mail: chamber@eufaulachamberofcommerce. com
URL: http://www.eufaulachamberofcommerce.com
Contact: Jimmie Phelan, Executive Director
Description: Promotes business and community development in the Eufaula, OK area.

56515 ■ Fairview Chamber of Commerce
624 N Main St.
Fairview, OK 73737-1216
Ph: (580)227-2527
Co. E-mail: fairviewchamber@att.net
URL: http://www.fairviewokchamber.net
Contact: Jeannie Marlin, Executive Director
Description: Promotes business and community development in Fairview, OK. Sponsors festivals including Fairview Follies, Wrangler Rodeo weekend, national John Deere Two-cylinder Show, Gloss Mt. cruisers car show/cruise-in, major county fair/farm and ranch expo, old time threshing bee, Boot Scoot'n 5k run, oldest free fly-in and air show, Fairview quilt festival and Christmas on Main, Easter Egg Hunt, and Business Seminars. Acts as Tourism Headquarters for major county. **Publications:** Chamber News (Monthly). **Educational Activities:** Business Women's Breakfast (Annual). **Awards:** Business of the Month (Monthly); Certified City (Semiannual).

56516 ■ Fort Gibson Chamber of Commerce
108 N Lee St.
Fort Gibson, OK 74434-0730
Ph: (918)478-4780
URL: http://www.fortgibson.com
Contact: Gary L. Perkins, Executive Director
Description: Promotes business and community development in Ft. Gibson, OK.

56517 ■ Frederick Chamber of Commerce and Industry
100 S Main St.
Frederick, OK 73542
Ph: (580)335-2126
Fax: (580)335-3767
Co. E-mail: frederickcc@pldi.net
URL: http://www.frederickokchamber.org
Contact: Sharon Bennett, Executive Director
Description: Promotes agriculture business, industry, and community development in Tillman County, OK. Involves in economic development, tourism promotion, and improving the quality of life. **Publications:** It's Happening in Frederick (Monthly).

56518 ■ Freedom Chamber of Commerce
PO Box 125
Freedom, OK 73842
Ph: (580)621-3276
Co. E-mail: freedomchamberofcommerce@yahoo. com
URL: http://www.freedomokla.com/aboutus.htm
Description: Promotes business and community development in Freedom, OK.

56519 ■ Grand Lake Area Chamber of Commerce
PO Box 215
Langley, OK 74350
Ph: (918)782-3214
Fax: (918)782-3215
Co. E-mail: info@grandlakechamber.org
URL: http://www.grandlakechamber.org
Contact: Jaime Dobbins, President
Description: Promotes business and community development in Grand Lake Area, OK.

56520 ■ Greater Enid Chamber of Commerce
210 Kenwood Blvd.
Enid, OK 73702
Ph: (580)237-2494

Fax: (580)237-2497
URL: http://www.enidchamber.com
Contact: Jon Blankenship, President
Description: Promotes business and community development in the Enid, OK area. **Publications:** Update (Monthly). **Educational Activities:** Camp Tomahawk (Annual). **Awards:** Academic Achievement Award (Annual); Special Recognition of Teacher (Annual).

56521 ■ Greater Muskogee Area Chamber of Commerce (GMCC)
310 W Broadway St.
Muskogee, OK 74401-6610
Ph: (918)682-2401
Free: 866-381-6543
Fax: (918)682-2403
Co. E-mail: info@muskogeechamber.org
URL: http://www.muskogeechamber.org
Contact: Treasure McKenzie, President
Description: Promotes business and community development in the greater Muskogee area. **Founded:** 1902. **Publications:** Chamber Directory (Biennial); Greater Muskogee Area Chamber of Commerce--Chamber Directory (Biennial); Chamber Directory (Biennial); The Muskogee Chamber Connection (Monthly). **Educational Activities:** Business After Hours (Monthly). **Awards:** Ambassador of the Month (Monthly).

56522 ■ Greater Oklahoma City Chamber of Commerce
123 Park Ave.
Oklahoma City, OK 73102
Ph: (405)297-8900
Fax: (405)297-8908
Co. E-mail: info@okcchamber.com
URL: http://www.okcchamber.com
Contact: Roy H. Williams, President
Description: Promotes business and community development in Oklahoma City, OK. **Founded:** 1889. **Publications:** OKC Action (Biweekly).

56523 ■ Greater Oklahoma City Hispanic Chamber of Commerce
309 SW 59th St., Ste. 302
Oklahoma City, OK 73109
Ph: (405)616-5031
Fax: (405)616-0600
Co. E-mail: info@okchispanicchamber.com
URL: http://www.okchispanicchamber.com
Contact: Guillermo Galindo, Chairman
Founded: 2000.

56524 ■ Greater Shawnee Area Chamber of Commerce
131 N Bell Ave.
Shawnee, OK 74801-6981
Ph: (405)273-6092
Fax: (405)275-9851
Co. E-mail: info@shawneechamber.com
URL: http://www.shawneechamber.com
Contact: Nancy Keith, President
Description: Promotes business and community development in Shawnee, OK. **Founded:** 1920.

56525 ■ Grove Area Chamber of Commerce (GACC)
9630 US Hwy. 59
Grove, OK 74344-4482
Ph: (918)786-9079
Fax: (918)786-2909
Co. E-mail: grovecc@sbcglobal.net
URL: http://www.groveok.org
Contact: Lisa Friden, President
Description: Promotes business, community development, and tourism in the Grove, OK area. Markets Grove as a retirement and recreation center. Sponsors Grovefest and annual Christmas parade. **Founded:** 1962.

56526 ■ Guide to Doing Business in Waterford
210 W Main St.
Weatherford, OK 73096-4839
Ph: (580)772-7744
Free: 800-725-7744

Fax: (580)772-7751
Co. E-mail: welcome@weatherfordchamber.com
URL: http://weatherfordchamber.com/new
Contact: Wes Magill, President
Released: Annual

56527 ▪ Guthrie Chamber of Commerce
212 W Oklahoma Ave.
Guthrie, OK 73044
Ph: (405)282-1947
Free: 800-299-1889
Fax: (405)282-0061
Co. E-mail: info@guthrieok.com
URL: http://www.guthrieok.com
Contact: Mary Coffin, President
Description: Promotes business and community development in Guthrie, OK. Sponsors annual Christmas Celebration. **Founded:** 1889.

56528 ▪ Hartshorne Chamber of Commerce
PO Box 343
Hartshorne, OK 74547
Ph: (918)297-3651
Co. E-mail: info@cityofhartshorneok.com
URL: http://www.cityofhartshorneok.com
Contact: Paula Thomson, Treasurer
Description: Promotes business and community development in Hartshorne, OK.

56529 ▪ Haskell Chamber of Commerce
PO Box 252
Haskell, OK 74436
Ph: (918)482-1245
Co. E-mail: info@haskellchamber.com
URL: http://www.haskellchamber.com
Description: Promotes business and community development in Haskell, OK.

56530 ▪ Healdton Chamber of Commerce
10734 Hwy. 76
Healdton, OK 73438-1714
Ph: (580)229-0900
Co. E-mail: healdton_chamber@yahoo.com
URL: http://www.healdtonchamber.com
Contact: Renee Miller, President
Description: Promotes business and community development in Healdton, OK.

56531 ▪ *The Heart of Oklahoma Chamber*
218 W Main St.
Purcell, OK 73080
Ph: (405)527-3093
Fax: (405)527-4351
Co. E-mail: chamberoffice@theheartofok.com
URL: http://www.theheartofok.com
Contact: Char Page, Executive Director
Released: Monthly

56532 ▪ Heart of Oklahoma Chamber of Commerce
218 W Main St.
Purcell, OK 73080
Ph: (405)527-3093
Fax: (405)527-4351
Co. E-mail: chamberoffice@theheartofok.com
URL: http://www.theheartofok.com
Contact: Char Page, Executive Director
Description: Promotes business and community development in Purcell, OK. **Publications:** *The Heart of Oklahoma Chamber* (Monthly).

56533 ▪ Henryetta Chamber of Commerce
115 S 4th St.
Henryetta, OK 74437-5272
Ph: (918)652-3331
Fax: (918)652-3332
Co. E-mail: chamber@henryetta.org
URL: http://www.henryetta.org
Contact: Roy Madden, Executive Director
Description: Promotes business and community development in Henryetta, OK.

56534 ▪ Hobart Chamber of Commerce
106 W 4th St.
Hobart, OK 73651

Ph: (580)726-2553
Co. E-mail: hobartchamber@cableone.net
URL: http://www.hobartok.com
Contact: Shirley Linville, President
Description: Promotes business and community development in Hobart, OK.

56535 ▪ Holdenville Chamber of Commerce (HCC)
121 N Creek St.
Holdenville, OK 74848
Co. E-mail: holdenvillecofc@okplus.com
URL: http://www.angelfire.com/ok5/chamberofcommerce
Description: Promotes business and community development in Holdenville, OK.

56536 ▪ Hominy Chamber of Commerce
c/o Robyn Ryan, Treas.
PO Box 8
Hominy, OK 74035
Ph: (918)885-4939
Co. E-mail: hominychamberofcommerce@windstream.net
URL: http://www.hominychamber.com
Contact: Jerry Stumpff, President
Description: Promotes business and community development in Hominy, OK.

56537 ▪ Idabel Chamber of Commerce and Agriculture (ICC)
7 SW Texas St.
Idabel, OK 74745
Ph: (580)286-3305
Fax: (580)286-6708
Co. E-mail: idabelchamber@yahoo.com
URL: http://idabelchamberofcommerce.com/contact.html
Contact: Betty Johnson, Executive Director
Description: Promotes business and community development in McCurtain County, OK. Sponsors community events. **Founded:** 1945. **Awards:** Agri-Business of the Year (Annual).

56538 ▪ *Infogram*
301 W Commerce St.
Altus, OK 73522-0518
Ph: (580)482-0210
Fax: (580)482-0223
Co. E-mail: altuschamber@altuschamber.com
URL: http://www.altuschamber.com
Contact: Holley Urbanski, President
Released: Monthly

56539 ▪ *It's Happening in Frederick*
100 S Main St.
Frederick, OK 73542
Ph: (580)335-2126
Fax: (580)335-3767
Co. E-mail: frederickcc@pldi.net
URL: http://www.frederickokchamber.org
Contact: Sharon Bennett, Executive Director
Released: Monthly **Price:** $12, /year.

56540 ▪ Jenks Chamber of Commerce (JCC)
224 E A St.
Jenks, OK 74037
Ph: (918)299-5005
Fax: (918)299-5799
Co. E-mail: info@jenkschamber.com
URL: http://www.jenkschamber.com
Contact: Josh Driskell, President
Description: Promotes business and community development in Jenks, OK. **Founded:** 1966.

56541 ▪ Kingfisher Chamber of Commerce
123 W Miles
Kingfisher, OK 73750
Ph: (405)375-4445
Fax: (405)375-5304
Co. E-mail: chamber@pldi.net
URL: http://www.kingfisher.org
Contact: Chase Farrar, President
Description: Works to promote economic and cultural development through business and individual participation.

56542 ▪ Laverne Area Chamber of Commerce
PO Box 634
Laverne, OK 73848
Ph: (580)921-3612
Co. E-mail: lvrnokcc@ptsi.net
URL: http://www.laverneok.com
Contact: Terri Wheeler, Executive Director
Description: Promotes business and community development in Laverne, OK. **Founded:** 1919. **Subscriptions:** books.

56543 ▪ Lawton - Fort Sill Chamber of Commerce and Industry
302 W Gore Blvd.
Lawton, OK 73501-3709
Ph: (580)355-3541
Free: 800-872-4540
Fax: (580)357-3642
Co. E-mail: dburch@lawtonfortsillchamber.com
URL: http://www.lawtonfortsillchamber.com
Contact: Debra Burch, President
Description: Promotes business and community development in Lawton, OK. **Publications:** *Action News* (Periodic).

56544 ▪ Lindsay Chamber of Commerce
107 N Main St.
Lindsay, OK 73052
Ph: (405)756-4312
Co. E-mail: lchamber@telepath.com
URL: http://www.angelfire.com/biz/lindsayok
Contact: Danny Siebel, President
Description: Promotes business and community development in Lindsay, OK. Sponsors golf tournament, kite festival, Christmas parade, fireworks display, Teacher Appreciation Day, and city-wide garage sale. **Publications:** *Chamber Communicant* (Monthly).

56545 ▪ Love County Chamber of Commerce
PO Box 422
Marietta, OK 73448
Ph: (580)276-3102
Co. E-mail: lovecountychamber@yahoo.com
URL: http://www.lovecountyokla.org
Description: Promotes business and community development in Love County, OK.

56546 ▪ *Mainstream*
5905 Trosper Rd.
Midwest City, OK 73140
Ph: (405)733-3801
Fax: (405)733-5633
Co. E-mail: information@midwestcityok.com
URL: http://www.midwestcityok.com
Contact: Bonnie Cheatwood, Executive Director
Released: Monthly

56547 ▪ McAlester Area Chamber of Commerce and Agriculture (MACCA)
345 E Adams
McAlester, OK 74502
Ph: (918)423-2550
Fax: (918)423-1345
Co. E-mail: karen@mcalester.org
URL: http://www.mcalester.org
Contact: Karen Stephens, President
Description: Promotes agriculture, business, and community development in McAlester, OK.

56548 ▪ *Membership Directory and Information Guide*
410 W Main St.
Ardmore, OK 73401
Ph: (580)223-7765
Fax: (580)223-7825
Co. E-mail: wstucky@ardmore.org
URL: http://chamber.ardmore.org
Contact: Wes Stucky, President
Released: Annual

56549 ▪ Miami Area Chamber of Commerce (MACC)
103 E Central Ave., Ste. 100
Miami, OK 74354
Ph: (918)542-4481

Fax: (918)540-1260
Co. E-mail: info@miamikchamber.com
URL: http://www.miamiokchamber.com/chamber
Contact: Cindy Morris, President
Description: Promotes business and community development in Miami, OK.

56550 ■ Midwest City Chamber of Commerce
5905 Trosper Rd.
Midwest City, OK 73140
Ph: (405)733-3801
Fax: (405)733-5633
Co. E-mail: information@midwestcityok.com
URL: http://www.midwestcityok.com
Contact: Bonnie Cheatwood, Executive Director
Description: Strives to create and maintain a favorable business climate in the community. Provides leadership necessary to advance the civic, commercial, industrial, and general interests of the business and professional community in the Midwest City trade area. **Founded:** 1947. **Publications:** *Mainstream* (Monthly).

56551 ■ Midwest City Chamber of Commerce Foundation for Progress
PO Box 10980
Midwest City, OK 73140-1980
Ph: (405)733-3801
Fax: (405)733-5633
Co. E-mail: information@midwestcityok.com
URL: http://www.midwestcityok.com
Contact: Mr. Kelly Brander, President
Description: Promotes and markets local businesses in Midwest City, to the Central Oklahoma region and in the global market.

56552 ■ *Moore Business Network*
305 W Main St.
Moore, OK 73160-5143
Ph: (405)794-3400
Fax: (405)794-8555
Co. E-mail: brendar@moorechamber.com
URL: http://www.moorechamber.com
Contact: Brenda Roberts, Executive Director
Released: Monthly

56553 ■ Moore Chamber of Commerce (MCC)
305 W Main St.
Moore, OK 73160-5143
Ph: (405)794-3400
Fax: (405)794-8555
Co. E-mail: brendar@moorechamber.com
URL: http://www.moorechamber.com
Contact: Brenda Roberts, Executive Director
Description: Promotes business and community development in Moore, OK. **Founded:** 1946. **Publications:** *Moore Business Network* (Monthly).

56554 ■ *The Muskogee Chamber Connection*
310 W Broadway St.
Muskogee, OK 74401-6610
Ph: (918)682-2401
Free: 866-381-6543
Fax: (918)682-2403
Co. E-mail: info@muskogeechamber.org
URL: http://www.muskogeechamber.org
Contact: Treasure McKenzie, President
Released: Monthly; every 2nd Tuesday.

56555 ■ Mustang Chamber of Commerce
1201 N Mustang Rd.
Mustang, OK 73064-7217
Ph: (405)376-2758
Fax: (405)376-4764
Co. E-mail: mustangc@icon.net
URL: http://www.mustangchamber.com
Contact: Becky Julian, Executive Director
Description: Promotes business and community development in the Mustang, OK area.

56556 ■ National Black Chamber of Commerce - Oklahoma
1216 E Kenosha St., Ste. 182
Broken Arrow, OK 74012
Ph: (918)712-4181

Fax: (918)712-4161
Co. E-mail: info@oklahomablackchamber.org
URL: http://www.oklahomablackchamber.org
Contact: Gail Crum, President
Description: Represents Black owned businesses. Seeks to empower and sustain African American communities through entrepreneurship and capitalistic activity. Provides advocacy, training and education to Black communities.

56557 ■ *Norman Business Journal*
115 E Gray St.
Norman, OK 73069-7203
Ph: (405)321-7260
Fax: (405)360-4679
Co. E-mail: normanchamber@normanchamber.com
URL: http://www.normanchamber.com
Contact: John Woods, President
Released: Monthly

56558 ■ Norman Chamber of Commerce
115 E Gray St.
Norman, OK 73069-7203
Ph: (405)321-7260
Fax: (405)360-4679
Co. E-mail: normanchamber@normanchamber.com
URL: http://www.normanchamber.com
Contact: John Woods, President
Description: Promotes business and community development in Norman, OK. Sponsors Leadership Norman and Tomorrow's Leaders programs. **Founded:** 1889. **Publications:** *Norman Business Journal* (Monthly); *Relocation Guide*; *Visitors Guide* (Periodic). **Educational Activities:** Business After Hours (Monthly); Business Before Hours (Monthly). **Awards:** Athena Award (Annual); Teachers of the Year (Annual).

56559 ■ Northwest Chamber of Commerce (NWC)
7440 NW 39th Expy.
Bethany, OK 73008
Ph: (405)789-1256
Fax: (405)789-2478
Co. E-mail: info@nwokc.com
URL: http://www.nwokc.com
Contact: Jill McCartney, President
Description: Promotes business and community development in Bethany, OK area. **Founded:** 1939. **Publications:** *Northwest Network* (Monthly).

56560 ■ *Northwest Network*
7440 NW 39th Expy.
Bethany, OK 73008
Ph: (405)789-1256
Fax: (405)789-2478
Co. E-mail: info@nwokc.com
URL: http://www.nwokc.com
Contact: Jill McCartney, President
Released: Monthly

56561 ■ *OKC Action*
123 Park Ave.
Oklahoma City, OK 73102
Ph: (405)297-8900
Fax: (405)297-8908
Co. E-mail: info@okcchamber.com
URL: http://www.okcchamber.com
Contact: Roy H. Williams, President
Released: Biweekly

56562 ■ Okemah Chamber of Commerce
PO Box 508
Okemah, OK 74859
Ph: (918)623-2440
Co. E-mail: chamber@okemahok.org
URL: http://www.okemahok.org/chamber.html
Contact: Alan Oatsvall, President
Description: Promotes business and community development in Okemah, OK.

56563 ■ Oologah Area Chamber of Commerce
PO Box 109
Oologah, OK 74053
Co. E-mail: chamber@oologah.org
URL: http://www.oologah.org
Description: Promotes business and economic development in Oologah, OK area. Serves as a civic organization and an advocate for the community.

56564 ■ Owasso Chamber of Commerce
315 S Cedar St.
Owasso, OK 74055
Ph: (918)272-2141
Fax: (918)272-8564
Co. E-mail: fayrene@owassochamber.com
URL: http://www.owassochamber.com
Contact: Fayrene Akin, Office Manager
Description: Promotes business and community development in Owasso, OK. **Founded:** 1950. **Publications:** *Owasso News Line* (Monthly). **Educational Activities:** Owasso Chamber of Commerce Luncheon (Monthly).

56565 ■ *Owasso News Line*
315 S Cedar St.
Owasso, OK 74055
Ph: (918)272-2141
Fax: (918)272-8564
Co. E-mail: fayrene@owassochamber.com
URL: http://www.owassochamber.com
Contact: Fayrene Akin, Office Manager
Released: Monthly

56566 ■ Pauls Valley Chamber of Commerce
112 E Paul St.
Drawer 638
Pauls Valley, OK 73075
Ph: (405)238-6491
Fax: (405)238-2335
Co. E-mail: pvchamber@sbcglobal.net
URL: http://www.paulsvalley.com/chamber.html
Description: Promotes business, economic and community development in the Pauls Valley, OK service area. **Founded:** 1921. **Publications:** *Chamber Chatter* (Monthly).

56567 ■ Pawhuska Chamber of Commerce
210 W Main
Pawhuska, OK 74056
Ph: (918)287-1208
Co. E-mail: pawhuskachamber2@sbcglobal.net
URL: http://www.pawhuskachamber.com
Description: Promotes business and community development in Pawhuska, OK. **Founded:** 1905.

56568 ■ Pawnee Community Chamber of Commerce
613 Harrison St.
Pawnee, OK 74058-2520
Ph: (918)762-2108
Fax: (918)762-2108
Co. E-mail: chamber@cityofpanwee.com
URL: http://www.cityofpawnee.com
Contact: Brett Scott, President
Description: Promotes business and tourism in Pawnee, OK area. Sponsors variety of events and activities throughout the year. **Awards:** Business of the Year (Annual); Citizen of the Year (Annual); Outstanding Building Design (Annual); Volunteer of the Year (Annual).

56569 ■ Perkins Chamber of Commerce
PO Box 502
Perkins, OK 74059
Ph: (405)747-6809
Co. E-mail: perkinschamber@gmail.com
URL: http://www.perkinscc.com
Contact: David Massey, President
Description: Promotes business and community development in Perkins, OK. **Publications:** *Chamber Chatter.*

56570 ■ Perry Chamber of Commerce (PCC)
327 N 7th St.
Perry, OK 73077-6405
Ph: (580)336-4684

Fax: (580)336-3522
Co. E-mail: information@perrychamber.net
URL: http://www.perryokchamber.com/ourChamber.
  htm
Contact: Brett Powers, President
Description: Promotes business and community development in Perry, OK. Sponsors Cherokee Strip Celebration, Springfest home, Sales Expo, Holidayfest, and Crazy Days. **Publications:** *Communicator* (Quarterly).

56571 ■ Piedmont Chamber of Commerce
c/o Gary Layton, Exec. Dir.
12 Monroe NW
Piedmont, OK 73078
Ph: (405)373-2234
Fax: (405)373-2234
Co. E-mail: piedmontokchamber@att.net
URL: http://www.piedmontokchamber.org
Contact: Cindy Cheatwood, President
Description: Promotes business and community development in Piedmont, OK.

56572 ■ Ponca City Area Chamber of Commerce (PCACC)
420 E Grand Ave.
Ponca City, OK 74601-5405
Ph: (580)765-4400
Fax: (580)765-2798
Co. E-mail: staff@poncacitychamber.com
URL: http://www.poncacitychamber.com
Contact: Rich Cantillon, President
Description: Promotes business, community tourism and economic development in the Ponca City, OK area. **Founded:** 1894.

56573 ■ *Positively Anadarko*
516 W Kentucky Ave.
Anadarko, OK 73005
Ph: (405)247-6651
Fax: (405)247-6652
Co. E-mail: coc@anadarko.org
URL: http://www.anadarko.org
Contact: Carla Hall, Executive Director
Released: Monthly **Price:** included in membership dues.

56574 ■ Poteau Chamber of Commerce
201 S Broadway St.
Poteau, OK 74953
Ph: (918)647-9178
Fax: (918)647-4099
Co. E-mail: poteauchamber@windstream.net
URL: http://poteauchamber.com
Contact: Karen Wages, Chief Executive Officer
Description: Promotes business and community development in Poteau, OK. **Founded:** 1917.

56575 ■ Prague Chamber of Commerce
820 Jim Thorpe Blvd.
Prague, OK 74864
Ph: (405)567-2616
Fax: (405)567-2616
Co. E-mail: praguecoc@windstream.net
URL: http://www.praguechamber.org
Contact: Harvey Robinson, President
Description: Promotes business and community development in Prague, OK. **Founded:** 1927.

56576 ■ Pryor Area Chamber of Commerce (PACC)
100 E Graham Ave.
Pryor, OK 74362-0367
Ph: (918)825-0157
Fax: (918)825-0158
Co. E-mail: pr@pryorchamber.com
URL: http://www.pryorchamber.com
Contact: Darren DeLozier, Chairman
Description: Promotes business and community development in Mayes County, OK. Sponsors Leadership Pryor, business seminars and workshops, FunFest, DAM J.A.M. Bicycle Tour of N.E. Oklahoma's Lakes and Dams and Lighted Christmas Parade. **Founded:** 1943.

56577 ■ *Quest*
1126 W Main St.
Collinsville, OK 74021-3113

Ph: (918)371-4703
Co. E-mail: cvillechamber3477@gmail.com
URL: http://www.collinsvillechamber.net
Contact: Bill Johnston, President
Released: Monthly **Price:** free for members.

56578 ■ *Relocation Guide*
115 E Gray St.
Norman, OK 73069-7203
Ph: (405)321-7260
Fax: (405)360-4679
Co. E-mail: normanchamber@normanchamber.com
URL: http://www.normanchamber.com
Contact: John Woods, President

56579 ■ Sallisaw Chamber of Commerce
PO Box 251
Sallisaw, OK 74955-0251
Ph: (918)775-2558
Fax: (918)775-4021
Co. E-mail: sallisawchamber@yahoo.com
URL: http://www.sallisawchamber.com
Contact: Mrs. Judy Martens, Executive Vice
  President
Description: Promotes business and community development in Sallisaw, OK.

56580 ■ Sand Springs Area Chamber of Commerce
121 N Main St.
Sand Springs, OK 74063
Ph: (918)245-3221
Fax: (918)245-2530
Co. E-mail: info@sandspringschamber.com
URL: http://www.sandspringschamber.com
Contact: Mr. J.C. Kinder, Jr., President
Description: Aims to advance the business community and improve the quality of life for the Sand Springs area citizens. **Founded:** 1946. **Publications:** *Chamber Comments*. **Educational Activities:** Sand Springs Area Chamber of Commerce Meeting (Monthly). **Awards:** Business Person of the Year (Annual); Volunteer of the Year (Annual).

56581 ■ Sapulpa Area Chamber of Commerce
101 E Dewey
Sapulpa, OK 74066
Ph: (918)224-0170
Fax: (918)224-0172
Co. E-mail: betty@sapulpachamber.com
URL: http://www.sapulpachamber.com
Contact: James Leewright, President
Description: Promotes business and community development in the Sapulpa, OK area.

56582 ■ Seminole Chamber of Commerce
326 E Evans Ave.
Seminole, OK 74868-3922
Ph: (405)382-3640
Fax: (405)382-3529
Co. E-mail: info@seminoleokchamber.org
URL: http://seminoleokchamber.org
Contact: Amy Britt, Executive Director
Description: Promotes business and community development in Seminole, Oklahoma. **Scope:** local and area attractions and businesses. **Founded:** 1928. **Subscriptions:** 100 books periodicals. **Publications:** *Seminole Chamber of Commerce Membership Directory and Visitor's Guide* (Biennial); *Seminole Chamber of Commerce Membership Directory and Visitor's Guide* (Annual). **Educational Activities:** Gusher Days (Annual). **Awards:** Citizen of the Year (Annual).

56583 ■ *Seminole Chamber of Commerce Membership Directory and Visitor's Guide*
326 E Evans Ave.
Seminole, OK 74868-3922
Ph: (405)382-3640
Fax: (405)382-3529
Co. E-mail: info@seminoleokchamber.org
URL: http://seminoleokchamber.org
Contact: Amy Britt, Executive Director
Released: Biennial **Price:** free.

56584 ■ Shattuck Chamber of Commerce
115 S Main St.
Shattuck, OK 73858-0400

Ph: (580)938-2818
Fax: (580)938-2852
Co. E-mail: shattuckcc@pldi.net
URL: http://www.shattuckchamber.org
Contact: David W. Romine, Executive Director
Description: Promotes business and community development in Shattuck, OK. **Founded:** 1949.

56585 ■ Skiatook Chamber of Commerce
304 E Rogers Blvd.
Skiatook, OK 74070-1206
Ph: (918)396-3702
URL: http://www.skiatookchamber.com
Contact: Stephanie Upton, Executive Director
Description: Promotes business and community development in Skiatook, OK. **Publications:** *ChamberNews* (Monthly).

56586 ■ South Oklahoma City Chamber of Commerce
701 SW 74th St.
Oklahoma City, OK 73139-4599
Ph: (405)634-1436
Fax: (405)634-1462
Co. E-mail: info@southokc.com
URL: http://www.southokc.com
Contact: Elaine Lyons, President
Description: Promotes business and community development in southern Oklahoma City, OK. **Founded:** 1905. **Publications:** *Achiever* (Bimonthly). **Educational Activities:** After 5 Mixers (Quarterly). **Awards:** Ambassador of the Month (Monthly).

56587 ■ Spiro Area Chamber of Commerce
210 S Main St.
Spiro, OK 74959
Ph: (918)962-3816
Fax: (918)962-3816
Co. E-mail: spirocc@sbcglobal.net
URL: http://www.myspiro.com
Contact: Dennis Peterson, President
Description: Works to create a positive business atmosphere by promoting industry, tourism, and agriculture in Spiro and Leflore County.

56588 ■ State Chamber - Oklahoma's Association of Business and Industry
330 NE 10th St.
Oklahoma City, OK 73104-3220
Ph: (405)235-3669
Fax: (405)235-3670
Co. E-mail: info@okstatechamber.com
URL: http://www.okstatechamber.com
Contact: Fred S. Morgan, President
Description: Promotes business and community development in Oklahoma. **Founded:** 1924. **Publications:** *The Advocate* (Periodic).

56589 ■ Stillwater Chamber of Commerce
409 S Main St.
Stillwater, OK 74074-3524
Ph: (405)372-5573
Free: 800-593-5573
Fax: (405)372-4316
Co. E-mail: info@stillwaterchamber.org
URL: http://stillwaterchamber.org
Contact: Lisa Navrkal, President
Description: Promotes business and community development in Stillwater, OK. **Founded:** 1892. **Publications:** *Stillwater Commerce* (Monthly); *Stillwater Connection* (Weekly). **Educational Activities:** Stillwater Chamber of Commerce Breakfast (Monthly); Business Showcase and Mixer (Semiannual).

56590 ■ *Stillwater Commerce*
409 S Main St.
Stillwater, OK 74074-3524
Ph: (405)372-5573
Free: 800-593-5573
Fax: (405)372-4316
Co. E-mail: info@stillwaterchamber.org
URL: http://stillwaterchamber.org
Contact: Lisa Navrkal, President
Released: Monthly **Price:** included in membership dues.

56591 ■ *Stillwater Connection*
409 S Main St.
Stillwater, OK 74074-3524

Ph: (405)372-5573
Free: 800-593-5573
Fax: (405)372-4316
Co. E-mail: info@stillwaterchamber.org
URL: http://stillwaterchamber.org
Contact: Lisa Navrkal, President
Released: Weekly **Price:** free to newspaper subscribers.

56592 ■ Stroud Chamber of Commerce
216 W Main St.
Stroud, OK 74079
Ph: (918)968-3321
Co. E-mail: stroudch@brightok.net
URL: http://stroudchamber.com
Contact: Tommy Smith, President
Description: Aims to advance the economic, civic, educational and cultural growth of Stroud and to enhance the quality of life in the community. Fosters continuous improvement of the Stroud area as a place to conduct business and enjoy life.

56593 ■ Sulphur Chamber of Commerce
717 W Broadway
Sulphur, OK 73086
Ph: (580)622-2824
Fax: (580)622-4217
Co. E-mail: info@sulphurokla.com
URL: http://www.sulphurokla.com
Contact: David Allen, President
Description: Promotes business and community development in Sulphur, OK. Sponsors 5k Run and Racewalk, annual Sulphur Days Festival, Hills of Oklahoma Tour (bicycle race), Christmas parade, and Arbuckle County Christmas Festivities.

56594 ■ Tahlequah Area Chamber of Commerce and Tourism Council (TACC)
123 E Delaware St.
Tahlequah, OK 74464
Ph: (918)456-3742
Fax: (918)456-3751
Co. E-mail: david@tahlequahchamber.com
URL: http://tahlequahchamber.com
Contact: David Moore, Executive Director
Description: Promotes business and community development in Tahlequah, OK. Sponsors 4-H Livestock Show, Moonlight Classic golf tournament, Christmas Parade, Festival of Lights, Cherokee Square Arts and Crafts Festival. **Founded:** 1898. **Publications:** Chamber Voice (Monthly).

56595 ■ Talihina Chamber of Commerce
900 2nd St., Ste. 12
Talihina, OK 74571
Ph: (918)567-3434
Fax: (918)567-3388
Co. E-mail: chamber@talihinacc.com
URL: http://www.talihinacc.com
Description: Promotes business and community development in Talihina, Oklahoma.

56596 ■ Tecumseh Chamber of Commerce (TCC)
114 N Broadway St.
Tecumseh, OK 74873
Ph: (405)598-8666
Fax: (405)598-6760
Co. E-mail: chamber@tecumsehok.org
URL: http://www.tecumsehok.com
Contact: Sharon Pattillo, President
Description: Promotes business and community development in Tecumseh, OK. **Publications:** Chamber Chimes (Monthly). **Awards:** Seniors of the Month (Monthly).

56597 ■ Tulsa Metro Chamber
Williams Center Tower II
2 W 2nd St., Ste. 150
Tulsa, OK 74103
Ph: (918)585-1201
Fax: (918)585-8106
Co. E-mail: mikeneal@tulsachamber.com
URL: http://www.tulsachamber.com
Contact: Mr. Mike Neal, President
Description: Promotes business and community development in the Tulsa and Northeastern Oklahoma areas. Convention/Meeting: none. **Founded:** 1903.

56598 ■ Update
210 Kenwood Blvd.
Enid, OK 73702
Ph: (580)237-2494
Fax: (580)237-2497
URL: http://www.enidchamber.com
Contact: Jon Blankenship, President
Released: Monthly

56599 ■ Vinita Area Chamber of Commerce (VACC)
105 W Delaware St.
Vinita, OK 74301
Ph: (918)256-7133
Fax: (918)256-8261
Co. E-mail: chamber@vinita.com
URL: http://www.vinita.com
Contact: J.C. Kinder, Executive Director
Description: Promotes business and community development in Vinita, OK. Sponsors competitions and festivals. **Founded:** 1904. **Publications:** Chamber News (Semimonthly). **Educational Activities:** Vinita Area Chamber of Commerce Meeting (Monthly).

56600 ■ Visit Roger Mills County and Cheyenne, Oklahoma
PO Box 57
Cheyenne, OK 73628
Ph: (580)497-3318
Free: 877-497-3318
Co. E-mail: cheyennecoc@yahoo.com
URL: http://www.cheyenneokcoc.com
Contact: Mrs. Rhonda Robertson, President

56601 ■ Visitors Guide
115 E Gray St.
Norman, OK 73069-7203
Ph: (405)321-7260
Fax: (405)360-4679
Co. E-mail: normanchamber@normanchamber.com
URL: http://www.normanchamber.com
Contact: John Woods, President
Released: Periodic

56602 ■ Watonga Chamber of Commerce
PO Box 537
Watonga, OK 73772-0537
Ph: (580)623-5452
Fax: (580)623-5428
Co. E-mail: cwatonga@pldi.net
URL: http://www.watongachamber.com
Contact: Mary Larson, Director, Administration
Description: Promotes business and community development in Watonga, OK. **Founded:** 1941. **Awards:** Business Beautification (Annual); Business of the Year (Annual); New Business of the Year (Annual); Teacher of the Year (Annual); Volunteer of the Year (Annual).

56603 ■ Waynoka Chamber of Commerce
PO Box 173
Waynoka, OK 73860
Ph: (580)824-4741
Co. E-mail: waynokachamberofcommerce@yahoo.com
URL: http://www.waynokachamber.com
Contact: Wayne LaMunyon, President
Description: Promotes business and community development in Waynoka, OK.

56604 ■ Weatherford Area Chamber of Commerce (WACC)
210 W Main St.
Weatherford, OK 73096-4839
Ph: (580)772-7744
Free: 800-725-7744
Fax: (580)772-7751
Co. E-mail: welcome@weatherfordchamber.com
URL: http://weatherfordchamber.com/new
Contact: Wes Magill, President
Description: Promotes business and community development in Weatherford, OK. Sponsors Southwest Festival of the Arts, Heartland/Route 66 Cruise, and IPRA Rodeo. **Founded:** 1907. **Publications:** Guide to Doing Business in Waterford (Annual).

56605 ■ Weekly Memo
419 W Will Rogers Blvd.
Claremore, OK 74017-6820
Ph: (918)341-2818
Fax: (918)342-0663
Co. E-mail: chamber@claremore.org
URL: http://www.claremore.org
Contact: Dell Davis, President
Released: Weekly

56606 ■ Wewoka Chamber of Commerce
PO Box 719
Wewoka, OK 74884
Ph: (405)257-5485
Fax: (405)257-2662
Co. E-mail: wewokachamber@sbcglobal.net
Contact: Debbie Melton, President
Description: Promotes business and community development in Wewoka, OK.

56607 ■ Who's Who in Business
10441 S Regal Blvd., Ste. 104
Bixby, OK 74008
Ph: (918)366-9445
Fax: (918)366-9443
Co. E-mail: info@bixbychamber.com
URL: http://www.bixbychamber.com
Contact: Russ Smith, Chairman
Released: Annual

56608 ■ Wilburton Chamber of Commerce
302 W Main St.
Wilburton, OK 74578
Ph: (918)465-2759
Fax: (918)465-2759
Co. E-mail: wilburtonchamber@sbcglobal.net
URL: http://wilburtonchamber.com
Contact: Dr. Robert Woodruff, President
Description: Promotes business and community development in Wilburton, OK.

56609 ■ Woodward Chamber of Commerce (WCC)
1006 Oklahoma Ave.
Woodward, OK 73801-4662
Ph: (580)256-7411
Free: 800-364-5352
Fax: (580)254-3585
Co. E-mail: wwchamber@sbcglobal.net
URL: http://www.woodwardchamber.com
Contact: C.J. Montgomery, President
Description: Promotes business and community development in Woodward, OK. Monitors issues such as minimum wage, educational funding, and worker's compensation. Lobbies for favorable legislation. Holds area festivals and other activities. **Telecommunication Services:** cjmontgomery@sbcglobal.net.

56610 ■ Wynnewood Chamber of Commerce
PO Box 616
Wynnewood, OK 73098-0616
Ph: (405)665-4466
Free: 800-400-1388
Fax: (405)665-4466
Co. E-mail: wynnewoodokla@sbcglobal.net
URL: http://www.wynnewoodokla.com
Description: Promotes business and community development in Wynnewood, OK. **Founded:** 1951.

56611 ■ Yukon Chamber of Commerce
510 Elm St.
Yukon, OK 73099
Ph: (405)354-3567
Fax: (405)350-0724
Co. E-mail: chamber@yukoncc.com
URL: http://www.yukoncc.com
Contact: Cathy Patton, President
Description: Promotes business and community development in Yukon, OK.

MINORITY BUSINESS ASSISTANCE PROGRAMS

56612 ■ Oklahoma City Minority Business Enterprise and Consultant Center
5350 S Western Ave., Ste. 103
Oklahoma City, OK 73109

Ph: (405)702-9009
Fax: (405)702-9993
URL: http://www.okcmbecc.org
Contact: Wayne A. Lawson, Chief Executive Officer
Description: Provides consulting, training, contract assistance, and other services to minority businesses.

56613 ■ Oklahoma Department of Commerce - New and Existing Businesses - Minority-Owned Businesses
900 N Stiles
Oklahoma City, OK 73126-0980
Ph: (405)815-6552
Free: 800-879-6552
Fax: (405)815-5199
Co. E-mail: bddinfo@odoc.state.ok.us
URL: http://www.okcommerce.gov
Contact: Natilie Sherili, Secretary
Description: Specializes in finance export programs to assist small Oklahoma companies.

56614 ■ Oklahoma Minority Supplier Development Council
The Pavilion Bldg.
6701 N Broadway, Ste. 216
Oklahoma City, OK 73116
Ph: (405)767-9900
Fax: (405)767-9901
Co. E-mail: oklamsdc@aol.com
URL: http://www.omsdc.org
Contact: Debra Ponder-Nelson, Chief Executive Officer
Description: Encourages the growth and development of minority businesses by fostering a greater utilization of minority businesses by major corporations.

56615 ■ Oklahoma Native American Business Enterprise Center
7915 E 63rd St., Ste. 201
Tulsa, OK 74133
Ph: (918)994-4370
Fax: (918)994-4394
Co. E-mail: james@ruralenterprises.com
URL: http://www.onabec.com
Contact: James Ray
Description: Provides business assistance to Native American and other minority-owned companies in Oklahoma.

FINANCING AND LOAN PROGRAMS

56616 ■ Chisholm Private Capital Partners
5400 N. Grand Blvd., Ste. 225
Oklahoma City, OK 73112
Ph: (405)605-1111
Fax: (405)605-1115
URL: http://www.chisholmvc.com
Contact: William D. Paiva, Partner
Preferred Investment Size: $1,000,000 to $4,000,000. **Industry Preferences:** Computer software and services, semiconductors and other electronics, Internet specific, communications and media, medical and health, industrial and energy, other products, and computer hardware. **Geographic Preference:** Oklahoma.

56617 ■ Davis, Tuttle Venture Partners, L.P. / DTVP (Tulsa)
110 W. 7th St., Ste. 1000
Tulsa, OK 74106-3703
Ph: (918)584-7272
Fax: (918)582-3404
URL: http://www.davistuttle.com
Contact: Barry M. Davis, Partner
Preferred Investment Size: $500,000 to $5,000,000. **Industry Preferences:** Other products, consumer related, medical and health, industrial and energy, computer software and services, semiconductors and other electronics, Internet specific, communications and media. **Geographic Preference:** Southwest.

PROCUREMENT ASSISTANCE PROGRAMS

56618 ■ Department of Central Services - Purchasing Division
2401 N Lincoln Blvd., Ste. 212
Oklahoma City, OK 73105
Ph: (405)521-2115
Fax: (405)521-4475
Co. E-mail: scott_schlotthauer@dcs.state.ok.us
URL: http://www.dcs.ok.gov
Contact: Scott Schlotthauer, Director

56619 ■ Oklahoma Bid Assistance Network (OBA) - Moore Norman Technology Center (MNTC) - Business Development Center - Bid Assistance Procurement Center
4701 12th Ave. NW
Norman, OK 73069-8399
Ph: (405)364-5763
Fax: (405)360-9989
URL: http://mntechnology.com
Contact: Lynda Kouri, Executive Director
E-mail: gbertoletti@mntechnology
Description: The center serves the businesses and individuals in MNTC's district of Moore, Norman, and south Oklahoma City. Services offered include: bid notification registration, bid matching, access to specifications, standards and drawings as well as introductions to a networks of procurement specialists.

56620 ■ Oklahoma Department of Career and Technology Education - Bid Assistance Centers
1500 W 7th Ave.
Stillwater, OK 74074-4364
Ph: (405)377-2000
Fax: (405)743-5541
Co. E-mail: pberk@okcareertech.org
URL: http://www.okcareertech.org
Contact: Phil Berkenbile, Director
Description: Provides federal contracting at 21 offices, located at vo-tech schools statewide.

56621 ■ Oklahoma Procurement Technical Assistance Center - Eastern Oklahoma County Technology Center
4601 N Choctaw Rd.
Choctaw, OK 73020
Ph: (405)390-9591
Fax: (405)390-9598
Co. E-mail: mailbox@ecotech.org
URL: http://www.eoctech.org
Contact: Julie Farmer, Coordinator
E-mail: jfarmer@eoctech.org
Description: Provides individuals with life-long career/technical training and personal development through quality programs, services and activities serving the school districts of Choctaw, Harrah, Jones and Luther.

56622 ■ Oklahoma Procurement Technical Assistance Center - Francis Tuttle Tech Center
12777 N Rockwell Ave.
Oklahoma City, OK 73142
Ph: (405)717-4740
Co. E-mail: jrobbins@francistuttle.com
URL: http://www.francistuttle.com
Contact: Judy Robbins, Director, Procurement
E-mail: jrobbins@francistuttle.com
Description: Helps client firms find potential government customers, register in government systems such as the Central Contractor Registration System, and market themselves to both government agencies and prime contractors.

56623 ■ Oklahoma Procurement Technical Assistance Center - Great Plains Technology Center
4500 W Lee Blvd.
Lawton, OK 73505
Ph: (580)250-5554

Fax: (580)250-5566
Co. E-mail: lmaddox@gptech.org
URL: http://www.gptech.org
Contact: Leslie Maddox, Coordinator
E-mail: imaddox@gptech.org
Description: Promotes the economic development of southwest Oklahoma by assisting businesses and organizations of the district to continually improve their operations.

56624 ■ Oklahoma Procurement Technical Assistance Center - Oklahoma Bid Assistance Network (OBAN) - Autry Technology Center
1201 W Willow
Enid, OK 73703-2598
Ph: (580)242-2750
Fax: (580)242-2015
Co. E-mail: thenneke@autrytech.com
URL: http://www.autrytech.com
Contact: Terry Henneke, Coordinator
E-mail: thenneke@autrytech.com
Description: Provides programs and services that enhance skill development and job opportunities.

56625 ■ Oklahoma Procurement Technical Assistance Center - Oklahoma Bid Assistance Network (OBA) - Gordon Cooper Tech Center
1 John C Bruton Blvd.
Shawnee, OK 74804
Ph: (405)273-7493
Fax: (405)273-6354
Co. E-mail: davidh@gctech.org
URL: http://www.gctech.org
Contact: David Hoffmeier, Coordinator
E-mail: davidh@gctech.org
Description: Provides timely information and training for businesses interested in government markets.

56626 ■ Oklahoma Procurement Technical Assistance Center - Oklahoma Bid Assistance Network (OBA) - High Plains Tech Center
3921 34th St.
Woodward, OK 73801-7000
Ph: (580)571-6185
Fax: (580)571-6051
Co. E-mail: vsmith@hptc.net
URL: http://www.hptc.net
Contact: Vonda Wills, Coordinator
E-mail: cevans@hptc.net
Description: To increase business activity and employment in our service area by giving local companies a chance to diversify. Provides information and tools needed for contracting with the federal, and state governments serving Woodward, Harper, Woods, Major, Kingfisher, and Blaine Counties.

56627 ■ Oklahoma Procurement Technical Assistance Center - Oklahoma Bid Assistance Network (OBA) - Indian Capital Technology Center (ICTC)
2403 N 41st St. E
Muskogee, OK 74403-1799
Ph: (918)348-7945
Fax: (918)682-5595
Co. E-mail: johnh@ictctech.com
URL: http://www.icavts.tec.ok.us
Contact: John Hasler, Coordinator
E-mail: johnh@ictctech.com
Description: Goal is to present potential contractors with a clear understanding of the bidding process as well as providing the most up-to-date information required for contract bidding.

56628 ■ Oklahoma Procurement Technical Assistance Center - Oklahoma Bid Assistance Network (OBA) - Kiamichi Tech Center - Kiamichi District Bid Assistance Center
1004 Highway 2, N
Wilburton, OK 74578
Ph: (918)465-2323

Fax: (918)465-3666
Co. E-mail: rdegiacomo@okktc.org
URL: http://www.okktc.org
Contact: Ron DeGiacomo, Coordinator
E-mail: rdegiacomo@okktc.org
Description: Provides training and assistance in locating and competing for government contracts.

56629 ■ Oklahoma Procurement Technical Assistance Center - Oklahoma Bid Assistance Network (OBA) - Mid-America Technology Center
27438 State Hwy. 59
Wayne, OK 73095
Ph: (405)449-3391
Fax: (405)449-7321
Co. E-mail: mslemp@matech.org
URL: http://www.matech.org
Contact: Mitchell Slemp, Consultant
E-mail: mslemp@matech.org
Description: Enriches economic stability and growth by providing educational and training opportunities for the citizens and businesses in the communities.

56630 ■ Oklahoma Procurement Technical Assistance Center - Oklahoma Bid Assistance Network (OBA) - Northeast Technology Center Pryor Campus
PO Box 825
Pryor, OK 74362
Ph: (918)825-5555
Fax: (918)825-6281
URL: http://www.netechcenters.com
Contact: Donna Martin, Coordinator
E-mail: dmartin@netechcenters.com
Description: Assists area businesses obtain government contracts. Help is available to cut through red tape, find what contracts are out for bid, how to request an opportunity to bid, and how to complete and submit a bid package.

56631 ■ Oklahoma Procurement Technical Assistance Center - Oklahoma Bid Assistance Network (OBA) - Pioneer Tech Center
2101 N Ash
Ponca City, OK 74601-1110
Ph: (580)762-8336
Fax: (580)762-1175
Co. E-mail: info@pioneertech.com
URL: http://www.pioneertech.org
Contact: Teresa Smith, Coordinator
Description: Assists companies to compete and win government contracts.

56632 ■ Oklahoma Procurement Technical Assistance Center - Oklahoma Bid Assistance Network (OBA) - Red River Technology Center
3300 W Bois D'Are
Duncan, OK 73534
Ph: (580)255-2903
Free: 888-607-2446
Co. E-mail: dharwell@rrtc.edu
URL: http://www.redriver.tec.ok.us
Contact: Dana Harwell, Coordinator
E-mail: dharwell@redriver.tec.ok.us
Description: Assists area businesses obtain government contracts. Help is available to cut through red tape, find what contracts are out for bid, how to request an opportunity to bid, and how to complete and submit a bid package.

56633 ■ Oklahoma Procurement Technical Assistance Center - Oklahoma Bid Assistance Network (OBA) - Southwest Technology Center
711 W Tamarack Rd.
Altus, OK 73521
Ph: (580)477-2250
URL: http://www.swtc.org
Contact: Dianna Thompson, Coordinator
E-mail: monica.cox@swtc.org
Description: Assists area businesses obtain government contracts. Help is available to cut through red tape, find what contracts are out for bid, how to request an opportunity to bid, and how to complete and submit a bid package.

56634 ■ Oklahoma Procurement Technical Assistance Center - Oklahoma Bid Assistance Network (OBA) - Tri-County Technology Center
6101 SE Nowata Rd.
Bartlesville, OK 74006
Ph: (918)331-3320
URL: http://www.tctc.org
Contact: Angela Cash, Specialist
E-mail: acash@tctc.org
Description: Assist in competing for government contracts and will help you develop a pro-active marketing strategy identifying bid opportunities from all levels of government covering Washington, Nowata, Craig, Ottawa, Mayes, Rogers, and Tulsa Counties.

56635 ■ Oklahoma Procurement Technical Assistance Center - Oklahoma Bid Assistance Network (OBA) - Tulsa Technology Center
6111 E Skelly Dr.
Tulsa, OK 74147-7200
Ph: (918)828-5464
Fax: (918)828-5439
URL: http://www.tulsatech.org
Contact: Joyce McClellan, Coordinator
E-mail: joyce.mcclellan@tulsatech.org
Description: Assist in competing for government contracts.

56636 ■ Oklahoma Procurement Technical Assistance Center - Tribal Government Institute
421 E Comanche, Ste. B
Norman, OK 73071
Ph: (405)329-5542
Fax: (405)329-5543
Co. E-mail: tgi@coxnet.net
URL: http://www.tgiok.com
Contact: Bob Gann, Program Manager
Description: Provides management training, consulting, technical assistance, program and project applications, and tribal government assistance in the fields of drafting housing codes, constitutional law, policies and procedures, coordinating housing bond issues, grant proposals, public health and safety codes, law and order codes and many types of legislative requirements of tribal governments and their agencies.

56637 ■ Rose State College - Oklahoma Small Business Development Center - Procurement Center
Professional Training and Education Ctr.
1720 Hudiburg Drive
Midwest City, OK 73110
Ph: (405)733-7348
Fax: (405)733-7495
Co. E-mail: varmstrong@rose.edu
URL: http://www.rose.edu
Contact: Vickie Armstrong, Director
Description: Procurement center for all area small business development centers.

INCUBATORS/RESEARCH AND TECHNOLOGY PARKS

56638 ■ Atoka Industrial Incubator - Atoka Kiamichi Area Vo-Tech/Atoka Campus
1301 W Liberty Rd.
Atoka, OK 74525
Ph: (580)889-7321
Fax: (580)889-5642
URL: http://www.kiamichi-atoka.tec.ok.us/

56639 ■ Central Oklahoma Business and Job Development Corp. - Center for Business, Technology, Research and Development
201 N Settle Dr.
Drumright, OK 74030
Ph: (918)352-4517

Fax: (918)352-9545
Co. E-mail: stacyP@ctechok.org
URL: http://cob-jdc.org/
Description: A non-profit program providing a supportive environment for small business start-up, survival, and growth.

56640 ■ McAlester Chamber of Commerce - SBDC
345 E Adams
McAlester, OK 74502
Ph: (918)423-2550
Free: 888-828-9901
Fax: (918)423-1345
Co. E-mail: jmills@onenet.net
URL: http://www.mcalester.org
Contact: Jim Mills, Executive Director
Description: Works to provide a business-friendly environment and business development programs.

56641 ■ Meridian Technology Center for Business Development Center - School
1312 S Sangre Rd.
Stillwater, OK 74074-1899
Ph: (405)377-3333
Fax: (405)377-9604
Co. E-mail: info@meridian-technology.com
URL: http://www.meridian-technology.com/cbd/index.asp
Description: A business incubator that fosters the development of new and emerging businesses. The Center offers office and manufacturing space, conference rooms, and other resources.

56642 ■ Pioneer Technology Center Business Incubator - Incubator
2101 N Ash St.
Ponca City, OK 74601
Ph: (580)762-8336
Fax: (580)762-1175
Co. E-mail: info@pioneertech.org
URL: http://www.pioneertech.org
Description: A certified business incubator for new businesses. Offers space for service, light manufacturing, or wholesale companies.

56643 ■ Poteau Kiamichi Technology Center - Incubator
1509 S McKenna
Poteau, OK 74953
Ph: (918)647-4525
Fax: (918)647-4527
Co. E-mail: kdavidson@okktc.org
URL: http://www.kiamichi-poteau.tec.ok.us
Contact: Doug Hall, Director

56644 ■ Rural Enterprises Inc.
2912 Enterprise Blvd.
Durant, OK 74701
Ph: (580)924-5094
Free: 800-658-2823
Fax: (580)920-2745
Co. E-mail: mwingfield@ruralenterprises.com
URL: http://www.ruralenterprises.com
Contact: Kenny Simpson, Executive Vice President
Description: Provides technology data searches to Oklahoma businesses, utilizing over 400 databases. Makes available a library of world technology information with assistance from the Rural Innovation and Finance Center.

56645 ■ Stigler Kiamichi Technology Center - Incubator
1410 Old Military Rd.
Stigler, OK 74462
Ph: (918)967-2801
Fax: (918)967-2804
URL: http://www.kiamichi-stigler.tec.ok.us
Contact: Jimmy Eakle, Director

56646 ■ Tri-County Economic Technology Center Incubator - Incubator
6101 SE Nowata Rd.
Bartlesville, OK 74006
Ph: (918)331-3257

Fax: (918)335-3795
Co. E-mail: edettle@tctc.org
URL: http://www.tctc.org
Description: A certified small business incubator offering office and light manufacturing space.

56647 ■ Wes Watkins Technology Center - Incubator
7892 Hwy. 9
Wetumka, OK 74883
Ph: (405)452-5500
Fax: (405)452-3561
URL: http://www.wwtech.org
Contact: Frank Alexander, Director

EDUCATIONAL PROGRAMS

56648 ■ Canadian Valley Technology Center
6505 E Hwy. 66
El Reno, OK 73036-9117
Ph: (405)262-2629
Fax: (405)422-2320
URL: http://www.cvtech.edu
Description: Trade and technical college offering a small business management program.

56649 ■ Center for Business Technology, Research and Development
201 N Settles Dr.
Drumright, OK 74030
Ph: (918)352-4516
Fax: (918)352-9545
URL: http://www.centraltech.edu
Description: Trade and technical college offering a small business management program.

56650 ■ Central Oklahoma Technology Center
1720 S Main St.
Sapulpa, OK 74066
Ph: (918)224-9300
Fax: (918)224-0744
URL: http://www.centraltech.edu
Description: Trade and technical college offering a small business management program.

56651 ■ EOC Technology Center
4601 N Choctaw Rd.
Choctaw, OK 73020
Ph: (405)390-9591
Fax: (405)390-9598
Co. E-mail: mailbox@eoctech.edu
URL: http://www.eoctech.edu
Description: Business college offering a small business management program.

56652 ■ Francis Tuttle Technology Center - Rockwell Campus
12777 N Rockwell Ave.
Oklahoma City, OK 73142
Ph: (405)717-7799
Fax: (405)717-4771
Co. E-mail: bis@francistuttle.edu
URL: http://www.francistuttle.edu
Description: Business college offering a small business management program.

56653 ■ Gordon Cooper Technology Center
1 John C Bruton Blvd.
Shawnee, OK 74804
Ph: (405)273-7493
Fax: (405)273-6354
Co. E-mail: info@gctech.org
URL: http://www.gctech.org
Description: Business college offering a small business management program.

56654 ■ Great Plains Technology Center
4500 W Lee Blvd.
Lawton, OK 73505
Ph: (580)355-6371

Free: 800-244-1024
Fax: (580)250-5677
Co. E-mail: info@greatplains.edu
URL: http://www.greatplains.edu
Description: Business college offering a small business management program.

56655 ■ High Plains Technology Center
3921 34th St.
Woodward, OK 73801
Ph: (580)256-6618
Free: 800-725-1492
Fax: (580)571-6190
URL: http://www.hptc.net
Description: Business college offering a small business management program.

56656 ■ Kiamichi Area Vo-Tech--Atoka
PO Box 240
Atoka, OK 74525
Ph: (580)889-7321
Fax: (580)889-5642
Co. E-mail: billsmith@ktc.edu
URL: http://www.ktc.edu
Description: Business college offering a small business management program.

56657 ■ Kiamichi Technology Center
301 Kiamichi Dr.
McAlester, OK 74501
Ph: (918)426-0940
Free: 888-567-6630
Fax: (918)426-1626
URL: http://www.ktc.edu
Description: Business college offering a small business management program.

56658 ■ Kiamichi Technology Center--Stigler
1410 Old Military Rd.
Stigler, OK 74462
Ph: (918)967-2801
Free: 888-567-6805
Fax: (918)967-2804
URL: http://www.ktc.edu
Description: Business college offering a small business management program.

56659 ■ Meridian Technology Center
1312 S Sangre Rd.
Stillwater, OK 74074-1899
Ph: (405)377-3333
Free: 888-607-2509
Fax: (405)377-9604
Co. E-mail: info@meridiantech.edu
URL: http://www.meridiantech.edu
Description: Business college offering a small business management program.

56660 ■ Metro Vocational Technical School
1900 Springlake Dr.
Oklahoma City, OK 73111
Ph: (405)424-8324
Fax: (405)424-8555
Co. E-mail: info@metrotech.edu
URL: http://www.metrotech.edu
Description: Business college offering a small business management program.

56661 ■ Mid-America Technology Center
PO Box H
Wayne, OK 73095
Ph: (405)449-3391
Free: 800-232-5580
Fax: (405)449-7321
URL: http://www.matech.edu
Description: Business college offering a small business management program.

56662 ■ Moore Norman Technology Center
4701 12th Ave. NW
Norman, OK 73069
Ph: (405)364-5763

Fax: (405)360-9989
URL: http://www.mntechnology.com
Description: Trade and technical college offering a small business management program.

56663 ■ Northeast Technology Center
PO Box 825
Pryor, OK 74362
Ph: (918)825-5555
Free: 888-832-7988
Fax: (918)825-6281
URL: http://www.netech.edu
Description: Business college offering a small business management program.

56664 ■ Pioneer Technology Center
2101 N Ash
Ponca City, OK 74601
Ph: (580)762-8336
Free: 866-612-4782
Fax: (580)762-1175
Co. E-mail: info@pioneertech.edu
URL: http://www.pioneertech.edu
Description: Business college offering a small business management program.

56665 ■ Red River Technology Center
3300 W Bois D'Arc
Duncan, OK 73534
Ph: (580)255-2903
Free: 888-607-2446
Fax: (580)255-0491
Co. E-mail: jjacobi@rrtc.edu
URL: http://www.rrtc.edu
Description: Business college offering a small business management program.

56666 ■ Tri-County Area Vo-Tech
6101 SE Nowata Rd.
Bartlesville, OK 74006
Ph: (918)333-2422
Free: 888-567-4610
Fax: (918)333-6797
URL: http://www.tctc.org
Description: Business college offering a small business management program.

56667 ■ Tulsa Community College
6111 E Skelly Dr.
Tulsa, OK 74135
Ph: (918)595-7000
Fax: (918)828-5429
URL: http://www.tulsacc.edu
Description: Two-year college offering a small business management program.

56668 ■ Western Technology Center - Burnes Flat Campus
621 Sooner Dr.
Burns Flat, OK 73624
Ph: (580)562-3181
Fax: (580)562-4476
Co. E-mail: lhefner@westtech.edu
URL: http://www.wtc.tec.ok.us
Description: Business college offering a small business management program.

LEGISLATIVE ASSISTANCE

56669 ■ Oklahoma Department of Commerce - Oklahoma Small Business Conference
900 N Stiles Ave.
Oklahoma City, OK 73104-3234
Ph: (405)815-6552
Free: 800-879-6552
Fax: (405)815-5142
Co. E-mail: info@okcommerce.gov
URL: http://www.okcommerce.gov
Description: Annual conference in which small business owners study legislative issues affecting their businesses, learn techniques to start or operate their businesses, and network with state, federal, and nonprofit entities offering small business assistance.

SMALL BUSINESS DEVELOPMENT CENTERS

56670 ■ Blue Mountain Community College Small Business Development Center
2411 NW Carden Ave.
Morrow Hall, Ste. M-11
Pendleton, OR 97801
Ph: (541)276-6233
Free: 888-441-7232
Fax: (541)276-6819
Co. E-mail: sbdc@bluecc.edu
URL: http://www.bluecc.edu/busind_sbdc
Description: Represents and promotes the small business sector. Provides management assistance to current and prospective small business owners. Helps to improve management skills and expand the products and services of members.

56671 ■ Chemeketa Community College Small Business Development Center
Center for Business and Industry
626 High St. NE, Ste. 210
Salem, OR 97301
Ph: (503)399-5088
Fax: (503)581-6017
Co. E-mail: sbdc@chemeketa.edu
URL: http://www.chemeketa.edu/busprofession/ccbi/sbdc
Description: Represents and promotes the small business sector. Provides management assistance to current and prospective small business owners. Helps to improve management skills and expand the products and services of members.

56672 ■ Clackamas Community College Small Business Development Center
OIT Bldg., Rm. 172
7736 SE Harmony Rd.
Milwaukie, OR 97222
Ph: (503)594-0738
Co. E-mail: bizcenter@clackamas.edu
URL: http://depts.clackamas.edu/sbdc
Description: Represents and promotes the small business sector. Provides management assistance to current and prospective small business owners. Helps to improve management skills and expand the products and services of members.

56673 ■ Clatsop Community College Small Business Development Center
1455 N Roosevelt Dr.
Seaside, OR 97138
Ph: (503)338-2402
Free: 800-206-7352
Co. E-mail: sbdc@clatsopcc.edu
URL: http://www.clatsopcc.edu
Description: Represents and promotes the small business sector. Provides management assistance to current and prospective small business owners. Helps to improve management skills and expand the products and services of members.

56674 ■ Columbia Gorge Community College Small Business Development Center
400 E Scenic Dr., Ste. 259
The Dalles, OR 97058
Ph: (541)506-6121
Fax: (541)506-6122
Co. E-mail: mmerrillr@cgcc.cc.or.us
URL: http://www.cgcc.cc.or.us/sbdc
Contact: Mary Merrill, Director
Description: Represents and promotes the small business sector. Provides management assistance to current and prospective small business owners. Helps to improve management skills and expand the products and services of members.

56675 ■ Eastern Oregon University Small Business Development Center
Integrated Services Bldg.
1607 Gekeler Ln., Rm. 148
La Grande, OR 97850
Ph: (541)962-1532
Fax: (541)962-1532
Co. E-mail: eousbdc@gmail.com
URL: http://clients.bizcenter.org/center.aspx?center=2011&subloc=0&mode=e
Description: Represents and promotes the small business sector. Provides management assistance to current and prospective small business owners. Helps to improve management skills and expand the products and services of members.

56676 ■ Hermiston Small Business Development Center
975 SE Columbia Dr.
Hermiston, OR 97838
Ph: (541)567-1800
URL: http://www.bluecc.edu/loc_herm
Description: Represents and promotes the small business sector. Provides management assistance to current and prospective small business owners. Helps to improve management skills and expand the products and services of members.

56677 ■ Klamath Community College Small Business Development Center
7390 S 6th St., Bldg. 5
Klamath Falls, OR 97603
Ph: (541)882-3521
Fax: (541)885-7758
Co. E-mail: sbdc@klamathcc.edu
URL: http://www.oit.edu/faculty-staff/small-business-development-center
Contact: Jamie Albert, Director
URL(s): www.klamathcc.edu/about/directory.aspx.
Description: Represents and promotes the small business sector. Provides management assistance to current and prospective small business owners. Helps to improve management skills and expand the products and services of members.

56678 ■ Mt. Hood Community College Small Business Development Center
501 NE Hood Ave., Ste. 240
Gresham, OR 97030
Ph: (503)491-7658
Co. E-mail: bizcenter@mhcc.edu
URL: http://www.mhcc.edu/sbdc
Description: Represents and promotes the small business sector. Provides management assistance to current and prospective small business owners. Helps to improve management skills and expand the products and services of members.

56679 ■ North County Recreation District Small Business Development Center
4301 3rd St.
Tillamook, OR 97141
Ph: (503)842-2236
Co. E-mail: nehalem@bizcenter.org
URL: http://www.tbcc.cc.or.us/~tbccbiz
Description: Represents and promotes the small business sector. Provides management assistance to current and prospective small business owners. Helps to improve management skills and expand the products and services of members.

56680 ■ Oregon Coast Community College Small Business Development Center
3788 SE High School Dr.
Lincoln City, OR 97367
Ph: (541)994-4166
Fax: (541)996-4958
URL: http://www.oregoncoastcc.org/small-business-management-program
Description: Represents and promotes the small business sector. Provides management assistance to current and prospective small business owners. Helps to improve management skills and expand the products and services of members.

56681 ■ Pendleton Small Business Development Center
Blue Mountain Community College
2411 NW Carden Ave.
Morrow Hall, Ste. M-11
Pendleton, OR 97801
Ph: (541)276-6233
Free: 888-441-7232
Fax: (541)276-6819
Co. E-mail: sbdc@bluecc.edu
URL: http://www.bluecc.edu/busind_sbdc
Contact: Art Hill, Director
Description: Represents and promotes the small business sector. Provides management assistance to current and prospective small business owners. Helps to improve management skills and expand the products and services of members.

56682 ■ Portland Community College Small Business Development Center
2025 Lloyd Center Mall
Portland, OR 97232
Co. E-mail: sbdc@pcc.edu
URL: http://www.pcc.edu/climb/small-business
Description: Represents and promotes the small business sector. Provides management assistance to current and prospective small business owners. Helps to improve management skills and expand the products and services of members.

56683 ■ Rogue Community College Small Business Development Center
214 SW 4th St.
Grants Pass, OR 97526
Ph: (541)956-7494
Co. E-mail: sbdc@roguecc.edu
URL: http://www.roguecc.edu/sbdc
Contact: Rick Leibowitz, Director
Description: Represents and promotes the small business sector. Provides management assistance to current and prospective small business owners. Helps to improve management skills and expand the products and services of members.

56684 ■ Southern Oregon University Small Business Development Center
RCC/SOU Higher Education Center
101 S Bartlett St., Rm. 101
Medford, OR 97501
Ph: (541)552-8300
Fax: (541)552-8101
URL: http://www.sou.edu/business/sbdc/index.html
Contact: Jack Vitacco, Director
Description: Represents and promotes the small business sector. Provides management assistance to current and prospective small business owners. Helps to improve management skills and expand the products and services of members.

56685 ■ Tillamook Bay Community College Small Business Development Center
4301 Third St.
Tillamook, OR 97141
Ph: (503)842-8222
Fax: (503)842-8334
URL: http://www.bizcenter.org/tillamook
Description: Represents and promotes the small business sector. Provides management assistance to current and prospective small business owners. Helps to improve management skills and expand the products and services of members.

56686 ■ Treasure Valley Community College Small Business Development Center
Albertson Center
650 College Blvd.
Ontario, OR 97914
Ph: (541)881-5762
Fax: (541)881-5511
Co. E-mail: bizcenter@tvcc.cc
URL: http://www.bizcenter.org
URL(s): www.tvcc.cc/academics/cbwcl/biz_center.cfm. **Description:** Represents and promotes the small business sector. Provides management assistance to current and prospective small business owners. Helps to improve management skills and expand the products and services of members.

SMALL BUSINESS ASSISTANCE PROGRAMS

56687 ■ Business Oregon - Global Strategy Section
121 SW Salmon St., Ste. 205
Portland, OR 97204
Ph: (503)229-5625
Fax: (503)222-5050
URL: http://www.oregon.gov/ECDD
Description: Provides assistance through one-to-one consultation, trade shows and exhibitions, export seminars, a Personalized Export Panel session, participation in an overseas trade mission, and student international market research program.

56688 ■ Oregon Department of Agriculture - Agricultural Development and Marketing Division
1207 NW Naito Pky., Ste. 104
Portland, OR 97209-2832
Ph: (503)872-6600
Fax: (503)872-6601
Co. E-mail: agmarket@oda.state.or.us
URL: http://oregon.gov/ODA/ADMD/index.shtml
Contact: Katy Coba, Director
Description: Operates a marketing program that assists in the development of new markets or in the expansion of existing markets for agricultural commodities produced or processed in the state.

56689 ■ Oregon Department of Business Development - Business Development Division
775 Summer St. NE, Ste. 200
Salem, OR 97301-1280
Ph: (503)986-0123
Fax: (503)581-5115
URL: http://econ.oregon.gov/
Contact: Tim McCabe, Director
Description: Helps to coordinate state programs with local community efforts in business expansion, recruitment, retention, and start-up efforts.

56690 ■ Oregon Department of Business Development - Business Development Division - Eastern Regional Business Development Office
775 Summer St. NE, Ste. 200
Salem, OR 97301-1280
Ph: (503)986-0123
Free: 800-233-3306
Fax: (503)581-5115
URL: http://www.oregon4biz.com/
Contact: Tim McCabe, Director
Description: Helps to coordinate state programs with local community efforts in business expansion, recruitment, retention, and start-up efforts.

56691 ■ Oregon Department of Business Development - Small Business Program
775 Summer St. NE, Ste. 200
Salem, OR 97301-1280
Ph: (503)986-0123
Fax: (503)581-5115
Co. E-mail: oregon.smallbiz@state.or.us
URL: http://www.oregon-smallbiz.com
Description: Helps small businesses resolve regulatory problems with state agencies.

56692 ■ Oregon Economic and Community Development Department
775 Summer St. NE, Ste. 200
Salem, OR 97301-1280
Ph: (503)986-0123
Fax: (503)581-5115
URL: http://econ.oregon.gov/
Description: Coordinates business, financial, job training, and community development resources for individuals, businesses, and local jurisdictions.

56693 ■ Oregon Economic and Community Development Department - Business Development Division - Southern Oregon Regional Economic Development, Inc.
673 Market St.
Medford, OR 97504
Ph: (541)773-8946
Free: 800-805-8740
Fax: (541)779-0953
Co. E-mail: colleen@soredi.org
URL: http://www.soredi.org
Contact: Ron Fox, Executive Director
Description: Helps to coordinate state programs with local community efforts in business expansion, recruitment, retention, and start-up efforts.

SCORE OFFICES

56694 ■ Central Oregon SCORE
Co. E-mail: office@centraloregonscore.org

56695 ■ Salem SCORE
Co. E-mail: score460@gmail.com

56696 ■ SCORE Portland
East Tower, 2nd Fl.
100 Middle St.
Portland, ME 04101
Ph: (207)772-1147
Fax: (207)772-5581
Co. E-mail: info@scoremaine.com
URL: http://portlandme.score.org
Description: Delivers expertise and resources to maximize the success of existing and emerging small businesses. Offers 3-hour workshops in how to start own business, writing a business plan, marketing and sales, face to face or email counseling at no cost.

56697 ■ Willamette SCORE
Co. E-mail: score@eugenechamber.com

BETTER BUSINESS BUREAUS

56698 ■ Better Business Bureau of Oregon and Western Washington
4004 SW Kruse Way Pl., Ste. 375
Lake Oswego, OR 97035
Ph: (503)212-3022
Fax: (503)212-3099
Co. E-mail: info@thebbb.org
URL: http://alaskaoregonwesternwashington.bbb.org
Contact: Robert Andrew, President
Description: Seeks to promote and foster the highest ethical relationship between businesses and the public through voluntary self-regulation, consumer and business education, and service excellence. Provides information to help consumers and businesses make informed purchasing decisions and avoid costly scams and frauds; settles consumer complaints through arbitration and other means.

CHAMBERS OF COMMERCE

56699 ■ African American Chamber of Commerce of Oregon (AACCO)
PO Box 2979
Clackamas, OR 97015-2979
Ph: (503)244-5794
Free: 800-909-2882
Fax: (503)293-2094
Co. E-mail: blackchamber@usa.net
URL: http://www.blackchamber.info
Contact: Roy Jay, President
Description: Seeks to enhance, educate, and empower individuals, businesses, and organizations regarding the economics of African American business, community, and government relations. Provides training, speakers' bureau, mentoring and first contact sources. **Founded:** 1995.

56700 ■ Albany Area Chamber of Commerce (AACC)
PO Box 548
Albany, OR 97321-0161
Ph: (503)926-1517
Fax: (503)926-7064
Co. E-mail: info@albanychamber.com
URL: http://www.albanychamber.com
Contact: Janet Steele, President
Description: Promotes business and community development in the Albany, OR area. Sponsors appreciation breakfasts, tradeshows, Albany and youth leadership, high school scholarships, distinguished services awards, and youth job fairs. **Founded:** 1904. **Publications:** *The Chamber Network* (Monthly); *Membership and Buyers Guide* (Periodic).

56701 ■ *Alliance E-Newsletter*
200 SW Market St., Ste. 1770
Portland, OR 97201
Ph: (503)224-8684
Fax: (503)323-9186
URL: http://www.portlandalliance.com
Contact: Sandra McDonough, President
Released: Monthly

56702 ■ *Alliance News*
200 SW Market St., Ste. 1770
Portland, OR 97201
Ph: (503)224-8684
Fax: (503)323-9186
URL: http://www.portlandalliance.com
Contact: Sandra McDonough, President
Released: Monthly

56703 ■ *Area Business Directory*
417 NW Adams St.
McMinnville, OR 97128
Ph: (503)472-6196
Fax: (503)472-6198
Co. E-mail: chamberinfo@mcminnville.org
URL: http://www.mcminnville.org
Contact: Phil Hutchinson, President
Released: Annual

56704 ■ Ashland Chamber of Commerce
PO Box 1360
Ashland, OR 97520-0046
Ph: (541)482-3486
Fax: (541)482-2350
Co. E-mail: dana@ashlandchamber.com
URL: http://ashlandchamber.com
Contact: Sandra Slattery, Executive Director
Description: Promotes business and community development in Ashland, OR. Sponsors Winter Wine, Food, and Arts festival and Cultural Heritage Month. **Founded:** 1889. **Publications:** *Ashland Chamber News* (Monthly).

56705 ■ *Ashland Chamber News*
PO Box 1360
Ashland, OR 97520-0046
Ph: (541)482-3486
Fax: (541)482-2350
Co. E-mail: dana@ashlandchamber.com
URL: http://ashlandchamber.com
Contact: Sandra Slattery, Executive Director
Released: Monthly **Price:** included in membership dues.

56706 ■ Astoria-Warrenton Area Chamber of Commerce (AWACC)
PO Box 176
Astoria, OR 97103-0176
Ph: (503)325-6311
Free: 800-875-6807
Fax: (503)325-9767
Co. E-mail: info@oldoregon.com
URL: http://www.oldoregon.com
Contact: Skip Hauke, Executive Director
Description: Promotes business and community development in Astoria, Warrenton, and the lower Columbia region. Sponsors Crab and Seafood Festival in April and Oktoberfish, a microbrew and seafood festival in October. **Founded:** 1873. **Publications:** *ChamberWorks* (Monthly); *Visitor Information Guide* (Annual). **Educational Activities:** Great Columbia Crossing (Annual). **Awards:** George Award (Annual).

56707 ■ Aurora Chamber of Commerce
PO Box 86
Aurora, OR 97002-0086
Ph: (503)939-0312
Co. E-mail: info@auroracolony.com
URL: http://www.auroracolony.com
Description: Promotes business and community development in Aurora, OR.

56708 ■ Baker County Unlimited Chamber of Commerce (BCCC)
490 Campbell St.
Baker City, OR 97814
Ph: (541)523-5855
Free: 800-523-1235
Fax: (541)523-9187
Co. E-mail: debi@visitbaker.com
URL: http://www.visitbaker.com
Contact: Debi Bainter, Executive Director
Description: Promotes business and community development in Baker County, OR. Sponsors community events, including Miner's Jubilee and community beautification program. Provides business referral service and visitor information; offers small business consultation services. Bestows Man, Woman and Business of the Year awards. **Publications:** *The Chamber Charge* (Monthly); *Business, Club, and Organizations* (Periodic). **Educational Activities:** Forum (Weekly).

56709 ■ Bandon Chamber of Commerce (BCC)
300 2nd St., Old Town
Bandon, OR 97411
Ph: (541)347-9616
Fax: (541)347-7006
Co. E-mail: bandoncc@mycomspan.com
URL: http://www.bandon.com
Contact: Julie Miller, Executive Director
Description: Promotes business and community development in Bandon, OR.

56710 ■ *Basin Business*
205 Riverside Dr., Ste. A
Klamath Falls, OR 97601
Ph: (541)884-5193
URL: http://www.klamath.org
Contact: Chip Massie, Executive Director
Released: Monthly **Price:** free.

56711 ■ Bay Area Chamber of Commerce (BACC)
145 Central Ave.
Coos Bay, OR 97420
Ph: (541)266-0868
Free: 800-824-8486
Fax: (541)267-6704
Co. E-mail: timmslater@oregonsbayarea.org
URL: http://www.oregonsbayarea.org
Contact: Mr. Timm Slater, Executive Director
Description: Promotes business and community development in the Coos Bay/North Bend, OR area. **Founded:** 1890. **Publications:** *Economic Profile* (Annual); *Your Bay Area Business Connection* (Monthly). **Awards:** Business of the Year (Annual); Citizen of the Year (Annual); 4 Star Customer Service Award (Quarterly).

56712 ■ Beaverton Area Chamber of Commerce (BACC)
12655 SW Center St., Ste. 140
Beaverton, OR 97005
Ph: (503)644-0123
Fax: (503)526-0349
Co. E-mail: info@beaverton.org
URL: http://www.beaverton.org
Contact: Lorraine Clarno, President
Description: Promotes business development and retention, advocate sound public policy. Provides innovative member services to sustain and enhances vibrant and diverse community. **Founded:** 1953. **Publications:** *Business Beat* (Monthly); *Business Directory* (Annual). **Educational Activities:** Beaverton Area Chamber of Commerce Luncheon (Monthly).

56713 ■ *Bend Chamber Business*
777 NW Wall St., Ste. 200
Bend, OR 97701
Ph: (541)382-3221
Free: 800-905-BEND
Fax: (541)385-9929
Co. E-mail: info@bendchamber.org
URL: http://www.bendchamber.org
Contact: Mr. Tim Casey, Executive Director
Released: Monthly **Price:** included in membership dues.

56714 ■ Bend Chamber of Commerce (BCC)
777 NW Wall St., Ste. 200
Bend, OR 97701
Ph: (541)382-3221
Free: 800-905-BEND
Fax: (541)385-9929
Co. E-mail: info@bendchamber.org
URL: http://www.bendchamber.org
Contact: Mr. Tim Casey, Executive Director
Description: Promotes business and community development in the Bend, OR area. **Founded:** 1926. **Publications:** *Bend Chamber Business* (Monthly). **Educational Activities:** City Club Forum (Monthly). **Awards:** Citizen of the Year (Annual); Distinguished Business of the Year (Annual); Large Business of the Year (Annual); Small Business of the Year (Annual).

56715 ■ Brookings-Harbor Chamber of Commerce
16330 Lower Harbor Rd.
Brookings, OR 97415
Ph: (541)469-3181
Free: 800-535-9469
Co. E-mail: info@brookingsharborchamber.com
URL: http://www.brookingsor.com
Description: Seeks to help create and maintain a viable economy that provides all citizens with a high quality of life. Promotes business and community development in the Brookings, OR area. Sponsors the Azalea Festival. **Founded:** 1951. **Publications:** *Brookings Harbor Light* (Monthly); *Business Review*; *Calendar of Events* (Annual); *Restaurant and Dining Guide* (Periodic).

56716 ■ *Brookings Harbor Light*
16330 Lower Harbor Rd.
Brookings, OR 97415
Ph: (541)469-3181
Free: 800-535-9469
Co. E-mail: info@brookingsharborchamber.com
URL: http://www.brookingsor.com
Released: Monthly

56717 ■ *Business Beat*
12655 SW Center St., Ste. 140
Beaverton, OR 97005
Ph: (503)644-0123
Fax: (503)526-0349
Co. E-mail: info@beaverton.org
URL: http://www.beaverton.org
Contact: Lorraine Clarno, President
Released: Monthly

56718 ■ *Business Beat*
290 Hwy. 101
Florence, OR 97439
Ph: (541)997-3128
Fax: (541)997-4101
Co. E-mail: cal@florencechamber.com
URL: http://www.florencechamber.com
Contact: Cal Applebee, Executive Director
Released: Monthly **Price:** free.

56719 ■ *Business, Club, and Organizations*
490 Campbell St.
Baker City, OR 97814
Ph: (541)523-5855
Free: 800-523-1235
Fax: (541)523-9187
Co. E-mail: debi@visitbaker.com
URL: http://www.visitbaker.com
Contact: Debi Bainter, Executive Director
Released: Periodic

56720 ■ *Business and Community Directory*
PO Box 298
Estacada, OR 97023-0298
Ph: (503)630-3483
Co. E-mail: info@estacadachamber.org
URL: http://estacadachamber.net/main
Contact: Jordan Winthrop, President
Released: Annual

56721 ■ *Business and Community Directory*
1110 Commercial St. NE
Salem, OR 97301-1020
Ph: (503)581-1466
Fax: (503)581-0972
Co. E-mail: info@salemchamber.org
URL: http://www.salemchamber.org
Contact: Jason Brandt, Chief Executive Officer
Released: Annual

56722 ■ *Business Directory*
12655 SW Center St., Ste. 140
Beaverton, OR 97005
Ph: (503)644-0123
Fax: (503)526-0349
Co. E-mail: info@beaverton.org
URL: http://www.beaverton.org
Contact: Lorraine Clarno, President
Released: Annual

56723 ■ *Business Directory*
415 S Hwy. 395
Hermiston, OR 97838
Ph: (541)567-6151
Fax: (541)564-9109
Co. E-mail: info@hermistonchamber.com
URL: http://www.hermistonchamber.com
Contact: Debbie Pedro, Executive Director
Released: Annual

56724 ■ *Business Informer*
191 SE 2nd Ave.
Canby, OR 97013
Ph: (503)266-4600
Fax: (503)266-4338
Co. E-mail: chamber@canby.com
URL: http://www.canbyareachamber.org
Contact: Beverly Doolittle, Executive Director
Released: Monthly **Price:** included in membership dues.

56725 ■ *Business News*
7740 SE Harmony Rd.
Milwaukie, OR 97222-1269
Ph: (503)654-7777
Fax: (503)653-9515
Co. E-mail: web1@yourchamber.com
URL: http://www.yourchamber.com
Contact: David A. Kelly, President
Released: Monthly

56726 ■ *Business News*
446 SW 7th St.
Redmond, OR 97756
Ph: (541)923-5191
Fax: (541)923-6442
Co. E-mail: info@visitredmondoregon.com
URL: http://www.visitredmondoregon.com
Contact: Dustin Hewitt, President
Released: Monthly; every 1st Wednesday.

56727 ■ *Business News*
1110 Commercial St. NE
Salem, OR 97301-1020
Ph: (503)581-1466
Fax: (503)581-0972
Co. E-mail: info@salemchamber.org
URL: http://www.salemchamber.org
Contact: Jason Brandt, Chief Executive Officer
Released: Monthly

56728 ■ *Business and Professional Directory*
7740 SE Harmony Rd.
Milwaukie, OR 97222-1269
Ph: (503)654-7777
Fax: (503)653-9515
Co. E-mail: web1@yourchamber.com
URL: http://www.yourchamber.com
Contact: David A. Kelly, President
Released: Annual

56729 ■ *Business Review*
16330 Lower Harbor Rd.
Brookings, OR 97415
Ph: (541)469-3181
Free: 800-535-9469
Co. E-mail: info@brookingsharborchamber.com
URL: http://www.brookingsor.com

56730 ■ *Business Review*
101 E 8th St.
Medford, OR 97501-7201
Ph: (541)779-4847
Fax: (541)776-4808
Co. E-mail: business@medfordchamber.com
URL: http://www.medfordchamber.com
Contact: Brad S. Hicks, President
Released: Monthly

56731 ■ *BusinessALERT*
101 E 8th St.
Medford, OR 97501-7201
Ph: (541)779-4847
Fax: (541)776-4808
Co. E-mail: business@medfordchamber.com
URL: http://www.medfordchamber.com
Contact: Brad S. Hicks, President
Released: Quarterly

56732 ■ *Calendar of Events*
16330 Lower Harbor Rd.
Brookings, OR 97415
Ph: (541)469-3181
Free: 800-535-9469
Co. E-mail: info@brookingsharborchamber.com
URL: http://www.brookingsor.com
Released: Annual

56733 ■ Canby Area Chamber of Commerce (CACC)
191 SE 2nd Ave.
Canby, OR 97013
Ph: (503)266-4600
Fax: (503)266-4338
Co. E-mail: chamber@canby.com
URL: http://www.canbyareachamber.org
Contact: Beverly Doolittle, Executive Director
Description: Promotes business and community development in the Canby, OR area. Sponsors annual holiday lighting competition, golf tournament and produces annual collectible Christmas ornament Monthly luncheon. **Founded:** 1947. **Publications:** *Business Informer* (Monthly); *Canby Area Chamber Directory and Buyer's Guide* (Periodic). **Awards:** Beautification Award (Annual); Community Caring Award (Annual); Educational Staff Award (Annual); Educator Award (Annual); Job Growth Award (Annual).

56734 ■ *Canby Area Chamber Directory and Buyer's Guide*
191 SE 2nd Ave.
Canby, OR 97013
Ph: (503)266-4600
Fax: (503)266-4338
Co. E-mail: chamber@canby.com
URL: http://www.canbyareachamber.org
Contact: Beverly Doolittle, Executive Director
Released: Periodic

56735 ■ Cannon Beach Chamber of Commerce (CBCC)
PO Box 64
Cannon Beach, OR 97110
Ph: (503)436-2623
Fax: (503)436-0910
Co. E-mail: chamber@cannonbeach.org
URL: http://www.cannonbeach.org
Contact: Carol Hungerford, President
Description: Promotes business and community development in Cannon Beach, OR. **Founded:** 1938. **Publications:** *Shore Lines* (Monthly).

56736 ■ *Catalyst*
29600 SW Park Pl.
Wilsonville, OR 97070
Ph: (503)682-0411
Free: 800-647-3843
Fax: (503)682-4189
Co. E-mail: info@wilsonvillechamber.com
URL: http://www.wilsonvillechamber.com
Contact: Wendy Veliz Buck, President
Released: Monthly **Price:** $70.

56737 ■ Central Point Area Chamber of Commerce
150 Manzanita St.
Central Point, OR 97502
Ph: (541)664-5301
Fax: (541)664-3667
URL: http://www.centralpointchamber.org
Contact: Cindy Hudson, Executive Director
Description: Promotes business and community development in Central Point, OR.

56738 ■ *Chamber Business Directory*
PO Box 536
Sandy, OR 97055
Ph: (503)668-4006
Fax: (503)668-3549
Co. E-mail: chamber@sandyoregonchamber.org
URL: http://www.sandyoregonchamber.org
Contact: Mitch Speck, Executive Director
Released: Annual **Price:** free.

56739 ■ *The Chamber Charge*
490 Campbell St.
Baker City, OR 97814
Ph: (541)523-5855
Free: 800-523-1235
Fax: (541)523-9187
Co. E-mail: debi@visitbaker.com
URL: http://www.visitbaker.com
Contact: Debi Bainter, Executive Director
Released: Monthly **Price:** included in membership dues.

56740 ■ *Chamber Chatter*
PO Box 217
Oakridge, OR 97463-0217
Ph: (541)782-4146
Fax: (541)782-1081
Co. E-mail: info@oakridgechamber.com
URL: http://www.oakridgechamber.com
Contact: Sandy Price, President
Released: Monthly **Price:** free.

56741 ■ *Chamber Connection*
415 S Hwy. 395
Hermiston, OR 97838
Ph: (541)567-6151
Fax: (541)564-9109
Co. E-mail: info@hermistonchamber.com
URL: http://www.hermistonchamber.com
Contact: Debbie Pedro, Executive Director
Released: Monthly

56742 ■ Chamber of Medford - Jackson County
101 E 8th St.
Medford, OR 97501-7201
Ph: (541)779-4847
Fax: (541)776-4808
Co. E-mail: business@medfordchamber.com
URL: http://www.medfordchamber.com
Contact: Brad S. Hicks, President
Description: Promotes business and community development in the Medford, OR area. Sponsors Pear Blossom Golf Tournament. **Founded:** 1895. **Publications:** *Business Review* (Monthly); *BusinessALERT* (Quarterly); *Community Profile and Membership Directory* (Annual).

56743 ■ *The Chamber Network*
PO Box 548
Albany, OR 97321-0161
Ph: (503)926-1517
Fax: (503)926-7064
Co. E-mail: info@albanychamber.com
URL: http://www.albanychamber.com
Contact: Janet Steele, President
Released: Monthly

56744 ■ *Chamber News*
484 N Broadway
Burns, OR 97720
Ph: (541)573-2636
Co. E-mail: info@harneycounty.com
URL: http://www.harneycounty.com
Contact: Jen Hoke, Executive Director
Released: Quarterly **Price:** included in membership dues.

56745 ■ *Chamber News*
700 E Gibbs, Ste. C
Cottage Grove, OR 97424
Ph: (541)942-2411
Free: 888-832-2045
URL: http://www.cgchamber.com
Released: Monthly **Price:** included in membership dues.

56746 ■ *Chamber News*
PO Box 536
Sandy, OR 97055
Ph: (503)668-4006
Fax: (503)668-3549
Co. E-mail: chamber@sandyoregonchamber.org
URL: http://www.sandyoregonchamber.org
Contact: Mitch Speck, Executive Director
Released: Periodic

56747 ■ *Chamber News*
1530 6th St.
Umatilla, OR 97882
Ph: (541)922-4825
Fax: (541)922-4825
Co. E-mail: karen@umatillachamber.net
URL: http://www.umatillaoregonchamber.org
Contact: Libby Bovent, President
Released: Monthly

56748 ■ *Chamber News*
274 SW 4th St.
Madras, OR 97741
Ph: (541)475-2350
Free: 800-967-3564
Fax: (541)475-4341
Co. E-mail: office@madraschamber.com
URL: http://www.madraschamber.com
Contact: Joe Krenowicz, Executive Director
Released: Monthly **Price:** free.

56749 ■ *Chamber Notes*
115 N College St., Ste. 2
Newberg, OR 97132-2858

Ph: (503)538-2014
Fax: (503)538-2463
Co. E-mail: sheryl@chehalemvalley.org
URL: http://www.chehalemvalley.org/web
Contact: Sheryl Kelsh, President
Released: Monthly **Price:** included in membership dues.

56750 ■ *Chamber Profiles*
1995 NW Vine St.
Grants Pass, OR 97528
Ph: (541)476-7717
Fax: (541)476-9574
Co. E-mail: gpcoc@grantspasschamber.org
URL: http://www.grantspasschamber.org
Contact: Colene Martin, President
Released: Annual

56751 ■ *Chamber Times*
207 Depot St.
La Grande, OR 97850
Ph: (541)963-8588
Free: 800-848-9969
Fax: (541)963-3936
Co. E-mail: info@unioncountychamber.org
URL: http://www.unioncountychamber.org
Contact: Judy Hector, Chief Executive Officer
Released: Monthly **Price:** free.

56752 ■ *Chamber Update*
1995 NW Vine St.
Grants Pass, OR 97528
Ph: (541)476-7717
Fax: (541)476-9574
Co. E-mail: gpcoc@grantspasschamber.org
URL: http://www.grantspasschamber.org
Contact: Colene Martin, President
Released: Monthly

56753 ■ *Chamber Update*
2194 Columbia Blvd.
St. Helens, OR 97051
Ph: (503)397-0685
Fax: (503)397-7196
Co. E-mail: mgr@sccchamber.org
URL: http://www.sccchamber.org
Contact: Tina Kammerzelt, Manager
Released: Monthly **Price:** included in membership dues.

56754 ■ *Chamber Update*
1401 Willamette St.
Eugene, OR 97401
Ph: (541)484-1314
Fax: (541)484-4942
Co. E-mail: admin@eugenechamber.com
URL: http://www.eugenechamber.com/cwt/external/wcpages/index.aspx
Contact: David Hauser, President
Released: Monthly

56755 ■ *Chamber Voice*
720 E Port Marina Dr.
Hood River, OR 97031
Ph: (541)386-2000
Free: 800-366-3530
Co. E-mail: andrewm@skylighttheater.com
URL: http://www.hoodriver.org
Contact: Andrew McElderry, President
Released: Monthly

56756 ■ *ChamberWire*
PO Box 226
Oregon City, OR 97045
Ph: (503)656-1619
Fax: (503)656-2274
Co. E-mail: chamberinfo@oregoncity.org
URL: http://www.oregoncity.org
Contact: Amber Holveck, Executive Director
Released: Monthly

56757 ■ *ChamberWorks*
PO Box 176
Astoria, OR 97103-0176
Ph: (503)325-6311
Free: 800-875-6807

Fax: (503)325-9767
Co. E-mail: info@oldoregon.com
URL: http://www.oldoregon.com
Contact: Skip Hauke, Executive Director
Released: Monthly **Price:** included in membership dues.

56758 ■ Chehalem Valley Chamber of Commerce
115 N College St., Ste. 2
Newberg, OR 97132-2858
Ph: (503)538-2014
Fax: (503)538-2463
Co. E-mail: sheryl@chehalemvalley.org
URL: http://www.chehalemvalley.org/web
Contact: Sheryl Kelsh, President
Description: Promotes business and community development in the Newberg, Dundee, and St. Paul, OR area. **Founded:** 1941. **Publications:** *Chamber Notes* (Monthly). **Educational Activities:** Harvest Festival (Annual).

56759 ■ Clatskanie Chamber of Commerce
PO Box 635
Clatskanie, OR 97016-0635
Ph: (503)728-2502
Co. E-mail: webmaster@clatskanie.com
URL: http://www.clatskanie.com/chamber
Contact: Debi Hazen, President
Description: Promotes business and community development in Clatskanie, OR. **Publications:** *Clatskanie Chamber Newsletter* (Monthly).

56760 ■ *Clatskanie Chamber Newsletter*
PO Box 635
Clatskanie, OR 97016-0635
Ph: (503)728-2502
Co. E-mail: webmaster@clatskanie.com
URL: http://www.clatskanie.com/chamber
Contact: Debi Hazen, President
Released: Monthly

56761 ■ *Communique*
555 SW Coast Hwy.
Newport, OR 97365-4934
Ph: (541)265-8801
Free: 800-COA-ST44
Fax: (541)265-5589
Co. E-mail: info@newportchamber.org
URL: http://www.newportchamber.org
Contact: Don Lindly, President
Released: Monthly

56762 ■ *Community Business Directory*
3705 Hwy. 101 N
Tillamook, OR 97141
Ph: (503)842-7525
Fax: (503)842-7526
Co. E-mail: tillchamber@oregoncoast.com
URL: http://www.tillamookchamber.org
Contact: Justin Aufdermauer, Executive Director
Released: Annual **Price:** included in membership dues.

56763 ■ *Community Profile and Membership Directory*
101 E 8th St.
Medford, OR 97501-7201
Ph: (541)779-4847
Fax: (541)776-4808
Co. E-mail: business@medfordchamber.com
URL: http://www.medfordchamber.com
Contact: Brad S. Hicks, President
Released: Annual

56764 ■ Coquille Chamber of Commerce and Visitor Information Center
119 N Birch St.
Coquille, OR 97423
Ph: (541)396-3414
Co. E-mail: coquillechamber@mycomspan.com
URL: http://coquillechamber.net
Description: Works to promote and foster a healthy economy in the Coquille area by supporting citizens and the business community. Places an emphasis on quality in business and life in the community, as well as willingness to invest in the area's future. **Founded:** 1924.

56765 ■ Cornelius Chamber of Commerce
120 N 13th Ave.
Cornelius, OR 97113
Ph: (503)359-4037
Fax: (503)992-1997
Co. E-mail: president@corneliuschamber.com
URL: http://www.corneliuschamber.org
Contact: Ms. Jenny Garner, Executive Director
Description: Promotes business and community development in Cornelius, OR.

56766 ■ Corvallis-Benton Chamber Coalition
420 NW Second St.
Corvallis, OR 97330-6442
Ph: (541)757-1505
Fax: (541)766-2996
Co. E-mail: info@cbchambercoalition.com
URL: http://www.cbchambercoalition.com
Contact: Mike McInally, Chairman
Description: Promotes business and community development in the Corvallis, OR area. **Founded:** 1930.

56767 ■ Cottage Grove Area Chamber of Commerce
700 E Gibbs, Ste. C
Cottage Grove, OR 97424
Ph: (541)942-2411
Free: 888-832-2045
URL: http://www.cgchamber.com
Description: Promotes business and community development in Cottage Grove, OR. **Founded:** 1949. **Publications:** *Chamber News* (Monthly). **Awards:** First Citizen and Business of the Year (Annual).

56768 ■ Creswell Chamber of Commerce
PO Box 577
Creswell, OR 97426
Ph: (541)895-4398
Co. E-mail: info@creswellchamber.com
URL: http://www.creswellchamber.com
Contact: Arlene Macauley, Administrator
Description: Promotes business and community activities in Creswell such as the July 4th Celebration and the Annual Banquet. **Founded:** 1964. **Telecommunication Services:** creswell-cc@centurytel.net.

56769 ■ Crooked River Ranch Chamber of Commerce
PO Box 1502
Crooked River, OR 97760
Ph: (541)923-2679
Fax: (541)923-2755
Co. E-mail: info@crrchamber.com
URL: http://www.crrchamber.com
Contact: Hope A. Johnson, Executive Director
Description: Promotes business development for members. Works with other community organizations to improve quality of life. **Founded:** 1997. **Publications:** *The Zephyr* (Monthly).

56770 ■ *Dallas Area*
119 SW Court St.
Dallas, OR 97338
Ph: (503)623-2564
Fax: (503)623-8936
Co. E-mail: info@dallasoregon.org
URL: http://www.dallasoregon.org
Contact: Chelsea Pope, Executive Director
Released: Biennial **Price:** free.

56771 ■ Dallas Area Chamber of Commerce
119 SW Court St.
Dallas, OR 97338
Ph: (503)623-2564
Fax: (503)623-8936
Co. E-mail: info@dallasoregon.org
URL: http://www.dallasoregon.org
Contact: Chelsea Pope, Executive Director
Description: Promotes the Dallas Area as an excellent place to live, work, play and do business. **Founded:** 1926. **Publications:** *Dallas Area* (Biennial); *Dallas Area* (Biennial). **Awards:** Business of the Year (Annual); Exceptional Family (Annual); First Citizen (Annual); Good Samaritan (Annual); Junior First Citizen (Annual); Most Improved Business of the Year (Annual); Outstanding Organization (Annual); Small Business of the Year (Annual).

56772 ■ *Dining and Shopping Guide*
4039 NW Logan Rd.
Lincoln City, OR 97367
Ph: (541)994-3070
Fax: (541)994-8339
Co. E-mail: info@lcchamber.com
URL: http://lcchamber.com
Contact: Lori Arce-Torres, President
Released: Annual

56773 ■ *Economic Profile*
145 Central Ave.
Coos Bay, OR 97420
Ph: (541)266-0868
Free: 800-824-8486
Fax: (541)267-6704
Co. E-mail: timmslater@oregonsbayarea.org
URL: http://www.oregonsbayarea.org
Contact: Mr. Timm Slater, Executive Director
Released: Annual

56774 ■ Estacada - Clackamas River Area Chamber of Commerce (ECRACC)
PO Box 298
Estacada, OR 97023-0298
Ph: (503)630-3483
Co. E-mail: info@estacadachamber.org
URL: http://estacadachamber.net/main
Contact: Jordan Winthrop, President
Description: Promotes business and community development in the Estacada, OR area. Sponsors local celebrations and competitions. Operates the Visitor Information Services Complex. **Scope:** Oregon tourism, Oregon history, Estacada history. **Founded:** 1956. **Subscriptions:** 75 articles maps photographs. **Publications:** *Business and Community Directory* (Annual); *Historical Estacada Walking Tour.* **Educational Activities:** Estacada - Clackamas River Area Chamber of Commerce Seminar (Monthly).

56775 ■ Eugene Area Chamber of Commerce
1401 Willamette St.
Eugene, OR 97401
Ph: (541)484-1314
Fax: (541)484-4942
Co. E-mail: admin@eugenechamber.com
URL: http://www.eugenechamber.com/cwt/external/wcpages/index.aspx
Contact: David Hauser, President
Description: Promotes a healthy local economy within the Eugene community by influencing business success, public policy and community development. **Publications:** *Chamber Update* (Monthly).

56776 ■ Florence Area Chamber of Commerce (FACC)
290 Hwy. 101
Florence, OR 97439
Ph: (541)997-3128
Fax: (541)997-4101
Co. E-mail: cal@florencechamber.com
URL: http://www.florencechamber.com
Contact: Cal Applebee, Executive Director
Description: Promotes business and community development in the Florence, OR area. **Founded:** 1958. **Publications:** *Business Beat* (Monthly).

56777 ■ *Focus on Business*
3705 Hwy. 101 N
Tillamook, OR 97141
Ph: (503)842-7525
Fax: (503)842-7526
Co. E-mail: tillchamber@oregoncoast.com
URL: http://www.tillamookchamber.org
Contact: Justin Aufdermauer, Executive Director
Released: Monthly **Price:** included in membership dues.

56778 ■ *Food, Lodging and Service Guide*
PO Box 217
Oakridge, OR 97463-0217
Ph: (541)782-4146
Fax: (541)782-1081
Co. E-mail: info@oakridgechamber.com
URL: http://www.oakridgechamber.com
Contact: Sandy Price, President

56779 ■ Forest Grove Chamber of Commerce (FGCC)
2417 Pacific Ave.
Forest Grove, OR 97116-2498
Ph: (503)357-3006
Fax: (503)357-2367
Co. E-mail: info@visitforestgrove.com
URL: http://www.fgchamber.org
Contact: Teri Koerner, Executive Director
Description: Promotes business and community development in the Forest Grove, OR area. **Founded:** 1917. **Telecommunication Services:** info@fgchamber.org.

56780 ■ *The Gem*
PO Box 728
Yachats, OR 97498
Ph: (541)547-3530
Free: 800-929-0477
Fax: (541)547-4930
Co. E-mail: info@yachats.org
URL: http://www.yachats.org

56781 ■ Gold Beach Chamber of Commerce
PO Box 489
Gold Beach, OR 97444
Ph: (541)247-0923
Fax: (541)247-4394
Co. E-mail: info@goldbeachchamber.com
URL: http://www.goldbeachchamber.com
Contact: Sandy Vieira, Executive Director
Description: Promotes business and community development in the Gold Beach, OR area. Sponsors America's Wild Rivers Coast Art, fireworks display, and seafood and wine festivals. Holds annual business conference. **Founded:** 1927. **Publications:** *Gold Beach Chamber of Commerce Annual Business Directory* (Annual); *Gold Beach Chamber of Commerce Annual Business Directory* (Annual). **Awards:** Business of the Year (Annual); Citizen of the Year (Annual); Volunteer of the Year (Annual).

56782 ■ *Gold Beach Chamber of Commerce Annual Business Directory*
PO Box 489
Gold Beach, OR 97444
Ph: (541)247-0923
Fax: (541)247-4394
Co. E-mail: info@goldbeachchamber.com
URL: http://www.goldbeachchamber.com
Contact: Sandy Vieira, Executive Director
Released: Annual

56783 ■ Grant County Chamber of Commerce (GCCC)
301 W Main St.
John Day, OR 97845-1026
Ph: (541)575-0547
Free: 800-769-5664
Co. E-mail: gcadmin@gcoregonlive.com
URL: http://www.gcoregonlive.com
Contact: Tammy Bremner, President
Description: Promotes business and community development in Grant County, OR.

56784 ■ Grants Pass - Josephine County Chamber of Commerce (GPJCCC)
1995 NW Vine St.
Grants Pass, OR 97528
Ph: (541)476-7717
Fax: (541)476-9574
Co. E-mail: gpcoc@grantspasschamber.org
URL: http://www.grantspasschamber.org
Contact: Colene Martin, President
Description: Encourages, assists, and promotes the business community in the Josephine County, OR area through programs and services. Sponsors concerts in the park. **Founded:** 1905. **Publications:** *Chamber Profiles* (Annual); *Chamber Update* (Monthly).

56785 ■ Greater Hermiston Chamber of Commerce (GHCC)
415 S Hwy. 395
Hermiston, OR 97838
Ph: (541)567-6151

Fax: (541)564-9109
Co. E-mail: info@hermistonchamber.com
URL: http://www.hermistonchamber.com
Contact: Debbie Pedro, Executive Director
Description: Promotes business growth, economic diversification, and livability in the Greater Hermiston, OR area. Sponsors Wine and Cheese Festival. **Founded:** 1933. **Publications:** *Business Directory* (Annual); *Chamber Connection* (Monthly); *Greater Hermiston Chamber of Commerce--Member Business Directory.* **Educational Activities:** DSA Banquet (Annual). **Telecommunication Services:** debbie@hermistonchamber.com.

56786 ■ Greater Newport Chamber of Commerce (GNCC)
555 SW Coast Hwy.
Newport, OR 97365-4934
Ph: (541)265-8801
Free: 800-COA-ST44
Fax: (541)265-5589
Co. E-mail: info@newportchamber.org
URL: http://www.newportchamber.org
Contact: Don Lindly, President
Description: Promotes business and community development in Newport, OR. Sponsors competitions and annual festival. **Founded:** 1939. **Publications:** *Communique* (Monthly); *Pocket Guide* (Annual).

56787 ■ Gresham Area Chamber of Commerce (GACC)
701 NE Hood Ave.
Gresham, OR 97030
Ph: (503)665-1131
Fax: (503)666-1041
Co. E-mail: gacc@greshamchamber.org
URL: http://www.greshamchamber.org
Contact: Keith Evans, President
Description: Promotes business and community development in eastern Multnomah County, OR. Participates in charitable activities, including Business Education Partnership, and Excellence in Business. Sponsors Windjam Music Festival, Mt. Hood Jazz Festival, annual children's week, and Christmas Festival. **Founded:** 1931.

56788 ■ Harney County Chamber of Commerce (HCCC)
484 N Broadway
Burns, OR 97720
Ph: (541)573-2636
Co. E-mail: info@harneycounty.com
URL: http://www.harneycounty.com
Contact: Jen Hoke, Executive Director
Description: Promotes economic well being through leadership and advocacy for business, industry, education and tourism. **Publications:** *Chamber News* (Quarterly).

56789 ■ Heppner Chamber of Commerce
PO Box 1232
Heppner, OR 97836
Ph: (541)676-5536
Fax: (541)676-9650
Co. E-mail: heppnerchamber@centurytel.net
URL: http://www.heppnerchamber.com
Contact: Sheryll Bates, Executive Director
Description: Promotes business and community development in the Heppner, Oregon area. **Founded:** 1954.

56790 ■ Hillsboro Chamber of Commerce
5193 NE Elam Young Pkwy., Ste. A
Hillsboro, OR 97124
Ph: (503)648-1102
Fax: (503)681-0535
Co. E-mail: info@hillchamber.org
URL: http://www.hillchamber.org
Contact: Deanna Palm, President
Description: Promotes business and community development in the Hillsboro, OR area. Convention/Meeting: none. **Publications:** *Hillsboro Chamber of Commerce Business Directory* (Annual); *Home Business Review* (Bimonthly); *Newsline* (Monthly).

56791 ■ *Hillsboro Chamber of Commerce Business Directory*
5193 NE Elam Young Pkwy., Ste. A
Hillsboro, OR 97124

Ph: (503)648-1102
Fax: (503)681-0535
Co. E-mail: info@hillchamber.org
URL: http://www.hillchamber.org
Contact: Deanna Palm, President
Released: Annual

56792 ■ Hispanic Metropolitan Chamber (HMC)
PO Box 1837
Portland, OR 97207
Ph: (503)222-0280
Fax: (503)243-5597
Co. E-mail: info@hmccoregon.com
URL: http://www.hmccoregon.com
Contact: Gale Castillo, President
Description: Works with all the members of the community to achieve the economic advancement of Hispanic-owned businesses in OR and Southwest WA. **Founded:** 1994. **Awards:** Hispanic Metropolitan Chamber Scholarship (Annual).

56793 ■ *Historical Estacada Walking Tour*
PO Box 298
Estacada, OR 97023-0298
Ph: (503)630-3483
Co. E-mail: info@estacadachamber.org
URL: http://estacadachamber.net/main
Contact: Jordan Winthrop, President

56794 ■ *Home Business Review*
5193 NE Elam Young Pkwy., Ste. A
Hillsboro, OR 97124
Ph: (503)648-1102
Fax: (503)681-0535
Co. E-mail: info@hillchamber.org
URL: http://www.hillchamber.org
Contact: Deanna Palm, President
Released: Bimonthly

56795 ■ Hood River County Chamber of Commerce (HRCCC)
720 E Port Marina Dr.
Hood River, OR 97031
Ph: (541)386-2000
Free: 800-366-3530
Co. E-mail: andrewm@skylighttheater.com
URL: http://www.hoodriver.org
Contact: Andrew McElderry, President
Description: Promotes business and community development in the Hood River County, OR area. Sponsors Harvestfest and Blossom Festival, and Cross Channel Swim. **Founded:** 1924. **Publications:** *Chamber Voice* (Monthly).

56796 ■ *Hot Deals*
1575 Main St.
Sweet Home, OR 97386
Ph: (541)367-6186
Co. E-mail: info@sweethomechamber.org
URL: http://www.sweethomechamber.org
Contact: Andrea Culy, Executive Director
Released: Monthly

56797 ■ *Hotline*
12345 SW Main St.
Tigard, OR 97223
Ph: (503)639-1656
Fax: (503)639-6302
Co. E-mail: debi@tigardchamber.org
URL: http://www.tigardchamber.org/site
Contact: Debi Mollahan, Chief Executive Officer
Released: Monthly

56798 ■ Jacksonville Chamber of Commerce and Visitor Center
PO Box 33
Jacksonville, OR 97530
Ph: (541)899-8118
Co. E-mail: chamber@jacksonvilleoregon.org
URL: http://www.jacksonvilleoregon.org
Description: Promotes business and community development in Jacksonville, OR. Sponsors annual Whole Town Garage Sale, Victorian Christmas Celebration, Chinese New Year, Block Party, Fritillaria Festival, Harvest Auction, and Harvest-Halloween Parade. **Founded:** 1974. **Awards:** Person of the Year (Annual).

56799 ■ Junction City-Harrisburg Chamber of Commerce
341 W 6th St.
Junction City, OR 97448-1235
Ph: (541)998-6154
Fax: (541)998-1037
Co. E-mail: info@jch-chamber.org
URL: http://www.jch-chamber.org/chamber/index.htm
Contact: Ms. Rick Kissock, Executive Director
Description: Promotes business and community development in the Junction City-Harrisburg, OR area. **Founded:** 1955.

56800 ■ Keizer Chamber of Commerce and Visitor Center
6075 Ulali Dr. NE Ste. 102
Keizer, OR 97303
Ph: (503)393-9111
Fax: (503)393-1003
Co. E-mail: christine@keizerchamber.com
URL: http://www.keizerchamber.com
Contact: Christine Dieker, Executive Director
Description: Promotes business and community development in Keizer, OR area.

56801 ■ Klamath County Chamber of Commerce (KCCC)
205 Riverside Dr., Ste. A
Klamath Falls, OR 97601
Ph: (541)884-5193
URL: http://www.klamath.org
Contact: Chip Massie, Executive Director
Description: Promotes business and community development in Klamath County, OR. **Founded:** 1905. **Publications:** *Basin Business* (Monthly).

56802 ■ La Pine Chamber of Commerce
PO Box 616
La Pine, OR 97739
Ph: (541)536-9771
Co. E-mail: director@lapine.org
URL: http://www.lapine.org
Contact: Ann Gawith, Executive Director
Description: Promotes business and community development in La Pine, OR area.

56803 ■ Lake County Chamber of Commerce
126 N St. E
Lakeview, OR 97630-1536
Ph: (541)947-6040
Free: 877-947-6040
Fax: (541)947-4892
Co. E-mail: ahenry@lakecountychamber.org
URL: http://www.lakecountychamber.org
Contact: Audrey Henry, Executive Director
Description: Promotes business and community development in Lake County, OR. **Founded:** 1945.

56804 ■ Lakeside Chamber of Commerce
PO Box 333
Lakeside, OR 97449
Ph: (541)759-3981
Co. E-mail: lkchamber@presys.com
URL: http://www.lakesideoregonchambers.com
Contact: Jonie Reeder, Vice President
Description: Promotes business and community development in Lakeside, OR area.

56805 ■ *Largest Employers in the Portland/ Vancouver Metropolitan Area*
200 SW Market St., Ste. 1770
Portland, OR 97201
Ph: (503)224-8684
Fax: (503)323-9186
URL: http://www.portlandalliance.com
Contact: Sandra McDonough, President

56806 ■ *Lincoln City Business Resource Guide and Membership Directory*
4039 NW Logan Rd.
Lincoln City, OR 97367
Ph: (541)994-3070
Fax: (541)994-8339
Co. E-mail: info@lcchamber.com
URL: http://lcchamber.com
Contact: Lori Arce-Torres, President
Released: Annual

56807 ■ Lincoln City Chamber of Commerce
4039 NW Logan Rd.
Lincoln City, OR 97367
Ph: (541)994-3070
Fax: (541)994-8339
Co. E-mail: info@lcchamber.com
URL: http://lcchamber.com
Contact: Lori Arce-Torres, President
Description: Promotes business and community development in Lincoln City, OR. Sponsors Community Days Banquet, Holiday Gala, a weekly forum, Business Trade Show, "A Bite at the Beach" event and "Radio Days". **Founded:** 1950. **Publications:** *Dining and Shopping Guide* (Annual); *Trade Winds*; *Lincoln City Business Resource Guide and Membership Directory* (Annual).

56808 ■ Madras-Jefferson County Chamber of Commerce
274 SW 4th St.
Madras, OR 97741
Ph: (541)475-2350
Free: 800-967-3564
Fax: (541)475-4341
Co. E-mail: office@madraschamber.com
URL: http://www.madraschamber.com
Contact: Joe Krenowicz, Executive Director
Description: Promotes business and community development in Jefferson County, OR area. **Publications:** *Chamber News* (Monthly).

56809 ■ McMinnville Area Chamber of Commerce (GMCC)
417 NW Adams St.
McMinnville, OR 97128
Ph: (503)472-6196
Fax: (503)472-6198
Co. E-mail: chamberinfo@mcminnville.org
URL: http://www.mcminnville.org
Contact: Phil Hutchinson, President
Description: Promotes business and community development in the greater McMinnville, OR area. Sponsors annual Turkey Rama Festival in July. **Founded:** 1915. **Publications:** *Area Business Directory* (Annual).

56810 ■ *Meeting and Tour Planner Guide*
876 SW 4th Ave.
Ontario, OR 97914
Ph: (541)889-8012
Free: 866-989-8012
Co. E-mail: info@ontariochamber.com
URL: http://www.ontariochamber.com
Contact: Dale Jeffries, Chairman

56811 ■ *Membership and Buyers Guide*
PO Box 548
Albany, OR 97321-0161
Ph: (503)926-1517
Fax: (503)926-7064
Co. E-mail: info@albanychamber.com
URL: http://www.albanychamber.com
Contact: Janet Steele, President
Released: Periodic

56812 ■ *Membership Directory and Resource Guide*
200 SW Market St., Ste. 1770
Portland, OR 97201
Ph: (503)224-8684
Fax: (503)323-9186
URL: http://www.portlandalliance.com
Contact: Sandra McDonough, President
Released: Annual

56813 ■ Molalla Area Chamber of Commerce (MACC)
180 S Industrial Way, Ste. A
Molalla, OR 97038-7414
Ph: (503)829-6941
URL: http://www.molallachamber.com
Description: Promotes business and community development in Molalla, OR. **Founded:** 1983. **Awards:** Chamber Person of the Year (Annual).

56814 ■ Monmouth-Independence Chamber of Commerce (MICC)
311 Monmouth Ave.
Independence, OR 97351

Ph: (503)838-4268
Co. E-mail: micc@minetfiber.com
URL: http://www.micc-or.org
Contact: Jean Love, Executive Director
Description: Promotes business and community development in Monmouth and Independence, OR. Sponsors charitable events and festivals. Holds community clean-up day. **Founded:** 1964.

56815 ■ Mount Angel Chamber of Commerce
PO Box 221
Mount Angel, OR 97362-0221
Ph: (503)845-9440
Co. E-mail: machamber@mtangelchamber.org
URL: http://www.mtangelchamber.org
Contact: Pete Wall, President
Description: Promotes business and community development in Mount Angel, OR.

56816 ■ Mount Hood Area Chamber of Commerce
PO Box 819
Welches, OR 97067
Ph: (503)622-3017
Fax: (503)622-4881
Co. E-mail: chamber@mthood.org
URL: http://www.mthood.org
Contact: Coni Scott, President
Description: Promotes business and community development in Welches, OR area. **Founded:** 1957. **Publications:** *Mt. Hood/Columbia River Gorge Travel Planner* (Annual).

56817 ■ *Mt. Hood/Columbia River Gorge Travel Planner*
PO Box 819
Welches, OR 97067
Ph: (503)622-3017
Fax: (503)622-4881
Co. E-mail: chamber@mthood.org
URL: http://www.mthood.org
Contact: Coni Scott, President
Released: Annual

56818 ■ *Newsline*
5193 NE Elam Young Pkwy., Ste. A
Hillsboro, OR 97124
Ph: (503)648-1102
Fax: (503)681-0535
Co. E-mail: info@hillchamber.org
URL: http://www.hillchamber.org
Contact: Deanna Palm, President
Released: Monthly

56819 ■ North Clackamas County Chamber of Commerce
7740 SE Harmony Rd.
Milwaukie, OR 97222-1269
Ph: (503)654-7777
Fax: (503)653-9515
Co. E-mail: web1@yourchamber.com
URL: http://www.yourchamber.com
Contact: David A. Kelly, President
Description: Promotes business and community development in Clackamas County, OR. Sponsors harvest festival. **Founded:** 1955. **Publications:** *Business News* (Monthly); *Business and Professional Directory* (Annual). **Educational Activities:** Business Forum (Monthly); Greeters (Weekly). **Awards:** Business Person of the Year (Annual); Large Business of the Year (Annual); Express Personnel-Small Business of the Year (Annual); Irwin Adams Memorial Lifetime Achievement Award (Annual); Rohn Bly Memorial Volunteer of the Year (Annual).

56820 ■ North Santiam Chamber of Commerce (NSCC)
PO Box 222
Mill City, OR 97360
Ph: (503)897-5000
Co. E-mail: director@nschamber.org
URL: http://www.nschamber.org
Contact: Michelle Gates, Executive Director
Description: Promotes business and community development in several communities of the Santiam Canyon.

56821 ■ Nyssa Chamber of Commerce and Agriculture
105 Main St.
Nyssa, OR 97913
Ph: (541)372-3091
Fax: (541)372-9990
Co. E-mail: nyssachamber@nyssachamber.com
URL: http://www.nyssachamber.com
Contact: Tom Cook, President
Description: Works to advance the commercial, industrial, farming, civic and general interests of the City of Nyssa and its business area.

56822 ■ Oakridge - Westfir Chamber of Commerce
PO Box 217
Oakridge, OR 97463-0217
Ph: (541)782-4146
Fax: (541)782-1081
Co. E-mail: info@oakridgechamber.com
URL: http://www.oakridgechamber.com
Contact: Sandy Price, President
Description: Promotes business, community development, and tourism in the Oakridge/Westfir, OR area. Sponsors tree-planting and covered bridge Christmas lighting. **Publications:** *Chamber Chatter* (Monthly); *Food, Lodging and Service Guide.*

56823 ■ Ontario Chamber of Commerce (OCC)
876 SW 4th Ave.
Ontario, OR 97914
Ph: (541)889-8012
Free: 866-989-8012
Co. E-mail: info@ontariochamber.com
URL: http://www.ontariochamber.com
Contact: Dale Jeffries, Chairman
Description: Promotes business and community development in Ontario, OR. Participates in local charitable activities. Sponsors America's Global Village and Festival. **Founded:** 1912. **Publications:** *Meeting and Tour Planner Guide.*

56824 ■ Oregon City Chamber of Commerce
PO Box 226
Oregon City, OR 97045
Ph: (503)656-1619
Fax: (503)656-2274
Co. E-mail: chamberinfo@oregoncity.org
URL: http://www.oregoncity.org
Contact: Amber Holveck, Executive Director
Description: Works to promote the economic vitality and quality of life in the community of Oregon City. **Founded:** 1909. **Publications:** *ChamberWire* (Monthly).

56825 ■ *Pendleton Business*
501 S Main St.
Pendleton, OR 97801
Ph: (541)276-7411
Free: 800-547-8911
Fax: (541)276-8849
Co. E-mail: info@pendletonchamber.com
URL: http://www.pendletonchamber.com
Contact: Leslie Carnes, Executive Director
Released: Monthly

56826 ■ Pendleton Chamber of Commerce (PCC)
501 S Main St.
Pendleton, OR 97801
Ph: (541)276-7411
Free: 800-547-8911
Fax: (541)276-8849
Co. E-mail: info@pendletonchamber.com
URL: http://www.pendletonchamber.com
Contact: Leslie Carnes, Executive Director
Description: Promotes business and community development in Pendleton, OR. Operates visitors and convention bureau. **Founded:** 1893. **Publications:** *Pendleton Business* (Monthly); *Pendleton Chamber of Commerce Directory* (Periodic).

56827 ■ *Pendleton Chamber of Commerce Directory*
501 S Main St.
Pendleton, OR 97801
Ph: (541)276-7411

Free: 800-547-8911
Fax: (541)276-8849
Co. E-mail: info@pendletonchamber.com
URL: http://www.pendletonchamber.com
Contact: Leslie Carnes, Executive Director
Released: Periodic

56828 ■ Philomath Area Chamber of Commerce
PO Box 606
Philomath, OR 97370-0606
Ph: (541)929-2454
Co. E-mail: director@philomathchamber.org
URL: http://www.philomathchamber.org
Contact: Marcia Gilson, President
Description: Promotes business and community development in Philomath, OR. **Founded:** 1963. **Awards:** Philomath Samaritan Awards (Biennial).

56829 ■ *Pocket Guide*
555 SW Coast Hwy.
Newport, OR 97365-4934
Ph: (541)265-8801
Free: 800-COA-ST44
Fax: (541)265-5589
Co. E-mail: info@newportchamber.org
URL: http://www.newportchamber.org
Contact: Don Lindly, President
Released: Annual

56830 ■ Port Orford and North Curry Chamber of Commerce—Port Orford Chamber of Commerce
PO Box 637
Port Orford, OR 97465
Ph: (541)332-8055
Co. E-mail: chamber@portorfordchamber.com
URL: http://www.portorfordchamber.com
Description: Promotes business and community development in Port Orford, OR. Encourages tourism. Sponsors the annual Volkswalk, 4th of July Fireworks, Labor Day Auto Races, and Circus. **Founded:** 1925.

56831 ■ Portland Business Alliance
200 SW Market St., Ste. 1770
Portland, OR 97201
Ph: (503)224-8684
Fax: (503)323-9186
URL: http://www.portlandalliance.com
Contact: Sandra McDonough, President
Description: Works to ensure economic prosperity in the Portland region by providing strong leadership, partnership and programs that encourage business growth and vitality. **Founded:** 1870. **Publications:** *Alliance E-Newsletter* (Monthly); *Alliance News* (Monthly); *Membership Directory and Resource Guide* (Annual); *The Top 25*; *Largest Employers of the Portland/Vancouver Metropolitan Area* (Annual); *Oregon International Trade Directory* (Irregular); *Taking Stocks: A Snapshot of Portland Metro-Area Public Companies* (Annual); *Portland Metropolitan Chamber of Commerce--Membership Directory* (Annual); *Portland's Top Stocks and Major Employers*; *Largest Employers in the Portland/Vancouver Metropolitan Area*; *Manufacturers of the Portland Metropolitan Area* (Annual).

56832 ■ Prineville-Crook County Chamber of Commerce (PCCCC)
102 NW 2nd St.
Prineville, OR 97754
Ph: (541)447-6304
Fax: (541)447-6537
Co. E-mail: info@visitprineville.org
URL: http://www.visitprineville.com
Contact: Joe Becker, Executive Director
Description: Promotes business and community development in Prineville, OR area. Holds weekly legislative committee meeting. **Founded:** 1919. **Awards:** Business of the Year (Annual); Citizen of the Year (Annual).

56833 ■ *RACC Business Perspectives*
410 Spruce St.
Roseburg, OR 97470-3132
Ph: (541)672-2648

Fax: (541)673-7868
Co. E-mail: info@roseburgareachamber.org
URL: http://www.roseburgareachamber.org
Contact: Debbie Fromdahl, President
Released: Monthly

56834 ■ Redmond Chamber of Commerce
446 SW 7th St.
Redmond, OR 97756
Ph: (541)923-5191
Fax: (541)923-6442
Co. E-mail: info@visitredmondoregon.com
URL: http://www.visitredmondoregon.com
Contact: Dustin Hewitt, President
Description: Promotes business and community
development in Redmond, OR. Sponsors events.
Publications: *Business News* (Monthly).

56835 ■ Reedsport - Winchester Bay
Chamber of Commerce
855 Highway Ave.
Reedsport, OR 97467-0011
Ph: (541)271-3495
Free: 800-247-2155
Co. E-mail: info@reedsportcc.com
URL: http://www.reedsportcc.com
Contact: Robin Dollar, Manager
Description: Promotes business and community
development in Reedsport, OR. Seeks to establish
the area as a tourist destination. Holds Ocean
Festival. **Founded:** 1968. **Awards:** Business Person
of the Year (Annual).

56836 ■ *Restaurant and Dining Guide*
16330 Lower Harbor Rd.
Brookings, OR 97415
Ph: (541)469-3181
Free: 800-535-9469
Co. E-mail: info@brookingsharborchamber.com
URL: http://www.brookingsor.com
Released: Periodic

56837 ■ Rogue River Area Chamber of
Commerce
PO Box 457
Rogue River, OR 97537
Ph: (541)582-0242
Co. E-mail: dean@deanstirm.com
URL: http://rogueriverchamber.com
Contact: Dean Stirm, President
Description: Promotes business and community
development in the Rogue River, OR area.

56838 ■ Roseburg Area Chamber of
Commerce (RACC)
410 Spruce St.
Roseburg, OR 97470-3132
Ph: (541)672-2648
Fax: (541)673-7868
Co. E-mail: info@roseburgareachamber.org
URL: http://www.roseburgareachamber.org
Contact: Debbie Fromdahl, President
Description: Promotes business and community
development in Roseburg and central Douglas
County, OR. **Founded:** 1920. **Publications:** *RACC
Business Perspectives* (Monthly). **Educational Ac-
tivities:** Business Fair (Annual). **Awards:** First
Citizens Awards (Annual); Outstanding Business
Educator (Quarterly); Outstanding Educator (Quar-
terly); Outstanding Volunteer (Quarterly).

56839 ■ Salem Area Chamber of Commerce
(SACC)
1110 Commercial St. NE
Salem, OR 97301-1020
Ph: (503)581-1466
Fax: (503)581-0972
Co. E-mail: info@salemchamber.org
URL: http://www.salemchamber.org
Contact: Jason Brandt, Chief Executive Officer
Description: Promotes business and community
development in Marion and Polk counties, OR. **Publi-
cations:** *Business and Community Directory* (An-
nual); *Business News* (Monthly); *Salem Area Cham-
ber of Commerce Business Directory and Resource
Guide* (Annual). **Awards:** Agri-Business of the Year
(Annual); Business of the Year (Annual); Crystal
Apple Awards (Annual); Employer of the Year (An-

nual); First Citizen of the Year (Annual); New Business of the Year (Annual); Regional Business of the
Year (Annual); Small Business of the Year (Annual).

56840 ■ Sandy Area Chamber of Commerce
PO Box 536
Sandy, OR 97055
Ph: (503)668-4006
Fax: (503)668-3549
Co. E-mail: chamber@sandyoregonchamber.org
URL: http://www.sandyoregonchamber.org
Contact: Mitch Speck, Executive Director
Description: Promotes business and community
development in the Sandy, OR area. **Publications:**
Chamber Business Directory (Annual); *Chamber
News* (Periodic). **Educational Activities:** Ambas-
sadors Meeting (Monthly); Education Committee
Meeting (Monthly).

56841 ■ Sherwood Chamber of Commerce
(SCC)
PO Box 805
Sherwood, OR 97140-0805
Ph: (503)625-7800
Fax: (503)625-7550
Co. E-mail: chamber@sherwoodchamber.org
URL: http://www.sherwoodchamber.org
Contact: Nancy Bruton, Executive Director
Description: Promotes business and community
development in the Sherwood, OR area. Sponsors
the Sherwood Cruisin in June and The Great Onion
Festival in October. **Publications:** *Sherwood Cham-
ber of Commerce Business and Community Directory*
(Annual); *Sherwood Chamber of Commerce Newslet-
ter* (Bimonthly).

56842 ■ *Sherwood Chamber of Commerce*
Business and Community Directory
PO Box 805
Sherwood, OR 97140-0805
Ph: (503)625-7800
Fax: (503)625-7550
Co. E-mail: chamber@sherwoodchamber.org
URL: http://www.sherwoodchamber.org
Contact: Nancy Bruton, Executive Director
Released: Annual

56843 ■ *Sherwood Chamber of Commerce*
Newsletter
PO Box 805
Sherwood, OR 97140-0805
Ph: (503)625-7800
Fax: (503)625-7550
Co. E-mail: chamber@sherwoodchamber.org
URL: http://www.sherwoodchamber.org
Contact: Nancy Bruton, Executive Director
Released: Bimonthly

56844 ■ *Shore Lines*
PO Box 64
Cannon Beach, OR 97110
Ph: (503)436-2623
Fax: (503)436-0910
Co. E-mail: chamber@cannonbeach.org
URL: http://www.cannonbeach.org
Contact: Carol Hungerford, President
Released: Monthly

56845 ■ Silverton Area Chamber of
Commerce (SACC)
PO Box 257
Silverton, OR 97381
Ph: (503)873-5615
Fax: (503)873-7144
Co. E-mail: info@silvertonchamber.org
URL: http://www.silvertonchamber.org
Contact: Stacy Palmer, Executive Director
Description: Promotes business, community devel-
opment, and tourism in the Silverton, OR area. Spon-
sors First Citizen banquet, farm and industrial tours,
hanging flower basket program, and Christmas
decorating contest. **Founded:** 1952. **Publications:**
Visitor's Guide and Business Directory.

56846 ■ Sisters Area Chamber of Commerce
PO Box 430
Sisters, OR 97759
Ph: (541)549-0251
Free: 866-549-0252

Fax: (541)549-4253
Co. E-mail: info@sisterscountry.com
URL: http://www.sisterscountry.com
Contact: Erin Borla, Executive Director
Description: Strives to promote the civic, industrial,
commercial, agricultural, environmental and general
welfare of the city of Sisters, Oregon and its economic
area. **Founded:** 1974.

56847 ■ *Slick Magazine*
207 Depot St.
La Grande, OR 97850
Ph: (541)963-8588
Free: 800-848-9969
Fax: (541)963-3936
Co. E-mail: info@unioncountychamber.org
URL: http://www.unioncountychamber.org
Contact: Judy Hector, Chief Executive Officer
Released: Annual **Price:** free to members.

56848 ■ South Columbia County Chamber of
Commerce
2194 Columbia Blvd.
St. Helens, OR 97051
Ph: (503)397-0685
Fax: (503)397-7196
Co. E-mail: mgr@sccchamber.org
URL: http://www.sccchamber.org
Contact: Tina Kammerzelt, Manager
Description: Promotes business and community
development in St. Helens, Scappoose, Warren,
Columbia City, and Deer Island, OR. **Founded:** 1919.
Publications: *Chamber Update* (Monthly). **Awards:**
Board Member of the Year (Annual); Chamber Busi-
ness of the Year (Annual); Member of the Year (An-
nual).

56849 ■ Springfield Area Chamber of
Commerce
101 S A St.
Springfield, OR 97477
Ph: (541)746-1651
Fax: (541)726-4727
Co. E-mail: dan@springfield-chamber.org
URL: http://www.springfield-chamber.org
Contact: Dan Egan, Executive Director
Description: Promotes business and community
development in the Springfield, OR area. **Founded:**
1949.

56850 ■ Stayton - Sublimity Chamber of
Commerce (SSCC)
175 E High St.
Stayton, OR 97383
Ph: (503)769-3464
Co. E-mail: sscoc@wvi.com
URL: http://www.staytonsublimitychamber.org
Contact: Kelly Schreiber, Executive Director
Description: Promotes business and community
development in the Stayton/Sublimity, OR area.
Sponsors area festivals and Christmas activities.
Founded: 1891.

56851 ■ Sunriver Area Chamber of
Commerce
PO Box 3246
Sunriver, OR 97707
Ph: (541)593-8149
Fax: (541)593-3581
Co. E-mail: dsmeage@sunriverchamber.com
URL: http://www.sunriverchamber.com
Contact: Dennis E. Smeage, President
Description: Promotes business and community
development in Sunriver, OR area. **Founded:** 1987.

56852 ■ Sutherlin Chamber of Commerce
and Visitors' Information Center
PO Box 1410
Sutherlin, OR 97479
Ph: (541)580-1122
URL: http://www.sutherlinchamber.com
Description: Promotes business and community
development in the Sutherlin, OR area. Sponsors
festivals. Assists in boy scouting activities. **Founded:**
1939.

56853 ■ Sweet Home Chamber of Commerce
1575 Main St.
Sweet Home, OR 97386

Ph: (541)367-6186
Co. E-mail: info@sweethomechamber.org
URL: http://www.sweethomechamber.org
Contact: Andrea Culy, Executive Director
Description: Promotes business and community development in Sweet Home, OR. Sponsors festival.
Publications: *Hot Deals* (Monthly).

56854 ■ Tigard Area Chamber of Commerce (TCC)
12345 SW Main St.
Tigard, OR 97223
Ph: (503)639-1656
Fax: (503)639-6302
Co. E-mail: debi@tigardchamber.org
URL: http://www.tigardchamber.org/site
Contact: Debi Mollahan, Chief Executive Officer
Description: Promotes business and community development in the Tigard, OR area. **Publications:** *Hotline* (Monthly). **Educational Activities:** Tigard Area Chamber of Commerce Luncheon (Monthly).
Awards: Shining Stars Award (Annual).

56855 ■ Tillamook Area Chamber of Commerce
3705 Hwy. 101 N
Tillamook, OR 97141
Ph: (503)842-7525
Fax: (503)842-7526
Co. E-mail: tillchamber@oregoncoast.com
URL: http://www.tillamookchamber.org
Contact: Justin Aufdermauer, Executive Director
URL(s): gotillamook.com. **Description:** Promotes business and community development in Tillamook, OR. Participates in area festivals. **Founded:** 1931.
Publications: *Community Business Directory* (Annual); *Focus on Business* (Monthly). **Awards:** Business of the Month (Monthly); Business Person of the Year (Annual); John Shelly Volunteer of the Year (Annual); Honorary Citizen and Junior Citizen of the Year (Annual).

56856 ■ *Trade Winds*
4039 NW Logan Rd.
Lincoln City, OR 97367
Ph: (541)994-3070
Fax: (541)994-8339
Co. E-mail: info@lcchamber.com
URL: http://lcchamber.com
Contact: Lori Arce-Torres, President

56857 ■ *Tualatin Business and Community Guide*
18791 SW Martinazzi Ave.
Tualatin, OR 97062
Ph: (503)692-0780
Fax: (503)692-6955
Co. E-mail: linda@tualatinchamber.com
URL: http://www.tualatinchamber.com
Contact: Linda Moholt, Chief Executive Officer
Released: Annual

56858 ■ *Tualatin Business Connection*
18791 SW Martinazzi Ave.
Tualatin, OR 97062
Ph: (503)692-0780
Fax: (503)692-6955
Co. E-mail: linda@tualatinchamber.com
URL: http://www.tualatinchamber.com
Contact: Linda Moholt, Chief Executive Officer
Released: Bimonthly

56859 ■ Tualatin Chamber of Commerce (TCC)
18791 SW Martinazzi Ave.
Tualatin, OR 97062
Ph: (503)692-0780
Fax: (503)692-6955
Co. E-mail: linda@tualatinchamber.com
URL: http://www.tualatinchamber.com
Contact: Linda Moholt, Chief Executive Officer
Description: Promotes business and community development in Tualatin, OR. Sponsors trade show. Conducts Tualatin Crawfish Festival, Membership luncheon, weekly Networking AMs, Golf Tournament, and Holiday Tree Lighting. **Founded:** 1980. **Publications:** *Tualatin Business and Community Guide* (Annual); *Tualatin Business Connection* (Bimonthly).

56860 ■ Umatilla Chamber of Commerce
1530 6th St.
Umatilla, OR 97882
Ph: (541)922-4825
Fax: (541)922-4825
Co. E-mail: karen@umatillachamber.net
URL: http://www.umatillaoregonchamber.org
Contact: Libby Bovent, President
Description: Promotes business and community development in Umatilla, OR. Hosts the Oregon Governor's Cup Walleye Tournament each Labor Day weekend. **Founded:** 1947. **Publications:** *Chamber News* (Monthly). **Educational Activities:** Business-to-Business Luncheon (Monthly). **Awards:** Distinguished Citizens Awards (Annual).

56861 ■ Union County Chamber of Commerce
207 Depot St.
La Grande, OR 97850
Ph: (541)963-8588
Free: 800-848-9969
Fax: (541)963-3936
Co. E-mail: info@unioncountychamber.org
URL: http://www.unioncountychamber.org
Contact: Judy Hector, Chief Executive Officer
Description: Promotes business and community development in Union County, OR. **Founded:** 1933.
Publications: *Chamber Times* (Monthly); *Slick Magazine* (Annual).

56862 ■ Vale Chamber of Commerce
PO Box 661
Vale, OR 97918
Ph: (541)473-3800
Co. E-mail: info@valechamber.com
URL: http://www.valechamber.com
Contact: Brian Wolfe, President
Description: Promotes business and community development in Vale, OR.

56863 ■ *Visitor Information Guide*
PO Box 176
Astoria, OR 97103-0176
Ph: (503)325-6311
Free: 800-875-6807
Fax: (503)325-9767
Co. E-mail: info@oldoregon.com
URL: http://www.oldoregon.com
Contact: Skip Hauke, Executive Director
Released: Annual

56864 ■ *Visitor's Guide and Business Directory*
PO Box 257
Silverton, OR 97381
Ph: (503)873-5615
Fax: (503)873-7144
Co. E-mail: info@silvertonchamber.org
URL: http://www.silvertonchamber.org
Contact: Stacy Palmer, Executive Director

56865 ■ *W-D Area Chamber News*
c/o Dan Strasser, Pres.
371 SW Main St.
Winston, OR 97496
Ph: (541)679-6129
Co. E-mail: winstonvic@charter.net
URL: http://www.winstonoregon.net/chamber.html
Contact: Dan Strasser, President

56866 ■ Waldport Chamber of Commerce
PO Box 669
Waldport, OR 97394
Ph: (541)563-2133
Co. E-mail: chamber@peak.org
URL: http://www.waldport-chamber.com
Contact: Mark Campbell, President
Description: Promotes business and community development in Waldport, OR. **Founded:** 1959.

56867 ■ Wallowa County Chamber of Commerce
PO Box 427
Enterprise, OR 97828-0427
Ph: (541)426-4622
Free: 800-585-4121

Fax: (541)426-2032
Co. E-mail: info@wallowacounty.org
URL: http://www.wallowacountychamber.com
Contact: Vicki Searles, Executive Director
Description: Promotes agricultural, business, and community development in the Wallowa County, OR area. Conducts annual Old Time Fiddlers Contest. Publications: none. **Awards:** Citizens Award (Annual).

56868 ■ Wilsonville Chamber of Commerce
29600 SW Park Pl.
Wilsonville, OR 97070
Ph: (503)682-0411
Free: 800-647-3843
Fax: (503)682-4189
Co. E-mail: info@wilsonvillechamber.com
URL: http://www.wilsonvillechamber.com
Contact: Wendy Veliz Buck, President
Description: Promotes business and community development in Wilsonville, OR area. **Founded:** 1973. **Publications:** *Catalyst* (Monthly); *Wilsonville Community and Business Directory* (Annual).

56869 ■ *Wilsonville Community and Business Directory*
29600 SW Park Pl.
Wilsonville, OR 97070
Ph: (503)682-0411
Free: 800-647-3843
Fax: (503)682-4189
Co. E-mail: info@wilsonvillechamber.com
URL: http://www.wilsonvillechamber.com
Contact: Wendy Veliz Buck, President
Released: Annual

56870 ■ Winston Dillard Area Chamber of Commerce
c/o Dan Strasser, Pres.
371 SW Main St.
Winston, OR 97496
Ph: (541)679-6129
Co. E-mail: winstonvic@charter.net
URL: http://www.winstonoregon.net/chamber.html
Contact: Dan Strasser, President
Description: Works for the advancement of commercial, industrial, civic, and general interests of the Winston-Dillard area. **Founded:** 1960. **Publications:** *W-D Area Chamber News*.

56871 ■ Woodburn Area Chamber of Commerce (WACC)
PO Box 194
Woodburn, OR 97071
Ph: (503)982-8221
Fax: (503)982-8410
Co. E-mail: welcome@woodburnchamber.org
URL: http://www.woodburnchamber.org
Contact: Don Judson, Executive Director
Description: Promotes business and community development in the Woodburn, OR area. Sponsors Woodburn Business Showcase. **Founded:** 1938.
Publications: *Woodburn Chamber News* (Monthly).
Awards: Crystal Apple Awards (Annual); Distinguished Service Awards (Annual).

56872 ■ *Woodburn Chamber News*
PO Box 194
Woodburn, OR 97071
Ph: (503)982-8221
Fax: (503)982-8410
Co. E-mail: welcome@woodburnchamber.org
URL: http://www.woodburnchamber.org
Contact: Don Judson, Executive Director
Released: Monthly **Price:** included in membership dues.

56873 ■ Yachats Area Chamber of Commerce (YACC)
PO Box 728
Yachats, OR 97498
Ph: (541)547-3530
Free: 800-929-0477

Fax: (541)547-4930
Co. E-mail: info@yachats.org
URL: http://www.yachats.org
Description: Promotes business and community development in south Lincoln County, OR. Sponsors Arts and Crafts Fair, Smelt Fry, and Kite Festival. **Publications:** *The Gem.* **Awards:** Business of the Year (Annual); Man and Woman of the Year (Annual); Volunteer of the Year (Annual).

56874 ■ *Your Bay Area Business Connection*
145 Central Ave.
Coos Bay, OR 97420
Ph: (541)266-0868
Free: 800-824-8486
Fax: (541)267-6704
Co. E-mail: timmslater@oregonsbayarea.org
URL: http://www.oregonsbayarea.org
Contact: Mr. Timm Slater, Executive Director
Released: Monthly

56875 ■ *The Zephyr*
PO Box 1502
Crooked River, OR 97760
Ph: (541)923-2679
Fax: (541)923-2755
Co. E-mail: info@crrchamber.com
URL: http://www.crrchamber.com
Contact: Hope A. Johnson, Executive Director
Released: Monthly **Price:** included in membership dues.

MINORITY BUSINESS ASSISTANCE PROGRAMS

56876 ■ Oregon Advocate's Office for Minority, Women, and Emerging Small Businesses
155 Cottage St. NE, 2nd Fl.
Salem, OR 97301
Ph: (503)378-3506
Fax: (503)378-3139
Co. E-mail: omwesb.web@state.or.us
URL: http://www.oregon.gov/GOV/MWESB/
Contact: Cheryl Myers

Description: Advocates for disadvantaged and emerging small businesses, allowing their participation in the state's targeted purchasing programs. Also identifies and seeks to remove barriers that prevent these businesses from entering the mainstream of commercial activity.

56877 ■ Portland Minority Business Development Center
IMPACT Business Consultants, Inc.
8959 SW Barbour Blvd., Ste. 102
Portland, OR 97219
Ph: (503)245-9253
Fax: (503)246-3841
Co. E-mail: impact1@teleport.com

FINANCING AND LOAN PROGRAMS

56878 ■ OVP Venture Partners / Olympic Venture Partners (Portland)
1 SW Columbia, Ste. 1675
Portland, OR 97239
Ph: (503)697-8766
Fax: (503)697-8863
Co. E-mail: info@ovp.com
URL: http://www.ovp.com
Contact: Bill Funcannon, Chief Financial Officer

Preferred Investment Size: $1,000,000 to $5,000,000. **Industry Preferences:** Computer software and services, Internet specific, medical and health, biotechnology, communications and media, consumer related, semiconductors and other electronics, computer hardware, industrial and energy, and other products. **Geographic Preference:** Northwest and West Coast.

PROCUREMENT ASSISTANCE PROGRAMS

56879 ■ Oregon Procurement Technical Assistance Center - Department of Administrative Services (DAS) - State Procurement Office - Oregon Cooperative Purchasing Program
1225 Ferry St., U-140
Salem, OR 97301-4285
Ph: (503)378-4642
Fax: (503)373-1626
Co. E-mail: purchasing.info@state.or.us
URL: http://egov.oregon.gov
Contact: Jacquie Spenner, Leader
E-mail: dianne.lancaster@state.or.us
Description: Oregon's Statewide Procurement Office (SPO) provides training and direction for public contracting in the State of Oregon. The Statewide Procurement is an office of the Department of Administrative Service's State Services Division. The Oregon Cooperative Purchasing Program allows qualified agencies and organizations access to state contracts to purchase goods and services, and procurement training opportunities.

56880 ■ Oregon Procurement Technical Assistance Center - Disadvantaged Business Enterprise (DBE)
c/o V. West Consulting Services
Portland, OR 97211
Ph: (503)493-6027
Fax: (503)493-6029
Co. E-mail: vwest@vwservices.com
URL: http://www.gcap.org
Description: Ensures nondiscrimination in the award and administration of Federal contracts. The program creates a level playing field for small companies that are Black, Hispanic, Native Americans, Asian-Pacific Islanders, Subcontinent Asians, or women owned.

56881 ■ Oregon Procurement Technical Assistance Center - Government Contract Assistance Center (GCAP) - Northwest Environmental Business Council (NEBC)
620 SW Fifth Ave., Ste. 1008
Portland, OR 97204
Ph: (503)227-6361
Free: 800-985-6322
Fax: (503)227-1007
Co. E-mail: Robert@nebc.org
URL: http://www.nebc.org
Contact: Robert Grott, Director
E-mail: robert@nebc.org
Description: Trade association representing the interests of its members, while promoting the health of the industry and the environment as a whole. The organization engages in a range of activities and services designed to connect members to customers, regulators and legislators, knowledge, resources, and each other.

56882 ■ Oregon Procurement Technical Assistance Center - Government Contract Assistance Center (GCAP) - Pacific Northwest Defense Coalition (PNDC)
2828 SW Corbett Ave., Ste. 115
Portland, OR 97201
Ph: (503)312-3175
Co. E-mail: brice.barrett@pndc.us
URL: http://www.pndc.us
Contact: Brice Barrett, Director
E-mail: brice.barret@pndc.us
Description: Provides educational programs, business-to-business networking, and outreach to government decision makers ensuring success.

56883 ■ Oregon Procurement Technical Assistance Center - North Bend Government Contract Assistance Program
2455 Maple Leaf Ln.
North Bend, OR 97459
Ph: (541)756-7505

Fax: (541)756-5735
Co. E-mail: info@gcap.org
URL: http://www.gcap.org
Contact: J. Rick Evans, Director
E-mail: revans@gcap.org
Description: Supports state and local government by providing leadership, training, oversight and a vehicle for public contracting.

56884 ■ Oregon Procurement Technical Assistance Center - The Organization for Economic Initiatives
1144 Gateway Loop, Ste. 203
Springfield, OR 97477
Ph: (541)736-1088
Free: 800-497-7551
Fax: (541)736-1090
Co. E-mail: info@gcap.org
URL: http://www.gcap.org
Contact: Jan Hurt, Program Manager
E-mail: jhurt@orednet.org

56885 ■ Oregon Procurement Technical Assistance Center - Portland Government Assistance Program
PO Box 1364
Lake Oswego, OR 97035
Ph: (503)635-3921
Fax: (503)635-3921
Co. E-mail: info@gcap.org
URL: http://www.gcap.org
Contact: Michael Bowen, Counselor
E-mail: mbowen@gcap.org
Description: Supports state and local government by providing leadership, training, oversight and a vehicle for public contracting.

56886 ■ Oregon Procurement Technical Assistance Center - Willamette Government Contract Assistance Program
1144 Gateway Loop, Ste. 203
Springfield, OR 97477
Ph: (541)736-1088
Free: 800-497-7551
Fax: (541)736-1090
Co. E-mail: info@gcap.org
URL: http://www.gcap.org
Contact: Dee Edwards, Program Manager
Description: Supports state and local government by providing leadership, training, oversight and a vehicle for public contracting.

INCUBATORS/RESEARCH AND TECHNOLOGY PARKS

56887 ■ Business Enterprise Center
1965 SW Airport Ave.
Corvallis, OR 97333
Ph: (541)758-4009
Fax: (541)758-7319
Co. E-mail: thebec@thebec.com
URL: http://www.thebec.com/
Contact: Kathleen Hutchinson, Director
Description: A non-profit organization business incubator that provides professionally-managed facilities and services at a subsidized rate for primarily start-up businesses.

56888 ■ Open Technology Business Center
8305 SW Creekside Pl., Ste. C
Beaverton, OR 97008
Ph: (971)223-4660
Fax: (971)223-4659
Co. E-mail: email@otbc.com
URL: http://www.otbc.org/
Contact: Steve Morris, Director
Description: A small business incubator devoted to supporting the growth of technology startups in Oregon by taking a company's technology and helping turn it into a growth business through individualized coaching programs and commercialization assistance that accelerate each company's progress.

56889 ■ Oregon Association Of Minority Entrepreneurs
4134 N Vancouver Ave.
Portland, OR 97217

Ph: (503)249-7744
Fax: (503)249-2027
URL: http://www.oame.org/
Description: A non-profit organization formed to promote and develop entrepreneurship and economic development for ethnic minorities in the state of Oregon and SW Washington.

56890 ■ The Oregon Innovation Center (OIC)
PO Box 8759
Bend, OR 97708
Ph: (541)312-5785
Fax: (541)312-5787
Co. E-mail: info@innovationcenter.org
URL: http://www.innovationcenter.org
Description: The OIC is a small business incubator for emerging technology firms and entrepreneurs. In addition to affordable space, the Center offers tenants capital sourcing, economic facilities and other services.

EDUCATIONAL PROGRAMS

56891 ■ Chemeketa Community College - Training and Economic Development Center
4000 Lancaster Dr. NE
Salem, OR 97307
Ph: (503)399-5000
Free: 800-398-6262
Fax: (503)581-6017
URL: http://www.chemeketa.edu
Description: Provides noncredit courses, workshops, and short-term in-house and on-site programs to help business owners, managers, and employees learn and improve business knowledge and skills. The Small Business Management Program is a one-year course of study renewable up to three years offered to small business operators. It includes weekly classes and visits to businesses by instructors for assistance in recordkeeping, cost analysis, and effective operations. State, Targeted Training Funds are coordinated by this area.

56892 ■ Mount Hood Community College
26000 SE Stark St.
Gresham, OR 97030
Ph: (503)491-6422
Fax: (503)491-7388
URL: http://www.mhcc.edu
Description: Two-year college offering a small business management program.

56893 ■ Southwestern Oregon Community College
1988 Newmark Ave.
Coos Bay, OR 97420

Ph: (541)888-2525
Free: 800-962-2838
Fax: (541)888-7247
URL: http://www.socc.edu
Description: Two-year college offering a small business management program.

56894 ■ Umpqua Community College
1140 Umpqua College Rd.
Roseburg, OR 97470
Ph: (541)440-4600
Fax: (541)440-4637
URL: http://www.umpqua.cc.or.us
Description: Two-year college offering a small business management program.

PUBLICATIONS

56895 ■ *Incorporation and Business Guide for Oregon*
Self-Counsel Press, Inc.
1704 N. State St.
Bellingham, WA 98225
Ph: (360)676-4530
Free: 800-663-3007
Fax: (360)676-4549
Ed: C. Thomas Davis. **Released:** Fourth edition, 1992. **Price:** $14.95. **Description:** Includes forms to help entrepreneurs incorporate in Oregon.

56896 ■ *Incorporation Forms*
Self-Counsel Press
1704 N State St.
Bellingham, WA 98225
Ph: (360)676-4530
Free: 800-663-3007
Fax: (360)676-4549
Released: 1993. **Price:** $12.95 (paper). **Description:** Includes forms necessary to form your own corporation in Oregon.

56897 ■ *Oregon Business Magazine*
715 SW Morrison St.
Ste. 800
Portland, OR 97205
Ph: (503)223-0304
Fax: (503)221-6544
URL: http://www.oregonbusiness.com

56898 ■ *Smart Start your Oregon Business*
PSI Research
300 N. Valley Dr.
Grants Pass, OR 97526
Ph: (503)479-9464
Free: 800-228-2275

Fax: (503)476-1479
Co. E-mail: info@psi-research.com
URL: http://www.psi-research.com
Ed: Michael D. Jenkins. **Released:** Revised edition, 1992. **Price:** $29.95 (looseleaf binder); $24.95 (paper). **Description:** Part of the Successful Business Library series.

56899 ■ *Your Business Plan*
44 W. Broadway, Ste. 501
Eugene, OR 97401-3021
Ph: (541)726-2250
Fax: (541)345-6006
URL: http://www.efru.org/~osbdcn
Price: $16.45. **Description:** Spanish version also available.

56900 ■ *Your International Business Plan*
44 W. Broadway, Ste. 501
Eugene, OR 97401
Ph: (541)726-2250
Fax: (541)345-6006
URL: http://culterslanecc.edu
Ed: James L. Otis. **Released:** Revised edition, 1990. **Price:** $16.95 (paper).

56901 ■ *Your Marketing Plan*
44 W. Broadway, Ste. 507
Eugene, OR 97401
Ph: (503)726-2250
Fax: (503)345-6006
URL: http://www.efru.org/~osbdcn
Price: $16.45. **Description:** Helps the small business manager identify and target the potential and actual markets for their goods and services. Also discusses fundamental marketing concepts.

PUBLISHERS

56902 ■ PSI Research Inc./Hellgate Press—Publishing Services Inc.PSI Research;
1375 Upper River Rd.
Gold Hill, OR 97525-9785
Ph: (541)855-5566
Free: 800-795-4059
Fax: (541)855-1360
Co. E-mail: info@hellgatepress.com
URL: http://www.hellgatepress.com
Contact: Emmett Ramey, President
Description: Description: Publishes books on all aspects of business including finance, marketing, law, human resources, communications, franchising, military, adventure and travel. Accepts unsolicited manuscripts. Reaches market through Distributor Midpoint Books. **Founded:** 1997. **Telecommunication Services:** admin@hellgatepress.com.

SMALL BUSINESS DEVELOPMENT CENTERS

56903 ■ *Advisor*
200 Innovation Blvd.
119 Technology Center
University Park, PA 16802
Ph: (814)863-4293
Fax: (814)865-6667
Co. E-mail: sbdc@psu.edu
URL: http://www.sbdc.psu.edu
Contact: Heather Fennessey, Director
Released: 3/year

56904 ■ Bucknell University Small Business Development Center
Bucknell University
112 Dana Engineering Bldg.
Lewisburg, PA 17837
Ph: (570)577-1249
Free: 866-375-6010
Fax: (570)577-1768
Co. E-mail: sbdc@bucknell.edu
URL: http://www.bucknell.edu/SBDC.xml
Contact: Jon R. Vernam, Director
Description: Represents and promotes the small business sector. Provides management assistance to current and prospective small business owners. Helps to improve management skills and expand the products and services of members.

56905 ■ Clarion University Small Business Development Center
330 N Point Dr., Ste. 100
Clarion, PA 16214-3873
Ph: (814)393-2060
Free: 877-292-1843
Fax: (814)393-2636
Co. E-mail: sbdc@clarion.edu
URL: http://web.clarion.edu/sbdc
Contact: Dr. Kevin J. Roth, Director
Description: Represents and promotes the small business sector. Provides management assistance to current and prospective small business owners. Helps to improve management skills and expand the products and services of members.

56906 ■ Duquesne University Small Business Development Center
108 Rockwell Hall
600 Forbes Ave.
Pittsburgh, PA 15282
Ph: (412)396-6233
Fax: (412)396-5884
Co. E-mail: duqsbdc@duq.edu
URL: http://www.sbdc.duq.edu
Contact: Dr. Mary McKinney, Director
Description: Represents and promotes the small business sector. Provides management assistance to current and prospective small business owners. Helps to improve management skills and expand the products and services of members.

56907 ■ Indiana University of Pennsylvania Small Business Development Center
c/o Tony Palamone, Dir.
664 Pratt Dr., Ste. 108
Indiana, PA 15705
Ph: (724)357-7915
Fax: (724)357-5985
Co. E-mail: iup-sbdc@iup.edu
URL: http://www.iup.edu/business/sbdc
Contact: Tony Palamone, Director
Description: Represents and promotes the small business sector. Provides management assistance to current and prospective small business owners. Helps to improve management skills and expand the products and services of members.

56908 ■ Kutztown University Small Business Development Center (KU SBDC)
15155 Kutztown Rd.
Kutztown, PA 19530
Ph: (484)646-4002
Free: 866-458-7232
Fax: (484)646-4009
Co. E-mail: sbdc@kutztownsbdc.org
URL: http://www.kutztownsbdc.org
Contact: Ernie Post, Director
Description: Represents and promotes the small business sector. Provides management assistance to current and prospective small business owners. Helps to improve management skills and expand the products and services of members.

56909 ■ Lehigh University Small Business Development Center
125 Goodman Dr.
Bethlehem, PA 18015
Ph: (610)758-3980
Fax: (610)758-5205
Co. E-mail: insbdc@lehigh.edu
URL: http://www.lehigh.edu/~insbdc/index.html
Contact:
Description: Represents and promotes the small business sector. Provides management assistance to current and prospective small business owners. Helps to improve management skills and expand the products and services of members.

56910 ■ Lock Haven University Small Business Development Center
301 W Church St.
Lock Haven, PA 17745
Ph: (570)484-2589
Co. E-mail: tkeohane@lhup.edu
URL: http://www.lhup.edu/sbdc
Contact: Timothy J. Keohane, Director
Description: Represents and promotes the small business sector. Provides management assistance to current and prospective small business owners. Helps to improve management skills and expand the products and services of members.

56911 ■ Penn State Small Business Development Center
200 Innovation Blvd.
119 Technology Center
University Park, PA 16802

Ph: (814)863-4293
Fax: (814)865-6667
Co. E-mail: sbdc@psu.edu
URL: http://www.sbdc.psu.edu
Contact: Heather Fennessey, Director
Description: Represents and promotes the small business sector. Provides management assistance to current and prospective small business owners. Helps to improve management skills and expand the products and services of members. **Publications:** *Advisor* (3/year); *SBDC News* (Semiannual).

56912 ■ Pennsylvania Small Business Development Center, Lead Office
3819-33 Chestnut St., Ste. 325
Philadelphia, PA 19104-3238
Ph: (215)898-1219
Fax: (215)573-2135
Co. E-mail: pasbdc@wharton.upenn.edu
URL: http://pasbdc.org
Contact: Christian Conroy, Director
Description: Represents and promotes the small business sector. Provides management assistance to current and prospective small business owners. Helps to improve management skills and expand the products and services of members.

56913 ■ St. Vincent College Small Business Development Center
Center for Global Competitiveness
Aurelius Hall, 1st Fl.
300 Fraser Purchase Rd.
Latrobe, PA 15650
Ph: (724)537-4572
Free: 866-723-2242
Fax: (724)537-0919
Co. E-mail: sbdc@stvincent.edu
URL: http://www.stvincent.edu/sbdc
Contact: James H. Kunkel, Executive Director
Description: Represents and promotes the small business sector. Provides management assistance to current and prospective small business owners. Helps to improve management skills and expand the products and services of members.

56914 ■ *SBDC News*
200 Innovation Blvd.
119 Technology Center
University Park, PA 16802
Ph: (814)863-4293
Fax: (814)865-6667
Co. E-mail: sbdc@psu.edu
URL: http://www.sbdc.psu.edu
Contact: Heather Fennessey, Director
Released: Semiannual

56915 ■ Shippensburg University Small Business Development Center
405 Grove Hall
1871 Old Main Dr.
Shippensburg, PA 17257
Ph: (717)477-1935

Fax: (717)477-4010
Co. E-mail: sbdc@ship.edu
URL: http://www.ship.edu/SBDC/Contact_Us
Contact: Michael H. Unruh, Director
Description: Represents and promotes the small business sector. Provides management assistance to current and prospective small business owners. Helps to improve management skills and expand the products and services of members.

56916 ■ Small Business Development Center at Gannon University
c/o Steve Overholt, Mgr. of Business Consulting
120 W 9th St.
Erie, PA 16501
Ph: (814)871-7232
Free: 877-258-6648
Co. E-mail: overholt001@gannon.edu
URL: http://www.sbdcgannon.org
Contact: Steve Overholt, Business Manager
Description: Represents and promotes the small business sector. Provides management assistance to current and prospective small business owners. Helps to improve management skills and expand the products and services of members.

56917 ■ Small Business Development Center at St. Francis University
PO Box 600
Loretto, PA 15940
Ph: (814)472-3200
Fax: (814)472-3202
Co. E-mail: sbdc@francis.edu
URL: http://www.francis.edu/sbdc
Contact: Ed Huttenhower, Director
URL(s): www.sfcpa.edu/sbdc.htm. **Description:** Represents and promotes the small business sector. Provides management assistance to current and prospective small business owners. Helps to improve management skills and expand the products and services of members.

56918 ■ Small Business Development Center at The University of Scranton
600 Linden St.
Scranton, PA 18510-4639
Ph: (570)941-7588
Co. E-mail: sbdc@scranton.edu
URL: http://www.scrantonsbdc.com
Contact: Lisa M. Hall, Director
Description: Represents and promotes the small business sector. Provides management assistance to current and prospective small business owners. Helps to improve management skills and expand the products and services of members.

56919 ■ Small Business Development Center at the University of Pittsburgh
1800 Posvar Hall
230 S Bouquet St.
Pittsburgh, PA 15213
Ph: (412)648-1542
Fax: (412)648-1636
Co. E-mail: rvargo@katz.pitt.edu
URL: http://www.pittentrepreneur.com/sbdc
Contact: Raymond L. Vargo, Director
Description: Represents and promotes the small business sector. Provides management assistance to current and prospective small business owners. Helps to improve management skills and expand the products and services of members.

56920 ■ Temple Small Business Development Center
Beech Bldg.
1510 Cecil B. Moore Ave., Ste. 200
Philadelphia, PA 19121
Ph: (215)204-7282
Fax: (215)204-4554
Co. E-mail: sbdc@temple.edu
URL: http://sbm.temple.edu/sbdc
Contact: Eustace Kangaju, Director
Description: Represents and promotes the small business sector. Provides management assistance to current and prospective small business owners. Helps to improve management skills and expand the products and services of members.

56921 ■ Wharton Small Business Development Center (WSBDC)
Vance Hall
3733 Spruce St.
Philadelphia, PA 19104
Ph: (215)898-4861
Fax: (215)898-1063
URL: http://whartonsbdc.wharton.upenn.edu
Contact: Therese Flaherty, Director
Description: Represents and promotes the small business sector. Provides management assistance to current and prospective small business owners. Helps to improve management skills and expand the products and services of members.

56922 ■ Widener University Small Business Development Center
University Technology Park II
1350 Edgmont Ave., Ste. 1300
Chester, PA 19013
Ph: (610)610-8490
Fax: (610)619-8496
Co. E-mail: info@widenersbdc.org
URL: http://www.widenersbdc.org
Contact: Glenn McAllister, Director
Description: Represents and promotes the small business sector. Provides management assistance to current and prospective small business owners. Helps to improve management skills and expand the products and services of members.

56923 ■ Wilkes University Small Business Development Center
Innovation Center
7 S Main St., Ste. 200
Wilkes-Barre, PA 18701
Ph: (570)408-4340
Fax: (570)408-7889
Co. E-mail: sbdc@wilkes.edu
URL: http://www.wilkes.edu/sbdc
Description: Represents and promotes the small business sector. Provides management assistance to current and prospective small business owners. Helps to improve management skills and expand the products and services of members.

SMALL BUSINESS ASSISTANCE PROGRAMS

56924 ■ Pennsylvania Department of Community and Economic Development, Center for Business Financing - Site Development Division (BID)
Commonwealth Keystone Bldg.
400 North St., 4th Fl.
Harrisburg, PA 17120-0225
Ph: (717)787-6245
Free: 800-379-7448
Fax: (717)772-2890
Co. E-mail: readysetsucceed@newpa.com
URL: http://www.newpa.com
Description: Provides financing for infrastructure improvements such as sewer and water systems, waste disposal facilities, transportation facilities, and fire and safety facilities.

56925 ■ Pennsylvania Department of Community and Economic Development, Center Entrepreneurial Assistance
Commonwealth Keystone Bldg.
400 North St., 4th Fl.
Harrisburg, PA 17120-0225
Ph: (717)787-6245
Free: 800-280-3801
Fax: (717)772-2890
Co. E-mail: readysetsucceed@newpa.com
URL: http://www.newpa.com
Description: Pennsylvania's advocate for small business; provides prompt information on licenses and permits needed to start and operate a business.

56926 ■ Pennsylvania Department of Community and Economic Development - Loans Division
Commonwealth Keystone Bldg.
400 North St., 4th Fl.
Harrisburg, PA 17120-0225

Ph: (717)787-6245
Fax: (717)772-2890
Co. E-mail: readysetsucceed@newpa.com
URL: http://www.newpa.com
Description: Provides funds to train employees in specific skills to meet an individual employer's needs.

56927 ■ Pennsylvania Department of Community and Economic Development, Office of International Business Development
Commonwealth Keystone Bldg.
400 North St., 4th Fl.
Harrisburg, PA 17120-0225
Ph: (717)787-6245
Fax: (717)772-2890
Co. E-mail: readysetsucceed@newpa.com
URL: http://www.newpa.com
Description: Provides assistance to companies seeking the latest information on potential foreign markets for their products, and regional economic development organizations and companies with information about all facets of international trade. Responds to inquiries from foreign importers in search of new suppliers.

56928 ■ Pennsylvania Department of Community and Economic Development, Pennsylvania Industrial Development Authority
Commonwealth Keystone Bldg.
400 North St., 4th Fl.
Harrisburg, PA 17120-0225
Ph: (717)787-6245
Fax: (717)772-2890
Co. E-mail: readysetsucceed@newpa.com
URL: http://www.newpa.com
Description: Established in 1956 to make long-term, low-interest business loans to firms engaged in manufacturing or industrial enterprises.

56929 ■ Pennsylvania Department of Community and Economic Development, Technology Innovation - Ben Franklin Technology Partners
Commonwealth Keystone Bldg.
400 North St., 4th Fl.
Harrisburg, PA 17120-0225
Ph: (866)466-3972
Fax: (717)772-2890
Co. E-mail: readysetsucceed@newpa.com
URL: http://www.newpa.com
Description: Programs promote advanced technology in an effort to make traditional industry more competitive in the international marketplace. BFP's Advanced Technology Centers represent consortia of businesses that provide joint applied research and development efforts, assistance to higher education institutions and entrepreneurial assistance services.

56930 ■ Pennsylvania State University - Technical Assistance Program
The 329 Bldg., Ste. 416-417
University Park, PA 16802
Ph: (814)865-0427
Fax: (814)865-3589
Co. E-mail: penntap@psu.edu
URL: http://www.penntap.psu.edu
Contact: Wayne Figurelle, Director
Description: Provides technical information and assistance in problem-solving, business start-up, and increasing productivity.

SCORE OFFICES

56931 ■ Altoona-Alleghenies SCORE
Co. E-mail: score575@atlanticcbb.net

56932 ■ Bedford-Alleghenies SCORE
Co. E-mail: score575@atlanticbb.net

56933 ■ Cumberland Valley SCORE
Co. E-mail: chamber@chambersburg.org

56934 ■ Johnstown-Alleghenies SCORE
Co. E-mail: score575@atlanticbb.net

56935 ■ Monroe-Stroudsburg SCORE
556 Main St.
Stroudsburg, PA 18360

Ph: (570)421-4433
Fax: (570)424-4431
Co. E-mail: info@scoremonroe.org
URL: http://www.scoremonroe.org
Description: Promotes business and community development in the Monroe County. Conducts business education seminars and workshops to those wanting to start a business.

56936 ■ Pottstown SCORE No. 594
244 High St., Ste. 102
Pottstown, PA 19464
Ph: (610)327-2673
Fax: (610)327-0150
Co. E-mail: info@pottstownscore.org
URL: http://www.pottstownscore.org
Description: Provides professional guidance and information to maximize the success of existing and emerging small businesses. Offers business counseling and workshops. **Founded:** 1991.

56937 ■ Reading SCORE
Co. E-mail: info@reading008score.org

56938 ■ SCORE Bucks County
Co. E-mail: score570@verizon.net

56939 ■ SCORE Central PA
Industry & Technology Ctr.
2820 E College Ave., Ste. E
State College, PA 16801
Ph: (814)234-9415
Fax: (814)234-9415
Co. E-mail: scorecentralpa@scorecpa.org
URL: http://www.scorecpa.org
Contact: William Asbury, Chairman
Description: Provides professional guidance and information to maximize the success of existing and emerging small businesses. Offers business counseling and workshops. **Founded:** 1991.

56940 ■ SCORE Chester County
601 Westtown Rd. No.281
West Chester, PA 19380
Ph: (610)344-6910
Fax: (610)344-6919
Co. E-mail: contact.0544@scorevolunteer.org
URL: http://chestercounty.score.org
Description: Serves as volunteer program in which working and retired business management professionals provide free business counseling to men and women who are considering starting a small business, encountering problems with their business, or expanding their business. Offers free one-on-one counseling, online counseling and low cost workshops on a variety of business topics.

56941 ■ SCORE Delaware County
Co. E-mail: info@scoredelco.org

56942 ■ SCORE Eastern Montgomery County
Baederwood Office Plz.
1653 The Fairway, Ste. 204
Jenkintown, PA 19046
Ph: (215)885-3027
Fax: (610)768-2895
Co. E-mail: counselor@score513.org
URL: http://montgomerycountypa.score.org
Description: Provides professional guidance and information to maximize the success of existing and emerging small businesses. Offers business counseling and workshops.

56943 ■ SCORE Erie
120 W 9th St.
Erie, PA 16501
Ph: (814)871-5650
Fax: (814)871-7530
URL: http://erie.score.org
Description: Strives for the formation, growth, and success of small businesses. Promotes entrepreneur education in Erie area, Pennsylvania.

56944 ■ SCORE Harrisburg
100 Cameron St.
Harrisburg, PA 17101
Ph: (717)213-0435

Fax: (717)761-4315
URL: http://harrisburg.score.org
Description: Strives for the formation, growth, and success of small businesses. Promotes entrepreneur education in Harrisburg area, Pennsylvania. **Founded:** 1964. **Subscriptions:** books.

56945 ■ SCORE Lancaster
Liberty Pl., Ste. 231
313 W Liberty St.
Lancaster, PA 17603-2798
Ph: (717)397-3092
Co. E-mail: scorelancaster@verizon.net
URL: http://www.scorelancaster.org
Description: Strives for the formation, growth, and success of small businesses. Promotes entrepreneur education throughout Lancaster County. **Founded:** 1965.

56946 ■ SCORE Lehigh Valley
2158 Ave. C
Bethlehem, PA 18017
Ph: (610)266-3000
Co. E-mail: admin@lvscore.org
URL: http://www.lehighvalleyscore.org
Description: Strives for the formation, growth, and success of small businesses. Promotes entrepreneur education in Bethlehem area, Pennsylvania. **Founded:** 1965.

56947 ■ SCORE North Central PA
330 Pine St., Ste. 305
Williamsport, PA 17701
Ph: (570)322-3720
Fax: (570)322-3720
Co. E-mail: score234@verizon.net
URL: http://www.lycoming.org/score
Description: Provides professional guidance and information to maximize the success of existing and emerging small businesses. Offers business counseling and workshops. **Founded:** 1970.

56948 ■ SCORE Philadelphia
Co. E-mail: scorephila@yahoo.com

56949 ■ SCORE Pittsburgh
411 - 7th Ave., Ste. 1450
Pittsburgh, PA 15219
Ph: (412)395-6560
Fax: (412)395-6562
Co. E-mail: info@scorepittsburgh.com
URL: http://www.scorepittsburgh.org
Description: Aims to help small businesses in Southwestern Pennsylvania to grow and prosper by providing workshops and one-on-one counseling by members that have many years of experience in managing businesses. **Founded:** 1965.

56950 ■ SCORE Uniontown
140 N Beeson Ave., Rm. 404
Uniontown, PA 15401
Ph: (724)437-4222
Co. E-mail: uniontownscore@lcsys.net
Description: Provides professional guidance and information to maximize the success of existing and emerging small businesses. Offers business counseling and workshops.

56951 ■ SCORE Westmoreland County
St. Vincent College
300 Fraser Purchase Rd.
Latrobe, PA 15650
Ph: (724)539-7505
Fax: (724)539-1850
Co. E-mail: score@email.stvincent.edu
URL: http://www.westmorelandscore.org
Description: Provides professional guidance and information to maximize the success of existing and emerging small businesses. Offers business counseling and workshops.

56952 ■ SCORE Wilkes Barre
Stegmaier Bldg.
7 Wilkes Barre Blvd., Ste. 362
Wilkes-Barre, PA 18702-5241
Ph: (570)826-6502

Fax: (570)826-6498
Co. E-mail: infoscore@wbscore.org
URL: http://www.wbscore.org
Description: Provides professional guidance and information to maximize the success of existing and emerging small businesses. Offers business counseling and workshops.

56953 ■ SCORE York—SCORE 441
HACC Goodling Center
2101 Pennsylvania Ave.
York, PA 17404
Ph: (717)845-8830
Co. E-mail: score441@yorkscore.org
URL: http://york.score.org
Description: Offers mentoring to existing businesses that are experiencing difficulties. Workshops are also given periodically throughout the year in conjunction with Kutztown University's Small Business Development Center to help people start a business, write a business plan, and market their business. **Scope:** marketing, business start-up, foreign and domestic trade, financing a business, sales, business plans, marketing plans, strategic plans, community resources, governmental resources and agencies. **Founded:** 1964. **Subscriptions:** 75 articles books periodicals video recordings.

BETTER BUSINESS BUREAUS

56954 ■ Better Business Bureau of Western Pennsylvania
400 Holiday Dr., Ste. 220
Pittsburgh, PA 15220
Ph: (412)456-2700
Fax: (412)922-8656
Co. E-mail: info@pittsburgh.bbb.org
URL: http://www.pittsburgh.bbb.org
Description: Seeks to promote and foster ethical relationship between businesses and the public through voluntary self-regulation, consumer and business education, and service excellence. Provides information to help consumers and businesses make informed purchasing decisions and avoid costly scams and frauds; settles consumer complaints through arbitration and other means.

CHAMBERS OF COMMERCE

56955 ■ Action!
3001 Jacks Run Rd.
McKeesport, PA 15131
Ph: (412)678-2450
Co. E-mail: rba@regionalbusinessalliance.com
URL: http://www.rca-pa.com
Contact: Constance Yarris, Executive Director
Released: Monthly

56956 ■ African-American Chamber of Commerce of Philadelphia
30 S 15th St., Ground Fl.
Philadelphia, PA 19102
Ph: (215)751-9501
Fax: (215)751-9509
Co. E-mail: info@aachamber.org
URL: http://www.aachamber.org
Contact: Sulaiman Rahman, Chairman
Description: Promotes business and community development in Philadelphia, PA. **Founded:** 1994. **Publications:** *Chamber News* (Quarterly).

56957 ■ Allegheny Valley Chamber of Commerce
1 Acee Dr., Ste. 2
Natrona Heights, PA 15065
Ph: (724)224-3400
Fax: (724)224-3442
Co. E-mail: staff@alleghenyvalleychamber.com
URL: http://alleghenyvalleychamber.com
Contact: Mary E. Bowlin, President
Description: Promotes business and community development in northeastern Allegheny County, PA. Sponsors business education program with schools. Holds annual golf outing, dinner dance, business mixers, seminars, and special events. Operates Allegh-

eny Valley Development Corp.. Bestows Small Business of the Year Award. **Founded:** 1911. **Publications:** *Chamber Climate* (Bimonthly).

56958 ■ Ambridge Area Chamber of Commerce (AACC)
562 Merchant St.
Ambridge, PA 15003
Ph: (724)266-3040
Fax: (724)266-3096
Co. E-mail: ambridgechamber@gmail.com
URL: http://ambridgechamberofcommerce.com
Contact: Jeremy G. Angus, Executive Director
Description: Promotes business and community development in the Ambridge, PA area. Sponsors Nationality Days. **Founded:** 1916. **Publications:** *Chamber Membership Roster* (Annual).

56959 ■ America-Israel Chamber of Commerce, Central Atlantic Region
200 S Broad St., Ste. 700
Philadelphia, PA 19102
Ph: (215)790-3722
Fax: (215)790-3601
Co. E-mail: aicc@greaterphilachamber.com
URL: http://www.americaisraelchamber.com
Contact: Beth Cohen, President
Description: Promotes the interests of the U.S.-Israel business community. **Founded:** 1987.

56960 ■ Armstrong County Chamber of Commerce (ACCC)
125 Market St., Ste. 1
Kittanning, PA 16201
Ph: (724)543-1305
Fax: (724)548-2951
Co. E-mail: accc1@accc1.comcastbiz.net
URL: http://www.armstrongchamber.org
Contact: Lynda Pozzuto, Executive Director
Description: Promotes business and community development in Armstrong County, PA. Conducts social activities, including golf outings, exhibits, and breakfast meetings with elected officials. Holds annual Expo. **Founded:** 1922. **Publications:** *The Bridge* (Bimonthly); *The Business Report*; *Commercial-Industrial Directory* (Triennial). **Awards:** Citizen of the Year (Annual).

56961 ■ Beaver County Chamber of Commerce
798 Turnpike St.
Beaver, PA 15009
Ph: (724)775-3944
Fax: (724)728-9737
Co. E-mail: info@bcchamber.com
URL: http://www.beavercountychamber.com
Contact: Erica Wachtel, President
Description: Advances the economic, industrial, physical, professional, cultural and civic welfare of Beaver County through its membership. Encourages and protects the trade and commerce of the area and promotes its orderly growth and development. **Publications:** *Connections* (Monthly). **Awards:** Business of the Year Award (Annual).

56962 ■ Bedford County Chamber of Commerce
125 S Juliana St.
Bedford, PA 15522-1304
Ph: (814)623-2233
Fax: (814)623-6089
Co. E-mail: info@bedfordcountychamber.org
URL: http://www.bedfordcountychamber.com
Contact: Kellie Goodman Shaffer, Executive Director
Description: Promotes business and community development in the Bedford County, PA area. **Founded:** 1986. **Publications:** *Chamber News* (Monthly). **Telecommunication Services:** director@bedfordcountychamber.org.

56963 ■ Bellefonte Intervalley Area Chamber of Commerce (BIACC)
320 W High St., Train Sta.
Bellefonte, PA 16823
Ph: (814)355-2917

Fax: (814)355-2761
Co. E-mail: bellefontecoc@aol.com
URL: http://www.bellefontechamber.org
Contact: Gary V. Hoover, Executive Director
Description: Promotes business and community development in the Bellefonte, PA area. **Founded:** 1938.

56964 ■ Berwick Area Chamber of Commerce (BACC)
206 Mulberry St.
Berwick, PA 18603
Ph: (570)752-3601
Fax: (570)752-3602
Co. E-mail: info@berwickpa.org
URL: http://www.columbiamontourchamber.com
Contact: Nathan Navely, Chairman
Description: Promotes business and community development in the Greater Berwick, PA area. **Founded:** 1922. **Publications:** *The BACC Beat* (Bimonthly). **Educational Activities:** Berwick Area Chamber of Commerce Dinner (Annual).

56965 ■ *Blair Business Mirror*
3900 Industrial Park Dr., Ste. 12
Altoona, PA 16602
Ph: (814)943-8151
Fax: (814)943-5239
Co. E-mail: chamber@blairchamber.com
URL: http://www.blairchamber.com
Contact: Joe Hurd, President
Released: Monthly **Price:** free.

56966 ■ Blair County Chamber of Commerce
3900 Industrial Park Dr., Ste. 12
Altoona, PA 16602
Ph: (814)943-8151
Fax: (814)943-5239
Co. E-mail: chamber@blairchamber.com
URL: http://www.blairchamber.com
Contact: Joe Hurd, President
Description: Promotes business and community development in Blair County, PA. **Founded:** 1887. **Publications:** *Blair Business Mirror* (Monthly); *Chamber Extra* (Monthly); *Blair Business Mirror* (Monthly). **Telecommunication Services:** jhurd@blairchamber.com.

56967 ■ Bradford Area Chamber of Commerce (BACC)
121 Main St.
Bradford, PA 16701
Ph: (814)368-7115
Fax: (814)368-6233
Co. E-mail: ed@bradfordchamber.com
URL: http://www.bradfordchamber.com
Contact: Ron Orris, Executive Director
Description: Promotes business and community development in the Bradford, PA area. **Founded:** 1882. **Publications:** *Small Street Journal* (Monthly).

56968 ■ Brentwood-Baldwin-Whitehall Chamber of Commerce (BBWCC)
3501 Brownsville Rd.
Pittsburgh, PA 15227-3115
Ph: (412)884-1233
Co. E-mail: secretary@bbwchamber.com
URL: http://www.bbwchamber.com
Contact: Debbie Maddock, President
Description: Promotes business and community development in Brentwood, Baldwin, and Whitehall, PA. Sponsors annual trade fair and seminars. **Founded:** 1959. **Publications:** *Chamber Chatter Box* (Monthly); *In the Spotlight* (Monthly). **Awards:** Student of the Year (Annual).

56969 ■ *The Bridge*
125 Market St., Ste. 1
Kittanning, PA 16201
Ph: (724)543-1305
Fax: (724)548-2951
Co. E-mail: accc1@accc1.comcastbiz.net
URL: http://www.armstrongchamber.org
Contact: Lynda Pozzuto, Executive Director
Released: Bimonthly

56970 ■ *Bridges to Business*
2170 Portzer Rd.
Quakertown, PA 18951

Ph: (215)536-3211
Fax: (215)536-7767
Co. E-mail: info@ubcc.org
URL: http://www.ubcc.org
Contact: Tara King, Executive Director
Released: Bimonthly

56971 ■ Brookville Area Chamber of Commerce (BACC)
100 Main St., Ste. A
Brookville, PA 15825
Ph: (814)849-8448
Co. E-mail: brookvillechamber@windstream.net
URL: http://www.brookvillechamber.com
Contact: Melanie Darrin, Executive Director
Description: Promotes business and community development in the Brookville, PA area.

56972 ■ *Brush Valley Buyer's Guide*
2 E Arch St., Ste. 313-A
Shamokin, PA 17872
Ph: (570)648-4675
Fax: (570)648-0679
Co. E-mail: swinhofer@censop.com
URL: http://www.brushvalleychamber.com
Contact: Sandy Winhofer, Director
Released: Annual **Price:** included in membership dues.

56973 ■ Brush Valley Regional Chamber of Commerce
2 E Arch St., Ste. 313-A
Shamokin, PA 17872
Ph: (570)648-4675
Fax: (570)648-0679
Co. E-mail: swinhofer@censop.com
URL: http://www.brushvalleychamber.com
Contact: Sandy Winhofer, Director
Description: Promotes business and community development in the Shamokin, Coal Township, Mt. Carmel, Kulpmont, Marion Heights, Trevorton, Elysburg, Paxinos and Ralpho Township, PA areas. Strives to forward the prosperity of the commercial, agricultural and industrial community; to promote general welfare; to procure and dispense such information as it will advance and elevate commercial dealings and extend just methods of business by the establishment and maintenance of a place for business and social meetings. **Founded:** 1926. **Publications:** *Brush Valley Buyer's Guide* (Annual).

56974 ■ *The Business Brief*
314 5th St.
Ellwood City, PA 16117
Ph: (724)758-5501
Co. E-mail: info@ellwoodchamber.org
URL: http://www.ellwoodchamber.org
Contact: Terri Stramba, Executive Director
Released: Bimonthly

56975 ■ *Business Development News*
100 S Queen St.
Lancaster, PA 17603
Ph: (717)397-3531
Fax: (717)293-3159
Co. E-mail: info@lcci.com
URL: http://www.lancasterchamber.com
Contact: Thomas Baldrige, President
Released: Monthly

56976 ■ *Business Directory*
1019 Philadelphia St.
Indiana, PA 15701-1689
Ph: (724)465-2511
Fax: (724)465-3706
Co. E-mail: dphenry@wpia.net
URL: http://www.indianapa.com/chamber
Contact: Dana P. Henry, President
Released: Periodic **Price:** free for members; $100, for nonmembers.

56977 ■ *Business Directory*
13 E High St.
Manheim, PA 17545-2002
Ph: (717)665-6330

Fax: (717)665-7656
Co. E-mail: info@manheimchamber.com
URL: http://manheimchamber.com
Contact: Teresa M. Shelly, Executive Director
Released: Periodic

56978 ■ *Business Directory*
53 S St. Marys St.
St. Marys, PA 15857
Ph: (814)781-3804
Fax: (814)781-7302
Co. E-mail: info@stmaryschamber.org
URL: http://www.stmaryschamber.org
Contact: Mark Rupprecht, President
Released: Monthly

56979 ■ *Business Directory*
Released: Annual **Price:** included in membership
dues.

56980 ■ *Business Guide and Community
Directory*
PO Box 991
McMurray, PA 15317-0991
Ph: (724)941-6345
Co. E-mail: info@peterstownshipchamber.com
URL: http://www.peterstownshipchamber.com
Contact: Joseph Jasek, President
Released: Annual **Price:** free.

56981 ■ *Business and Industrial Directory*
308 Market St.
Warren, PA 16365
Ph: (814)723-3050
Fax: (814)723-6024
Co. E-mail: info@wccbi.org
URL: http://www.wccbi.org
Contact: James L. Decker, President
Released: Annual

56982 ■ *Business and Industry*
65 W Main St.
Uniontown, PA 15401-2124
Ph: (724)437-4571
Free: 800-916-9365
Fax: (724)438-3304
Co. E-mail: info@faycham.org
URL: http://www.fayettechamber.com
Contact: Muriel J. Nuttall, Executive Director
Price: $5, for members; $10, for nonmembers.

56983 ■ *Business and Industry*
PO Box 572
Carlisle, PA 17013
Ph: (717)243-4515
Fax: (717)243-4446
Co. E-mail: mcrowley@carlislechamber.org
URL: http://www.carlislechamber.org
Contact: Ms. Michelle Hornick Crowley, President
Released: Quarterly

56984 ■ *The Business Report*
125 Market St., Ste. 1
Kittanning, PA 16201
Ph: (724)543-1305
Fax: (724)548-2951
Co. E-mail: accc1@accc1.comcastbiz.net
URL: http://www.armstrongchamber.org
Contact: Lynda Pozzuto, Executive Director
Price: included in membership dues.

56985 ■ *Business Review*
2525 Rochester Rd., Ste. 200
Cranberry Township, PA 16066-6422
Ph: (724)776-4949
Fax: (724)776-5344
Co. E-mail: cranberryoffice@thechamberinc.com
URL: http://thechamberinc.com
Contact: Kathleen Sain, Chairperson
Released: Monthly

56986 ■ *Business Spotlight*
PO Box 445
Hatfield, PA 19440-0445
Ph: (215)855-3335
Fax: (215)855-3335
Co. E-mail: admin@hatfieldchamber.com
URL: http://www.hatfieldchamber.com
Contact: Lawrence Stevens, Executive Director

56987 ■ *Business Voice*
96 S George St., 3rd Fl.
York, PA 17401-1611
Ph: (717)848-4000
Free: 800-673-2429
Fax: (717)843-6737
Co. E-mail: info@yorkchamber.com
URL: http://www.yorkchamber.com
Contact: Thomas E. Donley, President
E-mail: donley@yorkchamber.com
Released: Monthly **Price:** included in membership
dues.

56988 ■ *Business Voice Newsletter*
Released: Monthly

56989 ■ *BusinessLinks*
850 Beaver Grade Rd.
Moon Township, PA 15108
Ph: (412)264-6270
Fax: (412)264-1575
Co. E-mail: info@paacc.com
URL: http://www.paacc.com
Contact: Sally Haas, President
Released: Monthly

56990 ■ **Butler County Chamber of
Commerce and Tourism**
PO Box 1082
Butler, PA 16003-1082
Ph: (724)283-2222
Fax: (724)283-0224
Co. E-mail: info@butlercountychamber.com
URL: http://www.butlercountychamber.com
Contact: Stan M. Kosciuszko, President
Description: Enhances the economic prosperity of
the members and promotes free enterprise and
growth in Butler County. **Founded:** 1896.

56991 ■ *Buyer's Guide*
21 N 6th Ave.
Clarion, PA 16214
Ph: (814)226-9161
Fax: (814)226-4903
Co. E-mail: info@clarionpa.com
URL: http://www.clarionpa.com
Contact: Tracy J. Becker, Executive Director

56992 ■ *Buyer's Guide*
Citiscape
Hazleton, PA 18201-6288
Ph: (570)455-1509
Fax: (570)450-2013
Co. E-mail: dguydish@hazletonchamber.org
URL: http://www.hazletonchamber.org/
Contact: Donna Palermo, President
Price: free for members (first copy); $20, for non-
profits; $40, for nonmembers.

56993 ■ *Buyer's Guide*
100 S Queen St.
Lancaster, PA 17603
Ph: (717)397-3531
Fax: (717)293-3159
Co. E-mail: info@lcci.com
URL: http://www.lancasterchamber.com
Contact: Thomas Baldrige, President
Released: Periodic

56994 ■ *Calendar of Events*
2512 Rte. 6, Ste. 2
Hawley, PA 18428
Ph: (570)226-3191
Fax: (570)226-9387
Co. E-mail: visit@lakeregioncc.com
URL: http://www.lakeregioncc.com
Contact: Jim Shook, President
Released: Quarterly

56995 ■ *Calendar of Events - Information
Directory*
445 Linden St.
Columbia, PA 17512
Ph: (717)684-5249
Fax: (717)684-5142
Co. E-mail: svcc@parivertowns.com
URL: http://www.parivertowns.com
Contact: Melissa A. Glenn, Director
Released: Periodic

56996 ■ *Castle Views*
217 E Baltimore St.
Greencastle, PA 17225
Ph: (717)597-4610
Fax: (717)597-0709
Co. E-mail: info@greencastlepachamber.org
URL: http://www.greencastlepachamber.org
Contact: Joel Fridgen, Executive Director
Released: Bimonthly

56997 ■ *Catalyst*
417 Walnut St.
Harrisburg, PA 17101-1902
Ph: (717)255-3252
Free: 800-225-7224
Fax: (717)255-3298
Co. E-mail: info@pachamber.org
URL: http://www.pachamber.org
Contact: Gene Barr, President
Released: Quarterly

56998 ■ **Central Bradford County Chamber of
Commerce (CBCCC)**
PO Box 146
Towanda, PA 18848-0146
Ph: (570)268-2732
Fax: (570)265-2331
URL: http://cbradchamber.org
Contact: Susan Portnoff, Administrator
Description: Serves members and the community
with networking opportunities, business seminars,
promotion and referrals. **Founded:** 1925.

56999 ■ **Central Bucks Chamber of
Commerce (CBCC)**
Bailiwick, Ste. 23
Doylestown, PA 18901
Ph: (215)348-3913
Fax: (215)348-7154
Co. E-mail: info@centralbuckschamber.com
URL: http://www.centralbuckschamber.com
Contact: Dr. John C. Soffronoff, Chairman
Description: Promotes business and community
development in central Bucks County, PA. **Founded:**
1946. **Publications:** *Who, What, Where, When.*

57000 ■ **Central Pennsylvania Chamber of
Commerce**
30 Lawton Ln.
Milton, PA 17847
Ph: (570)742-7341
Free: 800-326-9211
Fax: (570)742-2008
Co. E-mail: mculp@centralpachamber.com
URL: http://www.centralpachamber.com/index.php
Contact: Maria A. Culp, President
Description: Promotes business and community
development in upper Northumberland and eastern
Union counties, PA. **Founded:** 1905. **Publications:**
News & Views (Monthly). **Awards:** Business and
Education Award (Annual); Business of the Year (An-
nual); Presidents Award (Annual); Volunteer of the
Year (Annual).

57001 ■ **Chamber of Business and Industry
of Centre County (CBICC)**
200 Innovation Blvd., Ste. 150
State College, PA 16803
Ph: (814)234-1829
Fax: (814)234-5869
Co. E-mail: cbicc@cbicc.org
URL: http://www.cbicc.org
Contact: David Wise, President
Description: Promotes business and community
development in State College, PA. **Founded:** 1992.
Publications: *ChamberNet* (Quarterly).

57002 ■ *Chamber Chat*
PO Box 182
Glenside, PA 19038
Ph: (215)500-4080
Co. E-mail: info@glensidechamber.org
URL: http://www.glensidechamber.org
Contact: Barbara A. Nye, President
Released: Bimonthly

57003 ■ *Chamber Chatter*
1st Commonwealth Bank Bldg.
3 S Brady St., Ste. 205
DuBois, PA 15801
Ph: (814)371-5010
Fax: (814)371-5005
Co. E-mail: dacc@duboispachamber.com
URL: http://www.duboispachamber.com
Contact: Nancy J. Micks, President
Released: Monthly

57004 ■ *Chamber Chatter*
18 Carlisle St., Ste. 203
Gettysburg, PA 17325
Ph: (717)334-8151
Fax: (717)334-3368
Co. E-mail: info@gettysburg-chamber.org
URL: http://www.gettysburg-chamber.org
Contact: Carrie S. Stuart, President
Released: Monthly

57005 ■ *Chamber Chatter*
119 N High St.
West Chester, PA 19380-3145
Ph: (610)696-4046
Fax: (610)696-9110
Co. E-mail: info@gwcc.org
URL: http://www.gwcc.org
Contact: Mark Yoder, President
Released: Monthly **Price:** free for members.

57006 ■ *Chamber Chatter*
143 E High St.
Waynesburg, PA 15370-2053
Ph: (724)627-5926
Fax: (724)627-8017
Co. E-mail: waynesburgchamber@windstream.net
URL: http://www.waynesburgchamber.com
Contact: Melody R. Longstreth, Executive Director
Released: Monthly **Price:** free.

57007 ■ *Chamber Chatter Box*
3501 Brownsville Rd.
Pittsburgh, PA 15227-3115
Ph: (412)884-1233
Co. E-mail: secretary@bbwchamber.com
URL: http://www.bbwchamber.com
Contact: Debbie Maddock, President
Released: Monthly

57008 ■ *Chamber Climate*
1 Acee Dr., Ste. 2
Natrona Heights, PA 15065
Ph: (724)224-3400
Fax: (724)224-3442
Co. E-mail: staff@alleghenyvalleychamber.com
URL: http://alleghenyvalleychamber.com
Contact: Mary E. Bowlin, President
Released: Bimonthly

57009 ■ Chamber of Commerce of Greater West Chester (CCGWC)
119 N High St.
West Chester, PA 19380-3145
Ph: (610)696-4046
Fax: (610)696-9110
Co. E-mail: info@gwcc.org
URL: http://www.gwcc.org
Contact: Mark Yoder, President
Description: Promotes business and community development in Greater West Chester. Conducts educational and networking opportunities. **Founded:** 1915. **Publications:** *Chamber Chatter* (Monthly); *Images of Greater West Chester* (Annual); *Membership & Resource Directory* (Annual). **Educational Activities:** Iron Hill Classic Golf Outing. **Awards:** Business of the Year (Annual); Outstanding Citizen (Annual); Volunteer of the Year (Annual); J. Dewees Mosteller Community Service Award (Annual).

57010 ■ *Chamber Connection*
100 W 3rd St.
Williamsport, PA 17701
Ph: (570)326-1971
Fax: (570)321-1209
Co. E-mail: chamber@williamsport.org
URL: http://www.williamsport.org
Contact: Vincent J. Matteo, President
Released: Monthly; every first Monday.

57011 ■ *Chamber Connections*
146 Carlisle St.
Hanover, PA 17331
Ph: (717)637-6130
Fax: (717)637-9127
Co. E-mail: office@hanoverchamber.com
URL: http://www.hanoverchamber.com
Contact: Gary Laird, President
Released: Monthly

57012 ■ *Chamber E-Central*
241 Tollgate Hill Rd.
Greensburg, PA 15601
Ph: (724)834-2900
Fax: (724)837-7635
Co. E-mail: info@westmorelandchamber.com
URL: http://www.westmorelandchamber.com
Contact: Chad Amond, President
Released: Monthly

57013 ■ *Chamber Extra*
3900 Industrial Park Dr., Ste. 12
Altoona, PA 16602
Ph: (814)943-8151
Fax: (814)943-5239
Co. E-mail: chamber@blairchamber.com
URL: http://www.blairchamber.com
Contact: Joe Hurd, President
Released: Monthly **Price:** included in membership dues.

57014 ■ *Chamber Media Network*
908 Diamond Park
Meadville, PA 16335
Ph: (814)337-8030
Fax: (814)337-8022
Co. E-mail: info@meadvillechamber.com
URL: http://www.meadvillechamber.com
Contact: Kathleen Bishop, President
Released: Monthly

57015 ■ *Chamber Membership Roster*
562 Merchant St.
Ambridge, PA 15003
Ph: (724)266-3040
Fax: (724)266-3096
Co. E-mail: ambridgechamber@gmail.com
URL: http://ambridgechamberofcommerce.com
Contact: Jeremy G. Angus, Executive Director
Released: Annual

57016 ■ *Chamber News*
100 S Queen St.
Lancaster, PA 17603
Ph: (717)397-3531
Fax: (717)293-3159
Co. E-mail: info@lcci.com
URL: http://www.lancasterchamber.com
Contact: Thomas Baldrige, President
Price: free for members.

57017 ■ *Chamber News*
125 S Juliana St.
Bedford, PA 15522-1304
Ph: (814)623-2233
Fax: (814)623-6089
Co. E-mail: info@bedfordcountychamber.org
URL: http://www.bedfordcountychamber.com
Contact: Kellie Goodman Shaffer, Executive Director
Released: Monthly

57018 ■ *Chamber News*
30 S 15th St., Ground Fl.
Philadelphia, PA 19102
Ph: (215)751-9501
Fax: (215)751-9509
Co. E-mail: info@aachamber.org
URL: http://www.aachamber.org
Contact: Sulaiman Rahman, Chairman
Released: Quarterly **Price:** free.

57019 ■ *Chamber News and Notes*
PO Box 991
McMurray, PA 15317-0991
Ph: (724)941-6345
Co. E-mail: info@peterstownshipchamber.com
URL: http://www.peterstownshipchamber.com
Contact: Joseph Jasek, President
Released: Quarterly

57020 ■ *Chamber Newsletter*
537 W Main St.
Mount Pleasant, PA 15666
Ph: (724)547-7521
Co. E-mail: marjorie@laurelhighlandschamber.com
URL: http://www.laurelhighlandschamber.com
Contact: Patty McGuire, Secretary
Released: Monthly **Price:** included in membership dues.

57021 ■ *Chamber Outlook*
100 Lincoln Way E, Ste. A
Chambersburg, PA 17201
Ph: (717)264-7101
Fax: (717)267-0399
Co. E-mail: chamber@chambersburg.org
URL: http://www.chambersburg.org
Contact: David G. Sciamanna, President
Released: 11/year

57022 ■ *Chamber Report*
221 N Center St.
Corry, PA 16407
Ph: (814)665-9925
Co. E-mail: cacc@velocity.net
URL: http://www.corrychamber.org
Contact: Jill Hall, Advisor
Released: Quarterly

57023 ■ *Chamber Report*
146 Carlisle St.
Hanover, PA 17331
Ph: (717)637-6130
Fax: (717)637-9127
Co. E-mail: office@hanoverchamber.com
URL: http://www.hanoverchamber.com
Contact: Gary Laird, President
Released: Monthly

57024 ■ *Chamber Update*
212 N Jay St.
Lock Haven, PA 17745
Ph: (570)748-5782
Free: 888-388-6991
Fax: (570)893-0433
Co. E-mail: flanagan@kcnet.org
URL: http://www.clintoncountyinfo.com
Contact: Michael Flanagan, President
Released: Monthly

57025 ■ *Chamber Update*
51-B S Main St.
Mansfield, PA 16933
Ph: (570)662-3442
Fax: (570)662-0259
Co. E-mail: info@mansfield.org
URL: http://www.mansfield.org
Contact: Gale Hall, Director
Released: Monthly

57026 ■ *Chamber Voice*
Red Barn Mall
120 S York Rd.
Hatboro, PA 19040
Ph: (215)956-9540
Fax: (215)956-9635
Co. E-mail: office@hatborochamber.org
URL: http://hatborochamber.org
Contact: Chris Dubil, President
Released: Quarterly **Price:** included in membership dues.

57027 ■ *Chamber X-Change*
326 McKinley Ave., Ste. 102
Latrobe, PA 15650
Ph: (724)537-2671
Fax: (724)537-2690
Co. E-mail: info@latrobearea.com
URL: http://www.latrobearea.com
Released: Monthly

57028 ■ *ChamberInk*
245 Market St., Ste. 100
Johnstown, PA 15901-2910
Ph: (814)536-5107
Free: 800-790-4522

Fax: (814)539-5800
Co. E-mail: chamber@johnstownchamber.com
URL: http://www.johnstownchamber.com
Contact: Mr. Robert F. Layo, President
Released: Biweekly

57029 ■ *Chamberline*
53 W King St.
Shippensburg, PA 17257
Ph: (717)532-5509
Fax: (717)532-7501
Co. E-mail: chamber@shippensburg.org
URL: http://www.shippensburg.org
Contact: Barbara Hoover, President
Released: Quarterly

57030 ■ *ChamberNet*
200 Innovation Blvd., Ste. 150
State College, PA 16803
Ph: (814)234-1829
Fax: (814)234-5869
Co. E-mail: cbicc@cbicc.org
URL: http://www.cbicc.org
Contact: David Wise, President
Released: Quarterly

57031 ■ *The Changing Times*
12013 Frankstown Rd.
Penn Hills, PA 15235-3435
Ph: (412)795-8741
Fax: (412)795-7993
Co. E-mail: admin@pennhillschamber.org
URL: http://www.pennhillschamber.org
Contact: Denise Graham Shealey, President
Released: Monthly

57032 ■ Chester County Chamber of Business and Industry (CCCBI)
1600 Paoli Pike
Malvern, PA 19355-3375
Ph: (610)725-9100
Fax: (610)725-8479
Co. E-mail: nkeefer@cccbi.org
URL: http://www.cccbi.org
Contact: Nancy Keefer, President
Description: Serves as the voice of business in Chester County to positively influence the business climate through developing effective relationships with government, media and the public. Provides effective, results-oriented training, networking information, resources and other services. **Founded:** 1992. **Publications:** *The Voice* (Bimonthly).

57033 ■ Chilean and American Chamber of Commerce of Greater Philadelphia (CACCGP)
200 S Broad St., Ste. 700
Philadelphia, PA 19102-3813
Ph: (215)790-3690
Fax: (215)790-3600
Co. E-mail: mvercillo@greaterphilachamber.com
URL: http://caccgp.com
Contact: Mary Vercillo, Assistant
Description: Fosters increased and improved commercial and trade relations between the Republic of Chile and the Greater Philadelphia Region. Participates in a variety of activities and programs. **Founded:** 1988.

57034 ■ Clarion Area Chamber of Business and Industry
21 N 6th Ave.
Clarion, PA 16214
Ph: (814)226-9161
Fax: (814)226-4903
Co. E-mail: info@clarionpa.com
URL: http://www.clarionpa.com
Contact: Tracy J. Becker, Executive Director
Description: Promotes business and community development in Clarion County, PA. Monitors legislation; holds special events, seminars, and shop talks. Sponsors Autumn Leaf Festival, Clarion Summer Fun Fest and Fishing Derby. **Founded:** 1954. **Publications:** *Buyer's Guide*; *Demographic Packet*; *In Touch* (Bimonthly). **Awards:** Business of the Year (Annual); Citizen of the Year (Annual). **Telecommunication Services:** tracy@clarionpa.com.

57035 ■ Clearfield Chamber of Commerce
125 E Market St.
Clearfield, PA 16830
Ph: (814)765-7567
Fax: (814)765-6948
Co. E-mail: info@clearfieldchamber.com
URL: http://www.clearfieldchamber.com
Contact: Holly Bloom, Director
Description: Promotes business and community development in the Clearfield and Curwensville, PA area. **Founded:** 1887.

57036 ■ Clinton County Economic Partnership (CCEP)
212 N Jay St.
Lock Haven, PA 17745
Ph: (570)748-5782
Free: 888-388-6991
Fax: (570)893-0433
Co. E-mail: flanagan@kcnet.org
URL: http://www.clintoncountyinfo.com
Contact: Michael Flanagan, President
Description: Promotes business and community development in Clinton County, PA. Provides promotional materials. Holds Business After Hours party. **Founded:** 1989. **Publications:** *Chamber Update* (Monthly); *Partnership Press* (Monthly). **Educational Activities:** Exposition of Business and Industry in Clinton County (Annual).

57037 ■ *Clubs and Organization*
Citiscape
Hazleton, PA 18201-6288
Ph: (570)455-1509
Fax: (570)450-2013
Co. E-mail: dguydish@hazletonchamber.org
URL: http://www.hazletonchamber.org/
Contact: Donna Palermo, President
Price: free for members (first copy); $10, for nonprofits; $15, for nonmembers.

57038 ■ *Clubs and Organizations*
840 Hamilton St., Ste. 205
Allentown, PA 18101
Ph: (610)841-5860
Fax: (610)437-4907
Co. E-mail: info@lehighvalleychamber.org
URL: http://www.lehighvalleychamber.org
Contact: T. Anthony Iannelli, President
Released: Annual

57039 ■ *Clubs and Organizations Directory*
1019 Philadelphia St.
Indiana, PA 15701-1689
Ph: (724)465-2511
Fax: (724)465-3706
Co. E-mail: dphenry@wpia.net
URL: http://www.indianapa.com/chamber
Contact: Dana P. Henry, President
Released: Periodic **Price:** free for members; $50, for nonmembers.

57040 ■ Columbia Montour Chamber of Commerce
238 Market St.
Bloomsburg, PA 17815
Ph: (570)784-2522
Fax: (570)784-2661
Co. E-mail: chamber@columbiamontourchamber.com
URL: http://columbiamontourchamber.com
Contact: Joe Scopelliti, Chairman
Description: Promotes business and community development in the Bloomsburg, PA area. **Founded:** 1941. **Publications:** *E-biz* (Weekly). **Awards:** Athena Award (Annual); Community Class Awards (Annual).

57041 ■ *Commerce Comments*
436 Old York Rd.
Jenkintown, PA 19046
Ph: (215)887-5122
Fax: (215)887-3220
Co. E-mail: info@emccc.org
URL: http://www.emccc.org
Contact: Ms. Wendy Klinghoffer, Executive Director
Released: Bimonthly

57042 ■ *Commercial-Industrial Directory*
125 Market St., Ste. 1
Kittanning, PA 16201
Ph: (724)543-1305
Fax: (724)548-2951
Co. E-mail: accc1@accc1.comcastbiz.net
URL: http://www.armstrongchamber.org
Contact: Lynda Pozzuto, Executive Director
Released: Triennial

57043 ■ *Communicator*
91 S Progress Ave.
Pottsville, PA 17901
Ph: (570)622-1942
Free: 800-755-1942
Fax: (570)622-1638
Co. E-mail: info@schuylkillchamber.com
URL: http://www.schuylkillchamber.com
Contact: Robert S. Carl, Jr., Executive Director
Released: Monthly

57044 ■ *The Communicator*
538 W Market St.
Perkasie, PA 18944
Ph: (215)257-5390
Fax: (267)354-6924
Co. E-mail: pennridgecc@pennridge.com
URL: http://www.pennridge.com
Contact: Keith Smith, President
Released: Monthly

57045 ■ *Community Audit*
908 Diamond Park
Meadville, PA 16335
Ph: (814)337-8030
Fax: (814)337-8022
Co. E-mail: info@meadvillechamber.com
URL: http://www.meadvillechamber.com
Contact: Kathleen Bishop, President
Released: Periodic

57046 ■ *Connection*
152 High St., Ste. 360
Pottstown, PA 19464-5555
Ph: (610)326-2900
Fax: (610)970-9705
Co. E-mail: eileen@tricountyareachamber.com
URL: http://www.tricountyareachamber.com
Contact: Eileen Dautrich, President
Released: Monthly

57047 ■ *Connections*
840 Hamilton St., Ste. 205
Allentown, PA 18101
Ph: (610)841-5860
Fax: (610)437-4907
Co. E-mail: info@lehighvalleychamber.org
URL: http://www.lehighvalleychamber.org
Contact: T. Anthony Iannelli, President
Released: Monthly **Price:** available for members.

57048 ■ *Connections*
4211 Trindle Rd.
Camp Hill, PA 17011
Ph: (717)761-0702
Fax: (717)761-4315
Co. E-mail: wschamber@wschamber.org
URL: http://www.wschamber.org
Contact: Kathleen M. Mangan, President
Released: Monthly

57049 ■ *Connections*
798 Turnpike St.
Beaver, PA 15009
Ph: (724)775-3944
Fax: (724)728-9737
Co. E-mail: info@bcchamber.com
URL: http://www.beavercountychamber.com
Contact: Erica Wachtel, President
Released: Monthly

57050 ■ Corry Area Chamber of Commerce
221 N Center St.
Corry, PA 16407

Ph: (814)665-9925
Co. E-mail: cacc@velocity.net
URL: http://www.corrychamber.org
Contact: Jill Hall, Advisor
URL(s): www.corrypa.com. **Description:** Promotes its members and the Corry Area Community. **Founded:** 1921. **Publications:** *Chamber Report* (Quarterly); *Industrial & Membership Directory* (Periodic).

57051 ■ Coudersport Area Chamber of Commerce
PO Box 261
Coudersport, PA 16915
Ph: (814)274-8165
Fax: (814)274-8165
Co. E-mail: cacoc@coudersport.org
URL: http://www.coudersport.org
Contact: Stan Swank, President
Description: Promotes business and community development in Coudersport, PA.

57052 ■ *County Guide*
601 N Center Ave.
Somerset, PA 15501
Ph: (814)445-6431
Fax: (814)443-4313
Co. E-mail: info@somersetcountychamber.com
URL: http://www.somersetcountychamber.com
Contact: Sean Isgan, President

57053 ■ Cranberry Area Chamber of Commerce
2525 Rochester Rd., Ste. 200
Cranberry Township, PA 16066-6422
Ph: (724)776-4949
Fax: (724)776-5344
Co. E-mail: cranberryoffice@thechamberinc.com
URL: http://thechamberinc.com
Contact: Kathleen Sain, Chairperson
Description: Business executives, professional people, and other concerned citizens united to provide leadership and direction for the economic and social development of the community. Improves the business environment and builds a better area to live and work. **Founded:** 1986. **Publications:** *Business Review* (Monthly). **Educational Activities:** Business Development Group (Weekly).

57054 ■ Cresson Area Chamber of Commerce
PO Box 113
Cresson, PA 16630
Ph: (814)886-8100
Co. E-mail: info@cressonarea.com
URL: http://www.cressonarea.com
Contact: Howard Harkins, Chairman
Description: Promotes business and economic development in the Cresson, PA area. Supports local business and community interest.

57055 ■ *Crossroads*
185 Exton Square Mall
Exton, PA 19341
Ph: (610)363-7746
Fax: (610)363-2374
Co. E-mail: chamber@ercc.net
URL: http://www.ercc.net
Contact: Don Anders, President
Released: Monthly

57056 ■ Delaware County Chamber of Commerce (DCCC)
602 E Baltimore Pike
Media, PA 19063-1735
Ph: (610)565-3677
Fax: (610)565-1606
Co. E-mail: info@delcochamber.org
URL: http://www.delcochamber.org
Contact: Alex Charlton, President
Description: Promotes business and community development in Delaware County, PA. **Founded:** 1930. **Publications:** *Delco Chamber of Commerce Membership Directory* (Annual). **Educational Activities:** Expo (Annual).

57057 ■ *Delco Chamber of Commerce Membership Directory*
602 E Baltimore Pike
Media, PA 19063-1735
Ph: (610)565-3677
Fax: (610)565-1606
Co. E-mail: info@delcochamber.org
URL: http://www.delcochamber.org
Contact: Alex Charlton, President
Released: Annual

57058 ■ *Demographic Packet*
21 N 6th Ave.
Clarion, PA 16214
Ph: (814)226-9161
Fax: (814)226-4903
Co. E-mail: info@clarionpa.com
URL: http://www.clarionpa.com
Contact: Tracy J. Becker, Executive Director

57059 ■ *Directory of Clubs & Organizations*
William Penn Pl.
2790 Mosside Blvd., Ste. 715
Monroeville, PA 15146
Ph: (412)856-0622
Fax: (412)856-1030
Co. E-mail: macc@monroevillechamber.com
URL: http://www.monroevillechamber.com
Contact: Frank Horrigan, President
Released: Periodic

57060 ■ *Down to Business*
16 E Main St., Ste. 1
Ephrata, PA 17522
Ph: (717)738-9010
Fax: (717)738-9012
Co. E-mail: info@ephrata-area.org
URL: http://ephrataareac.le3.getliveedit.com
Contact: Kurt Brown, President
Released: Bimonthly

57061 ■ Downingtown-Thorndale Regional Chamber of Commerce
38 W Lancaster Ave.
Downingtown, PA 19335
Ph: (610)269-1523
Fax: (610)269-8713
Co. E-mail: splaugher@dtrcc.com
URL: http://www.dtrcc.com
Contact: Jillian M. Fragale, Executive Director
Description: Promotes business and community development in the Downingtown, PA area. **Founded:** 1945. **Publications:** *Your Chamber Matters* (Monthly).

57062 ■ *E-biz*
238 Market St.
Bloomsburg, PA 17815
Ph: (570)784-2522
Fax: (570)784-2661
Co. E-mail: chamber@columbiamontourchamber.com
URL: http://columbiamontourchamber.com
Contact: Joe Scopelliti, Chairman
Released: Weekly

57063 ■ East Liberty Quarter Chamber of Commerce (ELQCC)
5907 Penn Ave., Ste. 305
Pittsburgh, PA 15206
Ph: (412)661-9660
Fax: (412)661-9661
Co. E-mail: pbrecht@eastlibertychamber.org
URL: http://www.eastlibertychamber.org
Contact: Paul G. Brecht, Executive Director
Description: Promotes business and community development in the East Liberty Quarter area of Pittsburgh, PA. **Founded:** 1927.

57064 ■ Eastern Montgomery County Chamber of Commerce (EMCCC)
436 Old York Rd.
Jenkintown, PA 19046
Ph: (215)887-5122

Fax: (215)887-3220
Co. E-mail: info@emccc.org
URL: http://www.emccc.org
Contact: Ms. Wendy Klinghoffer, Executive Director
Description: Promotes business and community development in southeastern Montgomery County. Sponsors business card exchanges. **Founded:** 1933. **Publications:** *Commerce Comments* (Bimonthly); *Membership Directory and Buyer's Guide* (Annual). **Awards:** Humanitarian Organization of the Year (Annual); Lifetime Achievement (Annual); Small Business of the Year (Annual); Business of the Year (Annual); Business Person of the Year (Annual); Technology Business of the Year (Annual).

57065 ■ *Economic Profile*
96 S George St., 3rd Fl.
York, PA 17401-1611
Ph: (717)848-4000
Free: 800-673-2429
Fax: (717)843-6737
Co. E-mail: info@yorkchamber.com
URL: http://www.yorkchamber.com
Contact: Thomas E. Donley, President
E-mail: donley@yorkchamber.com
Released: Annual

57066 ■ Ellwood City Area Chamber of Commerce
314 5th St.
Ellwood City, PA 16117
Ph: (724)758-5501
Co. E-mail: info@ellwoodchamber.org
URL: http://www.ellwoodchamber.org
Contact: Terri Stramba, Executive Director
Description: Serves as the information center for Ellwood City area businesses and the community. Provides business information, business counseling, tourism brochures, maps, and referrals to a wide network of agencies, businesses and government offices. **Publications:** *The Business Brief* (Bimonthly).

57067 ■ Ephrata Area Chamber of Commerce
16 E Main St., Ste. 1
Ephrata, PA 17522
Ph: (717)738-9010
Fax: (717)738-9012
Co. E-mail: info@ephrata-area.org
URL: http://ephrataareac.le3.getliveedit.com
Contact: Kurt Brown, President
Description: Promotes business and community development in the Ephrata, PA area. **Publications:** *Down to Business* (Bimonthly).

57068 ■ *Erie*
208 E Bayfront Pkwy., Ste. 100
Erie, PA 16507
Ph: (814)454-7191
Fax: (814)459-0241
Co. E-mail: jdible@eriepa.com
URL: http://www.eriepa.com/chamber
Released: Monthly

57069 ■ *Erie Business and Community Resource Guide*
208 E Bayfront Pkwy., Ste. 100
Erie, PA 16507
Ph: (814)454-7191
Fax: (814)459-0241
Co. E-mail: jdible@eriepa.com
URL: http://www.eriepa.com/chamber
Price: $15, for members; $25, for nonmembers.

57070 ■ *Erie City/County Map*
208 E Bayfront Pkwy., Ste. 100
Erie, PA 16507
Ph: (814)454-7191
Fax: (814)459-0241
Co. E-mail: jdible@eriepa.com
URL: http://www.eriepa.com/chamber

57071 ■ *Erie County Fact Packet*
208 E Bayfront Pkwy., Ste. 100
Erie, PA 16507
Ph: (814)454-7191
Fax: (814)459-0241
Co. E-mail: jdible@eriepa.com
URL: http://www.eriepa.com/chamber

57072 ■ *Erie Extra*
208 E Bayfront Pkwy., Ste. 100
Erie, PA 16507
Ph: (814)454-7191
Fax: (814)459-0241
Co. E-mail: jdible@eriepa.com
URL: http://www.eriepa.com/chamber
Released: Biweekly **Price:** included in membership dues.

57073 ■ *ERIE Industrial Directory*
208 E Bayfront Pkwy., Ste. 100
Erie, PA 16507
Ph: (814)454-7191
Fax: (814)459-0241
Co. E-mail: jdible@eriepa.com
URL: http://www.eriepa.com/chamber
Released: Periodic

57074 ■ Erie Regional Chamber and Growth Partnership
208 E Bayfront Pkwy., Ste. 100
Erie, PA 16507
Ph: (814)454-7191
Fax: (814)459-0241
Co. E-mail: jdible@eriepa.com
URL: http://www.eriepa.com/chamber

Description: Promotes business and community development in Erie County, PA. Promotes tourism. Provides assistance and information. Maintains Economic/Business Resource Center and Videoconference Center. **Founded:** 2002. **Publications:** *Erie* (Monthly); *Erie Extra* (Biweekly); *Tourist/Motorcoach* (Periodic); *Erie Business and Community Resource Guide*; *Erie City/County Map*; *Erie County Fact Packet*; *ERIE Industrial Directory* (Periodic). **Educational Activities:** North Coast Quality Week (Annual). **Awards:** ATHENA PowerLink Award (Annual); Louis J. Tullio Community Service Award (Annual); Team Quality Award of Western Pennsylvania (Annual); Tri-State Regional Quality Award (Annual).

57075 ■ Exton Region Chamber of Commerce (ERCC)
185 Exton Square Mall
Exton, PA 19341
Ph: (610)363-7746
Fax: (610)363-2374
Co. E-mail: chamber@ercc.net
URL: http://www.ercc.net
Contact: Don Anders, President

Description: Promotes business and community development in Exton and surrounding Central Chester County, PA area. Works on regional issues such as the environment, legislation, and road improvements. Conducts scholarship fundraisers and silent/live auction. Sponsors annual golf outing. **Founded:** 1960. **Publications:** *Crossroads* (Monthly); *Membership and Resource Directory* (Annual). **Educational Activities:** Awards Dinner (Annual). **Awards:** Chairman's Award (Annual); Community Service Award (Annual); Entrepreneur of the Year (Annual); Harold Martin Business Leadership Award (Annual); Presidents Award (Annual).

57076 ■ Fayette Chamber of Commerce
65 W Main St.
Uniontown, PA 15401-2124
Ph: (724)437-4571
Free: 800-916-9365
Fax: (724)438-3304
Co. E-mail: info@faycham.org
URL: http://www.fayettechamber.com
Contact: Muriel J. Nuttall, Executive Director

Description: Promotes business and community development in Fayette County, PA. **Founded:** 1945. **Publications:** *Business and Industry*.

57077 ■ Franklin Area Chamber of Commerce
1327 Liberty St.
Franklin, PA 16323-1528
Ph: (814)432-5823
Free: 888-547-2377

Fax: (814)437-2453
Co. E-mail: administrator@franklinareachamber.org
URL: http://www.franklinareachamber.org
Contact: Lynn Cochran, Executive Director
Description: Provides economic, educational, and legislative information and assistance which can be used by members to achieve profit, progress, and prosperity. Unites hundreds of business and professional firms, thus creating a unique central agency working to improve business and build a better community. **Founded:** 1913. **Awards:** Gold Shovel Awards; Man and Woman of the Year Awards (Annual).

57078 ■ French-American Chamber of Commerce
1528 Walnut St., Ste. 2020
Philadelphia, PA 19102-3613
Ph: (215)545-0123
Fax: (215)545-0144
Co. E-mail: info@faccphila.org
URL: http://www.faccphila.org
Contact: Judith L. Ujobai, Executive Director
Description: Seeks to contribute, through the efforts of the chapters and members, to the development and improvement of economic, commercial, and financial relations between France and the United States. **Founded:** 1989.

57079 ■ *From the Chamber...*
17 E Main St.
North East, PA 16428
Ph: (814)725-4262
Fax: (814)725-3994
Co. E-mail: info@nechamber.org
URL: http://www.nechamber.org
Contact: Anne Saxer, President
Released: Biweekly

57080 ■ Fulton County Chamber of Commerce and Tourism
PO Box 141
McConnellsburg, PA 17233
Ph: (717)485-4064
Fax: (717)325-0023
Co. E-mail: info@fultoncountypa.com
URL: http://www.fultoncountypa.com
Contact: Dwight Washabaugh, President
Description: Helps to promote business and stimulate the economic successes of Fulton County as a whole. **Founded:** 1951.

57081 ■ German American Chamber of Commerce - Philadelphia (GACC)
1 Penn Center, Ste. 340
1617 John F. Kennedy Blvd.
Philadelphia, PA 19103
Ph: (215)665-1585
Fax: (215)665-0375
Co. E-mail: admin@gaccphiladelphia.com
URL: http://www.gaccphiladelphia.com
Contact: Ms. Barbara Afanassiev, President
Description: Promotes development of trade and investment opportunities between the United States and Germany. **Founded:** 1989.

57082 ■ Gettysburg-Adams County Area Chamber of Commerce
18 Carlisle St., Ste. 203
Gettysburg, PA 17325
Ph: (717)334-8151
Fax: (717)334-3368
Co. E-mail: info@gettysburg-chamber.org
URL: http://www.gettysburg-chamber.org
Contact: Carrie S. Stuart, President
Description: Promotes business and community development in Adams County, PA. **Founded:** 1919. **Publications:** *Chamber Chatter* (Monthly); *Relocation Packet*; *Major Employers of Adams County*; *Major Manufacturers of Adams County*. **Awards:** Education Mini Grants (Annual); Volunteer of the Year (Annual); Outstanding Citizen of the Year (Annual); Small Business Person of the Year (Annual).

57083 ■ *Government Officials Guide*
3211 N Front St., Ste. 201
Harrisburg, PA 17110-1342
Ph: (717)232-4099
Free: 877-883-8339

Fax: (717)232-5184
Co. E-mail: info@hbgrc.org
URL: http://www.harrisburgregionalchamber.org
Contact: David E. Black, President
Price: $20, regular; $25, by mail.

57084 ■ *Great Pittston Life*
104 Kennedy Blvd.
Pittston, PA 18640-0704
Ph: (570)655-1424
Fax: (570)655-0336
Co. E-mail: info@pittstonchamber.org
URL: http://pittstonchamber.org/index_files/Page266.htm
Contact: Rosemary Dessoye, Executive Vice President

57085 ■ Great Valley Regional Chamber of Commerce (GVRCC)
5 Great Valley Pkwy.
Malvern, PA 19355
Ph: (610)889-2069
Fax: (610)889-2063
Co. E-mail: greatchamber@gvrcc.org
URL: http://www.gvrcc.org
Contact: Patrick Michaels, Chairperson
Description: Supports and promotes business and economic development which ensures that Great Valley Region remains an ideal area to live, work, and invest. **Founded:** 1989.

57086 ■ Greater BucksMont Chamber of Commerce
PO Box 3014
Warminster, PA 18974
Ph: (215)672-6633
Fax: (215)672-7637
Co. E-mail: admin@bucksmontchamber.com
URL: http://www.bucksmontchamber.com
Contact: Susan Kaminski, President

57087 ■ Greater Carbondale Chamber of Commerce
27 N Main St.
Carbondale, PA 18407
Ph: (570)282-1690
Fax: (570)282-1206
Co. E-mail: info@carbondalechamber.org
URL: http://www.carbondalechamber.org
Contact: Stephen Ursich, President
Description: Promotes business and community development in the Carbondale, PA area.

57088 ■ Greater Carlisle Area Chamber of Commerce
PO Box 572
Carlisle, PA 17013
Ph: (717)243-4515
Fax: (717)243-4446
Co. E-mail: mcrowley@carlislechamber.org
URL: http://www.carlislechamber.org
Contact: Ms. Michelle Hornick Crowley, President
Description: Promotes business and community development in the Carlisle, PA area. Conducts trade fairs, seminars, and social activities. **Scope:** business development, Carlisle area/Cumberland County. **Founded:** 1910. **Subscriptions:** 100 articles books. **Publications:** *Business and Industry* (Quarterly); *Quality of Life*; *News Briefs* (Bimonthly).

57089 ■ Greater Chambersburg Chamber of Commerce
100 Lincoln Way E, Ste. A
Chambersburg, PA 17201
Ph: (717)264-7101
Fax: (717)267-0399
Co. E-mail: chamber@chambersburg.org
URL: http://www.chambersburg.org
Contact: David G. Sciamanna, President
Description: Advocates and promotes economic growth through the free enterprise system, helps members prosper, promotes planned community growth and enhances the quality of life in the Chambersburg area. **Founded:** 1911. **Publications:** *Chamber Outlook* (11/year).

57090 ■ Greater Connellsville Chamber of Commerce
923 W Crawford Ave.
Connellsville, PA 15425
Ph: (724)628-5500
Fax: (724)628-5676
Co. E-mail: info@greaterconnellsville.org
URL: http://www.greaterconnellsville.org
Contact: Bryan S. Kisiel, President
Description: Promotes business and community development in Connellsville, PA area.

57091 ■ Greater DuBois Chamber of Commerce - Economic Development
1st Commonwealth Bank Bldg.
3 S Brady St., Ste. 205
DuBois, PA 15801
Ph: (814)371-5010
Fax: (814)371-5005
Co. E-mail: dacc@duboispachamber.com
URL: http://www.duboispachamber.com
Contact: Nancy J. Micks, President
Description: Promotes business and community development in the Du Bois, PA area. Holds monthly breakfast, annual dinner, ribbon cuttings, and business expo. **Founded:** 1944. **Publications:** *Chamber Chatter* (Monthly).

57092 ■ Greater Glenside Chamber of Commerce (GGCC)
PO Box 182
Glenside, PA 19038
Ph: (215)500-4080
Co. E-mail: info@glensidechamber.org
URL: http://www.glensidechamber.org
Contact: Barbara A. Nye, President
Description: Promotes business and community development in the Glenside, PA area. Sponsors craft show and car show. **Founded:** 1963. **Publications:** *Chamber Chat* (Bimonthly). **Awards:** Beautification Awards (Annual); Merchant of the Year.

57093 ■ Greater Hatboro Chamber of Commerce
Red Barn Mall
120 S York Rd.
Hatboro, PA 19040
Ph: (215)956-9540
Fax: (215)956-9635
Co. E-mail: office@hatborochamber.org
URL: http://hatborochamber.org
Contact: Chris Dubil, President
Description: Promotes business and community development in Hatboro, PA. Sponsors Christmas parade, Little Miss. and Mr. Hatboro Contest, County Music Festival, sidewalk sale festival, car show, Halloween and Christmas stroll. **Founded:** 1960. **Publications:** *Chamber Voice* (Quarterly); *Hatboro Online Business Directory*.

57094 ■ Greater Hazleton Chamber of Commerce
Citiscape
Hazleton, PA 18201-6288
Ph: (570)455-1509
Fax: (570)450-2013
Co. E-mail: dguydish@hazletonchamber.org
URL: http://www.hazletonchamber.org/
Contact: Donna Palermo, President
Description: Promotes business and community development in the Hazleton, PA area. **Founded:** 1953. **Publications:** *Greater Hazleton Image*; *Buyer's Guide*; *Clubs and Organization*; *Hazleton Area Image*; *Greater Hazleton Chamber of Commerce--Industrial Directory*; *Hazleton Industrial Directory*; *Greater Hazleton Chamber of Commerce--Club & Organization Directory*; *Greater Hazleton Chamber of Commerce--Clubs and Organization Directory*; *Greater Hazleton Chamber of Commerce--Membership Directory/Buyer's Guide*; *Greater Hazleton Chamber of Commerce--Membership Directory/Buyer's Guide*. **Educational Activities:** Golf Outing and On-Course Trade Show (Annual). **Telecommunication Services:** dpalermo@hazletonchamber.org.

57095 ■ Greater Johnstown/Cambria County Chamber of Commerce
245 Market St., Ste. 100
Johnstown, PA 15901-2910
Ph: (814)536-5107
Free: 800-790-4522
Fax: (814)539-5800
Co. E-mail: chamber@johnstownchamber.com
URL: http://www.johnstownchamber.com
Contact: Mr. Robert F. Layo, President
Description: Stimulates and encourage an informed membership, to be the advocate of business and to form private/public partnerships to promote the health and growth of area business and the community. **Publications:** *ChamberInk* (Biweekly). **Educational Activities:** Showcase for Commerce (Annual). **Telecommunication Services:** bob@johnstownchamber.com.

57096 ■ Greater Lehigh Valley Chamber of Commerce
840 Hamilton St., Ste. 205
Allentown, PA 18101
Ph: (610)841-5860
Fax: (610)437-4907
Co. E-mail: info@lehighvalleychamber.org
URL: http://www.lehighvalleychamber.org
Contact: T. Anthony Iannelli, President
Description: Seeks to improve the economy and quality of life in the Lehigh Valley, PA area. **Founded:** 1872. **Publications:** *Clubs and Organizations* (Annual); *Connections* (Monthly); *Relocation Guide*. **Awards:** Excellence in Business Awards (Annual). **Telecommunication Services:** tonyi@lehighvalleychamber.org.

57097 ■ Greater Mansfield Area Chamber of Commerce
51-B S Main St.
Mansfield, PA 16933
Ph: (570)662-3442
Fax: (570)662-0259
Co. E-mail: info@mansfield.org
URL: http://www.mansfield.org
Contact: Gale Hall, Director
Description: Promotes business and community development in the Mansfield, PA area. Sponsors annual Home for the Holidays Christmas Celebration and 1890s celebration. **Founded:** 1985. **Publications:** *Chamber Update* (Monthly). **Telecommunication Services:** ghall@pplweb.com.

57098 ■ Greater Northeast Philadelphia Chamber of Commerce (GNPCC)
8601 Roosevelt Blvd.
Philadelphia, PA 19152-2001
Ph: (215)332-3400
Fax: (215)332-6050
Co. E-mail: gnpccoffice@aol.com
URL: http://www.gnpcc.org
Contact: Al Taubenberger, President
Description: Represents business and professional interests. Serves as a catalyst for growth and promotes the area's residential and commercial assets. **Founded:** 1922.

57099 ■ Greater Philadelphia Chamber of Commerce
200 S Broad St., Ste. 700
Philadelphia, PA 19102
Ph: (215)545-1234
Fax: (215)790-3600
URL: http://www.greaterphilachamber.com
Contact: Rob Wonderling, President
Description: Seeks to facilitate and promote quality and excellence in business, governmental, and educational organizations in the Delaware Valley area of Delaware, New Jersey, and Pennsylvania. Offers custom designed and project team training and consultant referral. Provides print and video resources. Sponsors 20 seminars per year and PACE Network. **Founded:** 1983. **Subscriptions:** video recordings. **Awards:** Quality Recognition Award (Annual).

57100 ■ Greater Pittsburgh Chamber of Commerce
c/o Allegheny Conference on Community Development and Affiliates
11 Stanwix St., 17th Fl.
Pittsburgh, PA 15222-1312
Ph: (412)392-4500
Fax: (412)392-4520
Co. E-mail: info@pittsburghchamber.com
URL: http://www.alleghenyconference.org/Chamber
Contact: Greg Babe, Chairman
Description: Promotes business and community development in Greater Pittsburgh, PA.

57101 ■ Greater Pittston Chamber of Commerce
104 Kennedy Blvd.
Pittston, PA 18640-0704
Ph: (570)655-1424
Fax: (570)655-0336
Co. E-mail: info@pittstonchamber.org
URL: http://pittstonchamber.org/index_files/Page266.htm
Contact: Rosemary Dessoye, Executive Vice President Secretary
Description: Promotes business and community development in the Pittston, PA area. **Founded:** 1920. **Publications:** *Great Pittston Life*.

57102 ■ Greater Pocono Chamber of Commerce (GPCC)
556 Main St.
Stroudsburg, PA 18360-2093
Ph: (570)421-4433
Fax: (570)424-7281
Co. E-mail: rphillips@greaterpoconochamber.com
URL: http://www.greaterpoconochamber.com
Contact: Robert Phillips, President
Description: Promotes business and community development in the Monroe County, PA area. **Founded:** 1910. **Publications:** *Impact* (Monthly). **Educational Activities:** Business Trade Show (Annual). **Awards:** Athena (Annual); Business (Annual); Citizen (Annual); Humanitarians of the Year (Annual).

57103 ■ Greater Scranton Chamber of Commerce
c/o Joanne Stetz
PO Box 431
Scranton, PA 18501-0431
Ph: (570)342-7711
Fax: (570)347-6262
Co. E-mail: jstetz@scrantonchamber.com
URL: http://www.scrantonchamber.com
Contact: Austin J. Burke, President
Description: Provides members with the opportunity to forge bonds that serve as the foundations for the growth of Greater Scranton. **Founded:** 1867. **Publications:** *Leadership Lackawanna News* (Semiannual); *Newsbriefs* (Bimonthly); *The Scranton Plan News* (Quarterly).

57104 ■ Greater Susquehanna Valley Chamber of Commerce (GSVCC)
c/o Charlie Ross, Pres./CEO
PO Box 10
Shamokin Dam, PA 17876-0010
Ph: (570)743-4100
Free: 800-410-2880
Fax: (570)743-1221
Co. E-mail: info@gsvcc.org
URL: http://www.gsvcc.org
Contact: Charlie Ross, President
Description: Businesses in Snyder, Union, Northumberland, and Montour Counties. Strives to advance business environment and quality of life by providing programs and services which promote civic, social, business and economic growth and development. **Publications:** *The Voice of the Valley* (Monthly). **Awards:** Business of the Year (Annual); Karen L. Hackman Star of Excellence Award (Annual); Small Business of the Year (Annual).

57105 ■ Greater Waynesboro Chamber of Commerce
5 Roadside Ave.
Waynesboro, PA 17268-1694
Ph: (717)762-7123

Fax: (717)762-7124
Co. E-mail: director@waynesboro.org
URL: http://www.waynesboro.org
Contact: Ms. Carlene Willhide, Executive Director

Description: Promotes business and community development in the Waynesboro, PA area. Convention/Meeting: none. **Founded:** 1920. **Publications:** *Member Directory and Buyers Guide* (Annual).

57106 ■ Greater White Haven Chamber of Commerce
PO Box 363
White Haven, PA 18661
Ph: (570)443-0302
Co. E-mail: info@whitehavenchamber.org
URL: http://whitehavenchamber.org
Contact: Susan Eckert, President

Description: Facilitates the people to work together for the economic growth of the community. Raises the standard of living in the White Haven area.

57107 ■ Greencastle-Antrim Chamber of Commerce
217 E Baltimore St.
Greencastle, PA 17225
Ph: (717)597-4610
Fax: (717)597-0709
Co. E-mail: info@greencastlepachamber.org
URL: http://www.greencastlepachamber.org
Contact: Joel Fridgen, Executive Director

Description: Promotes business and community development in Antrim Township and Greencastle, PA. **Founded:** 1959. **Publications:** *Castle Views* (Bimonthly).

57108 ■ Grove City Area Chamber of Commerce
119 S Broad St.
Grove City, PA 16127
Ph: (724)458-6410
Fax: (724)458-6841
Co. E-mail: gcchamber@shopgrovecity.com
URL: http://www.shopgrovecity.com
Contact: Beth Black, Executive Director

Description: Promotes business and community development in the Grove City, PA area. **Founded:** 1952.

57109 ■ Hanover Area Chamber of Commerce (HACC)
146 Carlisle St.
Hanover, PA 17331
Ph: (717)637-6130
Fax: (717)637-9127
Co. E-mail: office@hanoverchamber.com
URL: http://www.hanoverchamber.com
Contact: Gary Laird, President

Description: Promotes business and community development in Hanover, Littlestown, McSherrystown, New Oxford, Spring Grove, Abbottstown, East Berlin, and Codrus, PA. **Founded:** 1923. **Publications:** *Chamber Connections* (Monthly); *Chamber Report* (Monthly); *Hanover Area Church Directory* (Annual); *Quality of Life Directory* (Biennial); *Relocation Packet* (Semiannual).

57110 ■ Hanover Area Church Directory
146 Carlisle St.
Hanover, PA 17331
Ph: (717)637-6130
Fax: (717)637-9127
Co. E-mail: office@hanoverchamber.com
URL: http://www.hanoverchamber.com
Contact: Gary Laird, President
Released: Annual

57111 ■ Harrisburg Regional Chamber of Commerce
3211 N Front St., Ste. 201
Harrisburg, PA 17110-1342
Ph: (717)232-4099
Free: 877-883-8339

Fax: (717)232-5184
Co. E-mail: info@hbgrc.org
URL: http://www.harrisburgregionalchamber.org
Contact: David E. Black, President

Description: Promotes business and community development in the Harrisburg, PA area. **Founded:** 1912. **Publications:** *Government Officials Guide*; *Harrisburg Regional Industrial Directory*; *The Harrisburg Regional News* (Quarterly); *Membership Directory and Regional Profile*; *Who's Who in the Capital Region* (Annual); *Harrisburg Regional Chamber of Commerce--Membership Directory and Regional Profile* (Annual). **Awards:** Athena Award (Annual); Small Business of the Year (Annual). **Telecommunication Services:** dblack@hbgrc.org.

57112 ■ Harrisburg Regional Industrial Directory
3211 N Front St., Ste. 201
Harrisburg, PA 17110-1342
Ph: (717)232-4099
Free: 877-883-8339
Fax: (717)232-5184
Co. E-mail: info@hbgrc.org
URL: http://www.harrisburgregionalchamber.org
Contact: David E. Black, President
Price: $45, regular; $50, by mail.

57113 ■ The Harrisburg Regional News
3211 N Front St., Ste. 201
Harrisburg, PA 17110-1342
Ph: (717)232-4099
Free: 877-883-8339
Fax: (717)232-5184
Co. E-mail: info@hbgrc.org
URL: http://www.harrisburgregionalchamber.org
Contact: David E. Black, President
Released: Quarterly

57114 ■ Hatboro Online Business Directory
Red Barn Mall
120 S York Rd.
Hatboro, PA 19040
Ph: (215)956-9540
Fax: (215)956-9635
Co. E-mail: office@hatborochamber.org
URL: http://hatborochamber.org
Contact: Chris Dubil, President
Price: $170, /year for members; $340, /year for nonmembers.

57115 ■ Hatfield Chamber of Commerce
PO Box 445
Hatfield, PA 19440-0445
Ph: (215)855-3335
Fax: (215)855-3335
Co. E-mail: admin@hatfieldchamber.com
URL: http://www.hatfieldchamber.com
Contact: Lawrence Stevens, Executive Director
Description: Organized to advance the economic, industrial, professional, cultural and civic welfare of Hatfield Borough and Hatfield Township. **Founded:** 1927. **Publications:** *Business Spotlight*. **Educational Activities:** Benevolence Fund Drive (Annual).

57116 ■ Hazleton Area Image
Citiscape
Hazleton, PA 18201-6288
Ph: (570)455-1509
Fax: (570)450-2013
Co. E-mail: dguydish@hazletonchamber.org
URL: http://www.hazletonchamber.org/
Contact: Donna Palermo, President
Price: free.

57117 ■ Historic Brochure
202 W Central Ave.
Titusville, PA 16354
Ph: (814)827-2941
Fax: (814)827-2914
Co. E-mail: christab@titusvillechamber.com
URL: http://titusvillechamber.com
Contact: Christa Battin, Executive Director
Released: Periodic

57118 ■ Historical Walking Tour of Ridgway
300 Main St.
Ridgway, PA 15853
Ph: (814)776-1424

Fax: (814)772-2188
Co. E-mail: ridgwaychamber@ncentral.com
URL: http://www.ridgwaychamber.com
Contact: Cathy Grove, President

57119 ■ Images
41 Chestnut St.
Sharon, PA 16146
Ph: (724)981-5880
Fax: (724)981-5480
Co. E-mail: deanne@svchamber.com
URL: http://www.svchamber.com
Contact: Eric Brown, President
Released: Bimonthly **Price:** $5, /year.

57120 ■ Images of Greater West Chester
119 N High St.
West Chester, PA 19380-3145
Ph: (610)696-4046
Fax: (610)696-9110
Co. E-mail: info@gwcc.org
URL: http://www.gwcc.org
Contact: Mark Yoder, President
Released: Annual **Price:** free for members.

57121 ■ Images Magazine
604 Cumberland St.
Lebanon, PA 17042-5272
Ph: (717)273-3727
Fax: (717)273-7940
Co. E-mail: info@lvchamber.org
URL: http://www.lvchamber.org
Contact: Larry Bowman, President
Released: Annual

57122 ■ Impact
556 Main St.
Stroudsburg, PA 18360-2093
Ph: (570)421-4433
Fax: (570)424-7281
Co. E-mail: rphillips@greaterpoconochamber.com
URL: http://www.greaterpoconochamber.com
Contact: Robert Phillips, President
Released: Monthly **Price:** included in membership dues.

57123 ■ Import/Export Directory
96 S George St., 3rd Fl.
York, PA 17401-1611
Ph: (717)848-4000
Free: 800-673-2429
Fax: (717)843-6737
Co. E-mail: info@yorkchamber.com
URL: http://www.yorkchamber.com
Contact: Thomas E. Donley, President
E-mail: donley@yorkchamber.com
Released: Annual

57124 ■ Import/Export Guide
100 S Queen St.
Lancaster, PA 17603
Ph: (717)397-3531
Fax: (717)293-3159
Co. E-mail: info@lcci.com
URL: http://www.lancasterchamber.com
Contact: Thomas Baldrige, President
Released: Annual

57125 ■ In the Spotlight
3501 Brownsville Rd.
Pittsburgh, PA 15227-3115
Ph: (412)884-1233
Co. E-mail: secretary@bbwchamber.com
URL: http://www.bbwchamber.com
Contact: Debbie Maddock, President
Released: Monthly

57126 ■ In Touch
21 N 6th Ave.
Clarion, PA 16214
Ph: (814)226-9161
Fax: (814)226-4903
Co. E-mail: info@clarionpa.com
URL: http://www.clarionpa.com
Contact: Tracy J. Becker, Executive Director
Released: Bimonthly

57127 ■ Indian Valley Chamber of Commerce (IVCC)
100 Penn Ave.
Telford, PA 18969
Ph: (215)723-9472
Fax: (215)723-2490
Co. E-mail: ivchamber@indianvalleychamber.com
URL: http://www.indianvalleychamber.com
Contact: Sharon L. Minninger, Executive Director
Description: Promotes business and community development in the Souderton, PA area. **Founded:** 1970. **Publications:** *The Participant* (Bimonthly).

57128 ■ Indian Valley Chamber of Commerce (IVCC)
PO Box 64077
Souderton, PA 18964
Ph: (215)723-9472
Fax: (215)723-2490
Co. E-mail: ivchamber@indianvalleychamber.com
URL: http://www.indianvalleychamber.com
Contact: Sharon L. Minninger, Executive Director
Description: Promotes business and community development in Indian Valley, PA area. **Founded:** 1970.

57129 ■ Indiana County Chamber of Commerce
1019 Philadelphia St.
Indiana, PA 15701-1689
Ph: (724)465-2511
Fax: (724)465-3706
Co. E-mail: dphenry@wpia.net
URL: http://www.indianapa.com/chamber
Contact: Dana P. Henry, President
Description: Promotes business and community development in Indiana County, PA. Provides New Business Assistance Kits and Newcomers Kits. Maintains liaison with government agencies. Operates Indiana County Development Corp.. Holds Business After Hours parties. **Founded:** 1912. **Publications:** *Business Directory* (Periodic); *Clubs and Organizations Directory* (Periodic); *Industrial Directory* (Periodic); *Update* (Periodic).

57130 ■ Industrial Directory
1019 Philadelphia St.
Indiana, PA 15701-1689
Ph: (724)465-2511
Fax: (724)465-3706
Co. E-mail: dphenry@wpia.net
URL: http://www.indianapa.com/chamber
Contact: Dana P. Henry, President
Released: Periodic

57131 ■ Industrial Directory
326 McKinley Ave., Ste. 102
Latrobe, PA 15650
Ph: (724)537-2671
Fax: (724)537-2690
Co. E-mail: info@latrobearea.com
URL: http://www.latrobearea.com
Released: Annual

57132 ■ Industrial Directory
908 Diamond Park
Meadville, PA 16335
Ph: (814)337-8030
Fax: (814)337-8022
Co. E-mail: info@meadvillechamber.com
URL: http://www.meadvillechamber.com
Contact: Kathleen Bishop, President
Released: Periodic

57133 ■ Industrial Directory
William Penn Pl.
2790 Mosside Blvd., Ste. 715
Monroeville, PA 15146
Ph: (412)856-0622
Fax: (412)856-1030
Co. E-mail: macc@monroevillechamber.com
URL: http://www.monroevillechamber.com
Contact: Frank Horrigan, President
Released: Periodic

57134 ■ Industrial Directory
300 Main St.
Ridgway, PA 15853
Ph: (814)776-1424

Fax: (814)772-2188
Co. E-mail: ridgwaychamber@ncentral.com
URL: http://www.ridgwaychamber.com
Contact: Cathy Grove, President
Released: Annual

57135 ■ Industrial Directory
53 S St. Marys St.
St. Marys, PA 15857
Ph: (814)781-3804
Fax: (814)781-7302
Co. E-mail: info@stmaryschamber.org
URL: http://www.stmaryschamber.org
Contact: Mark Rupprecht, President

57136 ■ Industrial Directory
202 W Central Ave.
Titusville, PA 16354
Ph: (814)827-2941
Fax: (814)827-2914
Co. E-mail: christab@titusvillechamber.com
URL: http://titusvillechamber.com
Contact: Christa Battin, Executive Director
Released: Periodic **Price:** free.

57137 ■ Industrial Directory
100 W 3rd St.
Williamsport, PA 17701
Ph: (570)326-1971
Fax: (570)321-1209
Co. E-mail: chamber@williamsport.org
URL: http://www.williamsport.org
Contact: Vincent J. Matteo, President
Released: Semiannual

57138 ■ Industrial Directory Labels
100 S Queen St.
Lancaster, PA 17603
Ph: (717)397-3531
Fax: (717)293-3159
Co. E-mail: info@lcci.com
URL: http://www.lancasterchamber.com
Contact: Thomas Baldrige, President
Released: Annual **Price:** $100, for members; $200, for nonmembers; $3, plus shipping and handling.

57139 ■ Industrial & Membership Directory
221 N Center St.
Corry, PA 16407
Ph: (814)665-9925
Co. E-mail: cacc@velocity.net
URL: http://www.corrychamber.org
Contact: Jill Hall, Advisor
Released: Periodic

57140 ■ Industrial Parks Guide
100 S Queen St.
Lancaster, PA 17603
Ph: (717)397-3531
Fax: (717)293-3159
Co. E-mail: info@lcci.com
URL: http://www.lancasterchamber.com
Contact: Thomas Baldrige, President
Released: Periodic

57141 ■ Insites
Released: Quarterly

57142 ■ Jim Thorpe Chamber of Commerce
PO Box 164
Jim Thorpe, PA 18229
Ph: (570)325-5810
Free: 888-JIM-THOR
Co. E-mail: info@jimthorpe.org
URL: http://jimthorpe.org
Description: Promotes business and tourism. Activities include Jim Thorpe Birthday weekend, Fall Foliage Festival, Renaissance Festival and Old Time Christmas Celebration. **Founded:** 1982. **Publications:** *Jim Thorpe' Visitor's Guide* (Annual).

57143 ■ Jim Thorpe' Visitor's Guide
PO Box 164
Jim Thorpe, PA 18229
Ph: (570)325-5810
Free: 888-JIM-THOR
Co. E-mail: info@jimthorpe.org
URL: http://jimthorpe.org
Released: Annual **Price:** free for members.

57144 ■ Johnsonburg Chamber of Commerce
501 High St.
Johnsonburg, PA 15845-1235
Ph: (814)965-4793
URL: http://www.co.elk.pa.us
Description: Promotes business and community development in Johnsonburg, PA.

57145 ■ Juniata River Valley Chamber of Commerce and Visitors Bureau (JVACC)
Historic Courthouse
1 W Market St., Ste. 119
Lewistown, PA 17044
Ph: (717)248-6713
Fax: (717)248-6714
Co. E-mail: info@juniatarivervalley.org
URL: http://www.juniatarivervalley.org
Contact: Jim Tunall, President
Description: Offers low-cost insurance and phone service to members and offers information on the community to people from the area and from other areas. Holds programs to inform the public about happenings in the community.

57146 ■ Lancaster Chamber of Commerce and Industry
100 S Queen St.
Lancaster, PA 17603
Ph: (717)397-3531
Fax: (717)293-3159
Co. E-mail: info@lcci.com
URL: http://www.lancasterchamber.com
Contact: Thomas Baldrige, President
Description: Promotes business and community development in Lancaster, PA. Provides governmental liaison. Promotes employment and training of unskilled workers. Sponsors Bizcorp, Economic Development Company of Lancaster County, Foundation of the Lancaster Chamber, Lancaster City Partnership, Lancaster County Business Group on Health, Lancaster Enterprise, and Leadership Lancaster. **Founded:** 1872. **Publications:** *Buyer's Guide* (Periodic); *Chamber News*; *Import/Export Guide* (Annual); *Industrial Directory Labels* (Annual); *Industrial Parks Guide* (Periodic); *Lancaster Marketplace*; *Legislative Update* (Periodic); *Major Employer Directory* (Annual); *Business Development News* (Monthly); *Sample Employee Policy Handbook*.

57147 ■ Lancaster Marketplace
100 S Queen St.
Lancaster, PA 17603
Ph: (717)397-3531
Fax: (717)293-3159
Co. E-mail: info@lcci.com
URL: http://www.lancasterchamber.com
Contact: Thomas Baldrige, President

57148 ■ Latrobe Area Chamber of Commerce
326 McKinley Ave., Ste. 102
Latrobe, PA 15650
Ph: (724)537-2671
Fax: (724)537-2690
Co. E-mail: info@latrobearea.com
URL: http://www.latrobearea.com
Description: Promotes business and community development in the Latrobe, PA area. **Founded:** 1945. **Publications:** *Chamber X-Change* (Monthly); *Industrial Directory* (Annual); *Welcome to Latrobe Area Neighborhood*. **Awards:** Community Service Award (Annual).

57149 ■ Laurel Highlands Chamber of Commerce (LHCC)
537 W Main St.
Mount Pleasant, PA 15666
Ph: (724)547-7521
Co. E-mail: marjorie@laurelhighlandschamber.com
URL: http://www.laurelhighlandschamber.com
Contact: Patty McGuire, Secretary Treasurer
Description: Promotes business and community development in the Mt. Pleasant, PA area. **Founded:** 1949. **Publications:** *Chamber Newsletter* (Monthly).

57150 ■ Lawrence County Chamber of Commerce
138 W Washington St.
New Castle, PA 16101-3910

Ph: (724)654-5593
Fax: (724)654-3330
Co. E-mail: info@lawrencecountychamber.org
URL: http://www.lawrencecountychamber.org
Contact: William J. Flannery, President
Description: Strives to recruit and enhance business, as well as foster community development in Lawrence County, Mississippi.

57151 ■ *Leadership Lackawanna News*
c/o Joanne Stetz
PO Box 431
Scranton, PA 18501-0431
Ph: (570)342-7711
Fax: (570)347-6262
Co. E-mail: jstetz@scrantonchamber.com
URL: http://www.scrantonchamber.com
Contact: Austin J. Burke, President
Released: Semiannual

57152 ■ Lebanon Valley Chamber of Commerce
604 Cumberland St.
Lebanon, PA 17042-5272
Ph: (717)273-3727
Fax: (717)273-7940
Co. E-mail: info@lvchamber.org
URL: http://www.lvchamber.org
Contact: Larry Bowman, President
Description: Promotes business and community development in the Lebanon County, PA area. Convention/Meeting: none. **Founded:** 1917. **Publications:** *Images Magazine* (Annual); *Manufacturers & Processors Directory* (Annual); *Memberandum* (Monthly).

57153 ■ *Legislative Update*
100 S Queen St.
Lancaster, PA 17603
Ph: (717)397-3531
Fax: (717)293-3159
Co. E-mail: info@lcci.com
URL: http://www.lancasterchamber.com
Contact: Thomas Baldrige, President
Released: Periodic

57154 ■ Lower Bucks County Chamber of Commerce (LBCCC)
409 Hood Blvd.
Fairless Hills, PA 19030
Ph: (215)943-7400
Fax: (215)943-7404
Co. E-mail: info@lbccc.org
URL: http://www.lbccc.org
Contact: Clark L. Shuster, President
Description: Promotes business and community development in Bucks County, PA. Holds annual Expo and job fairs. Sponsors semi-annual seminars. **Founded:** 1957. **Publications:** *Outlook* (Monthly); *Outlook* (Monthly). **Telecommunication Services:** cshuster@lbccc.org.

57155 ■ *MACConnections*
William Penn Pl.
2790 Mosside Blvd., Ste. 715
Monroeville, PA 15146
Ph: (412)856-0622
Fax: (412)856-1030
Co. E-mail: macc@monroevillechamber.com
URL: http://www.monroevillechamber.com
Contact: Frank Horrigan, President
Released: Monthly

57156 ■ Main Line Chamber of Commerce (MLCC)
175 Strafford Ave., Ste. 130
Wayne, PA 19087-3331
Ph: (610)687-6232
Fax: (610)687-8085
Co. E-mail: info@mlcc.org
URL: http://www.mlcc.org
Contact: Bernard Dagenais, President
Description: Promotes business and community development in Chester, Delaware, and Montgomery counties, PA. Conducts business card exchanges and Main Line Week activities. **Founded:** 1921. **Publications:** *NewsLine* (Bimonthly); *Membership Directory and Business Resource Guide* (Annual); *Main Line Chamber of Commerce--Membership Directory*

and Business Resource Guide (Annual); *Street Locator Atlas*. **Educational Activities:** Business Exposition (Annual); Inspirational Breakfast (Annual). **Telecommunication Services:** sschuck@mlcc.org.

57157 ■ *Major Employer Directory*
100 S Queen St.
Lancaster, PA 17603
Ph: (717)397-3531
Fax: (717)293-3159
Co. E-mail: info@lcci.com
URL: http://www.lancasterchamber.com
Contact: Thomas Baldrige, President
Released: Annual **Price:** $20, for members; $30, for nonmembers; $3, plus shipping and handling.

57158 ■ *Major Employers of Adams County*
18 Carlisle St., Ste. 203
Gettysburg, PA 17325
Ph: (717)334-8151
Fax: (717)334-3368
Co. E-mail: info@gettysburg-chamber.org
URL: http://www.gettysburg-chamber.org
Contact: Carrie S. Stuart, President
Price: $10.

57159 ■ *Major Manufacturers of Adams County*
18 Carlisle St., Ste. 203
Gettysburg, PA 17325
Ph: (717)334-8151
Fax: (717)334-3368
Co. E-mail: info@gettysburg-chamber.org
URL: http://www.gettysburg-chamber.org
Contact: Carrie S. Stuart, President
Price: $10.

57160 ■ Manheim Area Chamber of Commerce
13 E High St.
Manheim, PA 17545-2002
Ph: (717)665-6330
Fax: (717)665-7656
Co. E-mail: info@manheimchamber.com
URL: http://manheimchamber.com
Contact: Teresa M. Shelly, Executive Director
Description: Promotes business and community development in the Manheim, PA area. **Founded:** 1967. **Publications:** *Business Directory* (Periodic).

57161 ■ *Manufacturers & Processors Directory*
604 Cumberland St.
Lebanon, PA 17042-5272
Ph: (717)273-3727
Fax: (717)273-7940
Co. E-mail: info@lvchamber.org
URL: http://www.lvchamber.org
Contact: Larry Bowman, President
Released: Annual

57162 ■ *Map of York Area*
96 S George St., 3rd Fl.
York, PA 17401-1611
Ph: (717)848-4000
Free: 800-673-2429
Fax: (717)843-6737
Co. E-mail: info@yorkchamber.com
URL: http://www.yorkchamber.com
Contact: Thomas E. Donley, President
E-mail: donley@yorkchamber.com
Released: Annual

57163 ■ Meadville - Western Crawford County Chamber of Commerce
908 Diamond Park
Meadville, PA 16335
Ph: (814)337-8030
Fax: (814)337-8022
Co. E-mail: info@meadvillechamber.com
URL: http://www.meadvillechamber.com
Contact: Kathleen Bishop, President
Description: Promotes business and community development in western Crawford County, PA. Promotes tourism; provides educational programs. **Founded:** 1807. **Publications:** *Community Audit* (Periodic); *Chamber Media Network* (Monthly); *Industrial Directory* (Periodic).

57164 ■ *Member Directory and Buyers Guide*
5 Roadside Ave.
Waynesboro, PA 17268-1694
Ph: (717)762-7123
Fax: (717)762-7124
Co. E-mail: director@waynesboro.org
URL: http://www.waynesboro.org
Contact: Ms. Carlene Willhide, Executive Director
Released: Annual

57165 ■ *Memberandum*
604 Cumberland St.
Lebanon, PA 17042-5272
Ph: (717)273-3727
Fax: (717)273-7940
Co. E-mail: info@lvchamber.org
URL: http://www.lvchamber.org
Contact: Larry Bowman, President
Released: Monthly **Price:** free for members.

57166 ■ *Membership Directory and Business Resource Guide*
4211 Trindle Rd.
Camp Hill, PA 17011
Ph: (717)761-0702
Fax: (717)761-4315
Co. E-mail: wschamber@wschamber.org
URL: http://www.wschamber.org
Contact: Kathleen M. Mangan, President
Released: Annual

57167 ■ *Membership Directory and Business Resource Guide*
175 Strafford Ave., Ste. 130
Wayne, PA 19087-3331
Ph: (610)687-6232
Fax: (610)687-8085
Co. E-mail: info@mlcc.org
URL: http://www.mlcc.org
Contact: Bernard Dagenais, President
Released: Annual **Price:** $10, for members; $25, for nonmembers; $1.50, plus shipping and handling.

57168 ■ *Membership Directory and Buyer's Guide*
436 Old York Rd.
Jenkintown, PA 19046
Ph: (215)887-5122
Fax: (215)887-3220
Co. E-mail: info@emccc.org
URL: http://www.emccc.org
Contact: Ms. Wendy Klinghoffer, Executive Director
Released: Annual

57169 ■ *Membership Directory and Buyer's Guide*
308 Market St.
Warren, PA 16365
Ph: (814)723-3050
Fax: (814)723-6024
Co. E-mail: info@wccbi.org
URL: http://www.wccbi.org
Contact: James L. Decker, President
Released: Annual

57170 ■ *Membership Directory and Regional Profile*
3211 N Front St., Ste. 201
Harrisburg, PA 17110-1342
Ph: (717)232-4099
Free: 877-883-8339
Fax: (717)232-5184
Co. E-mail: info@hbgrc.org
URL: http://www.harrisburgregionalchamber.org
Contact: David E. Black, President
Price: $15, for members; $20, for members (by mail); $20, for nonmembers; $30, for nonmembers (by mail).

57171 ■ *Membership and Resource Directory*
185 Exton Square Mall
Exton, PA 19341
Ph: (610)363-7746
Fax: (610)363-2374
Co. E-mail: chamber@ercc.net
URL: http://www.ercc.net
Contact: Don Anders, President
Released: Annual

57172 ■ *Membership & Resource Directory*
119 N High St.
West Chester, PA 19380-3145
Ph: (610)696-4046
Fax: (610)696-9110
Co. E-mail: info@gwcc.org
URL: http://www.gwcc.org
Contact: Mark Yoder, President
Released: Annual

57173 ■ **Mercersburg Area Chamber of Commerce (MACC)**
19 N Main St.
Mercersburg, PA 17236
Ph: (717)328-5827
Fax: (717)328-4814
Co. E-mail: info@mercerburg.org
URL: http://www.mercersburg.org
Contact: Mary-Anne Gordon, Executive Director
Description: Promotes business and community development in the Mercersburg, PA area. Conducts charitable activities. Sponsors festival. **Founded:** 1975. **Publications:** *Mercersburg Area Chamber of Commerce Business Directory* (Annual). **Awards:** Business Person of the Year (Annual). **Telecommunication Services:** mercersburgchamber@embarqmail.com.

57174 ■ *Mercersburg Area Chamber of Commerce Business Directory*
19 N Main St.
Mercersburg, PA 17236
Ph: (717)328-5827
Fax: (717)328-4814
Co. E-mail: info@mercerburg.org
URL: http://www.mercersburg.org
Contact: Mary-Anne Gordon, Executive Director
Released: Annual **Price:** free.

57175 ■ **Mon Valley Regional Chamber of Commerce**
1 Chamber Plz.
Charleroi, PA 15022
Ph: (724)483-3507
Fax: (724)489-1045
Co. E-mail: info@mvrchamber.org
URL: http://www.mvrchamber.org
Contact: Debra Keefer, Executive Director
Description: Promotes business and community development in the Mid Mon Valley Region of Southwestern Pennsylvania. Encourages networking, educational, and economic development. **Founded:** 1921. **Publications:** *Regional Reporter* (Monthly). **Awards:** Excellence in Business (Annual).

57176 ■ *Mon-Yough Membership Directory*
3001 Jacks Run Rd.
McKeesport, PA 15131
Ph: (412)678-2450
Co. E-mail: rba@regionalbusinessalliance.com
URL: http://www.rca-alliance.com
Contact: Constance Yarris, Executive Director
Released: Annual

57177 ■ **Monroeville Area Chamber of Commerce**
William Penn Pl.
2790 Mosside Blvd., Ste. 715
Monroeville, PA 15146
Ph: (412)856-0622
Fax: (412)856-1030
Co. E-mail: macc@monroevillechamber.com
URL: http://www.monroevillechamber.com
Contact: Frank Horrigan, President
Description: Promotes business and community development in the Monroeville, PA area. Sponsors "Chamber Challenge" and annual Golf Invitational among other major events. **Founded:** 1953. **Publications:** *Directory of Clubs & Organizations* (Periodic); *Industrial Directory* (Periodic); *MACConnections* (Monthly).

57178 ■ *Mountains and Whitecaps*
2512 Rte. 6, Ste. 2
Hawley, PA 18428
Ph: (570)226-3191

Fax: (570)226-9387
Co. E-mail: visit@lakeregioncc.com
URL: http://www.lakeregioncc.com
Contact: Jim Shook, President
Released: Monthly

57179 ■ **Nazareth Area Chamber of Commerce**
201 N Main St.
Nazareth, PA 18064
Ph: (610)759-9188
Fax: (610)759-5262
Co. E-mail: tina@nazarethchamber.com
URL: http://nazarethchamber.com
Contact: Tina A. Smith, President
Description: Preserves and enhances the interests of the members and the business community by improving the general welfare and prosperity of the region. **Publications:** *Nazareth Chamber News* (Monthly).

57180 ■ *Nazareth Chamber News*
201 N Main St.
Nazareth, PA 18064
Ph: (610)759-9188
Fax: (610)759-5262
Co. E-mail: tina@nazarethchamber.com
URL: http://nazarethchamber.com
Contact: Tina A. Smith, President
Released: Monthly **Price:** included in membership dues.

57181 ■ *News Bulletin*
850 Beaver Grade Rd.
Moon Township, PA 15108
Ph: (412)264-6270
Fax: (412)264-1575
Co. E-mail: info@paacc.com
URL: http://www.paacc.com
Contact: Sally Haas, President
Released: Monthly

57182 ■ *Newsbriefs*
c/o Joanne Stetz
PO Box 431
Scranton, PA 18501-0431
Ph: (570)342-7711
Fax: (570)347-6262
Co. E-mail: jstetz@scrantonchamber.com
URL: http://www.scrantonchamber.com
Contact: Austin J. Burke, President
Released: Bimonthly

57183 ■ *NewsFlash*
209 E Hartford St.
Milford, PA 18337-0883
Ph: (570)296-8700
Fax: (570)296-3921
Co. E-mail: info@pikechamber.com
URL: http://www.pikechamber.com
Contact: Danielle Jordan, Executive Director
Released: Monthly

57184 ■ *NewsLine*
175 Strafford Ave., Ste. 130
Wayne, PA 19087-3331
Ph: (610)687-6232
Fax: (610)687-8085
Co. E-mail: info@mlcc.org
URL: http://www.mlcc.org
Contact: Bernard Dagenais, President
Released: Bimonthly

57185 ■ **North East Area Chamber of Commerce (NEACC)**
17 E Main St.
North East, PA 16428
Ph: (814)725-4262
Fax: (814)725-3994
Co. E-mail: info@nechamber.org
URL: http://www.nechamber.org
Contact: Anne Saxer, President
Description: Promotes business and community development in the North East, PA area. Promotes educational and recreational activities. Sponsors annual Wine Country Harvest Festival on last weekend of September. **Founded:** 1989. **Publications:** *From*

the Chamber... (Biweekly); *Welcome to Wine County* (Annual). **Educational Activities:** Wine Fest (Annual). **Awards:** Outstanding Contribution Award (Annual).

57186 ■ **Northampton Area Chamber of Commerce (NACC)**
PO Box 355
Northampton, PA 18067
Ph: (610)262-8669
Co. E-mail: allthingsframed@rcn.com
URL: http://www.northamptonpa.com
Contact: Mr. Tony Pristash, President
Description: Promotes business and community development in Northampton, PA area.

57187 ■ **Northern Allegheny County Chamber of Commerce (NACCC)**
5000 Brooktree Rd.
Wexford, PA 15090
Ph: (724)934-9700
Fax: (724)934-9710
Co. E-mail: naccc@naccc.com
URL: http://www.naccc.com
Contact: Mary Margaret Fisher, Executive Director
Description: Strives to promote the interests of the business community through encouraging growth in existing businesses and industries and giving assistance to new firms or individuals seeking to locate and/or conduct business in Northern Allegheny County. **Founded:** 1972. **Publications:** *Monday Morning Coffee with the Northern Allegheny County Chamber of Commerce* (Weekly). **Telecommunication Services:** mmfisher@naccc.com.

57188 ■ *Norwin Chamber of Commerce*
321 Main St.
Irwin, PA 15642-3437
Ph: (724)863-0888
Fax: (724)863-5133
Co. E-mail: info@norwinchamber.com
URL: http://www.norwinchamber.com
Contact: Rosanne Barry Novotnak, President
Description: Promotes business and community development in Irwin, North Huntingdon, and North Irwin, PA. **Founded:** 1942. **Publications:** *Vocal Point* (Monthly). **Educational Activities:** Norwin Chamber of Commerce Luncheon (Monthly).

57189 ■ *Outlook*
409 Hood Blvd.
Fairless Hills, PA 19030
Ph: (215)943-7400
Fax: (215)943-7404
Co. E-mail: info@lbccc.org
URL: http://www.lbccc.org
Contact: Clark L. Shuster, President
Released: Monthly **Price:** included in membership dues.

57190 ■ **Oxford Area Chamber of Commerce (OACC)**
PO Box 4
Oxford, PA 19363
Ph: (610)932-0740
Fax: (610)932-0827
Co. E-mail: oxfordchamber@zoominternet.net
URL: http://www.oxfordpa.org
Contact: Richard Hannum, President
Description: Promotes business and community development in southern Chester County, PA. **Founded:** 1964. **Publications:** *Oxfordian* (Semiannual).

57191 ■ *Oxfordian*
PO Box 4
Oxford, PA 19363
Ph: (610)932-0740
Fax: (610)932-0827
Co. E-mail: oxfordchamber@zoominternet.net
URL: http://www.oxfordpa.org
Contact: Richard Hannum, President
Released: Semiannual **Price:** free.

57192 ■ *The Pacesetter*
Manor Oak One, Ste. 140
1910 Cochan Rd.
Pittsburgh, PA 15220
Ph: (412)306-8090

Fax: (412)306-8093
Co. E-mail: office@shchamber.org
URL: http://www.shchamber.org
Contact: James W. Bentz, President
Released: Monthly

57193 ■ Palmerton Area Chamber of Commerce
410 Delaware Ave.
Palmerton, PA 18071
Ph: (610)824-6954
URL: http://www.palmertonpa.com/chamber
Contact: Peter L. Kern, President
Description: Promotes business and community development in Palmerton, PA.

57194 ■ *The Participant*
100 Penn Ave.
Telford, PA 18969
Ph: (215)723-9472
Fax: (215)723-2490
Co. E-mail: ivchamber@indianvalleychamber.com
URL: http://www.indianvalleychamber.com
Contact: Sharon L. Minninger, Executive Director
Released: Bimonthly

57195 ■ *Partnership Press*
212 N Jay St.
Lock Haven, PA 17745
Ph: (570)748-5782
Free: 888-388-6991
Fax: (570)893-0433
Co. E-mail: flanagan@kcnet.org
URL: http://www.clintoncountyinfo.com
Contact: Michael Flanagan, President
Released: Monthly

57196 ■ Penn Hills Chamber of Commerce (PHCC)
12013 Frankstown Rd.
Penn Hills, PA 15235-3435
Ph: (412)795-8741
Fax: (412)795-7993
Co. E-mail: admin@pennhillschamber.org
URL: http://www.pennhillschamber.org
Contact: Denise Graham Shealey, President
Description: Promotes the interests of the business community. Supports and encourages cultural and civic activities beneficial to the business community, and endorses those activities which will improve or expand the general quality of life in Penn Hills. **Publications:** *The Changing Times* (Monthly).

57197 ■ Pennridge Chamber of Commerce (PCC)
538 W Market St.
Perkasie, PA 18944
Ph: (215)257-5390
Fax: (267)354-6924
Co. E-mail: pennridgecc@pennridge.com
URL: http://www.pennridge.com
Contact: Keith Smith, President
Description: Represents business in the Pennridge community. Works with business and the community in striving to make the Pennridge area a better place to work and live. **Founded:** 1963. **Publications:** *The Communicator* (Monthly).

57198 ■ PennSuburban Chamber of Commerce
34 Susquehanna Ave.
Lansdale, PA 19446
Ph: (215)362-9200
Fax: (215)362-0393
Co. E-mail: info@northpenn.org
URL: http://www.pennsuburban.org
Contact: Lon Seitz, Chairperson
Description: Preserves and enhances the interests of the members and the business community by improving the general welfare and prosperity of the region. **Founded:** 1913. **Publications:** *PennSuburban Chamber of Commerce--Membership Directory* (Annual); *Prospector* (Monthly).

57199 ■ Pennsylvania Chamber of Business and Industry
417 Walnut St.
Harrisburg, PA 17101-1902
Ph: (717)255-3252

Free: 800-225-7224
Fax: (717)255-3298
Co. E-mail: info@pachamber.org
URL: http://www.pachamber.org
Contact: Gene Barr, President
Description: Seeks to advocate business by influencing legislative, regulatory, and judicial branches of state government. **Founded:** 1932. **Publications:** *Catalyst* (Quarterly). **Awards:** Business Leader of the Year (Annual); Community of the Year (Annual).

57200 ■ *Pennsylvania Pike County Magazine*
209 E Hartford St.
Milford, PA 18337-0883
Ph: (570)296-8700
Fax: (570)296-3921
Co. E-mail: info@pikechamber.com
URL: http://www.pikechamber.com
Contact: Danielle Jordan, Executive Director
Released: Annual

57201 ■ Perkiomen Valley Chamber of Commerce (PVCC)
351 E Main St.
Collegeville, PA 19426
Ph: (610)489-6660
Fax: (610)454-1270
Co. E-mail: info@pvchamber.net
URL: http://www.pvchamber.net
Contact: Arlene Magargal, Director, Operations
Description: Seeks to preserve, protect and promote members and their businesses. Programs include monthly meetings, educational seminars, legislative forums, social functions and business mixers. Serves boroughs of Collegeville, Schwenksville and Trappe and the townships of Limerick, Lower Frederick, Lower Providence, Perkiomen, Skippack and Upper Providence in Western Montgomery County, PA. **Founded:** 1957.

57202 ■ Peters Township Chamber of Commerce
PO Box 991
McMurray, PA 15317-0991
Ph: (724)941-6345
Co. E-mail: info@peterstownshipchamber.com
URL: http://www.peterstownshipchamber.com
Contact: Joseph Jasek, President
Description: Promotes business and community development in the Peters Township, PA area. Conducts community service projects. Recognizes graduating high school seniors and honors new teachers. Sponsors dinner dance, golf benefit, Community Day, and seminars. **Founded:** 1954. **Publications:** *Chamber News and Notes* (Quarterly); *Business Guide and Community Directory* (Annual).

57203 ■ Phoenixville Area Chamber of Commerce
171 E Bridge St.
Phoenixville, PA 19460
Ph: (610)933-3070
Fax: (610)917-0503
Co. E-mail: info@phoenixvillechamber.org
URL: http://www.phoenixvillechamber.org
Contact: Stephen Giampietro, Chairman of the Board
Description: Promotes business and community development in the Phoenixville, PA and the Valley Forge region. Conducts entrepreneurial education. Sponsors annual Summer Music Festival. **Founded:** 1927. **Publications:** *The Rising Phoenix* (Quarterly). **Educational Activities:** Phoenixville Area Chamber of Commerce Dinner (Monthly).

57204 ■ Pike County Chamber of Commerce
209 E Hartford St.
Milford, PA 18337-0883
Ph: (570)296-8700
Fax: (570)296-3921
Co. E-mail: info@pikechamber.com
URL: http://www.pikechamber.com
Contact: Danielle Jordan, Executive Director
Description: Promotes business and community development in Pike County, PA. Promotes tourism. Assists new businesses and homeowners. Operates information booth. Provides legislative representation and group insurance. Bestows Community Achievement Award. Sponsors business card exchanges,

grand openings, radio interviews, seminars, and social gatherings. Convenes board meetings. **Founded:** 1962. **Publications:** *NewsFlash* (Monthly); *Pennsylvania Pike County Magazine* (Annual).

57205 ■ Pittsburgh Airport Area Chamber of Commerce (PAACC)
850 Beaver Grade Rd.
Moon Township, PA 15108
Ph: (412)264-6270
Fax: (412)264-1575
Co. E-mail: info@paacc.com
URL: http://www.paacc.com
Contact: Sally Haas, President
Description: Promotes business and community development in the Pittsburgh, PA airport area. Sponsors scholarship programs and educational seminars. **Founded:** 1949. **Publications:** *BusinessLinks* (Monthly); *News Bulletin* (Monthly). **Educational Activities:** Business Expo (Annual). **Awards:** Business of the Year (Annual); Entrepreneur of the Year (Annual); Business of the Year: Nonprofit (Annual); Business Person of the Year (Annual).

57206 ■ Pocono Lake Region Chamber of Commerce
2512 Rte. 6, Ste. 2
Hawley, PA 18428
Ph: (570)226-3191
Fax: (570)226-9387
Co. E-mail: visit@lakeregioncc.com
URL: http://www.lakeregioncc.com
Contact: Jim Shook, President
Description: Strives to promote the civic and commercial progress, and enhance the environmental preservation of the Hawley-Lake Wallenpaupack Region. Initiates and supports tourism, education, and networking activities. **Publications:** *Calendar of Events* (Quarterly); *Mountains and Whitecaps* (Monthly); *Touring Wallenpaupack Visitor Guide and Directory* (Annual). **Educational Activities:** Fall Arts & Crafts Fair (Annual); Holiday Dinner (Annual); Summer Chicken Bar-B-Que (Annual).

57207 ■ *Progress*
601 N Center Ave.
Somerset, PA 15501
Ph: (814)445-6431
Fax: (814)443-4313
Co. E-mail: info@somersetcountychamber.com
URL: http://www.somersetcountychamber.com
Contact: Sean Isgan, President
Released: Monthly

57208 ■ *Prospector*
34 Susquehanna Ave.
Lansdale, PA 19446
Ph: (215)362-9200
Fax: (215)362-0393
Co. E-mail: info@northpenn.org
URL: http://www.pennsuburban.org
Contact: Lon Seitz, Chairperson
Released: Monthly

57209 ■ *Quality of Life*
PO Box 572
Carlisle, PA 17013
Ph: (717)243-4515
Fax: (717)243-4446
Co. E-mail: mcrowley@carlislechamber.org
URL: http://www.carlislechamber.org
Contact: Ms. Michelle Hornick Crowley, President

57210 ■ *Quality of Life Directory*
146 Carlisle St.
Hanover, PA 17331
Ph: (717)637-6130
Fax: (717)637-9127
Co. E-mail: office@hanoverchamber.com
URL: http://www.hanoverchamber.com
Contact: Gary Laird, President
Released: Biennial

57211 ■ *Quickletter*
1129 Industrial Park Rd., Ste. 108
Vandergrift, PA 15690-9646
Ph: (724)845-5426

Fax: (724)845-5428
Co. E-mail: strongland@alltel.net
URL: http://www.strongland.org
Contact: Al Pulice, Chairman
Released: Monthly

57212 ■ Regional Chamber Alliance (RCA)
3001 Jacks Run Rd.
McKeesport, PA 15131
Ph: (412)678-2450
Co. E-mail: rba@regionalbusinessalliance.com
URL: http://www.rca-pa.org
Contact: Constance Yarris, Executive Director
Description: Promotes business and community development in southeastern Allegheny County, PA. Provides business goods and services and industrial referrals. Holds small business seminars. Sponsors Mon-Yough Science Fair. **Founded:** 1906. **Publications:** *Action!* (Monthly); *Mon-Yough Membership Directory* (Annual).

57213 ■ Regional Reporter
1 Chamber Plz.
Charleroi, PA 15022
Ph: (724)483-3507
Fax: (724)489-1045
Co. E-mail: info@mvrchamber.org
URL: http://www.mvrchamber.org
Contact: Debra Keefer, Executive Director
Released: Monthly **Price:** free for members.

57214 ■ Relocation Guide
840 Hamilton St., Ste. 205
Allentown, PA 18101
Ph: (610)841-5860
Fax: (610)437-4907
Co. E-mail: info@lehighvalleychamber.org
URL: http://www.lehighvalleychamber.org
Contact: T. Anthony Iannelli, President

57215 ■ Relocation Packet
18 Carlisle St., Ste. 203
Gettysburg, PA 17325
Ph: (717)334-8151
Fax: (717)334-3368
Co. E-mail: info@gettysburg-chamber.org
URL: http://www.gettysburg-chamber.org
Contact: Carrie S. Stuart, President
Price: $15, per copy.

57216 ■ Relocation Packet
146 Carlisle St.
Hanover, PA 17331
Ph: (717)637-6130
Fax: (717)637-9127
Co. E-mail: office@hanoverchamber.com
URL: http://www.hanoverchamber.com
Contact: Gary Laird, President
Released: Semiannual

57217 ■ Ridgway Area Business Directory
300 Main St.
Ridgway, PA 15853
Ph: (814)776-1424
Fax: (814)772-2188
Co. E-mail: ridgwaychamber@ncentral.com
URL: http://www.ridgwaychamber.com
Contact: Cathy Grove, President
Released: Annual

57218 ■ Ridgway-Elk County Chamber of Commerce
300 Main St.
Ridgway, PA 15853
Ph: (814)776-1424
Fax: (814)772-2188
Co. E-mail: ridgwaychamber@ncentral.com
URL: http://www.ridgwaychamber.com
Contact: Cathy Grove, President
Description: Promotes business and community development in Ridgway and Elk County, PA. Holds educational seminars. **Founded:** 1892. **Publications:** *Industrial Directory* (Annual); *Historical Walking Tour of Ridgway*; *Ridgway Area Business Directory* (Annual). **Educational Activities:** Community Service Awards Dinner (Periodic).

57219 ■ The Rising Phoenix
171 E Bridge St.
Phoenixville, PA 19460
Ph: (610)933-3070
Fax: (610)917-0503
Co. E-mail: info@phoenixvillechamber.org
URL: http://www.phoenixvillechamber.org
Contact: Stephen Giampietro, Chairman of the Board
Released: Quarterly

57220 ■ Route 422 Business Advisor
152 High St., Ste. 360
Pottstown, PA 19464-5555
Ph: (610)326-2900
Fax: (610)970-9705
Co. E-mail: eileen@tricountyareachamber.com
URL: http://www.tricountyareachamber.com
Contact: Eileen Dautrich, President
Released: Monthly **Price:** free.

57221 ■ St. Marys Area Chamber of Commerce
53 S St. Marys St.
St. Marys, PA 15857
Ph: (814)781-3804
Fax: (814)781-7302
Co. E-mail: info@stmaryschamber.org
URL: http://www.stmaryschamber.org
Contact: Mark Rupprecht, President
Description: Promotes business and community development in St. Marys, PA. **Founded:** 1984. **Publications:** *Business Directory* (Monthly); *Industrial Directory*. **Educational Activities:** Business Expo (Annual).

57222 ■ Sample Employee Policy Handbook
100 S Queen St.
Lancaster, PA 17603
Ph: (717)397-3531
Fax: (717)293-3159
Co. E-mail: info@lcci.com
URL: http://www.lancasterchamber.com
Contact: Thomas Baldrige, President
Price: $30, for members; $60, for nonmembers; $5, plus shipping and handling.

57223 ■ Schuylkill Chamber of Commerce
91 S Progress Ave.
Pottsville, PA 17901
Ph: (570)622-1942
Free: 800-755-1942
Fax: (570)622-1638
Co. E-mail: info@schuylkillchamber.com
URL: http://www.schuylkillchamber.com
Contact: Robert S. Carl, Jr., Executive Director
Description: Serves members and affiliates with value-added programs and services and improves the quality of life and economic vitality of Schuylkill County. **Founded:** 1918. **Publications:** *Communicator* (Monthly); *Schuylkill Chamber of Commerce-- Membership Directory*.

57224 ■ Scottdale Area Chamber of Commerce
318 Pittsburgh St.
Scottdale, PA 15683
Ph: (724)887-3611
Co. E-mail: scottdalechamber@gmail.com
URL: http://www.scottdale.com
Contact: Andy Pinsky, President
Description: Promotes business and community development in the Scottdale, PA area. Sponsors festival and contests; participates in charitable activities. Publications: none. **Founded:** 1950.

57225 ■ The Scranton Plan News
c/o Joanne Stetz
PO Box 431
Scranton, PA 18501-0431
Ph: (570)342-7711
Fax: (570)347-6262
Co. E-mail: jstetz@scrantonchamber.com
URL: http://www.scrantonchamber.com
Contact: Austin J. Burke, President
Released: Quarterly

57226 ■ Shenango Valley Chamber of Commerce
41 Chestnut St.
Sharon, PA 16146
Ph: (724)981-5880
Fax: (724)981-5480
Co. E-mail: deanne@svchamber.com
URL: http://www.svchamber.com
Contact: Eric Brown, President
Description: Promotes business and community development in northwestern Pennsylvania and Brookfield and Masury, OH. Provides business assistance, educational programs, and government liaison. Holds breakfast and luncheon meetings with local, state and federal legislators. Sponsors Business and Industry Golf Classic, Business After Hours networking events, annual Business Expo, and other professional development and networking events. **Founded:** 1956. **Publications:** *Images* (Bimonthly); *Shenango Valley Chamber of Commerce Membership Directory and Buyer's Guide* (Annual). **Awards:** Chamber Person of the Year (Annual); Phoenix Award (Annual).

57227 ■ Shenango Valley Chamber of Commerce Membership Directory and Buyer's Guide
41 Chestnut St.
Sharon, PA 16146
Ph: (724)981-5880
Fax: (724)981-5480
Co. E-mail: deanne@svchamber.com
URL: http://www.svchamber.com
Contact: Eric Brown, President
Released: Annual

57228 ■ Shippensburg Area Chamber of Commerce (SACC)
53 W King St.
Shippensburg, PA 17257
Ph: (717)532-5509
Fax: (717)532-7501
Co. E-mail: chamber@shippensburg.org
URL: http://www.shippensburg.org
Contact: Barbara Hoover, President
Description: Promotes business and community development in Franklin and Cumberland counties, PA. **Founded:** 1938. **Publications:** *Chamberline* (Quarterly).

57229 ■ Small Street Journal
121 Main St.
Bradford, PA 16701
Ph: (814)368-7115
Fax: (814)368-6233
Co. E-mail: ed@bradfordchamber.com
URL: http://www.bradfordchamber.com
Contact: Ron Orris, Executive Director
Released: Monthly **Price:** free.

57230 ■ Somerset County Chamber of Commerce
601 N Center Ave.
Somerset, PA 15501
Ph: (814)445-6431
Fax: (814)443-4313
Co. E-mail: info@somersetcountychamber.com
URL: http://www.somersetcountychamber.com
Contact: Sean Isgan, President
Description: Established to network with businesses to enhance economic opportunities. **Founded:** 1912. **Publications:** *Somerset County Chamber of Commerce Business Directory*; *Business Directory* (Annual); *County Guide*; *Progress* (Monthly); *Somerset County Chamber of Commerce--Business Directory* (Annual). **Educational Activities:** Annual Antique Show (Annual).

57231 ■ South Hills Chamber of Commerce (SHCC)
Manor Oak One, Ste. 140
1910 Cochan Rd.
Pittsburgh, PA 15220
Ph: (412)306-8090

Fax: (412)306-8093
Co. E-mail: office@shchamber.org
URL: http://www.shchamber.org
Contact: James W. Bentz, President
Description: Promotes business and community development in the South Hills area of Pittsburgh, PA. **Founded:** 1981. **Publications:** *The Pacesetter* (Monthly).

57232 ■ South West Communities Chamber of Commerce (SWCCOC)
990 Washington Pike
Bridgeville, PA 15017
Ph: (412)221-4100
Fax: (412)257-1210
Co. E-mail: info@swccoc.org
URL: http://www.swccoc.org
Contact: Emerald VanBuskirk, Executive Director
Description: Promotes business and community development in Upper St. Clair, PA.

57233 ■ Southern Chester County Chamber of Commerce (SCCCC)
217 W State St.
Kennett Square, PA 19348
Ph: (610)444-0774
Fax: (610)444-5105
Co. E-mail: info@scccc.com
URL: http://www.scccc.com
Contact: Cheryl Kuhn, Executive Director
Description: Promotes business and community development in Southern Chester County, PA. **Founded:** 1930. **Awards:** Outstanding Citizen of the Year (Annual).

57234 ■ Southern Wayne Regional Chamber
PO Box 296
Hamlin, PA 18427
Ph: (570)689-4199
Fax: (570)689-4391
Co. E-mail: swrchamber@swrchamber.org
URL: http://www.swrchamber.org
Contact: Patty Blaum, Executive Director
Released: Quarterly

57235 ■ Southern Wayne Regional Chamber of Commerce (SWRCC)
PO Box 296
Hamlin, PA 18427
Ph: (570)689-4199
Fax: (570)689-4391
Co. E-mail: swrchamber@swrchamber.org
URL: http://www.swrchamber.org
Contact: Patty Blaum, Executive Director
Description: Business and professional people accomplishing collectively that none could do or would do individually. Sponsors several fundraisers throughout the year. **Publications:** *Southern Wayne Regional Chamber* (Quarterly). **Educational Activities:** Golf Tournament (Annual).

57236 ■ Steel Valley Chamber of Commerce
3910 Main St.
Munhall, PA 15120
Ph: (412)462-1600
Co. E-mail: iburym@verizon.net
URL: http://www.steelvalleychamber.com
Contact: John J. Karafa, Jr., President
Description: Enhances and promotes businesses and organizations in a supportive and visionary association providing benefits and leadership.

57237 ■ Strongland Chamber of Commerce (SCC)
1129 Industrial Park Rd., Ste. 108
Vandergrift, PA 15690-9646
Ph: (724)845-5426
Fax: (724)845-5428
Co. E-mail: strongland@alltel.net
URL: http://www.strongland.org
Contact: Al Pulice, Chairman
Description: Promotes business and community development in northern Westmoreland and Southern Armstrong counties, PA. Operates Kiski Valley Enterprises; sponsors cycling race. **Scope:** community, economic development. **Founded:** 1985. **Publications:** *Quickletter* (Monthly). **Educational**

Activities: Homexpo (Annual). **Awards:** Student Motivational Scholarship. **Telecommunication Services:** strongland@windstream.net.

57238 ■ Sullivan County Chamber of Commerce, Pennsylvania
PO Box 134
Muncy Valley, PA 17758
Ph: (570)482-4088
Fax: (570)482-4089
Co. E-mail: sulchamc@epix.net
URL: http://www.sullivanpachamber.com
Contact: Craig Harting, President
Description: Promotes business and community development in Sullivan County, PA. **Founded:** 1986.

57239 ■ Susquehanna Style Magazine
96 S George St., 3rd Fl.
York, PA 17401-1611
Ph: (717)848-4000
Free: 800-673-2429
Fax: (717)843-6737
Co. E-mail: info@yorkchamber.com
URL: http://www.yorkchamber.com
Contact: Thomas E. Donley, President
E-mail: donley@yorkchamber.com
Released: Bimonthly

57240 ■ Susquehanna Valley Chamber of Commerce and Visitors' Bureau (SVCCVB)
445 Linden St.
Columbia, PA 17512
Ph: (717)684-5249
Fax: (717)684-5142
Co. E-mail: svcc@parivertowns.com
URL: http://www.parivertowns.com
Contact: Melissa A. Glenn, Director
Description: Promotes business and community development in Columbia, Marietta, Mountville, and Wrightsville, PA. Sponsors annual Antique and Craft Fair. Operates Susquehanna Heritage Tourist and Information Center and Susquehanna Tri-Bourough Development Company. **Founded:** 1928. **Publications:** *Calendar of Events - Information Directory* (Periodic).

57241 ■ Swedish-American Chamber of Commerce, Philadelphia
200 S Broad St., Ste. 700
Philadelphia, PA 19102
Ph: (215)790-3785
Fax: (215)790-3888
Co. E-mail: info@sacc-philadelphia.org
URL: http://www.sacc-philadelphia.org

57242 ■ Titusville Area Chamber of Commerce (TACC)
202 W Central Ave.
Titusville, PA 16354
Ph: (814)827-2941
Fax: (814)827-2914
Co. E-mail: christab@titusvillechamber.com
URL: http://titusvillechamber.com
Contact: Christa Battin, Executive Director
Description: Promotes business, community development, and downtown revitalization in the Titusville, PA area. Conducts business advocacy through the legislative, transportation, and education committee programs. Sponsors leadership programs, golf outing, Chamber Week activities, community surveys, active tourism programs, $30,000 per year gift certificate program, and member insurance program. Maintains small business development and outreach center. **Scope:** tourist information. **Founded:** 1889. **Publications:** *Historic Brochure* (Periodic); *Industrial Directory* (Periodic). **Educational Activities:** Oil Festival (Annual).

57243 ■ Touring Wallenpaupack Visitor Guide and Directory
2512 Rte. 6, Ste. 2
Hawley, PA 18428
Ph: (570)226-3191
Fax: (570)226-9387
Co. E-mail: visit@lakeregioncc.com
URL: http://www.lakeregioncc.com
Contact: Jim Shook, President
Released: Annual

57244 ■ Tourist/Motorcoach
208 E Bayfront Pkwy., Ste. 100
Erie, PA 16507
Ph: (814)454-7191
Fax: (814)459-0241
Co. E-mail: jdible@eriepa.com
URL: http://www.eriepa.com/chamber
Released: Periodic

57245 ■ Township of Richland Chamber of Commerce
4011 Dickey Rd.
Gibsonia, PA 15044
Ph: (724)443-5921
Fax: (724)443-8860
URL: http://www.richland.pa.us
Contact: Herbert C. Dankmyer, Chairman

57246 ■ Treasures
96 S George St., 3rd Fl.
York, PA 17401-1611
Ph: (717)848-4000
Free: 800-673-2429
Fax: (717)843-6737
Co. E-mail: info@yorkchamber.com
URL: http://www.yorkchamber.com
Contact: Thomas E. Donley, President
E-mail: donley@yorkchamber.com

57247 ■ TriCounty Area Chamber of Commerce (TCACC)
152 High St., Ste. 360
Pottstown, PA 19464-5555
Ph: (610)326-2900
Fax: (610)970-9705
Co. E-mail: eileen@tricountyareachamber.com
URL: http://www.tricountyareachamber.com
Contact: Eileen Dautrich, President
Description: Promotes business and community development in the Pottstown, PA area. **Founded:** 1927. **Publications:** *Connection* (Monthly); *Route 422 Business Advisor* (Monthly). **Educational Activities:** Chamber 101 (Semimonthly).

57248 ■ Tyrone Area Chamber of Commerce
1004 Logan Ave.
Tyrone, PA 16686-9510
Ph: (814)684-0736
Fax: (814)684-6070
Co. E-mail: tyronechamber@nb.net
URL: http://www.tyronechamber.com
Contact: Ms. Rose Black, Executive Director
Description: Promotes business and community development in the Tyrone, PA area. **Founded:** 1916. **Publications:** *Tyrone Chamber Tab* (Monthly). **Educational Activities:** Business After Hours (Monthly). **Telecommunication Services:** info@tyronechamber.com.

57249 ■ Tyrone Chamber Tab
1004 Logan Ave.
Tyrone, PA 16686-9510
Ph: (814)684-0736
Fax: (814)684-6070
Co. E-mail: tyronechamber@nb.net
URL: http://www.tyronechamber.com
Contact: Ms. Rose Black, Executive Director
Released: Monthly **Price:** free.

57250 ■ Update
1019 Philadelphia St.
Indiana, PA 15701-1689
Ph: (724)465-2511
Fax: (724)465-3706
Co. E-mail: dphenry@wpia.net
URL: http://www.indianapa.com/chamber
Contact: Dana P. Henry, President
Released: Periodic

57251 ■ Upper Bucks Chamber of Commerce
2170 Portzer Rd.
Quakertown, PA 18951
Ph: (215)536-3211

Fax: (215)536-7767
Co. E-mail: info@ubcc.org
URL: http://www.ubcc.org
Contact: Tara King, Executive Director
Description: Promotes business and community development in Upper Bucks County, PA. **Founded:** 1954. **Publications:** *Bridges to Business* (Bimonthly). **Telecommunication Services:** tking@ubcc.org.

57252 ■ Venango Area Chamber of Commerce (VACC)
41 Main St.
Oil City, PA 16301-1440
Ph: (814)676-8521
Fax: (814)676-8185
Co. E-mail: chamber@venangochamber.org
URL: http://www.venangochamber.org
Contact: Susan R. Williams, Executive Director
Description: Provides services that promote successful business growth by coordinating activities and forums that address community issues. **Founded:** 1912.

57253 ■ *Vocal Point*
321 Main St.
Irwin, PA 15642-3437
Ph: (724)863-0888
Fax: (724)863-5133
Co. E-mail: info@norwinchamber.com
URL: http://www.norwinchamber.com
Contact: Rosanne Barry Novotnak, President
Released: Monthly

57254 ■ *The Voice*
1600 Paoli Pike
Malvern, PA 19355-3375
Ph: (610)725-9100
Fax: (610)725-8479
Co. E-mail: nkeefer@cccbi.org
URL: http://www.cccbi.org
Contact: Nancy Keefer, President
Released: Bimonthly

57255 ■ *The Voice of the Valley*
c/o Charlie Ross, Pres./CEO
PO Box 10
Shamokin Dam, PA 17876-0010
Ph: (570)743-4100
Free: 800-410-2880
Fax: (570)743-1221
Co. E-mail: info@gsvcc.org
URL: http://www.gsvcc.org
Contact: Charlie Ross, President
Released: Monthly

57256 ■ *Wage & Benefit Survey*
Released: Annual **Price:** $100, /year.

57257 ■ Warren County Chamber of Business and Industry (WCCBI)
308 Market St.
Warren, PA 16365
Ph: (814)723-3050
Fax: (814)723-6024
Co. E-mail: info@wccbi.org
URL: http://www.wccbi.org
Contact: James L. Decker, President
Description: Promotes business and community development in Warren County, PA. Sponsors business seminars, programs, and workshops. Maintains consulting service. Holds annual golf outing. **Founded:** 1938. **Publications:** *Business and Industrial Directory* (Annual); *Membership Directory and Buyer's Guide* (Annual). **Telecommunication Services:** jdecker@wccbi.org.

57258 ■ Washington County Chamber of Commerce (WCCOC)
20 E Beau St.
Washington, PA 15301
Ph: (724)225-3010
Fax: (724)228-7337
Co. E-mail: jeff@washcochamber.com
URL: http://www.washcochamber.com
Contact: Patrick G. O'Brien, Chairperson
Description: Promotes business and community development in the Washington, PA area. **Founded:** 1881.

57259 ■ Wayne County Chamber of Commerce
32 Commercial St., Ste. 200
Honesdale, PA 18431
Ph: (570)253-1960
Free: 800-433-9008
Fax: (570)253-1517
Co. E-mail: exec@waynecountycc.com
URL: http://www.waynecountycc.com
Contact: Todd Stephens, President
Description: Promotes business and community development in Wayne County, PA. **Founded:** 1929. **Awards:** Business Person of the Year (Annual).

57260 ■ Waynesburg Chamber of Commerce
143 E High St.
Waynesburg, PA 15370-2053
Ph: (724)627-5926
Fax: (724)627-8017
Co. E-mail: waynesburgchamber@windstream.net
URL: http://www.waynesburgchamber.com
Contact: Melody R. Longstreth, Executive Director
Description: Provides services and programs that will increase the success of member businesses and organizations and enhance the economy and quality of life in the Waynesburg area. **Founded:** 1949. **Publications:** *Chamber Chatter* (Monthly). **Awards:** Distinguished Service Award (Annual).

57261 ■ *Welcome to Latrobe Area Neighborhood*
326 McKinley Ave., Ste. 102
Latrobe, PA 15650
Ph: (724)537-2671
Fax: (724)537-2690
Co. E-mail: info@latrobearea.com
URL: http://www.latrobearea.com

57262 ■ *Welcome to Wine County*
17 E Main St.
North East, PA 16428
Ph: (814)725-4262
Fax: (814)725-3994
Co. E-mail: info@nechamber.org
URL: http://www.nechamber.org
Contact: Anne Saxer, President
Released: Annual

57263 ■ Wellsboro Area Chamber of Commerce
PO Box 733
Wellsboro, PA 16901
Ph: (570)724-1926
Fax: (570)724-5084
Co. E-mail: info@wellsboropa.com
URL: http://www.wellsboropa.com
Contact: Ms. Julie VanNess, Executive Director
Description: Promotes business and community development in the Wellsboro, PA area. **Telecommunication Services:** juliev@wellsboropa.com.

57264 ■ West Shore Chamber of Commerce
4211 Trindle Rd.
Camp Hill, PA 17011
Ph: (717)761-0702
Fax: (717)761-4315
Co. E-mail: wschamber@wschamber.org
URL: http://www.wschamber.org
Contact: Kathleen M. Mangan, President
Description: Promotes business and community development in the Camp Hill, PA area. **Scope:** demographic information. **Founded:** 1948. **Subscriptions:** audio recordings books. **Publications:** *Connections* (Monthly); *Membership Directory and Business Resource Guide* (Annual). **Educational Activities:** Business and Industry Night (Annual); Spotlight Breakfast (Bimonthly). **Awards:** George C. Hoopy Award (Annual); Les Ginanni Business and Community Connection Award (Annual).

57265 ■ Western Chester County Chamber of Commerce (WCCCC)
50 S 1st Ave.
Coatesville, PA 19320
Ph: (610)384-9550

Fax: (610)384-9550
Co. E-mail: info@westernchestercounty.com
URL: http://www.westernchestercounty.com
Contact: Bill Shaw, President
Description: Promotes business and community development in Western Chester County, PA. Maintains hall of fame. **Founded:** 1929. **Publications:** *Western View* (Monthly). **Awards:** Community Citizens' Awards; Student Awards.

57266 ■ *Western View*
50 S 1st Ave.
Coatesville, PA 19320
Ph: (610)384-9550
Fax: (610)384-9550
Co. E-mail: info@westernchestercounty.com
URL: http://www.westernchestercounty.com
Contact: Bill Shaw, President
Released: Monthly **Price:** included in membership dues.

57267 ■ Westmoreland Chamber of Commerce (WCC)
241 Tollgate Hill Rd.
Greensburg, PA 15601
Ph: (724)834-2900
Fax: (724)837-7635
Co. E-mail: info@westmorelandchamber.com
URL: http://www.westmorelandchamber.com
Contact: Chad Amond, President
Description: Provides leadership to facilitate, maintain, and advance an environment conducive to the economic well being and superior quality of life for Westmoreland County through leadership, growth, and vision. **Publications:** *Chamber E-Central* (Monthly); *Westmoreland Chamber of Commerce--Membership Directory.*

57268 ■ *Who's Who in the Capital Region*
3211 N Front St., Ste. 201
Harrisburg, PA 17110-1342
Ph: (717)232-4099
Free: 877-883-8339
Fax: (717)232-5184
Co. E-mail: info@hbgrc.org
URL: http://www.harrisburgregionalchamber.org
Contact: David E. Black, President
Released: Annual

57269 ■ Wilkinsburg Chamber of Commerce
PO Box 8638
Wilkinsburg, PA 15221
Ph: (412)242-0234
Co. E-mail: info@wilkinsburgchamber.com
URL: http://wilkinsburgchamber.com
Contact: Owen McAfee, President
Description: Promotes the improvement of the business community, being cognizant of the social and economic changes that have occurred in the borough over the past century. **Founded:** 1893.

57270 ■ Williamsport-Lycoming Chamber of Commerce
100 W 3rd St.
Williamsport, PA 17701
Ph: (570)326-1971
Fax: (570)321-1209
Co. E-mail: chamber@williamsport.org
URL: http://www.williamsport.org
Contact: Vincent J. Matteo, President
Description: Promotes business and community development in the Williamsport, PA area. **Founded:** 1885. **Publications:** *Chamber Connection* (Monthly); *Industrial Directory* (Semiannual).

57271 ■ York County Chamber of Commerce
96 S George St., 3rd Fl.
York, PA 17401-1611
Ph: (717)848-4000
Free: 800-673-2429
Fax: (717)843-6737
Co. E-mail: info@yorkchamber.com
URL: http://www.yorkchamber.com
Contact: Thomas E. Donley, President
E-mail: donley@yorkchamber.com
Description: Promotes business and community development in the York, PA area. Offers advocacy service. **Founded:** 1898. **Publications:** *Business Voice* (Monthly); *Economic Profile* (Annual); *Import/*

Export Directory (Annual); *Map of York Area* (Annual); *Susquehanna Style Magazine* (Bimonthly); *Treasures*; *York Economic Outlook* (Quarterly).

57272 ■ *York Economic Outlook*
96 S George St., 3rd Fl.
York, PA 17401-1611
Ph: (717)848-4000
Free: 800-673-2429
Fax: (717)843-6737
Co. E-mail: info@yorkchamber.com
URL: http://www.yorkchamber.com
Contact: Thomas E. Donley, President
E-mail: donley@yorkchamber.com
Released: Quarterly

57273 ■ *Your Chamber Matters*
38 W Lancaster Ave.
Downingtown, PA 19335
Ph: (610)269-1523
Fax: (610)269-8713
Co. E-mail: splaugher@dtrcc.com
URL: http://www.dtrcc.com
Contact: Jillian M. Fragale, Executive Director
Released: Monthly

MINORITY BUSINESS ASSISTANCE PROGRAMS

57274 ■ Pennsylvania Department of General Services - Bureau of Minority and Women's Business Opportunities (BMWBO)
North Office Bldg., Rm. 611
401 North St.
Harrisburg, PA 17120-0500
Ph: (717)783-3119
Fax: (717)787-7052
Co. E-mail: gs-bmwbo@state.pa.us
URL: http://www.dgs.state.pa.us
Contact: Peter Speaks
Description: Actively pursues contracting and subcontracting opportunities in state government and the private sector for minority and women business enterprises.

57275 ■ Pennsylvania Minority Business Development Authority
Commonwealth Keystone Bldg.
400 North St., 4th Fl.
Harrisburg, PA 17120-0225
Ph: (717)720-1442
Fax: (717)772-2890
Co. E-mail: ra-dcedsbfo@state.pa.us
URL: http://www.newpa.com
Description: Provides low-interest, long-term loans and equity guarantees to assist in the start-up or expansion of minority-owned businesses.

57276 ■ Pennsylvania Minority Business Enterprise Center
4548 Market St.
Philadelphia, PA 19139
Ph: (215)895-4046
Fax: (215)895-4094
Co. E-mail: clientservices@pambdc.com
URL: http://www.pa-mbec.com/
Contact: Jacqueline Hill, Director

FINANCING AND LOAN PROGRAMS

57277 ■ Adams Capital Management Inc.
500 Blackburn Ave.
Sewickley, PA 15143-1478
Ph: (412)749-9454
Fax: (412)749-9459
Co. E-mail: jpa@acm.com
URL: http://www.acm.com
Contact: Andrea L. Stephenson, Director, Finance
E-mail: jpa@acm.com
Founded: 1994. **Preferred Investment Size:** $5,000,000 to $30,000,000. **Industry Preferences:** Internet specific, semiconductors and other electron-

ics, computer software and services, medical and health, biotechnology, computer hardware, communications and media. **Geographic Preference:** U.S.

57278 ■ Ben Franklin Technology Partners
115 Technology Ctr.
University Park, PA 16802
Ph: (814)863-4558
Co. E-mail: info@cnp.benfranklin.org
URL: http://www.benfranklin.org
Contact: Stephen Brawley, Chief Executive Officer
Preferred Investment Size: $50,000 to $150,000. **Industry Preferences:** Biotechnology, Internet specific, medical and health, computer software and services, other products, industrial and energy, computer hardware, consumer related, semiconductors and other electronics, communications and media. **Geographic Preference:** Pennsylvania.

57279 ■ BioAdvance
3711 Market St., 8th Fl.
Philadelphia, PA 19104
Ph: (215)966-6214
Fax: (215)966-6215
Co. E-mail: info@bioadvance.com
URL: http://www.bioadvance.com
Contact: Barbara Schilberg, Chief Executive Officer
E-mail: bschilberg@bioadvance.com
Preferred Investment Size: $500,000 to $1,000,000. **Investment Policies:** Seed and early stage. **Industry Preferences:** Biotechnology, and medical and health. **Geographic Preference:** Southeastern Pennsylvania.

57280 ■ Birchmere Ventures
424 South 27th St., Ste. 203
Pittsburgh, PA 15203
Ph: (412)322-3300
Co. E-mail: businessplans@birchmerevc.com
URL: http://www.birchmerevc.com
Contact: Gary Glausser, Partner
E-mail: gary@birchmerevc.com
Preferred Investment Size: $1,000,000 to $2,500,000. **Industry Preferences:** Computer software and services, biotechnology, Internet specific, computer hardware, industrial and energy, medical and health, semiconductors and other electronics. **Geographic Preference:** Mid Atlantic.

57281 ■ Blue Hill Partners, LLC
40 W. Evergreen Ave.
Philadelphia, PA 19118
Ph: (215)247-2400
Fax: (215)248-2381
URL: http://www.bluehillpartners.com
Contact: Peter D. Williams, Principal
Preferred Investment Size: $500,000 to $2,000,000. **Investment Policies:** Early stage, mezzanine and expansion. **Industry Preferences:** Industrial and energy, agriculture, forestry and fishing. **Geographic Preference:** Pennsylvania.

57282 ■ CEO Venture Fund
1 North Shore Ctr.
12 federal St., Ste. 201
Pittsburgh, PA 15212
Ph: (412)322-2572
Fax: (412)322-3226
URL: http://www.ceoventurefund.com
Contact: James Colker, Managing Partner
Preferred Investment Size: $1,000,000 to $2,000,000. **Industry Preferences:** Computer software and services, biotechnology, semiconductors and other electronics, Internet specific, computer hardware, other products, industrial and energy, medical and health, communications and media, and consumer related. **Geographic Preference:** Mid Atlantic.

57283 ■ Cross Atlantic Capital Partners
5 Radnor Corporate Ctr., Ste. 555
100 Matsonford Rd.
Radnor, PA 19087
Ph: (610)995-2650

Fax: (610)971-2062
Co. E-mail: info@xacp.com
URL: http://www.xacp.com
Contact: Donald Caldwell, Managing Director
Preferred Investment Size: $2,000,000 to $7,000,000. **Industry Preferences:** Internet specific, computer software and services, communications and media, computer hardware, other products, semiconductors and other electronics, industrial and energy, and biotechnology. **Geographic Preference:** U.S.

57284 ■ Draper Triangle Ventures
2 Gateway Ctr., Ste. 2000
Pittsburgh, PA 15222
Ph: (412)288-9800
Fax: (412)288-9799
Co. E-mail: karen@dtvc.com
URL: http://www.dtvc.com
Contact: Donald Jones, Managing Director
E-mail: djones@dtvc.com
Preferred Investment Size: $250,000 to $2,000,000. **Industry Preferences:** Communications, Internet specific, semiconductors and other electronics, medical and health, computer software, industrial and energy, and consumer related. **Geographic Preference:** Midwest and Northeast.

57285 ■ Enertech Capital /Enertech Capital Partners, L.P.
625 W, Ridge Pike, Bldg. D, Ste. 105
Conshohocken, PA 19428
Ph: (484)539-1860
Fax: (484)-539-1870
Co. E-mail: businessplans@enertechcapital.com
URL: http://www.enertechcapital.com
Contact: Scott Ungerer, Managing Director
Preferred Investment Size: $1,000,000 to $7,000,000. **Industry Preferences:** Internet specific, computer software and services, industrial and energy, semiconductors and other electronics, consumer related, computer hardware, other products, communications and media. **Geographic Preference:** U.S.

57286 ■ Gamma Investors
555 Croton Rd.
King of Prussia, PA 19006
Ph: (610)203-9337
Fax: (215)827-5198
Co. E-mail: gammainvestorsllc@Gammalnvestors. com
URL: http://www.gammainvestors.com
Contact: Alec Petro, Managing Director
Preferred Investment Size: $250,000 to $3,000,000. **Industry Preferences:** Internet specific. **Geographic Preference:** U.S.

57287 ■ Innovation Works, Inc.
2000 Technology Dr., Ste. 250
Pittsburgh, PA 15219-3109
Ph: (412)681-1520
Fax: (412)681-2625
Co. E-mail: info@innovationworks.org
URL: http://www.innovationworks.org
Contact: Rich Lunak, Chief Executive Officer
Preferred Investment Size: $100,000 to $500,000. **Industry Preferences:** Communications and media, computer hardware and software, Internet specific, semiconductors and other electronics, biotechnology, medical and health, industrial and energy. **Geographic Preference:** Pennsylvania.

57288 ■ Katalyst Venture Partners
PO Box 198
Hartford, PA 19041
Ph: (610)585-0285
URL: http://www.katalyst.com
Contact: Johnathan Kalman, Chief Executive Officer
Industry Preferences: Communications and media, computer software, and Internet specific. **Geographic Preference:** U.S. and Canada.

57289 ■ Keystone Venture Capital Management Co.
1601 Market St., Ste. 2500
Philadelphia, PA 19103
Ph: (215)241-1200

Fax: (215)241-1211
Co. E-mail: rpace@keystonevc.com
URL: http://www.keystoneventures.com
Contact: Peter Ligeti, Partner
E-mail: pligeti@keystnevc.com
Preferred Investment Size: $1,000,000 to $4,000,000. **Industry Preferences:** Internet specific, consumer related, computer software and services, communications and media, industrial and energy, medical and health, other products, computer hardware, semiconductors and other electronics. **Geographic Preference:** Mid Atlantic and Northeast.

57290 ■ Lancet Capital / Caduceus Capital Partners
245 First St., Ste. 1800
Cambridge, MA 02142
Ph: (617)320-1234
Fax: (617)444-8405
URL: http://www.lancetcapital.com
Contact: George L. Sing, Managing Director
E-mail: sing@lancetcapital.com
Preferred Investment Size: $100,000 to $4,000,000. **Industry Preferences:** Biotechnology, medical and health. **Geographic Preference:** U.S.

57291 ■ LaunchCyte LLC
2403 Sidney St., Ste. 271
Pittsburgh, PA 15203
Ph: (412)481-2200
Fax: (412)592-0349
Co. E-mail: info@launchcyte.com
URL: http://www.launchcyte.com
Contact: Tom Petzinger, Chief Executive Officer
E-mail: tom@launchcyte.com
Investment Policies: Start-up. **Industry Preferences:** Biotechnology.

57292 ■ Liberty Venture Partners, Inc.
2 Commerce Sq.
2001 Market St., Ste. 3820
Philadelphia, PA 19103-7012
Ph: (267)861-5692
Fax: (267)861-5696
URL: http://www.libertyvp.com
Contact: Thomas R. Morse, Principal
E-mail: tmorse@liberyvp.com
Preferred Investment Size: $1,000,000 to $3,000,000. **Industry Preferences:** Medical and health, computer software and services, communications and media, and Internet specific, medical and health, industrial and energy, and biotechnology. **Geographic Preference:** Mid Atlantic.

57293 ■ Mid-Atlantic Capital Alliance / MAC Alliance
200 South Broad St., Ste. 700
Philadelphia, PA 19102-3896
Ph: (215)790-3800
Fax: (215)790-3601
Co. E-mail: PACT@PhiladelphiaPACT.com
URL: http://www.macalliance.org
Contact: Tom Balderston, Chief Executive Officer
Preferred Investment Size: $100,000 to $300,000. **Industry Preferences:** Technology and services, clean technology, and life sciences. **Geographic Preference:** Greater Philadelphia region.

57294 ■ Mid-Atlantic Venture Funds / Nepa Management Corp.
Ben Franklin Technology Ctr.
125 Goodman Dr.
Bethlehem, PA 18015
Ph: (610)865-6550
Fax: (610)865-6427
Co. E-mail: info@mavf.com
URL: http://www.mavf.com
Contact: Frederick J. Beste, III, Partner
Preferred Investment Size: $500,000 to $8,000,000. **Industry Preferences:** Internet specific, computer software and services, medical and health, industrial and energy, other products, computer hardware, semiconductors and other electronics, communications and media, consumer related, and biotechnology. **Geographic Preference:** Mid Atlantic Massachusetts, North Carolina, and Northeast.

57295 ■ MVP Capital Partners
201 King of Prussia Rd., Ste. 240
Radnor, PA 19087
Ph: (610)254-2999
Fax: (610)254-2996
URL: http://www.mvpcapitalpartners.com
Contact: Robert E. Brown, Jr., Partner
Preferred Investment Size: $2,000,000 to $8,000,000. **Industry Preferences:** Consumer related, Internet specific, computer software and services, medical and health, industrial and energy, other products, communications and media, biotechnology, and computer hardware. **Geographic Preference:** Central and Eastern U.S.

57296 ■ NewSpring Ventures
Radnor Financial Ctr.
555 E. Lancaster Ave., Ste. 444
Radnor, PA 19087
Ph: (610)567-2380
Fax: (610)567-2388
Co. E-mail: info@NewSpringCapital.com
URL: http://www.newspringventures.com
Contact: Janet Paroo, Partner
E-mail: MDiPiano@NewSpringCapital.com
Preferred Investment Size: $2,000,000 to $5,000,000. **Industry Preferences:** Communications and media, computer software, computer related, semiconductors and other electronics, Internet specific, medical and health, financial services, business service, and manufacturing. **Geographic Preference:** Mid Atlantic.

57297 ■ PA Early Stage / Pennsylvania Stage Partners
435 Devon Park Dr., Ste. 801
Wayne, PA 19087
Ph: (610)293-4075
Fax: (610)254-4240
Co. E-mail: info@novitascapital.com
URL: http://www.paearlystage.com
Contact: Michael Bolton, Managing Director
Preferred Investment Size: $250,000 to $2,000,000. **Industry Preferences:** Internet specific, computer software and services, biotechnology, other products, semiconductors and other electronics, medical and health, consumer related, industrial and energy, communications and media. **Geographic Preference:** Mid Atlantic.

57298 ■ Patricof & Co. Ventures, Inc.
601 Lexington Ave., 53rd Fl.
New York, NY 10022
Ph: (212)753-6300
Fax: (212)31906155
URL: http://www.patricof.com
Preferred Investment Size: $500,000 minimum. **Industry Preferences:** Financial and business services, medical and health, communications and media, consumer related, information technology, and other products. **Geographic Preference:** No preference.

57299 ■ Philadelphia Ventures, Inc.
The Bellevue
200 S. Broad St., 8th Fl.
Philadelphia, PA 19102
Ph: (215)732-4445
Fax: (215)732-4644
Contact: Charles Burton, Managing Director
E-mail: burton1110@aol.com
Industry Preferences: Computer hardware, computer software and services, communications and media, medical and health, biotechnology, industrial and energy, semiconductors and other electronics, other products, Internet specific, and consumer related. **Geographic Preference:** Pennsylvania.

57300 ■ RAF Netventures / RAF Ventures
One Pitcairn Pl.
165 Township Line Rd., Ste. 2100
Jenkintown, PA 19046-3593
Ph: (215)572-0738

Fax: (215)576-1640
Co. E-mail: acquisitions@rafind.com
URL: http://www.rafnetventures.com
Contact: Richard M. Horowitz, Chief Operating Officer
Preferred Investment Size: $20,000,000 to $200,000,000. **Industry Preferences:** Internet specific, medical and health, computer software and services, and biotechnology. **Geographic Preference:** Northeast.

57301 ■ The Reinvestment Fund (TRF)
1700 Market St., 19th Fl.
Philadelphia, PA 19103-3904
Ph: (215)574-5800
Fax: (215)574-5900
Co. E-mail: info@TRFund.com
URL: http://www.trfund.com
Contact: Jeremy Nowak, Chief Executive Officer
Preferred Investment Size: $1,000,000 to $5,000,000. **Industry Preferences:** Other products, medical and health, Internet specific, industrial and energy, consumer related, computer software and services. **Geographic Preference:** Mid Atlantic.

57302 ■ Rock Hill Ventures, Inc. / Hillman Medical Ventures, Inc.
1059 Indian Creek Rd.
Wynnewood, PA 19096
Ph: (610)896
Fax: (610)940-0363
Co. E-mail: Hal@RockHillVentures.com
URL: http://rockhill-ventures.com
Preferred Investment Size: $1,000,000 to $2,000,000. **Industry Preferences:** Medical and health, and biotechnology. **Geographic Preference:** Mid Atlantic, Northeast, and Southeast.

57303 ■ S.R. One, Limited
Eight Tower Bridge
161 Washington St., Ste. 500
Conshohocken, PA 19428-2077
Ph: (610)567-1000
Fax: (610)567-1039
Co. E-mail: info@srone.com
URL: http://srone.com
Contact: Rajeev Dadoo, Partner
Preferred Investment Size: $500,000 to $5,000,000. **Industry Preferences:** Biotechnology, medical and health, computer software and services, Internet specific, and consumer related. **Geographic Preference:** U.S.

57304 ■ TL Ventures / Radnor Venture Partners
435 Devon Park Dr.
700 Bldg.
Wayne, PA 19087
Ph: (610)971-1515
Fax: (610)975-9330
Co. E-mail: info@tlventures.com
URL: http://www.tlventures.com
Contact: Robert Keith, Managing Director
Preferred Investment Size: $3,000,000 to $20,000,000. **Industry Preferences:** Internet specific, computer software and services, communications and media, biotechnology, semiconductors and other electronics, medical and health, other products, computer hardware, and consumer related. **Geographic Preference:** Northeast, Northwest, Southwest, and West Coast.

PROCUREMENT ASSISTANCE PROGRAMS

57305 ■ Defense Supply Center Philadelphia
700 Robbins Ave.
Bldg. 36-2
Philadelphia, PA 19111
Ph: (215)737-2321
Free: 800-831-1110
Fax: (215)737-7116
URL: http://www.dscp.dla.mil
Description: Covers activities for GSA, Public Building Services (Philadelphia, PA), Army Corps of Engineers (Philadelphia, PA), Defense Personnel Support Center-Clothing & Textile (Philadelphia, PA),

Defense Personnel Support Center-Medical (Philadelphia, PA), Defense Personnel Support Center-Subsistence (Philadelphia, PA).

57306 ■ Navy Inventory Control Point
700 Robbins Ave.
Bldg. 1, Rm.3209 (SBS)
Philadelphia, PA 19111
Ph: (215)697-4950
Fax: (215)697-2616
Co. E-mail: Joseph.giordano@sba.gov
URL: http://www.navicp.navy.mil
Description: Covers activities for Navy Inventory Control Point (Philadelphia, PA).

57307 ■ Pennsylvania & Maryland Procurement Center
Fleet & Industrial Supply
Center Detachment Philadelphia
700 Robbins Ave., Bldg. 2B
Philadelphia, PA 19111-5083
Ph: (215)697-9555
Fax: (215)697-9554
Contact: Gerald Furey, Representative
Description: Covers activities for Navy, Fleet & Industrial Support, Center Detachment Philadelphia (Philadelphia, PA), NAVFAC (Philadelphia, PA), Naval Surface Weapons Center (Bethesda, MD), Army Chemical & Biological Defense Command (Edgewood, MD), and Army, Aberdeen Proving Ground (Aberdeen, MD).

57308 ■ Pennsylvania Procurement Technical Assistance Center
The Wharton School
Vance Hall, Rm. 435
3733 Spruce St.
Philadelphia, PA 19104-6374
Ph: (215)898-1219
Fax: (215)898-1063
Co. E-mail: clydes@wharton.upenn.edu
URL: http://www.pasbdc.org
Contact: Clyde Stoltzfus, Director

57309 ■ Pennsylvania Procurement Technical Assistance Center - Economic Development Council of Northeast Pennsylvania - The Northeastern Pennsylvania Alliance (NEPA) - Enterprise Development District
1151 Oak St.
Pittston, PA 18640-3726
Ph: (570)655-5581
Fax: (570)654-5137
Co. E-mail: info@nepa-alliance.org
URL: http://www.nepa-alliance.org
Contact: Bruce Parc Eckersley, Specialist
E-mail: dkern@nepa-alliance.org
Description: Helps businesses expand into new markets and get the financial assistance they need to grow.

57310 ■ Pennsylvania Procurement Technical Assistance Center - Government Agency Coordination Office - California University of Pennsylvania
250 University Ave., Box 20
3733 Spruce St.
4th Floor-Vance Hall
California, PA 15419
Ph: (724)938-5881
Fax: (724)938-4575
Co. E-mail: wojcik@cup.edu
URL: http://www.cup.edu/advancement/gaco/index.jsp
Contact: Deborah Wojcik, Program Manager
E-mail: wojcik@cup.edu
Description: Provides services to companies interested in pursuing federal, state and local contracting, subcontracting and export opportunities.

57311 ■ Pennsylvania Procurement Technical Assistance Center - Government Agency Coordination Office (GACO) - California University of Pennsylvania
700 River Ave., Ste. 220
Pittsburgh, PA 15212
Ph: (412)237-6098

Fax: (412)237-6099
Co. E-mail: gacopso@earthlink.net
URL: http://www.cup.edu/advancement/gaco
Contact: Kate Glodek, Manager
E-mail: gacopso@earthlink.net
Description: Provides services to companies interested in pursuing federal, state and local contracting, subcontracting and export opportunities.

57312 ■ Pennsylvania Procurement Technical Assistance Center - Government Agency Coordination Office (GACO) - Slippery Rock University
006 Eisenberg Classroom Bldg.
Slippery Rock, PA 16057
Ph: (724)738-2346
Fax: (724)738-2168
Co. E-mail: gcac@sru.edu
URL: http://academics.sru.edu/cbiss/gcac
Contact: Renee Decker, Manager
E-mail: renee.decker@sru.edu
Description: Provides services to companies interested in pursuing federal, state and local contracting, subcontracting and export opportunities.

57313 ■ Pennsylvania Procurement Technical Assistance Center - Indiana University of Pennsylvania - Government Contracting Assistance Program
IUP Robert Shaw Bldg., Rm. 10
650 S 13th St.
Indiana, PA 15705-1087
Ph: (724)357-7824
Fax: (724)357-3082
Co. E-mail: rfmoreau@iup.edu
URL: http://www.eberly.iup.edu/gcap
Contact: Ron Moreau, Program Manager
E-mail: rfmoreau@grove.iup.edu
Description: Provides procurement technical assistance to firms interested in selling their goods or services to the local, state, and/or federal government.

57314 ■ Pennsylvania Procurement Technical Assistance Center - Johnstown Area Regional Industries
245 Market St., Ste. 200
Johnstown, PA 15901
Ph: (814)539-4951
Fax: (814)535-8677
Co. E-mail: bshark@jari.com
URL: http://www.jari.com
Contact: Bob Shark, Program Manager

57315 ■ Pennsylvania Procurement Technical Assistance Center - North Central Pennsylvania Regional Planning & Development Commission
651 Montmorenci Rd.
Ridgeway, PA 15853
Ph: (814)773-3162
Fax: (814)772-7045
Co. E-mail: bimhof@ncentral.com
URL: http://www.ncentral.com
Contact: Bob Imhof, Program Manager
E-mail: bimhof@ncentral.com
Description: Designed to increase the number of area companies receiving government contracts by educating management on how to market their products to the government.

57316 ■ Pennsylvania Procurement Technical Assistance Center - Northeastern Pennsylvania Alliance
1151 Oak St.
Pittston, PA 18640-3726
Ph: (570)655-5581
Fax: (570)654-5137
Co. E-mail: info@nepa.alliance.org
URL: http://www.nepa.alliance.org
Contact: Bruce Parc Eckersley, Specialist
E-mail: dkk@microserve.net
Description: Serves as a liaison to help local companies, usually small businesses (suppliers) and local government contractors (buyers/procurers) increase sales and growth for our regional economy.

57317 ■ Pennsylvania Procurement Technical Assistance Center - Northern Tier Regional Planning & Development Commission
312 Main St.
Towanda, PA 18848-1697
Ph: (570)265-9103
Free: 888-868-8800
Fax: (570)265-7585
Co. E-mail: meehan@northerntier.org
URL: http://www.northerntier.org
Contact: Kerry Meehan, Program Manager
E-mail: sabatura@northerntier.org
Description: Providing resources to help businesses and entrepreneurs, local governments, and non-profit organizations.

57318 ■ Pennsylvania Procurement Technical Assistance Center - Northwest Pennsylvania Regional Planning and Development Commission
395 Seneca St.
Oil City, PA 16301
Ph: (814)677-4800
Fax: (814)677-7663
Co. E-mail: janeta@nwcommission.org
URL: http://www.nwcommission.org
Contact: Janet Anderson, Director
E-mail: christopher@nwcommission.org
Description: Local development district serving Clarion, Crawford, Erie, Forest, Lawrence, Mercer, Venango, and Warren Counties.

57319 ■ Pennsylvania Procurement Technical Assistance Center - SEDA Council of Governments
201 Furnace Rd.
Lewisburg, PA 17837
Ph: (570)524-4491
Free: 800-332-6701
Fax: (570)524-9190
Co. E-mail: procurement@seda-cog.org
URL: http://www.seda-cog.org
Contact: Robert Brown, Program Manager
Description: Assist companies in either entering the government market place or expanding their current market share.

57320 ■ Pennsylvania Procurement Technical Assistance Center - Small Business Development Center - Kutztown University
737 Constitution Dr.
Exton, PA 19341
Ph: (610)458-5700
Co. E-mail: boehm@kutztown.edu
URL: http://www.pasbdc.org
Contact: George Boehm, Counselor
E-mail: boehm@kutztown.edu
Description: To grow the economy of Pennsylvania by providing entrepreneurs with the education, information and tools necessary to build successful businesses.

57321 ■ Pennsylvania Procurement Technical Assistance Center - Small Business Development Center - Lehigh University
Rauch Business Center, No. 37
621 Taylor St.
Bethlehem, PA 18015
Ph: (610)758-4089
Co. E-mail: cmj0@lehigh.edu
URL: http://www.pasbdc.org/lehigh
Contact: Chris Jones, Counselor
E-mail: jps4@lehigh.edu
Description: To grow the economy of Pennsylvania by providing entrepreneurs with the education, information and tools necessary to build successful businesses.

57322 ■ Pennsylvania Procurement Technical Assistance Center - Small Business Development Center - Widener University
140 Edgemont Ave., Ste. 120
Chester, PA 19013

Ph: (610)499-1175
URL: http://www.pasbdc.org
Description: To grow the economy of Pennsylvania by providing entrepreneurs with the education, information and tools necessary to build successful businesses.

57323 ■ Pennsylvania Procurement Technical Assistance Center - Southwestern Pennsylvania Commission
Regional Enterprise Tower
425 6th Ave., Ste. 2500
Pittsburgh, PA 15219-1582
Ph: (412)391-5590
Fax: (412)391-9160
Co. E-mail: dpinkosky@spcregion.org
URL: http://www.spcregion.org
Contact: Dave Pinkosky, Counselor
Description: Helps companies to enter and succeed in the world of government contracting.

57324 ■ Pennsylvania Procurement Technical Assistance Center - Trustees of the University of Pennsylvania State Director's Office - Pennsylvania Small Business Development Centers - The Wharton School
3733 Spruce St.
Vance Hall, Rm. 435
Philadelphia, PA 19104-6374
Ph: (215)898-1219
Fax: (215)573-2135
Co. E-mail: pasbdc@wharton.upenn.edu
URL: http://www.pasbdc.org
Contact: Clyde M. Stoltzfus, Director
E-mail: clydes@wharton.upenn.edu
Description: The Pennsylvania SBDC State Director's office is hosted by the Wharton School at the University of Pennsylvania. The State Director's office is responsible for the administration and oversight of the Pennsylvania system of 18 centers.

57325 ■ Private Industry Council - Procurement Information Center of Westmoreland/Fay
219 Donohoe Rd.
Greensburg, PA 15601
Ph: (724)836-2600
Fax: (724)836-8058
Co. E-mail: info@privateindustrycouncil.com
URL: http://www.privateindustrycouncil.com
Contact: Tim Yurcisin, Chief Executive Officer

57326 ■ Southern Alleghenies Planning and Development Commission
541 58th St.
Altoona, PA 16602-1193
Ph: (814)949-6528
Fax: (814)949-6505
Co. E-mail: silvetti@sapdc.org
URL: http://www.sapdc.org
Contact: Edward Silvetti, Director
E-mail: shade@ssapdc.org

57327 ■ Temple University Small Business Development Center - Temple University
1510 Cecil B. Moore Ave.
Philadelphia, PA 19121
Ph: (215)204-7282
Fax: (215)204-4554
Co. E-mail: sbdc@temple.edu
URL: http://www.temple.edu/sbdc
Contact: Eustace Kangaju, Director
Description: Helps small business grow and succeed. We provide high quality business management consulting and training for aspiring entrepreneurs and small emerging growth companies in Southeastern Pennsylvania.

INCUBATORS/RESEARCH AND TECHNOLOGY PARKS

57328 ■ Altoona Blair County Development Corporation
3900 Industrial Park Dr.
Altoona, PA 16602
Ph: (814)944-6113

Fax: (814)946-0157
Co. E-mail: abcd@abcdcorp.org
URL: http://www.abcdcorp.org
Description: Provides business development and entrepreneurial assistance.

57329 ■ Ben Franklin Technology Partners
125 Goodman Dr.
Bethlehem, PA 18015-3715
Ph: (610)758-5200
Free: 800-445-9515
Fax: (610)861-5918
Co. E-mail: info@nep.benfranklin.org
URL: http://www.nep.benfranklin.org
Contact: Bob Thomson, Regional Manager
Description: The Northeast Tier is one of four BFTCs that operate in Pennsylvania. They are dedicated to nurturing the development of emerging technology firms.

57330 ■ Bridgeworks Enterprise Center
Allentown Economic Development Corp.
905 Harrison St.
Allentown, PA 18103
Ph: (610)770-1015
Fax: (610)770-1043
Co. E-mail: info@allentownedc.com
URL: http://www.thebridgeworks.com/bec.html
Contact: Lewis Edwards, Director
Description: A small business incubator providing a building and a program where new businesses receive special benefits and reduced costs in order to increase their likelihood of success.

57331 ■ Carbondale Technology Transfer Center
10 Enterprise Dr.
Carbondale, PA 18407
Ph: (570)282-1255
Fax: (570)282-1426
Co. E-mail: paul@cttc.org
URL: http://www.4cttc.org/
Description: A small business incubator providing technical support, business assistance, financial resources and appropriate facilities to entrepreneurs, small businesses, and light industry/light assembly manufacturers working with technology applications or innovative products or processes.

57332 ■ Catalyst Connection
2000 Technology Dr.
Pittsburgh, PA 15219
Ph: (412)918-4300
Free: 888-88-SPIRC
Fax: (412)687-2791
Co. E-mail: info@spirc.org
URL: http://www.catalystconnection.org/
Description: An economic development organization assisting small-to-mid sized manufacturing businesses in southwestern Pennsylvania.

57333 ■ Chamber of Business and Industry of Centre County
200 Innovation Blvd., Ste 150
State College, PA 16803
Ph: (814)234-1829
Fax: (814)234-5869
Co. E-mail: cbicc@cbicc.org
URL: http://www.cbicc.org
Contact: John Coleman, Chief Executive Officer
Description: Promotes commerce, business, and industry in Centre County.

57334 ■ Donald H. Jones Center for Entrepreneurship
Tepper School Of Business
Carnegie Mellon University
500 Forbes Ave,
Pittsburgh, PA 15213-3890
Ph: (412)268-8685
Fax: (412)268-4804
Co. E-mail: boni@andrew.cmu.edu
URL: http://www.tepper.cmu.edu
Description: Provides formal entrepreneurship training.

57335 ■ Executive Office Link
5 Great Valley Pky., Ste. 210
Malvern, PA 19355

Ph: (610)251-6850
Fax: (610)889-9726
Co. E-mail: info@execofficelink.com
URL: http://execofficelink.com
Contact: Sharon Nothnagle, President
Description: Provides office space, virtual offices, meeting rooms, and business services to entrepreneurs and small businesses.

57336 ■ Girard Area Industrial Development Corp. - Model Works Industrial Commons
227 Hathaway St.
Girard, PA 16427
Ph: (814)774-9339
Fax: (814)774-9235
Description: Provides incubation facilities and a multi-tenant facility for incubator graduates.

57337 ■ Greater Hazelton Business and Innovation Center
Can Be
103 Rotary Dr.
West Hazelton, PA 18202
Ph: (570)455-8334
Fax: (570)454-7787
Co. E-mail: jstpierre@canbe.biz
URL: http://www.canbe.biz/
Description: A small business incubator helping entrepreneurs grow new ventures in the community that will provide goods, services and jobs. Provides office and light industrial space.

57338 ■ McNeilly Business Center
Greenville Area Economic Development Corp.
12 N Diamond St.
Greenville, PA 16125
Ph: (724)588-1161
Fax: (724)588-9881
Co. E-mail: jim.lowry@gaedc.org
URL: http://www.gaedc.org/mcneilly.asp
Contact: Jim Lowry, Executive Director
Description: An incubator offering small business office space and financing assistance.

57339 ■ North Central Pennsylvania Regional Planning and Development Commission - Enterprise Development
651 Montmorency Rd.
Ridgeway, PA 15853
Ph: (814)773-3162
Free: 800-242-5872
Fax: (814)772-7045
Co. E-mail: ncprpdc@ncentral.com
URL: http://www.ncentral.com
Contact: Eric Bridges, Executive Director
Description: Works to foster the economic vitality of the county. Programs include: Export Marketing; Procurement Technical Assistance; Loan Assistance; Entrepreneurial Network; Keystone Opportunity Zones; and North Central Enterprises Inc.

57340 ■ Redevelopment Authority of the City of Meadville
984 Waters St., Ste. 2
Meadville, PA 16335-3497
Ph: (814)337-8200
Fax: (814)337-7257
Co. E-mail: info@redevelopmeadville.com
URL: http://www.redevelopmeadville.com/
Contact: Jill M. Groves, Executive Director
Description: Works to revitalize the city of Meadville through economic community growth.

57341 ■ University City Science Center
3711 Market St., 8th Fl.
Philadelphia, PA 19104
Ph: (215)966-6000
Fax: (215)382-0057
Co. E-mail: info@sciencecenter.org
URL: http://www.sciencecenter.org
Description: The UCSC is dedicated to fostering science and technology-based economic development. The incubator offers tenants office and laboratory space, business services, and research management assistance.

57342 ■ Warren/Forest Counties Economic Opportunity Council
1209 Pennsylvania Ave. W
Warren, PA 16365
Ph: (814)726-2400
Free: 800-231-1797
Fax: (814)723-0510
Co. E-mail: eoc@fcaa.org
URL: http://www.wfcaa.org

EDUCATIONAL PROGRAMS

57343 ■ Central Pennsylvania College
College Hill Rd.
Summerdale, PA 17093
Ph: (717)732-0702
Free: 800-759-2727
Fax: (717)732-5254
Co. E-mail: admissions@centralpenn.edu
URL: http://www.centralpenn.edu
Description: Two-year college offering a program in entrepreneurship and small business management.

57344 ■ Community College of Allegheny County, North Campus
8701 Perry Hwy.
Pittsburgh, PA 15237-5353
Ph: (412)366-7000
Fax: (412)369-3635
URL: http://www.ccac.edu
Description: Two-year college offering a small business management program.

57345 ■ Delaware County Community College
901 S Media Line Rd.
Media, PA 19063-1094
Ph: (610)359-5000
Free: 800-543-0146
Fax: (610)723-1530
Co. E-mail: wecare@dccc.edu
URL: http://www.dccc.edu
Description: Conducts small business courses, including financial management for small business; choosing microcomputer software; how to cash in on your crafts; how to start a consulting business; marketing for your small business; develop your own typing/word processing business; how to develop a business plan; fundamentals of small business management; start-up financing; record keeping and taxes for small business; and microcomputer awareness. Also offers consulting and technical assistance. Works with Community Accountants of Media to provide free accounting and financial assistance to eligible small business owners.

57346 ■ Northampton Community College (NCC)
3835 Green Pond Rd.
Bethlehem, PA 18020
Ph: (610)861-5300
Free: 877-543-0998
Fax: (610)861-4560
Co. E-mail: JRMccarthy@northampton.edu
URL: http://www.northampton.edu
Contact: James McCarthy, Director, Admissions
Description: Two-year college offering a small business management program. **Founded:** 1967. **Telecommunication Services:** adminfo@northampton.edu.

57347 ■ Penn Foster Career School
925 Oak St.
Scranton, PA 18515
Ph: (570)961-4033
Free: 800-275-4410
Fax: (570)702-8380
Co. E-mail: infoims@pennfoster.com
URL: http://www.pennfoster.edu
Contact: Richard W. Ferrin, President
URL(s): www.pennfoster.com, www.educationdirect.com. **Description:** Home-study school offering a small business management program. **Founded:** 1958. **Telecommunication Services:** info@pennfoster.com.

PUBLICATIONS

57348 ■ *Smart Start your Pennsylvania Business*
PSI Research
300 N. Valley Dr.
Grants Pass, OR 97526
Ph: (503)479-9464
Free: 800-228-2275
Fax: (503)476-1479
Co. E-mail: info@psi-research.com
URL: http://www.psi-research.com
Ed: Michael D. Jenkins. **Released:** Revised edition, 1992. **Price:** $29.95 (looseleaf binder); $24.95 (paper). **Description:** Part of the Successful Business Library series.

PUBLISHERS

57349 ■ The Danielle Adams Publishing Co.
PO Box 100
Wynnewood, PA 19096-1917
Ph: (610)642-1000
Free: 800-234-4332
Fax: (610)642-6832
Co. E-mail: jeff@dobkin.com
URL: http://www.dobkin.com
Contact: Jeffrey Dobkin, President
URL(s): www.danielleadams.com. **Description:** Description: Publishes books and articles of interest to small business owners, Investors, Marketers and Entrepreneurs. Does not accept unsolicited manuscripts. Reaches market through commission representatives, direct mail and wholesalers. **Scope:** Provider of marketing and direct marketing services and consulting. Offers a full range of services: Analysis, action plans, benchmarking, testing and reviews of marketing campaigns, advertising, copy writing and direct sell catalogs analysis. Assists clients in any industry worldwide. **Founded:** 1986. **Publications:** "A 15-Point Check List for Your Ads"; "12 Places to Buy a Mailing List"; "Forget Theory Here's What Works Best in Direct Marketing"; "How to Market a Product for Under 500"; "Uncommon Marketing Techniques"; "Direct Marketing Strategies"; "Successful Low Cost Direct Marketing Methods"; "Vital Signs"; "How to Get 1000 Worth of Advertising for 60"; "15Magic Words to Make Sure Your Press Release Gets Published"; "18 Marketing Assumptions that Aren't True"; "Marketing Through Associations"; "Marketing With Post Cards"; "16 Myths of Marketing"; "Inside Secrets of Direct Marketing: Bulleted Tips"; "Increasing Response Through Booklet Titles". **Seminars:** Marketing and Direct Marketing.

57350 ■ Bookhaven Press L.L.C.
249 Field Club Cir.
McKees Rocks, PA 15136
Ph: (412)494-6926
Free: 800-782-7424
Fax: (412)494-5749
Co. E-mail: info@bookhavenpress.com
URL: http://www.bookhavenpress.com
Contact: Dennis V. Damp, President
E-mail: ddamp@bookhavenpress.com
URL(s): federaljobs.net/us10.htm, www.bookhavenpress.com/reviews.htm#Post_Office_Jobs, bookhavenpress.com. **Description:** Description: Publishes trade books for general audience on business and employment. Reaches market through direct mail, Internet sales, trade sales and wholesalers. Does not accept unsolicited manuscripts. **Founded:** 1985. **Publications:** *The Book of U.S. Government Jobs: Where They Are, What's Available, and How to Get One* (Annual); *Take Charge of Your Federal Career*; *Post Office Jobs: Explore and Find Jobs, Prepare for the 473 Postal Exam, and Locate All Job Opportunities*; *Post Office Jobs: How to Get a Job With the U.S. Postal Service*; *The Book of US Government Jobs: Where They Are, What's Available and How to Write a Federal Resume*; *Health*

Care Job Explosion! High Growth Health Care Careers and Job Locator. **Telecommunication Services:** bookhaven@aol.com.

57351 ■ Dalton Directory
24 N Bryn Mawr Ave., Ste. 278
Bryn Mawr, PA 19010
Ph: (518)583-4545
Free: 800-221-1050
Fax: (518)583-4545
Co. E-mail: info@daltondirectory.com
URL: http://www.daltondirectory.com
Contact: Mark A. Dalton, Owner
Description: Description: Publishes business directories for the New York and Philadelphia metropolitan areas. Reaches market through direct mail and telephone sales. Does not accept unsolicited manuscripts. **Founded:** 1960. **Publications:** *Dalton Philadelphia Metro Business Directory* (Annual); *Lehigh Valley Metro Business Directory*; *Dalton's Baltimore/Washington Metropolitan Directory of Business/Industry*; *Lehigh Valley Metro Business Directory* (Biennial); *Dalton's New York Metropolitan Directory of Business/Industry* (Biennial); *Dalton's Baltimore/Washington Metropolitan Directory of Business/Industry* (Biennial).

57352 ■ Strategic Press
1460 Pittman Ave.
Sparks, NV 89431
Ph: (775)331-7047
Free: 800-767-5964
Fax: (775)358-9675
Co. E-mail: info@strategicpress.com
URL: http://www.strategicpress.com/links.htm
Contact: Brian Foote, President
Description: Description: Publishes business and marketing books and special reports for small business owners and entrepreneurs. Also offers audio cassettes, posters and prints Does not accept unsolicited manuscripts Reaches market through direct mail. **Founded:** 1998.

57353 ■ Windsor Press Inc.
6 N 3rd St.
Hamburg, PA 19526
Ph: (610)562-2267
Free: 800-562-5521
Fax: (610)562-2770
Co. E-mail: distribution@windsorpress.com
URL: http://www.windsorpress.com
Contact: George Mitten, President
E-mail: george@windsorpress.com
Description: Description: Publishes annual reports, manuals and a variety of books, including employer, ad and program books. Also offers post cards, brochures and newsletters. **Founded:** 1958. **Publications:** *East Penn Valley Merchandiser: Merchandiser* (Daily); *Northern Berks Merchandiser* (Daily).

57354 ■ Xlibris Corporation
1663 Liberty Dr.
Ste. 200
Bloomington, IN 47403
Ph: (610)915-5214
Free: 888-795-4274
Fax: (610)915-0294
Co. E-mail: info@xlibris.com
URL: http://www2.xlibris.com/
Contact: Joe Steinbach, President
URL(s): xlibris.com, www.xlibris.com. **Description:** Description: Publishes publishing kits to help the authors for publishing their works. Accepts unsolicited manuscripts. Reaches market through commission reps, direct mail, reviews, listings, telephone sales and wholesalers and distributors, including Amazon, BFN, borders, Ingram, books in print and lightning source. **Scope:** Provides the tools needed to publish using print-on-demand technology. Offers a variety of design, production and publishing services as well as online distribution availability and marketing products for self-publishing authors. **Founded:** 1997. **Publications:** "The Vineyard on Mulberry Street"; "Another Kind of Love Story"; "Dating Nightmares of A Single Woman".

SMALL BUSINESS DEVELOPMENT CENTERS

57355 ■ Rhode Island Small Business Development Center - Lead Office (RISBDC)
270 Weybosset St.
Richmond Bldg., 4th Fl.
Providence, RI 02903
Ph: (401)598-2702
Fax: (401)598-2722
Co. E-mail: john.cronin@jwu.edu
URL: http://www.risbdc.org
Contact: John Cronin, Director

SMALL BUSINESS ASSISTANCE PROGRAMS

57356 ■ Brown Forum for Enterprise
Brown University
Box 1991
Providence, RI 02912
Ph: (401)863-3528
Fax: (401)863-9822
Co. E-mail: leigh_kendall@brown.edu
URL: http://www.brownenterpriseforum.org
Contact: Leigh Kendall, Coordinator
Description: Brings together entrepreneurs, venture capitalists, executives, and others to discuss the problems of starting and expanding a business. Sponsors start-up workshops.

57357 ■ Rhode Island Department of Environmental Management - Division of Agriculture and Resource Marketing
235 Promenade St.
Providence, RI 02908-5767
Ph: (401)222-2781
Fax: (401)222-6047
URL: http://www.dem.ri.gov/programs/bnatres/agricult/
Contact: Kenneth Ayers, Section Chief
Description: Provides information on markets for agriculture, seafood, and aquaculture products.

57358 ■ Rhode Island Economic Development Corporation - Business Services
315 Iron Horse Way, Ste. 101
Providence, RI 02908
Ph: (401)278-9100
Fax: (401)273-8271
Co. E-mail: info@riedc.com
URL: http://www.riedc.com
Contact: Katharine Flynn, Director
Description: Provides assistance in finance packaging and information on finance programs, such as the Revolving Loan Fund, insured mortgage financing, and bond programs. The Procurement Program provides federal procurement information. The Office of Minority Business Affairs assists in business planning and loan packaging, and certifies minority-owned, women-owned, and disadvantaged businesses for participation in state procurement and set-

aside programs. The Business Retention Program offers advice to owners who are having problems with state agencies.

57359 ■ U.S. Department of Commerce - Rhode Island Economic Development Corp. (RIEDC)
315 Iron Horse Way, Ste. 101
Providence, RI 02908
Ph: (401)278-9100
Free: 800-250-7384
Fax: (401)273-8270
Co. E-mail: info@riedc.com
URL: http://www.riedc.com
Contact: J. Michael Saul, Executive Director
URL(s): www.visitrhodeisland.com/. **Description:** Provides site and building information to businesses expanding or relocating within the state. Also provides employee relocation assistance for out-of-state companies moving to Rhode Island. **Telecommunication Services:** visitrhodeisland@riedc.com.

SCORE OFFICES

57360 ■ SCORE JGE Knight
380 Westminster St.
Providence, RI 02903
Ph: (401)528-4561
Fax: (401)528-4539
Co. E-mail: info@riscore.org
URL: http://ri.score.org
Description: Provides professional guidance and information to maximize the success of existing and emerging small businesses. Offers business counseling and workshops.

CHAMBERS OF COMMERCE

57361 ■ *Annual Area Resource Guide and Directory*
4945 Old Post Rd.
Charlestown, RI 02813
Ph: (401)364-3878
Fax: (401)364-8794
URL: http://www.charlestownrichamber.com
Contact: Ann Cook, President
Released: Annual

57362 ■ *Business and Community Resource Guide*
6 Blackstone Valley Pl., Ste. 301
Lincoln, RI 02865
Ph: (401)334-1000
Fax: (401)334-1009
Co. E-mail: general@nrichamber.com
URL: http://www.nrichamber.com
Contact: John C. Gregory, President
Released: Annual; every spring. **Price:** free for members; $250, for nonmembers.

57363 ■ *Business Matters*
230 Old Tower Hill Rd.
Wakefield, RI 02879
Ph: (401)783-2801

Fax: (401)789-3120
Co. E-mail: info@skchamber.com
URL: http://www.skchamber.com/cwt/external/wcpages/index.aspx
Contact: Joe Viele, Chairman
Released: Monthly

57364 ■ *Business Pulse*
6 Blackstone Valley Pl., Ste. 301
Lincoln, RI 02865
Ph: (401)334-1000
Fax: (401)334-1009
Co. E-mail: general@nrichamber.com
URL: http://www.nrichamber.com
Contact: John C. Gregory, President
Released: Monthly

57365 ■ Central Rhode Island Chamber of Commerce
3288 Post Rd.
Warwick, RI 02886
Ph: (401)732-1100
Fax: (401)732-1107
Co. E-mail: info@centralrichamber.com
URL: http://www.centralrichamber.com
Contact: Lauren Slocum, President
Description: Promotes business and community development in Kent County, RI. Sponsors Management Assistance Team, Legislative Action Organization, and Commercial and Sales Leads programs. Provides health insurance program. Holds monthly luncheon and trade show series. **Founded:** 1980. **Publications:** *ChamberWorks* (Monthly).

57366 ■ *Chamber News*
PO Box 742
Narragansett, RI 02882
Ph: (401)783-7121
Fax: (401)789-0220
Co. E-mail: support@narragansettcoc.com
URL: http://narragansettri.com/chamber
Contact: Debbie Kelso, Executive Director
Released: Monthly

57367 ■ *Chamber News: A Focus on Business*
c/o Ms. Laura A. McNamara, Exec. Dir.
1011 Waterman Ave.
East Providence, RI 02914
Ph: (401)438-1212
Fax: (401)435-4581
Co. E-mail: office@eastprovchamber.com
URL: http://www.eastprovchamber.com
Contact: Ms. Laura A. McNamara, Executive Director
Released: Quarterly

57368 ■ *ChamberWorks*
3288 Post Rd.
Warwick, RI 02886
Ph: (401)732-1100
Fax: (401)732-1107
Co. E-mail: info@centralrichamber.com
URL: http://www.centralrichamber.com
Contact: Lauren Slocum, President
Released: Monthly **Price:** included in membership dues.

57369 ■ Charlestown Chamber of Commerce
4945 Old Post Rd.
Charlestown, RI 02813
Ph: (401)364-3878
Fax: (401)364-8794
URL: http://www.charlestownrichamber.com
Contact: Ann Cook, President
Description: Serves members and the community with networking opportunities, business seminars, and referrals. **Publications:** Annual Area Resource Guide and Directory (Annual). **Educational Activities:** Big Apple Circus (Annual).

57370 ■ Connections
8045 Post Rd.
North Kingstown, RI 02852
Ph: (401)295-5566
Fax: (401)295-5582
Co. E-mail: info@northkingstown.com
URL: http://www.northkingstown.com
Contact: Karla P. Driscoll, Executive Director
Released: Monthly **Price:** included in membership dues.

57371 ■ Cranston Chamber News
875 Oaklawn Ave., 3rd Fl., Ste. 1
Cranston, RI 02910
Ph: (401)785-3780
Fax: (401)785-3782
Co. E-mail: susan@cranstonchamber.com
URL: http://www.cranstonchamber.com
Contact: Susan Pagnozzi, President
Released: Monthly

57372 ■ East Bay Chamber of Commerce (EBCC)
16 Cutler St., Ste. 102
Warren, RI 02885
Ph: (401)245-0750
Fax: (401)245-0110
Co. E-mail: info@eastbaychamberri.org
URL: http://www.eastbaychamberri.org/cwt/external/wcpages/index.aspx
Contact: Betty J. Pleacher, President
Description: Strives to promote economic development and improve the quality of life for the East Bay, RI community. **Founded:** 1958. **Publications:** East Bay Community and Buyers' Guide (Annual); Moving Forward (Monthly); Who's Who in Bristol County Business (Annual). **Awards:** Citizen of the Year Award (Annual); Community Betterment (Semiannual). **Telecommunication Services:** betty@eastbaychamberri.org.

57373 ■ East Bay Community and Buyers' Guide
16 Cutler St., Ste. 102
Warren, RI 02885
Ph: (401)245-0750
Fax: (401)245-0110
Co. E-mail: info@eastbaychamberri.org
URL: http://www.eastbaychamberri.org/cwt/external/wcpages/index.aspx
Contact: Betty J. Pleacher, President
Released: Annual

57374 ■ East Greenwich Chamber of Commerce (EGCC)
580 Main St.
East Greenwich, RI 02818
Ph: (401)885-0020
Fax: (401)885-0048
Co. E-mail: egc@intap.net
URL: http://www.eastgreenwichchamber.com
Contact: Stephen M. Lombardi, Executive Director
Description: Promotes business and community development in East Greenwich, RI. **Founded:** 1929. **Publications:** Messenger (Monthly); Welcome to East Greenwich (Annual); Welcome to East Greenwich (Annual). **Educational Activities:** Business after Business (Monthly); Fest and Feast (Annual). **Awards:** Community Improvement Awards (Annual). **Telecommunication Services:** jerry@eastgreenwichchamber.com.

57375 ■ East Providence Area Chamber of Commerce (EPACC)
c/o Ms. Laura A. McNamara, Exec. Dir.
1011 Waterman Ave.
East Providence, RI 02914
Ph: (401)438-1212
Fax: (401)435-4581
Co. E-mail: office@eastprovchamber.com
URL: http://www.eastprovchamber.com
Contact: Ms. Laura A. McNamara, Executive Director
Description: Promotes business and community development in East Providence, Barrington, Rhode Island and Seekonk and Rehoboth, Massachusetts and surrounding areas. **Founded:** 1897. **Publications:** Chamber News: A Focus on Business (Quarterly). **Awards:** Business of the Year (Annual).

57376 ■ Go Westerly
1 Chamber Way
Westerly, RI 02891
Ph: (401)596-7761
Fax: (401)596-2190
Co. E-mail: info@westerlychamber.org
URL: http://www.westerlychamber.org
Contact: Lisa Konicki, Executive Director

57377 ■ Greater Cranston Chamber of Commerce (GCCC)
875 Oaklawn Ave., 3rd Fl., Ste. 1
Cranston, RI 02910
Ph: (401)785-3780
Fax: (401)785-3782
Co. E-mail: susan@cranstonchamber.com
URL: http://www.cranstonchamber.com
Contact: Susan Pagnozzi, President
Description: Promotes business and community development in Cranston, RI. Sponsors Adopt-A-School program. Holds business seminars. **Founded:** 1930. **Publications:** Cranston Chamber News (Monthly); Who's Who in Greater Cranston. **Educational Activities:** Business Expansion Network (Semimonthly); Statewide Business Expo (Annual). **Awards:** Business Person of the Month (Monthly).

57378 ■ Greater Providence Chamber of Commerce
30 Exchange Terr.
Providence, RI 02903
Ph: (401)521-5000
Fax: (401)621-6109
Co. E-mail: chamber@provchamber.com
URL: http://www.providencechamber.com
Contact: Laurie White, President
Description: Strives to develop a positive and productive business climate for the community through economic development, political action and civic endeavor. Helps member to grow and prosper in Rhode Island. Promotes program of a civic, social and cultural nature. Provides leadership, ideas, energy and finances to help address major community challenges. **Founded:** 1868.

57379 ■ Greater Westerly-Pawcatuck Area Chamber of Commerce
1 Chamber Way
Westerly, RI 02891
Ph: (401)596-7761
Fax: (401)596-2190
Co. E-mail: info@westerlychamber.org
URL: http://www.westerlychamber.org
Contact: Lisa Konicki, Executive Director
Description: Business owners. Promotes business and community development in the greater Westerly, RI and Pawcatuck, CT areas. **Publications:** Go Westerly. **Educational Activities:** Golf Tournament (Annual). **Awards:** Community Service Award (Annual).

57380 ■ Messenger
580 Main St.
East Greenwich, RI 02818
Ph: (401)885-0020
Fax: (401)885-0048
Co. E-mail: egc@intap.net
URL: http://www.eastgreenwichchamber.com
Contact: Stephen M. Lombardi, Executive Director
Released: Monthly

57381 ■ Moving Forward
16 Cutler St., Ste. 102
Warren, RI 02885
Ph: (401)245-0750
Fax: (401)245-0110
Co. E-mail: info@eastbaychamberri.org
URL: http://www.eastbaychamberri.org/cwt/external/wcpages/index.aspx
Contact: Betty J. Pleacher, President
Released: Monthly

57382 ■ Narragansett Chamber of Commerce
PO Box 742
Narragansett, RI 02882
Ph: (401)783-7121
Fax: (401)789-0220
Co. E-mail: support@narragansettcoc.com
URL: http://narragansettri.com/chamber
Contact: Debbie Kelso, Executive Director
Description: Businesses. Promotes business and community development in Narragansett, RI. Sponsors annual Heritage Days, Festival of Lights, and parades. **Publications:** Chamber News (Monthly).

57383 ■ Newport County Chamber of Commerce (NCCC)
35 Valley Rd.
Middletown, RI 02842-6377
Ph: (401)847-1600
Fax: (401)849-5848
Co. E-mail: info@newportchamber.com
URL: http://www.newportchamber.com
Contact: Jody J. Sullivan, Executive Director
Description: Promotes business and community development in Newport County, RI. **Founded:** 1927.

57384 ■ North Kingstown Chamber of Commerce
8045 Post Rd.
North Kingstown, RI 02852
Ph: (401)295-5566
Fax: (401)295-5582
Co. E-mail: info@northkingstown.com
URL: http://www.northkingstown.com
Contact: Karla P. Driscoll, Executive Director
Description: Individuals, businesses, and manufacturers. Promotes business, tourism, and community development in North Kingstown, RI area. **Founded:** 1929. **Publications:** Connections (Monthly); Resource Guide and Business Directory.

57385 ■ Northern Rhode Island Chamber of Commerce (NRICC)
6 Blackstone Valley Pl., Ste. 301
Lincoln, RI 02865
Ph: (401)334-1000
Fax: (401)334-1009
Co. E-mail: general@nrichamber.com
URL: http://www.nrichamber.com
Contact: John C. Gregory, President
Description: Strives to strengthen the economic climate of Northern Rhode Island, through business leadership that fosters member and community prosperity. **Founded:** 1991. **Publications:** Business Pulse (Monthly); Business and Community Resource Guide (Annual). **Educational Activities:** Golf Tournament (Annual); Table Top Expo (Annual).

57386 ■ Pawtuxet Valley Chamber of Commerce
1192 Main St.
West Warwick, RI 02893
Ph: (401)823-3349
Fax: (401)823-8162
Co. E-mail: carolyn@pvccommerce.org
URL: http://www.pvccommerce.org
Contact: Carolyn Zinno, Director

57387 ■ Resource Guide and Business Directory
8045 Post Rd.
North Kingstown, RI 02852
Ph: (401)295-5566
Fax: (401)295-5582
Co. E-mail: info@northkingstown.com
URL: http://www.northkingstown.com
Contact: Karla P. Driscoll, Executive Director

57388 ■ South Kingstown Chamber of Commerce (SKCC)
230 Old Tower Hill Rd.
Wakefield, RI 02879
Ph: (401)783-2801
Fax: (401)789-3120
Co. E-mail: info@skchamber.com
URL: http://www.skchamber.com/cwt/external/
    wcpages/index.aspx
Contact: Joe Viele, Chairman
Description: Banks, small businesses, lawyers, doctors, utilities, and hospitals. Promotes business and community development in the South Kingstown, RI area. Co-sponsors community holiday decorations; conducts annual Business Expo. **Founded:** 1933. **Publications:** *Business Matters* (Monthly).

57389 ■ *Welcome to East Greenwich*
580 Main St.
East Greenwich, RI 02818
Ph: (401)885-0020
Fax: (401)885-0048
Co. E-mail: egc@intap.net
URL: http://www.eastgreenwichchamber.com
Contact: Stephen M. Lombardi, Executive Director
Released: Annual

57390 ■ *Who's Who in Bristol County Business*
16 Cutler St., Ste. 102
Warren, RI 02885
Ph: (401)245-0750
Fax: (401)245-0110
Co. E-mail: info@eastbaychamberri.org
URL: http://www.eastbaychamberri.org/cwt/external/
    wcpages/index.aspx
Contact: Betty J. Pleacher, President
Released: Annual

57391 ■ *Who's Who in Greater Cranston*
875 Oaklawn Ave., 3rd Fl., Ste. 1
Cranston, RI 02910
Ph: (401)785-3780
Fax: (401)785-3782
Co. E-mail: susan@cranstonchamber.com
URL: http://www.cranstonchamber.com
Contact: Susan Pagnozzi, President

MINORITY BUSINESS ASSISTANCE PROGRAMS

57392 ■ Rhode Island Minority Business Enterprise
One Capital Hill, 2nd Fl.
Providence, RI 02908
Ph: (401)574-8670

Fax: (401)574-8387
Co. E-mail: CNewton@gw.doa.state.ri.us
URL: http://www.mbe.ri.gov
Description: Promotes the development of certified minority, women, and disadvantaged businesses in Rhode Island. Offers advocacy, business assistance, and certification.

FINANCING AND LOAN PROGRAMS

57393 ■ Providence Equity Partners, Inc. /Providence Ventures
50 Kennedy Plz., 18th Fl.
Providence, RI 02903
Ph: (401)751-1700
Fax: (401)751-1790
URL: http://www.provequity.com
Contact: Glenn M. Creamer, Managing Director
Preferred Investment Size: $10,000,000 to $600,000,000. **Industry Preferences:** Communications and media, Internet specific, semiconductors and other electronics, other products, computer hardware, computer software and services, and consumer related. **Geographic Preference:** U.S. and Canada.

PROCUREMENT ASSISTANCE PROGRAMS

57394 ■ Rhode Island Procurement Technical Assistance Center - Rhode Island Economic Development Corporation
315 Iron Horse Way, Ste. 101
Providence, RI 02908
Ph: (401)278-9100
Fax: (401)273-8270
Co. E-mail: info@riedc.com
URL: http://www.riptac.com
Contact: Dorothy Reynolds, Program Manager
E-mail: dilly@riedc.com
Description: Provides specialized and professional assistance to individuals and businesses seeking to sell, or currently selling, their goods or services to the Department of Defense, other federal agencies, state, and local governments.

INCUBATORS/RESEARCH AND TECHNOLOGY PARKS

57395 ■ Urban Ventures
200 Allens Ave., 3rd Fl.
Providence, RI 02903
Ph: (401)780-8866

Fax: (401)780-8844
Co. E-mail: jrenville@urbanventuresri.com
URL: http://www.urbanventuresri.com/
Contact: Neville Songwe, Executive Director (Acting)
Description: A small business incubator that assists entrepreneurs in the business start-up process and gives aid to new businesses to help ensure their survival. Also know as the Rhode Island Urban Business Incubator.

EDUCATIONAL PROGRAMS

57396 ■ Johnson & Wales University (Providence, Rhode Island)
8 Abbott Park Pl.
Providence, RI 02903
Ph: (401)598-1000
Free: 800-342-5598
Fax: (401)598-2880
Co. E-mail: pvd@admissions.jwu.edu
URL: http://www.jwu.edu
Contact: Mim L. Runey, President
URL(s): www.jwu.edu/providence. **Description:** Business college offering classes in small business management. **Founded:** 1914. **Telecommunication Services:** admissions@jwu.edu.

PUBLICATIONS

57397 ■ *Providence Business News*
400 Westminister St.
Ste. 600
Providence, RI 02903
Ph: (401)273-2201
Fax: (401)274-6580
URL: http://www.pbn.com

57398 ■ *Providence Journal Bulletin*
75 Fountain St.
Providence, RI 02902
Ph: (401)277-7000
Fax: (401)277-7346
Co. E-mail: projo@projo.com
URL: http://www.projo.com

PUBLISHERS

57399 ■ Smokin' Donut Books
381 Seaside Dr.
Jamestown, RI 02835
Ph: (401)423-2400
Free: 877-474-8738
Fax: (401)423-2700
Co. E-mail: info@smokindonut.com
URL: http://www.smokindonut.com
Contact: Kristin Zhivago, Manager
E-mail: press@smokindonut.com
Description: Description: Publishes business and how-to books. **Founded:** 2004.

SMALL BUSINESS DEVELOPMENT CENTERS

57400 ■ Aiken Small Business Development Center
471 University Pkwy.
Box 9
Aiken, SC 29801
Ph: (803)641-3646
Fax: (803)641-3647
Co. E-mail: rekam@usca.edu
Description: Represents and promotes the small business sector. Provides management assistance to current and prospective small business owners. Helps to improve management skills and expand the products and services of members.

57401 ■ Beaufort Area Small Business Development Center
801 Carteret St.
Beaufort, SC 29902
Ph: (843)521-4143
URL: http://scsbdc.moore.sc.edu/AreaOffices. html#Beaufort
Description: Represents and promotes the small business sector. Provides management assistance to current and prospective small business owners. Helps to improve management skills and expand the products and services of members.

57402 ■ Charleston Area Small Business Development Center
5900 Core Dr., Ste. 104
North Charleston, SC 29406
Ph: (843)740-6160
URL: http://scsbdc.moore.sc.edu/AreaOffices. html#Charleston
Description: Represents and promotes the small business sector. Provides management assistance to current and prospective small business owners. Helps to improve management skills and expand the products and services of members.

57403 ■ Clemson Area Small Business Development Center
Clemson University
College of Business and Public Affairs
425 Sirrine Hall
Clemson, SC 29634-1392
Ph: (864)710-4717
Fax: (864)656-4770
Co. E-mail: bennys@clemson.edu
URL: http://www.clemson.edu/centers-institutes/sbdc
Contact: Ben Smith, Manager
Description: Represents and promotes the small business sector. Provides management assistance to current and prospective small business owners. Helps to improve management skills and expand the products and services of members.

57404 ■ Florence Area Small Business Development Center
PO Box 100548
Florence, SC 29501-0548
Ph: (843)661-8256
URL: http://scsbdc.moore.sc.edu/AreaOffices. html#Florence
Description: Represents and promotes the small business sector. Provides management assistance to current and prospective small business owners. Helps to improve management skills and expand the products and services of members.

57405 ■ Greenville Area Small Business Development Center
Renaissance Center
135 S Main St., Ste. 600
Greenville, SC 29601
Ph: (864)370-1545
URL: http://scsbdc.moore.sc.edu/AreaOffices. html#Greenville
Description: Represents and promotes the small business sector. Provides management assistance to current and prospective small business owners. Helps to improve management skills and expand the products and services of members.

57406 ■ Greenwood Area Small Business Development Center
PO Box 246
Greenwood, SC 29648
Ph: (864)354-4182
URL: http://scsbdc.moore.sc.edu/AreaOffices. html#Greenwood
Description: Represents and promotes the small business sector. Provides management assistance to current and prospective small business owners. Helps to improve management skills and expand the products and services of members.

57407 ■ Hilton Head Area Small Business Development Center
University of South Carolina - Beaufort South Campus
One University Blvd.
Bluffton, SC 29909
Ph: (843)208-8259
URL: http://scsbdc.moore.sc.edu/AreaOffices. html#HiltonHead
Description: Represents and promotes the small business sector. Provides management assistance to current and prospective small business owners. Helps to improve management skills and expand the products and services of members.

57408 ■ Myrtle Beach Area Small Business Development Center
PO Box 261954
Conway, SC 29528-6054
Ph: (843)349-4010
URL: http://scsbdc.moore.sc.edu/AreaOffices. html#Myrtle
Description: Represents and promotes the small business sector. Provides management assistance to current and prospective small business owners. Helps to improve management skills and expand the products and services of members.

57409 ■ Orangeburg Area Small Business Development Center
South Carolina State University
School of Business
Algernon S. Belcher Hall
300 College St., Campus Box 7176
Orangeburg, SC 29117
Ph: (803)536-8445
URL: http://scsbdc.moore.sc.edu/AreaOffices. html#Orangeburg
Description: Represents and promotes the small business sector. Provides management assistance to current and prospective small business owners. Helps to improve management skills and expand the products and services of members.

57410 ■ Rock Hill Area Small Business Development Center
Winthrop University
118 Thurmond Bldg.
Rock Hill, SC 29733
Ph: (803)323-2283
URL: http://scsbdc.moore.sc.edu/AreaOffices. html#Rockhill
Description: Represents and promotes the small business sector. Provides management assistance to current and prospective small business owners. Helps to improve management skills and expand the products and services of members.

57411 ■ Spartanburg Small Business Development Center
Spartanburg Human Resource Ctr.
142 S Dean St., Ste. 216
Spartanburg, SC 29302
Ph: (864)316-9162
URL: http://scsbdc.moore.sc.edu/AreaOffices. html#Spartanburg
Description: Represents and promotes the small business sector. Provides management assistance to current and prospective small business owners. Helps to improve management skills and expand the products and services of members.

57412 ■ Sumter Small Business Development Center
University of South Carolina - Sumter
200 Miller Rd., Rm. 216
Sumter, SC 29150-2478
Ph: (803)938-3833
URL: http://scsbdc.moore.sc.edu/AreaOffices. html#Sumter
Description: Represents and promotes the small business sector. Provides management assistance to current and prospective small business owners. Helps to improve management skills and expand the products and services of members.

57413 ■ University of South Carolina Small Business Development Center
Moore School of Business
1705 College St.
Columbia, SC 29208
Ph: (803)777-4907

Fax: (803)777-7819
Co. E-mail: scsbdc@mailbox.sc.edu
URL: http://scsbdc.moore.sc.edu
Description: Represents and promotes the small business sector. Provides management assistance to current and prospective small business owners. Helps to improve management skills and expand the products and services of members.

SMALL BUSINESS ASSISTANCE PROGRAMS

57414 ■ South Carolina Department of Commerce
1201 Main St., Ste. 1600
Columbia, SC 29201-3200
Ph: (803)737-0400
Free: 800-868-7232
Fax: (803)737-0418
Co. E-mail: info@sccommerce.com
URL: http://www.sccommerce.com
Contact: Mandy Kibler, Director
E-mail: mkibler@sccommerce.com

Description: Offers a range of innovative services to assist entrepreneurs and expanding industries. Services include: Buyer/Supplier Match; Financing Assistance; International Trade Opportunities; Research Park System; Location, Training, and Labor Assistance; Market Research; and Entrepreneurial Support Services. **Founded:** 1905. **Publications:** *South Carolina Industrial Directory* (Annual); *International Companies in South Carolina* (Annual).

57415 ■ South Carolina Jobs-Economic Development Authority
1201 Main St., Ste. 1600
Columbia, SC 29201
Ph: (803)737-0268
Fax: (803)737-0628
Co. E-mail: generalinfo@scjeda.net
URL: http://www.scjeda.net
Contact: Harry A. Huntley, Executive Director

Description: Raises capital and provides technical assistance to small businesses in creating jobs; sells general and industrial revenue bonds.

57416 ■ South Carolina Office of Small and Minority Business Assistance
Edgar A. Brown Bldg.
1205 Pendleton St., Rm. 440-A
Columbia, SC 29201
Ph: (803)734-0657
Fax: (803)734-2498
Co. E-mail: mwoodson@oepp.sc.gov
URL: http://www.govoepp.state.sc.us/osmba
Contact: Margaret Woodson, Director

Description: Provides advocacy and referral services, training and other educational activities for small and minority businesses.

SCORE OFFICES

57417 ■ SCORE Aiken
Co. E-mail: chamber@aikenchamber.net

57418 ■ SCORE Coastal
4500 Leeds Ave., Ste. 100
North Charleston, SC 29405
Ph: (843)727-4778
Fax: (843)805-3112
Co. E-mail: info@score285.org
URL: http://coastal.score.org

Description: Provides professional guidance and information to maximize the success of existing and emerging small businesses. Offers business counseling and workshops.

57419 ■ SCORE Grand Strand
605 10th Ave. N
Myrtle Beach, SC 29577-3568
Ph: (843)918-1079

Fax: (843)918-1080
Co. E-mail: info@mbscore.org
URL: http://www.mbscore.org
Contact: Mr. Sam Bookhart, Chairman
Description: Provides business counseling to small business, both existing businesses and startups.
Founded: 1984.

57420 ■ SCORE Midlands
Strom Thurmond Bldg.
1835 Assembly St., Rm. 1425
Columbia, SC 29201
Ph: (803)765-5131
Fax: (803)765-5962
URL: http://midlands.score.org
Description: Provides professional guidance and information to maximize the success of existing and emerging small businesses. Offers business counseling and workshops.

57421 ■ SCORE Piedmont
Federal Bldg.
300 E Washington St.
Greenville, SC 29601
Ph: (864)271-3638
Fax: (864)271-3638
Co. E-mail: info@piedmontscore.org
URL: http://www.piedmontscore.org
Description: Provides professional guidance and information to maximize the success of existing and emerging small businesses. Offers business counseling and workshops.

57422 ■ SCORE S.C. Lowcountry
1 Chamber of Commerce Dr.
Hilton Head Island, SC 29938
Ph: (843)785-7107
Fax: (843)785-7110
URL: http://www.scorehiltonhead.com
URL(s): sclowcountry.score.org. **Description:** Provides professional guidance and information to maximize the success of existing and emerging small businesses. Offers business counseling and workshops.

BETTER BUSINESS BUREAUS

57423 ■ BBB Broadcaster
1121 3rd Ave.
Conway, SC 29526
Ph: (843)488-2227
Fax: (843)488-0998
Co. E-mail: operations@coastalcarolina.bbb.org
URL: http://myrtlebeach.bbb.org
Contact: Kathy Graham, President
Released: Monthly

57424 ■ BBB Business and Consumer Brochures
408 N Church St., Ste. C
Greenville, SC 29601
Ph: (864)242-5052
Fax: (864)271-9802
Co. E-mail: info@upstatesc.bbb.org
URL: http://upstatesc.bbb.org
Contact: Vee Daniel, President
Released: Periodic

57425 ■ Better Business Bureau of Central South Carolina and Charleston
2330 Devine St.
Columbia, SC 29205
Ph: (803)254-2525
Fax: (803)779-3117
Co. E-mail: info@columbia.bbb.org
URL: http://columbia.bbb.org
Contact: Paul Prince, Chairman
Description: Works to promote public confidence in business and stimulate fair competition between local businesses through effective self-regulation of local advertising and selling practices; conducts standardized evaluations of local charitable organizations; protects businesses, investors and consumers from fraudulent and unfair practices; provides programs for the resolution of disputes, including mediation and arbitration; promotes reliable and secure e-commerce

through the BBB Online Reliability and Privacy Seal programs; and educates consumers and the business community.

57426 ■ Better Business Bureau of Coastal Carolina
1121 3rd Ave.
Conway, SC 29526
Ph: (843)488-2227
Fax: (843)488-0998
Co. E-mail: operations@coastalcarolina.bbb.org
URL: http://myrtlebeach.bbb.org
Contact: Kathy Graham, President
Description: Seeks to promote and foster ethical relationship between businesses and the public through voluntary self-regulation, consumer and business education, and service excellence. Provides information to help consumers and businesses make informed purchasing decisions and avoid costly scams and frauds; settles consumer complaints through arbitration and other means. **Founded:** 1987.
Publications: *BBB Broadcaster* (Monthly).

57427 ■ Better Business Bureau Serving Upstate South Carolina
408 N Church St., Ste. C
Greenville, SC 29601
Ph: (864)242-5052
Fax: (864)271-9802
Co. E-mail: info@upstatesc.bbb.org
URL: http://upstatesc.bbb.org
Contact: Vee Daniel, President
Description: Seeks to promote and foster the highest ethical relationship between businesses and the public through voluntary self-regulation, consumer and business education, and service excellence.
Scope: business and consumer issues. **Founded:** 1982. **Publications:** *BBB Business and Consumer Brochures* (Periodic). **Educational Activities:** Local Ad Review Program (Monthly). **Awards:** Student of Integrity (Annual).

CHAMBERS OF COMMERCE

57428 ■ Anderson Area Chamber of Commerce (AACOC)
907 N Main St., Ste. 200
Anderson, SC 29621
Ph: (864)226-3454
Fax: (864)226-3300
Co. E-mail: info@andersonscchamber.com
URL: http://www.andersonscchamber.com
Contact: Mr. Lee R. Luff, President
Description: Promotes business and community development in the Anderson, SC area. **Founded:** 1902. **Publications:** *New Horizons* (Bimonthly).

57429 ■ Beaufort Regional Chamber of Commerce
PO Box 910
Beaufort, SC 29901-0910
Ph: (843)986-5400
Free: 800-638-3525
Fax: (843)986-5405
Co. E-mail: chamber@beaufortsc.org
URL: http://www.beaufortsc.org/cwo/Home
Contact: Ms. Carlotta Ungaro, President
Description: Advocates for and supports a positive business climate and leads the enhancement, expansion and diversification of the business community throughout Beaufort County, SC. **Founded:** 1892.
Publications: *On The Move* (Monthly).

57430 ■ Berkeley Chamber of Commerce
1004 Old Hwy. 52
Moncks Corner, SC 29461
Ph: (843)577-9549
Free: 800-882-0337
Fax: (843)899-6491
Co. E-mail: info@berkeleysc.org
URL: http://www.berkeleysc.org/index.html
Contact: Mr. Bill McCall, President
Description: Promotes business and community development in Berkeley County, SC.

57431 ■ Business Resource Guide
PO Box 590
Rock Hill, SC 29731

Ph: (803)324-7500
Fax: (803)324-1889
Co. E-mail: info@yorkcountychamber.com
URL: http://www.yorkcountychamber.com
Contact: Rob Youngblood, President
E-mail: ryoungblood@yorkcountychamber.com
Released: Annual **Price:** $5, plus shipping and handling.

57432 ■ Business World Language
PO Box 1636
Spartanburg, SC 29304-1636
Ph: (864)594-5000
Fax: (864)594-5055
Co. E-mail: jpoole@spartanburgchamber.com
URL: http://www.spartanburgchamber.com
Contact: Mr. David Cordeau, President
Released: Monthly **Price:** free for members.

57433 ■ Calhoun County Chamber of Commerce (CCCC)
Courthouse Annex, Ste. 114
St. Matthews, SC 29135
Ph: (803)655-5650
Fax: (803)655-6110
Co. E-mail: calhounchamber@sc.rr.com
URL: http://calhouncountychamber.org
Contact: Jane Dyches, Executive Director
Description: Promotes business and community development in Calhoun County, SC.

57434 ■ Carolinas Association of Chamber of Commerce Executives (CACCE)
930 Richland St.
Columbia, SC 29201
Ph: (803)733-1112
Fax: (803)733-1149
Co. E-mail: lluff@andersonscchamber.com
URL: http://www.cacce.org
Contact: Lee Luff, President
Description: Strives to advance comprehensive leadership and professional development for Chambers of Commerce through the efforts of the members of the association and their resources. **Founded:** 1994.

57435 ■ Chamber Chain
109 Benson St.
Walterboro, SC 29488-0027
Ph: (843)549-9595
Fax: (843)549-5775
Co. E-mail: info@walterboro.org
URL: http://www.walterboro.org
Contact: David M. Smalls, President
Released: Monthly **Price:** free.

57436 ■ Chamber Connection
109 Gadsden St.
Chester, SC 29706-0489
Ph: (803)581-4142
Fax: (803)581-2431
Co. E-mail: ccchamber@infoave.net
URL: http://www.chesterchamber.com
Contact: James W. Fuller, President
Released: Monthly

57437 ■ Chamber Connection
PO Box 6246
North Augusta, SC 29861
Ph: (803)279-2323
Fax: (803)279-0003
Co. E-mail: chamber@northaugusta.net
URL: http://www.northaugusta.net/chamber
Contact: Brian Tucker, President
Released: Monthly

57438 ■ Chamber Connection
1521 Highway 17 S
North Myrtle Beach, SC 29582
Ph: (843)281-2662
Free: 877-332-2662
Fax: (843)280-2930
Co. E-mail: info@northmyrtlebeachchamber.com
URL: http://www.northmyrtlebeachchamber.com
Contact: Marc Jordan, President
Released: Monthly

57439 ■ Chamber E-Gram
930 Richland St.
Columbia, SC 29201
Ph: (803)733-1110
Fax: (803)733-1149
Co. E-mail: info@columbiachamber.com
URL: http://www.columbiachamber.com
Contact: Luz Arpan, President
Released: Weekly

57440 ■ Chamber Heart Beat
PO Box 578
Hartsville, SC 29551
Ph: (843)332-6401
Fax: (803)332-8017
Co. E-mail: staff@hartsvillechamber.org
URL: http://www.hartsvillechamber.com
Contact: Johnna Shirley, President
Released: Quarterly

57441 ■ Chamber Link
610 W Palmetto St.
Florence, SC 29501
Ph: (843)665-0515
Fax: (843)662-2010
Co. E-mail: tmarschel@flochamber.com
URL: http://www.flochamber.com
Contact: Mr. Tom Marschel, President
Released: Monthly

57442 ■ Chamber Membership Directory
109 Benson St.
Walterboro, SC 29488-0027
Ph: (843)549-9595
Fax: (843)549-5775
Co. E-mail: info@walterboro.org
URL: http://www.walterboro.org
Contact: David M. Smalls, President
Released: Annual

57443 ■ Chamber News
PO Box 980
Greenwood, SC 29648
Ph: (864)223-8431
Fax: (864)229-9785
Co. E-mail: info@greenwoodscchamber.org
URL: http://www.greenwoodscchamber.org
Contact: Angelle LaBorde, President
Released: Monthly

57444 ■ The Chamber Quill
203 Main St.
Conway, SC 29528
Ph: (843)248-2273
Fax: (843)248-0003
URL: http://www.conwayscchamber.com
Contact: Tom Brown, President
Released: Bimonthly

57445 ■ Chamber Times
111 Trade St.
Greer, SC 29651-3427
Ph: (864)877-3131
Fax: (864)877-0961
Co. E-mail: info@greerchamber.com
URL: http://www.greerchamber.com
Contact: Allen Smith, President
Released: Monthly

57446 ■ ChamberChat Newsletters
PO Box 605
Simpsonville, SC 29681
Ph: (864)963-3781
Fax: (864)228-0003
Co. E-mail: info@simpsonvillechamber.com
URL: http://www.simpsonvillechamber.com
Contact: Deborah Hardwick, President
Released: Bimonthly **Price:** included in membership dues.

57447 ■ Charleston Metro Chamber of Commerce (CMCC)
4500 Leeds Ave., Ste. 100
North Charleston, SC 29405
Ph: (843)577-2510

Fax: (843)723-4853
Co. E-mail: mail@charlestonchamber.org
URL: http://chaschamber.com
Contact: Bryan Derreberry, President
E-mail: bderreberry@charlestonchamber.org
Description: Promotes business and community development in Charleston, SC. **Founded:** 1773. **Publications:** *Major Employers Directory* (Annual); *Manufacturers Directory* (Annual); *Visitors Guide* (Annual); *Visitors Guide* (Annual); *Charleston Metro Chamber of Commerce--Major Employers Directory* (Annual); *Membership Directory and Buyers Guide* (Annual); *Industrial & Technology-Based Firms Directory.*

57448 ■ Cherokee County Chamber of Commerce
225 S Limestone St.
Gaffney, SC 29340
Ph: (864)489-5721
Fax: (864)489-5788
Co. E-mail: krobbs@cherokeechamber.org
URL: http://www.cherokeechamber.org
Contact: Ed Elliott, President
Description: Promotes business and community development in Cherokee County. **Telecommunication Services:** pchilders@cherokeechamber.org; acrotzer@cherokeechamber.org.

57449 ■ Chester County Chamber of Commerce (CCCC)
109 Gadsden St.
Chester, SC 29706-0489
Ph: (803)581-4142
Fax: (803)581-2431
Co. E-mail: ccchamber@infoave.net
URL: http://www.chesterchamber.com
Contact: James W. Fuller, President
Description: Promotes business and community development in Chester County, SC. **Publications:** *Chamber Connection* (Monthly). **Telecommunication Services:** preschamber@truvista.net.

57450 ■ Clarendon County Chamber of Commerce (CCCC)
19 N Brooks St.
Manning, SC 29102
Ph: (803)435-4405
Free: 800-731-LAKE
Fax: (803)435-4406
Co. E-mail: chamber@clarendoncounty.com
URL: http://www.clarendoncounty.com
Contact: Dawn Griffith, Executive Director
Description: Promotes business and community development in Clarendon County, SC. Supports United Way. Conducts litter control program. Sponsors April Striped Bass Festival and Murah Program Education. **Founded:** 1986. **Publications:** *County Business Directory* (Annual). **Educational Activities:** Awards Banquet (Annual). **Awards:** Ambassador of the Year (Annual); Business Person of the Year (Annual); Citizen of the Year (Annual).

57451 ■ Clemson Area Chamber of Commerce
PO Box 1622
Clemson, SC 29633-1622
Ph: (864)654-1200
Free: 800-654-5096
Co. E-mail: chris@clemsonchamber.org
URL: http://www.clemsonchamber.org
Contact: Chris Hardy, President
Description: Promotes business and community development in the greater Clemson, SC area. Sponsors Clemson Bicycle Race.

57452 ■ Communicator
222 W Main St.
Pickens, SC 29671
Ph: (864)878-3258
Fax: (864)878-7317
Co. E-mail: thomas-realty@bellsouth.net
URL: http://www.pickenschamber.org
Contact: Mike Parrott, Executive Director
Released: Quarterly

57453 ■ Connections
PO Box 590
Rock Hill, SC 29731

Ph: (803)324-7500
Fax: (803)324-1889
Co. E-mail: info@yorkcountychamber.com
URL: http://www.yorkcountychamber.com
Contact: Rob Youngblood, President
E-mail: ryoungblood@yorkcountychamber.com

57454 ■ The Connector
32 E Calhoun St.
Sumter, SC 29150
Ph: (803)775-1231
Co. E-mail: chamber@sumterchamber.com
URL: http://www.sumterchamber.com
Contact: Grier U. Blackwelder, President
Released: Bimonthly

57455 ■ Conway Area Chamber of Commerce (CACC)
203 Main St.
Conway, SC 29528
Ph: (843)248-2273
Fax: (843)248-0003
URL: http://www.conwayscchamber.com
Contact: Tom Brown, President
Description: Promotes business and community development in Conway, SC. **Founded:** 1958. **Publications:** The Chamber Quill (Bimonthly).

57456 ■ County Business Directory
19 N Brooks St.
Manning, SC 29102
Ph: (803)435-4405
Free: 800-731-LAKE
Fax: (803)435-4406
Co. E-mail: chamber@clarendoncounty.com
URL: http://www.clarendoncounty.com
Contact: Dawn Griffith, Executive Director
Released: Annual

57457 ■ Demographics
24 Cleveland St.
Greenville, SC 29601
Ph: (864)242-1050
Free: 866-485-5262
Fax: (864)282-8509
Co. E-mail: bhaskew@greenvillechamber.org
URL: http://www.greenvillechamber.org
Contact: Ben Haskew, President

57458 ■ Employer's Desk Manual
24 Cleveland St.
Greenville, SC 29601
Ph: (864)242-1050
Free: 866-485-5262
Fax: (864)282-8509
Co. E-mail: bhaskew@greenvillechamber.org
URL: http://www.greenvillechamber.org
Contact: Ben Haskew, President
Released: Biennial

57459 ■ Fairfield County Chamber of Commerce (FCCC)
Town Clock Bldg.
100 Congress St.
Winnsboro, SC 29180
Ph: (803)635-4242
Fax: (803)712-2296
Co. E-mail: fchamber@truvista.net
URL: http://www.fairfieldchamber.sc
Contact: Mitchell Latham, Chairman
Description: Promotes business, community development and tourism in Fairfield County, SC. **Founded:** 1945.

57460 ■ Focal Points
930 Richland St.
Columbia, SC 29201
Ph: (803)733-1110
Fax: (803)733-1149
Co. E-mail: info@columbiachamber.com
URL: http://www.columbiachamber.com
Contact: Luz Arpan, President
Released: Monthly **Price:** included in membership dues.

57461 ■ Foothills Focus
c/o Kent Dykes, Pres.
PO Box 241
Easley, SC 29641-0241

Ph: (864)859-2693
Fax: (864)859-1941
Co. E-mail: kent@easleychamber.org
URL: http://easleychamber.net
Contact: Kent Dykes, President
Released: Monthly

57462 ■ Georgetown County Chamber of Commerce (GCCC)
531 Front St.
Georgetown, SC 29440
Ph: (843)546-8436
Free: 800-777-7705
Fax: (843)520-4876
Co. E-mail: info@georgetownchamber.com
URL: http://www.georgetownchamber.com
Contact: Lori Lowell, Chairperson
Description: Promotes business and community development in Georgetown County, SC. **Founded:** 1917. **Publications:** Georgetown County Chamber of Commerce Quarterly (Quarterly). **Telecommunication Services:** rdavila@visitgeorge.com.

57463 ■ Georgetown County Chamber of Commerce Quarterly
531 Front St.
Georgetown, SC 29440
Ph: (843)546-8436
Free: 800-777-7705
Fax: (843)520-4876
Co. E-mail: info@georgetownchamber.com
URL: http://www.georgetownchamber.com
Contact: Lori Lowell, Chairperson
Released: Quarterly

57464 ■ The Grand Strander
PO Box 2115
Myrtle Beach, SC 29578
Ph: (843)626-7444
Free: 800-356-3016
Fax: (843)448-3010
URL: http://www.myrtlebeachareachamber.com/
default.html
Contact: Brad Dean, President
Released: Monthly

57465 ■ Greater Aiken Chamber of Commerce
121 Richland Ave. E
Aiken, SC 29802
Ph: (803)641-1111
Fax: (803)641-4174
Co. E-mail: chamber@aikenchamber.net
URL: http://www.aikenchamber.net
Contact: Mr. J. David Jameson, President
Description: Promotes business and community development in Aiken, SC.

57466 ■ Greater Cheraw Chamber of Commerce (GCCC)
221 Market St.
Cheraw, SC 29520
Ph: (843)537-7681
Fax: (843)537-5886
Co. E-mail: cherawchamber@bellsouth.net
URL: http://www.cheraw.com
Contact: Mrs. Patsy J. Hendley, President
URL(s): www.cherawchamber.com. **Description:** Promotes business and community development in the Greater Cheraw, SC area. **Founded:** 1945.

57467 ■ Greater Chesterfield Chamber of Commerce
100 E Main St.
Chesterfield, SC 29709
Ph: (843)623-2343
Fax: (843)623-2424
Co. E-mail: info@chesterfieldscchamber.com
URL: http://www.chesterfieldscchamber.com
Contact: Donna Curtis, Executive Director
Description: Promotes business and community development in Chesterfield, SC.

57468 ■ Greater Columbia Chamber of Commerce (GCCVB)
930 Richland St.
Columbia, SC 29201
Ph: (803)733-1110

Fax: (803)733-1149
Co. E-mail: info@columbiachamber.com
URL: http://www.columbiachamber.com
Contact: Luz Arpan, President
Description: Promotes convention business and tourism in Columbia, SC. **Founded:** 1902. **Publications:** Chamber E-Gram (Weekly); Focal Points (Monthly); Major Employers Directory. **Awards:** Ambassador of the Year (Annual); Business Partner of the Year (Annual); Diplomats of the Month (Monthly); Small Business Person of the Year (Annual).

57469 ■ Greater Easley Chamber of Commerce (GECC)
c/o Kent Dykes, Pres.
PO Box 241
Easley, SC 29641-0241
Ph: (864)859-2693
Fax: (864)859-1941
Co. E-mail: kent@easleychamber.org
URL: http://easleychamber.net
Contact: Kent Dykes, President
Description: Promotes business and community development in Easley, SC and the surrounding area. Maintains economic development and tourism center. **Scope:** business. **Founded:** 1947. **Subscriptions:** books periodicals. **Publications:** Foothills Focus (Monthly).

57470 ■ Greater Florence Chamber of Commerce
610 W Palmetto St.
Florence, SC 29501
Ph: (843)665-0515
Fax: (843)662-2010
Co. E-mail: tmarschel@flochamber.com
URL: http://www.flochamber.com
Contact: Mr. Tom Marschel, President
Description: Provides leadership to promote and enhance a favorable business climate and improve the quality of life in Florence and the Pee Dee Area. **Founded:** 1916. **Publications:** Chamber Link (Monthly). **Awards:** Business Person of the Year (Annual); Chamber Champ of the Year (Annual); Small Business Person of the Year (Annual).

57471 ■ Greater Greenville Chamber of Commerce (GCC)
24 Cleveland St.
Greenville, SC 29601
Ph: (864)242-1050
Free: 866-485-5262
Fax: (864)282-8509
Co. E-mail: bhaskew@greenvillechamber.org
URL: http://www.greenvillechamber.org
Contact: Ben Haskew, President
Description: Promotes business and community development in the Greenville County, SC area. **Founded:** 1888. **Publications:** Demographics; Employer's Desk Manual (Biennial); International Business Directory (Annual); Market Facts; Outlook; Real Estate Report (Semiannual); Wage and Benefit Survey (Annual). **Awards:** Athena Award (Annual); Minority Business of the Year (Annual); Small Business of the Year (Annual); Buck Mickel Award for Business and Community Leadership (Annual); Max Heller Neighborhood Improvement Award (Annual).

57472 ■ Greater Greer Chamber of Commerce (GGCC)
111 Trade St.
Greer, SC 29651-3427
Ph: (864)877-3131
Fax: (864)877-0961
Co. E-mail: info@greerchamber.com
URL: http://www.greerchamber.com
Contact: Allen Smith, President
Description: Promotes business and community development in Greer, SC. **Publications:** Chamber Times (Monthly). **Educational Activities:** Communications Division Meeting (Quarterly). **Awards:** Educator of the Year Award (Annual).

57473 ■ Greater Hartsville Chamber of Commerce
PO Box 578
Hartsville, SC 29551
Ph: (843)332-6401

Fax: (803)332-8017
Co. E-mail: staff@hartsvillechamber.org
URL: http://www.hartsvillechamber.com
Contact: Johnna Shirley, President
Description: Provides business and community development in Hartsville, SC area. **Publications:** *Chamber Heart Beat* (Quarterly). **Telecommunication Services:** admin@hartsvillechamber.org.

57474 ■ Greater Lake City Chamber of Commerce
144 S Acline Ave.
Lake City, SC 29560
Ph: (843)374-8611
Fax: (843)374-7938
Co. E-mail: lccoc1@ftc-i.net
URL: http://www.lakecitysc.org
Description: Promotes Lake City, South Carolina's business and community.

57475 ■ Greater Mauldin Chamber of Commerce
PO Box 881
Mauldin, SC 29662
Ph: (864)297-1323
Fax: (864)297-5645
Co. E-mail: info@mauldinchamber.org
URL: http://www.mauldinchamber.org
Contact: Ms. Pat Pomeroy, Executive Director
Description: Works to provide an environment for business growth and development in the Mauldin area. **Founded:** 1982.

57476 ■ Greater Pickens Chamber of Commerce (GPCC)
222 W Main St.
Pickens, SC 29671
Ph: (864)878-3258
Fax: (864)878-7317
Co. E-mail: thomas-realty@bellsouth.net
URL: http://www.pickenschamber.org
Contact: Mike Parrott, Executive Director
Description: Promotes business and community development in the greater Pickens, SC area. Sponsors Azalea Festival. **Publications:** *Communicator* (Quarterly); *Pickens Directory* (Periodic). **Awards:** Award for Tourism (Annual); Beautification and Member of the Year (Annual).

57477 ■ Greater Summerville/Dorchester County Chamber of Commerce
PO Box 670
Summerville, SC 29484
Ph: (843)873-2931
Fax: (843)875-4464
Co. E-mail: jbrooks@greatersummerville.org
URL: http://www.gsdcchamber.org
Contact: Rita C. Berry, President
Description: Promotes business and community development in the Summerville, SC area. Sponsors Tour de Bloom Bike Race. Holds periodic board meeting. **Founded:** 1911. **Publications:** *Newcomer's Guide and Business Directory* (Annual).

57478 ■ Greater Sumter Chamber of Commerce
32 E Calhoun St.
Sumter, SC 29150
Ph: (803)775-1231
Co. E-mail: chamber@sumterchamber.com
URL: http://www.sumterchamber.com
Contact: Grier U. Blackwelder, President
Description: Promotes business and community development in the greater Sumter, SC area. **Founded:** 1910. **Publications:** *The Connector* (Bimonthly); *Who's Who in the Sumter Chamber* (Annual). **Awards:** Business Person of the Year (Annual); Large Manufacturer of the Year (Annual); Medium Manufacturer of the Year (Annual); Merchant of the Year (Annual); Military Citizen of the Year (Annual); Outstanding Achievement Award (Annual); Small Manufacturer of the Year (Annual); Minority Business Person of the Year (Annual).

57479 ■ Greater York Chamber of Commerce (GYCC)
23 E Liberty St.
York, SC 29745
Ph: (803)684-2590

Free: 877-684-2590
Fax: (803)684-2575
Co. E-mail: info@greateryorkchamber.com
URL: http://www.greateryorkchamber.com
Contact: Nancy Warren, President
Description: Promotes business and community development in Western York County, SC. Sponsors Summerfest and Christmas parade. **Founded:** 1939. **Publications:** *Industrial Guide* (Annual). **Educational Activities:** SummerFest (Annual).

57480 ■ Greenwood Area Chamber of Commerce
PO Box 980
Greenwood, SC 29648
Ph: (864)223-8431
Fax: (864)229-9785
Co. E-mail: info@greenwoodscchamber.org
URL: http://www.greenwoodscchamber.org
Contact: Angelle LaBorde, President
Description: Promotes business and community development in Greenwood, SC. **Publications:** *Chamber News* (Monthly).

57481 ■ Hampton County Chamber of Commerce
PO Box 122
Hampton, SC 29924
Ph: (803)914-2143
Co. E-mail: info@hamptoncountychamber.org
URL: http://hamptoncountychamber.org
Contact: Sally Dobson, President
Description: Promotes business and commerce in Hampton County, SC. **Founded:** 1986.

57482 ■ Hilton Head Island-Bluffton Chamber of Commerce
PO Box 5647
Hilton Head Island, SC 29938-5647
Ph: (843)785-3673
Free: 800-523-3373
Fax: (843)785-7110
Co. E-mail: info@hiltonheadisland.org
URL: http://www.hiltonheadchamber.org
Contact: Bill Miles, President
Publications: *Hilton Head Island-Bluffton Chamber of Commerce--Membership Directory* (Annual). **Telecommunication Services:** bmiles@hiltonheadisland.org.

57483 ■ *Industrial Directory*
PO Box 590
Rock Hill, SC 29731
Ph: (803)324-7500
Fax: (803)324-1889
Co. E-mail: info@yorkcountychamber.com
URL: http://www.yorkcountychamber.com
Contact: Rob Youngblood, President
E-mail: ryoungblood@yorkcountychamber.com
Released: Annual **Price:** $20, plus shipping and handling.

57484 ■ *Industrial Guide*
PO Box 605
Simpsonville, SC 29681
Ph: (864)963-3781
Fax: (864)228-0003
Co. E-mail: info@simpsonvillechamber.com
URL: http://www.simpsonvillechamber.com
Contact: Deborah Hardwick, President
Released: Annual **Price:** $5, /issue.

57485 ■ *Industrial Guide*
23 E Liberty St.
York, SC 29745
Ph: (803)684-2590
Free: 877-684-2590
Fax: (803)684-2575
Co. E-mail: info@greateryorkchamber.com
URL: http://www.greateryorkchamber.com
Contact: Nancy Warren, President
Released: Annual

57486 ■ *International Business Directory*
24 Cleveland St.
Greenville, SC 29601
Ph: (864)242-1050
Free: 866-485-5262

Fax: (864)282-8509
Co. E-mail: bhaskew@greenvillechamber.org
URL: http://www.greenvillechamber.org
Contact: Ben Haskew, President
Released: Annual

57487 ■ Jasper County Chamber of Commerce (JCCC)
451B E Wilson St.
Ridgeland, SC 29936
Ph: (843)726-8126
Co. E-mail: info@jaspercountychamber.com
URL: http://www.jaspercountychamber.com
Contact: Kendall Malphrus, Executive Director
Description: Promotes business and community development in Jasper County, SC. Sponsors local festival. **Founded:** 1961.

57488 ■ *Just One Minute*
1006 12th St.
Cayce, SC 29033
Ph: (803)794-6504
Free: 866-720-5400
Fax: (803)794-6505
Co. E-mail: westmetrochamber@aol.com
URL: http://www.westmetrochamber.com
Contact: Debra Gallup, Chairperson
Released: Bimonthly **Price:** included in membership dues.

57489 ■ Kershaw County Chamber of Commerce and Visitors' Center (KCCCVC)
607 S Broad St.
Camden, SC 29020
Ph: (803)432-2525
Free: 800-968-4037
Fax: (803)432-4181
Co. E-mail: lhorton@camden-sc.org
URL: http://www.camden-sc.org
Contact: Mrs. Liz Horton, Executive Director
Description: Promotes business and community development in Kershaw County, SC. **Founded:** 1910.

57490 ■ Lake Wylie Chamber of Commerce
PO Box 5233
Lake Wylie, SC 29710
Ph: (803)831-2827
Fax: (803)831-2460
Co. E-mail: info@lakewyliesc.com
URL: http://www.lakewyliesc.com
Contact: Susan Bromfield, President
Description: Promotes business and community development in Lake Wylie, SC area.

57491 ■ *Legislative Update*
1201 Main St., Ste. 1700
Columbia, SC 29201
Ph: (803)799-4601
Free: 800-799-4601
Fax: (803)779-6043
Co. E-mail: chamber@scchamber.net
URL: http://www.scchamber.net/cwt/external/ wcpages/index.aspx
Contact: Otis Rawl, President
Released: Weekly

57492 ■ Lexington Chamber of Commerce (LCC)
321 S Lake Dr.
Lexington, SC 29072
Ph: (803)359-6113
Fax: (803)359-0634
Co. E-mail: webmaster@lexingtonsc.org
URL: http://www.lexingtonsc.org
Contact: Randy Halfacre, President
Description: Promotes business and community development in Lexington, SC. **Founded:** 1959. **Awards:** Small Business Person of the Year (Annual).

57493 ■ Little River Chamber of Commerce
PO Box 400
Little River, SC 29566
Ph: (843)249-6604
Free: 866-817-8082

Fax: (843)249-9788
Co. E-mail: info@littleriverchamber.org
URL: http://www.littleriverchamber.org
Contact: Jennifer Walters, Executive Director
Description: Works to provide guidance and useful tips to entrepreneurs, residents and visitors. **Founded:** 2004. **Publications:** *Making Waves* (Monthly).

57494 ■ Loris Chamber of Commerce
4242 Main St.
Loris, SC 29569
Ph: (843)756-6030
Free: 866-664-6030
Fax: (843)756-5661
Co. E-mail: loriscoc@sccoast.net
URL: http://www.lorischambersc.com
Contact: Darlene Munn, President
Description: Promotes conventions and tourism in Loris, SC area.

57495 ■ *Major Employers Directory*
4500 Leeds Ave., Ste. 100
North Charleston, SC 29405
Ph: (843)577-2510
Fax: (843)723-4853
Co. E-mail: mail@charlestonchamber.org
URL: http://chaschamber.com
Contact: Bryan Derreberry, President
E-mail: bderreberry@charlestonchamber.org
Released: Annual **Price:** $75, for members; $150, for nonmembers.

57496 ■ *Major Employers Directory*
930 Richland St.
Columbia, SC 29201
Ph: (803)733-1110
Fax: (803)733-1149
Co. E-mail: info@columbiachamber.com
URL: http://www.columbiachamber.com
Contact: Luz Arpan, President
Price: $20, for members; $25, for nonmembers.

57497 ■ *Making Waves*
PO Box 400
Little River, SC 29566
Ph: (843)249-6604
Free: 866-817-8082
Fax: (843)249-9788
Co. E-mail: info@littleriverchamber.org
URL: http://www.littleriverchamber.org
Contact: Jennifer Walters, Executive Director
Released: Monthly

57498 ■ *Manufacturers Directory*
4500 Leeds Ave., Ste. 100
North Charleston, SC 29405
Ph: (843)577-2510
Fax: (843)723-4853
Co. E-mail: mail@charlestonchamber.org
URL: http://chaschamber.com
Contact: Bryan Derreberry, President
E-mail: bderreberry@charlestonchamber.org
Released: Annual **Price:** $15.

57499 ■ Marion Chamber of Commerce (MCC)
PO Box 35
Marion, SC 29571-0035
Ph: (843)423-3561
Fax: (843)423-0963
Co. E-mail: marionsc@bellsouth.net
URL: http://www.marionscchamber.com
Contact: Judy J. Johnson, Executive Vice President
Description: Promotes business and community development in Marion, SC.

57500 ■ *Market Facts*
24 Cleveland St.
Greenville, SC 29601
Ph: (864)242-1050
Free: 866-485-5262
Fax: (864)282-8509
Co. E-mail: bhaskew@greenvillechamber.org
URL: http://www.greenvillechamber.org
Contact: Ben Haskew, President

57501 ■ McCormick County Chamber of Commerce
100 S Main St.
McCormick, SC 29835
Ph: (864)852-2835
Fax: (864)852-2382
Co. E-mail: abarron@mccormickscchamber.org
URL: http://www.mccormickscchamber.org
Contact: Anne Barron, Office Manager
Description: Promotes business and community development in McCormick, SC. Promotes tourism. **Founded:** 1988.

57502 ■ *Membership Directory and Buyers Guide*
4500 Leeds Ave., Ste. 100
North Charleston, SC 29405
Ph: (843)577-2510
Fax: (843)723-4853
Co. E-mail: mail@charlestonchamber.org
URL: http://chaschamber.com
Contact: Bryan Derreberry, President
E-mail: bderreberry@charlestonchamber.org
Released: Annual **Price:** $20.

57503 ■ *Membership Directory/Buyers Guide*
PO Box 1636
Spartanburg, SC 29304-1636
Ph: (864)594-5000
Fax: (864)594-5055
Co. E-mail: jpoole@spartanburgchamber.com
URL: http://www.spartanburgchamber.com
Contact: Mr. David Cordeau, President
Released: Annual **Price:** $25, for nonmembers; free for members.

57504 ■ *Membership Guide*
PO Box 328
Orangeburg, SC 29116-0328
Ph: (803)534-6821
Free: 800-545-6153
Fax: (803)531-9435
Co. E-mail: chamber@orangeburgsc.net
URL: http://www.orangeburgchamber.com
Contact: David Coleman, President
Released: Semiannual

57505 ■ Myrtle Beach Area Chamber of Commerce
PO Box 2115
Myrtle Beach, SC 29578
Ph: (843)626-7444
Free: 800-356-3016
Fax: (843)448-3010
URL: http://www.myrtlebeachareachamber.com/default.html
Contact: Brad Dean, President
Description: Promotes business and community development in the Myrtle Beach, SC area. **Founded:** 1938. **Publications:** *The Grand Strander* (Monthly); *Progress Report and Program of Work* (Annual); *Sand and Surf Beach Safety*. **Educational Activities:** Membership Programs and Services Committee (Monthly). **Awards:** Ann DeBock Leadership Award (Annual); Leadership Grand Strand Scholarship (Annual).

57506 ■ *New Horizons*
907 N Main St., Ste. 200
Anderson, SC 29621
Ph: (864)226-3454
Fax: (864)226-3300
Co. E-mail: info@andersonscchamber.com
URL: http://www.andersonscchamber.com
Contact: Mr. Lee R. Luff, President
Released: Bimonthly **Price:** $12, /year for members; $24, /year for nonmembers.

57507 ■ *Newcomer's Guide and Business Directory*
PO Box 670
Summerville, SC 29484
Ph: (843)873-2931
Fax: (843)875-4464
Co. E-mail: jbrooks@greatersummerville.org
URL: http://www.gsdcchamber.org
Contact: Rita C. Berry, President
Released: Annual

57508 ■ North Augusta Chamber of Commerce
PO Box 6246
North Augusta, SC 29861
Ph: (803)279-2323
Fax: (803)279-0003
Co. E-mail: chamber@northaugusta.net
URL: http://www.northaugusta.net/chamber
Contact: Brian Tucker, President
Description: Promotes business and community development in the greater North Augusta, SC area. **Publications:** *Chamber Connection* (Monthly); *North Augusta Lifestyle Guide*; *North Augusta Lifestyle Guide*. **Awards:** Citizen of the Year (Annual); Small Business Person of the Year (Annual). **Telecommunication Services:** brian@northaugustachamber.org.

57509 ■ *North Augusta Lifestyle Guide*
PO Box 6246
North Augusta, SC 29861
Ph: (803)279-2323
Fax: (803)279-0003
Co. E-mail: chamber@northaugusta.net
URL: http://www.northaugusta.net/chamber
Contact: Brian Tucker, President

57510 ■ North Myrtle Beach Chamber of Commerce
1521 Highway 17 S
North Myrtle Beach, SC 29582
Ph: (843)281-2662
Free: 877-332-2662
Fax: (843)280-2930
Co. E-mail: info@northmyrtlebeachchamber.com
URL: http://www.northmyrtlebeachchamber.com
Contact: Marc Jordan, President
Description: Promotes North Myrtle Beach area and its businesses by providing strong leadership and supports economic, tourism and community development. **Publications:** *Chamber Connection* (Monthly).

57511 ■ Oconee County Chamber of Commerce (OCCC)
PO Box 855
Seneca, SC 29679
Ph: (864)882-2097
Fax: (864)882-2881
URL: http://www.oconeecountychamber.com
Contact: Pamela Ramey, Executive Director (Acting)
Description: Promotes business and community development in the greater Seneca, SC area.

57512 ■ *On The Move*
PO Box 910
Beaufort, SC 29901-0910
Ph: (843)986-5400
Free: 800-638-3525
Fax: (843)986-5405
Co. E-mail: chamber@beaufortsc.org
URL: http://www.beaufortsc.org/cwo/Home
Contact: Ms. Carlotta Ungaro, President
Released: Monthly

57513 ■ *Onward Orangeburg*
PO Box 328
Orangeburg, SC 29116-0328
Ph: (803)534-6821
Free: 800-545-6153
Fax: (803)531-9435
Co. E-mail: chamber@orangeburgsc.net
URL: http://www.orangeburgchamber.com
Contact: David Coleman, President

57514 ■ Orangeburg County Chamber of Commerce (OCCC)
PO Box 328
Orangeburg, SC 29116-0328
Ph: (803)534-6821
Free: 800-545-6153
Fax: (803)531-9435
Co. E-mail: chamber@orangeburgsc.net
URL: http://www.orangeburgchamber.com
Contact: David Coleman, President
Description: Promotes business and community development in Orangeburg County, SC. Conducts local festivals; makes available scholarships.

Founded: 1904. **Publications:** *Membership Guide* (Semiannual); *Onward Orangeburg*; *Orangeburg County Visitors Information Guide.*

57515 ■ *Orangeburg County Visitors Information Guide*
PO Box 328
Orangeburg, SC 29116-0328
Ph: (803)534-6821
Free: 800-545-6153
Fax: (803)531-9435
Co. E-mail: chamber@orangeburgsc.net
URL: http://www.orangeburgchamber.com
Contact: David Coleman, President

57516 ■ *Outlook*
24 Cleveland St.
Greenville, SC 29601
Ph: (864)242-1050
Free: 866-485-5262
Fax: (864)282-8509
Co. E-mail: bhaskew@greenvillechamber.org
URL: http://www.greenvillechamber.org
Contact: Ben Haskew, President

57517 ■ **Partnership for Tomorrow**
c/o Mr. Lawrence E. Wilson, Campaign Gen. Chm.
PO Box 507
Greer, SC 29652
Ph: (864)877-0330
Fax: (864)877-6489
URL: http://www.fcdusa.com/campaigns/partnr4tomrw.htm
Contact: Mr. Lawrence E. Wilson, Campaign Manager

57518 ■ *Pickens Directory*
222 W Main St.
Pickens, SC 29671
Ph: (864)878-3258
Fax: (864)878-7317
Co. E-mail: thomas-realty@bellsouth.net
URL: http://www.pickenschamber.org
Contact: Mike Parrott, Executive Director
Released: Periodic

57519 ■ *Progress Report and Program of Work*
PO Box 2115
Myrtle Beach, SC 29578
Ph: (843)626-7444
Free: 800-356-3016
Fax: (843)448-3010
URL: http://www.myrtlebeachareachamber.com/default.html
Contact: Brad Dean, President
Released: Annual

57520 ■ *Real Estate Report*
24 Cleveland St.
Greenville, SC 29601
Ph: (864)242-1050
Free: 866-485-5262
Fax: (864)282-8509
Co. E-mail: bhaskew@greenvillechamber.org
URL: http://www.greenvillechamber.org
Contact: Ben Haskew, President
Released: Semiannual

57521 ■ *Sand and Surf Beach Safety*
PO Box 2115
Myrtle Beach, SC 29578
Ph: (843)626-7444
Free: 800-356-3016
Fax: (843)448-3010
URL: http://www.myrtlebeachareachamber.com/default.html
Contact: Brad Dean, President

57522 ■ *SC Business Journal*
1201 Main St., Ste. 1700
Columbia, SC 29201
Ph: (803)799-4601
Free: 800-799-4601

Fax: (803)779-6043
Co. E-mail: chamber@scchamber.net
URL: http://www.scchamber.net/cwt/external/wcpages/index.aspx
Contact: Otis Rawl, President
Released: Monthly

57523 ■ *SC Business Magazine*
1201 Main St., Ste. 1700
Columbia, SC 29201
Ph: (803)799-4601
Free: 800-799-4601
Fax: (803)779-6043
Co. E-mail: chamber@scchamber.net
URL: http://www.scchamber.net/cwt/external/wcpages/index.aspx
Contact: Otis Rawl, President
Released: Annual

57524 ■ **Simpsonville Area Chamber of Commerce**
PO Box 605
Simpsonville, SC 29681
Ph: (864)963-3781
Fax: (864)228-0003
Co. E-mail: info@simpsonvillechamber.com
URL: http://www.simpsonvillechamber.com
Contact: Deborah Hardwick, President
Description: Promotes business and community development in the Simpsonville, SC area. Provides volunteering opportunities for members. **Publications:** *Simpsonville Membership Directory* (Annual); *Simpsonville Membership Directory* (Annual); *ChamberChat Newsletters* (Bimonthly); *Industrial Guide* (Annual); *Simpsonville Membership Directory* (Annual); *Industrial Guide* (Annual).

57525 ■ *Simpsonville Membership Directory*
PO Box 605
Simpsonville, SC 29681
Ph: (864)963-3781
Fax: (864)228-0003
Co. E-mail: info@simpsonvillechamber.com
URL: http://www.simpsonvillechamber.com
Contact: Deborah Hardwick, President
Released: Annual **Price:** free.

57526 ■ **South Carolina Chamber of Commerce (SCCC)**
1201 Main St., Ste. 1700
Columbia, SC 29201
Ph: (803)799-4601
Free: 800-799-4601
Fax: (803)779-6043
Co. E-mail: chamber@scchamber.net
URL: http://www.scchamber.net/cwt/external/wcpages/index.aspx
Contact: Otis Rawl, President
URL(s): www.scchamber.net. **Description:** Promotes business and community development in South Carolina. **Founded:** 1940. **Publications:** *South Carolina Chamber of Commerce Business Directory & Resource Guide*; *South Carolina Business Journal* (Monthly); *Legislative Update* (Weekly); *SC Business Journal* (Monthly); *SC Business Magazine* (Annual); *South Carolina Chamber of Commerce Business Directory & Resource Guide* (Annual). **Educational Activities:** Summit (Annual). **Awards:** Business Person of the Year (Annual); HR Professional of the Year (Annual); Public Servant of the Year (Annual).

57527 ■ **Spartanburg Area Chamber of Commerce**
PO Box 1636
Spartanburg, SC 29304-1636
Ph: (864)594-5000
Fax: (864)594-5055
Co. E-mail: jpoole@spartanburgchamber.com
URL: http://www.spartanburgchamber.com
Contact: Mr. David Cordeau, President
Description: Promotes business and community development in the Spartanburg, SC area. **Founded:** 1918. **Publications:** *Business World Language* (Monthly); *Membership Directory/Buyers Guide* (Annual). **Awards:** Ambassador of the Year Award (Annual); Duke Power Community Service Award (Annual); Neville Holcombe Distinguished Citizenship

Award (Annual); Small Business Person of the Year Award (Annual). **Telecommunication Services:** spartanburgchamber@spartanburgchamber.com.

57528 ■ **Tri-County Regional Chamber of Commerce (TCRCC)**
PO Box 1012
Holly Hill, SC 29059
Ph: (843)563-9091
Free: 800-788-5646
Fax: (843)496-3831
Co. E-mail: tcrcc@bellsouth.net
URL: http://www.tri-crcc.com
Contact: Teresa M. Hatchell, Executive Director
Description: Promotes business and community development in Berkeley, Dorchester, and Orangeburg counties.

57529 ■ **Union County Chamber of Commerce (UCCC)**
135 W Main St.
Union, SC 29379
Ph: (864)427-9039
Free: 877-202-8755
Fax: (864)427-9030
Co. E-mail: torance@unionsc.com
URL: http://www.unionsc.info
Contact: Torance Inman, Executive Director
Description: Promotes business and community development in Union County, SC as well as industrial and economic development. Develops grants and loan packages for economic development. Conducts preliminary engineering studies, site design, and environmental analysis on sites. **Scope:** business, commerce, census. **Founded:** 1965. **Subscriptions:** 100 books. **Awards:** Business of the Year (Annual); Volunteer of the Year (Annual).

57530 ■ *Visitors Guide*
4500 Leeds Ave., Ste. 100
North Charleston, SC 29405
Ph: (843)577-2510
Fax: (843)723-4853
Co. E-mail: mail@charlestonchamber.org
URL: http://chaschamber.com
Contact: Bryan Derreberry, President
E-mail: bderreberry@charlestonchamber.org
Released: Annual

57531 ■ *Wage and Benefit Survey*
24 Cleveland St.
Greenville, SC 29601
Ph: (864)242-1050
Free: 866-485-5262
Fax: (864)282-8509
Co. E-mail: bhaskew@greenvillechamber.org
URL: http://www.greenvillechamber.org
Contact: Ben Haskew, President
Released: Annual

57532 ■ **Walterboro-Colleton Chamber of Commerce (WCCC)**
109 Benson St.
Walterboro, SC 29488-0027
Ph: (843)549-9595
Fax: (843)549-5775
Co. E-mail: info@walterboro.org
URL: http://www.walterboro.org
Contact: David M. Smalls, President
Description: Citizens from all segments of the community, dedicated to promoting the business environment in Walterboro and Colleton Counties. **Founded:** 1951. **Publications:** *Chamber Chain* (Monthly); *Chamber Membership Directory* (Annual).

57533 ■ **West Metro Chamber of Commerce (WMCC)**
1006 12th St.
Cayce, SC 29033
Ph: (803)794-6504
Free: 866-720-5400
Fax: (803)794-6505
Co. E-mail: westmetrochamber@aol.com
URL: http://www.westmetrochamber.com
Contact: Debra Gallup, Chairperson
Description: Promotes business and community development in Cayce, Pine Ridge, South Congaree, Springdale, and West Columbia, SC. Sponsors fishing rodeo, Congaree Carnival river events, Christmas

parade, and golf tournament. **Founded:** 1957. **Publications:** *Just One Minute* (Bimonthly). **Telecommunication Services:** info@westmetrochamber.sc.

57534 ■ Westminster Chamber of Commerce
PO Box 155
Westminster, SC 29693
Ph: (864)647-5316
Co. E-mail: wcoc@nuvox.net
URL: http://www.westminstersc.com
Description: Promotes business and community development in Westminster, SC area.

57535 ■ *Who's Who in the Sumter Chamber*
32 E Calhoun St.
Sumter, SC 29150
Ph: (803)775-1231
Co. E-mail: chamber@sumterchamber.com
URL: http://www.sumterchamber.com
Contact: Grier U. Blackwelder, President
Released: Annual

57536 ■ Williamsburg HomeTown Chamber of Commerce
PO Box 696
Kingstree, SC 29556
Ph: (843)355-6431
Fax: (843)355-3343
Co. E-mail: whtc@ftc-i.net
URL: http://www.williamsburgsc.org
Contact: Leslee Spivey, Director
Description: Promotes business development and community involvement in Williamsbury County, SC. **Founded:** 1945. **Awards:** Citizen of the Year (Annual); Farmer of the Year (Annual); Merchant of the Year (Annual).

57537 ■ York County Regional Chamber of Commerce
PO Box 590
Rock Hill, SC 29731
Ph: (803)324-7500
Fax: (803)324-1889
Co. E-mail: info@yorkcountychamber.com
URL: http://www.yorkcountychamber.com
Contact: Rob Youngblood, President
E-mail: ryoungblood@yorkcountychamber.com
Description: Promotes business and community development in the Rock Hill, Fort Mill and Tega Cay, SC areas. **Publications:** *York County Regional Chamber of Commerce Business Directory*; *Industrial Directory* (Annual); *Business Resource Guide* (Annual); *Connections*; *Industrial Directory* (Annual); *York County Regional Chamber of Commerce--Business Directory* (Annual). **Awards:** Business Person of the Year; Business Woman of the Year; Small Business of the Year; Minority Business Person of the Year.

MINORITY BUSINESS ASSISTANCE PROGRAMS

57538 ■ South Carolina Statewide Minority Business Enterprise Center
400 Percival Rd.
Columbia, SC 29206
Ph: (803)743-1154
Fax: (803)743-1162
Co. E-mail: busdev@scmbec.com
URL: http://www.scmbec.com
Contact: Dawn Jennings
Description: Established to increase the growth of new minority owned business and strengthen existing ones, therefore making them more profitable.

FINANCING AND LOAN PROGRAMS

57539 ■ Capital Insights, LLC
PO Box 27162
Greenville, SC 29616-2162

Ph: (864)423-3060
Co. E-mail: jwarner@capitalinsights.com
URL: http://www.capitalinsights.com
Contact: John Warner, President
Preferred Investment Size: $130,000 to $2,800,000.
Industry Preferences: Communications and media, other products, semiconductors and other electronics, consumer related, industrial and energy. **Geographic Preference:** Southeast.

PROCUREMENT ASSISTANCE PROGRAMS

57540 ■ South Carolina Procurement Technical Assistance Center - Charleston Area Small Business Development Center
5900 Core Dr., Ste. 104
North Charleston, SC 29406
Ph: (843)740-6160
Co. E-mail: sbdc@moore.sc.edu
URL: http://scsbdc.moore.sc.edu
Contact: Milton Larson, Consultant
E-mail: mlarson@moore.sc.edu
Description: Offer a variety of services and management training courses tailored to meet the needs of small and medium sized businesses, including managerial and technical assistance to those wishing to start or expand and enterprise.

57541 ■ South Carolina Procurement Technical Assistance Center - The Frank L. Roddey Small Business Development Center - University of South Carolina - Moore School of Business
1705 College St.
Columbia, SC 29208
Ph: (803)777-7877
Fax: (803)777-4403
Co. E-mail: sbdc@moore.sc.edu
URL: http://scsbdc.moore.sc.edu
Contact: Scott Bellows, Program Manager
E-mail: fheape@moore.sc.edu
Description: Established to aid small business start-up ventures and to assist in the continued growth of small businesses across the country. The program is supported with federal, state and private funds and is open to any present or prospective small business owner generally fee free.

57542 ■ South Carolina Procurement Technical Assistance Center - Greenville Area Small Business Development Center
Clemson University Renaissance Center
135 S Main St., Ste. 600
Greenville, SC 29601
Ph: (864)370-1545
Co. E-mail: swhelch@clemson.edu
URL: http://business.clemson.edu/centers/sbdc/sbdc_about.htm
Contact: Scott Whelchel, Manager
Description: Offer a variety of services and management training courses tailored to meet the needs of small and medium sized businesses, including managerial and technical assistance to those wishing to start or expand and enterprise.

57543 ■ South Carolina Procurement Technical Assistance Center - Orangeburg Area Small Business Development Center - South Carolina State University - School of Business
Algernon S Belcher Hall
300 College St.
Campus Box 7176
Orangeburg, SC 29117
Ph: (803)536-8445
Fax: (803)536-8066
Co. E-mail: sthoma89@scsu.edu
URL: http://www.sbdc.scsu.edu/
Contact: John W. Goodwin, Consultant
E-mail: jgoodwin@scsu.edu
Description: Offer a variety of services and management training courses tailored to meet the needs of small and medium sized businesses, including managerial and technical assistance to those wishing to start or expand and enterprise.

57544 ■ South Carolina Procurement Technical Assistance Center - University of South Carolina Procurement Center
Merovan Center
College of Business Administration
1200 Woodruff, Ste. C-38
Greenville, SC 29607
Ph: (864)297-1016
Fax: (864)329-0453
Co. E-mail: kwilli2@clemson.edu
URL: http://business.clemson.edu/centers/sbdc/sbdc_about.htmwww.clemson.edu/cbbs/center s-institutes.htmlbusiness.clemson.edu/center

INCUBATORS/RESEARCH AND TECHNOLOGY PARKS

57545 ■ Florence/Darlington Technical College - SBDC
PO Box 100548
Florence, SC 29501
Ph: (843)661-8256
Fax: (843)664-2803

57546 ■ Marion County Small Business Incubator
1305 N. Main St.
Marion, SC 29571
Ph: (843)431-5009
Fax: (843)423-8306
Co. E-mail: hmcwhite@marionsc.org
URL: http://bcswonline.com/mcsbi/index.htm
Description: A small business incubator working with new and expanding businesses to improve their chances of success by providing workshops, seminars, mentoring, consulting, coaching, networking, office and manufacturing facilities, and access to financial resources.

EDUCATIONAL PROGRAMS

57547 ■ Florence-Darlington Technical College
2715 W Lucas St.
Florence, SC 29501
Ph: (843)661-8324
Free: 800-228-5745
Fax: (843)661-8208
URL: http://www.fdtc.edu
Description: Two-year college offering a small business management program.

57548 ■ Greenville Technical College - Northwest Campus
PO Box 5616
Greenville, SC 29606
Ph: (864)250-8000
Free: 800-723-0673
Fax: (864)250-8534
URL: http://www.gvltec.edu
Description: Offers a variety of business-oriented courses, seminars, workshops, and weekend courses for credit or noncredit status. Some courses offer continuing education units. Special emphasis is placed on small business start up, management, and computer and employee training.

57549 ■ Piedmont Technical College - Continuing Ed
620 N Emerald Rd.
Greenwood, SC 29648-1467
Ph: (864)941-8324
Fax: (864)941-8555
URL: http://www.ptc.edu
Description: Offer program/classes in small business/small business management.

57550 ■ Spartanburg Technical College - Industry and Business Training
800 Brisack Rd.
Spartanburg, SC 29305-4386
Ph: (864)592-4800
Free: 866-591-3700

Fax: (864)592-4564

Co. E-mail: admissions@sccsc.edu

URL: http://www.sccsc.edu

Description: Acts as an educational and technical resource center for the small businessperson and for those interested in starting their own businesses.

PUBLICATIONS

57551 ■ *Smart Start your South Carolina Business*

PSI Research

300 N. Valley Dr.

Grants Pass, OR 97526

Ph: (503)479-9464

Free: 800-228-2275

Fax: (503)476-1479

Co. E-mail: info@psi-research.com

URL: http://www.psi-research.com

Ed: Michael D. Jenkins. **Released:** Revised edition, 1992. **Price:** $29.95 (looseleaf binder); $24.95 (paper). **Description:** Part of the Successful Business Library series.

SMALL BUSINESS DEVELOPMENT CENTERS

57552 ■ Aberdeen Small Business Development Center
416 Production St. N
Aberdeen, SD 57401
Ph: (605)626-2565
Fax: (605)626-2667
Co. E-mail: kweaver@midco.net
Contact: Kelly Weaver, Manager

Description: Represents and promotes the small business sector. Provides management assistance to current and prospective small business owners. Helps to improve management skills and expand the products and services of members.

57553 ■ Pierre Small Business Development Center
3431 Airport Rd., Ste. 3
Pierre, SD 57501
Ph: (605)773-2783
Fax: (605)773-2784
Co. E-mail: marcella.hurley@usd.edu
URL: http://www.asbdc-us.org
Contact: Marcella Hurley, Regional Director

Description: Represents and promotes the small business sector. Provides management assistance to current and prospective small business owners. Helps to improve management skills and expand the products and services of members.

57554 ■ Rapid City Small Business Development Center
525 University Loop, Ste. 102
Rapid City, SD 57701
Ph: (605)394-5311
Co. E-mail: dleavens@tie.net
URL: http://www.asbdc-us.org
Contact: Dona Leavens, Regional Director

Description: Represents and promotes the small business sector. Provides management assistance to current and prospective small business owners. Helps to improve management skills and expand the products and services of members.

57555 ■ Sioux Falls Small Business Development Center
c/o Mark Slade, Regional Dir.
2329 N Career Ave., Ste. 106
Sioux Falls, SD 57107
Ph: (605)367-5757
Co. E-mail: mslade@usd.edu
URL: http://www.asbdc-us.org
Contact: Mark Slade, Regional Director

Description: Represents and promotes the small business sector. Provides management assistance to current and prospective small business owners. Helps to improve management skills and expand the products and services of members.

57556 ■ Watertown Small Business Development Center
c/o Belinda Engelhart, Regional Dir.
124 1st Ave. NW
Watertown, SD 57201-3503
Ph: (605)882-5115
Co. E-mail: belinda.engelhart@usd.edu
URL: http://www.asbdc-us.org
Contact: Belinda Engelhart, Regional Director

Description: Represents and promotes the small business sector. Provides management assistance to current and prospective small business owners. Helps to improve management skills and expand the products and services of members.

57557 ■ Yankton Small Business Development Center
c/o Sue Stoll, Regional Dir.
1808 Summit Ave.
Yankton, SD 57078
Ph: (605)665-0751
Co. E-mail: sues@districtiii.org
URL: http://www.asbdc-us.org
Contact: Sue Stoll, Regional Director

Description: Represents and promotes the small business sector. Provides management assistance to current and prospective small business owners. Helps to improve management skills and expand the products and services of members.

SMALL BUSINESS ASSISTANCE PROGRAMS

57558 ■ South Dakota Governors Office of Economic Development
711 E Wells Ave.
Pierre, SD 57501-3369
Ph: (605)773-3301
Free: 800-872-6190
Co. E-mail: goedinfo@state.sd.us
URL: http://www.sdreadytowork.com
Contact: Jeff Brusseau, Manager, Business Development

Description: Advocates on behalf of South Dakota's small business community regarding policy determinations and questions concerning other state agencies. **Publications:** *South Dakota Manufacturers Directory* (Continuous).

57559 ■ South Dakota Governor's Office of Economic Development - Export, Trade, and Marketing Division
711 E Wells Ave.
Pierre, SD 57501-3369
Ph: (605)626-3098
Free: 800-872-6190
Fax: (605)773-3256
Co. E-mail: goedinfo@state.sd.us
URL: http://www.sdreadytowork.com

Description: Promotes South Dakota's manufactured and processed products to domestic and international markets; fields international direct investment opportunities. Services include the South Dakota Made logotype; foreign buyers list; Trade Show Assistance Program; export services; and computerized trade leads.

SCORE OFFICES

57560 ■ SCORE Rapid City
525 University Loop, Ste. 102
Rapid City, SD 57701
Ph: (605)394-1707
Fax: (605)394-6140
Co. E-mail: lslezak@tie.net
URL: http://www.rapidcityscore.org/content/default. htm
Contact: Cal Diegel, Chairperson

Description: Provides professional guidance and information to maximize the success of existing and emerging small businesses. Promotes entrepreneur education in Rapid City area, South Dakota.

57561 ■ SCORE Sioux Falls
2329 N Career Ave., Ste. 105
Sioux Falls, SD 57107
Ph: (605)330-4243
Fax: (605)330-4215
URL: http://www.score.org/chapters/sioux-falls-score

Description: Provides professional guidance and information to maximize the success of existing and emerging small businesses. Offers business counseling and workshops. **Founded:** 1966.

CHAMBERS OF COMMERCE

57562 ■ Aberdeen Area Chamber of Commerce (AACC)
516 S Main St.
Aberdeen, SD 57401-4165
Ph: (605)225-2860
Fax: (605)225-2437
Co. E-mail: info@aberdeen-chamber.com
URL: http://www.aberdeen-chamber.com
Contact: Gail L. Ochs, President

Description: Promotes business and community development in the Brown County, SD area. **Founded:** 1884. **Publications:** *Progress* (Monthly). **Awards:** Athena Award (Annual); George Award (Annual); Star Award (Annual).

57563 ■ Beresford Chamber of Commerce (BCC)
PO Box 167
Beresford, SD 57004
Ph: (605)763-2021
Co. E-mail: chamber@bmtc.net
URL: http://www.bmtc.net/~chamber
Contact: Nicole Hyronimus, Executive Director

Description: Provides leadership to create a strong business climate while enhancing the quality of life in Beresford, SD area. **Founded:** 1950.

57564 ■ Brookings Area Chamber of Commerce and Convention Bureau
414 Main Ave.
Brookings, SD 57006
Ph: (605)692-6125
Fax: (605)697-8109
Co. E-mail: chamber@brookings.net
URL: http://www.brookingschamber.org
Contact: Jeff Harms, President
Description: Promotes business and community development in the Brookings, SD area.

57565 ■ *Business Directory*
106 W Kansas St.
Spearfish, SD 57783-2016
Ph: (605)642-2626
Free: 800-626-8013
URL: http://www.spearfishchamber.org
Contact: Kent Campbell, Executive Director
Released: Annual

57566 ■ Canton Chamber of Commerce (CCC)
PO Box 34
Canton, SD 57013-0034
Ph: (605)764-7864
Free: 866-445-9603
Fax: (605)764-7865
Co. E-mail: lisa.canton@iw.net
URL: http://www.cantonarea.com
Contact: Ms. Lisa Alden, Coordinator
Description: Promotes business and community development in the Canton, SD area. Sponsors Saturday in the Park & Fishing Derby in the summer and the annual Christmas Parade & Holiday Open House in December. **Founded:** 1926. **Publications:** *Community Education/Chamber of Commerce Newsletter* (Quarterly).

57567 ■ *The Chamber Advantage*
20 S Maple
Watertown, SD 57201-3650
Ph: (605)886-5814
Free: 800-658-4505
Fax: (605)886-5957
Co. E-mail: coc@watertownsd.com
URL: http://www.watertownsd.com
Contact: Tim Oviatt, Chairman
Released: Monthly **Price:** free.

57568 ■ *The Chamber Challenge*
100 3rd St. W
Lemmon, SD 57638
Ph: (605)374-5716
Co. E-mail: lchamber@sdplains.com
URL: http://www.lemmonsd.com
Contact: Ms. Stacy Daley, Coordinator
Released: Monthly

57569 ■ *Chamber Circuit*
767 Main St.
Deadwood, SD 57732
Ph: (605)578-1876
Free: 800-999-1876
Fax: (605)578-2429
Co. E-mail: visit@deadwood.org
URL: http://www.deadwood.org
Contact: George Milos, Executive Director
Released: Monthly

57570 ■ *Chamber Dialogue*
906 E Cherry St.
Vermillion, SD 57069-1602
Ph: (605)624-5571
Free: 800-809-2071
Fax: (605)624-0094
Co. E-mail: vacc@vermillionchamber.com
URL: http://www.vermillionchamber.com
Contact: Steve Howe, Executive Director
Released: Monthly **Price:** included in membership dues.

57571 ■ *Chamber News*
200 N Phillips Ave., Ste. 102
Sioux Falls, SD 57104-6059
Ph: (605)336-1620

Fax: (605)336-6499
Co. E-mail: sfacc@siouxfalls.com
URL: http://www.siouxfallschamber.com
Contact: Evan C. Nolte, President
Released: Monthly; every first Monday. **Price:** free.

57572 ■ *ChamberChatter*
115 W Lawler Ave.
Chamberlain, SD 57325
Ph: (605)234-4416
Co. E-mail: chamber@chamberlainsd.org
URL: http://www.chamberlainsd.org
Contact: April Reis, Executive Director
Released: Monthly

57573 ■ Chamberlain-Oacoma Area Chamber of Commerce
115 W Lawler Ave.
Chamberlain, SD 57325
Ph: (605)234-4416
Co. E-mail: chamber@chamberlainsd.org
URL: http://www.chamberlainsd.org
Contact: April Reis, Executive Director
Description: Promotes business and community development in Chamberlain, SD area. **Publications:** *ChamberChatter* (Monthly).

57574 ■ *The Chamberview*
601 N Main St.
Mitchell, SD 57301-1945
Ph: (605)996-5567
Fax: (605)996-8273
Co. E-mail: info@mitchellchamber.com
URL: http://www.mitchellchamber.com
Contact: Bryan Hisel, Executive Director
Released: Monthly; every 1st Monday.

57575 ■ *Closer Look*
200 N Phillips Ave., Ste. 102
Sioux Falls, SD 57104-6059
Ph: (605)336-1620
Fax: (605)336-6499
Co. E-mail: sfacc@siouxfalls.com
URL: http://www.siouxfallschamber.com
Contact: Evan C. Nolte, President
Released: Weekly

57576 ■ *Community Education/Chamber of Commerce Newsletter*
PO Box 34
Canton, SD 57013-0034
Ph: (605)764-7864
Free: 866-445-9603
Fax: (605)764-7865
Co. E-mail: lisa.canton@iw.net
URL: http://www.cantonarea.com
Contact: Ms. Lisa Alden, Coordinator
Released: Quarterly

57577 ■ Custer Area Chamber of Commerce and Visitors Bureau
615 Washington St.
Custer, SD 57730-2028
Ph: (605)673-2244
Free: 800-992-9818
Fax: (605)673-3726
Co. E-mail: info@custersd.com
URL: http://www.custersd.com/index.php
Contact: Mr. Dave Ressler, Executive Director
Description: Promotes the area of Custer County, SD as a tourist destination. Also promotes new and existing business, community development, and retail trade.

57578 ■ Deadwood Chamber of Commerce and Visitors' Bureau
767 Main St.
Deadwood, SD 57732
Ph: (605)578-1876
Free: 800-999-1876
Fax: (605)578-2429
Co. E-mail: visit@deadwood.org
URL: http://www.deadwood.org
Contact: George Milos, Executive Director
Description: Promotes business and community development in the Deadwood-Lead, SD area. **Founded:** 1962. **Publications:** *Chamber Circuit* (Monthly). **Telecommunication Services:** george@deadwood.org.

57579 ■ Faith Chamber of Commerce
PO Box 246
Faith, SD 57626-0246
Ph: (605)967-2001
Fax: (605)967-2002
Co. E-mail: faithchamber@faithsd.com
URL: http://www.faithsdchamber.com
Description: Promotes the town of Faith through economic development.

57580 ■ *Fish Bites*
106 W Kansas St.
Spearfish, SD 57783-2016
Ph: (605)642-2626
Free: 800-626-8013
URL: http://www.spearfishchamber.org
Contact: Kent Campbell, Executive Director
Released: Weekly

57581 ■ *Fish Wrapper*
106 W Kansas St.
Spearfish, SD 57783-2016
Ph: (605)642-2626
Free: 800-626-8013
URL: http://www.spearfishchamber.org
Contact: Kent Campbell, Executive Director
Released: Monthly

57582 ■ Greater Madison Area Chamber of Commerce (GMACC)
315 S Egan Ave.
Madison, SD 57042
Ph: (605)256-2454
Fax: (605)256-9606
URL: http://www.chamberofmadisonsd.com
Contact: Donna Uthe, President
Description: Promotes business and community development in the Madison, SD area. **Founded:** 1930.

57583 ■ Hot Springs Area Chamber of Commerce (HSACC)
801 S 6th St.
Hot Springs, SD 57747
Ph: (605)745-4140
Free: 800-325-6991
Fax: (605)745-5849
Co. E-mail: info@hotsprings-sd.com
URL: http://www.hotsprings-sd.com
Contact: Scott Haden, Executive Director
Description: Promotes business, community development, tourism & community events, and tourism in Hot Springs, SD. **Founded:** 1938.

57584 ■ *Investment Report*
444 Mt. Rushmore Rd. N
Rapid City, SD 57701-1147
Ph: (605)343-1744
Fax: (605)343-6550
Co. E-mail: info@rapidcitychamber.com
URL: http://www.rapidcitychamber.com
Contact: Linda Rabe, President
Released: Monthly **Price:** $15, /year.

57585 ■ Lead Area Chamber of Commerce
160 W Main St.
Lead, SD 57754
Ph: (605)584-1100
Fax: (605)584-2209
Co. E-mail: leadcoc@leadmethere.org
URL: http://www.leadmethere.org
Contact: Melissa Johnson, Executive Director
Description: Promotes business, community development, and tourism in Port Washington area.

57586 ■ *Legislative Lookout*
200 N Phillips Ave., Ste. 102
Sioux Falls, SD 57104-6059
Ph: (605)336-1620
Fax: (605)336-6499
Co. E-mail: sfacc@siouxfalls.com
URL: http://www.siouxfallschamber.com
Contact: Evan C. Nolte, President
Released: Daily

57587 ■ Lemmon Chamber of Commerce
100 3rd St. W
Lemmon, SD 57638

Ph: (605)374-5716
Co. E-mail: lchamber@sdplains.com
URL: http://www.lemmonsd.com
Contact: Ms. Stacy Daley, Coordinator
Description: Promotes business and community development in the Lemmon, SD area. Sponsors Boss Cowman Rodeo and Celebration in July and Christmas Craft Fair in November. **Publications:** *The Chamber Challenge* (Monthly).

57588 ■ Milbank Area Chamber of Commerce
1001 E 4th Ave., Ste. 101
Milbank, SD 57252
Ph: (605)432-6656
Free: 800-675-6656
Fax: (605)432-9507
Co. E-mail: chamber1@milbanksd.com
URL: http://www.milbanksd.com
Contact: Laura Foss, Executive Director
Description: Promotes business and community development in the Milbank, SD area.

57589 ■ Mitchell Area Chamber of Commerce
601 N Main St.
Mitchell, SD 57301-1945
Ph: (605)996-5567
Fax: (605)996-8273
Co. E-mail: info@mitchellchamber.com
URL: http://www.mitchellchamber.com
Contact: Bryan Hisel, Executive Director
Description: Provides leadership to unify community action that enhances the business environment and the quality of life in the Mitchell area. **Founded:** 1917. **Publications:** *The Chamberview* (Monthly).

57590 ■ Mobridge Chamber of Commerce
103 N Main St.
Mobridge, SD 57601
Ph: (605)845-2387
Fax: (605)845-3223
Co. E-mail: info@mobridge.org
URL: http://www.mobridge.org
Contact: Michele Harrison, Executive Director
Description: Promotes business and community development in Mobridge, SD.

57591 ■ Pierre Area Chamber of Commerce
800 W Dakota Ave.
Pierre, SD 57501
Ph: (605)224-7361
Free: 800-962-2034
Fax: (605)224-6485
Co. E-mail: contactchamber@pierre.org
URL: http://www.pierre.org
Contact: Ms. Laura Schoen Cabonneau, Chief Executive Officer
Description: Promotes the interests of local and regional individuals, businesses, and organizations. Provides quality services and representation in the areas of government, health, agriculture, education, and culture. **Telecommunication Services:** laurasc@pierre.org.

57592 ■ *Progress*
516 S Main St.
Aberdeen, SD 57401-4165
Ph: (605)225-2860
Fax: (605)225-2437
Co. E-mail: info@aberdeen-chamber.com
URL: http://www.aberdeen-chamber.com
Contact: Gail L. Ochs, President
Released: Monthly

57593 ■ *QUICKLY*
200 N Phillips Ave., Ste. 102
Sioux Falls, SD 57104-6059
Ph: (605)336-1620
Fax: (605)336-6499
Co. E-mail: sfacc@siouxfalls.com
URL: http://www.siouxfallschamber.com
Contact: Evan C. Nolte, President
Released: Weekly

57594 ■ Rapid City Area Chamber of Commerce (RCACC)
444 Mt. Rushmore Rd. N
Rapid City, SD 57701-1147
Ph: (605)343-1744

Fax: (605)343-6550
Co. E-mail: info@rapidcitychamber.com
URL: http://www.rapidcitychamber.com
Contact: Linda Rabe, President
Description: Seeks to enhance the economic well-being and quality of life in the Black Hills of SD. **Founded:** 1886. **Publications:** *Investment Report* (Monthly).

57595 ■ Redfield Area Chamber of Commerce
626 Main St.
Redfield, SD 57469
Ph: (605)472-0965
Fax: (605)472-4553
Co. E-mail: redfieldchamber@redfield-sd.com
URL: http://www.redfield-sd.com/chamber.html
Contact: Cathy Fink, Coordinator
Description: Promotes business and community development in Redfield, SD area.

57596 ■ *Report to Investors*
803 E 4th St.
Yankton, SD 57078-4512
Ph: (605)665-3636
Free: 800-888-1460
Fax: (605)665-7501
Co. E-mail: chamber@yanktonsd.com
URL: http://www.yanktonsd.com
Contact: Gary Dybsetter, President
Released: Annual

57597 ■ Sioux Falls Area Chamber of Commerce (SFACC)
200 N Phillips Ave., Ste. 102
Sioux Falls, SD 57104-6059
Ph: (605)336-1620
Fax: (605)336-6499
Co. E-mail: sfacc@siouxfalls.com
URL: http://www.siouxfallschamber.com
Contact: Evan C. Nolte, President
Description: Promotes business and community development in the Sioux Falls, SD area. Supports industry and agriculture. Maintains convention bureau. **Founded:** 1907. **Publications:** *Chamber News* (Monthly); *Closer Look* (Weekly); *Legislative Lookout* (Daily); *QUICKLY* (Weekly); *Sioux Falls Community Guide* (Annual). **Awards:** Farm Family of the Year (Annual); Agri-Business Citizen of the Year.

57598 ■ *Sioux Falls Community Guide*
200 N Phillips Ave., Ste. 102
Sioux Falls, SD 57104-6059
Ph: (605)336-1620
Fax: (605)336-6499
Co. E-mail: sfacc@siouxfalls.com
URL: http://www.siouxfallschamber.com
Contact: Evan C. Nolte, President
Released: Annual

57599 ■ Spearfish Area Chamber of Commerce—Spearfish Area Chamber of Commerce and Convention and Visitors Bureau
106 W Kansas St.
Spearfish, SD 57783-2016
Ph: (605)642-2626
Free: 800-626-8013
URL: http://www.spearfishchamber.org
Contact: Kent Campbell, Executive Director
Description: Seeks to advance a positive business climate and provide leadership to the promotion and managed growth of the Spearfish, SD area community. Markets Spearfish for the economic benefit of the community. **Founded:** 1919. **Publications:** *Business Directory* (Annual); *Fish Bites* (Weekly); *Fish Wrapper* (Monthly); *Spearfish Street Map* (Annual).

57600 ■ *Spearfish Street Map*
106 W Kansas St.
Spearfish, SD 57783-2016
Ph: (605)642-2626
Free: 800-626-8013
URL: http://www.spearfishchamber.org
Contact: Kent Campbell, Executive Director
Released: Annual

57601 ■ Sturgis Area Chamber of Commerce
2040 Junction Ave.
Sturgis, SD 57785
Ph: (605)347-2556
Fax: (605)347-6682
Co. E-mail: info@sturgisareachamber.com
URL: http://sturgisareachamber.com
Contact: J.D. Williams, President
Description: Promotes business and community development in Meade County, SD.

57602 ■ Vermillion Area Chamber of Commerce and Development Company
906 E Cherry St.
Vermillion, SD 57069-1602
Ph: (605)624-5571
Free: 800-809-2071
Fax: (605)624-0094
Co. E-mail: vacc@vermillionchamber.com
URL: http://www.vermillionchamber.com
Contact: Steve Howe, Executive Director
Description: Promotes business and community development in the Vermillion, SD area. Operates with the Vermillion Development Company. Sponsors competitions and festivals. **Publications:** *Chamber Dialogue* (Monthly).

57603 ■ Watertown Area Chamber of Commerce (WACC)
20 S Maple
Watertown, SD 57201-3650
Ph: (605)886-5814
Free: 800-658-4505
Fax: (605)886-5957
Co. E-mail: coc@watertownsd.com
URL: http://www.watertownsd.com
Contact: Tim Oviatt, Chairman
Description: Seeks to promote the economic prosperity and quality of life in the Watertown area. **Founded:** 1916. **Publications:** *The Chamber Advantage* (Monthly).

57604 ■ Winner Area Chamber of Commerce (WACC)
246 S Main St.
Winner, SD 57580-1831
Ph: (605)842-1533
Co. E-mail: winnerareachamber@gmail.com
URL: http://www.winnersd.com
Contact: Nicole Mathis, President
Description: Promotes business and community development in Winner, SD. **Founded:** 1946.

57605 ■ Yankton Area Chamber of Commerce (YACC)
803 E 4th St.
Yankton, SD 57078-4512
Ph: (605)665-3636
Free: 800-888-1460
Fax: (605)665-7501
Co. E-mail: chamber@yanktonsd.com
URL: http://www.yanktonsd.com
Contact: Gary Dybsetter, President
Description: Promotes business and community development in the Yankton, SD area. Convention/Meeting: none. **Founded:** 1920. **Publications:** *Report to Investors* (Annual); *Yankton Chamber News* (Bimonthly). **Awards:** P.A.Y. Scholarship (Annual).

57606 ■ *Yankton Chamber News*
803 E 4th St.
Yankton, SD 57078-4512
Ph: (605)665-3636
Free: 800-888-1460
Fax: (605)665-7501
Co. E-mail: chamber@yanktonsd.com
URL: http://www.yanktonsd.com
Contact: Gary Dybsetter, President
Released: Bimonthly **Price:** included in membership dues; $21, /year for nonmembers.

MINORITY BUSINESS ASSISTANCE PROGRAMS

57607 ■ Native American Economic Development Project - Yankton Sioux Tribe
PO Box 248
Marty, SD 57361
Ph: (605)384-3641
Fax: (605)384-5687
Co. E-mail: ysteppwr@charles-mix.com
Description: Provides individual counseling and technical assistance to entrepreneurs from the Yankton Sioux tribe. Also works to increase circulation of monies with the borders of the reservation.

57608 ■ South Dakota Indian Business Alliance - South Dakota Office of Tribal Government Relations
c/o Wakpa Sica Reconciliation Pl.
709 W Fort Chouteau Rd.
Fort Pierre, SD 57532-0001
Co. E-mail: dani.daughtery@hotmail.com
URL: http://www.sdtribalrelations.com/SDIBA/sdiba.asp
Description: Focuses on removing barriers to Native American business development in South Dakota.

PROCUREMENT ASSISTANCE PROGRAMS

57609 ■ South Dakota Procurement Technical Assistance Center
2329 N Career Pl., Ste. 106
Sioux Falls, SD 57107
Ph: (605)367-5252
Fax: (605)367-5755
Co. E-mail: Kareen.Dougherty@usd.edu
URL: http://www.usd.edu/sdptac/
Contact: Kareen Dougherty, Program Manager
Description: Helps businesses develop a marketing plan to sell their goods and services to the government. Also serves as a guide through the procurement process.

57610 ■ South Dakota Procurement Technical Assistance Center (East River) - University of South Dakota
2329 N Career Ave., Ste. 106
Sioux Falls, SD 57107
Ph: (605)367-5757
Fax: (605)367-5755
Co. E-mail: mslade@usd.edu
URL: http://www.usd.edu/sdptac
Contact: Mark Slade, Director
E-mail: Kareen.Dougherty@usd.edu
Description: Promotes early stage technology based companies to grow and prosper.

57611 ■ South Dakota Procurement Technical Assistance Center (West River) - University of South Dakota
Black Hill Business Development Center
525 University Loop, Ste. 102
Rapid City, SD 57701
Ph: (605)394-5311
Fax: (605)394-6140
Co. E-mail: dleavens@tie.net
URL: http://www.usd.edu/sdptac
Contact: Dona Leavens, Director
E-mail: echristianson@tie.net
Description: Promotes early stage technology based companies to grow and prosper.

57612 ■ South Dakota Procurement Technical Assistance Center - University of South Dakota - Business Research Bureau
414 Clark St.
Vermillion, SD 57069-2390
Ph: (605)677-5287
Fax: (605)677-5427
Co. E-mail: jshemmin@usd.edu
URL: http://www.usd.edu/sdptac
Contact: John S. Hemmingstad, Director
E-mail: kareen.dougherty@usd.edu
Description: Provides assistance to South Dakota businesses who wish to contract with local, state and federal government agencies.

INCUBATORS/RESEARCH AND TECHNOLOGY PARKS

57613 ■ Black Hills Business Development Center
525 University Loop, Ste. 101
Rapid City, SD 57701
Ph: (605)343-1880
Fax: (605)343-1916
Co. E-mail: jmirehouse@tie.net
URL: http://rapiddevelopment.com/BlackHillsBusinessDevelopmentCenter/
Contact: Jim Mirehouse, Chief Executive Officer
Description: A small business incubator committed to offering quality, affordable space to attract start-ups and businesses with growth potential by offering a full range of business services free or at a low cost through sharing.

57614 ■ The Enterprise Institute
2301 Research Park Way
Brookings, SD 57006
Ph: (605)697-5015
Co. E-mail: info@sdei.org
URL: http://www.sdei.org/
Description: A small business incubator designed to facilitate University and industry resources to encourage and assist the establishment of entrepreneurial growth enterprises in the region. Its objectives are to assist the development of commercially viable opportunities identified within the University, establish mentoring support and outreach for regional growth enterprises, and support and/or sponsor academic entrepreneurial programs.

EDUCATIONAL PROGRAMS

57615 ■ Mitchell Technical Institute
821 N Capital St.
Mitchell, SD 57301
Ph: (605)995-3024
Free: 800-684-1969
Fax: (605)995-3083
Co. E-mail: questions@mitchelltech.edu
URL: http://www.mitchelltech.edu
Description: School offers programs in small business management.

SMALL BUSINESS DEVELOPMENT CENTERS

57616 ■ Tennessee Small Business Development Centers, Austin Peay State University
601 College St.
McReynolds Bldg., Offices 111 & 113
Clarksville, TN 37040
Ph: (931)221-1370
Co. E-mail: fjohnson@tsbdc.org
URL: http://www.tsbdc.org
Description: Represents and promotes the small business sector. Provides management assistance to current and prospective small business owners. Helps to improve management skills and expand the products and services of members.

57617 ■ Tennessee Small Business Development Centers, Chattanooga State Technical Community College
Chattanooga Business Development Ctr.
100 Cherokee Blvd., Ste. 202
Chattanooga, TN 37405-0880
Ph: (423)756-8668
Fax: (423)756-6195
Co. E-mail: sharyn.moreland@chattanoogastate.edu
URL: http://www.tsbdc.org
Contact: Sharyn Moreland, Director
URL(s): www.chattanoogastate.edu/tsbdc. **Description:** Represents and promotes the small business sector. Provides management assistance to current and prospective small business owners. Helps to improve management skills and expand the products and services of members.

57618 ■ Tennessee Small Business Development Centers, Cleveland State Community College
Technologies Bldg., Rm.126
3535 Adkisson Dr.
Cleveland, TN 37320-3570
Ph: (423)478-6247
Free: 800-604-2722
Co. E-mail: dhudson@tsbdc.org
URL: http://www.tsbdc.org
URL(s): www.clevelandstatecc.edu/academics/divisions/business_technology. **Description:** Represents and promotes the small business sector. Provides management assistance to current and prospective small business owners. Helps to improve management skills and expand the products and services of members.

57619 ■ Tennessee Small Business Development Centers, Dyersburg State Community College
1510 Lake Rd.
Dyersburg, TN 38024-2411
Ph: (731)286-3201
Co. E-mail: jfrakes@mail.tsbdc.org
URL: http://www.tsbdc.org
Description: Represents and promotes the small business sector. Provides management assistance to

current and prospective small business owners. Helps to improve management skills and expand the products and services of members.

57620 ■ Tennessee Small Business Development Centers, Jackson State Community College
197 Auditorium St.
Jackson, TN 38301
Ph: (731)424-5389
Fax: (731)427-3942
Co. E-mail: racree@tsbdc.org
Contact: Ron Acree, Director
Description: Represents and promotes the small business sector. Provides management assistance to current and prospective small business owners. Helps to improve management skills and expand the products and services of members.

57621 ■ Tennessee Small Business Development Centers, Knoxville
17 Market Sq., No. 201
Knoxville, TN 37902-1405
Ph: (865)246-2663
Co. E-mail: lrossini@mail.tsbdc.org
URL: http://www.tsbdc.org/mapresults.aspx?Area=Knoxville&groupby=area
Description: Represents and promotes the small business sector. Provides management assistance to current and prospective small business owners. Helps to improve management skills and expand the products and services of members.

57622 ■ Tennessee Small Business Development Centers, Memphis
Memphis Renaissance Ctr.
555 Beale St.
Memphis, TN 38103
Ph: (901)526-9300
Co. E-mail: ddoyle@tsbdc.org
URL: http://www.tsbdc.org/mapresults.aspx?showall=y
Description: Represents and promotes the small business sector. Provides management assistance to current and prospective small business owners. Helps to improve management skills and expand the products and services of members.

57623 ■ Tennessee Small Business Development Centers, Middle Tennessee State University
Rutherford County Chamber of Commerce
3050 Medical Center Pkwy.
Murfreesboro, TN 37129
Ph: (615)898-2745
Co. E-mail: rklika@tsbdc.org
URL: http://www.tsbdc.org
Description: Represents and promotes the small business sector. Provides management assistance to current and prospective small business owners. Helps to improve management skills and expand the products and services of members.

57624 ■ Tennessee Small Business Development Centers, Middle Tennessee State University - Columbia
Maury Alliance
106 W 6th St.
Columbia, TN 38402
Ph: (931)388-2155
Co. E-mail: gosekowsky@tsbdc.org
URL: http://www.tsbdc.org
Description: Represents and promotes the small business sector. Provides management assistance to current and prospective small business owners. Helps to improve management skills and expand the products and services of members.

57625 ■ Tennessee Small Business Development Centers, Tennessee State University - Brentwood
Reliant Bank
1736 Carouthers Pkwy., Ste. 100
Brentwood, TN 37027-8167
Ph: (615)963-7179
Co. E-mail: info@nashvillesbdc.org
URL: http://www.tsbdc.org
Description: Represents and promotes the small business sector. Provides management assistance to current and prospective small business owners. Helps to improve management skills and expand the products and services of members.

57626 ■ Tennessee Small Business Development Centers, Tennessee State University - Nashville
330 10th Ave. N
Nashville, TN 37203-3401
Ph: (615)963-7179
Co. E-mail: proberts@tsbdc.org
URL: http://www.tsbdc.org
Description: Represents and promotes the small business sector. Provides management assistance to current and prospective small business owners. Helps to improve management skills and expand the products and services of members.

57627 ■ Tennessee Small Business Development Centers, Tennessee Tech University
College of Business Administration
1105 N Peachtree
Cookeville, TN 38505
Ph: (931)372-3670
Co. E-mail: vhenley@tsbdc.org
URL: http://www.tsbdc.org
Description: Represents and promotes the small business sector. Provides management assistance to current and prospective small business owners. Helps to improve management skills and expand the products and services of members.

57628 ■ Tennessee Small Business Development Centers, Volunteer State Community College
Betty Gibson Hall
1480 Nashville Pike
Gallatin, TN 37066-3148

Ph: (615)230-4780
URL: http://www.tsbdc.org
Description: Represents and promotes the small business sector. Provides management assistance to current and prospective small business owners. Helps to improve management skills and expand the products and services of members.

SMALL BUSINESS ASSISTANCE PROGRAMS

57629 ■ Tennessee Department of Agriculture, Market Development
PO Box 40627
Nashville, TN 37204
Ph: (615)837-5103
Fax: (615)837-5194
Co. E-mail: tn.agriculture@state.tn.us
URL: http://www.state.tn.us/agriculture
Contact: Ken Givens, Commissioner
Description: Develops domestic and international markets for farmers and agribusinesses.

57630 ■ Tennessee Department of Economic and Community Development - Business Enterprise Resource Office
312 Rosa L. Parks Ave., 11th Fl.
Nashville, TN 37243-0405
Ph: (615)741-1888
Free: 800-872-7201
Fax: (615)741-5829
Co. E-mail: ECD.Communications.Office@tn.gov
URL: http://www.state.tn.us/ecd
Contact: Matthew Kisber, Communications Specialist
Description: Serves as a first-stop office for businesses in the state, conducts programs aimed at increasing the success of small businesses.

57631 ■ Tennessee Department of Economic and Community Development - International Development Group
312 Rosa L. Parks Ave., 11th Fl.
Nashville, TN 37243
Ph: (615)741-1888
Free: 877-768-6374
Fax: (615)741-7306
Co. E-mail: ECD.Communications.Office@tn.gov
URL: http://www.state.tn.us/ecd
Contact: Lori Odom, Director
Description: Represents state manufacturers at foreign trade shows and missions International Development and co-sponsors seminars and workshops.

SCORE OFFICES

57632 ■ Greater Knoxville SCORE Chapter 435
412 N Cedar Bluff Rd., Ste. 450
Knoxville, TN 37923
Ph: (865)692-0716
Fax: (865)692-0718
Co. E-mail: downtown@scoreknox.org
URL: http://scoreknox.org
Description: Provides free counseling to those wanting to start a business, small business owners and nonprofit organizations.

57633 ■ Kingsport SCORE
Co. E-mail: kptscore@kingsportchamber.org

57634 ■ SCORE Bristol
30 6th St., 2nd Fl.
Bristol, TN 37620
Ph: (423)989-4866
Fax: (423)989-4867
URL: http://bristol.score.org

57635 ■ SCORE Chattanooga
Franklin Bldg.
5726 Marlin Rd., Ste. 515
Chattanooga, TN 37411
Ph: (423)553-1722

Fax: (423)553-1724
Co. E-mail: score.cha.tn@comcast.net
URL: http://www.scorechattanooga.org
URL(s): chattanooga.score.org. **Description:** Serves as volunteer program in which working and retired business management professionals provide free business counseling to men and women who are considering starting a small business, encountering problems with their business, or expanding their business. Offers free one-on-one counseling, online counseling and low cost workshops on a variety of business topics.

57636 ■ SCORE Greater Knoxville
412 N Cedar Bluff Rd., Ste. 450
Knoxville, TN 37923
Ph: (865)692-0716
Fax: (865)692-0718
Co. E-mail: counseling@scoreknox.org
URL: http://www.scoreknox.org
URL(s): greaterknoxville.score.org. **Description:** Serves as volunteer program in which working and retired business management professionals provide free business counseling to men and women who are considering starting a small business, encountering problems with their business, or expanding their business. Offers free one-on-one counseling, online counseling and low cost workshops on a variety of business topics. **Scope:** business. **Subscriptions:** articles.

57637 ■ SCORE Memphis
Clark Tower
5100 Poplar Ave., Ste. 1701
Memphis, TN 38137
Ph: (901)544-3588
Co. E-mail: scorememphis@comcast.net
URL: http://www.scorememphis.org
Contact: William Morris, Chairman
Description: Serves as volunteer program in which working and retired business management professionals provide free business counseling to men and women who are considering starting a small business, encountering problems with their business, or expanding their business. Offers free one-on-one counseling, online counseling and low cost workshops on a variety of business topics.

57638 ■ SCORE Nashville
50 Vantage Way, Ste. 201
Nashville, TN 37228-1500
Ph: (615)736-7621
URL: http://www.scorenashville.org
Description: Serves as volunteer program in which working and retired business management professionals provide free business counseling to men and women who are considering starting a small business, encountering problems with their business, or expanding their business. Offers free one-on-one counseling, online counseling and low cost workshops on a variety of business topics.

57639 ■ SCORE NE Tennessee
112 E Myrtle Ave., Ste. 408
Professional Bldg.
Johnson City, TN 37601
Ph: (423)461-8051
Fax: (423)461-8053
URL: http://netennessee.score.org
Description: Provides professional guidance and information to maximize the success of existing and emerging small businesses. Promotes entrepreneur education in NE Tennessee.

BETTER BUSINESS BUREAUS

57640 ■ Better Business Bureau, Chattanooga
1010 Market St., Ste. 200
Chattanooga, TN 37402
Ph: (423)266-6144
Free: 800-548-4456
Fax: (423)267-1924
Co. E-mail: tngabbb@bellsouth.net
URL: http://chattanooga.bbb.org
Contact: Jim Winsett, President
Description: Seeks to promote and foster the highest ethical relationship between businesses and the public through voluntary self-regulation, consumer

and business education, and service excellence. Provides information to help consumers and businesses make informed purchasing decisions and avoid costly scams and frauds; settles consumer complaints through arbitration and other means. **Founded:** 1960. **Awards:** Torch Award for Marketplace Ethics (Annual).

57641 ■ Better Business Bureau of Greater East Tennessee
PO Box 31377
Knoxville, TN 37930
Ph: (865)692-1600
Fax: (865)692-1590
Co. E-mail: info@knoxville.bbb.org
URL: http://knoxville.bbb.org
Contact: Jerry Tipton, President
Description: Seeks to promote and foster the highest ethical relationship between businesses and the public through voluntary self-regulation, consumer and business education, and service excellence. Provides information to help consumers and businesses make informed purchasing decisions and avoid costly scams and frauds; settles consumer complaints through arbitration and other means.

57642 ■ Better Business Bureau of the Mid-South
3693 Tyndale Dr.
Memphis, TN 38125-8537
Ph: (901)759-1300
Free: 800-222-8754
Fax: (901)757-2997
Co. E-mail: info@bbbmidsouth.org
URL: http://memphis.bbb.org
Description: Seeks to promote and foster ethical relationship between businesses and the public through voluntary self-regulation, consumer and business education, and service excellence. Provides information to help consumers and businesses make informed purchasing decisions and avoids costly scams and frauds; settles consumer complaints through arbitration and other means. **Founded:** 1948.

57643 ■ Better Business Bureau of Middle Tennessee (BBBN)
PO Box 198436
Nashville, TN 37219
Ph: (615)242-4222
Fax: (615)250-4245
Co. E-mail: bbbnash@aol.com
URL: http://nashville.bbb.org
Description: Promotes ethical business practices through self-regulation, rather than government or legal intervention, by providing factual reports on businesses, mediation and arbitration services, and advertising review. **Scope:** consumer, business, business tips. **Founded:** 1961. **Subscriptions:** articles.

CHAMBERS OF COMMERCE

57644 ■ *225 Keith*
PO Box 2275
Cleveland, TN 37320-2275
Ph: (423)472-6587
Fax: (423)472-2019
Co. E-mail: info@clevelandchamber.com
URL: http://clevelandchamber.com
Contact: Gary Farlow, President
Released: Monthly

57645 ■ *acorn*
1400 Oak Ridge Tpke.
Oak Ridge, TN 37830
Ph: (865)483-1321
Fax: (865)483-1678
Co. E-mail: ownby@orcc.org
URL: http://www.oakridgechamber.org
Contact: David Bradshaw, Chairman of the Board
Released: Monthly

57646 ■ *Alliance Membership Directory*
106 W 6th St.
Columbia, TN 38402
Ph: (931)388-2155

Fax: (931)380-0335
Co. E-mail: khuckaby@mauryalliance.com
URL: http://www.mauryalliance.com
Contact: Kara Huckaby, Director
Released: Annual

57647 ■ Anderson County Chamber of Commerce (ACCC)
245 N Main St., Ste. 200
Clinton, TN 37716
Ph: (865)457-2559
Fax: (865)483-7480
Co. E-mail: jackie@andersoncountychamber.org
URL: http://www.andersoncountychamber.org
Contact: Jackie L. Nichols, President
Description: Promotes business and community development in Anderson County, TN. Sponsors Antiques Festival, Teachers Appreciation Banquet, Scholarship Golf Tournament, Business Expo and Softball Classic. Conducts charitable activities. **Founded:** 1932. **Publications:** *Chamber News* (Monthly); *Guidebook and Directory* (Biennial). **Awards:** R.C. Hoskins Award (Annual).

57648 ■ *At Work*
2000 Commerce Ave.
Dyersburg, TN 38024
Ph: (731)285-3433
Fax: (731)286-4926
Co. E-mail: chamber@ecsis.net
URL: http://www.dyerchamber.com
Contact: Allen Hester, President
Released: Periodic

57649 ■ Athens Area Chamber of Commerce
13 N Jackson St.
Athens, TN 37303
Ph: (423)745-0334
Fax: (423)745-0335
Co. E-mail: info@athenschamber.org
URL: http://www.athenschamber.org
Contact: Rob Preston, President
Description: Promotes business and community development in Athens, TN area. **Founded:** 1982. **Publications:** *Athens Business* (Monthly).

57650 ■ *Athens Business*
13 N Jackson St.
Athens, TN 37303
Ph: (423)745-0334
Fax: (423)745-0335
Co. E-mail: info@athenschamber.org
URL: http://www.athenschamber.org
Contact: Rob Preston, President
Released: Monthly

57651 ■ Bartlett Area Chamber of Commerce (BACC)
2969 Elmore Park Rd.
Bartlett, TN 38134-8309
Ph: (901)372-9457
Fax: (901)372-9488
Co. E-mail: info@bartlettchamber.org
URL: http://www.bartlettchamber.org
Contact: John Threadgill, President
Description: Promotes business and community development in Shelby County, TN. Sponsors Leadership Bartlett program and annual Business Expo. Convention/Meeting: none. **Founded:** 1980. **Publications:** *Your Business Connection* (Monthly); *Bartlett Area Chamber of Commerce--Membership Directory* (Annual).

57652 ■ Bellevue Chamber of Commerce
177 A Belle Forest Cir.
Nashville, TN 37221
Ph: (615)662-2737
Fax: (615)662-0197
Co. E-mail: info@thebellevuechamber.com
URL: http://www.thebellevuechamber.com
Contact: Vincent Troia, Executive Director
Description: Promotes business and community development in Bellevue, TN.

57653 ■ Benton County/Camden Chamber of Commerce
266 Hwy. 641 N
Camden, TN 38320
Ph: (731)584-8395

Free: 877-584-8395
Fax: (731)584-5544
Co. E-mail: chamber1@usit.net
URL: http://www.bentoncountycamden.com
Description: Promotes business and community development in Camden, TN area.

57654 ■ Blount County Chamber of Commerce
201 S Washington St.
Maryville, TN 37804
Ph: (865)983-2241
Fax: (865)984-1386
Co. E-mail: info@blountpartnership.com
URL: http://www.blountchamber.com
Contact: Allan Cox, Chairman
Description: Promotes business and community development in Blount County, TN. **Founded:** 1920. **Publications:** *The Daily Times* (Annual); *Knoxville News Sentinel* (Annual).

57655 ■ Brentwood Cool Springs Chamber of Commerce
5211 Maryland Way, Ste. 1080
Brentwood, TN 37027
Ph: (615)373-1595
Fax: (615)373-8810
Co. E-mail: brad.dunn@pnfp.com
URL: http://www.brentwood.org
Contact: Brad Dunn, Chairman
Description: Seeks to promote and advance the business and commercial interests in Brentwood, TN and the surrounding area. Also sponsors members through various programs and services. **Founded:** 1955. **Publications:** *Brentwood Magazine* (Annual).

57656 ■ *Brentwood Magazine*
5211 Maryland Way, Ste. 1080
Brentwood, TN 37027
Ph: (615)373-1595
Fax: (615)373-8810
Co. E-mail: brad.dunn@pnfp.com
URL: http://www.brentwood.org
Contact: Brad Dunn, Chairman
Released: Annual

57657 ■ *Bristol Membership Directory-Newcomers Guide and Business Pages*
20 Volunteer Pkwy.
Bristol, TN 37620
Ph: (423)989-4850
Fax: (423)989-4867
Co. E-mail: phurt@bristolchamber.org
URL: http://www.bristolchamber.org
Contact: Paula Hurt, President
Released: Annual

57658 ■ Bristol Tennessee/Virginia Chamber of Commerce
20 Volunteer Pkwy.
Bristol, TN 37620
Ph: (423)989-4850
Fax: (423)989-4867
Co. E-mail: phurt@bristolchamber.org
URL: http://www.bristolchamber.org
Contact: Paula Hurt, President
Description: Promotes business and community development in Bristol, located in the states of Tennessee and Virginia. **Founded:** 1909. **Publications:** *Bristol Membership Directory-Newcomers Guide and Business Pages* (Annual). **Awards:** Ambassador of the Year (Annual); Volunteer of the Year (Annual).

57659 ■ *Business Directory*
115 Academy St.
Greeneville, TN 37743-5601
Ph: (423)638-4111
Fax: (423)638-5345
Co. E-mail: tferguson@greenecop.com
URL: http://www.greenecountypartnership.com/home.aspx
Contact: Tom R. Ferguson, President
Price: included in membership dues.

57660 ■ *The Business Link*
318 Angel Row
Loudon, TN 37774
Ph: (865)458-2067

Fax: (865)458-1206
Co. E-mail: info@loudoncountychamber.com
URL: http://www.loudoncountychamberofcommerce.com
Contact: Chip Miller, Chairman
Released: Monthly

57661 ■ *Business Pulse*
3050 Medical Center Pkwy.
Murfreesboro, TN 37129-3943
Ph: (615)893-6565
Free: 800-716-7560
Fax: (615)890-7600
Co. E-mail: info@rutherfordchamber.org
URL: http://www.rutherfordchamber.org
Contact: Paul Latture, President
Released: Monthly

57662 ■ Campbell County Chamber of Commerce
PO Box 305
Jacksboro, TN 37757
Ph: (423)566-0329
Fax: (423)562-0535
Co. E-mail: chamber@campbellcountygov.com
URL: http://www.campbellcountychamber.com
Contact: Betty Snodderly, Administrator
Description: Provides business and community development in the Campbell County, TN area.

57663 ■ Carroll County Chamber of Commerce
20740 E Main St.
Huntingdon, TN 38344
Ph: (731)986-4664
Fax: (731)986-2029
Co. E-mail: cchamber@earthlink.net
URL: http://carrollcounty-tn-chamber.com
Contact: Brad Hurley, President
Description: Organized for the purpose of advancing the commercial, industrial, civic, and general interests of the County of Carroll and its trade area.

57664 ■ *Chamber Chatter*
302 Betsy Pack Dr.
Jasper, TN 37347-3316
Ph: (423)942-5103
Fax: (423)942-0098
Co. E-mail: marioncoc@bellsouth.net
URL: http://www.marioncountychamber.com
Contact: Kevin Merrell, President
Released: Bimonthly

57665 ■ *The Chamber Community News*
500 W Market St.
Bolivar, TN 38008
Ph: (731)658-6554
Fax: (731)658-6874
Co. E-mail: infohcc@bellsouth.com
URL: http://hardemancountytn.com/chamber
Contact: Rob Jensik, Executive Director
Released: Bimonthly **Price:** included in membership dues.

57666 ■ *Chamber Connection*
123 S Jefferson Ave.
Ripley, TN 38063
Ph: (731)635-9541
Fax: (731)635-9064
Co. E-mail: info@lauderdalecountytn.org
URL: http://www.lauderdalecountytn.org
Contact: Keith Davidson, Chairman
Released: Quarterly

57667 ■ *Chamber Made News*
PO Box 387
Portland, TN 37148-0387
Ph: (615)325-9032
URL: http://www.portlandtn.com/chamber_of_commerce.htm
Contact: Paul Fuqua, President
Released: Monthly

57668 ■ *Chamber Membership Directory*
PO Box 180
Johnson City, TN 37605
Ph: (423)461-8000
Free: 800-852-3392

Fax: (423)461-8047
Co. E-mail: mentgen@johnsoncitytnchamber.com
URL: http://www.johnsoncitytnchamber.com
Contact: Gary Mabrey, President

57669 ■ *Chamber News*
245 N Main St., Ste. 200
Clinton, TN 37716
Ph: (865)457-2559
Fax: (865)463-7480
Co. E-mail: jackie@andersoncountychamber.org
URL: http://www.andersoncountychamber.org
Contact: Jackie L. Nichols, President
Released: Monthly **Price:** free for members.

57670 ■ *Chamber News*
107 Main St.
Dayton, TN 37321
Ph: (423)775-0361
Fax: (423)570-0105
Co. E-mail: chamber@volstate.net
URL: http://www.daytontnchamber.org
Contact: Lenita Sanders, President
Released: Monthly

57671 ■ *Chamber News*
PO Box 515
Fayetteville, TN 37334
Ph: (931)433-1234
Free: 888-433-1238
Fax: (931)433-9087
Co. E-mail: flcchamber@fpunet.com
URL: http://www.flcchamber.com
Contact: Carolyn Denton, Executive Director
Released: Monthly

57672 ■ *Chamber News*
110 N 2nd St.
Pulaski, TN 38478
Ph: (931)363-3789
Fax: (931)363-7279
Co. E-mail: secretary@gilescountychamber.com
URL: http://www.gilescountychamber.com
Contact: Margaret Campbell, Executive Secretary
Released: Monthly

57673 ■ *Chamber News*
PO Box 355
Spring City, TN 37381-0355
Ph: (423)365-5210
Fax: (423)365-9790
Co. E-mail: info@springcitychamberofcommerce.com
URL: http://www.springcitychamberofcommerce.com
Contact: Jim Reed, President
Released: Monthly

57674 ■ *Chamber Perspective*
City Hall
Franklin, TN 37065-0156
Ph: (615)794-1225
Free: 800-356-3445
Fax: (615)790-5337
Co. E-mail: info@wcfchamber.com
URL: http://www.williamson-franklinchamber.com
Contact: Nancy P. Conway, President
Released: Annual

57675 ■ *The Chamber Prosperity*
22 N Front St., Ste. 200
Memphis, TN 38101-0224
Ph: (901)543-3500
Fax: (901)543-3510
Co. E-mail: info@memphischamber.com
URL: http://welcome.memphischamber.com
Contact: Larry Cox, Chairman of the Board
Released: Monthly

57676 ■ *The Chamber Spirit*
575 S Main St., Ste. 101
Ashland City, TN 37015
Ph: (615)792-6722
Fax: (615)792-5001
Co. E-mail: info@cheathamchamber.org
URL: http://www.cheathamchamber.org
Contact: Ms. Stacey Luna, Executive Assistant
Released: Monthly

57677 ■ *Chamber Voice*
227 2nd Ave. N
Lewisburg, TN 37091
Ph: (931)359-3863
Fax: (931)359-3863
Co. E-mail: office@marshallchamber.org
URL: http://www.marshallchamber.org/business/
chamber
Contact: Eric Michael, President

57678 ■ *Chamber Works*
485 Halle Park Dr.
Collierville, TN 38017
Ph: (901)853-1949
Free: 888-853-1949
Fax: (901)853-2399
Co. E-mail: info@colliervillechamber.com
URL: http://www.colliervillechamber.com
Contact: Fran Persechini, President
Released: Monthly **Price:** free.

57679 ■ Chattanooga Area Chamber of Commerce
811 Broad St.
Chattanooga, TN 37402
Ph: (423)756-2121
Fax: (423)267-7242
Co. E-mail: rharr@chattanoogachamber.com
URL: http://www.chattanoogachamber.com
Contact: Ron Harr, President
Description: Promotes regional business growth that creates prosperity and enhances quality of life.
Awards: Chattanooga Nautilus Awards (Annual); Early Innovator Award (Annual); Kruesi Award for Innovation (Annual); Small Business Award (Annual).

57680 ■ Cheatham County Chamber of Commerce
575 S Main St., Ste. 101
Ashland City, TN 37015
Ph: (615)792-6722
Fax: (615)792-5001
Co. E-mail: info@cheathamchamber.org
URL: http://www.cheathamchamber.org
Contact: Ms. Stacey Luna, Executive Assistant
Description: Promotes business and community development in Cheatham County and Middle Tennessee. **Founded:** 1989. **Publications:** *The Chamber Spirit* (Monthly).

57681 ■ Claiborne County Chamber of Commerce (CCCC)
1732 Main St., Ste. 1
Tazewell, TN 37879
Ph: (423)626-4149
Free: 800-332-8164
Co. E-mail: chamber@claibornecounty.com
URL: http://claibornecounty.com
Contact: Dennis Shipley, Executive Director
Description: Promotes business and community development in Claiborne County, TN. Encourages tourism in the area. **Founded:** 1983.

57682 ■ Clarksville Area Chamber of Commerce
25 Jefferson St., Ste. 300
Clarksville, TN 37040
Ph: (931)245-4333
Free: 800-530-2487
Fax: (931)645-1574
Co. E-mail: cacc@clarksville.tn.us
URL: http://clarksvillechamber.com
Contact: James Chavez, President
Description: Works to enhance the quality of living for Clarksville residents by promoting business and economic development, improving the community's welfare, and representing the interests of its members. **Founded:** 1905.

57683 ■ Clay County Partnership Chamber of Commerce
424 Brown St.
Celina, TN 38551
Ph: (931)243-3338

Fax: (931)243-6809
Co. E-mail: director@dalehollowlake.org
URL: http://www.dalehollowlake.org
Contact: Ray Norris, Executive Director
Description: Promotes business and community development in Celina and Clay County, TN.

57684 ■ Cleveland/Bradley Chamber of Commerce
PO Box 2275
Cleveland, TN 37320-2275
Ph: (423)472-6587
Fax: (423)472-2019
Co. E-mail: info@clevelandchamber.com
URL: http://clevelandchamber.com
Contact: Gary Farlow, President
Publications: *225 Keith* (Monthly).

57685 ■ *Close Up*
503 W Court Sq.
Springfield, TN 37172
Ph: (615)384-3800
Fax: (615)384-1260
Co. E-mail: info@robertsonchamber.org
URL: http://www.robertsonchamber.org
Contact: Margot Fosnes, President
Released: Bimonthly

57686 ■ Collierville Area Chamber of Commerce (CACC)
485 Halle Park Dr.
Collierville, TN 38017
Ph: (901)853-1949
Free: 888-853-1949
Fax: (901)853-2399
Co. E-mail: info@colliervillechamber.com
URL: http://www.colliervillechamber.com
Contact: Fran Persechini, President
Description: Promotes business and community development in the Collierville, TN area. **Founded:** 1984. **Publications:** *Chamber Works* (Monthly); *Collierville Magazine* (Annual); *Collierville Magazine* (Annual). **Awards:** Person of the Year (Annual).

57687 ■ *Collierville Magazine*
485 Halle Park Dr.
Collierville, TN 38017
Ph: (901)853-1949
Free: 888-853-1949
Fax: (901)853-2399
Co. E-mail: info@colliervillechamber.com
URL: http://www.colliervillechamber.com
Contact: Fran Persechini, President
Released: Annual **Price:** free.

57688 ■ *Commerce Connection*
117 N Main St.
Goodlettsville, TN 37072
Ph: (615)859-7979
Fax: (615)859-1480
Co. E-mail: info@goodlettsvillechamber.com
URL: http://www.goodlettsvillechamber.com
Contact: Steve Otto, President
Released: Monthly

57689 ■ Cookeville Area-Putnam County Chamber of Commerce
1 W First St.
Cookeville, TN 38501
Ph: (931)526-2211
Free: 800-264-5541
Fax: (931)526-4023
Co. E-mail: info@cookevillechamber.com
URL: http://www.cookevillechamber.com
Contact: George Halford, President
Description: Promotes business and community development in the Putnam County, TN area and region. **Founded:** 1948.

57690 ■ Crockett County Chamber of Commerce (CCCC)
29 N Bells St.
Alamo, TN 38001
Ph: (731)696-5120

Fax: (731)696-4855
Co. E-mail: contact@crockettchamber.com
URL: http://www.crockettchamber.com
Contact: Diana Hart, Executive Director
Description: Promotes business and community development in Crockett County, TN.

57691 ■ Crossville-Cumberland County Chamber of Commerce
34 S Main St.
Crossville, TN 38555-4518
Ph: (931)484-8444
Free: 877-465-3861
Fax: (931)484-7511
Co. E-mail: thechamber@crossville.com
URL: http://www.crossville-chamber.com
Contact: Beth Alexander, President
Description: Promotes business and community development in Crossville, TN area.

57692 ■ The Daily Times
201 S Washington St.
Maryville, TN 37804
Ph: (865)983-2241
Fax: (865)984-1386
Co. E-mail: info@blountpartnership.com
URL: http://www.blountchamber.com
Contact: Allan Cox, Chairman
Released: Annual

57693 ■ Dayton Chamber of Commerce
107 Main St.
Dayton, TN 37321
Ph: (423)775-0361
Fax: (423)570-0105
Co. E-mail: chamber@volstate.net
URL: http://www.daytontnchamber.org
Contact: Lenita Sanders, President
Description: Strives to promote the advancement of civic, commercial, industrial, recreational, and agricultural interest in Dayton and Rhea County. **Publications:** Chamber News (Monthly).

57694 ■ Decatur County Chamber of Commerce
139 Tennessee Ave. N
Parsons, TN 38363
Ph: (731)847-4202
Fax: (731)847-4222
Co. E-mail: dccc@netease.net
URL: http://decaturcountytennessee.org
Contact: Charles P. Taylor, Sr., Executive Director
Description: Works to improve the economy and quality of life in Decatur County, TN.

57695 ■ Dickson County Chamber of Commerce
119 Hwy. 70 E
Dickson, TN 37055
Ph: (615)446-2349
Fax: (615)441-3112
Co. E-mail: contactus@dicksoncountychamber.com
URL: http://www.dicksoncountychamber.com
Contact: David Hamilton, President

57696 ■ Dyersburg-Dyer County Chamber of Commerce (DDCCC)
2000 Commerce Ave.
Dyersburg, TN 38024
Ph: (731)285-3433
Fax: (731)286-4926
Co. E-mail: chamber@ecsis.net
URL: http://www.dyerchamber.com
Contact: Allen Hester, President
Description: Promotes business and community development in Dyer County, TN. Encourages tourism in the area. **Founded:** 1942. **Publications:** At Work (Periodic). **Educational Activities:** Golf Tournament (Annual). **Awards:** Humanitarian of the Year (Annual); Man of the Year (Annual); Volunteer Diplomat of the Year (Annual); Woman of the Year (Annual).

57697 ■ Elizabethton - Carter County Chamber of Commerce
500 Veteran's Memorial Pkwy.
Elizabethton, TN 37644
Ph: (423)547-3850

Fax: (423)547-3854
Co. E-mail: director@elizabethtonchamber.com
URL: http://www.elizabethtonchamber.com
Contact: Richard Tester, President
URL(s): www.elizabethtonchamber.com. **Description:** Works to promote business and community development in Elizabethton-Carter County, TN area. **Publications:** Naturally Nice News (Monthly); Visitors Guide (Annual); Visitors Guide (Annual). **Awards:** Citizen of the Year (Annual).

57698 ■ Etowah Area Chamber of Commerce
PO Box 458
Etowah, TN 37331-0458
Ph: (423)263-2228
Fax: (423)263-1670
Co. E-mail: info@etowahcoc.org
URL: http://www.etowahcoc.org
Contact: Durant Tullock, Executive Director
Description: Works to promote business and community development in Etowah, TN area.

57699 ■ Fairview Area Chamber of Commerce
7100 City Center Cir.
Fairview, TN 37062
Ph: (615)799-9290
Co. E-mail: dianne@preferredcountry.com
URL: http://www.fairviewchamber.org
Contact: Dianne Ellis, Vice President
Description: Promotes business and community development in Fairview, TN area.

57700 ■ Fayette County Chamber of Commerce
PO Box 411
Somerville, TN 38068
Ph: (901)465-8690
Fax: (901)465-6497
Co. E-mail: info@fayettecountychamber.com
URL: http://www.fayettecountychamber.net
Contact: Barbara Walls, President
Description: Promotes business and community development in Fayette County, TN.

57701 ■ Fayetteville - Lincoln County Chamber of Commerce
PO Box 515
Fayetteville, TN 37334
Ph: (931)433-1234
Free: 888-433-1238
Fax: (931)433-9087
Co. E-mail: flcchamber@fpunet.com
URL: http://www.flcchamber.com
Contact: Carolyn Denton, Executive Director
Description: Promotes business and community development in Fayetteville and Lincoln County, TN area. **Publications:** Chamber News (Monthly).

57702 ■ Fentress County Chamber of Commerce
PO Box 1294
Jamestown, TN 38556
Ph: (931)879-9948
Free: 800-327-3945
Fax: (931)879-6767
Co. E-mail: wpage@jamestowntn.org
URL: http://www.jamestowntn.org
Contact: Kathy Perdue, President
Description: Provides business and community development in the Fentress County, TN area.

57703 ■ Franklin County Chamber of Commerce
44 Chamber Way
Winchester, TN 37398
Ph: (931)967-6788
Fax: (931)967-9418
URL: http://www.franklincountychamber.com
Contact: Judy Taylor, Executive Director
Description: Promotes business and community development in Franklin County, TN.

57704 ■ Gallatin Chamber of Commerce
118 W Main St.
Gallatin, TN 37066
Ph: (615)452-4000

Fax: (615)452-4021
Co. E-mail: info@gallatintn.org
URL: http://www.gallatintn.org
Contact: Paige Brown Strong, Executive Director
Description: Promotes business and community development in Gallatin, TN area.

57705 ■ Gatlinburg Chamber of Commerce
811 East Pkwy.
Gatlinburg, TN 37738
Ph: (865)436-4178
Free: 800-588-1817
Fax: (865)430-3876
Co. E-mail: info@gatlinburg.com
URL: http://www.gatlinburg.com/default.asp
Contact: Vicki Simms, Executive Director
Description: Promotes business and community development in Gatlinburg, TN. **Founded:** 1940.

57706 ■ Germantown Area Chamber of Commerce (GACC)
2195 Germantown Rd. S
Germantown, TN 38138
Ph: (901)755-1200
Fax: (901)755-9168
URL: http://www.germantownchamber.com
Contact: Ms. Pat Scroggs, President
Description: Promotes business and community development in Germantown, TN. Sponsors Business Expo, Taste of the Town, Holiday Tour of Homes and a Healthfest. **Founded:** 1973. **Publications:** Germantown Area Chamber News (Monthly); Germantown Magazine (Annual). **Educational Activities:** Networking at Noon (Monthly). **Awards:** Joe Roberts Award (Annual); New Teacher of the Year (Annual); Plus Scholarship (Annual); Teacher of the Year (Annual).

57707 ■ Germantown Area Chamber News
2195 Germantown Rd. S
Germantown, TN 38138
Ph: (901)755-1200
Fax: (901)755-9168
URL: http://www.germantownchamber.com
Contact: Ms. Pat Scroggs, President
Released: Monthly **Price:** free.

57708 ■ Germantown Magazine
2195 Germantown Rd. S
Germantown, TN 38138
Ph: (901)755-1200
Fax: (901)755-9168
URL: http://www.germantownchamber.com
Contact: Ms. Pat Scroggs, President
Released: Annual **Price:** free.

57709 ■ Giles County Chamber Business Directory
110 N 2nd St.
Pulaski, TN 38478
Ph: (931)363-3789
Fax: (931)363-7279
Co. E-mail: secretary@gilescountychamber.com
URL: http://www.gilescountychamber.com
Contact: Margaret Campbell, Executive Secretary
Released: Quarterly

57710 ■ Giles County Chamber of Commerce
110 N 2nd St.
Pulaski, TN 38478
Ph: (931)363-3789
Fax: (931)363-7279
Co. E-mail: secretary@gilescountychamber.com
URL: http://www.gilescountychamber.com
Contact: Margaret Campbell, Executive Secretary
Description: Strives to create a network to promote, educate and advance business by providing the leadership to generate economic growth and opportunities. **Founded:** 1909. **Publications:** Chamber News (Monthly); Giles County Chamber Business Directory (Quarterly); Giles County Chamber Quality of Life Book (Biennial); Giles County Chamber Business Directory (Quarterly); Giles County Chamber Quality of Life Book (Biennial). **Telecommunication Services:** gilesdirector@bellsouth.net.

57711 ■ *Giles County Chamber Quality of Life Book*
110 N 2nd St.
Pulaski, TN 38478
Ph: (931)363-3789
Fax: (931)363-7279
Co. E-mail: secretary@gilescountychamber.com
URL: http://www.gilescountychamber.com
Contact: Margaret Campbell, Executive Secretary
Released: Biennial

57712 ■ Goodlettsville Area Chamber of Commerce
117 N Main St.
Goodlettsville, TN 37072
Ph: (615)859-7979
Fax: (615)859-1480
Co. E-mail: info@goodlettsvillechamber.com
URL: http://www.goodlettsvillechamber.com
Contact: Steve Otto, President
Description: Promotes business and community development in the Goodlettsville area. **Founded:** 1961. **Publications:** *Commerce Connection* (Monthly).

57713 ■ Greater Gibson County Area Chamber of Commerce
200 E Eaton St.
Trenton, TN 38382
Ph: (731)855-0973
Fax: (731)855-0979
Co. E-mail: info@gibsoncountytn.com
URL: http://www.gibsoncountytn.com/chamber/information.htm
Contact: Tara Bradford, Executive Director
Description: Promotes business and community development in Greater Gibson County, TN.

57714 ■ Greene County Partnership
115 Academy St.
Greeneville, TN 37743-5601
Ph: (423)638-4111
Fax: (423)638-5345
Co. E-mail: tferguson@greenecop.com
URL: http://www.greenecountypartnership.com/home.aspx
Contact: Tom R. Ferguson, President
Description: Strives to promote, preserve, and enhance the quality of life and economic well being of all Greene Countians by providing collective leadership and serving as a facilitator, catalyst, and unifying force to achieve common community goals. **Founded:** 1993. **Publications:** *Business Directory*; *Partners* (Biweekly).

57715 ■ *Guidebook and Directory*
245 N Main St., Ste. 200
Clinton, TN 37716
Ph: (865)457-2559
Fax: (865)463-7480
Co. E-mail: jackie@andersoncountychamber.org
URL: http://www.andersoncountychamber.org
Contact: Jackie L. Nichols, President
Released: Biennial

57716 ■ Hardeman County Chamber of Commerce
500 W Market St.
Bolivar, TN 38008
Ph: (731)658-6554
Fax: (731)658-6874
Co. E-mail: infohccc@bellsouth.com
URL: http://hardemancountytn.com/chamber
Contact: Rob Jensik, Executive Director
Description: Promotes business and community development in Hardeman County, TN. **Founded:** 1940. **Publications:** *The Chamber Community News* (Bimonthly). **Educational Activities:** Chamber Community Coffee (Monthly).

57717 ■ Hartsville - Trousdale County Chamber of Commerce
240 Broadway
Hartsville, TN 37074-1336
Ph: (615)374-9243

Fax: (615)374-9243
Co. E-mail: jimfalco@hartsvilletrousdale.com
URL: http://www.hartsvilletrousdale.com
Contact: Natalie Knudsen, Executive Director
Description: Promotes business and community development in the Hartsville, TN area.

57718 ■ Henderson Chester County Chamber of Commerce
130 E Main St.
Henderson, TN 38340
Ph: (731)989-5222
Fax: (731)983-5518
Co. E-mail: khester@chestercountychamber.com
URL: http://www.chestercountychamber.com
Contact: Emily Shelton, Executive Director
Description: Promotes business and community development in Chester County, TN. **Founded:** 1976.

57719 ■ Henderson County Chamber of Commerce (HCCC)
149 Eastern Shores Dr.
Lexington, TN 38351
Ph: (731)968-2126
Fax: (731)968-7006
Co. E-mail: info@hctn.org
URL: http://www.hctn.org
Contact: Vicki Bunch, Executive Director
Description: Promotes business and community development in Henderson County, TN. **Founded:** 1983.

57720 ■ Hendersonville Area Chamber of Commerce
100 Country Club Dr., Ste. 104
Hendersonville, TN 37075
Ph: (615)824-2818
Fax: (615)250-3637
Co. E-mail: info@hendersonvillechamber.com
URL: http://www.hendersonvillechamber.com
Contact: Brenda Payne, President
Description: Promotes business and community development in Hendersonville, TN. **Founded:** 1970. **Publications:** *Portrait of Hendersonville* (Semiannual); *Preferred Business Directory* (Annual); *It's All About Business* (Monthly).

57721 ■ Hickman County Chamber of Commerce (HCCC)
c/o Nancy Roland, Exec. Dir.
405 W Public Sq.
Centerville, TN 37033
Ph: (931)729-5774
URL: http://www.hickmanco.org
Contact: Nancy Roland, Executive Director
Description: Promotes business and community development in Hickman County, TN. Sponsors annual Duck River Music and Arts Festival, Business Appreciation Day, Semi-Annual Countywide Yard Sales and various seminars.

57722 ■ Hohenwald-Lewis County Tennessee Chamber of Commerce
106 N Court St.
Hohenwald, TN 38462
Ph: (931)796-4084
Fax: (931)796-6020
URL: http://www.hohenwaldlewischamber.com
Description: Assures economic growth and opportunities; creates a network of business, industrial, and professional leaders; and enhances community's quality of life.

57723 ■ Humboldt Chamber of Commerce
1200 Main St.
Humboldt, TN 38343
Ph: (731)784-1842
Fax: (731)784-1573
Co. E-mail: sherri@humboldttnchamber.org
URL: http://www.humboldttnchamber.org
Contact: Sherri McCarter, Executive Director
Description: Promotes business and community development in the Humboldt, TN area. **Founded:** 1905.

57724 ■ Humphreys County Area Chamber of Commerce
PO Box 733
Waverly, TN 37185

Ph: (931)296-4865
Free: 877-296-4865
Fax: (931)899-1999
Co. E-mail: hcchamber@bellsouth.net
URL: http://www.hereyaare.com
Contact: Shirley Marrs, President
Description: Promotes business and community development in Humphreys County, TN.

57725 ■ *Industrial Directory*
PO Box 9
Morristown, TN 37815
Ph: (423)586-6382
Fax: (423)586-6576
Co. E-mail: macc@morristownchamber.com
URL: http://www.morristownchamber.com
Contact: C. Thomas Robinson, President
Released: Annual

57726 ■ *Industrial Relations Bulletin*
611 Commerce St., Ste. 3030
Nashville, TN 37203-3742
Ph: (615)256-5141
Fax: (615)256-6726
Co. E-mail: info@tnchamber.org
URL: http://www.tnchamber.org
Contact: Deborah K. Woolley, President
Released: Monthly

57727 ■ *Industrial Reporter*
611 Commerce St., Ste. 3030
Nashville, TN 37203-3742
Ph: (615)256-5141
Fax: (615)256-6726
Co. E-mail: info@tnchamber.org
URL: http://www.tnchamber.org
Contact: Deborah K. Woolley, President

57728 ■ *It's All About Business*
100 Country Club Dr., Ste. 104
Hendersonville, TN 37075
Ph: (615)824-2818
Fax: (615)250-3637
Co. E-mail: info@hendersonvillechamber.com
URL: http://www.hendersonvillechamber.com
Contact: Brenda Payne, President
Released: Monthly

57729 ■ Jackson Area Chamber of Commerce
PO Box 1904
Jackson, TN 38302-1904
Ph: (731)423-2200
Fax: (731)424-4860
Co. E-mail: chamber@jacksontn.com
URL: http://jacksontn.com
Contact: Bobby Arnold, Chairman of the Board
Description: Aims to develop and maintain an economic climate that creates and retains jobs and enhances the quality of life for all citizens of Jackson-Madison County and West Tennessee. **Founded:** 1905.

57730 ■ Jefferson County Chamber of Commerce
PO Box 890
Dandridge, TN 37725
Ph: (865)397-9642
Fax: (865)397-0164
Co. E-mail: Info@jeffersoncountytennessee.com
URL: http://www.jefferson-tn-chamber.org
Contact: Daryle Keck, Chairman of the Board
Description: Promotes business and community development in the Jefferson County, TN area.

57731 ■ *Johnson City Business Magazine*
PO Box 180
Johnson City, TN 37605
Ph: (423)461-8000
Free: 800-852-3392
Fax: (423)461-8047
Co. E-mail: mentgen@johnsoncitytnchamber.com
URL: http://www.johnsoncitytnchamber.com
Contact: Gary Mabrey, President

57732 ■ Johnson City - Jonesboro - Washington County Chamber of Commerce (JCJWCCC)
PO Box 180
Johnson City, TN 37605
Ph: (423)461-8000
Free: 800-852-3392
Fax: (423)461-8047
Co. E-mail: mentgen@johnsoncitytnchamber.com
URL: http://www.johnsoncitytnchamber.com
Contact: Gary Mabrey, President
Description: Promotes business and community development in Johnson City, Washington County, and northeastern TN. **Founded:** 1915. **Publications:** *Chamber Membership Directory*; *Johnson City Business Magazine*. **Telecommunication Services:** mabrey@johnsoncitytnchamber.com.

57733 ■ Johnson County Chamber of Commerce (JCCC)
PO Box 66
Mountain City, TN 37683
Ph: (423)727-5800
Fax: (423)727-4943
Co. E-mail: info@johnsoncountychamber.org
URL: http://www.johnsoncountychamber.org
Contact: David Sexton, President
Description: Promotes business and community development in Mountain City, TN. Operates Johnson County Welcome Center; sponsors annual Burley Festival.

57734 ■ Kingsport Area Chamber of Commerce
400 Clinchfield St., Ste. 100
Kingsport, TN 37660
Ph: (423)392-8800
Fax: (423)392-8834
Co. E-mail: kchamber@kingsportchamber.org
URL: http://www.kingsportchamber.org
Contact: Miles A. Burdine, President
Description: Provides business and community development in the Kingsport, TN area. **Awards:** Santa Train Scholarship (Annual).

57735 ■ Knoxville Area Chamber Partnership
17 Market Sq., No. 201
Knoxville, TN 37902
Ph: (865)637-4550
Fax: (865)523-2071
Co. E-mail: partnership@knoxvillechamber.com
URL: http://www.knoxvillechamber.com
Contact: Mitch Steenrod, Chairman
Description: Provides business and community development in the Knoxville, TN area. **Publications:** *Partners* (Monthly); *Regional Manufacturers Directory*. **Educational Activities:** Food for Thought (Periodic). **Telecommunication Services:** medwards@knoxvillechamber.com.

57736 ■ *Knoxville News Sentinel*
201 S Washington St.
Maryville, TN 37804
Ph: (865)983-2241
Fax: (865)984-1386
Co. E-mail: info@blountpartnership.com
URL: http://www.blountchamber.com
Contact: Allan Cox, Chairman
Released: Annual

57737 ■ Lauderdale County Chamber of Commerce
123 S Jefferson Ave.
Ripley, TN 38063
Ph: (731)635-9541
Fax: (731)635-9064
Co. E-mail: info@lauderdalecountytn.org
URL: http://www.lauderdalecountytn.org
Contact: Keith Davidson, Chairman
Description: Promotes business and community development in Lauderdale County, TN. **Publications:** *Chamber Connection* (Quarterly). **Telecommunication Services:** lhankins@lauderdalecountytn.org.

57738 ■ Lawrence County Chamber of Commerce
PO Box 86
Lawrenceburg, TN 38464
Ph: (931)762-4911
Free: 877-388-4911
Fax: (931)762-3153
Co. E-mail: info@selectlawrence.com
URL: http://www.selectlawrence.com
Contact: Daniel Webb, President
Description: Local industry, businesses and citizens. Promotes business and community development in Lawrence County. **Awards:** Citizen of the Year Award (Annual).

57739 ■ Lebanon/Wilson County Chamber of Commerce
149 Public Sq.
Lebanon, TN 37087-2736
Ph: (615)444-5503
Fax: (615)443-0596
URL: http://www.lebanonwilsontnchamber.org
Contact: Danny Stewart, Chairman
Description: Promotes business and community development in Lebanon-Wilson County, TN.

57740 ■ *Legislative Report*
611 Commerce St., Ste. 3030
Nashville, TN 37203-3742
Ph: (615)256-5141
Fax: (615)256-6726
Co. E-mail: info@tnchamber.org
URL: http://www.tnchamber.org
Contact: Deborah K. Woolley, President
Released: Weekly

57741 ■ Livingston - Overton County Chamber of Commerce
PO Box 354
Livingston, TN 38570
Ph: (931)823-6421
Free: 800-876-7393
Fax: (931)823-6422
Co. E-mail: chamber@twlakes.net
URL: http://www.overtonco.com
Contact: John Roberts, Director
Description: Promotes business and community development in Livingston-Overton County, TN. **Founded:** 1967.

57742 ■ Loudon County Chamber of Commerce (LCCC)
318 Angel Row
Loudon, TN 37774
Ph: (865)458-2067
Fax: (865)458-1206
Co. E-mail: info@loudoncountychamber.com
URL: http://www.loudoncountychamberofcommerce.com
Contact: Chip Miller, Chairman
Description: Seeks to develop and maintain a favorable business climate in Loudon County, TN and to provide leadership in the development of economic growth and quality of life. **Founded:** 1988. **Publications:** *The Business Link* (Monthly); *Loudon County Living Membership Guide* (Annual).

57743 ■ *Loudon County Living Membership Guide*
318 Angel Row
Loudon, TN 37774
Ph: (865)458-2067
Fax: (865)458-1206
Co. E-mail: info@loudoncountychamber.com
URL: http://www.loudoncountychamberofcommerce.com
Contact: Chip Miller, Chairman
Released: Annual

57744 ■ Lynchburg - Moore County Chamber of Commerce
PO Box 421
Lynchburg, TN 37352

Ph: (931)759-4111
Co. E-mail: info@lynchburgtn.com
URL: http://www.lynchburgtn.com
Contact: Woodye Bedford, President
Description: Promotes business and community development in Lynchburg-Moore County, TN.

57745 ■ Macon County Chamber of Commerce
685 Hwy. 52 BYP W
Lafayette, TN 37083
Ph: (615)666-5885
Fax: (615)666-6969
Co. E-mail: mchamber@nctc.com
URL: http://www.maconcountychamber.com
Description: Promotes business and community development in Macon County Lafayette, TN area.

57746 ■ Manchester Area Chamber of Commerce
110 E Main St.
Manchester, TN 37355
Ph: (931)728-7635
Fax: (931)723-0736
Co. E-mail: manchestercoc@macoc.org
URL: http://www.macoc.org
Contact: Bill Nickels, President
Description: Works to advance the commercial, industrial, and civic interests of Manchester and its trade area.

57747 ■ Marion County Chamber of Commerce
302 Betsy Pack Dr.
Jasper, TN 37347-3316
Ph: (423)942-5103
Fax: (423)942-0098
Co. E-mail: marioncoc@bellsouth.net
URL: http://www.marioncountychamber.com
Contact: Kevin Merrell, President
Description: Promotes business and community development in Marion County, TN area. **Publications:** *Chamber Chatter* (Bimonthly).

57748 ■ Marshall County Chamber of Commerce
227 2nd Ave. N
Lewisburg, TN 37091
Ph: (931)359-3863
Fax: (931)359-3863
Co. E-mail: office@marshallchamber.org
URL: http://www.marshallchamber.org/business/chamber
Contact: Eric Michael, President
Description: Promotes business and community development in Marshall County, TN. **Founded:** 1920. **Publications:** *Chamber Voice*.

57749 ■ Maury Alliance
106 W 6th St.
Columbia, TN 38402
Ph: (931)388-2155
Fax: (931)380-0335
Co. E-mail: khuckaby@mauryalliance.com
URL: http://www.mauryalliance.com
Contact: Kara Huckaby, Director
Description: Promotes business and community development in Columbia, TN area. **Publications:** *Alliance Membership Directory* (Annual).

57750 ■ McMinnville - Warren County Chamber of Commerce
PO Box 574
McMinnville, TN 37111
Ph: (931)473-6611
Fax: (931)473-4741
Co. E-mail: warrencotn@blomand.net
URL: http://www.warrentn.com
Contact: Bobby Cox, Chairman of the Board
Description: Promotes business and community development in McMinnville-Warren County, TN.

57751 ■ Memphis Regional Chamber of Commerce
22 N Front St., Ste. 200
Memphis, TN 38101-0224
Ph: (901)543-3500

Fax: (901)543-3510
Co. E-mail: info@memphischamber.com
URL: http://welcome.memphischamber.com
Contact: Larry Cox, Chairman of the Board
Description: Works to establish the Memphis region as a dynamic, growing, energetic metropolitan region strongly connected to the global marketplace. **Founded:** 1838. **Publications:** *The Chamber Prosperity* (Monthly).

57752 ■ **Millington Chamber of Commerce**
7743 Church St.
Millington, TN 38053
Ph: (901)872-1486
Fax: (901)872-0727
Co. E-mail: info@millingtonchamber.com
URL: http://www.millingtonchamber.com
Contact: Chris Murphy, Chairman
Description: Promotes business and community development in Millington, TN.

57753 ■ *Monday Morning Report*
211 Commerce St., Ste. 100
Nashville, TN 37201-1806
Ph: (615)743-3000
Fax: (615)743-3002
Co. E-mail: eboylan@nashvillechamber.com
URL: http://www.nashvillechamber.com
Contact: Ralph Schulz, President
E-mail: rschulz@nashvillechamber.com
Released: Weekly

57754 ■ **Monroe County Chamber of Commerce**
520 Cook St., Ste. A
Madisonville, TN 37354
Ph: (423)442-4588
Fax: (423)442-9016
Co. E-mail: info@monroecountychamber.org
URL: http://www.monroecountychamber.org
Contact: Mitch Millsaps, Chairman of the Board
Description: Promotes business and community development in Monroe County, TN.

57755 ■ **Monteagle Mountain Chamber of Commerce**
PO Box 353
Monteagle, TN 37356-0353
Ph: (931)924-5353
Fax: (931)924-5354
Co. E-mail: info@monteaglechamber.com
URL: http://www.monteaglechamber.com
Contact: Rhonda Pilkington, Executive Director
Description: Promotes economic growth and business development and strengthens cooperation and interaction of the various communities of Monteagle Mountain.

57756 ■ *Monthly Perspective*
City Hall
Franklin, TN 37065-0156
Ph: (615)794-1225
Free: 800-356-3445
Fax: (615)790-5337
Co. E-mail: info@wcfchamber.com
URL: http://www.williamson-franklinchamber.com
Contact: Nancy P. Conway, President
Released: Monthly

57757 ■ *Morristimes*
PO Box 9
Morristown, TN 37815
Ph: (423)586-6382
Fax: (423)586-6576
Co. E-mail: macc@morristownchamber.com
URL: http://www.morristownchamber.com
Contact: C. Thomas Robinson, President

57758 ■ **Morristown Area Chamber of Commerce (MACC)**
PO Box 9
Morristown, TN 37815
Ph: (423)586-6382

Fax: (423)586-6576
Co. E-mail: macc@morristownchamber.com
URL: http://www.morristownchamber.com
Contact: C. Thomas Robinson, President
Description: Promotes business and community development in Hamblen County, TN. **Founded:** 1911. **Publications:** *Industrial Directory* (Annual); *Morristimes*; *Morristown Magazine* (Periodic). **Awards:** Industrial Appreciation Awards (Annual); Meritorious Service Awards (Annual); The R. Jack Fishman Community Service Award (Annual); Small Business Awards of Excellence/Horizon Award (Annual).

57759 ■ *Morristown Magazine*
PO Box 9
Morristown, TN 37815
Ph: (423)586-6382
Fax: (423)586-6576
Co. E-mail: macc@morristownchamber.com
URL: http://www.morristownchamber.com
Contact: C. Thomas Robinson, President
Released: Periodic

57760 ■ **Mount Juliet - West Wilson County Chamber of Commerce**
46 W Caldwell St.
Mount Juliet, TN 37122
Ph: (615)758-3478
Fax: (615)754-8595
Co. E-mail: aspicer@tds.net
URL: http://www.mtjulietchamber.com
Contact: Mark Hinesley, President
Description: Promotes business and community development in the Mt. Juliet and West Wilson County, TN area. Conducts charitable programs; sponsors festival. **Founded:** 1963.

57761 ■ **Nashville Area Chamber of Commerce**
211 Commerce St., Ste. 100
Nashville, TN 37201-1806
Ph: (615)743-3000
Fax: (615)743-3002
Co. E-mail: eboylan@nashvillechamber.com
URL: http://www.nashvillechamber.com
Contact: Ralph Schulz, President
E-mail: rschulz@nashvillechamber.com
Description: Provides leadership that fosters growth and prosperity by ensuring the Nashville/Music City region is the best place to operate and grow a business, as well as the most desirable place to live, work, play and visit. **Founded:** 1847. **Publications:** *Monday Morning Report* (Weekly); *Return on Investment* (Quarterly); *Tennessee Manufacturers Directory*; *In Business for Yourself*; *Nashville Health Care Guide*; *Nashville Music Business Directory*; *Religious Resource Guide*; *Tennessee State Chambers Directory*; *Business and Professional Organizations Directory*; *Civic and Service Organizations Directory*; *Tennessee Business Services Directory*. **Telecommunication Services:** info@nashvillechamber.com.

57762 ■ *Naturally Nice News*
500 Veteran's Memorial Pkwy.
Elizabethton, TN 37644
Ph: (423)547-3850
Fax: (423)547-3854
Co. E-mail: director@elizabethtonchamber.com
URL: http://www.elizabethtonchamber.com
Contact: Richard Tester, President
Released: Monthly

57763 ■ **Newport/Cocke County Chamber of Commerce**
433-B Prospect Ave.
Newport, TN 37821
Ph: (423)623-7201
Fax: (423)623-7216
Co. E-mail: lramsey@cockecountypartnership.com
URL: http://www.cockecounty.org
Description: Promotes business and community development in Newport - Cocke County, TN.

57764 ■ **Oak Ridge Chamber of Commerce**
1400 Oak Ridge Tpke.
Oak Ridge, TN 37830
Ph: (865)483-1321

Fax: (865)483-1678
Co. E-mail: ownby@orcc.org
URL: http://www.oakridgechamber.org
Contact: David Bradshaw, Chairman of the Board
Description: Promotes business and community development in Oak Ridge, TN. **Publications:** *acorn* (Monthly); *Ridges* (Semiannual).

57765 ■ **Obion County Chamber of Commerce**
214 E Church St.
Union City, TN 38261
Ph: (731)885-0211
Free: 877-885-0211
Fax: (731)885-7155
Co. E-mail: lfrilling@obioncounty.org
URL: http://www.obioncounty.org/chamber
Contact: Dan Weber, President
Description: Promotes business and community development in Obion County, TN. **Founded:** 1922.

57766 ■ **Paris/Henry County Chamber of Commerce**
2508 E Wood St.
Paris, TN 38242
Ph: (731)642-3431
Free: 800-345-1103
Fax: (731)642-3454
Co. E-mail: pariscoc@paristnchamber.com
URL: http://www.paristnchamber.com
Contact: Jeff Seaton, President
Description: Works to improve the economy and quality of life in Paris-Henry County, TN.

57767 ■ *Partners*
115 Academy St.
Greeneville, TN 37743-5601
Ph: (423)638-4111
Fax: (423)638-5345
Co. E-mail: tferguson@greenecop.com
URL: http://www.greenecountypartnership.com/home.aspx
Contact: Tom R. Ferguson, President
Released: Biweekly **Price:** included in membership dues.

57768 ■ *Partners*
17 Market Sq., No. 201
Knoxville, TN 37902
Ph: (865)637-4550
Fax: (865)523-2071
Co. E-mail: partnership@knoxvillechamber.com
URL: http://www.knoxvillechamber.com
Contact: Mitch Steenrod, Chairman
Released: Monthly

57769 ■ **Pigeon Forge Chamber of Commerce**
247 LaFollette Cir.
Pigeon Forge, TN 37863-3207
Ph: (865)453-5700
Free: 800-221-9858
Co. E-mail: pifchamber@kmsfia.com
URL: http://www.pigeonforgechamber.com
Description: Works to improve the economy and quality of life in Pigeon Forge, TN.

57770 ■ **Pikeville - Bledsoe County Chamber of Commerce**
PO Box 205
Pikeville, TN 37367
Ph: (423)447-2791
Co. E-mail: directors@pikeville-bledsoe.com
URL: http://www.pikeville-bledsoe.com
Contact: Deena Swafford, Chairperson
Description: Works to improve the economy and quality of life in Pikeville-Bledsoe County, TN.

57771 ■ **Portland Chamber of Commerce (PCC)**
PO Box 387
Portland, TN 37148-0387
Ph: (615)325-9032
URL: http://www.portlandtn.com/chamber_of_commerce.htm
Contact: Paul Fuqua, President
Description: Promotes business and community development in Portland, TN. **Founded:** 1962. **Publications:** *Chamber Made News* (Monthly).

57772 ■ *Portrait of Hendersonville*
100 Country Club Dr., Ste. 104
Hendersonville, TN 37075
Ph: (615)824-2818
Fax: (615)250-3637
Co. E-mail: info@hendersonvillechamber.com
URL: http://www.hendersonvillechamber.com
Contact: Brenda Payne, President
Released: Semiannual

57773 ■ *Preferred Business Directory*
100 Country Club Dr., Ste. 104
Hendersonville, TN 37075
Ph: (615)824-2818
Fax: (615)250-3637
Co. E-mail: info@hendersonvillechamber.com
URL: http://www.hendersonvillechamber.com
Contact: Brenda Payne, President
Released: Annual

57774 ■ *Report to the Community*
3050 Medical Center Pkwy.
Murfreesboro, TN 37129-3943
Ph: (615)893-6565
Free: 800-716-7560
Fax: (615)890-7600
Co. E-mail: info@rutherfordchamber.org
URL: http://www.rutherfordchamber.org
Contact: Paul Latture, President

57775 ■ *Return on Investment*
211 Commerce St., Ste. 100
Nashville, TN 37201-1806
Ph: (615)743-3000
Fax: (615)743-3002
Co. E-mail: eboylan@nashvillechamber.com
URL: http://www.nashvillechamber.com
Contact: Ralph Schulz, President
E-mail: rschulz@nashvillechamber.com
Released: Quarterly; except July and December.
Price: included in membership dues.

57776 ■ *Ridges*
1400 Oak Ridge Tpke.
Oak Ridge, TN 37830
Ph: (865)483-1321
Fax: (865)483-1678
Co. E-mail: ownby@orcc.org
URL: http://www.oakridgechamber.org
Contact: David Bradshaw, Chairman of the Board
Released: Semiannual

**57777 ■ Roane County Chamber of
Commerce, Tennessee**
1209 N Kentucky St.
Kingston, TN 37763
Ph: (865)376-5572
Fax: (865)376-4978
Co. E-mail: tourism@roanealliance.org
URL: http://www.roanealliance.org
Contact: Kenyon Mee, Chairman
Description: Promotes business and community
development in Roane County, TN. **Founded:** 1956.

**57778 ■ Rutherford County Chamber of
Commerce**
3050 Medical Center Pkwy.
Murfreesboro, TN 37129-3943
Ph: (615)893-6565
Free: 800-716-7560
Fax: (615)890-7600
Co. E-mail: info@rutherfordchamber.org
URL: http://www.rutherfordchamber.org
Contact: Paul Latture, President
Description: Works to advance the commercial,
industrial, and civic interests of Rutherford County.
Founded: 1928. **Publications:** *Business Pulse*
(Monthly); *Report to the Community*. **Awards:** Business Legend of the Year (Annual); Business Person
of the Year (Annual).

**57779 ■ Scott County Chamber of Commerce
(SCCC)**
12025 Scott Hwy.
Helenwood, TN 37755-5248
Ph: (423)663-6900
Free: 800-645-6905

Fax: (423)663-6906
Co. E-mail: info@scottcountychamber.com
URL: http://www.scottcountychamber.com
Contact: Wayne King, President
Description: Promotes business and community
development in Scott County, TN. **Founded:** 1954.

57780 ■ Sevierville Chamber of Commerce
110 Gary Wade Blvd.
Sevierville, TN 37862
Ph: (865)453-6411
Free: 888-738-4378
Fax: (865)453-9649
Co. E-mail: info@seviervillechamber.com
URL: http://www.scoc.org
Contact: Allen Robins, Chairman
Description: Dedicated to the promotion of tourism,
industry and economic growth while preserving the
history and heritage of Sevierville and Sevier County.
Founded: 1963. **Publications:** *Sevierville Chamber
Newsletter* (5/year); *Sevierville Group Tour Planner*
(Annual); *Sevierville Marketing Plan*; *Smoky Mountain
Coupon Book* (Annual); *Smoky Mountain Wedding
Planner* (Annual).

57781 ■ *Sevierville Chamber Newsletter*
110 Gary Wade Blvd.
Sevierville, TN 37862
Ph: (865)453-6411
Free: 888-738-4378
Fax: (865)453-9649
Co. E-mail: info@seviervillechamber.com
URL: http://www.scoc.org
Contact: Allen Robins, Chairman
Released: 5/year

57782 ■ *Sevierville Group Tour Planner*
110 Gary Wade Blvd.
Sevierville, TN 37862
Ph: (865)453-6411
Free: 888-738-4378
Fax: (865)453-9649
Co. E-mail: info@seviervillechamber.com
URL: http://www.scoc.org
Contact: Allen Robins, Chairman
Released: Annual

57783 ■ *Sevierville Marketing Plan*
110 Gary Wade Blvd.
Sevierville, TN 37862
Ph: (865)453-6411
Free: 888-738-4378
Fax: (865)453-9649
Co. E-mail: info@seviervillechamber.com
URL: http://www.scoc.org
Contact: Allen Robins, Chairman

**57784 ■ Shelbyville-Bedford County
Chamber of Commerce (SBCCC)**
100 N Cannon Blvd.
Shelbyville, TN 37160
Ph: (931)684-3482
Free: 888-662-2525
Fax: (931)684-3483
Co. E-mail: bedfordchamber@bellsouth.net
URL: http://www.shelbyvilletn.com
Contact: Walter W. Wood, Chief Executive Officer
Description: Promotes business and community
development in Shelbyville-Bedford County, TN. **Publications:** *Walk With Us* (Quarterly).

**57785 ■ Smith County Chamber of
Commerce**
939 Upper Ferry Rd.
Carthage, TN 37030
Ph: (615)735-2093
Co. E-mail: info@smithcountychamber.org
URL: http://www.smithcountychamber.org
Contact: Denise Hackett, Executive Director
Description: Works to promote and support economic, civic, commercial, industrial and educational
interest and the welfare of the area. **Founded:** 1974.

**57786 ■ Smithville - DeKalb County Chamber
of Commerce**
c/o Suzanne Williams, Exec. Dir.
PO Box 64
Smithville, TN 37166
Ph: (615)597-4163

Fax: (615)597-4164
Co. E-mail: chamber@dekalbtn.com
URL: http://www.smithvilletn.com
Contact: Suzanne Williams, Executive Director
Description: Promotes economic development,
education, recreation and culture, and safety and
respect in Smithville-DeKalb County, TN.

57787 ■ *Smoky Mountain Coupon Book*
110 Gary Wade Blvd.
Sevierville, TN 37862
Ph: (865)453-6411
Free: 888-738-4378
Fax: (865)453-9649
Co. E-mail: info@seviervillechamber.com
URL: http://www.scoc.org
Contact: Allen Robins, Chairman
Released: Annual

57788 ■ *Smoky Mountain Wedding Planner*
110 Gary Wade Blvd.
Sevierville, TN 37862
Ph: (865)453-6411
Free: 888-738-4378
Fax: (865)453-9649
Co. E-mail: info@seviervillechamber.com
URL: http://www.scoc.org
Contact: Allen Robins, Chairman
Released: Annual

**57789 ■ South Tipton County Chamber of
Commerce**
PO Box 1198
Munford, TN 38058
Ph: (901)837-4600
Fax: (901)837-4602
Co. E-mail: chamber@southtipton.com
URL: http://www.southtipton.com
Contact: Rosemary Bridges, President
Description: Promotes business and community
development in South Tipton County, TN.

**57790 ■ Sparta - White County Chamber of
Commerce**
16 W Bockman Way
Sparta, TN 38583
Ph: (931)836-3552
Fax: (931)836-2216
Co. E-mail: sparta-chamber@charter.net
URL: http://www.sparta-chamber.net
Contact: Wallace G. Austin, President
Description: Promotes business and community
development in Sparta-White County, TN.

57791 ■ Spring City Chamber of Commerce
PO Box 355
Spring City, TN 37381-0355
Ph: (423)365-5210
Fax: (423)365-9790
Co. E-mail: info@springcitychamberofcommerce.com
URL: http://www.springcitychamberofcommerce.com
Contact: Jim Reed, President
Description: Promotes business and community
development. Preserves the competitive enterprise
system and represents member businesses in city,
county, and state affairs. **Scope:** state and national
economic indicators, state and local events and attractions. **Founded:** 1962. **Subscriptions:** 20 books
periodicals. **Publications:** *Chamber News* (Monthly).
Awards: Lucille Maybery Community Service (Annual).

57792 ■ Spring Hill Chamber of Commerce
PO Box 1815
Spring Hill, TN 37174
Ph: (931)486-0625
Co. E-mail: info@springhillchamber.com
URL: http://www.springhillchamber.com
Contact: Elizabeth Mefford, Secretary
Description: Works to provide networking and
marketing opportunities while providing access to
economic development assistance. Serves as a link
between the local businesses, their peers and the
community.

**57793 ■ Springfield - Robertson County
Chamber of Commerce**
503 W Court Sq.
Springfield, TN 37172

Ph: (615)384-3800
Fax: (615)384-1260
Co. E-mail: info@robertsonchamber.org
URL: http://www.robertsonchamber.org
Contact: Margot Fosnes, President
Description: Advances the economic, civic, social, cultural, and general interests of the City of Springfield, and the County of Robertson and the trade area. **Publications:** *Close Up* (Bimonthly). **Educational Activities:** Good Morning Robertson County (Monthly).

57794 ■ Stewart County Chamber of Commerce (SCCC)
117 Moore Rd.
Dover, TN 37058-0147
Ph: (931)232-8290
Fax: (931)232-4973
Co. E-mail: stewartcountycha@bellsouth.net
URL: http://www.stewartcountychamberofcommerce.com
Contact: Patty Page, President
Description: Promotes business and community development in Stewart County, TN. Sponsors festival.

57795 ■ Tennessee Chamber of Commerce and Industry
611 Commerce St., Ste. 3030
Nashville, TN 37203-3742
Ph: (615)256-5141
Fax: (615)256-6726
Co. E-mail: info@tnchamber.org
URL: http://www.tnchamber.org
Contact: Deborah K. Woolley, President
Description: Represents the interests of business. Lobbies on their behalf. Sponsors workshops and seminars. **Founded:** 1912. **Publications:** *Industrial Relations Bulletin* (Monthly); *Industrial Reporter*; *Legislative Report* (Weekly).

57796 ■ Tullahoma Area Chamber of Commerce
PO Box 1205
Tullahoma, TN 37388
Ph: (931)455-5497
Fax: (931)455-5350
Co. E-mail: tullahomachamber@tullahoma.org
URL: http://www.tullahoma.org
Contact: Renee Keene, President
Description: Promotes business and community development in Tullahoma, TN.

57797 ■ Unicoi County Chamber of Commerce
PO Box 713
Erwin, TN 37650
Ph: (423)743-3000
Co. E-mail: amanda@unicoicounty.org
URL: http://www.unicoicounty.org
Contact: Amanda Delp, Executive Director
Description: Promotes business and community development in Unicoi County, TN area.

57798 ■ *Visitors Guide*
500 Veteran's Memorial Pkwy.
Elizabethton, TN 37644
Ph: (423)547-3850
Fax: (423)547-3854
Co. E-mail: director@elizabethtonchamber.com
URL: http://www.elizabethtonchamber.com
Contact: Richard Tester, President
Released: Annual

57799 ■ *Walk With Us*
100 N Cannon Blvd.
Shelbyville, TN 37160
Ph: (931)684-3482
Free: 888-662-2525
Fax: (931)684-3483
Co. E-mail: bedfordchamber@bellsouth.net
URL: http://www.shelbyvilletn.com
Contact: Walter W. Wood, Chief Executive Officer
Released: Quarterly

57800 ■ Wayne County Chamber of Commerce
PO Box 574
Waynesboro, TN 38485

Ph: (931)722-3575
Fax: (931)724-4347
Co. E-mail: chamber@netease.net
URL: http://www.waynecountychamber.org
Contact: Rena Bolitho Purdy, Executive Director
Description: Promotes business, tourism and community in Wayne County TN. **Founded:** 1980. **Awards:** Person of the Year (Annual); Volunteer of the Year (Annual).

57801 ■ White House Area Chamber of Commerce (WCC)
414 Hwy. 76
White House, TN 37188-0521
Ph: (615)672-3937
Fax: (615)672-2828
Co. E-mail: whcoc@bellsouth.net
URL: http://www.whitehousechamber.org
Contact: Ms. Julie Bolton, Executive Director
Description: Promotes business and community development in White House, TN and surrounding area. Sponsors various community events. **Founded:** 1984.

57802 ■ Williamson County - Franklin Chamber of Commerce
City Hall
Franklin, TN 37065-0156
Ph: (615)794-1225
Free: 800-356-3445
Fax: (615)790-5337
Co. E-mail: info@wcfchamber.com
URL: http://www.williamson-franklinchamber.com
Contact: Nancy P. Conway, President
Description: Promotes business and community development in Franklin, TN area. **Publications:** *Chamber Perspective* (Annual); *Monthly Perspective* (Monthly); *Williamson County Magazine* (Annual); *Williamson County Magazine* (Annual). **Educational Activities:** Williamson County - Franklin Chamber of Commerce Luncheon (Monthly).

57803 ■ *Williamson County Magazine*
City Hall
Franklin, TN 37065-0156
Ph: (615)794-1225
Free: 800-356-3445
Fax: (615)790-5337
Co. E-mail: info@wcfchamber.com
URL: http://www.williamson-franklinchamber.com
Contact: Nancy P. Conway, President
Released: Annual

57804 ■ *Your Business Connection*
2969 Elmore Park Rd.
Bartlett, TN 38134-8309
Ph: (901)372-9457
Fax: (901)372-9488
Co. E-mail: info@bartlettchamber.org
URL: http://www.bartlettchamber.org
Contact: John Threadgill, President
Released: Monthly

MINORITY BUSINESS ASSISTANCE PROGRAMS

57805 ■ Memphis Minority Business Development Center
283 N Bellevue
Memphis, TN 38103
Ph: (901)726-5353
Fax: (901)726-5355
Contact: Gary Rowe, Director
Description: Provides business and consulting services to minority businesses and entrepreneurs.

57806 ■ Nashville Minority Business Center
Freedom Center Bldg.
223 Rosa L. Parks Ave. N, Ste. 205
Nashville, TN 37203-3513
Ph: (615)255-0432
Fax: (615)255-2377
Co. E-mail: nmbdc@bellsouth.net
URL: http://www.minoritybusinesscenter.com
Contact: Marilyn Robinson, Executive Director
Description: Works to foster the growth of minority businesses in Tennessee.

57807 ■ Tennessee Department of Economic and Community Development Center - Business Enterprise Resource Office (BERO)
312 Rosa L. Parks Ave., 11th Fl.
Nashville, TN 37243
Ph: (615)741-3282
Free: 877-768-6374
Fax: (615)741-5829
Co. E-mail: wisty.pender@tn.gov
URL: http://tennessee.gov/ecd/bero/
Contact: Wisty Pender, Director
Description: Provides services to minority entrepreneurs through offices located in Nashville, Chattanooga, Knoxville, and Memphis.

FINANCING AND LOAN PROGRAMS

57808 ■ Capital Across America
501 Union St., Ste. 201
Nashville, TN 37219
Ph: (615)254-1515
Fax: (615)254-1856
Co. E-mail: info@capitalacrossamerica.com
URL: http://www.capitalacrossamerica.com
Contact: Chris Brown, President
Industry Preferences: Women/minority-owned businesses. **Geographic Preference:** Mid Atlantic, Midwest, and Southeast.

57809 ■ Coleman Swenson Booth Inc. / Coleman Swenson Hoffman Booth
237 2nd Ave. S.
Franklin, TN 37064-2649
Ph: (615)791-9462
Fax: (615)791-9636
URL: http://www.colemanswenson.com
Contact: Larry H. Coleman, Partner
Preferred Investment Size: $1,000,000 to $7,000,000. **Industry Preferences:** Medical and health, Internet specific, other products, computer software and services, consumer related, biotechnology, computer hardware, communications and media. **Geographic Preference:** U.S.

57810 ■ Massey Burch Capital Corp.
4007 Hillsboro Rd., Ste. A
Nashville, TN 37215
Ph: (615)665-3227
Fax: (615)665-3240
URL: http://www.masseyburch.com
Contact: Donald M. Johnson, Partner
Preferred Investment Size: $500,000 to $2,000,000. **Industry Preferences:** Medical and health, Internet specific, communications and media, computer software and services, biotechnology. **Geographic Preference:** South.

57811 ■ MB Venture Partners, LLC
17 W. Pontotoc Ave., Ste. 200
Memphis, TN 38103
Ph: (901)322-0330
Fax: (901)332-0339
URL: http://www.mbventures.com
Contact: Gary Stevenson, Managing Partner
Investment Policies: Seed, early and later stage. **Industry Preferences:** Biotechnology, and medical and health. **Geographic Preference:** U.S.

57812 ■ Salix Ventures
30 Burton Hills Blvd., Ste. 370
Nashville, TN 37215
Ph: (615)665-1409
Fax: (615)665-2912
Co. E-mail: plans@salixventures.com
URL: http://www.salixventures.com
Contact: Mark Donovan, Partner
Preferred Investment Size: $5,000,000 to $7,000,000. **Industry Preferences:** Medical and health, computer software and services, Internet specific, biotechnology, other products, and consumer related. **Geographic Preference:** U.S.

57813 ■ SSM Partners
Crescent Ctr.
6075 Poplar Ave., Ste. 335
Memphis, TN 38119

Ph: (901)767-1131
Fax: (901)767-1135
URL: http://www.ssmventures.com
Contact: Jim Witherington, Managing Partner
Preferred Investment Size: $5,000,000 to
$20,000,000. **Industry Preferences:** Internet spe-
cific, computer software and services, communica-
tions and media, computer hardware, other products,
medical and health, consumer related, semiconduc-
tors and other electronics. **Geographic Preference:**
Southeast and Texas.

57814 ■ Valley Capital Corp.
535 Chestnut St., Ste. 368
Chattanooga, TN 37402
Ph: (423)265-1557
Fax: (423)265-1588
Contact: Lamar J. Partridge, President
Preferred Investment Size: $200,000 minimum. **In-
dustry Preferences:** Diversified. **Geographic Pref-
erence:** Southeast.

PROCUREMENT ASSISTANCE PROGRAMS

**57815 ■ Chattanooga Procurement Technical
Assistance Center - Center for Industrial
Services (CIS)**
Doctors Bldg., Ste. 502
744 McAllie Ave.
Chattanooga, TN 37403
Ph: (423)634-0848
Co. E-mail: paul.middlebrooks@tennessee.edu
URL: http://www.cis.tennessee.edu/government/
contracts
Contact: Paul Middlebrooks, Consultant
E-mail: paul.middlebrooks@tennessee.edu
Description: Tennessee business and industry are
assisted daily by CIS engineering and professional
staff in improving their economic competitiveness on
a national and global level.

**57816 ■ Jackson Procurement Technical
Assistance Center - Center for Industrial
Services (CIS)**
605 Airways Blvd., Ste. C
Jackson, TN 38301
Ph: (731)425-4777
Co. E-mail: russell.toone@tennessee.edu
URL: http://www.cis.tennessee.edu/PTAC
Contact: Russell Toone, Consultant
E-mail: russell.toone@tennessee.edu
Description: Tennessee business and industry are
assisted daily by CIS engineering and professional
staff in improving their economic competitiveness on
a national and global level.

**57817 ■ Knoxville Procurement Technical
Assistance Center - Center for Industrial
Services (CIS)**
105 Student Services Bldg.
Knoxville, TN 37996
Ph: (423)634-0848
Co. E-mail: paul.middlebrooks@tennessee.edu
URL: http://www.cis.tennessee.edu/government/
contracts
Contact: Paul Middlebrooks, Consultant
E-mail: paul.middlebrooks@tennessee.edu
Description: Tennessee business and industry are
assisted daily by CIS engineering and professional
staff in improving their economic competitiveness on
a national and global level.

**57818 ■ Memphis Procurement Technical
Assistance Center - Center for Industrial
Services (CIS)**
2670 Union Ave. Extended, Ste. 1123
Memphis, TN 38112
Ph: (901)323-9341
Co. E-mail: harry.kitchens@tennessee.edu
URL: http://www.cis.tennessee.edu/government/
contracts
Contact: Harry Kitchens, Consultant
E-mail: jcash@tennessee.edu
Description: Assists Utah small businesses who are
interested in bidding on federal, state and local
government procurements and commercial contract-
ing opportunities covering Box Elder, Cache, and
Rich Counties.

**57819 ■ Tennessee Procurement Technical
Assistance Center - Center for Industrial
Services (CIS)**
193 Polk Ave., Ste. C
Nashville, TN 37210
Ph: (615)532-8885
Fax: (615)532-4937
Co. E-mail: joe.flynn@tennessee.edu
URL: http://www.cis.tennessee.edu/government/
contracts
Contact: Joseph Flynn, Program Manager
E-mail: matheny@utk.edu

**57820 ■ Tennessee Procurement Technical
Assistance Center - University of Tennessee -
Center for Industrial Services (CIS)**
Doctors Bldg., Ste. 502
744 McAllie Ave.
Chattanooga, TN 37402
Ph: (423)634-0848
Co. E-mail: paul.middlebrooks@tennessee.edu
URL: http://www.cis.tennessee.edu/government/
contracts
Contact: Paul Middlebrooks, Counselor
E-mail: paul.middlebrooks@tennessee.edu
Description: Helps to utilize available resources to
leverage continual improvement in Tennessee's
industrial sector for the long-term sustainability of
business and jobs in our state.

**57821 ■ Tennessee Procurement Technical
Assistance Center - University of Tennessee -
Center for Industrial Services (CIS)**
605 Airways Blvd., Ste. 109
Jackson, TN 38301
Ph: (731)425-4777
Co. E-mail: russell.toone@tennessee.edu
URL: http://www.cis.tennessee.edu
Contact: Russell Toone, Counselor
E-mail: Russell.Toone@tennessee.edu
Description: Helps to utilize available resources to
leverage continual improvement in Tennessee's
industrial sector for the long-term sustainability of
business and jobs in our state.

**57822 ■ Tennessee Procurement Technical
Assistance Center - University of Tennessee -
Center for Industrial Services (CIS)**
2670 Union Ave. Extended, Ste. 1123
Memphis, TN 38112
Ph: (901)323-9341
URL: http://www.cis.tennessee.edu/government/
contracts
Contact: Harry Kitchens, Consultant
Description: To utilize available resources to lever-
age continual improvement in Tennessee's industrial
sector for the long-term sustainability of business and
jobs in our state.

**57823 ■ Tennessee Procurement Technical
Assistance Center - University of Tennessee -
Institute for Public Service**
105 Student Services Bldg.
Knoxville, TN 37996
Ph: (615)532-4916
Co. E-mail: debbie.barber@tennessee.edu
URL: http://www.cis.tennessee.edu/government/
contracts
Contact: Debbie Barber, Coordinator
Description: Helps to utilize available resources to
leverage continual improvement in Tennessee's
industrial sector for the long-term sustainability of
business and jobs in our state.

INCUBATORS/RESEARCH AND TECHNOLOGY PARKS

**57824 ■ Chattanooga/Hamilton County
Business Development Center**
100 Cherokee Blvd.
Chattanooga, TN 37405
Ph: (423)752-4301
Fax: (423)752-1700
URL: http://www.chattanoogachamber.com
Contact: Kathryn Foster, Director
Description: A business incubator offering office and
manufacturing space.

57825 ■ Emerge Memphis
516 Tennessee St.
Memphis, TN 38103
Ph: (901)312-7700
Fax: (901)544-7163
URL: http://www.emergememphis.org/
Description: A general business and technology-
based incubator and a focal point for entrepreneurial
activity in the Mid-South, whose mission is to foster a
dynamic, innovative culture and environment where
start-up companies have a first-rate opportunity to
grow and get the resources needed to most enable
their success.

57826 ■ Fairview Technology Center
Development Corporation of Knox County
17 Market Square, No. 201
Knoxville, TN 37902
Ph: (865)546-5887
Fax: (865)546-6170
Co. E-mail: tanapier@knoxdevelopment.org
URL: http://www.knoxdevelopment.org/BusinessIncu-
bator.aspx
Description: A small business incubator providing
office and laboratory facilities for start-up technology
businnses.

**57827 ■ Nashville Business Incubation
Center**
315 10th Ave. N., Ste. A
Nashville, TN 37203
Ph: (615)963-7184
Co. E-mail: mwalters_nbic@bellsouth.net
URL: http://www.nbiconline.com/
Contact: Mildred Townsend Waters, Executive Direc-
tor
Description: A small business incubator created to
help grow and develop small and micro-enterprise
businesses in the Metropolitan Nashville area.

57828 ■ Technology 2020
1020 Commerce Park Dr.
Oak Ridge, TN 37830
Ph: (865)220-2020
Fax: (865)220-2030
Co. E-mail: info@tech2020.org
URL: http://www.tech2020.org/
Contact: Mike Corley, Chief Executive Officer
Description: This small business incubator empha-
sizes the development of information technology and
science firms.

EDUCATIONAL PROGRAMS

**57829 ■ Chattanooga State Community
College**
4501 Amnicola Hwy.
Chattanooga, TN 37406-1097
Ph: (423)697-4400
Free: 866-547-3733
Fax: (423)756-6195
URL: http://www.chattanoogastate.edu
Description: Two-year college offering a small busi-
ness management program.

TRADE PERIODICALS

**57830 ■ *Tennessee Economic Development
Quarterly***
Pub: Department of Economic and Community
Development
Ed: Caroline Ragsdale, Editor, cragsdale@mail.state.
m.us. **Released:** Bimonthly. **Description:** Highlights
Tennessee's economic growth and business climate.

PUBLICATIONS

57831 ■ *Memphis Business Journal*
88 Union, Ste. 102
Memphis, TN 38103-5195
Ph: (901)523-1000
Fax: (901)526-5240
Co. E-mail: mbj@mem.net
URL: http://www.bizjournals.com/memphis/

57832 ■ *Nashville Business Journal*
PO Box 23229
Nashville, TN 37202-3229
Ph: (615)248-2222
Fax: (615)248-6246
URL: http://www.amcity.com/nashville

57833 ■ *Smart Start your Tennessee Business*
PSI Research
300 N. Valley Dr.
Grants Pass, OR 97526
Ph: (503)479-9464
Free: 800-228-2275

Fax: (503)476-1479
Co. E-mail: info@psi-research.com
URL: http://www.psi-research.com
Ed: Michael D. Jenkins. **Released:** Revised edition, 1992. **Price:** $29.95 (looseleaf binder); $24.95 (paper). **Description:** Part of the Successful Business Library series.

57834 ■ *The Tri-Cities Business Journal*
2203 McKinley Rd.
Ste. 133
Johnson City, TN 37604
Ph: (423)854-0140
Fax: (423)328-7226
URL: http://www.bjournal.com

PUBLISHERS

57835 ■ Doing Business in Memphis
1779 Kirby Pkwy., Ste. 128
Germantown, TN 38138-0631
Ph: (901)590-0050
Fax: (901)590-0100
URL: http://www.memphisbusiness.com
Contact: Deborah L. Camp, President
E-mail: dcamp@memphisbusiness.com
Description: Description: Publishes business-to-business directories. Does not accept unsolicited manuscripts. Reaches market through commission representatives, direct mail, reviews and listings, and telephone sales. **Founded:** 1990. **Publications:** *Doing Business in Memphis: A Directory of Business and Industry* (Biennial).

SMALL BUSINESS DEVELOPMENT CENTERS

57836 ■ Abilene Small Business Development Center
500 Chestnut St., Ste. 601
Abilene, TX 79602
Ph: (325)670-0300
Co. E-mail: j.willhelm@ttusbdc.org
URL: http://sbdctexas.com
Contact: Judy Wilhelm, Director
Description: Represents and promotes the small business sector. Provides management assistance to current and prospective small business owners. Helps to improve management skills and expand the products and services of members.

57837 ■ Angelina College Small Business Development Center
c/o Brian McClain, Dir.
3500 S First St.
Lufkin, TX 75902
Ph: (936)633-5400
Fax: (936)633-5494
Co. E-mail: bmcclain@angelina.edu
URL: http://www.angelina.sbdcnetwork.net
Contact: Brian McClain, Director
Description: Represents and promotes the small business sector. Provides management assistance to current and prospective small business owners. Helps to improve management skills and expand the products and services of members.

57838 ■ Angelo State University Small Business Development Center
ASU Station No. 10910
San Angelo, TX 76909
Ph: (325)942-2098
Fax: (325)942-2096
Co. E-mail: sbdc@angelo.edu
URL: http://www.angelo.edu/services/sbdc
Contact: Dave Erickson, Director
Description: Represents and promotes the small business sector. Provides management assistance to current and prospective small business owners. Helps to improve management skills and expand the products and services of members.

57839 ■ Best Southwest Small Business Development Center
Cedar Valley College Ctr.
207 N Cannady Dr.
Cedar Hill, TX 75104
Ph: (972)860-7894
Fax: (972)291-1320
Co. E-mail: rwyrick@dcccd.edu
URL: http://www.cedarvalleycollege.edu/ContinuingEducation/CVCCenteratCedarHill
Contact: Russell Wyrick, Director
Description: Represents and promotes the small business sector. Provides management assistance to current and prospective small business owners. Helps to improve management skills and expand the products and services of members.

57840 ■ Big Bend Small Business Development Center
PO Box C-47
Alpine, TX 79832
Ph: (915)837-8694
Fax: (432)837-8104
Co. E-mail: dwilson@sulross.edu
URL: http://www.sulross.edu/~sbdc
Contact: David Wilson, Director
Description: Represents and promotes the small business sector. Provides management assistance to current and prospective small business owners. Helps to improve management skills and expand the products and services of members.

57841 ■ Blinn College Small Business Development Center
902 College Ave.
Brenham, TX 77833
Ph: (979)830-4137
Fax: (979)830-4135
Co. E-mail: sbdc@blinn.edu
URL: http://www.blinn.edu/sbdc/index.htm
Contact: Matthew Wehring, Director
Description: Represents and promotes the small business sector. Provides management assistance to current and prospective small business owners. Helps to improve management skills and expand the products and services of members.

57842 ■ Brazos Valley Small Business Development Center
4001 E 29th St., Ste. 175
Bryan, TX 77805
Ph: (979)260-5222
Fax: (979)260-5229
Co. E-mail: info@bvsbdc.org
URL: http://www.brazosvalley.sbdcnetwork.net/brazosvalley/default.asp
Contact: James Pillans, Director
Description: Represents and promotes the small business sector. Provides management assistance to current and prospective small business owners. Helps to improve management skills and expand the products and services of members.

57843 ■ Brazosport College Small Business Development Center
500 College Dr.
Lake Jackson, TX 77566
Ph: (979)230-3380
Fax: (979)230-3482
Co. E-mail: sbdcinfo@brazosport.edu
URL: http://www.brazosport.edu/sbdc
Contact: Dr. Janice Gooines, Director
Description: Represents and promotes the small business sector. Provides management assistance to current and prospective small business owners. Helps to improve management skills and expand the products and services of members.

57844 ■ Collin Small Business Development Center
4800 Preston Park Blvd., Ste. 114
Plano, TX 75093
Ph: (972)985-3770
Fax: (972)985-3775
Co. E-mail: mfrey@collin.edu
URL: http://www.collin.edu/sbdc
Contact: Marta Gomez Frey, Director
Description: Represents and promotes the small business sector. Provides management assistance to current and prospective small business owners. Helps to improve management skills and expand the products and services of members.

57845 ■ Dallas Small Business Development Center
1402 Corinth St.
Dallas, TX 75215
Ph: (214)860-5865
Fax: (214)860-5867
Co. E-mail: dsbdc@dcccd.edu
URL: http://www.ntsbdc.org/c_dallas.html
Contact: Jeff Blatt, Director
Description: Represents and promotes the small business sector. Provides management assistance to current and prospective small business owners. Helps to improve management skills and expand the products and services of members.

57846 ■ Del Mar College Small Business Development Center
101 Baldwin Blvd., CED 146
Corpus Christi, TX 78404
Ph: (361)698-1021
Fax: (361)698-1024
Co. E-mail: afierova@delmar.edu
URL: http://www.delmar.edu/sbdc
Contact: Ann Fierova, Director
Description: Represents and promotes the small business sector. Provides management assistance to current and prospective small business owners. Helps to improve management skills and expand the products and services of members.

57847 ■ Denton County Small Business Development Center
414 W Parkway St.
Denton, TX 76201
Ph: (940)380-1849
Co. E-mail: nctcsbdc@denton-chamber.org
URL: http://www.nctc.edu/SBDC/sbdc.html
Description: Represents and promotes the small business sector. Provides management assistance to current and prospective small business owners. Helps to improve management skills and expand the products and services of members.

57848 ■ El Paso Community College Small Business Development Center
Bldg. B, Ste. B520
9050 Viscount Blvd.
El Paso, TX 79925
Ph: (915)831-7743
Fax: (915)831-7734
Co. E-mail: otavare1@epcc.edu
URL: http://elpasosbdc.net
Contact: Olga M. Tavarez, Director (Acting)
Description: Represents and promotes the small business sector. Provides management assistance to

current and prospective small business owners. Helps to improve management skills and expand the products and services of members.

57849 ■ Galveston County Small Business Development Center
8419 Emmett F. Lowry Expy.
Texas City, TX 77591
Ph: (409)933-1414
Fax: (409)933-3365
Co. E-mail: info@gcsbdc.com
URL: http://www.galvestoncounty.sbdcnetwork.net/galveston/default.asp
Contact: Carroll Cobb, Director
Description: Represents and promotes the small business sector. Provides management assistance to current and prospective small business owners. Helps to improve management skills and expand the products and services of members.

57850 ■ Grayson Small Business Development Center
6101 Grayson Dr.
Denison, TX 75020
Ph: (903)463-8787
Fax: (903)415-2565
Co. E-mail: stidhamk@grayson.edu
URL: http://www.ntsbdc.org/c_grayson.html
Contact: Karen Stidam, Director
URL(s): www.graysonsbdc.org. **Description:** Represents and promotes the small business sector. Provides management assistance to current and prospective small business owners. Helps to improve management skills and expand the products and services of members.

57851 ■ Kilgore Small Business Development Center
911 NW Loop 281, Ste. 209
Longview, TX 75604
Ph: (903)757-5857
Free: 800-388-7232
Fax: (903)753-7920
Co. E-mail: bbunt@kilgore.edu
URL: http://www.kilgore.edu/sbdc.asp
Contact: Brad Bunt, Director
Description: Represents and promotes the small business sector. Provides management assistance to current and prospective small business owners. Helps to improve management skills and expand the products and services of members.

57852 ■ Lamar State College Small Business Development Center
1401 Procter St.
Port Arthur, TX 77640
Ph: (409)984-6531
Free: 800-477-5872
Fax: (409)984-6063
Co. E-mail: taitli@lamarpa.edu
URL: http://www.lamarpa.edu/?url=/dept/sbdc/index.html
Contact: Linda Tait, Director
Description: Represents and promotes the small business sector. Provides management assistance to current and prospective small business owners. Helps to improve management skills and expand the products and services of members.

57853 ■ Lamar University Small Business Development Center
801 Pearl St.
Beaumont, TX 77701
Ph: (409)880-2367
Fax: (409)880-2201
Co. E-mail: sbdc@lamar.edu
URL: http://www.lamarbmt.sbdcnetwork.net/beaumont/default.asp?SnID=1263932212
Contact: David Mulcahy, Director
Description: Represents and promotes the small business sector. Provides management assistance to current and prospective small business owners. Helps to improve management skills and expand the products and services of members.

57854 ■ Lee College Small Business Development Center
1496 San Jacinto Mall, Ste. 1110
J.C. Penney Wing
Baytown, TX 77521
Ph: (281)425-6309
Fax: (281)425-6307
Co. E-mail: smccorquodale@lee.edu
URL: http://www.lee.edu/sbdc
Contact: Steve McCorquodale, Consultant
Description: Represents and promotes the small business sector. Provides management assistance to current and prospective small business owners. Helps to improve management skills and expand the products and services of members.

57855 ■ Lone Star College System Small Business Development Center
5000 Research Forest Dr.
The Woodlands, TX 77381-4356
Ph: (832)813-6674
Fax: (832)813-6624
Co. E-mail: sbdc@lonestar.edu
URL: http://www.lonestar.edu/sbdc
Contact: Sal Mira, Director
Description: Represents and promotes the small business sector. Provides management assistance to current and prospective small business owners. Helps to improve management skills and expand the products and services of members.

57856 ■ Lubbock Small Business Development Center
2579 S Loop 289
Lubbock, TX 79423
Ph: (806)745-1637
Free: 800-992-7232
Fax: (806)745-6717
Co. E-mail: e.melot@ttusbdc.org
URL: http://www.ttusbdc.org/lubbock
Contact: James Wilhelm, Director
Description: Represents and promotes the small business sector. Provides management assistance to current and prospective small business owners. Helps to improve management skills and expand the products and services of members.

57857 ■ McLennan Small Business Development Center
McLennan Community College
1400 College Dr.
Waco, TX 76708
Ph: (254)299-8141
Free: 800-349-7232
Fax: (254)299-8054
Co. E-mail: sbdc@mclennan.edu
URL: http://www.ntsbdc.org/c_mclennan.html
Contact: Steve Surguy, Director
Description: Represents and promotes the small business sector. Provides management assistance to current and prospective small business owners. Helps to improve management skills and expand the products and services of members.

57858 ■ Midwestern State University Small Business Development Center
3410 Taft Blvd.
Wichita Falls, TX 76308
Ph: (940)397-4373
Fax: (940)397-4374
Co. E-mail: msusbdc@mwsu.edu
URL: http://www.msusbdc.org
Contact: Vanda Wright, Director
Description: Represents and promotes the small business sector. Provides management assistance to current and prospective small business owners. Helps to improve management skills and expand the products and services of members.

57859 ■ Montague County Small Business Development Center
1525 W California
Gainesville, TX 76240
Ph: (940)688-4220

Fax: (940)668-6049
Co. E-mail: nctcsbdc@nctc.edu
URL: http://www.ntsbdc.org/c_n_cent.html
Contact: Cathy Keeler, Director
Description: Represents and promotes the small business sector. Provides management assistance to current and prospective small business owners. Helps to improve management skills and expand the products and services of members.

57860 ■ Navarro Small Business Development Center
Navarro College
3200 W 7th Ave.
Corsicana, TX 75110
Ph: (903)875-7667
Fax: (903)875-7468
Co. E-mail: sbdc@navarrocollege.edu
URL: http://www.ntsbdc.org/c_navarro.html
Contact: Robin Lasher, Director
Description: Represents and promotes the small business sector. Provides management assistance to current and prospective small business owners. Helps to improve management skills and expand the products and services of members.

57861 ■ North Central Texas College - Corinth Small Business Development Center
1404 N Corinth St., Ste. 307
Corinth, TX 76208
Ph: (940)498-6276
Fax: (940)668-6049
Co. E-mail: nctcsbdc@nctc.edu
URL: http://www.nctc.edu/SBDC/sbdc.html
Contact: Catherine Keeler, Director
Description: Represents and promotes the small business sector. Provides management assistance to current and prospective small business owners. Helps to improve management skills and expand the products and services of members.

57862 ■ North Central Texas Small Business Development Center
North Central Texas College
1525 W California St.
Gainesville, TX 76240
Ph: (940)668-4220
Free: 800-351-7232
Fax: (940)668-6049
Co. E-mail: nctcsbdc@nctc.edu
URL: http://www.ntsbdc.org
Contact: Catherine Keeler, Director
URL(s): www.nctc.edu/SBDC/sbdc.html. **Description:** Represents and promotes the small business sector. Provides management assistance to current and prospective small business owners. Helps to improve management skills and expand the products and services of members.

57863 ■ Northeast Texas Small Business Development Center
2886 FM 1735
Mount Pleasant, TX 75455-1089
Ph: (903)717-1552
Co. E-mail: twilson@ntcc.edu
URL: http://www.ntsbdc.org/c_texarkana.html
Contact: Tim Wilson, Director
URL(s): northeasttxsbdc.org. **Description:** Represents and promotes the small business sector. Provides management assistance to current and prospective small business owners. Helps to improve management skills and expand the products and services of members.

57864 ■ Northwest Texas Small Business Development Center (NWTSBDC)
2579 S Loop 289, Ste. 210
Lubbock, TX 79423
Ph: (806)745-3973
Free: 800-992-7232
Fax: (806)745-6207
Co. E-mail: s.caldwell@nwtsbdc.org
URL: http://www.nwtsbdc.org
Founded: 1986.

57865 ■ Paris Small Business Development Center
2400 Clarksville St.
Paris, TX 75460

Ph: (903)782-0223
Fax: (903)782-0219
Co. E-mail: bgottshalk@parisjc.edu
URL: http://www.sbdcparis.org/web
Contact: Bradley R. Gottshalk, Director
Description: Represents and promotes the small business sector. Provides management assistance to current and prospective small business owners. Helps to improve management skills and expand the products and services of members.

57866 ■ Prairie View A&M Small Business Development Center
Hobart Taylor Bldg., Rm. 1B119
FM 1098 Rd. & University Dr.
Prairie View, TX 77446
Ph: (936)261-9242
Fax: (936)261-9270
Co. E-mail: rlfaison@pvamu.edu
URL: http://www.pvamu.sbdcnetwork.net/prairieview/
    Default.asp
Contact: Rebecca L. Faison, Director
Description: Represents and promotes the small business sector. Provides management assistance to current and prospective small business owners. Helps to improve management skills and expand the products and services of members.

57867 ■ Sam Houston State University Small Business Development Center
2424 Sam Houston Ave., Bldg. A
Huntsville, TX 77340
Ph: (936)294-3737
Fax: (936)294-3738
Co. E-mail: sbdcinfo@shsu.edu
URL: http://www.samhoustonstateuniversity.sbdcnet-
    work.net/huntsville/Default.asp
Contact: Robert A. Barragan, Director
Description: Represents and promotes the small business sector. Provides management assistance to current and prospective small business owners. Helps to improve management skills and expand the products and services of members.

57868 ■ San Antonio Small Business Development Center (SA SBDC)
501 W Cesar E. Chavez Blvd.
San Antonio, TX 78207
Ph: (210)458-2460
Fax: (210)458-2464
URL: http://sasbdc.org
Contact: Morrison Woods, Director
Description: Represents and promotes the small business sector. Provides management assistance to current and prospective small business owners. Helps to improve management skills and expand the products and services of members.

57869 ■ San Jacinto College Small Business Development Center
6117 Broadway
Pearland, TX 77581
Ph: (281)485-5214
Fax: (281)867-1106
Co. E-mail: sbdc@sjcd.edu
URL: http://www.sjcd.sbdcnetwork.net/sanjacinto/
    Default.asp
Contact: Richard Prets, Director
Description: Represents and promotes the small business sector. Provides management assistance to current and prospective small business owners. Helps to improve management skills and expand the products and services of members.

57870 ■ South West Texas Border Small Business Development Center Network
University of Texas - San Antonio
501 W Cesar E. Chavez Blvd.
San Antonio, TX 78207-4415
Ph: (210)458-2450
Fax: (210)458-2464
Co. E-mail: morrison.woods@utsa.edu
URL: http://txsbdc.org
Contact: Albert Salgado, Director
Description: Represents and promotes the small business sector. Provides management assistance to current and prospective small business owners. Helps to improve management skills and expand the products and services of members.

57871 ■ SRSU Rio Grande College Small Business Development Center
4006 Bob Rogers Dr.
Eagle Pass, TX 78852
Ph: (830)758-5025
Fax: (830)758-5020
Co. E-mail: epena@sulross.edu
URL: http://rgc.sulross.edu/pages/106.asp
Contact: Elizabeth Pena, Director
Description: Represents and promotes the small business sector. Provides management assistance to current and prospective small business owners. Helps to improve management skills and expand the products and services of members.

57872 ■ Tarleton State University Small Business Development Center
105 N Stockton, Ste. A
Granbury, TX 76048
Ph: (817)573-7681
Fax: (817)573-5822
Co. E-mail: burch@tarleton.edu
URL: http://www.tsusbdc.org
Contact: Randy Burch, Program Manager
Description: Represents and promotes the small business sector. Provides management assistance to current and prospective small business owners. Helps to improve management skills and expand the products and services of members.

57873 ■ Tarrant Small Business Development Center
James E. Guinn Complex, Ste. 229
1150 South Fwy.
Fort Worth, TX 76104
Ph: (817)871-6028
Co. E-mail: tcc.sbdc@tccd.edu
URL: http://www.tccd.edu/Campuses_and_Centers.
    html
Contact: David Edmonds, Director
Description: Represents and promotes the small business sector. Provides management assistance to current and prospective small business owners. Helps to improve management skills and expand the products and services of members.

57874 ■ Texas State University - San Marcos Small Business Development Center
1340 Wonder World Dr., Ste. 108
San Marcos, TX 78666
Ph: (512)610-0996
Free: 888-880-4800
Co. E-mail: sbdc@txstate.edu
URL: http://www.business.txstate.edu
Contact: Larry Lucero, Director
URL(s): sbdc.mccoy.txstate.edu. **Description:** Represents and promotes the small business sector. Provides management assistance to current and prospective small business owners. Helps to improve management skills and expand the products and services of members.

57875 ■ Trinity Valley Small Business Development Center
100 Cardinal Dr.
Athens, TX 75751
Ph: (903)675-7403
Co. E-mail: mellsberry@tvcc.edu
URL: http://www.tvcc.edu/sbdc
Contact: Michael Ellsberry, Director
Description: Represents and promotes the small business sector. Provides management assistance to current and prospective small business owners. Helps to improve management skills and expand the products and services of members.

57876 ■ Tyler Small Business Development Center
Tyler Junior College
1530 S Southwest Loop 323, Ste. 100
Tyler, TX 75701
Ph: (903)510-2975

Fax: (903)510-2972
Co. E-mail: dpro@tjc.edu
URL: http://www.tylersbdc.com
Contact: Don Proudfoot, Director
Description: Represents and promotes the small business sector. Provides management assistance to current and prospective small business owners. Helps to improve management skills and expand the products and services of members.

57877 ■ University of Houston - Coastal Plains Small Business Development Center
c/o Kyle Smith, Dir.
1900 5th St.
Bay City, TX 77414
Ph: (979)244-8466
Fax: (979)244-8463
Co. E-mail: khsmith2@uh.edu
URL: http://www.coastalplains.sbdcnetwork.net/
    coastalplains/default.asp
Contact: Kyle Smith, Director
Description: Represents and promotes the small business sector. Provides management assistance to current and prospective small business owners. Helps to improve management skills and expand the products and services of members.

57878 ■ University of Houston - Fort Bend Small Business Development Center
2440 Texas Pkwy., Ste. 220
Missouri City, TX 77489
Ph: (281)499-9787
Fax: (281)499-6513
URL: http://sbdcnetwork.uh.edu/network/Default.asp
Description: Represents and promotes the small business sector. Provides management assistance to current and prospective small business owners. Helps to improve management skills and expand the products and services of members.

57879 ■ University of Houston - Victoria Small Business Development Center
3402 N Ben Wilson St.
Victoria, TX 77901-4497
Ph: (361)575-8944
Free: 877-895-SBDC
Co. E-mail: humphreysj@uhv.edu
URL: http://sbdc.uhv.edu/default.asp
Contact: Joe Humphreys, Director
Description: Represents and promotes the small business sector. Provides management assistance to current and prospective small business owners. Helps to improve management skills and expand the products and services of members.

57880 ■ University of Texas Pan American Small Business Development Center
ASA Rm. 160
1201 W University Dr.
Edinburg, TX 78539
Ph: (956)292-7535
Fax: (956)292-7561
Co. E-mail: mariaj2@utpa.edu
URL: http://txsbdc.org
Contact: Maria D. Juarez, Director
Description: Represents and promotes the small business sector. Provides management assistance to current and prospective small business owners. Helps to improve management skills and expand the products and services of members.

57881 ■ University of Texas of the Permian Basin Small Business Development Center
4901 E University Blvd.
Odessa, TX 79762
Ph: (432)552-2455
Fax: (432)552-3455
Co. E-mail: sbdc@utpb.edu
URL: http://www.utpbsbdc.org
Contact: Enrique Romero, Director
Description: Represents and promotes the small business sector. Provides management assistance to current and prospective small business owners. Helps to improve management skills and expand the products and services of members. **Publications:** *Making it Happen.*

57882 ■ West Texas A&M University Small Business Development Center
701 S Taylor St., Ste. 118
Amarillo, TX 79101
Ph: (806)372-5151
Co. E-mail: pj@wtsbdc.com
URL: http://www.smallbusinessdevelopmentcenter.com
Contact: P.J. Pronger, Director

Description: Represents and promotes the small business sector. Provides management assistance to current and prospective small business owners. Helps to improve management skills and expand the products and services of members.

SMALL BUSINESS ASSISTANCE PROGRAMS

57883 ■ Texas Department of Economic Development and Tourism - Business Development Division - Advisory Council on Small Business Issues
PO Box 12428
Austin, TX 78711-2728
Ph: (512)463-2000
Free: 800-888-0511
Fax: (512)463-1849
URL: http://www.governor.state.tx.us/ecodevo/
Contact: Roberto Dehoyos, Director

Description: Proposes long-range plans for small business activities.

SCORE OFFICES

57884 ■ Austin SCORE
Co. E-mail: info@scoreaustin.org

57885 ■ Cedar Park SCORE

57886 ■ Dripping Springs SCORE

57887 ■ Georgetown SCORE

57888 ■ Harker Heights SCORE

57889 ■ Marble Falls SCORE

57890 ■ Round Rock SCORE

57891 ■ SCORE 37 Houston
8701 S Gessner, Ste. 1200
Houston, TX 77074
Ph: (713)773-6565
Fax: (713)773-6551
Co. E-mail: score37@scorehouston.org
URL: http://www.scorehouston.org
Contact: Harland Andrews, Director

Description: Matches counselors experienced in every area of business management with small business owners in need of free expert advise; acts as a resource partner of the U.S. Small Business Administration. **Scope:** business. **Founded:** 1963. **Subscriptions:** 1000 articles books periodicals video recordings. **Publications:** The SCORE Sheet. **Educational Activities:** Mid America's Lenders Conference (Annual). **Awards:** Educational Vouchers (Monthly).

57892 ■ SCORE Corpus Christi
3649 Leopard St., Ste. 411
Corpus Christi, TX 78408-3260
Ph: (361)879-0017
Fax: (361)879-0764
Co. E-mail: score221@sbcglobal.net
URL: http://www.score-corpus-christi.org

Description: Advices entrepreneurs and would-be entrepreneurs with regards to starting and maintaining a small business. **Founded:** 1974.

57893 ■ SCORE Dallas
Meadows Bldg.
5646 Milton St., Ste. 303
Dallas, TX 75206
Ph: (214)987-9491

Fax: (214)987-9279
Co. E-mail: admin.0022@scorevolunteer.org
URL: http://www.dallas-score-22.org

Description: Creates business opportunities for small business owners and potential business owners to achieve success. Provides mentoring services to residents in Dallas, individual counseling and on-site business reviews. Develops business plans and evaluates financial projections.

57894 ■ SCORE East Texas
Tyler Junior College
1501 SSW Loop 323, Ste. 100
Tyler, TX 75701
Ph: (903)510-2975
Fax: (903)510-2972
Co. E-mail: mail@easttexasscore.org
URL: http://www.easttexassmallbusinesscounseling.com
Contact: Mr. Jerald Wolf, Chairman

Description: Provides counseling and mentoring to small businesses and persons wanting to start a small business. Counseling is free and confidential.

57895 ■ SCORE El Paso
10 Civic Center Plz.
El Paso, TX 79901
Ph: (915)534-0585
Fax: (915)534-0546
URL: http://www.score.org/chapters/el-paso-score
Contact: Chuck Wehmhoner, Chairman

Description: Creates business opportunities for small business owners and potential business owners to achieve success. Provides counseling, financial advice, business advise, various conferences and workshops in English and Spanish. Members include both currently working and retired executives and business owners on both sides of the U.S. and Mexico border.

57896 ■ SCORE Fort Worth
James E. Guinn School Complex
1150 South Fwy., Ste. 108
Fort Worth, TX 76104
Ph: (817)871-6002
Fax: (817)871-0531
Co. E-mail: scorefw@gmail.com
URL: http://www.fortworthsmallbusinesscounseling.com

Description: Serves as volunteer program in which working and retired business management professionals provide free business counseling to men and women who are considering starting a small business, encountering problems with their business, or expanding their business. Offers free one-on-one counseling, online counseling and low cost workshops on a variety of business topics. **Founded:** 1985.

57897 ■ SCORE Golden Triangle
PO Box 21664
Beaumont, TX 77720-1664
Ph: (409)861-2163
Fax: (409)722-5402
Co. E-mail: gtscore704@aol.com
URL: http://goldentriangle.scorechapter.org
Contact: Leo P. Flood, Chairman

Description: Provides professional guidance, mentoring services and financial assistance to maximize the success of existing and emerging small businesses. Promotes entrepreneur education in Beaumont, TX. **Founded:** 2008.

57898 ■ SCORE Lower Rio Grande Valley
222 E Van Buren
Harlingen, TX 78550
Ph: (956)427-8533
Fax: (956)427-8537
URL: http://www.rgvscore.org

Description: Provides professional guidance and information to maximize the success of existing and emerging small businesses. Promotes entrepreneur education in Lower Rio Grande Valley area, TX.

57899 ■ SCORE Lubbock
1205 Texas Ave., Rm. 411 D
Lubbock, TX 79401
Ph: (806)472-7462

Fax: (806)472-7487
URL: http://lubbock.score.org/chapters/lubbock-score

Description: Provides professional guidance, mentoring services and financial assistance to maximize the success of existing and emerging small businesses. Promotes entrepreneur education in Lubbock, TX.

57900 ■ SCORE San Antonio
1747 Citadel Plz., Ste. 103
San Antonio, TX 78209
Ph: (210)829-5776
URL: http://sanantonio.score.org/chapters/san-antonio-score
Contact: Carter Crews, Chairman

Description: Works for the formation, growth, and success of small businesses. Promotes entrepreneur education in San Antonio area, Texas. **Founded:** 1974.

57901 ■ The SCORE Sheet
8701 S Gessner, Ste. 1200
Houston, TX 77074
Ph: (713)773-6565
Fax: (713)773-6551
Co. E-mail: score37@scorehouston.org
URL: http://www.scorehouston.org
Contact: Harland Andrews, Director

57902 ■ Texarkana SCORE
Co. E-mail: score@texarkana.org

57903 ■ Waco SCORE
Co. E-mail: score@brc-waco.com

BETTER BUSINESS BUREAUS

57904 ■ Better Business Bureau of Abilene
3300 S 14th St., Ste. 307
Abilene, TX 79605-5052
Ph: (325)691-1533
Fax: (325)691-0309
Co. E-mail: info@abilene.bbb.org
URL: http://www.abilene.bbb.org

Description: Provides business reliability reports and complaint handling, including informal mediation, arbitration and alternative dispute resolution, business/consumer education resources and materials, national and local charitable information and the promotion of ethical business standards and voluntary self-regulation. **Scope:** consumer and business purchases. **Publications:** Consumer Resource Digest (Annual); Bulletin (Monthly); Consumer Resource Digest (Annual). **Awards:** Torch Award for Marketplace Ethics (Annual).

57905 ■ Better Business Bureau of Amarillo, Texas
720 S Tyler St., Ste. 112B
Amarillo, TX 79101-2354
Ph: (806)379-6222
Fax: (806)379-8206
Co. E-mail: info@txpanhandle.bbb.org
URL: http://txpanhandle.bbb.org
Contact: Janna Kiehl, Chief Executive Officer

Description: Seeks to promote and foster ethical relationship between businesses and the public through voluntary self-regulation, consumer and business education, and service excellence. Provides information to help consumers and businesses make informed purchasing decisions and avoid costly scams and frauds; settles consumer complaints through arbitration and other means.

57906 ■ Better Business Bureau, Austin
1005 La Posada Dr.
Austin, TX 78752
Ph: (512)445-2911
Fax: (512)445-2096
Co. E-mail: info@austin.bbb.org
URL: http://centraltx.bbb.org
Contact: Carrie A. Hurt, President

Description: Seeks to promote and foster the highest ethical relationship between businesses and the public through voluntary self-regulation, consumer and business education, and service excellence. Provides information to help consumers and businesses make informed purchasing decisions and avoid costly scams and frauds; settles consumer complaints through arbitration and other means.

57907 ▪ Better Business Bureau of Brazos Valley
418 Tarrow
College Station, TX 77840-1822
Ph: (979)260-2222
Free: 800-392-3798
Fax: (979)846-0276
Co. E-mail: info@bbbbryan.org
URL: http://www.bryan.bbb.org
Contact: Larry Lightfoot, President
Description: Seeks to promote and foster the highest ethical relationship between businesses and the public through voluntary self-regulation, consumer and business education, and service excellence. Provides information to help consumers and businesses make informed purchasing decisions and avoid costly scams and frauds; settles consumer complaints through arbitration and other means.

57908 ▪ Better Business Bureau of Central East Texas
3600 Old Bullard Rd., Bldg. 1
Tyler, TX 75701
Ph: (903)581-5704
Free: 800-443-0131
Fax: (903)534-8644
Co. E-mail: info@tyler.bbb.org
URL: http://www.tyler.bbb.org
Contact: Mechele Agbayani Mills, President
Description: Seeks to promote and foster the highest ethical relationship between businesses and the public through voluntary self-regulation, consumer and business education, and service excellence. Provides information to help consumers and businesses make informed purchasing decisions and avoid costly scams and frauds; settles consumer complaints through arbitration and other means.

57909 ▪ Better Business Bureau of Central and South Central Texas
445 Central TX Expwy., No. 1
Harker Heights, TX 76548
Ph: (254)699-0694
Fax: (254)699-0746
Co. E-mail: info@centraltx.bbb.org
URL: http://www.waco.bbb.org
Description: Promotes and fosters ethical relationship between businesses and the public through voluntary self-regulation, consumer and business education and service excellence.

57910 ▪ Better Business Bureau of the Coastal Bend
719 S Shoreline, Ste. 301B
Corpus Christi, TX 78401
Ph: (361)852-4949
Free: 800-379-4222
Fax: (361)885-0628
Co. E-mail: info@corpuschristi.bbb.org
URL: http://corpuschristi.bbb.org
Contact: Alan Bligh, Executive Director
Description: Seeks to promote and foster the highest ethical relationship between businesses and the public through voluntary self-regulation, consumer and business education, and service excellence. Provides information to help consumers and businesses make informed purchasing decisions and avoid costly scams and frauds; settles consumer complaints through arbitration and other means.
Founded: 1951.

57911 ▪ Better Business Bureau of Metropolitan Dallas
1601 Elm St., Ste. 3838
Dallas, TX 75201-4744
Ph: (214)220-2000
Free: 800-705-3994
Fax: (214)740-0321
Co. E-mail: info@dallas.bbb.org
URL: http://www.dallas.bbb.org
Contact: Jay Newman, President
Description: Seeks to promote and foster the highest ethical relationship between businesses and the public through voluntary self-regulation, consumer

and business education, and service excellence. Provides information to help consumers and businesses make informed purchasing decisions and avoid costly scams and frauds; settles consumer complaints through arbitration and other means.
Founded: 1920.

57912 ▪ Better Business Bureau of Metropolitan Houston
1333 W Loop S, Ste. 1200
Houston, TX 77027
Ph: (713)868-9500
Free: 877-468-9222
Fax: (713)867-4947
Co. E-mail: bbbinfo@bbbhou.org
URL: http://houston.bbb.org
Contact: Dan Parsons, President
Description: Seeks to promote and foster the highest ethical relationship between businesses and the public through voluntary self-regulation, consumer and business education, and service excellence. Provides information to help consumers and businesses make informed purchasing decisions and avoid costly scams and frauds; settles consumer complaints through arbitration and other means.

57913 ▪ Better Business Bureau of North Central Texas—Better Business Bureau, Wichita Falls
4245 Kemp Blvd., Ste. 900
Wichita Falls, TX 76308-2830
Ph: (940)691-1172
Fax: (940)691-1175
Co. E-mail: bbbnt@bbbnorcentx.org
URL: http://wichitafalls.bbb.org
Contact: Monica Horton, President
Description: Seeks to promote and foster the highest ethical relationship between businesses and the public through voluntary self-regulation, consumer and business education, and service excellence. Provides information to help consumers and businesses make informed purchasing decisions and avoid costly scams and frauds; settles consumer complaints through arbitration and other means.

57914 ▪ Better Business Bureau of San Angelo
3134 Executive Dr., Ste. A
San Angelo, TX 76904
Ph: (325)949-2989
Fax: (325)949-3514
Co. E-mail: gfriedrich@wcc.net
URL: http://sanangelo.bbb.org
Description: Seeks to promote and foster the highest ethical relationship between businesses and the public through voluntary self-regulation, consumer and business education, and service excellence. Provides information to help consumers and businesses make informed purchasing decisions and avoid costly scams and frauds; settles consumer complaints through arbitration and other means.

57915 ▪ Better Business Bureau, San Antonio
1800 NE Loop 410, Ste. 400
San Antonio, TX 78217-5296
Ph: (210)828-9441
Fax: (210)828-3101
Co. E-mail: info@sanantonio.bbb.org
URL: http://www.sanantonio.bbb.org
Contact: Dean Taylor, Executive Director
Description: Seeks to promote and foster the highest ethical relationship between businesses and the public through voluntary self-regulation, consumer and business education, and service excellence. Provides information to help consumers and businesses make informed purchasing decisions and avoid costly scams and frauds; settles consumer complaints through arbitration and other means.

57916 ▪ Better Business Bureau of South Texas
2017 West Expy. 83, Unit 4
Weslaco, TX 78596
Ph: (956)968-3678

Fax: (956)968-7638
Co. E-mail: bbbinfo@bbbhou.org
Description: Seeks to promote and foster the highest ethical relationship between businesses and the public through voluntary self-regulation, consumer and business education, and service excellence. Provides information to help consumers and businesses make informed purchasing decisions and avoid costly scams and frauds; settles consumer complaints through arbitration and other means.

57917 ▪ Better Business Bureau of Southeast Texas
550 Fannin, Ste. 100
Beaumont, TX 77701
Ph: (409)835-5348
Free: 800-658-7650
Fax: (409)838-6858
Co. E-mail: info@bbbsetexas.org
URL: http://www.beaumont.bbb.org
Contact: Michael Clayton, President
URL(s): southeasttexas.bbb.org. **Description:** Seeks to promote and foster the highest ethical relationship between businesses and the public through voluntary self-regulation, consumer and business education, and service excellence. Provides information to help consumers and businesses make informed purchasing decisions and avoid costly scams and frauds; settles consumer complaints through arbitration and other means.

57918 ▪ *Bulletin*
3300 S 14th St., Ste. 307
Abilene, TX 79605-5052
Ph: (325)691-1533
Fax: (325)691-0309
Co. E-mail: info@abilene.bbb.org
URL: http://www.abilene.bbb.org
Released: Monthly

57919 ▪ *Consumer Resource Digest*
3300 S 14th St., Ste. 307
Abilene, TX 79605-5052
Ph: (325)691-1533
Fax: (325)691-0309
Co. E-mail: info@abilene.bbb.org
URL: http://www.abilene.bbb.org
Released: Annual

CHAMBERS OF COMMERCE

57920 ▪ Abilene Chamber of Commerce
174 Cypress St., Ste. 200
Abilene, TX 79601-5850
Ph: (325)677-7241
Fax: (325)677-0622
Co. E-mail: info@abilenechamber.com
URL: http://www.abilenechamber.com
Contact: Mike McMahan, President
Description: Promotes business and community development in Abilene, TX. **Founded:** 1908. **Publications:** *Chamber Connection* (Monthly). **Telecommunication Services:** mmcmahan@abilenechamber.com.

57921 ▪ *Action Report*
418 W Ave. B
San Angelo, TX 76903-6027
Ph: (325)655-4136
Fax: (325)658-1110
Co. E-mail: chamber@sanangelo.org
URL: http://www.sanangelo.org
Contact: Phil Neighbors, President
Released: Monthly **Price:** $20, /year.

57922 ▪ *The Advocate*
602 E Commerce St.
San Antonio, TX 78295
Ph: (210)229-2100
Fax: (210)229-1600
Co. E-mail: infostore@sachamber.org
URL: http://sachamber.org
Contact: Richard Perez, President
Released: Monthly

57923 ▪ *Agriculture in Rio Grande Valley*
322 S Missouri
Weslaco, TX 78596

Ph: (956)968-3141
Fax: (956)968-0210
Co. E-mail: mail@valleychamber.com
URL: http://www.valleychamber.com
Contact: Allen Shields, Chairman

57924 ■ Alamo Chamber of Commerce
130 S 8th St.
Alamo, TX 78516
Ph: (956)787-2117
Co. E-mail: alamo.chamber@yahoo.com
URL: http://www.alamochamber.com
Contact: Carrol Moering, Office Manager
Description: Promotes business and community development in Alamo, TX.

57925 ■ Alamo City Black Chamber of Commerce
600 Hemisfair Plaza Way, Bldg. 406-10
San Antonio, TX 78205
Ph: (210)226-9055
Fax: (210)226-0524
Co. E-mail: info@alamocitychamber.org
URL: http://www.alamocitychamber.org
Contact: Andi Tiwari, Chairman
Description: Works to provide programs which contribute to the economic growth and development of African American minority and small businesses throughout the greater San Antonio area. **Founded:** 1938.

57926 ■ Albany Chamber of Commerce (ACC)
PO Box 2047
Albany, TX 76430
Ph: (325)762-2525
Fax: (325)762-3125
Co. E-mail: chamberc@albanytexas.com
URL: http://www.albanytexas.com
Description: Promotes business and community development in Albany, TX. Encourages tourism and supports educational and cultural activities. Preserves historical buildings. Gathers and disseminates information. Conducts community social and promotional events. **Awards:** Teacher of the Year (Annual).

57927 ■ *Alice Business Today*
612 E Main St.
Alice, TX 78333
Ph: (361)664-3454
Fax: (361)664-2291
Co. E-mail: jnavejar@alicetx.org
URL: http://www.alicetxchamber.org
Contact: Juan A. Navejar, Jr., Executive Vice President
Released: Monthly

57928 ■ Alice Chamber of Commerce (ACC)
612 E Main St.
Alice, TX 78333
Ph: (361)664-3454
Fax: (361)664-2291
Co. E-mail: jnavejar@alicetx.org
URL: http://www.alicetxchamber.org
Contact: Juan A. Navejar, Jr., Executive Vice President
Description: Promotes business and community development in Alice, TX. Maintains hall of honor. **Publications:** *Alice Business Today* (Monthly); *Membership Directory and Buyers Guide* (Annual). **Educational Activities:** Membership Banquet (Annual). **Awards:** Citizen of the Year (Annual); Junior Citizen of the Year (Annual); Law Enforcement Officer of the Year (Annual).

57929 ■ Allen Chamber of Commerce
210 W McDermott Dr.
Allen, TX 75013
Ph: (972)727-5585
Fax: (972)727-9000
Co. E-mail: info@allenchamber.com
URL: http://www.allenchamber.com
Contact: Sharon Mayer, President
Description: Promotes business and community development in Allen, TX.

57930 ■ Alpine Chamber of Commerce (ACC)
106 N 3rd St.
Alpine, TX 79830

Ph: (432)837-2326
Free: 800-561-3712
Co. E-mail: info@alpinetexas.com
URL: http://www.alpinetexas.com
Contact: Mark Hannan, President
Description: Promotes business, community development, and tourism in Alpine, TX and Big Bend National Park and region. **Founded:** 1907. **Publications:** *Travel Guide - Big Bend* (Periodic).

57931 ■ Alvin-Manvel Area Chamber of Commerce (AMCC)
105 W Willis St.
Alvin, TX 77511-2344
Ph: (281)331-3944
Free: 800-331-4063
Fax: (281)585-8662
Co. E-mail: chamber@amacc.org
URL: http://www.alvinmanvelchamber.org
Contact: Wendy Del Bello, Chairperson
Description: Promotes business and community development in the Alvin, TX area. **Publications:** *The Chamber Connection* (Monthly); *Alvin-Manvel Area Chamber of Commerce--Membership Directory* (Annual). **Telecommunication Services:** connie@alvintexas.org.

57932 ■ Amarillo Chamber of Commerce
1000 S Polk St.
Amarillo, TX 79101-3408
Ph: (806)373-7800
Fax: (806)373-3909
Co. E-mail: chamber@amarillo-chamber.org
URL: http://www.amarillo-chamber.org
Contact: Gary Molberg, President
Description: Promotes business and community development in Amarillo, TX. Sponsors local festival. **Founded:** 1926. **Publications:** *Clubs and Organizations* (Annual); *Community Leaders* (Annual); *Membership Directory and Buyers' Guide* (Annual).

57933 ■ Anahuac Area Chamber of Commerce
PO Box R
Anahuac, TX 77514
Ph: (409)267-4190
Fax: (409)267-3907
URL: http://www.anahuacchamber.com
Contact: Bob Pascasio, Chairman
Description: Works to promote business and community development in Anahuac, TX area.

57934 ■ Aransas Pass Chamber of Commerce
130 W Goodnight
Aransas Pass, TX 78336
Ph: (361)758-2750
Free: 800-633-3028
Fax: (361)758-8320
Co. E-mail: apcoc@cableone.net
URL: http://www.aransaspass.org
Contact: Rosemary Vega, Chief Executive Officer
Description: Promotes business and community development in Aransas Pass, TX. **Founded:** 1937.

57935 ■ *Area Business Councils/Small Business Update*
602 E Commerce St.
San Antonio, TX 78295
Ph: (210)229-2100
Fax: (210)229-1600
Co. E-mail: infostore@sachamber.org
URL: http://sachamber.org
Contact: Richard Perez, President
Released: Weekly

57936 ■ Arlington Chamber of Commerce (ACC)
505 E Border St.
Arlington, TX 76010
Ph: (817)275-2613
Fax: (817)261-7389
Co. E-mail: wjurey@arlingtontx.com
URL: http://www.arlingtontx.com
Contact: Wes Jurey, President
Description: Promotes business and community development in the Arlington, TX area. Seeks to create job opportunities and diversify the city's economic

base. Represents business leadership on policy issues affecting city's economic growth. **Founded:** 1945. **Publications:** *Business Update* (Monthly). **Awards:** Outstanding Small Business of the Year Award (Annual); Warren Green Free Enterprise Scholarship (Annual).

57937 ■ Arlington Hispanic Chamber of Commerce (AHCC)
301 S Center St., Ste. 500
Arlington, TX 76010
Ph: (682)367-1415
Fax: (682)367-1417
Co. E-mail: office@hispanic-chamber.org
URL: http://www.hispanic-chamber.org
Contact: Zeke Sanchez, Chairman
Description: Develops, promotes and protects Hispanic business in Arlington and surrounding areas.

57938 ■ Athens Chamber of Commerce
1206 S Palestine St.
Athens, TX 75751
Ph: (903)675-5181
Free: 800-755-7878
Fax: (903)675-5183
Co. E-mail: info@athenscc.org
URL: http://www.athenscc.org
Contact: Sarah J. Hueber, President
Description: Promotes business and community development in Athens, TX. **Publications:** *Athens Magazine* (Annual); *Discovery Line* (Monthly).

57939 ■ *Athens Magazine*
1206 S Palestine St.
Athens, TX 75751
Ph: (903)675-5181
Free: 800-755-7878
Fax: (903)675-5183
Co. E-mail: info@athenscc.org
URL: http://www.athenscc.org
Contact: Sarah J. Hueber, President
Released: Annual **Price:** free.

57940 ■ Atlanta Area Chamber of Commerce (AACC)
101 N East St.
Atlanta, TX 75551-2600
Ph: (903)796-3296
Fax: (903)796-5711
Co. E-mail: atlantaareacoc@sbcglobal.net
URL: http://www.atlantatexas.org/chamber/atlanta-chamber-of-commerce.aspx
Contact: Lisa Thompson, President
Description: Businesses, individuals, and professionals in northeastern Cass County, TX seeking to improve the area's economy and growth. Conducts annual Leadership Institute. Sponsors monthly mixer; Farmer's Market, Hoot and Holler BBQ Cookoff; and Christmas parade. **Founded:** 1945. **Publications:** *Communique* (Monthly).

57941 ■ Azle Area Chamber of Commerce (AACC)
252 W Main St., Ste. A
Azle, TX 76020
Ph: (817)444-1112
Fax: (817)444-1143
Co. E-mail: info@azlechamber.com
URL: http://www.azlechamber.com
Contact: Lorie Pack, President
Description: Promotes business and community development in Azle, TX. **Founded:** 1959. **Publications:** *Membership Directory and Buyers' Guide* (Annual). **Awards:** Educator of the Year (Annual); Citizen of the Year (Annual).

57942 ■ Baird Chamber of Commerce (BCC)
328 Market St.
Baird, TX 79504
Ph: (325)854-2003
Co. E-mail: baird@bairdtexas.com
URL: http://www.bairdtexas.com
Description: Promotes business and community development in Baird, TX. Sponsors annual Trade Festival, and annual art show and sale. **Founded:** 1960. **Telecommunication Services:** chamber@bairdtexas.com.

57943 ■ Balch Springs Chamber of Commerce
PO Box 800095
Balch Springs, TX 75180
Ph: (972)557-0988
Fax: (972)584-0320
Co. E-mail: info@balchspringschamber.org
URL: http://www.balchspringschamber.org
Contact: Alvester Gibson, President
Description: Promotes business and community development in Balch Springs, TX.

57944 ■ Ballinger Chamber of Commerce
PO Box 577
Ballinger, TX 76821
Ph: (325)365-2333
Fax: (325)365-3445
Co. E-mail: coc@balingertx.org
URL: http://www.ballingertx.org
Contact: Steve Smith, President
Description: Promotes business and community development in Ballinger, TX. Sponsors annual Texas State Festival of Ethnic Cultures and Arts and Crafts Show.

57945 ■ Bandera County Texas Chamber of Commerce
PO Box 2445
Bandera, TX 78003-2445
Ph: (830)796-3280
Fax: (830)796-3970
Co. E-mail: cowboy@banderatex.com
URL: http://banderatex.com
Contact: Scott Asher, President
Description: Promotes business and community development in Bandera County, TX. Sponsors Funtier Day Parade and Hunters' Barbecue. **Founded:** 1963. **Publications:** *Directory of Products and Services* (Periodic).

57946 ■ Bastrop Chamber of Commerce (BCC)
927 Main St.
Bastrop, TX 78602-3809
Ph: (512)303-0558
Fax: (512)303-0305
Co. E-mail: info@bastropchamber.us
URL: http://www.bastropchamber.com
Contact: Debbie Denny, Chairman
Description: Promotes business and community development in Bastrop, TX. Promotes a stable business environment. Sponsors local festival. **Founded:** 1922.

57947 ■ Baytown Chamber of Commerce (BCC)
Amegy Bank Bldg.
Baytown, TX 77521
Ph: (281)422-8359
Fax: (281)428-1758
Co. E-mail: info@baytownchamber.com
URL: http://www.baytownchamber.com
Contact: Tracey S. Wheeler, President
Description: Promotes business and community development in Baytown, TX. **Founded:** 1945. **Publications:** *Discover Baytown* (Annual); *Discover Baytown* (Annual). **Educational Activities:** Baytown Business EXPO (Annual). **Awards:** Baytown Chamber of Commerce Scholarship; Public Safety Recognition (Annual); Fire Fighter of the Quarter and Law Enforcer of Quarter (Quarterly). **Telecommunication Services:** tracey@baytownchamber.com.

57948 ■ Beaumont Chamber of Commerce (BCC)
1110 Park St.
Beaumont, TX 77701
Ph: (409)838-6581
Fax: (409)833-6718
Co. E-mail: chamber@bmtcoc.org
URL: http://www.bmtcoc.org
Contact: Jim Rich, President
Description: Promotes business and community development in Southeast Texas. Works with government agencies, educational institutions, and other development organizations to preserve existing jobs, promote better understanding of the free enterprise system, and diversify the industrial base of the region. **Founded:** 1901. **Publications:** *Metropolitan Beaumont* (Bimonthly); *Southeast Texas Business* (Monthly).

57949 ■ Bee County Chamber of Commerce
1705 N St. Mary's St.
Beeville, TX 78102
Ph: (361)358-3267
Fax: (361)358-3966
Co. E-mail: info@beecountychamber.org
URL: http://www.beecountychamber.org
Contact: Jessy T. Garza, Chairman
Description: Promotes business and community development in Bee County, TX. **Founded:** 1940.

57950 ■ Bellville Chamber of Commerce
10 S Holland St.
Bellville, TX 77418
Ph: (979)865-3407
Fax: (979)865-9760
Co. E-mail: bellvillechamber@sbcglobal.net
URL: http://www.bellville.com
Contact: Pat Burns, President
Description: Promotes business and community development in Bellville, OH area.

57951 ■ Belton Area Chamber of Commerce
412 E Central Ave.
Belton, TX 76513
Ph: (254)939-3551
Fax: (254)939-1061
Co. E-mail: info@beltonchamber.com
URL: http://www.beltonchamber.com
Contact: Stephanie O'Banion, President
Description: Promotes business and community development in the Belton, TX area. Sponsors 4th of July Celebration. **Founded:** 1913. **Publications:** *Return on Investment* (Monthly).

57952 ■ Big Lake Chamber of Commerce
121 N Main St.
Big Lake, TX 76932
Ph: (915)884-2980
Co. E-mail: blcoc@verizon.net
URL: http://www.biglaketx.com
Contact: Tina Robertson, Director
Description: Promotes business and community development in Big Lake, TX.

57953 ■ Big Spring Area Chamber of Commerce (BSACC)
215 W 3rd St.
Big Spring, TX 79720-2426
Ph: (432)263-7641
Free: 800-734-7641
Fax: (432)264-9111
Co. E-mail: debbyev@bigspringchamber.com
URL: http://www.bigspringchamber.com
Contact: Debbye Valverde, Executive Director
Description: Promotes business and community development in the Big Spring, TX area. Sponsors festival. **Founded:** 1930. **Publications:** *Focus* (Monthly). **Telecommunication Services:** chamber@bigspringchamber.com.

57954 ■ Bishop Chamber of Commerce (BCC)
213 E Main St.
Bishop, TX 78343-0426
Ph: (361)584-2214
Fax: (361)584-2214
Co. E-mail: bishopcc@intcomm.net
URL: http://www.bishoptx.com
Description: Promotes business and community development in Bishop, TX. Conducts charitable activities; sponsors Community Christmas Program. **Awards:** Junior Citizen of the Year (Annual); Lifetime Service Award (Periodic); Outstanding Business/Professional (Annual); Outstanding Citizen of the Year (Annual); Outstanding Newcomer (Periodic).

57955 ■ Blanco Chamber of Commerce
312 Pecan St.
Blanco, TX 78606-2607
Ph: (830)833-5101

Fax: (830)469-4455
Co. E-mail: info@blancochamber.com
URL: http://www.blancochamber.com
Contact: Marcy Westcott, Chairperson
Description: Promotes business and community development in Blanco, TX. Conducts charitable events. Sponsors car show and festival. **Publications:** *Blanco Chamber of Commerce--Member Directory and Resource Guide* (Annual).

57956 ■ Bolivar Peninsula Chamber of Commerce (BPCC)
PO Box 1170
Crystal Beach, TX 77650
Ph: (409)684-5940
Free: 800-386-7863
Fax: (409)684-3123
Co. E-mail: info@bolivarchamber.org
URL: http://www.bolivarchamber.org
Contact: Anne Willis, Vice President
Description: Promotes business and community development in the Bolivar Peninsula area of Texas. Addresses environmental and erosion control issues. Organizes Texas Crab Festival and Crystalland Christmas. Sponsors charities, scholarship programs, Volunteer Fire Departments, Emergency Medical Service, and youth athletic league. **Founded:** 1983. **Publications:** *Telephone Listing* (Monthly).

57957 ■ Bonham Area Chamber of Commerce and Economic Development (BACC)
119 E 5th St.
Bonham, TX 75418
Ph: (903)583-4811
Fax: (903)583-7972
Co. E-mail: bonhamchamber@cableone.net
URL: http://www.bonhamchamber.com
Contact: Bill Jones, Executive Director
Description: Promotes economic, cultural, and community development in Bonham and Fannin County, TX. **Founded:** 1929. **Publications:** *Chamber Chatter* (Monthly); *Image* (Annual).

57958 ■ Borger Chamber of Commerce
613 N Main St.
Borger, TX 79007-3528
Ph: (806)274-2211
Fax: (806)273-3488
Co. E-mail: borgerchamber@amaonline.com
URL: http://www.borgerchamber.org
Contact: Beverly Benton, President
Description: Promotes business and community development in Borger, TX. **Founded:** 1926. **Publications:** *Chamber Guide* (Annual); *Chamber Guide* (Annual); *Mid-Month Memo* (Quarterly). **Educational Activities:** World's Largest Fish Fry (Annual).

57959 ■ Bowie Chamber of Commerce (BCC)
309 N Smythe St.
Bowie, TX 76230
Ph: (940)872-1173
Free: 866-872-1173
Fax: (940)872-3291
Co. E-mail: bowiechamber@morgan.net
URL: http://www.bowietxchamber.org
Contact: Stacy Barber, President
Description: Promotes business, tourism and community development in Bowie, TX. **Founded:** 1928. **Publications:** *Chamber of Commerce Newsletter* (Monthly). **Telecommunication Services:** bowiechamber@communicomm.com.

57960 ■ Brady - McCulloch County Chamber of Commerce
101 E 1st St.
Brady, TX 76825-4906
Ph: (325)597-3491
Free: 888-577-5657
Fax: (325)792-9181
Co. E-mail: bradychamber@hotmail.com
URL: http://www.bradytx.com
Contact: Carla Landes, President
Description: Promotes business and community development in Brady, TX and McCulloch County. **Scope:** phone directories. **Founded:** 1920. **Subscriptions:** 152. **Publications:** *The Heartbeat* (Quarterly). **Awards:** Citizen of the Year (Annual);

Educator of the Year (Annual); Lifetime Achievement (Annual); Student of the Year (Annual). **Telecommunication Services:** erin@bradytx.com.

57961 ■ Breckenridge Chamber of Commerce
100 E Elm St.
Breckenridge, TX 76424
Ph: (254)559-2301
Fax: (254)559-7104
Co. E-mail: chamber@breckenridgetexas.com
URL: http://www.breckenridgetexas.com
Contact: Patsy Hagler, Vice President, Operations
Description: Promotes business and community development in Breckenridge, TX area.

57962 ■ Bridgeport Area Chamber of Commerce (BACC)
812 A Halsell St.
Bridgeport, TX 76426-3050
Ph: (940)683-2076
Fax: (940)683-3969
Co. E-mail: tiffanyevans@bridgeportchamber.org
URL: http://www.bridgeportchamber.org
Contact: Tiffany Evans, Executive Director
Description: Promotes business and community development in Wise County, TX. Sponsors Butterfield Stage Days, lighted Christmas Parade, Rodeo Parade, Wise County Youth Fair, and Holiday Spectacular. Assists in maintaining parks board. **Founded:** 1968. **Publications:** *Bridgeport Chamber of Commerce-The Voice of Business in Bridgeport* (10/year).

57963 ■ *Bridgeport Chamber of Commerce-The Voice of Business in Bridgeport*
812 A Halsell St.
Bridgeport, TX 76426-3050
Ph: (940)683-2076
Fax: (940)683-3969
Co. E-mail: tiffanyevans@bridgeportchamber.org
URL: http://www.bridgeportchamber.org
Contact: Tiffany Evans, Executive Director
Released: 10/year; every month except July and August.

57964 ■ Brownsville Chamber of Commerce (BCC)
1600 University Blvd.
Brownsville, TX 78520
Ph: (956)542-4341
Fax: (956)504-3348
Co. E-mail: info@brownsvillechamber.com
URL: http://www.brownsvillechamber.com
Contact: Angela R. Burton, President
Description: Promotes business and community development in Brownsville, TX. **Founded:** 1937. **Publications:** *Progress* (Monthly).

57965 ■ Brownwood Area Chamber of Commerce (BCC)
600 E Depot St.
Brownwood, TX 76801-7000
Ph: (915)646-9535
Fax: (915)643-6686
Co. E-mail: info@brownwoodchamber.org
URL: http://www.brownwoodchamber.org
Contact: Laura Terhune, Chief Executive Officer
Description: Promotes business and community development in Brown County, TX. **Founded:** 1906. **Publications:** *Partners* (Monthly). **Educational Activities:** Awards Banquet (Annual). **Telecommunication Services:** director@brownwoodchamber.org.

57966 ■ Buda Area Chamber of Commerce (BACC)
PO Box 904
Buda, TX 78610
Ph: (512)295-9999
Fax: (512)295-3569
Co. E-mail: info@budachamber.com
URL: http://www.budachamber.com
Contact: Richard Schneider, President
Description: Seeks to promote business and community development and enhance the relationship between local businesses and professionals with the public.

57967 ■ Buffalo Chamber of Commerce
PO Box 207
Buffalo, TX 75831-0207
Ph: (903)322-5810
Fax: (903)322-3849
Co. E-mail: chamber@buffalotxchamberofcommerce.org
URL: http://www.buffalotxchamberofcommerce.org
Contact: Molly Glick, President
Description: Promotes business and community development in Buffalo, TX. **Founded:** 1979.

57968 ■ Bulverde/Spring Branch Area Chamber of Commerce (BSBACOC)
PO Box 91
Bulverde, TX 78163
Ph: (830)438-4285
Free: 866-BUL-VERDE
Fax: (830)438-8572
Co. E-mail: bsbacoc@gvtc.com
URL: http://www.bulverdespringbranchchamber.com
Contact: Kathleen Banse, Director
Founded: 1995.

57969 ■ Burkburnett Chamber of Commerce (BCC)
104 W 3rd St.
Burkburnett, TX 76354
Ph: (940)569-3304
Fax: (940)569-3306
URL: http://www.burkburnett.org
Contact: Dick Vallon, Executive Director
Description: Promotes business and community development in Burkburnett, TX. **Founded:** 1925.

57970 ■ Burleson Area Chamber of Commerce (BACC)
1044 SW Wilshire Blvd.
Burleson, TX 76028-5717
Ph: (817)295-6121
Co. E-mail: alison.skirby@farmersagency.com
URL: http://burlesonchamber.com
Contact: Alison Bradham, Chairperson
Description: Promotes business and community development in northern Johnson County, TX. Sponsors the Texas Heritage Trail Ride. **Founded:** 1966. **Awards:** Citizen of the Year (Annual); Sportsman of the Year (Annual).

57971 ■ Burleson County Chamber of Commerce - Caldwell Office (BCCC)
301 N Main St.
Caldwell, TX 77836
Ph: (979)567-0000
Fax: (979)567-0818
Co. E-mail: info@burlesoncountytx.com
URL: http://www.burlesoncountytx.com
Contact: Louemma Polansky, Chairperson
Description: Promotes business and community development in Burleson County, TX. Sponsors Kolachee Festival and other special events.

57972 ■ Burnet Chamber of Commerce
229 S Pierce
Burnet, TX 78611
Ph: (512)756-4297
Co. E-mail: info@burnetchamber.org
URL: http://www.burnetchamber.org
Description: Promotes business and community development in Burnet, TX. **Founded:** 1955. **Awards:** Outstanding Director of the Year (Annual); Outstanding Volunteer of the Year (Annual).

57973 ■ *Business*
PO Box 346
Georgetown, TX 78627-0346
Ph: (512)930-3535
Fax: (512)930-3587
Co. E-mail: info@georgetownchamber.org
URL: http://www.georgetownchamber.org
Contact: Mel Pendland, President

57974 ■ *Business Barometer*
322 S Missouri
Weslaco, TX 78596
Ph: (956)968-3141

Fax: (956)968-0210
Co. E-mail: mail@valleychamber.com
URL: http://www.valleychamber.com
Contact: Allen Shields, Chairman
Released: Monthly

57975 ■ *Business Connection*
2713 Stonewall St.
Greenville, TX 75403-1055
Ph: (903)455-1510
Co. E-mail: chamber@greenvillechamber.com
URL: http://www.greenvillechamber.com
Contact: Sally Bird, President
Released: Monthly

57976 ■ *Business Desk Reference*
210 Barton Springs Rd., Ste. 400
Austin, TX 78704
Ph: (512)478-9383
Fax: (512)478-6389
Co. E-mail: communication@austinchamber.com
URL: http://www.austinchamber.com
Contact: Michael W. Rollins, President
Released: Periodic

57977 ■ *Business Directory*
100 Train Station Dr.
Llano, TX 78643
Ph: (325)247-5354
Free: 866-539-5535
Fax: (325)248-6917
Co. E-mail: info@llanochamber.org
URL: http://www.llanochamber.org
Contact: David Griffith, President
Released: Annual

57978 ■ *Business Directory*
505 W Davis
Conroe, TX 77305
Ph: (936)756-6644
Fax: (936)756-6462
Co. E-mail: info@conroe.org
URL: http://www.conroe.org
Contact: Scott Harper, President
Released: Periodic

57979 ■ *Business Line*
116 N Camp St.
Seguin, TX 78155
Ph: (830)379-6382
Fax: (830)379-6971
Co. E-mail: cofc@seguinchamber.com
URL: http://www.seguinchamber.com
Contact: Shanta Kuhl, President
Released: Monthly

57980 ■ *Business News*
2010 N Hampton Rd., Ste. 200
DeSoto, TX 75115
Ph: (972)224-3565
Fax: (972)354-1022
Co. E-mail: cjackson@desotochamber.org
URL: http://www.desotochamber.org
Contact: Cammy Jackson, President
Released: Monthly

57981 ■ *Business News*
600 Padre Blvd.
South Padre Island, TX 78597
Ph: (956)761-4412
Fax: (956)761-2739
Co. E-mail: info@spichamber.com
URL: http://www.spichamber.com
Contact: Roxanne Harris Guenzel, President
Released: Monthly

57982 ■ *Business News*
PO Box 12
Wimberley, TX 78676
Ph: (512)847-2201
Fax: (512)847-3189
Co. E-mail: info@wimberley.org
URL: http://www.wimberley.org
Contact: Linda Germain, Chairman of the Board
Released: Quarterly

57983 ■ *Business Plan*
1200 E 15th St.
Plano, TX 75074

Ph: (972)424-7547
Fax: (972)422-5182
Co. E-mail: info@planochamber.org
URL: http://www.planochamber.org/index.asp
Contact: Mabrie Jackson, President
Released: Annual

57984 ■ *Business Referral Guide*
1314 W Moore Ave.
Terrell, TX 75160
Ph: (972)563-5703
Free: 877-TER-RELL
Fax: (972)563-2363
Co. E-mail: info@terrelltexas.com
URL: http://www.terrelltexas.com
Contact: Danny R. Booth, President
Released: Annual

57985 ■ *Business Report*
4749 Twin City Hwy., Ste. 300
Port Arthur, TX 77642
Ph: (409)963-1107
Fax: (409)962-1997
Co. E-mail: portarthurchamber@portarthurtexas.com
URL: http://www.portarthurtexas.com
Contact: Mary Ann Reid, President
Released: Monthly

57986 ■ *Business Resource Directory*
1200 E 15th St.
Plano, TX 75074
Ph: (972)424-7547
Fax: (972)422-5182
Co. E-mail: info@planochamber.org
URL: http://www.planochamber.org/index.asp
Contact: Mabrie Jackson, President
Released: Annual

57987 ■ *The Business Spotlight*
PO Box 170132
Dallas, TX 75217
Ph: (214)398-9590
Fax: (214)398-9591
Co. E-mail: info@sedcc.org
URL: http://www.sedcc.org
Contact: Carl Raines, Chairman
Released: Monthly **Price:** included in membership dues.

57988 ■ *Business Spotlight*
110 Center St.
Deer Park, TX 77536-2734
Ph: (281)479-1559
Fax: (281)476-4041
Co. E-mail: info@deerpark.org
URL: http://www.deerpark.org
Contact: Tim Culp, President
Released: Monthly

57989 ■ *Business Update*
505 E Border St.
Arlington, TX 76010
Ph: (817)275-2613
Fax: (817)261-7389
Co. E-mail: wjurey@arlingtontx.com
URL: http://www.arlingtontx.com
Contact: Wes Jurey, President
Released: Monthly **Price:** free.

57990 ■ *Buyer's Guide*
c/o Rose Ryan, Exec. Dir.
9374 Valhalla
Selma, TX 78154
Ph: (210)658-8322
Fax: (210)658-1817
Co. E-mail: executive_director@metrocomchamber.
org
URL: http://www.randolphmetrocomchamber.org
Contact: Rose Ryan, Executive Director
Released: Periodic

57991 ■ **Calvert Chamber of Commerce**
PO Box 132
Calvert, TX 77837-0132
Ph: (979)364-2559
Co. E-mail: calverttx@calverttx.com
URL: http://www.calverttx.com
Description: Promotes business and community
development in Calvert, TX. **Founded:** 1868.

57992 ■ **Cameron Chamber of Commerce**
102 E 1st St.
Cameron, TX 76520
Ph: (254)697-4979
Fax: (254)697-2345
Co. E-mail: chamber@cameron-tx.com
URL: http://www.cameron-tx.com
Contact: Steven Wise, President
Description: Promotes business and community
development in the Cameron, TX area. Assists local
groups with community betterment projects; sponsors
local festival and the Center for Tourism. **Founded:**
1933. **Publications:** *Chamber Newsletter* (Monthly).
Awards: Banquet Award (Annual).

57993 ■ **Camp County Chamber of
Commerce**
202 Jefferson St.
Pittsburg, TX 75686
Ph: (903)856-3442
Fax: (903)856-3570
Co. E-mail: info@pittsburgchamber.com
URL: http://www.pittsburgchamber.com
Contact: Bob Sehon, President
Description: Promotes business and community
development in Camp County, TX. Sponsors festival.

57994 ■ **Canton Chamber of Commerce**
720 N Trade Days Blvd.
Canton, TX 75103
Ph: (903)567-2991
Co. E-mail: info@cantontexaschamber.com
URL: http://cantontexaschamber.com
Contact: Bob Reese, Chairman
Description: Promotes business and community
development in Canton, TX.

57995 ■ **Canyon Chamber of Commerce
(CCC)**
1518 5th Ave.
Canyon, TX 79015
Ph: (806)655-7815
Fax: (806)655-4608
Co. E-mail: info@canyonchamber.org
URL: http://www.canyonchamber.org
Contact: Cheryl Malcolm, Executive Director
Description: Promotes business, community devel-
opment, and tourism in the Canyon, TX area. Con-
ducts charitable activities. Sponsors Fourth of July
parade, fireworks, entertainment, craft/fun fair and
"Fair on the Square" event.

57996 ■ *The Catalyst*
5005 Woodway, Ste. 215
Houston, TX 77056-1780
Ph: (713)629-5555
Fax: (713)629-6403
Co. E-mail: dsweat@galleriachamber.com
URL: http://www.galleriachamber.com
Contact: Don P. Sweat, President
Released: Bimonthly

57997 ■ **Cedar Hill Chamber of Commerce
(CHCC)**
300 W Houston St.
Cedar Hill, TX 75104-2678
Ph: (972)291-7817
Fax: (972)291-8101
Co. E-mail: info@cedarhillchamber.org
URL: http://www.cedarhillchamber.org
Contact: Amanda Skinner, President
Description: Promotes business and community
development in Cedar Hill, TX.

57998 ■ **Cedar Park Chamber of Commerce
and Tourism**
1460 E Whitestone Blvd., Bldg. 2, Ste. 180
Cedar Park, TX 78613
Ph: (512)260-7800
Fax: (512)260-9269
URL: http://www.cedarparkchamber.org
Contact: Tony Moline, President
Description: Promotes business and community
development in Cedar Park, TX. **Founded:** 1973.
Publications: *Friday Facts* (Monthly).

57999 ■ **Cen-Tex Hispanic Chamber of
Commerce (CTHCC)**
915 La Salle Ave.
Waco, TX 76701
Ph: (254)754-7111
Fax: (254)754-3456
Co. E-mail: info@wacohispanicchamber.com
URL: http://www.wacohispanicchamber.com
Contact: Richard Contreras, President
Description: Promotes business and development
for the Hispanic community in Waco and Central
Texas. **Founded:** 1975.

58000 ■ **Centerville Chamber of Commerce**
PO Box 422
Centerville, TX 75833
Ph: (903)536-7261
Co. E-mail: centerville75833@yahoo.com
URL: http://www.centervilletexas.com
Contact: Dennis Coffey, President
Description: Promotes business and community
development in Centerville, TX area.

58001 ■ *The Chamber Business Report*
1125 Bonham St.
Paris, TX 75460
Ph: (903)784-2501
Fax: (903)784-2503
Co. E-mail: chamber@paristexas.com
URL: http://www.paristexas.com
Contact: Mindy Moree, President
Released: Monthly

58002 ■ *Chamber Chat*
PO Box 400
Slaton, TX 79364-0400
Ph: (806)828-6238
Fax: (806)828-5115
Co. E-mail: slatoncoc@sbcglobal.net
URL: http://www.slatonchamberofcommerce.org
Released: Monthly **Price:** included in membership
dues.

58003 ■ *Chamber Chat*
58 Spencer Hwy.
South Houston, TX 77587
Ph: (713)943-0244
Fax: (713)943-3978
URL: http://www.southhoustonchamber.org
Contact: JoAnn Parish, Executive Officer
Released: Monthly

58004 ■ *Chamber Chatter*
PO Box 4946
Lago Vista, TX 78645
Ph: (512)267-7952
Fax: (512)267-2338
Co. E-mail: info@lagovista.org
URL: http://www.lagovista.org
Contact: Sherri Campbell-Jander, Executive Director

58005 ■ *Chamber Chatter*
119 E 5th St.
Bonham, TX 75418
Ph: (903)583-4811
Fax: (903)583-7972
Co. E-mail: bonhamchamber@cableone.net
URL: http://www.bonhamchamber.com
Contact: Bill Jones, Executive Director
Released: Monthly **Price:** $25, /year.

58006 ■ *Chamber Chatter*
PO Box 474
Decatur, TX 76234
Ph: (940)627-3107
Fax: (940)627-3771
Co. E-mail: misty.hudson@netcommander.com
URL: http://www.decaturtx.com
Contact: Misty Hudson, Executive Director
Released: Monthly

58007 ■ *Chamber Chatter*
PO Box 426
Quitman, TX 75783-0426
Ph: (903)763-4411
Free: 866-302-3884

Fax: (903)763-4913
Co. E-mail: qtmncoc@peoplescom.net
URL: http://www.quitman.com
Contact: Toni Cole, Executive Director
Released: Monthly **Price:** free.

58008 ■ *Chamber Chatter*
105 E 12th St.
Shamrock, TX 79079
Ph: (806)256-2501
Fax: (806)256-3739
Co. E-mail: webmaster@cityofshamrock.com
URL: http://www.shamrocktx.net
Contact: David Rushing, Director
Released: Monthly

58009 ■ *Chamber Chatter*
PO Box 900
Kyle, TX 78640-0900
Ph: (512)268-4220
Free: 800-903-1564
Co. E-mail: ray@kylechamber.org
URL: http://www.kylechamber.org
Contact: Ray Hernandez, Executive Director
Released: Weekly

58010 ■ **Chamber of Commerce for Individuals with DisABILITIES—Chamber of Commerce for People with Barriers**
c/o Mr. Dan Howell, Pres.
PO Box 222008
Dallas, TX 75222-2008
Co. E-mail: ccidinfo@chamber4us.org
URL: http://chamber4us.org
Contact: Mr. Dan Howell, President
Description: Uses business principles to meet the economic needs of individuals with disabilities. Provides resources and avenues for the members to lessen their dependence on government and restore their self sufficiency. **Scope:** self-employment. **Founded:** 1996.

58011 ■ *Chamber of Commerce Newsletter*
309 N Smythe St.
Bowie, TX 76230
Ph: (940)872-1173
Free: 866-872-1173
Fax: (940)872-3291
Co. E-mail: bowiechamber@morgan.net
URL: http://www.bowietxchamber.org
Contact: Stacy Barber, President
Released: Monthly

58012 ■ *Chamber Connection*
509 W Bethel Rd., Ste. 200
Coppell, TX 75019-4483
Ph: (972)393-2829
Fax: (972)393-0659
Co. E-mail: info@coppellchamber.org
URL: http://www.coppellchamber.org
Contact: Tony Moline, President
Released: Monthly

58013 ■ *Chamber Connection*
174 Cypress St., Ste. 200
Abilene, TX 79601-5850
Ph: (325)677-7241
Fax: (325)677-0622
Co. E-mail: info@abilenechamber.com
URL: http://www.abilenechamber.com
Contact: Mike McMahan, President
Released: Monthly

58014 ■ *The Chamber Connection*
105 W Willis St.
Alvin, TX 77511-2344
Ph: (281)331-3944
Free: 800-331-4063
Fax: (281)585-8662
Co. E-mail: chamber@amacc.org
URL: http://www.alvinmanvelchamber.org
Contact: Wendy Del Bello, Chairperson
Released: Monthly

58015 ■ *Chamber Connection*
1000 Railroad Ave.
Fort Stockton, TX 79735
Ph: (432)336-2264
Free: 800-336-2166

Fax: (432)336-6114
Co. E-mail: director@ftstockton.org
URL: http://www.fortstockton.org
Contact: Arna McCorkle, Executive Vice President
Released: Quarterly **Price:** free for members.

58016 ■ *Chamber Connection*
PO Box 600
Livingston, TX 77351
Ph: (936)327-4929
Free: 800-918-1305
Fax: (936)327-2660
Co. E-mail: chamberadmin@livingston.net
URL: http://www.lpcchamber.com
Contact: Sydney Murphy, Executive Director
Released: Monthly

58017 ■ *Chamber Connection*
6117 Broadway St.
Pearland, TX 77581
Ph: (281)485-3634
Fax: (281)485-2420
Co. E-mail: chamber@pearlandchamber.org
URL: http://www.pearlandchamber.com
Contact: Carol R. Artz, President
Released: Monthly

58018 ■ *Chamber Connection*
700 Parker Sq., Ste. 100
Flower Mound, TX 75028
Ph: (972)539-0500
Fax: (972)539-4307
Co. E-mail: c.howard@flowermoundchamber.com
URL: http://www.flowermoundchamber.com
Contact: Cindi Howard, President (Acting)
Released: Monthly

58019 ■ *Chamber Dialogue*
PO Box 1135
Ozona, TX 76943-1135
Ph: (325)392-3737
Fax: (325)392-3485
Co. E-mail: oztxcoc@aol.com
URL: http://www.ozona.com/articles/view/4/chamber-of-commerce
Contact: Shanon Biggerstaff, Chief Executive Officer
Released: Monthly

58020 ■ *Chamber at a Glance*
2401 E Missouri St.
El Paso, TX 79903
Ph: (915)566-4066
Fax: (915)566-9714
Co. E-mail: cindyramosdavidson@ephcc.org
URL: http://www.ephcc.org
Contact: Cindy Ramos-Davidson, Chief Executive Officer
Released: Monthly

58021 ■ *Chamber Guide*
613 N Main St.
Borger, TX 79007-3528
Ph: (806)274-2211
Fax: (806)273-3488
Co. E-mail: borgerchamber@amaonline.com
URL: http://www.borgerchamber.org
Contact: Beverly Benton, President
Released: Annual **Price:** free.

58022 ■ *Chamber Guide*
551 N Valley Pkwy.
Lewisville, TX 75067
Ph: (972)436-9571
Fax: (972)436-5949
Co. E-mail: info@lewisvillechamber.org
URL: http://www.lewisvillechamber.org
Contact: Matt McCormick, President
Released: Annual

58023 ■ *Chamber Ink*
210 Barton Springs Rd., Ste. 400
Austin, TX 78704
Ph: (512)478-9383
Fax: (512)478-6389
Co. E-mail: communication@austinchamber.com
URL: http://www.austinchamber.com
Contact: Michael W. Rollins, President
Released: 10/year

58024 ■ *Chamber Link*
PO Box 346
Georgetown, TX 78627-0346
Ph: (512)930-3535
Fax: (512)930-3587
Co. E-mail: info@georgetownchamber.org
URL: http://www.georgetownchamber.org
Contact: Mel Pendland, President
Released: Weekly

58025 ■ *Chamber Magazine*
4120 Ave. H
Rosenberg, TX 77471
Ph: (281)342-5464
Fax: (281)342-2990
Co. E-mail: info@roserichchamber.org
Contact: Gail Parker, President
Released: Annual **Price:** free.

58026 ■ *Chamber Matters*
1604 N Jefferson
Mount Pleasant, TX 75455
Ph: (903)572-8567
Fax: (903)572-0613
Co. E-mail: info@mtpleasanttx.com
URL: http://www.mtpleasanttx.com
Contact: Faustine Curry, Chief Executive Officer
Released: Quarterly **Price:** included in membership dues.

58027 ■ *Chamber Matters*
275 W Princeton Dr., Ste. 105
Princeton, TX 75407
Ph: (972)736-6462
URL: http://www.princetontxchamber.com
Contact: Virginia Gathright, President

58028 ■ *Chamber Monthly Newsletter*
618 N Main St.
Schulenburg, TX 78956
Ph: (979)743-4514
Free: 866-504-5294
Fax: (979)743-9155
Co. E-mail: info@schulenburgchamber.org
URL: http://schulenburgchamber.org
Contact: Rachel Bolfik, Office Manager
Released: Monthly

58029 ■ *Chamber News*
PO Box 347
Sulphur Springs, TX 75483-0347
Ph: (903)885-6515
Free: 888-300-6623
Fax: (903)885-6516
Co. E-mail: chamber1@suddenlinkmail.net
URL: http://www.sulphursprings-tx.com
Contact: Meredith Caddell, President
Released: Monthly

58030 ■ *Chamber News*
PO Box 310
Weatherford, TX 76086
Ph: (817)596-3801
Free: 888-594-3801
Fax: (817)613-9216
Co. E-mail: info@weatherford-chamber.com
URL: http://www.weatherford-chamber.com
Contact: Tammy Gazzola, President
Released: Monthly

58031 ■ *Chamber News and Views*
201 N Main St.
Henderson, TX 75652
Ph: (903)657-5528
Fax: (903)657-9454
Co. E-mail: info@hendersontx.com
URL: http://www.hendersontx.com
Contact: Judy Sewell, Executive Director
Released: Monthly

58032 ■ *Chamber Newsletter*
102 E 1st St.
Cameron, TX 76520
Ph: (254)697-4979

Fax: (254)697-2345
Co. E-mail: chamber@cameron-tx.com
URL: http://www.cameron-tx.com
Contact: Steven Wise, President
Released: Monthly **Price:** free for members and associates.

58033 ■ *Chamber Newsletter*
777 Peters Ave.
Pleasanton, TX 94566
Ph: (925)846-5858
Fax: (925)846-9697
Co. E-mail: scott@pleasanton.org
URL: http://www.pleasanton.org
Contact: Scott Raty, President
Released: Monthly **Price:** available to members only.

58034 ■ *Chamber Newsletter*
1203 W Cameron Ave.
Rockdale, TX 76567
Ph: (512)446-2030
Fax: (512)446-5969
Co. E-mail: info@rockdalechamber.com
URL: http://www.rockdalechamber.com
Contact: Denice Doss, President
Released: Bimonthly **Price:** free.

58035 ■ *Chamber Notes*
124 E Church St.
Cuero, TX 77954
Ph: (361)275-2112
Fax: (361)275-6351
Co. E-mail: cuerocc@cuero.org
URL: http://www.cuero.org
Contact: Eric Draper, President
Released: Quarterly

58036 ■ *Chamber Notes*
813 N Kilgore St.
Kilgore, TX 75662
Ph: (903)984-5022
Free: 866-984-0400
Fax: (903)984-4975
Co. E-mail: info@kilgorechamber.com
URL: http://www.kilgorechamber.com
Contact: Donna Beets, Chairperson
Released: Monthly

58037 ■ *Chamber Notes*
100 N Center St.
New Boston, TX 75570-2935
Ph: (903)628-2581
Fax: (903)628-6340
Co. E-mail: chamber@newbostontx.org
URL: http://www.newbostontx.org
Contact: Deborah Cook, Executive Director
Released: Quarterly **Price:** free.

58038 ■ *Chamber Progress*
6900 S Rice Ave.
Bellaire, TX 77402-0788
Ph: (713)666-1521
Fax: (713)666-1523
Co. E-mail: trishw@gswhcc.org
URL: http://www.southwesthoustonchamber.com
Contact: Toni J. Franklin, President
Released: Monthly

58039 ■ *The Chamber Report*
PO Box 65
Comanche, TX 76442
Ph: (325)356-3233
Fax: (325)356-2940
Co. E-mail: info@comanchechamber.org
URL: http://www.comanchechamber.org
Contact: Marvin McKinnon, President
Released: Quarterly **Price:** free.

58040 ■ *The Chamber Report*
700 N Pearl St., Ste. 1200
Dallas, TX 75201
Ph: (214)746-6600
Fax: (214)712-1950
Co. E-mail: information@dallaschamber.org
URL: http://www.dallaschamber.org
Contact: Jim Oberwetter, President

58041 ■ *The Chamber Today*
602 E Commerce St.
San Antonio, TX 78295
Ph: (210)229-2100
Fax: (210)229-1600
Co. E-mail: infostore@sachamber.org
URL: http://sachamber.org
Contact: Richard Perez, President
Released: Weekly

58042 ■ *Chamber Update*
8224 White Settlement Rd., Ste. 100
White Settlement, TX 76108
Ph: (817)246-1121
Fax: (817)246-1121
Co. E-mail: wsacc@whitesettlement-tx.com
URL: http://www.whitesettlement-tx.com
Contact: Karla Barker, President
Released: Monthly

58043 ■ *The Chamber Voice*
519-25th St.
Galveston, TX 77550
Ph: (409)763-5326
Fax: (409)763-8271
Co. E-mail: gspagnola@galvestonchamber.com
URL: http://www.galvestonchamber.com
Contact: Gina Spagnola, President
Released: Quarterly

58044 ■ *Chamber Works*
PO Box 306
Stephenville, TX 76401
Ph: (254)965-5313
Fax: (254)965-3814
Co. E-mail: info@stephenvilletexas.org
URL: http://www.stephenvilletexas.org
Contact: July Danley, President
Released: Monthly

58045 ■ *Chambergram*
4334 Fairmont Pkwy.
Pasadena, TX 77504-3306
Ph: (281)487-7871
Fax: (281)487-5530
Co. E-mail: info@pasadenachamber.org
URL: http://www.pasadenachamber.org
Contact: Sherry Trainer, President
Released: Monthly

58046 ■ *Chambergram*
6117 Broadway St.
Pearland, TX 77581
Ph: (281)485-3634
Fax: (281)485-2420
Co. E-mail: chamber@pearlandchamber.org
URL: http://www.pearlandchamber.com
Contact: Carol R. Artz, President
Released: Weekly

58047 ■ *Chamber's Business*
700 Parker Sq., Ste. 100
Flower Mound, TX 75028
Ph: (972)539-0500
Fax: (972)539-4307
Co. E-mail: c.howard@flowermoundchamber.com
URL: http://www.flowermoundchamber.com
Contact: Cindi Howard, President (Acting)
Released: Annual

58048 ■ *ChamberWorks*
PO Box 325
Denison, TX 75020-0325
Ph: (903)465-1551
Fax: (903)465-8443
Co. E-mail: information@denisontexas.com
URL: http://www.denisontexas.us/default.aspx
Contact: Anna H. McKinney, President
Released: Monthly

58049 ■ Childress Chamber of Commerce
c/o Susan Leary, Exec. Dir.
PO Box 35
Childress, TX 79201

Ph: (940)937-2567
Co. E-mail: c_commerce@att.net
URL: http://biz.childresstexas.net/chamberofcommerce
Contact: Susan Leary, Executive Director
Description: Promotes business and community development in Childress, TX. Conducts charitable events. Sponsors festival. Sponsors charitable services and competitions. **Founded:** 1909. **Awards:** Man of the Year (Annual).

58050 ■ Cisco Chamber of Commerce (CCC)
309 Conrad Hilton Ave.
Cisco, TX 76437-2721
Ph: (254)442-2537
URL: http://www.ciscotx.com
Contact: Bridget Flores, Executive Director
Description: Promotes business and community development in Cisco, TX. Conducts charitable activities. Sponsors festival.

58051 ■ City of Eden
PO Box 367
Eden, TX 76837-0367
Co. E-mail: edenchamber@verizon.net
URL: http://edentexas.com
Contact: Keith Hall, President
Released: Quarterly **Price:** free.

58052 ■ *City Map*
1700 Sidney Baker St., Ste. 100
Kerrville, TX 78028
Ph: (830)896-1155
Fax: (830)896-1175
Co. E-mail: info@kerrvilletx.com
URL: http://kerrvilletx.le3.getliveedit.com/pages/home
Contact: Mark Tuschak, Chairman

58053 ■ City of South Houston Chamber of Commerce (CSHCC)
58 Spencer Hwy.
South Houston, TX 77587
Ph: (713)943-0244
Fax: (713)943-3978
URL: http://www.southhoustonchamber.org
Contact: JoAnn Parish, Executive Officer
Description: Promotes business and community development in the South Houston, TX area. Sponsors Strawberry Festival. **Publications:** *Chamber Chat* (Monthly).

58054 ■ *Citylife*
109 N Main St.
Midland, TX 79701
Ph: (432)683-3381
Free: 800-624-6435
Fax: (432)686-3556
Co. E-mail: info@midlandtxchamber.com
URL: http://www.midlandtxchamber.com
Contact: Bobby Burns, President
Released: Semiannual

58055 ■ Cleburne Chamber of Commerce
1511 W Henderson St.
Cleburne, TX 76033-4138
Ph: (817)645-2455
Fax: (817)641-3069
Co. E-mail: info@cleburnechamber.com
URL: http://www.cleburnechamber.com
Contact: Ms. Cathy Marchel, President
Description: Promotes business and community development in Cleburne, TX. **Founded:** 1916. **Publications:** *Demographics About Cleburne*.

58056 ■ Clifton Chamber of Commerce
115 N Ave. D
Clifton, TX 76634
Ph: (254)675-3720
Free: 800-344-3720
Co. E-mail: paigekey@cliftontexas.org
URL: http://www.cliftontexas.org
Contact: Paige A. Key, Executive Vice President
Description: Promotes business and community development in Clifton, TX.

58057 ■ *Clubs and Organizations*
1000 S Polk St.
Amarillo, TX 79101-3408
Ph: (806)373-7800

Fax: (806)373-3909
Co. E-mail: chamber@amarillo-chamber.org
URL: http://www.amarillo-chamber.org
Contact: Gary Molberg, President
Released: Annual

58058 ■ *Clubs and Organizations*
PO Box 1719
Denton, TX 76202-1719
Ph: (940)382-9693
Free: 888-381-1818
Fax: (940)382-0040
Co. E-mail: dcoc@denton-chamber.org
URL: http://www.denton-chamber.org
Contact: Charles W. Carpenter, President

58059 ■ *Clubs and Organizations Directory*
4749 Twin City Hwy., Ste. 300
Port Arthur, TX 77642
Ph: (409)963-1107
Fax: (409)962-1997
Co. E-mail: portarthurchamber@portarthurtexas.com
URL: http://www.portarthurtexas.com
Contact: Mary Ann Reid, President
Released: Periodic

58060 ■ Coldspring/San Jacinto County Chamber of Commerce (CCC)
PO Box 980
Coldspring, TX 77331
Ph: (936)653-2184
Fax: (936)653-2184
Co. E-mail: ccc@coldspringtexas.org
URL: http://www.coldspringtexas.org
Contact: Barbara Brock, President
Description: Promotes business and community development in San Jacinto County, TX. **Founded:** 1983.

58061 ■ Coleman County Chamber of Commerce, Agriculture and Tourist Bureau
218 Commercial Ave.
Coleman, TX 76834
Ph: (325)625-2163
Fax: (325)625-2164
Co. E-mail: chamber@colemantexas.org
URL: http://www.colemantexas.org
Description: Promotes business and community development in Coleman, TX.

58062 ■ Colleyville Area Chamber of Commerce (CACC)
6700 Colleyville Blvd.
Colleyville, TX 76034
Ph: (817)488-7148
Fax: (817)488-4242
Co. E-mail: info@colleyvillechamber.org
URL: http://www.colleyvillechamber.org
Contact: Mary Smith, President
Description: Promotes business and community development in Colleyville, TX area. **Founded:** 1976. **Publications:** *Community and Business Directory* (Annual).

58063 ■ Colony Chamber of Commerce
6900 Main St.
The Colony, TX 75056
Ph: (214)705-3075
Fax: (972)625-8027
Co. E-mail: info@thecolonychamber.org
URL: http://www.thecolonychamber.org
Contact: Scott Carpenter, President
Description: Promotes business and community development in The Colony, TX. **Publications:** *The Colony Connection* (Quarterly); *The Commerce Communicator* (Monthly); *The Colony Connection* (Quarterly). **Awards:** Citizen of the Year (Annual); Distinguished Service Award (Annual).

58064 ■ *The Colony Connection*
6900 Main St.
The Colony, TX 75056
Ph: (214)705-3075
Fax: (972)625-8027
Co. E-mail: info@thecolonychamber.org
URL: http://www.thecolonychamber.org
Contact: Scott Carpenter, President
Released: Quarterly

58065 ■ Colorado City Area Chamber of Commerce (CCACC)
157 W 2nd St.
Colorado City, TX 79512
Ph: (325)728-3403
Fax: (325)728-2911
Co. E-mail: chamber@cityofcoloradocity.org
URL: http://coloradocitychamberofcommerce.com
Description: Promotes business and community development in Mitchell County, TX. **Founded:** 1909.

58066 ■ Columbus Area Chamber of Commerce
425 Spring St.
Columbus, TX 78934
Ph: (979)725-8385
Fax: (979)725-5881
Co. E-mail: contactus@columbuscofc.org
Contact: George Fox, Executive Director
Description: Promotes business and community development in the Columbus, TX area. **Founded:** 1927.

58067 ■ Comanche Chamber of Commerce and Agriculture
PO Box 65
Comanche, TX 76442
Ph: (325)356-3233
Fax: (325)356-2940
Co. E-mail: info@comanchechamber.org
URL: http://www.comanchechamber.org
Contact: Marvin McKinnon, President
Description: Promotes business and community development in Comanche, TX. Sponsors Comanche County Pow-Wow. **Founded:** 1942. **Publications:** *The Chamber Report* (Quarterly).

58068 ■ Comfort Chamber of Commerce
PO Box 777
Comfort, TX 78013
Ph: (830)995-3131
Fax: (830)995-5252
Co. E-mail: info@comfort-texas.com
URL: http://www.comfortchamberofcommerce.com
Contact: Kathy Walters, President
Description: Promotes business and community development in Comfort, TX. Sponsors July 4th festivities, and Christmas in Comfort celebration. **Founded:** 1974. **Subscriptions:** 19500.

58069 ■ Commerce Chamber of Commerce (CCC)
PO Box 290
Commerce, TX 75429
Ph: (903)886-3950
Fax: (903)886-8012
Co. E-mail: commercechamber@embarqmail.com
URL: http://www.commerce-chamber.com
Contact: Trey Boyles, Manager
Description: Aims to promote the common business interests of merchants and citizens living and working in the city of Commerce, Texas, and in the immediate area; promote the free enterprise system; encourage the commercial, industrial and agricultural development of the city of Commerce and the immediate area; and assume a role of active leadership in community improvement. **Founded:** 1909.

58070 ■ *The Commerce Communicator*
6900 Main St.
The Colony, TX 75056
Ph: (214)705-3075
Fax: (972)625-8027
Co. E-mail: info@thecolonychamber.org
URL: http://www.thecolonychamber.org
Contact: Scott Carpenter, President
Released: Monthly **Price:** $20, /year.

58071 ■ *The Communicator*
PO Box 452
Crosby, TX 77532
Ph: (281)328-6984
Fax: (281)328-7296
Co. E-mail: chamber@crosbyhuffmancc.org
URL: http://www.crosbyhuffmancc.org
Contact: Julie Gilbert, President
Released: Monthly **Price:** free.

58072 ■ *Communicator*
PO Box 1220
Waco, TX 76703-1220
Ph: (254)757-5600
Fax: (254)752-6618
Co. E-mail: info@wacochamber.com
URL: http://www.wacochamber.com
Contact: Matthew T. Meadors, President
Released: Monthly

58073 ■ *Communique*
101 N East St.
Atlanta, TX 75551-2600
Ph: (903)796-3296
Fax: (903)796-5711
Co. E-mail: atlantaareacoc@sbcglobal.net
URL: http://www.atlantatexas.org/chamber/atlanta-chamber-of-commerce.aspx
Contact: Lisa Thompson, President
Released: Monthly

58074 ■ *The Communique*
1700 Sidney Baker St., Ste. 100
Kerrville, TX 78028
Ph: (830)896-1155
Fax: (830)896-1175
Co. E-mail: info@kerrvilletx.com
URL: http://kerrvilletx.le3.getliveedit.com/pages/home
Contact: Mark Tuschak, Chairman
Released: Monthly

58075 ■ *The Communique*
PO Box 2310
San Marcos, TX 78667
Ph: (512)393-5900
Fax: (512)393-5912
Co. E-mail: chamber@sanmarcostexas.com
URL: http://www.sanmarcostexas.com
Contact: Brian J. Bondy, President
Released: Monthly

58076 ■ *Community Book/Buyer's Guide*
420 Johnson Rd., Ste. 301
Keller, TX 76248
Ph: (817)431-2169
Fax: (817)431-3789
Co. E-mail: keller@kellerchamber.com
URL: http://www.kellerchamber.com
Contact: Susanne Johnson, President
Released: Annual **Price:** $25, additional listings.

58077 ■ *Community and Business Directory*
6700 Colleyville Blvd.
Colleyville, TX 76034
Ph: (817)488-7148
Fax: (817)488-4242
Co. E-mail: info@colleyvillechamber.org
URL: http://www.colleyvillechamber.org
Contact: Mary Smith, President
Released: Annual

58078 ■ *Community Directory*
1501 Corporate Cir., Ste. 100
Southlake, TX 76092
Ph: (817)481-8200
Fax: (817)749-8202
Co. E-mail: info@southlakechamber.com
URL: http://www.southlakechamber.com
Contact: Dana Davis, President
Released: Annual **Price:** free.

58079 ■ *Community Leaders*
1000 S Polk St.
Amarillo, TX 79101-3408
Ph: (806)373-7800
Fax: (806)373-3909
Co. E-mail: chamber@amarillo-chamber.org
URL: http://www.amarillo-chamber.org
Contact: Gary Molberg, President
Released: Annual

58080 ■ *Community Profile*
PO Box 1719
Denton, TX 76202-1719
Ph: (940)382-9693
Free: 888-381-1818

Fax: (940)382-0040
Co. E-mail: dcoc@denton-chamber.org
URL: http://www.denton-chamber.org
Contact: Charles W. Carpenter, President
Released: Periodic **Price:** $7.

58081 ■ *The Connecting Source*
520 N Glenbrook
Garland, TX 75040
Ph: (972)272-7551
Fax: (972)276-9261
URL: http://www.garlandchamber.com
Contact: Paul Mayer, Chief Executive Officer

58082 ■ *The Connection*
300 E Wheatland Rd.
Duncanville, TX 75116
Ph: (972)780-4990
Fax: (972)298-9370
Co. E-mail: info@duncanvillechamber.org
URL: http://duncanvillechamber.org
Contact: Allen Conley, Chairman
Released: Monthly

58083 ■ *Connection*
PO Box 1177
Palestine, TX 75802
Ph: (903)729-6066
Fax: (903)729-2083
URL: http://www.palestinechamber.org
Contact: Meghan Hill, Executive Director
Released: Weekly

58084 ■ *Connection*
110 E Hubbard St.
Lindale, TX 75771
Ph: (903)882-7181
Co. E-mail: info@lindalechamber.com
URL: http://www.lindalechamber.org
Contact: Shelbie Glover, Executive Director
Released: Quarterly

58085 ■ *Connections*
7610 Stemmons Freeway, Ste. 690
Dallas, TX 75229
Ph: (972)241-8250
Fax: (972)241-8270
Co. E-mail: info@gdaacc.com
URL: http://www.gdaacc.com
Contact: Galileo Jumaoas, President
Released: Monthly

58086 ■ Coppell Chamber of Commerce
509 W Bethel Rd., Ste. 200
Coppell, TX 75019-4483
Ph: (972)393-2829
Fax: (972)393-0659
Co. E-mail: info@coppellchamber.org
URL: http://www.coppellchamber.org
Contact: Tony Moline, President
Description: Strives to enhance and promote the business environment and quality of life in the Coppell community. **Publications:** *Chamber Connection* (Monthly).

58087 ■ Copperas Cove Chamber of Commerce and Visitors Bureau
204 E Robertson Ave.
Copperas Cove, TX 76522
Ph: (254)547-7571
Fax: (254)547-5015
Co. E-mail: chamber@copperascove.com
URL: http://www.copperascove.com
Contact: Marty Smith, President
Description: Promotes business and community development in Copperas Cove, TX.

58088 ■ Corpus Christi Area Hispanic Chamber of Commerce
c/o Mike Briones, CEO
615 N Upper Broadway, Ste. 410
Corpus Christi, TX 78401
Ph: (361)887-7408

Fax: (361)888-9473
Co. E-mail: mbriones@cchispanicchamber.org
URL: http://www.cchispanicchamber.org
Contact: Mike Briones, Chief Executive Officer
Description: Aims to serve the business community by developing positive changes through active participation in education, leadership, public affairs and creating business opportunities for its members. Works as the official Hispanic business liaison between the business community and the community at large. **Founded:** 1939.

58089 ■ *Correspondent*
3910 Main St.
Rowlett, TX 75030-0610
Ph: (972)475-3200
Fax: (972)463-1699
Co. E-mail: rowlett_chamber@rowlettchamber.com
URL: http://www.rowlettchamber.com
Contact: Diane Lemmons, President
Released: Monthly **Price:** included in membership dues.

58090 ■ Corsicana/Navarro County Chamber of Commerce
120 N 12th St.
Corsicana, TX 75110
Ph: (903)874-4731
Fax: (903)874-4187
Co. E-mail: chamber@corsicana.org
URL: http://www.corsicana.org
Contact: Paul Hooper, Executive Director
Description: Promotes business and community development in Corsicana, TX. **Founded:** 1918.

58091 ■ Crockett Area Chamber of Commerce
PO Box 307
Crockett, TX 75835
Ph: (936)544-2359
Free: 888-269-2359
Fax: (936)544-4355
Co. E-mail: jeana@crockettareachamber.org
URL: http://www.crockettareachamber.org
Contact: Jeana Culp, President
Description: Promotes business, community development, and tourism in Houston County, TX. **Founded:** 1928.

58092 ■ Crosby/Huffman Chamber of Commerce
PO Box 452
Crosby, TX 77532
Ph: (281)328-6984
Fax: (281)328-7296
Co. E-mail: chamber@crosbyhuffmancc.org
URL: http://www.crosbyhuffmancc.org
Contact: Julie Gilbert, President
Description: Promotes business and community development in Crosby, TX. **Publications:** *The Communicator* (Monthly).

58093 ■ Crowell Chamber of Commerce
PO Box 164
Crowell, TX 79227
Ph: (940)684-1310
URL: http://www.crowelltex.com
Contact: Taylor Fox, President
Description: Works to advance the commercial, financial, industrial and civic interests of the area.

58094 ■ Cuero Chamber of Commerce and Agriculture
124 E Church St.
Cuero, TX 77954
Ph: (361)275-2112
Fax: (361)275-6351
Co. E-mail: cuerocc@cuero.org
URL: http://www.cuero.org
Contact: Eric Draper, President
Description: Promotes agriculture, business, tourism, and community development in Cuero, TX. **Publications:** *Chamber Notes* (Quarterly).

58095 ■ Cy-Fair Houston Chamber of Commerce
11734 Barker Cypress, No. 105
Cypress, TX 77433
Ph: (281)373-1390

Fax: (281)373-1394
URL: http://www.cyfairchamber.com
Contact: Mary Evans, President
Description: Promotes business and community development in Cypress Fairbanks area, TX. **Publications:** *Cy-Fair Houston Chamber of Commerce Quarterly News Magazine* (Quarterly). **Awards:** Large Business of the Year (Annual); Small Business of the Year (Annual); Medium-Size Business of the Year (Annual).

58096 ■ *Cy-Fair Houston Chamber of Commerce Quarterly News Magazine*
11734 Barker Cypress, No. 105
Cypress, TX 77433
Ph: (281)373-1390
Fax: (281)373-1394
URL: http://www.cyfairchamber.com
Contact: Mary Evans, President
Released: Quarterly

58097 ■ Daingerfield Chamber of Commerce (DCC)
102 Coffey St.
Daingerfield, TX 75638
Ph: (903)645-2646
Fax: (903)645-2646
Co. E-mail: daingerfieldchamberofcommerce@ce-bridge.net
URL: http://www.daingerfieldtx.net
Contact: Sherry Ray, Office Manager
Description: Promotes business, community development, and tourism in Daingerfield, Texas. Sponsors Daingerfield Days Festival, Christmas parade, Awards Banquet and annual Easter Egg Hunt before Easter. **Founded:** 1900.

58098 ■ Dalhart Area Chamber of Commerce (DACC)
PO Box 967
Dalhart, TX 79022
Ph: (806)244-5646
Fax: (806)244-4945
Co. E-mail: chamber@dalhart.org
URL: http://www.dalhart.org
Contact: Aaron Meneses, Chairman
Description: Promotes business and community development in Dallam and Hartley counties, TX. **Founded:** 1924. **Publications:** *Directory of Businesses.* **Awards:** Citizen of the Year (Annual).

58099 ■ Dallas Black Chamber of Commerce (DBCC)
2838 Martin Luther King, Jr. Blvd.
Dallas, TX 75215
Ph: (214)421-5200
Fax: (214)421-5510
Co. E-mail: rgates@dbcc.org
URL: http://www.dbcc.org
Contact: Reginald Gates, President
Description: Promotes development of minority-owned businesses. **Founded:** 1926. **Publications:** *DBCC Update* (Bimonthly). **Awards:** Quest for Success Entrepreneur Awards (Annual); Willow Award for Community Service (Annual).

58100 ■ Dallas Northeast Chamber of Commerce
9543 Losa Dr., Ste. 118
Dallas, TX 75218
Ph: (214)328-4100
Fax: (214)328-4124
Co. E-mail: dncc@sbcglobal.net
URL: http://dnecc.org
Contact: Greg Solomon, President
Description: Promotes business and community development in Northeast Dallas, TX. **Founded:** 1997.

58101 ■ *DBCC Update*
2838 Martin Luther King, Jr. Blvd.
Dallas, TX 75215
Ph: (214)421-5200
Fax: (214)421-5510
Co. E-mail: rgates@dbcc.org
URL: http://www.dbcc.org
Contact: Reginald Gates, President
Released: Bimonthly

58102 ■ De Leon Chamber of Commerce and Agriculture
109 S Texas St.
De Leon, TX 76444
Ph: (254)893-2083
URL: http://www.deleontexas.com/chamber
Contact: Linda Levens, Executive Director
Description: Promotes business and community development in DeLeon, TX.

58103 ■ Deaf Smith County Chamber of Commerce
701 N Main
Hereford, TX 79045
Ph: (806)364-3333
Fax: (806)364-3342
Co. E-mail: info@herefordtx.org
URL: http://www.herefordtx.org
Description: Promotes business and community development in Deaf Smith County, TX.

58104 ■ Decatur Chamber of Commerce (DCC)
PO Box 474
Decatur, TX 76234
Ph: (940)627-3107
Fax: (940)627-3771
Co. E-mail: misty.hudson@netcommander.com
URL: http://www.decaturtx.com
Contact: Misty Hudson, Executive Director
Description: Promotes business and community development in Decatur, TX. Conducts Christmas fair for underprivileged youth, annual Fun Run, and Chisholm Trail Days. **Publications:** *Chamber Chatter* (Monthly).

58105 ■ Deer Park Chamber of Commerce (DPCC)
110 Center St.
Deer Park, TX 77536-2734
Ph: (281)479-1559
Fax: (281)476-4041
Co. E-mail: info@deerpark.org
URL: http://www.deerpark.org
Contact: Tim Culp, President
Description: Promotes business and community development in Deer Park, TX. Conducts charitable, fundraising, and social activities and educational forums. Monitors legislation. Sponsors annual Fall Festival. **Founded:** 1959. **Publications:** *Business Spotlight* (Monthly). **Awards:** Administrative Professional of the Year (Annual); Small Business of the Year (Annual).

58106 ■ Del Rio Chamber of Commerce (DRCC)
1915 Veterans Blvd.
Del Rio, TX 78840
Ph: (830)775-3551
Fax: (830)774-1813
URL: http://www.drchamber.com
Contact: Al Arreola, Jr., Executive Director
Description: Promotes business and community development in Val Verde County, TX. **Founded:** 1936.

58107 ■ Delta County Chamber of Commerce (DCCC)
41 Westside Sq.
Cooper, TX 75432
Ph: (903)395-4314
Fax: (903)395-4318
Co. E-mail: deltacounty@neto.com
URL: http://www.deltacounty.tx
Contact: Gracie Young, Office Manager
Description: Activities include Delta County Chigger Festival, Cooper Lake Bass Classic, and Dickens Christmas Parade. **Founded:** 1948.

58108 ■ *Demographics About Cleburne*
1511 W Henderson St.
Cleburne, TX 76033-4138
Ph: (817)645-2455
Fax: (817)641-3069
Co. E-mail: info@cleburnechamber.com
URL: http://www.cleburnechamber.com
Contact: Ms. Cathy Marchel, President

58109 ■ Denison Area Chamber of Commerce (DACC)
PO Box 325
Denison, TX 75020-0325
Ph: (903)465-1551
Fax: (903)465-8443
Co. E-mail: information@denisontexas.com
URL: http://www.denisontexas.us/default.aspx
Contact: Anna H. McKinney, President
Description: Promotes business and community development in the Denison, TX area. Sponsors National Aerobatic Competition, Lake Fest, and Western Week. **Founded:** 1912. **Publications:** *ChamberWorks* (Monthly); *Visions* (Annual).

58110 ■ Denton Chamber of Commerce (DCC)
PO Box 1719
Denton, TX 76202-1719
Ph: (940)382-9693
Free: 888-381-1818
Fax: (940)382-0040
Co. E-mail: dcoc@denton-chamber.org
URL: http://www.denton-chamber.org
Contact: Charles W. Carpenter, President
Description: Promotes business and community development in Denton, TX. Conducts new industry, convention, and visitor recruitment. Provides for leadership development and government relations. **Founded:** 1909. **Publications:** *Distinctly Denton* (Annual); *Community Profile* (Periodic); *Clubs and Organizations*; *Community Profile* (Periodic); *Distinctly Denton* (Annual).

58111 ■ *The Depot Connection*
PO Box 358
Hillsboro, TX 76645
Ph: (254)582-2481
Free: 800-HIL-LSBO
Fax: (254)582-0465
Co. E-mail: chamber@hillsborochamber.org
URL: http://www.hillsborochamber.org
Contact: Greg Solomon, President
Released: Bimonthly

58112 ■ DeSoto Chamber of Commerce (DCC)
2010 N Hampton Rd., Ste. 200
DeSoto, TX 75115
Ph: (972)224-3565
Fax: (972)354-1022
Co. E-mail: cjackson@desotochamber.org
URL: http://www.desotochamber.org
Contact: Cammy Jackson, President
Description: Promotes business and community development in southwestern Dallas County and northern Ellis County, TX. **Founded:** 1960. **Publications:** *Business News* (Monthly).

58113 ■ *Destination Guide*
PO Box 1408
Mineral Wells, TX 76068
Ph: (940)325-2557
Free: 800-252-6989
Fax: (940)328-0850
Co. E-mail: info@mineralwellstx.com
URL: http://www.mineralwellstx.com
Contact: Beth Watson, Executive Director
Released: Semiannual **Price:** free.

58114 ■ Dimmit County Chamber of Commerce
PO Box 699
Carrizo Springs, TX 78834-6699
Ph: (830)876-5205
Fax: (830)876-5206
Co. E-mail: chamberofcommerce@the-i.net
URL: http://www.dimmitcountytx.com
Contact: Efrain Garza, President
Description: Promotes business and community development in Dimmit County, TX. Sponsors Brush Country Days festival. **Founded:** 1930.

58115 ■ *Directory of Businesses*
PO Box 967
Dalhart, TX 79022
Ph: (806)244-5646

Fax: (806)244-4945
Co. E-mail: chamber@dalhart.org
URL: http://www.dalhart.org
Contact: Aaron Meneses, Chairman

58116 ■ *Directory of Manufacturers and Industrial Suppliers*
10 Civic Center Plz.
El Paso, TX 79901
Ph: (915)534-0500
Free: 800-651-8065
Fax: (915)534-0510
Co. E-mail: gepccreceptionist@elpaso.org
URL: http://www.elpaso.org/aboutUs.html
Contact: Richard E. Dayoub, President
Released: Annual

58117 ■ *Directory of Manufactures, Community Profile, Membership Directory*
PO Box 1860
Wichita Falls, TX 76307
Ph: (940)723-2741
Fax: (940)723-8773
Co. E-mail: ewaite@wf.net
URL: http://www.wichitafallscommerce.com
Contact: Tim Chase, President
Released: 10/year **Price:** $10.83.

58118 ■ *Directory of Products and Services*
PO Box 2445
Bandera, TX 78003-2445
Ph: (830)796-3280
Fax: (830)796-3970
Co. E-mail: cowboy@banderatex.com
URL: http://banderatex.com
Contact: Scott Asher, President
Released: Periodic

58119 ■ *Discover Baytown*
Amegy Bank Bldg.
Baytown, TX 77521
Ph: (281)422-8359
Fax: (281)428-1758
Co. E-mail: info@baytownchamber.com
URL: http://www.baytownchamber.com
Contact: Tracey S. Wheeler, President
Released: Annual **Price:** free.

58120 ■ *Discovery Line*
1206 S Palestine St.
Athens, TX 75751
Ph: (903)675-5181
Free: 800-755-7878
Fax: (903)675-5183
Co. E-mail: info@athenscc.org
URL: http://www.athenscc.org
Contact: Sarah J. Hueber, President
Released: Monthly **Price:** free for members.

58121 ■ *Distinctly Denton*
PO Box 1719
Denton, TX 76202-1719
Ph: (940)382-9693
Free: 888-381-1818
Fax: (940)382-0040
Co. E-mail: dcoc@denton-chamber.org
URL: http://www.denton-chamber.org
Contact: Charles W. Carpenter, President
Released: Annual

58122 ■ Dumas - Moore County Chamber of Commerce and Visitors Center
PO Box 735
Dumas, TX 79029-0735
Ph: (806)935-2123
Free: 888-840-8911
Fax: (806)935-2124
Co. E-mail: info@dumaschamber.com
URL: http://www.dumaschamber.com
Contact: Sam Cartwright, President
Description: Promotes business, community development, and tourism in Moore County, TX.

58123 ■ Duncanville Chamber of Commerce (DCC)
300 E Wheatland Rd.
Duncanville, TX 75116
Ph: (972)780-4990

Fax: (972)298-9370
Co. E-mail: info@duncanvillechamber.org
URL: http://duncanvillechamber.org
Contact: Allen Conley, Chairman
Description: Promotes business and community development in Duncanville, TX. **Founded:** 1954. **Publications:** *The Connection* (Monthly); *Healthy Living Guide* (Periodic); *Membership Directory/ Buyer's Guide* (Annual); *How To Go Into Business in Duncanville.* **Educational Activities:** Duncanville Chamber of Commerce Meeting (Periodic).

58124 ■ Eagle Pass Chamber of Commerce (EPCC)
PO Box 1188
Eagle Pass, TX 78853-1188
Ph: (830)773-3224
Free: 888-355-3224
Fax: (830)773-8844
Co. E-mail: chamber@eaglepasstexas.com
URL: http://eaglepasstexas.com
Contact: Sandra Martinez, Executive Director
Description: Promotes business and community development in Eagle Pass, TX. Sponsors International Friendship Fest. **Founded:** 1926. **Publications:** *Maquiladona Directory* (Quarterly).

58125 ■ Early Chamber of Commerce and Convention and Tourism Bureau (ECCCTB)
104 E Industrial Dr.
Early, TX 76802
Ph: (325)649-9317
Fax: (325)643-4746
Co. E-mail: ecoc@earlytx.com
URL: http://www.earlytx.com
Contact: Doug Scott, President
Description: Promotes business and community development in Brown County, TX. Sponsors annual Halloween Carnival and softball/volleyball competitions. Conducts seminars. **Founded:** 1980.

58126 ■ Eastland Chamber of Commerce
209 W Main St.
Eastland, TX 76448
Ph: (254)629-2332
Free: 877-265-3747
Fax: (254)629-1629
Co. E-mail: ecofc@eastland.net
URL: http://www.eastlandchamber.com
Contact: Angela Robinson, President
Description: Promotes business and community development in Eastland, TX. **Founded:** 1921. **Awards:** Business of the Year (Annual); Golden Deeds Award (Annual); Public Safety Award of Excellence (Annual).

58127 ■ ED Update
PO Box 1220
Waco, TX 76703-1220
Ph: (254)757-5600
Fax: (254)752-6618
Co. E-mail: info@wacochamber.com
URL: http://www.wacochamber.com
Contact: Matthew T. Meadors, President
Released: Quarterly

58128 ■ Eden Chamber of Commerce (ECC)
PO Box 367
Eden, TX 76837-0367
Co. E-mail: edenchamber@verizon.net
URL: http://edentexas.com
Contact: Keith Hall, President
Description: Promotes business and community development in Eden, TX. Sponsors Fall Festival and Concho County Stampede. Conducts newcomer's program. **Subscriptions:** 8000. **Publications:** *City of Eden* (Quarterly).

58129 ■ Edinburg Chamber of Commerce
Edinburg Depot
602 W University Dr.
Edinburg, TX 78539-3232
Ph: (956)383-4974
Free: 800-800-7214

Fax: (956)383-6942
Co. E-mail: chamber@edinburg.com
URL: http://www.edinburg.com
Contact: Letty Gonzalez, President
Description: Strives to improve and enhance the commerce and the quality of life in Edinburg and the region. Fosters service, development, and growth by forging positive relationships, advocating volunteerism, and leadership development. **Founded:** 1932.

58130 ■ El Campo Chamber of Commerce and Agriculture
PO Box 1400
El Campo, TX 77437
Ph: (979)543-2713
Fax: (979)543-5495
Co. E-mail: ecc@elcampochamber.com
URL: http://www.elcampochamber.com
Contact: Becca Socha, President
Description: Promotes the development of business, commerce, tourism, and agriculture in El Campo, TX. **Founded:** 1928.

58131 ■ El Paso Hispanic Chamber of Commerce (EPHCC)
2401 E Missouri St.
El Paso, TX 79903
Ph: (915)566-4066
Fax: (915)566-9714
Co. E-mail: cindyramosdavidson@ephcc.org
URL: http://www.ephcc.org
Contact: Cindy Ramos-Davidson, Chief Executive Officer
Description: Provides resources, information and education while promoting the awareness and preservation of the Hispanic culture. **Founded:** 1990. **Subscriptions:** articles. **Publications:** *Chamber at a Glance* (Monthly). **Educational Activities:** Cafe Pan Dulce (Semimonthly). **Awards:** Education Foundation Scholarship (Annual); Moving Forward Award (Annual).

58132 ■ Electra Chamber of Commerce
112 W Cleveland
Electra, TX 76360-2604
Ph: (940)495-3577
Co. E-mail: electracoc@electratel.net
URL: http://www.electratexas.com
Contact: Sherry Strange, Executive Director
Description: Promotes business and community development in Electra, TX. **Founded:** 1908.

58133 ■ Ennis Chamber of Commerce
108 Chamber of Commerce Dr.
Ennis, TX 75119
Ph: (972)878-2625
Fax: (972)875-1473
Co. E-mail: manager@ennis-chamber.com
URL: http://www.ennis-chamber.com
Contact: Jeannette J. Patak, President
Description: Promotes business and community development in the Ennis, TX area. Holds Ennis Polka Festival, annual Bluebonnet Trails, Ennis Heritage Antique Show and Sale, and Festival of the Train. Maintains Railroad and Cultural Heritage Museum. **Founded:** 1918. **Publications:** *TrendSetter News* (Quarterly). **Awards:** Industry of the Year (Annual); Small Business of the Quarter (Quarterly).

58134 ■ Facts by the Tracks
301 S Saginaw Blvd.
Saginaw, TX 76179
Ph: (817)232-0500
Fax: (817)232-2311
Co. E-mail: chamber@saginawtxchamber.org
URL: http://www.saginawtxchamber.org
Contact: Mr. Tracy Sutton, Executive
Released: Monthly

58135 ■ Fairfield Chamber of Commerce (FCC)
900 W Commerce St.
Fairfield, TX 75840
Ph: (903)389-5792

Fax: (903)389-8382
Co. E-mail: chamber@fairfieldtx.com
URL: http://fairfieldtexaschamber.com
Contact: Mary Small, President
Description: Promotes business and community development in Fairfield, TX. **Founded:** 1993.

58136 ■ Farmers Branch Chamber of Commerce
12875 Josey Ln., Ste. 150
Farmers Branch, TX 75234
Ph: (972)243-8966
Fax: (972)243-8968
Co. E-mail: fferguson@fbchamber.com
URL: http://www.fbchamber.com
Description: Promotes business and community development in Farmers Branch area. **Founded:** 1979.

58137 ■ Farmersville Chamber of Commerce (FCC)
201 S Main St.
Farmersville, TX 75442
Ph: (972)782-6533
Fax: (972)782-6603
Co. E-mail: chamber@ci.farmersville.tx.us
URL: http://www.farmersvilletx.com/chamber/index. jsp
Contact: Chris Lair, President
Description: Promotes business and community development in the Farmersville, TX area.

58138 ■ Flatonia Chamber of Commerce (FCC)
PO Box 610
Flatonia, TX 78941-0610
Ph: (361)865-3920
Fax: (361)865-2451
Co. E-mail: flatoniacofc@sbcglobal.net
URL: http://flatoniachamber.com
Description: Promotes business and community development in Flatonia, TX.

58139 ■ Floresville Chamber of Commerce
910 10th St.
Floresville, TX 78114
Ph: (830)393-0074
URL: http://www.floresvillechamber.com
Contact: Traci Jaskinia, Executive Director
Description: Promotes business and community development in Floresville, TX; Wilson County. **Founded:** 1957.

58140 ■ Flower Mound Chamber of Commerce
700 Parker Sq., Ste. 100
Flower Mound, TX 75028
Ph: (972)539-0500
Fax: (972)539-4307
Co. E-mail: c.howard@flowermoundchamber.com
URL: http://www.flowermoundchamber.com
Contact: Cindi Howard, President (Acting)
Description: Promotes business and community development in Flower Mound, TX. **Publications:** *Chamber Connection* (Monthly); *Chamber's Business* (Annual).

58141 ■ Focus
215 W 3rd St.
Big Spring, TX 79720-2426
Ph: (432)263-7641
Free: 800-734-7641
Fax: (432)264-9111
Co. E-mail: debbyev@bigspringchamber.com
URL: http://www.bigspringchamber.com
Contact: Debbye Valverde, Executive Director
Released: Monthly

58142 ■ Focus
900 Conover Dr.
Grand Prairie, TX 75051
Ph: (972)264-1558
Co. E-mail: info@grandprairiechamber.org
URL: http://www.grandprairiechamber.org
Contact: Lynn McGinley, President
Released: Monthly

58143 ■ *Focus*
213 W Austin St.
Marshall, TX 75671
Ph: (903)935-7868
Free: 800-953-7868
Fax: (903)935-9982
Co. E-mail: contactus@marshalltexas.com
URL: http://www.marshall-chamber.com
Contact: Connie Ware, President

58144 ■ *Focus*
4120 Ave. H
Rosenberg, TX 77471
Ph: (281)342-5464
Fax: (281)342-2990
Co. E-mail: info@roserichchamber.org
Contact: Gail Parker, President
Released: Monthly

58145 ■ Forney Area Chamber of Commerce
PO Box 570
Forney, TX 75126
Ph: (972)564-2233
Fax: (972)564-3677
URL: http://www.forneychamber.com
Contact: Laurie Barkham, President
Description: Promotes business and community development in Forney, TX and surrounding areas. Conducts fundraising activities. **Founded:** 1983. **Publications:** *Forney: The Antique Capital of Texas.* **Educational Activities:** Forney Area Chamber of Commerce Luncheon (Monthly). **Awards:** Citizen of the Year (Annual); Helping Hand Award (Annual).

58146 ■ *Forney: The Antique Capital of Texas*
PO Box 570
Forney, TX 75126
Ph: (972)564-2233
Fax: (972)564-3677
URL: http://www.forneychamber.com
Contact: Laurie Barkham, President

58147 ■ *Fort Bend Business Resource Book*
445 Commerce Green Blvd.
Sugar Land, TX 77478
Ph: (281)491-0800
Fax: (281)491-0112
Co. E-mail: keri@fortbendcc.org
URL: http://www.fortbendchamber.com
Contact: Keri Schmidt, President
Released: Biennial

58148 ■ Fort Bend Chamber of Commerce
445 Commerce Green Blvd.
Sugar Land, TX 77478
Ph: (281)491-0800
Fax: (281)491-0112
Co. E-mail: keri@fortbendcc.org
URL: http://www.fortbendchamber.com
Contact: Keri Schmidt, President
Description: Promotes business and community development in Sugar Land, Meadows, Missouri City, Stafford, Richmond, Rosenberg, and a portion of Katy, TX. **Founded:** 1972. **Publications:** *Fort Bend Business Resource Book* (Biennial); *Fort Bend Forward* (Monthly). **Educational Activities:** Fort Bend Business EXPO (Annual).

58149 ■ *Fort Bend Forward*
445 Commerce Green Blvd.
Sugar Land, TX 77478
Ph: (281)491-0800
Fax: (281)491-0112
Co. E-mail: keri@fortbendcc.org
URL: http://www.fortbendchamber.com
Contact: Keri Schmidt, President
Released: Monthly

58150 ■ *Fort Davis Brochure*
PO Box 378
Fort Davis, TX 79734
Ph: (432)426-3015
Free: 800-524-3015
Fax: (432)426-3978
Co. E-mail: info@fortdavis.com
URL: http://www.fortdavis.com
Contact: Ms. Lisa Nugent, Executive Director
Released: Annual **Price:** free.

58151 ■ Fort Davis Chamber of Commerce
PO Box 378
Fort Davis, TX 79734
Ph: (432)426-3015
Free: 800-524-3015
Fax: (432)426-3978
Co. E-mail: info@fortdavis.com
URL: http://www.fortdavis.com
Contact: Ms. Lisa Nugent, Executive Director
Description: Promotes business, community development, and Tourism in Ft. Davis, TX. **Founded:** 1979. **Publications:** *Fort Davis Brochure* (Annual); *Fort Davis Visitors' Guide* (Annual). **Awards:** JC Duncan Memorial (Annual).

58152 ■ *Fort Davis Visitors' Guide*
PO Box 378
Fort Davis, TX 79734
Ph: (432)426-3015
Free: 800-524-3015
Fax: (432)426-3978
Co. E-mail: info@fortdavis.com
URL: http://www.fortdavis.com
Contact: Ms. Lisa Nugent, Executive Director
Released: Annual **Price:** free.

58153 ■ Fort Stockton Chamber of Commerce (FSCC)
1000 Railroad Ave.
Fort Stockton, TX 79735
Ph: (432)336-2264
Free: 800-336-2166
Fax: (432)336-6114
Co. E-mail: director@ftstockton.org
URL: http://www.fortstockton.org
Contact: Arna McCorkle, Executive Vice President
Description: Promotes business and community development in Fort Stockton, TX. **Founded:** 1920. **Publications:** *Chamber Connection* (Quarterly). **Educational Activities:** Hospitality Training (Monthly).

58154 ■ Fort Worth Chamber of Commerce
777 Taylor St., Ste. 900
Fort Worth, TX 76102-4997
Ph: (817)336-2491
Fax: (817)877-4034
URL: http://www.fortworthchamber.com
Contact: William J. Thornton, Jr., President
Description: Promotes business and community development in Ft. Worth, TX.

58155 ■ Fredericksburg Chamber of Commerce
302 E Austin
Fredericksburg, TX 78624
Ph: (830)997-6523
Free: 888-997-3600
Fax: (830)997-8588
Co. E-mail: christie@fbgtxchamber.org
URL: http://www.fredericksburg-texas.com
Contact: Frances Rushing, President
Description: Promotes business and community development in Fredericksburg, TX. Sponsors Night in Old Fredericksburg festival. **Founded:** 1922.

58156 ■ French - American Chamber of Commerce - Dallas/Fort Worth
2665 Villa Creek Dr., Ste. 214
Dallas, TX 75234
Ph: (972)241-0111
Fax: (972)241-0901
Co. E-mail: admin@faccdallas.com
URL: http://www.faccdallas.com
Contact: L. Scott Brown, President

58157 ■ French - American Chamber of Commerce - Houston Chapter
3100 Timoins Ln., Ste. 350B
Houston, TX 77027
Ph: (713)960-0575
Co. E-mail: info@facchouston.com
URL: http://www.facchouston.com
Contact: Stephanie Thomsen, Executive Director

58158 ■ *Friday Facts*
1460 E Whitestone Blvd., Bldg. 2, Ste. 180
Cedar Park, TX 78613
Ph: (512)260-7800

Fax: (512)260-9269
URL: http://www.cedarparkchamber.org
Contact: Tony Moline, President
Released: Monthly

58159 ■ Friendswood Chamber of Commerce
1100 S Friendswood Dr.
Friendswood, TX 77546
Ph: (281)482-3329
Fax: (281)482-3911
Co. E-mail: fwdchmbr@swbell.net
URL: http://www.friendswood-chamber.com
Contact: Carol Jones, President
Description: Promotes business and community development in Friendswood, TX.

58160 ■ Frio Canyon Chamber of Commerce
PO Box 743
Leakey, TX 78873-0743
Ph: (830)232-5222
Co. E-mail: friochamber@hctc.net
URL: http://www.friocanyonchamber.com
Contact: Linda Hassell, Secretary
Description: Promotes business and community development in Frio Canyon, TX area.

58161 ■ Friona Chamber of Commerce and Agriculture
621 Main St.
Friona, TX 79035-0905
Ph: (806)250-3491
Fax: (806)250-2348
URL: http://www.frionachamber.com
Contact: Chris Alexander, Executive Vice President
Description: Promotes business and community development in Friona, TX.

58162 ■ Frisco Chamber of Commerce (FCC)
6843 Main St.
Frisco, TX 75034
Ph: (972)335-9522
Free: 877-832-0218
Fax: (972)335-6654
Co. E-mail: tfelker@friscochamber.com
URL: http://www.friscochamber.com/chamber/about.htm
Contact: Tony Felker, President
Description: Promotes business and community development in Frisco, TX. **Founded:** 1967. **Publications:** *Frisco Flyer* (Monthly).

58163 ■ *Frisco Flyer*
6843 Main St.
Frisco, TX 75034
Ph: (972)335-9522
Free: 877-832-0218
Fax: (972)335-6654
Co. E-mail: tfelker@friscochamber.com
URL: http://www.friscochamber.com/chamber/about.htm
Contact: Tony Felker, President
Released: Monthly

58164 ■ *FYI*
505 W Davis
Conroe, TX 77305
Ph: (936)756-6644
Fax: (936)756-6462
Co. E-mail: info@conroe.org
URL: http://www.conroe.org
Contact: Scott Harper, President
Released: Monthly

58165 ■ *FYI - Weekly Bulletin*
310 N 9th St., Ste. A
Midlothian, TX 76065-0609
Ph: (972)723-8600
Fax: (972)723-9300
Co. E-mail: info@midlothianchamber.org
URL: http://www.midlothianchamber.org
Contact: Marley Cherie, Chairperson
Released: Weekly

58166 ■ Galleria Chamber of Commerce
5005 Woodway, Ste. 215
Houston, TX 77056-1780
Ph: (713)629-5555

Fax: (713)629-6403
Co. E-mail: dsweat@galleriachamber.com
URL: http://www.galleriachamber.com
Contact: Don P. Sweat, President
Description: Promotes business and community development in the Galleria area of Houston, TX. **Founded:** 1985. **Publications:** *The Catalyst* (Bimonthly).

58167 ■ Galveston Chamber of Commerce
519-25th St.
Galveston, TX 77550
Ph: (409)763-5326
Fax: (409)763-8271
Co. E-mail: gspagnola@galvestonchamber.com
URL: http://www.galvestonchamber.com
Contact: Gina Spagnola, President
Description: Promotes business and community development in Galveston Island, TX. **Founded:** 1845. **Publications:** *The Chamber Voice* (Quarterly). **Telecommunication Services:** gcc@galveston-chamber.com.

58168 ■ Garland Chamber of Commerce
520 N Glenbrook
Garland, TX 75040
Ph: (972)272-7551
Fax: (972)276-9261
URL: http://www.garlandchamber.com
Contact: Paul Mayer, Chief Executive Officer
Description: Promotes business and community development in Garland, TX. **Publications:** *The Connecting Source*; *Membership Directory/Resource Guide*.

58169 ■ Gatesville Area Chamber of Commerce and Agribusiness (GCC)
2307 S Hwy. 36
Gatesville, TX 76528
Ph: (254)865-2617
Fax: (254)865-5581
URL: http://www.gatesvilletx.info
Contact: Gail Shelton, President
Description: Promotes tourism, business, and community development in the Gatesville, TX area. Sponsors Gatesville Shivaree and other festivals. **Founded:** 1939. **Publications:** *Gatesville Chamber of Commerce--Community Guide and Membership Directory* (Annual).

58170 ■ George West Chamber of Commerce
PO Box 359
George West, TX 78022
Ph: (361)449-2033
Free: 888-909-3514
Co. E-mail: chamber@georgewest.org
URL: http://www.georgewest.org
Description: Promotes business and community development in George West, TX.

58171 ■ Georgetown Chamber of Commerce (GCC)
PO Box 346
Georgetown, TX 78627-0346
Ph: (512)930-3535
Fax: (512)930-3587
Co. E-mail: info@georgetownchamber.org
URL: http://www.georgetownchamber.org
Contact: Mel Pendland, President
Description: Promotes business and community development in Georgetown, TX. **Founded:** 1947. **Publications:** *Business*; *Chamber Link* (Weekly); *Map* (Annual). **Educational Activities:** Fajita Supper (Annual); Mayfair (Annual).

58172 ■ Giddings Area Chamber of Commerce (GACC)
289 W Railroad
Giddings, TX 78942
Ph: (979)542-3455
Fax: (979)542-7060
Co. E-mail: giddingscofc@verizon.net
URL: http://www.giddingstx.com
Contact: Denice Harlan, Executive Director
Description: Promotes business and community development in Giddings, TX. Sponsors Giddings Gerburtstag. Operates Economic Development Council. **Founded:** 1920.

58173 ■ *The Gingerbread Times*
102 YMCA Dr.
Waxahachie, TX 75165
Ph: (972)937-2390
Fax: (972)938-9827
Co. E-mail: dwakeland@waxahachiechamber.com
URL: http://waxahachietxcoc.weblinkconnect.com/
cwt/External/WCPages/
Contact: Debra Wakeland, President
Released: Quarterly

58174 ■ Gladewater Chamber of Commerce (GCC)
215 N Main St.
Gladewater, TX 75647
Ph: (903)845-5501
Fax: (903)845-6326
URL: http://www.gladewaterchamber.com
Description: Promotes business and community development in Gladewater, TX. Sponsors promotional and fundraising events. **Founded:** 1931. **Publications:** *The Green Light is Go* (Monthly). **Educational Activities:** Christmas Time in Gusherville (Annual).

58175 ■ Glen Rose/Somervell County Chamber of Commerce
PO Box 605
Glen Rose, TX 76043
Ph: (254)897-2286
Fax: (254)897-7670
Co. E-mail: grcc@glenrosechamber.com
URL: http://www.glenrosechamber.com
Contact: Darrell Best, Chairman
Description: Promotes business and community development in Somervell County, TX. **Founded:** 1961.

58176 ■ Goliad County Chamber of Commerce
231 S Market St.
Goliad, TX 77963-0606
Ph: (361)645-3563
Free: 800-848-8674
Fax: (361)645-3579
Co. E-mail: goliadcc@goliad.net
URL: http://www.goliadcc.org
Contact: Mona Faust, Managing Director
Description: Promotes business and community development in Goliad County, TX.

58177 ■ Gonzales Chamber of Commerce (GCC)
c/o Barbara Hand, Exec. Dir.
PO Box 134
Gonzales, TX 78629-0134
Ph: (830)672-6532
Fax: (830)672-6533
Co. E-mail: info@gonzalestexas.com
URL: http://www.gonzalestexas.com
Contact: Barbara Hand, Executive Director
Description: Promotes business and community development in Gonzales County, TX. Sponsors Texan Independence celebration. Holds competition. **Founded:** 1923.

58178 ■ Grand Prairie Chamber of Commerce
900 Conover Dr.
Grand Prairie, TX 75051
Ph: (972)264-1558
Co. E-mail: info@grandprairiechamber.org
URL: http://www.grandprairiechamber.org
Contact: Lynn McGinley, President
Description: Promotes business and community development in Grand Prairie, TX. Sponsors Grand Prairie Grand Prix Bike Ride. **Publications:** *Focus* (Monthly).

58179 ■ Grapevine Chamber of Commerce
200 E Vine St.
Grapevine, TX 76051
Ph: (817)481-1522

Fax: (817)424-5208
Co. E-mail: info@grapevinechamber.org
URL: http://www.grapevinechamber.org
Contact: RaDonna Hessel, Chief Executive Officer
Description: Promotes business and community development in Grapevine, TX. **Telecommunication Services:** radonna@grapevinechamber.org.

58180 ■ Greater Angleton Chamber of Commerce
445 E Mulberry
Angleton, TX 77515
Ph: (979)849-6443
Fax: (979)849-4520
Co. E-mail: beth@angletonchamber.org
URL: http://www.angletonchamber.org
Contact: Beth Journeay, President
Description: Promotes business and community development in Angleton, TX.

58181 ■ Greater Austin Chamber of Commerce (ACC)
210 Barton Springs Rd., Ste. 400
Austin, TX 78704
Ph: (512)478-9383
Fax: (512)478-6389
Co. E-mail: communication@austinchamber.com
URL: http://www.austinchamber.com
Contact: Michael W. Rollins, President
Description: Promotes business and community development in Austin, TX. **Founded:** 1876. **Publications:** *Business Desk Reference* (Periodic); *Chamber Ink* (10/year); *Skyliner* (Periodic). **Telecommunication Services:** mrollins@austinchamber.com.

58182 ■ Greater Austin Hispanic Chamber of Commerce (GAHCC)
2800 S IH 35, Ste. 260
Austin, TX 78704
Ph: (512)476-7502
Fax: (512)476-6417
Co. E-mail: amartinez@gahcc.org
URL: http://www.gahcc.org
Contact: Andrew Martinez, President
Description: Promotes business and community development in the Hispanic communities of Austin, TX.

58183 ■ Greater Boerne Chamber of Commerce
126 Rosewood Ave.
Boerne, TX 78006
Ph: (830)249-8000
Fax: (830)249-9639
Co. E-mail: boerne@gvtc.com
URL: http://www.boerne.org
Contact: John Gonzalez, President
Description: Promotes business and community development in the Kendall County, TX area. Sponsors Weihnachts Fest parade. **Founded:** 1923. **Publications:** *Network News* (Monthly). **Educational Activities:** Fall Antique Show (Annual). **Awards:** Aubrey E. Sanderson Scholarship (Annual).

58184 ■ Greater Cedar Creek Lake Area Chamber of Commerce (CCLACC)
604 S 3rd St., Ste. E
Mabank, TX 75147
Ph: (903)887-3152
Fax: (903)887-3695
Co. E-mail: info@cclake.net
URL: http://www.cedarcreeklakechamber.com
Contact: Jo Ann Hanstrom, President
Description: Promotes business and community development in Mabank, TX. Sponsors Christmas Tour of Homes, Halloween Festival, annual Western Week, and Chili Cookoff. **Telecommunication Services:** info@cedarcreeklakechamber.com.

58185 ■ Greater Cleveland Chamber of Commerce
210 Peach Ave., Ste. B
Cleveland, TX 77327
Ph: (281)592-8786

Fax: (281)592-6949
Co. E-mail: info@clevelandtxchamber.com
URL: http://clevelandtxchamber.com
Contact: Tracey Walters, Chief Executive Officer
Description: Promotes business and community development in the Cleveland, TX area. **Awards:** Business of the Year (Annual); Citizen of the Year (Annual).

58186 ■ Greater Conroe - Lake Conroe Area Chamber of Commerce
505 W Davis
Conroe, TX 77305
Ph: (936)756-6644
Fax: (936)756-6462
Co. E-mail: info@conroe.org
URL: http://www.conroe.org
Contact: Scott Harper, President
Description: Promotes business and community development in Conroe, TX. **Founded:** 1934. **Publications:** FYI (Monthly); Greater Conroe/Lake Conroe Area Chamber of Commerce--Membership Directory (Annual); Business Directory (Periodic). **Educational Activities:** Board Retreat (Annual). **Telecommunication Services:** chamber@conroe.org.

58187 ■ Greater Dallas Asian American Chamber of Commerce (GDAACC)
7610 Stemmons Freeway, Ste. 690
Dallas, TX 75229
Ph: (972)241-8250
Fax: (972)241-8270
Co. E-mail: info@gdaacc.com
URL: http://www.gdaacc.com
Contact: Galileo Jumaoas, President
Description: Seeks to develop leaders, promotes community awareness, and develops business opportunities to members. **Founded:** 1986. **Publications:** Connections (Monthly). **Educational Activities:** Asian Charity Ball (Annual); Small Business Seminar Series.

58188 ■ Greater Dallas Chamber of Commerce
700 N Pearl St., Ste. 1200
Dallas, TX 75201
Ph: (214)746-6600
Fax: (214)712-1950
Co. E-mail: information@dallaschamber.org
URL: http://www.dallaschamber.org
Contact: Jim Oberwetter, President
Description: Works to unite and engage the Dallas region's business community. Provides dynamic business and civic leadership to develop and sustain a prosperous economy and a vibrant community. **Founded:** 1909. **Publications:** The Chamber Report. **Telecommunication Services:** jointhechamber@dallaschamber.org.

58189 ■ Greater El Paso Chamber of Commerce (GEPCC)
10 Civic Center Plz.
El Paso, TX 79901
Ph: (915)534-0500
Free: 800-651-8065
Fax: (915)534-0510
Co. E-mail: gepccreceptionist@elpaso.org
URL: http://www.elpaso.org/aboutUs.html
Contact: Richard E. Dayoub, President
Description: Promotes business and community development in El Paso, TX. **Founded:** 1899. **Publications:** Spotlight (Monthly); Manufacturers/Suppliers & Services Directory; Directory of Manufacturers and Industrial Suppliers (Annual).

58190 ■ Greater Elgin Chamber of Commerce (ECC)
PO Box 408
Elgin, TX 78621
Ph: (512)285-4515
Fax: (512)281-3393
Co. E-mail: genacarter@elgintxchamber.com
URL: http://www.elgintxchamber.com
Contact: Gena Carter, President
Description: Promotes business and community development in Elgin, TX. Conducts charitable activities and competitions. Sponsors festival. **Founded:** 1934.

58191 ■ Greater Heights Area Chamber of Commerce
545 W 19th St.
Houston, TX 77008
Ph: (713)861-6735
Fax: (713)861-9310
Co. E-mail: exasst@heightschamber.com
URL: http://www.heightschamber.com
Contact: Dee Farino, Chairman
Description: Promotes business and community development in Greater Heights Area, Houston, TX. **Founded:** 1988. **Awards:** Volunteer of the Month (Monthly).

58192 ■ Greater Hewitt Chamber of Commerce (GHCC)
PO Box 661
Hewitt, TX 76643
Ph: (254)666-1200
Fax: (254)666-3181
Co. E-mail: info@hewitt-texas.com
URL: http://www.hewitt-texas.com
Contact: Ian Dawson, President
Description: Promotes business and community development in the Greater Hewitt, TX area. **Founded:** 1978. **Publications:** Hewitt Why Not! (Biweekly). **Telecommunication Services:** hewittdirector@grandecom.net.

58193 ■ Greater Houston Partnership (GHP)
1200 Smith, Ste. 700
Houston, TX 77002-4400
Ph: (713)844-3600
Fax: (713)844-0200
Co. E-mail: ghp@houston.org
URL: http://www.houston.org
Contact: Lilyanne McClean, President
Description: Works to promote the business community in Houston. Seeks to establish economic prosperity in the region. **Founded:** 1989. **Publications:** Here is Houston (Quarterly); Partnership Houston (Annual); Partnership Houston: Membership Directory and Resource Guide (Annual); Houston: People, Opportunity, Success (Biennial).

58194 ■ Greater Irving - Las Colinas Chamber of Commerce
5201 N O'Connor Blvd., Ste. 100
Irving, TX 75039
Ph: (214)217-8484
Fax: (214)389-2513
Co. E-mail: chamber@irvingchamber.com
URL: http://www.irvingchamber.com
Contact: Chris E. Wallace, President
Description: Promotes business and community development in Irving, TX. **Founded:** 1934.

58195 ■ Greater Keller Chamber of Commerce
420 Johnson Rd., Ste. 301
Keller, TX 76248
Ph: (817)431-2169
Fax: (817)431-3789
Co. E-mail: keller@kellerchamber.com
URL: http://www.kellerchamber.com
Contact: Susanne Johnson, President
Description: Promotes business and community development in Keller, TX. **Publications:** Community Book/Buyer's Guide (Annual); Journal Sponsorship (Monthly).

58196 ■ Greater Killeen Chamber of Commerce (GKCC)
PO Box 548
Killeen, TX 76540-0548
Ph: (254)526-9551
Free: 866-790-4769
Fax: (254)526-6090
Co. E-mail: info@gkcc.com
URL: http://killeenchamber.com
Contact: John Crutchfield, President
Description: Promotes business and community development in Killeen, Fort Hood, and Harker Heights, TX. Encourages new settlement in the area. Sponsors Festival of Flags. Operates convention and visitors' bureau. **Publications:** Newsline (Monthly). **Telecommunication Services:** jcrutchfield@gkcc.com.

58197 ■ Greater Mission Chamber of Commerce
202 W Tom Landry St.
Mission, TX 78572
Ph: (956)585-2727
Fax: (956)585-3044
Co. E-mail: receptionist@missionchamber.com
URL: http://www.missionchamber.com
Contact: Arlene V. Rivera, President
Description: Promotes business and community development in Mission, TX. Encourages tourism; sponsors winter Texan activities. **Publications:** The Monitor (Monthly); Progress Times (Monthly).

58198 ■ Greater New Braunfels Chamber of Commerce
390 S Seguin Ave.
New Braunfels, TX 78130
Ph: (830)625-2385
Free: 800-572-2626
Fax: (830)625-7918
Co. E-mail: nbcc@nbcham.org
URL: http://www.nbcham.org/cwt/external/wcpages/index.aspx
Contact: Michael Meek, President
Description: Promotes business, economic, and community development in the Greater New Braunfels, TX area. **Founded:** 1920. **Publications:** Handelskammer (Monthly).

58199 ■ Greater Orange Area Chamber of Commerce (GOACC)
1012 Green Ave.
Orange, TX 77630
Ph: (409)883-3536
Fax: (409)866-3247
Co. E-mail: thechamber@sbcglobal.net
Contact: Julie Myers, Business Manager
Description: Promotes business and community development in the Orange, TX area. Holds annual Gumbo Cookoff. **Founded:** 1887. **Awards:** Citizen of the Year Alhena (Annual); Small Business Person (Annual).

58200 ■ Greater Pampa Area Chamber of Commerce (GPACC)
PO Box 1942
Pampa, TX 79065
Ph: (806)669-3241
Fax: (806)669-3244
Co. E-mail: harvest@pampachamber.com
URL: http://www.pampachamber.com
Contact: Joe Weaver, Executive Director
Description: Promotes business and community development in Pampa, TX. **Founded:** 1929.

58201 ■ Greater Pflugerville Chamber of Commerce (GPCC)
PO Box 483
Pflugerville, TX 78691-0483
Ph: (512)251-7799
Fax: (512)251-7802
Co. E-mail: gpcc@sbcglobal.net
URL: http://www.pfchamber.com/www
Contact: Patricia A. Gervan-Brown, President
Description: Promotes business and community development in Pflugerville, TX area. **Publications:** Weekly Wire (Weekly). **Educational Activities:** Chamber Chatter Luncheon (Monthly).

58202 ■ Greater Quitman Area Chamber of Commerce (GQACOC)
PO Box 426
Quitman, TX 75783-0426
Ph: (903)763-4411
Free: 866-302-3884
Fax: (903)763-4913
Co. E-mail: qtmncoc@peoplescom.net
URL: http://www.quitman.com
Contact: Toni Cole, Executive Director
Description: Provides quality service and leadership to its members and community, builds a healthier local economy and improves the quality of life through working together in a structured voluntary partnership of industrial, business, professional and concerned citizens. **Scope:** business. **Founded:** 1974. **Subscriptions:** 30000 articles audio recordings books papers periodicals video recordings. **Publications:**

Chamber Chatter (Monthly). **Educational Activities:** Dogwood Fiesta (Annual). **Awards:** Citizen of the Year (Annual); Member of the Month (Monthly).

58203 ■ Greater San Antonio Chamber of Commerce (GSACC)
602 E Commerce St.
San Antonio, TX 78295
Ph: (210)229-2100
Fax: (210)229-1600
Co. E-mail: infostore@sachamber.org
URL: http://sachamber.org
Contact: Richard Perez, President
Description: Promotes business and community development in the San Antonio, TX area. Represents the business community in legislative affairs and provides service programs. **Founded:** 1894. **Publications:** *The Advocate* (Monthly); *The Chamber Today* (Weekly); *Greater San Antonio Chamber of Commerce--Guide to Shopping Centers*; *Largest Employers Directory* (Annual); *The Greater San Antonio Chamber of Commerce--Clubs and OrganizatiDirectory* (Annual); *Area Business Councils/Small Business Update* (Weekly). **Telecommunication Services:** bbridges@sachamber.org.

58204 ■ Greater Southwest Houston Chamber of Commerce (GSWHCC)
6900 S Rice Ave.
Bellaire, TX 77402-0788
Ph: (713)666-1521
Fax: (713)666-1523
Co. E-mail: trishw@gswhcc.org
URL: http://www.southwesthoustonchamber.com
Contact: Toni J. Franklin, President
URL(s): www.gswhcc.org. **Description:** Promotes business and community development in Bellaire and Greater SW Houston, TX. Sponsors annual festival. **Founded:** 1949. **Publications:** *Chamber Progress* (Monthly). **Telecommunication Services:** info@gswhcc.org.

58205 ■ Greater Waco Chamber of Commerce
PO Box 1220
Waco, TX 76703-1220
Ph: (254)757-5600
Fax: (254)752-6618
Co. E-mail: info@wacochamber.com
URL: http://www.wacochamber.com
Contact: Matthew T. Meadors, President
Description: Promotes business and community development in the Waco, TX area. **Founded:** 1899. **Publications:** *Communicator* (Monthly); *ED Update* (Quarterly); *Waco Chamber and Business Quarterly* (Quarterly). **Awards:** Business Award (Annual).

58206 ■ *The Green Light is Go*
215 N Main St.
Gladewater, TX 75647
Ph: (903)845-5501
Fax: (903)845-6326
URL: http://www.gladewaterchamber.com
Released: Monthly **Price:** free for members.

58207 ■ Greenville Chamber of Commerce
2713 Stonewall St.
Greenville, TX 75403-1055
Ph: (903)455-1510
Co. E-mail: chamber@greenvillechamber.com
URL: http://www.greenvillechamber.com
Contact: Sally Bird, President
Description: Promotes business and community development in the Hunt County, TX area. Sponsors Cotton Jubilee and Fourth of July arts and crafts event. **Founded:** 1950. **Publications:** *Business Connection* (Monthly).

58208 ■ Gruver Chamber of Commerce
201 E Broadway
Gruver, TX 79040
Ph: (806)733-5114
Fax: (806)733-5038
URL: http://www.gruvertexas.com/chamber.html
Contact: Lisa Salmans, President
Description: Promotes business, community development, and tourism in the Gruver, TX area.

58209 ■ *Guide to the Rio Grande Valley*
322 S Missouri
Weslaco, TX 78596
Ph: (956)968-3141
Fax: (956)968-0210
Co. E-mail: mail@valleychamber.com
URL: http://www.valleychamber.com
Contact: Allen Shields, Chairman
Released: Annual

58210 ■ Hallettsville Chamber of Commerce
1614 N Texana St.
Hallettsville, TX 77964
Ph: (361)798-2662
Fax: (361)798-1553
Co. E-mail: visit@hallettsville.com
URL: http://www.hallettsville.com
Description: Promotes business, community development, and agriculture in Hallettsville, TX. Conducts membership drives and fundraisers.

58211 ■ Hamilton Chamber of Commerce (HCC)
204 E Main St.
Hamilton, TX 76531
Ph: (254)386-3216
Co. E-mail: chamber@hamiltontexas.com
URL: http://www.hamiltontexas.com
Contact: Mr. Sheldon Blackwell, President
Description: Promotes business and community development in Hamilton County, TX. Sponsors annual Hamilton County Dove Festival. **Awards:** Agriculturist of the Year (Annual); Business of the Year (Annual); Citizen of the Year (Annual).

58212 ■ *Handelskammer*
390 S Seguin Ave.
New Braunfels, TX 78130
Ph: (830)625-2385
Free: 800-572-2626
Fax: (830)625-7918
Co. E-mail: nbcc@nbcham.org
URL: http://www.nbcham.org/cwt/external/wcpages/index.aspx
Contact: Michael Meek, President
Released: Monthly

58213 ■ Harker Heights Chamber of Commerce
552 E FM 2410, Ste. B
Harker Heights, TX 76548
Ph: (254)699-4999
Fax: (254)699-5194
URL: http://www.hhchamber.com
Contact: Bill Kozlik, President
Description: Promotes business and community development in Harker Heights, TX area.

58214 ■ *Harlingen Area Business*
311 E Tyler St.
Harlingen, TX 78550-9121
Ph: (956)423-5440
Free: 800-531-7346
Fax: (956)425-3870
Co. E-mail: tsoule@harlingen.com
URL: http://harlingentxcoc.weblinkconnect.com/cwt/external/wcpages
Contact: Greg Quisenberry, Chairman
Released: Monthly

58215 ■ Harlingen Area Chamber of Commerce (HACC)
311 E Tyler St.
Harlingen, TX 78550-9121
Ph: (956)423-5440
Free: 800-531-7346
Fax: (956)425-3870
Co. E-mail: tsoule@harlingen.com
URL: http://harlingentxcoc.weblinkconnect.com/cwt/external/wcpages
Contact: Greg Quisenberry, Chairman
Description: Promotes business and community development in the Harlingen, TX area. **Publications:** *Harlingen Area Business* (Monthly); *Interplex Report and Memberandum* (Bimonthly).

58216 ■ Harlingen Hispanic Chamber of Commerce (HHCOC)
2309 N Ed Carey Dr.
Harlingen, TX 78550
Ph: (956)421-2400
Co. E-mail: brendarealtor05@yahoo.com
URL: http://www.harlingenchamber.com
Contact: Brenda Amaya, Secretary
Description: Works to promote the growth, development, and success of small businesses and to provide educational and leadership resources for the community. **Founded:** 1998. **Awards:** Embajador of the Year (Annual).

58217 ■ Hawkins Area Chamber of Commerce
109 Beaulah
Hawkins, TX 75765
Ph: (903)769-4482
Co. E-mail: chamber@hawkinschamberofcommerce.com
URL: http://www.hawkinschamberofcommerce.com
Description: Promotes business and community development in Hawkins, TX. Sponsors annual Hawkins Oil Festival.

58218 ■ *Healthy Living Guide*
300 E Wheatland Rd.
Duncanville, TX 75116
Ph: (972)780-4990
Fax: (972)298-9370
Co. E-mail: info@duncanvillechamber.org
URL: http://duncanvillechamber.org
Contact: Allen Conley, Chairman
Released: Periodic

58219 ■ Hearne Chamber of Commerce
304 S Market St.
Hearne, TX 77859
Ph: (979)279-2351
Fax: (979)279-2559
Co. E-mail: chamber@hearnetexas.info
URL: http://www.hearnetexas.info
Contact: Brad Ely, President
Description: Promotes business and community development in Robertson County, TX. Sponsors Booger Co. Glory Days the Dogwood Trails, and a Farmers' Market. **Founded:** 1914.

58220 ■ *The Heartbeat*
101 E 1st St.
Brady, TX 76825-4906
Ph: (325)597-3491
Free: 888-577-5657
Fax: (325)792-9181
Co. E-mail: bradychamber@hotmail.com
URL: http://www.bradytx.com
Contact: Carla Landes, President
Released: Quarterly **Price:** free for members.

58221 ■ Henderson Area Chamber of Commerce
201 N Main St.
Henderson, TX 75652
Ph: (903)657-5528
Fax: (903)657-9454
Co. E-mail: info@hendersontx.com
URL: http://www.hendersontx.com
Contact: Judy Sewell, Executive Director
Description: Promotes business and community development in Henderson, Tatum, Mt. Enterprise, Overton and New London in Rusk County, TX. **Founded:** 1926. **Publications:** *Chamber News and Views* (Monthly).

58222 ■ Henrietta - Clay County Chamber of Commerce
202 W Omega St.
Henrietta, TX 76365
Ph: (940)538-5261
Co. E-mail: claycountychamber@sbcglobal.net
URL: http://www.hccchamber.org
Contact: Kathy Pierce, President
Description: Promotes business and community development in Clay County, TX. **Founded:** 1927.

58223 ■ *Here is Houston*
1200 Smith, Ste. 700
Houston, TX 77002-4400

Ph: (713)844-3600
Fax: (713)844-0200
Co. E-mail: ghp@houston.org
URL: http://www.houston.org
Contact: Lilyanne McClean, President
Released: Quarterly **Price:** $3.50, for members; $7, for nonmembers.

58224 ■ *Hewitt Why Not!*
PO Box 661
Hewitt, TX 76643
Ph: (254)666-1200
Fax: (254)666-3181
Co. E-mail: info@hewitt-texas.com
URL: http://www.hewitt-texas.com
Contact: Ian Dawson, President
Released: Biweekly **Price:** free (paid by advertisers).

58225 ■ Hillsboro Chamber of Commerce (HCC)
PO Box 358
Hillsboro, TX 76645
Ph: (254)582-2481
Free: 800-HIL-LSBO
Fax: (254)582-0465
Co. E-mail: chamber@hillsborochamber.org
URL: http://www.hillsborochamber.org
Contact: Greg Solomon, President
Description: Promotes business and community development in the Hillsboro, TX area. **Publications:** *The Depot Connection* (Bimonthly).

58226 ■ *Hispanic Chamber News*
200 E Grayson, Ste. 203
San Antonio, TX 78215
Ph: (210)225-0462
Fax: (210)225-2485
URL: http://www.sahcc.org
Contact: Ramiro A. Cavazos, President
Released: Bimonthly

58227 ■ *Historic Llano*
100 Train Station Dr.
Llano, TX 78643
Ph: (325)247-5354
Free: 866-539-5535
Fax: (325)248-6917
Co. E-mail: info@llanochamber.org
URL: http://www.llanochamber.org
Contact: David Griffith, President

58228 ■ *Historic Port Isabel*
421 Queen Isabella Blvd.
Port Isabel, TX 78578
Ph: (956)943-2262
Free: 800-527-6102
Fax: (956)943-4001
Co. E-mail: director@portisabel.org
URL: http://portisabel.org
Contact: Betty Wells, President

58229 ■ Hondo Area Chamber of Commerce (HACC)
402 Carter
Hondo, TX 78861
Ph: (830)426-3037
Fax: (830)426-5357
Co. E-mail: info@hondochamber.com
URL: http://www.hondochamber.com
Contact: Rose Mary Mares, President
Description: Promotes business and community development in Hondo, TX.

58230 ■ Honey Grove Chamber of Commerce (HGCC)
PO Box 92
Honey Grove, TX 75446
Ph: (903)378-7888
Co. E-mail: info@honeygrovechamber.com
URL: http://www.honeygrovechamber.com
Contact: Jason White, President
Description: Promotes business and community development in Honey Grove, TX. Sponsors Davy Crockett Day and Christmas Parade.

58231 ■ Hopkins County Chamber of Commerce (HCCC)
PO Box 347
Sulphur Springs, TX 75483-0347

Ph: (903)885-6515
Free: 888-300-6623
Fax: (903)885-6516
Co. E-mail: chamber1@suddenlinkmail.net
URL: http://www.sulphursprings-tx.com
Contact: Meredith Caddell, President
Description: Promotes business and community development in Hopkins County, TX. Sponsors annual stew contest and annual dairy festival. **Founded:** 1926. **Publications:** *Chamber News* (Monthly). **Educational Activities:** Dairy Festival (Annual).

58232 ■ Houston Northwest Chamber of Commerce (HNWCC)
3920 FM 1960 W, Ste. 120
Houston, TX 77068
Ph: (281)440-4160
Fax: (281)440-5302
Co. E-mail: chamberinfo@houstonnwchamber.org
URL: http://www.hnwcc.com
Contact: Barbara Thompson, President
URL(s): www.houstonnwchamber.org. **Description:** Promotes business and community development in the Northwest Houston, TX area. **Founded:** 1974. **Publications:** *Houston's Great Northwest* (Monthly).

58233 ■ Houston West Chamber of Commerce (HWCC)
10370 Richmond, Ste. 125
Houston, TX 77042-4278
Ph: (713)785-4922
Fax: (713)785-4944
Co. E-mail: jeannie@hwcoc.org
URL: http://www.hwcoc.org
Contact: Jeannie Bollinger, President
Description: Promotes business and community development in Western Houston, TX. **Founded:** 1985. **Publications:** *Metro West Magazine* (Periodic). **Awards:** Star Award (Annual).

58234 ■ *Houston's Great Northwest*
3920 FM 1960 W, Ste. 120
Houston, TX 77068
Ph: (281)440-4160
Fax: (281)440-5302
Co. E-mail: chamberinfo@houstonnwchamber.org
URL: http://www.hnwcc.com
Contact: Barbara Thompson, President
Released: Monthly

58235 ■ *How To Go Into Business in Duncanville*
300 E Wheatland Rd.
Duncanville, TX 75116
Ph: (972)780-4990
Fax: (972)298-9370
Co. E-mail: info@duncanvillechamber.org
URL: http://duncanvillechamber.org
Contact: Allen Conley, Chairman

58236 ■ Howe Chamber of Commerce
PO Box 250
Howe, TX 75459-0250
Ph: (903)532-HOWE
Fax: (903)532-6012
Co. E-mail: contact@howetx.org
URL: http://www.ropesplace.com/howechamber
Contact: Wayne Swinford, President
Description: Promotes business and community development in Howe, TX. Sponsors festival and Christmas decoration contest. **Founded:** 1983.

58237 ■ *Hunting Lease Lists*
402 E Main
Junction, TX 76849
Ph: (325)446-3190
Free: 800-546-2534
Fax: (325)446-2871
Co. E-mail: junctiontx@cebridge.net
URL: http://www.junctiontexas.net
Contact: Laura Wilson, President
Released: Annual **Price:** free.

58238 ■ Hurst - Euless - Bedford Chamber of Commerce (HEBCC)
2109 Martin Dr.
Bedford, TX 76021-5910
Ph: (817)283-1521

Fax: (817)267-5111
Co. E-mail: chamber@heb.org
URL: http://www.heb.org
Contact: Ms. Mary Martin Frazior, President
Description: Promotes business and community development in Bedford, Euless, and Hurst, TX. **Founded:** 1954. **Publications:** *Member Update* (Bimonthly). **Awards:** HEB Chamber Community Service Award (Annual).

58239 ■ Hutto Chamber of Commerce
122 East St.
Hutto, TX 78634-0099
Ph: (512)759-4400
URL: http://www.hutto.org
Contact: Tom Britton, President
Description: Promotes business and community development in Hutto, TX. **Founded:** 1986.

58240 ■ *Image*
119 E 5th St.
Bonham, TX 75418
Ph: (903)583-4811
Fax: (903)583-7972
Co. E-mail: bonhamchamber@cableone.net
URL: http://www.bonhamchamber.com
Contact: Bill Jones, Executive Director
Released: Annual

58241 ■ *Impact*
410 N Center St.
Longview, TX 75601
Ph: (903)237-4000
Fax: (903)237-4049
Co. E-mail: info1@longviewtx.com
URL: http://www.longviewchamber.com
Contact: Kelly R. Hall, President
Released: Monthly

58242 ■ *The Informer*
PO Box 1100
Lancaster, TX 75146
Ph: (972)227-2579
Fax: (972)227-9555
Co. E-mail: chamber@lancastertx.org
URL: http://www.lancastertx.org
Contact: Joe Johnson, President
Released: Monthly

58243 ■ Ingleside Chamber of Commerce
PO Box 686
Ingleside, TX 78362
Ph: (361)776-2906
Free: 888-899-2906
Fax: (361)776-0678
Co. E-mail: ingchamber@cableone.net
URL: http://www.inglesidetxchamber.org
Contact: Michael Ladewig, Chairman
Description: Promotes business and community development in Ingleside, TX. **Scope:** chambers, state directory. **Founded:** 1984. **Subscriptions:** 2. **Publications:** *Ingleside Chamber of Commerce Newsletter* (Monthly).

58244 ■ *Ingleside Chamber of Commerce Newsletter*
PO Box 686
Ingleside, TX 78362
Ph: (361)776-2906
Free: 888-899-2906
Fax: (361)776-0678
Co. E-mail: ingchamber@cableone.net
URL: http://www.inglesidetxchamber.org
Contact: Michael Ladewig, Chairman
Released: Monthly **Price:** free.

58245 ■ *Insider*
551 N Valley Pkwy.
Lewisville, TX 75067
Ph: (972)436-9571
Fax: (972)436-5949
Co. E-mail: info@lewisvillechamber.org
URL: http://www.lewisvillechamber.org
Contact: Matt McCormick, President
Released: Monthly

58246 ■ *Interplex Report and Memberandum*
311 E Tyler St.
Harlingen, TX 78550-9121

Ph: (956)423-5440
Free: 800-531-7346
Fax: (956)425-3870
Co. E-mail: tsoule@harlingen.com
URL: http://harlingentxcoc.weblinkconnect.com/cwt/
external/wcpages
Contact: Greg Quisenberry, Chairman
Released: Bimonthly

58247 ■ Jacksboro Chamber of Commerce
302 S Main St.
Jacksboro, TX 76458
Ph: (940)567-2602
Fax: (940)567-3161
Co. E-mail: office@jacksborochamber.com
URL: http://www.jacksborochamber.com
Contact: Joe Mitchell, President
Description: Promotes business, tourism, and community development in Jacksboro, TX. Sponsors Weekend in Old Mesquiteville festival; conducts Halloween costume contest; promotes jamborees and community holiday festivities. **Founded:** 1947.

58248 ■ Jacksonville Chamber of Commerce
526 E Commerce St.
Jacksonville, TX 75766
Ph: (903)586-2217
Free: 800-376-2217
Fax: (903)586-6944
Co. E-mail: chamber@jacksonvilletexas.com
URL: http://www.jacksonvilletexas.com
Contact: Peggy Renfro, President
Description: Promotes business, community, and tourism development in Jacksonville, and Cherokee County, TX. **Founded:** 1928. **Subscriptions:** 45000.
Awards: Citizen of the Year (Annual); Spectrum Award (Annual).

58249 ■ Jasper Lake Sam Rayburn Area Chamber of Commerce
246 E Milam St.
Jasper, TX 75951
Ph: (409)384-2762
Fax: (409)384-4733
Co. E-mail: jaspercc@jaspercoc.org
URL: http://www.jaspercoc.org
Contact: Liz Street, Executive Director
Description: Promotes business and community development in Jasper, TX. **Founded:** 1919. **Publications:** *Jasper, TX* (Annual). **Awards:** Citizen of the Year (Annual); Newcomer of the Year (Annual); Small Business of the Year (Annual); Young Person of the Year (Annual).

58250 ■ *Jasper, TX*
246 E Milam St.
Jasper, TX 75951
Ph: (409)384-2762
Fax: (409)384-4733
Co. E-mail: jaspercc@jaspercoc.org
URL: http://www.jaspercoc.org
Contact: Liz Street, Executive Director
Released: Annual **Price:** free.

58251 ■ Johnson City Chamber of Commerce
PO Box 485
Johnson City, TX 78636
Fax: (830)868-5700
URL: http://www.johnsoncitytexaschamber.com
Contact: Robert Peterson, President
Description: Promotes business and community development in Johnson City, TX.

58252 ■ Joshua Area Chamber of Commerce (JACC)
104 N Main St.
Joshua, TX 76058
Ph: (817)558-2821
Fax: (817)645-7824
Co. E-mail: joshchamber@att.net
URL: http://www.joshuachamber.org
Contact: Paulette Hartman, Chairperson
Description: Promotes business and community development in the Joshua, TX area. **Founded:** 1986.

58253 ■ *Journal Sponsorship*
420 Johnson Rd., Ste. 301
Keller, TX 76248
Ph: (817)431-2169
Fax: (817)431-3789
Co. E-mail: keller@kellerchamber.com
URL: http://www.kellerchamber.com
Contact: Susanne Johnson, President
Released: Monthly **Price:** $150.

58254 ■ Katy Area Chamber of Commerce
23501 Cinco Ranch Blvd., Ste. B206
Katy, TX 77494
Ph: (281)391-5289
Fax: (281)391-7423
Co. E-mail: info@katychamber.com
URL: http://www.katychamber.com
Contact: Ann Hodge, President
Description: Promotes business and community development in Katy, TX area. **Founded:** 1962.

58255 ■ Kerens Chamber of Commerce (KCC)
PO Box 117
Kerens, TX 75144
Ph: (903)396-2391
Co. E-mail: kerenschamber@txun.net
URL: http://www.ci.kerens.tx.us
Contact: Cindy Scott, President
Description: Promotes business and community development in Kerens, TX.

58256 ■ *Kerrville*
1700 Sidney Baker St., Ste. 100
Kerrville, TX 78028
Ph: (830)896-1155
Fax: (830)896-1175
Co. E-mail: info@kerrvilletx.com
URL: http://kerrvilletx.le3.getliveedit.com/pages/home
Contact: Mark Tuschak, Chairman

58257 ■ Kerrville Area Chamber of Commerce
1700 Sidney Baker St., Ste. 100
Kerrville, TX 78028
Ph: (830)896-1155
Fax: (830)896-1175
Co. E-mail: info@kerrvilletx.com
URL: http://kerrvilletx.le3.getliveedit.com/pages/home
Contact: Mark Tuschak, Chairman
Description: Promotes business and community development in the Kerrville, TX area. **Founded:** 1922. **Publications:** *City Map*; *The Communique* (Monthly); *Kerrville*.

58258 ■ Kilgore Chamber of Commerce
813 N Kilgore St.
Kilgore, TX 75662
Ph: (903)984-5022
Free: 866-984-0400
Fax: (903)984-4975
Co. E-mail: info@kilgorechamber.com
URL: http://www.kilgorechamber.com
Contact: Donna Beets, Chairperson
Description: Promotes business and community development in Kilgore, TX. Convention/Meeting: none. **Founded:** 1931. **Publications:** *Chamber Notes* (Monthly). **Awards:** Citizen of the Year (Annual).

58259 ■ Kimble County Chamber of Commerce (KCCC)
402 E Main
Junction, TX 76849
Ph: (325)446-3190
Free: 800-546-2534
Fax: (325)446-2871
Co. E-mail: junctiontx@cebridge.net
URL: http://www.junctiontexas.net
Contact: Laura Wilson, President
Description: Promotes business, tourism, and community development in Kimble County, TX. Sponsors community activities and encourages hunting in the area. **Founded:** 1914. **Publications:** *Hunting Lease Lists* (Annual).

58260 ■ Kingsland - Lake LBJ Chamber of Commerce (KCC)
PO Box 465
Kingsland, TX 78639
Ph: (325)388-6211
Fax: (325)388-5391
Co. E-mail: info@kingslandchamber.org
URL: http://www.kingslandchamber.org
Contact: Cindy Miller, President
Description: Promotes business and community development in the Texas hill country. Conducts annual Bluebonnet Festival, Aquaboom, and Airfest. **Founded:** 1965.

58261 ■ Kingsville Chamber of Commerce (KCOC)
PO Box 1030
Kingsville, TX 78363
Ph: (361)592-6438
Fax: (361)592-0866
Co. E-mail: chamber@kingsville.org
URL: http://www.kingsville.org
Contact: Ms. Alice L. Byers, Executive Director
Description: Promotes business and community development in Kleberg County, TX. Provides individual and group assistance. Issues publications. **Founded:** 1908.

58262 ■ *Kirbyville Centennial Magazine 1995*
PO Box 417
Kirbyville, TX 75956
Ph: (409)423-5827
URL: http://kirbyvillechamberofcommerce.com
Contact: Charles Coleman, President
Price: $5.

58263 ■ Kirbyville Chamber of Commerce (KCC)
PO Box 417
Kirbyville, TX 75956
Ph: (409)423-5827
URL: http://kirbyvillechamberofcommerce.com
Contact: Charles Coleman, President
Description: Promotes business and community development in Kirbyville, TX. Sponsors Magnolia Festival. **Subscriptions:** articles books periodicals. **Publications:** *Kirbyville Centennial Magazine 1995*; *Kirbyville Centennial Magazine 1995*.

58264 ■ Kountze Chamber of Commerce (KCC)
PO Box 878
Kountze, TX 77625
Ph: (409)246-3413
Free: 866-456-8689
Fax: (409)246-2826
Co. E-mail: contact@kountzechamber.com
URL: http://www.kountzechamber.com
Contact: Ann Boyett, President
Description: Promotes business and community development in Kountze, TX.

58265 ■ *Kyle Area Chamber of Commerce Business Directory and Guidebook*
PO Box 900
Kyle, TX 78640-0900
Ph: (512)268-4220
Free: 800-903-1564
Co. E-mail: ray@kylechamber.org
URL: http://www.kylechamber.org
Contact: Ray Hernandez, Executive Director
Released: Biennial **Price:** free for members.

58266 ■ Kyle Area Chamber of Commerce and Visitors' Bureau
PO Box 900
Kyle, TX 78640-0900
Ph: (512)268-4220
Free: 800-903-1564
Co. E-mail: ray@kylechamber.org
URL: http://www.kylechamber.org
Contact: Ray Hernandez, Executive Director
Description: Strives to promote interaction among businesses, tourism, and commerce within the city of Kyle. **Founded:** 1998. **Publications:** *Chamber Chatter* (Weekly); *Kyle Area Chamber of Commerce Business Directory and Guidebook* (Biennial).

58267 ■ La Grange Area Chamber of Commerce
171 S Main
La Grange, TX 78945
Ph: (979)968-5756
Free: 800-524-7264
Fax: (979)968-8000
Co. E-mail: chamber@lagrangetx.org
URL: http://www.lagrangetx.org
Contact: Jonathan Hernandez, Chairman
Description: Promotes business and community development in Fayette County, TX.

58268 ■ La Porte-Bayshore Chamber of Commerce
PO Box 996
La Porte, TX 77572-0996
Ph: (281)471-1123
Fax: (281)471-1710
Co. E-mail: colleenhicks@laportechamber.org
URL: http://www.laportechamber.org
Contact: Colleen Hicks, President
Description: Promotes business and community development in La Porte, TX.

58269 ■ Lago Vista Area Chamber of Commerce
PO Box 4946
Lago Vista, TX 78645
Ph: (512)267-7952
Fax: (512)267-2338
Co. E-mail: info@lagovista.org
URL: http://www.lagovista.org
Contact: Sherri Campbell-Jander, Executive Director
Description: Provides services to members and community through marketing and management of economic development and tourism in the Lago Vista area. **Founded:** 1980. **Publications:** Chamber Chatter. **Awards:** Business of the Month (Monthly); Business of the Year (Annual); Citizen of the Year (Annual).

58270 ■ Lake Buchanan - Inks Lake Chamber of Commerce
19611 E State Hwy. 29
Buchanan Dam, TX 78609-4521
Ph: (512)793-2803
Fax: (512)793-2112
Co. E-mail: theedge@tstar.net
URL: http://www.buchanan-inks.com
Contact: Ray McCasland, President
Description: Promotes business and community development in Buchanan Dam, TX. **Founded:** 1958.

58271 ■ Lake Cities Chamber of Commerce
PO Box 1028
Lake Dallas, TX 75065
Ph: (940)497-3097
Fax: (972)534-1375
Co. E-mail: lccc@lakecitieschamber.com
URL: http://www.lakecitieschamber.com
Contact: Doug Gryder, President
Description: Strives to promote business and community development in Lake Cities Communities which include the City of Lake Dallas, the City of Corinth, the Town of Shady Shores, and the Town of Hickory Creek, TX.

58272 ■ Lake Granbury Area Chamber of Commerce (LGACC)
3408 E Hwy. 377
Granbury, TX 76049
Ph: (817)573-1622
Fax: (817)573-0805
Co. E-mail: mary@granburychamber.com
URL: http://www.granburychamber.com
Contact: Mike Scott, President
Description: Promotes business and community development in the Granbury, TX area.

58273 ■ Lake Houston Area Chamber of Commerce
110 W Main St.
Humble, TX 77338
Ph: (281)446-2128

Fax: (281)446-7483
Co. E-mail: chamber@lakehouston.org
URL: http://www.lakehouston.org
Contact: Charlie Dromgoole, President
Description: Promotes business and community development in Humble, Kingwood, and Atascosita areas, TX. Sponsors Good Oil Days festival. Holds Chamber Classic Golf Tournament and Health Fair Business-Fest. **Founded:** 1923. **Publications:** Member Business Link (Quarterly). **Educational Activities:** Aviation (Monthly).

58274 ■ Lake Whitney Chamber of Commerce
PO Box 604
Whitney, TX 76692
Ph: (254)694-2540
Fax: (855)870-7409
Co. E-mail: bluewater@lakewhitneychamber.com
URL: http://www.lakewhitneychamber.com
Contact: Diana Reed, Executive Secretary
Description: Promotes business, tourism, and community development in the Whitney, TX area.

58275 ■ Lamar County Chamber of Commerce
1125 Bonham St.
Paris, TX 75460
Ph: (903)784-2501
Fax: (903)784-2503
Co. E-mail: chamber@paristexas.com
URL: http://www.paristexas.com
Contact: Mindy Moree, President
Description: Promotes economic growth and quality of life in Paris and the Lamar County, TX area. **Founded:** 1904. **Publications:** The Chamber Business Report (Monthly).

58276 ■ Lampasas County Chamber of Commerce (LCCC)
PO Box 627
Lampasas, TX 76550
Ph: (512)556-5172
Free: 866-556-5172
Fax: (512)556-2195
Co. E-mail: lampasaschamber@sbcglobal.net
URL: http://www.lampasaschamber.org
Contact: Jill Carroll, Executive Director
Description: Promotes business and community development in Lampasas County, TX. **Founded:** 1918.

58277 ■ Lancaster Chamber of Commerce (LCC)
PO Box 1100
Lancaster, TX 75146
Ph: (972)227-2579
Fax: (972)227-9555
Co. E-mail: chamber@lancastertx.org
URL: http://www.lancastertx.org
Contact: Joe Johnson, President
Description: Promotes business and economic development in Lancaster, TX. **Founded:** 1953. **Publications:** The Informer (Monthly).

58278 ■ Laredo - Webb County Chamber of Commerce (LWCCC)
PO Box 790
Laredo, TX 78042
Ph: (956)722-9895
Free: 800-292-2122
Fax: (956)791-4503
Co. E-mail: chamber@laredochamber.com
URL: http://www.laredochamber.com
Contact: Miguel A. Conchas, President
Description: Promotes business and community development in Laredo, TX. Provides membership services and international trade information. **Founded:** 1915. **Publications:** Chamber Notes (Monthly); Inlandport (Monthly); Laredo Economic Activity Index (Annual). **Educational Activities:** Economic Outlook (Annual). **Awards:** Customer Service Award (Annual); Business Persons of the Year (Annual).

58279 ■ Levelland Area Chamber of Commerce (LACC)
c/o Mary Siders, Pres.
1101 Ave. H
Levelland, TX 79336
Ph: (806)894-3157
Fax: (806)894-4284
Co. E-mail: msiders@levelland.com
URL: http://www.levellandtexas.org/index.aspx-?nid=177
Contact: Mary Siders, President
Description: Promotes business and community development in the Levelland, TX area. Sponsors Easter egg hunt, Early Settlers Reunion, Marigolds Arts and Crafts Festival, and teachers' breakfast, Leadership Levelland Program, and Small Business Development Center. **Founded:** 1951.

58280 ■ Lewisville Area Chamber of Commerce
551 N Valley Pkwy.
Lewisville, TX 75067
Ph: (972)436-9571
Fax: (972)436-5949
Co. E-mail: info@lewisvillechamber.org
URL: http://www.lewisvillechamber.org
Contact: Matt McCormick, President
Description: Promotes business and community development in Lewisville, TX. **Founded:** 1962. **Publications:** Chamber Guide (Annual); Insider (Monthly).

58281 ■ Liberty-Dayton Area Chamber of Commerce (LDACC)
PO Box 1270
Liberty, TX 77575
Ph: (936)336-5736
Fax: (936)336-1159
Co. E-mail: chamber@imsday.com
URL: http://www.libertydaytonchamber.com
Contact: Sherry Mettlen, Chairperson
Description: Promotes business and community development in Dayton and Liberty, TX. Conducts lobbying activities; encourages proper maintenance of local highways. **Founded:** 1909.

58282 ■ Lindale Area Chamber of Commerce (LACC)
110 E Hubbard St.
Lindale, TX 75771
Ph: (903)882-7181
Co. E-mail: info@lindalechamber.com
URL: http://www.lindalechamber.org
Contact: Shelbie Glover, Executive Director
Description: Promotes business and community development in Lindale, TX area. **Publications:** Connection (Quarterly).

58283 ■ Livingston-Polk County Chamber of Commerce
PO Box 600
Livingston, TX 77351
Ph: (936)327-4929
Free: 800-918-1305
Fax: (936)327-2660
Co. E-mail: chamberadmin@livingston.net
URL: http://www.lpcchamber.com
Contact: Sydney Murphy, Executive Director
Description: Promotes business and community development in Livingston, TX and Polk County, TX. **Founded:** 1936. **Publications:** Chamber Connection (Monthly).

58284 ■ Llano County Chamber of Commerce (LCCC)
100 Train Station Dr.
Llano, TX 78643
Ph: (325)247-5354
Free: 866-539-5535
Fax: (325)248-6917
Co. E-mail: info@llanochamber.org
URL: http://www.llanochamber.org
Contact: David Griffith, President
Description: Promotes business and community development in Llano County, TX. Sponsors local festivals. **Founded:** 1919. **Publications:** Business Directory (Annual); Historic Llano; A Walking Tour of Historic Llano.

58285 ■ Lockhart Chamber of Commerce (LCC)
PO Box 840
Lockhart, TX 78644
Ph: (512)398-2818
Fax: (512)376-2632
Co. E-mail: staff@lockhartchamber.com
URL: http://www.lockhartchamber.com
Contact: Wayne Bock, President
Description: Promotes business and community development in Lockhart, TX. **Founded:** 1935. **Publications:** *Lockhart Enterprise* (Monthly).

58286 ■ *Lockhart Enterprise*
PO Box 840
Lockhart, TX 78644
Ph: (512)398-2818
Fax: (512)376-2632
Co. E-mail: staff@lockhartchamber.com
URL: http://www.lockhartchamber.com
Contact: Wayne Bock, President
Released: Monthly **Price:** free.

58287 ■ Longview Partnership
410 N Center St.
Longview, TX 75601
Ph: (903)237-4000
Fax: (903)237-4049
Co. E-mail: info1@longviewtx.com
URL: http://www.longviewchamber.com
Contact: Kelly R. Hall, President
Description: Promotes business and community development in Longview, TX. **Publications:** *Impact* (Monthly); *Uniquely Longview* (Annual).

58288 ■ Los Fresnos Chamber of Commerce
203 N Arroyo Blvd.
Los Fresnos, TX 78566
Ph: (956)233-4488
Co. E-mail: losfresnoschamber@yahoo.com
URL: http://www.losfresnoschamber.com
Contact: Debra Badeaux, Executive Director
Description: Promotes, extends and assists all commerce growth in the Los Fresnos area.

58289 ■ Louise-Hillje Chamber of Commerce
PO Box 156
Louise, TX 77455
Co. E-mail: member@work.com
URL: http://www.louisehilljechamber.org
Contact: Debbie Townsend, President
Description: Promotes business and community development in Louise, TX. **Founded:** 1959.

58290 ■ Lubbock Chamber of Commerce
1500 Broadway, Ste. 101
Lubbock, TX 79401
Ph: (806)761-7000
Fax: (806)761-7013
Co. E-mail: info@lubbockbiz.org
URL: http://lubbocktxcoc.weblinkconnect.com/cwt/
external/wcpages/index.aspx
Contact: Eddie McBride, President
Description: Promotes business and community development in Lubbock, TX area. **Founded:** 1913.

58291 ■ Lufkin - Angelina County Chamber of Commerce (LACCC)
1615 S Chestnut
Lufkin, TX 75901
Ph: (936)634-6644
Fax: (936)634-8726
Co. E-mail: jhuffman@lufkintexas.org
URL: http://www.lufkintexas.org
Contact: Jerry Huffman, President
Description: Promotes business and community development in Angelina County, TX. Sponsors annual Texas Forest Festival and Angelina County Youth Fair. **Founded:** 1919.

58292 ■ Madison County Chamber of Commerce
113 W Trinity
Madisonville, TX 77864
Ph: (936)348-3591

Fax: (936)348-2212
Co. E-mail: director@madisoncountytxchamber.com
URL: http://www.madisoncountytxchamber.com
Contact: Allen Griffith, Chairman
Description: Promotes business and community development in Madison County, TX. **Scope:** statistical and demographic data. **Subscriptions:** business records maps.

58293 ■ Mansfield Area Chamber of Commerce (MCC)
114 N Main St.
Mansfield, TX 76063
Ph: (817)473-0507
Fax: (817)473-8687
Co. E-mail: amiller@mansfieldchamber.org
URL: http://www.mansfieldchamber.org
Contact: Amanda M. Miller, President
Description: Promotes business and community development in Mansfield, TX. Sponsors annual Hometown Celebration, Golf Tournament, Allie Day, Circus (every two years), Spring and Fall Beautification days, Christmas Parade, Tour of Homes. **Founded:** 1895. **Publications:** *Welcome to Mansfield* (Annual); *Mansfield Chamber Communique* (Monthly).

58294 ■ *Mansfield Chamber Communique*
114 N Main St.
Mansfield, TX 76063
Ph: (817)473-0507
Fax: (817)473-8687
Co. E-mail: amiller@mansfieldchamber.org
URL: http://www.mansfieldchamber.org
Contact: Amanda M. Miller, President
Released: Monthly **Price:** free.

58295 ■ *Manufacturing Directory*
4749 Twin City Hwy., Ste. 300
Port Arthur, TX 77642
Ph: (409)963-1107
Fax: (409)962-1997
Co. E-mail: portarthurchamber@portarthurtexas.com
URL: http://www.portarthurtexas.com
Contact: Mary Ann Reid, President
Released: Periodic

58296 ■ *Map*
PO Box 346
Georgetown, TX 78627-0346
Ph: (512)930-3535
Fax: (512)930-3587
Co. E-mail: info@georgetownchamber.org
URL: http://www.georgetownchamber.org
Contact: Mel Pendland, President
Released: Annual

58297 ■ *Maquiladona Directory*
PO Box 1188
Eagle Pass, TX 78853-1188
Ph: (830)773-3224
Free: 888-355-3224
Fax: (830)773-8844
Co. E-mail: chamber@eaglepasstexas.com
URL: http://eaglepasstexas.com
Contact: Sandra Martinez, Executive Director
Released: Quarterly

58298 ■ Marble Falls - Lake LBJ Chamber of Commerce
916 Second St.
Marble Falls, TX 78654
Ph: (830)693-2815
Free: 800-759-8178
Fax: (830)693-1620
Co. E-mail: info@marblefalls.org
URL: http://www.marblefalls.org
Contact: Bill Rives, Executive Director
Description: Promotes business and community development in Marble Falls, TX.

58299 ■ Marfa Chamber of Commerce (MCC)
PO Box 635
Marfa, TX 79843
Ph: (432)729-4942
Free: 800-650-9696

Fax: (432)729-4956
Co. E-mail: info@marfacc.com
URL: http://www.marfacc.com
Contact: Kelly Sudderth, President
Description: Promotes business and community development in Marfa, TX.

58300 ■ Marion County Chamber of Commerce
101 N Polk St.
Jefferson, TX 75657-2213
Ph: (903)665-2672
Free: 888-GO-RELAX
Fax: (903)665-8233
Co. E-mail: jeffersontx1@att.net
URL: http://www.jefferson-texas.com
Contact: Kayanne Hollomon, Director
Description: Promotes business community and economic development in Marion County, TX. Encourages tourism. **Founded:** 1950. **Awards:** Citizen of the Year (Annual).

58301 ■ Marlin Chamber of Commerce (MCC)
245 Coleman St.
Marlin, TX 76661
Ph: (254)803-3301
Fax: (254)883-2171
Co. E-mail: marlintxchamber@aol.com
URL: http://www.marlintexas.com
Contact: Justin Hay, President
Description: Promotes business and community development in Marlin, TX.

58302 ■ Marshall Texas Chamber of Commerce
213 W Austin St.
Marshall, TX 75671
Ph: (903)935-7868
Free: 800-953-7868
Fax: (903)935-9982
Co. E-mail: contactus@marshalltexas.com
URL: http://www.marshall-chamber.com
Contact: Connie Ware, President
Description: Promotes business and community development in the Marshall, TX area. **Publications:** *Focus*.

58303 ■ *Mason Chamber News*
PO Box 156
Mason, TX 76856
Ph: (325)347-5758
Fax: (325)347-5259
Co. E-mail: masontexas@hctc.net
URL: http://www.masontxcoc.com
Contact: Bonnie Beam, President
Released: Bimonthly

58304 ■ Mason County Chamber of Commerce
PO Box 156
Mason, TX 76856
Ph: (325)347-5758
Fax: (325)347-5259
Co. E-mail: masontexas@hctc.net
URL: http://www.masontxcoc.com
Contact: Bonnie Beam, President
Description: Promotes business and community development in Mason County, TX. **Publications:** *Mason Chamber News* (Bimonthly).

58305 ■ McAllen Chamber of Commerce—McAllen Convention and Visitors Bureau
1200 Ash Ave.
McAllen, TX 78501
Ph: (956)682-2871
Fax: (956)687-2917
Co. E-mail: steve@mcallenchamber.com
URL: http://www.mcallenchamber.com
Contact: Steve Ahlenius, President
Description: Promotes business and community development in McAllen, TX. **Founded:** 1926.

58306 ■ McCamey Chamber of Commerce
201 E 6th St.
McCamey, TX 79752

Ph: (432)652-8202
Co. E-mail: jasonjmenefee@gmail.com
URL: http://mccameychamber.org
Contact: Jason Menefee, President
Description: Promotes business and community development in McCamey, TX. Conducts charitable activities, July 4th Activities, Teacher's Tea, Wind Energy Bluegrass Festival, Community Calendar, Lighted Christmas Parade, Santa at the Bank, and Merchant Auction.

58307 ■ McGregor Chamber of Commerce
303 S Main St.
McGregor, TX 76657
Ph: (254)840-2292
Fax: (254)840-4703
Co. E-mail: office@mcgregorchamber.com
URL: http://www.mcgregor-texas.com/chamber.html
Contact: Jon Mark Smith, Director
Description: Promotes business and community development in McGregor, TX. Conducts seasonal promotions with special events. **Awards:** Citizen of the Year Award (Annual).

58308 ■ McKinney Chamber of Commerce (MCC)
2150 S Central Expy., Ste. 150
Summit Office Park 1
McKinney, TX 75070
Ph: (972)542-0163
Fax: (972)548-0876
Co. E-mail: info@mckinneychamber.com
URL: http://www.mckinneytx.org/cwt/external/wcpages/index.aspx
Contact: Jodi Ann LaFreniere, President
Description: Promotes business and community development in McKinney, TX. Monitors legislation. **Founded:** 1906. **Publications:** *McKinney Focus* (Monthly); *McKinney Living Magazine* (Semiannual); *McKinney Living Magazine's Relocation & Referral Guide* (Annual). **Educational Activities:** Business after Hours (Monthly); Community Awards Celebration (Annual); State of the City (Annual). **Awards:** Citizen of the Year (Annual); Outstanding Business (Annual).

58309 ■ *McKinney Focus*
2150 S Central Expy., Ste. 150
Summit Office Park 1
McKinney, TX 75070
Ph: (972)542-0163
Fax: (972)548-0876
Co. E-mail: info@mckinneychamber.com
URL: http://www.mckinneytx.org/cwt/external/wcpages/index.aspx
Contact: Jodi Ann LaFreniere, President
Released: Monthly

58310 ■ *McKinney Living Magazine*
2150 S Central Expy., Ste. 150
Summit Office Park 1
McKinney, TX 75070
Ph: (972)542-0163
Fax: (972)548-0876
Co. E-mail: info@mckinneychamber.com
URL: http://www.mckinneytx.org/cwt/external/wcpages/index.aspx
Contact: Jodi Ann LaFreniere, President
Released: Semiannual **Price:** free.

58311 ■ *McKinney Living Magazine's Relocation & Referral Guide*
2150 S Central Expy., Ste. 150
Summit Office Park 1
McKinney, TX 75070
Ph: (972)542-0163
Fax: (972)548-0876
Co. E-mail: info@mckinneychamber.com
URL: http://www.mckinneytx.org/cwt/external/wcpages/index.aspx
Contact: Jodi Ann LaFreniere, President
Released: Annual **Price:** free.

58312 ■ *Member Business Link*
110 W Main St.
Humble, TX 77338
Ph: (281)446-2128

Fax: (281)446-7483
Co. E-mail: chamber@lakehouston.org
URL: http://www.lakehouston.org
Contact: Charlie Dromgoole, President
Released: Quarterly **Price:** free.

58313 ■ *Member Update*
2109 Martin Dr.
Bedford, TX 76021-5910
Ph: (817)283-1521
Fax: (817)267-5111
Co. E-mail: chamber@heb.org
URL: http://www.heb.org
Contact: Ms. Mary Martin Frazior, President
Released: Bimonthly **Price:** free for members.

58314 ■ *Membership Directory and Buyers Guide*
612 E Main St.
Alice, TX 78333
Ph: (361)664-3454
Fax: (361)664-2291
Co. E-mail: jnavejar@alicetx.org
URL: http://www.alicetxchamber.org
Contact: Juan A. Navejar, Jr., Executive Vice President
Released: Annual

58315 ■ *Membership Directory and Buyers' Guide*
1000 S Polk St.
Amarillo, TX 79101-3408
Ph: (806)373-7800
Fax: (806)373-3909
Co. E-mail: chamber@amarillo-chamber.org
URL: http://www.amarillo-chamber.org
Contact: Gary Molberg, President
Released: Annual

58316 ■ *Membership Directory and Buyers' Guide*
252 W Main St., Ste. A
Azle, TX 76020
Ph: (817)444-1112
Fax: (817)444-1143
Co. E-mail: info@azlechamber.com
URL: http://www.azlechamber.com
Contact: Lorie Pack, President
Released: Annual

58317 ■ *Membership Directory/Buyer's Guide*
300 E Wheatland Rd.
Duncanville, TX 75116
Ph: (972)780-4990
Fax: (972)298-9370
Co. E-mail: info@duncanvillechamber.org
URL: http://duncanvillechamber.org
Contact: Allen Conley, Chairman
Released: Annual

58318 ■ *Membership Directory/Buyer's Guide*
109 N Main St.
Midland, TX 79701
Ph: (432)683-3381
Free: 800-624-6435
Fax: (432)686-3556
Co. E-mail: info@midlandtxchamber.com
URL: http://www.midlandtxchamber.com
Contact: Bobby Burns, President
Released: Annual

58319 ■ *Membership Directory/Guide Book*
308 W Park Ave.
Pharr, TX 78577
Ph: (956)787-1481
Fax: (956)787-7972
Co. E-mail: info@pharrchamberofcommerce.com
URL: http://www.pharrchamberofcommerce.com
Contact: Luis A. Bazan, President
Released: Annual

58320 ■ *Membership Directory/Resource Guide*
520 N Glenbrook
Garland, TX 75040
Ph: (972)272-7551

Fax: (972)276-9261
URL: http://www.garlandchamber.com
Contact: Paul Mayer, Chief Executive Officer
Price: $30.

58321 ■ Mercedes Chamber of Commerce (MCC)
PO Box 37
Mercedes, TX 78570-0037
Ph: (956)565-2221
Co. E-mail: donna@mercedeschamber.com
URL: http://www.mercedeschamber.com
Description: Promotes business and community development in Mercedes, TX. **Founded:** 1930.

58322 ■ Merkel Chamber of Commerce
PO Box 536
Merkel, TX 79536
Ph: (325)928-5722
Co. E-mail: coc@merkeltx.com
URL: http://merkeltexas.com/html/chamber_of_commerce.html
Description: Promotes business and community development in Merkel, TX.

58323 ■ Mesquite Chamber of Commerce and Convention and Visitors Bureau (MCCCVB)
617 N Ebrite
Mesquite, TX 75149-3453
Ph: (972)285-0211
Fax: (972)285-3535
Co. E-mail: info@mesquitechamber.com
URL: http://www.mesquitechamber.com
Contact: Terry McCullar, President
Description: Promotes business and community development in the Mesquite, TX area. **Publications:** *Voice of Business.*

58324 ■ *Metro Brief*
c/o Rose Ryan, Exec. Dir.
9374 Valhalla
Selma, TX 78154
Ph: (210)658-8322
Fax: (210)658-1817
Co. E-mail: executive_director@metrocomchamber.org
URL: http://www.randolphmetrocomchamber.org
Contact: Rose Ryan, Executive Director
Released: Weekly

58325 ■ *Metro West Magazine*
10370 Richmond, Ste. 125
Houston, TX 77042-4278
Ph: (713)785-4922
Fax: (713)785-4944
Co. E-mail: jeannie@hwcoc.org
URL: http://www.hwcoc.org
Contact: Jeannie Bollinger, President
Released: Periodic

58326 ■ Metrocrest Chamber of Commerce
5100 Belt Line Rd., Ste. 430
Dallas, TX 75254
Ph: (469)587-0420
Fax: (469)587-0428
Co. E-mail: fmurray@metrocrestchamber.com
URL: http://metrocrestchamber.com
Contact: Charles B. Heath, Chairman
Description: Promotes business and community development in the area. **Publications:** *Metrocrest Membergram.*

58327 ■ *Metrocrest Membergram*
5100 Belt Line Rd., Ste. 430
Dallas, TX 75254
Ph: (469)587-0420
Fax: (469)587-0428
Co. E-mail: fmurray@metrocrestchamber.com
URL: http://metrocrestchamber.com
Contact: Charles B. Heath, Chairman

58328 ■ *Metropolitan Beaumont*
1110 Park St.
Beaumont, TX 77701
Ph: (409)838-6581

Fax: (409)833-6718
Co. E-mail: chamber@bmtcoc.org
URL: http://www.bmtcoc.org
Contact: Jim Rich, President
Released: Bimonthly **Price:** included in membership dues.

58329 ■ Mexia Area Chamber of Commerce
405 E Milam, Ste. 2
Mexia, TX 76667
Ph: (254)562-5569
Free: 888-535-5476
Fax: (254)562-7138
Co. E-mail: linda@mexiachamber.com
URL: http://www.mexiachamber.com
Contact: Tommy C. Tucker, Chairman
Description: Promotes business and community development in Mexia, TX.

58330 ■ *Mid-Month Memo*
613 N Main St.
Borger, TX 79007-3528
Ph: (806)274-2211
Fax: (806)273-3488
Co. E-mail: borgerchamber@amaonline.com
URL: http://www.borgerchamber.org
Contact: Beverly Benton, President
Released: Quarterly

58331 ■ *Midland Business Journal*
109 N Main St.
Midland, TX 79701
Ph: (432)683-3381
Free: 800-624-6435
Fax: (432)686-3556
Co. E-mail: info@midlandtxchamber.com
URL: http://www.midlandtxchamber.com
Contact: Bobby Burns, President
Released: Monthly

58332 ■ Midland Chamber of Commerce (MCC)
109 N Main St.
Midland, TX 79701
Ph: (432)683-3381
Free: 800-624-6435
Fax: (432)686-3556
Co. E-mail: info@midlandtxchamber.com
URL: http://www.midlandtxchamber.com
Contact: Bobby Burns, President
Description: Promotes business and community development in the Midland, TX area. **Founded:** 1931. **Publications:** *Citylife* (Semiannual); *Membership Directory/Buyer's Guide* (Annual); *Midland Business Journal* (Monthly).

58333 ■ Midlothian Chamber of Commerce (MCC)
310 N 9th St., Ste. A
Midlothian, TX 76065-0609
Ph: (972)723-8600
Fax: (972)723-9300
Co. E-mail: info@midlothianchamber.org
URL: http://www.midlothianchamber.org
Contact: Marley Cherie, Chairperson
Description: Promotes business and community development in Midlothian, TX. Conducts sporting competitions. Sponsors Mad Hatters Easter Parade, Christmas Light-Up Celebration, and a fall festival and craft sale. Conducts quarterly business seminar. **Founded:** 1936. **Publications:** *FYI - Weekly Bulletin* (Weekly). **Educational Activities:** Business Expo (Annual). **Awards:** Chamber Achievement Award (Annual); Community Service Award (Annual); Gene Page Award (Annual).

58334 ■ Mills County, Goldthwaite Area Chamber of Commerce (MCCOC)
PO Box 308
Goldthwaite, TX 76844
Ph: (325)648-3619
Fax: (325)648-3619
Co. E-mail: gcc@centex.net
URL: http://www.goldthwaite.biz
Contact: Lynn Knight, President
Description: Promotes business and community development in Mills County, TX. Publications: none. **Founded:** 1979.

58335 ■ Mineral Wells Area Chamber of Commerce
PO Box 1408
Mineral Wells, TX 76068
Ph: (940)325-2557
Free: 800-252-6989
Fax: (940)328-0850
Co. E-mail: info@mineralwellstx.com
URL: http://www.mineralwellstx.com
Contact: Beth Watson, Executive Director
Description: Promotes business and community development in Mineral Wells, TX. Sponsors festivals as well as athletic and community activities. **Founded:** 1925. **Publications:** *Destination Guide* (Semiannual); *Plan of Action* (Annual); *Visitors Guide* (Annual).

58336 ■ Monahans Chamber of Commerce (MCC)
401 S Dwight Ave.
Monahans, TX 79756-4609
Ph: (432)943-2187
Fax: (432)943-6868
Co. E-mail: chamber@monahans.org
URL: http://www.monahans.org
Contact: Teresa Burnett, Director
Description: Promotes business and community development in Monahans, TX.

58337 ■ *The Monitor*
202 W Tom Landry St.
Mission, TX 78572
Ph: (956)585-2727
Fax: (956)585-3044
Co. E-mail: receptionist@missionchamber.com
URL: http://www.missionchamber.com
Contact: Arlene V. Rivera, President
Released: Monthly

58338 ■ *Monthly Networking*
14011 Park Dr., Ste. 111
Tomball, TX 77377-0516
Ph: (281)351-7222
Free: 866-670-7222
Fax: (281)351-7223
Co. E-mail: bruceh@tomballchamber.org
URL: http://www.tomballchamber.org
Contact: Bruce E. Hillegeist, President

58339 ■ *More than News*
10707 Preston Rd.
Dallas, TX 75230
Ph: (214)368-6485
Fax: (214)368-6695
Co. E-mail: mailbox@ndcc.org
URL: http://www.ndcc.org
Contact: Steve Taylor, President

58340 ■ Moulton Chamber of Commerce and Agriculture
PO Box 482
Moulton, TX 77975
Ph: (361)596-7205
Fax: (361)596-4384
Co. E-mail: chamber@moultontexas.com
URL: http://www.moultontexas.com
Description: Promotes business and community development in Moulton, TX.

58341 ■ Mount Pleasant/Titus County Chamber of Commerce and Convention and Visitors' Bureau
1604 N Jefferson
Mount Pleasant, TX 75455
Ph: (903)572-8567
Fax: (903)572-0613
Co. E-mail: info@mtpleasanttx.com
URL: http://www.mtpleasanttx.com
Contact: Faustine Curry, Chief Executive Officer
Description: Promotes business and community development in Titus County, TX. **Publications:** *Chamber Matters* (Quarterly).

58342 ■ Muleshoe Chamber of Commerce and Agriculture
115 E American Blvd.
Muleshoe, TX 79347
Ph: (806)272-4248

Fax: (806)272-4614
Co. E-mail: chamber@fivearea.com
URL: http://www.muleshoe.org
Contact: Gina Wilkerson, President
Description: Promotes business and community development in Muleshoe, TX. **Founded:** 1955. **Publications:** *Muleshoe Journal* (Semiweekly).

58343 ■ *Muleshoe Journal*
115 E American Blvd.
Muleshoe, TX 79347
Ph: (806)272-4248
Fax: (806)272-4614
Co. E-mail: chamber@fivearea.com
URL: http://www.muleshoe.org
Contact: Gina Wilkerson, President
Released: Semiweekly **Price:** $12, /year.

58344 ■ Nacogdoches County Chamber of Commerce
2516 North St.
Nacogdoches, TX 75965
Ph: (936)560-5533
Fax: (936)560-3920
Co. E-mail: chamber@nactx.com
URL: http://www.nacogdoches.org
Contact: Bruce Partain, President
Description: Promotes business and community development in Nacogdoches County, TX.

58345 ■ National Black Chamber of Commerce (Corpus Christi, Texas)
PO Box 60574
Corpus Christi, TX 78466
Ph: (361)698-2116
Fax: (361)698-2112
Co. E-mail: info@texastechies.org
URL: http://ccblackchamber.tripod.com
Description: Represents Black owned businesses. Seeks to empower and sustain African American communities through entrepreneurship and capitalistic activity. Provides advocacy, training and education to Black communities.

58346 ■ National Black Chamber of Commerce - Alamo City
600 Hemisfair Plaza Way, Bldg. 406-10
San Antonio, TX 78205
Ph: (210)226-9055
URL: http://www.alamocitychamber.org
Contact: Gwendolyn Robinson, Executive Director
Description: Represents Black owned businesses. Seeks to empower and sustain African American communities through entrepreneurship and capitalistic activity. Provides advocacy, training and education to Black communities.

58347 ■ National Black Chamber of Commerce, Collin County
3001 S Central Expy., Ste. 301
McKinney, TX 75070
Ph: (469)424-0120
Free: 866-377-4002
Co. E-mail: hsatisfield@ccblackchamber.org
URL: http://www.ccblackchamber.org
Contact: Horace Satisfield, President
Description: Represents Black owned businesses. Seeks to empower and sustain African American communities through entrepreneurship and capitalistic activity. Provides advocacy, training and education to Black communities.

58348 ■ National Black Chamber of Commerce, Fort Worth Metropolitan
1150 South Fwy., Ste. 211
Fort Worth, TX 76104
Ph: (817)871-6538
Fax: (817)332-6438
Co. E-mail: djennings@fwmbcc.org
URL: http://www.fwmbcc.com
Contact: Mr. Devoyd Jennings, President
Description: Represents Black owned businesses. Seeks to empower and sustain African American communities through entrepreneurship and capitalistic activity. Provides advocacy, training and education to Black communities.

58349 ■ National Black Chamber of Commerce - Permian Basin (BCCPB)
PO Box 1006
Odessa, TX 79760
Ph: (432)332-5812
Fax: (432)333-7858
Co. E-mail: odel.crawford@sbcglobal.net
URL: http://www.odessablackchamber.com
Contact: Odel Crawford, President
Description: Represents Black owned businesses. Seeks to empower and sustain African American communities through entrepreneurship and capitalistic activity. Provides advocacy, training and education to Black communities.

58350 ■ National Black Chamber of Commerce, Tri-County
PO Box 88376
Houston, TX 77288
Ph: (832)875-3977
Fax: (713)839-7329
Co. E-mail: info@tcbcc.net
URL: http://www.tcbcc.org
Contact: Leondria R. Thompson, President
Description: Represents Black owned businesses. Seeks to empower and sustain African American communities through entrepreneurship and capitalistic activity. Provides advocacy, training and education to Black communities.

58351 ■ Navasota Grimes County Chamber of Commerce
117 S LaSalle
Navasota, TX 77868
Ph: (936)825-6600
Free: 800-252-6642
Fax: (936)825-3699
Co. E-mail: executivedirector@navasotagrimeschamber.com
URL: http://www.navasotagrimeschamber.com
Contact: Shanna Mayhall, Executive Director
Description: Promotes business and community development in Grimes County, TX. **Founded:** 1921.

58352 ■ Neches News
PO Box 445
Port Neches, TX 77651
Ph: (409)722-9155
Fax: (409)722-7380
Co. E-mail: pncoc@swbell.net
URL: http://www.portneccheschamber.com
Contact: Debbie Plaia, Executive Director
Released: Monthly **Price:** free.

58353 ■ NETwork
5001 Denton Hwy.
Haltom City, TX 76117-1439
Ph: (817)281-9376
Fax: (817)281-9379
Co. E-mail: bwoolsey@netarrant.org
URL: http://www.netarrant.org
Contact: Jack G. Bradshaw, President
Released: Bimonthly

58354 ■ Network News
126 Rosewood Ave.
Boerne, TX 78006
Ph: (830)249-8000
Fax: (830)249-9639
Co. E-mail: boerne@gvtc.com
URL: http://www.boerne.org
Contact: John Gonzalez, President
Released: Monthly **Price:** included in membership dues.

58355 ■ New Boston Chamber of Commerce
100 N Center St.
New Boston, TX 75570-2935
Ph: (903)628-2581
Fax: (903)628-6340
Co. E-mail: chamber@newbostontx.org
URL: http://www.newbostontx.org
Contact: Deborah Cook, Executive Director
Description: Promotes business and community development in New Boston, TX. **Founded:** 1971. **Subscriptions:** articles books maps periodicals. **Publications:** *Chamber Notes* (Quarterly).

58356 ■ Newsline
PO Box 548
Killeen, TX 76540-0548
Ph: (254)526-9551
Free: 866-790-4769
Fax: (254)526-6090
Co. E-mail: info@gkcc.com
URL: http://killeenchamber.com
Contact: John Crutchfield, President
Released: Monthly

58357 ■ Newton County Chamber of Commerce
PO Box 66
Newton, TX 75966
Ph: (409)379-5527
Fax: (409)379-9035
Co. E-mail: newtonchamber@hotmail.com
URL: http://www.newton-texas.com/chamber_of_commerce/index.htm
Contact: Wayne Whitehead, President
Description: Works to promote the business and economic development in Newton County. **Founded:** 1965.

58358 ■ Nocona Area Chamber of Commerce (NCC)
1522 E Hwy. 82
Nocona, TX 76255
Ph: (940)825-3526
Fax: (940)825-5389
URL: http://www.nocona.org
Description: Promotes business and community development in the Nocona, TX area. Sponsors bicycle and 5K races, Day in the Park, and Red River Romp. Conducts charitable activities.

58359 ■ North Chamber News
12930 Country Pkwy.
San Antonio, TX 78216
Ph: (210)344-4848
Fax: (210)525-8207
Co. E-mail: dwilson@northsachamber.com
URL: http://www.northsachamber.com
Contact: Mr. Duane Wilson, President
Released: Bimonthly

58360 ■ North Channel Area Chamber of Commerce
13301 I-10 E Fwy., No. 100
Houston, TX 77015
Ph: (713)450-3600
Fax: (713)450-0700
Co. E-mail: cgrant@ncachamber.com
URL: http://www.northchannelarea.com
Contact: Dr. Vickey Giles, Chairperson
Description: Promotes business and community development in Northeast Harris County, TX. Sponsors community festival. Conducts charitable activities. **Founded:** 1977.

58361 ■ North Dallas Chamber of Commerce (NDCC)
10707 Preston Rd.
Dallas, TX 75230
Ph: (214)368-6485
Fax: (214)368-6695
Co. E-mail: mailbox@ndcc.org
URL: http://www.ndcc.org
Contact: Steve Taylor, President
Description: Promotes business and community development in Northern Dallas, TX. **Founded:** 1954. **Publications:** *More than News.* **Awards:** Small Business of the Year (Annual).

58362 ■ North Galveston County Chamber of Commerce
PO Box 426
Dickinson, TX 77539
Ph: (281)534-4380
Fax: (281)534-4389
Co. E-mail: contact@northgalvestoncountychamber.com
URL: http://www.northgalvestoncountychamber.com
Contact: Michael Millo, Chairman
Description: Promotes business and community development in northern Galveston County, TX. **Publications:** *Wave* (Monthly).

58363 ■ North Houston Greenspoint Business
250 N Sam Houston Pkwy. E, Ste. 200
Houston, TX 77060
Ph: (281)874-8332
Fax: (281)248-4388
Co. E-mail: info@houstonicc.org
URL: http://houstonicc.org
Contact: Reggie Gray, President
Released: Annual

58364 ■ North Houston-Greenspoint Chamber of Commerce
250 N Sam Houston Pkwy. E, Ste. 200
Houston, TX 77060
Ph: (281)874-8332
Fax: (281)248-4388
Co. E-mail: info@houstonicc.org
URL: http://houstonicc.org
Contact: Reggie Gray, President
Description: Promotes business and community development in Northeastern Houston, TX. **Founded:** 1986. **Publications:** *North Houston Greenspoint Business* (Annual); *North Houston Greenspoint Business* (Annual); *Pacesetter* (Monthly). **Telecommunication Services:** rgray@houstonicc.org.

58365 ■ North San Antonio Chamber of Commerce (NSACC)
12930 Country Pkwy.
San Antonio, TX 78216
Ph: (210)344-4848
Fax: (210)525-8207
Co. E-mail: dwilson@northsachamber.com
URL: http://www.northsachamber.com
Contact: Mr. Duane Wilson, President
Description: Promotes business and community development in San Antonio, TX. **Founded:** 1974. **Publications:** *North Chamber News* (Bimonthly). **Educational Activities:** Enterprising Women's Conference (Annual). **Awards:** Athena Award (Annual).

58366 ■ Northeast Tarrant Chamber of Commerce
5001 Denton Hwy.
Haltom City, TX 76117-1439
Ph: (817)281-9376
Fax: (817)281-9379
Co. E-mail: bwoolsey@netarrant.org
URL: http://www.netarrant.org
Contact: Jack G. Bradshaw, President
Description: Promotes business and community development in Northeast Tarrant County, TX. **Publications:** *NETwork* (Bimonthly).

58367 ■ Nueces Canyon Chamber of Commerce
PO Box 369
Camp Wood, TX 78833
Ph: (830)597-6241
Co. E-mail: info@mycampwood.com
URL: http://www.mycampwood.com
Contact: Ben Cox, President
Description: Promotes business and community development in Camp Wood, TX.

58368 ■ Oak Cliff Chamber of Commerce (OCCC)
400 S Zang Blvd., Ste. 110
Dallas, TX 75208
Ph: (214)943-4567
URL: http://www.oakcliffchamber.org
Contact: Bob Stimson, President
Description: Promotes business and community development in Oak Cliff area. **Founded:** 1960. **Publications:** *Reporter.*

58369 ■ Official Guide to Portland
PO Box 388
Portland, TX 78374
Ph: (361)643-2475
Free: 877-643-2475
Fax: (361)643-7377
Co. E-mail: chamber@portlandtx.org
URL: http://www.portlandtx.org
Contact: Jane Gimler, President
Released: Periodic

58370 ■ Olney Chamber of Commerce
108 E Main St.
Olney, TX 76374
Ph: (940)564-5445
Fax: (940)564-3610
Co. E-mail: chamber@brazosnet.com
URL: http://www.olneytexas.com
Contact: Janell Hubbard, President
Description: Promotes business and community development in the Olney, Texas area.

58371 ■ Omaha Chamber of Commerce
PO Box 816
Omaha, TX 75571
Ph: (903)884-2302
Co. E-mail: andra04@sbcglobal.net
Description: Promotes business and community development in Omaha, TX.

58372 ■ Ozona Chamber of Commerce
PO Box 1135
Ozona, TX 76943-1135
Ph: (325)392-3737
Fax: (325)392-3485
Co. E-mail: oztxcoc@aol.com
URL: http://www.ozona.com/articles/view/4/chamber-of-commerce
Contact: Shanon Biggerstaff, Chief Executive Officer
Description: Promotes business and community development in Ozona, TX. **Founded:** 1962. **Publications:** *Chamber Dialogue* (Monthly).

58373 ■ *Pacesetter*
250 N Sam Houston Pkwy. E, Ste. 200
Houston, TX 77060
Ph: (281)874-8332
Fax: (281)248-4388
Co. E-mail: info@houstonicc.org
URL: http://houstonicc.org
Contact: Reggie Gray, President
Released: Monthly

58374 ■ Palacios Chamber of Commerce (PCC)
420 Main St.
Palacios, TX 77465
Ph: (361)972-2615
Co. E-mail: palcoc@tisd.net
URL: http://www.palacioschamber.com
Contact: Leland Singer, President
Description: Promotes business, tourism, and community development along the Central Texas coast. Conducts annual fishing tournament and annual awards banquet. **Founded:** 1910.

58375 ■ Palestine Area Chamber of Commerce
PO Box 1177
Palestine, TX 75802
Ph: (903)729-6066
Fax: (903)729-2083
URL: http://www.palestinechamber.org
Contact: Meghan Hill, Executive Director
Description: Promotes business and community development in the Palestine, TX area. Conducts annual Hot Pepper Festival. **Subscriptions:** business records. **Publications:** *Connection* (Weekly).

58376 ■ Panola County Chamber of Commerce (PCCC)
300 W Panola St.
Carthage, TX 75633
Ph: (903)693-6634
Fax: (903)693-8578
Co. E-mail: chamber@carthagetexas.com
URL: http://carthagetexas.us
Contact: Tommie Ritter Smith, President
Description: Promotes business and community development in Panola County, TX. **Founded:** 1946.

58377 ■ *Partners*
600 E Depot St.
Brownwood, TX 76801-7000
Ph: (915)646-9535
Fax: (915)643-6686
Co. E-mail: info@brownwoodchamber.org
URL: http://www.brownwoodchamber.org
Contact: Laura Terhune, Chief Executive Officer
Released: Monthly **Price:** free.

58378 ■ *Partnership Houston*
1200 Smith, Ste. 700
Houston, TX 77002-4400
Ph: (713)844-3600
Fax: (713)844-0200
Co. E-mail: ghp@houston.org
URL: http://www.houston.org
Contact: Lilyanne McClean, President
Released: Annual **Price:** $20, for members; $40, for nonmembers.

58379 ■ Pasadena Chamber of Commerce (PCC)
4334 Fairmont Pkwy.
Pasadena, TX 77504-3306
Ph: (281)487-7871
Fax: (281)487-5530
Co. E-mail: info@pasadenachamber.org
URL: http://www.pasadenachamber.org
Contact: Sherry Trainer, President
Description: Promotes business and community development in Pasadena, TX. Sponsors annual festival. Holds monthly After Hours business mixer and monthly business, industry, and professional luncheons with speakers per year. **Founded:** 1953. **Publications:** *Chambergram* (Monthly); *Pasadena Chamber of Commerce Membership Directory and Buyer's Guide* (Annual). **Awards:** Business of the Year (Annual).

58380 ■ *Pasadena Chamber of Commerce Membership Directory and Buyer's Guide*
4334 Fairmont Pkwy.
Pasadena, TX 77504-3306
Ph: (281)487-7871
Fax: (281)487-5530
Co. E-mail: info@pasadenachamber.org
URL: http://www.pasadenachamber.org
Contact: Sherry Trainer, President
Released: Annual

58381 ■ Pearland Area Chamber of Commerce
6117 Broadway St.
Pearland, TX 77581
Ph: (281)485-3634
Fax: (281)485-2420
Co. E-mail: chamber@pearlandchamber.org
URL: http://www.pearlandchamber.com
Contact: Carol R. Artz, President
URL(s): pearlandtx.usachamber.com. **Description:** Promotes business and community development in the Pearland, TX area. **Publications:** *Chamber Connection* (Monthly); *Chambergram* (Weekly). **Awards:** Business of the Year Award (Annual); Citizen of the Year Award (Annual).

58382 ■ Pecos Area Chamber of Commerce
111 S Cedar, Hwy. 285
Pecos, TX 79772-3206
Ph: (432)445-2406
Fax: (432)445-2407
URL: http://www.pecostx.com
Contact: Linda Gholson, President
Description: Promotes business and community development in Pecos, TX. **Founded:** 1957. **Publications:** *Pecos Billboard* (Quarterly).

58383 ■ *Pecos Billboard*
111 S Cedar, Hwy. 285
Pecos, TX 79772-3206
Ph: (432)445-2406
Fax: (432)445-2407
URL: http://www.pecostx.com
Contact: Linda Gholson, President
Released: Quarterly **Price:** free.

58384 ■ Perryton-Ochiltree Chamber of Commerce
2000 S Main
Perryton, TX 79070
Ph: (806)435-6575

Fax: (806)435-9821
Co. E-mail: pococ@ptsi.net
URL: http://www.perryton.org
Contact: Marilyn Reiswig, President
Description: Promotes business and community development in Perryton, TX. **Awards:** Citizen of the Year (Annual).

58385 ■ Pharr Chamber of Commerce (PCC)
308 W Park Ave.
Pharr, TX 78577
Ph: (956)787-1481
Fax: (956)787-7972
Co. E-mail: info@pharrchamberofcommerce.com
URL: http://www.pharrchamberofcommerce.com
Contact: Luis A. Bazan, President
Description: Promotes business and community development in Pharr, TX. **Founded:** 1946. **Publications:** *Membership Directory/Guide Book* (Annual).

58386 ■ Pilot Point Chamber of Commerce (PPCC)
PO Box 497
Pilot Point, TX 76258
Ph: (940)686-5385
Fax: (940)686-5385
Co. E-mail: jparker@pointbank.com
URL: http://www.pilotpoint.org
Contact: James Parker, President
Description: Promotes business and community development in Pilot Point, TX.

58387 ■ Plainview Chamber of Commerce (PCC)
710 W 5th St.
Plainview, TX 79072
Ph: (806)296-7431
Free: 800-658-2685
Fax: (806)296-0819
Co. E-mail: info@plainviewtexaschamber.com
URL: http://www.plainviewtexaschamber.com
Contact: Danny Glenn, President
Description: Promotes business and community development in Plainview, TX. Publications: none. **Telecommunication Services:** manager@plainview-texaschamber.com.

58388 ■ *Plan of Action*
PO Box 1408
Mineral Wells, TX 76068
Ph: (940)325-2557
Free: 800-252-6989
Fax: (940)328-0850
Co. E-mail: info@mineralwellstx.com
URL: http://www.mineralwellstx.com
Contact: Beth Watson, Executive Director
Released: Annual **Price:** free.

58389 ■ Plano Chamber of Commerce (PCC)
1200 E 15th St.
Plano, TX 75074
Ph: (972)424-7547
Fax: (972)422-5182
Co. E-mail: info@planochamber.org
URL: http://www.planochamber.org/index.asp
Contact: Mabrie Jackson, President
Description: Provides resources to maximize business performance through advocacy, education and networking. Over 1,500 business members from Plano and the surrounding area. **Founded:** 1946. **Publications:** *Business Plan* (Annual); *Business Resource Directory* (Annual). **Awards:** Athena Award (Annual); Citizen of the Year (Annual); Small Business Person of the Year (Annual).

58390 ■ Pleasanton Chamber of Commerce
777 Peters Ave.
Pleasanton, TX 94566
Ph: (925)846-5858
Fax: (925)846-9697
Co. E-mail: scott@pleasanton.org
URL: http://www.pleasanton.org
Contact: Scott Raty, President
Description: Promotes business and community development in Pleasanton, TX. **Founded:** 1950. **Publications:** *Chamber Newsletter* (Monthly).

58391 ■ Port Aransas Chamber of Commerce
403 W Cotter Ave.
Port Aransas, TX 78373
Ph: (361)749-5919
Free: 800-452-6278
URL: http://www.portaransas.org
Contact: Ms. Ann B. Vaughan, Executive Director
Description: Promotes business and community development in Port Aransas, TX area. **Founded:** 1974.

58392 ■ Port Arthur Chamber of Commerce (PACC)
4749 Twin City Hwy., Ste. 300
Port Arthur, TX 77642
Ph: (409)963-1107
Fax: (409)962-1997
Co. E-mail: portarthurchamber@portarthurtexas.com
URL: http://www.portarthurtexas.com
Contact: Mary Ann Reid, President
Description: Promotes business and community development in Mid-southern Jefferson County, TX. **Scope:** small business. **Founded:** 1899. **Subscriptions:** audio recordings audiovisuals books periodicals. **Publications:** *Business Report* (Monthly); *Clubs and Organizations Directory* (Periodic); *Manufacturing Directory* (Periodic). **Educational Activities:** Business Expo (Annual); Shrimp Fest (Annual).

58393 ■ Port Isabel Chamber of Commerce
421 Queen Isabella Blvd.
Port Isabel, TX 78578
Ph: (956)943-2262
Free: 800-527-6102
Fax: (956)943-4001
Co. E-mail: director@portisabel.org
URL: http://portisabel.org
Contact: Betty Wells, President
Description: Promotes business and community development in the Port Isabel, TX area. **Publications:** *Historic Port Isabel.*

58394 ■ Port Mansfield Chamber of Commerce
PO Box 75
Port Mansfield, TX 78598
Ph: (956)944-2354
Fax: (956)944-2515
Co. E-mail: pmft@granderiver.net
URL: http://www.port-mansfield.com/chamber.htm
Contact: Terry Neal, President
URL(s): www.portmansfieldchamber.org. **Description:** Promotes business and community development in Port Mansfield, TX.

58395 ■ Port Neches Chamber of Commerce (PNCC)
PO Box 445
Port Neches, TX 77651
Ph: (409)722-9155
Fax: (409)722-7380
Co. E-mail: pncoc@swbell.net
URL: http://www.portnecheschamber.com
Contact: Debbie Plaia, Executive Director
Description: Promotes business and community development in Port Neches, TX. **Founded:** 1941. **Publications:** *Neches News* (Monthly).

58396 ■ Portland Chamber of Commerce
PO Box 388
Portland, TX 78374
Ph: (361)643-2475
Free: 877-643-2475
Fax: (361)643-7377
Co. E-mail: chamber@portlandtx.org
URL: http://www.portlandtx.org
Contact: Jane Gimler, President
Description: Promotes business and community development in Portland, TX. Sponsors Portland WindFest, Taste of Portland, and Auction. **Founded:** 1963. **Publications:** *Official Guide to Portland* (Periodic).

58397 ■ Princeton Area Chamber of Commerce
275 W Princeton Dr., Ste. 105
Princeton, TX 75407
Ph: (972)736-6462
URL: http://www.princetontxchamber.com
Contact: Virginia Gathright, President
Description: Promotes business and community development in the Princeton, TX area. **Publications:** *Chamber Matters.* **Awards:** Princeton Area Chamber of Commerce Graduating Senior Scholarship (Annual).

58398 ■ *Progress*
1600 University Blvd.
Brownsville, TX 78520
Ph: (956)542-4341
Fax: (956)504-3348
Co. E-mail: info@brownsvillechamber.com
URL: http://www.brownsvillechamber.com
Contact: Angela R. Burton, President
Released: Monthly **Price:** included in membership dues.

58399 ■ *Progress*
14011 Park Dr., Ste. 111
Tomball, TX 77377-0516
Ph: (281)351-7222
Free: 866-670-7222
Fax: (281)351-7223
Co. E-mail: bruceh@tomballchamber.org
URL: http://www.tomballchamber.org
Contact: Bruce E. Hillegeist, President
Released: Bimonthly

58400 ■ *Progress*
c/o Rose Ryan, Exec. Dir.
9374 Valhalla
Selma, TX 78154
Ph: (210)658-8322
Fax: (210)658-1817
Co. E-mail: executive_director@metrocomchamber.org
URL: http://www.randolphmetrocomchamber.org
Contact: Rose Ryan, Executive Director

58401 ■ *Progress Times*
202 W Tom Landry St.
Mission, TX 78572
Ph: (956)585-2727
Fax: (956)585-3044
Co. E-mail: receptionist@missionchamber.com
URL: http://www.missionchamber.com
Contact: Arlene V. Rivera, President
Released: Monthly

58402 ■ Prosper Area Chamber of Commerce
PO Box 432
Prosper, TX 75078
Ph: (972)508-4200
URL: http://www.prosperchamberonline.com
Contact: Mr. Andy Thomas, Chairman
Description: Promotes business and community development in Prosper, TX area.

58403 ■ Ralls Chamber of Commerce
801 Ave. I
Ralls, TX 79357
Ph: (806)253-2342
Co. E-mail: rallscofc@esc17.net
URL: http://www.rallschamberofcommerce.com
Contact: Terry Acker, Manager
Description: Promotes business and community development in Ralls, TX. **Founded:** 1920.

58404 ■ Randolph Metrocom Chamber of Commerce (RMCC)
c/o Rose Ryan, Exec. Dir.
9374 Valhalla
Selma, TX 78154
Ph: (210)658-8322
Fax: (210)658-1817
Co. E-mail: executive_director@metrocomchamber.org
URL: http://www.randolphmetrocomchamber.org
Contact: Rose Ryan, Executive Director
Description: Promotes business and community development in Cibolo, Converse, Garden Ridge, Kirby, Live Oak, Marion, Schertz, Selma, Universal City, Windcrest and Randolph Air Force Base, TX. Encourages tourism; operates information center. **Founded:** 1975. **Publications:** *Buyer's Guide* (Periodic); *Metro Brief* (Weekly); *Progress.*

58405 ■ Red River County Chamber of Commerce
101 N Locust St.
Clarksville, TX 75426
Ph: (903)427-2645
Fax: (903)427-5454
Co. E-mail: redrivercc@lstarnet.com
URL: http://redrivercoc.com/chamber/chamber-info
Contact: Shelley Benton, Director
Description: Promotes business and community development in Clarksville, TX. **Founded:** 1921.

58406 ■ *Reporter*
400 S Zang Blvd., Ste. 110
Dallas, TX 75208
Ph: (214)943-4567
URL: http://www.oakcliffchamber.org
Contact: Bob Stimson, President

58407 ■ *Return on Investment*
412 E Central Ave.
Belton, TX 76513
Ph: (254)939-3551
Fax: (254)939-1061
Co. E-mail: info@beltonchamber.com
URL: http://www.beltonchamber.com
Contact: Stephanie O'Banion, President
Released: Monthly

58408 ■ Richardson Chamber of Commerce (RCC)
411 Belle Grove Dr.
Richardson, TX 75080-5297
Ph: (972)792-2800
Fax: (972)792-2825
Co. E-mail: bill@telecomcorridor.com
URL: http://www.richardsonchamber.com
Contact: Bill Sproull, President
Description: Promotes business and community development in Richardson, TX. **Founded:** 1946.

58409 ■ Rio Grande Valley Chamber of Commerce
322 S Missouri
Weslaco, TX 78596
Ph: (956)968-3141
Fax: (956)968-0210
Co. E-mail: mail@valleychamber.com
URL: http://www.valleychamber.com
Contact: Allen Shields, Chairman
Description: Promotes business and community development in the Rio Grande Valley of Texas. **Founded:** 1943. **Publications:** *Agriculture in Rio Grande Valley*; *Business Barometer* (Monthly); *Guide to the Rio Grande Valley* (Annual).

58410 ■ Rockdale Chamber of Commerce
1203 W Cameron Ave.
Rockdale, TX 76567
Ph: (512)446-2030
Fax: (512)446-5969
Co. E-mail: info@rockdalechamber.com
URL: http://www.rockdalechamber.com
Contact: Denice Doss, President
Description: Promotes business and community development in Rockdale, TX. **Founded:** 1952. **Publications:** *Chamber Newsletter* (Bimonthly). **Educational Activities:** Planning Conference (Annual).

58411 ■ Rockport-Fulton Chamber of Commerce (RFCC)
404 Broadway
Rockport, TX 78382
Ph: (361)729-6445
Free: 800-242-0071
Fax: (361)729-7681
Co. E-mail: visitor@1rockport.org
URL: http://www.1rockport.org
Contact: Peggy Mayo, Chairperson
URL(s): www.rockport-fulton.org. **Description:** Promotes business and community development in Aransas County, TX. Conducts charitable activities. **Founded:** 1912.

58412 ■ Rockwall Area Chamber of Commerce
697 E I-30
Rockwall, TX 75087
Ph: (972)771-5733

Fax: (972)772-3642
Co. E-mail: info@rockwallchamber.org
URL: http://www.rockwallchamber.org
Contact: Margie Hooper, President
Description: Represents the business' interests and promotes a positive growth environment in the Rockwall, Texas area. **Founded:** 1929.

58413 ■ **Rosenberg - Richmond Area Chamber of Commerce**
4120 Ave. H
Rosenberg, TX 77471
Ph: (281)342-5464
Fax: (281)342-2990
Co. E-mail: info@roserichchamber.org
Contact: Gail Parker, President
Description: Promotes business and community development in Rosenberg and Richmond, TX. **Publications:** *Chamber Magazine* (Annual); *Focus* (Monthly); *Chamber Magazine* (Annual). **Telecommunication Services:** gparker@roserichchamber. org.

58414 ■ **Round Rock Chamber of Commerce (RRCC)**
212 E Main St.
Round Rock, TX 78664
Ph: (512)255-5805
Fax: (512)255-3345
Co. E-mail: dkurkul@roundrockchamber.org
URL: http://www.roundrockchamber.org
Contact: Doug Kurkul, President
Description: Promotes business and community development in Round Rock, TX. Sponsors Frontier Days festival. **Founded:** 1959. **Publications:** *Round Rock Reporter* (Monthly); *Round Rock Welcome Packet* (Semiannual).

58415 ■ *Round Rock Reporter*
212 E Main St.
Round Rock, TX 78664
Ph: (512)255-5805
Fax: (512)255-3345
Co. E-mail: dkurkul@roundrockchamber.org
URL: http://www.roundrockchamber.org
Contact: Doug Kurkul, President
Released: Monthly **Price:** free.

58416 ■ *Round Rock Welcome Packet*
212 E Main St.
Round Rock, TX 78664
Ph: (512)255-5805
Fax: (512)255-3345
Co. E-mail: dkurkul@roundrockchamber.org
URL: http://www.roundrockchamber.org
Contact: Doug Kurkul, President
Released: Semiannual **Price:** $2.

58417 ■ **Rowlett Chamber of Commerce (RCC)**
3910 Main St.
Rowlett, TX 75030-0610
Ph: (972)475-3200
Fax: (972)463-1699
Co. E-mail: rowlett_chamber@rowlettchamber.com
URL: http://www.rowlettchamber.com
Contact: Diane Lemmons, President
Description: Promotes business and community development in Rowlett, TX. **Founded:** 1974. **Publications:** *Correspondent* (Monthly).

58418 ■ **Royse City Chamber of Commerce**
PO Box 547
Royse City, TX 75189
Ph: (972)636-5000
Fax: (972)636-0051
Co. E-mail: info@roysecitychamber.com
URL: http://www.roysecitychamber.com
Contact: Julia Bryant, Executive Director
Description: Promotes business and community development in Royse City, TX. **Founded:** 1973. **Awards:** Allison Cherry Memorial Scholarship (Annual); Chamber College Scholarship (Annual).

58419 ■ **Rusk Chamber of Commerce**
184 S Main St.
Rusk, TX 75785
Ph: (903)683-4242
Free: 800-933-2381

Fax: (903)683-1054
Co. E-mail: bgoldsberry@rusktexas.com
URL: http://www.ruskchamber.com
Contact: Robert Goldsberry, Executive Director
Description: Promotes business and community development in Rusk, TX. Sponsors Indian Summer Arts and Crafts Fair.

58420 ■ **Sabinal Chamber of Commerce**
PO Box 55
Sabinal, TX 78881
Ph: (830)988-2010
Co. E-mail: sab@sabinalchamber.com
URL: http://www.sabinalchamber.com
Description: Promotes business and community development in Sabinal, TX.

58421 ■ **Saginaw Area Chamber of Commerce (SACC)**
301 S Saginaw Blvd.
Saginaw, TX 76179
Ph: (817)232-0500
Fax: (817)232-2311
Co. E-mail: chamber@saginawtxchamber.org
URL: http://www.saginawtxchamber.org
Contact: Mr. Tracy Sutton, Executive
Description: Promotes the economic, civic, and cultural welfare of the Saginaw area community. **Founded:** 1972. **Publications:** *Facts by the Tracks* (Monthly).

58422 ■ **Salado Chamber of Commerce**
PO Box 219
Salado, TX 76571
Ph: (254)947-5040
Fax: (254)947-3126
Co. E-mail: saladochamber@vvm.com
URL: http://www.salado.com
Contact: Dawn Orange, Director, Administration
Description: Promotes business and community development in Salado. Provide donations to civic organizations; sponsor an annual art show and art fair. **Founded:** 1969.

58423 ■ **San Angelo Chamber of Commerce (SACC)**
418 W Ave. B
San Angelo, TX 76903-6027
Ph: (325)655-4136
Fax: (325)658-1110
Co. E-mail: chamber@sanangelo.org
URL: http://www.sanangelo.org
Contact: Phil Neighbors, President
Description: Promotes business and community development in San Angelo, TX. **Founded:** 1916. **Publications:** *Action Report* (Monthly).

58424 ■ **San Antonio Hispanic Chamber of Commerce (SAHCC)**
200 E Grayson, Ste. 203
San Antonio, TX 78215
Ph: (210)225-0462
Fax: (210)225-2485
URL: http://www.sahcc.org
Contact: Ramiro A. Cavazos, President
Description: Promotes Hispanic business in San Antonio, TX. **Founded:** 1929. **Publications:** *Hispanic Chamber News* (Bimonthly).

58425 ■ **San Antonio Women's Chamber of Commerce of Texas (SAWCC)**
600 Hemisfair Plaza Way, Bldg. 217
San Antonio, TX 78205
Ph: (210)299-2636
Fax: (210)299-4169
Co. E-mail: info@sawomenschamber.net
URL: http://www.sawomenschamber.org
Contact: Jennifer Scroggins, Chairperson
Description: Promotes activities for growth and development of women into leadership roles in business, politics, and community. **Founded:** 1988.

58426 ■ **San Augustine County Chamber of Commerce**
611 W Columbia St.
San Augustine, TX 75972
Ph: (936)275-3610

Fax: (936)288-0380
Co. E-mail: sacc611@sbcglobal.net
URL: http://www.sanaugustinetx.com
Contact: Woody Harrison, President
Description: Promotes business and community development in San Augustine County, TX.

58427 ■ **San Benito Chamber of Commerce**
210 E Heywood St.
San Benito, TX 78586
Ph: (956)361-0626
Fax: (956)399-5421
Co. E-mail: cgil@cityofsanbenito.com
URL: http://www.sanbenitochamber.org
Contact: Bill Elliott, President
Description: Promotes business and community development in the San Benito, TX area.

58428 ■ **San Marcos Area Chamber of Commerce (SMACC)**
PO Box 2310
San Marcos, TX 78667
Ph: (512)393-5900
Fax: (512)393-5912
Co. E-mail: chamber@sanmarcostexas.com
URL: http://www.sanmarcostexas.com
Contact: Brian J. Bondy, President
Description: Promotes business and community development in San Marcos, TX. **Founded:** 1906. **Publications:** *The Communique* (Monthly).

58429 ■ **San Saba County Chamber of Commerce**
302 E Wallace St.
San Saba, TX 76877
Ph: (325)372-5141
Co. E-mail: executive.director@sansabachamber. com
URL: http://www.sansabachamber.com
Contact: Fern Reed, Executive Director
Description: Works to enhance the quality of life and to promote the economic well-being of San Saba County through leadership, commitment, and participation. **Founded:** 1950. **Publications:** *San Saba County Chamber of Commerce News* (Quarterly).

58430 ■ *San Saba County Chamber of Commerce News*
302 E Wallace St.
San Saba, TX 76877
Ph: (325)372-5141
Co. E-mail: executive.director@sansabachamber. com
URL: http://www.sansabachamber.com
Contact: Fern Reed, Executive Director
Released: Quarterly

58431 ■ **Sanger Area Chamber of Commerce**
PO Box 537
Sanger, TX 76266
Ph: (940)458-7702
Fax: (940)458-7823
Co. E-mail: chamber@sangertexas.com
URL: http://www.sangertexas.com
Contact: Scott Stephens, President
Description: Promotes business and community development in the Sanger, TX area.

58432 ■ **Santa Fe Chamber of Commerce**
12406 Hwy. 6
Santa Fe, TX 77510
Ph: (409)925-8558
Fax: (409)925-8551
Co. E-mail: sfchamber@comcast.net
URL: http://www.santafetexaschamber.com
Contact: Fay Picard, President
Description: Promotes business and community development in the Santa Fe, TX area. Sponsors Easter and Christmas festivals.

58433 ■ **Schulenburg Chamber of Commerce (SCC)**
618 N Main St.
Schulenburg, TX 78956
Ph: (979)743-4514
Free: 866-504-5294

Fax: (979)743-9155
Co. E-mail: info@schulenburgchamber.org
URL: http://schulenburgchamber.org
Contact: Rachel Bolfik, Office Manager
Description: Promotes agricultural, business, and community development in Schulenburg, TX. Operates Travel Information Center. **Founded:** 1925. **Publications:** *Chamber Monthly Newsletter* (Monthly).

58434 ■ Seagoville Chamber of Commerce (SCC)
107 Hall St.
Seagoville, TX 75159
Ph: (972)287-5184
Fax: (972)287-5815
Co. E-mail: seagovillechamber@sbcglobal.net
URL: http://www.seagovillecoc.org
Contact: Craig McLamore, President
Description: Promotes business and community development in Seagoville, TX. Sponsors various annual activities. **Founded:** 1975.

58435 ■ Sealy Chamber of Commerce
309 Main St.
Sealy, TX 77474
Ph: (979)885-3222
Free: 877-558-7245
Fax: (979)885-7184
Co. E-mail: sealycoc@sbcglobal.net
URL: http://www.sealy-tx.com
Contact: Lou Cox, President
URL(s): www.sealychamber.com. **Description:** Promotes business and community development in the Sealy, TX area. Sponsors annual Sealybration and Fantasy of Lights festivals. **Founded:** 1936. **Publications:** *Sealy Newsletter* (Monthly). **Educational Activities:** General Membership Meeting (Monthly).

58436 ■ *Sealy Newsletter*
309 Main St.
Sealy, TX 77474
Ph: (979)885-3222
Free: 877-558-7245
Fax: (979)885-7184
Co. E-mail: sealycoc@sbcglobal.net
URL: http://www.sealy-tx.com
Contact: Lou Cox, President
Released: Monthly **Price:** free for members.

58437 ■ Seguin Area Chamber of Commerce (SACC)
116 N Camp St.
Seguin, TX 78155
Ph: (830)379-6382
Fax: (830)379-6971
Co. E-mail: cofc@seguinchamber.com
URL: http://www.seguinchamber.com
Contact: Shanta Kuhl, President
Description: Promotes business and community development in Guadalupe County, TX. **Publications:** *Business Line* (Monthly).

58438 ■ Seymour Chamber of Commerce (SCC)
401 N Main St.
Seymour, TX 76380
Ph: (940)889-2921
Fax: (940)888-2922
Co. E-mail: scoc@nts-online.net
URL: http://www.seymourtxchamber.org
Contact: Myra Busby, Managing Director
Description: United to build a healthy economy and to improve the quality of life in the community. Seeks to promote the civic, commercial, industrial and other interests of Seymour and its contiguous territory; to correlate the efforts of the citizens of Seymour and of the members of the organization; to make Seymour and Baylor County a better place in which to live; and to carry out the purposes specified in its charter. Strives to strengthen and improve the economic development and business environment throughout the city of Seymour and the county of Baylor. **Founded:** 1922.

58439 ■ Shamrock Chamber of Commerce (SCC)
105 E 12th St.
Shamrock, TX 79079
Ph: (806)256-2501

Fax: (806)256-3739
Co. E-mail: webmaster@cityofshamrock.com
URL: http://www.shamrocktx.net
Contact: David Rushing, Director
Description: Promotes business and community development in Shamrock, TX. Sponsors area festival. **Founded:** 1924. **Publications:** *Chamber Chatter* (Monthly).

58440 ■ Shelby County Chamber of Commerce
100 Courthouse Sq., A-101
Center, TX 75935
Ph: (936)598-3682
Fax: (936)598-8163
Co. E-mail: info@shelbycountychamber.com
URL: http://www.shelbycountychamber.com
Contact: Pam Phelps, Executive Director
Description: Promotes business and community development in Shelby County, TX. **Awards:** Distinguished Service Award (Annual); Farm Family of the Year (Annual); Young Citizen of the Year (Annual).

58441 ■ Shiner Chamber of Commerce
PO Box 221
Shiner, TX 77984-0221
Ph: (361)594-4180
Co. E-mail: shinercc@shinertx.com
URL: http://www.shinertx.com
Contact: Bernice Jalufka, Office Manager
Description: Promotes business and community development in Shiner, TX. **Founded:** 1920.

58442 ■ Sinton Chamber of Commerce (SCC)
218 W Sinton St.
Sinton, TX 78387
Ph: (361)364-2307
Fax: (361)364-3538
Co. E-mail: sintonchamber@sbcglobal.net
URL: http://www.sintontexas.org
Description: Promotes business and community development in Sinton, TX.

58443 ■ *Skyliner*
210 Barton Springs Rd., Ste. 400
Austin, TX 78704
Ph: (512)478-9383
Fax: (512)478-6389
Co. E-mail: communication@austinchamber.com
URL: http://www.austinchamber.com
Contact: Michael W. Rollins, President
Released: Periodic

58444 ■ Slaton Chamber of Commerce
PO Box 400
Slaton, TX 79364-0400
Ph: (806)828-6238
Fax: (806)828-5115
Co. E-mail: slatoncoc@sbcglobal.net
URL: http://www.slatonchamberofcommerce.org
Description: Promotes business and community development in Slaton, TX. **Publications:** *Chamber Chat* (Monthly). **Awards:** Boss of the Year (Annual); Man of the Year (Annual); Organization of the Year (Annual); Outstanding Volunteer of the Year (Annual); Outstanding Women's Division Member (Annual); Woman of the Year (Annual).

58445 ■ Smithville Area Chamber of Commerce
PO Box 716
Smithville, TX 78957
Ph: (512)237-2313
Fax: (512)237-2605
Co. E-mail: chamber@smithvilletx.org
URL: http://www.smithvilletx.org
Contact: Adena Lewis, President
Description: Promotes business and community development in Smithville, TX.

58446 ■ Snyder Chamber of Commerce
2302 Ave. R
Snyder, TX 79549
Ph: (325)573-3558

Fax: (325)573-9721
Co. E-mail: snychcom@snydertex.com
URL: http://www.snyderchamber.org
Contact: Melissa Elam, Executive Director
Description: Promotes business, community development and tourism in Snyder, TX.

58447 ■ Sonora Chamber of Commerce (SCOC)
PO Box 1172
Sonora, TX 76950-1172
Ph: (325)387-2880
Free: 888-387-2880
Fax: (325)387-5357
Co. E-mail: soncoc@sonoratx.net
URL: http://www.sonoratx-chamber.com
Contact: Donna Garrett, Executive Director
Description: Promotes business and community development in Sonora, TX. **Awards:** Business Person of the Year (Annual); Citizen of the Year (Annual); Educator of the Year (Annual); Employee of the Year (Annual); Landscape of the Month (Monthly); Landscape of the Year (Annual).

58448 ■ South Belt - Ellington Chamber of Commerce
10500 Scarsdale
Houston, TX 77089-2375
Ph: (281)481-5516
Co. E-mail: info@southbeltchamber.com
URL: http://southbeltchamber.com
Contact: Marie Flickinger, Chairperson
Description: Promotes business and community development in South Belt-Ellington, TX area.

58449 ■ South Montgomery County - Woodlands Chamber of Commerce (SMCWCC)
1400 Woodloch Forest Dr., Ste. 300
The Woodlands, TX 77380
Ph: (281)367-5777
Fax: (281)292-1655
Co. E-mail: karen.hoylman@woodlandschamber.org
URL: http://www.woodlandschamber.org
Contact: Karen Hoylman, President
Description: Promotes business and community development in the Spring, TX area. **Founded:** 1978.

58450 ■ South Padre Island Chamber of Commerce
600 Padre Blvd.
South Padre Island, TX 78597
Ph: (956)761-4412
Fax: (956)761-2739
Co. E-mail: info@spichamber.com
URL: http://www.spichamber.com
Contact: Roxanne Harris Guenzel, President
Description: Promotes business and community development in South Padre Island, TX. **Founded:** 1989. **Publications:** *Business News* (Monthly). **Educational Activities:** Ladies Kingfish Tournament (Annual).

58451 ■ South San Antonio Chamber of Commerce
c/o Cindy Taylor, Pres.
7902 Challenger Dr.
Brooks City-Base
San Antonio, TX 78235
Ph: (210)533-1600
Fax: (210)533-1611
Co. E-mail: ctaylor@southsachamber.org
URL: http://www.southsachamber.org
Contact: Cindy Taylor, President
Description: Works to enhance economic growth and planned development of South San Antonio and Southern Bexar County, TX.

58452 ■ Southeast Dallas Chamber of Commerce (SEDCC)
PO Box 170132
Dallas, TX 75217
Ph: (214)398-9590

Fax: (214)398-9591
Co. E-mail: info@sedcc.org
URL: http://www.sedcc.org
Contact: Carl Raines, Chairman
Description: Promotes business and community development in Southeastern Dallas, TX. **Publications:** *The Business Spotlight* (Monthly). **Awards:** Business of the Year (Annual); Community Service Award (Annual); DISD Educator of the Year (Annual); DISD Principal of the Year (Annual); Outstanding Firefighter (Annual); Outstanding Police Officer (Annual); SEDCC Awards Scholarship (Annual).

58453 ■ *Southeast Texas Business*
1110 Park St.
Beaumont, TX 77701
Ph: (409)838-6581
Fax: (409)833-6718
Co. E-mail: chamber@bmtcoc.org
URL: http://www.bmtcoc.org
Contact: Jim Rich, President
Released: Monthly **Price:** included in membership dues.

58454 ■ Southlake Chamber of Commerce
1501 Corporate Cir., Ste. 100
Southlake, TX 76092
Ph: (817)481-8200
Fax: (817)749-8202
Co. E-mail: info@southlakechamber.com
URL: http://www.southlakechamber.com
Contact: Dana Davis, President
Description: Promotes business and community development in Southlake, TX. Sponsors festivals and charitable events. **Founded:** 1984. **Publications:** *Community Directory* (Annual); *Southlake Chamber of Commerce--Community Directory* (Annual); *Community Directory* (Annual); *Southlake Chamber of Commerce News and Views* (Monthly). **Awards:** Citizen of the Year (Annual).

58455 ■ *Southlake Chamber of Commerce News and Views*
1501 Corporate Cir., Ste. 100
Southlake, TX 76092
Ph: (817)481-8200
Fax: (817)749-8202
Co. E-mail: info@southlakechamber.com
URL: http://www.southlakechamber.com
Contact: Dana Davis, President
Released: Monthly

58456 ■ Spearman Chamber of Commerce (SCC)
211 Main St.
Spearman, TX 79081
Ph: (806)659-5555
Co. E-mail: spearcc@hotmail.com
URL: http://www.spearman.org
Contact: Keith Hight, Executive Vice President
Description: Promotes business and community development in Spearman, TX.

58457 ■ *The Spirit of Tomball Texas*
14011 Park Dr., Ste. 111
Tomball, TX 77377-0516
Ph: (281)351-7222
Free: 866-670-7222
Fax: (281)351-7223
Co. E-mail: bruceh@tomballchamber.org
URL: http://www.tomballchamber.org
Contact: Bruce E. Hillegeist, President
Released: Annual

58458 ■ *Spotlight*
10 Civic Center Plz.
El Paso, TX 79901
Ph: (915)534-0500
Free: 800-651-8065
Fax: (915)534-0510
Co. E-mail: gepccreceptionist@elpaso.org
URL: http://www.elpaso.org/aboutUs.html
Contact: Richard E. Dayoub, President
Released: Monthly

58459 ■ Springtown Area Chamber of Commerce (SACOC)
112 S Main St.
Springtown, TX 76082

Ph: (817)220-7828
Fax: (817)523-3268
Co. E-mail: director@springtownchamber.org
URL: http://www.springtowntexas.com
Contact: Oleta Parker, Executive Director
Description: Promotes business and community development in Springtown, TX. **Founded:** 1979.

58460 ■ Stephenville Chamber of Commerce
PO Box 306
Stephenville, TX 76401
Ph: (254)965-5313
Fax: (254)965-3814
Co. E-mail: info@stephenvilletexas.org
URL: http://www.stephenvilletexas.org
Contact: July Danley, President
Description: Promotes business and community development in Stephenville, TX. **Founded:** 1920. **Publications:** *Chamber Works* (Monthly).

58461 ■ *Stonewall Bulletin*
PO Box 1
Stonewall, TX 78671
Ph: (830)644-2735
Fax: (830)644-2165
Co. E-mail: stonewallchamber@gmail.com
URL: http://www.stonewalltexas.com
Contact: Jason Englert, President
Released: Monthly **Price:** included in membership dues.

58462 ■ Stonewall Chamber of Commerce (SCC)
PO Box 1
Stonewall, TX 78671
Ph: (830)644-2735
Fax: (830)644-2165
Co. E-mail: stonewallchamber@gmail.com
URL: http://www.stonewalltexas.com
Contact: Jason Englert, President
Description: Promotes the peach industry, business and tourism, and community development in the Stonewall, TX area. Sponsors local festival. **Founded:** 1961. **Publications:** *Stonewall Bulletin* (Monthly).

58463 ■ Swedish American Chamber of Commerce, Texas (SACC TX)
c/o Soren Marklund, Pres.
PO Box 130706
Houston, TX 77219
Ph: (281)461-6215
Co. E-mail: info@sacctx.com
URL: http://www.sacctx.com
Contact: Soren Marklund, President

58464 ■ Sweetwater Chamber of Commerce and Convention and Visitors' Bureau (SCCCVB)
PO Box 1148
Sweetwater, TX 79556
Ph: (325)235-5488
Free: 800-658-6757
Fax: (325)235-1026
Co. E-mail: jacque@sweetwatertexas.org
URL: http://www.sweetwatertexas.org/Chamber.html
Contact: Jacque McCoy, Executive Director
Description: Promotes business and community development in Sweetwater, TX. **Founded:** 1964.

58465 ■ *TAMACC: The Voice of the Texas Hispanic Business Community*
c/o Ben Mendez, Chm.
P.O. Box 41780
Austin, TX 78704-0030
Ph: (512)444-5727
Co. E-mail: president@tamacc.org
URL: http://www.tamacc.org
Contact: Ben Mendez, Chairman
Released: Quarterly

58466 ■ *Taylor Business*
PO Box 231
Taylor, TX 76574-3053
Ph: (512)352-6364

Fax: (512)352-6366
Co. E-mail: info@taylorchamber.org
URL: http://www.taylorchamber.org
Contact: Thomas Martinez, President
Released: Monthly

58467 ■ Taylor Chamber of Commerce
PO Box 231
Taylor, TX 76574-3053
Ph: (512)352-6364
Fax: (512)352-6366
Co. E-mail: info@taylorchamber.org
URL: http://www.taylorchamber.org
Contact: Thomas Martinez, President
Description: Promotes business and community development in Taylor, TX. **Publications:** *Taylor Business* (Monthly).

58468 ■ *Telephone Listing*
PO Box 1170
Crystal Beach, TX 77650
Ph: (409)684-5940
Free: 800-386-7863
Fax: (409)684-3123
Co. E-mail: info@bolivarchamber.org
URL: http://www.bolivarchamber.org
Contact: Anne Willis, Vice President
Released: Monthly **Price:** free.

58469 ■ Terrell Chamber of Commerce
1314 W Moore Ave.
Terrell, TX 75160
Ph: (972)563-5703
Free: 877-TER-RELL
Fax: (972)563-2363
Co. E-mail: info@terrelltexas.com
URL: http://www.terrelltexas.com
Contact: Danny R. Booth, President
Description: Promotes business and community development in Terrell, TX. Provides community services; sponsors Heritage Jubilee and Civic Auction, Christmas activities, 4th of July fireworks, work in Terrell, and scholarships. **Publications:** *Business Referral Guide* (Annual).

58470 ■ *Texarkana*
c/o Jeff Sandford, Pres.
Texarkana, TX 75504
Ph: (903)792-7191
Free: 877-275-5289
Fax: (903)793-4304
Co. E-mail: chamber@texarkana.org
URL: http://texarkana.wliinc2.com
Contact: Jeff K. Sandford, President
E-mail: jsandford@texarkana.org
Released: Quarterly

58471 ■ Texarkana Chamber of Commerce
c/o Jeff Sandford, Pres.
Texarkana, TX 75504
Ph: (903)792-7191
Free: 877-275-5289
Fax: (903)793-4304
Co. E-mail: chamber@texarkana.org
URL: http://texarkana.wliinc2.com
Contact: Jeff K. Sandford, President
E-mail: jsandford@texarkana.org
Description: Promotes business and community development in Texarkana, TX. **Founded:** 1912. **Subscriptions:** maps reports. **Publications:** *Texarkana* (Quarterly); *Survey of Industries in Texarkana--Arkansas/Texas* (Quarterly). **Educational Activities:** Texarkana Chamber of Commerce Roundtable (Monthly). **Telecommunication Services:** jharris@texarkana.org; jsandford@texarkana.org.

58472 ■ Texas Association of Business and Chamber of Commerce (TABCC)
1209 Nueces St.
Austin, TX 78701-1719
Ph: (512)477-6721
Fax: (512)477-0836
Co. E-mail: bhammond@txbiz.org
URL: http://www.txbiz.org
Contact: Bill Hammond, President
Description: Aims to promote business and community development in Texas. **Founded:** 1995. **Publications:** *Texas Business Report* (Monthly); *Texas Employment Law Handbook* (Annual).

58473 ■ Texas Association of Mexican-American Chambers of Commerce (TAMACC)

c/o Ben Mendez, Chm.
P.O. Box 41780
Austin, TX 78704-0030
Ph: (512)444-5727
Co. E-mail: president@tamacc.org
URL: http://www.tamacc.org
Contact: Ben Mendez, Chairman

Description: Promotes the growth, development, and success of local Hispanic chambers of commerce and serves as the leading advocate of Hispanic business in TX. **Founded:** 1975. **Publications:** *TAMACC: The Voice of the Texas Hispanic Business Community* (Quarterly). **Educational Activities:** Convention and Business Expo (Annual).

58474 ■ *Texas Business Report*

1209 Nueces St.
Austin, TX 78701-1719
Ph: (512)477-6721
Fax: (512)477-0836
Co. E-mail: bhammond@txbiz.org
URL: http://www.txbiz.org
Contact: Bill Hammond, President

Released: Monthly **Price:** free for members.

58475 ■ Texas City - La Marque Chamber of Commerce (TCLMCC)

9702 E.F. Lowry Expy.
Texas City, TX 77590
Ph: (409)935-1408
Fax: (409)316-0901
Co. E-mail: jimmy@texascitychamber.com
URL: http://www.texascitychamber.com
Contact: Jimmy Hayley, President

Description: Promotes business and community development in Galveston County, TX. Conducts annual funfest and shrimp boil. **Founded:** 1969. **Publications:** *Texas City - La Marque Chamber Express* (Bimonthly); *Texas City-La Marque Magazine* (Periodic).

58476 ■ *Texas City - La Marque Chamber Express*

9702 E.F. Lowry Expy.
Texas City, TX 77590
Ph: (409)935-1408
Fax: (409)316-0901
Co. E-mail: jimmy@texascitychamber.com
URL: http://www.texascitychamber.com
Contact: Jimmy Hayley, President

Released: Bimonthly

58477 ■ *Texas City-La Marque Magazine*

9702 E.F. Lowry Expy.
Texas City, TX 77590
Ph: (409)935-1408
Fax: (409)316-0901
Co. E-mail: jimmy@texascitychamber.com
URL: http://www.texascitychamber.com
Contact: Jimmy Hayley, President

Released: Periodic

58478 ■ Three Rivers Chamber of Commerce

PO Box 1648
Three Rivers, TX 78071
Ph: (361)786-4330
Free: 888-600-3115
Co. E-mail: trchamber@threeriverstx.org
URL: http://www.threeriverstx.org

Description: Promotes business and community development in Three Rivers, TX area. **Founded:** 1913.

58479 ■ Tomball Area Chamber of Commerce (TCC)

14011 Park Dr., Ste. 111
Tomball, TX 77377-0516
Ph: (281)351-7222
Free: 866-670-7222
Fax: (281)351-7223
Co. E-mail: bruceh@tomballchamber.org
URL: http://www.tomballchamber.org
Contact: Bruce E. Hillegeist, President

Description: Seeks to further business growth and quality of life through business education, community development and partnership between business and government in Tomball, TX. **Founded:** 1965. **Publications:** *Monthly Networking*; *Progress* (Bimonthly); *The Spirit of Tomball Texas* (Annual); *The Spirit of Tomball Texas* (Annual). **Telecommunication Services:** admin@tomballchamber.org.

58480 ■ *Travel Guide - Big Bend*

106 N 3rd St.
Alpine, TX 79830
Ph: (432)837-2326
Free: 800-561-3712
Co. E-mail: info@alpinetexas.com
URL: http://www.alpinetexas.com
Contact: Mark Hannan, President

Released: Periodic

58481 ■ *TrendSetter News*

108 Chamber of Commerce Dr.
Ennis, TX 75119
Ph: (972)878-2625
Fax: (972)875-1473
Co. E-mail: manager@ennis-chamber.com
URL: http://www.ennis-chamber.com
Contact: Jeannette J. Patak, President

Released: Quarterly

58482 ■ Trinity County Chamber of Commerce

PO Box 366
Groveton, TX 75845-0366
Ph: (936)642-1715
Fax: (936)642-2144
Co. E-mail: tccoc@valornet.com
URL: http://www.trinitycountychamber.org

Description: Promotes business and community development in Groveton, TX. Sponsors annual East Texas Timber Fest and Groveton Indian Summer Days. Convention/Meeting: none.

58483 ■ Trinity Peninsula Chamber of Commerce (TPCC)

PO Box 549
Trinity, TX 75862
Ph: (936)594-3856
Fax: (936)594-0558
Co. E-mail: info@trinitychamber.org
URL: http://www.trinitychamber.org
Contact: Rowan Ljungdahl, President

Description: Promotes tourism, business, educational, and community development in the Upper Lake Livingston, TX area. Sponsors annual Christmas at the Crossroads Festival, co-sponsors annual Community Fair, and 4th of July Street Dance. **Founded:** 1949.

58484 ■ Troup Chamber of Commerce

PO Box 336
Troup, TX 75789
Ph: (903)842-4113
Co. E-mail: gwhitsell@embarqmail.com
URL: http://www.trouptexas.org/newsite/content/chamber-commerce
Contact: Marnie McElroy, President

Description: Promotes business and community development in Troup, TX.

58485 ■ Tulia Chamber of Commerce

127 SW 2nd St.
Tulia, TX 79088
Ph: (806)995-2296
Co. E-mail: exec@tuliachamber.com
URL: http://www.tuliachamber.com

Description: Promotes business and community development in Tulia, TX.

58486 ■ Tyler Area Chamber of Commerce (TACC)

PO Box 390
Tyler, TX 75702
Ph: (903)592-1661
Free: 800-235-5712
Fax: (903)593-2746
Co. E-mail: hbell@tylertexas.com
URL: http://www.tylertexas.com/index2.htm
Contact: Henry Bell, III, Chief Operating Officer

Description: Promotes business and community development in Tyler, TX. **Founded:** 1918. **Publications:** *Tyler Chamber News* (5/year).

58487 ■ *Tyler Chamber News*

PO Box 390
Tyler, TX 75702
Ph: (903)592-1661
Free: 800-235-5712
Fax: (903)593-2746
Co. E-mail: hbell@tylertexas.com
URL: http://www.tylertexas.com/index2.htm
Contact: Henry Bell, III, Chief Operating Officer

Released: 5/year

58488 ■ Tyler County Chamber of Commerce (TCCC)

717 W Bluff St.
Woodville, TX 75979
Ph: (409)283-2632
Fax: (409)283-6884
Co. E-mail: tylerctychamber@sbcglobal.net
URL: http://www.tylercountychamber.com
Contact: Bryan Weatherford, President

Description: Promotes business and community development in Tyler County, TX. Sponsors Dogwood Festival and promotes tourism. **Publications:** *Discover Tyler County* (Annual). **Telecommunication Services:** info@tylercountychamber.com.

58489 ■ *Uniquely Longview*

410 N Center St.
Longview, TX 75601
Ph: (903)237-4000
Fax: (903)237-4049
Co. E-mail: info1@longviewtx.com
URL: http://www.longviewchamber.com
Contact: Kelly R. Hall, President

Released: Annual **Price:** $25.

58490 ■ Uvalde Area Chamber of Commerce

207 N Getty
Uvalde, TX 78801
Ph: (830)278-3361
Fax: (830)278-3363
Co. E-mail: director@uvalde.org
URL: http://www.uvalde.org
Contact: Jesse Rodriguez, President

Description: Promotes business and community development in Uvalde, TX. **Founded:** 1920. **Publications:** *Uvalde Update* (Bimonthly).

58491 ■ *Uvalde Update*

207 N Getty
Uvalde, TX 78801
Ph: (830)278-3361
Fax: (830)278-3363
Co. E-mail: director@uvalde.org
URL: http://www.uvalde.org
Contact: Jesse Rodriguez, President

Released: Bimonthly

58492 ■ Van Alstyne Chamber of Commerce

228 E Marshall
Van Alstyne, TX 75495
Ph: (903)482-6066
Co. E-mail: info@vanalstynechamber.org
URL: http://www.vanalstynechamber.org
Contact: Brenda McDonald, President

Description: Promotes business and community development in Van Alstyne, TX.

58493 ■ Van Area Chamber of Commerce (VACC)

170 W Main St.
Van, TX 75790
Ph: (903)963-5051
Co. E-mail: vanchamber@vantexas.com
URL: http://van.gval.net
Contact: Victoria Tankersley, President

Description: Promotes business and community development in Van Zandt County, TX. Seeks to attract new industry to the area. Issues publications. **Founded:** 1945.

58494 ■ Van Horn Chamber of Commerce
PO Box 488
Van Horn, TX 79855
Ph: (915)283-2043
Free: 866-424-6939
Fax: (915)283-2682
Co. E-mail: info@vanhorntexas.org
URL: http://www.vanhorntexas.org
Contact: Larry Simpson, President
Description: Promotes business and community development in Van Horn, TX.

58495 ■ Vernon Chamber of Commerce (VCC)
PO Box 1538
Vernon, TX 76385-1538
Ph: (940)552-2564
Free: 800-687-3137
Fax: (940)552-0654
Co. E-mail: vernonchamber@sbcglobal.net
URL: http://vernontexas.net
Description: Promotes business and community development in Vernon, TX. Encourages diversification in the local economy; acts as official host for visiting individuals and groups; encourages use of Vernon as host of the Tri-State Area Wrestling tournament, Santa Rosa Rodeo, high school playoff games, and Barrel Racing Futurity events. Assists newcomers in locating rental housing; coordinates community events. **Founded:** 1910. **Subscriptions:** books periodicals.

58496 ■ Victoria Chamber of Commerce
3404 N Ben Wilson St.
Victoria, TX 77901
Ph: (361)573-5277
Fax: (361)573-5911
Co. E-mail: randyvivian@victoriachamber.org
URL: http://www.victoriachamber.org
Contact: Randy Vivian, President
Description: Promotes business and community development in Victoria, TX. **Founded:** 1923. **Publications:** Vision (Periodic).

58497 ■ Vision
3404 N Ben Wilson St.
Victoria, TX 77901
Ph: (361)573-5277
Fax: (361)573-5911
Co. E-mail: randyvivian@victoriachamber.org
URL: http://www.victoriachamber.org
Contact: Randy Vivian, President
Released: Periodic

58498 ■ Visions
PO Box 325
Denison, TX 75020-0325
Ph: (903)465-1551
Fax: (903)465-8443
Co. E-mail: information@denisontexas.com
URL: http://www.denisontexas.us/default.aspx
Contact: Anna H. McKinney, President
Released: Annual

58499 ■ Visitors Guide
PO Box 1408
Mineral Wells, TX 76068
Ph: (940)325-2557
Free: 800-252-6989
Fax: (940)328-0850
Co. E-mail: info@mineralwellstx.com
URL: http://www.mineralwellstx.com
Contact: Beth Watson, Executive Director
Released: Annual **Price:** free.

58500 ■ Visitor's Guide/Chamber Directory
105 Huck St.
Yoakum, TX 77995
Ph: (361)293-2309
Fax: (361)293-3507
Co. E-mail: info@yoakumareachamber.com
URL: http://www.yoakumareachamber.com
Contact: Dave Talbert, Chairman
Released: Annual

58501 ■ Voice of Business
617 N Ebrite
Mesquite, TX 75149-3453
Ph: (972)285-0211

Fax: (972)285-3535
Co. E-mail: info@mesquitechamber.com
URL: http://www.mesquitechamber.com
Contact: Terry McCullar, President

58502 ■ Waco Chamber and Business Quarterly
PO Box 1220
Waco, TX 76703-1220
Ph: (254)757-5600
Fax: (254)752-6618
Co. E-mail: info@wacochamber.com
URL: http://www.wacochamber.com
Contact: Matthew T. Meadors, President
Released: Quarterly

58503 ■ A Walking Tour of Historic Llano
100 Train Station Dr.
Llano, TX 78643
Ph: (325)247-5354
Free: 866-539-5535
Fax: (325)248-6917
Co. E-mail: info@llanochamber.org
URL: http://www.llanochamber.org
Contact: David Griffith, President

58504 ■ Waller Area Chamber of Commerce (WACC)
PO Box 53
Waller, TX 77484
Ph: (936)372-5300
Co. E-mail: info@wallerchamber.com
URL: http://www.wallerchamber.com
Contact: Trey Duhon, President
Description: Promotes business and community development in Waller, TX area. **Telecommunication Services:** tduhon@duhonlaw.com.

58505 ■ Washington County Chamber of Commerce (WCCC)
314 S Austin St.
Brenham, TX 77833
Ph: (979)836-3695
Free: 888-BRE-NHAM
Fax: (979)836-2540
Co. E-mail: info@brenhamtexas.com
URL: http://www.brenhamtexas.com
Contact: Page Michel, President
Description: Promotes business and community development in Washington County, TX. Sponsors blood drive and Taste of the Country. **Founded:** 1917. **Publications:** Washington County Magazine (Annual). **Educational Activities:** Washington County Chamber of Commerce Banquet (Annual). **Awards:** Man and Woman of the Year Lifetime Achievement Awards (Annual).

58506 ■ Washington County Magazine
314 S Austin St.
Brenham, TX 77833
Ph: (979)836-3695
Free: 888-BRE-NHAM
Fax: (979)836-2540
Co. E-mail: info@brenhamtexas.com
URL: http://www.brenhamtexas.com
Contact: Page Michel, President
Released: Annual

58507 ■ Wave
PO Box 426
Dickinson, TX 77539
Ph: (281)534-4380
Fax: (281)534-4389
Co. E-mail: contact@northgalvestoncountychamber.com
URL: http://www.northgalvestoncountychamber.com
Contact: Michael Millo, Chairman
Released: Monthly **Price:** free.

58508 ■ Waxahachie Chamber of Commerce (WCC)
102 YMCA Dr.
Waxahachie, TX 75165
Ph: (972)937-2390

Fax: (972)938-9827
Co. E-mail: dwakeland@waxahachiechamber.com
URL: http://waxahachietxcoc.weblinkconnect.com/cwt/External/WCPages/
Contact: Debra Wakeland, President
Description: Promotes business and community development in Waxahachie, TX. Conducts Gingerbread Trail Festival. Convention/Meeting: none. **Founded:** 1921. **Publications:** The Gingerbread Times (Quarterly).

58509 ■ Weatherford Chamber of Commerce (WCC)
PO Box 310
Weatherford, TX 76086
Ph: (817)596-3801
Free: 888-594-3801
Fax: (817)613-9216
Co. E-mail: info@weatherford-chamber.com
URL: http://www.weatherford-chamber.com
Contact: Tammy Gazzola, President
Description: Promotes business and community development in Parker County, TX. **Founded:** 1912. **Publications:** Chamber News (Monthly).

58510 ■ Weekly Wire
PO Box 483
Pflugerville, TX 78691-0483
Ph: (512)251-7799
Fax: (512)251-7802
Co. E-mail: gpcc@sbcglobal.net
URL: http://www.pfchamber.com/www
Contact: Patricia A. Gervan-Brown, President
Released: Weekly

58511 ■ Weimar Area Chamber of Commerce (WACC)
PO Box 90
Weimar, TX 78962-0090
Ph: (979)725-9511
Fax: (979)725-6890
Co. E-mail: weimarcc@cvctx.org
URL: http://www.weimartx.org
Contact: Fran Barr, Executive Secretary
Description: Promotes business and community development in Weimar, TX.

58512 ■ Welcome to Mansfield
114 N Main St.
Mansfield, TX 76063
Ph: (817)473-0507
Fax: (817)473-8687
Co. E-mail: amiller@mansfieldchamber.org
URL: http://www.mansfieldchamber.org
Contact: Amanda M. Miller, President
Released: Annual

58513 ■ Weslaco Area Chamber of Commerce
PO Box 8398
Weslaco, TX 78599
Ph: (956)968-2102
Free: 888-968-2102
Co. E-mail: martha@weslaco.com
URL: http://www.weslaco.com
Contact: Martha Noell, President
Description: Promotes business and community development in the Weslaco, TX area. **Founded:** 1935.

58514 ■ West Chambers County Chamber of Commerce (WCCC)
PO Box 750
Mont Belvieu, TX 77580
Ph: (281)576-5440
Fax: (281)576-2135
Co. E-mail: missy@thewcccc.com
URL: http://www.westchamberscoc.com
Contact: Melissa G. Malechek, President
Description: Promotes business and community development in Mont Belvieu, TX.

58515 ■ West Columbia Chamber of Commerce (WCCC)
PO Box 837
West Columbia, TX 77486
Ph: (979)345-3921

Fax: (979)345-6526
URL: http://www.westcolumbiachamber.com
Contact: Sheryl Rogers, Chairman of the Board
Description: Promotes business, tourism, and community development in Southeastern Texas. Sponsors San Jacinto Festival. **Founded:** 1957.

58516 ■ West I-10 Chamber of Commerce
PO Box 100
Pattison, TX 77466
Ph: (281)375-8100
Co. E-mail: chamber@westi10chamber.org
URL: http://www.westi10chamber.org
Contact: R. Gregory Turner, President
Description: Promotes business community along I-10 Corridor and surrounding region.

58517 ■ Wharton Chamber of Commerce
225 N Richmond Rd.
Wharton, TX 77488
Ph: (979)532-1862
Fax: (979)532-0102
Co. E-mail: admin@whartonchamber.com
URL: http://www.whartontexas.com
Contact: Ron Sanders, Executive Director
Description: Promotes business and community development in Wharton, TX.

58518 ■ White Settlement Area Chamber of Commerce (WSACC)
8224 White Settlement Rd., Ste. 100
White Settlement, TX 76108
Ph: (817)246-1121
Fax: (817)246-1121
Co. E-mail: wsacc@whitesettlement-tx.com
URL: http://www.whitesettlement-tx.com
Contact: Karla Barker, President
Description: Promotes business and community development in White Settlement, TX. Sponsors annual White Settlement Days parade. **Publications:** *Chamber Update* (Monthly). **Educational Activities:** General Membership (Monthly).

58519 ■ Whitehouse Area Chamber of Commerce
PO Box 1041
Whitehouse, TX 75791
Ph: (903)839-8200
Co. E-mail: info@whitehousetx.com
URL: http://www.whitehousetx.com
Contact: Phil Rogers, President
Description: Promotes business and community development in the Whitehouse, TX area.

58520 ■ Whitesboro Area Chamber of Commerce (WCC)
2535 Hwy. 82E, Ste. C
Whitesboro, TX 76273
Ph: (903)564-3331
Fax: (903)564-3397
Co. E-mail: chamber@whitesborotx.com
URL: http://www.whitesborotx.com
Contact: Keith Muldrew, Chairman
Description: Promotes business and community development in the Whitesboro, TX area. **Founded:** 1939. **Awards:** Citizen of the Year Award (Biweekly); Historian of the Year Award (Periodic); Humanitarian of the Year Award (Annual); Lifetime Achievement Award (Periodic); Volunteer of the Year (Annual).

58521 ■ Wichita Falls Board of Commerce and Industry
PO Box 1860
Wichita Falls, TX 76307
Ph: (940)723-2741
Fax: (940)723-8773
Co. E-mail: ewaite@wf.net
URL: http://www.wichitafallscommerce.com
Contact: Tim Chase, President
Description: Strives to promote the business interests and community development of Wichita Falls, TX. **Founded:** 1968. **Publications:** *Wichita Falls Board of Commerce and Industry--Membership Directory and Community Guide* (Monthly); *Directory of Manufactures, Community Profile, Membership Directory* (10/year). **Awards:** Small Business Person of Year (Annual). **Telecommunication Services:** chamber@wf.net.

58522 ■ Wills Point Chamber of Commerce
PO Box 178
Wills Point, TX 75169
Ph: (903)873-3111
Fax: (903)873-2199
Co. E-mail: contact@willspointchamber.com
URL: http://willspointchamber.com
Contact: Jennifer Ross, President
Description: Promotes business and community development in Wills Point, TX.

58523 ■ Wimberley Chamber of Commerce
PO Box 12
Wimberley, TX 78676
Ph: (512)847-2201
Fax: (512)847-3189
Co. E-mail: info@wimberley.org
URL: http://www.wimberley.org
Contact: Linda Germain, Chairman of the Board
Description: Promotes business and community development in Wimberley, TX. **Founded:** 1949. **Publications:** *Business News* (Quarterly). **Educational Activities:** Wimberley Chamber of Commerce Show (Annual).

58524 ■ Winnsboro Area Chamber of Commerce
100 E Broadway
Winnsboro, TX 75494-2624
Ph: (903)342-3666
Co. E-mail: info@winnsboro.com
URL: http://www.winnsboro.com
Contact: Brett Burnett, President
Description: Promotes business and community development in Winnsboro, TX. **Founded:** 1957.

58525 ■ Wolfforth Area Chamber of Commerce and Agriculture
PO Box 36
Wolfforth, TX 79382
Ph: (806)855-4159
Fax: (806)855-4159
Co. E-mail: info@wolfforthchamber.org
URL: http://www.wolfforthchamber.org
Contact: Cindy Stephens, President
URL(s): www.wolfforthtx.us/chamber_of_commerce.htm. **Description:** Promotes business and community development in Wolfforth, TX.

58526 ■ Women's Business
PO Box 26051
Austin, TX 78755-0051
Ph: (512)338-0839
Co. E-mail: austin@womenschambertexas.com
URL: http://www.womenschambertexas.com
Contact: Rose Batson, President
Released: Quarterly **Price:** free for members.

58527 ■ Women's Chamber of Commerce of Texas in Austin
PO Box 26051
Austin, TX 78755-0051
Ph: (512)338-0839
Co. E-mail: austin@womenschambertexas.com
URL: http://www.womenschambertexas.com
Contact: Rose Batson, President
Description: Promotes business and economic development for women in Texas. **Founded:** 1987. **Publications:** *Women's Business* (Quarterly). **Educational Activities:** MAPCon (Annual). **Awards:** Texas Business Woman of the Year (Annual).

58528 ■ Wylie Chamber of Commerce
250 S Hwy. 78
Wylie, TX 75098
Ph: (972)442-2804
Co. E-mail: magnew@wyliechamber.org
URL: http://www.wyliechamber.org
Contact: Mike Agnew, President
Description: Promotes business and community development in Wylie, TX. **Founded:** 1977.

58529 ■ Yoakum Area Chamber of Commerce (YACC)
105 Huck St.
Yoakum, TX 77995
Ph: (361)293-2309

Fax: (361)293-3507
Co. E-mail: info@yoakumareachamber.com
URL: http://www.yoakumareachamber.com
Contact: Dave Talbert, Chairman
Description: Promotes business and community development in Yoakum, TX. Conducts tours of saddle and belt factories and operates economic development board. **Founded:** 1967. **Publications:** *Visitor's Guide/Chamber Directory* (Annual).

58530 ■ Yorktown Chamber of Commerce
PO Box 488
Yorktown, TX 78164
Ph: (361)564-2661
Fax: (361)564-2518
Co. E-mail: yorktownchamber@sbcglobal.net
URL: http://www.yorktowntx.com
Contact: Clark Kerlick, President
Description: Promotes business and community development in Yorktown, TX.

MINORITY BUSINESS ASSISTANCE PROGRAMS

58531 ■ Brownsville Minority Business Development Center - Management Assistance Services
3505 Boca Chica Blvd., Ste. 174
International Plaza Bldg.
Brownsville, TX 78521-2265
Ph: (956)546-3400
Co. E-mail: mector@xanadu2.net

58532 ■ City of Corpus Christi Economic Development Division
PO Box 9277
Corpus Christi, TX 78469
Ph: (361)883-9917
Fax: (361)883-9918
URL: http://www.cctexas.com

58533 ■ Corpus Christi Minority Business Development Center
226 Enterprise Pkwy, No. 112
Corpus Christi, TX 78405
Ph: (361)883-1809
Fax: (361)888-9473
Co. E-mail: corpusnbdc@attglobal.net
URL: http://www.mbda.gov

58534 ■ Dallas/Fort Worth Minority Business Enterprise Center
545 E John Carpenter Fwy., Ste. 100
Irving, TX 75062
Ph: (214)688-1612
Fax: (214)688-1753
Co. E-mail: mmora@gacompanies.com
URL: http://www.dallasfwmbec.com
Contact: Antonio Grijalva, President

58535 ■ El Paso Minority Business and Certification Center - El Paso Hispanic Chamber of Commerce
2401 E Missouri Ave.
El Paso, TX 79903
Ph: (915)351-6232
Fax: (915)566-9714
Co. E-mail: jrivera@elpasombec.com
URL: http://www.ephcc.org/AboutMBRC.aspx
Contact: Jennifer Rivera, Consultant
Description: Offers business and financial advice along with technical assistance to start-up minority businesses in the El Paso area.

58536 ■ El Paso Minority Business Development Center - NEDA Business Consultants, Inc.
5959 Gateway Blvd. W, Ste. 425
El Paso, TX 79925-3318
Ph: (915)774-0626
Fax: (915)774-0680
Co. E-mail: epneda@aol.com
URL: http://www.nedainc.net
Contact: Jose Rocha
Description: Helps small and minority businesses succeed in the free enterprise system.

58537 ■ Historically Underutilized Business Program - Texas Comptroller of Public Accounts
Capital Sta.
Austin, TX 78711-3528
URL: http://www.window.state.tx.us/procurement/ prog/hub/
Description: Provides information and facilitates the use of Texas' in-state procurement process for minority and women-owned businesses.

58538 ■ Houston Minority Supplier Development Council
Three Riverway, Ste. 555
Houston, TX 77056
Ph: (713)271-7805
Fax: (713)271-9770
Co. E-mail: info@hmbc.org
URL: http://www.hmbc.org/
Contact: Rich Huebner, President
Description: Works to increase and expand business opportunities and business growth for minority business enterprises.

58539 ■ San Antonio Minority Business Development Enterprise - University of Texas at San Antonio, Downtown
University of Texas at San Antonio, Downtown
501 W Durango Blvd.
San Antonio, TX 78207-4415
Ph: (210)458-2488
Fax: (210)458-2425
Co. E-mail: ied@utsa.edu
URL: http://www.sa-mbec.org
Contact: Orestes Hubbard, Director
Description: Provides ongoing consulting, training, technical, research and information services, in tandem with University-based assets and resources, and other state, federal and local agencies, to facilitate economic, community, and business development throughout South Texas and the Border Region.

58540 ■ Texas Department of Economic Development and Tourism - Business Development Division
PO Box 12428
Austin, TX 78711-2428
Ph: (512)936-0100
Free: 800-888-8TEX
Fax: (512)936-0080
Co. E-mail: locatetx@governor.state.tx.us
URL: http://www.governor.state.tx.us
Contact: Erin Dimerson, Director
Description: Promotes and supports small, minority-owned, and women-owned businesses in the areas of government contracting, capital resource identification, and general business counseling.

58541 ■ Women's Business Border Center
2401 E Missouri Ave.
El Paso, TX 79903
Ph: (915)566-4066
Fax: (915)566-9714
URL: http://www.womenbordercenter.com
Contact: Mary Aldeis
Description: Provides women with financial assistance and training, management, marketing, and procurement services to expand or start a business.

58542 ■ Women's Business Center
2852 W Trenton Rd.
Edinburg, TX 78539
Ph: (956)618-2828
Fax: (956)618-2834
Co. E-mail: office@aswbc-rgv.org
URL: http://www.wbc-rgv.org
Contact: Maria Mann, Executive Director
Description: Provides business development services, such as financial analysis, market research, loan application assistance, mentoring, and workshops and seminars, to women who wish to begin or expand a business.

58543 ■ Women's Business Council Southwest
2201 N Collins
Arlington, TX 76011

Ph: (817)299-0566
Fax: (817)299-0949
Co. E-mail: dhurst@wbcsouthwest.org
URL: http://www.websouthwest.org
Contact: Debbie Hurst, President
Description: Works to facilitate business opportunities between women business enterprises and other businesses, corporations, government entities, and institutions.

FINANCING AND LOAN PROGRAMS

58544 ■ Abacus Ventures
1686 Sunset Blvd.
Boulder, CO 80304
Ph: (512)276-5140
Fax: (512)857-1049
Co. E-mail: inquiries@abacusventures.com
URL: http://www.abacusventures.com
Contact: Dave Kennedy, Principal
Investment Policies: Acquisition.

58545 ■ Akin Gump Investment Partners 2000, LP
1700 Pacific Ave., Ste. 4100
Dallas, TX 75201-4624
Ph: (214)969-2800
Fax: (214)969-4343
Co. E-mail: dallasinfo@akingump.com
URL: http://www.akingump.com
Contact: J. Kenneth Menges, Jr., Partner
Industry Preferences: Computer software, Internet specific, and biotechnology.

58546 ■ Amerimark Capital Corp.
545 E. John Carpenter Fwy., Ste. 300
Irving, TX 75062
Ph: (214)638-7878
Fax: (972)719-9174
URL: http://www.amcapital.com
Contact: Charles Martin, Chief Executive Officer
E-mail: martin@amcapital.com
Preferred Investment Size: $500,000 to $2,000,000.
Industry Preferences: Communications, Internet specific, computer hardware, consumer related, industrial and energy, and business service. **Geographic Preference:** U.S.

58547 ■ Austin Ventures
300 W. 6th St., Ste. 2300
Austin, TX 78701-3902
Ph: (512)485-1900
Fax: (512)651-8500
URL: http://www.austinventures.com
Contact: Joseph C. Aragona, Partner
E-mail: joea@ausven.com
Preferred Investment Size: $100,000 to $20,000,000. **Industry Preferences:** Internet specific, communications and media, computer software and services, computer hardware, other products, semiconductors and other electronics, consumer related, medical and health, industrial and energy, and biotechnology. **Geographic Preference:** U.S. with focus on Texas.

58548 ■ BCM Technologies, Inc.
1709 Dryden Rd., Ste. 1790
Houston, TX 77030
Ph: (713)795-0105
Fax: (713)795-4602
URL: http://www.bcmtechnologies.com
Contact: Marty Pendleton, Vice President
Preferred Investment Size: $100,000 minimum. **Industry Preferences:** Biotechnology, medical and health. **Geographic Preference:** Southwest.

58549 ■ Buena Venture Associates, L.P.
1201 Washington Terrace
Fort Worth, TX 76107
Ph: (817)800-5221

Fax: (817)457-8211
Co. E-mail: idea@buenaventure.com
URL: http://www.buenaventure.com
Contact: John F. Pergande, Principal
Preferred Investment Size: $250,000 to $3,000,000.
Industry Preferences: Communications, computer software, Internet specific, medical and health. **Geographic Preference:** U.S.

58550 ■ The Capital Network / Texas Capital Network
2700 Via Fortuna, Ste. 250
Austin, TX 78746
Ph: (512)314-0711
Fax: (512)306-1651
URL: http://www.thecapitalnetwork.com
Contact: Michael McAllister, Chief Executive Officer
Preferred Investment Size: $100,000 to $500,000.
Industry Preferences: Communications, computer related, semiconductors and other electronics, biotechnology, medical and health, consumer related, industrial and energy, financial services, business service, manufacturing, agriculture, forestry and fishing. **Geographic Preference:** U.S. and Canada.

58551 ■ Capital Southwest Corp.
12900 Preston Rd., Ste. 700
Dallas, TX 75230-1323
Ph: (972)233-8242
Fax: (972)233-7362
Co. E-mail: cscinfo@capitalsouthwest.com
URL: http://www.capitalsouthwest.com
Contact: Gary L. Martin, Chief Executive Officer
Founded: 1961. **Preferred Investment Size:** $5,000,000 to $15,000,000. **Industry Preferences:** Consumer related, industrial and energy, communications and media, computer hardware, computer software and services, other products, Internet specific, medical and health, biotechnology, semiconductors and other electronics. **Geographic Preference:** U.S. with focus on the Southwest, Southeast, Midwest, and Mountain Regions.

58552 ■ The Catalyst Group
2 Riverway, Ste. 1710
Houston, TX 77056
Ph: (713)623-8133
Fax: (713)623-0473
Co. E-mail: info@tcgfunds.com
URL: http://www.tcgfunds.com
Contact: Rick Herrman, Principal
E-mail: rherrman@tcgfunds.com
Preferred Investment Size: $1,000,000 to $7,000,000. **Industry Preferences:** Medical and health, business service and manufacturing. **Geographic Preference:** Southeast.

58553 ■ CenterPoint Venture Partners
Two Galleria Tower
13455 Noel Rd., 16th Fl.
Dallas, TX 75240
Ph: (972)702-1101
Fax: (972)702-1103
URL: http://www.cpventures.com
Contact: Robert Paluck, Managing Director
Preferred Investment Size: $60,000 to $10,000,000.
Industry Preferences: Communications and media, Internet specific, computer software and services, computer hardware, other products, semiconductors and other electronics, medical and health. **Geographic Preference:** Southwest and Texas.

58554 ■ DFJ Mercury Venture Partners / Draper Fisher Jurvetson
1 Greenway Plz., Ste. 930
Houston, TX 77046
Ph: (713)715-6820
Fax: (713)715-6826
Co. E-mail: info@dfjmercury.com
URL: http://www.dfjmercury.com
Contact: Blair Garrou, Managing Director
Preferred Investment Size: $100,000 to $1,500,000.
Investment Policies: Seed and early stage. **Industry Preferences:** Industrial and energy. **Geographic Preference:** Texas.

58555 ■ Essex Woodlands Health Ventures / Woodlands Venture (The Woodlands)
21 Waterway Ave., Ste. 225
The Woodlands, TX 77380
Ph: (281)364-1555
Fax: (281)364-9755
Co. E-mail: houston@essexwoodlands.com
URL: http://www.essexwoodlands.com
Contact: James Currie, Managing Director
Preferred Investment Size: $20,000,000 to $60,000,000. **Industry Preferences:** Medical and health, biotechnology, computer software and services, Internet specific, consumer related, communications and media, other products, industrial and energy. **Geographic Preference:** U.S.

58556 ■ First Capital Management Co. LLC / FCG
750 East Mulberry St., Ste. 305
San Antonio, TX 78212
Ph: (210)736-4233
Fax: (210)736-5449
Co. E-mail: info@firstcapitalgroup.com
URL: http://www.firstcapitalgroup.com
Contact: Jeffrey P. Blanchard, Managing Partner
E-mail: jpblanchard@firstcapitalgroup.com
Preferred Investment Size: $1,000,000 to $6,000,000. **Industry Preferences:** Communications and media, medical and health, consumer related, and business service. **Geographic Preference:** Texas and the Southwest.

58557 ■ G-51 Capital LLC
900 South Capital of Texas Hwy., Ste. 151
Las Cimas IV
Austin, TX 78746
Ph: (512)929-5151
Fax: (512)732-0886
Co. E-mail: info@g51.com
URL: http://www.g51.com
Contact: N. Rudy Garza, Founder
Preferred Investment Size: $250,000 to $2,000,000. **Industry Preferences:** Computer software and services, computer hardware, Internet specific, and consumer related. **Geographic Preference:** U.S.

58558 ■ Gefinor Ventures / Inman Ventures
375 Park Ave., Ste. 3607
New York, NY 10152
Ph: (212)308-1111
Fax: (212)308-1182
Co. E-mail: kreesing@gefinor.com
URL: http://www.gefinorventures.com
Contact: Bobby R. Inman, Managing Director
Preferred Investment Size: $1,000,000 to $2,000,000. **Investment Policies:** Early, first, second, later stage, and mezzanine. **Industry Preferences:** Communications, computer software, Internet specific, semiconductors and other electronics, medical and health, financial services, consumer products, and manufacturing. **Geographic Preference:** U.S.

58559 ■ Genesis Park LP
2131 San Felipe
Houston, TX 77019
Ph: (713)521-1980
Co. E-mail: info@genesis-park.com
URL: http://www.genesis-park.com
Contact: Paul W. Hobby, Founder
Preferred Investment Size: $500,000 to $2,000,000. **Investment Policies:** Start-up, early, first stage, and buyouts. **Industry Preferences:** Communications and media, computer software, finance, industrial and energy. **Geographic Preference:** Texas.

58560 ■ HO2 Partners
2 Galleria Tower
13455 Noel Rd., Ste. 1670
Dallas, TX 75240-6620
Ph: (972)702-1107
Fax: (972)702-8234
URL: http://www.ho2.com
Contact: Daniel T. Owen, Partner
E-mail: dan@ho2.com
Preferred Investment Size: $750,000 to $3,000,000. **Industry Preferences:** Communications and computer software. **Geographic Preference:** Texas.

58561 ■ Interwest Partners (Dallas)
2 Galleria Tower
13455 Noel Rd., 16th Fl.
Dallas, TX 75240-6615
Ph: (972)392-7279
Fax: (972)490-6348
Co. E-mail: info@interwest.com
URL: http://www.interwest.com
Contact: Doug Pepper, Principal
Preferred Investment Size: $7,000,000 to $15,000,000. **Industry Preferences:** Medical and health, Internet specific, consumer related, biotechnology, communications and media, computer hardware, computer software and services, semiconductors and other electronics, industrial and energy, and other products. **Geographic Preference:** U.S.

58562 ■ JatoTech Ventures
6300 Bridgepoint Pky.
Bldg. 1, Ste. 500
Austin, TX 78730
Ph: (512)795-5860
Fax: (512)692-2868
Co. E-mail: info@jatotech.com
URL: http://www.jatotech.com
Contact: Walt Thirion, Managing Director
Preferred Investment Size: $500,000 to $3,000,000. **Investment Policies:** Seed and early stage. **Industry Preferences:** Communications and semiconductors and other electronics. **Geographic Preference:** Northern California and Southwest.

58563 ■ MESBIC Ventures Holding Co.
3308 Preston Rd.
Plano, TX 75093
Ph: (972)725-0322
Co. E-mail: drl@pacesettercapital.com
URL: http://www.pacesettercapital.com
Contact: Divaker R. Kamath, Executive Vice President
Preferred Investment Size: $1,000,000 minimum. **Industry Preferences:** Communications and media, computer software, hardware and services, consumer related, semiconductors and other electronics, medical and health, Internet specific, industrial and energy. **Geographic Preference:** Southeast and Southwest.

58564 ■ Murphree Venture Partners
1100 Louisiana, Ste. 5005
Houston, TX 77002
Ph: (713)655-8500
Fax: (713)655-8503
URL: http://www.murphreeventures.com
Contact: Dennis E. Murphree, Partner
E-mail: dmurphree@murphreeventures.com
Preferred Investment Size: $2,000,000 to $10,000,000. **Industry Preferences:** Computer software and services, Internet specific, medical and health, industrial and energy, consumer related, semiconductors and other electronics, computer hardware, communications and media. **Geographic Preference:** The Sunbelt states of the South and Southwest.

58565 ■ Natural Gas Partners (NGP)
125 E. John Carpenter Fwy., Ste., 600
Irving, TX 75062
Ph: (972)432-1440
Fax: (972)432-1441
Co. E-mail: inquiries@ngptrs.com
URL: http://www.naturalgaspartners.com
Contact: Richard L. Covington, Managing Director
Preferred Investment Size: $10,000,000 to $500,000,000. **Industry Preferences:** Industrial and energy. **Geographic Preference:** U.S. and Central and Western, Canada.

58566 ■ Phillips-Smith-Machens Venture Partners
25 Highland Park Village, Ste. 100-371
Dallas, TX 75205-2789
Ph: (972)387-0725

Fax: (214)522-0167
Co. E-mail: cece@phillips-smith.com
URL: http://www.phillips-smith.com
Contact: CeCe Smith, Partner
Preferred Investment Size: $1,000,000 to $5,000,000. **Industry Preferences:** Consumer related, Internet specific, computer software and services, and other products. **Geographic Preference:** U.S.

58567 ■ Seed Capital Partners
3008 Taylor St.
Dallas, TX 75226
Ph: (214)432-5817
Fax: (214)651-1862
URL: http://www.seedco.com
Contact: Allen D. Fleener, Founder
Preferred Investment Size: $500,000 to $1,000,000. **Industry Preferences:** Computer software, and Internet specific. **Geographic Preference:** U.S.

58568 ■ Sevin Rosen Management Co. / Sevin Rosen Funds
2 Galleria Tower
13455 Noel Rd., Ste. 1670
Dallas, TX 75240
Ph: (972)702-1100
Fax: (972)702-1103
Co. E-mail: info@srfunds.com
URL: http://www.srfunds.com
Contact: John V. Jaggers, Partner
Preferred Investment Size: $100,000 to $10,000,000. **Industry Preferences:** Communications and media, computer software and services, semiconductors and other electronics, consumer related, medical and health, computer hardware, Internet specific, and other products. **Geographic Preference:** U.S.

58569 ■ STARTech Early Ventures
1302 E. Collins, Blvd.
Richardson, TX 75081
Ph: (214)576-9800
Fax: (214)576-9849
URL: http://www.startechev.com
Contact: Vinse Davidson, Chief Financial Officer
Preferred Investment Size: $500,000 to $900,000. **Industry Preferences:** Computer software, and Internet specific, information technology. **Geographic Preference:** Texas.

58570 ■ Sternhill Partners
777 Post Oak Blvd., Ste 250
Houston, TX 77056
Ph: (713)622-2727
Fax: (713)622-3529
Co. E-mail: ned.hill@sternhillpartners.com
URL: http://www.sternhillpartners.com
Contact: Marc Geller, Managing Director
Preferred Investment Size: $500,000 to $6,000,000. **Industry Preferences:** Internet specific, communications and media, computer software and services, semiconductors and other electronics. **Geographic Preference:** Southwest and West Coast.

58571 ■ Techxas Ventures LLC
4401 W. Gate Blvd., Ste. 300
Austin, TX 78745
Ph: (512)334-3140
Fax: (512)334-3121
Co. E-mail: ventures@techxas.com
URL: http://www.techxas.com
Contact: Bruce Ezell, Managing Director
Preferred Investment Size: $100,000 to $9,000,000. **Industry Preferences:** Computer software and services, computer hardware, semiconductors and other electronics, Internet specific, communications and media, industrial and energy, other products. **Geographic Preference:** Texas.

58572 ■ Triton Ventures
6300 Bridge Point Pky.
Bldg. 1, Ste. 500
Austin, TX 78730
Ph: (512)795-5820

Fax: (512)795-5828
URL: http://www.tritonventures.com
Contact: D. Scott Collier, Managing Director
E-mail: scott@tritonventures.com
Preferred Investment Size: $500,000 to $4,000,000.
Industry Preferences: Communications and media, computer software, Internet specific, semiconductors and other electronics, industrial and energy. **Geographic Preference:** U.S.

58573 ■ Wingate Partners, L.P.
750 N. St. Paul, Ste. 1200
Dallas, TX 75201
Ph: (214)720-1313
Fax: (214)871-8799
Co. E-mail: mailbox@wingatepartners.com
URL: http://www.wingatepartners.com
Contact: Frederick B. Hegi, Principal
Preferred Investment Size: $25,000,000 to $100,000,000. **Industry Preferences:** Semiconductors and other electronics, medical and health, consumer related, industrial and energy, business service, and manufacturing. **Geographic Preference:** U.S.

PROCUREMENT ASSISTANCE PROGRAMS

58574 ■ Texas Procurement Technical Assistance Center - Angelina College
PO Box 1768
Lufkin, TX 75904-9493
Ph: (936)633-5432
Free: 888-326-5223
Fax: (936)633-5478
Co. E-mail: director@acpactx.org
URL: http://www.acpactx.org
Contact: James R. Rollins, Director
Description: Providing free advice to small businesses and industries of East Texas to sell products and services to federal, state, and local government agencies.

58575 ■ Texas Procurement Technical Assistance Center - Cross Timbers Procurement Center
University of Texas at Arlington
7300 Jack Newell Blvd. S
Ft. Worth, TX 76118-7115
Ph: (817)272-5978
Fax: (817)272-5952
Co. E-mail: gharlin@arri.uta.edu
URL: http://www.ctpc-texas.org
Contact: Gary Harlin, Program Manager

58576 ■ Texas Procurement Technical Assistance Center - Del Mar College - Workforce and Economic Development
101 Baldwin, CED 146
Corpus Christi, TX 78404
Ph: (361)698-2221
Fax: (361)698-1024
Co. E-mail: spsmith@delmar.edu
URL: http://www.delmar.edu/sbdc
Contact: Sean P. Smith, Program Manager
E-mail: spsmith@delmar.edu
Description: Designed to increase the number and type of businesses selling products and services to government agencies.

58577 ■ Texas Procurement Technical Assistance Center - El Paso Community College - Contract Opportunities Center
9050 Viscount, Rm. B545
El Paso, TX 79935
Ph: (915)831-7748
Fax: (915)831-7755
Co. E-mail: jconway@epcc.edu
URL: http://www.elpasococ.org
Contact: Joseph Conway, Program Manager
E-mail: josephc@epcc.edu
Description: Provides specialized and professional assistance to individuals and businesses seeking to learn about contracting and subcontracting opportunities, who are actively seeking contracting and subcontracting opportunities and/or performing under

contracts and subcontracts with the U.S. Department of Defense (DOD), other federal agencies, or state and local governments.

58578 ■ Texas Procurement Technical Assistance Center - Midwestern State University - Wichita Falls Small Business Development Center (SBDC)
3410 Taft Blvd.
Wichita Falls, TX 76308
Ph: (940)397-4373
Co. E-mail: vanda.wright@mwsu.edu
URL: http://www.nwtsbdc.org
Contact: Vanda Wright, Director
Description: Midwestern State University Small Business Development Center provides business counseling, technical assistance, training workshops, and business plan development for small businesses in our 13 county area.

58579 ■ Texas Procurement Technical Assistance Center - Northwest Texas Regional Network - West Texas A&M University Small Business Development Center (SBDC)
701 S Taylor, Ste. 118
Amarillo, TX 79101
Ph: (806)372-5151
URL: http://www.nwtsbdc.org
Contact: David Dickerson, Consultant
Description: The WTAMU SBDC provides counseling and seminar training for potential and existing businesses located in the top twenty-five counties of the Texas Panhandle.

58580 ■ Texas Procurement Technical Assistance Center - Pan Handle Regional Planning Commission
415 W 8th Ave.
Amarillo, TX 79105
Ph: (806)372-3381
Fax: (806)372-3268
Co. E-mail: dnelson@theprpc.org
URL: http://www.prpc.cog.tx.us
Contact: Doug Nelson, Director
Description: Assists local governments in planning, developing, and implementing programs designed to improve the general health, safety, and welfare of the citizens in the Texas Panhandle.

58581 ■ Texas Procurement Technical Assistance Center - San Antonio Procurement Outreach Program
PO Box 839966
San Antonio, TX 78283-3966
Ph: (210)207-8080
Fax: (210)207-8151
URL: http://www.sanantonio.gov/edd
Contact: A.J. Rodriguez, Director

58582 ■ Texas Procurement Technical Assistance Center - Texas Facilities Commission (TFC)
1711 San Jacinto
Austin, TX 78701
Ph: (512)463-0209
Co. E-mail: richard.ehlert@tfc.state.tx.us
URL: http://www.tfc.state.tx.us
Contact: Richard Ehlert
E-mail: skip.bartek@tbpc.state.tx.us
Description: Lead the State of Texas procurement and contracting communities with enhanced services, innovative systems, and best practices to further encourage competition and operational efficiency for the benefit of state agencies, local government entities, and the vendor community.

58583 ■ Texas Procurement Technical Assistance Center - Texas Information Procurement Service
University of Houston
2302 Fannin, Ste. 200
Houston, TX 77002
Ph: (713)752-8477

Fax: (713)756-1515
Co. E-mail: sbdcptac@uh.edu
URL: http://www.sbdc.uh.edu
Description: Provides free one-on-one consulting to help business owners research and bid on government contracts.

58584 ■ Texas Procurement Technical Assistance Center - Texas Tech University
2579 S Loop 289, Ste. 214
Lubbock, TX 79423
Ph: (806)745-3973
Free: 800-992-7232
Fax: (806)745-6717
Co. E-mail: o.castellano@nwtsbdc.org
URL: http://www.nwtsbdc.org
Contact: Otilo Castellano, Director
E-mail: o.castellano@ttu.edu
Description: Provides training and technical assistance to area businesses interested in contracting with federal, state, and local governments.

58585 ■ Texas Procurement Technical Assistance Center - Texas Tech University - Abilene Small Business Development Center
500 Chestnut, Ste. 601
Abilene, TX 79602
Ph: (325)670-0300
Fax: (325)670-0311
URL: http://www.ttusbdc.org/abilene/
Contact: Judy Wilhelm, Director
Description: An outreach program that provides counseling, technical assistance, training workshops, and reference resources for small businesses and entrepreneurs.

58586 ■ Texas Procurement Technical Assistance Center - Texas Tech University - Midland Small Business Development Center (SBDC)
1400 N, FM 1788, Hwy. 191
Midland, TX 79707
Ph: (432)552-2455
Fax: (432)552-3455
URL: http://www.nwtsbdc.org
Contact: Tommy Baker, Director
Description: Provides quality service and assistance to business owners and potential entrepreneurs.

58587 ■ Texas Procurement Technical Assistance Center - University of Houston - Small Business Development Center
2302 Fannin, Ste. 200
Houston, TX 77002
Ph: (713)752-8444
Fax: (713)756-1500
Co. E-mail: sbdcmetro@uh.edu
URL: http://www.sbdc.uh.edu
Description: Provides business consulting and training to entrepreneurs of small and emerging companies.

58588 ■ Texas Procurement Technical Assistance Center - University of Texas - Permian Basin Small Business Development Center (SBDC)
4901 E University Blvd.
Odessa, TX 79762
Ph: (432)552-2455
Fax: (432)552-3455
URL: http://www.nwtsbdc.org
Contact: Tommy Baker, Director
Description: The University of Texas Permian Basin Small Business Development Center provides business counseling, technical assistance, training workshops, and business plan development for small businesses in our 16 county area.

58589 ■ Texas Procurement Technical Assistance Center - Valley Procurement Technical Assistance Center
301 Mexico Blvd., Ste F6-A
Brownsville, TX 78520
Ph: (956)548-8741

Fax: (956)548-8750
Co. E-mail: Rosalie.O.Manzano@utb.edu
Contact: Rosalie Manzano, Program Manager
E-mail: rosalie@utb1.edu
Description: Experienced counseling on how to do business with federal/state/local government agencies.

INCUBATORS/RESEARCH AND TECHNOLOGY PARKS

58590 ■ Austin Technology Incubator (IC2-ATI)
The University of Texas at Austin
3925 W Braker Ln., WPR Bldg. R5500
Austin, TX 78759-5321
Ph: (512)305-0000
Fax: (512)305-0009
Co. E-mail: slundquist@ati.utexas.edu
URL: http://www.ati.utexas.edu
Contact: Isaac Barchas, Director
Description: Located at the University of Texas at Austin, this incubator specializes in supporting emerging high-risk technology firms.

58591 ■ The Business Resource Center
801 Elm St.
Waco, TX 76704-2662
Ph: (254)754-8898
Fax: (254)756-0776
Co. E-mail: brc@brc-waco.com
URL: http://www.brc-waco.com
Contact: Toni Herbert, Executive Director
Description: This small business incubator supports the development of emerging firms through a variety of business assistance services.

58592 ■ Clean Energy Incubator
3925 West Braker Ln.
Austin, TX 78759
Ph: (512)305-0000
Fax: (512)305-0009
URL: http://www.cleanenergyincubator.com/
Contact: Mitch Jacobson, Director
Description: A small business incubator offering an environment dedicated specifically to helping young clean energy companies succeed by providing the resources and facilities necessary for qualified start-ups to attract funding and aggressively compete in the free market.

58593 ■ Entrepreneurial Development Center
9600 Long Point Rd., Ste. 150
Houston, TX 77055
Ph: (713)932-7495
Fax: (713)932-7498
Co. E-mail: service@servicesca.org
URL: http://www.servicesca.org/entrepreneurial_development_center.htm
Description: A small business incubator who pioneered business development and entrepreneurial education programs to accelerate business growth for entrepreneurs in emerging businesses without using public funding.

58594 ■ Houston Technology Center
410 Pierce St.
Houston, TX 77002
Ph: (713)658-1750
Fax: (713)658-1744
URL: http://www.houstontech.org/
Contact: Walter Ulrich, Chief Executive Officer
Description: A non-profit business accelerator, incubator, and resource center dedicated to supporting, promoting, and assisting entrepreneurs and emerging companies emanating from greater Houston's key technology sectors: energy, life sciences, information technology and NASA-originated technology. Its goal is to be a leading resource for starting and growing technology-based companies in Houston and to serve as a focal point for the city's burgeoning technology community.

58595 ■ TECH Fort Worth
1120 South Fwy.
Fort Worth, TX 76104
Ph: (817)339-8968

Fax: (817)810-0617
Co. E-mail: info@techfortworth.org
URL: http://techfortworth.org/
Contact: Darlene Ryan, Director
Description: A nonprofit business incubator and accelerator working with technology startup companies which have based their businesses on proprietary technology they have developed or acquired. It works closely with these companies to create feasible business plans, to develop effective marketing strategies, to build strong management teams, and to launch them successfully into the Fort Worth economy.

58596 ■ University of Texas College of Business - Center for Innovation and Technology Entrepreneurship
1 USTA Cir.
San Antonio, TX 78249-0631
Ph: (210)458-4313
Fax: (210)458-4308
URL: http://business.utsa.edu/cite/index.asp
Description: Fosters the growth of new technology ventures. Offers the Roadrunner Incubator, an incubator for early-stage student enterprises.

EDUCATIONAL PROGRAMS

58597 ■ El Paso Community College
PO Box 20500
El Paso, TX 79998
Ph: (915)831-2000
Fax: (915)831-2161
URL: http://www.epcc.edu
Description: Two-year college offering small business management courses.

58598 ■ Kilgore College
1100 Broadway
Kilgore, TX 75662-3204
Ph: (903)984-8531
Fax: (903)983-8607
URL: http://www.kilgore.edu
Description: Two-year college offering a program in small business management.

LEGISLATIVE ASSISTANCE

58599 ■ Texas Department of Economic Development
PO Box 12428
Austin, TX 78711
Ph: (512)463-2000
Free: 800-888-0511
Fax: (512)463-1849
URL: http://www.governor.state.tx.us/ecodevo/
Description: Brings together government efforts to support economic growth through world trade development, domestic business development, and small business assistance.

TRADE PERIODICALS

58600 ■ *Perspectives*
Pub: Federal Reserve Bank of Dallas
Contact: Richard W. Fisher, President
Ed: Kay Champagne, Editor. **Released:** Quarterly.
Description: Discusses various banking and community topics.

PUBLICATIONS

58601 ■ *How to Form Your Own Texas Corporation*
950 Parker St.
Berkeley, CA 94710
Ph: (510)549-1976
Free: 800-992-6656
URL: http://www.nolo.com
Ed: Anthony Mancuso. **Released:** Fourth edition, 1988. **Price:** $29.95 (paper).

58602 ■ *Smart Start your Texas Business Guide*
PSI Research
300 N. Valley Dr.
Grants Pass, OR 97526

Ph: (503)479-9464
Free: 800-228-2275
Fax: (503)476-1479
Co. E-mail: info@psi-research.com
URL: http://www.psi-research.com
Ed: Michael D. Jenkins. **Released:** Revised edition, 1992. **Price:** $29.95 (looseleaf binder); $24.95 (paper). **Description:** Part of the Successful Business Library series.

PUBLISHERS

58603 ■ ABS Consulting Training Services
16855 Northchase Dr.
Houston, TX 77060
Ph: (281)673-2800
Free: 800-769-1199
Fax: (281)673-2950
Co. E-mail: info@absconsulting.com
URL: http://www.absconsulting.com
Contact: Dr. A. Denise Turner, President
Description: Description: Publishes law, regulatory and technical books on subjects that include federal safety and code regulations. **Founded:** 1973.

58604 ■ Dockery House Publishing Inc.—Heritage Publishing Inc.
1225 Chateau Ln.
Lindale, TX 75771
Ph: (903)882-6900
Free: 800-520-2665
Fax: (903)882-7607
Co. E-mail: questions@dockerypublishing.com
URL: http://www.dockerypublishing.com
Contact: Rod Dockery, President
E-mail: rdockery@dockerypublishing.com
Description: Description: Publishes customized books for new business development. Publishes magazines and books for chain stores. Does not accept unsolicited manuscripts. Reaches market through commission representatives. **Founded:** 1980.

58605 ■ Mesa House Publishing
1124 S Owasso Ave.
Tulsa, OK 74120
Ph: (918)504-9929
Free: 888-306-0060
Fax: (918)295-8237
Co. E-mail: info@mesahouse.com
URL: http://www.mesahouse.com
Contact: Heino R. Erichsen, Manager
Description: Description: Publishes and distributes books and software for commercial real estate, site selection, site evaluation, market analysis and related fields. **Founded:** 1999. **Telecommunication Services:** books@mesahouse.com; orders@mesahouse.com.

58606 ■ MLM Consultants—Americas MLM Consultants
2410 Cinco Woods Plz.
San Antonio, TX 78259-3531
Ph: (210)494-3884
Fax: (210)494-9909
Co. E-mail: research@mlmconsultant.com
URL: http://www.mlmconsultant.com
Contact: Rod Cook, President
E-mail: rod@mlmconsultant.com
Description: Description: Publishes books, software and resources on business topics.

58607 ■ Mullaney Publishing Group
PO Box 833383
Richardson, TX 75083-3383
Ph: (972)234-5310
Fax: (972)234-3255
Contact: Chuck Wilson, Manager
E-mail: chuck.wilson3@gte.net
Description: Description: Publishes on retail business and ecommerce.

58608 ■ Penworth Publishing
6942 FM 1960 E, Ste. 152
Humble, TX 77346
Ph: (281)404-5019

Fax: (713)893-6107
Co. E-mail: info@penworth.com
URL: http://www.penworth.com
Contact: Carmen Wisenbaker, Manager
Description: Description: Publishes books on nonfiction and business information. **Founded:** 2000.

58609 ■ ShopKeeper Software
1005 Lakewood Ln.
Round Rock, TX 78681-4520

Ph: (512)388-3290
Fax: (512)310-9855
Co. E-mail: sales@shopkeeper.com
URL: http://www.shopkeeper.com
Contact: Eileen Nudd, President
Description: Description: Publishes small business software for Macintosh computers. Does not accept unsolicited manuscripts. Reaches market through direct mail, trade sales, wholesalers and distributors. **Founded:** 1985. **Publications:** *ShopKeeper Plus*;

Bill-It; *QwikBILL*; *Time Clock/Sign Out*. **Telecommunication Services:** help@shopkeeper.com.

58610 ■ World Gumbo Publishing
7801 Alma, Ste. 105-323
Plano, TX 75025-3483
Free: 888-318-2911
Contact: Dean Lindsay, Manager
Description: Description: Publishes business and personal growth books. **Founded:** 2004.

SMALL BUSINESS DEVELOPMENT CENTERS

58611 ■ Blanding Small Business Development Center
College of Eastern Utah - San Juan Campus
639 W 100 S
Blanding, UT 84511
Ph: (435)678-8102
URL: http://www.utahsbdc.org
Contact: William L. Olderog, Director
Description: Represents and promotes the small business sector. Provides management assistance to current and prospective small business owners. Helps to improve management skills and expand the products and services of members.

58612 ■ Cedar City Small Business Development Center
77 N Main St.
Cedar City, UT 84720
Ph: (435)856-7707
Co. E-mail: isom@suu.edu
URL: http://www.utahsbdc.org
Contact: Craig Isom, Director
URL(s): www.suu.edu/business/sbdc. **Description:** Represents and promotes the small business sector. Provides management assistance to current and prospective small business owners. Helps to improve management skills and expand the products and services of members.

58613 ■ Ephraim Small Business Development Center
Ave. Box 1019
150 E College Ave.
Ephraim, UT 84627
Ph: (435)283-7376
URL: http://www.utahsbdc.org/locations/ephraim
Description: Represents and promotes the small business sector. Provides management assistance to current and prospective small business owners. Helps to improve management skills and expand the products and services of members.

58614 ■ Kaysville Small Business Development Center
450 S Simmons Way, Ste. 202
Kaysville, UT 84037
Ph: (801)593-2202
URL: http://www.utahsbdc.org/locations/kaysville
Description: Represents and promotes the small business sector. Provides management assistance to current and prospective small business owners. Helps to improve management skills and expand the products and services of members.

58615 ■ Logan Small Business Development Center
Utah State University
UMC 8330
1330 E 700 N, No. 124
Logan, UT 84322-1300
Ph: (435)797-2277
Co. E-mail: frank.prante@usu.edu
URL: http://www.utahsbdc.org/locations/logan
URL(s): sbdc.usu.edu. **Description:** Represents and promotes the small business sector. Provides management assistance to current and prospective small business owners. Helps to improve management skills and expand the products and services of members.

58616 ■ Ogden Small Business Development Center
Weber State University
3806 University Cir.
Ogden, UT 84408-3806
Ph: (801)626-7232
Fax: (801)626-7423
Co. E-mail: bking1@weber.edu
URL: http://community.weber.edu/sbdc/Default.html
Contact: Beverly King, Director
Description: Represents and promotes the small business sector. Provides management assistance to current and prospective small business owners. Helps to improve management skills and expand the products and services of members.

58617 ■ Orem/Provo Small Business Development Center
Utah Valley University
800 W University Pkwy., MS 239
Orem, UT 84058
Ph: (801)863-8230
Fax: (801)863-7071
Co. E-mail: sbdc@uvu.edu
URL: http://www.uvu.edu/sbdc
Contact: Ken Fakler, Director
Description: Represents and promotes the small business sector. Provides management assistance to current and prospective small business owners. Helps to improve management skills and expand the products and services of members.

58618 ■ Price Small Business Development Center
451 E 400 N
Price, UT 84501
Ph: (435)613-5443
URL: http://www.utahsbdc.org
Description: Represents and promotes the small business sector. Provides management assistance to current and prospective small business owners. Helps to improve management skills and expand the products and services of members.

58619 ■ Richfield Small Business Development Center
Snow College
800 W 200 S, Rm. 155W
Richfield, UT 84701
Ph: (435)893-2252
Co. E-mail: keith.church@snow.edu
URL: http://www.utahsbdc.org
Description: Represents and promotes the small business sector. Provides management assistance to current and prospective small business owners. Helps to improve management skills and expand the products and services of members.

58620 ■ Vernal Small Business Development Center
Utah State University
320 N Aggie Blvd.
Vernal, UT 84078
Ph: (435)789-6100
URL: http://www.utahsbdc.org
Description: Represents and promotes the small business sector. Provides management assistance to current and prospective small business owners. Helps to improve management skills and expand the products and services of members.

SMALL BUSINESS ASSISTANCE PROGRAMS

58621 ■ Utah Community and Economic Development Department - International Development Office
324 S State St., Ste. 500
Salt Lake City, UT 84111
Ph: (801)538-8737
Fax: (801)538-8889
Co. E-mail: intlmail@utah.gov
URL: http://international.utah.gov/
Contact: Brett Heimburger, Director
Description: Assists businesses by developing marketing efforts, providing technical assistance in exporting, and matching foreign market opportunities with Utah sources.

SCORE OFFICES

58622 ■ Central Utah SCORE
Co. E-mail: scoreutah@hotmail.com

58623 ■ Ogden SCORE
Co. E-mail: ogdenscore158@netscape.net

58624 ■ SCORE Northern Utah
Cache Valley Chamber of Commerce
160 N Main St.
Logan, UT 84321
Ph: (435)213-8713
URL: http://northernutah.score.org
Description: Provides professional guidance, mentoring services and financial assistance to maximize the success of existing and emerging small businesses. Promotes entrepreneur education in Northern Utah.

58625 ■ SCORE Salt Lake
310 S Main St., N Mezzanine
Salt Lake City, UT 84101
Ph: (801)746-2269
Fax: (801)746-2273
Co. E-mail: loy.rasmuson@comcast.net
URL: http://www.saltlakescore.com
Description: Provides professional guidance, mentoring services and financial assistance to maximize the success of existing and merging small businesses. Promotes entrepreneur education in Salt Lake City, Utah.

58626 ■ **Southern Utah SCORE**
Co. E-mail: sutahscore@yahoo.com

BETTER BUSINESS BUREAUS

58627 ■ **Better Business Bureau of Utah**
5673 S Redwood Rd., No. 22
Salt Lake City, UT 84123
Ph: (801)892-6009
Free: 800-456-3907
Fax: (801)892-6002
Co. E-mail: info@utah.bbb.org
URL: http://utah.bbb.org
Contact: Jane Driggs, President
Description: Seeks to promote and foster the highest ethical relationship between businesses and the public through voluntary self-regulation, consumer and business education, and service excellence. Provides information to help consumers and businesses make informed purchasing decisions and avoid costly scams and frauds; settles consumer complaints through arbitration and other means. **Telecommunication Services:** jdriggs@utah.bbb.org.

CHAMBERS OF COMMERCE

58628 ■ **Bear Lake Rendezvous Chamber of Commerce (BLRCC)**
PO Box 55
Garden City, UT 84028
Ph: (435)946-2197
Free: 800-448-2327
Co. E-mail: info@bearlakechamber.com
URL: http://www.bearlakechamber.com
Contact: Angie McPhie, President
Description: Promotes business and community development in Bear Lake, UT area.

58629 ■ **Bear River Valley Chamber of Commerce (BRVCC)**
PO Box 311
Tremonton, UT 84337
Ph: (435)257-7585
Fax: (435)257-2947
Co. E-mail: nikkijdr@yahoo.com
URL: http://www.bearriverchamber.org
Contact: Nikki Anderson, Executive Director
Description: Works to promote and enhance the business environment in the Bear River Valley.

58630 ■ **Beaver Valley Chamber of Commerce**
PO Box 760
Beaver, UT 84713
Ph: (435)438-5081
Free: 888-848-5081
Co. E-mail: signs4u@netutah.com
URL: http://www.beaverutchamber.com
Description: Promotes business and community development in Beaver, UT. **Founded:** 1984.

58631 ■ **Blanding Chamber of Commerce (BCC)**
PO Box 792
Blanding, UT 84511
Ph: (435)678-3662
Co. E-mail: info@blandingutah.org
URL: http://www.blandingutah.org
Description: Promotes business and community development in Blanding, UT.

58632 ■ **Brigham City Area Chamber of Commerce**
6 N Main
Brigham City, UT 84302
Ph: (435)723-3931
Fax: (435)723-5761
Co. E-mail: chamber@brighamchamber.com
URL: http://www.bcareachamber.com
Contact: Scott Hendrickson, Chairman
Description: Promotes business and community development in Brigham City, UT area. **Founded:** 1965.

58633 ■ **Brigham City Chamber of Commerce Women in Business**
6 N Main St.
Brigham City, UT 84302
Ph: (435)723-3931
Fax: (435)723-5761
Co. E-mail: monica@brighamchamber.com
URL: http://www.bcareachamber.com
Contact: Monica Holdaway, Executive Director
Description: Enhances the overall quality of life and economic vitality in community through projects, programs, policies and events. Serves as an advocate for business on public, governmental or legislative issues. Encourages networking, information and provide education opportunities.

58634 ■ *Business Directory*
2484 Washington Blvd., Ste. 400
Ogden, UT 84401
Ph: (801)621-8300
Free: 866-990-1299
Fax: (801)392-7609
Co. E-mail: chamber@ogdenweberchamber.com
URL: http://ogdenweberchamber.com
Contact: Mr. Dave Hardman, President
Released: Annual **Price:** $50.

58635 ■ *Business Directory and Relocation Guide*
97 E St. George Blvd.
St. George, UT 84770-2853
Ph: (435)628-1658
Fax: (435)628-5638
Co. E-mail: gregg@stgeorgechamber.com
URL: http://www.stgeorgechamber.com
Contact: Russ Behrmann, President
E-mail: russ@stgeorgechamber.com
Released: Annual

58636 ■ *Business Focus*
175 E 400 S, Ste. 600
Salt Lake City, UT 84111-2329
Ph: (801)364-3631
Fax: (801)328-5098
Co. E-mail: info@saltlakechamber.org
URL: http://www.saltlakechamber.org
Contact: Lane Beattie, President
Released: Monthly

58637 ■ *Business and Professional Directory*
7355 S 900 E, No. 1
Midvale, UT 84047
Ph: (801)561-3880
Co. E-mail: info@midvalechambers.com
URL: http://www.midvalechamber.com
Contact: Marie Marshall, President
Released: Annual

58638 ■ *Business Pulse*
8000 S Redwood Rd.
West Jordan, UT 84088
Ph: (801)569-5151
Fax: (801)569-5153
Co. E-mail: info@westjordanchamber.com
URL: http://www.westjordanchamber.com
Contact: N. Craig Dearing, President
Released: Monthly **Price:** included in membership dues.

58639 ■ **Cache Chamber of Commerce (CCC)**
160 N Main St.
Logan, UT 84321
Ph: (435)752-2161
Fax: (435)753-5825
Co. E-mail: semile@cachechamber.com
URL: http://www.cachechamber.com
Contact: Sandra Emile, President
Description: Promotes business and community development in Cache and Rich counties, UT. **Founded:** 1911. **Publications:** *The Insider* (Biweekly). **Awards:** Business of the Year (Annual); Citizen of the Year (Annual).

58640 ■ **Carbon County Chamber of Commerce (CCCC)**
81 N 200 E, No. 3
Price, UT 84501
Ph: (435)637-2788

Fax: (435)637-7010
Co. E-mail: cccc@priceutah.net
URL: http://www.carboncountychamber.net
Contact: Ethan Migliori, President
Description: Promotes business and community development in Carbon County, UT. **Publications:** *Chamber Chatter* (Monthly).

58641 ■ **Cedar City Area Chamber of Commerce**
77 N Main St.
Cedar City, UT 84720
Ph: (435)586-4484
URL: http://www.cedarcitychamber.com
Description: Promotes business and community development in Cedar City, UT. **Publications:** *Chamber Times* (Monthly).

58642 ■ *Chamber Chatter*
81 N 200 E, No. 3
Price, UT 84501
Ph: (435)637-2788
Fax: (435)637-7010
Co. E-mail: cccc@priceutah.net
URL: http://www.carboncountychamber.net
Contact: Ethan Migliori, President
Released: Monthly

58643 ■ *Chamber Insider*
51 S University Ave., Ste. 215
Provo, UT 84606
Ph: (801)851-2555
Co. E-mail: vhale@thechamber.org
URL: http://www.thechamber.org
Contact: Val Hale, President

58644 ■ *Chamber Times*
77 N Main St.
Cedar City, UT 84720
Ph: (435)586-4484
URL: http://www.cedarcitychamber.com
Released: Monthly

58645 ■ **ChamberWest**
1241 W Village Main Dr., Ste. B
West Valley City, UT 84119
Ph: (801)969-8755
Fax: (801)977-8329
URL: http://www.chamberwest.com
Contact: Alan Anderson, President
Description: Promotes business and community development in West Valley City, Taylorsville, and Kearns, Utah. **Founded:** 1963. **Publications:** *ChamberWorks* (Monthly). **Educational Activities:** General Membership Meeting (Monthly). **Awards:** Business Champion (Annual); Business of the Year (Annual); ChamberWest Service Award (Annual); Civic Partner of the Year (Annual); Small Business of the Year (Annual); Volunteer of the Year (Annual).

58646 ■ *ChamberWorks*
1241 W Village Main Dr., Ste. B
West Valley City, UT 84119
Ph: (801)969-8755
Fax: (801)977-8329
URL: http://www.chamberwest.com
Contact: Alan Anderson, President
Released: Monthly

58647 ■ *Community Guide*
217 E Center St., Ste. 250
Moab, UT 84532
Ph: (435)259-7814
Fax: (435)259-8519
Co. E-mail: info@moabchamber.com
URL: http://www.moabchamber.com
Contact: Steve Lawry, President
Released: Biennial

58648 ■ **Davis Chamber of Commerce**
450 S Simmons Way, Ste. 220
Kaysville, UT 84037
Ph: (801)593-2200

Fax: (801)593-2212
Co. E-mail: jimsmith@davischamberofcommerce.
com
URL: http://www.davischamberofcommerce.com
Contact: Jim Smith, President
Description: Promotes business and community development in Kaysville, UT. **Publications:** *The Inside Track* (Weekly); *Wasatch Business Connection* (Monthly).

58649 ■ Delta Area Chamber of Commerce (DACC)
80 N 200 W
Delta, UT 84624-9440
Ph: (435)864-4316
Fax: (435)864-4313
Co. E-mail: daccinfo@deltautahchamber.com
URL: http://deltautahchamber.com
Contact: Jeffery D. Christensen, President
Description: Promotes business and community development in the Delta, UT area. Facilitates business-education partnerships. Provides secretarial services for the Western Utah Mining Association. **Founded:** 1982.

58650 ■ *Dinah Says*
134 W Main St.
Vernal, UT 84078-2504
Ph: (435)789-1352
Fax: (435)789-1355
Co. E-mail: vchambermgr@easilink.com
URL: http://www.vernalchamber.com
Contact: Adam Massey, Executive Director
Released: Quarterly

58651 ■ *Dinosaur Land*
134 W Main St.
Vernal, UT 84078-2504
Ph: (435)789-1352
Fax: (435)789-1355
Co. E-mail: vchambermgr@easilink.com
URL: http://www.vernalchamber.com
Contact: Adam Massey, Executive Director
Released: Annual

58652 ■ Duchesne County Chamber of Commerce (DCACC)
50 E 200 S
Roosevelt, UT 84066-1417
Ph: (435)722-4598
Fax: (435)722-4579
Co. E-mail: irene@uintabasin.org
URL: http://duchesne.net
Description: Promotes business and community development in the Duchesne County, UT area. Sponsors festival and conducts competitions.

58653 ■ *Focus*
5250 S Commerce Dr.
Murray, UT 84107
Ph: (801)263-2632
Fax: (801)263-8262
Co. E-mail: scott@murraychamber.net
URL: http://www.murraychamber.net
Contact: Scott Baker, President
Released: Monthly

58654 ■ *Heber Valley Chamber of Commerce Member Directory*
475 N Main St.
Heber City, UT 84032
Ph: (435)654-3666
Free: 866-994-3237
Fax: (435)654-3667
Co. E-mail: info@hebervalleycc.org
URL: http://www.GoHeberValley.com
Contact: Jennifer Kohler, Executive Director
Released: Annual

58655 ■ Heber Valley Chamber of Commerce and Visitor Center (HVCC)
475 N Main St.
Heber City, UT 84032
Ph: (435)654-3666
Free: 866-994-3237

Fax: (435)654-3667
Co. E-mail: info@hebervalleycc.org
URL: http://www.GoHeberValley.com
Contact: Jennifer Kohler, Executive Director
Description: Promotes business, tourism, and community development in Wasatch County, UT. Contributes to local charities. Sponsors competitions and festival. **Founded:** 1952. **Publications:** *Insider* (Annual); *Heber Valley Chamber of Commerce Member Directory* (Annual). **Educational Activities:** Membership Meeting (Monthly). **Awards:** Business of the Month (Monthly).

58656 ■ Hurricane Valley Chamber of Commerce
PO Box 101
Hurricane, UT 84737
Ph: (435)635-3402
Fax: (435)635-3402
Co. E-mail: info@hvchamber.com
URL: http://www.hvchamber.com
Contact: Cliff Holt, President
Description: Works to serve the interests of businesses throughout the Hurricane Valley. **Founded:** 1974.

58657 ■ *The Inside Track*
450 S Simmons Way, Ste. 220
Kaysville, UT 84037
Ph: (801)593-2200
Fax: (801)593-2212
Co. E-mail: jimsmith@davischamberofcommerce.
com
URL: http://www.davischamberofcommerce.com
Contact: Jim Smith, President
Released: Weekly

58658 ■ *The Insider*
160 N Main St.
Logan, UT 84321
Ph: (435)752-2161
Fax: (435)753-5825
Co. E-mail: semile@cachechamber.com
URL: http://www.cachechamber.com
Contact: Sandra Emile, President
Released: Biweekly

58659 ■ *Insider*
475 N Main St.
Heber City, UT 84032
Ph: (435)654-3666
Free: 866-994-3237
Fax: (435)654-3667
Co. E-mail: info@hebervalleycc.org
URL: http://www.GoHeberValley.com
Contact: Jennifer Kohler, Executive Director
Released: Annual

58660 ■ *Issues*
7355 S 900 E, No. 1
Midvale, UT 84047
Ph: (801)561-3880
Co. E-mail: info@midvalechambers.com
URL: http://www.midvalechamber.com
Contact: Marie Marshall, President
Released: Monthly

58661 ■ Kanab Chamber of Commerce (KCOC)
78 S 100 E
Kanab, UT 84741
Free: 800-733-5263
Fax: (435)644-5923
URL: http://www.kanabchamber.com
Contact: Kelly Stowell, President
Description: Promotes business and community development in the Kanab, UT area.

58662 ■ *Life in the Valley*
175 E 400 S, Ste. 600
Salt Lake City, UT 84111-2329
Ph: (801)364-3631
Fax: (801)328-5098
Co. E-mail: info@saltlakechamber.org
URL: http://www.saltlakechamber.org
Contact: Lane Beattie, President
Released: Annual **Price:** $10, /copy.

58663 ■ *Membership Directory and Buyer's Guide*
175 E 400 S, Ste. 600
Salt Lake City, UT 84111-2329
Ph: (801)364-3631
Fax: (801)328-5098
Co. E-mail: info@saltlakechamber.org
URL: http://www.saltlakechamber.org
Contact: Lane Beattie, President
Released: Annual **Price:** $50, /copy.

58664 ■ Midvale Area Chamber of Commerce
7355 S 900 E, No. 1
Midvale, UT 84047
Ph: (801)561-3880
Co. E-mail: info@midvalechambers.com
URL: http://www.midvalechamber.com
Contact: Marie Marshall, President
Description: Promotes business and community development in Midvale, UT. **Founded:** 1946. **Publications:** *Business and Professional Directory* (Annual); *Issues* (Monthly).

58665 ■ Moab Area Chamber of Commerce (MACC)
217 E Center St., Ste. 250
Moab, UT 84532
Ph: (435)259-7814
Fax: (435)259-8519
Co. E-mail: info@moabchamber.com
URL: http://www.moabchamber.com
Contact: Steve Lawry, President
Description: Promotes business and community development in Grand County, UT. Sponsors races and other special events. **Founded:** 1955. **Publications:** *Community Guide* (Biennial). **Educational Activities:** Art Walks (Monthly). **Awards:** Business of the Year (Annual); Citizen of the Year (Annual).

58666 ■ Monticello Chamber of Commerce
PO Box 217
Monticello, UT 84535
Ph: (435)587-2992
Co. E-mail: info@monticelloutahchamber.com
URL: http://www.monticelloutahchamber.com
Contact: Michael Martin, President
Description: Promotes business and community development in Monticello, UT. Sponsors annual fireworks display.

58667 ■ Murray Area Chamber of Commerce (MACC)
5250 S Commerce Dr.
Murray, UT 84107
Ph: (801)263-2632
Fax: (801)263-8262
Co. E-mail: scott@murraychamber.net
URL: http://www.murraychamber.net
Contact: Scott Baker, President
Description: Promotes business and community development in Murray, UT area. **Publications:** *Focus* (Monthly).

58668 ■ Ogden/Weber Chamber of Commerce
2484 Washington Blvd., Ste. 400
Ogden, UT 84401
Ph: (801)621-8300
Free: 866-990-1299
Fax: (801)392-7609
Co. E-mail: chamber@ogdenweberchamber.com
URL: http://ogdenweberchamber.com
Contact: Mr. Dave Hardman, President
Description: Seeks to advance prosperity in Weber County. Strives to strengthen relations with key community organizations and companies. Works with the state government to give support and resources for Weber County. **Founded:** 1887. **Subscriptions:** archival material articles. **Publications:** *Business Directory* (Annual); *Women in Business* (Quarterly). **Educational Activities:** Business After Hours (Monthly); Ogden/Weber Chamber of Commerce Dinner (Annual). **Awards:** Wall of Fame Award (Annual).

58669 ■ Park City Chamber of Commerce
PO Box 1630
Park City, UT 84060
Ph: (435)649-6100
Free: 800-453-1360

Fax: (435)649-4132
Co. E-mail: bill@visitparkcity.com
URL: http://www.parkcityinfo.com
Contact: Bill Malone, President
Description: Promotes business and community development in Park City, UT. **Publications:** *Summit Outlook* (Monthly).

58670 ■ Payson Chamber of Commerce
PO Box 176
Payson, UT 84651
Ph: (801)465-2634
Fax: (801)465-5173
Co. E-mail: paysonchamber@yahoo.com
URL: http://www.paysoncitychamber.org
Contact: Carolyn Bowman, Executive Director
Description: Promotes business and community development in Payson, UT area.

58671 ■ *Progress*
9350 S 150 E, Ste. 980
Sandy, UT 84070
Ph: (801)566-0344
Fax: (801)566-0346
Co. E-mail: sandychamber@sandychamber.com
URL: http://www.sandychamber.com
Contact: Stan Parrish, President
Released: Monthly

58672 ■ *Progress Business Journal*
9350 S 150 E, Ste. 980
Sandy, UT 84070
Ph: (801)566-0344
Fax: (801)566-0346
Co. E-mail: sandychamber@sandychamber.com
URL: http://www.sandychamber.com
Contact: Stan Parrish, President
Released: Bimonthly

58673 ■ *Recreation and Relocation Guide*
Released: Annual **Price:** $10, /issue.

58674 ■ St. George Area Chamber of Commerce (SGACC)
97 E St. George Blvd.
St. George, UT 84770-2853
Ph: (435)628-1658
Fax: (435)628-5638
Co. E-mail: gregg@stgeorgechamber.com
URL: http://www.stgeorgechamber.com
Contact: Russ Behrmann, President
E-mail: russ@stgeorgechamber.com
Description: Promotes business and community development in the Washington County, UT area. **Founded:** 1940. **Publications:** *St. George Area Chamber of Commerce Business Directory; Business Directory and Relocation Guide* (Annual); *Business Directory and Relocation Guide* (Annual); *St. George Area Chamber of Commerce--Business Directory and Relocation Guide* (Annual). **Educational Activities:** Membership Luncheon (Weekly). **Awards:** Entrepreneur of the Year (Annual); Executive of the Year (Annual); Lifetime Achievement Award (Annual); Community-Business Partnership of the Year (Annual); Community Service Volunteer of the Year (Annual); Junior Entrepreneur of the Year (Annual). **Telecommunication Services:** staceyg@netutah.com.

58675 ■ Salt Lake Chamber (SLACC)
175 E 400 S, Ste. 600
Salt Lake City, UT 84111-2329
Ph: (801)364-3631
Fax: (801)328-5098
Co. E-mail: info@saltlakechamber.org
URL: http://www.saltlakechamber.org
Contact: Lane Beattie, President
Description: Promotes business and community development in the Salt Lake City, UT area. **Founded:** 1902. **Publications:** *Life in the Valley* (Annual); *Business Focus* (Monthly); *Life in the Valley* (Annual); *Membership Directory and Buyer's Guide* (Annual). **Educational Activities:** Member Welcome (Monthly). **Awards:** Giant in our City Award (Annual); Giant Step Small Business Award (Annual). **Telecommunication Services:** info@slchamber.com.

58676 ■ Sandy Area Chamber of Commerce (SACC)
9350 S 150 E, Ste. 980
Sandy, UT 84070
Ph: (801)566-0344
Fax: (801)566-0346
Co. E-mail: sandychamber@sandychamber.com
URL: http://www.sandychamber.com
Contact: Stan Parrish, President
Description: Promotes business and community development in the Sandy, UT area. **Founded:** 1978. **Publications:** *Progress* (Monthly); *Progress Business Journal* (Bimonthly); *Sandy Area Metro Guide* (Annual). **Awards:** Service Award (Annual).

58677 ■ *Sandy Area Metro Guide*
9350 S 150 E, Ste. 980
Sandy, UT 84070
Ph: (801)566-0344
Fax: (801)566-0346
Co. E-mail: sandychamber@sandychamber.com
URL: http://www.sandychamber.com
Contact: Stan Parrish, President
Released: Annual

58678 ■ South Salt Lake Chamber of Commerce
220 E Morris Ave., Ste. 150
South Salt Lake, UT 84115
Ph: (801)466-3377
Fax: (801)467-3322
Co. E-mail: info@sslchamber.com
URL: http://www.sslchamber.com
Contact: Rick Taggart, Chairman
Description: Promotes business and community development in South Salt Lake, UT area.

58679 ■ Southwest Valley Chamber of Commerce
PO Box 330
Riverton, UT 84065
Ph: (801)280-0595
Fax: (801)280-3674
Co. E-mail: susan@swvchamber.org
URL: http://www.swvchamber.org
Contact: Pennie Rich, Chairperson
Description: Promotes business and community development in Southwest Valley Area, UT.

58680 ■ *Summit Outlook*
PO Box 1630
Park City, UT 84060
Ph: (435)649-6100
Free: 800-453-1360
Fax: (435)649-4132
Co. E-mail: bill@visitparkcity.com
URL: http://www.parkcityinfo.com
Contact: Bill Malone, President
Released: Monthly

58681 ■ Tooele County Chamber of Commerce (TCCC)
PO Box 460
Tooele, UT 84074-0460
Ph: (435)882-0690
Free: 800-378-0690
Fax: (435)833-0946
Co. E-mail: chamber@tooelechamber.com
URL: http://www.tooelechamber.com
Contact: Joyce Hogan, Chairperson
Description: Promotes business and community development in Tooele County, UT. **Founded:** 1948. **Publications:** *Visitors Guide and Business Directory* (Annual). **Educational Activities:** Membership Network Luncheon (Monthly). **Awards:** Tooele Citizen of the Year (Annual).

58682 ■ Utah Valley Chamber of Commerce
51 S University Ave., Ste. 215
Provo, UT 84606
Ph: (801)851-2555
Co. E-mail: vhale@thechamber.org
URL: http://www.thechamber.org
Contact: Val Hale, President
Description: Promotes business and community development in Provo and Orem, UT. Conducts networking activities. **Scope:** business, human resources. **Founded:** 1985. **Subscriptions:** 150

articles audio recordings books periodicals video recordings. **Publications:** *Chamber Insider*. **Educational Activities:** First Friday Forum (Monthly).

58683 ■ Vernal Area Chamber of Commerce (VACC)
134 W Main St.
Vernal, UT 84078-2504
Ph: (435)789-1352
Fax: (435)789-1355
Co. E-mail: vchambermgr@easilink.com
URL: http://www.vernalchamber.com
Contact: Adam Massey, Executive Director
Description: Promotes business and community development in the Vernal, UT area. **Founded:** 1949. **Publications:** *Dinah Says* (Quarterly); *Dinosaur Land* (Annual); *Vernal Directory* (Periodic). **Awards:** Beautification Award (Monthly); Business of the Month (Monthly); Outstanding Public Service (Quarterly); Total Citizen Award (Annual).

58684 ■ *Vernal Directory*
134 W Main St.
Vernal, UT 84078-2504
Ph: (435)789-1352
Fax: (435)789-1355
Co. E-mail: vchambermgr@easilink.com
URL: http://www.vernalchamber.com
Contact: Adam Massey, Executive Director
Released: Periodic

58685 ■ *Visitors Guide and Business Directory*
PO Box 460
Tooele, UT 84074-0460
Ph: (435)882-0690
Free: 800-378-0690
Fax: (435)833-0946
Co. E-mail: chamber@tooelechamber.com
URL: http://www.tooelechamber.com
Contact: Joyce Hogan, Chairperson
Released: Annual

58686 ■ *Wasatch Business Connection*
450 S Simmons Way, Ste. 220
Kaysville, UT 84037
Ph: (801)593-2200
Fax: (801)593-2212
Co. E-mail: jimsmith@davischamberofcommerce.com
URL: http://www.davischamberofcommerce.com
Contact: Jim Smith, President
Released: Monthly

58687 ■ *West Jordan Business and Professional Directory*
8000 S Redwood Rd.
West Jordan, UT 84088
Ph: (801)569-5151
Fax: (801)569-5153
Co. E-mail: info@westjordanchamber.com
URL: http://www.westjordanchamber.com
Contact: N. Craig Dearing, President
Released: Periodic

58688 ■ West Jordan Chamber of Commerce (WJCC)
8000 S Redwood Rd.
West Jordan, UT 84088
Ph: (801)569-5151
Fax: (801)569-5153
Co. E-mail: info@westjordanchamber.com
URL: http://www.westjordanchamber.com
Contact: N. Craig Dearing, President
Description: Promotes business and community development in West Jordan, UT. **Founded:** 1985. **Publications:** *Business Pulse* (Monthly); *West Jordan Business and Professional Directory* (Periodic). **Awards:** Citizen of the Year (Annual); Community Enhancement Award; Teacher of the Month (Monthly); Teacher of the Year (Annual).

58689 ■ *Women in Business*
2484 Washington Blvd., Ste. 400
Ogden, UT 84401
Ph: (801)621-8300
Free: 866-990-1299

Fax: (801)392-7609
Co. E-mail: chamber@ogdenweberchamber.com
URL: http://ogdenweberchamber.com
Contact: Mr. Dave Hardman, President
Released: Quarterly

MINORITY BUSINESS ASSISTANCE PROGRAMS

58690 ■ Utah Community and Culture Department - Office of Indian Affairs
324 S State, Ste. 500
Salt Lake City, UT 84114
Ph: (801)538-8808
Fax: (801)538-8803
Co. E-mail: fscuch@utah.gov
URL: http://indian.utah.gov/
Contact: Forrest Cuch, Director
Description: Works to improve the educational, employment, and economic status of minorities in the state.

58691 ■ Utah Community and Economic Development Department - Office of Ethnic Affairs - Asian Advisory Council
324 S State, Ste. 500
Salt Lake City, UT 84111
Ph: (801)538-8883
Fax: (801)538-8678
Co. E-mail: loda@utah.gov
URL: http://ethnicoffice.utah.gov/
Contact: Edith Mitko, Director
Description: Works to improve the educational, employment, and economic status of minorities in the state.

58692 ■ Utah Community and Economic Development Department - Office of Ethnic Affairs - Hispanic/Latino Advisory Council
324 S State, Ste. 500
Salt Lake City, UT 84111
Ph: (801)538-8755
Fax: (801)538-8678
Co. E-mail: jsoriano@utah.gov
URL: http://ethnicoffice.utah.gov/
Contact: Jesse Soriano, Director
Description: Works to improve the educational, employment, and economic status of minorities in the state.

58693 ■ Utah Office of Economic Development - Office of Ethnic Affairs - Black Advisory Council
324 S State St., Ste. 500
Salt Lake City, UT 84111
Ph: (801)538-8754
Fax: (801)538-8888
Co. E-mail: dcharleston@utah.gov
URL: http://ethnicoffice.utah.gov/
Contact: Debra Charleston, Director
Description: Works to improve the educational, employment, and economic status of minorities in the state.

FINANCING AND LOAN PROGRAMS

58694 ■ Utah Ventures II, L.P.
2755 E. Cottonwood Pky., Ste. 5
Salt Lake City, UT 84121
Ph: (801)365-0262
Fax: (801)365-0233
Co. E-mail: info@uvpartners.com
URL: http://www.utahventures.com
Contact: James C. Dreyfous, Managing Director
Preferred Investment Size: $3,000,000 to $10,000,000. **Industry Preferences:** Diversified technology. **Geographic Preference:** Northwest and Rocky Mountain region.

58695 ■ Wasatch Venture Corporation / EPIC Ventures
1 South Main St., 8th Fl.
Salt Lake City, UT 84111
Ph: (801)524-8939

Fax: (801)524-8941
Co. E-mail: neesha@epicvc.com
URL: http://www.wasatchvc.com
Contact: Todd Stevens, Managing Director
Preferred Investment Size: $500,000 to $3,000,000. **Industry Preferences:** Internet specific, computer software and services, computer hardware, communications and media, semiconductors and other electronics, consumer related, biotechnology, medical and health, and other products. **Geographic Preference:** Rocky Mountains, Southwest, and West Coast.

PROCUREMENT ASSISTANCE PROGRAMS

58696 ■ Utah Department of Community and Economic Development Department - Procurement Technical Assistance Center
324 S State St., Ste. 500
Salt Lake City, UT 84111
Ph: (801)538-8733
Fax: (801)538-8888
Co. E-mail: fglange@utah.gov
URL: http://goed.utah.gov/business_development/PTAC/
Contact: Fred Lange, Director
Description: Assists businesses in competing for government and commercial contracts.

58697 ■ Utah Procurement Technical Assistance Center - Bear River Association of Governments
170 N Main St.
Logan, UT 84321
Ph: (435)752-7242
Fax: (435)752-6962
Co. E-mail: kentw@brag.utah.gov
URL: http://goed.utah.gov
Contact: Kent Watson, Regional Manager
E-mail: kentw@brag.ut.gov
Description: Assists Utah small businesses who are interested in bidding on federal, state and local government procurements and commercial contracting opportunities covering Box Elder, Cache, and Rich Counties.

58698 ■ Utah Procurement Technical Assistance Center (UPTAC) - Bear River Association of Governments
170 N Main St.
Logan, UT 84321
Ph: (435)752-7242
Fax: (435)752-6962
Co. E-mail: kentw@brag.utah.gov
URL: http://goed.utah.gov
Contact: Kent Watson, Regional Manager
E-mail: kentw@brag.dst.us
Description: Serves Box Elder, Cache and Rich counties.

58699 ■ Utah Procurement Technical Assistance Center - Dixie Business Alliance
225 S 700 E
127 Hazy St.
St. George, UT 84770
Ph: (435)652-7754
Fax: (435)652-7870
Co. E-mail: keithchristiansen@utah.gov
URL: http://www.ptac.dixie.edu
Contact: Keith Christiansen, Regional Manager
Description: Assists Utah small businesses who are interested in bidding on federal, state and local government procurements and commercial contracting opportunities covering Washington and Kane Counties.

58700 ■ Utah Procurement Technical Assistance Center - Salt Lake Community College
9750 S 300 W, MCPC
Sandy, UT 84070
Ph: (801)957-6076

Fax: (801)957-3488
Co. E-mail: jwilkinson@utah.gov
URL: http://goed.utah.gov
Contact: Jonnie Wilkinson, Regional Manager
E-mail: jwilkinson@utah.gov
Description: Assists Utah small businesses who are interested in bidding on federal, state and local government procurements and commercial contracting opportunities covering South Salt Lake, Utah, and Tooele Counties.

58701 ■ Utah Procurement Technical Assistance Center - Six County Association of Governments
PO Box 820
Richfield, UT 84701
Ph: (435)893-0710
Fax: (435)893-0701
Co. E-mail: kchris@sixcounty.com
URL: http://goed.utah.gov
Contact: Kent Christensen, Regional Manager
E-mail: kchris@sixaog.state.ut.us
Description: Assists Utah small businesses who are interested in bidding on federal, state and local government procurements and commercial contracting opportunities covering Juab, Millard, Sanpete, Sevier, Piute, and Wayne Counties.

58702 ■ Utah Procurement Technical Assistance Center (UPTAC) - Southeastern Utah Association of Governments
375 S Carbon Ave.
Price, UT 84051
Ph: (435)586-5400
Co. E-mail: dpaletta@seualg.dst.ut.us
URL: http://goed.utah.gov
Description: The purpose of the program is to assist Utah small businesses who are interested in bidding on federal, state and local government procurements and commercial contracting opportunities serving Carbon, Emery, Grand and San Juan counties.

58703 ■ Utah Procurement Technical Assistance Center - Southern Utah University
351 W University Blvd.
Cedar City, UT 84720
Ph: (435)588-5400
Fax: (435)586-5493
Co. E-mail: andersonjoni@suu.edu
URL: http://goed.utah.gov
Contact: Joni Anderson, Director
E-mail: cisom@suu.edu
Description: Assists Utah small businesses who are interested in bidding on federal, state and local government procurements and commercial contracting opportunities covering Iron, Garfield, and Beaver Counties.

58704 ■ Utah Procurement Technical Assistance Center (UPTAC) - Southern Utah University
351 W Center St.
Cedar City, UT 84720
Ph: (435)586-5400
Fax: (435)586-5493
Co. E-mail: andersonjoni@suu.edu
URL: http://goed.utah.gov
Description: The purpose of the program is to assist Utah small businesses who are interested in bidding on federal, state and local government procurements and commercial contracting opportunities serving Iron, Garfield and Beaver counties.

58705 ■ Utah Procurement Technical Assistance Center (UPTAC) - Utah Defense Alliance/UBIDS
324 S State St., Ste. 500
Salt Lake City, UT 84111
Ph: (801)538-8655
Fax: (801)538-8888
Co. E-mail: cspence@utah.gov
URL: http://goed.utah.gov
Contact: Chuck Spence, Deputy Director
E-mail: cspence.utah.gov
Description: The purpose of the program is to assist Utah small businesses who are interested in bidding on federal, state and local government procurements and commercial contracting opportunities serving Weber, Davis and Morgan counties.

58706 ■ Utah Procurement Technical Assistance Center (UPTAC) - Utah Valley State College
1410 W 1200 S
Orem, UT 84058-5999
Ph: (801)863-8713
Fax: (801)957-3488
Co. E-mail: cholley@utah.gov
URL: http://goed.utah.gov
Contact: Cory Holley, Regional Manager
E-mail: cholley@utah.gov
Description: The purpose of the program is to assist Utah small businesses who are interested in bidding on federal, state and local government procurements and commercial contracting opportunities serving Utah and Wasatch counties.

58707 ■ Utah Procurement Technical Assistance Center - Utah Valley State College - Small Business Development Center
1410 W 1200 S
Orem, UT 84058-5999
Ph: (801)863-8713
Fax: (801)863-7071
Co. E-mail: cholley@utah.gov
URL: http://www.goed.utah.gov/PTAC
Contact: Cory Holley, Regional Manager
E-mail: cholley@utah.gov
Description: Assists Utah small businesses who are interested in bidding on federal, state and local government procurements and commercial contracting opportunities covering Utah and Wasatch Counties.

INCUBATORS/RESEARCH AND TECHNOLOGY PARKS

58708 ■ Grow Utah Ventures
450 S Simmons Way, Ste. 500
Kaysville, UT 84037
Ph: (801)593-2265
Co. E-mail: info@growutahventures.com
URL: http://www.growutahventures.com/
Contact: Craig T. Bott, Chief Executive Officer
Description: A small business incubator dedicated to providing education, financial, and management support to entrepreneurs and businesses along the Wasatch Front.

58709 ■ Miller Business Innovation Center
Salt Lake Community College
9750 S 300 W
Sandy, UT 84070

Ph: (801)957-5200
Fax: (801)957-3488
Co. E-mail: rex.falkenrath@slcc.edu
URL: http://www.mbrcslcc.edu/mbic/
Contact: Rex Falkenrath, Regional Director
Description: A small business incubator dedicated to the housing and the acceleration of some of Utah's most promising new ventures.

EDUCATIONAL PROGRAMS

58710 ■ Salt Lake Community College - Redwood Road Campus
4600 S Redwood Rd.
Salt Lake City, UT 84130-0808
Ph: (801)957-4111
Fax: (801)957-4444
URL: http://www.slcc.edu
Description: Provides courses and workshops on topics relevant to entrepreneurs and small business owners.

PUBLISHERS

58711 ■ Creating Keepsakes Books—Creative Crafts Group L.L.C.
14850 Pony Express Rd.
Bluffdale, UT 84065-4801
Ph: (801)984-2070
Free: 888-247-5282
Fax: (801)984-2080
Co. E-mail: customerservice@creativecraftsgroup.com
URL: http://www.creatingkeepsakes.com
Contact: Lisa Bearnson, President
Description: Description: Publishes books and CD-ROMs on photography, paper crafts and scrap booking.

58712 ■ Executive Excellence Publishing (EEP)
1806 North 1120 West
Provo, UT 84604
Ph: (801)375-4060
Free: 877-250-1983
Fax: (801)377-5960
Co. E-mail: info@eep.com
URL: http://eep.store.merchandizer.com
Contact: Ken Shelton, President
E-mail: kens@eep.com
URL(s): www.eep.com. **Description:** Description: Publishes business books and a newsletter. Accepts unsolicited manuscripts. Reaches market through

commission representatives, direct mail, reviews and listings, telephone sales, Ingram, Baker & Taylor and National Book Network. **Founded:** 1984. **Publications:** *Executive Excellence: The Newsletter of Personal Development, Managerial Effectiveness, and Organizational Productivity.* **Telecommunication Services:** execexcl@itsnet.com.

58713 ■ Janco Associates Inc.
11 Eagle Landing Ct.
Park City, UT 84060
Ph: (435)940-9300
Fax: (435)615-9302
Co. E-mail: info@e-janco.com
URL: http://www.e-janco.com
Contact: M. Victor Janulaitis, Chief Executive Officer
E-mail: victor@e-janco.com
Description: Description: Publishes paperless books on the Internet which focuses on management information systems. **Scope:** An international management consulting firm that specializes in the strategic and mission critical use of information technology to provide or restore a company's competitive edge. Has a proven approach to produce actions which lead to significant operational improvements. In today's climate, this often requires a fundamental restructuring of the way clients approach their business, both from a long- and short-term perspective. Manages both the technical and cultural aspects of this change with equal attention to detail. Firm's principals and consultants bring to the practice strong backgrounds in MIS as well as significant management experience in a wide range of industries. Clients consist primarily of the CFO's and CIO's of Fortune 500 corporations. Specific expertise includes: mission critical implementation, strategic competitive advantage, merger management paperless books, capacity planning, LAN/WAN implementation, compensation analysis, data center reorganization, organizational development and operations improvement. **Founded:** 1998. **Publications:** "Disaster Recovery/Business Continuity Template"; "Security Manual Template Bundle"; "Information Systems Position Description Hand guide"; "Personal Computer Policies and Procedures Hand guide"; "Information Systems Metrics Hand guide"; "Client Server Hand guide"; "Metrics Hand guide for the Internet and Information Technology and Practical Guide for it Outsourcing". **Seminars:** Paperless Books; In sourcing; Performance Metrics: Managing for Excellence; Gaining the Competitive Advantage; User Vision of Performance and Managing the Transition to Client Server. **Telecommunication Services:** support@e-janco.com. **Special Services:** Zinnote®.

SMALL BUSINESS DEVELOPMENT CENTERS

58714 ■ Vermont Small Business Development Center, Addison County
1590 Rte. 7 S, Ste. No. 8
Middlebury, VT 05753
Ph: (802)388-7953
Fax: (802)388-0119
Co. E-mail: spaddock@vtsbdc.org
URL: http://www.vtsbdc.org
Contact: Steve Paddock, Director, Programs
Description: Represents and promotes the small business sector. Provides management assistance to current and prospective small business owners. Helps to improve management skills and expand the products and services of members.

58715 ■ Vermont Small Business Development Center, Bennington County
PO Box 923
Bennington, VT 05201-0923
Ph: (802)442-8975
Fax: (802)442-1101
Co. E-mail: bdeclue@vtsbdc.org
URL: http://www.vtsbdc.org
Contact: Brian DeClue, Advisor
Description: Represents and promotes the small business sector. Provides management assistance to current and prospective small business owners. Helps to improve management skills and expand the products and services of members.

58716 ■ Vermont Small Business Development Center, Caledonia County
PO Box 630
St. Johnsbury, VT 05819
Ph: (802)748-1014
Fax: (802)748-1223
Co. E-mail: rhart@vtsbdc.org
URL: http://www.vtsbdc.org
Contact: Ross Hart, Advisor
Description: Represents and promotes the small business sector. Provides management assistance to current and prospective small business owners. Helps to improve management skills and expand the products and services of members.

58717 ■ Vermont Small Business Development Center, Franklin County
PO Box 1099
St. Albans, VT 05478-1099
Ph: (802)524-2194
Co. E-mail: sdensham@vtsbdc.org
URL: http://www.vtsbdc.org
Contact: Steve Densham, Advisor
Description: Represents and promotes the small business sector. Provides management assistance to current and prospective small business owners. Helps to improve management skills and expand the products and services of members.

58718 ■ Vermont Small Business Development Center, Grand Isle County
PO Box 213
North Hero, VT 05474-0213
Ph: (802)372-8400
Fax: (802)372-5107
Co. E-mail: sdensham@vtsbdc.org
URL: http://www.vtsbdc.org
Contact: Steve Densham, Advisor
Description: Represents and promotes the small business sector. Provides management assistance to current and prospective small business owners. Helps to improve management skills and expand the products and services of members.

58719 ■ Vermont Small Business Development Center, Lamoille County
PO Box 455
Morrisville, VT 05661-0455
Ph: (802)888-4542
Fax: (802)888-7612
Co. E-mail: drubel@vtsbdc.org
URL: http://www.vtsbdc.org
Contact: Dave Rubel, Advisor
Description: Represents and promotes the small business sector. Provides management assistance to current and prospective small business owners. Helps to improve management skills and expand the products and services of members.

58720 ■ Vermont Small Business Development Center - Lead Office (VTSBDC)
One Main St.
Randolph Center, VT 05061-0188
Ph: (802)728-9101
Free: 800-464-SBDC
Fax: (802)728-3026
Co. E-mail: lquillen@vtsbdc.org
URL: http://www.vtsbdc.org
Contact: Lenae Quillen-Blume, Director
Description: Works to assist start-ups and strengthen existing business entities through high quality, no cost business counseling, and affordable business training programs.

58721 ■ Vermont Small Business Development Center, Orange/Windsor Counties
PO Box 246
White River Junction, VT 05001-0246
Ph: (802)295-3710
Fax: (802)295-3779
Co. E-mail: deibner@vtsbdc.org
URL: http://www.vtsbdc.org
Contact: Deborah Eibner, Advisor
Description: Represents and promotes the small business sector. Provides management assistance to current and prospective small business owners. Helps to improve management skills and expand the products and services of members.

58722 ■ Vermont Small Business Development Center, Rutland County
112 Quality Ln.
Rutland, VT 05701

Ph: (802)773-9147
Co. E-mail: bdeclue@vtsbdc.org
URL: http://www.vtsbdc.org
Contact: Brian DeClue, Advisor
Description: Represents and promotes the small business sector. Provides management assistance to current and prospective small business owners. Helps to improve management skills and expand the products and services of members.

58723 ■ Vermont Small Business Development Center, Southern Windsor
14 Clinton St., Ste. 7
Springfield, VT 05156
Ph: (802)885-2071
Fax: (802)885-3027
Co. E-mail: dboudrieau@vtsbdc.org
URL: http://www.vtsbdc.org
Contact: Debra Boudrieau, Advisor
Description: Represents and promotes the small business sector. Provides management assistance to current and prospective small business owners. Helps to improve management skills and expand the products and services of members.

58724 ■ Vermont Small Business Development Center, Washington County
PO Box 1439
Montpelier, VT 05601-1439
Ph: (802)223-4654
Fax: (802)223-4655
Co. E-mail: drubel@vtsbdc.org
URL: http://www.vtsbdc.org
Contact: Dave Rubel, Advisor
Description: Represents and promotes the small business sector. Provides management assistance to current and prospective small business owners. Helps to improve management skills and expand the products and services of members.

58725 ■ Vermont Small Business Development Center, Windham County
76 Cotton Mill Hill, C-1
Brattleboro, VT 05301
Ph: (802)257-7731
Fax: (802)257-0294
Co. E-mail: dboudrieau@vtsbdc.org
URL: http://www.vtsbdc.org
Contact: Debra Boudrieau, Advisor
Description: Represents and promotes the small business sector. Provides management assistance to current and prospective small business owners. Helps to improve management skills and expand the products and services of members.

SMALL BUSINESS ASSISTANCE PROGRAMS

58726 ■ Agency of Commerce and Community Development - Economic Development Department
One National Life Dr.
Drawer 1
Montpelier, VT 05620-0501

Ph: (802)828-3080
Free: 800-622-4553
Fax: (802)828-3258
Co. E-mail: info@thinkvermont.com
URL: http://economicdevelopment.vermont.gov/
Contact: Tayt Brooks, Commissioner
Description: A full-service business consulting and referral network, coordinating the efforts of the state's regional development corporations, the Vermont Industrial Development Authority, and federal employment training and financing agencies.

58727 ■ Agency of Commerce and Community Development - Economic Development Department - Site Selection Office
National Life Bldg.
Drawer 20
Montpelier, VT 05620-0501
Ph: (802)828-3211
Free: 800-622-4553
Fax: (802)828-3258
Co. E-mail: info@thinkvermont.com
URL: http://www.thinkvermont.com
Description: Maintains a computerized inventory of industrial parks, sites, commercial and industrial buildings.

58728 ■ Agency of Commerce and Community Development - Economic Development Department - Vermont Business Expansion Program
National Life Bldg.
Drawer 20
Montpelier, VT 05620-0501
Ph: (802)828-3211
Free: 800-622-4553
Fax: (802)828-3258
Co. E-mail: info@thinkvermont.com
URL: http://www.thinkvermont.com
Description: Helps companies take advantage of international research and development in traditional manufacturing, high technology, and information applications.

58729 ■ Vermont Small Business Development Center - Economic Development Department
PO Box 188
Randolph Center, VT 05061-0188
Ph: (802)728-9101
Free: 800-622-4553
Fax: (802)728-3026
Co. E-mail: lquillen@vtsbdc.org
URL: http://www.vtsbdc.org/
Contact: Lenae Quillen-Blume, Director
Description: Directly assists small businesses, and offers referrals when necessary.

SCORE OFFICES

58730 ■ SCORE Champlain Valley
11 Lincoln St., Rm. 106
Essex Junction, VT 05452
Ph: (802)951-6762
URL: http://champlainvalley.score.org
Contact: Jerry Johnson, Chairman
Description: Offers free business counseling and mentoring in the area.

58731 ■ SCORE Montpelier
87 State St., Rm. 205
Montpelier, VT 05601
Ph: (802)828-4422
Co. E-mail: scorechapter275@aol.com
URL: http://www.montpelier.scorechapter.org
Description: Works to provide free counseling and training to small businesses and potential small businesses. **Scope:** business. **Founded:** 1965. **Subscriptions:** 1500 articles.

CHAMBERS OF COMMERCE

58732 ■ 60 Main Street News
60 Main St., Ste. 100
Burlington, VT 05401-8418
Ph: (802)863-3489

Free: 877-686-5253
Fax: (802)863-1538
Co. E-mail: vermont@vermont.org
URL: http://www.vermont.org
Contact: Tom Torti, President
Released: Monthly

58733 ■ Addison County Annual Guide & Map
93 Court St.
Middlebury, VT 05753
Ph: (802)388-7951
Free: 800-733-8376
Fax: (802)388-8066
Co. E-mail: info@addisoncounty.com
URL: http://www.addisoncounty.com
Contact: Andy Mayer, President
Released: Annual

58734 ■ Addison County Chamber of Commerce (ACCOC)
93 Court St.
Middlebury, VT 05753
Ph: (802)388-7951
Free: 800-733-8376
Fax: (802)388-8066
Co. E-mail: info@addisoncounty.com
URL: http://www.addisoncounty.com
Contact: Andy Mayer, President
Description: Promotes business and community development in Addison County, VT. **Founded:** 1969. **Publications:** Addison County Annual Guide & Map (Annual); The Chamber News (Monthly); Who's Who in Addison County (Annual); Addison County Business Directory & Community Profile; Addison County Business Directory & Community Profile (Annual). **Telecommunication Services:** info@midvermont.com.

58735 ■ Area Guide to Manchester and the Mountains
5046 Main St., Ste. 1
Manchester Center, VT 05255-9787
Ph: (802)824-5522
Free: 800-362-4144
Fax: (802)362-3451
Co. E-mail: bmaginniss@manchesterchamber.net
URL: http://www.manchestervermont.net
Contact: Berta Maginniss, Executive Director
Released: Semiannual

58736 ■ Area Map
PO Box 336
Barre, VT 05641-0336
Ph: (802)229-5711
Fax: (802)229-5713
Co. E-mail: cvchamber@aol.com
URL: http://www.central-vt.com
Contact: George Malek, President

58737 ■ Barton Area Chamber of Commerce
PO Box 776
Barton, VT 05822
Ph: (802)239-4147
Co. E-mail: info@centerofthekingdom.com
URL: http://www.centerofthekingdom.com
Description: Serves members and the community with networking opportunities, business seminars, and referrals.

58738 ■ Bennington Area Chamber of Commerce
100 Veterans Memorial Dr.
Bennington, VT 05201
Ph: (802)447-3311
Free: 800-229-0252
Fax: (802)447-1163
Co. E-mail: chamber@bennington.com
URL: http://www.bennington.com/chamber
Contact: Joann Erenhouse, Executive Director
Description: Serves members and the community with networking opportunities, business seminars, and referrals. **Founded:** 1911. **Publications:** Bennington Area Guide (Annual).

58739 ■ Bennington Area Guide
100 Veterans Memorial Dr.
Bennington, VT 05201
Ph: (802)447-3311

Free: 800-229-0252
Fax: (802)447-1163
Co. E-mail: chamber@bennington.com
URL: http://www.bennington.com/chamber
Contact: Joann Erenhouse, Executive Director
Released: Annual

58740 ■ Brandon Area Chamber of Commerce (BACC)
PO Box 267
Brandon, VT 05733
Ph: (802)247-6401
Co. E-mail: info@brandon.org
URL: http://brandon.org
Contact: Janet Mondlak, Executive Director
Description: Promotes business and community development in Brandon, VT. **Publications:** Chamber News (Monthly). **Educational Activities:** Brandon HarvestFest (Annual).

58741 ■ Brattleboro Area Chamber of Commerce (BACC)
180 Main St.
Brattleboro, VT 05301
Ph: (802)254-4565
Free: 877-254-4565
Co. E-mail: info@brattleborochamber.org
URL: http://www.brattleborochamber.org
Contact: Jerry Goldberg, Executive Director
Description: Promotes business and community development in the Brattleboro, VT area. Sponsors festivals and social activities. **Founded:** 1904. **Publications:** The Chamber Window (Bimonthly). **Telecommunication Services:** jerry@brattleborochamber.org.

58742 ■ Business to Business Buyers Guide
PO Box 697
White River Junction, VT 05001
Ph: (802)295-6200
Fax: (802)295-3779
Co. E-mail: director@uppervalleychamber.com
URL: http://uppervalleychamber.com
Contact: Catherine Carter, President
Price: included in membership dues.

58743 ■ Calendar of Events
PO Box 173
Waitsfield, VT 05673
Ph: (802)496-3409
Free: 800-828-4748
Co. E-mail: info@madrivervalley.com
URL: http://www.madrivervalley.com
Contact: Susan Roy, Executive Director
Released: Annual

58744 ■ Central Vermont Chamber of Commerce
PO Box 336
Barre, VT 05641-0336
Ph: (802)229-5711
Fax: (802)229-5713
Co. E-mail: cvchamber@aol.com
URL: http://www.central-vt.com
Contact: George Malek, President
Description: Works to improve the climate for doing business, promotes community, and provides travel marketing in Central Vermont. **Founded:** 1971. **Publications:** Area Map; Community Profile; Regional Tourist Brochures. **Telecommunication Services:** cvermont1@aol.com.

58745 ■ Chamber E-News
PO Box 9
Randolph, VT 05060
Ph: (802)728-9027
Co. E-mail: chamber@randolphvt.com
URL: http://www.randolphvt.com
Contact: Mike Van Dyke, President
Released: Monthly

58746 ■ The Chamber News
93 Court St.
Middlebury, VT 05753
Ph: (802)388-7951
Free: 800-733-8376

Fax: (802)388-8066
Co. E-mail: info@addisoncounty.com
URL: http://www.addisoncounty.com
Contact: Andy Mayer, President
Released: Monthly

58747 ■ *Chamber News*
PO Box 267
Brandon, VT 05733
Ph: (802)247-6401
Co. E-mail: info@brandon.org
URL: http://brandon.org
Contact: Janet Mondlak, Executive Director
Released: Monthly

58748 ■ *Chamber Outlook*
2 N Main St., Ste. 101
St. Albans, VT 05478
Ph: (802)524-2444
Fax: (802)527-2256
Co. E-mail: info@fcrccvt.com
URL: http://www.stalbanschamber.com/default.asp-
  ?Key=1
Contact: Jim Walsh, Executive Director
Released: Bimonthly **Price:** included in membership
dues.

58749 ■ *The Chamber Window*
180 Main St.
Brattleboro, VT 05301
Ph: (802)254-4565
Free: 877-254-4565
Co. E-mail: info@brattleborochamber.org
URL: http://www.brattleborochamber.org
Contact: Jerry Goldberg, Executive Director
Released: Bimonthly

58750 ■ *Community Profile*
PO Box 336
Barre, VT 05641-0336
Ph: (802)229-5711
Fax: (802)229-5713
Co. E-mail: cvchamber@aol.com
URL: http://www.central-vt.com
Contact: George Malek, President

58751 ■ *Courier*
50 Merchants Row
Rutland, VT 05701
Ph: (802)773-2747
Free: 800-756-8880
Fax: (802)773-2772
Co. E-mail: info@rutlandvermont.com
URL: http://www.rutlandvermont.com
Contact: Thomas L. Donahue, Chief Executive Of-
  ficer
Released: Monthly

58752 ■ *Experience Burlington*
60 Main St., Ste. 100
Burlington, VT 05401-8418
Ph: (802)863-3489
Free: 877-686-5253
Fax: (802)863-1538
Co. E-mail: vermont@vermont.org
URL: http://www.vermont.org
Contact: Tom Torti, President
Released: Annual

**58753 ■ Franklin County Regional Chamber
of Commerce**
2 N Main St., Ste. 101
St. Albans, VT 05478
Ph: (802)524-2444
Fax: (802)527-2256
Co. E-mail: info@fcrccvt.com
URL: http://www.stalbanschamber.com/default.asp-
  ?Key=1
Contact: Jim Walsh, Executive Director
Description: Promotes business and community
development in the St. Albans, VT area. **Founded:**
1947. **Publications:** *Chamber Outlook* (Bimonthly);
St. Albans Brochure (Biennial); *Just To Let You
Know...* (Bimonthly).

**58754 ■ Great Falls Regional Chamber of
Commerce (GFRC)**
5 Westminster St.
Bellows Falls, VT 05101

Ph: (802)463-4280
Co. E-mail: info@gfrcc.org
URL: http://www.gfrcc.org/index.html
Contact: Roger Riccio, Executive Director
Description: Promotes business and community
development in Windham County, VT and Cheshire
County, NH. Sponsors Rockingham Old Home Days
Festival and various other events to promote the
areas. **Founded:** 1957. **Awards:** Citizen of the Year
(Annual).

**58755 ■ Hardwick Area Chamber of
Commerce (HACC)**
PO Box 111
Hardwick, VT 05843
Ph: (802)472-5906
Fax: (802)472-6865
Co. E-mail: chamber@heartofvt.com
URL: http://www.hardwickvtarea.com
Contact: Ron Sanville, President
Description: Promotes business and community
development in the Hardwick, VT area. **Telecom-
munication Services:** sanville2@vtlink.net.

**58756 ■ Hartford Area Chamber of
Commerce (HACC)**
35 Railroad Row
White River Junction, VT 05001
Ph: (802)295-7900
Fax: (802)296-8280
Co. E-mail: info@hartfordvtchamber.com
URL: http://www.hartfordvtchamber.com
Contact: Bill Blaiklock, President
Description: Promotes business and community
development in Quechee, VT. Sponsors annual Bal-
loon Festival and crafts fair.

58757 ■ Island Pond Chamber of Commerce
PO Box 255
Island Pond, VT 05846
Ph: (802)673-1854
Co. E-mail: info@islandpondchamber.org
URL: http://www.islandpondchamber.org
Contact: Justin Hannington, Secretary
Description: Aims to improve the business climate in
the Island Pond Area. Participates on the Board of
the Brighton Community Forum. Plans activities to
draw business and tourists into the area.

58758 ■ *Just To Let You Know...*
2 N Main St., Ste. 101
St. Albans, VT 05478
Ph: (802)524-2444
Fax: (802)527-2256
Co. E-mail: info@fcrccvt.com
URL: http://www.stalbanschamber.com/default.asp-
  ?Key=1
Contact: Jim Walsh, Executive Director
Released: Bimonthly

58759 ■ Killington Chamber of Commerce
PO Box 114
Killington, VT 05751
Ph: (802)773-4181
Free: 800-337-1928
Fax: (802)775-7070
URL: http://www.killingtonchamber.com
Description: Serves members and the community
with networking opportunities and business seminars.
Founded: 1974.

**58760 ■ Lake Champlain Islands Chamber of
Commerce**
PO Box 213
North Hero, VT 05474
Ph: (802)372-8400
Free: 800-262-5226
Fax: (802)372-5107
Co. E-mail: info@champlainislands.com
URL: http://www.champlainislands.com
Contact: Kim Kinney, President
Description: Promotes business and community
development in Grand Isle County. **Publications:**
The Vessel (Quarterly). **Educational Activities:** Busi-
ness Fair (Annual). **Awards:** Business Person of the
Year (Annual); Teddy Award (Annual).

**58761 ■ Lake Champlain Regional Chamber
of Commerce (LCRCC)**
60 Main St., Ste. 100
Burlington, VT 05401-8418
Ph: (802)863-3489
Free: 877-686-5253
Fax: (802)863-1538
Co. E-mail: vermont@vermont.org
URL: http://www.vermont.org
Contact: Tom Torti, President
Description: Promotes business and community
development in Chittenden County, VT. Advocates for
issues favorable to business and the community.
Founded: 1910. **Publications:** *Experience Burling-
ton* (Annual); *60 Main Street News* (Monthly).

58762 ■ *Legislative Updates*
PO Box 37
Montpelier, VT 05601
Ph: (802)223-3443
Fax: (802)223-4257
Co. E-mail: info@vtchamber.com
URL: http://www.vtchamber.com
Contact: Mark Saba, President
Released: Weekly; during legislative sessions.

58763 ■ Lyndon Area Chamber of Commerce
PO Box 886
Lyndonville, VT 05851
Ph: (802)626-9696
Fax: (802)626-1167
Co. E-mail: info@lyndonvermont.com
URL: http://www.lyndonvermont.com
Contact: Mary Marceau, President
Description: Provides information on vacationing,
business and residential relocation, activities, and
world famous bridges. Offers excellent education
system.

**58764 ■ Manchester and the Mountains
Regional Chamber of Commerce**
5046 Main St., Ste. 1
Manchester Center, VT 05255-9787
Ph: (802)824-5522
Free: 800-362-4144
Fax: (802)362-3451
Co. E-mail: bmaginniss@manchesterchamber.net
URL: http://www.manchestervermont.net
Contact: Berta Maginniss, Executive Director
Description: Works to provide resources, services,
education and promotion for members, communities
and visitors. Stimulates economic growth and suc-
cess while improving the quality of life. **Publications:**
Area Guide to Manchester and the Mountains (Semi-
annual). **Educational Activities:** Norman's Attic (An-
nual). **Telecommunication Services:** visitor@
manchesterchamber.net.

**58765 ■ *Mount Snow/Haystack Chamber -
Guide to Southern Vermont***
PO Box 3
Wilmington, VT 05363
Ph: (802)464-8092
Free: 877-887-6884
Fax: (802)464-0287
Co. E-mail: info@visitvermont.com
URL: http://www.visitvermont.com/
Contact: Laura Sibilia, Executive Director
Released: Annual **Price:** free.

**58766 ■ Mount Snow Valley Chamber of
Commerce**
PO Box 3
Wilmington, VT 05363
Ph: (802)464-8092
Free: 877-887-6884
Fax: (802)464-0287
Co. E-mail: info@visitvermont.com
URL: http://www.visitvermont.com/
Contact: Laura Sibilia, Executive Director
Description: Promotes business and community
development in the Deerfield Valley, VT area. **Publi-
cations:** *Mount Snow/Haystack Chamber - Guide to
Southern Vermont* (Annual); *Mount Snow/Haystack
Chamber - Guide to Southern Vermont* (Annual).
Telecommunication Services: laura@visitvermont.
com.

58767 ■ Northeast Kingdom Chamber of Commerce (NEKCC)
51 Depot Sq., Ste. 3
St. Johnsbury, VT 05819
Ph: (802)748-3678
Free: 800-639-6379
Fax: (802)748-0731
Co. E-mail: nekinfo@nekchamber.com
URL: http://www.nekchamber.com
Contact: Darcie McCann, Executive Director
Description: Promotes business, economic and community development in Vermont's St. Johnsbury and Northeast Kingdom area. Handles travel promotion, community/economic development, legislative/governmental relations, business training and promotion of regional projects. **Founded:** 1957.

58768 ■ Randolph Chamber of Commerce (RACOC)
PO Box 9
Randolph, VT 05060
Ph: (802)728-9027
Co. E-mail: chamber@randolphvt.com
URL: http://www.randolphvt.com
Contact: Mike Van Dyke, President
Description: Commercial and industrial organizations and interested individuals. Promotes business and community development, and tourism in Randolph Center, Braintree, and Brookfield, VT. Sponsors educational programs, 4th of July celebration, Christmas promotion, fall golf classic and operates information booth from June until October. **Publications:** *Chamber E-News* (Monthly); *Randolph Map Brochure* (Semiannual). **Educational Activities:** Business After Hours (Quarterly); Randolph Chamber of Commerce Dinner (Quarterly). **Awards:** Business Executive of the Year (Annual). **Telecommunication Services:** director@randolph-chamber.com.

58769 ■ *Randolph Map Brochure*
PO Box 9
Randolph, VT 05060
Ph: (802)728-9027
Co. E-mail: chamber@randolphvt.com
URL: http://www.randolphvt.com
Contact: Mike Van Dyke, President
Released: Semiannual

58770 ■ *Regional Tourist Brochures*
PO Box 336
Barre, VT 05641-0336
Ph: (802)229-5711
Fax: (802)229-5713
Co. E-mail: cvchamber@aol.com
URL: http://www.central-vt.com
Contact: George Malek, President

58771 ■ Rutland Region Chamber of Commerce (RRCC)
50 Merchants Row
Rutland, VT 05701
Ph: (802)773-2747
Free: 800-756-8880
Fax: (802)773-2772
Co. E-mail: info@rutlandvermont.com
URL: http://www.rutlandvermont.com
Contact: Thomas L. Donahue, Chief Executive Officer
Description: Promotes and serves businesses and the public through a commitment to the economic vitality, community spirit, and the quality of life in the Rutland, VT region. Speaks as an active voice for the interest of business. Committed to meeting the needs of members, advocacy, and the use of information to expand the market and business opportunities for members. **Founded:** 1912. **Publications:** *Courier* (Monthly); *MAP*; *Area Profile Book and Membership Directory* (Annual). **Educational Activities:** Business After Hours (Monthly). **Telecommunication Services:** rrccvt@aol.com.

58772 ■ *St. Albans Brochure*
2 N Main St., Ste. 101
St. Albans, VT 05478
Ph: (802)524-2444

Fax: (802)527-2256
Co. E-mail: info@fcrccvt.com
URL: http://www.stalbanschamber.com/default.asp-?Key=1
Contact: Jim Walsh, Executive Director
Released: Biennial

58773 ■ Smugglers' Notch Area Chamber of Commerce (SNACC)
PO Box 364
Jeffersonville, VT 05464-0364
Co. E-mail: info@smugnotch.com
URL: http://www.smugnotch.com
Contact: Ray Saloomey, President
Description: Promotes business and community development in the Smugglers Notch and Lamoille County area of Vermont. **Founded:** 1973. **Publications:** *Smugglers Notch Area Vacation Guide* (Annual).

58774 ■ *Smugglers Notch Area Vacation Guide*
PO Box 364
Jeffersonville, VT 05464-0364
Co. E-mail: info@smugnotch.com
URL: http://www.smugnotch.com
Contact: Ray Saloomey, President
Released: Annual **Price:** free.

58775 ■ *Springfield Community Guide*
56 Main St., Ste. 2
Springfield, VT 05156
Ph: (802)885-2779
Fax: (802)885-6826
Co. E-mail: chamber@springfieldvt.com
URL: http://www.springfieldvt.com
Contact: Carol Cole, Executive Vice President

58776 ■ Springfield Regional Chamber of Commerce
56 Main St., Ste. 2
Springfield, VT 05156
Ph: (802)885-2779
Fax: (802)885-6826
Co. E-mail: chamber@springfieldvt.com
URL: http://www.springfieldvt.com
Contact: Carol Cole, Executive Vice President
Description: Businesses, organizations, and interested individuals. Promotes business and community development in Springfield, VT. Sponsors Business After Hours Program, Citizens' Forum, radio program, Springfield Home Show, annual Vermont Apple Festival, workshops, and social activities. **Founded:** 1916. **Publications:** *Springfield Community Guide*. **Awards:** Springfield Citizen of the Year (Annual).

58777 ■ Stowe Area Association
PO Box 1320
Stowe, VT 05672
Ph: (802)253-7321
Free: 877-467-8693
Fax: (802)253-6628
Co. E-mail: askus@gostowe.com
URL: http://www.gostowe.com
Contact: Ed Stahl, Executive Director
Description: Promotes business and community development in Stowe, VT area. **Founded:** 1947.

58778 ■ Sugarbush Chamber of Commerce
PO Box 173
Waitsfield, VT 05673
Ph: (802)496-3409
Free: 800-828-4748
Co. E-mail: info@madrivervalley.com
URL: http://www.madrivervalley.com
Contact: Susan Roy, Executive Director
Description: Inns, lodges, ski resorts, retailers, restaurants, and sports centers. Promotes business and community development in central Vermont. **Founded:** 1977. **Publications:** *Calendar of Events* (Annual).

58779 ■ Swanton Chamber of Commerce
PO Box 237
Swanton, VT 05488

Ph: (802)868-7200
Co. E-mail: chamberoffice@swantonchamber.com
URL: http://www.swantonchamber.com
Contact: Adam P. Paxman, President
Description: Promotes business and community development in Swanton, VT.

58780 ■ Upper Valley Bi-State Regional Chamber of Commerce (UVB-SRCC)
PO Box 697
White River Junction, VT 05001
Ph: (802)295-6200
Fax: (802)295-3779
Co. E-mail: director@uppervalleychamber.com
URL: http://uppervalleychamber.com
Contact: Catherine Carter, President
Description: Promotes business and community development in White River Junction, VT. **Publications:** *Business to Business Buyers Guide*.

58781 ■ *Vermont Business*
PO Box 37
Montpelier, VT 05601
Ph: (802)223-3443
Fax: (802)223-4257
Co. E-mail: info@vtchamber.com
URL: http://www.vtchamber.com
Contact: Mark Saba, President
Released: Annual

58782 ■ Vermont Chamber of Commerce
PO Box 37
Montpelier, VT 05601
Ph: (802)223-3443
Fax: (802)223-4257
Co. E-mail: info@vtchamber.com
URL: http://www.vtchamber.com
Contact: Mark Saba, President
Description: Promotes business and community development in the state of Vermont. Conducts educational programs. Lobbies state government. Promotes travel and tourism in the state. **Founded:** 1950. **Publications:** *Legislative Updates* (Weekly); *Vermont Business* (Annual); *Vermont Connections* (Quarterly). **Awards:** Citizen of the Year (Annual); Diane C. Davis Business of the Year (Annual).

58783 ■ *Vermont Connections*
PO Box 37
Montpelier, VT 05601
Ph: (802)223-3443
Fax: (802)223-4257
Co. E-mail: info@vtchamber.com
URL: http://www.vtchamber.com
Contact: Mark Saba, President
Released: Quarterly

58784 ■ *The Vessel*
PO Box 213
North Hero, VT 05474
Ph: (802)372-8400
Free: 800-262-5226
Fax: (802)372-5107
Co. E-mail: info@champlainislands.com
URL: http://www.champlainislands.com
Contact: Kim Kinney, President
Released: Quarterly

58785 ■ *Who's Who in Addison County*
93 Court St.
Middlebury, VT 05753
Ph: (802)388-7951
Free: 800-733-8376
Fax: (802)388-8066
Co. E-mail: info@addisoncounty.com
URL: http://www.addisoncounty.com
Contact: Andy Mayer, President
Released: Annual

58786 ■ *Window on Woodstock*
PO Box 486
Woodstock, VT 05091
Ph: (802)457-3555
Free: 888-496-6378
Fax: (802)457-1601
Co. E-mail: info@woodstockvt.com
URL: http://www.woodstockvt.com
Contact: David Kanal, President

58787 ■ Woodstock Area Chamber of Commerce
PO Box 486
Woodstock, VT 05091
Ph: (802)457-3555
Free: 888-496-6378
Fax: (802)457-1601
Co. E-mail: info@woodstockvt.com
URL: http://www.woodstockvt.com
Contact: David Kanal, President
Description: Promotes business and community development in the Woodstock, VT area. Sponsors Wassail Festival. **Publications:** *Window on Woodstock.* **Educational Activities:** Woodstock Wassail Celebration.

MINORITY BUSINESS ASSISTANCE PROGRAMS

58788 ■ Vermont Women's Business Center - Central Vermont Community Action Council
8 S Main St.
Barre, VT 05641
Ph: (802)479-9813
Co. E-mail: vwbc@cvcac.org
URL: http://www.cvcac.org
Description: Provides assistance, support, and training for women to start or grow a business in Vermont.

FINANCING AND LOAN PROGRAMS

58789 ■ Aggregate Capital Partners, LLC
2463 Stowe Hollow Rd.
Stowe, VT 05672

Ph: (802)253-6843
Co. E-mail: info@aggregatecapital.com
URL: http://www.aggregatecapital.com
Contact: David Bradbury, Managing Partner
Preferred Investment Size: $25,000 to $500,000.
Investment Policies: Start-up, seed, early and first stage, and expansion. **Industry Preferences:** Internet specific. **Geographic Preference:** Mid Atlantic, Northeast, and Southeast U.S., Ontario, and Quebec Canada.

INCUBATORS/RESEARCH AND TECHNOLOGY PARKS

58790 ■ Bennington County Industrial Corp.
215 South St., 2nd Fl.
Bennington, VT 05201
Ph: (802)442-8975
Fax: (802)447-1101
Co. E-mail: peter@bcic.org
URL: http://www.bcic.org
Description: Provides a variety of free business assistance services.

58791 ■ Precision Valley Development Corp.
100 River St.
Springfield, VT 05156
Ph: (802)885-2138
Fax: (802)885-3745
Co. E-mail: twparker@vermontel.net
URL: http://www.springfieldvt.com/pvdc/home.htm
Description: Provides business office and manufacturing facilities.

58792 ■ Vermont Small Business Development Center
Vermont Technical College
1 Main St.
Randolph Center, VT 05061-0188
Ph: (802)728-9101
Fax: (802)728-3026
Co. E-mail: lquillen@vtsbdc.org
URL: http://www.vtsbdc.org/
Contact: Lenae Quillen-Blume, Director
Description: A non-profit partnership of government, education, and business seeking to spur Vermont's economy by helping its small businesses succeed and grow.

EDUCATIONAL PROGRAMS

58793 ■ Lyndon State College - Continuing Education Department
PO Box 919
Lyndonville, VT 05851
Ph: (802)626-6200
Free: 800-225-1998
Co. E-mail: admissions@lyndonstate.edu
URL: http://www.lsc.vsc.edu
Description: Offers courses for professional, personal, and academic enrichment. Conducts business and management courses on a credit or noncredit basis. Presents institutes, seminars, and workshops. Offers degree programs in small business management, management training, and personnel management.

SMALL BUSINESS DEVELOPMENT CENTERS

58794 ■ Alexandria Small Business Development Center
625 N Washington St., Ste. 400
Alexandria, VA 22314
Ph: (703)778-1292
Fax: (703)778-1293
Co. E-mail: info@alexandriasbdc.org
URL: http://www.alexandriasbdc.org
Contact: Bill Reagan, Executive Director
Description: Represents and promotes the small business sector. Provides management assistance to current and prospective small business owners. Helps to improve management skills and expand the products and services of members.

58795 ■ Blue Ridge Community College Small Business Development Center (BRCC SBDC)
Augusta Center, Rm. 140
15 Sports Medicine Dr.
Fishersville, VA 22939
Ph: (540)453-2246
Free: 888-750-2722
Co. E-mail: wrightd@brcc.edu
URL: http://www.valleysbdc.org
Contact: Joyce Krech, Director
URL(s): www.virginiasbdc.org/center. aspx?center=46061&subloc=0. **Description:** Represents and promotes the small business sector. Provides management assistance to current and prospective small business owners. Helps to improve management skills and expand the products and services of members.

58796 ■ Central Virginia Small Business Development Center
c/o Nora Gillespie, Dir.
2211 Hydraulic Rd., Ste. 107
Charlottesville, VA 22901
Ph: (434)295-8198
Fax: (434)979-4123
Co. E-mail: sbdc@cstone.net
URL: http://www.avenue.org/sbdc
Contact: Nora Gillespie, Director
Description: Represents and promotes the small business sector. Provides management assistance to current and prospective small business owners. Helps to improve management skills and expand the products and services of members.

58797 ■ Fairfax Small Business Development Center
Mason Enterprise Ctr.
4031 University Dr., Ste. 200
Fairfax, VA 22030
Ph: (703)277-7747
URL: http://www.virginiasbdc.org
Description: Represents and promotes the small business sector. Provides management assistance to current and prospective small business owners. Helps to improve management skills and expand the products and services of members.

58798 ■ Greater Richmond Small Business Development Center (GRSBDC)
600 E Main St., Ste. 700
Richmond, VA 23219
Ph: (804)783-9314
Fax: (804)783-9366
Co. E-mail: mike.leonard@grcc.com
URL: http://www.grsbdc.com
Contact: Mike Leonard, Executive Director
Description: Represents and promotes the small business sector. Provides management assistance to current and prospective small business owners. Helps to improve management skills and expand the products and services of members.

58799 ■ James Madison University Small Business Development Center (JMU SBDC)
1598 S Main St., MSC 5502
Harrisonburg, VA 22807
Ph: (540)568-3227
Fax: (540)801-8469
Co. E-mail: krechjh@jmu.edu
URL: http://www.valleysbdc.org
Contact: Joyce Krech, Director
Description: Represents and promotes the small business sector. Provides management assistance to current and prospective small business owners. Helps to improve management skills and expand the products and services of members.

58800 ■ Longwood University Small Business Development Center - Crater
PO Box 1808
Petersburg, VA 23805
Ph: (804)518-2003
Fax: (804)518-2004
Co. E-mail: hoodpa@longwood.edu
URL: http://www.longwood.edu/sbdc
Contact: Pat Hood, Director
Description: Represents and promotes the small business sector. Provides management assistance to current and prospective small business owners. Helps to improve management skills and expand the products and services of members.

58801 ■ Longwood University Small Business Development Center - Danville
300 Ringgold Industrial Pkwy.
Danville, VA 24540
Ph: (434)791-7321
Fax: (434)791-7341
Co. E-mail: arnoldjd@longwood.edu
URL: http://www.sbdc-longwood.com
Contact: Diane Arnold, Director
Description: Represents and promotes the small business sector. Provides management assistance to current and prospective small business owners. Helps to improve management skills and expand the products and services of members.

58802 ■ Longwood University Small Business Development Center - Farmville
515 Main St.
Farmville, VA 23909
Ph: (434)395-2086

Fax: (434)395-2359
Co. E-mail: mcguiresr@longwood.edu
URL: http://www.sbdc-longwood.com/farmville.html
Contact: Sheri McGuire, Director
Description: Represents and promotes the small business sector. Provides management assistance to current and prospective small business owners. Helps to improve management skills and expand the products and services of members.

58803 ■ Longwood University Small Business Development Center - Martinsville
PO Box 709
Martinsville, VA 24114
Ph: (276)632-4462
Fax: (276)632-5059
Co. E-mail: ephgraverg@longwood.edu
URL: http://www.sbdc-longwood.com/martinsville. html
Contact: Dick Ephgrave, Director
Description: Represents and promotes the small business sector. Provides management assistance to current and prospective small business owners. Helps to improve management skills and expand the products and services of members.

58804 ■ Longwood University Small Business Development Center - South Boston
515 Broad St.
South Boston, VA 24592
Ph: (434)572-4533
Fax: (434)572-1733
Co. E-mail: harrislb@longwood.edu
URL: http://www.longwood.edu/sbdc
Contact: Larry Harris, Director
Description: Represents and promotes the small business sector. Provides management assistance to current and prospective small business owners. Helps to improve management skills and expand the products and services of members.

58805 ■ Lord Fairfax Small Business Development Center - Culpeper
233 E Davis St., Ste. 300
Culpeper, VA 22701
Ph: (540)727-0638
Co. E-mail: dreardon@lfsbdc.org
URL: http://www.lfsbdc.org
Description: Represents and promotes the small business sector. Provides management assistance to current and prospective small business owners. Helps to improve management skills and expand the products and services of members.

58806 ■ Lord Fairfax Small Business Development Center - Fauquier
6480 College St.
Warrenton, VA 20187
Ph: (540)351-1595
Fax: (540)351-1597
Co. E-mail: dmaza@lfsbdc.org
URL: http://www.lfsbdc.org
Contact: Dale Maza, Counselor
Description: Represents and promotes the small business sector. Provides management assistance to

current and prospective small business owners. Helps to improve management skills and expand the products and services of members.

58807 ■ Lord Fairfax Small Business Development Center - Middletown
173 Skirmisher Ln.
Middletown, VA 22645
Ph: (540)868-7093
Fax: (540)868-7095
Co. E-mail: bsirbaugh@lfsbdc.org
URL: http://www.lfsbdc.org
Contact: Bill Sirbaugh, Jr., Director
Description: Represents and promotes the small business sector. Provides management assistance to current and prospective small business owners. Helps to improve management skills and expand the products and services of members.

58808 ■ Loudoun County Small Business Development Center
21145 Whitfield Pl., Ste. 104
Sterling, VA 20165
Ph: (703)430-7222
Fax: (703)430-7258
Co. E-mail: sbdc@loudounsbdc.org
URL: http://www.loudounsbdc.org
Contact: Robin Suomi, Executive Director
Description: Represents and promotes the small business sector. Provides management assistance to current and prospective small business owners. Helps to improve management skills and expand the products and services of members.

58809 ■ Lynchburg Small Business Development Center
Business Development Centre
147 Mill Ridge Rd.
Lynchburg, VA 24502
Ph: (434)582-6170
Co. E-mail: sbdcdir@lbdc.com
URL: http://www.virginiasbdc.org/center.
  aspx?center=46080&subloc=0
Description: Represents and promotes the small business sector. Provides management assistance to current and prospective small business owners. Helps to improve management skills and expand the products and services of members.

58810 ■ Mason Small Business Development Center
4031 University Dr., Ste. 200
Fairfax, VA 22030
Ph: (703)277-7747
Fax: (703)277-7722
Co. E-mail: help@masonsbdc.org
URL: http://www.masonsbdc.org
Contact: John Casey, Director
Description: Represents and promotes the small business sector. Provides management assistance to current and prospective small business owners. Helps to improve management skills and expand the products and services of members.

58811 ■ Mountain Empire Small Business Development Center
Mountain Empire Community College
3441 Mountain Empire Rd.
Big Stone Gap, VA 24219
Ph: (276)523-2400
Fax: (276)523-8297
Co. E-mail: tblankenbecler@me.vccs.edu
URL: http://www.me.cc.va.us/sbdc
Contact: Tim Blankenbecler, Director
Description: Represents and promotes the small business sector. Provides management assistance to current and prospective small business owners. Helps to improve management skills and expand the products and services of members.

58812 ■ New River Valley Small Business Development Center
Radford University
704 Fairfax St., Ste. H
Radford, VA 24142
Ph: (540)831-6056

Fax: (540)831-6735
Co. E-mail: dshanks@radford.edu
URL: http://bac.asp.radford.edu/SBDC
Contact: David Shanks, Director
Description: Represents and promotes the small business sector. Provides management assistance to current and prospective small business owners. Helps to improve management skills and expand the products and services of members.

58813 ■ Rappahannock Region Small Business Development Center - Fredericksburg
University of Mary Washington
College of Graduate and Profession
121 University Blvd.
Fredericksburg, VA 22406
Ph: (540)286-8060
Fax: (540)286-8042
Co. E-mail: sbdc@umw.edu
URL: http://www.umw.edu/rrsbdc
Contact: Brian Baker, Executive Director
Description: Represents and promotes the small business sector. Provides management assistance to current and prospective small business owners. Helps to improve management skills and expand the products and services of members.

58814 ■ Rappahannock Region Small Business Development Center - Warsaw
PO Box 490
Warsaw, VA 22572
Ph: (804)333-0286
Free: 800-524-8915
Fax: (804)333-0187
Co. E-mail: jcorprew@umw.edu
URL: http://www.umw.edu/rrsbdc
Contact: Joy Corprew, Director
Description: Represents and promotes the small business sector. Provides management assistance to current and prospective small business owners. Helps to improve management skills and expand the products and services of members.

58815 ■ Roanoke Regional Small Business Development Center
Roanoke Regional Chamber of Commerce
210 S Jefferson St.
Roanoke, VA 24011-1702
Ph: (540)983-0717
Fax: (540)983-0723
Co. E-mail: sbdc@roanokechamber.org
URL: http://www.rrsbdc.org/small_business_services
Contact: Wayne E. Flippen, Director
URL(s): www.roanokechamber.org. **Description:** Represents and promotes the small business sector. Provides management assistance to current and prospective small business owners. Helps to improve management skills and expand the products and services of members.

58816 ■ Small Business Development Center of Hampton Roads
600 Butler Farm Rd.
Hampton, VA 23666
Ph: (757)865-3128
Fax: (757)865-5885
Co. E-mail: farleyd@tncc.edu
URL: http://www.hrsbdc.org
Contact: Debra Farley, Associate Director Counselor
Description: Represents and promotes the small business sector. Provides management assistance to current and prospective small business owners. Helps to improve management skills and expand the products and services of members.

58817 ■ Small Business Development Center of Hampton Roads - Eastern Shore
c/o Eastern Shore Chamber of Commerce
10956 Pkwy.
Melfa, VA 23410
Ph: (757)789-3418
Co. E-mail: gbryan7600@gmail.com
URL: http://www.hrsbdc.org/about-hrsbdc/contact/
  eastern-shore
Contact: George Bryan, Counselor
Description: Represents and promotes the small business sector. Provides management assistance to

current and prospective small business owners. Helps to improve management skills and expand the products and services of members.

58818 ■ Small Business Development Center of Hampton Roads - Franklin
108 3rd St.
Franklin, VA 23851
Ph: (757)562-4900
Co. E-mail: join@fsachamber.com
URL: http://www.hrsbdc.org/about-hrsbdc/contact/
  franklin
Description: Represents and promotes the small business sector. Provides management assistance to current and prospective small business owners. Helps to improve management skills and expand the products and services of members.

58819 ■ Small Business Development Center of Hampton Roads - Smithfield
100 Main St.
Smithfield, VA 23431
Ph: (757)357-3502
Co. E-mail: lwhite@theisle.org
URL: http://www.hrsbdc.org/about-hrsbdc/contact/
  smithfield
Description: Represents and promotes the small business sector. Provides management assistance to current and prospective small business owners. Helps to improve management skills and expand the products and services of members.

58820 ■ Small Business Development Center of Hampton Roads - Suffolk
127 E Washington St.
Suffolk, VA 23434
Ph: (757)664-2613
Co. E-mail: jleach5@verizon.net
URL: http://www.hrsbdc.org/about-hrsbdc/contact/
  suffolk
Contact: Jack Leach, Counselor
Description: Represents and promotes the small business sector. Provides management assistance to current and prospective small business owners. Helps to improve management skills and expand the products and services of members.

58821 ■ Small Business Development Center of Hampton Roads - Thomas Nelson
Thomas Nelson Community College
600 Butler Farm Rd., Ste. A1105
Hampton, VA 23666
Ph: (757)865-3128
Fax: (757)865-5885
Co. E-mail: farleyd@tncc.edu
URL: http://www.hrsbdc.org
Contact: Debra Farley, Associate Director Counselor
Description: Represents and promotes the small business sector. Provides management assistance to current and prospective small business owners. Helps to improve management skills and expand the products and services of members.

58822 ■ Small Business Development Center of Hampton Roads - Williamsburg
PO Box 3495
Williamsburg, VA 23187
Ph: (757)229-6511
Fax: (757)229-2047
Co. E-mail: sethrift@verizon.net
URL: http://www.hrsbdc.org/about-hrsbdc/contact/
  williamsburg
Contact: Sherri Thrift, Counselor
Description: Represents and promotes the small business sector. Provides management assistance to current and prospective small business owners. Helps to improve management skills and expand the products and services of members.

58823 ■ South Fairfax Small Business Development Center
7001 Loisdale Rd., Ste. C
Springfield, VA 22150
Ph: (703)768-1440

Fax: (703)768-0547
Co. E-mail: mark@cbponline.org
URL: http://www.cbponline.org/content/view/16/85
Contact: Mark Brown, Director
Description: Represents and promotes the small business sector. Provides management assistance to current and prospective small business owners. Helps to improve management skills and expand the products and services of members.

58824 ■ Southwest Virginia Small Business Development Center
Southwest Virginia Community College
Tazewell Hall
635 Community College Rd.
Richlands, VA 24641
Ph: (276)964-7345
Co. E-mail: joyce.kinder@sw.edu
URL: http://www.sw.edu/sbdc
Contact: Joyce Kinder, Director
URL(s): www.virginiasbdc.org. **Description:** Represents and promotes the small business sector. Provides management assistance to current and prospective small business owners. Helps to improve management skills and expand the products and services of members.

58825 ■ Virginia Highlands Small Business Development Center
PO Box 828
Abingdon, VA 24212
Ph: (276)739-2474
Fax: (276)739-2577
Co. E-mail: swagner@vhcc.edu
URL: http://vhcc2.vhcc.edu/sbdc
Description: Represents and promotes the small business sector. Provides management assistance to current and prospective small business owners. Helps to improve management skills and expand the products and services of members.

SMALL BUSINESS ASSISTANCE PROGRAMS

58826 ■ Virginia Department of Agriculture and Consumer Services - Office of International Marketing
102 Governor St.
Richmond, VA 23219
Ph: (804)786-2373
Fax: (804)371-6097
Co. E-mail: keith.long@vdacs.virginia.gov
URL: http://www.vdacs.virginia.gov/international/index.html
Contact: Keith Long, Director
Description: Works to maximize the export of Virginia's agricultural products; provides market, exporter, and sales development assistance.

58827 ■ Virginia Department of Business Assistance - Small Business Development Division
PO Box 446
Richmond, VA 23218-0446
Ph: (804)371-8200
Fax: (804)371-8111
Co. E-mail: vbic@vdba.virginia.gov
URL: http://www.dba.virginia.gov
Contact: Lynda Sharp Anderson, Director
Description: Small business persons appointed by the governor to advise the Department of Economic Development on small business programs and concerns.

58828 ■ Virginia Department of Business Assistance - Small Business and Financing Authority
PO Box 446
Richmond, VA 23218-0446
Ph: (804)371-8200
Fax: (804)371-8111
Co. E-mail: vbic@vdba.virginia.gov
URL: http://www.dba.virginia.gov
Contact: Lynda Sharp Anderson, Director
Description: Assists small businesses by providing information on sources of technical, management, and financial assistance programs. Serves as an ombudsman, helping small businesses to resolve state regulatory problems.

58829 ■ Virginia Economic Development Partnership - International Trade and Export
901 E Byrd St.
Richmond, VA 23218-0798
Ph: (804)545-5752
Fax: (804)545-5751
Co. E-mail: info@yesvirginia.org
URL: http://www.yesvirginia.org
Contact: Paul Grossman, Director
Description: Consulting program designed to assist Virginia firms in identifying and developing foreign markets for their goods and services.

SCORE OFFICES

58830 ■ SCORE Central Virginia
E Market and Firth St., Ste. 200
Charlottesville, VA 22902
Ph: (434)295-6712
Fax: (434)295-3144
Co. E-mail: chairperson@score-494.org
URL: http://www.score-494.org
Contact: Steve Cooper, Chairman
Description: Strives for the formation, growth and success of small businesses. Provides consulting services to existing and emerging small businesses in Central Virginia. Counselors include men and women who have many years of business experience in various fields. Develops business plans and evaluates financial projections.

58831 ■ SCORE - Greater Lynchburg
Federal Bldg.
1101 Court St., Ste. A42
Lynchburg, VA 24504
Ph: (434)846-3235
Fax: (434)846-1798
Co. E-mail: info@lynchburgscore.org
URL: http://www.lynchburgscore.org
URL(s): greaterlynchburg.score.org. **Description:** Represents owners and managers of mobile offshore units. Aims to promote and protect the interests of British rig owners and managers in respect of all aspects of design, construction, equipment, and operation of mobile offshore units. **Founded:** 1984.

58832 ■ SCORE Hampton Roads
838 Granby St.
Norfolk, VA 23510
Ph: (757)455-9338
Co. E-mail: admin@scorehr.org
URL: http://www.scorehr.org
Description: Provides professional guidance, mentoring services and financial assistance to maximize the success of existing and emerging small businesses. Promotes entrepreneur education in Norfolk, VA. **Founded:** 1965.

58833 ■ SCORE Martinsville
115 Broad St.
Martinsville, VA 24112
Ph: (276)632-6401
Co. E-mail: score@mhcchamber.com
URL: http://www.martinsvillescore.com
Description: Provides free and confidential counseling to individuals and groups wishing to start or improve a small business. Membership consists of both retired and active businessmen and women with a wide variety of experiences and backgrounds. Hold monthly meetings for counselor training and development and offer counseling appointments on a weekly basis.

58834 ■ SCORE Peninsula
c/o Virginia Peninsula Chamber of Commerce
21 Enterprise Pkwy., Ste. 100
Hampton, VA 23666
Ph: (757)262-2000
Co. E-mail: info@peninsulascore.com
URL: http://www.peninsulascore.com
Description: Strives for the formation, growth and success of existing and emerging small businesses in Hampton Roads region. Provides professional guidance, mentoring services and financial assistance. Develops business plans and evaluates financial projections.

58835 ■ SCORE Richmond
Federal Bldg., Ste. 1150
SBA Offices
400 N 8th St.
Richmond, VA 23219-4829
Ph: (804)771-2400
Fax: (804)771-2764
Co. E-mail: information@richmondscore.org
URL: http://www.richmondscore.org
Contact: Fred Eyerman, Chairman
Description: Serves as volunteer program in which working and retired business management professionals provide free business counseling to men and women who are considering starting a small business, encountering problems with their business, or expanding their business. Offers free one-on-one counseling, online counseling and low cost workshops on a variety of business topics.

58836 ■ SCORE Roanoke
105 Franklin Rd. SW, Ste. 150
Roanoke, VA 24011
Ph: (540)857-2834
Fax: (540)857-2043
URL: http://roanoke.score.org
Description: Provides professional guidance, mentoring services and financial assistance to maximize the success of existing and emerging small businesses. Promotes entrepreneur education in Roanoke area, VA.

58837 ■ SCORE Shenandoah Valley
301 W Main St.
Waynesboro, VA 22980
Ph: (540)949-4423
Fax: (540)942-6755
Co. E-mail: score427@ci.waynesboro.va.us
URL: http://www.scorevavalley.org
Description: Provides professional guidance, mentoring services and financial assistance to maximize the success of existing and emerging small businesses. Promotes entrepreneur education in Waynesboro, VA. **Founded:** 1992.

58838 ■ SCORE Williamsburg
c/o Greater Williamsburg Chamber and Tourism Alliance
421 N Boundary St.
Williamsburg, VA 23185-3614
Ph: (757)229-6511
Co. E-mail: info@scorewilliamsburg.org
URL: http://www.scorewilliamsburg.org
Contact: Kenneth W. Carr, Chairman
Description: Provides free and confidential business advice to small businesses and, to people who want to start their own business.

BETTER BUSINESS BUREAUS

58839 ■ Better Business Bureau of Central Virginia
720 Moorefield Park Dr., Ste. 300
Richmond, VA 23236
Ph: (804)648-0016
Fax: (804)320-0248
Co. E-mail: info@richmond.bbb.org
URL: http://richmond.bbb.org
Contact: Thomas J. Gallagher, President
Description: Seeks to promote and foster the highest ethical relationship between businesses and the public through voluntary self-regulation, consumer and business education, and service excellence. Provides information to help consumers and businesses make informed purchasing decisions and avoid costly scams and frauds; settles consumer complaints through arbitration and other means.

58840 ■ Better Business Bureau of Greater Hampton Roads
586 Virginian Dr.
Norfolk, VA 23505
Ph: (757)531-1300

Fax: (757)531-1388
Co. E-mail: info@hamptonroadsbbb.org
URL: http://norfolk.bbb.org
Contact: Rosemary Nye, President
Description: Seeks to promote and foster ethical relationship between businesses and the public through voluntary self-regulation, consumer and business education, and service excellence. Provides information to help consumers and businesses make informed purchasing decisions and avoid costly scams and frauds; settles consumer complaints through arbitration and other means.

58841 ■ Better Business Bureau of Western Virginia
31 W Campbell Ave.
Roanoke, VA 24011-1301
Ph: (540)342-3455
Free: 800-533-5501
Fax: (540)345-2289
Co. E-mail: info@roanoke.bbb.org
URL: http://vawest.bbb.org
Contact: Julie Wheeler, President
URL(s): roanoke.bbb.org. **Description:** Seeks to promote and foster the highest ethical relationship between businesses and the public through voluntary self-regulation, consumer and business education, and service excellence. Provides information to help consumers and businesses make informed purchasing decisions and avoid costly scams and frauds; settles consumer complaints through arbitration and other means.

CHAMBERS OF COMMERCE

58842 ■ Advocate
9 S 5th St.
Richmond, VA 23219
Ph: (804)644-1607
Fax: (804)783-6112
Co. E-mail: b.duval@vachamber.com
URL: http://www.vachamber.com
Contact: Barry DuVal, President
Released: Monthly

58843 ■ Advocate
800 Country Club Rd.
Harrisonburg, VA 22802
Ph: (540)434-3862
Fax: (540)434-4508
Co. E-mail: information@hrchamber.org
URL: http://www.hrchamber.org
Contact: Roy Kelly, Administrative Assistant
Released: Quarterly

58844 ■ Alexandria Business Guide
801 N Fairfax St., Ste. 402
Alexandria, VA 22314
Ph: (703)549-1000
Fax: (703)739-3805
Co. E-mail: tleone@alexchamber.com
URL: http://www.alexchamber.com
Contact: Tina Leone, President
Released: Annual; every fall. **Price:** included in membership dues.

58845 ■ Alexandria Chamber of Commerce (ACC)
801 N Fairfax St., Ste. 402
Alexandria, VA 22314
Ph: (703)549-1000
Fax: (703)739-3805
Co. E-mail: tleone@alexchamber.com
URL: http://www.alexchamber.com
Contact: Tina Leone, President
Description: Promotes business and community development in Alexandria, VA. **Founded:** 1906. **Publications:** Alexandria Business Guide (Annual); Chamber Currents (Bimonthly); Who's Who in Alexandria Business (Annual); Who's Who in Alexandria Business.

58846 ■ Alleghany Highlands Chamber of Commerce (AHCC)
241 W Main St.
Covington, VA 24426
Ph: (540)962-2178
Free: 888-430-5786

Fax: (540)962-2179
Co. E-mail: info@ahchamber.com
URL: http://www.ahchamber.com
Contact: Teresa A. Hammond, Executive Director
Description: Promotes business and community development in the Alleghany Highlands, VA area. **Founded:** 1906.

58847 ■ Altavista Area Chamber of Commerce (ACC)
PO Box 606
Altavista, VA 24517
Ph: (434)369-6665
Fax: (434)369-4202
Co. E-mail: info@altavistachamber.com
URL: http://www.altavistachamber.org
Contact: Morgan Allen, Chairman
Description: Promotes business and community development in the Altavista, VA area. **Publications:** Vistas (Monthly). **Telecommunication Services:** info@altavistachamber.org.

58848 ■ Amherst County Chamber of Commerce (ACCC)
PO Box 560
Amherst, VA 24521
Ph: (434)946-0990
Fax: (434)946-0879
Co. E-mail: information@amherstvachamber.com
URL: http://www.amherstvachamber.com
Contact: Wanda Beverly, President
Description: Aims to advance the commercial, industrial, professional, domestic and global interests of Amherst County and its trade area. **Publications:** Amherst County Guidebook (Annual); Chamber Business (Bimonthly).

58849 ■ Amherst County Guidebook
PO Box 560
Amherst, VA 24521
Ph: (434)946-0990
Fax: (434)946-0879
Co. E-mail: information@amherstvachamber.com
URL: http://www.amherstvachamber.com
Contact: Wanda Beverly, President
Released: Annual

58850 ■ Annandale Chamber of Commerce (ACC)
7263 Maple Pl., Ste. 207
Annandale, VA 22003-3004
Ph: (703)256-7232
Fax: (703)256-7233
Co. E-mail: info@annandalechamber.com
URL: http://www.annandalechamber.com/root/index.aspx
Contact: Gavin Dock, President
Description: Promotes business and community development in Annandale, VA. Sponsors parade, Health fair and other community activities. **Founded:** 1946. **Publications:** Annandale Chamber of Commerce Newsletter (Monthly); Annandale Community Directory (Annual). **Awards:** Business of the Year (Annual); Chamber Member of the Year (Annual); Citizen of the Year (Annual).

58851 ■ Annandale Chamber of Commerce Newsletter
7263 Maple Pl., Ste. 207
Annandale, VA 22003-3004
Ph: (703)256-7232
Fax: (703)256-7233
Co. E-mail: info@annandalechamber.com
URL: http://www.annandalechamber.com/root/index.aspx
Contact: Gavin Dock, President
Released: Monthly

58852 ■ Annandale Community Directory
7263 Maple Pl., Ste. 207
Annandale, VA 22003-3004
Ph: (703)256-7232
Fax: (703)256-7233
Co. E-mail: info@annandalechamber.com
URL: http://www.annandalechamber.com/root/index.aspx
Contact: Gavin Dock, President
Released: Annual

58853 ■ Appomattox County Chamber of Commerce (ACCC)
PO Box 704
Appomattox, VA 24522
Ph: (434)352-2621
Fax: (434)352-0294
Co. E-mail: chamber@appomattoxchamber.org
URL: http://www.appomattoxchamber.org
Contact: Patricia D'Amario, Office Manager
Description: Promotes business and community development in the Appomattox County, VA area. Sponsors anniversary festival for the surrender at Appomattox. **Founded:** 1958. **Publications:** Business Directory (Annual).

58854 ■ Arlington Chamber of Commerce
2009 14th St. N, Ste. 111
Arlington, VA 22201
Ph: (703)525-2400
Fax: (703)522-5273
Co. E-mail: chamber@arlingtonchamber.org
URL: http://www.arlingtonchamber.org
Contact: Richard V. Doud, Jr., President
Description: Promotes business and community development in Arlington, VA. **Founded:** 1924. **Publications:** The Arlingtonian (Monthly); Membership Directory and Referral Guide (Periodic); Arlington Chamber of Commerce Membership Directory (Annual). **Awards:** Police, Fire, Sheriff Valor Awards (Annual); Small Business of the Year Awards (Annual).

58855 ■ The Arlingtonian
2009 14th St. N, Ste. 111
Arlington, VA 22201
Ph: (703)525-2400
Fax: (703)522-5273
Co. E-mail: chamber@arlingtonchamber.org
URL: http://www.arlingtonchamber.org
Contact: Richard V. Doud, Jr., President
Released: Monthly

58856 ■ Bath County Chamber of Commerce
PO Box 718
Hot Springs, VA 24445
Ph: (540)839-5409
Free: 800-628-8092
Fax: (540)839-5409
Co. E-mail: bathco@va.tds.net
URL: http://www.bathcountyva.org/clubs_organizations/Chamber%20of%20Commerce.htm
Contact: Patrick Sheridan, President
Description: Promotes business and community development in the Bath County, VA area. **Founded:** 1942.

58857 ■ Bedford Area Chamber of Commerce (BACC)
305 E Main St.
Bedford, VA 24523
Ph: (540)586-9401
Fax: (540)587-6650
URL: http://www.bedfordareachamber.com
Contact: Susan Martin, President
Description: Promotes business and community development in Bedford, VA.

58858 ■ BizConnect
PO Box 1298
Leesburg, VA 20177
Ph: (703)777-2176
Fax: (703)777-1392
Co. E-mail: thoward@loudounchamber.org
URL: http://www.loudounchamber.org
Contact: Tony Howard, President
Released: Monthly

58859 ■ Blackstone Chamber of Commerce (BCC)
PO Box 295
Blackstone, VA 23824-0295

Ph: (434)292-1677
Co. E-mail: chamber@blackstoneva.com
URL: http://blackstoneva.com
Contact: Brenda R. Carter, Executive Director
Description: Promotes business and community development in Blackstone, VA. Committed in supporting, promoting, and creating economic opportunities that benefit the community. **Founded:** 1960. **Publications:** *FYI* (Monthly).

58860 ■ Botetourt County Chamber of Commerce (BCCC)
PO Box 81
Fincastle, VA 24090-0081
Ph: (540)473-8280
Fax: (540)473-8365
Co. E-mail: bccoc@rbnet.com
URL: http://www.bot-co-chamber.com
Contact: Dan Naff, Secretary Treasurer
Description: Promotes business and community development in the Botetourt County, VA area. **Founded:** 1962. **Publications:** *Chamber Monitor* (Quarterly).

58861 ■ The Bridge
PO Box 1868
Kilmarnock, VA 22482
Ph: (804)435-6092
Fax: (804)435-3092
Co. E-mail: info@lancasterva.com
URL: http://www.lancasterva.com
Contact: Thomas Richardson, President
Released: Monthly

58862 ■ Broadway-Timberville Chamber of Commerce (BTCC)
233 McCauley Dr.
Timberville, VA 22853
Ph: (540)896-7413
Fax: (540)896-2825
Co. E-mail: secretary@btchamber.org
URL: http://www.btchamber.org
Contact: Crystal R. Collins, Executive Secretary
Description: Promotes business and community development in the Broadway-Timberville, VA area. Participates in annual Fall Festival and Arts and Crafts Show. Plans periodic special events. **Founded:** 1959.

58863 ■ Buckingham Chamber of Commerce
PO Box 951
Dillwyn, VA 23936
Ph: (434)983-2372
Co. E-mail: info@buckinghamchamber.org
URL: http://www.buckinghamchamber.org
Contact: Nan Holt, President
Description: Promotes business and community development in Buckingham County, VA area.

58864 ■ Business Agenda
407 S Loudoun St.
Winchester, VA 22601
Ph: (540)662-4118
Fax: (540)722-6365
Co. E-mail: rcollins@regionalchamber.biz
URL: http://www.regionalchamber.biz
Contact: Randy Collins, President
Released: Monthly

58865 ■ Business Connections
210 S Jefferson St.
Roanoke, VA 24011
Ph: (540)983-0700
Fax: (540)983-0723
Co. E-mail: business@roanokechamber.org
URL: http://www.roanokechamber.org
Contact: Joyce Waugh, President
E-mail: jwaugh@roanokechamber.org
Released: Quarterly **Price:** included in membership dues.

58866 ■ Business Directory
PO Box 704
Appomattox, VA 24522
Ph: (434)352-2621

Fax: (434)352-0294
Co. E-mail: chamber@appomattoxchamber.org
URL: http://www.appomattoxchamber.org
Contact: Patricia D'Amario, Office Manager
Released: Annual

58867 ■ Business Directory
2300 Fall Hill Ave., Ste. 240
Fredericksburg, VA 22404-7476
Ph: (540)373-9400
Fax: (540)373-9570
Co. E-mail: linda@fredericksburgchamber.org
URL: http://www.fredericksburgchamber.org
Contact: Susan Spears, President
Released: Biennial

58868 ■ Business and Information
9720 Capital Ct., Ste. 203
Manassas, VA 20110-2050
Ph: (703)368-6600
Fax: (703)368-4733
Co. E-mail: djones@pwcgmcc.org
URL: http://www.pwcgmcc.org
Contact: Robert H. Clapper, II, President
Released: Annual

58869 ■ The Catalyst
PO Box 226
Norton, VA 24273
Ph: (276)679-0961
Fax: (276)679-2655
Co. E-mail: coc@naxs.com
URL: http://www.wisecountychamber.org
Contact: Joyce M. Payne, Chief Executive Officer
Released: Monthly

58870 ■ Central Fairfax Chamber of Commerce (CFCC)
11166 Fairfax Blvd., Ste. 407
Fairfax, VA 22030
Ph: (703)591-2450
Fax: (703)591-2820
Co. E-mail: info@cfcc.org
URL: http://www.cfcc.org
Contact: Traci Claar, Director
E-mail: tclaar@gmu.edu
Description: Promotes business and community development in Central Fairfax, VA area. **Founded:** 1956. **Publications:** *Central Fairfax Chamber of Commerce--Membership Directory*; *Central Fairfax Directory* (Annual).

58871 ■ Chamber Bits
PO Box 1564
Charlottesville, VA 22902-1564
Ph: (434)295-3141
Fax: (434)295-3144
Co. E-mail: desk@cvillechamber.com
URL: http://www.cvillechamber.com
Contact: Timothy Hulbert, President
Released: Weekly

58872 ■ Chamber Business
PO Box 560
Amherst, VA 24521
Ph: (434)946-0990
Fax: (434)946-0879
Co. E-mail: information@amherstvachamber.com
URL: http://www.amherstvachamber.com
Contact: Wanda Beverly, President
Released: Bimonthly

58873 ■ Chamber Business Directory
PO Box 223
Monterey, VA 24465-0223
Ph: (540)468-2550
Fax: (540)468-2551
Co. E-mail: info@highlandcounty.org
URL: http://www.highlandcounty.org
Contact: Carolyn Pohowsky, Executive Director
Released: Annual

58874 ■ Chamber Chat
205-1 Keith St.
Warrenton, VA 20186
Ph: (540)347-4414

Fax: (540)347-7510
Co. E-mail: mailbox@fauquierchamber.org
URL: http://www.fauquierchamber.org
Contact: Priscilla Hottle, Chairperson
Released: Monthly

58875 ■ Chamber Chatter
PO Box 510
Floyd, VA 24091
Ph: (540)745-4407
Co. E-mail: chamber@swva.net
URL: http://www.visitfloyd.org
Contact: John McEnhill, President
Released: Quarterly **Price:** free for members.

58876 ■ Chamber Comments
PO Box 1564
Charlottesville, VA 22902-1564
Ph: (434)295-3141
Fax: (434)295-3144
Co. E-mail: desk@cvillechamber.com
URL: http://www.cvillechamber.com
Contact: Timothy Hulbert, President
Released: Bimonthly

58877 ■ The Chamber Comments
PO Box 928
Petersburg, VA 23804-0928
Ph: (804)733-8131
Fax: (804)733-9891
Co. E-mail: info@petersburgvachamber.com
URL: http://www.petersburgvachamber.com
Contact: Cynthia Raitt Devereaux, President
Released: Quarterly; February, May, July, November.

58878 ■ Chamber of Commerce of Smyth County
214 W Main St.
Marion, VA 24354
Ph: (276)783-3161
Fax: (276)783-8003
Co. E-mail: info@smythchamber.org
URL: http://www.smythchamber.org
Contact: Kristin Untiedt-Barnett, Executive Director
Description: Promotes business and community development in the Smyth County, VA area. **Founded:** 1981.

58879 ■ Chamber Connection
30 Ladd Rd.
Fishersville, VA 22939
Ph: (540)324-1133
Fax: (540)324-1136
Co. E-mail: chamber@ntelos.net
URL: http://www.augustachamber.org
Contact: Linda Hershey, President
Released: Bimonthly

58880 ■ Chamber Connections
PO Box 99
Blairs, VA 24527
Ph: (434)836-6990
Fax: (434)836-6955
Co. E-mail: chamber@dpchamber.org
URL: http://www.dpchamber.org
Contact: Laurie S. Moran, President
Released: Monthly

58881 ■ Chamber Currents
600 E Main St., Ste. 700
Richmond, VA 23219
Ph: (804)648-1234
Fax: (804)783-9366
Co. E-mail: contactus@grcc.com
URL: http://www.grcc.com
Contact: Douglas M. Roth, Chairman
Released: Monthly

58882 ■ Chamber Currents
801 N Fairfax St., Ste. 402
Alexandria, VA 22314
Ph: (703)549-1000
Fax: (703)739-3805
Co. E-mail: tleone@alexchamber.com
URL: http://www.alexchamber.com
Contact: Tina Leone, President
Released: Bimonthly

58883 ■ Chamber Monitor
PO Box 81
Fincastle, VA 24090-0081
Ph: (540)473-8280
Fax: (540)473-8365
Co. E-mail: bccoc@rbnet.com
URL: http://www.bot-co-chamber.com
Contact: Dan Naff, Secretary
Released: Quarterly

58884 ■ Chamber News
109 S Commerce St.
Culpeper, VA 22701
Ph: (540)825-8628
Free: 888-285-7373
Fax: (540)825-1449
Co. E-mail: info@culpeperchamber.com
URL: http://www.culpeperchamber.com
Contact: Raven Yates, Chairperson
Released: Bimonthly

58885 ■ Chamber Newsletter
PO Box 93
Palmyra, VA 22963-0093
Ph: (434)589-3262
Fax: (434)589-6212
Co. E-mail: fluvannacountycoc@embarqmail.com
URL: http://www.fluvannachamber.org
Contact: Mr. Jim Bogdan, President
Released: Monthly **Price:** free for members.

58886 ■ Chamber Notes
201 Temple Ave., Ste. E
Colonial Heights, VA 23834
Ph: (804)526-5872
Fax: (804)526-9637
Co. E-mail: chchamber@colonialheights.cc
URL: http://www.colonial-heights.com
Contact: Roger Green, Executive Director
Released: Monthly **Price:** free.

58887 ■ Chamber Voice
9097 Atlee Sta. Rd., Ste. 117
Mechanicsville, VA 23116
Ph: (804)798-8130
Fax: (804)798-0014
Co. E-mail: jennifer@touchpointspr.com
URL: http://www.habcc.com
Contact: Jennifer Y. Scott, Executive Director
Released: Monthly

58888 ■ ChamberAlert
2300 Fall Hill Ave., Ste. 240
Fredericksburg, VA 22404-7476
Ph: (540)373-9400
Fax: (540)373-9570
Co. E-mail: linda@fredericksburgchamber.org
URL: http://www.fredericksburgchamber.org
Contact: Susan Spears, President

58889 ■ ChamberLink
2300 Fall Hill Ave., Ste. 240
Fredericksburg, VA 22404-7476
Ph: (540)373-9400
Fax: (540)373-9570
Co. E-mail: linda@fredericksburgchamber.org
URL: http://www.fredericksburgchamber.org
Contact: Susan Spears, President
Released: Monthly

58890 ■ Charlottesville Regional Chamber of Commerce (CRCC)
PO Box 1564
Charlottesville, VA 22902-1564
Ph: (434)295-3141
Fax: (434)295-3144
Co. E-mail: desk@cvillechamber.com
URL: http://www.cvillechamber.com
Contact: Timothy Hulbert, President
Description: Promotes business and community development in Albemarle County, VA area. **Founded:** 1913. **Publications:** Chamber Bits (Weekly); Chamber Comments (Bimonthly).

58891 ■ Chesterfield County Chamber of Commerce
9330 Iron Bridge Rd., Ste. B
Chesterfield, VA 23832
Ph: (804)748-6364
Fax: (804)425-5669
Co. E-mail: lenita@chesterfieldchamber.com
URL: http://www.chesterfieldchamber.com
Contact: Lenita Gilreath, President
Description: Works to build an involved and informed Chesterfield business community. Educates and informs both county elected officials and county professional staff as to the consequences and alternatives regarding proposed regulations and processes. Educates the community at large as to the problems and challenges of the business community and the advantage to residents of a healthy and vibrant business community. Provides valuable resources to the members that help their businesses succeed. **Founded:** 1999.

58892 ■ Chincoteague Chamber of Commerce (CCC)
6733 Maddox Blvd.
Chincoteague Island, VA 23336
Ph: (757)336-6161
Fax: (757)336-1242
Co. E-mail: chincochamber@verizon.net
URL: http://www.chincoteaguechamber.com
Contact: Suzanne Taylor, Executive Director
Description: Promotes business and community development in Chincoteague, VA. **Founded:** 1954. **Publications:** Island Adventure.

58893 ■ Clarkesville Lake Country Chamber of Commerce
105 2nd St.
Clarksville, VA 23927-1017
Ph: (434)374-2436
Free: 800-557-5582
Fax: (434)374-8174
Co. E-mail: clarksville@kerrlake.com
URL: http://clarksvilleva.com
Contact: Sheila Cuykendall, Executive Director
Description: Promotes business and community development in Clarkesville, VA and the surrounding area. Sponsors and hosts downtown events such as Big Lake Flea Market, The Virginia Lake Festival and Harvest Days Festival. Supports other events and activities such as the Clarksville Hydroplane Challenge/2006 World Inboard Championship. **Founded:** 1970. **Publications:** Shoreline (Bimonthly). **Awards:** Citizen of the Year for Clarksville, VA (Annual); Distinguished Citizen Award for Clarksville, VA (Annual).

58894 ■ Colonial Beach Chamber of Commerce (CBCC)
PO Box 475
Colonial Beach, VA 22443
Ph: (804)224-8145
Fax: (804)224-8145
Co. E-mail: info@colonialbeach.org
URL: http://www.colonialbeach.org
Contact: Carey Geddes, President
Description: Promotes business and community service in the Colonial Beach, VA area.

58895 ■ Colonial Heights Chamber of Commerce (CHCC)
201 Temple Ave., Ste. E
Colonial Heights, VA 23834
Ph: (804)526-5872
Fax: (804)526-9637
Co. E-mail: chchamber@colonialheights.cc
URL: http://www.colonial-heights.com
Contact: Roger Green, Executive Director
Description: Promotes business and community development in Colonial Heights, VA. **Founded:** 1949. **Publications:** Chamber Notes (Monthly). **Awards:** Business of the Year (Annual).

58896 ■ Commerce Report
2015 Memorial Ave.
Lynchburg, VA 24501
Ph: (434)845-5966
Fax: (434)522-9592
Co. E-mail: info@lynchburgchamber.org
URL: http://www.lynchburgchamber.org
Contact: Rex K. Hammond, President
Released: Monthly

58897 ■ Community Resource Guide and Membership Directory
PO Box 99
Blairs, VA 24527
Ph: (434)836-6990
Fax: (434)836-6955
Co. E-mail: chamber@dpchamber.org
URL: http://www.dpchamber.org
Contact: Laurie S. Moran, President
Released: Annual

58898 ■ Connections
16430 Booker T. Washington Hwy., No. 2
Moneta, VA 24121
Ph: (540)721-1203
Free: 800-676-8203
Fax: (540)721-7796
Co. E-mail: vgardner@visitsmithmountainlake.com
URL: http://www.visitsmithmountainlake.com
Contact: Vicki Gardner, Director
Released: Bimonthly

58899 ■ Country Sampler Calendar of Events
PO Box 475
Eastville, VA 23347
Ph: (757)678-0010
Co. E-mail: chamber@northamptoncountychamber.com
URL: http://www.northamptoncountychamber.com
Contact: Jeff Holland, President
Released: Monthly

58900 ■ Crewe - Burkeville Chamber of Commerce
PO Box 305
Crewe, VA 23930
Ph: (434)645-8413
Fax: (434)645-8413
Co. E-mail: chamber@creweburkeville.org
URL: http://www.creweburkeville.org
Description: Seeks to have more community involvement, more involvement from chamber members, induce more businesses into the area, and provide employment opportunities for local citizens in the Crewe-Burkeville, VA area. **Founded:** 1981. **Awards:** Business Advocate of the Year Award (Annual); Business of the Year (Annual); Lifetime Achievement Award (Annual).

58901 ■ Culpeper County Chamber of Commerce
109 S Commerce St.
Culpeper, VA 22701
Ph: (540)825-8628
Free: 888-285-7373
Fax: (540)825-1449
Co. E-mail: info@culpeperchamber.com
URL: http://www.culpeperchamber.com
Contact: Raven Yates, Chairperson
Description: Promotes business and community development in Culpeper County, VA. **Publications:** Chamber News (Bimonthly). **Awards:** CulpeperFest Award of Excellence (Annual); President's Award (Annual); Small Business Person of the Year (Annual); L.B. Henretty Memorial Outstanding Citizen Award (Annual); Most Improved Small Business Location (Annual). **Telecommunication Services:** jcharapich@culpeperchamber.com.

58902 ■ Danville Pittsylvania County Chamber of Commerce
PO Box 99
Blairs, VA 24527
Ph: (434)836-6990
Fax: (434)836-6955
Co. E-mail: chamber@dpchamber.org
URL: http://www.dpchamber.org
Contact: Laurie S. Moran, President
Description: Improves the business environment of Danville/Pittsylvania County, VA by providing leadership, products, programs and services which promote the success of members. **Founded:** 2001. **Publications:** Chamber Connections (Monthly); Community Resource Guide and Membership Directory (Annual); Images of Danville and Pittsylvania County (Annual). **Awards:** Education Grant Awards (Annual); Educator

of the Year (Annual); Emerging Enterprise Award (Annual); Enduring Enterprise Award (Annual); Entrepreneurial Excellence Awards (Annual).

58903 ■ Dickenson County Chamber of Commerce
PO Box 1990
Clintwood, VA 24228
Ph: (276)926-6074
Co. E-mail: chamber@dcwin.org
URL: http://www.dickensonchamber.net
Contact: Rita Surratt, President
Description: Promotes business and community development in Dickenson County, VA. **Scope:** businesses, literature on Dickenson County, tourist attractions. **Subscriptions:** 30 articles books periodicals video recordings.

58904 ■ Doorways
100 E Washington St.
Lexington, VA 24450
Ph: (540)463-5375
Fax: (540)463-3567
Co. E-mail: chamber@lexrockchamber.com
URL: http://www.lexrockchamber.com
Contact: Sammy Moore, Executive Director
Released: Monthly

58905 ■ Dulles Regional Chamber of Commerce
PO Box 327
Herndon, VA 20172
Ph: (571)323-5301
Fax: (703)787-8859
URL: http://www.dullesregionalchamber.org
Contact: Eileen Curtis, President
Description: Promotes business and community development in the Greater Dulles area, including Herndon, Reston, Chantilly, Great Falls, Potomac Falls, Sterling, Ashburn and Centreville. **Founded:** 1959.

58906 ■ Eastern Shore of Virginia Chamber of Commerce
PO Box 460
Melfa, VA 23410-0460
Ph: (757)787-2460
Fax: (757)787-8687
Co. E-mail: chamber@esvachamber.org
URL: http://www.esvachamber.org/home/home.asp
Contact: Dr. Terris Kennedy, Chairman
Description: Promotes business and community development in the eastern shore of Virginia. **Founded:** 1953.

58907 ■ Edinburg Area Chamber of Commerce (EACC)
PO Box 511
Edinburg, VA 22824
Ph: (540)984-8318
Co. E-mail: chamcom@shentel.net
URL: http://www.edinburgchamber.com
Contact: Steve Wood, President
Description: Promotes business and community development in the Edinburgh, VA area. **Founded:** 1961.

58908 ■ Emporia - Greensville Chamber of Commerce
400 Halifax St.
Emporia, VA 23847
Ph: (434)634-9441
Fax: (434)634-3485
Co. E-mail: ontrack@telpage.net
URL: http://www.emporia-greensvillechamber.com
Publications: On Track.

58909 ■ Enterprise
21 Enterprise Pkwy., Ste. 100
Hampton, VA 23666
Ph: (757)262-2000
Free: 800-556-1822
Fax: (757)262-2009
Co. E-mail: vpcc@vpcc.org
URL: http://www.vpcc.org
Contact: Dottie Jordan, President
Released: Monthly **Price:** $10, /year for nonmembers.

58910 ■ Enterprise
513 Maple Ave. W, 2nd Fl.
Vienna, VA 22180-4229
Ph: (703)281-1333
Fax: (703)242-1482
Co. E-mail: info@vtrcc.org
URL: http://www.vtrcc.org
Contact: Lisa Huffman, President
Released: Biweekly

58911 ■ Fairfax County Chamber of Commerce
8230 Old Courthouse Rd., Ste. 350
Vienna, VA 22182-3853
Ph: (703)749-0400
Fax: (703)749-9075
Co. E-mail: jcorcoran@fairfaxchamber.org
URL: http://www.fairfaxchamber.org
Contact: Lovey Hammel, Chairperson
Description: Promotes business and community development in Fairfax County. **Founded:** 1925.

58912 ■ Farmville Chamber of Commerce (FCC)
PO Box 361
Farmville, VA 23901
Ph: (434)392-3939
Fax: (434)392-3818
Co. E-mail: tory@farmvilleareachamber.org
URL: http://www.farmvilleareachamber.org
Contact: Lee Minix, Chairman
Description: Promotes business and community development in Farmville, VA. Sponsors Heart of Virginia Festival, candidate debates, and annual Farmville Christmas Show. **Founded:** 1948. **Publications:** Newcomer's Guide (Periodic).

58913 ■ Fauquier County Chamber of Commerce
205-1 Keith St.
Warrenton, VA 20186
Ph: (540)347-4414
Fax: (540)347-7510
Co. E-mail: mailbox@fauquierchamber.org
URL: http://www.fauquierchamber.org
Contact: Priscilla Hottle, Chairperson
Description: Promotes business and community development in Fauquier County and its trade area. **Founded:** 1921. **Publications:** Chamber Chat (Monthly). **Educational Activities:** After 5 Business Socials (Monthly). **Awards:** Business Person of the Year (Annual).

58914 ■ Floyd County Chamber of Commerce
PO Box 510
Floyd, VA 24091
Ph: (540)745-4407
Co. E-mail: chamber@swva.net
URL: http://www.visitfloyd.org
Contact: John McEnhill, President
Description: Promotes business and community development in Floyd County, VA. **Publications:** Chamber Chatter (Quarterly).

58915 ■ Fluvanna County Chamber of Commerce (FCCC)
PO Box 93
Palmyra, VA 22963-0093
Ph: (434)589-3262
Fax: (434)589-6212
Co. E-mail: fluvannacountycoc@embarqmail.com
URL: http://www.fluvannachamber.org
Contact: Mr. Jim Bogdan, President
Description: Promotes business and community development in Fluvanna County, VA. **Founded:** 1977. **Publications:** Chamber Newsletter (Monthly); Guide to Fluvanna County (Annual); Fluvanna County Chamber of Commerce--Membership Directory. **Educational Activities:** Bostf Meetings (Monthly). **Awards:** Business Person of the Year (Annual).

58916 ■ Franklin County Chamber of Commerce (FCCC)
52 Franklin St.
Rocky Mount, VA 24151
Ph: (540)483-9542

Fax: (540)483-0653
Co. E-mail: danny@ssisecurityva.com
URL: http://franklincounty.org
Contact: Danny Reynolds, President
Description: Promotes business and community development in the Franklin County, VA area. **Founded:** 1962.

58917 ■ Franklin-Southampton Area Chamber of Commerce
PO Box 531
Franklin, VA 23851
Ph: (757)562-4900
Fax: (757)562-6138
Co. E-mail: join@fsachamber.com
URL: http://www.fsachamber.com
Contact: Teresa B. Beale, Executive Director
Description: Promotes business and community development in the Franklin-Southampton, VA area. **Founded:** 1954. **Publications:** Speaking of Business (Monthly).

58918 ■ Fredericksburg Regional Chamber of Commerce (FRCC)
2300 Fall Hill Ave., Ste. 240
Fredericksburg, VA 22404-7476
Ph: (540)373-9400
Fax: (540)373-9570
Co. E-mail: linda@fredericksburgchamber.org
URL: http://www.fredericksburgchamber.org
Contact: Susan Spears, President
Description: Promotes business and community development in Fredericksburg, and Stafford and Spotsylvania Counties, VA. **Founded:** 1916. **Publications:** Business Directory (Biennial); ChamberAlert; ChamberLink (Monthly); Business Directory (Annual). **Awards:** Business of the Year (Annual); Chamber Goodwill Awards (Annual); Community Service Award (Annual); Prince B. Woodard Citizenship Award (Annual).

58919 ■ Front Royal - Warren County Chamber of Commerce
104 E Main St.
Front Royal, VA 22630
Ph: (540)635-3185
Fax: (540)635-9758
Co. E-mail: info@frontroyalchamber.com
URL: http://www.frontroyalchamber.com
Contact: Nicole Foster, President
Description: Promotes business and community development in Front Royal, VA. Sponsors Virginia Mushroom Festival. **Founded:** 1940. **Publications:** Gazebo Gazette (Monthly).

58920 ■ FYI
PO Box 295
Blackstone, VA 23824-0295
Ph: (434)292-1677
Co. E-mail: chamber@blackstoneva.com
URL: http://blackstoneva.com
Contact: Brenda R. Carter, Executive Director
Released: Monthly

58921 ■ Galax - Carroll - Grayson Chamber of Commerce
608 W Stuart Dr.
Galax, VA 24333
Ph: (276)236-2184
Fax: (276)236-1338
Co. E-mail: info@gcgchamber.com
URL: http://www.gcgchamber.com
Contact: Kenneth Belton, President
Description: Promotes business and community development in the City of Galax and counties of Carroll and Grayson, VA.

58922 ■ Gazebo Gazette
104 E Main St.
Front Royal, VA 22630
Ph: (540)635-3185
Fax: (540)635-9758
Co. E-mail: info@frontroyalchamber.com
URL: http://www.frontroyalchamber.com
Contact: Nicole Foster, President
Released: Monthly

58923 ■ *Glance at the Virginia Peninsula*
21 Enterprise Pkwy., Ste. 100
Hampton, VA 23666
Ph: (757)262-2000
Free: 800-556-1822
Fax: (757)262-2009
Co. E-mail: vpcc@vpcc.org
URL: http://www.vpcc.org
Contact: Dottie Jordan, President

58924 ■ Gloucester County Chamber of Commerce (GLOCO)
6699 Fox Centre Pkwy., No. 609
Gloucester, VA 23061
Ph: (804)693-2425
Fax: (804)693-7193
Co. E-mail: chamberexec@glocochamber.org
URL: http://gloucestervachamber.org
Contact: Makalia Records, Executive Director
Description: Promotes business and community development in the Gloucester County, VA area. **Scope:** business. **Founded:** 1965. **Publications:** *Insider* (Monthly). **Educational Activities:** After Hours (Monthly).

58925 ■ Goochland County Chamber of Commerce
2941 River Rd. W
Goochland, VA 23063
Ph: (804)556-3811
Fax: (804)556-2131
Co. E-mail: director@goochlandchamber.org
URL: http://www.goochlandchamber.org
Contact: Travis Chewning, President
Description: Promotes business and community development in Goochland County, VA.

58926 ■ *Government Textbook*
9 S 5th St.
Richmond, VA 23219
Ph: (804)644-1607
Fax: (804)783-6112
Co. E-mail: b.duval@vachamber.com
URL: http://www.vachamber.com
Contact: Barry DuVal, President
Released: Periodic

58927 ■ Greater Augusta Regional Chamber of Commerce
30 Ladd Rd.
Fishersville, VA 22939
Ph: (540)324-1133
Fax: (540)324-1136
Co. E-mail: chamber@ntelos.net
URL: http://www.augustachamber.org
Contact: Linda Hershey, President
Description: Promotes business and community development in the Staunton-Augusta County, VA area. Sponsors Annual Christmas Parade. **Founded:** 1999. **Publications:** *Chamber Connection* (Bimonthly); *Industrial Directory* (Periodic); *Industrial Directory* (Periodic); *Membership and Business Services Guide*; *Greater Augusta Regional Chamber of Commerce--Industrial Directory* (Periodic). **Educational Activities:** Business After Hours (Monthly); Awards (Annual).

58928 ■ Greater Reston Chamber of Commerce (GRCC)
1763 Fountain Dr.
Reston, VA 20190
Ph: (703)707-9045
Fax: (703)707-9049
Co. E-mail: info@restonchamber.org
URL: http://www.restonchamber.org
Contact: C. Michael Ferraro, Chairman
Description: Promotes business and community development in Reston, VA.

58929 ■ Greater Richmond Chamber of Commerce (GRCC)
600 E Main St., Ste. 700
Richmond, VA 23219
Ph: (804)648-1234

Fax: (804)783-9366
Co. E-mail: contactus@grcc.com
URL: http://www.grcc.com
Contact: Douglas M. Roth, Chairman
Description: Seeks to improve the economy and quality of life of Greater Richmond region through its programs and initiatives. **Founded:** 1867. **Publications:** *Chamber Currents* (Monthly). **Awards:** Impact Award (Annual).

58930 ■ Greater Springfield Chamber of Commerce (GSCC)
6434 Brandon Ave., Ste. 3A
Springfield, VA 22150
Ph: (703)866-3500
Fax: (703)866-3501
Co. E-mail: manney@springfieldchamber.org
URL: http://www.springfieldchamber.org
Contact: Nancy-jo Manney, Executive Director
Description: Promotes business and community development in Springfield, VA. **Founded:** 1957. **Awards:** Businessperson of the Year (Annual); Commerce Advocate Award (Annual); Corporate Citizen Award (Annual); Outstanding Food Service Award (Annual); Arthur E. Morisette Top Hat Service Award (Annual).

58931 ■ *Greater Vienna Handbook*
513 Maple Ave. W, 2nd Fl.
Vienna, VA 22180-4229
Ph: (703)281-1333
Fax: (703)242-1482
Co. E-mail: info@vtrcc.org
URL: http://www.vtrcc.org
Contact: Lisa Huffman, President
Released: Annual

58932 ■ Greater Williamsburg Chamber and Tourism Alliance
421 N Boundary St.
Williamsburg, VA 23187-3495
Ph: (757)229-6511
Free: 800-368-6511
Fax: (757)229-2047
Co. E-mail: wacc@williamsburgcc.com
URL: http://www.williamsburgcc.com
Contact: Kevin P. Walsh, Chairman of the Board
Description: Business people united to enhance, promote and serve the business community. Provides the leadership to strengthen the community's economic base and quality of life. **Awards:** Corporate Citizen Award (Annual); Mini-Grant Program (Annual).

58933 ■ *Guide to Fluvanna County*
PO Box 93
Palmyra, VA 22963-0093
Ph: (434)589-3262
Fax: (434)589-6212
Co. E-mail: fluvannacountycoc@embarqmail.com
URL: http://www.fluvannachamber.org
Contact: Mr. Jim Bogdan, President
Released: Annual

58934 ■ Halifax County Chamber of Commerce (HCCC)
515 Broad St.
South Boston, VA 24592
Ph: (434)572-3085
Co. E-mail: info@halifaxchamber.net
URL: http://www.halifaxchamber.net
Contact: Nancy L. Pool, President
Description: Promotes business and community development in the Halifax County, VA area. Sponsors the Virginia Cantaloupe Festival. **Founded:** 1955.

58935 ■ Hampton Roads Chamber of Commerce
500 E Main St., Ste. 700
Norfolk, VA 23510
Ph: (757)622-2312
Fax: (757)622-5563
URL: http://www.hamptonroadschamber.com
Contact: John A. Hornbeck, Jr., President
Description: Promotes business and community development in the Hampton Roads region of Southeast Virginia. **Founded:** 1984.

58936 ■ Hanover Association of Businesses and Chamber of Commerce
9097 Atlee Sta. Rd., Ste. 117
Mechanicsville, VA 23116
Ph: (804)798-8130
Fax: (804)798-0014
Co. E-mail: jennifer@touchpointspr.com
URL: http://www.habcc.org
Contact: Jennifer Y. Scott, Executive Director
Description: Promotes business and community development in the town of Ashland and Hanover County, VA. **Founded:** 2002. **Publications:** *Chamber Voice* (Monthly); *Strictly Business* (Bimonthly). **Educational Activities:** Hanover Association of Businesses and Chamber of Commerce Meeting (Annual).

58937 ■ Harrisonburg-Rockingham Chamber of Commerce (HRCC)
800 Country Club Rd.
Harrisonburg, VA 22802
Ph: (540)434-3862
Fax: (540)434-4508
Co. E-mail: information@hrchamber.org
URL: http://www.hrchamber.org
Contact: Roy Kelly, Administrative Assistant
Description: Promotes business and community development in the Harrisonburg-Rockingham, VA area. Sponsors festivals. **Founded:** 1916. **Publications:** *Advocate* (Quarterly); *Industrial Directory*; *Market Data Population Information* (Annual). **Awards:** Business Person of the Year (Annual); Entrepreneur of the Year (Annual); Farm Family Stewardship (Annual).

58938 ■ Highland County Chamber of Commerce (HCCC)
PO Box 223
Monterey, VA 24465-0223
Ph: (540)468-2550
Fax: (540)468-2551
Co. E-mail: info@highlandcounty.org
URL: http://www.highlandcounty.org
Contact: Carolyn Pohowsky, Executive Director
Description: Promotes business and community development in the Highland County, VA area. Sponsors McDowell Days: Battle of McDowell Reenactment, The Highland County Fair, Hands and Harvest and Wintertide. **Founded:** 1967. **Publications:** *Chamber Business Directory* (Annual). **Educational Activities:** Hands and Harvest Fall Foliage (Annual).

58939 ■ Hopewell-Prince George Chamber of Commerce (HPGCC)
PO Box 1297
Hopewell, VA 23860-1297
Ph: (804)458-5536
Fax: (804)458-0041
Co. E-mail: becky@hpgchamber.org
URL: http://www.hpgchamber.org
Contact: Becky McDonough, Executive Vice President
Description: Promotes business and community development in the Hopewell, VA area. **Founded:** 1926.

58940 ■ *Images of Danville and Pittsylvania County*
PO Box 99
Blairs, VA 24527
Ph: (434)836-6990
Fax: (434)836-6955
Co. E-mail: chamber@dpchamber.org
URL: http://www.dpchamber.org
Contact: Laurie S. Moran, President
Released: Annual

58941 ■ *Industrial Directory*
179 E Main St.
Abingdon, VA 24210
Ph: (276)628-8141
Fax: (276)628-3984
Co. E-mail: chamber@eva.org
URL: http://www.washingtonvachamber.org
Contact: Cathy Andersen, President
Released: Periodic

58942 ■ *Industrial Directory*
800 Country Club Rd.
Harrisonburg, VA 22802
Ph: (540)434-3862
Fax: (540)434-4508
Co. E-mail: information@hrchamber.org
URL: http://www.hrchamber.org
Contact: Roy Kelly, Administrative Assistant
Price: $10.

58943 ■ *Industrial Directory*
30 Ladd Rd.
Fishersville, VA 22939
Ph: (540)324-1133
Fax: (540)324-1136
Co. E-mail: chamber@ntelos.net
URL: http://www.augustachamber.org
Contact: Linda Hershey, President
Released: Periodic **Price:** $6.

58944 ■ *Inprint*
9720 Capital Ct., Ste. 203
Manassas, VA 20110-2050
Ph: (703)368-6600
Fax: (703)368-4733
Co. E-mail: djones@pwcgmcc.org
URL: http://www.pwcgmcc.org
Contact: Robert H. Clapper, II, President
Released: Bimonthly

58945 ■ *Insider*
6699 Fox Centre Pkwy., No. 609
Gloucester, VA 23061
Ph: (804)693-2425
Fax: (804)693-7193
Co. E-mail: chamberexec@glocochamber.org
URL: http://gloucestervachamber.org
Contact: Makalia Records, Executive Director
Released: Monthly **Price:** free.

58946 ■ *Island Adventure*
6733 Maddox Blvd.
Chincoteague Island, VA 23336
Ph: (757)336-6161
Fax: (757)336-1242
Co. E-mail: chincochamber@verizon.net
URL: http://www.chincoteaguechamber.com
Contact: Suzanne Taylor, Executive Director

58947 ■ *Isle of Wight - Smithfield - Windsor Chamber of Commerce*
100 Main St.
Smithfield, VA 23431
Ph: (757)357-3502
Free: 888-284-3475
Fax: (757)357-6884
Co. E-mail: chamber@theisle.org
URL: http://www.theisle.org
Contact: Russell Parrish, Chairman
Description: Promotes business and community development in Isle of Wight County. **Awards:** Agricultural Business of the Year (Annual); Business of the Year (Annual); Educator of the Year (Annual).

58948 ■ *Lancaster County Chamber of Commerce*
PO Box 1868
Kilmarnock, VA 22482
Ph: (804)435-6092
Fax: (804)435-3092
Co. E-mail: info@lancasterva.com
URL: http://www.lancasterva.com
Contact: Thomas Richardson, President
Description: Promotes business and community development in Lancaster County, VA. **Publications:** *The Bridge* (Monthly); *Lancaster Life* (Monthly); *Lancaster Life* (Monthly).

58949 ■ *Lancaster Life*
PO Box 1868
Kilmarnock, VA 22482
Ph: (804)435-6092
Fax: (804)435-3092
Co. E-mail: info@lancasterva.com
URL: http://www.lancasterva.com
Contact: Thomas Richardson, President
Released: Monthly

58950 ■ *Lee County Area Chamber of Commerce*
PO Box 417
Pennington Gap, VA 24277
Ph: (276)337-9277
Co. E-mail: director@leecountyvachamber.org
URL: http://leecountyvachamber.org
Contact: James Miller, President
Description: Promotes business and community development in Lee County, VA area.

58951 ■ *Lexington-Rockbridge County Chamber of Commerce (LRCCC)*
100 E Washington St.
Lexington, VA 24450
Ph: (540)463-5375
Fax: (540)463-3567
Co. E-mail: chamber@lexrockchamber.com
URL: http://www.lexrockchamber.com
Contact: Sammy Moore, Executive Director
Description: Promotes business and community development in the Lexington-Rockbridge County, VA area. Sponsors small business seminars. **Founded:** 1937. **Publications:** *Doorways* (Monthly); *Rockbridge Almanac* (Annual). **Awards:** Education of the Year (Annual); Business Individual of the Year (Annual).

58952 ■ *Loudoun Chamber Business Directory and Resource Guide*
PO Box 1298
Leesburg, VA 20177
Ph: (703)777-2176
Fax: (703)777-1392
Co. E-mail: thoward@loudounchamber.org
URL: http://www.loudounchamber.org
Contact: Tony Howard, President
Released: Annual

58953 ■ *Loudoun County Chamber of Commerce (LCCC)*
PO Box 1298
Leesburg, VA 20177
Ph: (703)777-2176
Fax: (703)777-1392
Co. E-mail: thoward@loudounchamber.org
URL: http://www.loudounchamber.org
Contact: Tony Howard, President
Description: Promotes business and community development in the Loudoun County, VA area. **Founded:** 1960. **Publications:** *BizConnect* (Monthly); *Loudounclear* (Bimonthly); *Loudoun Chamber Business Directory and Resource Guide* (Annual). **Educational Activities:** Dulles Connection Expo (Annual).

58954 ■ *Loudounclear*
PO Box 1298
Leesburg, VA 20177
Ph: (703)777-2176
Fax: (703)777-1392
Co. E-mail: thoward@loudounchamber.org
URL: http://www.loudounchamber.org
Contact: Tony Howard, President
Released: Bimonthly

58955 ■ *Louisa County Chamber of Commerce*
PO Box 955
Louisa, VA 23093
Ph: (540)967-0944
Co. E-mail: info@louisachamber.org
URL: http://www.louisachamber.org/outside_home.asp
Contact: Dr. Jack Manzari, Chairman
Description: Promotes business and community development in Louisa County, VA.

58956 ■ *Luray-Page County Chamber of Commerce*
18 Campbell St.
Luray, VA 22835
Ph: (540)743-3915
Free: 888-743-3915

Fax: (540)743-3944
Co. E-mail: info@luraypage.com
URL: http://www.luraypage.com
Contact: Dave Tong, President
Description: Promotes business tourism and community development in the Luray-Page County, VA area.

58957 ■ *Lynchburg Life/Business Directory*
2015 Memorial Ave.
Lynchburg, VA 24501
Ph: (434)845-5966
Fax: (434)522-9592
Co. E-mail: info@lynchburgchamber.org
URL: http://www.lynchburgchamber.org
Contact: Rex K. Hammond, President
Released: Annual

58958 ■ *Lynchburg Regional Chamber of Commerce (LRCC)*
2015 Memorial Ave.
Lynchburg, VA 24501
Ph: (434)845-5966
Fax: (434)522-9592
Co. E-mail: info@lynchburgchamber.org
URL: http://www.lynchburgchamber.org
Contact: Rex K. Hammond, President
Description: Promotes business and community development in the Lynchburg, VA area. **Founded:** 1833. **Publications:** *Commerce Report* (Monthly); *Lynchburg Life/Business Directory* (Annual). **Educational Activities:** Board Retreat (Biennial). **Awards:** ATHENA Award (Annual); Small Business Award (Annual).

58959 ■ *Madison Chamber of Commerce (MCC)*
PO Box 373
Madison, VA 22727-0373
Ph: (540)948-4455
Co. E-mail: tourism@madison-va.com
URL: http://www.madison-va.com
Contact: Marge Berry, Director
Description: Promotes business and community development in the Madison County, VA area. **Founded:** 1980. **Publications:** *Madison Chamber of Commerce Business News* (Monthly).

58960 ■ *Madison Chamber of Commerce Business News*
PO Box 373
Madison, VA 22727-0373
Ph: (540)948-4455
Co. E-mail: tourism@madison-va.com
URL: http://www.madison-va.com
Contact: Marge Berry, Director
Released: Monthly

58961 ■ *Market Data Population Information*
800 Country Club Rd.
Harrisonburg, VA 22802
Ph: (540)434-3862
Fax: (540)434-4508
Co. E-mail: information@hrchamber.org
URL: http://www.hrchamber.org
Contact: Roy Kelly, Administrative Assistant
Released: Annual **Price:** $5.

58962 ■ *Martinsville - Henry County Chamber of Commerce (MHCCC)*
115 Broad St.
Martinsville, VA 24114
Ph: (276)632-6401
Fax: (276)632-5059
Co. E-mail: mhccoc@mhcchamber.com
URL: http://www.martinsville.com
Contact: Guy Stanley, Chairman
Description: Encourages a strong local economy by creating an environment where businesses thrive and community and commerce work together for the future of Martinsville-Henry County. **Founded:** 1959. **Telecommunication Services:** amanda@mhcchamber.com.

58963 ■ *Membership and Business Services Guide*
30 Ladd Rd.
Fishersville, VA 22939
Ph: (540)324-1133

Fax: (540)324-1136
Co. E-mail: chamber@ntelos.net
URL: http://www.augustachamber.org
Contact: Linda Hershey, President

58964 ■ *Membership Directory and Referral Guide*
2009 14th St. N, Ste. 111
Arlington, VA 22201
Ph: (703)525-2400
Fax: (703)522-5273
Co. E-mail: chamber@arlingtonchamber.org
URL: http://www.arlingtonchamber.org
Contact: Richard V. Doud, Jr., President
Released: Periodic

58965 ■ Montgomery County Chamber of Commerce (MCCC)
103 Professional Park Dr.
Blacksburg, VA 24060
Ph: (540)552-2636
Fax: (540)552-2639
Co. E-mail: dlyons@montgomerycc.org
URL: http://montgomerycc.org
Contact: Shane Adams, President
E-mail: sadams@montgomerycc.org
Description: Promotes business and community development in Montgomery County, VA. **Founded:** 2003. **Publications:** *Montgomery County Chamber of Commerce--Directory & QOL* (Annual). **Telecommunication Services:** chamber@montgomerycc.org.

58966 ■ Mount Vernon - Lee Chamber of Commerce
6911 Richmond Hwy., Ste. 320
Alexandria, VA 22306
Ph: (703)360-6925
Fax: (703)360-6928
Co. E-mail: info@mtvernon-leechamber.org
URL: http://www.mtvernon-leechamber.org
Contact: Barbara Doyle, President
Description: Promotes a successful business climate. Provides public policy representation. Supports economic revitalization. **Founded:** 1954. **Telecommunication Services:** hollydougherty@mtvernon-leechamber.org.

58967 ■ New Kent Chamber of Commerce (NKCC)
7324 Vineyard Pkwy.
Providence Forge, VA 23140
Ph: (804)966-8581
Co. E-mail: presidentelect@newkentchamber.org
URL: http://www.newkentchamber.org
Contact: Larry Ragsdale, President
Description: Promotes business and community development in the New Kent, VA area.

58968 ■ *Newcomer's Guide*
PO Box 361
Farmville, VA 23901
Ph: (434)392-3939
Fax: (434)392-3818
Co. E-mail: tory@farmvilleareachamber.org
URL: http://www.farmvilleareachamber.org
Contact: Lee Minix, Chairman
Released: Periodic

58969 ■ Northampton County Chamber of Commerce
PO Box 475
Eastville, VA 23347
Ph: (757)678-0010
Co. E-mail: chamber@northamptoncountychamber.com
URL: http://www.northamptoncountychamber.com
Contact: Jeff Holland, President
Description: Promotes business and community development in Northampton County, VA area. **Publications:** *Country Sampler Calendar of Events* (Monthly). **Educational Activities:** Cape Charles Fall Festival (Annual).

58970 ■ *On Track*
400 Halifax St.
Emporia, VA 23847
Ph: (434)634-9441

Fax: (434)634-3485
Co. E-mail: ontrack@telpage.net
URL: http://www.emporia-greensvillechamber.com

58971 ■ Orange County Chamber of Commerce (OCCC)
PO Box 146
Orange, VA 22960
Ph: (540)672-5216
Fax: (540)672-2304
Co. E-mail: occhamber@verizon.net
URL: http://www.orangevachamber.com
Contact: Barbara Bannar, Executive Director
Description: Promotes business and community development in Orange County, VA. **Founded:** 1924.

58972 ■ Patrick County Chamber of Commerce
PO Box 577
Stuart, VA 24171-0577
Ph: (276)694-6012
Co. E-mail: patcchamber@embargmail.com
URL: http://www.patrickchamber.com
Contact: Phyllis Nester, President
Description: Promotes business and community development in the Patrick County, VA area. Sponsors the Virginia Peach Festival. Publications: none. **Founded:** 1975.

58973 ■ Petersburg Chamber of Commerce (PCC)
PO Box 928
Petersburg, VA 23804-0928
Ph: (804)733-8131
Fax: (804)733-9891
Co. E-mail: info@petersburgvachamber.com
URL: http://www.petersburgvachamber.com
Contact: Cynthia Raitt Devereaux, President
Description: Promotes business and community development in Petersburg, VA. **Founded:** 1881. **Publications:** *The Chamber Comments* (Quarterly).

58974 ■ Powhatan Chamber of Commerce
3887 Old Buckingham Rd.
Powhatan, VA 23139
Ph: (804)598-2636
Fax: (804)598-0223
Co. E-mail: info@powhatanchamberofcommerce.org
URL: http://powhatanchamber.org
Contact: Mary Kay Gates, President
Description: Association of business, professional and civic-minded individuals. Promotes free enterprise system, economic growth and prosperity of Powhatan County. **Founded:** 1988.

58975 ■ Prince William County - Greater Manassas Chamber of Commerce (PWCGMCC)
9720 Capital Ct., Ste. 203
Manassas, VA 20110-2050
Ph: (703)368-6600
Fax: (703)368-4733
Co. E-mail: djones@pwcgmcc.org
URL: http://www.pwcgmcc.org
Contact: Robert H. Clapper, II, President
Description: Promotes business and community development in the Greater Manassas area. **Publications:** *Business and Information* (Annual); *Inprint* (Bimonthly); *Inprint* (Bimonthly); *Business and Information* (Annual).

58976 ■ Pulaski County Chamber of Commerce (PCCC)
4440 Cleburne Blvd., Ste. B
Dublin, VA 24084
Ph: (540)674-1991
Fax: (540)674-4163
Co. E-mail: pcchamber2@swva.net
URL: http://www.pulaskichamber.info
Contact: Ms. Peggy White, Executive Director
Description: Promotes business and community development in Pulaski County, VA. **Founded:** 1952.

58977 ■ Radford Chamber of Commerce (RCC)
200 3rd Ave., Ste. C
Radford, VA 24141
Ph: (540)639-2202

Fax: (540)639-2228
Co. E-mail: info@radfordchamber.com
URL: http://radfordchamber.net
Contact: Keith Weltens, President
Description: Promotes business and community development in Radford, VA. **Founded:** 1944.

58978 ■ *Resource Guide*
21 Enterprise Pkwy., Ste. 100
Hampton, VA 23666
Ph: (757)262-2000
Free: 800-556-1822
Fax: (757)262-2009
Co. E-mail: vpcc@vpcc.org
URL: http://www.vpcc.org
Contact: Dottie Jordan, President
Released: Annual

58979 ■ Roanoke Regional Chamber of Commerce (RRCC)
210 S Jefferson St.
Roanoke, VA 24011
Ph: (540)983-0700
Fax: (540)983-0723
Co. E-mail: business@roanokechamber.org
URL: http://www.roanokechamber.org
Contact: Joyce Waugh, President
E-mail: jwaugh@roanokechamber.org
Description: Promotes business and community development in the Roanoke Valley, VA area. **Founded:** 1890. **Publications:** *Business Connections* (Quarterly); *Roanoke Area Industrial Directory*.

58980 ■ *Rockbridge Almanac*
100 E Washington St.
Lexington, VA 24450
Ph: (540)463-5375
Fax: (540)463-3567
Co. E-mail: chamber@lexrockchamber.com
URL: http://www.lexrockchamber.com
Contact: Sammy Moore, Executive Director
Released: Annual

58981 ■ Scott County Chamber of Commerce
PO Box 609
Gate City, VA 24251
Ph: (540)386-6665
Fax: (540)386-9198
URL: http://www.mounet.com/~scottcc
Description: Promotes business and community development in Scott County, VA. **Founded:** 1985.

58982 ■ Scottsville Community Chamber of Commerce (SCCC)
PO Box 11
Scottsville, VA 24590
Ph: (434)286-6000
Fax: (434)286-9102
Co. E-mail: scccpresident@gmail.com
URL: http://scottsvilleva.com
Contact: Cynthia Bruce, President
Description: Promotes business and community development in Scottsville, VA. **Founded:** 1964.

58983 ■ *Shoreline*
105 2nd St.
Clarksville, VA 23927-1017
Ph: (434)374-2436
Free: 800-557-5582
Fax: (434)374-8174
Co. E-mail: clarksville@kerrlake.com
URL: http://clarksvilleva.com
Contact: Sheila Cuykendall, Executive Director
Released: Bimonthly **Price:** free.

58984 ■ Smith Mountain Lake Chamber of Commerce/Partnership (SMLCC/P)
16430 Booker T. Washington Hwy., No. 2
Moneta, VA 24121
Ph: (540)721-1203
Free: 800-676-8203
Fax: (540)721-7796
Co. E-mail: vgardner@visitsmithmountainlake.com
URL: http://www.visitsmithmountainlake.com
Contact: Vicki Gardner, Director
Description: Smith Mountain Lake business and professional people. Promotes tourism, business, and community growth. Develops and promotes programs designed to encourage economic, social,

cultural, and recreational interests of Lake area residents. **Publications:** *Connections* (Bimonthly); *Visitors and Newcomers' Guide to Smith Mountain Lake* (Annual); *Visitors and Newcomers Guide to Smith Mountain Lake* (Annual). **Educational Activities:** Awards (Annual); Business After Hours (Monthly). **Telecommunication Services:** sburt@visitsmithmountainlake.com.

58985 ■ South Hill Chamber of Commerce (SHCC)
201 S Mecklenburg Ave.
South Hill, VA 23970
Ph: (434)447-4547
Free: 800-524-4347
Fax: (434)447-4461
Co. E-mail: frank@southhillchamber.com
URL: http://www.southhillchamber.com
Contact: Frank Malone, Executive Director
Description: Promotes business and community development in South Hill, VA. Sponsors festival. **Founded:** 1941.

58986 ■ *Speaking of Business*
PO Box 531
Franklin, VA 23851
Ph: (757)562-4900
Fax: (757)562-6138
Co. E-mail: join@fsachamber.com
URL: http://www.fsachamber.com
Contact: Teresa B. Beale, Executive Director
Released: Monthly

58987 ■ Strasburg Chamber of Commerce (SCC)
PO Box 42
Strasburg, VA 22657
Ph: (540)465-3187
Fax: (540)465-2812
Co. E-mail: schamber@shentel.net
URL: http://www.strasburgva.com
Contact: Rich Orndorff, Jr., President
URL(s): www.strasburgvachamber.com. **Description:** Promotes business and community development in Strasburg, VA. Sponsors annual Mayfest Celebration. **Founded:** 1951.

58988 ■ *Strictly Business*
9097 Atlee Sta. Rd., Ste. 117
Mechanicsville, VA 23116
Ph: (804)798-8130
Fax: (804)798-0014
Co. E-mail: jennifer@touchpointspr.com
URL: http://www.habcc.com
Contact: Jennifer Y. Scott, Executive Director
Released: Bimonthly

58989 ■ Surry County Chamber of Commerce
PO Box 353
Surry, VA 23883
Ph: (757)294-0066
Free: 877-290-0066
Co. E-mail: harold.jones@dom.com
URL: http://www.surrychamber.org
Contact: Harold Jones, President
Description: Promotes business and community development in Surry County, VA area.

58990 ■ Tappahannock-Essex County Chamber of Commerce (TECC)
c/o E. Stanley Langford, Jr., Chm.
PO Box 1651
Tappahannock, VA 22560
Ph: (804)443-4230
Fax: (804)443-4157
URL: http://www.essex-virginia.org
Contact: E. Stanley Langford, Jr., Chairman
Description: Promotes business and community development in the Tappahannock-Essex, VA area. Conducts annual Summer Festival and business fair; sponsors 10K race. **Founded:** 1970. **Publications:** *Update* (Monthly).

58991 ■ Tazewell Area Chamber of Commerce (TACC)
Tazewell Mall Box 6
Tazewell, VA 24651-9998
Ph: (276)988-5091

Fax: (276)988-5093
Co. E-mail: info@tazewellchamber.org
URL: http://www.tazewellchamber.org
Contact: John Boothe, President
Description: Promotes business and community development in the Tazewell, VA area. **Founded:** 1972.

58992 ■ Top of Virginia Regional Chamber (TVRC)
407 S Loudoun St.
Winchester, VA 22601
Ph: (540)662-4118
Fax: (540)722-6365
Co. E-mail: rcollins@regionalchamber.biz
URL: http://www.regionalchamber.biz
Contact: Randy Collins, President
Description: Promotes business and community development in the Winchester City, Frederick, and Clarke County, VA area. **Publications:** *Business Agenda* (Monthly).

58993 ■ *Update*
c/o E. Stanley Langford, Jr., Chm.
PO Box 1651
Tappahannock, VA 22560
Ph: (804)443-4230
Fax: (804)443-4157
URL: http://www.essex-virginia.org
Contact: E. Stanley Langford, Jr., Chairman
Released: Monthly

58994 ■ Vienna-Tysons Regional Chamber of Commerce (VTRCC)
513 Maple Ave. W, 2nd Fl.
Vienna, VA 22180-4229
Ph: (703)281-1333
Fax: (703)242-1482
Co. E-mail: info@vtrcc.org
URL: http://www.vtrcc.org
Contact: Lisa Huffman, President
Description: Promotes business and community development in the Vienna, VA area. Sponsors Halloween Parade and annual Chili Cook-Off. **Founded:** 1963. **Publications:** *Enterprise* (Biweekly); *Greater Vienna Handbook* (Annual). **Educational Activities:** Business Expo (Annual).

58995 ■ Vinton Area Chamber of Commerce
116 S Poplar St., Ste. 1-A
Vinton, VA 24179
Ph: (540)343-1364
Co. E-mail: info@vintonchamber.com
URL: http://www.vintonchamber.com
Contact: Sabrina Weeks, President
Description: Promotes business and community development in the Vinton Area, VA.

58996 ■ *Virginia All-Business Directory*
9 S 5th St.
Richmond, VA 23219
Ph: (804)644-1607
Fax: (804)783-6112
Co. E-mail: b.duval@vachamber.com
URL: http://www.vachamber.com
Contact: Barry DuVal, President
Released: Annual **Price:** $160, for members; $180, for nonmembers.

58997 ■ Virginia Association of Chamber of Commerce Executives (VACCE)
9 S Fifth St.
Richmond, VA 23219-3890
Ph: (804)644-1607
Fax: (804)783-6112
Co. E-mail: b.duval@vachamber.com
URL: http://www.vachamber.com
Contact: Barry DuVal, President
Description: Represents large and small chambers of commerce from localities throughout the state. Strives to develop the professional skills of chamber executives, staff and volunteer leaders. Conducts a forum for integrating the work of the local chambers of commerce to contribute to the growth and development of local communities.

58998 ■ Virginia Chamber of Commerce (VCC)
9 S 5th St.
Richmond, VA 23219
Ph: (804)644-1607
Fax: (804)783-6112
Co. E-mail: b.duval@vachamber.com
URL: http://www.vachamber.com
Contact: Barry DuVal, President
Description: Promotes business and community development in Virginia. **Founded:** 1924. **Publications:** *Advocate* (Monthly); *Government Textbook* (Periodic); *Virginia All-Business Directory* (Annual).

58999 ■ Virginia Peninsula Chamber of Commerce (VPCC)
21 Enterprise Pkwy., Ste. 100
Hampton, VA 23666
Ph: (757)262-2000
Free: 800-556-1822
Fax: (757)262-2009
Co. E-mail: vpcc@vpcc.org
URL: http://www.vpcc.org
Contact: Dottie Jordan, President
Description: Promotes the economic and business interests of the Virginia Peninsula. **Founded:** 1898. **Publications:** *Enterprise* (Monthly); *Glance at the Virginia Peninsula*; *Resource Guide* (Annual). **Educational Activities:** SeaFest (Annual). **Awards:** Distinguished Citizen (Annual).

59000 ■ *Visitors and Newcomers' Guide to Smith Mountain Lake*
16430 Booker T. Washington Hwy., No. 2
Moneta, VA 24121
Ph: (540)721-1203
Free: 800-676-8203
Fax: (540)721-7796
Co. E-mail: vgardner@visitsmithmountainlake.com
URL: http://www.visitsmithmountainlake.com
Contact: Vicki Gardner, Director
Released: Annual **Price:** free.

59001 ■ *Vistas*
PO Box 606
Altavista, VA 24517
Ph: (434)369-6665
Fax: (434)369-4202
Co. E-mail: info@altavistachamber.com
URL: http://www.altavistachamber.org
Contact: Morgan Allen, Chairman
Released: Monthly

59002 ■ Warsaw-Richmond County Chamber of Commerce (WRCCC)
PO Box 1141
Warsaw, VA 22572
Ph: (804)313-2252
Co. E-mail: warsawrcchamber@gmail.com
URL: http://www.warsaw-rcchamber.com
Contact: David Mann, President
Description: Promotes business and community development in the Warsaw, VA area. **Founded:** 1987.

59003 ■ Washington County Chamber of Commerce (WCCC)
179 E Main St.
Abingdon, VA 24210
Ph: (276)628-8141
Fax: (276)628-3984
Co. E-mail: chamber@eva.org
URL: http://www.washingtonvachamber.org
Contact: Cathy Andersen, President
Description: Promotes business and community development in Washington County, VA. Organizes Business Night Out mixers, industrial appreciation dinner, Salute to Education banquet, and other events. **Founded:** 1927. **Publications:** *Industrial Directory* (Periodic).

59004 ■ *Who's Who in Alexandria Business*
801 N Fairfax St., Ste. 402
Alexandria, VA 22314
Ph: (703)549-1000

Fax: (703)739-3805
Co. E-mail: tleone@alexchamber.com
URL: http://www.alexchamber.com
Contact: Tina Leone, President
Released: Annual **Price:** included in membership dues.

59005 ■ Wise County Chamber of Commerce
PO Box 226
Norton, VA 24273
Ph: (276)679-0961
Fax: (276)679-2655
Co. E-mail: coc@naxs.com
URL: http://www.wisecountychamber.org
Contact: Joyce M. Payne, Chief Executive Officer
Description: Promotes business and community development in the Wise County, VA area. **Founded:** 1955. **Publications:** *The Catalyst* (Monthly). **Tele-communication Services:** wisecountycoc@verizon.net.

59006 ■ Woodstock Chamber of Commerce
PO Box 605
Woodstock, VA 22664
Ph: (540)459-2542
Co. E-mail: barry.fadely@axa-advisors.com
URL: http://www.woodstockvachamber.com
Contact: Jenna French, Executive Director
Description: Promotes business and community development in the Woodstock, VA area.

59007 ■ Wytheville-Wythe-Bland Chamber of Commerce (WWBCC)
150 E Monroe St.
Wytheville, VA 24382
Ph: (276)223-3365
Fax: (276)223-3412
Co. E-mail: chamber@wytheville.org
URL: http://www.wwbchamber.com
Contact: Dr. Charlie White, President
E-mail: wcwhitc@wcc.vccs.edu
URL(s): www.wytheville.org. **Description:** Promotes business and community development in the Wytheville-Wythe-Bland, VA area. **Founded:** 1946. **Publications:** *Wytheville Chamber of Commerce Business Directory*; *Wytheville-Wythe-Bland Chamber of Commerce Business Directory* (Annual); *Wytheville/Wythe/Bland Chamber of Commerce Business Directory* (Annual).

59008 ■ *Wytheville-Wythe-Bland Chamber of Commerce Business Directory*
150 E Monroe St.
Wytheville, VA 24382
Ph: (276)223-3365
Fax: (276)223-3412
Co. E-mail: chamber@wytheville.org
URL: http://www.wwbchamber.com
Contact: Dr. Charlie White, President
E-mail: wcwhitc@wcc.vccs.edu
Released: Annual

MINORITY BUSINESS ASSISTANCE PROGRAMS

59009 ■ National Capital Area Minority Business Opportunity Center - Performance-Based Solutions Inc.
5113 Leesburg Pike, Ste. 306
Falls Church, VA 22041
Ph: (703)575-6464
Fax: (703)575-6467
Co. E-mail: wguinn@ncamboc.com
URL: http://www.ncamboc.com
Contact: Emmett Anderson, Executive Director
Description: Assists high-growth minority businesses in the Washington DC area with financing and other business development needs.

59010 ■ Virginia Department of Minority Business Enterprise (DMBE)
1111 E Main St., Ste. 300
Richmond, VA 23219
Ph: (804)786-6585

Fax: (804)786-9736
Co. E-mail: dmbe@dmbe.virginia.gov
URL: http://www.dmbe.state.va.us/
Contact: Ida Outlaw McPherson, Director
Description: Assists minority firms in identifying and targeting state agencies, as well as other public and private sector entities; sponsors seminars and workshops; provides a support program and one-on-one consultations.

FINANCING AND LOAN PROGRAMS

59011 ■ Calvert Social Venture Partners, L.P.
402 Maple Ave., W.
Vienna, VA 22180
Ph: (703)255-4930
Fax: (703)255-4931
URL: http://www.calvertventures.com
Contact: John May, Managing Partner
Preferred Investment Size: $250,000 to $1,000,000.
Industry Preferences: Environment. **Geographic Preference:** U.S.

59012 ■ ECentury Capital Partners, L.P.
8180 Greensboro Dr., Ste. 1150
McLean, VA 22102
Ph: (703)442-4480
Fax: (703)448-1816
Co. E-mail: info@ecenturycapital.com
URL: http://www.ecenturycapital.com
Contact: Hank Tuten, Managing Director
Preferred Investment Size: $126,000 to $4,000,000.
Investment Policies: Seed, early, first, and second stage, and expansion. **Industry Preferences:** Communications, computer software, semiconductors and other electronics, and industrial and energy. **Geographic Preference:** Eastern U.S.

59013 ■ Fairfax Partners, LLC
8300 Greensboro Dr., Ste. 1040
McLean, VA 22102
Ph: (703)847-9486
Fax: (703)847-0911
URL: http://www.fairfaxpartners.com
Contact: Robert Carlin, Managing Partner
Preferred Investment Size: $1,000,000 to $5,000,000. **Industry Preferences:** Communications, Internet specific, medical and health, and business service. **Geographic Preference:** Mid Atlantic.

59014 ■ Global Internet Ventures / GIV Venture Partners
8150 Leesburg Pike, Ste. 1210
Vienna, VA 22182
Ph: (703)442-3300
Fax: (703)442-3388
URL: http://www.givinc.com
Contact: Jim McGregor, Managing Director
Preferred Investment Size: $2,000,000 to $4,000,000. **Industry Preferences:** Communications, computer software, Internet specific, medical and health. **Geographic Preference:** Mid Atlantic.

59015 ■ Harbert Venture Partners LLC
1210 E. Cary St., Ste. 400
Richmond, VA 23219
Ph: (804)782-3800
Fax: (804)782-3810
URL: http://www.harbert.net
Contact: William W. Brooke, Managing Partner
Preferred Investment Size: $1,000,000 to $4,000,000. **Investment Policies:** Start-up, seed, and early stage. **Industry Preferences:** Communications and media, computer related, software and services, biotechnology and life sciences, medical and health, and industrial and energy. **Geographic Preference:** Southeastern U.S.

59016 ■ NeuroVentures Capital LLC
Zero Court Sq.
Charlottesville, VA 22902
Ph: (434)297-1000

Fax: (434)297-1001
Co. E-mail: info@neuroventures.com
URL: http://www.neuroventures.com
Contact: Daniel J. O'Connell, Managing Partner
E-mail: djo@neuroventures.com
Preferred Investment Size: $200,000 to $2,000,000.
Investment Policies: Start-up, early and first stage, and expansion. **Industry Preferences:** Biotechnology, and medical and health. **Geographic Preference:** U.S.

59017 ■ New Horizons Venture Capital
1808 Eye St. NW, Ste. 200
Washington, DC 20006
Ph: (202)955-7965
Fax: (202)955-7966
Co. E-mail: info@newhorizonsvc.com
URL: http://www.newhorizonsvc.com
Contact: T.J. Jubeir, Managing Partner
Preferred Investment Size: $1,000,000 to $4,000,000. **Investment Policies:** Early, first and second stage. **Industry Preferences:** Internet specific, communications and media, and computer software and services. **Geographic Preference:** Mid Atlantic.

59018 ■ Renaissance Ventures
33 S. 13th St., 3rd Fl.
Richmond, VA 23218
Ph: (804)643-5500
Fax: (804)643-5322
URL: http://www.renventures.com
Contact: Herbert W. Jackson, Managing Director
Investment Policies: Early stage. **Industry Preferences:** Biotechnology. **Geographic Preference:** National.

59019 ■ Taylor Corporation
209 Madison St., Ste. 300
Alexandria, VA 22314
Ph: (703)739-1000
Fax: (703)997-2392
URL: http://www.taylorventure.com
Contact: Ken Snyder, President
Investment Policies: Start-up, early stage, and balanced. **Industry Preferences:** Business service, and manufacturing. **Geographic Preference:** U.S. and Canada.

59020 ■ Virginia Capital
1801 Libbie Ave., Ste. 201
Richmond, VA 23226
Ph: (804)648-4802
Fax: (804)648-4809
Co. E-mail: vacapital@vacapital.com
URL: http://www.vacapital.com
Contact: Fred Russell, Managing Partner
Preferred Investment Size: $1,000,000 to $5,000,000. **Industry Preferences:** Communications and media, medical and health, consumer related, and transportation, financial services, and business service. **Geographic Preference:** Mid Atlantic.

PROCUREMENT ASSISTANCE PROGRAMS

59021 ■ American Indian Procurement Technical Assistance Center - UIDA Business Services - UBS Sub Office Northeast Region
2340 Dulles Corner Blvd.
Mail Stop 1N01
Herndon, VA 20171
Ph: (703)561-4415
Fax: (703)561-4419
Co. E-mail: cpierce@uida.org
URL: http://www.uida.org
Contact: Chris Pierce, Specialist
E-mail: georgew@uida.org
Description: Helps to develop and expand an American Indian private sector which employs Indian labor, increases the number of viable tribal and individual Indian businesses, and positively impacts and involves reservation communities, by establishing business relationships between Indian enterprises and private industry.

59022 ■ Central Virginia Procurement Technical Assistance Center
2211 Hydraulic Rd., Ste. 103
Charlottesville, VA 22901
Ph: (434)293-2136
Co. E-mail: gmcmulli@gmu.edu
Contact: Greg McMullin, Counselor
E-mail: gmcmulli@gmu.edu
Description: Provides assistance to businesses interested in doing business with federal, state, and local governments. Covers cities and counties from Danville to Highland and Shenandoah counties on the Northwestern border across to the eastern shore.

59023 ■ Hampton Roads Virginia Procurement Technical Assistance Center
5200 Palmer Ln., Ste. 2A
Williamsburg, VA 23188
Ph: (757)719-1767
Fax: (757)277-0129
Co. E-mail: jmorret@gmu.edu
URL: http://www.hrptac.org
Contact: Joseph D. Moore, Director
E-mail: jmooret@gmu.edu
Description: Serves Tidewater, Hampton Roads area in helping business with government at federal, state, and local levels.

59024 ■ Procurement Technical Assistance Center of Northern Virginia - Mason Enterprise Center
4031 University Dr., Ste. 200
Fairfax, VA 22030
Ph: (703)277-7700
Fax: (703)352-8195
Co. E-mail: ptap@gmu.edu
URL: http://www.vaptap.org
Contact: James Regan, Program Manager
E-mail: jregan@gmu.edu
Description: The center services nine counties in Northern Virginia and the cities they contain. Goal is to increase contracting activity between small businesses, prime government contractors, and the government.

59025 ■ Virginia Department of General Services - Division of Purchases and Supply - Procurement Assistance
1111 E Broad St., 7th Fl.
Richmond, VA 23219
Ph: (804)786-3842
Fax: (804)371-8937
URL: http://dps.dgs.virginia.gov/training/index.htm

59026 ■ Virginia Procurement Center - Defense Supply Center-Richmond
8000 Jefferson Davis Hwy.
Richmond, VA 23297-5100
Ph: (804)279-5242
Fax: (804)279-6615
URL: http://www.dscr.dla.mil/
Description: Covers activities for Defense Supply Center Richmond (Richmond, VA), Army Training & Doctrine Command, Army Corps of Engineers (Norfolk, VA), Navy FISC (Norfolk, VA), NAVFAC (Norfolk, VA), NASA, Langley Research Center (Hampton, VA).

59027 ■ Virginia Procurement Technical Assistance Center - Crater Planning District Commission
1964 Wakefield St.
Petersburg, VA 23805
Ph: (804)861-1666
Fax: (804)732-8972
Co. E-mail: info@craterpdc.org
URL: http://www.craterpdc.org
Contact: Dennis Morris, Executive Director
Description: The major focus of the Commission's Work program is economic, industrial and small business development.

59028 ■ Virginia Procurement Technical Assistance Center - Southwest Virginia Community College
PO Box SVCC
Richlands, VA 24641
Ph: (276)964-7334

Fax: (276)964-7361
Co. E-mail: pac.info@sw.edu
URL: http://www.sw.edu/ptac
Contact: Glenda D. Calver, Director
E-mail: glenda.calver@sw.edu
Description: Provide businesses with the marketing know how and technical tools they need to obtain and perform successfully under federal, state and local government contracts with the mission of creating and retaining jobs, fostering competition and lower costs for the government, and helping to sustain our armed forces' readiness.

59029 ■ Virginia Procurement Technical Assistance Program - George Mason University
4031 University Dr., Ste. 200
Fairfax, VA 22030-3409
Ph: (703)277-7750
Fax: (703)352-8195
Co. E-mail: jregan@gmu.edu
URL: http://www.vaptap.org
Contact: James Regan, Program Manager
Description: Exists to increase contracting activity between small businesses, prime government contractors and the government.

INCUBATORS/RESEARCH AND TECHNOLOGY PARKS

59030 ■ Business Development Centre Inc.
147 Mill Ridge Rd.
Lynchburg, VA 24502
Ph: (434)582-6100
Fax: (434)582-6170
Co. E-mail: sbdcdir@lbdc.com
URL: http://www.lbdc.com/
Description: A small business incubator offering services to business owners and prospective business owners in the cities of Lynchburg and Bedford, the towns of Altavista and Amherst, and the counties of Amherst, Appomattox, Bedford, and Campbell in Central Virginia.

59031 ■ The New Century Venture Center
1354 Eighth St. SW
Roanoke, VA 24015-1812
Ph: (540)344-6402
Fax: (540)345-0262
Co. E-mail: lison@ncvc.com
URL: http://www.ncvc.com
Description: The Center is a small business incubator that serves emerging firms through shared resources and a variety of financial services.

59032 ■ New River Valley Development Corporation
6580 Valley Center Dr., Ste. 302
Radford, VA 24141
Ph: (540)633-6731
Fax: (540)633-6768
Co. E-mail: mbarber@firstbancorp.com
URL: http://www.nrvdc.org
Contact: Wayne Carpenter, Manager
Description: This incubator serves as a seeding location for emerging businesses hoping to expand operations. These include entrepreneurs and manufacturing/industrial companies.

59033 ■ Virginia Biotechnology Research Park
800 E Leigh St.
Richmond, VA 23219
Ph: (804)828-5390
Free: 888-822-4675
Fax: (804)828-8566
Co. E-mail: vbrp@vabiotech.com
URL: http://vabiotech.com
Contact: Robert T. Skunda
Description: An incubator for early and mid-stage life science, research, and state/federal lab enterprises. Offers tenants a variety of services including a biotechnology library, talent bank, fiber optic telecommunications, conference and office space, and more.

EDUCATIONAL PROGRAMS

59034 ■ Bryant and Stratton College - Virginia Beach Campus
301 Center Pointe Dr.
Virginia Beach, VA 23462
Ph: (757)499-7900
Free: 866-948-0571
Co. E-mail: VABeach@bryanstratton.edu
URL: http://www.bryantstratton.edu
Description: Business college offering a course in small business management.

59035 ■ John Tyler Community College
13101 Jefferson Davis Hwy.
Chester, VA 23831-5316
Ph: (804)796-4000
Fax: (804)796-4362
URL: http://www.jtcc.edu
Description: Two-year college offering a small business management program.

59036 ■ Mountain Empire Community College
3441 Mountain Empire Rd.
Big Stone Gap, VA 24219
Ph: (276)523-2400
Fax: (276)523-8297
URL: http://www.me.cc.va.us
Description: Two-year college offering programs in business management.

59037 ■ Northern Virginia Community College
8333 Little River Tpke.
Annandale, VA 22003-3796
Ph: (703)323-3000
Free: 877-408-2028
Fax: (703)323-3367
URL: http://www.nvcc.edu
Contact: Kimberly Ellis, Officer, Student Services Registrar
Description: Two-year college offering a small business management course. **Founded:** 1964. **Publications:** *The Peashooter* (Biweekly).

LEGISLATIVE ASSISTANCE

59038 ■ Virginia Senate Committee on Commerce and Labor
Senate Committee Operations
Richmond, VA 23218
Ph: (804)698-7450
Fax: (804)698-7672
Co. E-mail: jlance@sov.state.virginia.us
URL: http://legis.state.va.us/
Contact: Richard L. Saslaw, Chairperson
Description: Handles small business legislation.

PUBLICATIONS

59039 ■ Smart Start your Virginia Business
PSI Research
300 N. Valley Dr.
Grants Pass, OR 97526
Ph: (503)479-9464
Free: 800-228-2275
Fax: (503)476-1479
Co. E-mail: info@psi-research.com
URL: http://www.psi-research.com
Ed: Michael D. Jenkins. **Released:** Revised edition, 1992. **Price:** $29.95 (looseleaf binder); $24.95 (paper). **Description:** Part of the Successful Business Library series.

59040 ■ Virginia Business
411 E. Franklin St., Ste. 105
Richmond, VA 23219
Ph: (804)649-6999
Fax: (804)649-6311
Co. E-mail: lugincius@va-business.com
URL: http://www.virginiabusiness.com

PUBLISHERS

59041 ■ Capital Books Inc.
22841 Quicksilver Dr.
Sterling, VA 20166
Ph: (703)661-1586
Free: 800-758-3756
Fax: (703)661-1547
Co. E-mail: newcaplital@aol.com
Contact: Azad Ajamian, President
Description: Description: Publishes historical fiction, cookbooks, how-to, travel, home and garden, business, and lifestyles. **Founded:** 1998.

59042 ■ GOALS Institute—Humdinger Books
2540 Brenton Point Dr., Ste. 100
Reston, VA 20191
Ph: (703)264-2000
Fax: (703)264-2408
Co. E-mail: info@goalsinstitute.com
URL: http://www.goalsinstitute.com
Contact: James R. Ball, President
Description: Description: Publishes self-help, business and personal development books. Does not accept unsolicited manuscripts. Reaches market through direct mail, telephone and trade sales. **Founded:** 1992.

59043 ■ GTM Co.
6729 Glenmont St.
Falls Church, VA 22042
Ph: (703)241-4915
Fax: (703)241-9586
Co. E-mail: wfpenoyar@hotmail.com
Contact: William F. Penoyar, President
Description: Description: Publishes a book on how to do business with the U.S. government. **Founded:** 1984.

59044 ■ Information International
10814 Fawn Dr.
Great Falls, VA 22066-3315
Ph: (703)450-7049
Fax: (925)226-4865
Co. E-mail: robert@isquare.com
URL: http://www.isquare.com
Contact: William Bliss, President
E-mail: robert@isquare.com
Description: Description: Publishes business publications and software, especially start-up and entrepreneurial related. Does not accept unsolicited manuscripts. Reaches market through direct mail, and the internet. **Founded:** 1986.

59045 ■ Ivy Software Inc.
1146 Richmond-Tappahannock Hwy.
Manquin, VA 23106
Ph: (804)769-7193
Free: 800-342-5489
Fax: (804)769-7019
Co. E-mail: ivyinfo@ivysoftware.com
URL: http://www.ivysoftware.com
Contact: Robert Holt, Owner
Description: Description: Publishes on business management, accounting and finance. offers seminars, microcomputer training and stand-up instruc-
tion. Reaches market through telephone sales, trade sales and in-office contact. Does not accept unsolicited manuscripts. **Founded:** 1986.

59046 ■ Management Concepts Inc.
8230 Leesburg Pke.
Tysons Corner, VA 22182
Ph: (703)790-9595
Free: 800-506-4450
Fax: (703)790-1371
Co. E-mail: info@managementconcepts.com
URL: http://www.managementconcepts.com
Contact: Phil Davidson, Manager
E-mail: pdavidson@managementconcepts.com
Description: Description: Publishes books on federal government contracting, including marketing and proposal development and small business resources. Also publishes newsletters. Accepts unsolicited manuscripts. Reaches market through direct mail and the National Contract Management Association. **Founded:** 1973.

59047 ■ Stylus Publishing, LLC—KIT Publishers
22883 Quicksilver Dr.
Sterling, VA 20166-2012
Ph: (703)661-1504
Free: 800-232-0223
Fax: (703)661-1547
Co. E-mail: stylusinfo@styluspub.com
URL: http://www.styluspub.com
URL(s): stylus.styluspub.com. **Description:** Description: Publishes books on higher education, corporate training, business and management and third world development. **Founded:** 1996. **Publications:** *Idea-Based Learning*; *Job Search in Academe: How to Get the Position You Deserve.*

SMALL BUSINESS DEVELOPMENT CENTERS

59048 ■ Aberdeen Small Business Development Center
Grays Harbor College
1620 Edward P. Smith Dr., Bldg. 200
Aberdeen, WA 98520
Ph: (360)538-2530
Co. E-mail: erik.stewart@wsbdc.org
URL: http://www.wsbdc.org
Contact: Erik Stewart, Advisor
Description: Represents and promotes the small business sector. Provides management assistance to current and prospective small business owners. Helps to improve management skills and expand the products and services of members.

59049 ■ Auburn Small Business Development Center
110 2nd St. SW, Ste. 135
Auburn, WA 98001
Ph: (253)333-4953
Fax: (253)333-4640
Co. E-mail: dburnett@greenriver.edu
URL: http://www.wsbdc.org
Contact: Deanna Burnett-Keener, Director
Description: Represents and promotes the small business sector. Provides management assistance to current and prospective small business owners. Helps to improve management skills and expand the products and services of members.

59050 ■ Bellingham Small Business Development Center
115 Unity St., Ste. 101
Bellingham, WA 98225
Ph: (360)778-1762
Fax: (360)647-9413
Co. E-mail: jennifer.shelton@wwu.edu
URL: http://www.wsbdc.org
Contact: Jennifer Shelton, Director
Description: Represents and promotes the small business sector. Provides management assistance to current and prospective small business owners. Helps to improve management skills and expand the products and services of members.

59051 ■ Bremerton Small Business Development Center
345 6th St., Ste. 568
Bremerton, WA 98337
Ph: (360)307-4220
Fax: (360)337-4864
URL: http://www.wsbdc.org
Description: Represents and promotes the small business sector. Provides management assistance to current and prospective small business owners. Helps to improve management skills and expand the products and services of members.

59052 ■ Edmonds Small Business Development Center
728 134th St. SW, Ste. 128
Everett, WA 98204

Ph: (425)640-1435
Fax: (425)743-5726
Co. E-mail: sbdc@edcc.edu
URL: http://www.wsbdc.org/advisor-location?locid=8
Contact: Peter Quist, Director
Description: Represents and promotes the small business sector. Provides management assistance to current and prospective small business owners. Helps to improve management skills and expand the products and services of members.

59053 ■ Highline Community College Small Business Development Center
PO Box 98000
Des Moines, WA 98198
Ph: (206)878-3710
Fax: (206)870-5929
Co. E-mail: rshockley@highline.edu
URL: http://www.wsbdc.org/advisor-location?locid=16
Contact: Rich Shockley, Advisor
Description: Represents and promotes the small business sector. Provides management assistance to current and prospective small business owners. Helps to improve management skills and expand the products and services of members.

59054 ■ Lewis County Small Business Development Center
c/o David Baria, Business Advisor
1611 N National Ave.
Chehalis, WA 98532
Ph: (360)748-0114
Fax: (360)748-1238
Co. E-mail: dbaria@lewisedc.com
URL: http://www.wsbdc.org/
   advisor?empid=39&locid=35&s
Contact: David Baria, Advisor
Description: Represents and promotes the small business sector. Provides management assistance to current and prospective small business owners. Helps to improve management skills and expand the products and services of members.

59055 ■ Longview Small Business Development Center
Don Talley Bldg., Rm. 103A
1600 Maple St.
Longview, WA 98632
Ph: (360)442-2946
Fax: (360)422-2948
Co. E-mail: jerry.petrick@wsbdc.org
URL: http://www.wsbdc.org
Contact: Jerry Petrick, Advisor
Description: Represents and promotes the small business sector. Provides management assistance to current and prospective small business owners. Helps to improve management skills and expand the products and services of members.

59056 ■ Moses Lake Small Business Development Center
Bldg. 1800, Rm. 1857A
7662 Chanute St. NE
Moses Lake, WA 98837
Ph: (509)793-2373

Fax: (509)762-4703
Co. E-mail: allanp@bigbend.edu
URL: http://www.wsbdc.org
Contact: Allan Peterson, Advisor
Description: Represents and promotes the small business sector. Provides management assistance to current and prospective small business owners. Helps to improve management skills and expand the products and services of members.

59057 ■ Mount Vernon Small Business Development Center
204 W Montgomery St.
Mount Vernon, WA 98273
Ph: (360)336-6114
Fax: (360)336-6116
Co. E-mail: dean@skagit.org
URL: http://www.wsbdc.org
Contact: Dean Shellan, Advisor
Description: Represents and promotes the small business sector. Provides management assistance to current and prospective small business owners. Helps to improve management skills and expand the products and services of members.

59058 ■ Okanogan Small Business Development Center
320 Omak Ave., No. 400
Omak, WA 98841
Ph: (509)826-5107
Fax: (509)826-7425
Co. E-mail: blakeney@methow.com
URL: http://www.wsbdc.org/
   advisor?empid=10&locid=20&s
Contact: Lewis Blakeney, Advisor
Description: Represents and promotes the small business sector. Provides management assistance to current and prospective small business owners. Helps to improve management skills and expand the products and services of members.

59059 ■ Olympia Small Business Development Center
665 Woodland Sq. SE, Ste. 201
Lacey, WA 98503
Ph: (360)407-0014
Fax: (360)407-0012
Co. E-mail: rnielsen@spscc.ctc.edu
URL: http://www.wsbdc.org/
   advisor?empid=494&locid=42&s
Contact: Ron Nielsen, Advisor
Description: Represents and promotes the small business sector. Provides management assistance to current and prospective small business owners. Helps to improve management skills and expand the products and services of members.

59060 ■ Port Angeles Small Business Development Center
Lincoln Center
905 S B St., Ste. 128
Port Angeles, WA 98363
Ph: (360)417-5657

Fax: (360)344-3079
Co. E-mail: kathleen.purdy@wsbdc.org
URL: http://www.wsbdc.org
Contact: Kathleen Purdy, Director
Description: Represents and promotes the small business sector. Provides management assistance to current and prospective small business owners. Helps to improve management skills and expand the products and services of members.

59061 ■ Port Townsend Small Business Development Center
211 Taylor St., Ste. 402A
Port Townsend, WA 98368
Ph: (360)334-3078
Fax: (360)344-3079
Co. E-mail: kathleen.purdy@wsbdc.org
URL: http://www.wsbdc.org
Contact: Kathleen Purdy, Advisor
Description: Represents and promotes the small business sector. Provides management assistance to current and prospective small business owners. Helps to improve management skills and expand the products and services of members.

59062 ■ Pullman Small Business Development Center
1610 NE Eastgate Blvd., Ste. 650
Pullman, WA 99163
Ph: (509)335-8081
Fax: (509)335-8082
Co. E-mail: tlcornelison@wsu.edu
URL: http://www.wsbdc.org
Contact: Terry Cornelison, Advisor
Description: Represents and promotes the small business sector. Provides management assistance to current and prospective small business owners. Helps to improve management skills and expand the products and services of members.

59063 ■ Renton Small Business Development Center
Bldg. J, Ste. 214
3000 NE 4th St.
Renton, WA 98056
Ph: (425)235-7819
Co. E-mail: asbury.lockett@wsbdc.org
URL: http://www.wsbdc.org
Description: Represents and promotes the small business sector. Provides management assistance to current and prospective small business owners. Helps to improve management skills and expand the products and services of members.

59064 ■ Seattle Small Business Development Center
Washington State University West
520 Pike St., Ste. 1101
Seattle, WA 98101
Ph: (206)428-3022
Fax: (206)448-1334
Co. E-mail: mfranz@wsu.edu
URL: http://www.wsbdc.org/advisor-location?locid=49
Contact: Michael Franz, Advisor
Description: Represents and promotes the small business sector. Provides management assistance to current and prospective small business owners. Helps to improve management skills and expand the products and services of members.

59065 ■ Spokane Small Business Development Center
SIRTI Bldg.
665 N Riverpoint Blvd., Ste. 201
Spokane, WA 99202
Ph: (509)358-7890
Fax: (509)358-7896
Co. E-mail: cdoyl@wsu.edu
URL: http://www.wsbdc.org
Description: Represents and promotes the small business sector. Provides management assistance to current and prospective small business owners. Helps to improve management skills and expand the products and services of members.

59066 ■ Tacoma Small Business Development Center
1101 S Yakima Ave., M-123
Tacoma, WA 98405

Ph: (253)680-7768
Fax: (253)680-7771
Co. E-mail: jrodenberg@bates.ctc.edu
URL: http://www.wsbdc.org
Contact: John Rodenberg, Advisor
Description: Represents and promotes the small business sector. Provides management assistance to current and prospective small business owners. Helps to improve management skills and expand the products and services of members.

59067 ■ Tri-Cities Small Business Development Center
c/o Bruce Davis, Dir.
7130 W Grandridge, Ste. A
Kennewick, WA 99336
Ph: (509)735-6222
Fax: (509)735-6609
Co. E-mail: bdavis@columbiabasin.edu
URL: http://www.wsbdc.org
Contact: Bruce Davis, Director
URL(s): www.columbiabasin.edu/home/index.asp-?page=617. **Description:** Represents and promotes the small business sector. Provides management assistance to current and prospective small business owners. Helps to improve management skills and expand the products and services of members.

59068 ■ Vancouver Small Business Development Center
11700 NE 95th St., Ste. 102
Vancouver, WA 98682
Ph: (360)260-6372
Fax: (360)260-6369
Co. E-mail: jharte@vancouver.wsu.edu
URL: http://www.wsbdc.org/advisor-location?locid=10
Contact: Jan Harte, Advisor
Description: Represents and promotes the small business sector. Provides management assistance to current and prospective small business owners. Helps to improve management skills and expand the products and services of members.

59069 ■ Washington Small Business Development Center - Lead Office (WSBDC)
SIRTI Bldg.
665 N Riverpoint Blvd., Ste. 201
Spokane, WA 99202
Ph: (509)358-7890
Fax: (509)358-7896
Co. E-mail: terry.chamber@wsbdc.org
URL: http://www.wsbdc.org
Contact: Terry Chambers, Director

59070 ■ Wenatchee Small Business Development Center
238 Olds Station Rd., Ste. A
Wenatchee, WA 98801
Ph: (509)888-7252
Co. E-mail: jim.fletcher@wsbdc.org
URL: http://www.wsbdc.org
Contact: Jim Fletcher, Director
URL(s): wenatcheesbdc.blogspot.com/p/contact-sbdc-wenatchee-office.html. **Description:** Represents and promotes the small business sector. Provides management assistance to current and prospective small business owners. Helps to improve management skills and expand the products and services of members.

59071 ■ Yakima Small Business Development Center
10 N 9th St.
Yakima, WA 98901
Ph: (509)454-7612
Fax: (509)248-0601
Co. E-mail: linda@yakima.org
URL: http://www.wsbdc.org/advisor-location?locid=3
Contact: Linda Johnson, Advisor
Description: Represents and promotes the small business sector. Provides management assistance to current and prospective small business owners. Helps to improve management skills and expand the products and services of members.

SMALL BUSINESS ASSISTANCE PROGRAMS

59072 ■ Washington Department of Commerce - International Trade & Economic Development Division
128 10th Ave. SW
Olympia, WA 98504-2525
Ph: (360)725-4100
Fax: (360)586-0873
Co. E-mail: trade@cted.wa.gov
URL: http://www.cted.wa.gov
Contact: Larry Williams, Assistant Director
Description: Assists Washington state businesses in profitably accessing the global markets by providing training and assistance.

59073 ■ Washington State Department of Commerce - Business Development Division
128 10th Ave. SW
Olympia, WA 98504-2525
Ph: (360)725-4100
Fax: (360)586-0873
URL: http://www.cted.wa.gov
Contact: Larry Williams, Assistant Director
Description: Intercedes with government agencies on behalf of businesses experiencing licensing, taxation, and regulation difficulties.

59074 ■ Washington State Department of Revenue
1025 Union Ave. SE, Ste. 500
Olympia, WA 98501
Ph: (360)753-5574
Free: 800-647-7706
Fax: (360)586-5543
Co. E-mail: communication@dor.wa.gov
URL: http://www.dor.wa.gov
Contact: Cindi L. Holmstrom, Director
Description: Provides information about Washington taxes for prospective businesses.

SCORE OFFICES

59075 ■ Central Washington SCORE
300 S Columbia St.
Wenatchee, WA 98801
Ph: (509)662-2116
Fax: (509)662-2022
Co. E-mail: score@wenatchee.org
URL: http://www.centralwashingtonscore.org
Description: Promotes business and community development in the Wenatchee, WA area. **Founded:** 1902.

59076 ■ SCORE Bellingham
Chase Bank, 2nd Fl.
1336 Cornwall Ave.
Bellingham, WA 98225
Ph: (360)685-4259
URL: http://www.scorechapter591.org
Description: Provides consulting services to individuals wishing to start a new business or who have problems with established businesses.

59077 ■ SCORE Fort Vancouver
4001 Main St., Ste. 120,121
Vancouver, WA 98663
Ph: (360)699-1079
Co. E-mail: scorevan@iinet.com
URL: http://www.scorevancouver.org
Description: Provides best source of free and confidential small business advice to help build business from idea to start-up to success. Helps small businesses flourish. Volunteers share their wisdom and lessons learned in business.

59078 ■ SCORE Mid-Columbia
PO Box 336
Richland, WA 99352
Ph: (509)375-3582
Co. E-mail: score@paktec.com
URL: http://www.score-wa.org
Description: Provides professional guidance and information to America's small business in order to strengthen the local and national economy.

59079 ■ SCORE Seattle
2401 4th Ave., Ste. 450
Seattle, WA 98121
Ph: (206)553-7320
Fax: (206)553-0194
URL: http://seattle.score.org
Description: Provides free and personalized business counseling, throughout the Pudget Sound area, to help start up and existing businesses become successful. Holds many workshops on various topics directed toward the entrepreneur. **Scope:** business. **Founded:** 1965. **Subscriptions:** articles books papers periodicals reports software. **Publications:** *SCORE Workshop Brochure* (Annual).

59080 ■ SCORE Spokane
801 W Riverside Ave., Ste. 444
Spokane, WA 99201-0908
Ph: (509)353-2821
Fax: (509)353-2600
Co. E-mail: info@scorespokane.org
URL: http://www.scorespokane.org
Description: Provides professional guidance, mentoring services and financial assistance to maximize the success of existing and emerging small businesses. **Founded:** 1973.

59081 ■ SCORE Tacoma
Tacoma Business Ctr., Rm. M-123
Bates Technical School
1101 S Yakima Ave.
Tacoma, WA 98405
Ph: (253)680-7770
Fax: (253)680-7771
Co. E-mail: score@bates.ctc.edu
URL: http://www.tacomabusinesscenter.org
Description: Provides public service to America by offering small business advice and training.

59082 ■ *SCORE Workshop Brochure*
2401 4th Ave., Ste. 450
Seattle, WA 98121
Ph: (206)553-7320
Fax: (206)553-0194
URL: http://seattle.score.org
Released: Annual

59083 ■ Yakima Valley SCORE
Co. E-mail: yakimascore@yahoo.com

BETTER BUSINESS BUREAUS

59084 ■ Better Business Bureau of the Inland Northwest—Better Business Bureau Serving Eastern Washington, North Idaho and Montana
152 S Jefferson, Ste. 200
Spokane, WA 99201-4532
Ph: (509)455-4200
Free: 800-356-1007
Fax: (509)838-1079
Co. E-mail: info@spokane.bbb.org
URL: http://spokane.bbb.org
Contact: Jan Quintrall, President
Description: Seeks to promote and foster the highest ethical relationship between businesses and the public through voluntary self-regulation, consumer and business education, and service excellence. Provides information to help consumers and businesses make informed purchasing decisions and avoid costly scams and frauds; settles consumer complaints through arbitration and other means. **Telecommunication Services:** jquintrall@spokane.bbb.org.

59085 ■ Better Business Bureau, Oregon/Western Washington
1000 Station Dr., Ste. 222
DuPont, WA 98327
Ph: (206)431-2222
Fax: (206)431-2200
Co. E-mail: info@thebbb.org
URL: http://www.alaskaoregonwesternwashington.bbb.org
Contact: Robert W.G. Andrew, President
Description: Seeks to promote and foster the highest ethical relationship between businesses and the public through voluntary self-regulation, consumer

and business education, and service excellence. Provides information to help consumers and businesses make informed purchasing decisions and avoid costly scams and frauds; settles consumer complaints through arbitration and other means.

CHAMBERS OF COMMERCE

59086 ■ *Action Report*
10 N 9th St.
Yakima, WA 98901
Ph: (509)248-2021
Fax: (509)248-0601
Co. E-mail: chamber@yakima.org
URL: http://www.yakima.org
Contact: Betty Wilkinson, President
E-mail: betty@yakima.org
Released: Monthly

59087 ■ Anacortes Chamber of Commerce (ACC)
819 Commercial Ave.
Anacortes, WA 98221
Ph: (360)293-3832
Fax: (360)293-1595
Co. E-mail: info@anacortes.org
URL: http://www.anacortes.org
Contact: Mitch Everton, Executive Director
Description: Promotes business and community development in the Anacortes, WA area. Sponsors Anacortes Waterfront Festival. **Founded:** 1904. **Publications:** *The Anacortes Communicator* (Monthly).

59088 ■ *The Anacortes Communicator*
819 Commercial Ave.
Anacortes, WA 98221
Ph: (360)293-3832
Fax: (360)293-1595
Co. E-mail: info@anacortes.org
URL: http://www.anacortes.org
Contact: Mitch Everton, Executive Director
Released: Monthly

59089 ■ *Around Town - What's Going On*
PO Box 94
Chewelah, WA 99109
Ph: (509)935-8595
Fax: (509)935-8520
Co. E-mail: info@chewelah.org
URL: http://www.chewelah.org
Contact: Jeanne Nixon, Manager
Released: Bimonthly

59090 ■ Asotin Chamber of Commerce
PO Box 574
Asotin, WA 99402
Ph: (509)243-4242
URL: http://www.wcce.org
Description: Promotes business and community development in the Asotin, WA area.

59091 ■ Auburn Area Chamber of Commerce
108 S Division St., Ste. B
Auburn, WA 98001-5305
Ph: (253)833-0700
Fax: (253)735-4091
Co. E-mail: auburncc@auburnareawa.org
URL: http://www.auburnareawa.org
Contact: Rod Luke, Chairman
Description: Strives to serve the needs of the members and the greater Auburn Business community by providing leadership and a forum to promote, enhance and encourage business growth. **Founded:** 1925. **Publications:** *Auburn Works* (Monthly); *Auburn Works*.

59092 ■ *Auburn Works*
108 S Division St., Ste. B
Auburn, WA 98001-5305
Ph: (253)833-0700
Fax: (253)735-4091
Co. E-mail: auburncc@auburnareawa.org
URL: http://www.auburnareawa.org
Contact: Rod Luke, Chairman
Released: Monthly

59093 ■ Bainbridge Island Chamber of Commerce
395 Winslow Way E
Bainbridge Island, WA 98110
Ph: (206)842-3700
Fax: (206)842-3713
Co. E-mail: info@bainbridgechamber.com
URL: http://www.bainbridgechamber.com
Contact: Kevin Dwyer, Executive Director
Description: Promotes business and community development in Bainbridge Island, Washington. Sponsors Celebrity Auction, and community school activities. **Founded:** 1927. **Publications:** *Business News* (Monthly). **Educational Activities:** General Membership Meeting (Monthly).

59094 ■ Ballard Chamber of Commerce (BCC)
2208 NW Market St., Ste. 100
Seattle, WA 98107
Ph: (206)784-9705
Fax: (206)783-8154
Co. E-mail: info@ballardchamber.com
URL: http://www.ballardchamber.com
Contact: Beth Williamson Miller, Executive Director
Description: Promotes business and community development in the Ballard neighborhood of Seattle, WA. Sponsors annual SeafoodFest. **Founded:** 1927. **Publications:** *Membership Roster* (Annual).

59095 ■ Battle Ground Chamber of Commerce (BGCC)
1419 W Main St., Ste. 110
Battle Ground, WA 98604
Ph: (360)687-1510
Fax: (360)687-4505
Co. E-mail: info@battlegroundchamber.org
URL: http://www.battlegroundchamber.org
Contact: Diane Rivera, Executive Director
Description: Promotes business and community development in Northern Clark County, WA. Conducts annual Harvest Days Festival. **Founded:** 1964. **Publications:** *Business News and Views* (Monthly); *Battle Ground Chamber of Commerce--Business Directory*; *Battle Ground--North Clark County Directory* (Annual). **Educational Activities:** Halloween Fun (Annual); Harvest Days (Annual). **Awards:** Business Person of the Year (Annual); Citizen of the Year (Annual); Honorable Mention Citation for All American City (Annual).

59096 ■ *Battle Ground--North Clark County Directory*
1419 W Main St., Ste. 110
Battle Ground, WA 98604
Ph: (360)687-1510
Fax: (360)687-4505
Co. E-mail: info@battlegroundchamber.org
URL: http://www.battlegroundchamber.org
Contact: Diane Rivera, Executive Director
Released: Annual; in July. **Price:** $5, /year.

59097 ■ Bellevue Chamber of Commerce
302 Bellevue Sq.
Bellevue, WA 98004
Ph: (425)454-2464
Fax: (425)462-4660
Co. E-mail: staffteam@bellevuechamber.org
URL: http://www.bellevuechamber.org
Contact: Betty Nokes, President
Description: Fosters a healthy business environment by providing strategic leadership, advocacy, tools and resources for business success. **Publications:** *The Edge* (Monthly); *The Voice of Business* (Monthly); *The Membership Directory & Business Resource Guide* (Annual). **Awards:** Corporate Citizenship Award (Annual); Eastside Business of the Year Award (Annual); Eastside Economic Leadership Award (Annual); Eastside Tourism Award (Annual); Innovative Service Award (Annual); Innovative Technology Award (Annual).

59098 ■ Bellingham/Whatcom Chamber of Commerce and Industry (B/WCCI)
119 N Commercial St., Ste. 110
Bellingham, WA 98225
Ph: (360)734-1330

Fax: (360)734-1332
Co. E-mail: chamber@bellingham.com
URL: http://www.bellingham.com
Contact: Ken Oplinger, President
Description: County-wide Chamber of Commerce; organizes community festivals and special events.

59099 ■ **Benton City Chamber of Commerce**
PO Box 401
Benton City, WA 99320
Ph: (509)588-4984
Co. E-mail: info@bentoncitychamber.org
URL: http://www.bentoncitychamber.org
Contact: Heather Duncan, President

59100 ■ **Birch Bay Chamber of Commerce**
7900 Birch Bay Dr.
Birch Bay, WA 98230
Ph: (360)371-5004
Co. E-mail: info@birchbaychamber.com
URL: http://www.birchbaychamber.com
Description: Promotes a healthy business climate while recognizing the quality of life at Birch Bay.
Founded: 1972. **Publications:** *Chamber News* (Monthly).

59101 ■ *Biz2Biz*
2000 Hewitt Ave., Ste. 205
Everett, WA 98201
Ph: (425)257-3222
Fax: (425)257-2074
Co. E-mail: info@everettchamber.com
URL: http://www.everettchamber.com
Contact: Louise Stanton-Masten, President
Released: Monthly

59102 ■ **Blaine Community Chamber of Commerce**
728 Peace Portal Dr.
Blaine, WA 98230
Ph: (360)332-6484
Free: 800-624-3555
Fax: (360)332-4544
Co. E-mail: info@blainechamber.com
URL: http://www.blainechamber.com
Contact: Ms. Carroll Solomon, Secretary
Description: Promotes business and community development in Blaine, WA. **Founded:** 1950.

59103 ■ **Bonney Lake Chamber of Commerce**
PO Box 7171
Bonney Lake, WA 98391
Ph: (253)222-5945
Co. E-mail: lora@bonneylake.com
URL: http://www.bonneylake.com
Contact: Lora Butterfield, Executive Director
Description: Promotes business and community development in Bonney Lake, WA. **Founded:** 1982.
Publications: *Chamber News.*

59104 ■ **Bremerton Area Chamber of Commerce (BACC)**
286 4th St.
Bremerton, WA 98337
Ph: (360)479-3579
Fax: (360)479-1033
Co. E-mail: chamber@bremertonchamber.org
URL: http://www.bremertonchamber.org
Contact: Mike Strube, President
Description: Promotes business and community development in the Bremerton, WA area. **Founded:** 1907. **Publications:** *Bremerton Business News* (Monthly). **Educational Activities:** Membership Luncheon (Monthly).

59105 ■ *Bremerton Business News*
286 4th St.
Bremerton, WA 98337
Ph: (360)479-3579
Fax: (360)479-1033
Co. E-mail: chamber@bremertonchamber.org
URL: http://www.bremertonchamber.org
Contact: Mike Strube, President
Released: Monthly

59106 ■ **Brewster Chamber of Commerce**
PO Box 1087
Brewster, WA 98812

Ph: (509)689-3464
Co. E-mail: contact@brewsterchamber.org
URL: http://www.brewsterchamber.org
Contact: Janet Jordan, President
Description: Promotes business and community development in Brewster.

59107 ■ **Bridgeport Area Chamber of Commerce**
Box 1060
Bridgeport, WA 98813-1060
Ph: (509)686-9501
Fax: (509)686-4052
Co. E-mail: gschmidt@bridgeport.wednet.edu
URL: http://www.bridgeportwashington.com
Contact: Gene Schmidt, President
Description: Promotes business and community development in Bridgeport, WA.

59108 ■ **Buckley Chamber of Commerce**
PO Box 168
Buckley, WA 98321
Ph: (360)829-0975
Fax: (360)829-9201
Co. E-mail: information@buckleychamber.org
URL: http://www.buckleychamber.org/chamber.htm
Contact: Ron Callis, President
Description: Promotes business and community development in Buckley, WA. Holds monthly board meeting.

59109 ■ *The Bulletin*
3614-A California Ave. SW
Seattle, WA 98116-4413
Ph: (206)932-5685
Fax: (206)938-7437
Co. E-mail: info@wschamber.com
URL: http://www.wschamber.com
Contact: Dave Montoure, Chairman
Released: Monthly

59110 ■ **Burlington Chamber of Commerce (BCC)**
111 S Cherry St.
Burlington, WA 98233
Ph: (360)757-0994
Fax: (360)757-0821
URL: http://www.burlington-chamber.com
Contact: Cheri Adkins, Chairperson
Description: Promotes business and community development in Burlington, WA. Sponsors Berry Dairy Days festival, Easter Egg Hunt, and Santa's Farm Parade, and Northwest Coffee Festival. **Founded:** 1961. **Publications:** *In Motion* (Monthly). **Educational Activities:** Social After Hours/Business Over Breakfast (Monthly).

59111 ■ *Business Advocate*
14220 Interurban Ave. S., Ste. 134
Tukwila, WA 98168
Ph: (206)575-1633
Free: 800-638-8613
Fax: (206)575-2007
Co. E-mail: staff@swkcc.org
URL: http://www.swkcc.org
Contact: Lynn Wallace, President
Released: Monthly **Price:** free.

59112 ■ *Business Connections*
500 NW Chamber of Commerce Way
Chehalis, WA 98532
Ph: (360)748-8885
Free: 800-525-3323
Fax: (360)748-8763
Co. E-mail: thechamber@chamberway.com
URL: http://www.chamberway.com
Contact: Bob Jackins, Chairman
Released: Monthly

59113 ■ *Business Directory*
422 NE 4th Ave.
Camas, WA 98607
Ph: (360)834-2472
Fax: (360)834-9171
Co. E-mail: brent@cwchamber.com
URL: http://www.cwchamber.com/cwdata
Contact: Brent Erickson, Executive Director
Released: Annual

59114 ■ *Business Directory*
111 W Main
Ritzville, WA 99169-0122
Ph: (509)659-1936
Fax: (509)659-0142
Co. E-mail: chamber@ritzville.com
URL: http://www.ritzvillechamber.org
Contact: Melanie Strecker, Administrator
Released: Periodic

59115 ■ *Business Directory and Community Profile*
625 S. 4th St.
Renton, WA 98057
Ph: (425)226-4560
Free: 877-467-3686
Fax: (425)226-4287
URL: http://www.gorenton.com
Contact: Jason Parker, Chairman
Released: Annual

59116 ■ *Business Matters*
2026 54th Ave. E
Fife, WA 98424
Ph: (253)922-9320
Free: 800-305-9926
URL: http://www.fifechamber.org
Contact: Aaron Williams, Executive Director
Released: Monthly

59117 ■ *Business News*
395 Winslow Way E
Bainbridge Island, WA 98110
Ph: (206)842-3700
Fax: (206)842-3713
Co. E-mail: info@bainbridgechamber.com
URL: http://www.bainbridgechamber.com
Contact: Kevin Dwyer, Executive Director
Released: Monthly

59118 ■ *Business News and Views*
1419 W Main St., Ste. 110
Battle Ground, WA 98604
Ph: (360)687-1510
Fax: (360)687-4505
Co. E-mail: info@battlegroundchamber.org
URL: http://www.battlegroundchamber.org
Contact: Diane Rivera, Executive Director
Released: Monthly

59119 ■ *Business Phone Directory*
PO Box 668
Quincy, WA 98848-0668
Ph: (509)787-2140
Fax: (509)787-4500
Co. E-mail: qvcc@quincyvalley.org
URL: http://www.quincyvalley.org
Contact: Karen Vizena, Executive Director
Released: Annual

59120 ■ **Camas-Washougal Chamber of Commerce (CWCC)**
422 NE 4th Ave.
Camas, WA 98607
Ph: (360)834-2472
Fax: (360)834-9171
Co. E-mail: brent@cwchamber.com
URL: http://www.cwchamber.com/cwdata
Contact: Brent Erickson, Executive Director
Description: Promotes business and community development in Camas and Washougal, WA. Sponsors Camas Days festival. **Founded:** 1953. **Publications:** *Business Directory* (Annual); *Chamber News* (Monthly); *Camas-Washougal Chamber of Commerce--Business Directory.*

59121 ■ *The Cashmere Business Journal*
PO Box 834
Cashmere, WA 98815
Ph: (509)782-7404
Fax: (509)782-1265
URL: http://www.cashmerechamber.com
Contact: Mr. Ben Ellis, President
Released: Bimonthly

59122 ■ **Cashmere Chamber of Commerce**
PO Box 834
Cashmere, WA 98815
Ph: (509)782-7404

Fax: (509)782-1265
URL: http://www.cashmerechamber.com
Contact: Mr. Ben Ellis, President
Description: Promotes business and community development in Cashmere, WA area. **Founded:** 1924. **Publications:** *The Cashmere Business Journal* (Bimonthly). **Awards:** Business of the Year (Annual); Citizen of the Year (Annual).

59123 ■ Central Washington SCORE
300 S Columbia St.
Wenatchee, WA 98801
Ph: (509)662-2116
Fax: (509)662-2022
Co. E-mail: score@wenatchee.org
URL: http://www.centralwashingtonscore.org
Description: Promotes business and community development in the Wenatchee, WA area. **Founded:** 1902.

59124 ■ Central Whidbey Chamber of Commerce (CWCC)
PO Box 152
Coupeville, WA 98239
Ph: (360)678-5434
Co. E-mail: cwcc@centralwhidbeychamber.com
URL: http://www.centralwhidbeychamber.com
Contact: Lynda Eccles, Executive Director
Description: Serves the business and community interests of Coupeville and Greenbank on Whidbey Island and produces local festivals. Maintains a visitor and Information Center. **Publications:** *The Chamber Notes* (Monthly). **Educational Activities:** Central Whidbey Island Harvest-Time Bed & Breakfast Tour & Tastes (Annual). **Telecommunication Services:** director@centralwhidbeychamber.com.

59125 ■ Centralia-Chehalis Chamber of Commerce
500 NW Chamber of Commerce Way
Chehalis, WA 98532
Ph: (360)748-8885
Free: 800-525-3323
Fax: (360)748-8763
Co. E-mail: thechamber@chamberway.com
URL: http://www.chamberway.com
Contact: Bob Jackins, Chairman
Description: Promotes business and community development in Lewis and Southern Thurston counties, WA. Provides regional tourist information. Sponsors community social and promotional events. Maintains information center. **Founded:** 1926. **Publications:** *Business Connections* (Monthly).

59126 ■ The Chamber
PO Box 3440
Federal Way, WA 98063
Ph: (253)838-2605
Fax: (253)661-9050
Co. E-mail: federalway@federalwaychamber.com
URL: http://www.federalwaychamber.com
Contact: Tom Pierson, Chief Executive Officer
Released: Monthly

59127 ■ Chamber Business Monthly
3815 196th St. SW, Ste. 136
Lynnwood, WA 98036
Ph: (425)774-0507
Fax: (425)774-4636
Co. E-mail: info@s2c3.com
URL: http://www.s2c3.com
Contact: Jean Hales, President
Released: Monthly

59128 ■ Chamber Chat
12345 30th Ave. NE, Ste. F-G
Seattle, WA 98125-5436
Ph: (206)363-3287
Fax: (206)363-6456
Co. E-mail: lakecitychamberofcommerce@gmail.com
URL: http://www.lakecitychamber.org
Contact: Tracy Heims, President
Released: Monthly

59129 ■ The Chamber Chat
5304 Littlerock Rd. SW
Tumwater, WA 98512
Ph: (360)357-5153

Fax: (360)786-1685
Co. E-mail: office@tumwaterchamber.com
URL: http://www.tumwaterchamber.com
Contact: David Bills, President
Released: Periodic

59130 ■ Chamber Chatter
PO Box 1249
Forks, WA 98331
Ph: (360)374-2531
Free: 800-443-6757
Fax: (360)374-9253
Co. E-mail: info@forkswa.com
URL: http://www.forkswa.com
Contact: Marcia Bingham, Director
Released: Monthly

59131 ■ The Chamber Connection
111 W Main St.
Monroe, WA 98272
Ph: (360)794-5488
Fax: (360)794-2044
Co. E-mail: info@chamber-monroe.org
URL: http://www.monroewachamber.com
Contact: Neil Watkins, Executive Director
Released: Monthly

59132 ■ Chamber Connection
PO Box 357
North Bend, WA 98045-0357
Ph: (425)888-4440
Fax: (425)888-4665
Co. E-mail: info@snovalley.org
URL: http://www.snovalley.org
Contact: Fritz Ribary, Chief Executive Officer
Released: Monthly

59133 ■ Chamber Connections
625 S. 4th St.
Renton, WA 98057
Ph: (425)226-4560
Free: 877-467-3686
Fax: (425)226-4287
URL: http://www.gorenton.com
Contact: Jason Parker, Chairman
Released: Monthly

59134 ■ Chamber Current
950 Pacific Ave., Ste. 300
Tacoma, WA 98402
Ph: (253)627-2175
Fax: (253)597-7305
Co. E-mail: info@tacomachamber.org
URL: http://www.tacomachamber.org
Contact: Tom Pierson, President
Released: Monthly

59135 ■ Chamber Journal
903 E Broadway St.
Goldendale, WA 98620
Ph: (509)773-3400
Fax: (509)773-3411
Co. E-mail: info@goldendalechamber.org
URL: http://www.goldendalechamber.org
Contact: Ray LaFond, President
Released: Periodic

59136 ■ Chamber Membership Directory and Profile
8300 Quinault Dr. NE, Ste. A
Lacey, WA 98516
Ph: (360)491-4141
Fax: (360)491-9403
Co. E-mail: info@laceychamber.com
URL: http://www.laceychamber.com
Contact: Sceni Foster, Coordinator, Administrative Services
Released: Annual

59137 ■ Chamber Monthly
PO Box 46
Sultan, WA 98294
Ph: (360)793-0983
Fax: (360)793-3241
Co. E-mail: debbie@skyvalleyvic.net
URL: http://www.skyvalleychamber.com
Contact: Brian Copple, President
Released: Monthly

59138 ■ Chamber News
PO Box 7171
Bonney Lake, WA 98391
Ph: (253)222-5945
Co. E-mail: lora@bonneylake.com
URL: http://www.bonneylake.com
Contact: Lora Butterfield, Executive Director

59139 ■ Chamber News
422 NE 4th Ave.
Camas, WA 98607
Ph: (360)834-2472
Fax: (360)834-9171
Co. E-mail: brent@cwchamber.com
URL: http://www.cwchamber.com/cwdata
Contact: Brent Erickson, Executive Director
Released: Monthly

59140 ■ Chamber News
133 W 2nd St.
Grandview, WA 98930
Ph: (509)882-2100
Fax: (509)882-5014
Co. E-mail: info@visitgrandview.org
URL: http://www.grandviewchamber.com
Contact: Brad Smith, President
Released: Monthly

59141 ■ Chamber News
PO Box 2389
Shelton, WA 98584
Ph: (360)426-2021
Free: 800-576-2021
Fax: (360)426-8678
Co. E-mail: heidi@sheltonchamber.org
URL: http://sheltonchamber.org
Released: Monthly

59142 ■ Chamber News
29 E Sumach St.
Walla Walla, WA 99362
Ph: (509)525-0850
Free: 877-998-4748
Fax: (509)522-2038
Co. E-mail: info@wwchamber.com
URL: http://www.wwvchamber.com
Contact: Jon Bren, Chairman of the Board
Released: Monthly

59143 ■ CHAMBER NEWS
PO Box 1012
Woodland, WA 98674
Ph: (360)225-9552
Fax: (360)225-3490
Co. E-mail: sknight@woodlandwachamber.com
URL: http://www.lewisriver.com/woodlandchamber
Contact: Tammie Howard, Director
Released: Annual

59144 ■ Chamber News
7900 Birch Bay Dr.
Birch Bay, WA 98230
Ph: (360)371-5004
Co. E-mail: info@birchbaychamber.com
URL: http://www.birchbaychamber.com
Released: Monthly

59145 ■ Chamber News
PO Box 824
Kalama, WA 98625
Ph: (360)673-6299
URL: http://www.kalamachamber.com
Contact: Brad Whittaker, President
Released: Monthly

59146 ■ Chamber Newsletter
415 N Grand Ave.
Pullman, WA 99163
Ph: (509)334-3565
Free: 800-365-6948
Fax: (509)332-3232
Co. E-mail: chamber@pullmanchamber.com
URL: http://www.pullmanchamber.com
Contact: Tammy Lewis, Executive Director
Released: Monthly

59147 ■ The Chamber Notes
PO Box 152
Coupeville, WA 98239

Ph: (360)678-5434
Co. E-mail: cwcc@centralwhidbeychamber.com
URL: http://www.centralwhidbeychamber.com
Contact: Lynda Eccles, Executive Director
Released: Monthly

59148 ■ *Chamber Scoop*
PO Box 1249
Forks, WA 98331
Ph: (360)374-2531
Free: 800-443-6757
Fax: (360)374-9253
Co. E-mail: info@forkswa.com
URL: http://www.forkswa.com
Contact: Marcia Bingham, Director
Released: Monthly **Price:** included in membership dues.

59149 ■ *Chamber Trends*
Bldg. 19, Ste. No. 109
4650 Steilacoom Blvd. SW
Lakewood, WA 98499-1599
Ph: (253)582-9400
Fax: (253)581-5241
Co. E-mail: chamber@lakewood-wa.com
URL: http://www.lakewood-wa.com
Contact: Linda K. Smith, President
Released: Monthly **Price:** $150, /issue for members; $450, /issue for nonmembers.

59150 ■ Chewelah Chamber of Commerce (CCoC)
PO Box 94
Chewelah, WA 99109
Ph: (509)935-8595
Fax: (509)935-8520
Co. E-mail: info@chewelah.org
URL: http://www.chewelah.org
Contact: Jeanne Nixon, Manager
Description: Promotes business and community development in Chewelah, WA. Participates in Miss Chewelah - Auction Beautification. Maintains tourism and visitor's center. **Founded:** 1907. **Publications:** *Around Town - What's Going On* (Bimonthly).

59151 ■ Clallam Bay - Sekiu Chamber of Commerce
PO Box 355
Clallam Bay, WA 98326-0355
Ph: (360)963-2339
Free: 877-694-9433
Co. E-mail: info@clallambay.com
URL: http://www.clallambay.com
Contact: Patti Adler, President
URL(s): www.sekiu.com. **Description:** Assists in the development of the Clallam Bay-Sekiu and the surrounding areas.

59152 ■ Clarkston Chamber of Commerce (CCC)
502 Bridge St.
Clarkston, WA 99403
Ph: (509)758-7712
Free: 800-933-2128
Fax: (509)751-8767
Co. E-mail: info@clarkstonchamber.org
URL: http://www.clarkstonchamber.org
Contact: Kristin Kemak, Executive Director
Description: Promotes business and community development in Clarkston, WA. **Publications:** *Connection* (Monthly).

59153 ■ Cle Elum-Roslyn Chamber of Commerce (CECC)
401 W 1st St.
Cle Elum, WA 98922
Ph: (509)674-5958
Fax: (509)674-1674
Co. E-mail: cle_elum@cleelum.com
URL: http://cleelumroslyn.org
Contact: Ryan Munsey, President
Description: Promotes business and community development and tourism in the Cle Elum, WA area. Sponsors festivals and charitable events.

59154 ■ Colville Chamber of Commerce
121 E Astor
Colville, WA 99114
Ph: (509)684-5973

Fax: (509)684-1344
Co. E-mail: colvillecoc@colville.com
URL: http://www.colville.com
Contact: Andy Hydorn, President
Description: Promotes business and community development in Colville, WA. Sponsors Rendezvous festival. Serves as a leader in tourism promotions. Sponsors Colville Junior Miss Program and Colville Float. **Founded:** 1910.

59155 ■ *Commerce Communicator*
PO Box 1264
Ferndale, WA 98248
Ph: (360)384-3042
Free: 888-722-2062
Fax: (360)384-3009
Co. E-mail: info@ferndale-chamber.com
URL: http://www.ferndale-chamber.com
Contact: Wayne Galloway, President
Released: Monthly

59156 ■ *Commerce Report*
c/o Lori Mattson, Pres./CEO
7130 W Grandridge Blvd., Ste. C
Kennewick, WA 99336
Ph: (509)736-0510
Fax: (509)783-1733
Co. E-mail: info@tricityregionalchamber.com
URL: http://www.tcrchamber.com
Contact: Lori Mattson, President
Released: Monthly

59157 ■ Concrete Chamber of Commerce
PO Box 743
Concrete, WA 98237
Ph: (360)853-8767
Co. E-mail: chamber@concrete-wa.com
URL: http://www.concrete-wa.com
Contact: Karen Ganion, Office Manager
Description: Promotes business and community development in Concrete, WA. **Founded:** 1976.

59158 ■ *Connection*
502 Bridge St.
Clarkston, WA 99403
Ph: (509)758-7712
Free: 800-933-2128
Fax: (509)751-8767
Co. E-mail: info@clarkstonchamber.org
URL: http://www.clarkstonchamber.org
Contact: Kristin Kemak, Executive Director
Released: Monthly

59159 ■ *Connections*
PO Box 850
Wenatchee, WA 98807-0850
Ph: (509)662-2116
Fax: (509)663-2022
Co. E-mail: info@wenatchee.org
URL: http://www.wenatchee.org
Contact: Craig Larsen, Executive Director
Released: Monthly **Price:** included in membership dues.

59160 ■ Coulee City Chamber of Commerce
PO Box 896
Coulee City, WA 99115-0896
Ph: (509)681-2018
Co. E-mail: tns@accima.com
URL: http://www.couleecity.com
Description: Promotes business and community development in Coulee City, WA.

59161 ■ Cranberry Coast Chamber of Commerce
PO Box 305
Grayland, WA 98547
Ph: (360)267-2003
Free: 800-473-6018
Fax: (360)267-2003
Co. E-mail: info@2thebeach.org
URL: http://www.cranberrycoastcoc.com
Contact: Beverly Ripley, Coordinator, Events
Description: Aims to promote the growth, economic development, and enhanced quality of life of Cranberry Coast.

59162 ■ Davenport Chamber of Commerce (DCC)
PO Box 869
Davenport, WA 99122
Ph: (509)725-6711
Co. E-mail: chamberofcommercedavenport@gmail.com
URL: http://www.davenportwa.org
Contact: Kathryn Jump, President
Description: Promotes business and community development in the Davenport, WA area.

59163 ■ Dayton Chamber of Commerce (DCC)
166 E Main St.
Dayton, WA 99328
Ph: (509)382-4825
Free: 800-882-6299
Co. E-mail: chamber@historicdayton.com
URL: http://www.historicdayton.com
Contact: Claudia Nysoe, Executive Director
Description: Promotes business and community development in Dayton, WA. Conducts area festival. **Founded:** 1946.

59164 ■ Deer Park Chamber of Commerce
316 E Crawford Ave.
Deer Park, WA 99006
Ph: (509)276-5900
Fax: (509)276-5900
Co. E-mail: info@deerparkchamber.com
URL: http://www.deerparkchamber.com
Contact: Joyce Simmons, President
Description: Promotes business and community development in Deer Park, WA.

59165 ■ *Destination Sequim, Travel Planner*
1192 E Washington St.
Sequim, WA 98382-0907
Ph: (360)683-6197
Free: 800-737-8462
Fax: (360)683-6349
Co. E-mail: info@sequimchamber.com
URL: http://www.sequimchamber.com
Contact: Shelli Robb Kahler, Executive Director
Price: free for members.

59166 ■ *E-Bulletin*
10 N 9th St.
Yakima, WA 98901
Ph: (509)248-2021
Fax: (509)248-0601
Co. E-mail: chamber@yakima.org
URL: http://www.yakima.org
Contact: Betty Wilkinson, President
E-mail: betty@yakima.org

59167 ■ *Economic and Community Profile/ Directory*
14220 Interurban Ave. S., Ste. 134
Tukwila, WA 98168
Ph: (206)575-1633
Free: 800-638-8613
Fax: (206)575-2007
Co. E-mail: staff@swkcc.org
URL: http://www.swkcc.org
Contact: Lynn Wallace, President
Released: Annual

59168 ■ *The Edge*
302 Bellevue Sq.
Bellevue, WA 98004
Ph: (425)454-2464
Fax: (425)462-4660
Co. E-mail: staffteam@bellevuechamber.org
URL: http://www.bellevuechamber.org
Contact: Betty Nokes, President
Released: Monthly **Price:** included in membership dues.

59169 ■ Ellensburg Chamber of Commerce (ECC)
609 N Main St.
Ellensburg, WA 98926
Ph: (509)925-2002
Free: 888-925-2204

Fax: (509)962-6148
Co. E-mail: info@ellensburg-chamber.com
URL: http://www.ellensburg-chamber.com
Contact: Susan Grindle, President
Description: Promotes agricultural, business, and community development in Ellensburg, WA area. Sponsors triathlon, annual Windfest, and local holiday festivities. **Founded:** 1908. **Publications:** *Chamber Membership Directory* (Annual).

59170 ■ Elma Chamber of Commerce
PO Box 798
Elma, WA 98541
Ph: (360)482-3055
Co. E-mail: info@elmachamber.org
URL: http://www.elmachamber.org
Contact: Renee Dunham, President
Description: Promotes business and community development in Elma, WA.

59171 ■ Enumclaw Chamber of Commerce (EACC)
1421 Cole St.
Enumclaw, WA 98022
Ph: (360)825-7666
Fax: (360)825-8369
Co. E-mail: tracey@enumclawchamber.com
URL: http://www.enumclawchamber.com
Contact: Tracey McCallum, Executive Director
Description: Promotes business and community development in the Enumclaw, WA area. Hosts Fourth of July Freedom Celebration and annual Christmas parade. **Publications:** *View Point* (Monthly). **Awards:** Business Award (Annual); Business of the Month (Monthly); Individual Citizen Award (Annual); Organization Award (Annual); Pioneer Award (Annual).

59172 ■ Ephrata Chamber of Commerce (ECC)
1 Basin St. SW
Ephrata, WA 98823
Ph: (509)754-4656
Fax: (509)754-5788
Co. E-mail: info@ephratawachamber.com
URL: http://www.ephratawachamber.com
Contact: Tia Tracy, Executive Director
Description: Promotes business and community development in Ephrata, WA. **Publications:** *Ephrata Newsletter* (Monthly). **Educational Activities:** Auction (Annual).

59173 ■ Ephrata Newsletter
1 Basin St. SW
Ephrata, WA 98823
Ph: (509)754-4656
Fax: (509)754-5788
Co. E-mail: info@ephratawachamber.com
URL: http://www.ephratawachamber.com
Contact: Tia Tracy, Executive Director
Released: Monthly **Price:** free for members.

59174 ■ Event Directory
202 Hwy. 20
Winthrop, WA 98862
Ph: (509)996-2125
Free: 888-463-8469
Co. E-mail: info@winthropwashington.com
URL: http://winthropwashington.com
Released: Annual

59175 ■ eVents Update
1301 5th Ave., Ste. 2500
Seattle, WA 98101-2611
Ph: (206)389-7200
Fax: (206)389-7288
Co. E-mail: info@seattlechamber.com
URL: http://www.seattlechamber.com
Contact: Phil Bussey, President
Released: Biweekly

59176 ■ Everett Area Chamber of Commerce
2000 Hewitt Ave., Ste. 205
Everett, WA 98201
Ph: (425)257-3222

Fax: (425)257-2074
Co. E-mail: info@everettchamber.com
URL: http://www.everettchamber.com
Contact: Louise Stanton-Masten, President
Description: Promotes business and community development in the Everett, WA area. Emphasizes downtown revitalization. **Founded:** 1892. **Publications:** *Biz2Biz* (Monthly); *Everett Guide* (Annual). **Awards:** Corporate Executive of the Year Award (Annual); Henry M. Jackson (Annual); Service-to-Business Award (Annual); Small Business Executive of the Year Award (Annual). **Telecommunication Services:** louise@everettchamber.com.

59177 ■ Everett Guide
2000 Hewitt Ave., Ste. 205
Everett, WA 98201
Ph: (425)257-3222
Fax: (425)257-2074
Co. E-mail: info@everettchamber.com
URL: http://www.everettchamber.com
Contact: Louise Stanton-Masten, President
Released: Annual

59178 ■ The Exchange
714-B Metcalf St.
Sedro Woolley, WA 98284
Ph: (360)855-1841
Co. E-mail: swchamber@sedro-woolley.com
URL: http://www.sedro-woolley.com
Contact: Pola Kelley, Executive Director
Released: Monthly **Price:** available to members only.

59179 ■ Facility Directory
17401 33rd Ave. NE
Woodinville, WA 98072
Ph: (425)481-8300
Fax: (425)481-9743
URL: http://www.woodinvillechamber.org
Contact: David Witt, Executive Director
Released: Periodic

59180 ■ Federal Way Chamber of Commerce
PO Box 3440
Federal Way, WA 98063
Ph: (253)838-2605
Fax: (253)661-9050
Co. E-mail: federalway@federalwaychamber.com
URL: http://www.federalwaychamber.com
Contact: Tom Pierson, Chief Executive Officer
Description: Promotes business and community development in the Federal Way, WA area. **Founded:** 1953. **Publications:** *The Chamber* (Monthly). **Educational Activities:** Ambassador Committee (Monthly). **Awards:** Ambassadors of the Month (Monthly).

59181 ■ Ferndale Chamber of Commerce (FCC)
PO Box 1264
Ferndale, WA 98248
Ph: (360)384-3042
Free: 888-722-2062
Fax: (360)384-3009
Co. E-mail: info@ferndale-chamber.com
URL: http://www.ferndale-chamber.com
Contact: Wayne Galloway, President
Description: Promotes business and community development in Ferndale, WA. Conducts hot air balloon festival, international folk dance festival, garage sale, pumpkin contest, and Christmas-tree lighting. Sponsors charitable activities. **Founded:** 1955. **Publications:** *Commerce Communicator* (Monthly). **Awards:** Business of the Month (Monthly); Business of the Year (Annual).

59182 ■ Fife Area Chamber of Commerce
2026 54th Ave. E
Fife, WA 98424
Ph: (253)922-9320
Free: 800-305-9926
URL: http://www.fifechamber.org
Contact: Aaron Williams, Executive Director
Description: Promotes commerce, assists in area businesses, and advances the business image of the Fife area. **Publications:** *Business Matters* (Monthly). **Educational Activities:** Fife Area Chamber of Commerce Luncheon (Monthly).

59183 ■ FOCUS
325 W 4th St.
Newport, WA 99156
Ph: (509)447-5812
Free: 877-818-1008
Co. E-mail: info@newportareachamber.com
URL: http://www.newportoldtownchamber.org
Contact: Barb Smith, President
Released: Monthly

59184 ■ Forks Chamber of Commerce
PO Box 1249
Forks, WA 98331
Ph: (360)374-2531
Free: 800-443-6757
Fax: (360)374-9253
Co. E-mail: info@forkswa.com
URL: http://www.forkswa.com
Contact: Marcia Bingham, Director
Description: Promotes business and community development in Forks, WA. **Scope:** business, customer service. **Founded:** 1926. **Subscriptions:** 40 books video recordings. **Publications:** *Chamber Chatter* (Monthly); *Chamber Scoop* (Monthly); *News and Views* (Periodic). **Awards:** Best Business of the Year (Annual); Best Citizen of the Year (Annual); Best Volunteer of the Year (Annual); HS Scholarship (Annual). **Telecommunication Services:** chamber@forkswa.com.

59185 ■ Gig Harbor Peninsula Area Chamber of Commerce (GHPA)
3311 Harborview Dr., Ste. 101
Gig Harbor, WA 98332
Ph: (253)851-6865
Free: 800-359-8804
Fax: (253)851-6881
Co. E-mail: info@gigharborchamber.com
URL: http://www.gigharborchamber.com
Contact: Warren Zimmerman, President
Description: Promotes business and community development in the Gig Harbor, WA area. Conducts annual parade and picnic; conducts photo competitions. **Founded:** 1980.

59186 ■ Grand Coulee Dam Area Chamber of Commerce (GCDACC)
PO Box 760
Grand Coulee, WA 99133-0760
Ph: (509)633-3074
Free: 800-268-5332
Fax: (509)633-2366
Co. E-mail: chamber@grandcouleedam.org
URL: http://www.grandcouleedam.org
Contact: Susan Miller, Manager
Description: Promotes business and community development in the Grand Coulee Dam, WA area. Sponsors Colorama, Laser Light, and 4th of July festivities. **Founded:** 1978.

59187 ■ Grandview Chamber of Commerce
133 W 2nd St.
Grandview, WA 98930
Ph: (509)882-2100
Fax: (509)882-5014
Co. E-mail: info@visitgrandview.org
URL: http://www.grandviewchamber.com
Contact: Brad Smith, President
Description: Promotes business and community development in Grandview, WA. **Publications:** *Chamber News* (Monthly). **Educational Activities:** Summer Eve in the Park (Annual).

59188 ■ Granger Chamber of Commerce
PO Box 250
Granger, WA 98932
Ph: (509)854-7304
Co. E-mail: grangerchamber@gmail.com
URL: http://www.grangerchamber.org
Contact: Gabriel Martinez, President
Description: Promotes the economic growth and quality of life in Granger, WA.

59189 ■ Grays Harbor Chamber of Commerce
506 Duffy St.
Aberdeen, WA 98520-3531
Ph: (360)532-1924
Free: 800-321-1924

Fax: (360)533-7945
Co. E-mail: info@graysharbor.org
URL: http://www.graysharbor.org
Contact: Kellie Daniels, Chairperson
Description: Promotes business and community development in Grays Harbor County, WA. Holds business forums, retreats, seminars, and workshops. Provides information, advocacy and networking. **Founded:** 1892. **Publications:** *The Insider* (Monthly).

59190 ■ Greater Eatonville Chamber of Commerce
PO Box 845
Eatonville, WA 98328
Ph: (360)832-4000
Co. E-mail: info@eatonvillechamber.com
URL: http://www.eatonvillechamber.com
Contact: Louise Carson, Secretary
Description: Promotes business and community development in the Eatonville, WA area. **Publications:** *Greater Eatonville Chamber of Commerce Newsletter* (Bimonthly).

59191 ■ *Greater Eatonville Chamber of Commerce Newsletter*
PO Box 845
Eatonville, WA 98328
Ph: (360)832-4000
Co. E-mail: info@eatonvillechamber.com
URL: http://www.eatonvillechamber.com
Contact: Louise Carson, Secretary
Released: Bimonthly

59192 ■ Greater Edmonds Chamber of Commerce
121 5th Ave. N
Edmonds, WA 98020
Ph: (425)670-1496
Fax: (425)712-1808
Co. E-mail: chamberofcommerce@edmondswa.com
URL: http://www.edmondswa.com
Contact: Jim Hills, President
E-mail: jhills@heraldnet.com
Description: Promotes business and community development in Edmonds, WA. Sponsors A Taste of Edmonds Festival. **Founded:** 1907. **Publications:** *Edmonds Chamber of Commerce Preferred Business Directory*; *Chamber Directory of Preferred Businesses*.

59193 ■ Greater Goldendale Area Chamber of Commerce
903 E Broadway St.
Goldendale, WA 98620
Ph: (509)773-3400
Fax: (509)773-3411
Co. E-mail: info@goldendalechamber.org
URL: http://www.goldendalechamber.org
Contact: Ray LaFond, President
Description: Promotes business and community development in Goldendale, WA. **Publications:** *Chamber Journal* (Periodic).

59194 ■ Greater Issaquah Chamber of Commerce (GICC)
155 NW Gilman Blvd.
Issaquah, WA 98027
Ph: (425)392-7024
Fax: (425)392-8101
Co. E-mail: info@issaquahchamber.com
URL: http://www.issaquahchamber.com
Contact: Matthew Bott, Chief Executive Officer
Description: Promotes business and community development in Issaquah, WA. Sponsors festival. **Publications:** *Issaquah! Chamber Business News* (Monthly). **Awards:** Greater Issaquah Chamber Scholarship (Annual).

59195 ■ Greater Kingston Community Chamber of Commerce
PO Box 78
Kingston, WA 98346
Ph: (360)297-3813
URL: http://kingstonchamber.com
Contact: Donna Etchey, President
Description: Promotes business and community development in Kingston, WA area.

59196 ■ Greater Kirkland Chamber of Commerce (GKCC)
401 Parkplace, Ste. 102
Kirkland, WA 98033
Ph: (425)822-7066
Fax: (425)827-4878
Co. E-mail: info@kirklandchamber.org
URL: http://www.kirklandchamber.org
Contact: Bill Vadino, Executive Director
Description: Promotes business and community development in the Greater Kirkland, WA area. **Publications:** *Kirkland Works* (Monthly).

59197 ■ Greater Lake Stevens Chamber of Commerce (GLSCC)
PO Box 439
Lake Stevens, WA 98258-0439
Ph: (425)334-0433
Co. E-mail: info@lakestevenschamber.com
URL: http://www.lschamber.org
Contact: Pam Stevens, President
Description: Promotes business and community development in the Lake Stevens, WA area. Operates Visitor Information Center. **Founded:** 1981. **Awards:** Business of the Year (Annual); Citizen of the Year (Annual); Junior Citizen of the Year (Annual).

59198 ■ Greater Maple Valley - Black Diamond Chamber of Commerce
23745 225th Way SE, Ste. 205
Maple Valley, WA 98038
Ph: (425)432-0222
Fax: (888)778-6823
Co. E-mail: info@maplevalleychamber.org
URL: http://www.maplevalleychamber.org
Contact: Susie Davies, Office Manager
Description: Promotes the general welfare and prosperity of the area and its surrounding territory. **Founded:** 1965.

59199 ■ Greater Marysville - Tulalip Chamber of Commerce
8825 34th Ave. NE, Ste. C
Tulalip, WA 98271
Ph: (360)659-7700
Fax: (360)653-7539
Co. E-mail: sandy@marysvilletulalipchamber.com
URL: http://www.marysvilletulalipchamber.com
Contact: Caldie Rogers, President
Description: Promotes the community and its total economy and fosters business-government relations to help members operate their business in the best possible environment. Serves as a civic clearinghouse, a public relations counselor, a legislative representative at the local, state, and national levels of government, an information and referral bureau and a research and promotion medium. **Founded:** 1908. **Publications:** *Memberandum* (Monthly).

59200 ■ Greater Oak Harbor Chamber of Commerce (GOHCC)
PO Box 883
Oak Harbor, WA 98277
Ph: (360)675-3755
Fax: (360)679-1624
Co. E-mail: info@oakharborchamber.com
URL: http://www.oakharborchamber.com
Contact: Jill Johnson, Executive Director
Description: Promotes business and community development in the Oak Harbor, WA area. Sponsors Holland Happening and Fourth of July festivals. **Founded:** 1957. **Awards:** Business of the Month (Monthly).

59201 ■ Greater Othello Chamber of Commerce
PO Box 2813
Othello, WA 99344
Ph: (509)488-2683
Free: 866-OTH-ELLO
Fax: (509)488-3123
Co. E-mail: manager@othellochamber.com
URL: http://www.othellochamber.com
Contact: Janelle Andersen, President
Description: Promotes business and community development in Othello, WA. Sponsors 4th of July celebration.

59202 ■ Greater Pasco Area Chamber of Commerce (GPACC)
1925 N 20th Ave.
Pasco, WA 99301
Ph: (509)547-9755
Fax: (509)547-9756
Co. E-mail: admin@pascochamber.org
URL: http://www.pascochamber.org
Contact: Ms. Steve Lee, Assistant Director
Description: Promotes business and community development in the Pasco, WA area. **Founded:** 1912.

59203 ■ Greater Poulsbo Chamber of Commerce (GPCC)
19351 8th Ave., Ste. 108
Poulsbo, WA 98370
Ph: (360)779-4848
Free: 877-768-5726
Fax: (360)779-3115
URL: http://www.poulsbochamber.com
Contact: Kathleen Haag, President
Description: Promotes business and community development and tourism in the Poulsbo, WA area. Provides visitor and relocation information. **Founded:** 1950. **Publications:** *Poulsbo Exchange* (Monthly); *Visitor Guide* (Annual). **Awards:** Volunteer of the Year (Annual).

59204 ■ Greater Redmond Chamber of Commerce
PO Box 628
Redmond, WA 98073-0628
Ph: (425)885-4014
Fax: (425)882-0996
Co. E-mail: chrish@redmondchamber.org
URL: http://www.redmondchamber.org
Contact: Christine Hoffmann, President
Description: Promotes business and community development in the Redmond, WA area. **Publications:** *Redmond Business* (Monthly).

59205 ■ Greater Renton Chamber of Commerce
625 S. 4th St.
Renton, WA 98057
Ph: (425)226-4560
Free: 877-467-3686
Fax: (425)226-4287
URL: http://www.gorenton.com
Contact: Jason Parker, Chairman
Description: Promotes business and community development in the Renton, WA area. **Publications:** *Chamber Connections* (Monthly); *Business Directory and Community Profile* (Annual).

59206 ■ Greater Seattle Chamber of Commerce
1301 5th Ave., Ste. 2500
Seattle, WA 98101-2611
Ph: (206)389-7200
Fax: (206)389-7288
Co. E-mail: info@seattlechamber.com
URL: http://www.seattlechamber.com
Contact: Phil Bussey, President
Description: Promotes business and community development in Seattle, WA area. **Founded:** 1890. **Publications:** *eVents Update* (Biweekly); *Directory of Seattle-King County Manufacturers*; *Greater Seattle Chamber of Commerce--Membership and Business Directory*; *Directory of Major Corporations: Central Puget Sound Region* (Biennial); *Directory of Major Manufacturers: Central Puget Sound Region*.

59207 ■ Greater University Chamber of Commerce (GUCC)
4710 University Way NE, Ste. 144
Seattle, WA 98105
Ph: (206)527-4417
Co. E-mail: director@udistrictchamber.org
URL: http://www.udistrictchamber.org
Contact: Teresa Lord Hugel, Executive Director
Description: Promotes business and community development in the University District of Seattle, WA. Sponsors University District Streetfair, University Farmers Market, and Junior Grand Seafair Parade. **Founded:** 1915. **Publications:** *University District Business News* (Monthly). **Telecommunication Services:** info@udistrictchamber.org.

59208 ■ Greater Vancouver Chamber of Commerce
1101 Broadway, Ste. 100
Vancouver, WA 98660
Ph: (360)694-2588
Fax: (360)693-8279
Co. E-mail: yourchamber@vancouverusa.com
URL: http://www.vancouverusa.com
Contact: Kim Capeloto, President

59209 ■ Greater Woodinville Chamber of Commerce
17401 33rd Ave. NE
Woodinville, WA 98072
Ph: (425)481-8300
Fax: (425)481-9743
URL: http://www.woodinvillechamber.org
Contact: David Witt, Executive Director
Description: Aims to promote, strengthen, and represent business community in Woodinville, WA. Serves as a voice to help focus government on the needs of the business community. Provides an environment for business networking and leads economic development efforts within the community. **Founded:** 1962. **Publications:** *Facility Directory* (Periodic); *Off the Vine* (Monthly). **Awards:** Business of the Year (Annual); Carol Edwards Community Award (Annual); Citizen of the Year (Annual); Volunteer of the Year (Annual).

59210 ■ Greater Yakima Chamber of Commerce
10 N 9th St.
Yakima, WA 98901
Ph: (509)248-2021
Fax: (509)248-0601
Co. E-mail: chamber@yakima.org
URL: http://www.yakima.org
Contact: Betty Wilkinson, President
E-mail: betty@yakima.org
Description: Strives to improve and preserve the business community of greater Yakima area. **Founded:** 1920. **Publications:** *Action Report* (Monthly); *E-Bulletin*; *Greater Yakima Chamber of Commerce--Membership Guide* (Annual); *Greater Yakima Chamber of Commerce--Clubs & Organizations Directory* (Annual); *Top Employer's List* (Annual); *Manufacturing Directory for Yakima Valley* (Annual); *Meeting, Reception, Banquet Rooms, and Caterers in the Greater Yakima Area* (Annual).

59211 ■ *In Motion*
111 S Cherry St.
Burlington, WA 98233
Ph: (360)757-0994
Fax: (360)757-0821
URL: http://www.burlington-chamber.com
Contact: Cheri Adkins, Chairperson
Released: Monthly **Price:** included in membership dues.

59212 ■ *The Insider*
506 Duffy St.
Aberdeen, WA 98520-3531
Ph: (360)532-1924
Free: 800-321-1924
Fax: (360)533-7945
Co. E-mail: info@graysharbor.org
URL: http://www.graysharbor.org
Contact: Kellie Daniels, Chairperson
Released: Monthly

59213 ■ *Insight*
8300 Quinault Dr. NE, Ste. A
Lacey, WA 98516
Ph: (360)491-4141
Fax: (360)491-9403
Co. E-mail: info@laceychamber.com
URL: http://www.laceychamber.com
Contact: Sceni Foster, Coordinator, Administrative Services
Released: Monthly

59214 ■ *Issaquah! Chamber Business News*
155 NW Gilman Blvd.
Issaquah, WA 98027
Ph: (425)392-7024

Fax: (425)392-8101
Co. E-mail: info@issaquahchamber.com
URL: http://www.issaquahchamber.com
Contact: Matthew Bott, Chief Executive Officer
Released: Monthly

59215 ■ Kalama Chamber of Commerce
PO Box 824
Kalama, WA 98625
Ph: (360)673-6299
URL: http://www.kalamachamber.com
Contact: Brad Whittaker, President
Description: Promotes business and community development in Kalama, WA area. **Publications:** *Chamber News* (Monthly). **Awards:** Citizen of the Year (Annual); Totem Award (Annual).

59216 ■ Kelso Longview Chamber of Commerce
1563 Olympia Way
Longview, WA 98632
Ph: (360)423-8400
Fax: (360)423-0432
Co. E-mail: info@kelsolongviewchamber.org
URL: http://www.kelsolongviewchamber.org
Contact: Frank McShane, Chairman
Description: Represents business communities and promotes community development of both Kelso and Longview. **Founded:** 1924.

59217 ■ Kent Chamber of Commerce
524 W Meeker St., Ste. 1
Kent, WA 98032
Ph: (253)854-1770
Fax: (253)854-8567
Co. E-mail: info@kentchamber.com
URL: http://www.kentchamber.com
Contact: Andrea Keikkala, Executive Director
Description: Promotes business and community development in Kent, WA. **Founded:** 1948. **Publications:** *The Voice of Business* (Monthly). **Awards:** Best Practices Award (Annual); Company Citizenship Award (Annual); Diversity Award (Annual); Economic Engine Award (Annual); Education Service Award (Annual); Green Award (Annual); Innovation Award (Annual); President's Leadership Award (Annual); Robert E. Lee Membership Development Award (Annual); Volunteer of the Month (Monthly); Legislator or Government Employee of the Year Award (Annual).

59218 ■ *Kirkland Works*
401 Parkplace, Ste. 102
Kirkland, WA 98033
Ph: (425)822-7066
Fax: (425)827-4878
Co. E-mail: info@kirklandchamber.org
URL: http://www.kirklandchamber.org
Contact: Bill Vadino, Executive Director
Released: Monthly **Price:** included in membership dues.

59219 ■ La Conner Chamber of Commerce
PO Box 1610
La Conner, WA 98257
Ph: (360)466-4778
Free: 888-642-9284
Fax: (360)466-0204
Co. E-mail: info@laconnerchamber.com
URL: http://www.laconnerchamber.com
Contact: Marci Plank, Executive Director
Description: Promotes business and commerce in La Conner, WA area. **Scope:** tourism in Washington. **Founded:** 1981. **Publications:** *La Connerite* (Monthly).

59220 ■ *La Connerite*
PO Box 1610
La Conner, WA 98257
Ph: (360)466-4778
Free: 888-642-9284
Fax: (360)466-0204
Co. E-mail: info@laconnerchamber.com
URL: http://www.laconnerchamber.com
Contact: Marci Plank, Executive Director
Released: Monthly

59221 ■ Lacey Thurston County Chamber of Commerce (LTCCC)
8300 Quinault Dr. NE, Ste. A
Lacey, WA 98516
Ph: (360)491-4141
Fax: (360)491-9403
Co. E-mail: info@laceychamber.com
URL: http://www.laceychamber.com
Contact: Sceni Foster, Coordinator, Administrative Services
Description: Promotes business and community development in the Lacey, WA area. **Founded:** 1960. **Publications:** *Insight* (Monthly); *Chamber Membership Directory and Profile* (Annual). **Educational Activities:** FORUM Luncheon (Monthly); Lacey Thurston County Chamber of Commerce Meeting (Annual). **Awards:** Ambassador of the Year (Annual); Large Business of the Year (Annual); Small Business of the Year (Annual); Volunteer of the Year (Annual).

59222 ■ Lake Chelan Chamber of Commerce
PO Box 216
Chelan, WA 98816-0216
Ph: (509)682-3503
Free: 800-4CH-ELAN
Fax: (509)682-3538
Co. E-mail: info@lakechelan.com
URL: http://www.lakechelan.com
Contact: Morgan Picton, President
Description: Seeks to support and encourage the economic and business development in the Chelan, WA area. Coordinates the efforts of commerce, industry and the professions in maintaining and strengthening a sound and healthy business climate in the region. Provides networking and learning opportunities for the business community in and around Chelan. **Founded:** 1931. **Publications:** *Lake Chelan Visitors Guide* (Annual); *Lake Chelan Visitors Guide* (Annual). **Educational Activities:** Business After Hours (Monthly). **Awards:** Beautification Award (Annual); Best New Business (Annual); Business of the Year (Annual); Citizen of the Year (Annual).

59223 ■ *Lake Chelan Visitors Guide*
PO Box 216
Chelan, WA 98816-0216
Ph: (509)682-3503
Free: 800-4CH-ELAN
Fax: (509)682-3538
Co. E-mail: info@lakechelan.com
URL: http://www.lakechelan.com
Contact: Morgan Picton, President
Released: Annual **Price:** free.

59224 ■ Lake City Chamber of Commerce
12345 30th Ave. NE, Ste. F-G
Seattle, WA 98125-5436
Ph: (206)363-3287
Fax: (206)363-6456
Co. E-mail: lakecitychamberofcommerce@gmail.com
URL: http://www.lakecitychamber.org
Contact: Tracy Heims, President
Description: Promotes business and community development in Lake City, WA. Sponsors festival and awards scholarships. **Founded:** 1958. **Publications:** *Chamber Chat* (Monthly).

59225 ■ Lakewood Chamber of Commerce
Bldg. 19, Ste. No. 109
4650 Steilacoom Blvd. SW
Lakewood, WA 98499-1599
Ph: (253)582-9400
Fax: (253)581-5241
Co. E-mail: chamber@lakewood-wa.com
URL: http://www.lakewood-wa.com
Contact: Linda K. Smith, President
Description: Promotes business and community development in Lakewood. Seeks to help enhance business activity and develops partnership for a vital community through political, social, and community leadership. **Founded:** 1972. **Publications:** *Chamber Trends* (Monthly). **Educational Activities:** Lakewood Chamber of Commerce Meeting (Annual).

59226 ■ Langley South Whidbey Chamber of Commerce
PO Box 403
Langley, WA 98260
Ph: (360)221-6765

Fax: (360)221-2979
Co. E-mail: langley@whidbey.com
URL: http://www.whidbeylodging.com
Contact: Mary Ann Mansfield, President
Description: Promotes business and community development in Langley, Washington. **Founded:** 1976.

59227 ■ Leavenworth Chamber of Commerce
940 Hwy. 2
Leavenworth, WA 98826
Ph: (509)548-5807
Fax: (509)548-1014
Co. E-mail: info@leavenworth.org
URL: http://www.leavenworth.org/modules/pages/index.php?pageid=1
Contact: Nancy Smith, Executive Director
Description: Promotes business and community development in Leavenworth, WA.

59228 ■ Lopez Island Chamber of Commerce
PO Box 102
Lopez Island, WA 98261
Ph: (360)468-4664
Free: 877-433-2789
Co. E-mail: lopezchamber@lopezisland.com
URL: http://www.lopezisland.com
Contact: Becky Smith, President
Description: Promotes business and commerce in Lopez Island, WA.

59229 ■ Lynden Chamber of Commerce (LCC)
PO Box 647
Lynden, WA 98264
Ph: (360)354-5995
Fax: (360)354-0401
Co. E-mail: lynden@lynden.org
URL: http://www.lynden.org
Contact: Gary A. Vis, Executive Director
Description: Promotes business, tourism, and community development in Lynden, WA. Sponsors local charitable events and festivals. **Founded:** 1928.

59230 ■ Magnolia Chamber of Commerce
3214 W McGraw St., Ste. 301B
Seattle, WA 98199
Ph: (206)284-5836
Fax: (206)352-7494
Co. E-mail: info@magnoliachamber.org
URL: http://www.magnoliachamber.org
Contact: Nancy Callaghan, Executive Director
Description: Promotes and develops business and commerce in Magnolia, Seattle, WA.

59231 ■ McCleary Community Chamber of Commerce
PO Box 53
McCleary, WA 98557-0053
Ph: (360)495-3667
URL: http://mcclearychamber.com
Contact: Pauline Martin, President
Description: Promotes the general welfare and prosperity of McCleary and all areas of its business community.

59232 ■ *Memberandum*
8825 34th Ave. NE, Ste. C
Tulalip, WA 98271
Ph: (360)659-7700
Fax: (360)653-7539
Co. E-mail: sandy@marysvilletulalipchamber.com
URL: http://www.marysvilletulalipchamber.com
Contact: Caldie Rogers, President
Released: Monthly

59233 ■ *Membership and Community Resource Directory*
111 W Main St.
Monroe, WA 98272
Ph: (360)794-5488
Fax: (360)794-2044
Co. E-mail: info@chamber-monroe.org
URL: http://www.monroewachamber.com
Contact: Neil Watkins, Executive Director
Released: Annual; in January.

59234 ■ *The Membership Directory & Business Resource Guide*
302 Bellevue Sq.
Bellevue, WA 98004
Ph: (425)454-2464
Fax: (425)462-4660
Co. E-mail: staffteam@bellevuechamber.org
URL: http://www.bellevuechamber.org
Contact: Betty Nokes, President
Released: Annual **Price:** $30.

59235 ■ *Membership Roster*
2208 NW Market St., Ste. 100
Seattle, WA 98107
Ph: (206)784-9705
Fax: (206)783-8154
Co. E-mail: info@ballardchamber.com
URL: http://www.ballardchamber.com
Contact: Beth Williamson Miller, Executive Director
Released: Annual

59236 ■ Mercer Island Chamber of Commerce
PO Box 108
Mercer Island, WA 98040
Ph: (206)232-3404
Fax: (206)232-8903
Co. E-mail: mi_chamber@msn.com
URL: http://www.mercerislandchamber.com
Contact: James Murphy, President
Description: Supports the growth, development, and advancement of the businesses of Mercer Island.

59237 ■ Monroe Chamber of Commerce
111 W Main St.
Monroe, WA 98272
Ph: (360)794-5488
Fax: (360)794-2044
Co. E-mail: info@chamber-monroe.org
URL: http://www.monroewachamber.com
Contact: Neil Watkins, Executive Director
Description: Comprises of representatives of the business community. Strives to foster business growth and community development. Sponsors Fair Days Parade, annual auction and Community Awards Recognition. Operates Visitor Information Center year round. **Founded:** 1962. **Publications:** *The Chamber Connection* (Monthly); *Membership and Community Resource Directory* (Annual).

59238 ■ Morton Chamber of Commerce
PO Box 10
Morton, WA 98356
Ph: (360)496-6086
Fax: (360)496-6210
Co. E-mail: chamber@lewiscounty.com
URL: http://mortonchamber.lewiscounty.com
Description: Promotes business and commerce in Morton, WA area.

59239 ■ Moses Lake Area Chamber of Commerce
324 S Pioneer Way
Moses Lake, WA 98837-1737
Ph: (509)765-7888
Free: 800-992-6234
Fax: (509)765-0000
Co. E-mail: information@moseslake.com
URL: http://www.moseslake.com
Contact: Michelle Price, President
Description: Promotes business and community development in the Moses Lake, WA area. **Founded:** 1941. **Awards:** President's Award (Annual).

59240 ■ Mount Adams Chamber of Commerce
PO Box 449
White Salmon, WA 98672
Ph: (509)493-3630
Free: 866-493-3630
Co. E-mail: info@mtadamschamber.com
URL: http://www.mtadamschamber.com
Contact: James L. Kacena, President
Description: Promotes business and community development in the Mid-Columbia area of Washington. Provides relocation and tourism information. Promotes festival, art and wine event. **Founded:** 1950.

59241 ■ *Mount Vernon Chamber Chat*
PO Box 1007
Mount Vernon, WA 98273
Ph: (360)428-8547
Fax: (360)424-6237
Co. E-mail: info@mountvernonchamber.com
URL: http://www.mountvernonchamber.com/members
Contact: Kristen Whitener, President
Released: Monthly

59242 ■ Mount Vernon Chamber of Commerce
PO Box 1007
Mount Vernon, WA 98273
Ph: (360)428-8547
Fax: (360)424-6237
Co. E-mail: info@mountvernonchamber.com
URL: http://www.mountvernonchamber.com/members
Contact: Kristen Whitener, President
Description: Promotes business and community development in Mt. Vernon, WA. Sponsors Skagit River Festival. **Publications:** *Mount Vernon Chamber Chat* (Monthly). **Educational Activities:** Networking Meeting (Monthly).

59243 ■ *The New Market*
5304 Littlerock Rd. SW
Tumwater, WA 98512
Ph: (360)357-5153
Fax: (360)786-1685
Co. E-mail: office@tumwaterchamber.com
URL: http://www.tumwaterchamber.com
Contact: David Bills, President
Released: Monthly

59244 ■ *New Wave*
PO Box 382
Ocean Shores, WA 98569
Ph: (360)289-2451
Free: 800-762-3224
Co. E-mail: chamber@oceanshores.org
URL: http://www.oceanshores.org
Contact: Mr. Mark Plackett, Executive Director
Released: Monthly

59245 ■ Newport - Oldtown Chamber of Commerce
325 W 4th St.
Newport, WA 99156
Ph: (509)447-5812
Free: 877-818-1008
Co. E-mail: info@newportareachamber.com
URL: http://www.newportoldtownchamber.org
Contact: Barb Smith, President
Description: Works to promote and strengthen the business and economic climate of the area while preserving and enhancing the area's quality of life. **Founded:** 1950. **Publications:** *FOCUS* (Monthly). **Educational Activities:** Newport - Oldtown Chamber of Commerce Meeting (Monthly).

59246 ■ *News and Views*
PO Box 1249
Forks, WA 98331
Ph: (360)374-2531
Free: 800-443-6757
Fax: (360)374-9253
Co. E-mail: info@forkswa.com
URL: http://www.forkswa.com
Contact: Marcia Bingham, Director
Released: Periodic

59247 ■ North Mason Chamber of Commerce
PO Box 416
Belfair, WA 98528
Ph: (360)275-4267
Fax: (360)275-0853
Co. E-mail: greg@northmasonchamber.com
URL: http://www.northmasonchamber.com
Contact: Rhonda Brown, Chairman of the Board
Description: Encourages and promotes business, tourism, social, educational, and environmental interests and activities of the North Mason community. Provides a representative voice for the busi-

ness community on transportation, growth and land use management, health care, education and workforce development issues.

59248 ■ Oakville Chamber of Commerce
PO Box 331
Oakville, WA 98568-0331
Ph: (360)273-2702
Co. E-mail: info@oakville-wa.org
URL: http://www.oakville-wa.org

Description: Strives to improve the general welfare and prosperity of the Oakville community. Promotes economic, civic, commercial, cultural, industrial, and educational interests of the area.

59249 ■ Ocean Park Area Chamber of Commerce
PO Box 403
Ocean Park, WA 98640
Ph: (360)665-4448
Free: 888-751-9354
Co. E-mail: opchamber@opwa.com
URL: http://www.opwa.com
Contact: Bob Beezley, President

Description: Aims to preserve the competitive enterprise system of business and to promote business and community growth and development. Supports worthwhile civic and/or cultural events for the community. Hosts a Garlic Festival in June, and an Old Fashioned 4th of July including a parade and Art In The Park. **Founded:** 1983.

59250 ■ Ocean Shores/North Beach Chamber of Commerce
PO Box 382
Ocean Shores, WA 98569
Ph: (360)289-2451
Free: 800-762-3224
Co. E-mail: chamber@oceanshores.org
URL: http://www.oceanshores.org
Contact: Mr. Mark Plackett, Executive Director

Description: Promotes business, tourism and support for non-profits in Ocean Shores, WA. **Founded:** 1970. **Publications:** *New Wave* (Monthly). **Educational Activities:** Chamber Business After Hours (Monthly). **Awards:** Business of the Quarter (Quarterly); Business of the Year (Annual).

59251 ■ Odessa Chamber of Commerce
PO Box 355
Odessa, WA 99159
Ph: (509)982-0049
URL: http://www.odessachamber.net
Contact: Marlon Schafer, President

Description: Non-competitive sports enthusiasts.

59252 ■ Off the Vine
17401 33rd Ave. NE
Woodinville, WA 98072
Ph: (425)481-8300
Fax: (425)481-9743
URL: http://www.woodinvillechamber.org
Contact: David Witt, Executive Director
Released: Monthly

59253 ■ Omak Chamber of Commerce
PO Box 3100
Omak, WA 98841
Ph: (509)826-1880
Free: 800-225-6625
Fax: (509)826-6201
Co. E-mail: omakchamber@northcascades.net
URL: http://www.omakchamber.com
Contact: Corina Radford, President

Description: Promotes business and community development in Omak, WA.

59254 ■ Oroville Chamber of Commerce
PO Box 2140
Oroville, WA 98844-2140
Ph: (509)476-2739

Fax: (509)476-2739
Co. E-mail: orovillechamber@gdicom.net
URL: http://www.orovillewashington.com
Contact: Gary DeVon, President
Description: Promotes business and commerce in the Oroville, WA area. **Publications:** *Oroville Chamber Update!* (Periodic). **Educational Activities:** Oroville Chamber of Commerce Meeting (Bimonthly). **Telecommunication Services:** orovillewashington@gmail.com.

59255 ■ Oroville Chamber Update!
PO Box 2140
Oroville, WA 98844-2140
Ph: (509)476-2739
Fax: (509)476-2739
Co. E-mail: orovillechamber@gdicom.net
URL: http://www.orovillewashington.com
Contact: Gary DeVon, President
Released: Periodic; no less than 2 times a month.
Price: free.

59256 ■ Palouse Chamber of Commerce
PO Box 174
Palouse, WA 99161-0174
Co. E-mail: palousechamber@visitpalouse.com
URL: http://VisitPalouse.com
Contact: Patti Green-Kent, President
Description: Promotes business and community development in Palouse, WA area.

59257 ■ Point Roberts Chamber of Commerce and Visitor's Bureau
PO Box 128
Point Roberts, WA 98281
Ph: (360)945-2313
Fax: (360)945-2855
Co. E-mail: membership@pointrobertschamber-ofcommerce.com
URL: http://pointrobertschamberofcommerce.com
Contact: Heather McPhee, Director
Description: Promotes business and community development in Point Roberts, WA.

59258 ■ Port Ludlow Chamber of Commerce
PO Box 65305
Port Ludlow, WA 98365
Ph: (360)437-9798
Fax: (360)437-7684
Co. E-mail: info@portludlowchamber.org
URL: http://www.portludlowchamber.org
Contact: Paula Zimmerman, Co-President
Description: Promotes business and commerce in Port Ludlow, WA area.

59259 ■ Port Orchard Chamber of Commerce (POCOC)
1014 Bay St., No. 8
Port Orchard, WA 98366-5205
Ph: (360)876-3505
Free: 800-982-8139
Fax: (360)895-1920
Co. E-mail: office@portochard.com
URL: http://www.portorchard.com
Contact: Desiree Steffens, President
Description: Promotes business and community development in the Port Orchard, WA area. Sponsors charitable events. **Founded:** 1943.

59260 ■ Port Townsend Chamber of Commerce
440 12th St.
Port Townsend, WA 98368
Ph: (360)385-2722
Free: 888-ENJOY-PT
Fax: (360)379-8204
Co. E-mail: info@jeffcountychamber.org
URL: http://www.ptchamber.org
Contact: Jennifer Wells-MacGillonie, Executive Director
URL(s): jeffcountychamber.org. **Description:** Promotes business and community development in Port Townsend, WA. **Founded:** 1889.

59261 ■ Poulsbo Exchange
19351 8th Ave., Ste. 108
Poulsbo, WA 98370
Ph: (360)779-4848
Free: 877-768-5726

Fax: (360)779-3115
URL: http://www.poulsbochamber.com
Contact: Kathleen Haag, President
Released: Monthly

59262 ■ Profile Booklet
c/o Lori Mattson, Pres./CEO
7130 W Grandridge Blvd., Ste. C
Kennewick, WA 99336
Ph: (509)736-0510
Fax: (509)783-1733
Co. E-mail: info@tricityregionalchamber.com
URL: http://www.tcrchamber.com
Contact: Lori Mattson, President
Released: Annual

59263 ■ Prosser Chamber of Commerce
1230 Bennett Ave.
Prosser, WA 99350
Ph: (509)786-3177
Free: 800-408-1517
Fax: (509)786-2399
Co. E-mail: info@prosserchamber.org
URL: http://www.prosserchamber.org
Contact: Jim Milne, Executive Director
Description: Promotes business and community development in Prosser, WA area.

59264 ■ Pullman Chamber of Commerce (PCC)
415 N Grand Ave.
Pullman, WA 99163
Ph: (509)334-3565
Free: 800-365-6948
Fax: (509)332-3232
Co. E-mail: chamber@pullmanchamber.com
URL: http://www.pullmanchamber.com
Contact: Tammy Lewis, Executive Director
Description: Promotes business and community development in Pullman, WA. Sponsors 4th of July Community Celebration and National Lentil Festival. **Founded:** 1910. **Publications:** *Chamber Newsletter* (Monthly).

59265 ■ Quincy Chamber Update
PO Box 668
Quincy, WA 98848-0668
Ph: (509)787-2140
Fax: (509)787-4500
Co. E-mail: qvcc@quincyvalley.org
URL: http://www.quincyvalley.org
Contact: Karen Vizena, Executive Director
Released: Monthly

59266 ■ Quincy Valley Chamber of Commerce (QVCC)
PO Box 668
Quincy, WA 98848-0668
Ph: (509)787-2140
Fax: (509)787-4500
Co. E-mail: qvcc@quincyvalley.org
URL: http://www.quincyvalley.org
Contact: Karen Vizena, Executive Director
Description: Promotes business and community development and tourism in the Quincy, WA area. Sponsors Farmer-Consumer Awareness day. Conducts fundraising auction. **Founded:** 1947. **Publications:** *Business Phone Directory* (Annual); *Quincy Chamber Update* (Monthly).

59267 ■ Real Estate Magazine
c/o Lori Mattson, Pres./CEO
7130 W Grandridge Blvd., Ste. C
Kennewick, WA 99336
Ph: (509)736-0510
Fax: (509)783-1733
Co. E-mail: info@tricityregionalchamber.com
URL: http://www.tcrchamber.com
Contact: Lori Mattson, President
Price: $2, in U.S.; $5, postage for foreign mail.

59268 ■ Redmond Business
PO Box 628
Redmond, WA 98073-0628
Ph: (425)885-4014

Fax: (425)882-0996
Co. E-mail: chrish@redmondchamber.org
URL: http://www.redmondchamber.org
Contact: Christine Hoffmann, President
Released: Monthly

59269 ■ Ritzville Area Chamber of Commerce
111 W Main
Ritzville, WA 99169-0122
Ph: (509)659-1936
Fax: (509)659-0142
Co. E-mail: chamber@ritzville.com
URL: http://www.ritzvillechamber.org
Contact: Melanie Strecker, Administrator
Description: Promotes business and community development in Ritzville, WA. **Founded:** 1903. **Publications:** *Business Directory* (Periodic). **Educational Activities:** Business Meeting (Monthly).

59270 ■ Rosalia Chamber of Commerce
PO Box 132
Rosalia, WA 99170-0132
Ph: (509)999-0909
Co. E-mail: rosaliachamber@gmail.com
Contact: Pat Voge, President

59271 ■ San Juan Island Chamber of Commerce
PO Box 98
Friday Harbor, WA 98250
Ph: (360)378-5240
Fax: (360)370-5289
Co. E-mail: chamberinfo@sanjuanisland.org
URL: http://www.sanjuanisland.org
Contact: Julie Corey, President
Description: Promotes business and community development in the Friday Harbor, WA area. **Publications:** *San Juan Island Chamber of Commerce News* (Monthly).

59272 ■ *San Juan Island Chamber of Commerce News*
PO Box 98
Friday Harbor, WA 98250
Ph: (360)378-5240
Fax: (360)370-5289
Co. E-mail: chamberinfo@sanjuanisland.org
URL: http://www.sanjuanisland.org
Contact: Julie Corey, President
Released: Monthly

59273 ■ Sedro-Woolley Chamber of Commerce
714-B Metcalf St.
Sedro Woolley, WA 98284
Ph: (360)855-1841
Co. E-mail: swchamber@sedro-woolley.com
URL: http://www.sedro-woolley.com
Contact: Pola Kelley, Executive Director
Description: Promotes business and community development in Sedro-Woolley, WA. Sponsors Woodfest, Tulip Festival, Blast From the Past, Founders Days, Christmas Parade and tree lighting, and Breakfast with Santa. **Founded:** 1914. **Publications:** *The Exchange* (Monthly). **Educational Activities:** Steelhead Days (Annual). **Awards:** Sedro-Woolley Business of the Year (Annual).

59274 ■ Sequim-Dungeness Valley Chamber of Commerce
1192 E Washington St.
Sequim, WA 98382-0907
Ph: (360)683-6197
Free: 800-737-8462
Fax: (360)683-6349
Co. E-mail: info@sequimchamber.com
URL: http://www.sequimchamber.com
Contact: Shelli Robb Kahler, Executive Director
Description: Promotes business and community development in the Sequim, WA area. **Founded:** 1936. **Publications:** *Destination Sequim, Travel Planner.*

59275 ■ *Shelton Journal*
PO Box 2389
Shelton, WA 98584
Ph: (360)426-2021
Free: 800-576-2021

Fax: (360)426-8678
Co. E-mail: heidi@sheltonchamber.org
URL: http://sheltonchamber.org
Released: Weekly

59276 ■ Shelton-Mason County Chamber of Commerce (SMCCC)
PO Box 2389
Shelton, WA 98584
Ph: (360)426-2021
Free: 800-576-2021
Fax: (360)426-8678
Co. E-mail: heidi@sheltonchamber.org
URL: http://sheltonchamber.org
Description: Promotes business and community development in Shelton and Mason County, WA. Conducts seminars and workshops; sponsors festivals and parades. Sponsors the Christmas Parade and Annual Auction Bazaar. Conducts community tours. Offers quarterly seminar. **Founded:** 1920. **Publications:** *Chamber News* (Monthly); *Shelton Journal* (Weekly). **Educational Activities:** Shelton-Mason County Chamber of Commerce Dinner (Monthly).

59277 ■ Shoreline Chamber of Commerce (SCC)
18560 1st Ave. NE
Shoreline, WA 98155-2148
Ph: (206)361-2260
Fax: (206)361-2268
Co. E-mail: info@shorelinechamber.com
URL: http://www.shorelinechamber.com
Contact: Rick Stephens, President
Description: Promotes commerce in the Greater Shoreline Area by providing value to its members through business education, networking opportunities and effective representation. **Founded:** 1976. **Publications:** *ShoreLines* (Monthly); *Shoreline Chamber of Commerce--Membership Directory & Buyer's Guide.*

59278 ■ *ShoreLines*
18560 1st Ave. NE
Shoreline, WA 98155-2148
Ph: (206)361-2260
Fax: (206)361-2268
Co. E-mail: info@shorelinechamber.com
URL: http://www.shorelinechamber.com
Contact: Rick Stephens, President
Released: Monthly **Price:** included in membership dues.

59279 ■ Silverdale Chamber of Commerce
PO Box 1218
Silverdale, WA 98383
Ph: (360)692-6800
Fax: (360)692-1379
Co. E-mail: kathleen@silverdalechamber.com
URL: http://www.silverdalechamber.com
Contact: Julie Jennings, President
Description: Promotes business and community development in Silverdale, WA. **Founded:** 1973.

59280 ■ Skamania County Chamber of Commerce
PO Box 1037
Stevenson, WA 98648
Ph: (509)427-8911
Free: 800-989-9178
Fax: (509)427-5122
Co. E-mail: info@skamania.org
URL: http://www.skamania.org
Contact: Casey Roeder, Executive Director
Description: Promotes and develops business and commerce in Skamania County, WA.

59281 ■ Sky Valley Chamber of Commerce
PO Box 46
Sultan, WA 98294
Ph: (360)793-0983
Fax: (360)793-3241
Co. E-mail: debbie@skyvalleyvic.net
URL: http://www.skyvalleychamber.com
Contact: Brian Copple, President
Description: Promotes business and community development in Sultan, WA. Conducts Sultan Summer Shindig and other community activities. **Publications:** *Chamber Monthly* (Monthly); *Snohomish County Tourist Bureau* (Periodic).

59282 ■ Snohomish Chamber of Commerce
PO Box 135
Snohomish, WA 98291-0135
Ph: (360)568-2526
Fax: (360)568-3869
Co. E-mail: manager@cityofsnohomish.com
URL: http://www.cityofsnohomish.com
Contact: Jeff Rasmussen, President
Description: Promotes business and community development in Snohomish, WA. **Founded:** 1953.

59283 ■ *Snohomish County Tourist Bureau*
PO Box 46
Sultan, WA 98294
Ph: (360)793-0983
Fax: (360)793-3241
Co. E-mail: debbie@skyvalleyvic.net
URL: http://www.skyvalleychamber.com
Contact: Brian Copple, President
Released: Periodic

59284 ■ Snoqualmie Valley Chamber of Commerce (SVCC)
PO Box 357
North Bend, WA 98045-0357
Ph: (425)888-4440
Fax: (425)888-4665
Co. E-mail: info@snovalley.org
URL: http://www.snovalley.org
Contact: Fritz Ribary, Chief Executive Officer
Description: Promotes business/community growth and development by promoting economic programs designed to strengthen and expand the economic potential of all businesses within the area. **Publications:** *Chamber Connection* (Monthly). **Educational Activities:** After Hours (Monthly). **Awards:** New Business of the Year (Annual); President's Award (Annual); Volunteer of the Year (Annual); Business of the Year (Annual); Director's Award (Annual).

59285 ■ Soap Lake Chamber of Commerce
PO Box 433
Soap Lake, WA 98851
Ph: (509)246-1821
Co. E-mail: slcoc@soaplakecoc.org
URL: http://www.soaplakecoc.org
Description: Promotes business and commerce in Soap Lake, WA area.

59286 ■ South Snohomish County Chamber of Commerce (SSCCC)
3815 196th St. SW, Ste. 136
Lynnwood, WA 98036
Ph: (425)774-0507
Fax: (425)774-4636
Co. E-mail: info@s2c3.com
URL: http://www.s2c3.com
Contact: Jean Hales, President
Description: Promotes business and community development in southern Snohomish County, WA. **Founded:** 1964. **Publications:** *Chamber Business Monthly* (Monthly); *South Snohomish County Chamber of Commerce Buyer's Guide and Membership Directory* (Annual); *South Snohomish County Chamber of Commerce Buyer's Guide and Membership Directory* (Annual). **Educational Activities:** General Membership Meeting/Luncheon (Monthly); Good Morning South County Breakfast Networking (Monthly). **Awards:** Small Business Award; John M. Fluke, Sr., Community Service Award (Annual).

59287 ■ *South Snohomish County Chamber of Commerce Buyer's Guide and Membership Directory*
3815 196th St. SW, Ste. 136
Lynnwood, WA 98036
Ph: (425)774-0507
Fax: (425)774-4636
Co. E-mail: info@s2c3.com
URL: http://www.s2c3.com
Contact: Jean Hales, President
Released: Annual

59288 ■ Southwest King County Chamber of Commerce (SWKCC)
14220 Interurban Ave. S., Ste. 134
Tukwila, WA 98168
Ph: (206)575-1633
Free: 800-638-8613

Fax: (206)575-2007
Co. E-mail: staff@swkcc.org
URL: http://www.swkcc.org
Contact: Lynn Wallace, President
Description: Promotes business and community development in Southwest King County, Burien, SeaTac, and Tukwila, WA. **Scope:** small business resources, demographics, economic indicators. **Founded:** 1989. **Subscriptions:** periodicals. **Publications:** *Business Advocate* (Monthly); *Economic and Community Profile/Directory* (Annual). **Awards:** Southwest King County Business Award (Annual); Small Business of the Year Award (Annual).

59289 ■ Spokane Regional Chamber of Commerce (SRCC)
801 W Riverside, Ste. 100
Spokane, WA 99201
Ph: (509)624-1393
Free: 800-776-5263
Fax: (509)747-0077
Co. E-mail: info@greaterspokane.org
URL: http://www.spokanechamber.org
Contact: Richard Hadley, President
Description: Promotes business and community development in the Spokane, WA area.

59290 ■ Stanwood Chamber of Commerce
PO Box 641
Stanwood, WA 98292-0641
Ph: (360)629-0562
Fax: (360)629-0562
Co. E-mail: info@stanwoodchamber.org
URL: http://www.stanwoodchamber.org/
Contact: Stacy Johnson, Executive Director
Description: Promotes a positive business climate in the city of Stanwood. Sponsors several community events including the Man/Woman/Business Person of the Year Banquet, Chamber Golf Classic, An Old Fashioned Christmas in Stanwood, the Port Susan Snow Goose & Birding Festival and Bowling Family Fun Day. **Publications:** *Stanwood Chamber of Commerce Directory* (Annual); *Stanwood Chamber of Commerce Directory* (Annual).

59291 ■ *Stanwood Chamber of Commerce Directory*
PO Box 641
Stanwood, WA 98292-0641
Ph: (360)629-0562
Fax: (360)629-0562
Co. E-mail: info@stanwoodchamber.org
URL: http://www.stanwoodchamber.org/
Contact: Stacy Johnson, Executive Director
Released: Annual **Price:** free.

59292 ■ Steilacoom Chamber of Commerce
PO Box 88584
Steilacoom, WA 98388
Ph: (253)353-6982
URL: http://www.steilacoom.org
Contact: Cindy McKirtick, President

59293 ■ Sunnyside Chamber of Commerce (SCC)
230 E Edison Ave.
Sunnyside, WA 98944
Ph: (509)837-5939
Free: 800-457-8089
Fax: (509)837-8015
Co. E-mail: info@sunnysidechamber.com
URL: http://sunnysidechamber.com
Contact: Gerald Roy, President
Description: Promotes business and community development in Sunnyside, WA. **Awards:** Outstanding Agri-Business Person (Annual); Outstanding Business Person (Annual); Outstanding Community Beautification (Annual); Outstanding Educator (Annual); Outstanding Health Care Person (Annual); Outstanding Public Official (Annual); Outstanding Senior Citizen (Annual); Outstanding Youth (Annual).

59294 ■ *Tacoma-Pierce County Business Directory*
950 Pacific Ave., Ste. 300
Tacoma, WA 98402
Ph: (253)627-2175

Fax: (253)597-7305
Co. E-mail: info@tacomachamber.org
URL: http://www.tacomachamber.org
Contact: Tom Pierson, President
Released: Annual **Price:** included in membership dues; $19.95, for nonmembers.

59295 ■ Tacoma-Pierce County Chamber of Commerce (TPCC)
950 Pacific Ave., Ste. 300
Tacoma, WA 98402
Ph: (253)627-2175
Fax: (253)597-7305
Co. E-mail: info@tacomachamber.org
URL: http://www.tacomachamber.org
Contact: Tom Pierson, President
Description: Promotes business and community development in Pierce County, WA. **Founded:** 1884. **Publications:** *Chamber Current* (Monthly); *Tacoma-Pierce County Business Directory* (Annual); *Tacoma-Pierce County Manufacturing Directory* (Annual); *Tacoma-Pierce County Chamber of Commerce--Membership Directory/Buyers Guide* (Annual). **Awards:** Tahoma Environmental Business Award (Annual).

59296 ■ Thurston County Chamber of Commerce
PO Box 1427
Olympia, WA 98507
Ph: (360)357-3362
Fax: (360)357-3376
Co. E-mail: info@thurstonchamber.com
URL: http://www.thurstonchamber.com
Contact: David Schaffert, President
Description: Promotes business and community development in Thurston County, WA. **Founded:** 1873. **Publications:** *The Voice-For Free Enterprise* (Monthly). **Educational Activities:** Chamber Forum (Monthly). **Awards:** Distinguished Leader Award (Annual).

59297 ■ Tonasket Chamber of Commerce
PO Box 523
Tonasket, WA 98855
Ph: (509)486-4429
Free: 866-440-8828
Fax: (509)486-4543
Co. E-mail: info@tonasketchamber.com
URL: http://tonasketchamber.com
Contact: Kari Alexander, President
Description: Promotes business and community development in Tonasket, WA. **Founded:** 1973.

59298 ■ Toppenish Chamber of Commerce
PO Box 28
Toppenish, WA 98948-0028
Ph: (509)865-3262
Free: 800-863-6375
Fax: (509)865-3549
Co. E-mail: chamber@toppenish.net
URL: http://www.toppenish.net
Contact: Zachary Dorr, Executive Director
Description: Promotes business and community development in Toppenish, WA. Sponsors arts, crafts, food fair, 4th of July parade, and ranch party. **Founded:** 1941.

59299 ■ Town of Conconully Chamber of Commerce
PO Box 309
Conconully, WA 98819-0309
Ph: (509)826-9050
Free: 877-826-9050
Fax: (509)826-3374
Co. E-mail: northfork04@wmconnect.com
URL: http://www.conconully.com
Contact: Tom Gibson, President
Description: Promotes business and community development in the Conconully, WA area.

59300 ■ Tri-City Regional Chamber of Commerce
c/o Lori Mattson, Pres./CEO
7130 W Grandridge Blvd., Ste. C
Kennewick, WA 99336
Ph: (509)736-0510

Fax: (509)783-1733
Co. E-mail: info@tricityregionalchamber.com
URL: http://www.tcrchamber.com
Contact: Lori Mattson, President
Description: Promotes business and community development in the Kennewick, WA area. **Founded:** 1986. **Publications:** *Commerce Report* (Monthly); *Profile Booklet* (Annual); *Real Estate Magazine*. **Educational Activities:** General Membership Meeting (Monthly). **Awards:** Student Academic Recognition (Periodic). **Telecommunication Services:** camille.kellison@tricityregionalchamber.com.

59301 ■ Tumwater Area Chamber of Commerce
5304 Littlerock Rd. SW
Tumwater, WA 98512
Ph: (360)357-5153
Fax: (360)786-1685
Co. E-mail: office@tumwaterchamber.com
URL: http://www.tumwaterchamber.com
Contact: David Bills, President
Description: Promotes business and community development in Tumwater, WA area. **Founded:** 1989. **Publications:** *The Chamber Chat* (Periodic); *The New Market* (Monthly).

59302 ■ Twisp Chamber of Commerce
PO Box 686
Twisp, WA 98856
Ph: (509)997-2020
Co. E-mail: rebmeadows@gmail.com
URL: http://www.twispinfo.com
Description: Promotes business and community development in Twisp, WA.

59303 ■ *University District Business News*
4710 University Way NE, Ste. 144
Seattle, WA 98105
Ph: (206)527-4417
Co. E-mail: director@udistrictchamber.org
URL: http://www.udistrictchamber.org
Contact: Teresa Lord Hugel, Executive Director
Released: Monthly

59304 ■ *View Point*
1421 Cole St.
Enumclaw, WA 98022
Ph: (360)825-7666
Fax: (360)825-8369
Co. E-mail: tracey@enumclawchamber.com
URL: http://www.enumclawchamber.com
Contact: Tracey McCallum, Executive Director
Released: Monthly

59305 ■ *Viewpoint*
PO Box 444
Yelm, WA 98597
Ph: (360)458-6608
Fax: (360)458-6383
Co. E-mail: info@yelmchamber.com
URL: http://www.yelmchamber.com
Contact: Cecelia Jenkins, Committee Chairman
Released: Monthly

59306 ■ *Visitor Guide*
19351 8th Ave., Ste. 108
Poulsbo, WA 98370
Ph: (360)779-4848
Free: 877-768-5726
Fax: (360)779-3115
URL: http://www.poulsbochamber.com
Contact: Kathleen Haag, President
Released: Annual **Price:** free.

59307 ■ *The Voice of Business*
524 W Meeker St., Ste. 1
Kent, WA 98032
Ph: (253)854-1770
Fax: (253)854-8567
Co. E-mail: info@kentchamber.com
URL: http://www.kentchamber.com
Contact: Andrea Keikkala, Executive Director
Released: Monthly

59308 ■ *The Voice of Business*
302 Bellevue Sq.
Bellevue, WA 98004
Ph: (425)454-2464

Fax: (425)462-4660
Co. E-mail: staffteam@bellevuechamber.org
URL: http://www.bellevuechamber.org
Contact: Betty Nokes, President
Released: Monthly

59309 ■ The Voice-For Free Enterprise
PO Box 1427
Olympia, WA 98507
Ph: (360)357-3362
Fax: (360)357-3376
Co. E-mail: info@thurstonchamber.com
URL: http://www.thurstonchamber.com
Contact: David Schaffert, President
Released: Monthly

59310 ■ Walla Walla Valley Chamber of Commerce (WWVCC)
29 E Sumach St.
Walla Walla, WA 99362
Ph: (509)525-0850
Free: 877-998-4748
Fax: (509)522-2038
Co. E-mail: info@wwwchamber.com
URL: http://www.wvvchamber.com
Contact: Jon Bren, Chairman of the Board
Description: Promotes business and community development in the Walla Walla, WA area. Sponsors Walla Walla Balloon Stampede and Walla Walla Sweet Onion Festival. **Scope:** business. **Founded:** 1934. **Subscriptions:** 20 books. **Publications:** *Chamber News* (Monthly); *Walla Walla Valley Chamber of Commerce--Business Directory.* **Awards:** Award of Merit (Annual); Volunteer of the Year (Annual). **Telecommunication Services:** info@wwv-chamber.com.

59311 ■ Wallingford Chamber of Commerce (WCC)
2100-A N 45th St.
Seattle, WA 98103
Ph: (206)632-0645
Co. E-mail: info@wallingfordchamber.org
URL: http://wallingfordchamber.org
Contact: Colleen Kurke, President
Description: Promotes business and community development in the Wallingford neighborhood of Seattle, WA. **Founded:** 1929.

59312 ■ Wenatchee Valley Chamber of Commerce (WVCC)
PO Box 850
Wenatchee, WA 98807-0850
Ph: (509)662-2116
Fax: (509)663-2022
Co. E-mail: info@wenatchee.org
URL: http://www.wenatchee.org
Contact: Craig Larsen, Executive Director
Description: Promotes business and community development in East Wenatchee, WA. **Publications:** *Connections* (Monthly); *Wenatchee Valley Chamber of Commerce Business Directory and Relocation Guide* (Annual). **Awards:** Business of the Chelan (Annual); Douglas Counties Business of the Year (Annual).

59313 ■ Wenatchee Valley Chamber of Commerce Business Directory and Relocation Guide
PO Box 850
Wenatchee, WA 98807-0850
Ph: (509)662-2116
Fax: (509)663-2022
Co. E-mail: info@wenatchee.org
URL: http://www.wenatchee.org
Contact: Craig Larsen, Executive Director
Released: Annual

59314 ■ West Plains Chamber of Commerce (WPCC)
8727 W Hwy. 2
Spokane, WA 99224
Ph: (509)235-8480

Fax: (509)624-5244
Co. E-mail: chamberoffice@westplainschamber.org
URL: http://www.westplainschamber.org
Contact: Matthew Pederson, Executive Director
Description: Promotes business and community development in Cheney, WA. **Founded:** 1942.

59315 ■ West Seattle Chamber of Commerce
3614-A California Ave. SW
Seattle, WA 98116-4413
Ph: (206)932-5685
Fax: (206)938-7437
Co. E-mail: info@wschamber.com
URL: http://www.wschamber.com
Contact: Dave Montoure, Chairman
Description: Provides a professional forum to discuss and influence policies and programs affecting business and social climate. **Founded:** 1922. **Publications:** *The Bulletin* (Monthly).

59316 ■ Westport-Grayland Chamber of Commerce
2985 S Montesano Ave.
Westport, WA 98595
Free: 800-345-6223
Co. E-mail: info@westportgrayland-chamber.org
URL: http://www.westportgrayland-chamber.org
Description: Promotes business and community development in the Westport, WA area. Sponsors crab races, Seafood festival, Kite Fest, and Surf Festival.

59317 ■ White Center Chamber of Commerce
1612 SW 114th St., Ste. 108
Seattle, WA 98146-3562
Ph: (206)763-4196
Fax: (206)763-1042
Co. E-mail: wcchamber@hotmail.com
URL: http://www.whitecenterchamber.org
Contact: Mark Ufkes, President

59318 ■ Willapa Harbor Chamber of Commerce (RCC)
PO Box 1249
South Bend, WA 98586
Ph: (360)942-5419
URL: http://www.visit.willapabay.org
Contact: Ms. Anne Steele, Director
Description: Promotes business, tourism and community development in North Pacific County.

59319 ■ Winthrop Chamber of Commerce
202 Hwy. 20
Winthrop, WA 98862
Ph: (509)996-2125
Free: 888-463-8469
Co. E-mail: info@winthropwashington.com
URL: http://winthropwashington.com
Description: Promotes business and community development in Winthrop, WA. **Publications:** *Event Directory* (Annual); *Winthrop Washington Business Directory* (Annual); *Winthrop Washington Business Directory* (Annual).

59320 ■ Winthrop Washington Business Directory
202 Hwy. 20
Winthrop, WA 98862
Ph: (509)996-2125
Free: 888-463-8469
Co. E-mail: info@winthropwashington.com
URL: http://winthropwashington.com
Released: Annual

59321 ■ Woodland Chamber of Commerce
PO Box 1012
Woodland, WA 98674
Ph: (360)225-9552
Fax: (360)225-3490
Co. E-mail: sknight@woodlandwachamber.com
URL: http://www.lewisriver.com/woodlandchamber
Contact: Tammie Howard, Director
URL(s): www.woodlandwachamber.com. **Description:** Promotes business and community development in Woodland, WA. Operates information center. **Founded:** 1967. **Publications:** *CHAMBER NEWS* (Annual). **Awards:** Citizen of the Year (Annual); Quarterly Business (Quarterly).

59322 ■ Yelm Area Chamber of Commerce
PO Box 444
Yelm, WA 98597
Ph: (360)458-6608
Fax: (360)458-6383
Co. E-mail: info@yelmchamber.com
URL: http://www.yelmchamber.com
Contact: Cecelia Jenkins, Committee Chairman
Description: Promotes business and community development in Yelm, WA area. **Publications:** *Viewpoint* (Monthly).

MINORITY BUSINESS ASSISTANCE PROGRAMS

59323 ■ Northwest Native American Business Enterprise Center
3327 NE 125th St., Ste. 101
Seattle, WA 98125
Ph: (206)365-7738
Fax: (206)365-7764
Co. E-mail: mine.smith@nwnabec.org
URL: http://www.nwnabec.org
Contact: Mine Smith
Description: Offers management services and technical assistance to Native American business owners in Washington, Oregon, and Idaho.

59324 ■ Washington Minority Business Enterprise Center - Community Capital Development
1437 S Jackson St., Ste. 301
Seattle, WA 98144
Ph: (206)267-3131
Fax: (206)267-3132
Co. E-mail: info@mbecwa.com
URL: http://www.mbecwa.com
Contact: Jim Thomas
Description: Works to create, grow, and sustain minority entrepreneurial opportunities in Washington.

59325 ■ Washington State Office of Minority and Women's Business Enterprises
PO Box 41160
Olympia, WA 98504-1160
Ph: (360)753-9693
Free: 866-208-1064
Fax: (360)586-7079
Co. E-mail: ccanorro@omwbe.wa.gov
URL: http://www.omwbe.wa.gov
Contact: Cathy Canorro
Description: Created to increase opportunities for minorities and women wishing to obtain state contracts.

FINANCING AND LOAN PROGRAMS

59326 ■ Bear Creek Venture Partners
1000 2nd Ave., Ste. 1200
Seattle, WA 98104
Ph: (425)765-5333
Fax: (425)883-0270
URL: http://www.bearcreekvp.com
Contact: Jay Powers, Partner
E-mail: jay@bearcreekvp.com
Investment Policies: Early stage. **Industry Preferences:** Communications, computer software, and Internet specific. **Geographic Preference:** Northwest.

59327 ■ Benaroya Capital Company
3600 136th Pl. SE, Ste. 250
Bellevue, WA 98006
Ph: (425)440-6700
Fax: (425)440-6730
Co. E-mail: general@benaroya.com
URL: http://www.benaroya.com
Contact: Larry Benaroya, Principal
E-mail: larryb@benaroya.com
Preferred Investment Size: $500,000 to $3,000,000. **Investment Policies:** Seed, first and second stage. **Industry Preferences:** Communications, and semiconductors and other electronics. **Geographic Preference:** Northwest.

59328 ■ EFund, LLC
2607 2nd Ave., Ste. 300
Seattle, WA 98121
Ph: (206)389-4901
Fax: (206)389-4901
Co. E-mail: plans@edundllc.com
URL: http://www.efundllc.com
Contact: Daniel Kranzler, Managing Partner
Investment Policies: Early stage. **Industry Preferences:** Communications and media, and Internet specific. **Geographic Preference:** U.S.

59329 ■ Fluke Venture Partners
11400 SE Sixth St., Ste. 230
Bellevue, WA 98004
Ph: (425)453-4590
Fax: (425)453-4675
URL: http://www.flukeventures.com
Contact: Denny Weston, Managing Director
E-mail: weston@flukeventures.com
Preferred Investment Size: $1,000,000 to $3,000,000. **Industry Preferences:** Computer software and services, computer hardware, Internet specific, medical and health, communications and media, consumer related, industrial and energy, biotechnology, semiconductors and other electronics, and other products. **Geographic Preference:** U.S. Pacific Northwest.

59330 ■ Frazier & Company / Frazier Healthcare and Technology Ventures
601 Union, 2 Union Sq., Ste. 3200
Seattle, WA 98101
Ph: (206)621-7200
Fax: (206)621-1848
URL: http://www.frazierco.com
Contact: Alan Frazier, Founder
E-mail: alan@frazierhealthcare.com
Preferred Investment Size: $10,000,000 to $40,000,000. **Industry Preferences:** Computer software and services, Internet specific, medical and health, communications and media, computer hardware, other products, consumer related, industrial and energy, biotechnology, semiconductors and other electronics. **Geographic Preference:** Midwest and Northwest.

59331 ■ Kirlan Venture Capital, Inc.
221 First Ave. W., Ste. 108
Seattle, WA 98119-4223
Ph: (206)281-8610
Fax: (206)285-3451
Co. E-mail: lisa@kirlanvc.com
URL: http://www.kirlanvc.com
Contact: Kirk Lanterman, Chairman
Preferred Investment Size: $100,000 to $2,000,000. **Industry Preferences:** Communications and media, medical and health, computer software and services, Internet specific, industrial and energy, and computer hardware. **Geographic Preference:** Washington.

59332 ■ Northwest Venture Associates, Inc. / Spokane Capital MGMT
221 N. Wall St., Ste. 628
Spokane, WA 99201
Ph: (509)747-0728
Fax: (509)747-0758
URL: http://www.nwva.com
Contact: Robert Wolfe, Managing Partner
E-mail: bob@nwva.com
Preferred Investment Size: $500,000 to $5,000,000. **Industry Preferences:** Internet specific, computer software and services, communications and media, and consumer related. **Geographic Preference:** Northwest, Colorado, Utah, and Western Canada.

59333 ■ OVP Venture Partners / Olympic Venture Partners (Kirkland)
1010 Market St.
Kirkland, WA 98033
Ph: (425)889-9192
Fax: (425)889-0152
Co. E-mail: info@ovp.com
URL: http://www.ovp.com
Contact: Bill Funcannon, Chief Financial Officer
Preferred Investment Size: $1,000,000 to $5,000,000. **Industry Preferences:** Computer software and services, Internet specific, medical and

health, biotechnology, communications and media, consumer related, semiconductors and other electronics, computer hardware, and other products. **Geographic Preference:** Northwest and West Coast.

59334 ■ Pacific Northwest Partners L.P.
305 108th Ave. NE, 2nd Fl.
Bellevue, WA 98004
Ph: (425)455-9967
Fax: (425)455-9404
URL: http://www.pnwp.com
Contact: Louis Kertesz, Partner
Preferred Investment Size: $500,000 minimum. **Industry Preferences:** Internet specific, medical and health, consumer related, computer software and services, and other products. **Geographic Preference:** Northwest and West Coast.

59335 ■ Paladin Partners
838 Kirkland Ave.
Kirkland, WA 98033
Ph: (425)260-5354
Fax: (425)822-5305
URL: http://www.paladinpartners.com
Contact: Janis Machala, Managing Partner
E-mail: JanisM@paladinpartners.com
Industry Preferences: Communications, computer software, Internet specific, and business service. **Geographic Preference:** West Coast.

59336 ■ The Phoenix Partners
1000 2nd Ave., Ste. 3950
Seattle, WA 98104
Ph: (206)624-8968
Fax: (206)624-1907
Co. E-mail: kfitterer@phoenixvc.com
URL: http://www.phoenixvc.com
Contact: William B. Horne, Chief Financial Officer
Preferred Investment Size: $1,000,000 to $3,000,000. **Industry Preferences:** Biotechnology, Internet specific, computer software and services, computer hardware, consumer related, medical and health, semiconductors and other electronics, communications and media, and other products. **Geographic Preference:** West Coast.

59337 ■ Seapoint Ventures
719 2nd Ave., Ste. 1405
Seattle, WA 98104
Ph: (206)438-1880
Fax: (206)438-1886
Co. E-mail: info@seapointventures.com
URL: http://www.seapointventures.com
Contact: Thomas S. Huseby, Managing Partner
Preferred Investment Size: $300,000 to $4,000,000. **Industry Preferences:** Internet specific, computer software and services, computer hardware, communications and media, and biotechnology. **Geographic Preference:** Northwest and West Coast.

59338 ■ Timberline Venture Partners
400 Seaport Ct., Ste. 250
Redwood City, CA 94063
Ph: (650)599-9000
Fax: (650)599-9726
Co. E-mail: mail@timberlinevc.com
URL: http://www.timberlinevc.com
Contact: Jeffrey C. Tung, Managing Partner
Preferred Investment Size: $500,000 to $5,000,000. **Industry Preferences:** Communications, computer software, Internet specific, semiconductors and other electronics. **Geographic Preference:** California and Northwest.

59339 ■ Voyager Capital
719 2nd Ave., Ste. 1400
Seattle, WA 98104
Ph: (206)438-1800
Fax: (206)438-1900
URL: http://www.voyagercap.com
Contact: Erik D. Benson, Managing Director
E-mail: benson@voyagercapital.com
Preferred Investment Size: $3,000,000 to $12,000,000. **Industry Preferences:** Internet specific, computer software and services, semiconductors and other electronics, communications and media, computer hardware, and other products. **Geographic Preference:** Seattle, Portland, and California.

PROCUREMENT ASSISTANCE PROGRAMS

59340 ■ Washington Procurement Technical Assistance Center - Columbia River Economic Development Council (CREDC)
805 Broadway, Ste. 412
Vancouver, WA 98660
Ph: (360)694-5006
Fax: (360)694-9927
Co. E-mail: info@credc.org
URL: http://www.credc.org
Contact: Jerry Petrick, Director
E-mail: jlehner@crdc.org
Description: A proactive, results-oriented public/ private partnership working with over 180 associates to assist businesses to relocate or expand in Clark, Cowlitz, and Skamania counties.

59341 ■ Washington Procurement Technical Assistance Center - Community Capital Development
1437 S Jackson, Ste. 201
Seattle, WA 98144
Ph: (206)324-4330
Fax: (206)324-4322
Co. E-mail: info@seattleccd.com
URL: http://www.seattleccd.com
Contact: Josephine Tamayo Murry, Director
E-mail: adavis@seattleccd.com
Description: Provides access to capital and business assistance to low-income, women and minority entrepreneurs and small businesses in King County.

59342 ■ Washington Procurement Technical Assistance Center - Economic Development Association of Skagit County (EDASC)
204 W Montgomery St.
Mount Vernon, WA 98273
Ph: (360)336-6114
Fax: (360)336-6116
Co. E-mail: info@skagit.org
URL: http://www.skagit.org
Contact: Diane McLeod, Manager, Business Development
E-mail: diane@skagit.org
Description: Assists companies who are interested in doing business with the government in Island, San Juan, Skagit and Whatcom counties.

59343 ■ Washington Procurement Technical Assistance Center - Northwest Economic Council
115 Unity St., Ste. 101
Bellingham, WA 98227-2803
Ph: (360)676-4255
Free: 800-810-4255
Fax: (360)647-9413
Co. E-mail: nancy@nwecon.org
URL: http://www.nwecon.org/
Contact: Nancy Jordan, Executive Director
Description: Encourages existing industrial and commercial businesses to expand, and works to attract new industrial and commercial businesses to Whatcom County. Formerly Bellingham Whatcom Economic Development Council.

59344 ■ Washington Procurement Technical Assistance Center - The Northwest Native American Business Enterprise Center - NWNABEC
3237 NE 125th St., Ste. 101
Seattle, WA 98125
Ph: (206)365-7738
Fax: (206)365-7764
Co. E-mail: mine.smith@ncaied.org
URL: http://www.nwnabec.org
Contact: Mine Smith, Director
E-mail: mine.smith@ncaied.org
Description: Provides management and technical assistance for Native Americans residing in the state of Washington, Oregon, and Idaho. This assistance extends to both tribes and individuals living both on and off the reservation. Assistance is available for all stages of business from start-up through expansion.

59345 ■ Washington Procurement Technical Assistance Center - Snohomish County Economic Development Council - PTAC
728 134th St. SW, Ste. 128
Everett, WA 98204
Ph: (425)743-4567
Fax: (425)745-5726
Co. E-mail: info@snoedc.org
URL: http://www.snoedc.org
Contact: Lily Keeffe, Director
Description: Helps companies find and successfully achieve contracts for work with the local, state and federal governments.

59346 ■ Washington Procurement Technical Assistance Center - Spokane Regional Chamber of Commerce
BIZStreet Resource Ctr.
801 W Riverside Ave., Ste. 100
Spokane, WA 99201
Ph: (509)624-1393
Free: 800-776-5263
Fax: (509)747-0077
Co. E-mail: bizstreet@greaterspokane.com
URL: http://www.greaterspokane.org/bizstreet. aspx?name=BIZStreet
Contact: Louise Fendrich, Manager
E-mail: lfendrich@chamber.spokane.net
Description: Assists businesses with any aspect of federal, state and local government contracting. Serving 13 counties in Eastern Washington including Spokane, Ferry, Lincoln, Stevens, Pend Orielle, Adams, Franklin, Benton, Whitman, Walla Walla, Columbia, Garfield and Asotin counties.

59347 ■ Washington Procurement Technical Assistance Center - William Factory - Tacoma-Pierce Small Business Incubator
1423 East 29th
Tacoma, WA 98404
Ph: (253)722-5800
Fax: (253)722-5801
Co. E-mail: jeremy@williamfactory.com
URL: http://www.williamfactory.com
Description: Provides an opportunity to nurture carefully selected, smaller, locally owned entrepreneurs through their formative years serving Pierce County.

59348 ■ Washington Procurement Technical Center - Grays Harbor Economic Development Council
506 Duffy St.
Aberdeen, WA 98520
Ph: (360)532-7888
Free: 800-553-6618
Fax: (360)532-7922
Co. E-mail: info@ghedc.com
URL: http://www.ghedc.com
Contact: Roger Milliman, Manager, Business Development
Description: Assist local government and businesses to promote the overall economic vitality of the county and its communities, to market and capitalize on the County's assets serving Clallam, Grays Harbor, Jefferson, Kitsap, Mason, Pacific, and Wahkiakum counties.

59349 ■ Washington Technical Assistance Center - Thurston County Economic Development Council
West Coast Bank Bldg.
665 Woodland Sq. Loop SE, Ste. 201
Lacey, WA 98053
Ph: (360)754-6320
Fax: (360)407-3980
Co. E-mail: office@thurstonedc.com
URL: http://www.thurstonedc.com
Contact: John Tamble, Administrator
E-mail: tkennedy@thurstonedc.com
Description: Specializes in identifying opportunity and applying effort that results in creating a vibrant and vital economy.

59350 ■ Yakima County Development Associations - Washington Procurement Technical Assistance Center
PO Box 1387
Yakima, WA 98907-1387

Ph: (509)575-1140
Fax: (509)575-1508
Co. E-mail: info@ycda.com
URL: http://www.ycda.com
Contact: Tammy Everts, Director
E-mail: mmochel@ycda.com
Description: A public-private non-profit corporation created to enhance the income and employment stability of the local economy serving Asotin, Benton, Columbia, Franklin, Garfield, Kittitas, Walla Walla and Yakima counties.

INCUBATORS/RESEARCH AND TECHNOLOGY PARKS

59351 ■ Tri-Cities Enterprise Center
2000 Logston Blvd.
Richland, WA 99352
Ph: (509)375-3268
Fax: (509)375-4838
Co. E-mail: info@enterprisecenter.net
URL: http://www.enterprisecenter.net
Contact: Stanley Stave, General Manager
Description: A non-profit incubator dedicated to ensuring the survival of emerging firms in Benton and Franklin counties of Washington state.

59352 ■ Washington Technology Center
300 Fluke Hall
University of Washington Campus
Seattle, WA 98195-2140
Ph: (206)685-1920
Fax: (206)543-3059
Co. E-mail: info@watechcenter.org
URL: http://www.watechcenter.org
Contact: Chris Coleman, Executive Director
Description: A joint industry/state/university enterprise engaged in commercially promising research and technology development.

EDUCATIONAL PROGRAMS

59353 ■ Big Bend Community College
7662 Chanute St. NE
Moses Lake, WA 98837
Ph: (509)793-2061
Free: 877-745-1212
Co. E-mail: admissions@bigbend.edu
URL: http://www.bigbend.edu/
Description: Two-year college offering a small business management program. **Publications:** *Tumbleweed Times* (Semimonthly); *Tumbleweed Times* (Semimonthly).

59354 ■ Olympic College
1600 Chester Ave.
Bremerton, WA 98337-1699
Ph: (360)792-6050
Free: 800-259-6718
Fax: (360)475-7150
Co. E-mail: prospect@olympic.edu
URL: http://www.olympic.edu
Description: Provides a variety of certificate programs and courses specifically designed to assist small businesses.

59355 ■ South Seattle Community College
6000 16th Ave. SW, JMB 119
Seattle, WA 98106-1499
Ph: (206)934-5300
Free: 800-833-6384
Fax: (206)934-7945
Co. E-mail: sentinel@sccd.ctc.edu
URL: http://www.seattlecolleges.com/
URL(s): www.southseattle.edu. **Description:** Two-year college offering a program in small business management. **Publications:** *The South Seattle Sentinel* (Biweekly); *The South Seattle Sentinel* (Biweekly).

59356 ■ Spokane Falls Community College (SFCC)
3410 W Fort George Wright Dr.
Spokane, WA 99224-5288
Ph: (509)533-3500
Free: 888-509-7944

Fax: (509)533-3237
Co. E-mail: sfccinfo@spokanefalls.edu
URL: http://www.spokanefalls.edu
Contact: Steve Bays, Dean, Student Services
URL(s): www.spokanefalls.edu/businessmgmt. **Description:** Two-year college offering a small business management program. **Founded:** 1967. **Publications:** *Communicator* (Semiweekly). **Telecommunication Services:** steveb@spokanefalls.edu.

59357 ■ Tacoma Community College - Business and Industry Resource Center
6501 S 19th St.
Tacoma, WA 98466
Ph: (253)566-5000
Fax: (253)272-7968
URL: http://www.tacomacc.edu
Description: Offers day and evening small business courses, for credit or noncredit, at the main campus and at the downtown center. Selected courses also are held on Saturdays to meet the scheduling needs of working students. Classes are co-sponsored by the Tacoma-Pierce County Chamber of Commerce as part of its Small Business Profit Center. Customized training for business and organizations is designed to meet the needs of employees and managers. Training workshops are held on site for the convenience of the participants.

PUBLICATIONS

59358 ■ *Incorporation and Business Guide for Wahsington*
Self-Counsel Press, Inc.
1704 N. State St.
Bellingham, WA 98225
Ph: (360)676-4530
Free: 800-663-3007
Fax: (360)676-4549
Ed: Victoria Van Hof. **Released:** Sixth edition, 1993. **Price:** $12.95. **Description:** Includes forms to help entrepreneurs incorporate in Washington.

59359 ■ *Incorporation Forms For Washington*
Self-Counsel Press
1704 N State St.
Bellingham, WA 98225
Ph: (360)676-4530
Free: 800-663-3007
Fax: (360)676-4549
Released: 1993. **Price:** $12.95 (paper). **Description:** Provides forms for forming your own corporation in the state of Washington.

59360 ■ *Smart Start your Washington Business*
PSI Research
300 N. Valley Dr.
Grants Pass, OR 97526
Ph: (503)479-9464
Free: 800-228-2275
Fax: (503)476-1479
Co. E-mail: info@psi-research.com
URL: http://www.psi-research.com
Ed: Michael D. Jenkins. **Released:** Revised edition, 1992. **Price:** $29.95 (looseleaf binder); $24.95 (paper). **Description:** Part of the Successful Business Library series.

PUBLISHERS

59361 ■ Cleaning Consultant Services Inc. (CCS)
3693 E Marginal Way S
Seattle, WA 98134
Ph: (206)682-9748
Fax: (206)622-6876
Co. E-mail: wgriffin@cleaningconsultants.com
URL: http://www.cleaningbusiness.com
Contact: William R. Griffin, President
E-mail: wgriffin@cleaningconsultants.com
URL(s): www.cleaningbusiness.com. **Description:** Description: Publishes books on floor care, carpet care, self-employment, window washing, custodial training and many other areas related to the cleaning industry. Reaches market through direct mail, reviews and listings, telephone sales, ads, catalogs and trade

shows. **Scope:** Provider of engineering and consulting services. It deals with claim and dispute resolution, program and material development, and cleaning services. **Founded:** 1973. **Publications:** "Raising the Bar with Science, Training and Upward Mobility," Jan, 2010; "Technology Revolutionizes the Cleaning Process "Cleaning for Health" is the New Mantra," Distribution Sales and Management Magazine, May, 2003; "Bill Griffin's Crystal Balls-Cleaning Trends in the Usa 2001," Floor Care is Hot in 2001," Mar, 2001; "Inclean Magazine (Australia), Feb, 2001; "Maintaining Swimming Pools, Spas, Whirlpool Tubs and Saunas," Executive House keeping, Feb, 2001; "Whats New with Floor Care," 2001. **Seminars:** Stone Maintenance Technician (SMT) IICRC Certification Course; Carpet Cleaning Technician; Apprentice/Basic Skills; Organizing Custodial Operations for Maximum Efficiency: How to Sell & Price Contract Cleaning; Starting a House cleaning Business; Rugs & Carpet Cleaning; How to Start and Operate a Successful Cleaning Business; Cleaning Schools in the 2000and Beyond; Bringing About and Working Through Change; Organizing Custodial Operations for Maximum Efficiency; Floor Care Technician (FCT)11 CPC Certified Course; Administering Cleaning Service Contracts. **Telecommunication Services:** ccs@cleaningconsultants.com; marketing@cleaningconsultants.com.

59362 ■ Madson Group Inc.—Fina A Groomer Inc.
PO Box 2489
Yelm, WA 98597
Ph: (360)446-5348
Free: 800-556-5131
Fax: (360)446-5234
Co. E-mail: findagroomer@earthlink.net
URL: http://www.groomingbusinessinabox.com
Contact: Dr. Madeline Bright Ogle, President

Description: Description: Publishes on careers and business, pets, travel, education and management. Also publishes newsletters. Offers online services. Accepts unsolicited manuscripts. Reaches market through direct mail. **Founded:** 1987.

59363 ■ Online Training Solutions Inc.
602 Bellevue Way SE
Bellevue, WA 98004-6633
Free: 888-308-6874
Fax: (888)308-6875
Co. E-mail: customer.service@otsi.com
URL: http://www.otsi.com
Contact: Joan Lambert, President

Description: Description: Publishes training books. **Scope:** Consultants involved in CBT and WBT preparation and traditional publishing services (writing, editing, design, and layout). Publishes computer training books. Serves private industries world wide. Services include: management, authoring, editorial services, graphics, book production and technical services. **Founded:** 1986. **Publications:** "Quick Course Series"; "Step by Step Series"; "Microsoft Windows XP Step by Step"; "Microsoft Windows XP Step by Step Deluxe". **Special Services:** Quick Course®; Fast-track training®; eclecticClassroom™.

59364 ■ Redmond Technology Press
8434 154th Ave. NE
Redmond, WA 98052
Ph: (425)881-7350
Fax: (425)671-0585
Co. E-mail: steve.nelson@stephenlnelson.com
URL: http://www.redtechpress.com
Contact: Stephen L. Nelson, President
E-mail: steve.nelson@stephenlnelson.com

Description: Description: Publishes computer books for business people, including MBA's guides, effective executive's guides and new webmaster's guides. **Founded:** 1986.

59365 ■ Stat Communications Ltd.
250 H St.
Blaine, WA 98230
URL: http://www.statpub.com
Contact: P. Pao, Manager

Description: Description: Publishes on international trade and agriculture. Accepts unsolicited manuscripts, should be business-related and include a self-addressed, stamped envelope. Reaches market through direct mail. **Founded:** 1988. **Publications:** Grey Book (Monthly).

SMALL BUSINESS DEVELOPMENT CENTERS

59366 ■ Charleston Small Business Development Center
c/o Anne Lane, Mgr.
1116 Smith St.
Charleston, WV 25301
Ph: (304)558-2960
Co. E-mail: anne.c.lane@wv.gov
Contact: Anne Lane, Manager
Description: Represents and promotes the small business sector. Provides management assistance to current and prospective small business owners. Helps to improve management skills and expand the products and services of members.

59367 ■ Eastern Panhandle Small Business Development Center
142 N Queen St.
Martinsburg, WV 25401
Ph: (304)596-6642
Fax: (304)596-6646
Co. E-mail: christina.m.lundberg@wv.gov
URL: http://wvsbdc.wvcommerce.org
Contact: Christina Lundberg, Manager
Description: Represents and promotes the small business sector. Provides management assistance to current and prospective small business owners. Helps to improve management skills and expand the products and services of members.

59368 ■ Eastern West Virginia Small Business Development Center
1929 State Rd., No. 55
Moorefield, WV 26836
Ph: (304)434-8000
Fax: (304)434-7003
Co. E-mail: mludewig@eastern.wvnet.edu
URL: http://wvsbdc.wvcommerce.org/default.aspx
Contact: Beth Ludewig, Manager
Description: Represents and promotes the small business sector. Provides management assistance to current and prospective small business owners. Helps to improve management skills and expand the products and services of members.

59369 ■ Marshall University Small Business Development Center
348 15th St.
Huntington, WV 25701
Ph: (304)399-1040
Fax: (304)525-1467
Co. E-mail: amber.c.wilson@wv.gov
URL: http://wvsbdc.wvcommerce.org
Contact: Amber Wilson, Manager
Description: Represents and promotes the small business sector. Provides management assistance to current and prospective small business owners. Helps to improve management skills and expand the products and services of members.

59370 ■ Pierpont Community and Technical College of Fairmont State University Small Business Development Center
320 Adams St., Ste. G01
Fairmont, WV 26554
Free: 888-982-7232
Description: Represents and promotes the small business sector. Provides management assistance to current and prospective small business owners. Helps to improve management skills and expand the products and services of members.

59371 ■ Pierpont Community and Technical College of Fairmont State University Small Business Development Center - Buckhannon
99 Edminston Way, Ste. 204
Buckhannon, WV 26201
Ph: (304)439-1290
Co. E-mail: v.m.karickhoff@wv.gov
Contact: Vicki Karickhoff, Coach
Description: Represents and promotes the small business sector. Provides management assistance to current and prospective small business owners. Helps to improve management skills and expand the products and services of members.

59372 ■ Pierpont Community and Technical College Small Business Development Center - Fairmont
Veterans Sq., Ste. G-01
320 Adams St.
Fairmont, WV 26554
Ph: (304)367-4931
Free: 888-982-7232
Fax: (304)558-0127
Description: Represents and promotes the small business sector. Provides management assistance to current and prospective small business owners. Helps to improve management skills and expand the products and services of members.

59373 ■ Southern West Virginia Small Business Development Center
PO Box 2900
Mount Gay, WV 25637
Ph: (304)767-0532
Fax: (304)862-3071
Co. E-mail: harold.d.patterson@wv.gov
URL: http://wvsbdc.wvcommerce.org
Contact: Harold Patterson, Manager
URL(s): www.sba.gov/localresources/district/wv/WV_WVSBDC.html. **Description:** Represents and promotes the small business sector. Provides management assistance to current and prospective small business owners. Helps to improve management skills and expand the products and services of members.

59374 ■ West Virginia Northern Community College Small Business Development Center
c/o Donna Schramm, Dir.
1704 Market St.
Wheeling, WV 26003

Ph: (304)233-5900
Co. E-mail: dschramm@wvncc.edu
URL: http://www.wvncc.edu/workforce-development/small-business-development-center/112
Contact: Donna Schramm, Manager
Description: Represents and promotes the small business sector. Provides management assistance to current and prospective small business owners. Helps to improve management skills and expand the products and services of members.

59375 ■ West Virginia Small Business Development Center - Lead Office (WVSBDC)
West Virginia Department of Commerce
Capitol Complex Bldg. 6, Rm. 525
1900 Kanawha Blvd. E
Charleston, WV 25305-0311
Ph: (304)558-2234
Free: 800-982-3386
Fax: (304)558-1189
Co. E-mail: kristina.j.oliver@wv.gov
URL: http://wvsbdc.wvcommerce.org
Contact: Kristina Oliver, Director
Description: Offers free business counseling on topics such as marketing, financing, and management. Conducts loan packaging. **Awards:** Small Business Workforce Training Grant (Monthly).

59376 ■ West Virginia University Small Business Development Center
PO Box 6884
Morgantown, WV 26506
Ph: (304)293-5839
Fax: (304)225-2510
Co. E-mail: sharon.stratton@mail.wvu.edu
URL: http://wvsbdc.wvcommerce.org
Contact: Sharon Stratton, Manager
URL(s): wvubi.com/small-business-development-center. **Description:** Represents and promotes the small business sector. Provides management assistance to current and prospective small business owners. Helps to improve management skills and expand the products and services of members.

59377 ■ West Virginia University Small Business Development Center - Parkersburg
300 Campus Dr.
Parkersburg, WV 26104
Ph: (304)424-8391
Fax: (304)424-8266
Co. E-mail: greg.a.hill@wv.gov
URL: http://www.sbdcwv.org
Contact: Greg Hill, Manager
URL(s): www.wvup.edu/WCE/sbdc.htm. **Description:** Represents and promotes the small business sector. Provides management assistance to current and prospective small business owners. Helps to improve management skills and expand the products and services of members.

59378 ■ Workforce Small Business Development Center - Beckley
200 Value City Ctr., Ste. 500
Beckley, WV 25801
Ph: (304)252-0406

Fax: (304)253-0176
Co. E-mail: ramorgan@r1workforcewv.org
URL: http://wvsbdc.wvcommerce.org
URL(s): www.sba.gov/localresources/district/wv/WV_WVSBDC.html. **Description:** Represents and promotes the small business sector. Provides management assistance to current and prospective small business owners. Helps to improve management skills and expand the products and services of members.

59379 ■ Workforce Small Business Development Center - Summersville
830 Northside Dr., Ste. 166
Summersville, WV 26651
Ph: (304)872-0020
Fax: (304)872-0020
Co. E-mail: james.e.epling@wv.gov
URL: http://www.sbdcwv.org
Contact: James Epling, Manager
Description: Represents and promotes the small business sector. Provides management assistance to current and prospective small business owners. Helps to improve management skills and expand the products and services of members.

SMALL BUSINESS ASSISTANCE PROGRAMS

59380 ■ West Virginia Development Office - Business and Industrial Development Division
State Capitol Complex, Bldg. 6, Rm. 553
1900 Kanawha Blvd. E
Charleston, WV 25305-0311
Ph: (304)558-2234
Free: 800-982-3386
Fax: (304)558-0449
URL: http://www.wvdo.org
Contact: Kelley Goes, Executive Director
Description: Offers assistance to small business.

SCORE OFFICES

59381 ■ Buckhannon SCORE
Co. E-mail: agovernorsinn@aol.com

59382 ■ Greenbrier Valley SCORE
Co. E-mail: scorel70@hotmail.com

59383 ■ Huntington SCORE
Co. E-mail: score488@unlimitedfuture.org

59384 ■ SCORE Charleston
1116 Smith St.
Charleston, WV 25301
Ph: (304)347-5463
Co. E-mail: score256@wvscore.org
URL: http://charleston.score.org
Description: Provides free business counseling for small business managers or individuals going into business. **Founded:** 1978. **Subscriptions:** 30.

59385 ■ SCORE Wheeling
1310 Market St.
Wheeling Chamber of Commerce
Wheeling, WV 26003
Ph: (304)233-2575
Fax: (304)233-1320
Co. E-mail: wwvscore@juno.com

59386 ■ Upper Mon Valley SCORE
Co. E-mail: score@ma.rr.com

CHAMBERS OF COMMERCE

59387 ■ Beckley - Raleigh County Chamber of Commerce (BRCCC)
245 N Kanawha St.
Beckley, WV 25801
Ph: (304)252-7328
Free: 877-987-3847

Fax: (304)252-7373
Co. E-mail: chamber@brccc.com
URL: http://www.brccc.com
Contact: Ellen Taylor, President
Description: Coordinates the efforts of commerce, industry, and the professions in maintaining and strengthening a sound and healthy business climate in the Beckley-Raleigh County area. Sponsors aggressive programs of work and stimulate activities which will provide for full development and employment of the human and economic resources. **Founded:** 1920.

59388 ■ Berkeley Springs - Morgan County Chamber of Commerce (BSMCCC)
127 Fairfax St.
Berkeley Springs, WV 25411
Ph: (304)258-3738
Co. E-mail: chamber@berkeleysprings.com
URL: http://www.berkeleyspringschamber.com
Contact: Beth Peters Curtin, Executive Director
Description: Promotes business and community development in Berkeley Springs, WV. Sponsors festival. Conducts charitable activities. **Founded:** 1952.

59389 ■ Business Ledger
PO Box 737
Franklin, WV 26807
Ph: (304)358-3884
Co. E-mail: pendletoncoc@verizon.net
URL: http://www.visitpendleton.com
Contact: Carolyn Simmons, Chairman
Released: Quarterly

59390 ■ Buyers' Guide
110 Adams St.
Fairmont, WV 26554
Ph: (304)363-0442
Fax: (304)363-0480
Co. E-mail: mccc@marionchamber.com
URL: http://www.marionchamber.com
Contact: Butch Osbourne, Chairman
Released: Periodic

59391 ■ The Chamber Challenge
1522 N Walker St.
Princeton, WV 24740
Ph: (304)487-1502
Fax: (304)425-0227
Co. E-mail: pmccc@frontiernet.net
URL: http://www.pmccc.com
Contact: Mr. Robert Farley, President
Released: Monthly

59392 ■ Chamber Chat
200 1/2 W Main St.
Kingwood, WV 26537
Ph: (304)329-0576
Fax: (304)329-1407
Co. E-mail: prestoncoc@labyrinth.net
URL: http://www.prestonchamber.com
Contact: Kim Riley, President
Released: Monthly **Price:** free for members.

59393 ■ Chamber Chatter
604 Jefferson Ave.
Moundsville, WV 26041
Ph: (304)845-2773
Co. E-mail: chamber@marshallcountychamber.com
URL: http://www.marshallcountychamber.com
Contact: David W. Knuth, Executive Director
Released: Monthly

59394 ■ Chamber Chatter Calendar of Events
1302 N Randolph Ave.
Elkins, WV 26241
Ph: (304)636-2780
Free: 800-422-3304
Fax: (304)636-2780
Co. E-mail: bpritt@randolphcountycvb.com
URL: http://www.elkinswv.com
Contact: Brenda J. Pritt, Executive Director
Released: Monthly

59395 ■ Chamber Links
1624 Kanawha Blvd. E
Charleston, WV 25311
Ph: (304)342-1115

Fax: (304)342-1130
Co. E-mail: forjobs@wvchamber.com
URL: http://www.wvchamber.com
Contact: Steve Roberts, President
Released: Weekly

59396 ■ ChamberLink
1108 3rd Ave., Ste. 300
Huntington, WV 25701
Ph: (304)525-5131
Fax: (304)525-5158
Co. E-mail: mark@huntingtonchamber.org
URL: http://www.huntingtonchamber.org
Contact: Jim Withers, Chairman
Released: Monthly **Price:** free.

59397 ■ Charleston Regional Chamber of Commerce and Development
c/o Charleston Area Alliance
1116 Smith St.
Charleston, WV 25301
Ph: (304)340-4253
Free: 800-792-4326
Fax: (304)340-4275
Co. E-mail: info@charlestonwvchamber.org
URL: http://www.charlestonareaalliance.org
Contact: Matthew G. Ballard, President
Description: Promotes business and community development in Charleston, WV.

59398 ■ Community Directory
PO Box 487
Wellsburg, WV 26070-0487
Ph: (304)479-2115
Fax: (304)737-1660
Co. E-mail: kjroberts@comcast.net
URL: http://www.wellsburgchamber.com
Released: Annual

59399 ■ Economic Profile
110 Adams St.
Fairmont, WV 26554
Ph: (304)363-0442
Fax: (304)363-0480
Co. E-mail: mccc@marionchamber.com
URL: http://www.marionchamber.com
Contact: Butch Osbourne, Chairman

59400 ■ Fayette County Chamber of Commerce (FCCC)
310 Oyler Ave.
Oak Hill, WV 25901
Ph: (304)465-5617
Fax: (304)465-5618
Co. E-mail: fayette@wvdsl.net
URL: http://www.fayettecounty.com
Description: Promotes business and community development in Fayette County, WV.

59401 ■ Grant County Chamber of Commerce
126 S Main St., Ste. 1
Petersburg, WV 26847
Ph: (304)257-2722
Co. E-mail: gowv@gowv.com
URL: http://www.gowv.com
Contact: Tammy Kesner, President
Description: Promotes business, community development, and tourism in Grant County area. **Founded:** 1991.

59402 ■ Greater Bluefield Chamber of Commerce
PO Box 4098
Bluefield, WV 24701
Ph: (304)327-7184
Fax: (304)325-3085
Co. E-mail: info@bluefieldchamber.com
URL: http://www.bluefieldchamber.com
Contact: Marc Meachum, President
Description: Promotes business and community development in Bluefield, WV.

59403 ■ Green Piece
1624 Kanawha Blvd. E
Charleston, WV 25311
Ph: (304)342-1115

Fax: (304)342-1130
Co. E-mail: forjobs@wvchamber.com
URL: http://www.wvchamber.com
Contact: Steve Roberts, President
Released: Semiannual

59404 ■ Greenbrier County Convention and Visitors Bureau (GCCVB)
200 W Washington St.
Lewisburg, WV 24901-1354
Ph: (304)645-1000
Free: 800-833-2068
Fax: (304)647-3001
Co. E-mail: info@greenbrierwv.com
URL: http://greenbrierwv.com
Contact: Kara Dense, Executive Director
Description: Promotes business and community development in Lewisburg, WV and the Greenbrier Valley area. **Publications:** *Greenbrier County Visitors Guide* (Annual); *Travel Wise* (Semiannual).

59405 ■ *Greenbrier County Visitors Guide*
200 W Washington St.
Lewisburg, WV 24901-1354
Ph: (304)645-1000
Free: 800-833-2068
Fax: (304)647-3001
Co. E-mail: info@greenbrierwv.com
URL: http://greenbrierwv.com
Contact: Kara Dense, Executive Director
Released: Annual

59406 ■ Hampshire County Chamber of Commerce
91 S High St.
Romney, WV 26757
Ph: (304)822-7221
Co. E-mail: hampshirechamberofcommerce@citlink. net
URL: http://hcweekender.com/hampshirereview/Websites/HCChamberCommerce
Contact: Sandra Hunt, President
Description: Promotes business and community development in Hampshire County, WV. **Publications:** *News You Can Use.*

59407 ■ Harrison County Chamber of Commerce (HCCC)
520 W Main St.
Clarksburg, WV 26301-2819
Ph: (304)624-6331
Fax: (304)624-5190
Co. E-mail: info@harrisoncountychamber.com
URL: http://www.harrisoncountychamber.com
Contact: Katherine D. Wagner, President
Description: Promotes business and community development in Harrison County, WV. Sponsors symposium. **Founded:** 1919. **Publications:** *The Rising Star* (Quarterly). **Educational Activities:** Harrison County Chamber of Commerce Dinner (Annual). **Awards:** Citizen of the Year (Annual). **Telecommunication Services:** kathy@harrisoncountychamber.com.

59408 ■ Huntington Regional Chamber of Commerce (HRCC)
1108 3rd Ave., Ste. 300
Huntington, WV 25701
Ph: (304)525-5131
Fax: (304)525-5158
Co. E-mail: mark@huntingtonchamber.org
URL: http://www.huntingtonchamber.org
Contact: Jim Withers, Chairman
Description: Promotes business and community development in Cabell and Wayne Counties. **Publications:** *ChamberLink* (Monthly); *Membership Directory and Lifestyle Guide* (Annual).

59409 ■ Jefferson County Chamber of Commerce
201 Frontage Rd.
Charles Town, WV 25414-0426
Ph: (304)725-2055
Free: 800-624-0577

Fax: (304)728-8307
Co. E-mail: info@jeffersoncountywvchamber.org
URL: http://www.jeffersoncountywvchamber.org/index.html
Contact: Heather Morgan, Executive Director
Description: Promotes business and community development in Jefferson County, WV.

59410 ■ Logan County Chamber of Commerce
300 Main St.
Logan, WV 25601
Ph: (304)752-1324
Fax: (304)752-5988
Co. E-mail: logancountychamber@frontier.com
URL: http://www.logancountychamberofcommerce.com
Contact: Debrina J. Williams, Managing Director
Description: Promotes business and community development in Logan County, WV. **Founded:** 1913.

59411 ■ Marion County Chamber of Commerce (MCCC)
110 Adams St.
Fairmont, WV 26554
Ph: (304)363-0442
Fax: (304)363-0480
Co. E-mail: mccc@marionchamber.com
URL: http://www.marionchamber.com
Contact: Butch Osbourne, Chairman
Description: Promotes business and community development in Marion County, WV. **Founded:** 1953. **Publications:** *Buyers' Guide* (Periodic); *Economic Profile*; *Momentum* (Monthly). **Educational Activities:** Cavalcade of Trade (Annual). **Telecommunication Services:** tms@marionchamber.com.

59412 ■ Marshall County Chamber of Commerce (MCCC)
604 Jefferson Ave.
Moundsville, WV 26041
Ph: (304)845-2773
Co. E-mail: chamber@marshallcountychamber.com
URL: http://www.marshallcountychamber.com
Contact: David W. Knuth, Executive Director
Description: Promotes business, community development, and tourism in Marshall County, WV. Sponsors annual Christmas parade and annual Riverfront Festival (featuring a Native American Pow Wow). **Publications:** *Chamber Chatter* (Monthly).

59413 ■ Martinsburg-Berkeley County Chamber of Commerce
198 Viking Way
Martinsburg, WV 25401-5338
Ph: (304)267-4841
Free: 800-322-9007
Fax: (304)263-4695
Co. E-mail: chamber@berkeleycounty.org
URL: http://www.berkeleycounty.org
Contact: Tina H. Combs, President
Description: Promotes business and community development in Martinsburg-Berkeley County, WV. **Founded:** 1926.

59414 ■ Mason County Area Chamber of Commerce (MCACC)
305 Main St.
Point Pleasant, WV 25550
Ph: (304)675-1050
Fax: (304)675-1601
Co. E-mail: mccofc@pointpleasantwv.org
URL: http://www.masoncountychamber.org
Contact: Hilda Austin, Executive Director
Description: Promotes business and community development in Mason County, WV. Sponsors Mason County Fair Queen Contest. Holds annual dinner.

59415 ■ *Membership Directory and Lifestyle Guide*
1108 3rd Ave., Ste. 300
Huntington, WV 25701
Ph: (304)525-5131
Fax: (304)525-5158
Co. E-mail: mark@huntingtonchamber.org
URL: http://www.huntingtonchamber.org
Contact: Jim Withers, Chairman
Released: Annual **Price:** free for members.

59416 ■ Mineral County Chamber of Commerce
1 Grand Central Park
Keyser, WV 26726
Ph: (304)788-2513
Co. E-mail: office@mineralchamber.com
URL: http://www.mineralchamber.com
Description: Works to stimulate and enhance the business environment and quality of life in Mineral County. **Founded:** 1866.

59417 ■ *Momentum*
110 Adams St.
Fairmont, WV 26554
Ph: (304)363-0442
Fax: (304)363-0480
Co. E-mail: mccc@marionchamber.com
URL: http://www.marionchamber.com
Contact: Butch Osbourne, Chairman
Released: Monthly

59418 ■ Morgantown Area Chamber of Commerce (MACoC)
1029 University Ave., Ste. 101
Morgantown, WV 26505-5586
Ph: (304)292-3311
Free: 800-618-2525
Fax: (304)296-6619
Co. E-mail: info@morgantownchamber.org
URL: http://www.morgantownchamber.org
Contact: Kenneth Busz, President
Description: Promotes business and community development in the Morgantown, WV area. **Founded:** 1920.

59419 ■ *News You Can Use*
91 S High St.
Romney, WV 26757
Ph: (304)822-7221
Co. E-mail: hampshirechamberofcommerce@citlink. net
URL: http://hcweekender.com/hampshirereview/Websites/HCChamberCommerce
Contact: Sandra Hunt, President

59420 ■ Pendleton County Chamber of Commerce
PO Box 737
Franklin, WV 26807
Ph: (304)358-3884
Co. E-mail: pendletoncoc@verizon.net
URL: http://www.visitpendleton.com
Contact: Carolyn Simmons, Chairman
Description: Promotes business and community development in Pendleton County, KY. Sponsors annual awards banquet. **Publications:** *Business Ledger* (Quarterly).

59421 ■ Preston County Chamber of Commerce
200 1/2 W Main St.
Kingwood, WV 26537
Ph: (304)329-0576
Fax: (304)329-1407
Co. E-mail: prestoncoc@labyrinth.net
URL: http://www.prestonchamber.com
Contact: Kim Riley, President
Description: Promotes business and community development in Preston, WV. **Founded:** 1988. **Publications:** *Chamber Chat* (Monthly); *Preston County Chamber of Commerce Business, Services and Information Directory*.

59422 ■ *Preston County Chamber of Commerce Business, Services and Information Directory*
200 1/2 W Main St.
Kingwood, WV 26537
Ph: (304)329-0576
Fax: (304)329-1407
Co. E-mail: prestoncoc@labyrinth.net
URL: http://www.prestonchamber.com
Contact: Kim Riley, President

59423 ■ Princeton-Mercer County Chamber of Commerce (PMCCC)
1522 N Walker St.
Princeton, WV 24740

Ph: (304)487-1502
Fax: (304)425-0227
Co. E-mail: pmccc@frontiernet.net
URL: http://www.pmccc.com
Contact: Mr. Robert Farley, President

Description: Promotes economic development and advances professional and educational growth to businesses and communities. **Founded:** 1927. **Publications:** *The Chamber Challenge* (Monthly). **Awards:** Citizen of the Year (Annual); Volunteer of the Year (Annual); Excel Award Business of the Year (Annual).

59424 ■ Putnam County Chamber of Commerce (PCCC)
5664 State, Rte. 34
Winfield, WV 25213
Ph: (304)757-6510
Fax: (304)757-6562
Co. E-mail: chamber@putnamcounty.org
URL: http://www.putnamcounty.org
Contact: Mr. Marty S. Chapman, President

URL(s): putnamchamber.org. **Description:** Promotes programs of an economic, industrial, commercial, civic, and cultural nature in Putnam County, WV so that its citizens and business community can prosper. Seeks to enlighten the obstacles which inhibit business expansion and community growth and public awareness regarding local, state, and national issues. **Founded:** 1979. **Awards:** Mayo Lester Community Service Award (Annual).

59425 ■ Randolph County Convention and Visitors Bureau (RCCVB)
1302 N Randolph Ave.
Elkins, WV 26241
Ph: (304)636-2780
Free: 800-422-3304
Fax: (304)636-2780
Co. E-mail: bpritt@randolphcountycvb.com
URL: http://www.elkinswv.com
Contact: Brenda J. Pritt, Executive Director

Description: Promotes business and community development in Randolph County, WV. Sponsors area festival. Convention/Meeting: none. **Founded:** 1923. **Publications:** *Visitors Guide* (Semiannual); *Chamber Chatter Calendar of Events* (Monthly).

59426 ■ Richwood Chamber of Commerce (RCC)
PO Box 267
Richwood, WV 26261
Ph: (304)846-6790
URL: http://www.richwoodwv.com/chamber.html
Contact: Maxine Corbett, Executive Director

Description: Promotes business and community development in the Richwood, WV area. Sponsors educational and recreational programs. Conducts charitable activities. Sponsors competitions and festival. Publications: none. Convention/Meeting: none. **Founded:** 1960.

59427 ■ *The Rising Star*
520 W Main St.
Clarksburg, WV 26301-2819
Ph: (304)624-6331
Fax: (304)624-5190
Co. E-mail: info@harrisoncountychamber.com
URL: http://www.harrisoncountychamber.com
Contact: Katherine D. Wagner, President
Released: Quarterly

59428 ■ Roane County Chamber of Commerce (RCCC)
PO Box 1
Spencer, WV 25276-0001
Ph: (304)927-1780
Fax: (304)927-5953
Co. E-mail: rchamber@commission.state.wv.us
URL: http://www.roanechamberwv.org
Contact: Chuck Ricks, Vice President

Description: Promotes business and community development in Roane County, WV. Publications: none. **Founded:** 1928. **Awards:** Citizen of the Year (Annual).

59429 ■ St. Albans Area Chamber of Commerce
PO Box 675
St. Albans, WV 25177-0675
Ph: (304)727-7251
Fax: (304)727-7251
Co. E-mail: stacoc@netzero.net
URL: http://www.stalbanswv.com/about.shtml
Contact: Janet Painter, President

59430 ■ Summersville Area Chamber of Commerce (SACC)
PO Box 567
Summersville, WV 26651
Ph: (304)872-1588
Co. E-mail: info@summersvillechamber.com
URL: http://www.summersvillechamber.com
Contact: Teresa Clevenger, President

Description: Promotes business and community development in the Summersville, WV area. Sponsors festival. **Founded:** 1968.

59431 ■ *The Town Crier*
3174 Pennsylvania Ave., Ste. 1
Weirton, WV 26062
Ph: (304)748-7212
Fax: (304)748-0241
Co. E-mail: info@weirtonchamber.com
URL: http://www.weirtonchamber.com
Contact: Brenda Mull, President
Released: Monthly **Price:** included in membership dues.

59432 ■ *Travel Wise*
200 W Washington St.
Lewisburg, WV 24901-1354
Ph: (304)645-1000
Free: 800-833-2068
Fax: (304)647-3001
Co. E-mail: info@greenbrierwv.com
URL: http://greenbrierwv.com
Contact: Kara Dense, Executive Director
Released: Semiannual

59433 ■ *Visitors Guide*
1302 N Randolph Ave.
Elkins, WV 26241
Ph: (304)636-2780
Free: 800-422-3304
Fax: (304)636-2780
Co. E-mail: bpritt@randolphcountycvb.com
URL: http://www.elkinswv.com
Contact: Brenda J. Pritt, Executive Director
Released: Semiannual

59434 ■ Weirton Area Chamber of Commerce (WCC)
3174 Pennsylvania Ave., Ste. 1
Weirton, WV 26062
Ph: (304)748-7212
Fax: (304)748-0241
Co. E-mail: info@weirtonchamber.com
URL: http://www.weirtonchamber.com
Contact: Brenda Mull, President

Description: Promotes business and community development in Weirton, WV. **Founded:** 1935. **Publications:** *The Town Crier* (Monthly). **Telecommunication Services:** services@weirtonchamber.com.

59435 ■ Wellsburg Chamber of Commerce (WCC)
PO Box 487
Wellsburg, WV 26070-0487
Ph: (304)479-2115
Fax: (304)737-1660
Co. E-mail: kjroberts@comcast.net
URL: http://www.wellsburgchamber.com

Description: Promotes business and community development in Wellsburg, WV. **Founded:** 1916. **Publications:** *Community Directory* (Annual). **Awards:** Citizen of the Year (Annual).

59436 ■ West Virginia Chamber of Commerce
1624 Kanawha Blvd. E
Charleston, WV 25311
Ph: (304)342-1115

Fax: (304)342-1130
Co. E-mail: forjobs@wvchamber.com
URL: http://www.wvchamber.com
Contact: Steve Roberts, President

Description: Represents all business sectors in every region of the state. Serves as "a proactive leader in the search for solutions to problems, a voice for free competition and streamlined government, a catalyst for progressive thinking and problem solving, and a partner with government as appropriate". **Founded:** 1936. **Publications:** *Chamber Links* (Weekly); *Green Piece* (Semiannual); *West Virginia Human Resources Journal* (Quarterly). **Educational Activities:** West Virginia Chamber of Commerce Conference (Periodic); West Virginia Chamber of Commerce Meeting (Annual).

59437 ■ *West Virginia Human Resources Journal*
1624 Kanawha Blvd. E
Charleston, WV 25311
Ph: (304)342-1115
Fax: (304)342-1130
Co. E-mail: forjobs@wvchamber.com
URL: http://www.wvchamber.com
Contact: Steve Roberts, President
Released: Quarterly

59438 ■ Wheeling Area Chamber of Commerce (WACC)
1310 Market St.
Wheeling, WV 26003
Ph: (304)233-2575
Fax: (304)233-1320
Co. E-mail: terrysterling@wheelingchamber.com
URL: http://www.wheelingchamber.com
Contact: Terry A. Sterling, President

Description: Promotes business and community development in Wheeling, WV. **Founded:** 1966.

PROCUREMENT ASSISTANCE PROGRAMS

59439 ■ Mid-Ohio Valley Regional Council
531 Market St.
Parkersburg, WV 26101
Ph: (304)422-4993
Free: 800-924-7047
Fax: (304)422-4998
Co. E-mail: dberkey@mountain.net
URL: http://www.movrc.org
Contact: Fred Rader, Director

Description: Provides advice, assistance, and technical support to businesses and industries interested in becoming involved in the government procurement process.

59440 ■ Regional Contracting Assistance Center - Robert C. Byrd Institute - Huntington
1050 4th Ave.
Huntington, WV 25701-1522
Ph: (304)781-1625
Free: 800-469-7224
Fax: (304)781-1623
Co. E-mail: info@rcbi.org
URL: http://rcbi.org
Contact: Tom Minnich, Director

Description: Serves as a clearinghouse for information on contracting/subcontracting opportunities, and as a source for technical resources, information, and training. Offers an electronic bid match, access to government and industry regulations and standards, past procurement histories, technical assistance in understanding bid and contract requirements, assistance in bid proposal preparation, training in various aspects of contracting, and assistance in understanding contract pricing, packaging, and administration.

59441 ■ Regional Contracting Assistant Center - Princeton
195 Davis St., Ste. 103
Princeton, WV 24740
Ph: (304)425-9438

Fax: (425)648-4751
Co. E-mail: dbailey@rcacwv.com
URL: http://www.rcacwv.com
Contact: Donna George, Director, Marketing

59442 ■ Regional Contracting Assisting Center - Southern West Virginia Community & Technical College
300 Main St.
Logan, WV 25601
Ph: (304)792-7234
Fax: (304)792-7239
Co. E-mail: rcac@rcawv.com
URL: http://www.rcacwv.com
Contact: Jackie Whitley, Specialist
E-mail: jeffreyh@southern.wvnet.edu
Description: Provides advice and assistance in areas specific to company's government contracting needs such as federal acquisition regulation serving Boone, Lincoln, Logan, McDowell, Mingo, and Wyoming Counties.

59443 ■ West Virginia Procurement Technical Assistance Center
PO Box 5528
Vienna, WV 26105
Ph: (304)428-6889
Free: 800-868-3924

Fax: (304)428-6891
Co. E-mail: belinda@cssiwv.com
URL: http://www.wvptac.org
Contact: Belinda Sheridan, Director
E-mail: snyder@access.mountain.net

INCUBATORS/RESEARCH AND TECHNOLOGY PARKS

59444 ■ Unlimited Future, Inc.
1650 8th Ave.
Huntington, WV 25703
Ph: (304)697-3007
Fax: (304)522-0367
Co. E-mail: ufi@unlimitedfuture.org
URL: http://unlimitedfuture.org
Description: This incubator is dedicated to eliminated barriers to the creation of successful businesses. The non-profit center specializes in assisting disadvantaged businesses through the reduction of overhead and other services.

EDUCATIONAL PROGRAMS

59445 ■ Southern West Virginia Community and Technical College
128 College Dr.
Saulsville, WV 25876

Ph: (304)294-8346
Fax: (304)294-8534
URL: http://www.southernwv.edu
Description: Two-year college offering a program in small business management.

59446 ■ West Virginia Northern Community College (Wheeling)
1704 Market St.
Wheeling, WV 26003
Ph: (304)233-5900
Fax: (304)232-8187
URL: http://www.wvncc.edu
Description: Two-year college offering a small business management program.

59447 ■ West Virginia University (Parkersburg)
300 Campus Dr.
Parkersburg, WV 26101-9577
Ph: (304)424-8000
Free: 800-982-9887
Fax: (304)424-8315
Co. E-mail: info@mail.wvup.edu
URL: http://www.wvup.edu
Description: Conducts management and supervisory training courses. Also offers training programs and free consultation for small business owners.

SMALL BUSINESS DEVELOPMENT CENTERS

59448 ■ Southwestern Wisconsin Small Business Development Center (SWSBDC)
510 Pioneer Tower
Platteville, WI 53818-3099
Ph: (608)342-1038
Fax: (608)342-1599
Co. E-mail: swsbdc@uwplatt.edu
URL: http://www.uwplatt.edu/swsbdc/index.html
Contact: Gary M. Smith, Program Director
Description: Represents and promotes the small business sector. Provides management assistance to current and prospective small business owners. Helps to improve management skills and expand the products and services of members.

59449 ■ University of Wisconsin - Eau Claire Small Business Development Center
210 Water St.
Eau Claire, WI 54702-4004
Ph: (715)836-5811
Free: 800-582-5182
Fax: (715)836-5263
URL: http://www.uwec.edu/CE/cbs/aboutsbdc.htm
Contact: Jim Mishefske, Director
Description: Represents and promotes the small business sector. Provides management assistance to current and prospective small business owners. Helps to improve management skills and expand the products and services of members.

59450 ■ University of Wisconsin - Green Bay Small Business Development Center
2420 Nicolet Dr.
Green Bay, WI 54311
Ph: (920)496-2117
Free: 800-940-SBDC
Co. E-mail: tromblec@uwgb.edu
URL: http://www.uwgb.edu/sbdc/index.html
Contact: Christina Trombley, Director
Description: Represents and promotes the small business sector. Provides management assistance to current and prospective small business owners. Helps to improve management skills and expand the products and services of members.

59451 ■ University of Wisconsin - La Crosse Small Business Development Center
1725 State St.
La Crosse, WI 54601
Ph: (608)785-8782
Fax: (608)785-6919
Co. E-mail: sbdc@uwlax.edu
URL: http://www.uwlax.edu/sbdc/index.html
Contact: Anne Hlavacka, Director
Description: Represents and promotes the small business sector. Provides management assistance to current and prospective small business owners. Helps to improve management skills and expand the products and services of members.

59452 ■ University of Wisconsin - Madison Small Business Development Center
975 University Ave., No. 3260
Madison, WI 53706
Ph: (608)263-7680
Free: 800-940-7232
Fax: (608)263-0818
URL: http://sbdc.wisc.edu
Description: Represents and promotes the small business sector. Provides management assistance to current and prospective small business owners. Helps to improve management skills and expand the products and services of members.

59453 ■ University of Wisconsin - Milwaukee Small Business Development Center
161 W Wisconsin Ave., Ste. 6000
Milwaukee, WI 53203
Ph: (414)227-3240
Co. E-mail: sbdc@uwm.edu
URL: http://www4.uwm.edu/SCE/dci.cfm?id=15
Contact: Kristine Kruepke, Program Manager
Description: Represents and promotes the small business sector. Provides management assistance to current and prospective small business owners. Helps to improve management skills and expand the products and services of members.

59454 ■ University of Wisconsin - Oshkosh Small Business Development Center
800 Algoma Blvd.
Oshkosh, WI 54901-3551
Ph: (920)424-1453
Free: 800-232-8939
Fax: (920)424-2005
Co. E-mail: sbdc@uwosh.edu
URL: http://www.uwosh.edu/sbdc
Contact: Mr. Robert O'Donnell, Director
Description: Represents and promotes the small business sector. Provides management assistance to current and prospective small business owners. Helps to improve management skills and expand the products and services of members.

59455 ■ University of Wisconsin - Parkside Small Business Development Center
900 Wood Rd.
Kenosha, WI 53141
Ph: (262)595-3363
Free: 800-940-7232
Co. E-mail: mcphaul@uwp.edu
URL: http://www.parksidesbdc.com
Contact: Jim McPhaul, Director (Acting)
Description: Represents and promotes the small business sector. Provides management assistance to current and prospective small business owners. Helps to improve management skills and expand the products and services of members.

59456 ■ University of Wisconsin - River Falls Small Business Development Center
College of Business and Economics
South Hall, Rm. 128
410 S Third St.
River Falls, WI 54022

Ph: (715)425-0620
Fax: (715)425-0707
Co. E-mail: steven.e.dewald@uwrf.edu
URL: http://www.uwrf.edu/CBE/SBDC.cfm
Contact: Steve DeWald, Director
Description: Represents and promotes the small business sector. Provides management assistance to current and prospective small business owners. Helps to improve management skills and expand the products and services of members.

59457 ■ University of Wisconsin - Stevens Point Small Business Development Center
032 Main Bldg.
2100 Main St.
Stevens Point, WI 54481
Ph: (715)346-2288
Free: 800-898-9472
Co. E-mail: vloberme@uwsp.edu
URL: http://www.uwsp.edu/conted/sbdc
Contact: Vicki Lobermeier, Director
Description: Represents and promotes the small business sector. Provides management assistance to current and prospective small business owners. Helps to improve management skills and expand the products and services of members.

59458 ■ University of Wisconsin - Superior Small Business Development Center
PO Box 2000
Superior, WI 54880
Ph: (715)394-8351
Free: 800-410-8351
Fax: (715)394-8592
Co. E-mail: jraymond@uwsuper.edu
URL: http://www.uwsuper.edu/sbdc
Contact: Ms. Julianne Raymond, Director
Description: Represents and promotes the small business sector. Provides management assistance to current and prospective small business owners. Helps to improve management skills and expand the products and services of members.

59459 ■ University of Wisconsin - Whitewater Small Business Development Center
1200 Hyland Hall
Whitewater, WI 53190
Ph: (262)472-3217
Fax: (262)472-1600
Co. E-mail: ask-sbdc@uww.edu
URL: http://sbdc.uww.edu
Contact: Sheila Vold, Business Manager Office Manager
Description: Represents and promotes the small business sector. Provides management assistance to current and prospective small business owners. Helps to improve management skills and expand the products and services of members.

59460 ■ Wisconsin Small Business Development Center - Lead Office (WSBDC)
423 Extension Bldg.
432 N Lake St., Rm. 423
Madison, WI 53706-1496
Ph: (608)263-7794
Free: 800-940-7232

Fax: (608)263-7830
Co. E-mail: gayle.kugler@uwex.edu
URL: http://www.wisconsinsbdc.org
Contact: Gayle Kugler, Director
Description: Provides educational services, counseling and free business answer line assistance for entrepreneurs and small business owners. **Founded:** 1980.

SMALL BUSINESS ASSISTANCE PROGRAMS

59461 ■ Wisconsin Department of Agriculture, Trade and Consumer Protection (DATCP)—Wisconsin Consumer Protection Office
2811 Agriculture Dr.
Madison, WI 53708-8911
Ph: (608)224-4949
Free: 800-422-7128
Fax: (608)224-4939
Co. E-mail: winocall@datcp.state.wi.us
URL: http://datcp.wi.gov
Contact: Dr. Richard L. Cates, Director
E-mail: rlcates@mhtc.net
URL(s): www.datcp.state.wi.us/index.jsp. **Description:** Provides marketing services to promote the interests of agriculture and agricultural products domestically and in international markets. **Founded:** 1839. **Publications:** *Something Special from Wisconsin Suppliers Guide* (Annual); *Wisconsin Poultry & Egg Directory* (Biennial). **Telecommunication Services:** datcphotline@datcp.state.wi.us; hotline@datcp.state.wi.us.

59462 ■ Wisconsin Department of Commerce - Business Development Division
201 W Washington Ave., 5th Fl.
Madison, WI 53707-7970
Ph: (608)264-7837
Fax: (608)264-6151
Co. E-mail: comwebmailbd@wisconsin.gov
URL: http://www.commerce.state.wi.us
Contact: Jim O'Keefe, Administrator
Description: Develops resources, programs, and policies to strengthen Wisconsin's entrepreneurial network. Cosponsors business development and training workshops and conferences.

59463 ■ Wisconsin Department of Commerce - Entrepreneurs/Start-ups
201 W Washington Ave., 5th Fl.
Madison, WI 53707-7970
Ph: (608)264-7837
Fax: (608)264-6151
URL: http://www.commerce.state.wi.us
Contact: Jim O'Keefe, Administrator
Description: Develops resources, programs, and policies to strengthen Wisconsin's entrepreneurial network. Cosponsors business development and training workshops and conferences.

59464 ■ Wisconsin Department of Commerce - International Division
201 W Washington Ave., 6th Fl.
Madison, WI 53703
Ph: (608)267-0639
Fax: (608)266-5551
Co. E-mail: international@wisconsin.gov
URL: http://www.commerce.state.wi.us/IE/
Contact: Mary Regel, Director
Description: Assists Wisconsin manufacturers in exploring international sales opportunities, joint ventures and licensing, and encouraging foreign manufacturers to establish companies in Wisconsin.

SCORE OFFICES

59465 ■ SCORE Central Wisconsin
700 S Central Ave.
Marshfield, WI 54449
Ph: (715)384-3454
Co. E-mail: cwscore@centralwisconsinscore.org
Description: Provides free counseling and low-cost workshops for the Stevens Point, Marshfield and Wisconsin Rapids area.

59466 ■ SCORE Chapter 28, Milwaukee, WI
310 W Wisconsin Ave., Ste. 425
Milwaukee, WI 53203
Ph: (414)297-3942
Fax: (414)297-1377
Co. E-mail: score@scorewisconsin.org
URL: http://www.scoresewisconsin.org
Description: Provides counseling, workshops, and seminars to help entrepreneurs start and operate small businesses. **Founded:** 1965.

59467 ■ SCORE Eau Claire
Federation Bldg., Rm. B11
500 S Barstow St.
Eau Claire, WI 54701
Ph: (715)834-1573
Fax: (715)834-6047
Co. E-mail: score@score-eauclaire.org
URL: http://www.score-eauclaire.org
Description: Provides professional guidance, mentoring services and financial assistance to maximize the success of existing and emerging small businesses.

59468 ■ SCORE Fox Cities
125 N Superior St.
Appleton, WI 54913
Ph: (920)734-7101
Co. E-mail: score@foxcitiesbusiness.com
URL: http://www.scorefoxcities.com
Description: Provides free counseling and low-cost workshops within the Fox Valley.

59469 ■ SCORE Green Bay
Northeast Wisconsin Technical Center
Business Assistance Center, Rm. 130
2701 Larsen Rd.
Green Bay, WI 54303
Ph: (920)496-8930
Fax: (920)496-6009
Co. E-mail: cgokey@titletown.org
URL: http://www.greenbayscore.org
Contact: Steven Greenfield, Chairman
Description: Provides free and confidential business counseling tailored to meet the needs of small business owners and personal objectives.

59470 ■ SCORE La Crosse
712 Main St.
La Crosse, WI 54601
Ph: (608)784-4880
Co. E-mail: scorelax@centurytel.net
URL: http://lacrossescore.org
Description: Provides professional guidance, mentoring services and financial assistance to maximize the success of existing and emerging small businesses.

59471 ■ SCORE Madison
MGE Innovation Center - Lower Level
505 S Rosa Rd., Ste. 37
Madison, WI 53719
Ph: (608)441-2820
Co. E-mail: rlw-score145@charter.net
URL: http://scoremadison145.org
Contact: Kent Anderson, Chairman
Description: Provides entrepreneur education for the formation, growth and success of small businesses in the area.

59472 ■ SCORE Wausau
200 Washington St., Ste. 120
Wausau, WI 54403
Ph: (715)845-6231
Description: Provides professional guidance, mentoring services and financial assistance to maximize the success of existing and emerging small businesses.

59473 ■ South Central Wisconsin SCORE
Co. E-mail: jcedc@mwt.net

BETTER BUSINESS BUREAUS

59474 ■ Better Business Bureau of Wisconsin
10101 W Greenfield Ave., No. 125
Milwaukee, WI 53214

Ph: (414)847-6000
Free: 800-273-1002
Co. E-mail: info@wisconsin.bbb.org
URL: http://wisconsin.bbb.org
Contact: Randall Hoth, President
Description: Seeks to promote and foster the highest ethical relationship between businesses and the public through voluntary self-regulation, consumer and business education, and service excellence. Provides information to help consumers and businesses make informed purchasing decisions and avoid costly scams and frauds; settles consumer complaints through arbitration and other means.

CHAMBERS OF COMMERCE

59475 ■ *Action Update*
N88 W16621 Appleton Ave.
Menomonee Falls, WI 53052
Ph: (262)251-2430
Fax: (262)251-0969
Co. E-mail: toni@fallschamber.com
URL: http://fallschamber.com
Contact: Toni M. Yates, Executive Director
Released: Periodic **Price:** free.

59476 ■ *Active Voice*
5501 Vern Holmes Dr.
Stevens Point, WI 54481
Ph: (715)344-1940
Fax: (715)344-4473
Co. E-mail: info@portagecountybiz.com
URL: http://www.portagecountybiz.com
Contact: Lori Dehlinger, Executive Director
Released: Monthly

59477 ■ *Adams County Chamber of Commerce Newsletter*
PO Box 576
Adams, WI 53910
Ph: (608)339-6997
Free: 888-339-6997
Fax: (608)339-8079
Co. E-mail: chamber@adamscountywi.com
URL: http://www.adamscountywi.com
Contact: Alice Parr, Executive Director
Released: Quarterly

59478 ■ Adams County Chamber of Commerce and Tourism (ACCC&T)
PO Box 576
Adams, WI 53910
Ph: (608)339-6997
Free: 888-339-6997
Fax: (608)339-8079
Co. E-mail: chamber@adamscountywi.com
URL: http://www.adamscountywi.com
Contact: Alice Parr, Executive Director
Description: Promotes business and community development in Adams County, WI. Sponsors annual Crazy Days business and retail festival, Castle Rock Triathlon, Waterfest Boat Parade and Holiday Parade & seasonal events. **Founded:** 1945. **Publications:** *Adams County Chamber of Commerce Newsletter* (Quarterly); *Adams County Visitors Guide* (Annual). **Awards:** JEM Grant from the Wisconsin State Department of Tourism (Annual); High School Outstanding Student/s (Annual).

59479 ■ *Adams County Visitors Guide*
PO Box 576
Adams, WI 53910
Ph: (608)339-6997
Free: 888-339-6997
Fax: (608)339-8079
Co. E-mail: chamber@adamscountywi.com
URL: http://www.adamscountywi.com
Contact: Alice Parr, Executive Director
Released: Annual

59480 ■ Algoma Area Chamber of Commerce (AACC)
1226 Lake St.
Algoma, WI 54201
Ph: (920)487-2041
Free: 800-498-4888

Fax: (920)487-5519
Co. E-mail: chamber@algoma.org
URL: http://www.algoma.org
Description: Seeks to improve the business climate and promote community development in the Algoma, WI area. Sponsors festivals, promotes tourism and operates visitor center. **Scope:** local history, Algoma record Herald 1873-present, birth/death/marriage records. **Founded:** 1946. **Publications:** *Chamber Beacon* (Quarterly). **Educational Activities:** Wet Whistle Wine Fest (Annual); Doll and Teddy Bear Show and Sale (Annual). **Awards:** Business of the Year (Annual); Educator of the Year (Annual); Industry of the Year (Annual).

59481 ■ *The Ambassador*
111 Milwaukee Ave.
Sparta, WI 54656
Ph: (608)269-4123
Free: 888-540-8434
Fax: (608)269-3350
Co. E-mail: spartachamber@centurytel.net
URL: http://www.spartachamber.com
Contact: Sharon Folcey, Executive Director
Released: Monthly

59482 ■ *America's Little Switzerland*
418 Railroad St.
New Glarus, WI 53574
Ph: (608)527-2095
Free: 800-527-6838
Co. E-mail: info@swisstown.com
URL: http://www.swisstown.com
Released: Weekly **Price:** free.

59483 ■ Ashland Area Chamber of Commerce (AACC)
PO Box 746
Ashland, WI 54806
Ph: (715)682-2500
Free: 800-284-9484
Co. E-mail: info@visitashland.com
URL: http://www.visitashland.com
Description: Represents retailers and businesses. Promotes business and community development in the Ashland, WI area. **Founded:** 1888.

59484 ■ Baileys Harbor Community Association (BHCA)
PO Box 31
Baileys Harbor, WI 54202
Ph: (920)839-2366
Co. E-mail: info@baileysharbor.com
URL: http://www.baileysharbor.com
Description: Works to advance the commercial, financial, industrial and civic interests of the area. **Founded:** 1979. **Publications:** *Fall is a Favorite Time of Year.* **Educational Activities:** Collector Car and Truck Show (Annual).

59485 ■ Baldwin Area Chamber of Commerce (BCC)
PO Box 142
Baldwin, WI 54002
Ph: (715)760-0518
Co. E-mail: bwchamber@baldwin-telecom.net
URL: http://www.baldwin-woodvillechamber.org
Contact: Aaron Van Ranst, President
Description: Works for the improvement of the business community in Baldwin. **Founded:** 1982.

59486 ■ Baraboo Area Chamber of Commerce (BCC)
PO Box 442
Baraboo, WI 53913
Ph: (608)356-8333
Free: 800-BAR-ABOO
Fax: (608)356-8422
Co. E-mail: chamber@baraboo.com
URL: http://www.baraboo.com/chamber.html
Contact: Gene Dalhoff, Executive Director
Description: Represents agribusiness, manufacturing, professional, retail, and tourism businesses. Promotes business and community development in Baraboo, WI. **Founded:** 1950. **Publications:** *Chamber Review* (Monthly). **Educational Activities:** Golf Outing (Annual).

59487 ■ *Bay Business Journal*
PO Box 1660
Green Bay, WI 54305
Ph: (920)437-8704
Fax: (920)437-1024
Co. E-mail: info@titletown.org
URL: http://www.titletown.org
Contact: Laurie Radke, President
Released: Bimonthly

59488 ■ Bayfield Chamber of Commerce
PO Box 138
Bayfield, WI 54814
Ph: (715)779-3335
Free: 800-447-4094
Co. E-mail: chamber@bayfield.org
URL: http://bayfield.org
Contact: Cari Obst, Executive Director
Description: Promotes business and community development in Bayfield, WI area. **Awards:** Good Neighbor Award (Annual). **Telecommunication Services:** cari@bayfield.org.

59489 ■ *Bear Tracks*
801 Main St., Ste. 1
Mukwonago, WI 53149
Ph: (262)363-7758
Fax: (262)363-7730
Co. E-mail: director@mukwonagochamber.org
URL: http://www.mukwonagochamber.org
Contact: April Reszka, Executive Director
Released: 5/year **Price:** free.

59490 ■ Beaver Dam Area Chamber of Commerce (BDACC)
127 S Spring St.
Beaver Dam, WI 53916
Ph: (920)887-8879
Fax: (920)887-9750
Co. E-mail: info@beaverdamchamber.com
URL: http://www.beaverdamchamber.com
Contact: Philip Fritsche, Executive Director
Description: Promotes business and community development in the Beaver Dam, WI area. Offers a Beaver Dam Health Program to members. **Founded:** 1922. **Publications:** *Chamber Newsletter* (Monthly).

59491 ■ Berlin Chamber of Commerce (BCC)
Ferndale Center
40 Chamberlain Hwy.
Kensington, CT 06037
Ph: (860)829-1033
Fax: (860)829-1243
Co. E-mail: director@berlinctchamber.org
URL: http://www.berlinctchamber.org
Contact: Katherine A. Fuechsel, Executive Director
Description: Promotes business and community development in Berlin, Kensington, and East Berlin, WI. Conducts various programs to assist small businesses to compete successfully. **Founded:** 1948. **Publications:** *CommUNITY* (Quarterly); *Visitor's Guide.* **Educational Activities:** Berlin Chamber of Commerce Meeting (Quarterly).

59492 ■ Bloomer Chamber of Commerce
PO Box 273
Bloomer, WI 54724
Ph: (715)568-3339
Fax: (715)568-3346
Co. E-mail: bchamber@bloomer.net
URL: http://www.bloomerchamber.com
Contact: Rod Turner, Executive Director
Description: Promotes business and community development in Bloomer, WI area.

59493 ■ Boscobel Chamber of Commerce
800 Wisconsin Ave.
Boscobel, WI 53805
Ph: (608)375-2672
Fax: (608)375-2672
Co. E-mail: chamber@boscobelwisconsin.com
URL: http://www.boscobelwisconsin.com
Contact: Tom Richter, President
Description: Promotes business and community development in Boscobel, WI area.

59494 ■ Boulder Junction Chamber of Commerce
PO Box 286
Boulder Junction, WI 54512-0286
Ph: (715)385-2400
Free: 800-466-8759
Co. E-mail: boulderjct@boulderjct.org
URL: http://www.boulderjct.org
Contact: Theresa Smith, Executive Director
Description: Promotes business and community development in Boulder Junction, WI area.

59495 ■ Brillion Area Chamber of Commerce
PO Box 123
Brillion, WI 54110
Ph: (920)875-0125
Co. E-mail: info@brillionchamber.com
URL: http://www.brillionchamber.com
Contact: Joy Buboltz, Secretary Treasurer
Description: Promotes business and community development in Brillion, WI area.

59496 ■ Brodhead Chamber of Commerce
PO Box 16
Brodhead, WI 53520-0016
Ph: (608)897-8411
Co. E-mail: nancy@brodheadchamber.org
URL: http://www.brodheadchamber.org
Description: Promotes business and community development in Brodhead, WI area.

59497 ■ Brooklyn Area Chamber of Commerce
108 Hotel St.
Brooklyn, WI 53521
Ph: (608)455-1627
Co. E-mail: info@brooklynwisconsin.com
URL: http://www.brooklynwisconsin.com
Contact: LaVorn Dvorak, President
Description: Promotes and develop Brooklyn area business and at the same time provides education and supports its members businesses.

59498 ■ Burlington Area Chamber of Commerce (BACC)
113 E Chestnut St., Ste. B
Burlington, WI 53105
Ph: (262)763-6044
Fax: (262)763-3631
Co. E-mail: info@burlingtonchamber.org
URL: http://www.burlingtonchamber.org
Contact: Janice Ludtke, Executive Director
Description: Promotes business and community development in the Burlington, WI area. Holds festival. **Founded:** 1944. **Publications:** *Burlington, Discover the Treasures* (Monthly); *FOCUS* (Monthly); *Burlington, Discover the Treasures* (Monthly).

59499 ■ *Burlington, Discover the Treasures*
113 E Chestnut St., Ste. B
Burlington, WI 53105
Ph: (262)763-6044
Fax: (262)763-3631
Co. E-mail: info@burlingtonchamber.org
URL: http://www.burlingtonchamber.org
Contact: Janice Ludtke, Executive Director
Released: Monthly

59500 ■ *Business Beat*
615 E Washington Ave., 2nd Fl.
Madison, WI 53701-0071
Ph: (608)256-8348
Fax: (608)256-0333
Co. E-mail: info@greatermadisonchamber.com
URL: http://greatermadisonchamber.com
Contact: Jennifer Alexander, President
E-mail: jalexander@greatermadisonchamber.com
Released: Monthly

59501 ■ *Business to Business*
102 E Main St.
Waterford, WI 53185
Ph: (262)534-5911
Fax: (262)534-6507
Co. E-mail: chamber@waterford-wi.org
URL: http://www.waterford-wi.org
Contact: Jennifer Thomas, Executive Director
Released: Quarterly

59502 ■ *Business Directory*
1634 Wisconsin Ave.
Grafton, WI 53024
Ph: (262)377-1650
Fax: (262)375-7087
Co. E-mail: info@grafton-wi.org
URL: http://grafton-wi.org
Contact: Pam King, Executive Director
Released: Annual

59503 ■ *Business Directory*
PO Box 141
Luxemburg, WI 54217-0307
Ph: (920)845-2062
Co. E-mail: info@luxemburgchamber.com
URL: http://luxemburgchamber.com
Contact: Jeff Blemke, President
Released: Biennial

59504 ■ *Business Directory*
6331 W Mequon Rd.
Mequon, WI 53092
Ph: (262)512-9358
Fax: (262)512-9359
Co. E-mail: info@mtchamber.org
URL: http://www.mtchamber.org
Contact: Tina Schwantes, Executive Director
Released: Annual

59505 ■ *Business Directory*
PO Box 66
Randolph, WI 53956
Ph: (920)326-4769
Fax: (920)326-5032
URL: http://www.randolphwi.net
Contact: Kathy Nehmer, President
Released: Periodic

59506 ■ *Businessmatters*
PO Box 6190
Wausau, WI 54402-6190
Ph: (715)845-6231
Fax: (715)845-6235
Co. E-mail: info@wausauchamber.com
URL: http://www.wausauchamber.com
Contact: Jeff Zriny, President
Released: Quarterly

59507 ■ *Butler Area Chamber of Commerce*
(BACC)
12808 W Hampton Ave.
Butler, WI 53007-1606
Ph: (262)781-5195
Fax: (262)781-7870
Co. E-mail: linda@butlerchamber.org
URL: http://www.butlerchamber.org
Contact: Linda C. Ryfinski, Executive Director
Description: Promotes business and community
development in the Butler, WI area. Offers special
health insurance program for small businesses and
real estate and employment referrals. **Founded:**
1970. **Publications:** *Butler Area Chamber of Com-
merce Newsletter* (Monthly). **Educational Activities:**
Christmas Business After Hours (Annual). **Awards:**
Distinguished Business of the Year (Annual); Distinguished Citizen of the Year (Annual).

59508 ■ *Butler Area Chamber of Commerce*
Newsletter
12808 W Hampton Ave.
Butler, WI 53007-1606
Ph: (262)781-5195
Fax: (262)781-7870
Co. E-mail: linda@butlerchamber.org
URL: http://www.butlerchamber.org
Contact: Linda C. Ryfinski, Executive Director
Released: Monthly **Price:** included in membership
dues.

59509 ■ *Cable Area Chamber of Commerce*
PO Box 217
Cable, WI 54821
Ph: (715)798-3833
Free: 800-533-7454
Co. E-mail: info@cable4fun.com
URL: http://www.cable4fun.com
Contact: James Bolen, Executive Director
Description: Promotes business and economic
development in Cable Area, WI.

59510 ■ *Caddott Chamber*
PO Box 84
Cadott, WI 54727
Ph: (715)289-3338
Fax: (715)289-5454
Co. E-mail: info@cadottchamber.org
URL: http://www.cadottchamber.org
Contact: Huntz Geissler, President
Released: Monthly

59511 ■ *Cadott Area Chamber of Commerce*
PO Box 84
Cadott, WI 54727
Ph: (715)289-3338
Fax: (715)289-5454
Co. E-mail: info@cadottchamber.org
URL: http://www.cadottchamber.org
Contact: Huntz Geissler, President
Description: Supports and promotes business in
Caddott Area. **Publications:** *Caddott Chamber*
(Monthly).

59512 ■ *Cambridge Chamber of Commerce*
PO Box 572
Cambridge, WI 53523-0572
Ph: (608)423-3780
Fax: (608)423-7558
Co. E-mail: wivictorian@aol.com
URL: http://www.cambridgewi.com
Contact: Simone Mausser, President
Description: Promotes business and community
development in Cambridge, WI area.

59513 ■ *Capitol Watch*
501 E Washington Ave.
Madison, WI 53701-0352
Ph: (608)258-3400
Fax: (608)258-3413
Co. E-mail: jhaney@wmc.org
URL: http://www.wmc.org
Contact: James S. Haney, President
Released: Weekly

59514 ■ *CCGB News*
500 Public Ave.
Beloit, WI 53511
Ph: (608)365-8835
Fax: (608)365-6850
Co. E-mail: info@greaterbeloitchamber.com
URL: http://greaterbeloitchamber.com
Contact: Randall Upton, President
Released: Monthly **Price:** $15, /year for individuals.

59515 ■ *Cedarburg Chamber of Commerce*
(CCC)
PO Box 104
Cedarburg, WI 53012
Ph: (262)377-5856
Free: 800-237-2874
Fax: (262)377-6470
Co. E-mail: info@cedarburg.org
URL: http://www.cedarburg.org
Contact: Kristine Hage, Executive Director
Description: Businesses and individuals. Promotes
business and community development in Cedarburg,
WI. **Founded:** 1902.

59516 ■ *Chamber Beacon*
1226 Lake St.
Algoma, WI 54201
Ph: (920)487-2041
Free: 800-498-4888
Fax: (920)487-5519
Co. E-mail: chamber@algoma.org
URL: http://www.algoma.org
Released: Quarterly

59517 ■ *Chamber Business*
PO Box 128
Richland Center, WI 53581
Ph: (608)647-6205
Free: 800-422-1318
Fax: (608)647-5449
Co. E-mail: chamber@richlandalliance.com
URL: http://www.richlandchamber.com
Contact: Shannon Clark, President
Released: Semiannual

59518 ■ *Chamber to Chamber*
501 E Washington Ave.
Madison, WI 53701-0352
Ph: (608)258-3400
Fax: (608)258-3413
Co. E-mail: jhaney@wmc.org
URL: http://www.wmc.org
Contact: James S. Haney, President

59519 ■ *Chamber Chronicles*
PO Box 180171
Delafield, WI 53018
Ph: (262)646-8100
Free: 888-294-1082
Fax: (262)646-8237
Co. E-mail: info@visitdelafield.org
URL: http://www.visitdelafield.org
Contact: Debra Smith, Executive Director
Released: Bimonthly

59520 ■ *Chamber Connection*
245 S Knowles Ave.
New Richmond, WI 54017
Ph: (715)246-2900
Free: 800-654-6380
Fax: (715)246-7100
Co. E-mail: info@newrichmondchamber.com
URL: http://www.newrichmondchamber.com
Contact: Angela Olson, President
Released: Monthly **Price:** included in membership
dues.

59521 ■ *The Chamber Connection*
7447 W Greenfield Ave.
West Allis, WI 53214
Ph: (414)302-9901
URL: http://www.wawmchamber.com
Contact: Diane Brandt, Executive Director
Released: Monthly

59522 ■ *Chamber Connection*
712 Main St.
La Crosse, WI 54601
Ph: (608)784-4880
Fax: (608)784-4919
Co. E-mail: lse_chamber@centurytel.net
URL: http://www.lacrossechamber.com
Contact: Dick Granchalek, President
Released: Monthly **Price:** included in membership
dues; $15, /year for nonmembers.

59523 ■ *The Chamber Link*
PO Box 584
Plymouth, WI 53073
Ph: (920)893-0079
Free: 888-693-8263
Fax: (920)893-8473
Co. E-mail: plymouthchamber@frontier.com
URL: http://www.plymouthwisconsin.com
Contact: Ron Nielsen, President
Released: Monthly

59524 ■ *Chamber Member Directory &*
Community Guide
116 W Capitol Dr.
Hartland, WI 53029-2104
Ph: (262)367-7059
Fax: (262)367-2980
Co. E-mail: admin@hartland-wi.org
URL: http://www.hartland-wi.org
Contact: Ms. Lynn Minturn, Executive Director
Released: Annual

59525 ■ *Chamber News*
8 W Main St.
Evansville, WI 53536
Ph: (608)882-5131
Co. E-mail: evansvillecoc@litewire.net
URL: http://evansvillechamber.com
Contact: John Morning, President
Released: Quarterly **Price:** included in membership
dues.

59526 ■ *Chamber News*
6331 W Mequon Rd.
Mequon, WI 53092
Ph: (262)512-9358

Fax: (262)512-9359
Co. E-mail: info@mtchamber.org
URL: http://www.mtchamber.org
Contact: Tina Schwantes, Executive Director
Released: Monthly

59527 ■ *Chamber News*
37 S Main St.
Rice Lake, WI 54868
Ph: (715)234-2126
Free: 877-234-2126
Fax: (715)234-2085
Co. E-mail: chamber@rice-lake.com
URL: http://www.rice-lake.com
Contact: Dan Jirik, President
Released: Monthly

59528 ■ *The Chamber News*
259 E Jefferson St.
Spring Green, WI 53588
Ph: (608)588-2054
Free: 800-588-2042
Co. E-mail: info@springgreen.com
URL: http://www.springgreen.com
Contact: Nancy Viste, President

59529 ■ *Chamber News*
PO Box 74
Washburn, WI 54891
Ph: (715)373-5017
Free: 800-253-4495
Co. E-mail: info@washburnchamber.com
URL: http://washburnchamber.com
Contact: Diane Brander, President
Released: Monthly

59530 ■ *Chamber News*
10 S Bridge St.
Chippewa Falls, WI 54729
Ph: (715)723-0331
Free: 888-723-0024
Fax: (715)723-0332
Co. E-mail: info@chippewachamber.org
URL: http://www.chippewachamber.org
Contact: Mike D. Jordan, President
Released: Monthly

59531 ■ *Chamber News*
224 Main St.
Mosinee, WI 54455
Ph: (715)693-4330
Fax: (715)693-9555
Co. E-mail: macoc@mtc.net
URL: http://www.mosineechamber.org
Contact: Tammy Lechnir-Campo, Executive Director
Released: Monthly

59532 ■ *Chamber News*
106 S Washington St.
St. Croix Falls, WI 54024
Ph: (715)483-3580
Co. E-mail: director@fallschamber.org
URL: http://www.fallschamber.org
Contact: Shelly Staeven, Coordinator

59533 ■ *Chamber Newsletter*
127 S Spring St.
Beaver Dam, WI 53916
Ph: (920)887-8879
Fax: (920)887-9750
Co. E-mail: info@beaverdamchamber.com
URL: http://www.beaverdamchamber.com
Contact: Philip Fritsche, Executive Director
Released: Monthly

59534 ■ *Chamber Newsletter*
PO Box 87
Lakewood, WI 54138
Ph: (715)276-6500
Co. E-mail: info@lakewoodareachamber.com
URL: http://www.lakewoodareachamber.com
Released: Monthly **Price:** free.

59535 ■ *The Chamber Newsletter*
122 W Garland St.
Jefferson, WI 53549-1717
Ph: (920)674-4511

Fax: (920)674-1499
Co. E-mail: info@jeffersonchamberwi.com
URL: http://www.jeffersonchamberwi.com
Contact: Traci Skolaski, President
Released: Monthly

59536 ■ *Chamber Review*
PO Box 442
Baraboo, WI 53913
Ph: (608)356-8333
Free: 800-BAR-ABOO
Fax: (608)356-8422
Co. E-mail: chamber@baraboo.com
URL: http://www.baraboo.com/chamber.html
Contact: Gene Dalhoff, Executive Director
Released: Monthly **Price:** included in membership dues.

59537 ■ *Chamber Review*
10437 Innovation Dr., Ste. 130
Wauwatosa, WI 53226
Ph: (414)453-2330
Fax: (414)453-2336
Co. E-mail: info@westsuburbanchamber.com
URL: http://www.westsuburbanchamber.com
Released: Monthly

59538 ■ *Chamber Talk*
1515 Memorial Dr.
Manitowoc, WI 54220
Ph: (920)684-5575
Free: 866-727-5575
Fax: (920)684-1915
Co. E-mail: info@chambermanitowoccounty.org
URL: http://www.manitowocchamber.com
Contact: Karen Szyman, Executive Director
Released: Monthly

59539 ■ Chetek Area Chamber of Commerce
PO Box 747
Chetek, WI 54728
Ph: (715)924-3200
Free: 800-317-1720
Co. E-mail: info@chetekwi.net
URL: http://www.chetekwi.net
Description: Promotes business and community development in Chetek, WI area.

59540 ■ Chilton Chamber of Commerce
PO Box 122
Chilton, WI 53014
Ph: (920)418-1650
Co. E-mail: info@chiltonchamber.com
URL: http://chiltonchamber.com
Contact: Tammy Pethan, Secretary
Description: Strives to unite and promote the commercial mercantile and manufacturing interests of the City of Chilton. Improves civic, industrial, and business principles among its members. **Founded:** 1948. **Awards:** Citizens of the Year (Annual).

59541 ■ Chippewa Falls Area Chamber of Commerce
10 S Bridge St.
Chippewa Falls, WI 54729
Ph: (715)723-0331
Free: 888-723-0024
Fax: (715)723-0332
Co. E-mail: info@chippewachamber.org
URL: http://www.chippewachamber.org
Contact: Mike D. Jordan, President
Description: Works to improve quality of life in the community by providing leadership to promote business interest of members. **Founded:** 1910. **Publications:** *Chamber News* (Monthly). **Educational Activities:** Chippewa Falls Area Chamber of Commerce Meeting (Monthly). **Awards:** Excellence in Education (Annual).

59542 ■ Cleveland Chamber of Commerce
PO Box 56
Cleveland, WI 53015-0056
Ph: (920)693-8256
Co. E-mail: info@clevelandwi.net
URL: http://clevelandwi.net
Contact: Tim Schueler, President
Description: Strives to bring new business and industry to Cleveland while helping the existing ones to become more viable.

59543 ■ Clintonville Area Chamber of Commerce
18 S Main St.
Clintonville, WI 54929
Ph: (715)823-4606
Fax: (715)823-7318
Co. E-mail: cvlchmbr@frontiernet.net
URL: http://www.clintonvillewi.org/chamber
Contact: Dan Gast, President
Description: Works to encourage communication and cooperation among business, industry, education, and community by providing leadership to promote the community. **Founded:** 1910.

59544 ■ *Comment*
304 S Main St.
West Bend, WI 53095
Ph: (262)338-2666
Free: 888-338-8666
Fax: (262)338-1771
Co. E-mail: info@wbachamber.org
URL: http://www.wbchamber.org
Contact: Craig Farrell, Executive Director
Released: Monthly

59545 ■ *Commerce Comments*
203 E Walworth St.
Elkhorn, WI 53121
Ph: (262)723-5788
Fax: (262)723-5784
Co. E-mail: info@elkhornchamber.com
URL: http://www.elkhorn-wi.org
Contact: Bill Rogers, President
Released: Monthly

59546 ■ *The Communicator*
130 W Larrabee St.
Omro, WI 54963
Ph: (920)685-6960
Fax: (920)685-0384
Co. E-mail: ssalfai@omro-wi.com
URL: http://www.omro-wi.com/chamber.html
Released: Monthly **Price:** free for members.

59547 ■ *Community Profile*
6331 W Mequon Rd.
Mequon, WI 53092
Ph: (262)512-9358
Fax: (262)512-9359
Co. E-mail: info@mtchamber.org
URL: http://www.mtchamber.org
Contact: Tina Schwantes, Executive Director

59548 ■ *Community Resource Guide*
225 High St.
Mineral Point, WI 53565
Ph: (608)987-3201
Free: 888-POI-NTWI
Fax: (608)987-4425
Co. E-mail: info@mineralpoint.com
URL: http://www.mineralpoint.com
Contact: Joy Gieseke, Executive Director

59549 ■ Crandon Area Chamber of Commerce
116 S Lake Ave.
Crandon, WI 54520
Ph: (715)478-3450
Free: 800-334-3387
Co. E-mail: crandon@newnorth.net
URL: http://www.visitforestcounty.com
Description: Seeks to promote the tourism and economic development of Crandon and Forest County. **Founded:** 1978.

59550 ■ Cumberland Chamber of Commerce (CCC)
PO Box 665
Cumberland, WI 54829
Ph: (715)822-3378
Co. E-mail: bagafest@cumberland-wisconsin.com
URL: http://www.cumberland-wisconsin.com
Description: Represents businesses and professionals promoting economic and community development in Cumberland, WI. Sponsors annual Rutabaga Festival. **Founded:** 1966.

59551 ■ Darlington Chamber of Commerce
447 Main St.
Darlington, WI 53530
Ph: (608)776-3067
Co. E-mail: mainstprogram@centurytel.net
URL: http://www.darlingtonwi.org
Contact: Suzanne Osterday, Director
Description: Promotes business and community development in Darlington, WI area.

59552 ■ De Forest Area Chamber of Commerce
c/o Lisa Beck, Exec. Dir.
201 De Forest St.
De Forest, WI 53532
Ph: (608)846-2922
Co. E-mail: dacc1@centurytel.net
URL: http://www.deforestarea.com
Contact: Lisa Beck, Executive Director
Description: Strives to provide leadership to improve business environment and promote economic growth through membership participation and involvement.

59553 ■ Delafield Chamber of Commerce (DCC)
PO Box 180171
Delafield, WI 53018
Ph: (262)646-8100
Free: 888-294-1082
Fax: (262)646-8237
Co. E-mail: info@visitdelafield.org
URL: http://www.visitdelafield.org
Contact: Debra Smith, Executive Director
Description: Promotes business and community development in Delafield, WI. **Founded:** 1930. **Publications:** Chamber Chronicles (Bimonthly).

59554 ■ Delavan - Delavan Lake Area Chamber of Commerce
52 E Walworth Ave.
Delavan, WI 53115
Ph: (262)728-5095
Free: 800-624-0052
Fax: (262)728-9199
Co. E-mail: info@delavanwi.org
URL: http://www.delavanwi.org
Contact: Travis Egan, President
Description: Promotes business and community development in Delavan, WI area.

59555 ■ *Destination Guide*
342 E Main St.
Menomonie, WI 54751
Ph: (715)235-9087
Free: 800-283-1862
Fax: (715)235-2824
Co. E-mail: info@menomoniechamber.org
URL: http://www.menomoniechamber.org
Contact: Lisa Montgomery, Chief Executive Officer
Released: Annual

59556 ■ Dodgeville Area Chamber of Commerce
338 N Iowa St.
Dodgeville, WI 53533
Ph: (608)935-9200
Free: 877-863-6343
Co. E-mail: info@dodgeville.com
URL: http://www.dodgeville.com
Contact: Bob Berglin, Executive Director
Description: Promotes business and community development in Dodgeville, WI area.

59557 ■ Door County Chamber of Commerce
PO Box 406
Sturgeon Bay, WI 54235-0406
Ph: (920)743-4456
Free: 800-527-3529
Fax: (920)743-7873
Co. E-mail: info@doorcounty.com
URL: http://www.doorcounty.com/
Contact: Jack Moneypenny, President
Description: Promotes the civic and commercial progress of the Door community. **Publications:** *Door County Vacation Planning Guide* (Annual); *Door County Winter Guide*. **Telecommunication Services:** cathy@doorcounty.com.

59558 ■ East Troy Area Chamber of Commerce
PO Box 312
East Troy, WI 53120
Ph: (262)642-3770
Fax: (262)642-8769
Co. E-mail: info@easttroywi.org
URL: http://www.easttroywi.org
Contact: Dan Heidelmeier, President
Description: Promotes business and community development in East Troy, WI area.

59559 ■ Eau Claire Area Chamber of Commerce
101 N Farwell St., Ste. 101
Eau Claire, WI 54703
Ph: (715)834-1204
Fax: (715)834-1956
Co. E-mail: information@eauclairechamber.org
URL: http://www.eauclairechamber.org
Contact: Robert S. McCoy, President
Description: Promotes business and community development in the Eau Claire, WI area. **Founded:** 1915. **Publications:** *Valley Business* (Monthly). **Awards:** Ambassador of the Year (Annual); Athena Award (Annual); Outstanding Volunteer (Annual); Small Business Person (Annual).

59560 ■ Edgerton Area Chamber of Commerce (EACC)
20 S Main St.
Edgerton, WI 53534
Ph: (608)884-4408
Free: 888-298-4408
Fax: (608)884-4408
Co. E-mail: edgertonchamber@edgertonchamber. com
URL: http://www.edgertonchamber.com
Contact: Andy Aleson, President
Description: Promotes business and community development in the Edgerton, WI area.

59561 ■ Elkhart Lake Area Chamber of Commerce
41 E Rhine St.
Elkhart Lake, WI 53020
Ph: (920)876-2922
Free: 877-355-3554
Fax: (920)876-3659
Co. E-mail: elcoc@verizon.net
URL: http://www.elkhartlake.com
Contact: Mary Johnston, Executive Director
Description: Promotes business and community development in Elkhart Lake, WI area.

59562 ■ Elkhorn Area Chamber of Commerce (EACC)
203 E Walworth St.
Elkhorn, WI 53121
Ph: (262)723-5788
Fax: (262)723-5784
Co. E-mail: info@elkhornchamber.com
URL: http://www.elkhorn-wi.org
Contact: Bill Rogers, President
Description: Promotes business and community development in the Elkhorn, WI area. Holds annual Christmas Carol town parade. **Subscriptions:** audio recordings books periodicals video recordings. **Publications:** *Commerce Comments* (Monthly). **Educational Activities:** Elkhorn Area Chamber of Commerce Meeting (Annual). **Awards:** $500 Scholarship (Annual).

59563 ■ Ellsworth Area Chamber of Commerce (EACC)
PO Box 927
Ellsworth, WI 54011
Ph: (715)273-6442
Fax: (715)273-6442
Co. E-mail: info@ellsworthchamber.com
URL: http://www.ellsworthchamber.com
Contact: Peggy A. Nelson, President
Description: Works to promote the development of Ellsworth community.

59564 ■ Elroy Area Advancement Corporation
225 Main St.
Elroy, WI 53929
Ph: (608)462-5872
Fax: (608)462-2404
Co. E-mail: elroy@comantenna.com
URL: http://www.elroywi.com
Description: Promotes community advancement in the Elroy, WI area.

59565 ■ *The Endeavor*
PO Box 726
Hayward, WI 54843
Ph: (715)634-8662
Free: 800-724-2992
Fax: (715)634-8498
Co. E-mail: info@haywardareachamber.com
URL: http://www.haywardareachamber.com
Contact: Kevin Ruetten, Executive Director
Released: Monthly

59566 ■ Evansville Area Chamber of Commerce and Tourism
8 W Main St.
Evansville, WI 53536
Ph: (608)882-5131
Co. E-mail: evansvillecoc@litewire.net
URL: http://evansvillechamber.org
Contact: John Morning, President
Description: Promotes business and community development in Evansville, WI. **Publications:** *Chamber News* (Quarterly).

59567 ■ *Everybody's Business*
420 N Shawano St.
New London, WI 54961
Ph: (920)982-5822
Fax: (920)982-6344
Co. E-mail: chamber@newlondonwi.org
URL: http://www.newlondonchamber.com
Contact: Laurie A. Shaw, Executive Director
Released: Monthly

59568 ■ *Fall is a Favorite Time of Year*
PO Box 31
Baileys Harbor, WI 54202
Ph: (920)839-2366
Co. E-mail: info@baileysharbor.com
URL: http://www.baileysharbor.com

59569 ■ Falls Chamber of Commerce
106 S Washington St.
St. Croix Falls, WI 54024
Ph: (715)483-3580
Co. E-mail: director@fallschamber.org
URL: http://www.fallschamber.org
Contact: Shelly Staeven, Coordinator
Description: Promotes business and community development in the city of St. Croix Falls and its trade area. **Founded:** 1999. **Publications:** *Chamber News*. **Educational Activities:** Falls Chamber of Commerce Meeting (Monthly).

59570 ■ *FDLAC*
207 N Main St.
Fond du Lac, WI 54935
Ph: (920)921-9500
Fax: (920)921-9559
Co. E-mail: info@fdlac.com
URL: http://www.fdlac.com
Contact: Steve Little, Chairman
Released: Monthly

59571 ■ Fennimore Area Chamber of Commerce
c/o Linda Parrish, Promotions Coor.
850 Lincoln Ave.
Fennimore, WI 53809
Ph: (608)822-3599
Fax: (608)822-6007
Co. E-mail: promo@fennimore.com
URL: http://fennimore.com
Contact: Steve Birkett, President
Description: Promotes business, tourism, and community development in Fennimore, WI. **Founded:** 1970.

59572 ■ *FOCUS*
113 E Chestnut St., Ste. B
Burlington, WI 53105
Ph: (262)763-6044
Fax: (262)763-3631
Co. E-mail: info@burlingtonchamber.org
URL: http://www.burlingtonchamber.org
Contact: Janice Ludtke, Executive Director
Released: Monthly **Price:** free for members only.

59573 ■ *Focus on Fort Atkinson*
244 N Main St.
Fort Atkinson, WI 53538
Ph: (920)563-3210
Free: 888-SEE-FORT
Fax: (920)563-8946
Co. E-mail: facoc@fortchamber.com
URL: http://www.fortchamber.com
Contact: Dianne Hrobsky, Executive Vice President
Released: Monthly

59574 ■ Fond du Lac Area Association of Commerce (FDLAAC)
207 N Main St.
Fond du Lac, WI 54935
Ph: (920)921-9500
Fax: (920)921-9559
Co. E-mail: info@fdlac.com
URL: http://www.fdlac.com
Contact: Steve Little, Chairman
Description: Promotes business and community development in the Fond du Lac, WI area. **Founded:** 1912. **Publications:** *FDLAC* (Monthly). **Telecommunication Services:** joer@fdlac.com.

59575 ■ Fort Atkinson Area Chamber of Commerce (FAACC)
244 N Main St.
Fort Atkinson, WI 53538
Ph: (920)563-3210
Free: 888-SEE-FORT
Fax: (920)563-8946
Co. E-mail: facoc@fortchamber.com
URL: http://www.fortchamber.com
Contact: Dianne Hrobsky, Executive Vice President
  Secretary
Description: Represents commercial, industrial, professional, retail, and service businesses. Promotes business and community development in the Fort Atkinson, WI area. **Founded:** 1889. **Publications:** *Focus on Fort Atkinson* (Monthly). **Telecommunication Services:** evp@fortchamber.com

59576 ■ Forward Janesville (FJI)
14 S Jackson St.
Janesville, WI 53548
Ph: (608)757-3160
Fax: (608)757-3170
Co. E-mail: forward@forwardjanesville.com
URL: http://www.forwardjanesville.com
Contact: Mr. John Beckord, President
Description: Leads private sector economic and community development efforts to ensure the continued health and prosperity of business and industry in Janesville. **Founded:** 1991. **Publications:** *The Report* (Quarterly).

59577 ■ *Fox Cities Business*
PO Box 1855
Appleton, WI 54912-1855
Ph: (920)734-7101
Free: 800-999-3224
Fax: (920)734-7161
Co. E-mail: information@foxcitieschamber.com
URL: http://www.foxcitieschamber.com
Contact: Shannon Full, President
Released: Monthly

59578 ■ Fox Cities Chamber of Commerce and Industry (FCCCI)
PO Box 1855
Appleton, WI 54912-1855
Ph: (920)734-7101
Free: 800-999-3224

Fax: (920)734-7161
Co. E-mail: information@foxcitieschamber.com
URL: http://www.foxcitieschamber.com
Contact: Shannon Full, President
Description: Business, industry, and individuals in east central Wisconsin. Works to enhance the community's economic well-being, promote balanced development, and assure continued improvement of the quality of life. **Founded:** 1976. **Publications:** *Fox Cities Business* (Monthly); *Manufacturer Directory* (Periodic); *Organizations Guide*. **Educational Activities:** License to Cruise (Periodic). **Awards:** Athena Award (Annual); Manufacturer of the Year (Annual); Small Business of the Year (Annual).

59579 ■ Fox Lake Area Chamber of Commerce
PO Box 94
Fox Lake, WI 53933-0094
Ph: (920)928-3777
Free: 800-858-4904
Co. E-mail: info@foxlakechamber.com
URL: http://www.foxlakechamber.com
Contact: Keri Gossink, President
Description: Promotes economic, industrial, and community development and tourism in Fox Lake, WI. **Publications:** *Fox Lake Visitors Guide* (Annual).

59580 ■ *Fox Lake Visitors Guide*
PO Box 94
Fox Lake, WI 53933-0094
Ph: (920)928-3777
Free: 800-858-4904
Co. E-mail: info@foxlakechamber.com
URL: http://www.foxlakechamber.com
Contact: Keri Gossink, President
Released: Annual **Price:** free.

59581 ■ Fremont Area Chamber of Commerce (FACC)
PO Box 114
Fremont, WI 54940
Ph: (920)446-3838
Co. E-mail: info@travelfremont.com
URL: http://www.travelfremont.com
Contact: Doug Arndt, President
Description: Promotes business and community development in Fremont, WI area.

59582 ■ Galesville Area Chamber of Commerce
PO Box 196
Galesville, WI 54630
Ph: (608)582-2868
Co. E-mail: info@galesvillewi.com
URL: http://www.galesvillewi.com
Contact: Bob Ristow, President
Description: Promotes business and community development in Galesville, WI.

59583 ■ Geneva Lake Area Chamber of Commerce (GLACC)
201 Wrigley Dr.
Lake Geneva, WI 53147-2004
Ph: (262)248-4416
Free: 800-345-1020
Fax: (262)248-1000
Co. E-mail: lgcc@lakegenevawi.com
URL: http://www.lakegenevawi.cc
Contact: George F. Hennerley, Executive Vice
  President
Description: Promotes business and community development in the Geneva Lakes, WI area. **Founded:** 1947.

59584 ■ Germantown Area Chamber of Commerce (GACC)
PO Box 12
Germantown, WI 53022
Ph: (262)255-1812
Fax: (262)255-9033
Co. E-mail: lgrgich@germantownchamber.org
URL: http://germantownchamber.org
Contact: Lynn Grgich, Executive Director
Description: Promotes business and community development in the Germantown, WI area. Sponsors seminars, parades, social events, and annual dinner. **Founded:** 1982.

59585 ■ Glendale Association of Commerce
5909 N Milwaukee River Pkwy.
Glendale, WI 53209-3815
Ph: (414)228-1716
Fax: (414)332-6182
URL: http://www.shopcpn.com/webpage/display.
  cfm?ID=42962
Description: Aims to foster tourism, as well as to protect and advance the commercial, industrial, cultural, educational, and civic interests of the City of Glendale.

59586 ■ Grafton Area Chamber of Commerce (GACC)
1634 Wisconsin Ave.
Grafton, WI 53024
Ph: (262)377-1650
Fax: (262)375-7087
Co. E-mail: info@grafton-wi.org
URL: http://grafton-wi.org
Contact: Pam King, Executive Director
Description: Promotes commercial, financial, industrial, and civic development in the Grafton, WI area. Sponsors annual Christmas Party, Holiday Tree Lighting, Farmer's Market, and Grafton Grand Prix. **Founded:** 1975. **Publications:** *Business Directory* (Annual).

59587 ■ Grantsburg Chamber of Commerce
PO Box 451
Grantsburg, WI 54840
Ph: (715)463-2405
Co. E-mail: info@grantsburgchamber.com
URL: http://www.grantsburgchamber.com
Contact: Nicki Peterson, President
Description: Promotes business and community development in Grantsburg, WI area.

59588 ■ Greater Beloit Chamber of Commerce (GBCC)
500 Public Ave.
Beloit, WI 53511
Ph: (608)365-8835
Fax: (608)365-6850
Co. E-mail: info@greaterbeloitchamber.com
URL: http://greaterbeloitchamber.com
Contact: Randall Upton, President
Description: Promotes business and community development in the Beloit, WI area. Holds annual festival, seminars, and high school career expo. Maintains speaker's bureau. **Founded:** 1927. **Publications:** *CCGB News* (Monthly); *The Network*.

59589 ■ Greater Brookfield Chamber of Commerce (GBCC)
1305 N Barker Rd., Ste. 5
Brookfield, WI 53045
Ph: (262)786-1886
Fax: (262)786-1959
Co. E-mail: carol@brookfieldchamber.com
URL: http://www.brookfieldchamber.com
Contact: Carol White, President
Description: Promotes business and community development in Brookfield, WI. **Publications:** *Net Works* (Monthly). **Educational Activities:** Active Business Leader Exchange (Monthly).

59590 ■ Greater Madison Chamber of Commerce (GMCC)
615 E Washington Ave., 2nd Fl.
Madison, WI 53701-0071
Ph: (608)256-8348
Fax: (608)256-0333
Co. E-mail: info@greatermadisonchamber.com
URL: http://greatermadisonchamber.com
Contact: Jennifer Alexander, President
E-mail: jalexander@greatermadisonchamber.com
Description: Promotes business and community development in Dane County, WI. **Founded:** 1869. **Publications:** *Business Beat* (Monthly); *Madison/Dane County Manufacturers* (Biennial); *Madison/Dane County Businesses with 50 or More Employees* (Biennial).

59591 ■ Greater Mauston Area Chamber of Commerce
PO Box 171
Mauston, WI 53948
Ph: (608)847-4142

Fax: (608)847-4142
Co. E-mail: chamber@mauston.com
URL: http://www.mauston.com
Contact: Mary Hudack, Office Manager
Description: Promotes business and community development in the Mauston, WI area. Sponsors 4th of July Freedomfest. **Founded:** 1945.

59592 ■ Greater Menomonie Area Chamber of Commerce (GMACC)
342 E Main St.
Menomonie, WI 54751
Ph: (715)235-9087
Free: 800-283-1862
Fax: (715)235-2824
Co. E-mail: info@menomoniechamber.org
URL: http://www.menomoniechamber.org
Contact: Lisa Montgomery, Chief Executive Officer
Description: Promotes business and community development in the Menomonie, WI area. Holds summer and winter festivals. **Founded:** 1937. **Publications:** *Destination Guide* (Annual); *Greater Menomonie Area Chamber of Commerce--Member Directory* (Annual).

59593 ■ Greater Princeton Area Chamber of Commerce (GPACC)
PO Box 45
Princeton, WI 54968
Ph: (920)295-3877
Co. E-mail: info@princetonwi.com
URL: http://www.princetonwi.com
Contact: Mark Judas, President
Description: Promotes business and community development in Princeton, WI. Makes charitable contributions; sponsors annual summer flea market.

59594 ■ Greater Tomah Area Chamber of Commerce
PO Box 625
Tomah, WI 54660
Ph: (608)372-2166
Free: 800-948-6624
Fax: (608)372-2167
Co. E-mail: info@tomahwisconsin.com
URL: http://www.tomahwisconsin.com
Contact: Christopher Hanson, Executive Director
Description: Works to foster a cohesive environment where businesses, families, and community can prosper.

59595 ■ Greater Union Grove Area Chamber of Commerce (GUGACC)
PO Box 44
Union Grove, WI 53182-0044
Ph: (262)878-4606
Fax: (262)878-9125
Co. E-mail: ugchamber@att.net
URL: http://www.uniongrovechamber.org
Contact: Terri Gray, Executive Director
Description: Promotes business and community development in the Union Grove, WI area. Conducts Fourth of July Parade, Christmas Cookie Walk, and other community gatherings. Sponsors political candidate forums. **Founded:** 1986.

59596 ■ *Greater Waunakee Area Chamber of Commerce News*
100 E Main St.
Waunakee, WI 53597
Ph: (608)849-5977
Fax: (608)849-9825
Co. E-mail: waunakeechamber@tds.net
URL: http://www.webmger.com/WebMgmt/Content/waunakee/Default.asp
Contact: Ellen K. Schaaf, Executive Director
Released: Monthly

59597 ■ Green Bay Area Chamber of Commerce (GBACC)
PO Box 1660
Green Bay, WI 54305
Ph: (920)437-8704

Fax: (920)437-1024
Co. E-mail: info@titletown.org
URL: http://www.titletown.org
Contact: Laurie Radke, President
Description: Promotes business and community development in the Green Bay, WI area. **Founded:** 1917. **Publications:** *Bay Business Journal* (Bimonthly); *Green Bay Area Chamber of Commerce-- Membership Resource Directory* (Annual). **Educational Activities:** Power Networking Breakfast (Monthly).

59598 ■ Green Lake Area Chamber of Commerce (GLACC)
PO Box 337
Green Lake, WI 54941
Ph: (920)294-3231
Free: 800-253-7354
Fax: (920)294-3415
Co. E-mail: info@visitgreenlake.com
URL: http://visitgreenlake.com
Contact: Debra Beirman, President
Description: Promotes business and community development in the Green Lake, WI area. Sponsors community social and promotional activities. **Founded:** 1965. **Publications:** *Visitors' Guide* (Annual). **Educational Activities:** Harvest Days Festival (Annual).

59599 ■ Greendale Chamber of Commerce (GCC)
PO Box 467
Greendale, WI 53129
Ph: (414)423-3900
Co. E-mail: info@greendalechamber.com
URL: http://www.greendalechamber.com
Contact: Gregory Turay, President
Description: Promotes business and community development in Greendale, WI area. **Founded:** 1980.

59600 ■ Greenfield Chamber of Commerce (GCC)
4818 S 76th St., Ste. 129
Greenfield, WI 53220
Ph: (414)327-8500
Fax: (877)327-0084
Co. E-mail: gcc@greenfieldchamber.com
URL: http://www.thegreenfieldchamber.com
Contact: Judy Baxter, President
Description: Promotes business and community development in Greenfield, WI area. **Founded:** 1957. **Awards:** Student of the Year (Annual); Volunteer of the Year (Annual).

59601 ■ Hartford Area Chamber of Commerce
225 N Main St.
Hartford, WI 53027
Ph: (262)673-7002
Fax: (262)673-7057
Co. E-mail: info@hartfordchamber.org
URL: http://www.hartfordchamber.org
Contact: Barb Laabs, Executive Director
Description: Works to support and foster development in Hartford area.

59602 ■ Hartland Area Chamber of Commerce
116 W Capitol Dr.
Hartland, WI 53029-2104
Ph: (262)367-7059
Fax: (262)367-2980
Co. E-mail: admin@hartland-wi.org
URL: http://www.hartland-wi.org
Contact: Ms. Lynn Minturn, Executive Director
Description: Serves the members by providing programs and services, which enhance the business climate and community. **Publications:** *Hartland Matters* (Semiweekly); *Chamber Member Directory & Community Guide* (Annual).

59603 ■ *Hartland Matters*
116 W Capitol Dr.
Hartland, WI 53029-2104
Ph: (262)367-7059

Fax: (262)367-2980
Co. E-mail: admin@hartland-wi.org
URL: http://www.hartland-wi.org
Contact: Ms. Lynn Minturn, Executive Director
Released: Semiweekly

59604 ■ Hayward Area Chamber of Commerce (HACC)
PO Box 726
Hayward, WI 54843
Ph: (715)634-8662
Free: 800-724-2992
Fax: (715)634-8498
Co. E-mail: info@haywardareachamber.com
URL: http://www.haywardareachamber.com
Contact: Kevin Ruetten, Executive Director
Description: Promotes business and community development in Hayward, WI. **Publications:** *The Endeavor* (Monthly); *Hayward's Calendar of Events* (Annual). **Educational Activities:** Hayward Fall Festival (Annual).

59605 ■ *Hayward's Calendar of Events*
PO Box 726
Hayward, WI 54843
Ph: (715)634-8662
Free: 800-724-2992
Fax: (715)634-8498
Co. E-mail: info@haywardareachamber.com
URL: http://www.haywardareachamber.com
Contact: Kevin Ruetten, Executive Director
Released: Annual

59606 ■ Heart of the Valley Chamber of Commerce
101 E Wisconsin Ave.
Kaukauna, WI 54130-2153
Ph: (920)766-1616
Fax: (920)766-5504
Co. E-mail: bbeckman@heartofthevalleychamber.com
URL: http://www.heartofthevalleychamber.com
Contact: Bobbie Beckman, Executive Director
Description: Aims to assist new and existing Heart of Valley businesses and communities in the endeavors to be successful. Serves its member businesses through educational programs, chamber committees, special events, new hire paperwork and members only benefits. Works year round in diverse ways to strengthen this area's prosperity and livability. **Founded:** 1927.

59607 ■ *Hilites*
13825 W National Ave.
New Berlin, WI 53151
Ph: (262)786-5280
Co. E-mail: office@newberlinchamber.org
URL: http://newberlinchamber.org/dnn/april13/Home.aspx
Contact: Kimberly Dort, President
Released: Periodic

59608 ■ Horicon Chamber of Commerce (HCC)
PO Box 23
Horicon, WI 53032-0023
Ph: (920)485-3200
Co. E-mail: writeus@horiconchamber.com
URL: http://www.horiconchamber.com
Description: Promotes business and community development in Horicon, WI.

59609 ■ *Horn Blower*
PO Box 305
Ripon, WI 54971
Ph: (920)748-6764
Fax: (920)748-6784
Co. E-mail: chamber@ripon-wi.com
URL: http://www.ripon-wi.com/ripon-wi/page.asp?p=home
Contact: Paula Price, Executive Director
Released: Bimonthly **Price:** no charge.

59610 ■ Hudson Area Chamber of Commerce and Tourism Bureau
502 Second St.
Hudson, WI 54016
Ph: (715)386-8411
Free: 800-657-6775

Fax: (715)386-8432
Co. E-mail: info@hudsonwi.org
URL: http://www.hudsonwi.org
Contact: Kim Heinemann, President
Description: Strives to serve its members by promoting the local economy and advocating the interests of the business community while advancing the recreational and cultural opportunities in the Hudson area. **Founded:** 1953.

59611 ■ *Human Resources Report*
501 E Washington Ave.
Madison, WI 53701-0352
Ph: (608)258-3400
Fax: (608)258-3413
Co. E-mail: jhaney@wmc.org
URL: http://www.wmc.org
Contact: James S. Haney, President
Released: Periodic

59612 ■ Iola - Scandinavia Area Chamber of Commerce
PO Box 167
Iola, WI 54945
Ph: (715)445-4000
Co. E-mail: aasen@mwwb.net
URL: http://www.ischamber.org
Contact: Chris Aasen, President
Description: Promotes business and community development in Iola and Scandinavia, WI.

59613 ■ *Issues*
1505 9th St.
Monroe, WI 53566
Ph: (608)325-7648
Fax: (608)328-2241
Co. E-mail: thechamber@tds.net
URL: http://www.monroechamber.org
Contact: Pamela L. Christopher, Executive Director
Released: Monthly

59614 ■ Jefferson Chamber of Commerce
122 W Garland St.
Jefferson, WI 53549-1717
Ph: (920)674-4511
Fax: (920)674-1499
Co. E-mail: info@jeffersonchamberwi.com
URL: http://www.jeffersonchamberwi.com
Contact: Traci Skolaski, President
Description: Promotes business and community development in Jefferson, WI area. **Publications:** *The Chamber Newsletter* (Monthly).

59615 ■ Johnson Creek Area Chamber of Commerce
PO Box 527
Johnson Creek, WI 53038-0527
Ph: (920)699-4949
Co. E-mail: admin@johnsoncreekchamber.com
URL: http://www.johnsoncreekchamber.com
Contact: Rick Kaltenberg, President
Description: Promotes business and community development in Johnson Creek, WI.

59616 ■ Juneau Chamber of Commerce
PO Box 4
Juneau, WI 53039
Ph: (920)386-3359
Co. E-mail: juneau@juneauwi.org
URL: http://www.juneauwi.org
Contact: Gretchen Last, President
Description: Promotes business and community development in Juneau, WI area.

59617 ■ Kenosha Area Chamber of Commerce
600 52nd St., Ste. 130
Kenosha, WI 53140
Ph: (262)654-1234
Fax: (262)654-4655
Co. E-mail: kacc@acronet.net
URL: http://www.kenoshaareachamber.com
Contact: Matt Carlson, Chairman
Description: Promotes business and community development in Kenosha, WI area. **Founded:** 1916. **Publications:** *Manufacturers Directory of Kenosha: Area Guide* (Annual). **Telecommunication Services:** info@kenoshaareachamber.com.

59618 ■ Kewaunee Area Chamber of Commerce (KCC)
308 N Main St.
Kewaunee, WI 54216
Ph: (920)388-4822
Free: 800-666-8214
Co. E-mail: kalesvariety@sbcglobal.net
URL: http://www.kewaunee.org
Contact: Charley Butchart, President
Description: Seeks to provide the leadership necessary to promote Kewaunee's tourism, business and industrial development, while preserving its maritime heritage. Sponsors Trout Festival and Parade.

59619 ■ La Crosse Area Chamber of Commerce
712 Main St.
La Crosse, WI 54601
Ph: (608)784-4880
Fax: (608)784-4919
Co. E-mail: lse_chamber@centurytel.net
URL: http://www.lacrossechamber.com
Contact: Dick Granchalek, President
Description: Works to improve the business community and regional economy of La Crosse area. **Publications:** *Chamber Connection* (Monthly).

59620 ■ Lake Mills Area Chamber of Commerce (LMCC)
200C Water St.
Lake Mills, WI 53551
Ph: (920)648-3585
Fax: (920)648-6751
Co. E-mail: chamber@lakemills.org
URL: http://www.lakemills.org
Contact: Kate Anderson, Executive Director
Description: Works to enhance, preserve, and protect the quality of life and business in the Lake Mills, WI area.

59621 ■ Lake Wisconsin Chamber of Commerce
PO Box 43
Lodi, WI 53555
Ph: (608)592-4412
Co. E-mail: info@lakewisconsin.org
URL: http://www.lakewisconsin.org
Contact: Karla Faust, President
Description: Promotes business and community development in the Lake Wisconsin area. **Publications:** *Lake Wisconsin Chamber of Commerce Brochure* (Annual).

59622 ■ *Lake Wisconsin Chamber of Commerce Brochure*
PO Box 43
Lodi, WI 53555
Ph: (608)592-4412
Co. E-mail: info@lakewisconsin.org
URL: http://www.lakewisconsin.org
Contact: Karla Faust, President
Released: Annual

59623 ■ Lakewood Area Chamber of Commerce
PO Box 87
Lakewood, WI 54138
Ph: (715)276-6500
Co. E-mail: info@lakewoodareachamber.com
URL: http://www.lakewoodareachamber.com
Description: Promotes business and community development and tourism in the Lakewood, WI area. Sponsors Lakewood Mardi Gras Spring Fling festival. **Publications:** *Chamber Newsletter* (Monthly).

59624 ■ Lancaster Area Chamber of Commerce
206 S Madison St.
Lancaster, WI 53813
Ph: (608)723-2820
Fax: (608)723-7409
Co. E-mail: chamber@lancasterwisconsin.com
URL: http://www.lancasterwisconsin.com
Contact: Kyle Vesperman, President
Description: Promotes agricultural, business, community, and industrial development in the Lancaster, WI area.

59625 ■ *The Link*
2717 N Grandview Blvd., Ste. 204
Waukesha, WI 53188
Ph: (262)542-4249
Fax: (262)542-8068
Co. E-mail: alliance@waukesha.org
URL: http://www.waukesha.org
Contact: Suzanne Kelley, President

59626 ■ Lomira Area Chamber of Commerce
c/o Ann Welak, Pres.
PO Box 386
Lomira, WI 53048
Ph: (920)269-4112
Co. E-mail: warehousewebs@charter.net
URL: http://www.lomira.com/Servgrop/COC/Index-COC.htm
Contact: Ann Welak, President
Description: Promotes business and community development in Lomira, WI.

59627 ■ Luxemburg Chamber of Commerce (LCC)
PO Box 141
Luxemburg, WI 54217-0307
Ph: (920)845-2062
Co. E-mail: info@luxemburgchamber.com
URL: http://luxemburgchamber.com
Contact: Jeff Blemke, President
Description: Promotes business and community development in the Luxemburg, WI area. **Founded:** 1945. **Publications:** *Business Directory* (Biennial).

59628 ■ *MACC News*
48 N Main St.
Mayville, WI 53050
Ph: (920)387-5776
Free: 800-256-7670
Co. E-mail: info@mayvillechamber.com
URL: http://www.mayvillechamber.com
Contact: Linda Turk, Member

59629 ■ Madeline Island Chamber of Commerce
PO Box 274
La Pointe, WI 54850
Ph: (715)747-2801
Free: 888-475-3386
Co. E-mail: vacation@madelineisland.com
URL: http://www.madelineisland.com
Description: Promotes business and community development in Madeline Island, WI.

59630 ■ Manitowish Waters Chamber of Commerce (MWCC)
PO Box 251
Manitowish Waters, WI 54545
Ph: (715)543-8488
Free: 888-626-9877
Fax: (715)543-2519
Co. E-mail: funinfo@manitowishwaters.org
URL: http://www.manitowishwaters.org
Contact: Eric Behnke, President
Description: Promotes the organization's members and tourism-based, four-season community. Sponsors several seasonal festivals. **Founded:** 1939. **Publications:** *Manitowish Waters Visitor Guide* (Annual).

59631 ■ *Manitowish Waters Visitor Guide*
PO Box 251
Manitowish Waters, WI 54545
Ph: (715)543-8488
Free: 888-626-9877
Fax: (715)543-2519
Co. E-mail: funinfo@manitowishwaters.org
URL: http://www.manitowishwaters.org
Contact: Eric Behnke, President
Released: Annual

59632 ■ Manitowoc/Two Rivers Area Chamber of Commerce
1515 Memorial Dr.
Manitowoc, WI 54220
Ph: (920)684-5575
Free: 866-727-5575

Fax: (920)684-1915
Co. E-mail: info@chambermanitowoccounty.org
URL: http://www.manitowocchamber.com
Contact: Karen Szyman, Executive Director
Description: Businesses. Promotes business and community development in Manitowoc County, WI. **Founded:** 1970. **Publications:** *Chamber Talk* (Monthly); *Visitor Guide* (Annual); *Visitor Guide* (Annual). **Awards:** Athena Award (Annual); Industry of the Year (Annual); Non-Profit of the Year (Annual); Small Business of the Year (Annual).

59633 ■ *Manufacturer Directory*
PO Box 1855
Appleton, WI 54912-1855
Ph: (920)734-7101
Free: 800-999-3224
Fax: (920)734-7161
Co. E-mail: information@foxcitieschamber.com
URL: http://www.foxcitieschamber.com
Contact: Shannon Full, President
Released: Periodic

59634 ■ *Manufacturing Report*
501 E Washington Ave.
Madison, WI 53701-0352
Ph: (608)258-3400
Fax: (608)258-3413
Co. E-mail: jhaney@wmc.org
URL: http://www.wmc.org
Contact: James S. Haney, President
Released: Periodic

59635 ■ *Map Brochure*
221 S Main St.
Waupaca, WI 54981-1522
Ph: (715)258-7343
Free: 888-417-4040
Fax: (715)258-7868
Co. E-mail: discoverwaupaca@waupacaareachamber.com
URL: http://www.waupacaareachamber.com
Contact: Terri Schulz, President
Released: Semiannual

59636 ■ *Marinette Chamber Memo*
601 Marinette Ave.
Marinette, WI 54143
Ph: (715)735-6681
Free: 800-236-6681
Fax: (715)735-6682
Co. E-mail: chambernews@centurytel.net
URL: http://mandmchamber.com
Contact: Mary D. Johns, Chief Executive Officer
Released: Monthly

59637 ■ Marinette Menominee Area Chamber of Commerce
601 Marinette Ave.
Marinette, WI 54143
Ph: (715)735-6681
Free: 800-236-6681
Fax: (715)735-6682
Co. E-mail: chambernews@centurytel.net
URL: http://mandmchamber.com
Contact: Mary D. Johns, Chief Executive Officer
Description: Promotes business and community development in both cities and counties of Marinette, WI and Menominee, MI. **Founded:** 1939. **Publications:** *Marinette Chamber Memo* (Monthly).

59638 ■ Marshfield Area Chamber of Commerce and Industry (MACCI)
700 S Central Ave.
Marshfield, WI 54449
Ph: (715)384-3454
Fax: (715)387-8925
Co. E-mail: info@marshfieldchamber.com
URL: http://www.marshfieldchamber.com
Contact: Cindy Burns, President
Description: Promotes business and community development in the Marshfield, WI area. Sponsors annual Dairy Fest and Arts Weekend. Holds monthly board of directors meeting. **Founded:** 1946. **Publications:** *Perspectives* (Monthly).

59639 ■ Mayville Area Chamber of Commerce (MACC)
48 N Main St.
Mayville, WI 53050
Ph: (920)387-5776
Free: 800-256-7670
Co. E-mail: info@mayvillechamber.com
URL: http://www.mayvillechamber.com
Contact: Linda Turk, Member
URL(s): www.audubondays.com. **Description:** Area business personnel striving to promote business and community development in Mayville, WI. Supports community projects, children's holiday programs, and the Audubon Days festival. Provides opportunities to network, "to belong, and to make a difference". **Founded:** 1945. **Publications:** *MACC News.* **Awards:** Citizen of the Year (Annual).

59640 ■ Mazomanie Chamber of Commerce
PO Box 26
Mazomanie, WI 53560
Ph: (608)795-2100
Fax: (608)795-2102
Co. E-mail: kpena@villageofmazomanie.com
URL: http://www.villageofmazomanie.com
Contact: Kia Pena, Treasurer
Description: Promotes business and community development in Mazomanie, WI area.

59641 ■ McFarland Chamber of Commerce
4869 Larson Beach Rd., Ste. B
McFarland, WI 53558
Ph: (608)838-4011
Co. E-mail: info@mcfarlandchamber.com
URL: http://www.mcfarlandchamber.com
Contact: Jim Hartman, President
Description: Seeks to unite and direct the various businesses in the McFarland area in development and stimulation of the civic, industrial and commercial life. Activities include Family Festival, Citizen of the Year Banquet and Christmas in the Village festivities. **Founded:** 1980. **Awards:** Citizen of the Year (Annual).

59642 ■ Medford Area Chamber of Commerce
104 E Perkins St.
Medford, WI 54451
Ph: (715)748-4729
Free: 888-682-9567
Fax: (715)748-6899
Co. E-mail: medfordchamber@tds.net
URL: http://www.medfordwis.com
Description: Promotes business and community development in Medford, WI area.

59643 ■ Mellen Area Chamber of Commerce
PO Box 193
Mellen, WI 54546
Ph: (715)274-2330
Co. E-mail: mellen001@centurytel.net
URL: http://www.mellenwi.com
Contact: Sue Amman, President
Description: Promotes business and community development in Mellen, WI.

59644 ■ *Member Matters*
120 Jackson St.
Oshkosh, WI 54901
Ph: (920)303-2266
Fax: (920)303-2263
Co. E-mail: info@oshkoshchamber.com
URL: http://www.oshkoshchamber.com
Contact: John T. Anderson, Chairman
Released: Bimonthly

59645 ■ *Member Service Update*
501 E Washington Ave.
Madison, WI 53701-0352
Ph: (608)258-3400
Fax: (608)258-3413
Co. E-mail: jhaney@wmc.org
URL: http://www.wmc.org
Contact: James S. Haney, President

59646 ■ *Membermatters*
PO Box 6190
Wausau, WI 54402-6190
Ph: (715)845-6231

Fax: (715)845-6235
Co. E-mail: info@wausauchamber.com
URL: http://www.wausauchamber.com
Contact: Jeff Zriny, President
Released: Monthly

59647 ■ Menomonee Falls Community Chamber of Commerce (MFCC)
N88 W16621 Appleton Ave.
Menomonee Falls, WI 53052
Ph: (262)251-2430
Fax: (262)251-0969
Co. E-mail: toni@fallschamber.com
URL: http://fallschamber.com
Contact: Toni M. Yates, Executive Director
Description: Provides support and services for the ongoing economic development in the area. Brings together business and community leaders to promote, develop and support the economic, educational, and civic interests of the community. **Founded:** 1932. **Publications:** *Action Update* (Periodic). **Awards:** Business of the Year Award (Annual); Chairperson of the Year Award (Annual); Citizen of the Year (Annual); Community Betterment Award (Annual); Community Improvement Award (Annual); Leadership Menomonee Falls Award (Annual); President's Award (Annual); Leading the Way/Women of Achievement Award (Periodic).

59648 ■ Mequon-Thiensville Chamber of Commerce (MTACC)
6331 W Mequon Rd.
Mequon, WI 53092
Ph: (262)512-9358
Fax: (262)512-9359
Co. E-mail: info@mtchamber.org
URL: http://www.mtchamber.org
Contact: Tina Schwantes, Executive Director
Description: Promotes business and community development in Mequon and Thiensville, WI and its surrounding area. **Founded:** 1980. **Publications:** *Business Directory* (Annual); *Chamber News* (Monthly); *Community Profile.* **Educational Activities:** Mequon-Thiensville Chamber of Commerce Luncheon (Monthly).

59649 ■ Mercer Area Chamber of Commerce
5150 N Hwy. 51
Mercer, WI 54547
Ph: (715)476-2389
Co. E-mail: info@mercercc.com
URL: http://www.mercercc.com
Contact: Tina Brunell, Administrator Secretary
Description: Promotes business and community development in Mercer, WI area.

59650 ■ Merrill Area Chamber of Commerce (MACC)
705 N Center Ave.
Merrill, WI 54452
Ph: (715)536-9474
Free: 877-907-2757
Fax: (715)539-2043
Co. E-mail: info@merrillchamber.org
URL: http://merrillchamber.org/merrill_commerce
Contact: Debbe Kinsey, Executive Director
Description: Promotes business and community development in the Merrill, WI area. **Founded:** 1911. **Publications:** *Merrill City Directory* (Periodic); *Merrill, Wisconsin, A City of Progress and Promise.*

59651 ■ *Merrill City Directory*
705 N Center Ave.
Merrill, WI 54452
Ph: (715)536-9474
Free: 877-907-2757
Fax: (715)539-2043
Co. E-mail: info@merrillchamber.org
URL: http://merrillchamber.org/merrill_commerce
Contact: Debbe Kinsey, Executive Director
Released: Periodic **Price:** $14, /copy.

59652 ■ *Merrill, Wisconsin, A City of Progress and Promise*
705 N Center Ave.
Merrill, WI 54452
Ph: (715)536-9474
Free: 877-907-2757

Fax: (715)539-2043
Co. E-mail: info@merrillchamber.org
URL: http://merrillchamber.org/merrill_commerce
Contact: Debbe Kinsey, Executive Director
Price: $2, /copy.

59653 ■ Metropolitan Milwaukee Association of Commerce (MMAC)
756 N Milwaukee St., Ste. 400
Milwaukee, WI 53202
Ph: (414)287-4100
Fax: (414)271-7753
Co. E-mail: info@mmac.org
URL: http://www.mmac.org
Contact: Timothy Sullivan, Chairman
Description: Works to serve as advocate for metro Milwaukee companies to encourage business development, capital investment and job creation. **Founded:** 1861.

59654 ■ Middleton Chamber of Commerce (MCC)
7507 Hubbard Ave.
Middleton, WI 53562
Ph: (608)827-5797
Fax: (608)831-7765
Co. E-mail: nutt@middletonchamber.com
URL: http://www.middletonchamber.com
Contact: Mr. Van Nutt, Executive Director
Description: Represents businesses in Middleton, WI united to promote economic development. Aims to act as a liaison for business people and the community, and to provide governmental advocacy. **Founded:** 1952. **Telecommunication Services:** chamber@middletonchamber.com.

59655 ■ Mineral Point Chamber of Commerce (MPCCMS)
225 High St.
Mineral Point, WI 53565
Ph: (608)987-3201
Free: 888-POI-NTWI
Fax: (608)987-4425
Co. E-mail: info@mineralpoint.com
URL: http://www.mineralpoint.com
Contact: Joy Gieseke, Executive Director
Description: Represents business owners. Strives to enrich the economic well being and supports local business and industry in Mineral Point, WI. **Founded:** 1945. **Publications:** *Community Resource Guide*; *Visitor's Guide.*

59656 ■ Minocqua - Arbor Vitae - Woodruff Chamber of Commerce
PO Box 1006
Minocqua, WI 54548
Ph: (715)356-5266
Free: 800-446-6784
Fax: (715)358-2446
Co. E-mail: mavwacc@minocqua.org
URL: http://minocqua.org
Contact: Diane L. Geis Hapka, Executive Director
Description: Works to develop, promote and maintain a positive economic climate which supports the community. **Founded:** 1993. **Publications:** *Northwoods News* (Monthly). **Telecommunication Services:** dhapka@minocqua.org.

59657 ■ Mishicot Area Growth and Improvement Committee (MAGIC)
PO Box 237
Mishicot, WI 54228
Ph: (920)755-3411
Fax: (920)755-3411
Co. E-mail: magic@tm.net
URL: http://www.mishicot.org
Description: Promotes business and community development in Mishicot, WI area. **Founded:** 1847. **Publications:** *Mishicot Newsletter* (3/year). **Awards:** Abracadabra Award (Annual); Design Award (Annual); Genie Award (Annual); Red Carpet Award (Annual).

59658 ■ Mishicot Newsletter
PO Box 237
Mishicot, WI 54228
Ph: (920)755-3411

Fax: (920)755-3411
Co. E-mail: magic@tm.net
URL: http://www.mishicot.org
Released: 3/year **Price:** free, for members only; $1, for nonmembers.

59659 ■ Monona Chamber of Commerce
6320 Monona Dr., Ste. 100
Monona, WI 53716-3952
Ph: (608)222-8565
Fax: (608)222-8596
Co. E-mail: chamber@monona.com
URL: http://monona.com
Contact: April Carlisle, President
Description: Promotes business and community development in Monona, WI area. **Founded:** 1990.

59660 ■ Monroe Chamber of Commerce and Industry (MCCI)
1505 9th St.
Monroe, WI 53566
Ph: (608)325-7648
Fax: (608)328-2241
Co. E-mail: thechamber@tds.net
URL: http://www.monroechamber.org
Contact: Pamela L. Christopher, Executive Director
Description: Promotes business, industry, and tourism in the Monroe, WI area. Sponsors Balloon Rally. **Publications:** *Issues* (Monthly); *Visitor Guide* (Annual).

59661 ■ Montello Area Chamber of Commerce (MCC)
PO Box 219
Montello, WI 53949
Ph: (608)297-7420
Free: 888-318-0362
URL: http://www.montellowi.com
Description: Promotes business and community development in the Montello, WI area. Sponsors annual Father Marquette Days festival. Convention/Meeting: none. **Founded:** 1946.

59662 ■ Mosinee Area Chamber of Commerce
224 Main St.
Mosinee, WI 54455
Ph: (715)693-4330
Fax: (715)693-9555
Co. E-mail: macoc@mtc.net
URL: http://www.mosineechamber.org
Contact: Tammy Lechnir-Campo, Executive Director
Description: Strives to serve as a resource in order to promote the interests of area businesses and the community of Mosinee. **Publications:** *Chamber News* (Monthly).

59663 ■ Mount Horeb Area Chamber of Commerce
300 E Main St.
Mount Horeb, WI 53572
Ph: (608)437-5914
Free: 888-765-5929
Co. E-mail: info@trollway.com
URL: http://www.trollway.com
Contact: Dale Hatfield, President
Description: Promotes business and community development in Mount Horeb, WI.

59664 ■ Mukwonago Area Chamber of Commerce and Tourism Center
801 Main St., Ste. 1
Mukwonago, WI 53149
Ph: (262)363-7758
Fax: (262)363-7730
Co. E-mail: director@mukwonagochamber.org
URL: http://www.mukwonagochamber.org
Contact: April Reszka, Executive Director
Description: Promotes business and community development in Mukwonago, WI. **Scope:** Mukwonago, tourism information. **Founded:** 1985. **Subscriptions:** 150 articles books video recordings. **Publications:** *Bear Tracks* (5/year); *Paw Prints* (Bimonthly). **Awards:** Partnership Award; President Award; Employer Recognition Award (Annual); Entrepreneur of the Year (Annual); Retailer of the Year (Annual).

59665 ■ Muskego Area Chamber of Commerce
PO Box 234
Muskego, WI 53150
Ph: (414)422-1155
Fax: (414)422-1415
Co. E-mail: info@muskego.org
URL: http://www.muskego.org
Contact: Tina Weiss, Executive Director
Description: Promotes business and community development in Muskego, WI area. **Founded:** 1957.

59666 ■ National Black Chamber of Commerce, Wisconsin
3020 W Vliet St.
Milwaukee, WI 53208
Ph: (414)551-6649
Fax: (414)933-1652
Co. E-mail: rubenhopkins@aol.com
URL: http://www.twbcc.com
Contact: Ruben W. Hopkins, President
Description: Represents Black owned businesses. Seeks to empower and sustain African American communities through entrepreneurship and capitalistic activity. Provides advocacy, training and education to Black communities.

59667 ■ Nebagamon Community Association
11507 E Waterfront Dr.
Lake Nebagamon, WI 54849
Ph: (715)374-2741
Co. E-mail: ccoletta@centurytel.net
URL: http://www.lakenebagamonwi.com

59668 ■ Neillsville Area Chamber of Commerce (NACC)
500 W St.
Neillsville, WI 54456
Ph: (715)743-6444
Co. E-mail: neillsvillechamber@gmail.com
URL: http://www.neillsville.org
Contact: Deanna Heiman, Executive Director
Description: Represents retail and business owners; clubs and organizations. Promotes business and community development in the Neillsville, WI area. Conducts charitable activities. Sponsors annual Harvest Festival. **Publications:** *Teamwork for a Prosperous Community* (Monthly). **Educational Activities:** Chamber Dinner Meeting (Quarterly).

59669 ■ Net Works
1305 N Barker Rd., Ste. 5
Brookfield, WI 53045
Ph: (262)786-1886
Fax: (262)786-1959
Co. E-mail: carol@brookfieldchamber.com
URL: http://www.brookfieldchamber.com
Contact: Carol White, President
Released: Monthly

59670 ■ The Network
500 Public Ave.
Beloit, WI 53511
Ph: (608)365-8835
Fax: (608)365-6850
Co. E-mail: info@greaterbeloitchamber.com
URL: http://greaterbeloitchamber.com
Contact: Randall Upton, President

59671 ■ New Berlin Chamber of Commerce and Visitors Bureau (NBCC/VB)
13825 W National Ave.
New Berlin, WI 53151
Ph: (262)786-5280
Co. E-mail: office@newberlinchamber.org
URL: http://newberlinchamber.org/dnn/april13/Home.aspx
Contact: Kimberly Dort, President
Description: Promotes business and community development in New Berlin, WI. **Founded:** 1959. **Publications:** *Hilites* (Periodic).

59672 ■ New Glarus Chamber of Commerce
418 Railroad St.
New Glarus, WI 53574
Ph: (608)527-2095

Free: 800-527-6838
Co. E-mail: info@swisstown.com
URL: http://www.swisstown.com
Description: Promotes business and community development in New Glarus, WI. **Publications:** *America's Little Switzerland* (Weekly).

59673 ■ New Lisbon Area Chamber of Commerce (NLCC)
PO Box 79
New Lisbon, WI 53950
Ph: (608)562-3555
Fax: (608)562-5625
Co. E-mail: nlchambr@mwt.net
URL: http://www.newlisbonchamber.com
Contact: Jenny Kochie, President
Description: Strives to promote economy and provide leadership that could influence public policy for the benefit of members.

59674 ■ New London Area Chamber of Commerce (NLACC)
420 N Shawano St.
New London, WI 54961
Ph: (920)982-5822
Fax: (920)982-6344
Co. E-mail: chamber@newlondonwi.org
URL: http://www.newlondonchamber.com
Contact: Laurie A. Shaw, Executive Director
Description: Represents businesses and individuals organized to promote economic and community development in the New London, WI area. **Founded:** 1932. **Publications:** *Everybody's Business* (Monthly). **Educational Activities:** Expo (Annual). **Awards:** Ambassador of the Year Award (Annual); Business and Industry Award (Annual); Chamber Service Award (Annual); Community Service Award (Annual); Excellence in Industry Award (Annual); President's Award (Annual); Quality of Life Award (Annual); New Business of the Year Award (Annual).

59675 ■ New Richmond Area Chamber of Commerce and Visitors Bureau
245 S Knowles Ave.
New Richmond, WI 54017
Ph: (715)246-2900
Free: 800-654-6380
Fax: (715)246-7100
Co. E-mail: info@newrichmondchamber.com
URL: http://www.newrichmondchamber.com
Contact: Angela Olson, President
Description: Promotes economic and community development in the New Richmond, WI area. Conducts business, industry, community, and education partnership program. Sponsors annual Park Art Fair and Fun Festival. **Founded:** 1947. **Publications:** *Chamber Connection* (Monthly). **Educational Activities:** Ambassadors (Monthly).

59676 ■ *News Break!*
104 W Cook St., Ste. A
Portage, WI 53901
Ph: (608)742-6242
Free: 800-474-2525
Fax: (608)742-3799
Co. E-mail: pacc@portagewi.com
URL: http://www.portagewi.com
Contact: Marianne Hanson, Executive Director
Released: Monthly **Price:** free for members.

59677 ■ *Newswave*
120 Jackson St.
Oshkosh, WI 54901
Ph: (920)303-2266
Fax: (920)303-2263
Co. E-mail: info@oshkoshchamber.com
URL: http://www.oshkoshchamber.com
Contact: John T. Anderson, Chairman
Released: Bimonthly

59678 ■ *Northwoods News*
PO Box 1006
Minocqua, WI 54548
Ph: (715)356-5266
Free: 800-446-6784

Fax: (715)358-2446
Co. E-mail: mavwacc@minocqua.org
URL: http://minocqua.org
Contact: Diane L. Geis Hapka, Executive Director
Released: Monthly **Price:** included in membership dues.

59679 ■ Oconomowoc Area Chamber of Commerce (OACC)
175 E Wisconsin Ave.
Oconomowoc, WI 53066
Ph: (262)567-2666
Fax: (262)567-3477
URL: http://www.oconomowoc.org
Contact: Patricia Ornberg, Executive Director
Description: Promotes business and community development in the Oconomowoc, WI area. Offers numerous networking and advertising opportunities. **Founded:** 1969. **Publications:** *Oconomowoc Talk* (Monthly).

59680 ■ *Oconomowoc Talk*
175 E Wisconsin Ave.
Oconomowoc, WI 53066
Ph: (262)567-2666
Fax: (262)567-3477
URL: http://www.oconomowoc.org
Contact: Patricia Ornberg, Executive Director
Released: Monthly

59681 ■ Oconto Falls Area Chamber of Commerce
PO Box 24
Oconto Falls, WI 54154
Ph: (920)846-8306
Co. E-mail: ofchamber@bayland.net
URL: http://www.ocontofallschamber.com
Contact: Pam Lemorande, President
Description: Promotes business and community development in Oconto Falls, WI.

59682 ■ Omro Area Chamber of Commerce
130 W Larrabee St.
Omro, WI 54963
Ph: (920)685-6960
Fax: (920)685-0384
Co. E-mail: ssalfai@omro-wi.com
URL: http://www.omro-wi.com/chamber.html
Description: Promotes business and community development in Omro, WI. **Scope:** sales, marketing, customer service, advertisement. **Founded:** 1986. **Subscriptions:** articles books. **Publications:** *The Communicator* (Monthly). **Educational Activities:** Omro Area Chamber of Commerce Meeting (Monthly).

59683 ■ *Organizations Guide*
PO Box 1855
Appleton, WI 54912-1855
Ph: (920)734-7101
Free: 800-999-3224
Fax: (920)734-7161
Co. E-mail: information@foxcitieschamber.com
URL: http://www.foxcitieschamber.com
Contact: Shannon Full, President

59684 ■ Osceola Area Chamber of Commerce
PO Box 251
Osceola, WI 54020-0251
Ph: (715)755-3300
Free: 800-947-0581
Co. E-mail: osceolachamber@centurytel.net
URL: http://www.vil.osceola.wi.us
Contact: Timm Johnson, President
Description: Seeks to unite area businesses, industry, and services into a unified voice to promote, preserve, and protect Osceola and the surrounding area for the present and future.

59685 ■ Oshkosh Chamber of Commerce
120 Jackson St.
Oshkosh, WI 54901
Ph: (920)303-2266

Fax: (920)303-2263
Co. E-mail: info@oshkoshchamber.com
URL: http://www.oshkoshchamber.com
Contact: John T. Anderson, Chairman
Description: Promotes business and community development in Oshkosh area. **Founded:** 1907. **Publications:** *Member Matters* (Bimonthly); *Newswave* (Bimonthly). **Awards:** Ambassador of the Year (Annual); Community Service (Annual); Distinguished Service (Annual); Small Business Person of the Year (Annual); Volunteer of the Year (Annual).

59686 ■ Park Falls Area Chamber of Commerce (PFACC)
400 4th Ave. S
Park Falls, WI 54552
Ph: (715)762-2703
Free: 877-762-2703
Co. E-mail: chamber@parkfalls.com
URL: http://www.parkfalls.com
Contact: Sue Holm, Executive Director
Description: Serves resorts, industries, retailers, and service organizations in Ashland, Iron, Price, and Sawyer counties, WI. Promotes community and economic development; provides information; sponsors promotions and events. **Founded:** 1947. **Publications:** *Park Falls - Gateway to the Good Life*; *Chamber Chatter* (Weekly). **Educational Activities:** Flambeau Rama Celebration (Annual).

59687 ■ *Park Falls - Gateway to the Good Life*
400 4th Ave. S
Park Falls, WI 54552
Ph: (715)762-2703
Free: 877-762-2703
Co. E-mail: chamber@parkfalls.com
URL: http://www.parkfalls.com
Contact: Sue Holm, Executive Director

59688 ■ *Paw Prints*
801 Main St., Ste. 1
Mukwonago, WI 53149
Ph: (262)363-7758
Fax: (262)363-7730
Co. E-mail: director@mukwonagochamber.org
URL: http://www.mukwonagochamber.org
Contact: April Reszka, Executive Director
Released: Bimonthly **Price:** free.

59689 ■ Pelican Lake Area Chamber of Commerce
PO Box 45
Pelican Lake, WI 54463
Ph: (715)487-5222
Co. E-mail: pelicanlakecc@frontiernet.net
URL: http://www.pelicanlakewi.org
Description: Businesses. Promotes business and community development in the Pelican Lake, WI area. Sponsors annual Ice Fishing Jamboree. **Founded:** 1962.

59690 ■ *Perspectives*
700 S Central Ave.
Marshfield, WI 54449
Ph: (715)384-3454
Fax: (715)387-8925
Co. E-mail: info@marshfieldchamber.com
URL: http://www.marshfieldchamber.com
Contact: Cindy Burns, President
Released: Monthly

59691 ■ Pewaukee Chamber of Commerce
1285 Sunnyridge Rd.
Pewaukee, WI 53072
Ph: (262)691-8851
Fax: (262)691-0922
Co. E-mail: info@pewaukeechamber.org
URL: http://www.pewaukeechamber.org
Contact: Kathy Eckhardt, Executive Director
Description: Works to serve the needs of business community. **Publications:** *Pewaukee Chamber of Commerce--Community Directory*.

59692 ■ Phelps Chamber of Commerce (PCC)
PO Box 217
Phelps, WI 54554
Ph: (715)545-3800

Free: 877-669-7077
Co. E-mail: phelpschamber@gmail.com
URL: http://www.phelpscofc.org
Contact: Marti Primich, President
Description: Promotes business and community development in Phelps, WI. Sponsors annual Col-orama Brunch.

59693 ■ Platteville Chamber of Commerce
PO Box 724
Platteville, WI 53818
Ph: (608)348-8888
Fax: (608)348-8890
Co. E-mail: chamber@platteville.com
URL: http://www.platteville.com
Description: Promotes business and community development in Platteville, WI.

59694 ■ Plymouth Chamber of Commerce
PO Box 584
Plymouth, WI 53073
Ph: (920)893-0079
Free: 888-693-8263
Fax: (920)893-8473
Co. E-mail: plymouthchamber@frontier.com
URL: http://www.plymouthwisconsin.com
Contact: Ron Nielsen, President
Description: Promotes business and community development in Plymouth, WI. **Founded:** 1921. **Publications:** *The Chamber Link* (Monthly). **Awards:** Business of the Year (Annual); Family of the Year (Annual). **Telecommunication Services:** plymouth-chamber@excel.net.

59695 ■ Port Washington Chamber of Commerce
126 E Grand Ave.
Port Washington, WI 53074
Ph: (262)284-0900
Free: 800-719-4881
Fax: (262)284-0591
Co. E-mail: info@portwashingtonchamber.com
URL: http://www.portwashingtonchamber.com
Contact: Barb Beattie, President
Description: Promotes business, community development, and tourism in Port Washington area.

59696 ■ Portage Area Chamber of Commerce (PACC)
104 W Cook St., Ste. A
Portage, WI 53901
Ph: (608)742-6242
Free: 800-474-2525
Fax: (608)742-3799
Co. E-mail: pacc@portagewi.com
URL: http://www.portagewi.com
Contact: Marianne Hanson, Executive Director
Description: Individuals and businesses working to enhance the quality of life and improve business in the Portage, WI area. Sponsors Taste of Portage. **Founded:** 1929. **Publications:** *News Break!* (Monthly); *Portage Visitor Guides.*

59697 ■ Portage County Business Council (PCBC)
5501 Vern Holmes Dr.
Stevens Point, WI 54481
Ph: (715)344-1940
Fax: (715)344-4473
Co. E-mail: info@portagecountybiz.com
URL: http://www.portagecountybiz.com
Contact: Lori Dehlinger, Executive Director
Description: Represents over 500 Portage County businesses. Strengthens Portage County's quality of life by promoting a business climate that encourages growth and stability. **Publications:** *Active Voice* (Monthly).

59698 ■ *Portage Visitor Guides*
104 W Cook St., Ste. A
Portage, WI 53901
Ph: (608)742-6242
Free: 800-474-2525
Fax: (608)742-3799
Co. E-mail: pacc@portagewi.com
URL: http://www.portagewi.com
Contact: Marianne Hanson, Executive Director

59699 ■ Potosi - Tennyson Area Chamber of Commerce
PO Box 11
Potosi, WI 53820
Ph: (608)763-2261
Co. E-mail: potositennysoncc@tds.net
URL: http://www.potosiwisconsin.com
Contact: Lisa Droessler, President
Description: Promotes business and community development in Potosi/Tennyson, WI.

59700 ■ Poynette Chamber of Commerce
PO Box 625
Poynette, WI 53955
Ph: (608)635-2425
Co. E-mail: info@poynettechamber.com
URL: http://www.poynettechamber.com/index.html
Contact: Brita Schoeneberg, President
Description: Promotes business and community development in Poynette, WI.

59701 ■ Prairie Du Chien Area Chamber of Commerce (PDCACC)
PO Box 326
Prairie Du Chien, WI 53821
Ph: (608)326-8555
Free: 800-732-1673
Fax: (608)326-7744
Co. E-mail: info@prairieduchien.org
URL: http://www.prairieduchien.org
Contact: J.J. Jackson, President
Description: Promotes business and community development in the Prairie du Chien, WI area. Convention/Meeting: none. **Founded:** 1950. **Publications:** *Prairie du Chien Area* (Annual). **Telecommunication Services:** pdccoc@mhtc.net.

59702 ■ Prescott Area Chamber of Commerce (PACC)
237 Broad St.
Prescott, WI 54021
Ph: (715)262-3284
Fax: (715)262-5943
Co. E-mail: info@prescottwi.com
URL: http://www.prescottwi.com
Contact: Char Magee, President
Description: Promotes business and community development in the Prescott, WI area. Assists with local festivals. **Founded:** 1979. **Publications:** *Prescott Visitor and New Residents Guide* (Annual).

59703 ■ *Prescott Visitor and New Residents Guide*
237 Broad St.
Prescott, WI 54021
Ph: (715)262-3284
Fax: (715)262-5943
Co. E-mail: info@prescottwi.com
URL: http://www.prescottwi.com
Contact: Char Magee, President
Released: Annual

59704 ■ Presque Isle Chamber of Commerce (PICC)
PO Box 135
Presque Isle, WI 54557
Ph: (715)686-2910
Free: 888-835-6508
Co. E-mail: info@presqueisle.com
URL: http://www.presqueislewi.org
Contact: George Nelson, Supervisor
Description: Promotes business and community development in Presque Isle, WI.

59705 ■ Pulaski Area Chamber of Commerce
159 W Pulaski St.
Pulaski, WI 54162-0401
Ph: (920)822-4400
Fax: (920)822-4455
Co. E-mail: pacc@netnet.net
URL: http://www.pulaskichamber.org
Contact: Marlene Carey, President
Description: Promotes business and community development in the Pulaski, WI area.

59706 ■ Racine Area Manufacturers and Commerce (RAMAC)
300 5th St.
Racine, WI 53403

Ph: (262)634-1931
Fax: (262)634-7422
Co. E-mail: ramac@racinechamber.com
URL: http://www.racinechamber.com
Contact: Michael Kobylka, President
Description: Strives to strengthen the economic and business community of Racine area. **Founded:** 1982.

59707 ■ *Randolph: A Great Place to Grow*
PO Box 66
Randolph, WI 53956
Ph: (920)326-4769
Fax: (920)326-5032
URL: http://www.randolphwi.net
Contact: Kathy Nehmer, President

59708 ■ Randolph Chamber of Commerce (RCC)
PO Box 66
Randolph, WI 53956
Ph: (920)326-4769
Fax: (920)326-5032
URL: http://www.randolphwi.net
Contact: Kathy Nehmer, President
Description: Promotes business and community development in Randolph, WI. Sponsors annual Maxwell Street Festival. **Publications:** *Business Directory* (Periodic); *Randolph: A Great Place to Grow.*

59709 ■ *The Report*
14 S Jackson St.
Janesville, WI 53548
Ph: (608)757-3160
Fax: (608)757-3170
Co. E-mail: forward@forwardjanesville.com
URL: http://www.forwardjanesville.com
Contact: Mr. John Beckord, President
Released: Quarterly

59710 ■ Rhinelander Area Chamber of Commerce (RACC)
450 W Kemp St.
Rhinelander, WI 54501
Ph: (715)365-7464
Free: 800-236-4386
Fax: (715)365-7467
Co. E-mail: info@rhinelanderchamber.com
URL: http://www.explorerhinelander.com/chamber-info
Contact: Lara Reed, Executive Director
Description: Promotes business and community development in the Rhinelander, WI area. **Founded:** 1928.

59711 ■ Rice Lake Area Chamber of Commerce (RLACC)
37 S Main St.
Rice Lake, WI 54868
Ph: (715)234-2126
Free: 877-234-2126
Fax: (715)234-2085
Co. E-mail: chamber@rice-lake.com
URL: http://www.rice-lake.com
Contact: Dan Jirik, President
Description: Businesses. Promotes business and community development in the Rice Lake, WI area. **Founded:** 1941. **Publications:** *Chamber News* (Monthly). **Educational Activities:** Salute to Industry.

59712 ■ Richland Area Chamber of Commerce/Main Street Partnership (RACC)
PO Box 128
Richland Center, WI 53581
Ph: (608)647-6205
Free: 800-422-1318
Fax: (608)647-5449
Co. E-mail: chamber@richlandalliance.com
URL: http://www.richlandchamber.com
Contact: Shannon Clark, President
Description: Promotes business and community development in the Richland Center, WI area. Sponsors celebration on Frank Lloyd Wright's birthday, Centerfest, and June Dairy Days. **Founded:** 1936. **Publications:** *Chamber Business* (Semiannual); *Chamber Business* (Semiannual). **Awards:** Certificates of Appreciation (Annual). **Telecommunication Services:** chamber1@richlandchamber.com; info@richlandchamber.com.

59713 ■ Ripon Area Chamber of Commerce (RACC)
PO Box 305
Ripon, WI 54971
Ph: (920)748-6764
Fax: (920)748-6784
Co. E-mail: chamber@ripon-wi.com
URL: http://www.ripon-wi.com/ripon-wi/page.asp?p=home
Contact: Paula Price, Executive Director
Description: Promotes business and community development in the Ripon, WI area. Sponsors Dickens of A Christmas festival, Cookie Daze, Maxwell Street Day and Duck-tona $500 Rubber Duck Race. **Founded:** 1940. **Publications:** *Horn Blower* (Bimonthly); *The Ripon Guide* (Annual). **Awards:** Community Service (Annual); Distinguished Service (Annual); Outstanding Business/Industry (Annual).

59714 ■ *The Ripon Guide*
PO Box 305
Ripon, WI 54971
Ph: (920)748-6764
Fax: (920)748-6784
Co. E-mail: chamber@ripon-wi.com
URL: http://www.ripon-wi.com/ripon-wi/page.asp?p=home
Contact: Paula Price, Executive Director
Released: Annual

59715 ■ River Falls Area Chamber of Commerce and Tourism Bureau
214 N Main St.
River Falls, WI 54022
Ph: (715)425-2533
Fax: (715)425-2305
Co. E-mail: info@rfchamber.com
URL: http://www.rfchamber.com
Contact: Rosanne Bump, Chief Executive Officer
Description: Works to improve economic development and quality of life in the community through education, promotion and leadership. Sponsors River Falls Days, Town N' Country Day, Ambassadors Golf Outing, Business Show Case, and many more events. **Founded:** 1955. **Awards:** Ambassador of the Year (Annual); Business of the Year (Annual); Citizen of the Year (Annual); Small Business of the Year (Annual).

59716 ■ St. Germain Chamber of Commerce
PO Box 155
St. Germain, WI 54558
Ph: (715)477-2205
Co. E-mail: info@st-germain.com
URL: http://www.st-germain.com
Contact: Loren Anderson, President
Description: Promotes business and community development in St. Germain, WI.

59717 ■ *Sales and Exchange*
501 E Washington Ave.
Madison, WI 53701-0352
Ph: (608)258-3400
Fax: (608)258-3413
Co. E-mail: jhaney@wmc.org
URL: http://www.wmc.org
Contact: James S. Haney, President
Released: Monthly

59718 ■ Sauk Prairie Area Chamber of Commerce (SPACC)
421 Water St., Ste. 105
Prairie Du Sac, WI 53578
Ph: (608)643-4168
Free: 800-68-EAGLE
Fax: (608)643-3544
Co. E-mail: spacc@saukprairie.com
URL: http://www.saukprairie.com
Contact: Todd Baker, President
Description: Promotes business and community development in the Sauk City and Prairie du Sac, WI area. **Founded:** 1956. **Publications:** *Sauk Prairie Area Chamber of Commerce Business/Membership Directory* (Periodic).

59719 ■ *Sauk Prairie Area Chamber of Commerce Business/Membership Directory*
421 Water St., Ste. 105
Prairie Du Sac, WI 53578

Ph: (608)643-4168
Free: 800-68-EAGLE
Fax: (608)643-3544
Co. E-mail: spacc@saukprairie.com
URL: http://www.saukprairie.com
Contact: Todd Baker, President
Released: Periodic

59720 ■ Saukville Chamber of Commerce
PO Box 80238
Saukville, WI 53080
Ph: (262)268-1970
Co. E-mail: saukvillechamber@earthlink.net
URL: http://www.saukvillechamber.org
Contact: Russ Lund, President
Description: Promotes business and community development in the Saukville, WI area.

59721 ■ Sayner-Star Lake Chamber of Commerce (SSLCC)
PO Box 191
Sayner, WI 54560
Ph: (715)542-3789
Free: 888-722-3789
Co. E-mail: saynerstarlake@wildblue.net
URL: http://www.sayner-starlake.org
Description: Promotes business and community development in the Sayner, WI area. **Founded:** 1980.

59722 ■ Shawano Country Chamber of Commerce (SACC)
PO Box 38
Shawano, WI 54166-0038
Ph: (715)524-2139
Co. E-mail: nsmith@shawano.com
URL: http://www.shawanocountry.com
Contact: Nancy J. Smith, Executive Director
Description: Promotes business and community development in the Shawano, WI area. Acts as civic clearinghouse, public relations counselor, and legislative representative. **Founded:** 1926.

59723 ■ Sheboygan County Chamber of Commerce and Convention and Visitors Bureau
712 Riverfront Dr., Ste. 101
Sheboygan, WI 53081
Ph: (920)457-9491
Fax: (920)457-6269
Co. E-mail: chamber@sheboygan.org
URL: http://www.sheboygan.org
Contact: Betsy Alles, Executive Director
Description: Improves the economic, social and political conditions of Sheboygan County. Advances the status of the county by engaging in forums, addressing the needs of the community and developing beneficial programs for the members.

59724 ■ Sheboygan Falls Chamber Main Street
504 Broadway
Sheboygan Falls, WI 53085
Ph: (920)467-6206
Fax: (920)467-9571
Co. E-mail: chambermnst@sheboyganfalls.org
URL: http://www.sheboyganfalls.org
Contact: Nancy L. Verstrate, Executive Director
Description: Promotes commerce and redevelopment of downtown Sheboygan Falls. **Founded:** 1988. **Publications:** *Word on the Street* (Bimonthly).

59725 ■ Shell Lake Chamber of Commerce (SLCC)
PO Box 121
Shell Lake, WI 54871
Ph: (715)468-4340
Co. E-mail: shelllake_chamberofcommerce@yahoo.com
URL: http://www.shelllakeonline.com/contacts.htm
Contact: Doug Panek, Manager
Description: Promotes business and community development in Shell Lake, WI. Sponsors Town and Country Days. **Publications:** none.

59726 ■ *Solutions*
PO Box 34
Whitewater, WI 53190

Ph: (262)473-4005
Co. E-mail: info@whitewaterchamber.com
URL: http://www.whitewaterchamber.com
Released: Monthly **Price:** free for members.

59727 ■ Sparta Area Chamber of Commerce
111 Milwaukee Ave.
Sparta, WI 54656
Ph: (608)269-4123
Free: 888-540-8434
Fax: (608)269-3350
Co. E-mail: spartachamber@centurytel.net
URL: http://www.spartachamber.org
Contact: Sharon Folcey, Executive Director
Description: Fosters community prosperity and improvement of quality of life in the Sparta, WI area through cooperation, education, and active leadership. **Founded:** 1940. **Publications:** *The Ambassador* (Monthly). **Educational Activities:** Board and Executive Committee Meeting (Annual). **Telecommunication Services:** info@bikesparta.com.

59728 ■ Spooner Area Chamber of Commerce (SACC)
122 N River St.
Spooner, WI 54801
Ph: (715)635-2168
Free: 800-367-3306
Co. E-mail: spoonerchamber@spoonerchamber.org
URL: http://www.spoonerchamber.org
Contact: Aaron Arf, Executive Director
Description: Promotes business and community development in the Spooner, WI area. Sponsors Jack Pine Savage Days; Jack's A Hack Golf Tournament; Old Fashioned Saturday Night Woman's Day; conducts promotional activities. **Founded:** 1936. **Awards:** Business Person of the Year (Annual); Chamber Member of the Year (Annual); Citizen of the Year (Annual); Educator of the Year (Annual).

59729 ■ Spring Green Area Chamber of Commerce (SGACC)
259 E Jefferson St.
Spring Green, WI 53588
Ph: (608)588-2054
Free: 800-588-2042
Co. E-mail: info@springgreen.com
URL: http://www.springgreen.com
Contact: Nancy Viste, President
Description: Promotes business and community development in the Spring Green, WI area. Sponsors Arts and Crafts Fair and Country Christmas Festival. Conducts charitable activities. **Founded:** 1968. **Publications:** *The Chamber News.*

59730 ■ Stoughton Chamber of Commerce
532 E Main St.
Stoughton, WI 53589
Ph: (608)873-7912
Free: 888-873-7912
Fax: (608)873-7743
Co. E-mail: stoughton@stoughtonwi.com
URL: http://www.stoughtonwi.com
Contact: Randall McLaury, President
Description: Promotes business and community development in the Stoughton, WI area.

59731 ■ Stratford Area Chamber of Commerce
PO Box 312
Stratford, WI 54484
Ph: (715)687-4466
Co. E-mail: bergsd@firstweber.com
URL: http://www.stratfordwi.com
Contact: Dan Bergs, President

59732 ■ *Suburban Visitor Guide*
10437 Innovation Dr., Ste. 130
Wauwatosa, WI 53226
Ph: (414)453-2330
Fax: (414)453-2336
Co. E-mail: info@westsuburbanchamber.com
URL: http://www.westsuburbanchamber.com

59733 ■ Superior - Douglas County Chamber of Commerce
205 Belknap St.
Superior, WI 54880
Ph: (715)394-7716

Free: 800-942-5313
Fax: (715)394-3810
Co. E-mail: chamber@superiorchamber.org
URL: http://www.superiorchamber.org
Contact: David W. Minor, President
Description: Business people. Works to improve the economic, civic, and cultural welfare of the area through community development programs.

59734 ■ Sussex Area Chamber of Commerce
N64W23760 Main St., Ste. 101
Sussex, WI 53089
Ph: (262)246-4940
Fax: (262)246-7350
Co. E-mail: info@sussexareachamber.org
URL: http://www.sussexareachamber.org
Contact: Sheri Pellechia, Executive Director
Description: Works to advance the economic well-being of the community through commercial, civic, cultural, industrial and educational interest.

59735 ■ *Teamwork for a Prosperous Community*
500 W St.
Neillsville, WI 54456
Ph: (715)743-6444
Co. E-mail: neillsvillechamber@gmail.com
URL: http://www.neillsville.org
Contact: Deanna Heiman, Executive Director
Released: Monthly **Price:** free.

59736 ■ Tomahawk Chamber of Commerce
PO Box 412
Tomahawk, WI 54487-0412
Ph: (715)453-5334
Free: 800-569-2160
Co. E-mail: chambert@gototomahawk.com
URL: http://www.gototomahawk.com
Contact: Guy Klopatek, President
Description: Promotes business and community development in the Tomahawk, WI area. **Founded:** 1949. **Publications:** *Tomatalk* (Monthly); *Visitor Vacation Guide and Membership Directory* (Annual).

59737 ■ *Tomatalk*
PO Box 412
Tomahawk, WI 54487-0412
Ph: (715)453-5334
Free: 800-569-2160
Co. E-mail: chambert@gototomahawk.com
URL: http://www.gototomahawk.com
Contact: Guy Klopatek, President
Released: Monthly

59738 ■ *Valley Business*
101 N Farwell St., Ste. 101
Eau Claire, WI 54703
Ph: (715)834-1204
Fax: (715)834-1956
Co. E-mail: information@eauclairechamber.org
URL: http://www.eauclairechamber.org
Contact: Robert S. McCoy, President
Released: Monthly

59739 ■ Verona Area Chamber of Commerce
205 S Main St.
Verona, WI 53593-0003
Ph: (608)845-5777
Fax: (608)845-2519
Co. E-mail: info@veronawi.com
URL: http://veronawi.com
Contact: Karl Curtis, Executive Director
Description: Works to build a healthy Verona economy and improve the quality of life in the communities. Aims to proactively support, promote and enhance economic development and community well-being in Verona.

59740 ■ *Visitor Guide*
1515 Memorial Dr.
Manitowoc, WI 54220
Ph: (920)684-5575
Free: 866-727-5575
Fax: (920)684-1915
Co. E-mail: info@chambermanitowoccounty.org
URL: http://www.manitowocchamber.com
Contact: Karen Szyman, Executive Director
Released: Annual

59741 ■ *Visitor Guide*
1505 9th St.
Monroe, WI 53566
Ph: (608)325-7648
Fax: (608)328-2241
Co. E-mail: thechamber@tds.net
URL: http://www.monroechamber.org
Contact: Pamela L. Christopher, Executive Director
Released: Annual

59742 ■ *Visitor Vacation Guide and Membership Directory*
PO Box 412
Tomahawk, WI 54487-0412
Ph: (715)453-5334
Free: 800-569-2160
Co. E-mail: chambert@gototomahawk.com
URL: http://www.gototomahawk.com
Contact: Guy Klopatek, President
Released: Annual

59743 ■ *Visitors' Guide*
PO Box 337
Green Lake, WI 54941
Ph: (920)294-3231
Free: 800-253-7354
Fax: (920)294-3415
Co. E-mail: info@visitgreenlake.com
URL: http://visitgreenlake.com
Contact: Debra Beirman, President
Released: Annual **Price:** available to members only.

59744 ■ *Visitor's Guide*
225 High St.
Mineral Point, WI 53565
Ph: (608)987-3201
Free: 888-POI-NTWI
Fax: (608)987-4425
Co. E-mail: info@mineralpoint.com
URL: http://www.mineralpoint.com
Contact: Joy Gieseke, Executive Director

59745 ■ *WACC News*
440 W Main St.
Wautoma, WI 54982-0065
Ph: (920)787-3488
Free: 877-WAU-TOMA
Fax: (920)787-3788
Co. E-mail: wacc@wausarachamber.com
URL: http://www.wausharachamber.com
Contact: Rick Schmitz, President
Released: Monthly

59746 ■ Washburn Area Chamber of Commerce (WACC)
PO Box 74
Washburn, WI 54891
Ph: (715)373-5017
Free: 800-253-4495
Co. E-mail: info@washburnchamber.com
URL: http://washburnchamber.com
Contact: Diane Brander, President
Description: Promotes business and community development in Washburn, WI. **Founded:** 1975. **Publications:** *Chamber News* (Monthly).

59747 ■ Waterford Area Chamber of Commerce (WACC)
102 E Main St.
Waterford, WI 53185
Ph: (262)534-5911
Fax: (262)534-6507
Co. E-mail: chamber@waterford-wi.org
URL: http://www.waterford-wi.org
Contact: Jennifer Thomas, Executive Director
Description: Strives to promote business, tourism and community of the Waterford area through services and representation of the business community. **Publications:** *Business to Business* (Quarterly).

59748 ■ Waterloo Chamber of Commerce (WCC)
PO Box 1
Waterloo, WI 53594

Ph: (920)478-2500
Co. E-mail: chamber@waterloowi.us
URL: http://waterloowi.us/chamber/home2.php
Contact: William Hogan, President
Description: Promotes business and community development in Waterloo, WI.

59749 ■ Watertown Area Chamber of Commerce
519 E Main St.
Watertown, WI 53094
Ph: (920)261-6320
Fax: (920)261-6434
Co. E-mail: watncofc@powercom.net
URL: http://www.watertownchamber.com
Contact: Kim Erdmann, Executive Director
Description: Promotes business and community development in Watertown, WI. **Founded:** 1920.

59750 ■ Waukesha County Chamber of Commerce (WCCC)
2717 N Grandview Blvd., Ste. 204
Waukesha, WI 53188
Ph: (262)542-4249
Fax: (262)542-8068
Co. E-mail: alliance@waukesha.org
URL: http://www.waukesha.org
Contact: Suzanne Kelley, President
Description: Strives to enhance the business community of Waukesha County. **Publications:** *The Link.*

59751 ■ Waunakee/Westport Chamber of Commerce
100 E Main St.
Waunakee, WI 53597
Ph: (608)849-5977
Fax: (608)849-9825
Co. E-mail: waunakeechamber@tds.net
URL: http://www.webmger.com/WebMgmt/Content/waunakee/Default.asp
Contact: Ellen K. Schaaf, Executive Director
Description: Promotes business and community development in the Waunakee, WI area. **Founded:** 1979. **Publications:** *Greater Waunakee Area Chamber of Commerce News* (Monthly).

59752 ■ Waupaca Area Chamber of Commerce (WACC)
221 S Main St.
Waupaca, WI 54981-1522
Ph: (715)258-7343
Free: 888-417-4040
Fax: (715)258-7868
Co. E-mail: discoverwaupaca@waupacaareachamber.com
URL: http://www.waupacaareachamber.com
Contact: Terri Schulz, President
Description: Represents retailers, manufacturers, professionals, and service and community organizations united to promote economic and community development in the Waupaca, WI area. **Founded:** 1931. **Publications:** *Map Brochure* (Semiannual); *Waupaca Area Chamber of Commerce Newsline* (Monthly); *Waupaca Area Chamber of Commerce Progress Report* (Annual). **Telecommunication Services:** terri@waupacaareachamber.com

59753 ■ *Waupaca Area Chamber of Commerce Newsline*
221 S Main St.
Waupaca, WI 54981-1522
Ph: (715)258-7343
Free: 888-417-4040
Fax: (715)258-7868
Co. E-mail: discoverwaupaca@waupacaareachamber.com
URL: http://www.waupacaareachamber.com
Contact: Terri Schulz, President
Released: Monthly

59754 ■ *Waupaca Area Chamber of Commerce Progress Report*
221 S Main St.
Waupaca, WI 54981-1522
Ph: (715)258-7343
Free: 888-417-4040

Fax: (715)258-7868
Co. E-mail: discoverwaupaca@waupacaareachamber.com
URL: http://www.waupacaareachamber.com
Contact: Terri Schulz, President
Released: Annual

59755 ■ Waupun Area Chamber of Commerce
324 E Main St., Ste. 200
Waupun, WI 53963
Ph: (920)324-3491
Fax: (920)324-4357
Co. E-mail: info@waupunchamber.com
URL: http://www.waupunchamber.com
Contact: Jason Zweifel, President
Description: Aims to provide business leadership, promote its members' interests and encourage the long-term sustainable development, quality of life and prosperity of the area.

59756 ■ Wausau/Marathon County Chamber of Commerce (WACC)
PO Box 6190
Wausau, WI 54402-6190
Ph: (715)845-6231
Fax: (715)845-6235
Co. E-mail: info@wausauchamber.com
URL: http://www.wausauchamber.com
Contact: Jeff Zriny, President
Description: Promotes business and community development in the Wausau, WI area. **Publications:** *Businessmatters* (Quarterly); *Membermatters* (Monthly); *Businessmatters* (Quarterly); *Speakers Bureau Booklet.*

59757 ■ Waushara Area Chamber of Commerce (WACC)
440 W Main St.
Wautoma, WI 54982-0065
Ph: (920)787-3488
Free: 877-WAU-TOMA
Fax: (920)787-3788
Co. E-mail: wacc@wausharachamber.com
URL: http://www.wausharachamber.com
Contact: Rick Schmitz, President
Description: Promotes business and community development in Waushara County, WI. **Publications:** *WACC News* (Monthly). **Awards:** Business Person of the Year (Annual); Citizen of the Year (Annual). **Telecommunication Services:** info@wausharachamber. com.

59758 ■ Webster Area Chamber of Commerce
PO Box 48
Webster, WI 54893
Ph: (715)349-5999
Free: 800-788-3164
Co. E-mail: websterchamber@yahoo.com
URL: http://www.websterwisconsin.com
Description: Promotes business and community development in Webster, WI.

59759 ■ West Allis/West Milwaukee Chamber of Commerce (WACC)
7447 W Greenfield Ave.
West Allis, WI 53214
Ph: (414)302-9901
URL: http://www.wawmchamber.com
Contact: Diane Brandt, Executive Director
Description: Promotes business and community development in West Allis and West Milwaukee. **Founded:** 1958. **Publications:** *The Chamber Connection* (Monthly).

59760 ■ West Bend Area Chamber of Commerce (WBACC)
304 S Main St.
West Bend, WI 53095
Ph: (262)338-2666
Free: 888-338-8666

Fax: (262)338-1771
Co. E-mail: info@wbachamber.org
URL: http://www.wbchamber.org
Contact: Craig Farrell, Executive Director
Description: Businesses and individuals organized to promote economic and community development in the West Bend, WI area. **Founded:** 1970. **Publications:** *Comment* (Monthly).

59761 ■ West Suburban Chamber of Commerce (WSCC)
10437 Innovation Dr., Ste. 130
Wauwatosa, WI 53226
Ph: (414)453-2330
Fax: (414)453-2336
Co. E-mail: info@westsuburbanchamber.com
URL: http://www.westsuburbanchamber.com
Description: Promotes business and community development in Wauwatosa, WI. **Publications:** *Chamber Review* (Monthly); *Suburban Visitor Guide.*

59762 ■ Westfield Chamber of Commerce
PO Box 393
Westfield, WI 53964
Ph: (608)296-4146
Co. E-mail: pioneermotorinn@verizon.net
URL: http://www.westfieldwi.com
Description: Promotes business and community development in Westfield, WI.

59763 ■ Weyauwega Area Chamber of Commerce
PO Box 531
Weyauwega, WI 54983-0531
Ph: (920)867-2500
Co. E-mail: info@weyaugachamber.com
URL: http://www.weyauwegachamber.com
Contact: Becca Eckhardt, President
Description: Promotes business and community development in Weyauwega, WI.

59764 ■ Whitehall Area Chamber of Commerce
PO Box 281
Whitehall, WI 54773
Ph: (715)538-4353
Fax: (715)538-2301
Co. E-mail: kwitte@wppienergy.org
URL: http://whitehall-chamber.com
Contact: Rosanne Hoff, President
Description: Promotes business and community development in Whitehall, WI.

59765 ■ Whitewater Area Chamber of Commerce (WACC)
PO Box 34
Whitewater, WI 53190
Ph: (262)473-4005
Co. E-mail: info@whitewaterchamber.com
URL: http://www.whitewaterchamber.com
Description: Promotes business and community development in the Whitewater, WI area. **Founded:** 1941. **Publications:** *Solutions* (Monthly). **Educational Activities:** Badger State Games - Summer (Annual). **Telecommunication Services:** wacc@idc-net.com.

59766 ■ Wisconsin Manufacturers and Commerce (WMC)
501 E Washington Ave.
Madison, WI 53701-0352
Ph: (608)258-3400
Fax: (608)258-3413
Co. E-mail: jhaney@wmc.org
URL: http://www.wmc.org
Contact: James S. Haney, President
Description: Wisconsin manufacturers and service companies. Fosters and advances policies which are in the public interest of the state and nation. **Founded:** 1911. **Publications:** *Capitol Watch* (Weekly); *Chamber to Chamber*; *Human Resources Report* (Periodic); *Manufacturing Report* (Periodic); *Member Service Update*; *Sales and Exchange* (Monthly). **Educational Activities:** Wisconsin Safety Congress (Annual). **Awards:** The Besadny Scholarship (Annual); Business Friend of the Environment Awards (Annual); Excellence in Education Award (Annual); Wisconsin Business Friend of the Environment

Award (Annual); Wisconsin Corporate Safety Award (Annual); Wisconsin Manufacturer of the Year Award (Annual); Working for Wisconsin Award (Biennial).

59767 ■ Wittenberg Area Chamber of Commerce (WACC)
PO Box 284
Wittenberg, WI 54499
Ph: (715)253-3525
Co. E-mail: wittcham@wittenbergchamber.org
URL: http://wittenbergchamber.org
Description: Promotes business and community development in the Wittenberg, WI area.

59768 ■ *Word on the Street*
504 Broadway
Sheboygan Falls, WI 53085
Ph: (920)467-6206
Fax: (920)467-9571
Co. E-mail: chambermnst@sheboyganfalls.org
URL: http://www.sheboyganfalls.org
Contact: Nancy L. Verstrate, Executive Director
Released: Bimonthly

MINORITY BUSINESS ASSISTANCE PROGRAMS

59769 ■ Small Business Development Center - UWSP Continuing Education - University of Wisconsin-Stevens Point
Main Bldg., Rm. 032
2100 Main St.
Stevens Point, WI 54481-3897
Ph: (715)346-3838
Free: 800-898-9472
Fax: (715)346-3504
Co. E-mail: dl-cecserv@uwsp.edu
URL: http://www.uwsp.edu/conted/sbdc
Contact: Vicki Lobermeier, Director
Description: Provides counseling, in-depth studies, workshops, seminars, and communication development to American Indian tribes and individuals in Wisconsin.

59770 ■ Wisconsin Department of Commerce - Bureau of Minority Business Development
201 W Washington Ave.
Madison, WI 53707-7970
Ph: (608)266-1018
Fax: (608)264-6151
Co. E-mail: aggo.akyea@wisconsin.gov
URL: http://www.commerce.state.wi.us
Contact: Seyoum Mengasha, Consultant
Description: Provides assistance to existing and potential minority businesses in market assessment, access to credit, capital formation, and coordination of public and private resources. Also certifies minority vendors.

59771 ■ Wisconsin Department of Commerce - Women-Owned Business Enterprises
201 W Washington Ave.
Madison, WI 53707-7970
Ph: (608)267-0297
Free: 800-HELP-BUS
Co. E-mail: carol.dunn@wisconsin.gov
Contact: Carol Dunn, Ombudsman
Description: Helps women entrepreneurs start or expand their businesses. Identifies accessible sources of financing; assists in business planning, financial projections, and cash-flow statement preparations.

59772 ■ Wisconsin Minority Business Opportunity Center
1915 N Dr. Martin Luther King Jr. Dr., 213-F
Milwaukee, WI 53212
Ph: (414)372-3773
Fax: (414)372-4005
Co. E-mail: heather@wisconsinmboc.org
URL: http://www.wisconsinmboc.org
Contact: Heather N. Olson
Description: Works to expand and support minority business opportunities in Wisconsin.

FINANCING AND LOAN PROGRAMS

59773 ■ Capital Investments, Inc.
1009 W. Glen Oaks Ln., Ste. 103
Mequon, WI 53092
Ph: (262)241-0303
Fax: (262)241-8451
Co. E-mail: info@capitalinvestmentsinc.com
URL: http://www.capitalinvestmentsinc.com
Preferred Investment Size: $500,000 to $5,000,000.
Industry Preferences: Industrial and energy, computer software and services, computer hardware, other products, medical and health, consumer related, communications and media. **Geographic Preference:** U.S.

59774 ■ Lubar & Co.
700 N. Water St., Ste. 1200
Milwaukee, WI 53202
Ph: (414)291-9000
Fax: (414)291-9061
Co. E-mail: info@lubar.com
URL: http://www.lubar.com
Contact: David J. Lubar, President
Preferred Investment Size: $10,000,000 minimum.
Industry Preferences: Communications, computer hardware and software, semiconductors and other electronics, medical and health, consumer related, industrial and energy, transportation, business services, and manufacturing. **Geographic Preference:** Midwest.

59775 ■ Mason Wells Private Equity / M&I Ventures
411 E. Wisconsin Ave., Ste. 1280
Milwaukee, WI 53202
Ph: (414)727-6400
Fax: (414)727-6410
URL: http://www.masonwells.com
Contact: John Byrnes, Managing Director
Preferred Investment Size: $500,000 to $8,000,000.
Investment Policies: Start-up, seed, management buyouts, leveraged buyout, and early stage. **Industry Preferences:** Computer software, biotechnology, financial services, and business service. **Geographic Preference:** Midwest.

59776 ■ Venture Investors LLC
University Research Park
505 S. Rosa Rd., Ste. 201
Madison, WI 53719
Ph: (608)441-2700
Fax: (608)441-2727
Co. E-mail: viweb@ventureinvestors.com
URL: http://www.ventureinvesters.com
Contact: Roger Ganser, Managing Director
E-mail: roger@ventureinvestors.com
Preferred Investment Size: $50,000 to $8,000,000.
Industry Preferences: Biotechnology, medical and health, computer software and services, semiconductors and other electronics, consumer related, Internet specific, industrial and energy, communications and media, and computer hardware. **Geographic Preference:** Midwest and Wisconsin.

PROCUREMENT ASSISTANCE PROGRAMS

59777 ■ Madison Area Technical College - Business Procurement Assistance Center (BPAC)
3513 Anderson St., Ste. 108
Madison, WI 53704
Ph: (608)243-4490
Fax: (608)243-4486
Co. E-mail: bpac@matcmadison.edu
URL: http://matcmadison.edu/bpac/
Contact: Ralph Steckmam, Specialist
E-mail: steckman@matcmadison.edu
Description: Provides technical and marketing assistance to Wisconsin businesses interested in selling their products and services to the government.

59778 ■ Wisconsin Procurement Institute (WPI) - Regional PTAC
10437 Innovation Dr., Ste. 228
Milwaukee, WI 53226
Ph: (414)270-3600
Fax: (414)270-3610
Co. E-mail: ainav@wispro.org
URL: http://www.b2gconnect.org
Contact: Aina Vilumsons, Director
E-mail: josephe@wispro.org
Description: For Wisconsin companies interested in supplying their products and or services to federal, state, local agencies and prime contractors. WPI guides, trains and provides hands-on assistance to firms in developing government business and improving process and technical capabilities to access and compete in the Government marketplace.

59779 ■ Wisconsin Procurement Technical Assistance Center - American Indian Chamber of Commerce of Wisconsin - Regional PTAC
10809 W Lincoln Ave., Ste. 201
West Allis, WI 53227
Ph: (414)604-2044
Fax: (414)604-2070
Co. E-mail: craiga@aiccw.org
URL: http://www.aiccw.org
Contact: Craig Anderson, Director
E-mail: craig@aiccw.org
Description: Helps generate economic growth and wealth creation in Wisconsin Indian Country through directed service delivery to American Indian entrepreneurs.

59780 ■ Wisconsin Procurement Technical Assistance Center - Metropolitan Milwaukee Association of Commerce (MMAC) - Regional PTAC
756 N Milwaukee St., Ste. 400
Milwaukee, WI 53202
Ph: (414)287-4100
Fax: (414)271-7753
Co. E-mail: info@mmac.org
URL: http://www.mmac.org
Contact: Timothy R. Sheehy, President
Description: The Metropolitan Milwaukee Association of Commerce (MMAC) and its Council of Small Business Executives (COSBE) serve as advocates for metro Milwaukee companies to encourage business development, capital investment and job creation.

INCUBATORS/RESEARCH AND TECHNOLOGY PARKS

59781 ■ ADVOCAP, Inc. - Business Development Center
19 W 1st St.
Fond du Lac, WI 54935
Ph: (920)922-7760
Free: 800-631-7760
Fax: (920)922-7214
Co. E-mail: kathyd@advocap.org
URL: http://www.advocap.org/bd.html
Contact: Michael Bonertz, Executive Director
Description: Works to help low-income individuals become self-employed. Offers a variety of business development, marketing, and loan assistance services.

59782 ■ Madison Enterprise Center
1501 Williamson St.
Madison, WI 53703
Ph: (608)256-6565
Fax: (608)256-6561
Co. E-mail: sarah@cwd.org
URL: http://www.cwd.org/business/commercial-space/madison-enterprise-center/
Description: A small business incubator for emerging office and light industrial companies.

59783 ■ The Superior Business Center Inc.
1423 N 8th St.
Superior, WI 54880
Ph: (715)392-4749

Fax: (715)392-6131
Co. E-mail: info@sbc.com
URL: http://www.superiorbusinesscenter.com
Description: The SBC serves emerging businesses through a variety of resources including affordable office space. The Center also assists home-based businesses with telecommunications support.

LEGISLATIVE ASSISTANCE

59784 ■ Representative Jeff Mursau
State Capitol, Rm 18 N
Madison, WI 53708
Ph: (608)266-3780
Fax: (608)282-3636
Co. E-mail: rep.mursau@legis.state.wi.us

TRADE PERIODICALS

59785 ■ *Focus*
Pub: Wisconsin Taxpayers Alliance
Contact: Todd A. Berry, President
Released: 27/year. **Price:** $49, individuals; $109 three years. **Description:** Contains analysis of Wisconsin's government and policy.

PUBLICATIONS

59786 ■ *Corporate Report-Wisconsin*
PO Box 1080
Williams Bay, WI 53191
Ph: (262)245-1000
Fax: (262)245-2000
URL: http://www.crwmag.com

59787 ■ *Entrepreneurial Assistance in Wisconsin: Sources of Management and Technical Support*
201 W. Washington Ave.
Madison, WI 53707
Ph: (608)267-6876
Free: 800-HELP-BUS
Fax: (608)267-0436
URL: http://www.badger.state.wi.us/agency/commerce
Released: 1990. **Price:** $5.00. **Description:** Lists programs offering small business assistance. Includes alphabetical, geographical, and subject indexes.

59788 ■ *Going Into Business in Wisconsin: An Entrepreneur's Guide*
201 W. Washington Ave.
Madison, WI 53707
Ph: (608)267-6876
Free: 800-HELP-BUS
Fax: (608)267-0436
URL: http://www.badger.state.wi.us/agency/commerce
Released: Second editon, 1992. **Price:** Free. **Description:** Topics covered include going into business, business planning, legal forms of organization, financing, taxation/regulation/permits, marketing, finding personnel, legal assistance, accounting, location decisions, technology, international trade, and assistance for women and minority entrepreneurs. Includes worksheets and a bibliography.

59789 ■ *Smart Start your Wisconsin Business*
PSI Research
300 N. Valley Dr.
Grants Pass, OR 97526
Ph: (541)479-9464
Free: 800-228-2275
Fax: (541)476-1479
Co. E-mail: info@psi-research.com
URL: http://www.psi-research.com
Ed: Michael D. Jenkins. **Released:** Revised edition, 1992. **Price:** $29.95 (looseleaf binder); $24.95 (paper). **Description:** Part of the Successful Business Library series.

59790 ■ *Technology Resources for Business in Wisconsin*
201 W. Washington Ave.
Madison, WI 53707
Ph: (608)267-6876

Free: 800-HELP-BUS
Fax: (608)267-0436
URL: http://www.badger.state.wi.us/agency/commerce
Released: 1990. **Price:** $3.50. **Description:** Lists and describes university, public, and private resources for technology-driven firms; includes sources of assistance for research and development, technology transfer, testing, patenting, start-up, product introduction, and marketing.

59791 ■ *Venture Financing: Raising Capital in Wisconsin*
201 W. Washington Ave.
Madison, WI 53707
Ph: (608)267-6876
Fax: (608)267-0436
URL: http://www.badger.state.wi.us/agency/commerce
Released: 1990. **Price:** Free. **Description:** Topics covered include equity financing, 'mezzanine' financing, strategic partnering, government financing, debt financing, leasing, and other sources of financing.

59792 ■ *Wisconsin Financing Alternatives*
201 West Washington Ave.
Madison, WI 53707

Ph: (608)267-6876
Fax: (608)267-0436
URL: http://www.badger.state.wi.us/agency/commerce
Released: Reprinted October 1991. **Price:** $2.00. **Description:** Listing and description of programs with financing, finance labor training support, and incubator facilities for businesses in Wisconsin.

59793 ■ *Wisconsin Minority Business Resource Directory*
201 W. Washington Ave.
Madison, WI 53707
Ph: (608)266-5381
Fax: (608)267-0436
URL: http://www.badger.state.wi.us/agency/commerce
Released: Second edition. **Price:** $5.00. **Description:** Listing and description of general business assistance and financial resources for minority-owned and -run businesses in Wisconsin.

PUBLISHERS

59794 ■ **American Society for Quality Press (ASQ)**
600 N Plankinton Ave.
Milwaukee, WI 53201-3005

Ph: (414)272-8575
Free: 800-248-1946
Fax: (414)272-1734
Co. E-mail: help@asq.org
URL: http://www.asq.org
Contact: Mary Uttech, Director
E-mail: muttech@asq.org

Description: Description: Publishes technical books on quality control, ISO900, and management books on TQM, human resources, teamwork, and benchmarking. **Founded:** 1983.

59795 ■ **Guild Publishing**
931 E Main St., Ste. 9
Madison, WI 53703-2955
Ph: (608)257-2590
Free: 877-223-4600
Fax: (608)257-2690
Co. E-mail: art-info@guild.com
URL: http://www.artfulhome.com
Contact: Toni Sikes, Chief Executive Officer
E-mail: tsikes@guild.com

Description: Description: Publishes artists source books and books on contemporary art for architects and interior designers. **Founded:** 1985.

SMALL BUSINESS DEVELOPMENT CENTERS

59796 ■ Wyoming Small Business Development Center - Lead Office (WSBDC)
University of Wyoming
1000 E University Ave., Dept. 3922
Laramie, WY 82071
Ph: (307)766-3505
Free: 800-348-5194
Co. E-mail: ddw@uwyo.edu
URL: http://www.wyomingentrepreneur.biz
Contact: Diane Wolverton, Director

59797 ■ Wyoming Small Business Development Center - Region II
c/o Bruce Morse, Regional Dir.
143 S Bent St., Ste. A
Powell, WY 82435
Ph: (307)754-2139
Fax: (307)754-0368
Co. E-mail: bmorse1@uwyo.edu
Contact: Bruce Morse, Regional Director
Description: Represents and promotes the small business sector. Provides management assistance to current and prospective small business owners. Helps to improve management skills and expand the products and services of members.

59798 ■ Wyoming Small Business Development Center - Region III
c/o Leonard Holler, Regional Dir.
300 S Wolcott St., Ste. 300
Casper, WY 82601
Ph: (307)234-6683
Fax: (307)577-7014
Co. E-mail: lholler@uwyo.edu
Contact: Leonard Holler, Regional Director
Description: Represents and promotes the small business sector. Provides management assistance to current and prospective small business owners. Helps to improve management skills and expand the products and services of members.

59799 ■ Wyoming Small Business Development Center - Region IV
c/o Anya Petersen-Frey, Regional Dir.
1400 E College Dr.
Cheyenne, WY 82007-3204
Ph: (307)632-6141
Fax: (307)632-6061
Co. E-mail: apeter35@uwyo.edu
Contact: Anya Petersen-Frey, Regional Director
Description: Represents and promotes the small business sector. Provides management assistance to current and prospective small business owners. Helps to improve management skills and expand the products and services of members.

59800 ■ Wyoming Small Business Development Center - Region V
c/o Susan Jerke, Regional Dir.
2001 W Lakeway Rd., Ste. D
Gillette, WY 82718
Ph: (307)682-5232

Fax: (307)686-5792
Co. E-mail: sjerke@uwyo.edu
Contact: Susan Jerke, Regional Director
Description: Represents and promotes the small business sector. Provides management assistance to current and prospective small business owners. Helps to improve management skills and expand the products and services of members.

59801 ■ Wyoming Small Business Development Center - Region VI
c/o Margie Rowell, Regional Dir.
213 W Main St., Ste. C
Riverton, WY 82501
Ph: (307)857-1174
Fax: (307)857-0873
Co. E-mail: mrowell@uwyo.edu
Contact: Margie Rowell, Regional Director
Description: Represents and promotes the small business sector. Provides management assistance to current and prospective small business owners. Helps to improve management skills and expand the products and services of members.

SMALL BUSINESS ASSISTANCE PROGRAMS

59802 ■ Wyoming Department of Commerce - Wyoming Business Council
214 W 15th St.
Cheyenne, WY 82002-0240
Ph: (307)777-2800
Fax: (307)777-2838
Co. E-mail: info@wyomingbusiness.org
URL: http://www.wyomingbusiness.org
Contact: Robert Jenson, Chief Executive Officer
Description: Works to attract new businesses; provides technical assistance.

SCORE OFFICES

59803 ■ Casper SCORE
Co. E-mail: casper@scorewyoming.org

59804 ■ SCORE Casper
301 E 1st Ave.
Cheyenne, WY 82001
Ph: (307)632-1588
Co. E-mail: casper@scorewyoming.org
URL: http://www.scorewyoming.org
Contact: David Rippe, Chairman
Description: Provides professional guidance, mentoring services and financial assistance to maximize the success of existing and emerging small businesses.

CHAMBERS OF COMMERCE

59805 ■ Buffalo, Wyoming Chamber of Commerce
55 N Main St.
Buffalo, WY 82834
Ph: (307)684-5544

Free: 800-227-5122
Fax: (307)684-0291
Co. E-mail: info@buffalowyo.com
URL: http://www.buffalowyo.com
Contact: Angela Jarvis, Executive Director
Description: Promotes business, economic and community development in Buffalo, WY. **Founded:** 1941.

59806 ■ *Business Directory*
PO Box 550
Jackson, WY 83001-0550
Ph: (307)733-3316
Fax: (307)733-5585
Co. E-mail: info@jacksonholechamber.com
URL: http://www.jacksonholechamber.com
Contact: Tim O'Donoghue, Executive Director
Released: Periodic

59807 ■ *Business News, Business Agenda, Programs and Services*
314 S Gillette Ave.
Gillette, WY 82716
Ph: (307)682-3673
Fax: (307)682-0538
Co. E-mail: frontoffice@gillettechamber.com
URL: http://www.gillettechamber.com
Contact: Julie Simon, President
Released: Monthly

59808 ■ Campbell County Chamber of Commerce
314 S Gillette Ave.
Gillette, WY 82716
Ph: (307)682-3673
Fax: (307)682-0538
Co. E-mail: frontoffice@gillettechamber.com
URL: http://www.gillettechamber.com
Contact: Julie Simon, President
Description: Promotes business and community development in Campbell County, WY. **Founded:** 1956. **Publications:** *Business News, Business Agenda, Programs and Services* (Monthly).

59809 ■ Casper Area Chamber of Commerce (CACC)
500 N Center St.
Casper, WY 82601
Ph: (307)234-5311
Free: 866-234-5311
Fax: (307)265-2643
Co. E-mail: chamber@casperwyoming.org
URL: http://www.casperwyoming.org
Contact: Lori Becker, Executive Director
Description: Promotes economic prosperity and quality of life in Casper, WY area. **Founded:** 1903. **Publications:** *Progress* (Monthly).

59810 ■ *Chamber Chatter*
121 Brownfield Rd.
Douglas, WY 82633
Ph: (307)358-2950
Free: 877-937-4996

Fax: (307)358-2972
Co. E-mail: chamber@jackalope.org
URL: http://www.jackalope.org
Contact: Helga Bull, Executive Director
Released: Monthly **Price:** free.

59811 ■ *Chamber News*
1155 W Flaming Gorge Way
Green River, WY 82935
Ph: (307)875-5711
Free: 800-354-6743
Fax: (307)875-8993
Co. E-mail: jhartford@sweetwaterhsa.com
URL: http://www.grchamber.com
Released: Periodic

59812 ■ *Chamber News*
PO Box 550
Jackson, WY 83001-0550
Ph: (307)733-3316
Fax: (307)733-5585
Co. E-mail: info@jacksonholechamber.com
URL: http://www.jacksonholechamber.com
Contact: Tim O'Donoghue, Executive Director
Released: 8/year

59813 ■ *Chamber News*
160 N 1st St.
Lander, WY 82520
Ph: (307)332-3892
Free: 800-433-0662
Fax: (307)332-3893
Co. E-mail: info@landerchamber.org
URL: http://www.landerchamber.org
Contact: Scott Goetz, Executive Director
Released: Monthly

59814 ■ *Cheyenne Business Weekly*
One Depot Sq.
121 W 15th St., Ste. 204
Cheyenne, WY 82001
Ph: (307)638-3388
Fax: (307)778-1407
Co. E-mail: info@cheyennechamber.org
URL: http://www.cheyennechamber.org
Contact: Mr. Dale Steenbergen, President
Released: Weekly

59815 ■ *Choice Voice*
800 S 3rd St.
Laramie, WY 82070
Ph: (307)745-7339
Free: 866-876-1012
Fax: (307)745-4624
Co. E-mail: chamberofcommerce@laramie.org
URL: http://www.laramie.org
Contact: Debbie Moewes, President
Released: Monthly

59816 ■ Cody Country Chamber of Commerce (CCCC)
836 Sheridan Ave.
Cody, WY 82414
Ph: (307)587-2777
Co. E-mail: info@codychamber.org
URL: http://www.codychamber.org
Contact: Scott Baylo, Executive Director
Description: Promotes business and community development in Cody Country, WY. **Founded:** 1900.

59817 ■ Douglas Area Chamber of Commerce
121 Brownfield Rd.
Douglas, WY 82633
Ph: (307)358-2950
Free: 877-937-4996
Fax: (307)358-2972
Co. E-mail: chamber@jackalope.org
URL: http://www.jackalope.org
Contact: Helga Bull, Executive Director
Description: Promotes business and community development in the Douglas, WY area. Sponsors High Plains Country Music Competition and the Douglas Invitational Art Show. **Publications:** *Chamber Chatter* (Monthly).

59818 ■ Dubois Chamber of Commerce
PO Box 632
Dubois, WY 82513

Ph: (307)455-2556
Co. E-mail: duboiscc@detworld.com
URL: http://www.duboiswyomingchamber.org
Contact: Tammy Reed, President
Description: Promotes business and community development in Dubois, WY. Provides visitor information. Sponsors 4th of July festivities, Hometown Holidays, Cowboy Casino and 10,000 raffles. Assists local charities and organizations promote events. **Founded:** 1963. **Publications:** *Dubois Chamber News* (Quarterly).

59819 ■ *Dubois Chamber News*
PO Box 632
Dubois, WY 82513
Ph: (307)455-2556
Co. E-mail: duboiscc@detworld.com
URL: http://www.duboiswyomingchamber.org
Contact: Tammy Reed, President
Released: Quarterly

59820 ■ Evanston Chamber of Commerce
PO Box 365
Evanston, WY 82931-0365
Ph: (307)783-0370
Free: 800-328-9708
Fax: (307)789-4807
Co. E-mail: chamber@etownchamber.com
URL: http://www.etownchamber.com
Contact: David Bassett, President
Description: Promotes business and community development in Evanston, WY.

59821 ■ Glenrock Chamber of Commerce
506 W Birch St.
Glenrock, WY 82637
Ph: (307)436-5652
Fax: (307)436-5477
Co. E-mail: glenrockchamber@sdwinc.com
URL: http://www.glenrockchamber.com
Contact: Mary Kay Kindt, Executive Director
Description: Promotes business and community development in Glenrock, WY.

59822 ■ *Goshen Co. Chamber Action Update*
c/o Rhonda Schulte, Exec. Dir.
350 W 21st Ave.
Torrington, WY 82240
Ph: (307)532-3879
Fax: (307)534-2360
Co. E-mail: goshencountychamber@yahoo.com
URL: http://www.goshencountychamber.com
Contact: Martin Gubbels, President
Released: Monthly

59823 ■ Goshen County Chamber of Commerce (GCCC)
c/o Rhonda Schulte, Exec. Dir.
350 W 21st Ave.
Torrington, WY 82240
Ph: (307)532-3879
Fax: (307)534-2360
Co. E-mail: goshencountychamber@yahoo.com
URL: http://www.goshencountychamber.com
Contact: Martin Gubbels, President
Description: Promotes business and community development in Goshen County, WY. **Founded:** 1964. **Publications:** *Goshen Co. Chamber Action Update* (Monthly). **Awards:** Big Chief Award (Annual).

59824 ■ *The Grand Solution*
213 W Main St., Ste. C
Riverton, WY 82501
Ph: (307)856-4801
Free: 800-325-2732
Co. E-mail: info@rivertonchamber.org
URL: http://www.rivertonchamber.org
Contact: Ms. Anya Petersen-Frey, Executive Director
Released: Monthly

59825 ■ Greater Cheyenne Chamber of Commerce
One Depot Sq.
121 W 15th St., Ste. 204
Cheyenne, WY 82001
Ph: (307)638-3388

Fax: (307)778-1407
Co. E-mail: info@cheyennechamber.org
URL: http://www.cheyennechamber.org
Contact: Mr. Dale Steenbergen, President
Description: Promotes business and community development in the Cheyenne, WY area. **Founded:** 1907. **Publications:** *Cheyenne Business Weekly* (Weekly).

59826 ■ Green River Chamber of Commerce
1155 W Flaming Gorge Way
Green River, WY 82935
Ph: (307)875-5711
Free: 800-354-6743
Fax: (307)875-8993
Co. E-mail: jhartford@sweetwaterhsa.com
URL: http://www.grchamber.com
Description: Promotes business and community development and tourism in the Green River, WY area. **Founded:** 1921. **Publications:** *Chamber News* (Periodic). **Awards:** Volunteer Appreciation Award (Annual).

59827 ■ Greybull Area Chamber of Commerce
521 Greybull Ave.
Greybull, WY 82426
Ph: (307)765-2100
Free: 877-765-2100
Fax: (307)765-2100
Co. E-mail: chamber@greybull.com
URL: http://www.greybull.com
Description: Promotes business and community development in the Greybull, WY area.

59828 ■ *Hot Spot*
PO Box 768
Thermopolis, WY 82443
Ph: (307)864-3192
Free: 877-864-3192
Co. E-mail: thercc@rtconnect.net
URL: http://www.thermopolis.com
Contact: Kathy A. Wallingford, Executive Director
Released: Bimonthly

59829 ■ Jackson Hole Chamber of Commerce
PO Box 550
Jackson, WY 83001-0550
Ph: (307)733-3316
Fax: (307)733-5585
Co. E-mail: info@jacksonholechamber.com
URL: http://www.jacksonholechamber.com
Contact: Tim O'Donoghue, Executive Director
Description: Promotes business and community development in Jackson Hole, WY. Bestows scholarships. Sponsors Fall Arts Festival and Old West Days. **Founded:** 1946. **Publications:** *Business Directory* (Periodic); *Chamber News* (8/year).

59830 ■ Kemmerer/Diamondville Area Chamber of Commerce
800 Pine Ave.
Kemmerer, WY 83101
Ph: (307)877-9761
Free: 888-300-3413
Co. E-mail: chamber@kemmererchamber.com
URL: http://www.kemmererchamber.com
Description: Promotes business and community development in the Kemmerer, WY area. Sponsors annual flatpick guitar contest in August. **Founded:** 1980.

59831 ■ Lander Area Chamber of Commerce (LACC)
160 N 1st St.
Lander, WY 82520
Ph: (307)332-3892
Free: 800-433-0662
Fax: (307)332-3893
Co. E-mail: info@landerchamber.org
URL: http://www.landerchamber.org
Contact: Scott Goetz, Executive Director
Description: Promotes business and community development in the Lander, WY area. Sponsors committees such as Beautification, Tourism, Convention

and Visitors Bureau. **Publications:** *Chamber News* (Monthly). **Educational Activities:** Business After Hours (Monthly). **Awards:** Community Awards (Annual).

59832 ■ Laramie Area Chamber of Commerce (LACC)
800 S 3rd St.
Laramie, WY 82070
Ph: (307)745-7339
Free: 866-876-1012
Fax: (307)745-4624
Co. E-mail: chamberofcommerce@laramie.org
URL: http://www.laramie.org
Contact: Debbie Moewes, President
Description: Promotes business and community development in the Laramie, WY area. Conducts charitable activities, including a community clean up. **Founded:** 1945. **Publications:** *Choice Voice* (Monthly); *News Column* (Weekly). **Educational Activities:** Fishing Derby (Annual).

59833 ■ *Member Services Directory*
120 N 10th St.
Worland, WY 82401
Ph: (307)347-3226
Fax: (307)347-3025
Co. E-mail: wtschamber@rtconnect.net
URL: http://www.worlandchamber.com
Contact: Terry Sutherland, Executive Director
Released: Annual

59834 ■ Newcastle Area Chamber of Commerce
1323 Washington Blvd.
Newcastle, WY 82701
Ph: (307)746-2739
Free: 800-835-0157
Fax: (307)746-2739
Co. E-mail: chamber@newcastlewyo.com
URL: http://newcastlewyo.com/newc
Contact: Norman Shelton, Executive Director
Description: Seeks to be a collective voice representing the business interests of Northeastern Wyoming, the Western gateway to the Black Hills. **Telecommunication Services:** nacoc@rtconnect.net.

59835 ■ *News Column*
800 S 3rd St.
Laramie, WY 82070
Ph: (307)745-7339
Free: 866-876-1012
Fax: (307)745-4624
Co. E-mail: chamberofcommerce@laramie.org
URL: http://www.laramie.org
Contact: Debbie Moewes, President
Released: Weekly

59836 ■ Niobrara Chamber of Commerce
PO Box 1367
Lusk, WY 82225
Ph: (307)334-2950
Free: 800-223-5875
Co. E-mail: lusk@vistabeam.com
URL: http://www.luskwyoming.com
Description: Promotes business and community development in Lusk, WY.

59837 ■ Platte County Chamber of Commerce (PCCC)
65 16th St.
Wheatland, WY 82201
Ph: (307)322-2322
Fax: (307)322-3419
Co. E-mail: info@plattechamber.com
URL: http://www.plattechamber.com
Contact: Cheryl Deuel, Executive Director
Description: Promotes business and community development in Platte County, WY. Sponsors annual Bike Race, Community Fest, agricultural appreciation banquet, pancake breakfast, and Chugwater Chili Cook-off. **Founded:** 1968.

59838 ■ Powell Valley Chamber of Commerce (PVCC)
111 S Day St.
Powell, WY 82435-1258
Ph: (307)754-3494

Free: 800-325-4278
Fax: (307)754-3483
Co. E-mail: info@powellchamber.org
URL: http://powellchamber.org/content
Contact: Kim Dillivan, Executive Director
Description: Promotes business and community development in Powell, WY. Sponsors festivals. **Founded:** 1909.

59839 ■ *Progress*
500 N Center St.
Casper, WY 82601
Ph: (307)234-5311
Free: 866-234-5311
Fax: (307)265-2643
Co. E-mail: chamber@casperwyoming.org
URL: http://www.casperwyoming.org
Contact: Lori Becker, Executive Director
Released: Monthly

59840 ■ Rawlins-Carbon County Chamber of Commerce
519 W Cedar St.
Rawlins, WY 82301-1331
Ph: (307)324-4111
Fax: (307)324-5078
Co. E-mail: rawlinschamber@qwestoffice.net
URL: http://www.rawlinschamberofcommerce.org
Contact: Erin Essary, Director
Description: Promotes business and community development in Carbon County, WY. Sponsors annual Carbon County Business Expo and performing arts events. **Founded:** 1949.

59841 ■ Riverton Chamber of Commerce (RCC)
213 W Main St., Ste. C
Riverton, WY 82501
Ph: (307)856-4801
Free: 800-325-2732
Co. E-mail: info@rivertonchamber.org
URL: http://www.rivertonchamber.org
Contact: Ms. Anya Petersen-Frey, Executive Director
Description: Promotes business and community development in the Riverton, WY area. **Founded:** 1941. **Publications:** *The Grand Solution* (Monthly).

59842 ■ Rock Springs Chamber of Commerce (RSCC)
1897 Dewar Dr.
Rock Springs, WY 82902-0398
Ph: (307)362-3771
Free: 800-46-DUNES
Fax: (307)362-3838
Co. E-mail: rschamber@sweetwaterhsa.com
URL: http://www.rockspringswyoming.net
Contact: Dave Hanks, Chief Executive Officer
Description: Promotes business and community development in Rock Springs, WY. **Founded:** 1938.

59843 ■ Saratoga/Platte Valley Chamber of Commerce (SPVCC)
210 W Elm St.
Saratoga, WY 82331
Ph: (307)326-8855
Fax: (307)326-8850
Co. E-mail: info@saratogachamber.info
URL: http://www.saratogachamber.info
Contact: Russell Waldner, President
Description: Promotes business and community development and tourism in the upper Platte River area of Wyoming. Sponsors ice fishing derby; conducts competitions.

59844 ■ Sheridan County Chamber of Commerce
PO Box 707
Sheridan, WY 82801-0707
Ph: (307)672-2485
Free: 800-453-3650
Fax: (307)672-7321
Co. E-mail: info@sheridanwyomingchamber.org
URL: http://www.sheridanwyomingchamber.org
Contact: Janelle Anderson, Executive Director
Description: Promotes business and community development in Sheridan County, WY. **Founded:** 1913.

59845 ■ Star Valley Chamber of Commerce (SVCCOM)
PO Box 190
Afton, WY 83110
Ph: (307)885-2759
Free: 800-426-8833
Fax: (307)885-2758
Co. E-mail: info@starvalleychamber.com
URL: http://www.starvalleychamber.com
Contact: Melanie S. Wilkes, Executive Director
Description: Promotes business and community development in the Star Valley, WY area. **Founded:** 1988.

59846 ■ Sublette County Chamber of Commerce
PO Box 176
Pinedale, WY 82941
Ph: (307)367-2242
Free: 888-285-7282
Fax: (307)367-2248
Co. E-mail: membership@sublettechamber.com
URL: http://www.sublettechamber.com
Contact: Terrie Swift, Executive Director
Description: Promotes business and community development in the Pinedale, WY area. **Founded:** 1960.

59847 ■ Sundance Area Chamber of Commerce (SACC)
PO Box 1004
Sundance, WY 82729
Ph: (307)283-1000
Free: 800-477-9340
Fax: (307)437-6689
Co. E-mail: chamber@sundancewyoming.com
URL: http://www.sundancewyoming.com
Contact: Robyn Finch, President
Description: Promotes business and community development in the Sundance, WY area. Conducts annual appreciation barbecue. **Founded:** 1929.

59848 ■ Thermopolis - Hot Springs Chamber of Commerce
PO Box 768
Thermopolis, WY 82443
Ph: (307)864-3192
Free: 877-864-3192
Co. E-mail: thercc@rtconnect.net
URL: http://www.thermopolis.com
Contact: Kathy A. Wallingford, Executive Director
Description: Promotes business and community development in the Thermopolis, WY area. Seeks to attract tourists. Sponsors Fishing Has No Boundaries festival for the handicapped. Conducts the annual Gift of the Water Pageant, commemorating treaty with the Indians. **Founded:** 1919. **Publications:** *Hot Spot* (Bimonthly).

59849 ■ Worland Area Chamber of Commerce
120 N 10th St.
Worland, WY 82401
Ph: (307)347-3226
Fax: (307)347-3025
Co. E-mail: wtschamber@rtconnect.net
URL: http://www.worlandchamber.com
Contact: Terry Sutherland, Executive Director
Description: Promotes business and community development in the Worland, WY area. **Founded:** 1947. **Publications:** *Member Services Directory* (Annual); *Worland Business Advocate* (Monthly).

59850 ■ *Worland Business Advocate*
120 N 10th St.
Worland, WY 82401
Ph: (307)347-3226
Fax: (307)347-3025
Co. E-mail: wtschamber@rtconnect.net
URL: http://www.worlandchamber.com
Contact: Terry Sutherland, Executive Director
Released: Monthly

PROCUREMENT ASSISTANCE PROGRAMS

59851 ■ Wyoming Administration and Information Department - Procurement Services
Herschler Bldg.
122 W 25th St.
Cheyenne, WY 82002
Ph: (307)777-7253
Fax: (307)757-5852
Co. E-mail: mlande@state.wy.us
URL: http://ai.state.wy.us/generalservices/Procurement/index.asp
Contact: Mac Landen, Director

59852 ■ Wyoming Procurement Technical Assistance Center - Government Resources and Opportunities for Business (GRO-Biz) -

Northern Region
245 Broadway St., Ste. 7
Sheridan, WY 82801
Ph: (307)672-3700
Co. E-mail: grobiz@actacces.net
URL: http://www.gro-biz.com
Contact: Justin Hansen, Counselor
Description: Helping companies complete the necessary registrations so that they can compete for bids with federal, state and local entities.

59853 ■ Wyoming Procurement Technical Assistance Center - University of Wyoming - Southwest Region
1400 Dewar Dr., Ste. 208C
Rock Springs, WY 82901
Ph: (307)352-6894
Contact: Mark Atkinson, Director
E-mail: stille@wyoming.com
Description: Generates employment and enhances Wyoming's economy by helping businesses market their goods and services to all branches of the government, and to implement E-commerce in their business to improve their global competitiveness. Formerly Government Resources and Opportunities for Business (GRO-Biz).

PUBLICATIONS

59854 ■ *Guide to Business Permitting and Licensing in Wyoming*
Barrett Bldg.
6101 N. Yellowstone Rd., 4th Fl.
Cheyenne, WY 82002
Ph: (307)777-7696
Fax: (307)777-6005

Ed: Paul Howard. **Description:** Includes general and specific permit requirements, permits listed by business type, a listing of state agencies administering professional licenses, a checklist and worksheet, and two appendices.

SMALL BUSINESS DEVELOPMENT CENTERS

59855 ■ Pacific Islands Small Business Development Center Network (PISBDCN)
c/o Mr. Casey Jeszenka, Network Dir.
University of Guam
UOG Station
Mangilao, GU 96923
Ph: (671)735-2590
Fax: (671)734-2002
Co. E-mail: casey@pacificsbdc.com
URL: http://www.pacificsbdc.com
Contact: Mr. Casey Jeszenka, Director
Description: Works to support the growth and economic development of the U.S.-affiliated Pacific Islands in the Western Pacific region by providing high quality, confidential counseling and training to existing and prospective small businesses. **Founded:** 1995.

CHAMBERS OF COMMERCE

59856 ■ *Directory of Members*
Ada Plaza Center
Hagatna, GU 96910
Ph: (671)472-6311
Fax: (671)472-6202
Co. E-mail: david.john@ascpac.com
URL: http://www.guamchamber.com.gu
Contact: Kaleo S. Moylan, Chairman
Released: Annual **Price:** $10, /year.

59857 ■ Guam Chamber of Commerce
Ada Plaza Center
Hagatna, GU 96910
Ph: (671)472-6311
Fax: (671)472-6202
Co. E-mail: david.john@ascpac.com
URL: http://www.guamchamber.com.gu
Contact: Kaleo S. Moylan, Chairman
Description: Businesses and trade organizations. Promotes increased international trade and tourism. Gathers and disseminates information; conducts promotional activities; represents members' interests. **Founded:** 1924. **Publications:** *Directory of Members* (Annual); *President's Report* (Monthly); *Small Business Focus* (Quarterly); *Guam Chamber of Commerce--Directory of Members*; *The President's Report* (Monthly). **Educational Activities:** Guam Chamber of Commerce Meeting (Annual). **Awards:** Commerce Scholarship Award (Annual); Small Business Awards (Annual).

59858 ■ *President's Report*
Ada Plaza Center
Hagatna, GU 96910
Ph: (671)472-6311
Fax: (671)472-6202
Co. E-mail: david.john@ascpac.com
URL: http://www.guamchamber.com.gu
Contact: Kaleo S. Moylan, Chairman
Released: Monthly **Price:** $10, for members.

59859 ■ *Small Business Focus*
Ada Plaza Center
Hagatna, GU 96910
Ph: (671)472-6311
Fax: (671)472-6202
Co. E-mail: david.john@ascpac.com
URL: http://www.guamchamber.com.gu
Contact: Kaleo S. Moylan, Chairman
Released: Quarterly

CHAMBERS OF COMMERCE

59860 ■ *Camara En Accion*
PO Box 9024033
San Juan, PR 00902-4033
Ph: (787)721-6060
Fax: (787)723-1891
Co. E-mail: camarapr@camarapr.net
URL: http://camarapr.org
Contact: Edgardo Bigas Valladares, Executive Vice
 President
Released: Monthly

59861 ■ *Comercio y Produccion*
PO Box 9024033
San Juan, PR 00902-4033
Ph: (787)721-6060
Fax: (787)723-1891
Co. E-mail: camarapr@camarapr.net
URL: http://camarapr.org
Contact: Edgardo Bigas Valladares, Executive Vice
 President
Released: Bimonthly

59862 ■ *Maritime Register*
PO Box 9024033
San Juan, PR 00902-4033
Ph: (787)721-6060
Fax: (787)723-1891
Co. E-mail: camarapr@camarapr.net
URL: http://camarapr.org
Contact: Edgardo Bigas Valladares, Executive Vice
 President
Released: Monthly

**59863 ■ Puerto Rico Chamber of Commerce
(PRCC)**
PO Box 9024033
San Juan, PR 00902-4033
Ph: (787)721-6060

Fax: (787)723-1891
Co. E-mail: camarapr@camarapr.net
URL: http://camarapr.org
Contact: Edgardo Bigas Valladares, Executive Vice
 President
Description: Promotes business and community
development in Puerto Rico. Sponsors trade fairs,
exhibitions, seminars, and commercial missions.
Conducts lobbying. **Founded:** 1913. **Publications:**
Camara En Accion (Monthly); *Comercio y Produccion*
(Bimonthly); *Maritime Register* (Monthly).

MINORITY BUSINESS ASSISTANCE PROGRAMS

**59864 ■ Ponce Minority Business
Development Center**
M. L. Prats & Associates, Inc.
Edificio El Pardo, 19 Salud St.
Ponce, PR
Ph: (787)840-8100
Fax: (787)840-8115

**59865 ■ Puerto Rico Minority Business
Enterprise Center**
PO Box 363631
San Juan, PR 00936-3631
Ph: (787)753-8484
Fax: (787)753-0855
Co. E-mail: mbecsj@mbecpr.com
URL: http://mbecpr.com
Contact: Teresa Berrios, Director

FINANCING AND LOAN PROGRAMS

59866 ■ Advent-Morro Equity Partners
Banco Popular Bldg.
206 Tetuan St., Ste. 903
Old San Juan, PR 00902

Ph: (787)725-5285
Fax: (787)721-1735
Co. E-mail: info@adventmorro.com
URL: http://www.adventmorro.com
Contact: Cyril Meduna, President
E-mail: cmeduna@adventmorro.com
Preferred Investment Size: $2,500,000 to
$7,500,000. **Industry Preferences:** Communica-
tions, computer hardware and software, Internet
specific, medical and health, consumer related,
financial services, business service, and manufactur-
ing. **Geographic Preference:** Puerto Rico.

PROCUREMENT ASSISTANCE PROGRAMS

**59867 ■ Puerto Rico Procurement Technical
Assistance Center - Commonwealth of Puerto
Rico**
PO Box 362350
San Juan, PR 00936-2350
Ph: (787)753-4747
Fax: (787)751-6239
Co. E-mail: pacevedo@pridco.com
URL: http://www.ptacpr.com
Contact: Pedro Acevedo, Program Manager

LEGISLATIVE ASSISTANCE

**59868 ■ Puerto Rico House Standing
Committee on Industry and Commerce**
PO Box 2228
San Juan, PR
Ph: (787)722-0704
Fax: (787)722-1567
Co. E-mail: info@camaraderepresentantes.org
URL: http://www.camaraderepresentantes.org/

SMALL BUSINESS DEVELOPMENT CENTERS

59869 ■ University of the Virgin Islands Small Business Development Center
University of the Virgin Islands
8000 Nisky Center, Ste. 720
Charlotte Amalie, VI 00802-5804
Ph: (340)776-3206
Fax: (340)775-3756
Co. E-mail: ldottin@uvi.edu
URL: http://sbdcvi.org
Contact: Leonor Dottin, Director
Description: Promotes a more efficient and effective small business sector. Provides assistance to the management of existing and emerging small businesses. Helps to survive and expand their products and services. Gives resources to learn and improve management skills, opportunity to gain a broader perspective of their markets and new technologies and to access more timely information. **Founded:** 1985.

59870 ■ University of the Virgin Islands Small Business Development Center - St. Croix
Sunshine Mall, Ste. 104
Frederiksted, VI 00840
Ph: (340)692-5270
Fax: (340)692-5629
Co. E-mail: kjones2@uvi.edu
URL: http://sbdcvi.org
Contact: Karen Jones, Director
Description: Represents and promotes the small business sector. Provides management assistance to current and prospective small business owners. Helps to improve management skills and expand the products and services of members.

59871 ■ University of the Virgin Islands Small Business Development Center - St. Thomas/St. John
8000 Nisky Ctr., Ste. 720
St. Thomas, VI 00802
Ph: (340)776-3206
Fax: (340)775-3756
Co. E-mail: ldottin@uvi.edu
URL: http://sbdcvi.org
Contact: Leonor Dottin, Director
Description: Represents and promotes the small business sector. Provides management assistance to current and prospective small business owners. Helps to improve management skills and expand the products and services of members.

CHAMBERS OF COMMERCE

59872 ■ St. Thomas - St. John Chamber of Commerce (STSJCC)
PO Box 324
Charlotte Amalie, VI 00804
Ph: (340)776-0100
Fax: (340)776-0588
URL: http://www.usvichamber.com

Description: Promotes business and community development in the St. Thomas and St. John, VI area.

LEGISLATIVE ASSISTANCE

59873 ■ Legislature Of the Virgin Islands - Virgin Islands Senate Standing Committee on Economic Development Center
1 Lagoon St. Complex
Frederiksted
St. Croix, VI 00840
Ph: (340)773-2424
URL: http://www.legvi.org/

BETTER BUSINESS BUREAUS

59874 ■ Better Business Bureau Central and Northern Alberta
No. 888 Capital Pl.
9707-110 St.
Edmonton, AB, Canada T5K 2L9
Ph: (780)482-2341
Free: 800-232-7298
Fax: (780)482-1150
Co. E-mail: info@edmontonbbb.org
URL: http://www.edmontonbbb.org

59875 ■ Better Business Bureau of Southern Alberta
7330 Fisher St., SE, Ste. 350
Calgary, AB, Canada T2H 2H8
Ph: (403)531-8780
Fax: (403)640-2514
Co. E-mail: info@betterbusinessbureau.ca
URL: http://www.betterbusinessbureau.ca

PUBLISHERS

59876 ■ Platypus Publisher
2323E 3rd Ave. NW
Calgary, AB, Canada T2N 0K9
Ph: (403)283-0498
Fax: (403)270-3023
Co. E-mail: platypus@cadvision.com
Contact: Nattalia Lea, President
E-mail: nattalia@shaw.ca
Description: Description: Publishes how-to on entrepreneurs and small business for individuals. Offers T-shirts and cartoons. Does not accept unsolicited manuscripts. Reaches market through commission representatives, One-On-One, and Temeron Books. **Founded:** 1996.

59877 ■ Unlimited Learning Publications
123-28342 Township Rd., Ste. 384
Red Deer County, AB, Canada T4S 2B6
Ph: (403)347-0008
Free: 888-535-5059
Fax: (403)343-6688
Co. E-mail: dunning1@telusplanet.net
Contact: Donna Dunning, President
Description: Description: Publishes books on learning, career development, and work performance. Does not accept unsolicited manuscripts. Reaches market through distributors. **Founded:** 1992.

59878 ■ Visions International Publishing—VIP Books
10518-68 Ave.
Edmonton, AB, Canada T6H 2B1
Ph: (780)434-9202
Free: 800-661-3649
Fax: (780)436-1798
Co. E-mail: vip-books@telus.net
URL: http://www.thejoyofnotworking.com
Contact: Ernie J. Zelinski, President
E-mail: ez-books@telus.net
Description: Description: Publishes on personal growth in business. Reaches market through direct mail and Sandhill Book Marketing in Canada and Ten Speed Press in the U.S. **Founded:** 1989.

59879 ■ Word Engines Press Inc.
2125 Summerfield Blvd. SE
Airdrie, AB, Canada T4B 1X2
Ph: (403)630-6422
Free: 866-467-4550
Fax: (403)912-0199
Co. E-mail: abbottr@managersguide.com
URL: http://www.managersguide.com
Contact: Robert F. Abbott, President
E-mail: abbottr@managersguide.com
Description: Description: Publishes books for managers and professionals. Does not accept unsolicited manuscripts. Reaches market through direct mail and their website. **Founded:** 1998.

BETTER BUSINESS BUREAUS

59880 ■ Better Business Bureau of Mainland British Columbia
788 Beatty St., Ste. 404
Vancouver, BC, Canada V68 2M1
Ph: (604)682-2711
Fax: (604)681-1544
Co. E-mail: bbbmail@bbbvan.org
URL: http://www.bbbvan.org

59881 ■ Better Business Bureau of Vancouver Island
No. 220-1175 Cook St.
Victoria, BC, Canada V8V 4A1
Ph: (250)386-6348
Free: 877-826-4222
Fax: (250)386-2367
Co. E-mail: info@bbbvanisland.org
URL: http://www.bbbvanisland.org

FINANCING AND LOAN PROGRAMS

59882 ■ Discovery Capital
1285 West Pender St., Ste, 570
Vancouver, BC, Canada V6E 4B1
Ph: (604)683-3000
Fax: (604)662-3457
Co. E-mail: info@discoverycapital.com
URL: http://www.discoverycapital.com
Contact: John McEwen, Chief Executive Officer
Industry Preferences: Communications and media, Internet specific, health and life sciences. **Geographic Preference:** British Columbia and Canada.

59883 ■ Greenstone Venture Partners
1111 West Hastings St., Ste. 777
Vancouver, BC, Canada V6E 2J3
Ph: (604)717-1977
Fax: (604)717-1976
URL: http://www.greenstonevc.com
Contact: Brent Holliday, Partner
E-mail: bh@greenstonevc.com
Preferred Investment Size: $300,000 to $300,000,000. **Industry Preferences:** Communications and media, computer software, Internet specific,

semiconductors and other electronics. **Geographic Preference:** Northern California, Northwest U.S., and Western Canada.

59884 ■ GrowthWorks
2600-1055 W Georgia St., Royal Ctr.
Vancouver, BC, Canada V6E 3R5
Ph: (604)633-1418
Free: 800-268-8244
Fax: (604)688-9039
Co. E-mail: info@growthworks.ca
URL: http://www.growthworks.ca
Contact: David Levi, President
Founded: 1999. **Preferred Investment Size:** $100,000 to $5,000,000. **Industry Preferences:** Communications and media, Internet specific, computer related, semiconductors and other electronics, biotechnology, medical and health, consumer related, industrial and energy, transportation, manufacturing, agriculture, forestry and fishing, and environment. **Geographic Preference:** Canada.

59885 ■ Ventures West Management, Inc.
999 West Hastings St., Ste. 400
Vancouver, BC, Canada V6C 2W2
Ph: (604)688-9495
Fax: (604)687-2145
URL: http://www.ventureswest.com
Contact: Ted Anderson, Partner

Preferred Investment Size: $1,000,000 minimum to $9,999,000. **Industry Preferences:** Communications and media, computer software and services, computer hardware, biotechnology, Internet specific, medical and health, semiconductors and other electronics, industrial and energy related. **Geographic Preference:** Canada.

PUBLISHERS

59886 ■ J.A. Hall Publications—Hall Publications
2401-9304 Salish Ct.
Burnaby, BC, Canada V3J 7C5
Ph: (604)738-9688
Free: 888-993-6133

Fax: (604)738-9425
Co. E-mail: info@hallpublications.com
URL: http://www.hallpublications.com
Contact: Joan Ruddell, Manager
E-mail: joan.ruddell@hallpublications.com
Description: Description: Publishes health science books and manuals. Does not accept unsolicited manuscripts. Reaches market through direct mail, distributors and their website. **Founded:** 1997.

59887 ■ Self-Counsel Press Ltd.
1481 Charlotte Rd.
North Vancouver, BC, Canada V7J 1H1
Ph: (604)986-3366
Free: 800-663-3007
Fax: (604)986-3947
Co. E-mail: service@self-counsel.com
URL: http://www.self-counsel.com
Contact: Roger Kettyls, Manager
E-mail: rkettyls@self-counsel.com
Description: Description: Publishes legal, business, and reference books. **Founded:** 1971.

59888 ■ Sound Current Music & Books
RR 1
Bowen Island, BC, Canada V0N 1G0
Ph: (604)222-0060
Free: 877-777-6863
Fax: (604)947-0975
Co. E-mail: soundcurrent@sprint.ca
URL: http://www.soundcurrent.homestead.com
Contact: Deborah van Dyke, President
E-mail: soundcurrent@sprint.ca
Description: Description: Publishes sound healing resources in print and audio. Does not accept unsolicited manuscripts. Reaches market through direct mail, wholesalers and distributors. **Founded:** 1998.

59889 ■ Turnagain Enterprises Ltd.
1401 W Broadway, Ste. 601
Vancouver, BC, Canada V6H 1H6
Ph: (604)757-1312
Fax: (604)737-1317
Co. E-mail: info@albertgivton.com
URL: http://www.albertgivton.com
Contact: Shannon Hallett, Office Manager
Description: Description: Publishes book on wines. Does not accept unsolicited manuscripts. Reaches market through direct mail, distributors, print ads, and the Web. **Founded:** 1974.

SMALL BUSINESS ASSISTANCE PROGRAMS

59890 ■ **Canada Manitoba Business Service Centre**
240 Graham Ave., Rm. 250
Winnipeg, MB, Canada R3C 0J7
Ph: (204)984-2272
Free: 800-665-2019
Fax: (204)983-3852
Co. E-mail: manitoba@canadabusiness.ca
URL: http://www.canadabusiness.ca/manitoba
Description: Offers assistance, training, and expertise to business and entrepreneurs. Offers a variety of programs.

59891 ■ **Canada Manitoba Business Service Centre - Business Start Program**
240 Graham Ave., Rm. 250
Winnipeg, MB, Canada R3C 0J7
Ph: (204)984-2272
Free: 800-665-2019
Fax: (204)983-3852
Co. E-mail: manitoba@canadabusiness.ca
URL: http://www.canadabusiness.ca/manitoba
Description: Offers assistance, training, and expertise to business and entrepreneurs. Offers a variety of programs.

59892 ■ **Canada Manitoba Business Service Centre - Manitoba Marketing Network, Inc.**
240 Graham Ave., Rm. 250
Winnipeg, MB, Canada R3C 0J7
Ph: (204)945-1230
Free: 800-665-2019
Fax: (204)983-3852
Co. E-mail: info@manitobamarketingnetwork.ca
URL: http://www.manitobamarketingnetwork.ca
Contact: Gord Kraemer, Executive Director
Description: Offers assistance, training, and expertise to business and entrepreneurs. Offers a variety of programs.

59893 ■ **Canada Manitoba Business Service Centre - One-on-One Business Counseling**
240 Graham Ave., Rm. 250
Winnipeg, MB, Canada R3C 0J7
Ph: (204)984-2272
Free: 800-665-2019
Fax: (204)983-3852
Co. E-mail: manitoba@canadabusiness.ca
URL: http://www.canadabusiness.ca/manitoba
Description: Offers assistance, training, and expertise to business and entrepreneurs. Offers a variety of programs.

59894 ■ **Canada Manitoba Business Service Centre - Reference Library**
240 Graham Ave., Rm. 250
Winnipeg, MB, Canada R3C 0J7
Ph: (204)984-2272
Free: 800-665-2019

Fax: (204)983-3852
Co. E-mail: manitoba@canadabusiness.ca
URL: http://www.canadabusiness.ca/manitoba
Description: Offers assistance, training, and expertise to business and entrepreneurs along with an on-line catalog. Offers a variety of programs.

59895 ■ **Canada/Manitoba Business Services Centre - Importing/Exporting**
240 Graham Ave., Rm. 250
Winnipeg, MB, Canada R3C 0J7
Ph: (204)984-2272
Free: 800-665-2019
Fax: (204)983-3852
Co. E-mail: manitoba@canadabusiness.ca
URL: http://www.canadabusiness.ca/manitoba
Description: Provides information on import/export permits.

59896 ■ **Industry Economic Development and Mines - Technology Commercialization Program**
259 Portage Ave., Rm. 1040
Winnipeg, MB, Canada R3B 2A9
Ph: (204)945-2432
Fax: (204)945-1193
Co. E-mail: amy.thiessen@gov.mb.ca
URL: http://www.canadabusiness.ca/manitoba
Description: Negotiates individual agreements with private sector firms whereby, in return for certain provincial incentives, a firm will establish new operations or expand existing operations in Manitoba, undertaking specific capital investment as well as creating long-term jobs.

59897 ■ **Industry Economic Development - Western Regional Office**
131 9th St., Rm. 107
Brandon, MB, Canada R7A 6C2
Ph: (204)726-6250
Fax: (204)726-6403
Co. E-mail: keglemie@gov.mb.ca
URL: http://www.gov.mb.ca/iedm/
Description: Provides program assistance to small businesses.

59898 ■ **Manitoba Intergovernmental Affairs and Trade - Community Economic Development Branch - Neighbourhoods Alive!**
800 Portage Ave., 6th Fl.
Winnipeg, MB, Canada R3G 0N4
Ph: (204)945-3379
Free: 866-479-6155
Fax: (204)945-5059
Co. E-mail: nalive@gov.mb.ca
URL: http://www.gov.mb.ca/ia
Description: Supports local businesses and workers in creating employment and ownership opportunities.

59899 ■ **Manitoba Intergovernmental Affairs and Trade - Rural Economic Development Initiative (REDI)**
800 Portage Ave., 6th Fl.
Winnipeg, MB, Canada R3G 0N4
Ph: (204)945-2157

Fax: (204)945-5059
URL: http://www.gov.mb.ca/agriculture
Description: Offers consulting to owners/managers of small and medium-sized Manitoba businesses in the areas of marketing, accounting, and production.

59900 ■ **Manitoba Tax Assistance Office**
809-386 Broadway
Winnipeg, MB, Canada R3C 3R6
Ph: (204)948-2115
Fax: (204)948-2263
Co. E-mail: tao@gov.mb.ca
URL: http://www.gov.mb.ca/finance/tao
Description: Administers the Small Business Tax Reduction program.

BETTER BUSINESS BUREAUS

59901 ■ **Better Business Bureau of Manitoba**
1030B Empress St.
Winnipeg, MB, Canada R3G 3H4
Ph: (204)989-9010
Free: 800-385-3074
Fax: (204)989-9016
Co. E-mail: bbbinquiries@bbbmanitoba.ca
URL: http://www.bbbmanitoba.ca

MINORITY BUSINESS ASSISTANCE PROGRAMS

59902 ■ **Aboriginal Youth Mean Business!**
Partners for Careers
510 Selkirk Ave.
Winnipeg, MB, Canada R2W 2M7
Ph: (204)945-0447
Fax: (204)948-2714
Co. E-mail: rhewson@gov.mb.ca
URL: http://www.aymb.ca
Contact: Roberta Hewson, Executive Director
Description: Encourages and supports Aboriginal youth in starting or expanding businesses.

59903 ■ **Manitoba Industry, Trade and Tourism - Canada Manitoba Business Service Centre - Women's Entrepreneurial Programs**
240 Graham Ave., 2nd Fl. Rm. 250
Winnipeg, MB, Canada R3C 4B3
Ph: (204)984-2272
Fax: (204)983-3852
Co. E-mail: manitoba@cbsc.ic.gc.ca
URL: http://www.gov.mb.ca/business/
Contact: Shannon Coughlin, Manager
Description: Promotes entrepreneurship as an economic alternative for women. Liaison is provided between women business owners and provincial programs and services. Business information, seminars, and counseling are also provided to individuals and community organizations.

59904 ■ **Women's Enterprise Centre of Manitoba**
100-207 Donald St.
Winnipeg, MB, Canada R3C 1M5
Ph: (204)988-1860

Fax: (204)988-1871
Co. E-mail: wecinfo@wecm.ca
URL: http://www.wecm.ca
Contact: Sandra Altner, Chief Executive Officer
Description: Aids women in Manitoba with starting or expanding businesses.

PUBLISHERS

59905 ■ Gateway Publishing Company Ltd. (Winnipeg, Manitoba)
385 DeBaets St.
Winnipeg, MB, Canada R2J 4J8
Ph: (204)222-4294

Free: 800-665-4878
Fax: (204)224-4410
Co. E-mail: cookbooks@gatebook.com
URL: http://www.gatebook.com
Contact: Andrew's Trenton, Editor
Description: Description: Publishes books about child safety. Also publishes cookbooks. **Founded:** 1965.

SMALL BUSINESS ASSISTANCE PROGRAMS

59906 ■ Business New Brunswick - Finance and Administration
Centennial Bldg., Rm. 371, 3rd Fl.
Fredericton, NB, Canada E3B 5H1
Ph: (506)453-2451
Free: 800-561-0123

Fax: (506)457-4989
URL: http://www.gnb.ca/0024

INCUBATORS/RESEARCH AND TECHNOLOGY PARKS

59907 ■ Enterprise UNB
2 Garland Ct.
Fredericton, NB, Canada E3B 6C2

Ph: (506)453-4500
Fax: (506)453-3541
Co. E-mail: enterprise@unb.ca
URL: http://www.unb.ca/welcome/maps/fredericton/
show.php?id=27

Description: Jointly sponsored by the University of New Brunswick and the Research and Productivity Council, this incubator supports emerging technology firms.

BETTER BUSINESS BUREAUS

59908 ■ **Better Business Bureau of Newfoundland and Labrador**
360 Topsail Rd., Ste. 301
Saint John's, NL, Canada A1E 2B6
Ph: (709)364-2222
Free: 877-663-2363
Fax: (709)364-2255
Co. E-mail: info@bbbnl.org
URL: http://www.bbbnl.org
Publications: *Better Business Bureau of Newfoundland and Labrador--Directory and Consumer Guide* (Annual).

SMALL BUSINESS ASSISTANCE PROGRAMS

59909 ■ Nova Scotia Business, Inc. - Business Services Center
1800 Argyle St., Ste. 701
Halifax, NS, Canada B3J 3E4
Ph: (902)424-6650
Free: 800-668-1010
Fax: (902)424-5739
Co. E-mail: nsbi@gov.ns.ca
URL: http://www.novascotiabusiness.com/
Contact: Craig Stanfield, Director
Description: Provides counseling to Nova Scotia businesses on such areas as start-up, finance, management, marketing, and technical assessment to enhance overall effectiveness and growth. Services include review of business plans, financial statements, and projections.

59910 ■ Nova Scotia Economic Development
1660 Hollis St., Ste. 600
Halifax, NS, Canada B3J 1V7
Ph: (902)424-0377
Free: 800-565-2009
Fax: (902)424-7008
Co. E-mail: comm@gov.ns.ca
URL: http://www.gov.ns.ca/econ/
Contact: Percy Paris, Minister

BETTER BUSINESS BUREAUS

59911 ■ Better Business Bureau of the Maritime Provinces Inc.
1888 Brunswick St., Ste. 805
Halifax, NS, Canada B3J 3J8
Ph: (902)422-6581
Fax: (902)429-6457
Co. E-mail: bbbmp@bbbmp.ca
URL: http://www.bbbmp.ca

FINANCING AND LOAN PROGRAMS

59912 ■ ACF Equity Atlantic, Inc.
Purdy's Wharf Tower II, Ste. 210
Halifax, NS, Canada B3J 3R7
Ph: (902)492-5164
Fax: (902)421-1808
URL: http://www.acf.ca
Preferred Investment Size: $250,000 to $3,000,000.
Industry Preferences: Communications and media, computer hardware and software, Internet specific, semiconductors and other electronics, biotechnology, medical and health, consumer related, industrial and energy related, agriculture, forestry and fishing. **Geographic Preference:** Canada.

INCUBATORS/RESEARCH AND TECHNOLOGY PARKS

59913 ■ Agritech Park Inc.
90 Research Dr.
Bible Hill, NS, Canada B6L 2R2
Ph: (902)893-4145
Fax: (902)896-7276
Co. E-mail: ksanderson@nsac.ca
URL: http://www.agritechpark.com
Contact: Lauri K. Sanderson, Director
Description: This incubator assists emerging firms in the agriculture and biotechnology industries.

PUBLISHERS

59914 ■ Time-Use Research Program (TURP)
St. Mary's University
5670 Spring Garden Rd., Ste. 601
Halifax, NS, Canada B3H 3C3
Ph: (902)420-5676
Fax: (902)420-5129
Co. E-mail: timeuse@stmarys.ca
URL: http://www.stmarys.ca/partners/turp/main.html
Contact: Dr. Andrew S. Harvey, Director
E-mail: andrew.harvey@stmarys.ca
Description: Description: Publishes research findings, time-use literature and newsletters. Aimed towards academic audiences. Does not accept unsolicited manuscripts. **Founded:** 1992.

PUBLISHERS

59915 ■ Nortext Multimedia Inc. (Iqaluit, Northwest Territories)—Nortex PressInuit Cultural Institute;
Bldg. 157
Iqaluit, NT, Canada X0A 0H0
Ph: (867)979-4376
Fax: (867)979-7841
Co. E-mail: ads@nortext.com
URL: http://www.nortext.com
Contact: Michael Roberts, President
E-mail: michaelr@nortext.com

Description: Description: Publishes school books, aboriginal language, business, Nunavut and travel books. **Founded:** 1990.

BETTER BUSINESS BUREAUS

59916 ■ Better Business Bureau of Greater Toronto Area (GTA)
354 Charles St., E
Kitchener, ON, Canada N2G 4L5
Ph: (519)579-3080
Free: 800-459-8875
Fax: (519)570-0072
Co. E-mail: info@bbbmwo.ca
URL: http://www.bbbmwo.ca

59917 ■ Better Business Bureau of Ottawa
505-700 Industrial Ave.
Ottawa, ON, Canada K1G 0Y9
Ph: (613)237-4856
Free: 877-859-8566
Fax: (613)237-4878
Co. E-mail: info@ottawa.bbb.org
URL: http://www.ottawa.bbb.org

59918 ■ Better Business Bureau of South Central Ontario
100 James Street South
Hamilton, ON, Canada L8P 2Z2
Ph: (905)526-1111
Fax: (905)526-1225
Co. E-mail: info@thebbb.ca
URL: http://www.thebbb.ca

59919 ■ Better Business Bureau of Western Ontario
308-200 Queens Ave.
London, ON, Canada N6A 4E3
Ph: (519)673-3222
Free: 877-283-9222
Fax: (519)673-5966
Co. E-mail: info@bbblondon.on.ca
URL: http://www.bbblondon.on.ca

59920 ■ Better Business Bureau of Windsor and South Western Ontario
880 Ouellette Ave., Ste. 302
Windsor, ON, Canada N9A 1C7
Ph: (519)258-7222
Fax: (519)258-1198
Co. E-mail: inquiries@windsor.net
URL: http://www.windsorbbb.com

MINORITY BUSINESS ASSISTANCE PROGRAMS

59921 ■ Canadian Aboriginal and Minority Supplier Council
95 Berkeley St., 2nd Fl.
Toronto, ON, Canada M5A 2W8
Ph: (416)941-0004
Fax: (416)941-9282
Co. E-mail: info@camsc.ca
URL: http://www.camsc.ca
Contact: Orrin O. Benn, President
Description: Aims to promote the economic development of disadvantaged communities and groups in Canada.

FINANCING AND LOAN PROGRAMS

59922 ■ Celtic House Venture Partners
80 Aberdeen St., Ste. 300
Ottawa, ON, Canada K1S 5R5
Ph: (613)569-7200
Fax: (613)569-7209
Co. E-mail: info@celtic-house.com
URL: http://www.celtic-house.com
Contact: David Adderley, Managing Partner
Industry Preferences: Computer software and services, semiconductors and other electronics, communications and media, Internet specific, medical and health, and computer hardware. **Geographic Preference:** U.S. and Canada.

59923 ■ Clairvest Group Inc.
22 St. Clair Ave. E., Ste. 1700
Toronto, ON, Canada M4T 2S3
Ph: (416)925-9270
Fax: (416)925-5753
URL: http://www.clairvest.com
Contact: Joseph Rotman, Chief Executive Officer
Preferred Investment Size: $15,000,000 to $50,000,000. **Geographic Preference:** Canada.

59924 ■ Crosbie & Co. Inc.
150 King St., W, 15th Fl.
Toronto, ON, Canada M5H 1J9
Ph: (416)362-7726
Fax: (416)362-3447
Co. E-mail: info@crosbieco.com
URL: http://www.crosbieco.com
Contact: Allan Crosbie
E-mail: acrosbie@crosbieco.com
Industry Preferences: Communications and media, computer software, semiconductors and other electronics, medical and health, consumer related, industrial and energy, business service, manufacturing, agriculture, forestry and fishing. **Geographic Preference:** Ontario, Canada.

59925 ■ DRI Capital Inc.
22 St. Clair Ave., E., Ste. 200
Toronto, ON, Canada M4T 2S5
Ph: (416)863-1865
Fax: (416)863-5161
Co. E-mail: info@dricapital.com
URL: http://www.dricapital.com
Contact: Joshua Salisbury, Managing Director
E-mail: js@dricapital.com
Preferred Investment Size: $3,000,000 to $4,000,000. **Industry Preferences:** Biotechnology, medical and health.

59926 ■ IPS Industrial Promotion Services, Ltd.
60 Columbia Way, Ste. 720
Markham, ON, Canada L3R 0C9
Ph: (905)475-9400

Fax: (905)475-5003
URL: http://www.ipscanada.com
Contact: Nizar Alibhai, President
Preferred Investment Size: $500,000 minimum. **Industry Preferences:** Communication and media, computer hardware, semiconductors and other electronics, biotechnology, medical and health, consumer related, industrial and energy, and transportation. **Geographic Preference:** U.S. and Canada.

59927 ■ Jefferson Partners
260 Queen St. W., 4th Fl.
Toronto, ON, Canada M5V 1Z8
Ph: (416)367-1533
Fax: (416)367-5827
Co. E-mail: info@jefferson.com
URL: http://www.jefferson.com
Contact: David Folk, Partner
E-mail: dfolk@jefferson.com
Preferred Investment Size: $5,000,000 to $15,000,000. **Industry Preferences:** Communications and media, computer software, and Internet specific. **Geographic Preference:** Northeast U.S. and Canada.

59928 ■ J.L. Albright Venture Partners / JLA Ventures
Bay Adelaide Centre
333 Bay St., Ste. 1640
Toronto, ON, Canada M5H 2R2
Ph: (416)367-2440
Fax: (416)367-4604
URL: http://www.jlaventures.com
Contact: John Albright, Partner
Preferred Investment Size: $500,000 to $10,000,000. **Industry Preferences:** Internet specific, other products, computer software and services, and computer hardware. **Geographic Preference:** Ontario and Quebec.

59929 ■ McLean Watson Capital Inc.
One First Canadian Pl., Ste. 2810
Toronto, ON, Canada M5X 1A4
Ph: (416)363-2000
Free: 866-665-3566
Fax: (416)363-2010
Co. E-mail: information@mcleanwatson.com
URL: http://www.mcleanwatson.com
Contact: John F. Eckert, Partner
Preferred Investment Size: $1,000,000 to $5,000,000. **Industry Preferences:** Communications and media, computer software, computer related, semiconductors and other electronics. **Geographic Preference:** U.S. and Canada.

59930 ■ Middlefield Capital Fund
First Canadian Pl., 58th Fl.
Toronto, ON, Canada M5X 1A6
Ph: (416)362-0714
Fax: (416)362-7925
Co. E-mail: invest@middlefield.com
URL: http://www.middlefield.com
Contact: M.J. Brasseur, Chief Executive Officer
E-mail: gjestley@middlefield.com
Preferred Investment Size: $3,000,000 minimum. **Industry Preferences:** Communications and media,

computer hardware, semiconductors and other electronics, medical and health, consumer related, industrial and energy, transportation, financial services, agriculture, forestry and fishing. **Geographic Preference:** U.S. and Canada.

59931 ■ Mosaic Venture Partners
65 front St. E., Ste. 200
Toronto, ON, Canada M5E 1B5
Ph: (416)367-2888
Fax: (416)367-8146
URL: http://www.mosaicvp.com
Contact: Vernon Lobo, Managing Director
Industry Preferences: Internet specific. **Geographic Preference:** Canada.

59932 ■ Onex Corp.
161 Bay St.
Toronto, ON, Canada M5J 2S1
Ph: (416)362-7711
Fax: (416)362-5765
Co. E-mail: info@onexcorp.com
URL: http://www.onexcorp.com
Contact: Gerald W. Schwartz, President
URL(s): www.onex.com. **Founded:** 1984. **Preferred Investment Size:** $10,000,000 minimum. **Geographic Preference:** U.S. and Canada. **Telecommunication Services:** investor@onex.com; info@onex.com.

59933 ■ Penfund Partners, Inc.
390 Bay St., Ste. 1720
Toronto, ON, Canada M5H 2Y2
Ph: (416)865-0707
Fax: (416)364-4149
URL: http://www.penfund.com
Contact: John Bradlow, Partner
E-mail: jbradlow@penfund.com
Preferred Investment Size: $10,000 to $50,000,000.
Geographic Preference: U.S. and Canada.

59934 ■ Primaxis Technology Ventures Inc.
MaRS Centre, Heritage Bldg.
101 College St., Ste. 230
Toronto, ON, Canada M5G 1L7
Ph: (416)673-8188
Fax: (416)977-3403
Co. E-mail: kerri.golden@primaxis.com
URL: http://www.primaxis.com
Contact: Paul Russo, Chief Executive Officer
Industry Preferences: Communications and media, semiconductors and other electronics, and manufacturing. **Geographic Preference:** Canada.

59935 ■ Priveq Capital Funds
1500 Don Mills Rd., Ste. 711
Toronto, ON, Canada M3B 3K4
Ph: (416)447-3330
Fax: (416)447-3331
Co. E-mail: priveq@sympatico.ca
URL: http://www.priveq.ca
Contact: Bradley W. Ashley, Managing Partner
Preferred Investment Size: $3,000,000 to $7,000,000. **Industry Preferences:** Semiconductors and other electronics, consumer related, industrial and energy, transportation, business services, and manufacturing. **Geographic Preference:** U.S. and Canada.

59936 ■ Roynat Ventures / Roynat Capital Corp.
Scotia Plz.
40 King St. W., 26th Fl.
Toronto, ON, Canada M5H 1H1
Ph: (416)933-2730
Fax: (416)933-2783
Co. E-mail: info@roynat.com
URL: http://www.roynatcapital.com
Contact: Richard Kanemy, Regional Vice President
E-mail: kanemyr@roynat.com
Preferred Investment Size: $250,000 to $50,000,000. **Industry Preferences:** Business services, consumer related, industrial and energy, manufacturing, and other products. **Geographic Preference:** Canada.

59937 ■ Summerhill Venture Partners
21 St. Clair Ave. E, Ste. 1400
Toronto, ON, Canada M4T 1L8

Ph: (416)408-0700
Fax: (416)585-9749
URL: http://www.summerhillvp.com
Contact: Gary Rubinoff, Managing Director
Preferred Investment Size: $500,000 to $4,000,000.
Industry Preferences: Communications and media, information technology, Internet specific, semiconductors and other electronics, computer software and services. **Geographic Preference:** Northeastern U.S., primarily New York, Boston, and D.C., and Central and Eastern Canada.

59938 ■ Tera Capital Corp.
8 King St. E., Ste. 1905
Toronto, ON, Canada M5C 1B6
Ph: (416)368-8372
Free: 888-368-8372
Fax: (416)368-1427
Co. E-mail: info@teracap.com
URL: http://www.teracap.com
Contact: Howard Sutton, Partner
Preferred Investment Size: $250,000 to $1,000,000.
Industry Preferences: Industrial and energy, biotechnology, financial services, computer hardware, semiconductors and other electronics, biotechnology, and consumer related. **Geographic Preference:** Canada.

59939 ■ Working Ventures Canadian Fund Inc.
250 Bloor St. E., Ste. 1600
Toronto, ON, Canada M4W 1E6
Ph: (416)934-7777
Fax: (416)929-2421
Co. E-mail: WVID@workingventures.ca
URL: http://www.workingventures.ca
Preferred Investment Size: $334,000 to $10,008,000. **Industry Preferences:** Consumer related, communications and media, other products, computer software and services, computer hardware, Internet specific, industrial and energy, semiconductors and other electronics, biotechnology, and medical and health. **Geographic Preference:** Ontario and Western Canada.

TRADE PERIODICALS

59940 ■ In Touch
Pub: The City Centre Business Association of Windsor

Contact: Fran Funaro, Managing Editor
Released: Quarterly. **Description:** Acts as the publication of The City Centre Business Association of Windsor. Recurring features include news of members and a calendar of events.

PUBLISHERS

59941 ■ Canadian Small Business Institute
4936 Yonge St., Ste. 250
Toronto, ON, Canada M2N 6S3
Ph: (905)886-4674
Free: 866-992-6687
Fax: (905)886-4672
Co. E-mail: information@bsma.ca
URL: http://www.bsma.ca
Contact: Henry Tse, President
E-mail: htse@bsma.ca

Description: Description: Publishes materials to help people start their own business. Offers home study courses and distributes books and magazines on related topics. Also offers audio cassettes, seminars, and consulting and business services. Accepts unsolicited manuscripts. Distributes for Prentice Hall, Stoddart, John Wiley, Wade World Trade, Made in Europe, Trade Winds, and Business Opportunities Monthly. Reaches market through direct mail. **Founded:** 1982.

59942 ■ Digital Leisure Inc.
33 Cedar Ridge Rd.
Gormley, ON, Canada L0H 1G0
Ph: (905)888-9550
Free: 888-836-4383

Fax: (905)888-9440
Co. E-mail: info@digitalleisure.com
URL: http://www.digitalleisure.com
Contact: Elizabeth Foster, President
E-mail: elizabethf@digitalleisure.com
Description: Description: Publishes on video games.
Founded: 1997.

59943 ■ DreamCatcher Interactive Inc.
5000 Dufferin St., Bldg. R
Toronto, ON, Canada M3H 5T5
Ph: (416)638-5000
Free: 888-611-9999
Fax: (416)398-4476
Co. E-mail: info@dreamcatchergames.com
URL: http://www.dreamcatcherinc.com
Contact: Richard Wah Kan, President
Description: Description: Publishes games and software. **Founded:** 1996.

59944 ■ Dun & Bradstreet Canada
5770 Hurontario St.
Mississauga, ON, Canada L5R 3G5
Ph: (905)568-6000
Free: 800-463-6362
Fax: (800)668-7800
Co. E-mail: customercarecan@dnb.com
URL: http://www.dnb.ca
Contact: Jeff Stuek, President
Description: Description: Publishes business information reports and directories. Reaches market through sales and service representatives, telephone sales and direct mail. **Founded:** 1841. **Publications:** DunsPrint Canada (Continuous); DUNSERVE II (Bimonthly); Canadian Key Business Directory (Annual); Dun & Bradstreet United States (Quarterly). **Telecommunication Services:** cic@dnb.com.

59945 ■ Frasers Trade Directories Company Ltd.
1 Mt. Pleasant Rd., 7th Fl.
Toronto, ON, Canada M4Y 2Y5
Ph: (416)764-1467
Free: 888-297-7195
Fax: (416)764-1710
Co. E-mail: info@canadianmanufacturing.com
URL: http://www.frasers.com
Contact: Melissa Crook, Director
E-mail: mel.crook@rci.rogers.com
Description: Description: Publishes directories on Canadian industry, manufacturing and trade. **Founded:** 1913.

59946 ■ G7 Report Inc.- G7 Books
69 Medford Ave.
Toronto, ON, Canada M5R 3K4
Ph: (416)699-3530
Fax: (416)699-5683
Co. E-mail: g7report@passport.ca
Contact: William B. Z. Vukson, Publisher
E-mail: g7report@passport.ca
Description: Description: Publishes books on business and economic reference, currency, globalized markets, investing, organized crime, financial crises, and laundering. Does not accept unsolicited manuscripts. Reaches market through commission representatives, wholesalers and distributors, including Lavis Marketing/Femma. **Founded:** 1991.

59947 ■ Innovation Canada Inc.
2 Woodpark Rd.
Weston, ON, Canada M9P 1M1
Ph: (416)240-9003
Fax: (416)240-9008
Co. E-mail: innovation_canada@sympatico.ca
URL: http://www3.sympatico.ca/innovation_canada
Contact: William O. Munns, Chief Executive Officer
Description: Description: Publishes books on business and Canada. Reaches market through direct mail. Accepts unsolicited manuscripts. **Founded:** 1977.

59948 ■ Ivey Publishing
Richard Ivey School of Business
The University of Western Ontario
London, ON, Canada N6A 3K7
Ph: (519)661-3208
Free: 800-649-6355

Fax: (519)661-3882
Co. E-mail: cases@ivey.uwo.ca
URL: http://www.ivey.uwo.ca/cases
Contact: Donald L. Triggs, Director
Description: Description: Publishes business case studies. Publishes CD-ROM's. Reaches market through direct mail and telephone sales. Accepts unsolicited manuscripts. **Founded:** 1922.

59949 ■ Laurier Institute
Wilfrid Laurier University, 75 University Ave. W
Waterloo, ON, Canada N2L 3C5
Ph: (519)884-1970
Free: 888-646-8338
Fax: (519)746-3655
Co. E-mail: laurinst@wlu.ca
URL: http://www.wlu.ca
Contact: Dr. Robert Rosehart, President
E-mail: rrosehart@wlu.ca
Description: Description: Publishes management case studies in all areas of business and economics in English and French. **Scope:** Designs and delivers management training and development programs to organizations throughout the business community. **Founded:** 1983. **Telecommunication Services:** mgmtdev@wlu.ca.

59950 ■ Life Untangled Publishing
1 Humbercrest Blvd.
Toronto, ON, Canada M6S 4K6
Description: Description: Publishes books of biographical accounts.

59951 ■ maranGraphics Inc.
5755 Coopers Ave.
Mississauga, ON, Canada L4Z 1R9
Ph: (905)890-3300
Free: 800-469-6616
Fax: (905)890-9434
Co. E-mail: family@maran.com
URL: http://www.maran.com
Contact: Rob Maran, President
E-mail: rob@maran.com
Description: Description: Publishes computer books and manuals. **Founded:** 1975.

59952 ■ Multi-Media Publications Inc. (MMP)
227 Summit Dr.
Scugog, ON, Canada L0B 1E0
Ph: (905)986-5848

Free: 866-721-1540
Fax: (905)986-5777
Co. E-mail: info@mmpubs.com
URL: http://www.mmpubs.com
Contact: Troy O'Brien, Manager
E-mail: troy.obrien@obriendesign.biz
Description: Description: Publishes nonfiction books on a variety of business topics. **Founded:** 1988.

59953 ■ Nortext Multimedia Inc. (Ottawa, Ontario)
52 Antares Dr., Ste. 9
Ottawa, ON, Canada K2E 7Z1
Ph: (613)727-5466
Free: 800-263-1452
Fax: (613)727-6910
Co. E-mail: ads@nortext.com
URL: http://www.nortext.com
Contact: Michael Roberts, President
E-mail: michaelr@nortext.com
Description: Description: Publishes school books, aboriginal language, business, Nunavut and travel books. **Founded:** 1990.

59954 ■ Pearson Canada Inc.
26 Prince Andre Pl.
Don Mills
Toronto, ON, Canada M3C 2T8
Ph: (416)447-5101
Free: 800-263-9965
Fax: (416)443-0948
Co. E-mail: pubcanada@pearsoned.ca
URL: http://www.pearsoned.ca
Contact: Susan Dimock, Manager
Description: Description: Publishes fiction, nonfiction, textbooks, reference books and trade books. **Founded:** 1966.

59955 ■ Productive Publications
7-B Pleasant Blvd., Ste. 1210
Toronto, ON, Canada M4T 1K2
Ph: (416)483-0634
Free: 877-879-2669
Fax: (416)322-7434
Co. E-mail: productivepublications@rogers.com
URL: http://www.productivepublications.com
Contact: Iain Williamson, President
Description: Description: Publishes books relating to small business companies on self help, business management, personal finance and personal comput-

ers. Audience includes entrepreneurs, individuals, computer users and business managers. Reaches market through direct mail and wholesalers. Accepts unsolicited manuscripts. **Founded:** 1985.

59956 ■ Summit Group
263 Holmwood Ave., Ste. 100
Ottawa, ON, Canada K1S 2P8
Ph: (613)688-0763
Free: 800-575-1146
Fax: (613)688-0767
Co. E-mail: info@summitconnects.com
URL: http://www.summitconnects.com
Contact: Mcevoy Galbreath, President
E-mail: mcegalbreath@summitconnects.com
Description: Description: Publishes business and trade publications for Canadian government and businesses. Also publishes a professional journal for public sector procurement managers and a magazine for Canadians with chronic illness. Offers CD-ROMS, diskettes, and online. **Founded:** 1998. **Publications:** *Optimum: The Journal of Public Sector Management* (Quarterly).

59957 ■ Treehouse Publishing
403-10 Preston St.
Ottawa, ON, Canada K1R 7W4
Ph: (613)231-7601
Fax: (613)231-5873
Contact: John Ross Trinnell, Publisher
Description: Description: Publishes books on forestry and lumbering. Published J. R. Booth: The Life and Times of an Ottawa Lumberking. Does not accept unsolicited manuscripts. Reaches market through personal visits. **Founded:** 1998.

59958 ■ White Mountain Publications
174 Drive-In-Theatre Rd., RR 2
New Liskeard, ON, Canada P0J 1P0
Ph: (705)647-5424
Free: 800-258-5451
Fax: (705)647-8366
Co. E-mail: wmpub@wmpub.ca
URL: http://www.wmpub.ca
Contact: Deborah Ranchuk, President
Description: Description: Publishes books about the Baha'i faith, children's literature, poetry, nonfiction and how-to books. Accepts unsolicited manuscripts. Reaches market through direct mail, telephone sales, the Internet, wholesalers and distributors. **Founded:** 1982.

BETTER BUSINESS BUREAUS

59959 ■ Better Business Bureau of Quebec
1370 Notre-Dame Quest
Montreal, QC, Canada H3C 1K8
Ph: (514)286-9281
Fax: (514)323-1511
Co. E-mail: bbbbec@bbb-bec.com
URL: http://www.bbb-bec.com

MINORITY BUSINESS ASSISTANCE PROGRAMS

59960 ■ Aboriginal Business Canada - Indian and Northern Affairs Canada
10 Wellington St., 9th Fl.
Gatineau, QC, Canada K1A 0H4
Fax: (819)994-7223
URL: http://www.ainc-inac.gc.ca
Description: Provides a variety of services and support to promote Aboriginal businesses in Canada.

FINANCING AND LOAN PROGRAMS

59961 ■ Federal Business Development Bank
BDC Bldg.
5 Place Ville Marie, Ste. 400
Montreal, QC, Canada H3B 5E7

Ph: (514)283-1896
Free: 877-232-2269
Fax: (877)329-9232
URL: http://www.bdc.ca
Contact: Charles Cazabon, Vice President
Preferred Investment Size: $40,000,000 minimum.
Industry Preferences: Biotechnology, Internet specific, computer software, energy and environment.
Geographic Preference: Canada.

59962 ■ Investissement Desjardins
2 Complexe Desjardins, Ste. 1717
C.P. 760
Montreal, QC, Canada H5B 1B8
Ph: (514)281-2322
Free: 888-522-3222
Fax: (514)286-7876
URL: http://www.desjardins.com/id
Preferred Investment Size: $5,000,000 minimum.
Industry Preferences: Computer software and services, Internet specific, communications and media, biotechnology, other products, medical and health, and industrial and energy. **Geographic Preference:** Quebec, Canada.

59963 ■ TechnoCap, Inc.
4028 Marlowe
Montreal, QC, Canada H4A 3M2

Ph: (514)483-6000
Co. E-mail: Cpedroso@TechnoCap.com
URL: http://www.technocap.com
Contact: Richard Prytula, Managing Partner
Preferred Investment Size: $1,000,000 to $10,000,000. **Industry Preferences:** Communications and media, computer software, computer related, Internet specific, semiconductors and other electronics, medical and health, industrial and energy.
Geographic Preference: Canada.

PUBLISHERS

59964 ■ White Rock Publishing
2700 Du Mont-Joli Rue
Sainte Foy, QC, Canada G1V 1C8
Ph: (418)580-9019
Free: 800-363-7177
Fax: (418)658-7177
Co. E-mail: info@whiterockpub.com
URL: http://www.whiterockpub.com
Contact: Luc Dupont, President
E-mail: dupontluc@videotron.ca

Description: Description: Publishes advertising and marketing books. Accepts unsolicited manuscripts. Reaches market through direct mail and wholesalers.
Founded: 1996.

SMALL BUSINESS ASSISTANCE PROGRAMS

59965 ■ Regina Economic Development Authority
1919 Rose St., Ste. 255
Regina, SK, Canada S4P 3P1
Ph: (306)522-0227
Free: 800-866-5644
Fax: (306)352-1630
Co. E-mail: info@reginaroc.com
URL: http://www.rreda.com
Contact: Larry Miles, Chief Executive Officer

Description: Provides business information as well as counseling and consulting services to the business community, with emphasis on management information. Acts as facilitators in accessing a variety of program initiatives provided by other departments, the federal government, Crown corporations, and financial institutions.

59966 ■ Tourism Saskatchewan
189-1621 Albert St.
Regina, SK, Canada S4P 2S5
Ph: (306)787-9600
Free: 877-237-2273
URL: http://www.sasktourism.com

Description: Promotes growth of the tourism industry in Saskatchewan. Subprograms include Tourism Product Development, Tourism Market Development, Industry Organization Support, and Research and Planning Support. **Publications:** *Saskatchewan Vacation Guide* (Annual); *Saskatchewan Events Guide* (Annual); *Saskatchewan Winter* (Annual); *Saskatchewan Fishing & Hunting Guide* (Annual); *Saskatchewan Accommodation Resort and Campground Guide*; *Great Saskatchewan Gift Book* (Semiannual).

BETTER BUSINESS BUREAUS

59967 ■ Better Business Bureau of Saskatchewan
No. 201-2080 Broad St.
Regina, SK, Canada S4P 1Y3
Ph: (306)352-7601
Free: 888-352-7601
Fax: (306)565-6236
Co. E-mail: info@bbbsask.com
URL: http://www.bbbsask.com

SMALL BUSINESS ASSISTANCE PROGRAMS

59968 ■ Yukon Department of Economic Development
212 Main St., Ste. 209
Whitehorse, YT, Canada Y1A 2C6

Ph: (867)456-3914
Fax: (867)393-6412
Co. E-mail: economics@gov.yk.ca

URL: http://www.economicdevelopment.gov.yk.ca

AGENCY FOR INTERNATIONAL DEVELOPMENT

59969 ■ **Agency for International Development (AID) - Office of Small and Disadvantaged Business Utilization - Minority Resource Center**
Ronald Reagan Bldg.
1300 Pennsylvania Ave., NW, Ste. 5.8C
Washington, DC 20523
Ph: (202)712-1500
Fax: (202)216-3065
Co. E-mail: osdbu@usaid.gov
URL: http://www.usaid.gov/business/small_business/
Description: A small business advocacy and advisory office with the responsibility for ensuring that these enterprises receive access to USAID programs. The office maintains the USAID Consultant Registry Information System (ACRIS) and publishes The Guide to Doing Business with the Agency for International Development.

59970 ■ **Agency for International Development - Office of Small and Disadvantaged Business Utilization - Minority Resource Center**
Ronald Reagan Bldg.
1300 Pennsylvania Ave., NW, Ste. 7.8E
Washington, DC 20523-7800
Ph: (202)712-1500
Fax: (202)216-3056
Co. E-mail: osdbu@usaid.gov
URL: http://www.usaid.gov/business/small_business/
Description: A small business advocacy and advisory office with the responsibility for ensuring that these enterprises receive access to USAID programs. The office maintains the USAID Consultant Registry Information System (ACRIS) and publishes The Guide to Doing Business with the Agency for International Development.

59971 ■ **International Franchise Association - Office of Small and Disadvantaged Business Utilization - Minorities in Franchising**
1501 K St., NW, Ste. 350
Washington, DC 20005
Ph: (202)628-8000
Fax: (202)628-0812
URL: http://www.franchise.org
Description: A place where minority prospects can explore franchise offerings of companies actively looking to recruit minority franchisees.

59972 ■ **International Franchise Association - Office of Small and Disadvantaged Business Utilization - Minorities in Franchising**
1501 K St. NW, Ste. 350
Washington, DC 20005
Ph: (202)628-8000
Fax: (202)628-0812
URL: http://www.franchise.org
Description: A place where minority prospects can explore franchise offerings of companies actively looking to recruit minority franchisees.

59973 ■ **U.S. Agency for International Development - Freedom of Information Act Request - Bureau for Management/Information and Records Division**
Ronald Reagan Bldg.
Washington, DC 20523
Ph: (202)712-0960
Fax: (202)216-3070
URL: http://www.usaid.gov

59974 ■ **U.S. Agency for International Development - Freedom of Information Act Request - Bureau for Management/Information and Records Division**
Ronald Reagan Bldg.
Washington, DC 20523
Ph: (202)712-0960
Fax: (202)216-3070
URL: http://transition.usaid.gov/contact.html

59975 ■ **U.S. Agency for International Development - Office of the Inspector General**
PO Box 657
Washington, DC 20044-0657
Ph: (202)712-1023
Free: 800-230-6539
Co. E-mail: ig.hotline@usaid.gov
URL: http://www.usaid.gov/oig/
Description: Responsible for providing audit and investigative services to the U.S. Agency for International Development (USAID), the Millennium Challenge Corporation (MCC), the African Development Foundation (ADF), and the Inter-American Foundation (IAF).

59976 ■ **U.S. Agency for International Development - Office of the Inspector General**
PO Box 657
Washington, DC 20044-0657
Ph: (202)712-1023
Free: 800-230-6539
Co. E-mail: ig.hotline@usaid.gov
URL: http://transition.usaid.gov/oig/
Description: Responsible for providing audit and investigative services to the U.S. Agency for International Development (USAID), the Millennium Challenge Corporation (MCC), the African Development Foundation (ADF), and the Inter-American Foundation (IAF).

59977 ■ **U.S. Agency for International Development - USAID Library**
Ronald Reagan Bldg.
Mezzanine Level
Washington, DC 20523
Ph: (202)712-0579
Co. E-mail: ksc@usaid.gov
URL: http://library.info.usaid.gov/

59978 ■ **U.S. Agency for International Development - USAID Library**
Ronald Reagan Bldg.
Mezzanine Level
Washington, DC 20523

Ph: (202)712-0579
Co. E-mail: ksc@usaid.gov
URL: http://transition.usaid.gov/contact.html

59979 ■ **U.S. Agency for International Development - USAID Office of Procurement**
Ronald Reagan Bldg.
Washington, DC 20523
Ph: (202)712-5130
Fax: (202)216-3395
Co. E-mail: AandAOmbudsman@usaid.gov
URL: http://www.usaid.gov

59980 ■ **U.S. Agency for International Development - USAID Office of Procurement**
1300 Pennsylvania Ave., Bldg. SA-44
M/OAA/OD, Rm. 852H
Washington, DC 20004
Ph: (202)567-4624
Co. E-mail: aandaombudsman@usaid.gov
URL: http://transition.usaid.gov/contact.html#proc

BUREAU OF THE CENSUS

The Bureau of the Census is a part of the U.S. Department of Commerce. The following is a list of the state coordinating organizations in the Census Bureau's State Data Center Program and Business and Industry Data Center Program, arranged alphabetically by state.

59981 ■ **Maryland Small Business Development Center (SBDC)**
7100 Baltimore Ave., Ste. 401
College Park, MD 20740-3640
Ph: (301)403-0501
Co. E-mail: sbdcctr@umd.edu
URL: http://www.mdsbdc.umd.edu/region_capital.html
Contact: Renee Sprow, Director
Description: Represents and promotes the small business sector. Provides management assistance to current and prospective small business owners. Helps to improve management skills and expand the products and services of members. **Telecommunication Services:** training@mdsbdc.umd.edu.

59982 ■ **U.S. Department of Commerce - Ohio Department of Development - Office of Policy Research and Strategic Planning**
77 S. High St., 27th Fl.
Columbus, OH 43215-6130
Ph: (614)466-2116
Fax: (614)466-9697
Co. E-mail: osr@odod.state.oh.us
URL: http://www.odod.state.oh.us/research/

CORPORATION FOR NATIONAL SERVICE

59983 ■ **Corporation for National and Community Service - Department of AmeriCorps**
1201 New York Ave., NW, Rm. 9601
Washington, DC 20525-0001

Ph: (202)606-6818
Fax: (202)565-3475
URL: http://www.nationalservice.org/about/programs/
americorps.asp

59984 ■ Corporation for National and Community Service - Department of AmeriCorps
1201 New York Ave. NW, Rm. 9201
Washington, DC 20525
Ph: (202)606-6818
Fax: (202)606-3475
Co. E-mail: dc@cns.gov
URL: http://www.nationalservice.gov/about/programs/
americorps.asp

59985 ■ Corporation for National and Community Service - Field Liaison
1201 New York Ave., NW, Room 9205
Washington, DC 20525-0001
Ph: (202)606-6924
URL: http://www.learnandserve.gov

59986 ■ Corporation for National and Community Service - Field Liaison
1201 New York Ave. NW, Rm. 9205
Washington, DC 20525
Ph: (202)606-6924
URL: http://www.learnandserve.gov

59987 ■ Corporation for National and Community Service - Office of Learn and Serve
1201 New York Ave., NW
Washington, DC 20525-0001
Ph: (202)606-5000
Fax: (202)606-3472
Co. E-mail: LSAabout@cns.gov
URL: http://www.nationalservice.org/about/programs/
learnandserve.asp

59988 ■ Corporation for National and Community Service - Office of Learn and Serve
1201 New York Ave. NW
Washington, DC 20525-0001
Ph: (202)606-5000
Fax: (202)606-3472
Co. E-mail: LSAabout@cns.gov
URL: http://www.learnandserve.gov/

59989 ■ Corporation for National and Community Service (CNCS) - Office of Procurement
1201 New York Ave., NW
Washington, DC 20525-0001
Ph: (202)606-5000
Fax: (202)606-3472
Co. E-mail: info@cns.gov
URL: http://www.nationalservice.org

59990 ■ Corporation for National and Community Service (CNCS) - Office of Procurement
1201 New York Ave. NW
Washington, DC 20525-0001
Ph: (202)606-5000
Fax: (202)606-3472
Co. E-mail: info@cns.gov
URL: http://www.nationalservice.org

59991 ■ Corporation for National and Community Service - Office of Public Affairs
1201 New York Ave., NW, Rm. 10307
Washington, DC 20525-0001
Ph: (202)606-6924
Fax: (202)565-2782
URL: http://www.nationalservice.org

59992 ■ Corporation for National and Community Service - Office of Public Affairs
1201 New York Ave. NW, Rm. 10307
Washington, DC 20525-0001
Ph: (202)606-6724
Fax: (202)565-2782
Co. E-mail: sscott@cns.gov
URL: http://www.nationalservice.gov

ENVIRONMENTAL PROTECTION AGENCY

The following are State Superfund Offices for EPA Region Six.

59993 ■ Environmental Protection Agency (EPA) - Office of Small Business Programs
1200 Pennsylvania Ave. NW
Mail Code 1230T
Washington, DC 20460
Ph: (202)566-2075
URL: http://www.epa.gov/osdbu
Description: The Environmental Protection Agency's Office of Small and Disadvantaged Business Utilization performs the following duties: provides a convenient way for small businesses to access the EPA; facilitates communication between small businesses and the EPA; helps small businesses understand and comply with environmental regulations; investigates and resolves individual small business disputes with the EPA; and works with EPA personnel to increase their understanding of small businesses in the development and enforcement of environmental regulations. Provides procurement information as it regards to small businesses, small and disadvantaged businesses, minority-owned businesses, and women-owned businesses.

59994 ■ Environmental Protection Agency - Office of Small Business Programs
1200 Pennsylvania Ave. NW
Mail Code 1230T
Washington, DC 20460
Ph: (202)566-2075
Fax: (202)566-1505
URL: http://www.epa.gov/sbo/
Description: The Environmental Protection Agency's Office of Small and Disadvantaged Business Utilization performs the following duties: provides a convenient way for small businesses to access the EPA; facilitates communication between small businesses and the EPA; helps small businesses understand and comply with environmental regulations; investigates and resolves individual small business disputes with the EPA; and works with EPA personnel to increase their understanding of small businesses in the development and enforcement of environmental regulations. Provides procurement information as it regards to small businesses, small and disadvantaged businesses, minority-owned businesses, and women-owned businesses.

59995 ■ Environmental Protection Agency, Region 1
John F. Kennedy Federal Bldg.
1 Congress St., Ste. 1100
Boston, MA 02114-2023
Ph: (617)918-1111
Free: 888-372-7341
Fax: (617)918-0101
Co. E-mail: r1web.mail@epa.gov
URL: http://www.epa.gov/region01
Description: Serves Connecticut, Massachusetts, Maine, New Hampshire, Rhode Island, and Vermont.

59996 ■ Environmental Protection Agency, Region 1
5 Post Office Sq., Ste. 100
Boston, MA 02109-3912
Ph: (617)918-1111
Free: 888-372-7341
Fax: (617)918-0101
URL: http://www.epa.gov/aboutepa/region1.html
Description: Serves Connecticut, Massachusetts, Maine, New Hampshire, Rhode Island, and Vermont.

59997 ■ Environmental Protection Agency, Region 2
290 Broadway
New York, NY 10007-1866
Ph: (212)637-3660
Fax: (212)637-3518
Co. E-mail: R2_Web_Inquiry@epamail.epa.gov
URL: http://www.epa.gov/region02
Description: Serves New Jersey, New York, Puerto Rico, and the Virgin Islands.

59998 ■ Environmental Protection Agency, Region 2
290 Broadway
New York, NY 10007-1866
Ph: (212)637-3660
Free: 877-251-4575
Fax: (212)637-3518
URL: http://www.epa.gov/aboutepa/region2.html
Description: Serves New Jersey, New York, Puerto Rico, and the Virgin Islands.

59999 ■ Environmental Protection Agency, Region 3
1650 Arch St.
Philadelphia, PA 19103-2029
Ph: (215)814-5000
Free: 800-438-2474
Fax: (215)814-5108
Co. E-mail: teller.lawrence@epa.gov
URL: http://www.epa.gov/region03
Description: Serves Delaware, Maryland, Pennsylvania, Virginia, West Virginia, and the District of Columbia.

60000 ■ Environmental Protection Agency, Region 3
1650 Arch St.
Philadelphia, PA 19103-2029
Ph: (215)814-5000
Free: 800-438-2474
Fax: (215)814-5108
URL: http://www.epa.gov/aboutepa/region3.html
Description: Serves Delaware, Maryland, Pennsylvania, Virginia, West Virginia, and the District of Columbia.

60001 ■ Environmental Protection Agency, Region 4
61 Forsyth St., SW
Atlanta, GA 30303-8960
Ph: (404)562-9900
Free: 800-241-1754
Fax: (404)562-8174
Co. E-mail: maddox.sherry@epa.gov
URL: http://www.epa.gov/region04
Description: Serves Alabama, Florida, Georgia, Kentucky, Mississippi, North Carolina, South Carolina, and Tennessee.

60002 ■ Environmental Protection Agency, Region 4
61 Forsyth St. SW
Atlanta, GA 30303-8960
Ph: (404)562-9900
Free: 800-241-1754
Fax: (404)562-8174
URL: http://www.epa.gov/aboutepa/region4.html
Description: Serves Alabama, Florida, Georgia, Kentucky, Mississippi, North Carolina, South Carolina, and Tennessee.

60003 ■ Environmental Protection Agency, Region 5
77 W. Jackson Blvd.
Chicago, IL 60604-3507
Ph: (312)353-2000
Free: 800-621-8431
Fax: (312)353-9096
Co. E-mail: r5hotline@epa.gov
URL: http://www.epa.gov/region5/
Description: Serves Illinois, Indiana, Michigan, Minnesota, Ohio, and Wisconsin.

60004 ■ Environmental Protection Agency, Region 5
77 W. Jackson Blvd.
Chicago, IL 60604-3590
Ph: (312)353-2000
Free: 800-621-8431
Fax: (312)353-9096
URL: http://www.epa.gov/aboutepa/region5.html
Description: Serves Illinois, Indiana, Michigan, Minnesota, Ohio, and Wisconsin.

60005 ■ Environmental Protection Agency, Region 6
Fountain Pl., 12th Fl.
1445 Ross Ave., Ste. 1200
Dallas, TX 75202-2733
Ph: (214)665-7406
Free: 800-887-6063
Fax: (214)665-7284
URL: http://www.epa.gov/Region6/
Description: Serves Arkansas, Louisiana, New Mexico, Oklahoma, and Texas.

60006 ■ Environmental Protection Agency, Region 6
1445 Ross Ave., Ste. 1200
Dallas, TX 75202-2733
Ph: (214)665-7406
Free: 800-887-6063
Fax: (214)665-7284
URL: http://www.epa.gov/aboutepa/region6.html
Description: Serves Arkansas, Louisiana, New Mexico, Oklahoma, and Texas.

60007 ■ Environmental Protection Agency, Region 7
901 N. 5th St.
Kansas City, KS 66101
Ph: (913)551-7003
Free: 800-223-0425
Fax: (913)551-7066
Co. E-mail: r7actionline@epa.gov.
URL: http://www.epa.gov/region07
Description: Serves Iowa, Kansas, Missouri, and Nebraska.

60008 ■ Environmental Protection Agency, Region 7
11201 Renner Blvd.
Lenexa, KS 66219
Ph: (913)551-7003
Free: 800-223-0425
Fax: (913)551-7066
URL: http://www.epa.gov/aboutepa/region7.html
Description: Serves Iowa, Kansas, Missouri, and Nebraska.

60009 ■ Environmental Protection Agency, Region 8
1595 Wynkoop St.
Denver, CO 80202-1129
Ph: (303)312-6312
Free: 800-227-8917
Fax: (303)312-6685
Co. E-mail: r8eisc@epa.gov
URL: http://www.epa.gov/region08
Description: Serves Colorado, Montana, North Dakota, South Dakota, Utah, Wyoming, and 27 Tribal Nations.

60010 ■ Environmental Protection Agency, Region 8
1595 Wynkoop St.
Denver, CO 80202-1129
Ph: (303)312-6312
Free: 800-227-8917
Fax: (303)312-6685
URL: http://www.epa.gov/aboutepa/region8.html
Description: Serves Colorado, Montana, North Dakota, South Dakota, Utah, and Wyoming.

60011 ■ Environmental Protection Agency, Region 9
75 Hawthorne St.
San Francisco, CA 94105
Ph: (415)947-8000
Free: 866-EPA-WEST
Fax: (415)947-3556
URL: http://www.epa.gov/region09
Description: Serves Arizona, California, Hawaii, Nevada, American Samoa, Guam, the Trust Territory of the Pacific Islands, and 147 Tribes.

60012 ■ Environmental Protection Agency, Region 9
75 Hawthorne St.
San Francisco, CA 94105
Ph: (415)947-8000
Free: 866-EPA-WEST

Fax: (415)947-3556
Co. E-mail: nastri.wayne@epa.gov
URL: http://www.epa.gov/aboutepa/region9.html
Description: Serves Arizona, California, Hawaii, Nevada, American Samoa, Guam, and the Trust Territory of the Pacific Islands.

60013 ■ Environmental Protection Agency, Region 10
1200 6th Ave., Ste. 900
Seattle, WA 98101
Ph: (206)553-1200
Free: 800-424-4372
Fax: (206)553-4957
Co. E-mail: epa-seattle@epa.gov
URL: http://www.epa.gov/region10
Description: Serves Alaska, Idaho, Oregon, Washington, and 271 Native Tribes.

60014 ■ Environmental Protection Agency, Region 10
1200 6th Ave., Ste. 900
Seattle, WA 98101
Ph: (206)553-1200
Free: 800-424-4372
Fax: (206)553-4957
URL: http://www.epa.gov/aboutepa/region10.html
Description: Serves Alaska, Idaho, Oregon, and Washington.

60015 ■ Environmental Protection Agency State Superfund Office (Austin, Texas) - Commission of Environmental Quality - Hazardous and Solid Waste Division - Superfund and Emergency Response Section
PO Box 13087
Austin, TX 78711-3087
Ph: (512)239-5500
Fax: (512)239-5533
Co. E-mail: ac@tceq.tx.gov
URL: http://www.tceq.state.tx.us/nav/eq/eq_waste.html

60016 ■ Environmental Protection Agency State Superfund Office (Olympia, Washington) - Department of Ecology - Hazardous Waste and Toxics Reduction - Investigations and Cleanup Program
PO Box 47600
Olympia, WA 98504-7600
Ph: (360)407-6700
Free: 800-258-5990
Fax: (360)407-6715
URL: http://www.ecy.wa.gov/programs/hwtr/index.html

60017 ■ Environmental Protection Agency State Superfund Office (Olympia, Washington) - Department of Ecology - Waste Management Program - Investigations and Cleanup Program
PO Box 47600
Olympia, WA 98504-7600
Ph: (206)407-6700
Free: 800-258-5990
URL: http://www.ecy.wa.gov/programs/hwtr/index.html

60018 ■ Environmental Protection Agency State Superfund Office (Hartford, Connecticut) - Department of Energy and Environmental Protection - Small Business Assistance
79 Elm St.
Hartford, CT 06106-5127
Ph: (860)424-3000
Fax: (860)424-4051
Co. E-mail: deep.webmaster@ct.us
URL: http://www.ct.gov/dep/site/default.asp

60019 ■ Environmental Protection Agency State Superfund Office (Nashville, Tennessee) - Department of Environment and Conservation - Division of Solid and Hazardous Waste Management
L & C Annex, 1st Fl.
401 Church St.
Nashville, TN 37243-0435

Ph: (615)532-0109
Free: 888-891-8332
Co. E-mail: ask.tdec@tn.gov
URL: http://www.state.tn.us/environment/org/

60020 ■ Environmental Protection Agency State Superfund Office (Nashville, Tennessee) - Department of Environment and Conservation - Division of Solid and Hazardous Waste Management
L & C Tower, 1st Fl.
401 Church St.
Nashville, TN 37243-0435
Ph: (615)532-0780
Free: 888-891-8332
Co. E-mail: ask.tdec@tn.gov
URL: http://www.state.tn.us/environment/org/

60021 ■ Environmental Protection Agency State Superfund Office (Raleigh, North Carolina) - Department of Environment and Natural Resources
1601 Mail Service Center
Raleigh, NC 27699-1601
Ph: (919)733-4984
Fax: (919)715-3060
URL: http://www.enr.state.nc.us

60022 ■ Environmental Protection Agency State Superfund Office (Raleigh, North Carolina) - Department of Environment and Natural Resources
1601 Mail Service Center
Raleigh, NC 27699-1601
Ph: (919)733-4984
Free: 877-623-6748
Fax: (919)715-3060
URL: http://www.enr.state.nc.us

60023 ■ Environmental Protection Agency State Superfund Office (Pierre, South Dakota) - Department of Environment and Natural Resources - Waste Management Program
Joe Foss Bldg.
523 E. Capitol Ave.
Pierre, SD 57501-3181
Ph: (605)773-3153
Fax: (605)773-6035
Co. E-mail: denrinternetet@state.sd.us
URL: http://www.state.sd.us/denr/

60024 ■ Environmental Protection Agency State Superfund Office (Pierre, South Dakota) - Department of Environment and Natural Resources - Waste Management Program
Joe Foss Bldg.
523 E. Capitol Ave.
Pierre, SD 57501-3181
Ph: (605)773-3151
Fax: (605)773-6035
Co. E-mail: denrinternet@state.sd.us
URL: http://denr.sd.gov/

60025 ■ Environmental Protection Agency State Superfund Office (Baltimore, Maryland) - Department of the Environment - Recycling in Maryland
1800 Washington Blvd.
Baltimore, MD 21230
Ph: (410)537-3000
Free: 800-633-6101
Co. E-mail: webmaster@mdestate.md.us
URL: http://www.mde.state.md.us/Programs/Land-Programs/Recycling/

60026 ■ Environmental Protection Agency State Superfund Office (Baltimore, Maryland) - Department of the Environment - Recycling in Maryland
1800 Washington Blvd.
Baltimore, MD 21230
Ph: (410)537-3000
Free: 800-633-6101
URL: http://www.mde.maryland.gov/programs/land/recyclingandoperationsprogram/recyclinginmaryland/pages/programs/landprograms/recycling/md_recycling/index.aspx

60027 ■ Environmental Protection Agency State Superfund Office (Waterbury, Virginia) - Department of Environmental Conservation
One South Bldg.
103 S. Main St.
Waterbury, VA 05671-0401
Ph: (802)241-3800
Fax: (802)244-5141
URL: http://www.anr.state.vt.us/dec/dec.htm

60028 ■ Environmental Protection Agency State Superfund Office (Juneau, Alaska) - Department of Environmental Conservation - Division of Air Quality
410 Willoughby Ave., Ste. 303
Juneau, AK 99801
Ph: (907)465-5105
Fax: (907)465-5129
Co. E-mail: commissioner@alaska.gov
URL: http://dec.alaska.gov/air/index.htm

60029 ■ Environmental Protection Agency State Superfund Office (Juneau, Alaska) - Department of Environmental Conservation - Division of Environmental Quality
410 Willoughby Ave., Ste. 303
Juneau, AK 99801-1795
Ph: (907)465-5066
Fax: (907)465-5070
Co. E-mail: dec.commissioner@alaska.gov
URL: http://www.state.ak.us/local/akpages/ENV. CONSERV

60030 ■ Environmental Protection Agency State Superfund Office (Albany, New York) - Department of Environmental Conservation - Division of Environmental Remediation
625 Broadway
Albany, NY 12233-7012
Ph: (518)402-9764
Fax: (518)402-9016
Co. E-mail: derweb@gw.dec.state.ny.us
URL: http://www.dec.ny.gov/chemical/292.html

60031 ■ Environmental Protection Agency State Superfund Office (Albany, New York) - Department of Environmental Conservation - Division of Environmental Remediation - Hazardous Waste Management
625 Broadway
Albany, NY 12233-0001
Ph: (518)402-8560
Fax: (518)402-9016
Co. E-mail: derweb@gw.dec.state.ny.us
URL: http://www.dec.ny.gov/chemical/292.html

60032 ■ Environmental Protection Agency State Superfund Office (Montgomery, Alabama) - Department of Environmental Management - Land Division
1400 Coliseum Blvd.
Montgomery, AL 36110-2400
Ph: (334)271-7700
Fax: (334)271-7950
Co. E-mail: landmail@adem.state.al.us
URL: http://www.adem.state.al.us

60033 ■ Environmental Protection Agency State Superfund Office (Montogomery, Alabama) - Department of Environmental Management - Land Division
1400 Coliseum Blvd.
Montgomery, AL 36130-1463
Ph: (334)271-7700
Fax: (334)271-7950
Co. E-mail: landmail@adem.state.al.us
URL: http://www.adem.state.al.us

60034 ■ Environmental Protection Agency State Superfund Office (Providence, Rhode Island) - Department of Environmental Management - Office of Waste Management
235 Promenade St.
Providence, RI 02908-5767
Ph: (401)222-2797

Fax: (401)222-3812
Co. E-mail: owminfo@dem.ri.gov
URL: http://www.dem.ri.gov/programs/benviron/ waste/index.htm

60035 ■ Environmental Protection Agency State Superfund Office (Providence, Rhode Island) - Department of Environmental Management - Waste Management
235 Promenade St.
Providence, RI 02908-5767
Ph: (401)222-2797
Fax: (401)222-3812
Co. E-mail: tracee.lewis@dem.ri.gov
URL: http://www.dem.ri.gov/programs/benviron/ waste/index.htm

60036 ■ Environmental Protection Agency State Superfund Office (Harrisburg, Pennsylvania) - Department of Environmental Protection - Bureau of Waste Management
PO Box 8471
Harrisburg, PA 17105-8471
Ph: (717)783-2388
Fax: (717)787-1904
Co. E-mail: RA-epcontactus@state.pa.us
URL: http://www.depweb.state.pa.us/landrecwaste/ cwp/view.asp?a=1242Q=455143
URL(s): www.depweb.state.pa.us/portal/server.pt/ community/waste_management/14069. **Telecommunication Services:** RA-epcontactus@pa.gov.

60037 ■ Environmental Protection Agency State Superfund Office (Boston, Massachusetts) - Department of Environmental Protection - Bureau of Waste and Recycling
1 Winter St.
Boston, MA 02108
Ph: (617)292-5500
Fax: (617)556-1049
URL: http://www.mass.gov/dep/recycle/

60038 ■ Environmental Protection Agency State Superfund Office (Frankfort, Kentucky) - Department for Environmental Protection - Division of Waste Management
200 Fair Oaks Ln.
Frankfort, KY 40601
Ph: (502)564-6716
Fax: (502)564-4049
Co. E-mail: waste@ky.gov
URL: http://www.waste.ky.gov

60039 ■ Environmental Protection Agency State Superfund Office (Frankfort, Kentucky) - Department for Environmental Protection - Division of Waste Management
200 Fair Oaks Ln.
Frankfort, KY 40601
Ph: (502)564-6716
Fax: (502)564-4049
Co. E-mail: waste@ky.gov
URL: http://www.waste.ky.gov

60040 ■ Environmental Protection Agency State Superfund Office (Tallahassee, Florida) - Department of Environmental Protection - Division of Waste Management
2600 Blair Stone Rd.
Mail Stop 4500
Tallahassee, FL 32399-2400
Ph: (850)245-8705
Fax: (850)-245-8703
URL: http://www.dep.state.fl.us/waste

60041 ■ Environmental Protection Agency State Superfund Office (Tallahassee, Florida) - Department of Environmental Protection - Division of Waste Management
2600 Blair Stone Rd.
Mail Stop 4500
Tallahassee, FL 32399-2400
Ph: (850)245-8705
Fax: (850)245-8703
URL: http://www.dep.state.fl.us/waste

60042 ■ Environmental Protection Agency State Superfund Office (Trenton, New Jersey) - Department of Environmental Protection - Hazardous Waste Management Division
401 E. State St.
Mail code 401-02C
Trenton, NJ 08625
Ph: (609)633-1418
Fax: (609)633-1112
URL: http://www.nj.gov/dep/dshw/

60043 ■ Environmental Protection Agency State Superfund Office (Augusta, Maine) - Department of Environmental Protection - Office of the Commissioner
17 State House Station
Augusta, ME 04333-0017
Ph: (207)287-7688
Free: 800-452-1942
Fax: (207)287-7826
URL: http://www.maine.gov/dep/index.shtml

60044 ■ Environmental Protection Agency State Superfund Office (Augusta, Maine) - Department of Environmental Protection - Office of the Commissioner
17 State House Station
Augusta, ME 04333-0017
Ph: (207)287-7688
Free: 800-452-1942
Fax: (207)287-7826
URL: http://www.maine.gov/dep/index.shtml

60045 ■ Environmental Protection Agency State Superfund Office (Hartford, Connecticut) - Department of Environmental Protection - Small Business Assistance
79 Elm St.
Hartford, CT 06106-5127
Ph: (860)424-3000
Fax: (860)424-4051
Co. E-mail: dep.webmaster@po.state.ct.us
URL: http://www.ct.gov/dep/cwp/view. asp?a=2715q=324950depNav_GID=1626depNav=l

60046 ■ Environmental Protection Agency State Superfund Office (Trenton, New Jersey) - Department of Environmental Protection - Solid and Hazardous Waste Management Program
401 E. State St.
Trenton, NJ 08625
Ph: (609)633-1418
Fax: (609)633-1112
URL: http://www.nj.gov/dep/dshw/

60047 ■ Environmental Protection Agency State Superfund Office (Boston, Massachusetts) - Department of Environmental Protection - Waste and Recycling
1 Winter St.
Boston, MA 02108
Ph: (617)292-5500
Fax: (617)556-1049
Co. E-mail: john.fischer@state.ma.us
URL: http://www.mass.gov/dep/recycle/

60048 ■ Environmental Protection Agency State Superfund Office (Helena, Montana) - Department of Environmental Quality
Lee Metcalf Bldg.
1520 E. 6th Ave.
Helena, MT 59620-0901
Ph: (406)444-2544
Fax: (406)444-4386
URL: http://deq.mt.gov

60049 ■ Environmental Protection Agency State Superfund Office (Helena, Montana) - Department of Environmental Quality
Lee Metcalf Bldg.
1520 E. 6th Ave.
Helena, MT 59620-0901
Ph: (406)444-2544
Fax: (406)444-4386
URL: http://deq.mt.gov

60050 ■ Environmental Protection Agency State Superfund Office (Jackson, Mississippi) - Department of Environmental Quality
PO Box 2249
Jackson, MS 39225
Ph: (601)961-5171
Free: 888-786-0661
Fax: (601)354-6612
URL: http://www.deq.state.ms.us/MDEQ.nsf/page/
About_Commission?OpenDocument

60051 ■ Environmental Protection Agency State Superfund Office (Jackson, Mississippi) - Department of Environmental Quality
PO Box 2249
Jackson, MS 39225
Ph: (601)961-5171
Free: 888-786-0661
Fax: (601)354-6612
URL: http://www.deq.state.ms.us/

60052 ■ Environmental Protection Agency State Superfund Office (Waterbury, Virginia) - Department of Environmental Quality
One South Bldg.
103 S. Main St.
Waterbury, VA 05671-0401
Ph: (802)241-3800
Fax: (802)244-5141
URL: http://www.anr.state.vt.us/dec/dec.htm

60053 ■ Environmental Protection Agency State Superfund Office (Lincoln, Nebraska) - Department of Environmental Quality - Air and Waste Management Division
1200 N St., Ste. 400
Lincoln, NE 68509
Ph: (402)471-2186
Fax: (402)471-2909
URL: http://www.deq.state.ne.us

60054 ■ Environmental Protection Agency State Superfund Office (Lincoln, Nebraska) - Department of Environmental Quality - Air and Waste Management Division
1200 N St., Ste. 400
Lincoln, NE 68509
Ph: (402)471-2186
Fax: (402)471-2909
URL: http://www.deq.state.ne.us

60055 ■ Environmental Protection Agency State Superfund Office (Salt Lake City, Utah) - Department of Environmental Quality - Division of Air Quality
150 N. 1950 W.
Salt Lake City, UT 84114-4810
Ph: (801)536-4022
Free: 800-224-5434
URL: http://www.airquality.utah.gov/

60056 ■ Environmental Protection Agency State Superfund Office (Salt Lake City, Utah) - Department of Environmental Quality - Division of Air Quality
195 N. 1950 W., 4th Fl.
Salt Lake City, UT 84116
Ph: (801)536-4000
Free: 800-224-5434
Fax: (801)536-4099
URL: http://www.airquality.utah.gov/

60057 ■ Environmental Protection Agency State Superfund Office (Portland, Oregon) - Department of Environmental Quality - Environmental Cleanup Division
811 6th Ave.
Portland, OR 97204-1390
Ph: (503)229-5696
Free: 800-452-4011
Fax: (503)229-6124
Co. E-mail: wistar.gil@deq.state.or.us
URL: http://www.deq.state.or.us/lq/ecsi/ecsi.htm

60058 ■ Environmental Protection Agency State Superfund Office (Portland, Oregon) - Department of Environmental Quality -

Environmental Cleanup Site Information
811 SW 6th Ave.
Portland, OR 97204-1390
Ph: (503)229-5696
Free: 800-452-4011
Fax: (503)229-6124
Co. E-mail: wistar.gil@deq.state.or.us
URL: http://www.deq.state.or.us/lq/ecsi/ecsi.htm

60059 ■ Environmental Protection Agency State Superfund Office (Boise, Idaho) - Department of Environmental Quality - Hazardous Waste Management
1410 N. Hilton
Boise, ID 83706
Ph: (208)373-0502
Fax: (208)373-0417
URL: http://www.deq.state.id.us/waste/prog_issues.
cfm#haz

60060 ■ Environmental Protection Agency State Superfund Office (Oaklahoma City, Oklahoma) - Department of Environmental Quality - Land Protection Division
PO Box 1677
Oklahoma City, OK 73101-1677
Ph: (405)702-5100
Fax: (405)702-5101
Co. E-mail: scott.thompson@deq.state.ok.us
URL: http://www.deq.state.ok.us/LPDnew/index.htm

60061 ■ Environmental Protection Agency State Superfund Office (Oklahoma City, Oklahoma) - Department of Environmental Quality - Land Protection Division
PO Box 1677
Oklahoma City, OK 73101-1677
Ph: (405)702-5100
Fax: (405)702-5101
Co. E-mail: scott.thompson@deq.state.ok.us
URL: http://www.deq.state.ok.us/LPDnew/index.htm

60062 ■ Environmental Protection Agency State Superfund Office (Phoenix, Arizona) - Department of Environmental Quality - Office of Waste and Water Quality
1110 W. Washington St.
Phoenix, AZ 85007
Ph: (602)771-2300
Free: 800-234-5677
URL: http://www.azdeq.gov

60063 ■ Environmental Protection Agency State Superfund Office (Phoenix, Arizona) - Department of Environmental Quality - Office of Waste and Water Quality
1110 W. Washington St.
Phoenix, AZ 85007
Ph: (602)771-2300
Free: 800-234-5677
URL: http://www.azdeq.gov

60064 ■ Environmental Protection Agency State Superfund Office (North Little Rock, Arkansas) - Department of Environmental Quality - Waste Programs Division
5301 Northshore Dr.
North Little Rock, AR 72118-5317
Ph: (501)682-0833
Fax: (501)682-0565
Co. E-mail: rhodesc@adeq.state.ar.us
URL: http://www.adeq.state.ar.us/hazwaste/

60065 ■ Environmental Protection Agency State Superfund Office (North Little Rock, Arkansas) - Department of Environmental Quality - Waste Programs Division
5301 Northshore Dr.
North Little Rock, AR 72118-5317
Ph: (501)682-0831
Fax: (501)682-0565
Co. E-mail: hynum@adeq.state.ar.us
URL: http://www.adeq.state.ar.us/hazwaste/

60066 ■ Environmental Protection Agency State Superfund Office (Cheyenne, Wyoming) - Department of Environmental Quality -

Water Quality Division
Herscler Bldg., 4th Fl. W.
122 W. 25th St.
Cheyenne, WY 82001
Ph: (307)777-7781
Fax: (307)777-5973
Co. E-mail: kguill@wyo.gov
URL: http://deq.state.wy.us

60067 ■ Environmental Protection Agency State Superfund Office (Cheyenne, Wyoming) - Department of Environmental Quality - Water Quality Division
Herscler Bldg., 4th Fl. W.
122 W. 25th St.
Cheyenne, WY 82002
Ph: (307)777-7781
Fax: (307)777-5973
URL: http://deq.state.wy.us/wqd/

60068 ■ Environmental Protection Agency State Superfund Office (Concord, New Hampshire) - Department of Environmental Services - Commissioners Office
29 Hazen Dr.
Concord, NH 03301
Ph: (603)271-4974
Fax: (603)271-2867
URL: http://des.nh.gov

60069 ■ Environmental Protection Agency State Superfund Office (Concord, New Hampshire) - Department of Environmental Services - Office of the Commissioner
29 Hazen Dr.
Concord, NH 03302-0095
Ph: (603)271-4974
Fax: (603)271-2867
Co. E-mail: Thomas.burack@des.nh.gov
URL: http://des.nh.gov

60070 ■ Environmental Protection Agency State Superfund Office (Bismarck, North Dakota) - Department of Health - Division of Waste Management
918 E. Divide Ave., 3rd Fl.
Bismarck, ND 58501-1947
Ph: (701)328-5166
Fax: (701)328-5200
Co. E-mail: health@nd.gov
URL: http://www.health.state.nd.us/WM/

60071 ■ Environmental Protection Agency State Superfund Office (Topeka, Kansas) - Department of Health and Environment - Bureau of Waste Management - Storage Tank Section
Curtis State Office Bldg.
1000 SW Jackson, Ste. 320
Topeka, KS 66612-1366
Ph: (785)296-1600
Fax: (785)368-8909
Co. E-mail: bwm_web@kdhe.state.ks.us
URL: http://www.kdheks.gov/waste/index.html

60072 ■ Environmental Protection Agency State Superfund Office (Topeka, Kansas) - Department of Health and Environment - Bureau of Waste Management - Storage Tank Section
Curtis State Office Bldg.
1000 SW Jackson, Ste. 320
Topeka, KS 66612-1366
Ph: (785)296-1600
Fax: (785)296-8909
Co. E-mail: bwm_web@kdhe.state.ks.us
URL: http://www.kdheks.gov/waste/index.html

60073 ■ Environmental Protection Agency State Superfund Office (Columbia, South Carolina) - Department of Health and Environmental Control
2600 Bull St.
Columbia, SC 29201
Ph: (803)898-4000
Fax: (803)896-4001
URL: http://www.scdhec.gov/

60074 ■ Environmental Protection Agency State Superfund Office (Columbia, South Carolina) - Department of Health and Environmental Control
2600 Bull St.
Columbia, SC 29201
Ph: (803)898-4000
Fax: (803)896-4001
URL: http://www.scdhec.gov/

60075 ■ Environmental Protection Agency State Superfund Office (Boise, Idaho) - Department of Health - Environmental Health - Solid and Hazardous Waste Branch
1410 N. Hilton
Boise, ID 83706
Fax: (208)373-0417

60076 ■ Environmental Protection Agency State Superfund Office (Honolulu, Hawaii) - Department of Health - Environmental Management Division
1250 Punchbowl St.
Honolulu, HI 96813
Ph: (808)586-4304
Fax: (808)586-4444
URL: http://www.hawaii.gov/health/about/admin/en-viro.html

60077 ■ Environmental Protection Agency State Superfund Office (Honolulu, Hawaii) - Department of Health - Environmental Management Division
1250 Punchbowl St.
Honolulu, HI 96813
Ph: (808)586-4304
Fax: (808)586-4444
URL: http://www.hawaii.gov/health/about/admin/en-viro.html

60078 ■ Environmental Protection Agency State Superfund Office (Bismarck, North Dakota) - Department of Health - Waste Management Division
918 E. Divide Ave., 3rd Fl.
Bismarck, ND 58501-1947
Ph: (701)328-5166
Fax: (701)328-5200
Co. E-mail: sradig@nd.gov
URL: http://www.health.state.nd.us/WM/

60079 ■ Environmental Protection Agency State Superfund Office (Madison, Wisconsin) - Department of Natural Resources - Bureau of Waste Management
101 S. Webster St.
Madison, WI 53707
Ph: (608)266-2621
Fax: (608)261-4380
Co. E-mail: DNRWasteMaterials@Wisconsin.gov
URL: http://dnr.wi.gov/staffdir/dynamic/hazwaste.asp

60080 ■ Environmental Protection Agency State Superfund Office (Dover, Delaware) - Department of Natural Resources and Environmental Control - Air and Waste Management Section
89 Kings Hwy.
Dover, DE 19901
Ph: (302)739-9400
Fax: (302)739-3106
URL: http://www.dnrec.delaware.gov/Pages/default.aspx

60081 ■ Environmental Protection Agency State Superfund Office (Dover, Delaware) - Department of Natural Resources and Environmental Control - Division of Waste and Hazardous Substances
89 Kings Hwy.
Dover, DE 19901
Ph: (302)739-9400
Fax: (302)739-5060
URL: http://www.dnrec.delaware.gov/Pages/default.aspx

60082 ■ Environmental Protection Agency State Superfund Office (Jefferson City, Missouri) - Department of Natural Resources - Hazardous Waste Management Program
PO Box 176
Jefferson City, MO 65102
Ph: (573)751-5401
Free: 800-361-4827
Fax: (573)571-7569
Co. E-mail: swmp@dnr.mo.gov
URL: http://www.dnr.mo.gov/env/swmp/

60083 ■ Environmental Protection Agency State Superfund Office (Jerfferson City, Missouri) - Department of Natural Resources - Hazardous Waste Management Program
PO Box 176
Jefferson City, MO 65102
Ph: (573)751-5401
Free: 800-361-4827
Fax: (573)571-7569
Co. E-mail: hazwaste@dnr.mo.gov
URL: http://www.dnr.mo.gov/env/swmp/

60084 ■ Environmental Protection Agency State Superfund Office (Atlanta, Georgia) - Department of Natural Resources - Land Protection Branch - Solid Waste Management Program
East Tower
2 Martin Luther King Jr. Dr. SE, Ste. 1252
Atlanta, GA 30334
Ph: (404)656-3500
URL: http://www.gadnr.org

60085 ■ Environmental Protection Agency State Superfund Office (Atlanta, Georgia) - Department of Natural Resources - Land Protection Branch - Solid Waste Management Program
2 Martin Luther King Jr. Dr. SE, Ste. 1252
Atlanta, GA 30334
Ph: (404)656-3500
URL: http://www.gadnr.org

60086 ■ Environmental Protection Agency State Superfund Office (Des Moines, Iowa) - Department of Natural Resources Waste Management - Air Quality Bureau - Water Supply Section
Wallace Bldg.
502 E. 9th St.
Des Moines, IA 50319-0034
Ph: (515)281-5918
Fax: (515)281-8895
URL: http://www.iowadnr.com/air/

60087 ■ Environmental Protection Agency State Superfund Office (Des Moines, Iowa) - Department of Natural Resources Waste Management - Air Quality Bureau - Water Supply Section
7900 Hickman Rd., Ste. 1
Windsor Heights, IA 50324
Ph: (515)242-5100
Fax: (515)242-5094
URL: http://www.iowadnr.gov/air/

60088 ■ Environmental Protection Agency State Superfund Office (Madison, Wisconsin) - Department of Natural Resources - Waste and Materials Management
101 S. Webster St.
Madison, WI 53707
Ph: (608)266-2621
Fax: (608)261-4380
Co. E-mail: DNR_WasteMaterials@Wisconsin.gov
URL: http://dnr.wi.gov/org/aw/wm/

60089 ■ Environmental Protection Agency State Superfund Office (Denver, Colorado) - Department of Public Health and Environment - Hazardous Materials and Waste Management Division
4300 Cherry Creek Dr., S.
Denver, CO 80246-1530
Ph: (303)692-3320

Free: 888-569-1831
Fax: (303)759-5355
Co. E-mail: comments.hmwmd@state.co.us
URL: http://www.cdphe.state.co.us/hm/index.htm

60090 ■ Environmental Protection Agency State Superfund Office (Denver, Colorado) - Department of Public Health and Environment - Hazardous Materials and Waste Management Division
4300 Cherry Creek Dr. S.
Denver, CO 80246-1530
Ph: (303)692-3320
Free: 888-569-1831
Fax: (303)759-5355
Co. E-mail: comments.hmwmd@state.co.us
URL: http://www.cdphe.state.co.us/hm/index.htm

60091 ■ Environmental Protection Agency State Superfund Office (Sacramento, California) - Department of Toxic Substances Control
PO Box 806
Sacramento, CA 95812-0806
Ph: (916)255-3545
Free: 800-728-6942
Fax: (916)255-3785
Co. E-mail: webcoord@dtsc.ca.gov
URL: http://www.dtsc.ca.gov

60092 ■ Environmental Protection Agency State Superfund Office (Sacramento, California) - Department of Toxic Substances Control
PO Box 806
Sacramento, CA 95812-0806
Ph: (916)255-3545
Free: 800-728-6942
Fax: (916)255-3785
Co. E-mail: webcoord@dtsc.ca.gov
URL: http://www.dtsc.ca.gov

60093 ■ Environmental Protection Agency State Superfund Office (Carson City, Nevada) - Division of Environmental Protection - Department of Conservation and Natural Resources
901 S. Stewart St., Ste. 4001
Carson City, NV 89701-5249
Ph: (775)687-4670
Fax: (775)687-5856
URL: http://www.ndep.nv.gov

60094 ■ Environmental Protection Agency State Superfund Office (Carson City, Nevada) - Division of Environmental Protection - Department of Conservation and Natural Resources
901 S. Stewart St., Ste. 4001
Carson City, NV 89701-5249
Ph: (775)687-4670
Fax: (775)687-5856
URL: http://www.ndep.nv.gov

60095 ■ Environmental Protection Agency State Superfund Office (Charleston, West Virginia) - Division of Environmental Protection - Office of Waste Management
601 57th St.
Charleston, WV 25304
Ph: (304)926-0455
Fax: (304)368-3959

60096 ■ Environmental Protection Agency State Superfund Office (Charleston, West Virginia) - Division of Environmental Protection - Office of Waste Management
601 57th St.
Charleston, WV 25304
Ph: (304)926-0455
Fax: (304)368-3959

60097 ■ Environmental Protection Agency State Superfund Office (Columbus, Ohio) - Division of Environmental Response and Revitalization
50 W. Town St., Ste. 700
Columbus, OH 43215

Ph: (614)644-2924
Fax: (614)644-3146
Co. E-mail: epaderrweb@epa.state.oh.us
URL: http://www.epa.state.oh.us/derr/

60098 ■ Environmental Protection Agency State Superfund Office (Washington, District of Columbia) - Environmental Health Administration - Hazardous Materials, Pesticides and Underground Storage Tank Management
51 N. St., NE
Washington, DC 20020
Ph: (202)532-2500
URL: http://www.doh.dc.gov

60099 ■ Environmental Protection Agency State Superfund Office (Washington, District of Columbia) - Environmental Health Administration - Hazardous Materials, Pesticides and Underground Storage Tank Management
51 N. St., NE
Washington, DC 20020
URL: http://www.doh.dc.gov

60100 ■ Environmental Protection Agency State Superfund Office (Santa Fe, New Mexico) - Environmental Improvement Division - Hazardous Waste Bureau
2905 Rodeo Park Dr. E., Bldg. 1
Santa Fe, NM 87505-6313
Ph: (505)476-6000
Fax: (505)476-6030
URL: http://www.nmenv.state.nm.us/hwb/

60101 ■ Environmental Protection Agency State Superfund Office (Santa Fe, New Mexico) - Environmental Improvement Division - Hazardous Waste Bureau
2905 Rodeo Park Dr. E., Bldg. 1
Santa Fe, NM 87505-6303
Ph: (505)476-6000
Fax: (505)476-6030
URL: http://www.nmenv.state.nm.us/HWB/

60102 ■ Environmental Protection Agency State Superfund Office (Barrigada, Guam) - Environmental Protection Agency
GMF
Barrigada, GU 96921
Ph: (671)475-1658
Fax: (671)477-9402
URL: http://www.guamepa.govguam.net

60103 ■ Environmental Protection Agency State Superfund Office (Barrigada, Guam) - Environmental Protection Agency
Bldg. 17-3304, Mariner Ave.
Barrigada, GU 96921
Ph: (671)475-1658
Fax: (671)475-8007
URL: http://epa.guam.gov/

60104 ■ Environmental Protection Agency State Superfund Office (Springfield, Illinois) - Environmental Protection Agency - Bureau of Land - Pollution Prevention
1021 North Grand Ave., E.
Springfield, IL 62794-9276
Ph: (217)557-8761
Co. E-mail: David.Jansen@illinois.gov
URL: http://www.epa.state.il.us/land/

60105 ■ Environmental Protection Agency State Superfund Office (Springfield, Illinois) - Environmental Protection Agency - Bureau of Land - Pollution Prevention
1021 North Grand Ave. E., MC No. 10
Springfield, IL 62794-9276
Ph: (217)557-8761
Co. E-mail: David.Jansen@illinois.gov
URL: http://www.epa.state.il.us/land/

60106 ■ Environmental Protection Agency State Superfund Office (Columbus, Ohio) - Environmental Protection Agency - Division of Environmental Response and

Revitalization
50 W. Town St., Ste. 700
Columbus, OH 43216-1049
Ph: (614)644-2924
Fax: (614)644-3146
Co. E-mail: derrwebmail@epa.state.oh.us
URL: http://www.epa.state.oh.us/derr/

60107 ■ Environmental Protection Agency State Superfund Office (Indianapolis, Indiana) - Indiana Department of Environmental Management - Office of Environmental Response - Office of Land Quality
Indiana Government Center-North
100 N. Senate Ave.
Indianapolis, IN 46204-2251
Ph: (317)232-8603
Free: 800-451-6027
Fax: (317)233-6647
URL: http://www.in.gov/idem/

60108 ■ Environmental Protection Agency State Superfund Office (Indianapolis, Indiana) - Indiana Department of Environmental Management - Office of Environmental Response - Office of Land Quality
Indiana Government Center-North
100 N. Senate Ave.
Indianapolis, IN 46204-2251
Ph: (317)232-8603
Free: 800-451-6027
Fax: (317)233-6647
URL: http://www.in.gov/idem/

60109 ■ Environmental Protection Agency State Superfund Office (Lansing, Michigan) - Michigan Department of Environmental Quality - Waste Management Division
525 W. Allegan St.
Lansing, MI 48909-7973
Ph: (517)373-7917
Free: 800-292-4706
Fax: (517)373-7917
URL: http://www.michigan.gov/deq

60110 ■ Environmental Protection Agency State Superfund Office (Lansing, Michigan) - Michigan Department of Environmental Quality - Waste Management Division
525 W. Allegan St.
Lansing, MI 48909-7973
Ph: (517)373-7917
Free: 800-292-4706
Fax: (517)241-7401
Co. E-mail: deq-officeofcommunications@michigan.
   gov
URL: http://www.michigan.gov/deq

60111 ■ Environmental Protection Agency State Superfund Office (St. Paul, Minnesota) - Pollution Control Agency - Groundwater & Solid Waste Division
520 Lafayette Rd., N.
St. Paul, MN 55155-4194
Ph: (651)296-6300
Free: 800-657-3864
URL: http://www.pca.state.mn.us/index.cfm

60112 ■ Environmental Protection Agency State Superfund Office (St. Paul, Minnesota) - Pollution Control Agency - Groundwater & Solid Waste Division
520 Lafayette Rd. N.
St. Paul, MN 55155-4194
Ph: (651)296-6300
Free: 800-657-3864
URL: http://www.pca.state.mn.us/index.cfm

60113 ■ Environmental Protection Agency State Superfund Office (Austin, Texas) - Water Commission - Hazardous and Solid Waste Division - Superfund and Emergency Response Section
PO Box 13087
Austin, TX 78711-3087
Ph: (512)239-5500

Fax: (512)239-5533
Co. E-mail: ac@tceq.tx.gov
URL: http://www.tceq.texas.gov/response/

EXECUTIVE OFFICE OF THE PRESIDENT

60114 ■ Executive Office of the President - Office of Management and Budget - Administrator of the Small Business Administration
409 3rd St., Ste. 7000
Washington, DC 20416
URL: http://www.sba.gov/administrator/7585/3215

60115 ■ Executive Office of the President - Office of Management and Budget - Office of Federal Procurement Policy
725 17th St. NW
Washington, DC 20503
Ph: (202)395-3080
Fax: (202)395-3888
URL: http://www.whitehouse.gov/omb/

60116 ■ Executive Office of the President - Office of Management and Budget - Office of Federal Procurement Policy
725 17th St. NW
Washington, DC 20503
Ph: (202)395-3080
Fax: (202)395-3888
URL: http://www.whitehouse.gov/omb/procurement_
   default/

60117 ■ Executive Office of the President - Office of Management and Budget - Small Business Administration
725 17th St. NW
Washington, DC 20503
Ph: (202)395-1096
Fax: (202)395-3888
URL: http://www.whitehouse.gov/omb/

EXPORT-IMPORT BANK OF THE UNITED STATES

60118 ■ Export-Import Bank of the United States
811 Vermont Ave. NW
Washington, DC 20571
Ph: (202)565-3946
Free: 800-565-3946
Fax: (202)565-3931
URL: http://www.exim.gov/

Description: The Export-Import Bank of the United States assists in financing and in facilitating the export sales of U.S. goods and services. Programs directed at small businesses include pre-export guarantees to assist small and medium-sized businesses in obtaining working capital from financial entities for export-related activities such as inventory purchases or the manufacture of goods; a small business insurance policy, that assists in providing risk protection on export receivables for companies just beginning to export or with limited export volumes; and loan and guarantee programs that enable U.S. banks to offer medium-term, fixed-rate export loans to finance the sales of products and services produced or performed by small businesses. Nonfinancial assistance includes the operation of the Eximbank Hotline (800-565-EXIM). Through this service, Eximbank International Business Development Division is available to assist more business owners in developing competitive export financing plans, answer questions regarding Eximbank financing programs, and explain how to apply for Eximbank assistance, where to locate credit insurance, or how to make maximum use of complementary export programs offered by other U.S. government agencies. In addition, Eximbank offers monthly seminars in Washington, D.C., to help firms new to exporting understand the programs available from the federal government.

60119 ■ Export-Import Bank of the United States
811 Vermont Ave. NW
Washington, DC 20571
Ph: (202)565-3946
Free: 800-565-3946
Fax: (202)565-3931
Co. E-mail: smallbizhelp@exim.gov
URL: http://www.exim.gov/

Description: The Export-Import Bank of the United States assists in financing and in facilitating the export sales of U.S. goods and services. Programs directed at small businesses include pre-export guarantees to assist small and medium-sized businesses in obtaining working capital from financial entities for export-related activities such as inventory purchases or the manufacture of goods; a small business insurance policy, that assists in providing risk protection on export receivables for companies just beginning to export or with limited export volumes; and loan and guarantee programs that enable U.S. banks to offer medium-term, fixed-rate export loans to finance the sales of products and services produced or performed by small businesses. Nonfinancial assistance includes the operation of the Eximbank Hotline (800-565-EXIM). Through this service, Eximbank International Business Development Division is available to assist more business owners in developing competitive export financing plans, answer questions regarding Eximbank financing programs, and explain how to apply for Eximbank assistance, where to locate credit insurance, or how to make maximum use of complementary export programs offered by other U.S. government agencies. In addition, Eximbank offers monthly seminars in Washington, D.C., to help firms new to exporting understand the programs available from the federal government.

60120 ■ Export-Import Bank of the United States - Domestic Business Development
811 Vermont Ave., NW, Rm. 919
Washington, DC 20571-0002
Ph: (202)565-3900
Fax: (202)565-7731
Co. E-mail: info@exim.gov
URL: http://www.exim.gov

60121 ■ Export-Import Bank of the United States - Domestic Business Development
811 Vermont Ave., NW, Rm. 919
Washington, DC 20571-0002
Ph: (202)565-3900
Fax: (202)565-7731
Co. E-mail: info@exim.gov
URL: http://www.exim.gov

60122 ■ Export-Import Bank of the United States - Global Business Development
811 Vermont Ave., NW, Rm. 907
Washington, DC 20571-0002
Ph: (202)565-3674
Fax: (202)565-3961
Co. E-mail: ray.ellis@exim.gov
URL: http://www.exim.gov

60123 ■ Export-Import Bank of the United States - International Business Development
811 Vermont Ave., NW, Rm. 1123
Washington, DC 20571-0002
Ph: (202)565-3224
Fax: (202)565-3961
Co. E-mail: info@exim.gov
URL: http://www.exim.gov

60124 ■ Export-Import Bank of the United States - International Business Development Division
811 Vermont Ave., NW, Rm. 1123
Washington, DC 20571-0002
Ph: (202)565-3939
Fax: (202)565-3961
Co. E-mail: Michael.Forgione@exim.gov
URL: http://www.exim.gov

60125 ■ Export-Import Bank of the United States - Midwest Regional Office - Chicago Regional Office & U.S. Export Assistance Center
200 W. Adams St., Ste. 2450
Chicago, IL 60606
Ph: (312)353-8081
Fax: (312)353-8098
URL: http://www.exim.gov/contact/con_chi.cfm

60126 ■ Export-Import Bank of the United States - Midwest Regional Office - Chicago Regional Office & U.S. Export Assistance Center
200 W. Adams St., Ste. 2450
Chicago, IL 60606
Ph: (312)353-8081
Fax: (312)353-8098
URL: http://www.exim.gov/contact/con_chi.cfm

60127 ■ Export-Import Bank of the United States - Northeast and Mid-Atlantic Regional Office - New York City Regional Office
33 Whitehall St., 2nd Fl., Ste. B
New York, NY 10004
Ph: (212)809-2650
Fax: (212)809-2687
URL: http://www.exim.gov/contact/con_nyc.cfm

60128 ■ Export-Import Bank of the United States - Northeast and Mid-Atlantic Regional Office - New York City Regional Office
33 Whitehall St., 22nd Fl., Ste. B
New York, NY 10004
Ph: (212)809-2650
Fax: (212)809-2687
URL: http://www.exim.gov/contact/con_nyc.cfm

60129 ■ Export-Import Bank of the United States - Office of Administration and Security
811 Vermont Ave., NW, Rm. 1023
Washington, DC 20571-0002
Ph: (202)565-3312
Co. E-mail: jt.mcmullen@.emim.gov
URL: http://www.exim.gov

60130 ■ Export-Import Bank of the United States - Office of Administration and Security
811 Vermont Ave., NW, Rm. 1023
Washington, DC 20571-0002
Co. E-mail: jt.mcmullen@.emim.gov
URL: http://www.exim.gov

60131 ■ Export-Import Bank of the United States - Office of Contracting Services
811 Vermont Ave., NW, Rm. 1023
Washington, DC 20571-0002
Ph: (202)565-3330
Fax: (202)565-3528
Co. E-mail: angela.fortune@exim.gov
URL: http://www.exim.gov

60132 ■ Export-Import Bank of the United States - Office of Contracting Services
811 Vermont Ave. NW
Washington, DC 20571
Ph: (202)565-3946
Free: 800-565-3946
Fax: (202)565-3380
URL: http://www.exim.gov

60133 ■ Export-Import Bank of the United States - Office of Operations
811 Vermont Ave. NW, Rm. 907
Washington, DC 20571-0002
Ph: (202)565-3946
Fax: (202)565-3961
Co. E-mail: ray.ellis@exim.gov
URL: http://www.exim.gov

60134 ■ Export-Import Bank of the United States - Southeast Regional Office - Miami Regional Office
5835 Blue Lagoon Dr., Ste. 203
Miami, FL 33126
Ph: (305)526-7436
Fax: (305)526-7435
URL: http://www.exim.gov/contact/con_mia.cfm

60135 ■ Export-Import Bank of the United States - Southeast Regional Office - Miami Regional Office
5835 Blue Lagoon Dr., Ste. 203
Miami, FL 33126
Ph: (305)526-7436
Fax: (305)526-7435
URL: http://www.exim.gov/contact/con_mia.cfm

60136 ■ Export-Import Bank of the United States - Southwest Regional Office - Houston Regional Office
1880 S. Dairy Ashford II, Ste. 585
Houston, TX 77077
Ph: (281)721-0465
Fax: (281)679-0156
URL: http://www.exim.gov/contact/con_mia.cfm

60137 ■ Export-Import Bank of the United States - Southwest Regional Office - Houston Regional Office
1880 S. Dairy Ashford II, Ste. 405
Houston, TX 77077
Ph: (281)721-0465
Fax: (281)679-0156
URL: http://www.exim.gov/contact/con_hou.cfm

60138 ■ Export-Import Bank of the United States - Western Regional Office - Long Beach Regional Office
1 World Trade Center, St. 1670
Long Beach, CA 90831
Ph: (562)980-4580
Fax: (562)980-4590
URL: http://www.exim.gov

60139 ■ Export-Import Bank of the United States - Western Regional Office - Long Beach Regional Office
1 World Trade Center, St. 1670
Long Beach, CA 90831
URL: http://www.exim.gov

60140 ■ Export-Import Bank of the United States - Western Regional Office - Northern California Office
250 Montgomery St., 14th Fl.
San Francisco, CA 94104
Ph: (415)705-2285
Fax: (415)705-1156
URL: http://www.exim.gov/contact/con_sf.cfm

60141 ■ Export-Import Bank of the United States - Western Regional Office - Northern California Office
50 Fremont St., Ste. 2450
San Francisco, CA 94105
Ph: (415)705-2285
Fax: (415)705-1156
URL: http://www.exim.gov/contact/con_sf.cfm

60142 ■ Export-Import Bank of the United States - Western Regional Office - San Diego Office
9449 Balboa Ave., Ste. 111
San Diego, CA 92123
Ph: (858)467-7035
Fax: (858)467-7043
URL: http://www.exim.gov/contact/con_sd.cfm

60143 ■ Export-Import Bank of the United States - Western Regional Office - San Diego Office
9449 Balboa Ave., Ste. 111
San Diego, CA 92123
Ph: (858)467-7035
Fax: (858)467-7043
URL: http://www.exim.gov/contact/con_sd.cfm

FARM CREDIT ADMINISTRATION

60144 ■ Farm Credit Administration - Office of Equal Employment Opportunity
1501 Farm Credit Dr., Rm. 4301
McLean, VA 22102-5090
Ph: (703)883-4353

Fax: (703)883-4200
URL: http://www.fca.gov

60145 ■ Farm Credit Administration - Office of Equal Employment Opportunity and Inclusion
1501 Farm Credit Dr.
McLean, VA 22102-5090
Ph: (703)883-4353
Fax: (703)883-4200
Co. E-mail: info-line@fca.gov
URL: http://www.fca.gov

60146 ■ Farm Credit Administration - Office of Inspector General
1501 Farm Credit Dr., Rm. 2328
McLean, VA 22102-5090
Ph: (703)883-4030
Co. E-mail: info-line@fca.gov
URL: http://www.fca.gov/home/inspector.html

60147 ■ Farm Credit Administration - Office of Inspector General
1501 Farm Credit Dr.
McLean, VA 22102-5090
Ph: (703)883-4030
Co. E-mail: clinefelterc@fca.gov
URL: http://www.fca.gov/home/inspector.html

60148 ■ Farm Credit Administration - Office of Management Services
1501 Farm Credit Dr.
McLean, VA 22102-5090
Ph: (703)883-4200
URL: http://www.fca.gov

60149 ■ Farm Credit Administration - Office of Management Services
1501 Farm Credit Dr.
McLean, VA 22102-5090
Ph: (703)883-4200
Co. E-mail: smiths@fca.gov
URL: http://www.fca.gov/about/offices/offices.html

60150 ■ Farm Credit Administration (FCA) - Office of Management Services - Office of Procurement
1501 Farm Credit Dr.
McLean, VA 22102-5090
Ph: (703)883-4378
Co. E-mail: info-line@fca.gov
URL: http://www.fca.gov/FCA-Web/
fca%20new%20site/about/procurement.html

60151 ■ Farm Credit Administration (FCA) - Office of Procurement
1501 Farm Credit Dr.
McLean, VA 22102-5090
Ph: (703)883-4056
Co. E-mail: info-line@fca.gov
URL: http://www.fca.gov

FEDERAL COMMUNICATIONS COMMISSION

60152 ■ Federal Communications Commission - Administrative Law Division
445 12th St., SW
Washington, DC 20554
Ph: (202)418-1720
Free: 888-835-5322
Fax: (866)418-0232
Co. E-mail: fccinfo@fcc.gov
URL: http://www.fcc.gov/ogc/admain.html

60153 ■ Federal Communications Commission - Administrative Law Division
445 12th St. SW
Washington, DC 20554
Free: 888-835-5322
Fax: (866)418-0232
Co. E-mail: fccinfo@fcc.gov
URL: http://www.fcc.gov/ogc/admain.html

60154 ■ Federal Communications Commission - Consumer Inquiries and Complaints Division
445 12th St., SW, Rm. 4C763
Washington, DC 20554
Ph: (202)418-2512
Free: 888-225-5322
Co. E-mail: fccinfo@fcc.gov
URL: http://www.fcc.gov/cgb/cgb_offices.html#CICD

60155 ■ Federal Communications Commission - Consumer Inquiries and Complaints Division
445 12th St. SW
Washington, DC 20554
Free: 888-225-5322
Co. E-mail: fccinfo@fcc.gov
URL: http://www.fcc.gov/cgb/cgb_offices.html#CICD

60156 ■ Federal Communications Commission - Enforcement Bureau
445 12th St., SW, Rm. 7-C723
Washington, DC 20554
Ph: (202)418-7450
Fax: (202)418-2810
Co. E-mail: fccinfo@fcc.gov
URL: http://www.fcc.gov/eb

60157 ■ Federal Communications Commission - Enforcement Bureau
445 12th St., SW, Rm. 7-C723
Washington, DC 20554
Free: 888-225-5322
Fax: (866)418-0232
Co. E-mail: fccinfo@fcc.gov
URL: http://www.fcc.gov/eb

60158 ■ Federal Communications Commission (FCC) - Office of Communications Business Opportunities
445 12th St. SW
Washington, DC 20554
Ph: (202)418-0990
Free: 888-225-5322
Fax: (866)418-0235
Co. E-mail: OCBOinfo@fcc.gov
URL: http://www.fcc.gov/ocbo

60159 ■ Federal Communications Commission - Office of Communications Business Opportunities
445 12th St. SW
Washington, DC 20554
Ph: (202)418-0990
Free: 888-225-5322
Fax: (866)418-0235
Co. E-mail: OCBOinfo@fcc.gov
URL: http://www.fcc.gov/ocbo

60160 ■ Federal Communications Commission - Office of Media Relations
445 12th St., Rm. CY-C314
Washington, DC 20554-0001
Ph: (202)418-0503
Fax: (202)418-7286
Co. E-mail: david.fiske@fcc.gov
URL: http://www.fcc.gov/omr/

60161 ■ Federal Communications Commission - Office of Media Relations
445 12th St. SW
Washington, DC 20554
Ph: (202)418-0503
Fax: (202)418-7286
URL: http://www.fcc.gov/omr/

60162 ■ Federal Communications Commission - Office of Workplace Diversity
445 12th St., SW, Rm. 5-C750
Washington, DC 20554
Ph: (202)418-1799
Fax: (202)418-0379
Co. E-mail: fccinfo@fcc.gov
URL: http://www.fcc.gov/owd/

60163 ■ Federal Communications Commission - Office of Workplace Diversity
445 12th St. SW
Washington, DC 20554
Ph: (202)418-1799
Fax: (202)418-0379
Co. E-mail: fccinfo@fcc.gov
URL: http://www.fcc.gov/owd/

60164 ■ Federal Communications Commission - Wireless Telecommunications Bureau
445 12th St., SW
Washington, DC 20554
Ph: (202)418-7320
Fax: (202)418-2644
Co. E-mail: fccinfo@fcc.gov
URL: http://www.fcc.gov/wtb

60165 ■ Federal Communications Commission - Wireless Telecommunications Bureau
445 12th St. SW
Washington, DC 20554
Free: 888-225-5322
Fax: (866)418-0232
Co. E-mail: fccinfo@fcc.gov
URL: http://www.fcc.gov/wtb

FEDERAL DEPOSIT INSURANCE CORPORATION

The following FDIC service centers are arranged alphabetically by region.

60166 ■ Federal Deposit Insurance Corporation - Boston Area Office
15 Braintree Hill Office Pk.
Braintree, MA 02184-8701
Ph: (781)794-5632
Free: 866-728-9953
Co. E-mail: BOSCommunityAffairs@fdic.gov
URL: http://www.fdic.gov/consumers/community/offices.html
Contact: Timothy W. DeLessio, Director, Community Affairs
Description: Serves Connecticut, Maine, Massachusetts, New Hampshire, Rhode Island, and Vermont.

60167 ■ Federal Deposit Insurance Corporation - Chicago Regional Office
300 S. Riverside Plaza., Ste. 1700
Chicago, IL 60606
Ph: (312)382-7500
Free: 800-944-5343
Fax: (312)382-6901
Co. E-mail: CHICommunityAffairs@fdic.gov
URL: http://www.fdic.gov/about/contact/ask/regionaloffices.html
Contact: Angelisa Harris, Director, Community Affairs
URL(s): www.fdic.gov, www.fdic.gov/consumers/community/offices.html. **Description:** Serves Illinois, Indiana, Kentucky, Michigan, Ohio, and Wisconsin.

60168 ■ Federal Deposit Insurance Corporation - Kansas City Regional Office
2345 Grand Blvd., Ste. 1200
Kansas City, MO 64108-2638
Ph: (816)234-8000
Free: 800-209-7459
URL: http://www.fdic.gov
Description: Serves Iowa, Kansas, Minnesota, Missouri, Nebraska, North Dakota, and South Dakota.

60169 ■ Federal Deposit Insurance Corporation - Kansas City Regional Office
1100 Walnut St., Ste. 2100
Kansas City, MO 64106
Ph: (816)234-8000

Free: 800-209-7459
Co. E-mail: KSCommunityAffairs@fdic.gov
URL: http://www.fdic.gov/about/contact/ask/region-aloffices.html
Contact: Teresa Perez, Director, Community Affairs
URL(s): www.fdic.gov/consumers/community/offices.html. **Description:** Serves Iowa, Kansas, Minnesota, Missouri, Nebraska, North Dakota, and South Dakota.

60170 ■ Federal Deposit Insurance Corporation - New York Regional Office
350 5th Ave., Ste. 1200
New York, NY 10118-0110
Ph: (917)320-2500
Free: 800-334-9593
Co. E-mail: NYCommunityAffairs@fdic.gov
URL: http://www.fdic.gov/about/contact/ask/region-aloffices.html
Contact: Valerie J. Williams, Director, Community Affairs
URL(s): www.fdic.gov, www.fdic.gov/consumers/community/offices.html. **Description:** Serves Delaware, District of Columbia, Maryland, New Jersey, New York, Pennsylvania, Puerto Rico, and Virgin Islands.

60171 ■ Federal Deposit Insurance Corporation - Office of Diversity and Economic Opportunity - Minority and Women Outreach Program - Midwest Service Center
500 W. Monroe, Ste. 3300
Chicago, IL 60661-3697
Ph: (312)382-6000
Free: 800-944-5343
Fax: (312)382-6901
URL: http://www.fdic.gov
Contact: Judith M. Wood
Description: Serves Illinois, Indiana, Kentucky, Michigan, Ohio, and Wisconsin.

60172 ■ Federal Deposit Insurance Corporation - Office of Diversity and Economic Opportunity - Minority and Women Outreach Program - Midwest Service Center
500 W. Monroe, Ste. 3300
Chicago, IL 60661-3697
Ph: (312)382-6000
Free: 800-944-5343
Fax: (312)382-6901
URL: http://www.fdic.gov
Description: Serves Illinois, Indiana, Kentucky, Michigan, Ohio, and Wisconsin.

60173 ■ Federal Deposit Insurance Corporation - Office of Diversity and Economic Opportunity - Minority and Women Outreach Program - Northeast Service Center (East Hartford, Connecticut)
North Tower, Rm. 3026
101 East River Dr.
East Hartford, CT 06108
Ph: (860)520-2612
Fax: (860)541-5170
Contact: Herbert Chin

60174 ■ Federal Deposit Insurance Corporation - Office of Diversity and Economic Opportunity - Minority and Women Outreach Program - Northeast Service Center (East Hartford, Connecticut)
North Tower, Rm. 3026
101 East River Dr.
East Hartford, CT 06108
Ph: (860)520-2612
Fax: (860)541-5170

60175 ■ Federal Deposit Insurance Corporation - Office of Diversity and Economic Opportunity - Minority and Women Outreach Program - Northeast Service Center (Franklin, Massachusetts)
124 Grove St.
Franklin, MA 02038
Ph: (508)520-2612
Fax: (508)541-5170
Contact: Herbert Chin

60176 ■ Federal Deposit Insurance Corporation - Office of Diversity and Economic Opportunity - Minority and Women Outreach Program - Northeast Service Center (Franklin, Massachusetts)
124 Grove St.
Franklin, MA 02038
Ph: (508)520-2612
Fax: (508)541-5170

60177 ■ Federal Deposit Insurance Corporation - Office of Diversity and Economic Opportunity - Minority and Women Outreach Program - Southeast Service Center
10th St. NE, Ste. 800
Atlanta, GA 30309-3849
Ph: (678)916-2200
Free: 800-765-3342
Fax: (404)817-8817
URL: http://www.fdic.gov
Contact: Angelisa M. Harris
Description: Serves Alabama, Florida, Georgia, North Carolina, South Carolina, Virginia, and West Virginia.

60178 ■ Federal Deposit Insurance Corporation - Office of Diversity and Economic Opportunity - Minority and Women Outreach Program - Southeast Service Center
10th St. NE, Ste. 800
Atlanta, GA 30309-3849
Ph: (678)916-2200
Free: 800-765-3342
Fax: (404)817-8817
URL: http://www.fdic.gov
Description: Serves Alabama, Florida, Georgia, North Carolina, South Carolina, Virginia, and West Virginia.

60179 ■ Federal Deposit Insurance Corporation - Office of Diversity and Economic Opportunity - Minority and Women Outreach Program - Southwest Service Center
1601 Bryan St.
Dallas, TX 75201
Ph: (214)754-0098
Free: 800-568-9161
URL: http://www.fdic.gov
Contact: Robert Elcan
Description: Serves Colorado, New Mexico, Oklahoma, and Texas.

60180 ■ Federal Deposit Insurance Corporation - Office of Diversity and Economic Opportunity - Minority and Women Outreach Program - Southwest Service Center
1601 Bryan St.
Dallas, TX 75201
Ph: (214)754-0098
Free: 800-568-9161
URL: http://www.fdic.gov
Description: Serves Colorado, New Mexico, Oklahoma, and Texas.

60181 ■ Federal Deposit Insurance Corp. - Office of Diversity and Economic Opportunity - Minority and Women Outreach Program - Western Service Center
4 Park Plaza, Rm. J-1014
Irvine, CA 92714
Ph: (714)263-7669
Fax: (714)263-7202
Co. E-mail: mwoboutreach@fdic.gov
URL: http://www.fdic.gov
Contact: Otis Felton

60182 ■ Federal Deposit Insurance Corp. - Office of Diversity and Economic Opportunity - Minority and Women Outreach Program - Western Service Center
4 Park Plaza, Rm. J-1014
Irvine, CA 92714
Ph: (714)263-7669
Fax: (714)263-7202
URL: http://www.fdic.gov

60183 ■ Federal Deposit Insurance Corporation - San Francisco Regional Office
25 Jessie St. at Ecker Sq., Ste. 2300
San Francisco, CA 94105-2760
Ph: (415)546-0160
Free: 800-756-3558
Co. E-mail: SFCommunityAffairs@fdic.gov
URL: http://www.fdic.gov
Contact: Linda D. Ortega, Director, Community Affairs
URL(s): www.fdic.gov/about/contact/ask/regionaloffices.html. **Description:** Serves Alaska, Arizona, California, Guam, Hawaii, Idaho, Montana, Nevada, Oregon, Utah, Washington, and Wyoming.

FEDERAL EMERGENCY MANAGEMENT AGENCY

60184 ■ U.S. Department of Homeland Security - Customs and Border Protection Procurement
1300 Pennsylvania Ave., NW, Ste. 1310
Washington, DC 20229
Ph: (317)614-4562
Fax: (317)290-3187
Co. E-mail: clarence.abernathy@dhs.gov
URL: http://www.cbp.gov
Description: Procures search/detection equipment, data processing services, computer related services, computer programming, uniforms, construction, computer equipment, personal/household goods, repair/maintenance, administrative/general management consulting, investigative services, computer systems design, schools/instruction, security guards, and facilities support services.

60185 ■ U.S. Department of Homeland Security - Customs and Border Protection Procurement
1300 Pennsylvania Ave. NW, Ste. 1310
Washington, DC 20229
Ph: (703)526-4200
URL: http://www.cbp.gov
Description: Procures search/detection equipment, data processing services, computer related services, computer programming, uniforms, construction, computer equipment, personal/household goods, repair/maintenance, administrative/general management consulting, investigative services, computer systems design, schools/instruction, security guards, and facilities support services.

60186 ■ U.S. Department of Homeland Security - Federal Communications Commission (FCC) - Homeland Security Policy Council
445 12th St., SW, Rm. 7-C751
Washington, DC 20554
Ph: (202)418-7450
Co. E-mail: homeland@fcc.gov
URL: http://www.fcc.gov/hspc

60187 ■ U.S. Department of Homeland Security (FCC) - Federal Communications Commission - Homeland Security Policy Council
445 12th St. SW, Rm. 7-C751
Washington, DC 20554
Ph: (202)418-7450
Co. E-mail: homeland@fcc.gov
URL: http://www.fcc.gov/hspc

60188 ■ U.S. Department of Homeland Security - Federal Emergency Management Agency
500 C St., SW
Washington, DC 20472
Ph: (202)646-2500
Free: 800-621-3362
Co. E-mail: femasb@dhs.gov
URL: http://www.fema.gov

60189 ■ U.S. Department of Homeland Security - Federal Emergency Management Agency
500 C St. SW
Washington, DC 20472

Ph: (202)646-2500
Free: 800-621-3362
Co. E-mail: femasb@dhs.gov
URL: http://www.fema.gov

60190 ▪ U.S. Department of Homeland Security - Federal Emergency Management Agency - Office of Procurement
Patriot Ctr, SW
395 E. St., 2nd Fl.
Washington, DC 20472
Ph: (202)646-4216
Co. E-mail: pamela.mcclam@dhs.gov
URL: http://www.dhs.gov/xopnbiz/smallbusiness/gc_
1178570919850.shtm
Description: Procures information technology services directorate: information systems support, telecommunication equipment and services, computer maintenance and support, computer software and hardware, wide area network support, local area network support INTERNET services, systems development, engineering and integration, iand communications security, configuration management, and disaster response support.

60191 ▪ U.S. Department of Homeland Security - Federal Emergency Management Agency - Office of Procurement
Patriot Ctr. SW
395 E. St., 2nd Fl.
Washington, DC 20472
Ph: (202)212-1975
Co. E-mail: pamela.mcclam@fema.dhs.gov
URL: http://www.dhs.gov/small-business-specialists
Description: Procures information technology services directorate: information systems support, telecommunication equipment and services, computer maintenance and support, computer software and hardware, wide area network support, local area network support INTERNET services, systems development, engineering and integration, iand communications security, configuration management, and disaster response support.

60192 ▪ U.S. Department of Homeland Security - Federal Emergency Management Agency, Region 1 - Boston Regional Office
99 High St., 6th Fl.
Boston, MA 02110
Ph: (617)956-7506
URL: http://www.fema.gov/about/regions/regioni/re-gioni.shtm
Description: Serves New Hampshire, Vermont, Rhode Island, Connecticut, Maine, and Massachusetts.

60193 ▪ U.S. Department of Homeland Security - Federal Emergency Management Agency, Region 1 - Boston Regional Office
99 High St., 5th Fl.
Boston, MA 02110
Ph: (617)956-7506
URL: http://www.mmrs.fema.gov/about/contact/re-gioni.shtm
Description: Serves New Hampshire, Vermont, Rhode Island, Connecticut, and Massachusetts.

60194 ▪ U.S. Department of Homeland Security - Federal Emergency Management Agency, Region 2 - New York Regional Office
26 Federal Plz., Ste. 1337
New York, NY 10278-0002
Ph: (212)680-3612
URL: http://www.fema.gov/about/contact/regioni.shtm
Description: Serves New York, New Jersey, Puerto Rico, and the Virgin Islands.

60195 ▪ U.S. Department of Homeland Security - Federal Emergency Management Agency, Region 2 - New York Regional Office
26 Federal Plz., Ste. 1337
New York, NY 10278-0002
Ph: (212)680-3612
URL: http://www.mmrs.fema.gov/about/contact/regio-nii.shtm
Description: Serves New York, New Jersey, Puerto Rico, and the Virgin Islands.

60196 ▪ U.S. Department of Homeland Security - Federal Emergency Management Agency, Region 3 - Philadelphia Regional Office
One Independence Mall, 6th Fl.
615 Chestnut St.
Philadelphia, PA 19106-4404
Ph: (215)931-5608
URL: http://www.fema.gov/about/regions/regioniii/index.shtm
Description: Serves Delaware, District of Columbia, Maryland, Pennsylvania, Virginia, and West Virginia.

60197 ▪ U.S. Department of Homeland Security - Federal Emergency Management Agency, Region 3 - Philadelphia Regional Office
One Independence Mall, 6th Fl.
615 Chestnut St.
Philadelphia, PA 19106-4404
Free: 800-621-3362
URL: http://www.mmrs.fema.gov/about/contact/regio-niii.shtm
Description: Serves Delaware, District of Columbia, Maryland, Pennsylvania, Virginia, and West Virginia.

60198 ▪ U.S. Department of Homeland Security - Federal Emergency Management Agency, Region 4 - Atlanta Regional Office
3003 Chamblee Tucker Rd.
Atlanta, GA 30341
Ph: (770)220-5200
Fax: (770)220-5230
URL: http://www.fema.gov/about/regions/regioniv/index.shtm
Description: Serves Georgia, Florida, Kentucky, Mississippi, North Carolina, South Carolina, and Tennessee.

60199 ▪ U.S. Department of Homeland Security - Federal Emergency Management Agency, Region 4 - Atlanta Regional Office
3003 Chamblee Tucker Rd.
Atlanta, GA 30341
Ph: (770)220-5200
Fax: (770)220-5230
URL: http://www.mmrs.fema.gov/about/contact/re-gioniv.shtm
Description: Serves Georgia, Florida, Kentucky, Mississippi, North Carolina, South Carolina, and Tennessee.

60200 ▪ U.S. Department of Homeland Security - Federal Emergency Management Agency, Region 5 - Chicago Regional Office
536 S. Clark St., 6th Fl.
Chicago, IL 60605
Ph: (312)408-5500
URL: http://www.fema.gov/about/regions/regionv/index.shtm
Description: Serves Illinois, Indiana, Michigan, Ohio, Minnesota, and Wisconsin.

60201 ▪ U.S. Department of Homeland Security - Federal Emergency Management Agency, Region 5 - Chicago Regional Office
536 S. Clark St., 6th Fl.
Chicago, IL 60605
Ph: (312)408-5500
URL: http://www.mmrs.fema.gov/about/contact/re-gionv.shtm
Description: Serves Illinois, Indiana, Michigan, Ohio, Minnesota, and Wisconsin.

60202 ▪ U.S. Department of Homeland Security - Federal Emergency Management Agency, Region 6 - Denton Regional Office
Federal Emergency Management Ctr.
800 N. Loop 288
Denton, TX 76209-3698
Ph: (940)898-5399
URL: http://www.fema.gov/about/regions/regionvi/index.shtm
Description: Serves Arkansas, Louisiana, New Mexico, Oklahoma, and Texas.

60203 ▪ U.S. Department of Homeland Security - Federal Emergency Management Agency, Region 6 - Denton Regional Office
Federal Emergency Management Ctr.
800 N. Loop 288
Denton, TX 76209-3698
Ph: (940)898-5399
URL: http://www.fema.gov/about/regions/regionvi/index.shtm
Description: Serves Arkansas, Louisiana, New Mexico, Oklahoma, and Texas.

60204 ▪ U.S. Department of Homeland Security - Federal Emergency Management Agency, Region 7 - Kansas City Regional Office
9221 Ward Pkwy., Ste. 300
Kansas City, MO 64114-3372
Ph: (816)283-7061
URL: http://www.fema.gov/about/regions/regionvii/index.shtm
Description: Serves Iowa, Kansas, Missouri, and Nebraska.

60205 ▪ U.S. Department of Homeland Security - Federal Emergency Management Agency, Region 7 - Kansas City Regional Office
9221 Ward Pkwy., Ste. 300
Kansas City, MO 64114-3372
Ph: (816)283-7061
URL: http://www.mmrs.fema.gov/about/contact/re-gionvii.shtm
Description: Serves Iowa, Kansas, Missouri, and Nebraska.

60206 ▪ U.S. Department of Homeland Security - Federal Emergency Management Agency, Region 8 - Denver Regional Office
Denver Federal Ctr., Bldg. 710
Denver, CO 80225-0267
Ph: (303)235-4800
Fax: (303)235-4976
URL: http://www.fema.gov/about/regions/regionviii/index.shtm
Description: Serves Colorado, Montana, North Dakota, South Dakota, Utah, and Wyoming.

60207 ▪ U.S. Department of Homeland Security - Federal Emergency Management Agency, Region 8 - Denver Regional Office
Denver Federal Ctr., Bldg. 710
Denver, CO 80225-0267
Ph: (303)235-4800
Fax: (303)235-4976
URL: http://www.mmrs.fema.gov/about/contact/re-gionviii.shtm
Description: Serves Colorado, Montana, North Dakota, South Dakota, Utah, and Wyoming.

60208 ▪ U.S. Department of Homeland Security - Federal Emergency Management Agency, Region 9 - Oakland Regional Office
1111 Broadway, Ste. 1200
Oakland, CA 94607-4052
Ph: (510)627-7100
URL: http://www.fema.gov/about/regions/regionix/index.shtm
Description: Serves Arizona, California, Hawaii, Nevada, Guam, American Samoa, Commonwealth of the Northern Mariana Islands, Republic of the Marshall Islands, and Federated States of Micronesia.

60209 ▪ U.S. Department of Homeland Security - Federal Emergency Management Agency, Region 9 - Oakland Regional Office
1111 Broadway, Ste. 1200
Oakland, CA 94607-4052
Ph: (510)627-7100
URL: http://www.mmrs.fema.gov/about/contact/re-gionix.shtm
Description: Serves Arizona, California, Hawaii, and Nevada.

60210 ■ U.S. Department of Homeland Security - Federal Emergency Management Agency, Region 10 - Bothell Regional Office
130 228th St., SW
Bothell, WA 98021-8627
Ph: (425)487-4600
URL: http://www.fema.gov/about/regions/regionx/index.shtm
Description: Serves Alaska, Idaho, Washington, and Oregon.

60211 ■ U.S. Department of Homeland Security - Federal Emergency Management Agency, Region 10 - Bothell Regional Office
130 228th St. SW
Bothell, WA 98021-8627
Ph: (425)487-4600
URL: http://www.mmrs.fema.gov/about/contact/regionx.shtm
Description: Serves Alaska, Idaho, Washington, and Oregon.

60212 ■ U.S. Department of Homeland Security - Federal Law Enforcement Training Center - Artesia Facility
1300 W. Richey Ave.
Artesia, NM 88210
Ph: (575)748-8000
Co. E-mail: fletc-artesia@dhs.gov
URL: http://www.fletc.gov/about-fletc/locations/artesia

60213 ■ U.S. Department of Homeland Security - Federal Law Enforcement Training Center - Charleston Facility
2000 Bainbridge Ave.
Charleston, SC 29405-2607
Ph: (843)566-8550
Co. E-mail: FLETC-Charleston@dhs.gov
URL: http://www.fletc.gov/about-fletc/locations/charleston

60214 ■ U.S. Department of Homeland Security - Federal Law Enforcement Training Center - Cheltenham Facility
9000 Commo Rd., Stop 4000
Cheltenham, MD 20588-4000
Ph: (301)868-5830
Fax: (301)868-6549
Co. E-mail: fletc-webmasterche@dhs.gov
URL: http://www.fletc.gov/about-fletc/locations/cheltenham

60215 ■ U.S. Department of Homeland Security - Federal Law Enforcement Training Center - Glynco Facility
1131 Chapel Crossing Rd.
Glynco, GA 31524
Ph: (912)267-2100
Fax: (912)267-2071
URL: http://www.fletc.gov

60216 ■ U.S. Department of Homeland Security - Federal Law Enforcement Training Center - Washington Operations
555 11th St. NW, Ste. 400
Washington, DC 20528
Ph: (202)233-0260
Fax: (202)233-0258
Co. E-mail: FLETC-WashingtonOffice@dhs.gov
URL: http://www.fletc.gov/about-fletc/locations/washingtonDC/

60217 ■ U.S. Department of Homeland Security - National Urban Security Technology Laboratory
201 Varick St., 5th Fl.
New York, NY 10014-7447
Ph: (212)620-3576
Fax: (212)620-3651
Co. E-mail: adam.hutter@dhs.gov
URL: http://www.nustl.st.dhs.gov/

60218 ■ U.S. Department of Homeland Security - National Urban Security Technology Laboratory
201 Varick St., 5th Fl.
New York, NY 10014-7447
Ph: (212)620-3576

Fax: (212)620-3651
Co. E-mail: nustil@dhs.gov
URL: http://www.dhs.gov/st-nustl

60219 ■ U.S. Department of Homeland Security - Office of Procurement Operations
245 Murray Dr., SW, Bldg. 410, Rm. 3523-28
Washington, DC 20528
Ph: (202)447-5578
Co. E-mail: faye.jones@hq.dhs.gov
URL: http://www.dhs.gov/xopnbiz/smallbusiness/gc_1178570919850.shtm

60220 ■ U.S. Department of Homeland Security - Office of Procurement Operations
245 Murray Dr. SW, Bldg. 410, Rm. 3523-28
Washington, DC 20528
Ph: (202)447-5572
Co. E-mail: faye.jones@hq.dhs.gov
URL: http://www.dhs.gov/small-business-specialists

60221 ■ U.S. Department of Homeland Security - Office of Small and Disadvantaged Business Utilization
7th and D Sts., SW, Rm. 3124-A
Washington, DC 20528
Ph: (202)447-5555
Co. E-mail: Kevin.boeshears@dhs.gov
URL: http://www.dhs.gov/xopnbiz/smallbusiness/editorial_0715.shtm

60222 ■ U.S. Department of Homeland Security - Office of Small and Disadvantaged Business Utilization
245 Murray Dr., Bldg. 410, Rm. 3124-A
Washington, DC 20528
Ph: (202)447-5555
URL: http://www.dhs.gov/xopnbiz/smallbusiness/gc_1178570919850.shtm

60223 ■ U.S. Department of Homeland Security - Office of Small and Disadvantaged Business Utilization
245 Murray Dr., Bldg. 410
Attn: OSDBU/Rm. 3636
Washington, DC 20528
Ph: (202)447-5555
Fax: (202)447-5552
URL: http://www.dhs.gov/office-small-and-disadvantaged-business-utilization-staff

60224 ■ U.S. Department of Homeland Security - Office of Small and Disadvantaged Business Utilization
245 Murray Dr. SW, Bldg. 410
Washington, DC 20528
Ph: (202)447-5555
Fax: (202)447-5552
URL: http://www.dhs.gov/office-small-and-disadvantaged-business-utilization-staff

60225 ■ U.S. Department of Homeland Security - Transportation Security Administration - Small and Disadvantaged Business Office
10th Fl., TSA-25, W. Bldg.
601 S. 12th St.
Arlington, VA 22202-4220
Ph: (571)227-1067
Fax: (571)227-3219
Co. E-mail: tsa-contactcenter@dhs.gov
URL: http://www.tsa.gov/join/smallbiz/smallbiz_ready_for_business.shtm
Description: Procures simulators, training development, training courses, installation of checked baggage equipment, health and safety assessments on TSA screening operations, acquisition planning & program management support, safety equipment and supplies, and investigative services.

60226 ■ U.S. Department of Homeland Security - Transportation Security Administration - Small and Disadvantaged Business Office
601 S. 12th St., 10th Fl.
TSA-25, W. Bldg.
Arlington, VA 20598-4220
Ph: (571)227-1067

Fax: (571)227-3219
Co. E-mail: Robert.boone@dhs.gov
URL: http://www.tsa.gov/join/smallbiz/smallbiz_ready_for_business.shtm
Description: Procures simulators, training development, training courses, installation of checked baggage equipment, health and safety assessments on TSA screening operations, acquisition planning & program management support, safety equipment and supplies, and investigative services.

60227 ■ U.S. Department of Homeland Security - U.S. Citizenship and Immigration Services - Procurement Division
70 Kimball Ave.
South Burlington, VT 05403
Ph: (802)872-4111
Fax: (802)951-6455
Co. E-mail: richard.march@dhs.gov
URL: http://www.uscis.gov/portal/site/uscis

60228 ■ U.S. Department of Homeland Security - U.S. Citizenship and Immigration Services - Procurement Division
70 Kimball Ave.
South Burlington, VT 05403
Ph: (802)660-1116
Fax: (802)951-6455
URL: http://www.uscis.gov/portal/site/uscis

60229 ■ U.S. Department of Homeland Security - U.S. Coast Guard - Aircraft Logistics Center
Center Bldg. 63
Elizabeth City, NC 27909-5001
Ph: (252)335-6145
Fax: (252)335-6840
Co. E-mail: judith.a.knotts@uscg.mil
URL: http://www.dhs.gov/xopnbiz/smallbusiness/gc_1178570919850.shtm
Description: Procures aircraft parts for HH-60, HU-25, HC-130, HH-65; ground service equipment, engines, turbines and components, engine accessories, maintenance and repair, aircraft maintenance/overhaul/repair, electronics, avionics, life support equipment, HAZMAT material, engineering tech support, and ADP services.

60230 ■ U.S. Department of Homeland Security - U.S. Coast Guard - Aircraft Repair & Supply
Center Bldg. 63
Elizabeth City, NC 27909-5001
Ph: (252)335-6145
Fax: (252)335-6840
Co. E-mail: Judith.a.knotts@uscg.mil
URL: http://www.uscg.mil/acquisition/business/small-businessrep.asp
Description: Procures aircraft parts for HH-60, HU-25, HC-130, HH-65; ground service equipment, engines, turbines and components, engine accessories, maintenance and repair, aircraft maintenance/overhaul/repair, electronics, avionics, life support equipment, HAZMAT material, engineering tech support, and ADP services.

60231 ■ U.S. Department of Homeland Security - U.S. Coast Guard - Engineering Logistics Center
2401 Hawkins Pt. Rd., Code 043
Baltimore, MD 21226-5000
Ph: (410)762-6442
Fax: (410)762-6410
Co. E-mail: Corrine.m.sherman@uscg.dhs.gov
URL: http://www.dhs.gov/xopnbiz/smallbusiness/gc_1178570919850.shtm
Description: Procures electrical equipment (switches, fuses, microcircuits, relays, cords,) ropes, cables, chains and fittings, supplies and services, medical/dental equipment, instruments and laboratory equipment, lighting fixtures and lamps, ordnance (arms, ammunition), deck machinery, fuel, fuel oils, miscellaneous engines and components, diesel engines and components, custodial and janitorial services, power and hand pumps, pipe, tubing, hose and fittings, valves, gasses (compressed and liquefied), and electrical motors.

60232 ■ U.S. Department of Homeland Security - U.S. Coast Guard - Engineering Logistics Center
2401 Hawkins Pt. Rd., Code 043
Baltimore, MD 21226-5000
Ph: (410)762-6463
Fax: (410)762-6410
Co. E-mail: sharon.j.jackson@uscg.mil
URL: http://www.uscg.mil/acquisition/business/small-businessrep.asp
Description: Procures electrical equipment (switches, fuses, microcircuits, relays, cords,) ropes, cables, chains and fittings, supplies and services, medical/dental equipment, instruments and laboratory equipment, lighting fixtures and lamps, ordnance (arms, ammunition), deck machinery, fuel, fuel oils, miscellaneous engines and components, diesel engines and components, custodial and janitorial services, power and hand pumps, pipe, tubing, hose and fittings, valves, gasses (compressed and liquefied), and electrical motors.

60233 ■ U.S. Department of Homeland Security - U.S. Coast Guard - Maintenance and Logistics Command, Atlantic
300 E. Main St., Ste. 600
Norfolk, VA 23510-9107
Ph: (757)628-4654
Fax: (757)628-4676
Co. E-mail: mia.r.mayers@uscg.mil
URL: http://www.uscg.mil/acquisition/business/small-businessrep.asp
Description: Procures dry dock and ship repair, engine overhaul, spare parts for vessels, construction, ship repair, and dry-docking of new vessels.

60234 ■ U.S. Department of Homeland Security - U.S. Coast Guard - Maintenance and Logistics Command, Pacific
1301 Clay St., Ste. 807N
Oakland, CA 94612-5249
Ph: (510)637-5960
Fax: (510)637-5978
Co. E-mail: john.c.porter@uscg.mil
URL: http://www.uscg.mil/acquisition/business/small-businessrep.asp
Description: Procures dry dock and ship repair, engine overhaul, spare parts for vessels, construction, ship repair, and dry-docking of new vessels.

60235 ■ U.S. Department of Homeland Security - U.S. Coast Guard - Office of Contract Operations
1900 Half St. SW, Rm. 11-0222
Washington, DC 20593
Ph: (202)475-3271
Fax: (202)475-3905
Co. E-mail: sara.h.marcheggiani@uscg.dhs.gov
URL: http://www.dhs.gov/xopnbiz/smallbusiness/gc_1178570919850.shtm
Description: Procures aircraft, vessels, educational services, major electronics equipment, and all equipment and supplies to outfit new vessels and aircraft, with emphasis in oceanography and other marine sciences, including pollution control and abatement.

60236 ■ U.S. Department of Homeland Security - U.S. Coast Guard - Office of Contract Operations
2100 2nd St. SW, Stop 7112
Washington, DC 20593
Ph: (202)475-3746
Fax: (202)475-3905
Co. E-mail: sara.h.marcheggiani@uscg.mil
URL: http://www.uscg.mil/acquisition/business/small-businessrep.asp
Description: Procures aircraft, vessels, educational services, major electronics equipment, and all equipment and supplies to outfit new vessels and aircraft, with emphasis in oceanography and other marine sciences, including pollution control and abatement.

60237 ■ U.S. Department of Homeland Security - U.S. Coast Guard - Office of Procurement Management
2100 2nd St. SW, Rm. 11-0209
Washington, DC 20593

Ph: (202)475-5786
Co. E-mail: nauman.ansari@uscg.dhs.gov
URL: http://www.dhs.gov/xopnbiz/smallbusiness/gc_1178570919850.shtm

60238 ■ U.S. Department of Homeland Security - U.S. Coast Guard - Office of Procurement Management
2100 2nd St. SW, Stop 7112
Washington, DC 20593
Ph: (202)475-5786
Co. E-mail: nauman.ansari@uscg.mil
URL: http://www.uscg.mil/acquisition/business/small-businessrep.asp

60239 ■ U.S. Department of Homeland Security - U.S. Coast Guard - Research & Development Center
1082 Shennecossett Rd.
Groton, CT 06340-6048
Ph: (860)441-2843
Fax: (860)441-2888
Co. E-mail: Helen.r.nelson@uscg.dhs.gov
URL: http://www.dhs.gov/xopnbiz/smallbusiness/gc_1178570919850.shtm
Description: Procures special studies and analyses, applied research and development.

60240 ■ U.S. Department of Homeland Security - U.S. Coast Guard - Research & Development Center
1 Chelsea St.
New London, CT 06320-5506
Ph: (860)441-2843
Fax: (860)441-2888
Co. E-mail: Helen.r.nelson@uscg.mil
URL: http://www.uscg.mil/acquisition/business/small-businessrep.asp
Description: Procures special studies and analyses, applied research and development.

60241 ■ U.S. Department of Homeland Security - U.S. Coast Guard - Surface Forces Logistics Command, Atlantic
300 E. Main St., Ste. 600
Norfolk, VA 23510-9107
Ph: (757)628-4631
Fax: (757)628-4676
Co. E-mail: sharon.j.jackson@uscg.mil
URL: http://www.dhs.gov/xopnbiz/smallbusiness/gc_1178570919850.shtm
Description: Procures dry dock and ship repair, engine overhaul, spare parts for vessels, construction, ship repair, and dry-docking of new vessels.

60242 ■ U.S. Department of Homeland Security - U.S. Coast Guard - Surface Forces Logistics Command, Pacific
1301 Clay St., Ste. 807N
Oakland, CA 94612-5249
Ph: (510)637-5960
Fax: (510)637-5978
Co. E-mail: john.c.porter@uscg.mil
URL: http://www.dhs.gov/xopnbiz/smallbusiness/gc_1178570919850.shtm
Description: Procures dry dock and ship repair, engine overhaul, spare parts for vessels, construction, ship repair, and dry-docking of new vessels.

60243 ■ U.S. Department of Homeland Security - U.S. Secret Service - Procurement Division
245 Murray Dr., Bldg. 410
Washington, DC 20223
Ph: (202)406-6940
Fax: (202)406-6801
URL: http://www.secretservice.gov
Description: Procures computer equipment, computer facilities management, passenger car leasing, software, computer systems design, telecommunications, custom computer programming, hardware manufacturing, computer repair, and janitorial services.

60244 ■ U.S. Department of Homeland Security - U.S. Secret Service - Procurement Division
245 Murray Dr., Bldg. 410
Washington, DC 20223
Ph: (202)406-6940
Fax: (202)406-6801
URL: http://www.secretservice.gov
Description: Procures computer equipment, computer facilities management, passenger car leasing, software, computer systems design, telecommunications, custom computer programming, hardware manufacturing, computer repair, and janitorial services.

FEDERAL HOME LOAN MORTGAGE CORPORATION

60245 ■ Federal Home Loan Mortgage Corporation, Freddie Mac
401 9th St., NW, Ste. 600 S.
Washington, DC 20004
Ph: (202)434-8600
URL: http://www.freddiemac.gov

60246 ■ Federal Home Loan Mortgage Corporation, Freddie Mac
401 9th St., NW, Ste. 600 S.
Washington, DC 20004
Ph: (202)434-8600
URL: http://www.freddiemac.gov

60247 ■ Federal Home Loan Mortgage Corporation - Northeast Region
8000 Jones Branch Dr.
McLean, VA 22102
Ph: (703)388-7000
URL: http://www.freddiemac.com

60248 ■ Federal Home Loan Mortgage Corporation - Northeast Region
8200 Jones Branch Dr.
McLean, VA 22102-3110
Free: 800-424-5401
URL: http://www.freddiemac.com

60249 ■ Federal Home Loan Mortgage Corporation - Southeast Region
North Tower, Ste. 200
2300 Windy Ridge Pkwy., SE
Atlanta, GA 30339-5665
Ph: (770)857-8800
URL: http://www.freddiemac.com

60250 ■ Federal Home Loan Mortgage Corporation - Southeast Region
North Tower
2300 Windy Ridge Pkwy. SE, Ste. 200
Atlanta, GA 30339-5665
Ph: (770)857-8800
URL: http://www.freddiemac.com

60251 ■ Federal Home Loan Mortgage Corporation - Southwest Region
5000 Plano Pkwy.
Carrollton, TX 75010-4902
Ph: (972)395-4000
URL: http://www.freddiemac.com

60252 ■ Federal Home Loan Mortgage Corporation - Southwest Region
5000 Plano Pkwy.
Carrollton, TX 75010-4902
Ph: (972)395-4000
URL: http://www.freddiemac.com

60253 ■ Federal Home Loan Mortgage Corporation - Western Region
21700 Oxnard St., Ste. 1900
Woodland Hills, CA 91367-3642
Ph: (818)-710-3000
URL: http://www.freddiemac.com

60254 ■ Federal Home Loan Mortgage Corporation - Western Region
21700 Oxnard St., Ste. 1900
Woodland Hills, CA 91367-3642

Ph: (818)710-3000
URL: http://www.freddiemac.com

FEDERAL MEDIATION AND CONCILIATION SERVICE

60255 ■ Federal Mediation and Conciliation Service - Eastern Region
6161 Oak Tree Blvd., Ste. 120
Independence, OH 44131
Ph: (216)520-4800
Fax: (216)520-4815
Co. E-mail: jbuettner@fmcs.gov
URL: http://www.fmcs.gov/internet/itemDetail.
   asp?categoryID=82itemID=16282

60256 ■ Federal Mediation and Conciliation Service - Eastern Region - Cleveland, Ohio Regional Office
6161 Oak Tree Blvd., Ste. 120
Independence, OH 44131
Ph: (216)520-4800
Fax: (216)520-4815
Co. E-mail: rditillo@fmcs.gov
URL: http://www.fmcs.gov/internet/itemDetail.
   asp?categoryID=107&itemID=16282

60257 ■ Federal Mediation and Conciliation Service (FMCS) - Information Technology and Administrative Services - Procurement
2100 K St. NW
Washington, DC 20427
Ph: (202)606-8100
Fax: (202)606-4251
URL: http://www.fmcs.gov/internet/itemDetail.
   asp?categoryID=102&itemID=15960

60258 ■ Federal Mediation and Conciliation Service (FMCS) - Office of Procurement
2100 K St., NW
Washington, DC 20427
Ph: (202)606-8100
Fax: (202)606-4251
URL: http://www.fmcs.gov

60259 ■ Federal Mediation and Conciliation Service - Office of Public Affairs
2100 K St., NW
Washington, DC 20427
Ph: (202)606-5442
Fax: (202)606-4251
Co. E-mail: jarnold@fmcs.gov
URL: http://www.fmcs.gov/internet/categoryList.asp-
   ?categoryID=230

60260 ■ Federal Mediation and Conciliation Service - Office of Public Affairs
2100 K St., NW
Washington, DC 20427
Ph: (202)606-5442
Fax: (202)606-4251
Co. E-mail: jarnold@fmcs.gov
URL: http://www.fmcs.gov/internet/categoryList.asp-
   ?categoryID=230

60261 ■ Federal Mediation and Conciliation Service - Western Region
6161 Oak Tree Blvd., Ste. 120
Independence, OH 44131
Ph: (216)520-4800
Fax: (216)520-4815
Co. E-mail: jbuettner@fmcs.gov
URL: http://www.fmcs.gov/internet/itemDetail.
   asp?categoryID=82itemID=16282

60262 ■ Federal Mediation and Conciliation Service - Western Region - Minneapolis, Minnesota Sub-Regional Office
1300 Godward St., Ste. 3950
Broadway Plc. W.
Minneapolis, MN 55413
Ph: (612)331-6670
Fax: (612)331-5272
Co. E-mail: gtarkowski@fmcs.gov
URL: http://www.fmcs.gov/internet/itemDetail.
   asp?categoryID=107&itemID=16282

FEDERAL NATIONAL MORTGAGE ASSOCIATION

60263 ■ Government National Mortgage Association, Ginnie Mae - Procurement and Contracts
Potomac Ctr. S.
550 12th St., SW, 3rd Fl.
Washington, DC 20024
Ph: (202)708-1535
Fax: (202)485-0208
URL: http://www.ginniemae.gov

60264 ■ Government National Mortgage Association, Ginnie Mae - Procurement Management Division
Potomac Ctr. S.
550 12th St. SW, 3rd Fl.
Washington, DC 20024
Ph: (202)708-1535
Fax: (202)485-0208
URL: http://www.ginniemae.gov/about/contracts.
   asp?subTitle=About

FEDERAL TRADE COMMISSION

The following regional offices are arranged alphabetically by city.

60265 ■ Federal Trade Commission - Atlanta Regional Office - Southeast Region
225 Peachtree St., NE, Ste. 1500
Atlanta, GA 30303
Ph: (404)656-1356
Free: 877-382-4357
Fax: (404)656-1379
URL: http://www.ftc.gov/ro/southeast.shtm
Description: Serves Alabama, Florida, Georgia, Mississippi, North Carolina, South Carolina, and Tennessee.

60266 ■ Federal Trade Commission - Atlanta Regional Office - Southeast Region
225 Peachtree St. NE, Ste. 1500
Atlanta, GA 30303
Free: 877-382-4357
Fax: (404)656-1379
URL: http://www.ftc.gov/ro/southeast.shtm
Description: Serves Alabama, Florida, Georgia, Mississippi, North Carolina, South Carolina, and Tennessee.

60267 ■ Federal Trade Commission - Bureau of Consumer Protection
600 Pennsylvania Ave., NW, Rm. H-470
Washington, DC 20580
Ph: (202)326-3240
Free: 877-382-4357
Fax: (202)326-3799
URL: http://www.ftc.gov/bcp/index.shtml
Publications: *Consumer Protection.*

60268 ■ Federal Trade Commission - Chicago Regional Office - Midwest Region
55 W. Monroe St., Ste. 1825
Chicago, IL 60603
Ph: (312)960-5628
Free: 877-382-4357
Fax: (312)960-5600
URL: http://www.ftc.gov/ro/midwest.htm
Description: Serves Illinois, Indiana, Iowa, Kansas, Kentucky, Nebraska, North Dakota, Minnesota, Missouri, South Dakota, and Wisconsin.

60269 ■ Federal Trade Commission - Chicago Regional Office - Midwest Region
55 W. Monroe St., Ste. 1825
Chicago, IL 60603
Free: 877-382-4357
Fax: (312)960-5600
URL: http://www.ftc.gov/ro/midwest.htm
Description: Serves Illinois, Indiana, Iowa, Kansas, Kentucky, Nebraska, North Dakota, Minnesota, Missouri, South Dakota, and Wisconsin.

60270 ■ Federal Trade Commission - Cleveland Regional Office - East Central Region
1111 Superior Ave., Ste. 200
Cleveland, OH 44114-2507
Ph: (216)263-3418
Free: 877-382-4357
Fax: (216)263-3426
URL: http://www.ftc.gov/ro/eastcentral.htm
Description: Serves Delaware, District of Columbia, Maryland, Michigan, Ohio, Pennsylvania, Virginia, and West Virginia.

60271 ■ Federal Trade Commission - Cleveland Regional Office - East Central Region
1111 Superior Ave., Ste. 200
Cleveland, OH 44114-2507
Free: 877-382-4357
Fax: (216)263-3426
URL: http://www.ftc.gov/ro/eastcentral.shtm
Description: Serves Delaware, District of Columbia, Maryland, Michigan, Ohio, Pennsylvania, Virginia, and West Virginia.

60272 ■ Federal Trade Commission - Dallas Regional Office - Southwest Region
1999 Bryan St., Ste. 2150
Dallas, TX 75201-6808
Ph: (214)979-9374
Free: 877-382-4357
Fax: (214)953-3079
URL: http://www.ftc.gov/ro/southwest.shtm
Description: Serves Arkansas, Louisiana, New Mexico, Oklahoma, and Texas.

60273 ■ Federal Trade Commission - Dallas Regional Office - Southwest Region
1999 Bryan St., Ste. 2150
Dallas, TX 75201-6808
Free: 877-382-4357
Fax: (214)953-3079
URL: http://www.ftc.gov/ro/southwest.shtm
Description: Serves Arkansas, Louisiana, New Mexico, Oklahoma, and Texas.

60274 ■ Federal Trade Commission - Denver Regional Office
1405 Curtis St., Ste. 2900
Denver, CO 80202-2393
Description: Serves Colorado, Kansas, Montana, Nebraska, North Dakota, South Dakota, Utah, and Wyoming.

60275 ■ Federal Trade Commission - Los Angeles Regional Office - Western Region
10877 Wilshire Blvd., Ste. 700
Los Angeles, CA 90024
Ph: (310)824-4324
Free: 877-382-4357
Fax: (310)824-4380
URL: http://www.ftc.gov/ro/western.shtm
Description: Serves Arizona, northern California, southern California, Colorado, Hawaii, Nevada, and Utah.

60276 ■ Federal Trade Commission - Los Angeles Regional Office - Western Region
10877 Wilshire Blvd., Ste. 700
Los Angeles, CA 90024
Free: 877-382-4357
Fax: (310)824-4380
URL: http://www.ftc.gov/ro/western.shtm
Description: Serves Arizona, northern California, southern California, Colorado, Hawaii, Nevada, and Utah.

60277 ■ Federal Trade Commission - New York Regional Office - Northeast Region
1 Bowling Green
New York, NY 10004
Ph: (212)607-2801
Free: 877-382-4357
Fax: (212)607-2822
URL: http://www.ftc.gov/ro/northeast.shtm
Description: Serves Connecticut, Maine, Massachusetts, New Hampshire, New Jersey New York, Puerto Rico, Rhode Island, Vermont, and U.S. Virgin Islands.

60278 ■ Federal Trade Commission - New York Regional Office - Northeast Region
1 Bowling Green
New York, NY 10004
Free: 877-382-4357
Fax: (212)607-2822
URL: http://www.ftc.gov/ro/northeast.shtm
Description: Serves Connecticut, Maine, Massachusetts, New Hampshire, New Jersey New York, Puerto Rico, Rhode Island, Vermont, and U.S. Virgin Islands.

60279 ■ Federal Trade Commission - Office of Inspector General
600 Pennsylvania Ave. NW, Rm. 1110
Washington, DC 20580
Ph: (202)326-2800
Fax: (202)326-2034
Co. E-mail: oig@ftc.gov
URL: http://www.ftc.gov/oig/index.shtml

60280 ■ Federal Trade Commission - Office of Inspector General
600 Pennsylvania Ave. NW, Rm. 1110
Washington, DC 20580
Ph: (202)326-2800
Fax: (202)326-2034
Co. E-mail: oig@ftc.gov
URL: http://www.ftc.gov/oig/index.shtml

60281 ■ Federal Trade Commission (FTC) - Procurement and General Services Division
600 Pennsylvania Ave. NW
Washington, DC 20580
Ph: (202)326-2258
Fax: (202)326-2502
URL: http://www.ftc.gov/os/ar97/manage.shtm
Description: The Federal Trade Commission works to preserve a free marketplace by acting as the advocate of consumers and by resisting efforts of any one group to profit at the expense of the general public. The FTC maintains three bureaus and ten regional offices through which to carry out its responsibilities: the Bureau of Competition seeks to prevent business practices that restrain competition by investigating alleged violations, by recommending enforcement action when appropriate, and by participating in an advocacy program; the Bureau of Consumer Protection helps to preserve competition by prohibiting deceptive claims or practices that interfere with the public's ability to make informed purchasing decisions; and the Bureau of Economics offers support to these activities by ensuring that the FTC's actions are based on sound economic principles. FTC regional offices conduct investigations and litigations, offer advice, recommend cases, provide outreach services, sponsor conferences, and coordinate activities with local, state, and regional authorities.

60282 ■ Federal Trade Commission - Procurement and General Services Division
600 Pennsylvania Ave. NW
Washington, DC 20580
Ph: (202)326-2258
Fax: (202)326-2502
URL: http://www.ftc.gov/os/ar97/manage.shtm
Description: The Federal Trade Commission works to preserve a free marketplace by acting as the advocate of consumers and by resisting efforts of any one group to profit at the expense of the general public. The FTC maintains three bureaus and ten regional offices through which to carry out its responsibilities: the Bureau of Competition seeks to prevent business practices that restrain competition by investigating alleged violations, by recommending enforcement action when appropriate, and by participating in an advocacy program; the Bureau of Consumer Protection helps to preserve competition by prohibiting deceptive claims or practices that interfere with the public's ability to make informed purchasing decisions; the Bureau of Economics offers support to these activities by ensuring that the FTC's actions are based on sound economic principles. FTC regional offices conduct investigations and litigations, offer advice, recommend cases, provide outreach services, sponsor conferences, and coordinate activities with local, state, and regional authorities.

60283 ■ Federal Trade Commission - San Francisco Regional Office - Western Region
901 Market St., Ste. 570
San Francisco, CA 94103
Ph: (415)848-5124
Free: 877-382-4357
Fax: (415)848-5184
URL: http://www.ftc.gov/ro/western.htm
Description: Serves northern California, southern California, Colorado, Hawaii, Nevada, and Utah.

60284 ■ Federal Trade Commission - San Francisco Regional Office - Western Region
901 Market St., Ste. 570
San Francisco, CA 94103
Free: 877-382-4357
Fax: (415)848-5184
URL: http://www.ftc.gov/ro/western.htm
Description: Serves northern California, southern California, Colorado, Hawaii, Nevada, and Utah.

60285 ■ Federal Trade Commission - Seattle Regional Office - Northwest Region
2896 Federal Bldg.
915 2nd Ave.
Seattle, WA 98174
Ph: (206)220-4480
Free: 877-382-4357
Fax: (206)220-6366
URL: http://www.ftc.gov/ro/northwest.htm
Description: Serves Alaska, Montana, Idaho, Oregon, Washington, and Wyoming.

60286 ■ Federal Trade Commission - Seattle Regional Office - Northwest Region
915 2nd Ave., Rm. 2896
Seattle, WA 98174
Free: 877-382-4357
Fax: (206)220-6366
URL: http://www.ftc.gov/ro/northwest.htm
Description: Serves Alaska, Montana, Idaho, Oregon, Washington, and Wyoming.

GENERAL SERVICES ADMINISTRATION

The following business service centers are arranged alphabetically by city.

60287 ■ General Services Administration - Atlanta Business Service Center
401 W. Peachtree St.
Atlanta, GA 30308-3510
Ph: (404)562-2753
Co. E-mail: dawn.norman@gsa.gov
URL: http://www.iolp.gsa.gov/iolp/BuildingInfo.asp?bID=GA0087
Description: Serves Alabama, Florida, Georgia, Kentucky, Mississippi, North Carolina, South Carolina, and Tennessee.

60288 ■ General Services Administration - Auburn Business Service Center
400 15th St., SW
Rm. 9AB-10
Auburn, WA 98001
URL: http://www.gsa.gov
Description: Serves Alaska, Idaho, Oregon, and Washington.

60289 ■ General Services Administration - Boston Business Service Center
Thomas P. O'Neill Federal Bldg.
10 Causeway St.
Boston, MA 02222-1048
Ph: (617)565-4693
Free: 866-734-1727
Fax: (617)565-5967
Co. E-mail: roman.piaskoski@gsa.gov
URL: http://www.gsa.gov/portal/staffDirectory/topic/48@@
Description: Serves Connecticut, Maine, Massachusetts, New Hampshire, Rhode Island, and Vermont.

60290 ■ General Services Administration - Chicago Business Service Center
230 S. Dearborn St., Rm. 3600
Chicago, IL 60604
Ph: (312)886-3348
Fax: (312)353-7387
Co. E-mail: roger.blummer@gsa.gov
URL: http://www.gsa.gov
Description: Serves Illinois, Indiana, Michigan, Minnesota, Ohio, and Wisconsin.

60291 ■ General Services Administration - Denver Business Service Center
201 W. Colfax Ave., No. 1110
Denver, CO 80225-0506
Fax: (303)236-7403
Description: Serves Colorado, Montana, North Dakota, South Dakota, Utah, and Wyoming.

60292 ■ General Services Administration (FTS) - Federal Technology Service - Office of Regional Services
10304 Eaton Pl., 3rd Fl.
Fairfax, VA 22030
Co. E-mail: margaret.binns@gsa.gov
URL: http://www.fts.gsa.gov

60293 ■ General Services Administration - Ft. Worth Business Service Center
819 Taylor St.
Ft. Worth, TX 76102
Ph: (817)978-2321
Fax: (817)978-2577
URL: http://www.gsa.gov/portal/content/104716
Description: Serves Arkansas, Louisiana, New Mexico, Oklahoma, and Texas.

60294 ■ General Services Administration - Kansas City Business Service Center
1500 E. Bannister Rd., Rm. 2101
Kansas City, MO 64131-3009
Ph: (816)823-5120
Fax: (816)926-1779
Co. E-mail: chris.cockrill@gsa.gov
URL: http://www.gsa.gov/portal/staffDirectory/topic/48@@
Description: Serves Iowa, Kansas, Missouri, and Nebraska.

60295 ■ General Services Administration - New York Business Service Center
26 Federal Plz.
New York, NY 10278
Ph: (212)264-0591
Fax: (212)264-2746
Co. E-mail: brian.magden@gsa.gov
URL: http://www.gsa.gov/portal/staffDirectory/topic/48@@
Description: Serves New Jersey, New York, Puerto Rico, and the Virgin Islands.

60296 ■ General Services Administration - Office of Electronic Government and Technology
7th & D Sts., SW
Washington, DC 20405
Fax: (202)401-3722
Co. E-mail: roger.mason@gsa.gov

60297 ■ General Services Administration - Office of Global Supply - Logistics Operations Ctr.
Crystal Mall Bldg. 4
1901 S. Bell St., Rm. 1005
Arlington, VA 20406
Free: 800-525-8027
Co. E-mail: GSAglobalsupply@gsa.gov
URL: http://www.gsa.gov/portal/content/264345

60298 ■ General Services Administration - Office of Small Business Utilization - GSA
1275 1st St.
Washington, DC 20417
Ph: (202)501-1021

Free: 800-672-8472

Co. E-mail: small.business@gsa.gov

URL: http://www.gsa.gov/portal/category/21015

Description: The General Services Administration (GSA), the Federal government's purchasing agent, real estate developer, telecommunications manager, and computer overseer, contracts for over $10 billion worth of commodities and services each year. The GSA's Office of Enterprise Development (OED) develops and oversees GSA procurement preference programs for small, disadvantaged and women-owned businesses. In addition to other pamphlets, the OED publishes four major publications to assist businesses in their marketing efforts: Doing Business with GSA, GSA Small Purchases, GSA Subcontracting Directory (published semiannually), and Forecast of GSA Contracting Opportunities (published annually). Information about upcoming contracting opportunities is placed on GSA's Electronic Bulletin Board. GSA operates Business Service Centers (BSCs) in 11 major metropolitan areas throughout the country. The BSCs implement GSA procurement preference programs by providing assistance, information and counseling to small businesses interested in pursuing Federal Government contracts. Counselors at the BSCs help small businesses understand GSA contracting procedures and locate GSA buyers for their products or services. The BSCs are also involved in monitoring local GSA contracting programs to insure that small, disadvantaged and women-owned businesses are given access to contracts and subcontracts and to find ways to expand their participation. As part of GSA's program, the BSCs sponsor breakfasts and networking seminars to give small businesses an opportunity to meet contracting personnel and each other.

60299 ■ General Services Administration - Philadelphia Business Service Center - Office of Business and Public Affairs

John Wanamaker Bldg., Rm. 808

100 Penn Sq. E

Philadelphia, PA 19107

Ph: (215)656-5525

Fax: (215)656-6404

URL: http://www.gsa.gov

Description: Serves Delaware, Maryland, Pennsylvania, Virginia, and West Virginia.

60300 ■ General Services Administration - San Francisco Business Service Center

450 Golden Gate Ave.

San Francisco, CA 94102

Ph: (415)522-3001

Fax: (415)522-2815

URL: http://www.gsa.gov/portal/content/104695

Description: Serves California, Hawaii, Nevada, and Arizona.

60301 ■ General Services Administration - Washington, DC, Business Services Center

7th & D Sts. SW

Washington, DC 20407

Ph: (202)708-9100

Fax: (202)202-3722

URL: http://www.gsa.gov/portal/content/104717

Description: Serves the metropolitan Washington, D.C., area.

60302 ■ U.S. General Services Administration (FAS) - Federal Acquisition Service - Office of Regional Services

10304 Eaton Pl., 3rd Fl.

Fairfax, VA 22030

Ph: (703)306-6500

Co. E-mail: contactfas@gsa.gov

URL: http://www.fts.gsa.gov

60303 ■ U.S. General Services Administration - Great Lakes Region - Business Service Center

230 S. Dearborn St., Rm. 3600

Chicago, IL 60604

Ph: (312)886-3348

Fax: (312)353-7387

URL: http://www.gsa.gov

Description: Serves Illinois, Indiana, Michigan, Minnesota, Ohio, and Wisconsin.

60304 ■ U.S. General Services Administration - Greater Southwest Region - Business Service Center

819 Taylor St.

Ft. Worth, TX 76102

Ph: (817)978-2553

Fax: (817)978-2577

URL: http://www.gsa.gov

Description: Serves Arkansas, Louisiana, New Mexico, Oklahoma, and Texas.

60305 ■ U.S. General Services Administration - The Heartland Region - Business Service Center

1500 E. Bannister Rd., Rm. 2101

Kansas City, MO 64131-3088

Ph: (816)823-5120

Fax: (816)926-6878

URL: http://www.gsa.gov

Description: Serves Iowa, Kansas, Missouri, and Nebraska.

60306 ■ U.S. General Services Administration - Mid-Atlantic Region - Office of Business and Public Affairs

John Wanamaker Bldg., Rm. 808

100 Penn Sq. E

Philadelphia, PA 19107

Ph: (215)656-5525

Fax: (215)656-6404

URL: http://www.gsa.gov

Description: Serves Delaware, Maryland, New Jersey, Pennsylvania, Virginia, and West Virginia.

60307 ■ U.S. General Services Administration - National Capital Region - Business Services Center

7th & D Sts. SW

Washington, DC 20407

Ph: (202)202-6222

Fax: (202)202-3722

URL: http://www.gsa.gov

Description: Serves the metropolitan Washington, D.C., area.

60308 ■ U.S. General Services Administration - New England Region - Business Service Center

Thomas P. O'Neill Federal Bldg.

10 Causeway St., Rm. 900

Boston, MA 02222

Ph: (617)406-0052

Free: 866-734-1727

Fax: (617)565-5967

URL: http://www.gsa.gov

Description: Serves Connecticut, Maine, Massachusetts, New Hampshire, Rhode Island, and Vermont.

60309 ■ U.S. General Services Administration - Northeast and Caribbean Region - Business Service Center

26 Federal Plz.

New York, NY 10278

Ph: (212)264-0591

Fax: (212)264-2746

Co. E-mail: R2Contact@gsa.gov

URL: http://www.gsa.gov

Description: Serves New Jersey, New York, Puerto Rico, and the Virgin Islands.

60310 ■ U.S. General Services Administration - Northwest/Arctic Region - Business Service Center

400 15th St., SW

Rm. 9AB-10

Auburn, WA 98001

Ph: (206)931-7200

Co. E-mail: kay.pope@gsa.gov

URL: http://www.gsa.gov

Description: Serves Alaska, Idaho, Oregon, and Washington.

60311 ■ U.S. General Services Administration - Office of Global Supply - Logistics Operations Ctr.

Crystal Mall Bldg. 4

1901 S. Bell St., Rm. 1005

Arlington, VA 20406

Ph: (703)605-5514

Free: 800-525-8027

Fax: (800)856-7057

Co. E-mail: GSAglobalsupply@gsa.gov

URL: http://www.gsa.gov/Portal/gsa/ep/

60312 ■ U.S. General Services Administration - Office of Management and Budget - Office of E-Government and Information Technology

7th & D Sts., SW

Washington, DC 20405

Ph: (202)708-6222

Fax: (202)401-3722

URL: http://www.egov.gov

60313 ■ U.S. General Services Administration (GSA) - Office of Small Business Utilization

Regional Office Bldg.

7th and D. Sts. SW

Washington, DC 20407-0002

Ph: (202)501-1021

Free: 800-0ED-IGSA

Fax: (202)208-5938

Co. E-mail: small.business@gsa.gov

URL: http://www.gsa.gov/

Description: The General Services Administration (GSA), the Federal government's purchasing agent, real estate developer, telecommunications manager, and computer overseer, contracts for over $10 billion worth of commodities and services each year. The GSA's Office of Enterprise Development (OED) develops and oversees GSA procurement preference programs for small, disadvantaged and women-owned businesses. In addition to other pamphlets, the OED publishes four major publications to assist businesses in their marketing efforts: Doing Business with GSA, GSA Small Purchases, GSA Subcontracting Directory (published semiannually), and Forecast of GSA Contracting Opportunities (published annually). Information about upcoming contracting opportunities is placed on GSA's Electronic Bulletin Board. GSA operates Business Service Centers (BSCs) in 11 major metropolitan areas throughout the country. The BSCs implement GSA procurement preference programs by providing assistance, information and counseling to small businesses interested in pursuing Federal Government contracts. Counselors at the BSCs help small businesses understand GSA contracting procedures and locate GSA buyers for their products or services. The BSCs are also involved in monitoring local GSA contracting programs to insure that small, disadvantaged and women-owned businesses are given access to contracts and subcontracts and to find ways to expand their participation. As part of GSA's program, the BSCs sponsor breakfasts and networking seminars to give small businesses an opportunity to meet contracting personnel and each other.

60314 ■ U.S. General Services Administration - Pacific Rim Region - Business Service Center

450 Golden Gate Ave., 4th Fl.

San Francisco, CA 94102

Ph: (415)522-2845

Fax: (415)522-2815

URL: http://www.gsa.gov

Description: Serves California, Hawaii, Nevada, and Arizona.

60315 ■ U.S. General Services Administration - Rocky Mountain Region - Business Service Center

201 W. Colfax Ave., No. 1110

Denver, CO 80225-0506

Ph: (720)865-7100

Fax: (303)236-7403

Description: Serves Colorado, Montana, North Dakota, South Dakota, Utah, and Wyoming.

60316 ■ U.S. General Services Administration - Southeast Sunbelt Region - Business Service Center
401 W. Peachtree St.
Atlanta, GA 30308-3510
Ph: (404)331-2750
Co. E-mail: shyam.reddy@gsa.gov
URL: http://www.iolp.gsa.gov/iolp/BuildingInfo.
  asp?bID=GA0087
Description: Serves Alabama, Florida, Georgia, Kentucky, Mississippi, North Carolina, South Carolina, and Tennessee.

INTERNATIONAL TRADE ADMINISTRATION

The International Trade Administration is a part of the U.S. Department of Commerce. The following is a list of ITA Export Assistance Centers, arranged alphabetically by state.

60317 ■ International Trade Administration (ITA) - Office of Public Affairs
Herbert Clark Hoover Bldg., Rm. 3416
1401 Constitution Ave., NW
Washington, DC 20230
Ph: (202)482-3809
Free: 800-872-8723
Fax: (202)482-4821
Co. E-mail: public_affairs@ita.doc.gov
URL: http://trade.gov/press/index.asp
Description: The International Trade Administration's domestic and overseas programs are designed to stimulate the expansion of U.S. exports. Major programs include export counseling and assistance; promotion of U.S. products abroad; coordination and conduct of overseas trade missions; support for the Export Trading Company formation; and management of federal participation in international expositions held in the United States. The ITA gathers, analyzes, and disseminates commercially usable trade and marketing information, including advice on marketing opportunities abroad; information about government assistance available for expanding trade with other nations; location of needed materials and resources; and advice on international trade policy and tariff questions. The ITA operates a network of 48 U.S. and foreign Commercial Service district offices through which to carry out its programs. The ITA's information services, market research, and overseas promotion programs provide opportunities to introduce products abroad at small costs. The ITA, with its variety of low-cost marketing aids, also may assist small firms in locating overseas outlets for their products, namely agents, distributors, licensees, buyers, and suppliers.

60318 ■ International Trade Administration - Office of Public Affairs
Herbert Clark Hoover Bldg., Rm. 3416
1401 Constitution Ave., NW
Washington, DC 20230
Ph: (202)482-3809
Free: 800-872-8723
Fax: (202)482-5819
Co. E-mail: publicaffairs@trade.gov
URL: http://trade.gov/press/index.asp
Description: The International Trade Administration's domestic and overseas programs are designed to stimulate the expansion of U.S. exports. Major programs include export counseling and assistance; promotion of U.S. products abroad; coordination and conduct of overseas trade missions; support for the Export Trading Company formation; and management of federal participation in international expositions held in the United States. The ITA gathers, analyzes, and disseminates commercially usable trade and marketing information, including advice on marketing opportunities abroad; information about government assistance available for expanding trade with other nations; location of needed materials and resources; and advice on international trade policy and tariff questions. The ITA operates a network of 48 U.S. and foreign Commercial Service district offices through which to carry out its programs. The ITA's information services, market research, and overseas promotion programs provide opportunities

to introduce products abroad at small costs. The ITA, with its variety of low-cost marketing aids, also may assist small firms in locating overseas outlets for their products, namely agents, distributors, licensees, buyers, and suppliers.

60319 ■ International Trade Administration - U.S. Commercial Service - Export Assistance Center (Anchorage, Alaska)
World Trade Center Alaska
431 W. 7th Ave., Ste. 108
Anchorage, AK 99501-0700
Ph: (907)278-7233
Fax: (907)278-2982
Co. E-mail: info@wtcak.org
URL: http://www.wtcak.org

60320 ■ International Trade Administration - U.S. Commercial Service - Export Assistance Center (Austin, Texas)
211 E. 11th St., 4th Fl.
Austin, TX 78711
Ph: (512)916-5939
Fax: (512)916-5940
Co. E-mail: austin.office.box@trade.gov
URL: http://www.buyusa.gov/austin

60321 ■ International Trade Administration - U.S. Commercial Service - Export Assistance Center (Baltimore, Maryland)
U.S. Export Assistance Center
300 W. Pratt St., Ste. 300
Baltimore, MD 21202-6504
Ph: (410)962-4539
Fax: (410)962-4529
Co. E-mail: jansen.weaver@mail.doc.gov
URL: http://www.buyusa.gov/baltimore
Description: Serves as both the Baltimore and Washington, D.C., district office.

60322 ■ International Trade Administration - U.S. Commercial Service - Export Assistance Center (Birmingham, Alabama)
950 22nd St. N, Ste. 707
Birmingham, AL 35203-5309
Ph: (205)731-1331
Fax: (205)731-0076
Co. E-mail: Office.Birmingham@trade.gov
URL: http://www.buyusa.gov/alabama/

60323 ■ International Trade Administration - U.S. Commercial Service - Export Assistance Center (Boise, Idaho)
700 W. State St., 2nd Fl.
Boise, ID 83720
Ph: (208)364-7791
Fax: (208)334-2783
Co. E-mail: boise.office.box@trade.gov
URL: http://www.buyusa.gov/boise

60324 ■ International Trade Administration - U.S. Commercial Service - Export Assistance Center (Boston, Massachusetts)
JFK Federal Bldg., Ste. 1826A
55 New Sudbury St.
Boston, MA 02203
Ph: (617)565-4301
Fax: (617)565-4313
Co. E-mail: Office.Boston@mail.doc.gov
URL: http://www.buyusa.gov/newengland
Description: Boston office also services the states of New Hampshire and Vermont.

60325 ■ International Trade Administration - U.S. Commercial Service - Export Assistance Center (Buffalo, New York)
130 S. Elmwood Ave., Ste. 530
Buffalo, NY 14202
Ph: (585)551-4191
Fax: (585)551-5290
Co. E-mail: james.mariano@mail.doc.gov
URL: http://www.buyusa.gov/buffalo/

60326 ■ International Trade Administration - U.S. Commercial Service - Export Assistance Center (Carmel, Indiana)
11405 N. Pennsylvania St., Ste. 106
Carmel, IN 46032

Ph: (317)582-2300
Fax: (317)582-2301
Co. E-mail: mark.cooper@mail.doc.gov
URL: http://www.buyusa.gov/indiana

60327 ■ International Trade Administration - U.S. Commercial Service - Export Assistance Center (Charleston, South Carolina)
1362 McMillan Ave., Ste. 100
North Charleston, SC 29405
Ph: (843)746-3404
Fax: (843)529-0305
Co. E-mail: phil.minard@mail.doc.gov
URL: http://www.buyusa.gov/southcarolina/location.
  html

60328 ■ International Trade Administration - U.S. Commercial Service - Export Assistance Center (Charlotte, North Carolina)
521 E. Morehead St., Ste. 435
Charlotte, NC 28202
Ph: (704)333-4886
Fax: (704)332-2681
Co. E-mail: office.charlotte@mail.doc.gov
URL: http://www.buyusa.gov/northcarolina/

60329 ■ International Trade Administration - U.S. Commercial Service - Export Assistance Center (Chicago, Illinois)
200 W. Adams St., Rm. 2450
Chicago, IL 60603
Ph: (312)353-8490
Fax: (312)353-8120
Co. E-mail: Julie.carducci@mail.doc.gov
URL: http://www.buyusa.gov/midwest/

60330 ■ International Trade Administration - U.S. Commercial Service - Export Assistance Center (Cincinnati, Ohio)
36 E. 7th St., Ste. 2650
Cincinnati, OH 45202
Ph: (513)684-2944
Fax: (513)684-3227
Co. E-mail: office.cincinnati@trade.gov
URL: http://www.buyusa.gov/cincinnati/

60331 ■ International Trade Administration - U.S. Commercial Service - Export Assistance Center (Clearwater, Florida)
13805 58 St. N., Ste. 1-200
Clearwater, FL 33760
Ph: (727)893-3738
Fax: (727)893-3839
Co. E-mail: office.clearwater@trade.gov
URL: http://www.buyusa.gov/florida/

60332 ■ International Trade Administration - U.S. Commercial Service - Export Assistance Center (Cleveland, Ohio)
600 Superior Ave. E, Ste. 700
Cleveland, OH 44114
Ph: (216)522-4750
Fax: (216)522-2235
Co. E-mail: office.cleveland@mail.doc.gov
URL: http://www.buyusa.gov/northeastohio/cleve-
  landuseac.html

60333 ■ International Trade Administration - U.S. Commercial Service - Export Assistance Center (Columbia, South Carolina)
USC Moore School of Business
1705 College St., Ste. 600
Columbia, SC 29208
Ph: (803)777-2571
Fax: (803)777-2615
Co. E-mail: office.columbia@mail.doc.gov
URL: http://www.buyusa.gov/southcarolina/

60334 ■ International Trade Administration - U.S. Commercial Service - Export Assistance Center (Columbus, Ohio)
401 N. Front St., Ste. 200
Columbus, OH 43215
Ph: (614)365-9510
Fax: (614)365-9598
Co. E-mail: roberta.ford@trade.gov
URL: http://www.buyusa.gov/greatlakes/columbus.
  html

60335 ■ International Trade Administration - U.S. Commercial Service - Export Assistance Center (Dallas, Texas)
2050 N. Stemmons Fwy., Ste. 170
Dallas, TX 75207
Ph: (214)767-0018
Fax: (214)767-8240

60336 ■ International Trade Administration - U.S. Commercial Service - Export Assistance Center (Denver, Colorado)
World Trade Center
1625 Broadway, Ste. 680
Denver, CO 80202
Ph: (303)844-6001
Fax: (303)844-5651
Co. E-mail: Denver.office.box@trade.gov
URL: http://www.buyusa.gov/colorado/
Description: Denver office also services the states of Montana and Wyoming.

60337 ■ International Trade Administration - U.S. Commercial Service - Export Assistance Center (Des Moines, Iowa)
210 Walnut St., Rm. 749
Des Moines, IA 50309
Ph: (515)284-4590
Fax: (515)288-1437
Co. E-mail: office.desmoines@trade.gov
URL: http://www.buyusa.gov/iowa/

60338 ■ International Trade Administration - U.S. Commercial Service - Export Assistance Center (Detroit, Michigan)
8109 E. Jefferson Ave., Ste. 110
Detroit, MI 48214
Ph: (313)226-3650
Fax: (313)226-3657
Co. E-mail: office.detroit@trade.gov
URL: http://www.buyusa.gov/greatlakes/detroit.html

60339 ■ International Trade Administration - U.S. Commercial Service - Export Assistance Center (Eugene, Oregon)
1401 Willamette St.
Eugene, OR 97401-4003
Ph: (541)484-6575
Fax: (541)484-6704

60340 ■ International Trade Administration - U.S. Commercial Service - Export Assistance Center (Ft. Worth, Texas)
808 Throckmorton St.
Ft. Worth, TX 76102
Ph: (817)392-2673
Fax: (817)392-2668
Co. E-mail: fort.worth.office.box@trade.gov
URL: http://www.buyusa.gov/fortworth/

60341 ■ International Trade Administration - U.S. Commercial Service - Export Assistance Center (Gaithersburg, Maryland)
c/o National Institute of Standards and Technology
100 Bureau Dr.
Mail Stop 2160
Gaithersburg, MD 20899-2160
Ph: (301)975-4040
Fax: (301)926-1559
URL: http://www.buyusa.gov

60342 ■ International Trade Administration - U.S. Commercial Service - Export Assistance Center (Grand Rapids, Michigan)
401 W. Fulton St., Ste. 349C
Grand Rapids, MI 49504-6495
Ph: (616)458-3564
Fax: (616)458-3872
Co. E-mail: Thomas.Maguire@trade.gov
URL: http://www.buyusa.gov/greatlakes/

60343 ■ International Trade Administration - U.S. Commercial Service - Export Assistance Center (Greensboro, North Carolina)
342 N. Elm St.
Greensboro, NC 27401
Ph: (336)333-5345

Fax: (336)333-5158
Co. E-mail: debbie.strader@trade.gov
URL: http://www.buyusa.gov/northcarolina/
Description: Serves the business needs of Davidson, Forsyth, Guilford, Montgomery, Randolph, Rockingham, and Stokes counties.

60344 ■ International Trade Administration - U.S. Commercial Service - Export Assistance Center (Harrisburg, Pennsylvania)
2 S. George St., Cumberland House
Harrisburg, PA 17551-0302
Ph: (717)872-4386
Fax: (717)871-2132
Co. E-mail: antonio.ceballos@trade.gov
URL: http://www.buyusa.gov/harrisburg/

60345 ■ International Trade Administration - U.S. Commercial Service - Export Assistance Center (Highland Park, Illinois)
610 Central Ave., Ste. 150
Highland Park, IL 60035
Ph: (847)681-8010
Fax: (847)681-8012

60346 ■ International Trade Administration - U.S. Commercial Service - Export Assistance Center (Honolulu, Hawaii)
521 Ala Moana Blvd., Rm. 214
Foreign Trade Zone No. 9
Honolulu, HI 96813
Ph: (808)522-8040
Fax: (808)522-8045
Co. E-mail: john.holman@mail.doc.gov
URL: http://www.buyusa.gov/hawaii/

60347 ■ International Trade Administration - U.S. Commercial Service - Export Assistance Center (Houston, Texas)
1919 Smith St., Ste. 1026
Houston, TX 77002
Ph: (713)209-3104
Fax: (713)209-3135
Co. E-mail: office.houston@trade.gov
URL: http://www.buyusa.gov/houston

60348 ■ International Trade Administration - U.S. Commercial Service - Export Assistance Center (Jackson, Mississippi)
175 E. Capitol St., Ste. 255
Jackson, MS 39201
Ph: (601)965-4130
Fax: (601)965-4132
Co. E-mail: carol.moore@trade.gov
URL: http://www.buyusa.gov/jackson/

60349 ■ International Trade Administration - U.S. Commercial Service - Export Assistance Center (Kansas City, Missouri)
2509 Commerce Tower
911 Main St.
Kansas City, MO 64105
Ph: (816)421-1876
Fax: (816)471-7839
Co. E-mail: office.kansascity@trade.gov
URL: http://www.buyusa.gov/kansascity
Description: Affiliated with the Wichita district office.

60350 ■ International Trade Administration - U.S. Commercial Service - Export Assistance Center (Knoxville, Florida)
Historic City
17 Market Sq., Ste. 201
Knoxville, TN 37902-1405
Ph: (865)-545-4637
Fax: (865)545-4435
Co. E-mail: robert.leach@mail.doc.gov
URL: http://www.buyusa.gov/tennesse/

60351 ■ International Trade Administration - U.S. Commercial Service - Export Assistance Center (Little Rock)
425 W. Capitol Ave., Ste. 425
Little Rock, AR 72201
Ph: (501)324-5794
Fax: (501)324-7380
Co. E-mail: office.littlerock@trade.gov
URL: http://www.buyusa.gov/arkansas

60352 ■ International Trade Administration - U.S. Commercial Service - Export Assistance Center (Long Beach)
One World Trade Center, Ste. 1670
Long Beach, CA 90831
Fax: (310)980-4561

60353 ■ International Trade Administration - U.S. Commercial Service - Export Assistance Center (Long Island)
College at Old Westbury, PO Box 210
Academic Village - Marshall Hallam Bldg 10
223 Store Hill Road
Old Westbury, NY 11568-0210
Ph: (516)876-3418
Fax: (516)876-7563
Co. E-mail: shakir.farsakh@mail.doc.gov
URL: http://www.buyusa.gov/longisland/

60354 ■ International Trade Administration - U.S. Commercial Service - Export Assistance Center (Los Angeles, California)
11150 West Olympic Blvd., Ste. 975
Los Angeles, CA 90064
Ph: (310)235-7206
Fax: (310)235-7220
Co. E-mail: julianne.hennessy@trade.gov
URL: http://www.buyusa.gov/westlosangeles/

60355 ■ International Trade Administration - U.S. Commercial Service - Export Assistance Center (Louisville, Kentucky)
601 W. Broadway, Rm. 634B
Louisville, KY 40202
Ph: (502)582-5066
Fax: (502)582-6573
Co. E-mail: office.louisville@trade.gov
URL: http://www.buyusa.gov/greatlakes/louisville.html

60356 ■ International Trade Administration - U.S. Commercial Service - Export Assistance Center (Memphis, Tennessee)
22 N. Front St., Ste. 200
Memphis, TN 38103
Ph: (901)544-0930
Fax: (901)543-3510
Co. E-mail: david.spann@mail.doc.gov
URL: http://www.buyusa.gov/tennessee/

60357 ■ International Trade Administration - U.S. Commercial Service - Export Assistance Center (Miami, Florida)
5835 Blue Lagoon Dr., Ste. 203
Miami, FL 33126
Ph: (305)526-7425
Fax: (305)526-7434
Co. E-mail: linda.santucci@trade.gov
URL: http://www.buyusa.gov/sunbelt/24.html

60358 ■ International Trade Administration - U.S. Commercial Service - Export Assistance Center (Middletown, Connecticut)
213 Court St., Ste. 903
Middletown, CT 06457-3382
Ph: (860)638-6950
Fax: (860)638-6970
Co. E-mail: office.middletown@trade.gov
URL: http://www.buyusa.gov/connecticut/
Description: Affiliated with the Providence district office.

60359 ■ International Trade Administration - U.S. Commercial Service - Export Assistance Center (Milwaukee, Wisconsin)
1025 N. Broadway, Rm. R01
1235 N. Milwaukee St.
Milwaukee, WI 53202
Ph: (414)297-3473
Fax: (414)297-3470
Co. E-mail: office.milwaukee@trade.gov
URL: http://www.buyusa.gov/midwest

60360 ■ International Trade Administration - U.S. Commercial Service - Export Assistance Center (Minneapolis, Minnesota)
Butler Square Bldg., Ste. 210-C
100 N. 6th St.
Minneapolis, MN 55403

Ph: (612)348-1638
Fax: (612)348-1650
Co. E-mail: Minneapolis.box@trade.gov
URL: http://www.buyusa.gov/minnesota/

**60361 ■ International Trade Administration -
U.S. Commercial Service - Export Assistance
Center (Monterey, California)**
411 Pacific St., Ste. 316A
Monterey, CA 93940
Ph: (831)641-9850
Fax: (831)641-9849
Co. E-mail: chris.damm@mail.doc.gov
URL: http://www.buyusa.gov/monterey/ts.html

**60362 ■ International Trade Administration -
U.S. Commercial Service - Export Assistance
Center (Montpelier, Vermont)**
National Life Bldg., 6th Fl.
Montpelier, VT 05602
Ph: (802)828-4508
Fax: (802)828-3258
Co. E-mail: susan.murray@trade.gov
URL: http://www.buyusa.gov/newengland/montpelier.
html

**60363 ■ International Trade Administration -
U.S. Commercial Service - Export Assistance
Center (Nashville, Tennessee)**
312 8th Ave. N., 10th Fl.
Nashville, TN 37243
Ph: (615)736-2222
Fax: (615)736-2226
Co. E-mail: office.nashville@trade.gov
URL: http://www.buyusa.gov/greatlakes/nashville.
html

**60364 ■ International Trade Administration -
U.S. Commercial Service - Export Assistance
Center (Newark, New Jersey)**
744 Broad St., Ste. 1505
Newark, NJ 07102
Ph: (973)645-4682
Fax: (973)645-4783
Co. E-mail: joel.reynoso@trade.gov
URL: http://www.buyusa.gov/newark/

**60365 ■ International Trade Administration -
U.S. Commercial Service - Export Assistance
Center (Newport Beach, California)**
3300 Irvine Ave., Ste. 307
Newport Beach, CA 92660
Ph: (949)660-1688
Fax: (949)660-1338
Co. E-mail: office.NewportBeach@trade.gov
URL: http://www.buyusa.gov/newportbeach/

**60366 ■ International Trade Administration -
U.S. Commercial Service - Export Assistance
Center (Novato, California)**
50 Acacia Ave.
San Rafael, CA 94901
Ph: (415)485-6200
Fax: (415)485-6219
Co. E-mail: north.bay.office.box@NOSPAM.mail.doc.
gov
URL: http://www.buyusa.gov/northbay/

**60367 ■ International Trade Administration -
U.S. Commercial Service - Export Assistance
Center (Oakland, California)**
Oakland Federal Bldg. - North Tower
1301 Clay St., Ste. 630 N
Oakland, CA 94612
Ph: (510)273-7350
Fax: (510)273-7352
Co. E-mail: oakland.office.box@mail.doc.gov
URL: http://www.buyusa.gov/oakland/

**60368 ■ International Trade Administration -
U.S. Commercial Service - Export Assistance
Center (Oklahoma City, Oklahoma)**
301 NW 63rd St., Ste. 330
Oklahoma City, OK 73116
Ph: (405)608-5302
Fax: (405)608-4211
Co. E-mail: Ronald.wilson@trade.gov
URL: http://www.buyusa.gov/oklahomacity/

**60369 ■ International Trade Administration -
U.S. Commercial Service - Export Assistance
Center (Omaha, Nebraska)**
13006 W. Center Rd.
Omaha, NE 68144
Ph: (402)597-0193
Fax: (402)595-1194
Co. E-mail: Meredith.bond@trade.gov
URL: http://www.buyusa.gov/nebraska/
Description: Omaha office also services the states
of North Dakota and South Dakota.

**60370 ■ International Trade Administration -
U.S. Commercial Service - Export Assistance
Center (Orlando, Florida)**
315 E. Robinson St., Ste. 100
Orlando, FL 32801
Ph: (407)648-6592
Fax: (407)648-6756
Co. E-mail: kenneth.mouradian@mail.doc.gov
URL: http://www.buyusa.gov/sunbelt/20.html

**60371 ■ International Trade Administration -
U.S. Commercial Service - Export Assistance
Center (Philadelphia, Pennsylvania)**
The Curtis Ctr., Ste. 580 W.
Independence Sq. W.
Philadelphia, PA 19106-3304
Ph: (215)597-6101
Fax: (215)597-6123
Co. E-mail: office.philadelphia@mail.doc.gov
URL: http://www.buyusa.gov/philadelphia/
Description: Philadelphia office also services the
state of Delaware.

**60372 ■ International Trade Administration -
U.S. Commercial Service - Export Assistance
Center (Phoenix, Arizona)**
2828 N. Central Ave., Ste. 800
Phoenix, AZ 85012
Ph: (602)640-2513
Fax: (602)640-2518
Co. E-mail: eric.nielsen@trade.gov
URL: http://www.azexport.com

**60373 ■ International Trade Administration -
U.S. Commercial Service - Export Assistance
Center (Pittsburgh, Pennsylvania)**
Regional Enterprise Tower
425 6th Ave., Ste. 2950
Pittsburgh, PA 15219-1854
Ph: (412)644-2820
Fax: (412)644-2803
Co. E-mail: Lyn.Doverspike@mail.doc.gov
URL: http://www.buyusa.gov/pittsburgh/

**60374 ■ International Trade Administration -
U.S. Commercial Service - Export Assistance
Center (Pontiac, Michigan)**
Oakland Pointe Office Bldg.
250 Elizabeth Lake Rd., Ste. 1300 W.
Pontiac, MI 48341
Ph: (248)975-9600
Fax: (248)975-9606
Co. E-mail: office.pontiac@mail.doc.gov
URL: http://www.buyusa.gov/greatlakes/pontiac.html

**60375 ■ International Trade Administration -
U.S. Commercial Service - Export Assistance
Center (Portland, ME)**
c/o Maine International Trade Center
511 Congress St.
Portland, ME 04101
Ph: (207)541-7430
Fax: (207)541-7420
Co. E-mail: jeffrey.porter@trade.gov
URL: http://www.buyusa.gov/newengland/portland.
html
Description: Affiliated with the Boston, Massachu-
setts, district office.

**60376 ■ International Trade Administration -
U.S. Commercial Service - Export Assistance
Center (Portland, Oregon)**
1 World Trade Center
121 SW Salmon St., Ste. 242
Portland, OR 97204
Ph: (503)326-3001

Fax: (503)326-6351
Co. E-mail: scott.goddin@trade.gov
URL: http://www.buyusa.gov/oregon/

**60377 ■ International Trade Administration -
U.S. Commercial Service - Export Assistance
Center (Portsmouth, New Hampshire)**
17th New Hampshire Ave.
Portsmouth, NH 03801-2838
Ph: (603)334-6074
Fax: (603)334-6110
URL: http://www.buyusa.gov/newhampshire

**60378 ■ International Trade Administration -
U.S. Commercial Service - Export Assistance
Center (Providence, Rhode Island)**
315 Iron Horse Way, Ste. 101
Providence, RI 02908
Ph: (401)528-5104
Fax: (401)528-5067
Co. E-mail: keith.yatsuhashi@trade.gov
URL: http://www.buyusa.gov/rhodeisland/
Description: Affiliated with the Hartford district office.

**60379 ■ International Trade Administration -
U.S. Commercial Service - Export Assistance
Center (Reno, Nevada)**
1 E. 1st St., 16th Fl.
Reno, NV 89501
Ph: (775)784-5203
Fax: (775)784-5343
Co. E-mail: bill.cline@trade.gov
URL: http://www.buyusa.gov/nevada/

**60380 ■ International Trade Administration -
U.S. Commercial Service - Export Assistance
Center (Richmond, Virginia)**
400 N. 8th St., Ste. 412
Richmond, VA 23240-0026
Ph: (804)771-2246
Fax: (804)771-2390
Co. E-mail: eric.mcdonald@mail.doc.gov
URL: http://www.buyusa.gov/virginia/

**60381 ■ International Trade Administration -
U.S. Commercial Service - Export Assistance
Center (Rochester, New York)**
400 Andrews St., Ste. 710
Rochester, NY 14604
Ph: (585)263-6480
Fax: (585)325-6505
Co. E-mail: Timothy.McCall@mail.doc.gov
URL: http://www.buyusa.gov/rochester/

**60382 ■ International Trade Administration -
U.S. Commercial Service - Export Assistance
Center (Rockford, Illinois)**
605 Fulton Ave., Ste. E103
Rockford, IL 61103
Ph: (815)316-2380
Fax: (888)628-2571
Co. E-mail: office.rockford@trade.gov
URL: http://www.buyusa.gov/midwest/useac.html

**60383 ■ International Trade Administration -
U.S. Commercial Service - Export Assistance
Center (Sacramento, California)**
1410 Ethan Way
Sacramento, CA 95825
Ph: (916)566-7170
Fax: (916)566-7123
Co. E-mail: george.tastard@trade.gov
URL: http://www.buyusa.gov/sacramento/

**60384 ■ International Trade Administration -
U.S. Commercial Service - Export Assistance
Center (St. Louis, Missouri)**
8235 Forsyth Blvd., Ste. 520
St. Louis, MO 63105
Ph: (314)425-3302
Fax: (314)425-3381
Co. E-mail: office.stlouis@trade.gov
URL: http://www.buyusa.gov/stlouis

60385 ■ International Trade Administration - U.S. Commercial Service - Export Assistance Center (Salt Lake City, Utah)
9690 S. 300 W., Ste. 201
Sandy, UT 84070
Ph: (801)255-1871
Fax: (801)255-3147
Co. E-mail: office.saltlakecity@trade.gov
URL: http://www.buyusa.gov/utah

60386 ■ International Trade Administration - U.S. Commercial Service - Export Assistance Center (San Antonio, Texas)
203 S. Saint Mary St., Ste. 360
San Antonio, TX 78205
Ph: (210)228-9878
Fax: (210)228-9874
Co. E-mail: san.antonio.office.box@trade.gov
URL: http://www.buyusa.gov/sanantonio/

60387 ■ International Trade Administration - U.S. Commercial Service - Export Assistance Center (San Diego, California)
9449 Balboa Ave., Ste. 111
San Diego, CA 92123
Ph: (858)467-7032
Fax: (858)467-7043
Co. E-mail: matt.andersen@mail.doc.gov
URL: http://www.buyusa.gov/sandiego/

60388 ■ International Trade Administration - U.S. Commercial Service - Export Assistance Center (San Francisco, California)
250 Montgomery St., 14th Fl.
San Francisco, CA 94104
Ph: (415)705-2300
Fax: (415)705-2299
Co. E-mail: san.francisco.office.box@mail.doc.gov
URL: http://www.buyusa.gov/sanfrancisco/

60389 ■ International Trade Administration - U.S. Commercial Service - Export Assistance Center (San Jose, California)
55 S. Market St., Ste. 1040
San Jose, CA 95113
Ph: (408)535-2757
Fax: (408)535-2758
Co. E-mail: silicon.valley.office.box@mail.doc.gov
URL: http://www.buyusa.gov/siliconvalley/

60390 ■ International Trade Administration - U.S. Commercial Service - Export Assistance Center (San Juan, Puerto Rico)
Centro Internacional de Mercadeo Torre II, Ste. 702
Carr. 165
Guaynabo, PR 00968-8058
Ph: (787)775-1992
Fax: (787)781-7178
Co. E-mail: jose.burgos@trade.gov
URL: http://www.buyusa.gov/sunbelt/puertorico.html

60391 ■ International Trade Administration - U.S. Commercial Service - Export Assistance Center (Santa Clara, California)
5201 Great American Pkwy., Ste. 456
Santa Clara, CA 95054
Ph: (408)970-4610
Fax: (408)970-4618
Co. E-mail: santa.clara.office.box@mail.doc.gov

60392 ■ International Trade Administration - U.S. Commercial Service - Export Assistance Center (Santa Fe, New Mexico)
c/o New Mexico Dept. of Economic Development
Santa Fe, NM 87504-5003
Ph: (505)231-0075
Fax: (505)827-0211
Co. E-mail: sandra.necessary@mail.doc.gov
URL: http://www.buyusa.gov/newmexico

60393 ■ International Trade Administration - U.S. Commercial Service - Export Assistance Center (Scranton, Pennsylvania)
One Montage Mountain Rd., Ste. B
Moosic, PA 18507
Ph: (717)969-2530
Fax: (717)969-2539

60394 ■ International Trade Administration - U.S. Commercial Service - Export Assistance Center (Seattle, Washington)
2601 4th Ave., Ste. 320
Seattle, WA 98121
Ph: (206)553-5615
Fax: (206)553-7253
Co. E-mail: seattle.office.box@mail.doc.gov
URL: http://www.buyusa.gov/seattle

60395 ■ International Trade Administration - U.S. Commercial Service - Export Assistance Center (Sioux Falls, South Dakota)
Augustana College
2001 S. Summit Ave.
Sioux Falls, SD 57197
Ph: (605)330-4265
Fax: (605)330-4266
Co. E-mail: cinnamon.king@mail.doc.gov
URL: http://www.buyusa.gov/southdakota/

60396 ■ International Trade Administration - U.S. Commercial Service - Export Assistance Center (Somerset, Kentucky)
2292 S. Hwy. 27, Ste. 320
Somerset, KY 42501
Ph: (606)677-6160
Fax: (606)677-6161
URL: http://www.buyusa.gov/kentucky/

60397 ■ International Trade Administration - U.S. Commercial Service - Export Assistance Center (Spokane, Washington)
801 W. Riverside Ave., Ste. 100
Spokane, WA 99201
Ph: (509)353-2625
Fax: (509)353-2449
Co. E-mail: spokane.office.box@mail.doc.gov
URL: http://www.buyusa.gov/spokane/

60398 ■ International Trade Administration - U.S. Commercial Service - Export Assistance Center (Tallahassee, Florida)
The Atrium Bldg.
325 John Knox Rd., Ste. 201
Tallahassee, FL 32303
Ph: (850)942-9635
Fax: (850)922-9595
Co. E-mail: Michael.higgins@mail.doc.gov
URL: http://www.buyusa.gov/sunbelt/25.html

60399 ■ International Trade Administration - U.S. Commercial Service - Export Assistance Center (Toledo, Ohio)
420 Madison Ave., Ste. 510
Toledo, OH 43604
Ph: (216)522-4732
Fax: (216)522-2235
Co. E-mail: danielle.rust@mail.doc.gov
URL: http://www.buyusa.gov/greatlakes/toledo.html

60400 ■ International Trade Administration - U.S. Commercial Service - Export Assistance Center (Trenton, New Jersey)
20 W. State St.
Trenton, NJ 08625-0820
Ph: (609)989-2100
Fax: (609)989-2395
Co. E-mail: office.trenton@mail.doc.gov
URL: http://www.buyusa.gov/trenton/

60401 ■ International Trade Administration - U.S. Commercial Service - Export Assistance Center (Tulsa, Oklahoma)
700 N. Greenwood Ave., Ste. 1400
Tulsa, OK 74106
Ph: (918)581-7650
Fax: (918)581-6263
Co. E-mail: jim.williams@mail.doc.gov
URL: http://www.buyusa.gov/tulsa/

60402 ■ International Trade Administration - U.S. Commercial Service - Export Assistance Center (Westchester, New York)
707 Westchester Ave., Ste. 209
White Plains, NY 10604
Ph: (914)682-6712

Fax: (914)682-6698
Co. E-mail: Joan.Kanlian@mail.doc.gov
URL: http://www.buyusa.gov/westchester/

60403 ■ International Trade Administration - U.S. Commercial Service - Export Assistance Center (Wheaton, Illinois)
Illinois Institute of Technology
201 E. Loop Dr.
Wheaton, IL 60187
Ph: (708)353-4332
Fax: (708)353-4336

60404 ■ International Trade Administration - U.S. Commercial Service - Export Assistance Center (Wheeling, West Virgina)
c/o Wheeling Jesuit University/NTTC
316 Washington Ave.
Wheeling, WV 26003
Ph: (304)243-5493
Fax: (304)243-5494
Co. E-mail: diego.gattesco@mail.doc.gov
URL: http://www.buyusa.gov/westvirginia/

60405 ■ International Trade Administration - U.S. Commercial Service - Export Assistance Center (Wichita, Kansas)
150 N. Main St., Ste. 200
Wichita, KS 67202-1305
Ph: (316)263-4067
Fax: (316)263-8306
Co. E-mail: andrew.anderson@mail.doc.gov
URL: http://www.buyusa.gov/wichita/
Description: Affiliated with the Kansas City, Missouri, district office.

60406 ■ International Trade Administration - U.S. Commercial Service - Export Assistance Center (Ypsilanti, Michigan)
c/o Eastern Michigan University
300 W. Michigan Ave., Ste. 306G
Ypsilanti, MI 48197
Ph: (734)487-0259
Fax: (734)485-2396
Co. E-mail: joseph.kramer@mail.doc.gov
URL: http://www.buyusa.gov/greatlakes/ypsilanti.html

60407 ■ International Trade Administration - U.S. and Foreign Commercial Service - Export Assistance Center (Anchorage, Alaska)
World Trade Center Alaska
431 W. 7th Ave., Ste. 108
Anchorage, AK 99501-0700
Ph: (907)271-6237
Fax: (907)278-2982
Co. E-mail: greg@wtcak.org
URL: http://export.gov/alaska/

60408 ■ International Trade Administration - U.S. and Foreign Commercial Service - Export Assistance Center (Austin, Texas)
211 E. 11th St., 4th Fl.
Austin, TX 78701
Ph: (512)916-5939
Fax: (512)916-5940
Co. E-mail: office.austin@trade.gov
URL: http://export.gov/texas/austin/

60409 ■ International Trade Administration - U.S. and Foreign Commercial Service - Export Assistance Center (Baltimore, Maryland)
300 W. Pratt St., Ste. 300
Baltimore, MD 21201
Ph: (410)962-4539
Fax: (410)962-4529
Co. E-mail: bill.burwell@trade.gov
URL: http://export.gov/michigan/
Description: Serves as both the Baltimore and Washington, D.C., district office.

60410 ■ International Trade Administration - U.S. and Foreign Commercial Service - Export Assistance Center (Birmingham, Alabama)
950 22nd St. N, Ste. 773
Birmingham, AL 35203

Ph: (205)731-1331
Fax: (205)731-0076
Co. E-mail: Birmingham.Office.box@trade.gov
URL: http://export.gov/alabama/

60411 ■ International Trade Administration - U.S. and Foreign Commercial Service - Export Assistance Center (Boise, Idaho)
700 W. State St., 2nd Fl.
Boise, ID 83720
Ph: (208)364-7791
Fax: (208)334-2783
Co. E-mail: boise.office.box@trade.gov
URL: http://export.gov/idaho/

60412 ■ International Trade Administration - U.S. and Foreign Commercial Service - Export Assistance Center (Boston, Massachusetts)
JFK Federal Bldg.
55 New Sudbury St., Ste. 1826A
Boston, MA 02203
Ph: (617)565-4301
Fax: (617)565-4313
URL: http://www.buyusa.gov/massachusetts/

60413 ■ International Trade Administration - U.S. and Foreign Commercial Service - Export Assistance Center (Boston, Massachusetts)
JFK Federal Bldg.
55 New Sudbury St., Ste. 1826A
Boston, MA 02203
Ph: (617)565-4301
Fax: (617)565-4313
Co. E-mail: Office.Boston@trade.gov
URL: http://export.gov/massachusetts/
Description: Boston office also services the states of New Hampshire and Vermont.

60414 ■ International Trade Administration - U.S. and Foreign Commercial Service - Export Assistance Center (Boston, Massachusetts)
JFK Federal Bldg.
55 New Sudbury St., Ste. 1826A
Boston, MA 02203
Ph: (617)565-4301
Fax: (617)565-4313
URL: http://export.gov/massachusetts/

60415 ■ International Trade Administration - U.S. and Foreign Commercial Service - Export Assistance Center (Buffalo, New York)
130 S. Elmwood Ave., Ste. 530
Buffalo, NY 14202
Ph: (716)551-4191
Fax: (716)551-5290
Co. E-mail: rosanna.masucci@trade.gov
URL: http://export.gov/newyork/bflorochsyr/

60416 ■ International Trade Administration - U.S. and Foreign Commercial Service - Export Assistance Center (Carmel, Indiana)
11405 N. Pennsylvania St., Ste. 106
Carmel, IN 46032
Ph: (317)582-2300
Fax: (317)582-2301
Co. E-mail: mark.cooper@trade.gov
URL: http://export.gov/indiana/

60417 ■ International Trade Administration - U.S. and Foreign Commercial Service - Export Assistance Center (Charleston, South Carolina)
1362 McMillan Ave., Ste. 100
North Charleston, SC 29405
Ph: (843)746-3404
Fax: (843)529-0305
Co. E-mail: phil.minard@trade.gov
URL: http://export.gov/southcarolina/

60418 ■ International Trade Administration - U.S. and Foreign Commercial Service - Export Assistance Center (Charlotte, North Carolina)
521 E. Morehead St., Ste. 435
Charlotte, NC 28202

Ph: (704)333-4886
Fax: (704)332-2681
Co. E-mail: office.charlotte@trade.gov
URL: http://export.gov/northcarolina/

60419 ■ International Trade Administration - U.S. and Foreign Commercial Service - Export Assistance Center (Chicago, Illinois)
200 W. Adams St., Rm. 2450
Chicago, IL 60606
Ph: (312)353-8490
Fax: (312)353-8120
Co. E-mail: office.chicago@trade.gov
URL: http://export.gov/illinois/

60420 ■ International Trade Administration - U.S. and Foreign Commercial Service - Export Assistance Center (Cincinnati, Ohio)
36 E. 7th St., Ste. 2650
Cincinnati, OH 45202
Ph: (513)684-2944
Fax: (513)684-3227
Co. E-mail: office.cincinnati@trade.gov
URL: http://export.gov/ohio/southernohio/

60421 ■ International Trade Administration - U.S. and Foreign Commercial Service - Export Assistance Center (Clearwater, Florida)
13805 58 St. N., Ste. 1-200
Clearwater, FL 33760
Ph: (727)893-3738
Fax: (727)893-3839
Co. E-mail: sandra.campbell@trade.gov
URL: http://export.gov/florida/

60422 ■ International Trade Administration - U.S. and Foreign Commercial Service - Export Assistance Center (Cleveland, Ohio)
600 Superior Ave. E, Ste. 700
Cleveland, OH 44114
Ph: (216)522-4750
Fax: (216)522-2235
Co. E-mail: office.cleveland@trade.gov
URL: http://export.gov/ohio/northernohio/

60423 ■ International Trade Administration - U.S. and Foreign Commercial Service - Export Assistance Center (Columbia, South Carolina)
USC Moore School of Business
1705 College St., Ste. 600
Columbia, SC 29208
Ph: (803)777-2571
Fax: (803)777-2615
Co. E-mail: dorette.coetsee@trade.gov
URL: http://export.gov/southcarolina/

60424 ■ International Trade Administration - U.S. and Foreign Commercial Service - Export Assistance Center (Columbus, Ohio)
401 N. Front St., Ste. 200
Columbus, OH 43215
Ph: (614)365-9510
Fax: (614)365-9598
Co. E-mail: office.columbus@trade.gov
URL: http://export.gov/ohio/centralohio/

60425 ■ International Trade Administration - U.S. and Foreign Commercial Service - Export Assistance Center (Dallas, Texas)
2050 N. Stemmons Fwy., Ste. 170
Dallas, TX 75207

60426 ■ International Trade Administration - U.S. and Foreign Commercial Service - Export Assistance Center (Denver, Colorado)
World Trade Center
1625 Broadway, Ste. 680
Denver, CO 80202
Ph: (303)844-6623
Fax: (303)844-5651
Co. E-mail: Denver.office.box@trade.gov
URL: http://export.gov/colorado/
Description: Denver office also services the states of Montana and Wyoming.

60427 ■ International Trade Administration - U.S. and Foreign Commercial Service - Export Assistance Center (Des Moines, Iowa)
210 Walnut St.
749 Federal Bldg.
Des Moines, IA 50309
Ph: (515)284-4590
Fax: (515)288-1437
Co. E-mail: office.desmoines@trade.gov
URL: http://export.gov/iowa/

60428 ■ International Trade Administration - U.S. and Foreign Commercial Service - Export Assistance Center (Detroit, Michigan)
440 Burroughs St., Ste. 315
Mail Drop No. 64
Detroit, MI 48202
Ph: (313)872-6794
Fax: (313)872-6795
Co. E-mail: office.detroit@trade.gov
URL: http://export.gov/michigan/

60429 ■ International Trade Administration - U.S. and Foreign Commercial Service - Export Assistance Center (Eugene, Oregon)
1401 Willamette St.
Eugene, OR 97401-4003

60430 ■ International Trade Administration - U.S. and Foreign Commercial Service - Export Assistance Center (Ft. Worth, Texas)
4300 Amon Carter Blvd., Ste. 114
Ft. Worth, TX 76155
Ph: (817)684-5347
Fax: (817)684-5345
Co. E-mail: office.northtexas@trade.gov
URL: http://export.gov/texas/fortworth/

60431 ■ International Trade Administration - U.S. and Foreign Commercial Service - Export Assistance Center (Gaithersburg, Maryland)
c/o National Institute of Standards and Technology
100 Bureau Dr.
Mail Stop 2160
Gaithersburg, MD 20899-2160
Ph: (301)975-4040
Fax: (301)926-1559
Co. E-mail: notifyus@N0SPAM.nist.gov
URL: http://www.buyusa.gov

60432 ■ International Trade Administration - U.S. and Foreign Commercial Service - Export Assistance Center (Grand Rapids, Michigan)
401 W. Fulton St., Ste. 349C
Grand Rapids, MI 49504-6495
Ph: (616)458-3564
Fax: (616)458-3872
Co. E-mail: Thomas.Maguire@trade.gov
URL: http://export.gov/michigan/

60433 ■ International Trade Administration - U.S. and Foreign Commercial Service - Export Assistance Center (Greensboro, North Carolina)
342 N. Elm St.
Greensboro, NC 27401
Ph: (336)333-5345
Fax: (336)333-5158
Co. E-mail: debbie.strader@trade.gov
URL: http://export.gov/northcarolina/
Description: Serves the business needs of Davidson, Forsyth, Guilford, Montgomery, Randolph, Rockingham, and Stokes counties.

60434 ■ International Trade Administration - U.S. and Foreign Commercial Service - Export Assistance Center (Harrisburg, Pennsylvania)
2 S. George St., Cumberland House
Harrisburg, PA 17551-0302
Co. E-mail: deborah.doherty@.mail.doc.gov

60435 ■ International Trade Administration - U.S. and Foreign Commercial Service - Export Assistance Center (Highland Park, Illinois)
610 Central Ave., Ste. 150
Highland Park, IL 60035

60436 ■ International Trade Administration - U.S. and Foreign Commercial Service - Export Assistance Center (Honolulu, Hawaii)
521 Ala Moana Blvd., Rm. 214
Foreign Trade Zone No. 9
Honolulu, HI 96813
Ph: (808)522-8041
Fax: (808)522-8045
Co. E-mail: john.holman@trade.gov
URL: http://export.gov/hawaii/

60437 ■ International Trade Administration - U.S. and Foreign Commercial Service - Export Assistance Center (Houston, Texas)
1919 Smith St., Ste. 1026
Houston, TX 77002
Ph: (713)209-3104
Fax: (713)209-3135
Co. E-mail: steve.recobs@trade.gov
URL: http://export.gov/texas/houston/

60438 ■ International Trade Administration - U.S. and Foreign Commercial Service - Export Assistance Center (Jackson, Mississippi)
1230 Raymond Rd., Box 600
Jackson, MS 39204
Ph: (601)373-0773
Fax: (601)373-0959
Co. E-mail: carol.moore@trade.gov
URL: http://export.gov/mississippi/

60439 ■ International Trade Administration - U.S. and Foreign Commercial Service - Export Assistance Center (Kansas City, Missouri)
1000 Walnut St., Ste. 500
Kansas City, MO 64106
Ph: (816)421-1876
Fax: (816)471-7839
Co. E-mail: regina.heise@trade.gov
URL: http://export.gov/missouri/kansascity/
Description: Affiliated with the Wichita district office.
Telecommunication Services: office.kansascity@trade.gov.

60440 ■ International Trade Administration - U.S. and Foreign Commercial Service - Export Assistance Center (Knoxville, Tennessee)
17 Market Sq., Ste. 201
Knoxville, TN 37902-1405
Ph: (865)545-4637
Fax: (865)545-4435
Co. E-mail: robert.leach@trade.gov
URL: http://export.gov/tennessee/

60441 ■ International Trade Administration - U.S. and Foreign Commercial Service - Export Assistance Center (Little Rock)
425 W. Capitol Ave., Ste. 425
Little Rock, AR 72201
Ph: (501)324-5794
Fax: (501)324-7380
Co. E-mail: office.littlerock@trade.gov
URL: http://export.gov/arkansas/

60442 ■ International Trade Administration - U.S. and Foreign Commercial Service - Export Assistance Center (Long Beach)
One World Trade Center, Ste. 1670
Long Beach, CA 90831

60443 ■ International Trade Administration - U.S. and Foreign Commercial Service - Export Assistance Center (Long Island)
College at Old Westbury, PO Box 210
Academic Village - Marshall Hallam Bldg 10
223 Store Hill Rd.
Old Westbury, NY 11568-0210
Ph: (516)876-3418

Fax: (516)876-7563
Co. E-mail: shakir.farsakh@trade.gov
URL: http://export.gov/newyork/longisland/

60444 ■ International Trade Administration - U.S. and Foreign Commercial Service - Export Assistance Center (Los Angeles (West), California)
11150 West Olympic Blvd., Ste. 975
Los Angeles, CA 90064
Ph: (310)235-7206
Fax: (310)235-7220
Co. E-mail: office.losangeles@trade.gov
URL: http://export.gov/california/losangeleswest/index.asp

60445 ■ International Trade Administration - U.S. and Foreign Commercial Service - Export Assistance Center (Louisville, Kentucky)
601 W. Broadway, Rm. 634B
Louisville, KY 40202
Ph: (502)582-5066
Fax: (502)582-6573
Co. E-mail: office.louisville@trade.gov
URL: http://export.gov/kentucky/

60446 ■ International Trade Administration - U.S. and Foreign Commercial Service - Export Assistance Center (Memphis, Tennessee)
22 N. Front St., Ste. 200
Memphis, TN 38103
Ph: (901)544-0930
Fax: (901)543-3510
Co. E-mail: david.spann@trade.gov
URL: http://export.gov/tennessee/

60447 ■ International Trade Administration - U.S. and Foreign Commercial Service - Export Assistance Center (Miami, Florida)
5835 Blue Lagoon Dr., Ste. 203
Miami, FL 33126
Ph: (305)526-7425
Fax: (305)526-7434
Co. E-mail: andrew.gately@trade.gov
URL: http://export.gov/florida/

60448 ■ International Trade Administration - U.S. and Foreign Commercial Service - Export Assistance Center (Middletown, Connecticut)
213 Court St., Ste. 903
Middletown, CT 06457-3382
Ph: (860)638-6950
Fax: (860)638-6970
Co. E-mail: office.middletown@trade.gov
URL: http://www.buyusa.gov/connecticut/
Description: Affiliated with the Providence district office.

60449 ■ International Trade Administration - U.S. and Foreign Commercial Service - Export Assistance Center (Milwaukee, Wisconsin)
1235 N. Milwaukee St.
Milwaukee, WI 53202
Ph: (414)297-3473
Fax: (414)297-3470
Co. E-mail: damion.felton@trade.gov
URL: http://export.gov/wisconsin/

60450 ■ International Trade Administration - U.S. and Foreign Commercial Service - Export Assistance Center (Minneapolis, Minnesota)
Butler Square Bldg.
100 N. 6th St., Ste. 210-C
Minneapolis, MN 55403
Ph: (612)348-1638
Fax: (612)348-1650
Co. E-mail: minneapolis@trade.gov
URL: http://export.gov/minnesota/

60451 ■ International Trade Administration - U.S. and Foreign Commercial Service - Export Assistance Center (Monterey, California)
411 Pacific St., Ste. 316A
Monterey, CA 93940
Ph: (408)535-2757
Fax: (831)641-9849
Co. E-mail: chris.damm@trade.gov
URL: http://export.gov/california/monterey/

60452 ■ International Trade Administration - U.S. and Foreign Commercial Service - Export Assistance Center (Montpelier, Vermont)
National Life Bldg., 6th Fl.
Montpelier, VT 05620-0501
Ph: (802)828-4508
Fax: (802)828-3258
Co. E-mail: susan.murray@trade.gov
URL: http://export.gov/vermont/

60453 ■ International Trade Administration - U.S. and Foreign Commercial Service - Export Assistance Center (Nashville, Tennessee)
312 Rosa Parks Blvd., 10th Fl.
Nashville, TN 37243
Ph: (615)736-2222
Fax: (615)736-2226
Co. E-mail: office.nashville@trade.gov
URL: http://export.gov/tennessee/

60454 ■ International Trade Administration - U.S. and Foreign Commercial Service - Export Assistance Center (Newark, New Jersey)
744 Broad St., Ste. 1505
Newark, NJ 07102
Ph: (973)645-4682
Fax: (973)645-4783
Co. E-mail: susan.widmer@trade.gov
URL: http://export.gov/newjersey/contactus/index.asp

60455 ■ International Trade Administration - U.S. and Foreign Commercial Service - Export Assistance Center (Newport Beach, California)
2302 Martin Court, Ste. 315
Irvine, CA 92612
Ph: (949)660-1688
Fax: (949)660-1338
Co. E-mail: Newport.beach.office.box@trade.gov
URL: http://export.gov/california/irvine/index.asp

60456 ■ International Trade Administration - U.S. and Foreign Commercial Service - Export Assistance Center (Novato, California)
50 Acacia Ave.
San Rafael, CA 94901
Ph: (415)485-6200
Fax: (415)485-6219
Co. E-mail: north.bay.office.box@trade.gov
URL: http://export.gov/california/northbay/

60457 ■ International Trade Administration - U.S. and Foreign Commercial Service - Export Assistance Center (Oakland, California)
Oakland Federal Bldg., North Tower
1301 Clay St., Ste. 630 N
Oakland, CA 94612
Ph: (510)273-7350
Fax: (510)273-7352
Co. E-mail: rod.hirsch@trade.gov
URL: http://export.gov/california/oakland/

60458 ■ International Trade Administration - U.S. and Foreign Commercial Service - Export Assistance Center (Oklahoma City, Oklahoma)
301 NW 63rd St., Ste. 330
Oklahoma City, OK 73116
Ph: (405)608-5302
Fax: (405)608-4211
URL: http://export.gov/oklahoma/

60459 ■ International Trade Administration - U.S. and Foreign Commercial Service - Export Assistance Center (Omaha, Nebraska)
6708 Pine St., Rm. 205
Omaha, NE 68182-1101
Ph: (402)597-0193
Fax: (402)554-3473
Co. E-mail: meredith.bond@trade.gov
URL: http://export.gov/nebraska/
Description: Omaha office also services the states of North Dakota and South Dakota.

60460 ■ International Trade Administration - U.S. and Foreign Commercial Service - Export Assistance Center (Orlando, Florida)
3201 E. Colonial Dr., Ste. A-20
Orlando, FL 32803
Ph: (407)420-4877
Fax: (407)420-4425
Co. E-mail: kenneth.mouradian@trade.gov
URL: http://export.gov/florida/contactus/index.asp

60461 ■ International Trade Administration - U.S. and Foreign Commercial Service - Export Assistance Center (Philadelphia, Pennsylvania)
The Curtis Ctr.--Independence Sq. W.
601 Walnut St., Ste. 580 W.
Philadelphia, PA 19106-3304
Ph: (215)597-6101
Fax: (215)597-6123
Co. E-mail: office.philadelphia@trade.gov
URL: http://export.gov/pennsylvania/philadelphia/
Description: Philadelphia office also services the state of Delaware.

60462 ■ International Trade Administration - U.S. and Foreign Commercial Service - Export Assistance Center (Phoenix, Arizona)
2828 N. Central Ave., Ste. 800
Phoenix, AZ 85004
Ph: (602)640-2513
Fax: (602)745-7210
Co. E-mail: Office.Phoenix@trade.gov
URL: http://export.gov/arizona/eg_us_az_028116.asp

60463 ■ International Trade Administration - U.S. and Foreign Commercial Service - Export Assistance Center (Pittsburgh, Pennsylvania)
Regional Enterprise Tower
425 6th Ave., Ste. 2950
Pittsburgh, PA 15219-1854
Ph: (412)644-2800
Fax: (412)644-2803
Co. E-mail: office.pittsburgh@trade.gov
URL: http://export.gov/pennsylvania/pittsburgh/

60464 ■ International Trade Administration - U.S. and Foreign Commercial Service - Export Assistance Center (Pontiac, Michigan)
1025 Campus Dr. S., Bldg. 47 W.
Waterford, MI 48328
Ph: (248)975-9600
Fax: (248)975-9606
URL: http://export.gov/michigan/

60465 ■ International Trade Administration - U.S. and Foreign Commercial Service - Export Assistance Center (Portland, ME)
c/o Maine International Trade Center
511 Congress St.
Portland, ME 04101
Ph: (207)541-7430
Fax: (207)541-7420
Co. E-mail: jeffrey.porter@trade.gov
URL: http://export.gov/maine/
Description: Affiliated with the Boston, Massachusetts, district office.

60466 ■ International Trade Administration - U.S. and Foreign Commercial Service - Export Assistance Center (Portland, Oregon)
1 World Trade Center
121 SW Salmon St., Ste. 242
Portland, OR 97204
Ph: (503)326-3001

Fax: (503)326-6351
Co. E-mail: scott.goddin@trade.gov
URL: http://export.gov/oregon/

60467 ■ International Trade Administration - U.S. and Foreign Commercial Service - Export Assistance Center (Portsmouth, New Hampshire)
17th New Hampshire Ave.
Portsmouth, NH 03801-2838
Ph: (603)953-0210
Co. E-mail: justin.oslowski@trade.gov
URL: http://export.gov/newhampshire/

60468 ■ International Trade Administration - U.S. and Foreign Commercial Service - Export Assistance Center (Providence, Rhode Island)
315 Iron Horse Way, Ste. 101
Providence, RI 02908
Ph: (401)528-5104
Fax: (401)528-5067
Co. E-mail: keith.yatsuhashi@trade.gov
URL: http://export.gov/rhodeisland/
Description: Affiliated with the Hartford district office.

60469 ■ International Trade Administration - U.S. and Foreign Commercial Service - Export Assistance Center (Reno, Nevada)
449 S. Virginia St., 2nd Fl.
Reno, NV 89501
Ph: (775)784-5342
Fax: (775)784-5343
Co. E-mail: bill.cline@trade.gov
URL: http://export.gov/nevada/

60470 ■ International Trade Administration - U.S. and Foreign Commercial Service - Export Assistance Center (Richmond, Virginia)
800 E. Leigh St.
Richmond, VA 23219
Ph: (804)771-2246
Fax: (804)771-2390
Co. E-mail: eric.mcdonald@trade.gov
URL: http://export.gov/virginia/

60471 ■ International Trade Administration - U.S. and Foreign Commercial Service - Export Assistance Center (Rochester, New York)
400 Andrews St., Ste. 300
Rochester, NY 14604
Ph: (585)399-7065
Fax: (585)423-7570
Co. E-mail: Timothy.McCall@trade.gov
URL: http://export.gov/newyork/bflorochsyr/

60472 ■ International Trade Administration - U.S. and Foreign Commercial Service - Export Assistance Center (Rockford, Illinois)
605 Fulton Ave., Ste. E103
Rockford, IL 61103
Ph: (815)316-2380
Fax: (888)628-2571
Co. E-mail: patrick.hope@trade.gov
URL: http://export.gov/illinois/

60473 ■ International Trade Administration - U.S. and Foreign Commercial Service - Export Assistance Center (Sacramento, California)
1410 Ethan Way
Sacramento, CA 95825
Ph: (916)566-7170
Fax: (916)566-7123
Co. E-mail: george.tastard@trade.gov
URL: http://export.gov/california/sacramento/

60474 ■ International Trade Administration - U.S. and Foreign Commercial Service - Export Assistance Center (St. Louis, Missouri)
8235 Forsyth Blvd., Ste. 520
St. Louis, MO 63105
Ph: (314)425-3302

Fax: (314)425-3381
Co. E-mail: office.stlouis@trade.gov
URL: http://export.gov/missouri/st.louis/

60475 ■ International Trade Administration - U.S. and Foreign Commercial Service - Export Assistance Center (Salt Lake City, Utah)
9690 S. 300 W., Ste. 201D
Sandy, UT 84070
Ph: (801)255-1871
Fax: (801)255-3147
Co. E-mail: office.saltlakecity@trade.gov
URL: http://export.gov/utah/

60476 ■ International Trade Administration - U.S. and Foreign Commercial Service - Export Assistance Center (San Antonio, Texas)
203 S. Saint Mary's St., Ste. 101
San Antonio, TX 78205
Ph: (210)228-9878
Fax: (210)228-9874
Co. E-mail: san.antonio.office@trade.gov
URL: http://export.gov/texas/sanantonio/

60477 ■ International Trade Administration - U.S. and Foreign Commercial Service - Export Assistance Center (San Diego, California)
9449 Balboa Ave., Ste. 111
San Diego, CA 92123
Ph: (858)467-7043
Co. E-mail: matt.andersen@trade.gov
URL: http://export.gov/california/sandiego/index.asp

60478 ■ International Trade Administration - U.S. and Foreign Commercial Service - Export Assistance Center (San Francisco, California)
50 Fremont St., Ste. 2450
San Francisco, CA 94105
Ph: (415)705-2300
Fax: (415)705-2299
Co. E-mail: office.sanfrancisco@trade.gov
URL: http://export.gov/california/sanfrancisco/

60479 ■ International Trade Administration - U.S. and Foreign Commercial Service - Export Assistance Center (San Jose, California)
55 S. Market St., Ste. 1040
San Jose, CA 95113
Ph: (408)535-2757
Fax: (408)535-2758
Co. E-mail: silicon.valley.office.box@trade.gov
URL: http://export.gov/california/sanjose/

60480 ■ International Trade Administration - U.S. and Foreign Commercial Service - Export Assistance Center (San Juan, Puerto Rico)
165 Centro Internacional de Mercadeo Tower II, Ste. 702
Guaynabo, PR 00968-8058
Ph: (787)775-1992
Fax: (787)781-7178
Co. E-mail: jose.burgos@trade.gov
URL: http://export.gov/puertorico/

60481 ■ International Trade Administration - U.S. and Foreign Commercial Service - Export Assistance Center (Santa Clara, California)
5201 Great American Pkwy., Ste. 456
Santa Clara, CA 95054

60482 ■ International Trade Administration - U.S. and Foreign Commercial Service - Export Assistance Center (Santa Fe, New Mexico)
c/o New Mexico Dept. of Economic Development
Santa Fe, NM 87504-5003
Ph: (505)231-0075
Fax: (505)827-0211
Co. E-mail: sandra.necessary@trade.gov
URL: http://export.gov/newjersey/

60483 ■ International Trade Administration - U.S. and Foreign Commercial Service - Export Assistance Center (Scranton, Pennsylvania)
One Montage Mountain Rd., Ste. B
Moosic, PA 18507

60484 ■ International Trade Administration - U.S. and Foreign Commercial Service - Export Assistance Center (Seattle, Washington)
2001 6th Ave., Ste. 2610
Seattle, WA 98121
Ph: (206)553-5615
Fax: (206)553-7253
Co. E-mail: office.seattle@trade.gov
URL: http://export.gov/washington/seattle/

60485 ■ International Trade Administration - U.S. and Foreign Commercial Service - Export Assistance Center (Sioux Falls, South Dakota)
Augustana College
2001 S. Summit Ave.
Sioux Falls, SD 57197
Ph: (605)330-4265
Fax: (605)330-4266
Co. E-mail: cinnamon.king@trade.gov
URL: http://export.gov/southdakota/

60486 ■ International Trade Administration - U.S. and Foreign Commercial Service - Export Assistance Center (Somerset, Kentucky)
2292 S. Hwy. 27, Ste. 320
Somerset, KY 42501

60487 ■ International Trade Administration - U.S. and Foreign Commercial Service - Export Assistance Center (Spokane, Washington)
801 W. Riverside Ave., Ste. 100
Spokane, WA 99201
Ph: (509)344-9398
Fax: (509)326-6351
Co. E-mail: spokane.office.box@trade.gov
URL: http://www.buyusa.gov/spokane/

60488 ■ International Trade Administration - U.S. and Foreign Commercial Service - Export Assistance Center (Tallahassee, Florida)
The Atrium Bldg.
325 John Knox Rd., Ste. 201
Tallahassee, FL 32303
Ph: (850)942-9635
Fax: (850)298-6659
Co. E-mail: Michael.higgins@trade.gov
URL: http://export.gov/florida/

60489 ■ International Trade Administration - U.S. and Foreign Commercial Service - Export Assistance Center (Toledo, Ohio)
420 Madison Ave., Ste. 510
Toledo, OH 43604
Ph: (216)522-4732
Fax: (216)522-2235
Co. E-mail: melissa.blackledge@trade.gov
URL: http://export.gov/ohio/northernohio/

60490 ■ International Trade Administration - U.S. and Foreign Commercial Service - Export Assistance Center (Trenton, New Jersey)
20 W. State St.
Trenton, NJ 08625-0820
Ph: (609)896-2734
Co. E-mail: office.trenton@trade.gov
URL: http://export.gov/newjersey/

60491 ■ International Trade Administration - U.S. and Foreign Commercial Service - Export Assistance Center (Tulsa, Oklahoma)
700 N. Greenwood Ave., Ste. 1400
Tulsa, OK 74106
Ph: (918)581-7650
Fax: (918)581-6263
URL: http://export.gov/oklahoma/

60492 ■ International Trade Administration - U.S. and Foreign Commercial Service - Export Assistance Center (Westchester, New York)
707 Westchester Ave., Ste. 209
White Plains, NY 10604
Ph: (914)682-6712
Fax: (914)682-6698
Co. E-mail: Joan.Kanlian@mail.doc.gov
URL: http://export.gov/newyork/westchester/

60493 ■ International Trade Administration - U.S. and Foreign Commercial Service - Export Assistance Center (Wheaton, Illinois)
Illinois Institute of Technology
201 E. Loop Dr.
Wheaton, IL 60187

60494 ■ International Trade Administration - U.S. and Foreign Commercial Service - Export Assistance Center (Wheeling, West Virginia)
c/o Wheeling Jesuit University
316 Washington Ave.
NTTC Bldg., Rm. 134
Wheeling, WV 26003-6295
Ph: (304)243-5493
Fax: (304)243-5494
Co. E-mail: diego.gattesco@trade.gov
URL: http://export.gov/westvirginia/

60495 ■ International Trade Administration - U.S. and Foreign Commercial Service - Export Assistance Center (Wichita, Kansas)
150 N. Main St., Ste. 200
Wichita, KS 67202-1305
Ph: (316)263-4067
Fax: (316)263-8306
Co. E-mail: andrew.anderson@trade.gov
URL: http://export.gov/kansas/
Description: Affiliated with the Kansas City, Missouri, district office.

60496 ■ International Trade Administration - U.S. and Foreign Commercial Service - Export Assistance Center (Ypsilanti, Michigan)
c/o Eastern Michigan University College of Business
300 W. Michigan Ave., Ste. 306G
Ypsilanti, MI 48197
Ph: (616)458-3564
Fax: (616)458-3872
URL: http://export.gov/michigan/

INTERNATIONAL TRADE COMMISSION

60497 ■ International Trade Commission - Office of Economics
500 E St., SW, Rm. 602F
Washington, DC 20436
Ph: (202)205-3216
Fax: (202)205-2340
Co. E-mail: robert.koopman@usitc.gov
URL: http://www.usitc.gov

60498 ■ International Trade Commission - Office of Economics
500 E St., SW, Rm. 602F
Washington, DC 20436
Ph: (202)205-3216
Fax: (202)205-2340
URL: http://www.usitc.gov/research_and_analysis/office_economics.htm

60499 ■ International Trade Commission - Office of Industries
500 E St., SW, Rm. 504A
Washington, DC 20436
Ph: (202)205-3296
Fax: (202)205-3161
Co. E-mail: karen.laney-cummings@usitc.gov
URL: http://www.usitc.gov/ind_econ_ana/about/ind/index.htm

60500 ■ International Trade Commission - Office of Industries
500 E St. SW, Rm. 504A
Washington, DC 20436
Ph: (202)205-3296
Fax: (202)205-3161
URL: http://www.usitc.gov/research_and_analysis/office_industry.htm

60501 ■ International Trade Commission - Office of Operations
500 E St., SW, Rm. 715A
Washington, DC 20436
Ph: (202)205-2230
Fax: (202)205-1893
Co. E-mail: robert.rogowsky@usitc.gov
URL: http://www.usitc.gov

60502 ■ International Trade Commission - Office of Operations
500 E St., SW, Rm. 715A
Washington, DC 20436
Co. E-mail: robert.rogowsky@usitc.gov
URL: http://www.usitc.gov

60503 ■ International Trade Commission - Office of Tariff Affairs and Trade Agreements
500 E St., SW, Rm. 404B
Washington, DC 20436
Ph: (202)205-2603
Fax: (202)205-2616
Co. E-mail: david.beck@usitc.gov
URL: http://www.usitc.gov

60504 ■ International Trade Commission - Office of Tariff Affairs and Trade Agreements
500 E St. SW, Rm. 404B
Washington, DC 20436
Ph: (202)205-2593
Fax: (202)205-2616
Co. E-mail: david.beck@usitc.gov
URL: http://www.usitc.gov/tariff_affairs/

60505 ■ International Trade Commission - Office of Unfair Import Investigations
500 E St., SW, Rm. 401-O
Washington, DC 20436
Ph: (202)205-2561
Fax: (202)205-2158
Co. E-mail: lynn.levine@usitc.gov
URL: http://www.usitc.gov

60506 ■ International Trade Commission - Office of Unfair Import Investigations
500 E St., SW, Rm. 401-O
Washington, DC 20436
Ph: (202)205-2560
Fax: (202)205-2158
Co. E-mail: lynn.levine@usitc.gov
URL: http://www.usitc.gov/intellectual_property/contacts.htm

LIBRARY OF CONGRESS

60507 ■ Library of Congress
101 Independence Ave, SE
Washington, DC 20540
Ph: (202)707-5000
URL: http://www.loc.gov/

60508 ■ Library of Congress
101 Independence Ave. SE
Washington, DC 20540
Ph: (202)707-5000
URL: http://www.loc.gov/

NATIONAL AERONAUTICS AND SPACE ADMINISTRATION

The following NASA Industrial Applications Centers are arranged alphabetically by state.

60509 ■ Aerospace Research Applications Center
611 N. Capitol Ave.
Indianapolis, IN 46204
Ph: (317)262-5036

Fax: (317)262-5044

60510 ■ Aerospace Research Applications Center
611 N. Capitol Ave.
Indianapolis, IN 46204

60511 ■ Earth Data Analysis Center
1 University of New Mexico
MSC01 1110
Albuquerque, NM 87131-0001
Ph: (505)277-3622
Fax: (505)277-3614
URL: http://edac.unm.edu/

60512 ■ Earth Data Analysis Center
1 University of New Mexico
MSC01 1110
Albuquerque, NM 87131-0001
Ph: (505)277-3622
Fax: (505)277-3614
URL: http://edac.unm.edu/

60513 ■ NASA Industrial Applications Center (Los Angeles, California)
University of Southern California
3716 S. Hope St.
Research Annex, Rm. 200
Los Angeles, CA 90007-4344
Ph: (213)743-6132
Free: 800-872-7477
Fax: (213)746-9043

60514 ■ NASA Industrial Applications Center (Los Angeles, California)
University of Southern California
3716 S. Hope St.
Research Annex, Rm. 200
Los Angeles, CA 90007-4344

60515 ■ NASA Industrial Applications Center (Pittsburgh, Pennsylvania)
823 William Pitt Union
Pittsburgh, PA 15260
Ph: (412)648-7008
Fax: (412)648-7003

60516 ■ NASA Industrial Applications Center (Pittsburgh, Pennsylvania)
823 William Pitt Union
Pittsburgh, PA 15260

60517 ■ National Aeronautics and Space Administration - Ames Research Center - Small Business Specialist
Mail Stop 241-1
Moffett Field, CA 94035-1000
Ph: (650)604-4522
Fax: (650)604-4646
Co. E-mail: lupe.m.velasquez@nasa.gov
URL: http://osbp.nasa.gov/about-arc.html

60518 ■ National Aeronautics and Space Administration - Ames Research Center - Small Business Specialist
Mail Stop 241-1
Moffett Field, CA 94035-1000
Ph: (650)604-4695
Fax: (650)604-0912
Co. E-mail: christine.l.munroe@nasa.gov
URL: http://osbp.nasa.gov/about-arc.html

60519 ■ National Aeronautics and Space Administration - Goddard Space Flight Center - Small Business Specialist
Mail Stop 210
8800 Greenbelt Rd.
Greenbelt, MD 20771
Ph: (301)286-8136
Fax: (301)286-3041
Co. E-mail: giberto.delvalle-1@nasa.gov
URL: http://osbp.nasa.gov/about-goddard.html

60520 ■ National Aeronautics and Space Administration - Goddard Space Flight Center - Small Business Specialist
Mail Stop 210
8800 Greenbelt Rd.
Greenbelt, MD 20771-0001

Ph: (301)286-8136
Fax: (301)286-3041
Co. E-mail: giberto.delvalle-1@nasa.gov
URL: http://osbp.nasa.gov/about-goddard.html

60521 ■ National Aeronautics and Space Administration - Jet Propulsion Laboratory - Contractor Capabilities Office
800 Oak Grove Dr.
Pasadena, CA 91109-8099
Ph: (818)354-4379
Fax: (818)393-1746
Co. E-mail: stuart.t.imai@nasa.gov
URL: http://osbp.nasa.gov/about-jpl.html

60522 ■ National Aeronautics and Space Administration - Jet Propulsion Laboratory - Contractor Capabilities Office
800 Oak Grove Dr.
Pasadena, CA 91109-8099
Ph: (818)354-2070
Fax: (818)393-1746
Co. E-mail: stuart.t.imai@jpl.nasa.gov
URL: http://osbp.nasa.gov/about-jpl.html

60523 ■ National Aeronautics and Space Administration - John C. Stennis Space Center - Small Business Specialist - Procurement Office
Mail Stop DA30
Stennis Space Center, MS 39529-6000
Ph: (228)688-1720
Fax: (228)688-1141
Co. E-mail: michelle.m.stracener@nasa.gov
URL: http://osbp.nasa.gov/about-stennis.html

60524 ■ National Aeronautics and Space Administration - John C. Stennis Space Center - Small Business Specialist - Procurement Office
Mail Stop DA30
Stennis Space Center, MS 39529-6000
Ph: (228)688-1720
Fax: (228)688-1141
Co. E-mail: michelle.m.stracener@nasa.gov
URL: http://osbp.nasa.gov/about-stennis.html

60525 ■ National Aeronautics and Space Administration (NASA) - John H. Glenn Research Center at Lewis Field - Small Business Specialist
21000 Brookpark Rd.
Cleveland, OH 44135
Ph: (216)433-2147
Fax: (216)433-5185
Co. E-mail: timothy.c.piece@nasa.gov
URL: http://www.nasa.gov/centers/glenn/home/index.html

60526 ■ National Aeronautics and Space Administration (NASA) - John H. Glenn Research Center at Lewis Field - Small Business Specialist
21000 Brookpark Rd.
Cleveland, OH 44135
Ph: (216)433-4000
Fax: (216)433-5185
URL: http://www.nasa.gov/centers/glenn/home/index.html

60527 ■ National Aeronautics and Space Administration - Johnson Space Center - Small Business Specialist
Mail Stop BD3
Houston, TX 77058
Ph: (281)483-5933
Fax: (281)483-4326
Co. E-mail: charles.t.williams@nasa.gov
URL: http://osbp.nasa.gov/about-johnson.html

60528 ■ National Aeronautics and Space Administration - Johnson Space Center - Small Business Specialist
Mail Stop BD3
Houston, TX 77058-3696
Ph: (281)483-5933

Fax: (281)483-4326
Co. E-mail: charles.t.williams@nasa.gov
URL: http://osbp.nasa.gov/about-johnson.html

60529 ■ National Aeronautics and Space Administration - Kennedy Space Center - Small Business Specialist
Mail Stop OP-CIAO
Kennedy Space Center, FL 32899
Ph: (321)867-7357
Fax: (321)867-9999
Co. E-mail: larry.m.third@nasa.gov
URL: http://osbp.nasa.gov/about-kennedy.html

60530 ■ National Aeronautics and Space Administration - Kennedy Space Center - Small Business Specialist
Mail Stop OP-CIAO
Kennedy Space Center, FL 32899-0001
Ph: (321)867-7357
Fax: (321)867-9999
Co. E-mail: larry.m.third@nasa.gov
URL: http://osbp.nasa.gov/about-kennedy.html

60531 ■ National Aeronautics and Space Administration - Langley Research Center - Small Business Specialist
Mail Stop 144
Hampton, VA 23681-0001
Ph: (757)864-2456
Fax: (757)864-8541
Co. E-mail: randy.a.manning@nasa.gov
URL: http://osbp.nasa.gov/about-larc.html

60532 ■ National Aeronautics and Space Administration - Langley Research Center - Small Business Specialist
Mail Stop 144
Hampton, VA 23681-2199
Ph: (757)864-6074
Fax: (757)864-8541
Co. E-mail: randy.a.manning@nasa.gov
URL: http://osbp.nasa.gov/about-larc.html

60533 ■ National Aeronautics and Space Administration - Marshall Space Flight Center - Small Business Specialist
Mail Stop PS01
Huntsville, AL 35812-0001
Ph: (256)544-0267
Fax: (256)544-5851
Co. E-mail: david.e.brock@nasa.gov
URL: http://osbp.nasa.gov/about-marshall.html

60534 ■ National Aeronautics and Space Administration - Marshall Space Flight Center - Small Business Specialist
Mail Stop PS01
Huntsville, AL 35812-0001
Ph: (256)544-0267
Fax: (256)544-5851
Co. E-mail: david.e.brock@nasa.gov
URL: http://osbp.nasa.gov/about-marshall.html

60535 ■ National Aeronautics and Space Administration (NASA) - Office of Small Business Programs
NASA Headquarters, Rm. 2K39
300 E. St., SW
Washington, DC 20546-0001
Ph: (202)358-2088
Fax: (202)358-3261
Co. E-mail: smallbusiness@nasa.gov
URL: http://osdbu.nasa.gov

Description: The development and management of the National Aeronautics and Space Administration's programs to assist small businesses are administered by its Office of Small and Disadvantaged Business Utilization. Services include individual counseling sessions for business owners seeking advice on how to best pursue contracting opportunities at NASA. NASA's procurement program is decentralized, with procurements planned and accomplished by field installations that also maintain small and minority business specialists. NASA's Technology Utilization Program provides information and other assistance to small business owners seeking to apply the results of NASA research and development projects to new commercial products or processes.

60536 ■ National Aeronautics and Space Administration - Office of Small Business Programs
NASA Headquarters, Rm. 2K39
300 E. St., SW
Washington, DC 20546-0001
Ph: (202)358-2088
Fax: (202)358-3261
Co. E-mail: smallbusiness@nasa.gov
URL: http://osbp.nasa.gov/
Description: The development and management of the National Aeronautics and Space Administration's programs to assist small businesses are administered by its Office of Small and Disadvantaged Business Utilization. Services include individual counseling sessions for business owners seeking advice on how to best pursue contracting opportunities at NASA. NASA's procurement program is decentralized, with procurements planned and accomplished by field installations that also maintain small and minority business specialists. NASA's Technology Utilization Program provides information and other assistance to small business owners seeking to apply the results of NASA research and development projects to new commercial products or processes.

60537 ■ National Aeronautics and Space Administration - Resident Office--Jet Propulsion Laboratory - Small Business Specialist
4800 Oak Grove Dr.
Mail Code 180-802K
Pasadena, CA 91109
Ph: (818)354-4321
URL: http://www.jpl.nasa.gov

60538 ■ National Aeronautics and Space Administration - Resident Office--JPL - Small Business Specialist
4800 Oak Grove Dr.
Mail Code 180-802K
Pasadena, CA 91011
Ph: (818)354-4321
URL: http://www.jpl.nasa.gov

60539 ■ National Aeronautics and Space Administration (NASA) - Small Business Innovation Research Office
300 E. St., SW
Washington, DC 20546
Ph: (202)358-4652
Co. E-mail: sbir@reisys.gov
URL: http://sbir.gsfc.nasa.gov/SBIR/SBIR.html

60540 ■ National Aeronautics and Space Administration - Small Business Innovation Research Office
300 E. St., SW
Washington, DC 20546
Ph: (202)358-4652
Co. E-mail: richard.b.lesher@nasa.gov
URL: http://sbir.gsfc.nasa.gov/SBIR/SBIR.html

60541 ■ NERAC, Inc.
60 Temple Pl.
Boston, MA 02111
Fax: (617)423-0584
Co. E-mail: info@nerac.us
URL: http://www.nerac.us/

60542 ■ Northeast Homeland Security Regional Advisory Council (NERAC)
60 Temple Pl.
Boston, MA 02111
Co. E-mail: info@nerac.us
URL: http://www.nerac.us/

60543 ■ Rural Enterprises of Oklahoma
2912 Enterprise Blvd.
Durant, OK 74701
Ph: (580)924-5094
Free: 800-658-2823
Fax: (580)920-2745
URL: http://www.ruralenterprises.com/index.php

60544 ■ Rural Enterprises of Oklahoma
2912 Enterprise Blvd.
Durant, OK 74701
Ph: (580)924-5094
Free: 800-658-2823
Fax: (580)920-2745
URL: http://www.ruralenterprises.com/index.php

60545 ■ Southern Technology Applications Center
1 Progress Blvd.
Alachua, FL 32615
Ph: (904)462-3913
Free: 800-225-0308
Fax: (904)462-3898

NATIONAL CREDIT UNION ADMINISTRATION

60546 ■ National Credit Union Administration - Office of Small and Disadvantaged Business Utilization
1775 Duke St.
Alexandria, VA 22314-3428
Ph: (703)518-6300
Fax: (703)518-6661
URL: http://www.ncua.gov
Description: The National Credit Union Administration's Office of Small and Disadvantaged Business Utilization offers small businesses information and guidance on procurement procedures, how to be placed on a bidder's mailing list, and identification of both prime and subcontracting opportunities.

60547 ■ National Credit Union Administration - Office of Small and Disadvantaged Business Utilization
1775 Duke St.
Alexandria, VA 22314-3428
Ph: (703)518-6300
Fax: (703)518-6661
URL: http://www.ncua.gov
Description: The National Credit Union Administration's Office of Small and Disadvantaged Business Utilization offers small businesses information and guidance on procurement procedures, how to be placed on a bidder's mailing list, and identification of both prime and subcontracting opportunities.

60548 ■ National Credit Union Administration, Region 1 - Albany Regional Office
9 Washington Sq.
Washington Ave. Extension
Albany, NY 12205
Ph: (518)862-7400
Fax: (518)862-7420
Co. E-mail: region1@ncua.gov
URL: http://www.ncua.gov/AboutNcua/org/Region1.htm
Contact: Mark Treichel, Director

60549 ■ National Credit Union Administration, Region 2 - Alexandria Regional Office
1775 Duke St.
Alexandria, VA 22314-3437
Ph: (703)519-4600
Fax: (703)518-6674
Co. E-mail: region2@ncua.gov
URL: http://www.ncua.gov/AboutNcua/org/Region2.htm

60550 ■ National Credit Union Administration, Region 2 - Alexandria Regional Office
1900 Duke St., Ste. 300
Alexandria, VA 22314
Ph: (703)519-4600
Fax: (703)519-4620
Co. E-mail: region2@ncua.gov
URL: http://www.ncua.gov/about/Leadership/Reg/Pages/Region-2.aspx

60551 ■ National Credit Union Administration, Region 3 - Atlanta Regional Office
7000 Central Pkwy., Ste. 1600
Atlanta, GA 30328
Ph: (678)443-3000
Fax: (678)443-3020
Co. E-mail: region3@ncua.gov
URL: http://www.ncua.gov/AboutNcua/org/Region3.htm

60552 ■ National Credit Union Administration, Region 3 - Atlanta Regional Office
7000 Central Pkwy., Ste. 1600
Atlanta, GA 30328
Ph: (678)443-3000
Fax: (678)443-3020
Co. E-mail: region3@ncua.gov
URL: http://www.ncua.gov/about/Leadership/Reg/Pages/Region-3.aspx

60553 ■ National Credit Union Administration, Region 4 - Austin Regional Office
4807 Spicewood Springs Rd., Ste. 5200
Austin, TX 78759-8490
Ph: (512)342-5600
Fax: (512)342-5620
Co. E-mail: region4@ncua.gov
URL: http://www.ncua.gov/AboutNcua/org/Region4.htm

60554 ■ National Credit Union Administration, Region 4 - Austin Regional Office
4807 Spicewood Springs Rd., Ste. 5200
Austin, TX 78759-8490
Ph: (512)342-5600
Fax: (512)342-5620
Co. E-mail: region4@ncua.gov
URL: http://www.ncua.gov/about/Leadership/Reg/Pages/Region-4.aspx

60555 ■ National Credit Union Administration, Region 5 - Tempe Regional Office
1230 W. Washington St., Ste. 301
Tempe, AZ 85281
Ph: (602)302-6000
Fax: (602)302-6024
Co. E-mail: region5@ncua.gov
URL: http://www.ncua.gov/AboutNcua/org/Region5.htm

60556 ■ National Credit Union Administration, Region 5 - Tempe Regional Office
1230 W. Washington St., Ste. 301
Tempe, AZ 85281
Ph: (602)302-6000
Fax: (602)302-6024
Co. E-mail: region5@ncua.gov
URL: http://www.ncua.gov/about/Leadership/Reg/Pages/Region-5.aspx

NATIONAL LABOR RELATIONS BOARD

60557 ■ National Labor Relation Board, Region 30 - Milwaukee Regional Office
310 W. Wisconsin Ave., Ste. 700
Milwaukee, WI 53203-2211
Ph: (414)297-3861
Fax: (414)297-3880
URL: http://www.nlrb.gov

60558 ■ National Labor Relations Board
1099 14th St., NW, Rm. 5400 E.
Washington, DC 20570-0001
Ph: (202)273-1000
Fax: (202)501-8686
URL: http://www.nlrb.gov

60559 ■ National Labor Relations Board
1099 14th St. NW, Ste. 6300
Washington, DC 20570-0001

Ph: (202)208-3000
Fax: (202)208-3013
URL: http://www.nlrb.gov

60560 ■ National Labor Relations Board - Office of Small and Disadvantaged Business Utilization
1099 14th St., NW, Ste. 1708
Washington, DC 20570
Ph: (202)273-2928
Fax: (202)273-2928
URL: http://www.nlrb.gov

60561 ■ National Labor Relations Board - Office of Small and Disadvantaged Business Utilization
1099 14th St., NW, Ste. 1708
Washington, DC 20570
Co. E-mail: paula.roy@nlrb.gov
URL: http://www.nlrb.gov

60562 ■ National Labor Relations Board, Region 1 - Boston Regional Office
10 Causeway St., 6th Fl.
Boston, MA 02222-1072
Ph: (617)565-6700
Fax: (617)565-6725
URL: http://www.nlrb.gov

60563 ■ National Labor Relations Board, Region 1 - Boston Regional Office
10 Causeway St., 6th Fl.
Boston, MA 02222-1072
Ph: (617)565-6700
Fax: (617)565-6725
URL: http://www.nlrb.gov

60564 ■ National Labor Relations Board, Region 2 - New York Regional Office
26 Federal Plz., Rm. 3614
New York, NY 10278-0104
Ph: (212)264-0300
Fax: (212)264-2450
URL: http://www.nlrb.gov

60565 ■ National Labor Relations Board, Region 2 - New York Regional Office
26 Federal Plz., Rm. 3614
New York, NY 10278-0104
Ph: (212)264-0300
Fax: (212)264-2450
URL: http://www.nlrb.gov

60566 ■ National Labor Relations Board, Region 3 - Buffalo Regional Office
Niagara Center Bldg.
130 S. Elmwood Ave., Ste. 630
Buffalo, NY 14202-2387
Ph: (716)551-4931
Fax: (716)551-4972
URL: http://www.nlrb.gov

60567 ■ National Labor Relations Board, Region 3 - Buffalo Regional Office
Niagara Center Bldg.
130 S. Elmwood Ave., Ste. 630
Buffalo, NY 14202-2387
Ph: (716)551-4931
Fax: (716)551-4972
URL: http://www.nlrb.gov

60568 ■ National Labor Relations Board, Region 4 - Philadelphia Regional Office
615 Chestnut St., 7th Fl.
Philadelphia, PA 19106-4404
Ph: (215)597-7601
Fax: (215)597-7658
URL: http://www.nlrb.gov

60569 ■ National Labor Relations Board, Region 4 - Philadelphia Regional Office
615 Chestnut St., 7th Fl.
Philadelphia, PA 19106-4404
Ph: (215)597-7601
Fax: (215)597-7658
URL: http://www.nlrb.gov

60570 ■ National Labor Relations Board, Region 5 - Baltimore Regional Office
Bank of America Ctr., Tower II
100 S. Charles St., 6th Fl.
Baltimore, MD 21202-4061
Ph: (410)962-2822
Fax: (410)962-2198
URL: http://www.nlrb.gov

60571 ■ National Labor Relations Board, Region 6 - Pittsburgh Regional Office
William S. Moorhead Federal Bldg.
1000 Liberty Ave., Rm. 904
Pittsburgh, PA 15222-4111
Ph: (412)395-4400
Fax: (412)395-5986
URL: http://www.nlrb.gov

60572 ■ National Labor Relations Board, Region 6 - Pittsburgh Regional Office
William S. Moorhead Federal Bldg.
1000 Liberty Ave., Rm. 904
Pittsburgh, PA 15222-4111
Ph: (412)395-4400
Fax: (412)395-5986
URL: http://www.nlrb.gov

60573 ■ National Labor Relations Board, Region 7 - Detroit Regional Office
477 Michigan Ave., Rm. 300
Detroit, MI 48226-2569
Ph: (313)226-3200
Fax: (313)226-2090
URL: http://www.nlrb.gov

60574 ■ National Labor Relations Board, Region 7 - Detroit Regional Office
477 Michigan Ave., Rm. 300
Detroit, MI 48226-2569
Ph: (313)226-3200
Fax: (313)226-2090
URL: http://www.nlrb.gov

60575 ■ National Labor Relations Board, Region 8 - Cleveland Regional Office
1240 E. 9th St., Rm. 1695
Cleveland, OH 44199-2086
Ph: (216)522-3715
Fax: (216)522-2418
URL: http://www.nlrb.gov

60576 ■ National Labor Relations Board, Region 8 - Cleveland Regional Office
1240 E. 9th St., Rm. 1695
Cleveland, OH 44199-2086
Ph: (216)522-3715
Fax: (216)522-2418
URL: http://www.nlrb.gov

60577 ■ National Labor Relations Board, Region 9 - Cincinnati Regional Office
John Weld Peck Federal Bldg.
550 Main St., Rm. 3003
Cincinnati, OH 45202-3271
Ph: (513)684-3686
Fax: (513)684-3946
URL: http://www.nlrb.gov

60578 ■ National Labor Relations Board, Region 9 - Cincinnati Regional Office
John Weld Peck Federal Bldg.
550 Main St., Rm. 3003
Cincinnati, OH 45202-3271
Ph: (513)684-3686
Fax: (513)684-3946
URL: http://www.nlrb.gov

60579 ■ National Labor Relations Board, Region 10 - Atlanta Regional Office
Harris Tower, Ste. 1000
233 Peachtree St., NE
Atlanta, GA 30303-1531
Ph: (404)331-2896
Fax: (404)331-2858
URL: http://www.nlrb.gov

60580 ■ National Labor Relations Board, Region 10 - Atlanta Regional Office
Harris Tower, Ste. 1000
233 Peachtree St. NE
Atlanta, GA 30303-1531
Ph: (404)331-2896
Fax: (404)331-2858
URL: http://www.nlrb.gov

60581 ■ National Labor Relations Board, Region 11 - Winston-Salem Regional Office
Republic Sq.
4035 University Pkwy., Ste. 200
Winston-Salem, NC 27106-3325
Ph: (336)631-5201
Fax: (336)631-5210
URL: http://www.nlrb.gov

60582 ■ National Labor Relations Board, Region 11 - Winston-Salem Regional Office
Republic Sq.
4035 University Pkwy., Ste. 200
Winston-Salem, NC 27106-3325
Ph: (336)631-5201
Fax: (336)631-5210
URL: http://www.nlrb.gov

60583 ■ National Labor Relations Board, Region 12 - Tampa Regional Office
S. Trust Plz., Ste. 530
201 E. Kennedy Blvd.
Tampa, FL 33602-5824
Ph: (813)228-2641
Fax: (813)228-2874
URL: http://www.nlrb.gov

60584 ■ National Labor Relations Board, Region 12 - Tampa Regional Office
S. Trust Plz., Ste. 530
201 E. Kennedy Blvd.
Tampa, FL 33602-5824
Ph: (813)228-2641
Fax: (813)228-2874
URL: http://www.nlrb.gov

60585 ■ National Labor Relations Board, Region 13 - Chicago Regional Office
The Rookery Bldg.
209 S. LaSalle St., Ste. 900
Chicago, IL 60604-5208
Ph: (312)353-7570
Fax: (312)886-1341
URL: http://www.nlrb.gov

60586 ■ National Labor Relations Board, Region 13 - Chicago Regional Office
The Rookery Bldg.
209 S. LaSalle St., Ste. 900
Chicago, IL 60604-5208
Ph: (312)353-7570
Fax: (312)886-1341
URL: http://www.nlrb.gov

60587 ■ National Labor Relations Board, Region 14 - St. Louis Regional Office
1222 Spruce St., Rm. 8.302
St. Louis, MO 63103-2829
Ph: (314)539-7770
Fax: (314)539-7794
URL: http://www.nlrb.gov

60588 ■ National Labor Relations Board, Region 14 - St. Louis Regional Office
1222 Spruce St., Rm. 8.302
St. Louis, MO 63103-2829
Ph: (314)539-7770
Fax: (314)539-7794
URL: http://www.nlrb.gov

60589 ■ National Labor Relations Board, Region 16 - Ft. Worth Regional Office
819 Taylor St., Rm. 8A24
Ft. Worth, TX 76102-6178
Ph: (817)978-2921
Fax: (817)978-2928
URL: http://www.nlrb.gov

60590 ■ National Labor Relations Board, Region 16 - Ft. Worth Regional Office
819 Taylor St., Rm. 8A24
Ft. Worth, TX 76102-6178
Ph: (817)978-2921
Fax: (817)978-2928
URL: http://www.nlrb.gov

60591 ■ National Labor Relations Board, Region 17 - Overland Park Regional Office
8600 Farley St., Ste. 100
Overland Park, KS 66212-4677
Ph: (913)967-3000
Fax: (913)967-3010
URL: http://www.nlrb.gov

60592 ■ National Labor Relations Board, Region 17 - Overland Park Regional Office
8600 Farley St., Ste. 100
Overland Park, KS 66212-4677
Ph: (913)967-3000
Fax: (913)967-3010
URL: http://www.nlrb.gov

60593 ■ National Labor Relations Board, Region 18 - Minneapolis Regional Office
Towle Bldg., Ste. 790
330 2nd Ave., S.
Minneapolis, MN 55401-2221
Ph: (612)348-1757
Fax: (612)348-1785
URL: http://www.nlrb.gov

60594 ■ National Labor Relations Board, Region 18 - Minneapolis Regional Office
Towle Bldg., Ste. 790
330 2nd Ave. S.
Minneapolis, MN 55401-2221
Ph: (612)348-1757
Fax: (612)348-1785
URL: http://www.nlrb.gov

60595 ■ National Labor Relations Board, Region 19 - Seattle Regional Office
915 2nd Ave., Rm. 2948
Seattle, WA 98174-1078
Ph: (206)220-6300
Fax: (206)220-6305
URL: http://www.nlrb.gov

60596 ■ National Labor Relations Board, Region 19 - Seattle Regional Office
915 2nd Ave., Rm. 2948
Seattle, WA 98174-1078
Ph: (206)220-6300
Fax: (206)220-6305
URL: http://www.nlrb.gov

60597 ■ National Labor Relations Board, Region 20 - San Francisco Regional Office
901 Market St., Ste. 400
San Francisco, CA 94103-1735
Ph: (415)356-5130
Fax: (415)356-5156
URL: http://www.nlrb.gov

60598 ■ National Labor Relations Board, Region 20 - San Francisco Regional Office
901 Market St., Ste. 400
San Francisco, CA 94103-1735
Ph: (415)356-5130
Fax: (415)356-5156
URL: http://www.nlrb.gov

60599 ■ National Labor Relations Board, Region 21 - Los Angeles Regional Office
888 S. Figueroa St., 9th Fl.
Los Angeles, CA 90017-5449
Ph: (213)894-5200
Fax: (213)894-2778
URL: http://www.nlrb.gov

60600 ■ National Labor Relations Board, Region 21 - Los Angeles Regional Office
888 S. Figueroa St., 9th Fl.
Los Angeles, CA 90017-5449
Ph: (213)894-5200
Fax: (213)894-2778
URL: http://www.nlrb.gov

60601 ■ National Labor Relations Board, Region 22 - Newark Regional Office
20 Washington Pl., 5th Fl.
Newark, NJ 07102-3110
Ph: (973)645-2100
Fax: (973)645-3852
URL: http://www.nlrb.gov

60602 ■ National Labor Relations Board, Region 22 - Newark Regional Office
20 Washington Pl., 5th Fl.
Newark, NJ 07102-3110
Ph: (973)645-2100
Fax: (973)645-3852
URL: http://www.nlrb.gov

60603 ■ National Labor Relations Board, Region 24 - Hato Rey Regional Office
La Torre de Plz., Ste. 1002
525 F.D. Roosevelt Ave.
San Juan, PR 00918-1002
Ph: (787)766-5347
Fax: (787)766-5478
URL: http://www.nlrb.gov

60604 ■ National Labor Relations Board, Region 24 - Hato Rey Regional Office
La Torre de Plz., Ste. 1002
525 F.D. Roosevelt Ave.
San Juan, PR 00918-1002
Ph: (787)766-5347
Fax: (787)766-5478
URL: http://www.nlrb.gov

60605 ■ National Labor Relations Board, Region 25 - Indianapolis Regional Office
575 N. Pennsylvania St., Rm. 238
Indianapolis, IN 46204-1577
Ph: (317)226-7381
Fax: (317)226-5103
URL: http://www.nlrb.gov

60606 ■ National Labor Relations Board, Region 25 - Indianapolis Regional Office
575 N. Pennsylvania St., Rm. 238
Indianapolis, IN 46204-1577
Ph: (317)226-7381
Fax: (317)226-5103
URL: http://www.nlrb.gov

60607 ■ National Labor Relations Board, Region 26 - Memphis Regional Office
Brinkley Plz. Bldg., Ste. 350
80 Monroe Ave.
Memphis, TN 38103-2481
Ph: (901)544-0018
Fax: (901)544-0008
URL: http://www.nlrb.gov

60608 ■ National Labor Relations Board, Region 26 - Memphis Regional Office
Brinkley Plz. Bldg., Ste. 350
80 Monroe Ave.
Memphis, TN 38103-2481
Ph: (901)544-0018
Fax: (901)544-0008
URL: http://www.nlrb.gov

60609 ■ National Labor Relations Board, Region 27 - Denver Regional Office
600 17th St.
7th Fl., North Tower
Denver, CO 80202-5433
Ph: (303)844-3551
Fax: (303)844-6249
URL: http://www.nlrb.gov

60610 ■ National Labor Relations Board, Region 27 - Denver Regional Office
600 17th St.
7th Fl., North Tower
Denver, CO 80202-5433
Ph: (303)844-3551
Fax: (303)844-6249
URL: http://www.nlrb.gov

60611 ■ National Labor Relations Board, Region 28 - Phoenix Regional Office
2600 N. Central Ave., Ste. 1800
Phoenix, AZ 85004-3099
Ph: (602)640-2160
Fax: (602)640-2178
URL: http://www.nlrb.gov

60612 ■ National Labor Relations Board, Region 28 - Phoenix Regional Office
2600 N. Central Ave., Ste. 1400
Phoenix, AZ 85004-3099
Ph: (602)640-2160
Fax: (602)640-2178
URL: http://www.nlrb.gov

60613 ■ National Labor Relations Board, Region 29 - Brooklyn Regional Office
2 Metro Tech Ctr.
100 Myrtle Ave., 5th Fl.
Brooklyn, NY 11201-4201
Ph: (718)330-7713
Fax: (718)330-7579
URL: http://www.nlrb.gov

60614 ■ National Labor Relations Board, Region 29 - Brooklyn Regional Office
2 Metro Tech Ctr., 5th Fl.
Brooklyn, NY 11201-3838
Ph: (718)330-7713
Fax: (718)330-7579
URL: http://www.nlrb.gov

60615 ■ National Labor Relations Board, Region 30 - Milwaukee Regional Office
310 W. Wisconsin Ave., Ste. 700
Milwaukee, WI 53203-2211
Ph: (414)297-3861
Fax: (414)297-3880
URL: http://www.nlrb.gov

60616 ■ National Labor Relations Board, Region 31 - Los Angeles Regional Office
11150 W. Olympic Blvd., Ste. 700
Los Angeles, CA 90064-1824
Ph: (310)235-7352
Fax: (310)235-7420
URL: http://www.nlrb.gov

60617 ■ National Labor Relations Board, Region 31 - Los Angeles Regional Office
11150 W. Olympic Blvd., Ste. 700
Los Angeles, CA 90064-1824
Ph: (310)235-7352
Fax: (310)235-7420
URL: http://www.nlrb.gov

60618 ■ National Labor Relations Board, Region 32 - Oakland Regional Office
Oakland Federal Bldg.
1301 Clay St., Rm. 300-N
Oakland, CA 94612-5211
Ph: (510)637-3300
Fax: (510)637-3315
URL: http://www.nlrb.gov

60619 ■ National Labor Relations Board, Region 32 - Oakland Regional Office
Oakland Federal Bldg.
1301 Clay St., Rm. 300-N
Oakland, CA 94612-5211
Ph: (510)637-3300
Fax: (510)637-3315
URL: http://www.nlrb.gov

60620 ■ National Labor Relations Board, Region 34 - Hartford Regional Office
280 Trumbull St., 21st Fl.
Hartford, CT 06103-3503
Ph: (860)240-3522
Fax: (860)240-3564
URL: http://www.nlrb.gov

60621 ■ National Labor Relations Board, Region 34 - Hartford Regional Office
A.A. Ribicoff Federal Bldg. and Courthouse, 4th Fl.
Hartford, CT 06103-3503
Ph: (860)240-3522

Fax: (860)240-3564
URL: http://www.nlrb.gov

60622 ■ National Labor Relations, Region 5 - Baltimore Regional Office
The Appraisers Store Bldg.
103 S. Gay St., 8th Fl.
Baltimore, MD 21202-4061
Ph: (410)962-2822
Fax: (410)962-2198
URL: http://www.nlrb.gov

NATIONAL SCIENCE FOUNDATION

60623 ■ National Science Foundation - Office of Small and Disadvantaged Business Utilization
4201 Wilson Blvd., Rm. 550 S
Arlington, VA 22203
Ph: (703)292-7082
Fax: (703)292-9056
Co. E-mail: dsenich@nsf.gov
URL: http://www.nsf.gov/
Description: The National Science Foundation's Office of Small and Disadvantaged Business Utilization offers small businesses information and guidance on procurement procedures, how to be placed on a bidder's mailing list, and identification of both prime and subcontracting opportunities.

60624 ■ National Science Foundation - Office of Small and Disadvantaged Business Utilization
4201 Wilson Blvd., Rm. 550 S
Arlington, VA 22203
Co. E-mail: dsenich@nsf.gov
URL: http://www.nsf.gov/
Description: The National Science Foundation's Office of Small and Disadvantaged Business Utilization offers small businesses information and guidance on procurement procedures, how to be placed on a bidder's mailing list, and identification of both prime and subcontracting opportunities.

60625 ■ National Science Foundation - Small Business Innovation Research Programs
4201 Wilson Blvd., Rm. 590 N
Arlington, VA 22230
Ph: (703)292-8050
Fax: (703)292-9057
URL: http://www.nsf.gov/eng/iip/sbir/

60626 ■ National Science Foundation - Small Business Innovation Research Programs
4201 Wilson Blvd., Rm. 1135
Arlington, VA 22230
Ph: (703)292-7100
Fax: (703)292-9158
URL: http://www.nsf.gov/eng/iip/sbir/

60627 ■ National Science Foundation - Small Business Technology Transfer Program
4201 Wilson Blvd., Rm. 590 N
Arlington, VA 22230
Ph: (703)292-8050
Fax: (703)292-9057
URL: http://www.nsf.gov/eng/iip/sbir/

60628 ■ National Science Foundation - Small Business Technology Transfer Program
4201 Wilson Blvd., Rm. 590 N
Arlington, VA 22230
Ph: (703)292-8050
Fax: (703)292-9057
URL: http://www.nsf.gov/eng/iip/sbir/

OFFICE OF PERSONNEL MANAGEMENT

60629 ■ Office of Personnel Management - Center for National Security - Office of Operations
Theodore Roosevelt Bldg., Rm. 7412
1900 E St., NW
Washington, DC 20415-0001

Ph: (202)606-1868
Fax: (202)606-2663
Co. E-mail: michael.carmichael@opm.gov
URL: http://www.opm.gov

60630 ■ Office of Personnel Management - Center for National Security - Office of Operations
Theodore Roosevelt Bldg., Rm. 7412
1900 E St. NW
Washington, DC 20415-0001
Ph: (202)606-1868
Fax: (202)606-2663
Co. E-mail: michael.carmichael@opm.gov
URL: http://www.opm.gov

60631 ■ Office of Personnel Management - Division for Human Capital Leadership and Merit System Accountability
Theodore Roosevelt Bldg., Rm. 7470
1900 E. St., NW
Washington, DC 20415-0001
Ph: (202)606-1575
Fax: (202)606-1798
URL: http://apps.opm.gov/opmorgchart/index.cfm?orgid=11#orgchart

60632 ■ Office of Personnel Management - Division for Human Capital Leadership and Merit System Accountability
Theodore Roosevelt Bldg., Rm. 7470
1900 E. St., NW
Washington, DC 20415-0001
Ph: (202)606-1575
Fax: (202)606-1798
URL: http://apps.opm.gov/opmorgchart/index.cfm?orgid=11#orgchart

60633 ■ Office of Personnel Management - Office of Communications and Public Liaison
Theodore Roosevelt Federal Bldg., Rm. 5347
1900 E St., NW
Washington, DC 20415-0001
Ph: (202)606-2402
Fax: (202)606-2264
URL: http://apps.opm.gov/opmorgchart/index.cfm?orgid=all

60634 ■ Office of Personnel Management - Office of Communications and Public Liaison
Theodore Roosevelt Federal Bldg., Rm. 5347
1900 E St. NW
Washington, DC 20415-0001
Ph: (202)606-2402
Fax: (202)606-2264
URL: http://apps.opm.gov/opmorgchart/index.cfm?orgid=all

60635 ■ Office of Personnel Management - Office of Small and Disadvantaged Business Utilization - Contracting Division
Theodore Roosevelt Federal Bldg.
1900 E. St. NW
Washington, DC 20415-1000
Ph: (202)606-1800
URL: http://www.opm.gov/doingbusiness/smallbusiness/overview.aspx
Description: The Office of Personnel Management's Office of Small and Disadvantaged Business Utilization offers small businesses information and guidance on procurement procedures, how to be placed on a bidder's mailing list, and identification of both prime and subcontracting opportunities.

60636 ■ U.S. Office of Personnel Management - Office of Small and Disadvantaged Business Utilization - Contracting Division
Theodore Roosevelt Federal Bldg.
1900 E. St., NW
Washington, DC 20415-1000
Ph: (202)606-0583
Fax: (202)606-1464
Co. E-mail: stvanree@opm.gov
URL: http://opm.gov/
Description: The Office of Personnel Management's Office of Small and Disadvantaged Business Utilization offers small businesses information and guid-

ance on procurement procedures, how to be placed on a bidder's mailing list, and identification of both prime and subcontracting opportunities.

ONE STOP CAPITAL SHOP

The following is a list of One Stop Capital Shops, arranged alphabetically by state.

60637 ■ Jamaica Business Resource Center
90-33 160th St.
Jamaica, NY 11432-6125
Ph: (718)206-2255
Fax: (718)206-3693
Co. E-mail: jbrc@jbrc.org
URL: http://www.jbrc.org

60638 ■ Jamaica Business Resource Center
90-33 160th St.
Jamaica, NY 11432-6125
Ph: (718)206-2255
Fax: (718)206-3693
Co. E-mail: jbrc@jbrc.org
URL: http://www.jbrc.org

60639 ■ One Stop Capital Shop (Atlanta)
675 Ponce de Leon Ave. N., 1st Fl.
Atlanta, GA 30308
Ph: (404)853-7675
Fax: (404)853-7677
URL: http://apps.atlantaga.gov/resserv/atlonestop.html
Contact: David W. Perry, Facilitator
E-mail: dwperry1@sba.gov

60640 ■ One Stop Capital Shop (Atlanta)
675 Ponce de Leon Ave. N., 1st Fl.
Atlanta, GA 30308

60641 ■ One Stop Capital Shop (Baltimore, Maryland)
34 Market Pl., Ste. 800
Baltimore, MD 21202
Ph: (410)783-4222
Fax: (410)783-4637
Contact: Hallot Watkins, Facilitator
E-mail: Hallot.Watkins@sba.gov

60642 ■ One Stop Capital Shop (Baltimore, Maryland)
34 Market Pl., Ste. 800
Baltimore, MD 21202

60643 ■ One Stop Capital Shop (Bismarck)
700 E. Main Ave., 2nd Fl.
Bismarck, ND 58506
Ph: (701)328-5850
Free: 800-544-4674
Fax: (701)250-4304
Contact: Mike Gallagher, Facilitator
E-mail: michael.gallagher@aba.gov

60644 ■ One Stop Capital Shop (Bismarck)
700 E. Main Ave., 2nd Fl.
Bismarck, ND 58506

60645 ■ One Stop Capital Shop (Detroit, Michigan)
2051 Rosa Parks Blvd.
Detroit, MI 48216
Ph: (313)965-1100
Fax: (313)965-1101
Contact: Connie Logan, Facilitator
E-mail: connie.logan@sba.gov

60646 ■ One Stop Capital Shop (Detroit, Michigan)
2051 Rosa Parks Blvd.
Detroit, MI 48216

60647 ■ One Stop Capital Shop (Edinburg)
1201 W. University Dr.
Edinburg, TX 78539-2999
Ph: (956)316-2610
Fax: (956)316-2612
Contact: Alonzo Gracia, Facilitator
E-mail: alonzo.gracia@sba.gov

60648 ■ **One Stop Capital Shop (Edinburg)**
1201 W. University Dr.
Edinburg, TX 78539-2999
Ph: (956)316-2610
Fax: (956)316-2612

60649 ■ **One Stop Capital Shop (Glendale)**
330 N. Brand, Ste. 1200
Glendale, CA 91203-2304
Ph: (818)552-3308
Fax: (818)552-3286
Contact: Cyndi Jones, Facilitator
E-mail: cyndi.jones@sba.gov

60650 ■ **One Stop Capital Shop (Glendale)**
330 N. Brand, Ste. 1200
Glendale, CA 91203-2304
Ph: (818)552-3308
Fax: (818)552-3286

60651 ■ **One Stop Capital Shop (Hugo)**
Little Dixie Community Action Agency
502 W. Duke St.
Hugo, OK 74743
Ph: (580)326-3351
Fax: (580)326-2305
Contact: Jerry Reese, Facilitator
E-mail: jerry.reese@sba.gov

60652 ■ **One Stop Capital Shop (Hugo)**
Little Dixie Community Action Agency
502 W. Duke St.
Hugo, OK 74743
Ph: (580)326-3351
Fax: (580)326-2305

60653 ■ **One Stop Capital Shop (Kansas City, Kansas)**
UMB Bank Bldg.
601 Minnesota Ave., 3rd Fl.
Kansas City, KS 66101
Ph: (913)371-6007
Fax: (913)371-3207
Co. E-mail: debra.ramsey@sba.gov
Contact: Ray Williams, Facilitator
E-mail: ray.williams@sba.gov

60654 ■ **One Stop Capital Shop (Kansas City, Kansas)**
UMB Bank Bldg.
601 Minnesota Ave., 3rd Fl.
Kansas City, KS 66101
Ph: (913)371-6007
Fax: (913)371-3207
Co. E-mail: debra.ramsey@sba.gov

60655 ■ **One Stop Capital Shop (Mississippi Mid-Delta)**
L.S. Rogers Bldg.
14000 Hwy. 82 W.
Itta Bena, MS 38941
Ph: (601)254-3730
Fax: (601)254-3734
URL: http://www.mvsu.edu/campus_facilities_
services/main_campus/
Contact: John Greer, Facilitator
E-mail: john.greer@sba.gov

60656 ■ **One Stop Capital Shop (Mississippi Mid-Delta)**
L.S. Rogers Bldg.
14000 Hwy. 82 W.
Itta Bena, MS 38941
Ph: (601)254-3730
Fax: (601)254-3734
URL: http://www.mvsu.edu/campus_facilities_
services/main_campus/

60657 ■ **One Stop Capital Shop (New York, New York)**
290 Lenox Ave., 2nd Fl.
New York, NY 10027
Ph: (212)876-2246
Fax: (212)876-4236
Contact: Norman Hunt, Facilitator

60658 ■ **One Stop Capital Shop (New York, New York)**
290 Lenox Ave., 2nd Fl.
New York, NY 10027
Ph: (212)876-2246
Fax: (212)876-4236

60659 ■ **One Stop Capital Shop (Oakland, California)**
519 17th St., 6th Fl.
Oakland, CA 94612
Ph: (510)238-3703
Fax: (510)238-7999
Co. E-mail: ggarrett@oakland1stop.org
URL: http://www.caratnet.org/CommPartPages/Oak-
landOneStop.pdf
Contact: Michael Elkin, Facilitator
E-mail: michael.elkin@sba.gov

60660 ■ **One Stop Capital Shop (Oakland, California)**
519 17th St., 6th Fl.
Oakland, CA 94612
Ph: (510)238-3703
Fax: (510)238-7999
Co. E-mail: ggarrett@oakland1stop.org
URL: http://www.caratnet.org/CommPartPages/Oak-
landOneStop.pdf

60661 ■ **One Stop Capital Shop (Philadelphia/Camden)**
The Small Business Support Center
1315 Walnut St.
Philadelphia, PA 19107
Ph: (215)790-5000
Fax: (215)790-2222
Contact: Joseph McDevitt, Facilitator
E-mail: Joseph.McDevitt@sba.gov

60662 ■ **One Stop Capital Shop (Philadelphia/Camden)**
The Small Business Support Center
1315 Walnut St.
Philadelphia, PA 19107
Ph: (215)790-5000
Fax: (215)790-2222

60663 ■ **One Stop Capital Shop (Roxbury)**
20 Hampden St.
Roxbury, MA 02119
Ph: (617)445-3413
Fax: (617)445-5675
Contact: Armando Fernandez, Facilitator
E-mail: armando.fernandez@sba.gov

60664 ■ **One Stop Capital Shop (Roxbury)**
20 Hampden St.
Roxbury, MA 02119
Ph: (617)445-3413
Fax: (617)445-5675

60665 ■ **One Stop Capital Shop (Somerset, Kentucky)**
Small Business Development Center
2292 S. Hwy. 27, Ste. 260
Somerset, KY 42501
Ph: (606)677-6120
Fax: (606)622-1413
Contact: Kay Stucker, Facilitator
E-mail: kstucker@centertech.com

60666 ■ **One Stop Capital Shop (Somerset, Kentucky)**
Small Business Development Center
2292 S. Hwy. 27, Ste. 260
Somerset, KY 42501
Ph: (606)677-6120
Fax: (606)622-1413

60667 ■ **One Stop Capital Shop (Tacoma)**
KeyBank Bldg.
1101 Pacific Ave.
Tacoma, WA 98402
Fax: (253)274-1289
Contact: Bill Bell, Facilitator
E-mail: bill.bell@sba.gov

60668 ■ **One Stop Capital Shop (Houston, Texas) - U.S. General Store**
5330 Griggs Rd.
Houston, TX 77021
Fax: (713)643-8193
Co. E-mail: james.blanton@sba.gov
Contact: Neal Blanton, Facilitator

60669 ■ **One Stop Capital Shop (Houston, Texas) - U.S. General Store**
5330 Griggs Rd.
Houston, TX 77021
Ph: (713)643-8000
Fax: (713)643-8193
Co. E-mail: james.blanton@sba.gov

SECURITIES AND EXCHANGE COMMISSION

The following branch and district offices are arranged alphabetically by city.

60670 ■ **Securities and Exchange Commission - Atlanta Regional Office**
3475 Lenox Rd. NE, Ste. 1000
Atlanta, GA 30326-1232
Ph: (404)842-7600
Fax: (404)842-7666
Co. E-mail: Atlanta@sec.gov
URL: http://www.sec.gov
Description: Serves Georgia, North Carolina, South Carolina, Puerto Rico, South Carolina, Tennessee, and Alabama.

60671 ■ **Securities and Exchange Commission - Atlanta Regional Office**
950 E. Paces Ferry NE, Ste. 900
Atlanta, GA 30326-1382
Ph: (404)842-7600
Fax: (404)842-7666
Co. E-mail: Atlanta@sec.gov
URL: http://www.sec.gov
Description: Serves Georgia, North Carolina, South Carolina, Puerto Rico, South Carolina, Tennessee, and Alabama.

60672 ■ **Securities and Exchange Commission - Boston Regional Office**
33 Arch St., 23rd Fl.
Boston, MA 02110-1424
Ph: (617)573-8900
Co. E-mail: boston@sec.gov
URL: http://www.sec.gov
Description: Serves Connecticut, Maine, Mas-sachusetts, New Hampshire, Rhode Island, and Vermont.

60673 ■ **Securities and Exchange Commission - Boston Regional Office**
33 Arch St., 23rd Fl.
Boston, MA 02110-1424
Ph: (617)573-8900
Co. E-mail: boston@sec.gov
URL: http://www.sec.gov
Description: Serves Connecticut, Maine, Mas-sachusetts, New Hampshire, Rhode Island, and Vermont.

60674 ■ **Securities and Exchange Commission - Chicago Regional Office**
175 W. Jackson Blvd., Ste. 900
Chicago, IL 60604
Ph: (312)353-7390
Fax: (312)353-7398
Co. E-mail: Chicago@sec.gov
URL: http://www.sec.gov
Description: Serves Illinois, Indiana, Iowa, Kentucky, Michigan, Minnesota, Missouri, Ohio, and Wisconsin.

60675 ■ **Securities and Exchange Commission - Chicago Regional Office**
175 W. Jackson Blvd., Ste. 900
Chicago, IL 60604
Ph: (312)353-7390

Fax: (312)353-7398
Co. E-mail: Chicago@sec.gov
URL: http://www.sec.gov
Description: Serves Illinois, Indiana, Iowa, Kentucky, Michigan, Minnesota, Missouri, Ohio, and Wisconsin.

60676 ■ Securities and Exchange Commission - Denver Regional Office
1801 California St., Ste. 1500
Denver, CO 80202-2656
Ph: (303)844-1000
Fax: (303)391-6868
Co. E-mail: Denver@sec.gov
URL: http://www.sec.gov
Description: Serves Colorado, Kansas, Nebraska, New Mexico, North Dakota, South Dakota, and Wyoming.

60677 ■ Securities and Exchange Commission - Denver Regional Office
1801 California St., Ste. 1500
Denver, CO 80202-2656
Ph: (303)844-1000
Fax: (303)391-6868
Co. E-mail: Denver@sec.gov
URL: http://www.sec.gov
Description: Serves Colorado, Kansas, Nebraska, New Mexico, North Dakota, South Dakota, and Wyoming.

60678 ■ Securities and Exchange Commission - Fort Worth Regional Office
Burnett Plz., Ste. 1900
801 Cherry St., Unit 18
Ft. Worth, TX 76102
Ph: (817)978-3821
Fax: (817)334-2700
Co. E-mail: dfw@sec.gov
URL: http://www.sec.gov
Description: Serves Arkansas, Kansas, Oklahoma, Texas (except for the exam program which is administered by the Denver Regional Office).

60679 ■ Securities and Exchange Commission - Fort Worth Regional Office
Burnett Plz., Ste. 1900
801 Cherry St., Unit 18
Ft. Worth, TX 76102
Ph: (817)978-3821
Fax: (817)334-2700
Co. E-mail: dfw@sec.gov
URL: http://www.sec.gov
Description: Serves Arkansas, Kansas, Oklahoma, Texas (except for the exam program which is administered by the Denver Regional Office).

60680 ■ Securities and Exchange Commission - Los Angeles Regional Office
5670 Wilshire Blvd., 11th Fl.
Los Angeles, CA 90036-3648
Ph: (323)965-3998
Fax: (323)965-3815
Co. E-mail: losangeles@sec.gov
URL: http://www.sec.gov
Description: Serves Arizona, Hawaii, Guam, Nevada, southern California (zip codes 93599 and below, except for 93200-93299).

60681 ■ Securities and Exchange Commission - Los Angeles Regional Office
5670 Wilshire Blvd., 11th Fl.
Los Angeles, CA 90036-3648
Ph: (323)965-3998
Fax: (323)965-3815
Co. E-mail: losangeles@sec.gov
URL: http://www.sec.gov
Description: Serves Arizona, Hawaii, Guam, Nevada, southern California (zip codes 93599 and below, except for 93200-93299).

60682 ■ Securities and Exchange Commission - Miami Regional Office
801 Brickell Ave., Ste. 1800
Miami, FL 33131
Ph: (305)982-6300
Co. E-mail: miami@sec.gov
URL: http://www.sec.gov
Description: Serves Florida, Mississippi, Louisiana, U.S. Virgin Islands, and Puerto Rico.

60683 ■ Securities and Exchange Commission - Miami Regional Office
801 Brickell Ave., Ste. 1800
Miami, FL 33131
Ph: (305)982-6300
Co. E-mail: miami@sec.gov
URL: http://www.sec.gov
Description: Serves Florida, Mississippi, Louisiana, U.S. Virgin Islands, and Puerto Rico.

60684 ■ Securities and Exchange Commission - New York Regional Office
3 World Financial Center, Ste. 400
New York, NY 10281-1022
Ph: (212)336-1100
Co. E-mail: newyork@sec.gov
URL: http://www.sec.gov
Description: Serves New Jersey and New York.

60685 ■ Securities and Exchange Commission - New York Regional Office
3 World Financial Center, Ste. 400
New York, NY 10281-1022
Ph: (212)336-1100
Co. E-mail: newyork@sec.gov
URL: http://www.sec.gov
Description: Serves New Jersey and New York.

60686 ■ Securities and Exchange Commission (SEC) - Office of Small Business Policy - Small Business Ombudsman
100 F St., NE
Washington, DC 20549-0310
Ph: (202)551-3460
Co. E-mail: smallbusiness@sec.gov
URL: http://www.sec.gov/info/smallbus/reachsec.htm
Contact: William E. Toomey, Deputy Chief
Description: The Security and Exchange Commission's responsibilities under the securities laws are to protect investors and to ensure that capital markets operate in a fair and orderly manner. Nevertheless, the SEC believes that its regulations should not have the effect of inadvertently impairing capital formation by small businesses. Therefore the SEC has taken a number of steps to facilitate capital-raising by small businesses and to reduce undue regulatory burdens arising from the federal securities laws. The SEC is in a continuous process of examining other ways to further aid in accomplishing these goals. The SEC's Office of Small Business Policy, for example, directs the commission's small business rulemaking initiatives. It also reviews and comments on the impact of SEC rule proposals on smaller issuers and serves as a liaison with Congressional committees, government agencies, and other groups concerned with small business.

60687 ■ Securities and Exchange Commission - Office of Small Business Policy - Small Business Ombudsman
100 F St. NE
Washington, DC 20549-3628
Ph: (202)551-3460
Co. E-mail: smallbusiness@sec.gov
URL: http://www.sec.gov/info/smallbus/reachsec.htm
Description: The Security and Exchange Commission's responsibilities under the securities laws are to protect investors and to ensure that capital markets operate in a fair and orderly manner. Nevertheless, the SEC believes that its regulations should not have the effect of inadvertently impairing capital formation by small businesses. Therefore the SEC has taken a number of steps to facilitate capital-raising by small businesses and to reduce undue regulatory burdens arising from the federal securities laws. The SEC is in a continuous process of examining other ways to further aid in accomplishing these goals. The SEC's Office of Small Business Policy, for example, directs the commission's small business rulemaking initiatives. It also reviews and comments on the impact of SEC rule proposals on smaller issuers and serves as a liaison with Congressional committees, government agencies, and other groups concerned with small business.

60688 ■ Securities and Exchange Commission - Philadelphia Regional Office
Mellon Independence Center
701 Market St., Ste. 2000
Philadelphia, PA 19106-1538
Ph: (215)597-3100
Fax: (215)597-5885
Co. E-mail: philadelphia@sec.gov
URL: http://www.sec.gov
Description: Serves Delaware, the District of Columbia, Maryland, Pennsylvania, Virginia, and West Virginia.

60689 ■ Securities and Exchange Commission - Philadelphia Regional Office
Mellon Independence Center
701 Market St.
Philadelphia, PA 19106-1532
Ph: (215)597-3100
Fax: (215)597-5885
Co. E-mail: philadelphia@sec.gov
URL: http://www.sec.gov
Description: Serves Delaware, the District of Columbia, Maryland, Pennsylvania, Virginia, and West Virginia.

60690 ■ Securities and Exchange Commission - Salt Lake Regional Office
15 W. South Temple St., Ste. 1800
Salt Lake City, UT 84101
Ph: (801)524-5796
Fax: (801)524-3558
Co. E-mail: saltlake@sec.gov
URL: http://www.sec.gov
Description: Serves Utah.

60691 ■ Securities and Exchange Commission - Salt Lake Regional Office
15 W. South Temple St., Ste. 1800
Salt Lake City, UT 84101
Ph: (801)524-5796
Fax: (801)524-3558
Co. E-mail: saltlake@sec.gov
URL: http://www.sec.gov
Description: Serves Utah.

60692 ■ Securities and Exchange Commission - San Francisco Regional Office
44 Montgomery St., Ste. 2600
San Francisco, CA 94104
Ph: (415)705-2500
Co. E-mail: sanfrancisco@sec.gov
URL: http://www.sec.gov
Description: Serves Washington, Oregon, Alaska, Southern California (zip codes 93599 and below, except for 93200-93299).

60693 ■ Securities and Exchange Commission - San Francisco Regional Office
44 Montgomery St., Ste. 2800
San Francisco, CA 94104
Ph: (415)705-2500
Co. E-mail: sanfrancisco@sec.gov
URL: http://www.sec.gov/contact/addresses.htm
Description: Serves Washington, Oregon, Alaska, Southern California (zip codes 93599 and below, except for 93200-93299).

SMITHSONIAN INSTITUTION

60694 ■ Smithsonian Institute - Office of Equal Employment and Minority Affairs
ATTN: Supplier Diversity Program Manager
Capital Gallery, Ste. 2091, MRC 521
Washington, DC 20013-7012
Ph: (202)633-6430
Fax: (202)633-6427
Co. E-mail: sdphelp@si.edu
URL: http://www.si.edu/oeema/

60695 ■ Smithsonian Institute - Office of Equal Employment and Minority Affairs
ATTN: Supplier Diversity Program Manager
Capital Gallery, Ste. 2091, MRC 521
Washington, DC 20013-7012
Ph: (202)633-6430

Fax: (202)633-6427
Co. E-mail: sdphelp@si.edu
URL: http://www.si.edu/oeema/

TENNESSEE VALLEY AUTHORITY

60696 ■ **Tennessee Valley Authority (TVA)**
400 W Summit Hill Dr.
Knoxville, TN 37902-1499
Ph: (865)632-2101
Co. E-mail: tvainfo@tva.com
URL: http://www.tva.gov
Contact: Bill Johnson, President
Founded: 1933. **Publications:** *Directory of Terminals on the Tennessee River Waterway* (Irregular).

60697 ■ **Tennessee Valley Authority (TVA) - Minority Economic and Small Business Development**
PO Box 292409
Nashville, TN 37229-2409
Ph: (615)232-6225
Co. E-mail: econdev@tva.com
URL: http://www.tvaed.com/bus_serv.htm
Description: The Tennessee Valley Authority maintains agency-wide Minority Economic Development initiatives that assist small minority and women-owned businesses (SMWOBs) that seek TVA business opportunities, as well as, the entire business community of the Valley. TVA's Economic Development organization provides capital, technical, and managerial assistance for SMWOBs, start-ups, retention and expansions. Assistance takes the form of revolving loan funds, public/private partnerships that administer training programs, and in-house technical assistance. Through its Procurement organizations, TVA encourages minority participation in prime and subcontracting opportunities. Its policy is to promote the full participation of SMWOBs in all of its procurement and contracting activities. Further, priority shall be given to fostering the economic development of the Valley through use of products and services of such firms located in the Valley region. TVA's commitment is to maximize participation through the development of mutually beneficial business relationships with these firms consistent with achieving the best value to TVA.

60698 ■ **Tennessee Valley Authority - Minority Economic and Small Business Development**
PO Box 292409
Nashville, TN 37229-2409
Ph: (615)232-6225
Co. E-mail: econdev@tva.com
URL: http://www.tvaed.com/bus_serv.htm
Description: The Tennessee Valley Authority maintains agency-wide Minority Economic Development initiatives that assist small minority and women-owned businesses (SMWOBs) that seek TVA business opportunities, as well as, the entire business community of the Valley. TVA's Economic Development organization provides capital, technical, and managerial assistance for SMWOBs, start-ups, retention and expansions. Assistance takes the form of revolving loan funds, public/private partnerships that administer training programs, and in-house technical assistance. Through its Procurement organizations, TVA encourages minority participation in prime and subcontracting opportunities. Its policy is to promote the full participation of SMWOBs in all of its procurement and contracting activities. Further, priority shall be given to fostering the economic development of the Valley through use of products and services of such firms located in the Valley region. TVA's commitment is to maximize participation through the development of mutually beneficial business relationships with these firms consistent with achieving the best value to TVA.

U.S. DEPARTMENT OF AGRICULTURE

The following USDA agencies are arranged alphabetically.

60699 ■ **U.S. Department of Agriculture - Acquisition Management Division - Farm**

Service Agency - Office of Small and Disadvantaged Business Utilization Coordinator
1400 Independence Ave., SW
Mail Stop 0567
Washington, DC 20250-0567
Ph: (202)690-0723
Co. E-mail: joyce.bowie@usda.gov
URL: http://www.fsa.usda.gov/amb

60700 ■ **U.S. Department of Agriculture (APD) - Acquisition and Property Division (AFM) - Administrative and Financial Management**
14th St. & Independence Ave. SW
South Bldg., Rm. 1310
Washington, DC 20250
Ph: (202)720-3998
Co. E-mail: wendy.jones@ars.usda.gov

60701 ■ **U.S. Department of Agriculture - Administrative Services Division - Farmers Home Administration - Office of Small and Disadvantaged Business Utilization Coordinator**
1400 Independence Ave. SW
South Bldg., Rm. 1085
AG Stop 9501
Washington, DC 20250-9501
Ph: (202)720-7117
Fax: (202)720-3001
Co. E-mail: joe.ware@usda.gov
URL: http://www.usda.gov/osdbu

60702 ■ **U.S. Department of Agriculture - Administrative Services Division - Farmers Home Administration - Office of Small and Disadvantaged Business Utilization Coordinator**
1400 Independence Ave. SW
South Bldg., Rm. 1085
AG Stop 9501
Washington, DC 20250-9501
Ph: (202)720-7117
Fax: (202)720-3001
Co. E-mail: jamese.house@usda.gov
URL: http://www.usda.gov/osdbu

60703 ■ **U.S. Department of Agriculture - Administrative Services Division - Food and Nutrition Service - Office of Small and Disadvantaged Business Utilization Coordinator**
3101 Park Center Dr., Rm. 914
Alexandria, VA 22302
Ph: (703)305-2265
Co. E-mail: sabrina.mathis@fns.udsa.gov
URL: http://www.usda.gov/da/smallbus/sbcoord.htm

60704 ■ **U.S. Department of Agriculture - Administrative Services Division - Food and Nutrition Service - Office of Small and Disadvantaged Business Utilization Coordinator**
3101 Park Center Dr., Rm. 914
Alexandria, VA 22302
Ph: (703)305-2265
Co. E-mail: tina.nevitt@FNS.udsa.gov
URL: http://www.usda.gov/da/smallbus/sbcoord.htm

60705 ■ **U.S. Department of Agriculture - Administrative Services Division - U.S. Forest Service - Office of Small and Disadvantaged Business Utilization Coordinator**
Rosslyn Plz.E, Rm. 706
Washington, DC 20090-6090
Ph: (703)605-4744
Co. E-mail: cagguirebravo@fs.fed.us
URL: http://www.usda.gov/da/smallbus/sbcoord.htm

60706 ■ **U.S. Department of Agriculture - Administrative Services Division - U.S. Forest Service - Office of Small and Disadvantaged Business Utilization Coordinator**
1621 N. Kent St., Ste. 707
Arlington, VA 22209-2131

Ph: (703)605-5144
Co. E-mail: caguirrebravo@fs.fed.us
URL: http://www.usda.gov/da/smallbus/sbcoord.htm

60707 ■ **U.S. Department of Agriculture - Agricultural Research Service - Administrative and Financial Management - Acquisition and Property Division**
5601 Sunnyside Ave.
Beltsville, MD 20705-5117
Ph: (301)504-1734
Co. E-mail: michael.barnes@ars.usda.gov
URL: http://www.afm.ars.usda.gov/aboutAFM/APD/contacts.htm

60708 ■ **U.S. Department of Agriculture - Agricultural Research Service - Office of Small and Disadvantaged Business Utilization**
5601 Sunnyside Ave.
Beltsville, MD 20705-5117
Ph: (301)504-1734
Co. E-mail: jennifer.friel@ars.usda.gov
URL: http://www.usda.gov/da/smallbus/sbcoord.htm

60709 ■ **U.S. Department of Agriculture - Contracting and Acquisition Management Division - Agricultural Stabilization and Conservation Service - Office of Small and Disadvantaged Business Utilization Coordinator**
1400 Independence Ave. SW, Rm. 1085
South Bldg., AG STOP 9501
Washington, DC 20250-9501
Ph: (202)720-7117
Fax: (202)720-3001
URL: http://www.usda.gov/osdbu

60710 ■ **U.S. Department of Agriculture - Contracts and Procurement Branch - Office of the Inspector General - Office of Small and Disadvantaged Business Utilization Coordinator**
1400 Independence Ave., SW
W. Jamie Whitten Bldg., Rm. 117
Washington, DC 20250
Ph: (202)720-8001
Fax: (202)690-1278
URL: http://www.usda.gov/oig/

60711 ■ **U.S. Department of Agriculture - Contracts and Procurement Branch - Office of the Inspector General - Office of Small and Disadvantaged Business Utilization Coordinator**
1400 Independence Ave. SW
W. Jamie Whitten Bldg., Rm. 117
Washington, DC 20250
Ph: (202)720-8001
Fax: (202)690-1278
URL: http://www.usda.gov/oig/

60712 ■ **U.S. Department of Agriculture (USDA) - Cooperative State Research, Education, and Extension Service (CSREES) - Small Business Innovation Research Representative**
1400 Independence Ave., SW
800 Ninth St., SW
Mail Stop 2201
Washington, DC 20250-2201
Ph: (202)401-4002
Fax: (202)401-6070
Co. E-mail: ccleland@csrees.usda.gov
URL: http://www.csrees.usda.gov/fo/sbir.cfm

60713 ■ **U.S. Department of Agriculture (CSREES) - Cooperative State Research, Education, and Extension Service - Small Business Innovation Research Representative**
1400 Independence Ave. SW, Stop 2243
Mail Stop 2201
Washington, DC 20250-2243
Ph: (202)401-4002

Fax: (202)401-6070
Co. E-mail: ccleland@csrees.usda.gov
URL: http://www.csrees.usda.gov/fo/sbir.cfm
URL(s): www.dm.usda.gov/procurement/business/smallbiz.htm.

60714 ■ U.S. Department of Agriculture (OSDBU) - Departmental Management Branch - Extension Service - Office of Small and Disadvantaged Business Utilization Coordinator
South Agriculture Bldg.
1400 Independence Ave., SW, Rm. 1085
AG Stop 9501
Washington, DC 20250
Ph: (202)720-7117
Fax: (202)720-3001
URL: http://www.usda.gov/da/smallbus

60715 ■ U.S. Department of Agriculture - Departmental Management - Office of Small and Disadvantaged Business Utilization Coordinator
South Bldg., Rm. 1085
1400 Independence Ave. SW
AG Stop 9501
Washington, DC 20250
Ph: (202)720-7117
Free: 877-996-7328
Fax: (202)720-3001
Co. E-mail: joe.ware@dm.usda.gov
URL: http://www.dm.usda.gov/osdbu

60716 ■ U.S. Department of Agriculture - Management Services Branch - Extension Service - Office of Small and Disadvantaged Business Utilization Coordinator
South Agriculture Bldg.
1400 Independence Ave. SW, Rm. 1085
AG Stop 9501
Washington, DC 20250
Ph: (202)720-7117
Fax: (202)720-3001
URL: http://www.dm.usda.gov/da/smallbus

60717 ■ U.S. Department of Agriculture - Management Services Division - Animal and Plant Health Inspection Service - Office of Small and Disadvantaged Business Utilization Coordinator
4700 River Rd., Unit 111, Cub. 3D
Riverdale, MD 20737
Ph: (301)734-8110
Co. E-mail: Estela.M.Diaz@usda.gov
URL: http://www.usda.gov/da/smallbus/sbcoord.htm

60718 ■ U.S. Department of Agriculture - Management Services Division - Animal and Plant Health Inspection Service - Office of Small and Disadvantaged Business Utilization Coordinator
4700 River Rd., Unit 111, Cub. 3D
Riverdale, MD 20737
Ph: (301)734-8110
Co. E-mail: Estela.M.Diaz@usda.gov
URL: http://www.dm.usda.gov/da/smallbus/sbcoord.htm

60719 ■ U.S. Department of Agriculture - Management Services Division - Farm Service Agency - Office of Small and Disadvantaged Business Utilization Coordinator
1400 Independence Ave. SW
Washington, DC 20250
Ph: (202)690-0723
URL: http://www.dm.usda.gov/procurement/hcadlist.htm

60720 ■ U.S. Department of Agriculture - Management Services Division - Natural Resources Conservation Service - Office of Small and Disadvantaged Business Utilization Coordinator
1400 Independence Ave. SW
South Bldg., Rm. 6202
Washington, DC 20250

Ph: (202)720-8758
Co. E-mail: edward.biggers@wdc.usda.gov

60721 ■ U.S. Department of Agriculture - Management Services Division - Natural Resources Conservation Service - Office of Small and Disadvantaged Business Utilization Coordinator
1400 Independence Ave., SW
South Bldg., Rm. 1602
Washington, DC 20250
Ph: (202)720-8758
Co. E-mail: Terry.Kirby@wdc.usda.gov

60722 ■ U.S. Department of Agriculture (USDA) - Office of Small and Disadvantaged Business Utilization
1400 Independence Ave., SW
South Bldg., Rm. 1085
Washington, DC 20250
Ph: (202)720-7117
Fax: (202)720-3001
URL: http://www.usda.gov/osdbu
Description: The USDA's Office of Small and Disadvantaged Business Utilization offers information and other services to minority-owned, women-owned, and small and disadvantaged businesses to assist them in increasing and maintaining their participation in the department's procurement and other program opportunities. The department has 18 major procurement offices, and an additional 260 offices across the country that offer procurement assistance to the small business community. These services are provided to increase the overall viability and competitiveness of businesses as part of maintaining an economically strong national industrial and commercial base. Emphasis is given to assisting firms that can contribute to revitalizing the nation's rural communities, improving the private agricultural sector's foreign trade competitiveness, and/or increasing the federal government's productivity. The department procures approximately $2 billion in products and services each year, $1 billion of which is awarded to minority-owned, women-owned, and small and disadvantaged businesses.

60723 ■ U.S. Department of Agriculture - Office of Small and Disadvantaged Business Utilization
1400 Independence Ave. SW
South Bldg., Rm. 1085
AG STOP 9501
Washington, DC 20250-9501
Ph: (202)720-7117
Fax: (202)720-3001
Co. E-mail: joe.ware@dm.usda.gov
URL: http://www.dm.usda.gov/smallbus/contactus.htm
Description: The USDA's Office of Small and Disadvantaged Business Utilization offers information and other services to minority-owned, women-owned, and small and disadvantaged businesses to assist them in increasing and maintaining their participation in the department's procurement and other program opportunities. The department has 18 major procurement offices, and an additional 260 offices across the country that offer procurement assistance to the small business community. These services are provided to increase the overall viability and competitiveness of businesses as part of maintaining an economically strong national industrial and commercial base. Emphasis is given to assisting firms that can contribute to revitalizing the nation's rural communities, improving the private agricultural sector's foreign trade competitiveness, and/or increasing the federal government's productivity. The department procures approximately $2 billion in products and services each year, $1 billion of which is awarded to minority-owned, women-owned, and small and disadvantaged businesses.

60724 ■ U.S. Department of Agriculture - Procurement Division - Office of Operations - Office of Procurement and Property Management
USDA Reporters Bldg.
300 7th St. SW, Ste. 377
Washington, DC 20250-9852

Ph: (202)720-8946
Co. E-mail: Brinder.Billups@usda.gov
URL: http://www.usda.gov/da/smallbus/sbcoord.htm

60725 ■ U.S. Department of Agriculture - Procurement Division - Office of Operations - Office of Procurement and Property Management
USDA Reporters Bldg.
300 7th St. SW, Ste. 353
Washington, DC 20024
Ph: (202)720-8946
Co. E-mail: Brinder.Billups@usda.gov
URL: http://www.dm.usda.gov/smallbus/sbcoord.htm

60726 ■ U.S. Department of Agriculture - Procurement Management Branch - Food Safety and Inspection Service
5601 Sunnyside Ave.
2-L-175
Beltsville, MD 20705-5230
Ph: (301)504-2010
Free: 301--504-4276
Co. E-mail: angela.thomas@fsis.usda.gov
URL: http://www.usda.gov/da/smallbus/sbcoord.htm

60727 ■ U.S. Department of Agriculture - Procurement Management Branch - Food Safety and Inspection Service
5601 Sunnyside Ave., Location 2-L188C
Beltsville, MD 20705-5230
Ph: (301)504-4211
Fax: (301)504-4276
Co. E-mail: angela.thomas@fsis.usda.gov
URL: http://www.usda.gov/da/smallbus/sbcoord.htm

60728 ■ U.S. Department of Agriculture - Procurement, Property and Space - Economics Management Staff
14th St. & Independence Ave. SW
South Bldg., Rm. 1310
Washington, DC 20250
Ph: (202)720-3998

60729 ■ U.S. Department of Agriculture - Resources Management Staff - Office of Communications
James L. Whitten Bldg., Rm. 535-A
1400 Independence Ave., SW
Washington, DC 20250
Ph: (202)720-3118
Co. E-mail: terry.logan@oc.usda.gov
URL: http://www.usda.gov/da/smallbus/sbcoord.htm

60730 ■ U.S. Department of Agriculture - Resources Management Staff - Office of Communications
James L. Whitten Bldg., Rm. 434-A
1400 Independence Ave. SW
Washington, DC 20250
Ph: (202)720-3118
Co. E-mail: terry.logan@oc.usda.gov
URL: http://www.usda.gov/da/smallbus/sbcoord.htm

60731 ■ U.S. Department of Agriculture - Rural Development Division - Electric Program
South Bldg., Rm. 1085
1400 Independence Ave., SW
AG Stop 9501
Washington, DC 20250
Ph: (202)720-7117
Fax: (202)720-3001
URL: http://www.usda.gov/osdbu

U.S. DEPARTMENT OF COMMERCE

60732 ■ U.S. Department of Commerce - Alabama Department of Economic and Community Affairs (ADECA)
401 Adams Ave.
Montgomery, AL 36103-5690
Ph: (334)242-5100
Fax: (334)242-5099
URL: http://www.adeca.state.al.us

60733 ■ U.S. Department of Commerce - Alabama Department of Economic and Community Affairs
401 Adams Ave.
Montgomery, AL 36104
Ph: (334)242-5100
Fax: (334)242-5099
Co. E-mail: adeca.webmaster.info@adeca.alabama.
gov
URL: http://www.adeca.state.al.us

60734 ■ U.S. Department of Commerce - Alabama Public Library Service
6030 Monticello Dr.
Montgomery, AL 36130
Ph: (334)213-3900
Free: 800-723-8459
Fax: (334)213-3993
Co. E-mail: aplref01@asnmail.asc.edu
URL: http://statelibrary.alabama.gov/Content/Index.
aspx

60735 ■ U.S. Department of Commerce - Alabama Public Library Service
6030 Monticello Dr.
Montgomery, AL 36130
Ph: (334)213-3900
Free: 800-723-8459
Fax: (334)213-3993
Co. E-mail: aplref01@asnmail.asc.edu
URL: http://statelibrary.alabama.gov/Content/Index.
aspx

60736 ■ U.S. Department of Commerce - Alaska Department of Commerce, Community, and Economic Development - Alaska State Community Service Commission
550 W. 7th St.
Anchorage, AK 99501
Ph: (907)269-4659
Co. E-mail: nita_madsen@commerce.state.ak.us
URL: http://www.commerce.state.ak.us

60737 ■ U.S. Department of Commerce - Alaska Department of Commerce, Community and Economic Development - Alaska State Community Service Commission
550 W. 7th St.
Anchorage, AK 99501
Ph: (907)269-4659
Co. E-mail: nita_madsen@alaska.gov
URL: http://www.commerce.state.ak.us

60738 ■ U.S. Department of Commerce - Alaska Department of Labor - Census and Geographic Information Network - Research and Analysis
1111 W. 8th St., Ste. 301
Juneau, AK 99811-5504
Ph: (907)465-2439
Fax: (907)465-2101
Co. E-mail: Ingrid.Zaruba@alaska.gov
URL: http://www.census.gov/sdc/www.aksdc.html

60739 ■ U.S. Department of Commerce - Alaska Department of Labor - Census and Geographic Information Network - Research and Analysis
1111 W. 8th St., Ste. 301
Juneau, AK 99802
Ph: (907)465-2439
Fax: (907)465-2101
Co. E-mail: Ingrid.Zaruba@alaska.gov
URL: http://labor.alaska.gov/research/census/cginaf-
filiates.pdf

60740 ■ U.S. Department of Commerce - Alaska State Library - Government Publications/Technical Services
State Office Building, 8th Fl.
333 Willoughby Ave.
Juneau, AK 99811-0571
Ph: (907)465-2927
Fax: (907)465-2665
Co. E-mail: Dan_Cornwall@eed.state.ak.us
URL: http://library.state.ak.us/pub/publications.html

60741 ■ U.S. Department of Commerce - Alaska State Library - Government Publications/Technical Services
333 Willoughby Ave., 8th Fl.
Juneau, AK 99811-0571
Ph: (907)465-2920
Fax: (907)465-2151
Co. E-mail: asl@alaska.gov
URL: http://library.state.ak.us/pub/publications.html

60742 ■ U.S. Department of Commerce - Albany State College - State Data Center Program - Documents Librarian
504 College Dr.
Albany, GA 31705-2797
Ph: (229)430-4900
Fax: (229)430-3936

60743 ■ U.S. Department of Commerce - Albany State College - State Data Center Program - Documents Librarian
504 College Dr.
Albany, GA 31705-2797
Ph: (229)430-4600
Fax: (229)430-3936

60744 ■ U.S. Department of Commerce - Arizona Department of Economic Security
1789 W. Jefferson St.
1st Fl., NE Wing
Phoenix, AZ 85007
Ph: (602)542-5746
Free: 800-352-8168
Fax: (602)542-7425
Co. E-mail: abarnes@azdes.gov
URL: http://www.azdes.gov
Contact: Liz Barker, Director, Communications
Telecommunication Services: LizBarker@azdes.
gov.

60745 ■ U.S. Department of Commerce - Arizona State Department of Economic Security
1717 W. Jefferson St., O50Z-1, Rm. 119
Phoenix, AZ 85007
Ph: (602)542-4791
Fax: (602)254-8457
URL: http://www.azdes.gov

60746 ■ U.S. Department of Commerce - Arizona State Department of Economic Security
1717 W. Jefferson St., O50Z-1, Rm. 119
Phoenix, AZ 85007
Ph: (602)542-4791
Fax: (602)254-8457
URL: http://www.azdes.gov

60747 ■ U.S. Department of Commerce - Arizona State Department of Library, Archives, and Public Records - Law and Research Library
1700 W. Washington, Ste. 300
Phoenix, AZ 85007
Ph: (602)926-3870
Free: 800-228-4710
Fax: (602)256-7984
Co. E-mail: research@lib.az.us/is/state/government.
cfm
URL: http://www.lib.az.us/is/

60748 ■ U.S. Department of Commerce - Arizona State Department of Library, Archives, and Public Records - Law and Research Library
1700 W. Washington, Ste. 300
Phoenix, AZ 85007
Ph: (602)926-3870
Free: 800-228-4710
Fax: (602)256-7984
URL: http://www.azlibrary.gov/is/

60749 ■ U.S. Department of Commerce - Arkansas Employment Security Department - Research and Analysis Section - Department of Workforce Service
2 Capitol Mall
Little Rock, AR 72201

Ph: (501)682-2121
Co. E-mail: artee.williams@arkansas.gov
URL: http://www.state.ar.us/esd

60750 ■ U.S. Department of Commerce - Arkansas Employment Security Department - Research and Analysis Section - Department of Workforce Services
2 Capitol Mall
Little Rock, AR 72201
Ph: (501)682-2257
Fax: (501)682-7797
Co. E-mail: artee.williams@arkansas.gov
URL: http://www.state.ar.us/esd

60751 ■ U.S. Department of Commerce - Arkansas State Library
900 West Capitol Mall
Suite 100
Little Rock, AR 72201
Ph: (501)682-2053
Fax: (501)682-1529
Co. E-mail: carolyn@library.arkansas.gov
URL: http://www.asl.lib.ar.us/index.html

60752 ■ U.S. Department of Commerce - Arkansas State Library
900 W. Capitol, Ste. 100
Little Rock, AR 72201
Ph: (501)682-2053
Fax: (501)682-1529
Co. E-mail: aslref@asl.lib.ar.us
URL: http://www.library.arkansas.gov

60753 ■ U.S. Department of Commerce - Association of Bay Area Governments
Joseph P. Bort MetroCenter
101 8th St.
Oakland, CA 94607-2050
Ph: (510)464-7900
Fax: (510)464-7970
Co. E-mail: info@abag.ca.gov
URL: http://www.abag.ca.gov

60754 ■ U.S. Department of Commerce - Association of Bay Area Governments
Joseph P. Bort MetroCenter
101 8th St.
Oakland, CA 94607-2050
Ph: (510)464-7900
Fax: (510)464-7970
Co. E-mail: info@abag.ca.gov
URL: http://www.abag.ca.gov

60755 ■ U.S. Department of Commerce - Association of Monterey Bay Area Governments
445 Reservation Rd., Ste. G
Marina, CA 93933
Ph: (831)883-3750
Fax: (831)883-3755
Co. E-mail: info@ambag.org
URL: http://www.ambag.org

60756 ■ U.S. Department of Commerce - Association of Monterey Bay Area Governments
445 Reservation Rd., Ste. G
Marina, CA 93933
Ph: (831)883-3750
Fax: (831)883-3755
Co. E-mail: info@ambag.org
URL: http://www.ambag.org

60757 ■ U.S. Department of Commerce - Boise State University - Division of Research
Albertsons Library, Rm. 153
1910 University Dr.
Boise, ID 83725-1135
Ph: (208)426-5732
Fax: (208)426-1048
Co. E-mail: markrudin@boisestate.edu
URL: http://www.boisestate.edu/research

60758 ■ U.S. Department of Commerce - Boise State University - Division of Research
1910 University Dr.
Albertsons Library, Rm. 153
Boise, ID 83725-1135
Ph: (208)426-5732
Fax: (208)426-1048
Co. E-mail: markrudin@boisestate.edu
URL: http://www.boisestate.edu/research

60759 ■ U.S. Department of Commerce - Brown University - Social Science Research Lab (SSRL) - Department of Sociology
Maxcy Hall
112 George St.
Providence, RI 02912
Ph: (401)863-2367
Fax: (401)863-3213
Co. E-mail: Sociology@brown.edu
URL: http://www.brown.edu/Departments/Sociology/ssrl.html

60760 ■ U.S. Department of Commerce - Brown University - Social Science Research Lab - Department of Sociology
Maxcy Hall
112 George St.
Providence, RI 02912
Ph: (401)863-2367
Fax: (401)863-3213
Co. E-mail: Sociology@brown.edu
URL: http://www.brown.edu/Departments/Sociology/ssrl.html

60761 ■ U.S. Department of Commerce - Buckeye Hills Hocking Valley - Regional Development District
1400 Pike St.
Reno, OH 45773
Ph: (740)374-9436
Fax: (740)374-8038
Co. E-mail: info@buckeyehills.org
URL: http://www.buckeyehills.org/

60762 ■ U.S. Department of Commerce - Buckeye Hills Hocking Valley - Regional Development District
1400 Pike St.
Marietta, OH 45750
Ph: (740)374-9436
Fax: (740)374-8038
Co. E-mail: info@buckeyehills.org
URL: http://www.buckeyehills.org/

60763 ■ U.S. Department of Commerce - Bureau of Business and Economic Research - West Virginia University - College of Business and Economics
PO Box 6025
Morgantown, WV 26506-6025
Ph: (304)293-4092
Fax: (304)293-5652
Co. E-mail: bebureau@mail.wvu.edu
URL: http://www.be.wvu.edu/bber/

60764 ■ U.S. Department of Commerce - Bureau of Business and Economic Research - West Virginia University - College of Business and Economics
150 Clay St.
Morgantown, WV 26501
Ph: (304)293-7381
Co. E-mail: bebureau@mail.wvu.edu
URL: http://www.be.wvu.edu/bber/

60765 ■ U.S. Department of Commerce - Bureau of the Census
4600 Silver Hill Rd.
Washington, DC 20233
Ph: (301)763-4636
Free: 800-923-8282
URL: http://www.census.gov/
Description: The Census Bureau gathers and disseminates a wide variety of statistics about the people and economy of the United States. It is the principal source in the federal government for business information relating to manufacturers, retail trade, wholesale trade, construction trade, and

services. These data are generated both from the regular five-year census programs and from annual, quarterly, and monthly survey programs. Data concerning the number of establishments, production, value added by manufacture, shipments, receipts, employees, payrolls--as well as other general and specific business statistics--are compiled and published periodically. Small business owners interested in learning more about the statistics available from the Census Bureau and how to use them may obtain a set of introductory materials and order forms by contacting Customer Services. Other information may be obtained from Census Bureau regional. In addition, the Census Bureau sponsors a state data center program, which provides (for a fee) local access to the bureau's computer products in all states, the District of Columbia, Puerto Rico, Guam, and the U.S. Virgin Islands.

60766 ■ U.S. Department of Commerce - Bureau of the Census - Atlanta Regional Office
101 Marietta St. NW, Ste. 3200
Atlanta, GA 30303-2700
Ph: (404)730-3832
Free: 800-424-6974
Fax: (404)730-3835
Co. E-mail: Atlanta.regional.office@census.gov
URL: http://www.census.gov/regions/atlanta/

60767 ■ U.S. Department of Commerce - Bureau of the Census - Boston Regional Office
4 Copley Pl., Ste. 301
Boston, MA 02117-9108
Ph: (617)424-4501
Free: 800-562-5721
Fax: (617)424-0547
Co. E-mail: boston.regional.office@census.gov
URL: http://www.census.gov/regions/boston/

60768 ■ U.S. Department of Commerce - Bureau of the Census - Charlotte Regional Office
901 Center Park Dr., Ste. 106
Charlotte, NC 28217-2935
Ph: (704)424-6400
Free: 800-331-7360
Fax: (704)424-6944
Co. E-mail: charlotte.regional.office@census.gov
URL: http://www.census.gov/regions/charlotte/

60769 ■ U.S. Department of Commerce - Bureau of the Census - Chicago Regional Office
1111 W. 22nd St., Ste. 400
Oak Brook, IL 60523-1918
Ph: (630)288-9200
Free: 800-865-6384
Fax: (630)288-9288
Co. E-mail: Chicago.regional.office@census.gov
URL: http://www.census.gov/regions/chicago/

60770 ■ U.S. Department of Commerce - Bureau of the Census - Dallas Regional Office
8585 N. Stemmons Fwy., Ste. 800 S
Dallas, TX 75247-3836
Ph: (214)253-4400
Free: 800-835-9752
Fax: (214)253-4419
Co. E-mail: dallas.regional.office@census.gov
URL: http://www.census.gov/regions/dallas/

60771 ■ U.S. Department of Commerce - Bureau of the Census - Denver Regional Office
6950 W. Jefferson Ave., Ste. 250
Denver, CO 80235
Ph: (720)962-3700
Free: 800-852-6159
Fax: (303)969-6777
Co. E-mail: Denver.regional.office@census.gov
URL: http://www.census.gov/regions/denver/

60772 ■ U.S. Department of Commerce - Bureau of the Census - Detroit Regional Office
1395 Brewery Park Blvd., Ste. 100
Detroit, MI 48207
Ph: (313)259-0056
Free: 800-432-1495
Fax: (313)259-5045
Co. E-mail: Detroit.regional.office@census.gov
URL: http://www.census.gov/regions/detroit/

60773 ■ U.S. Department of Commerce - Bureau of the Census - Kansas City Regional Office
1211 N. 8th St.
Kansas City, KS 66101-2129
Ph: (913)551-6728
Free: 800-728-4748
Fax: (913)551-6789
Co. E-mail: kansas.city.regional.office@census.gov
URL: http://www.census.gov/regions/kansas_city/

60774 ■ U.S. Department of Commerce - Bureau of the Census - Los Angeles Regional Office
15350 Sherman Way, Ste. 400
Van Nuys, CA 91406-4224
Ph: (818)267-1700
Free: 800-992-3530
Fax: (818)267-1711
Co. E-mail: los.angeles.regional.office@census.gov
URL: http://www.census.gov/regions/los_angeles/

60775 ■ U.S. Department of Commerce - Bureau of the Census - New York City Regional Office
395 Hudson St., Ste. 800
New York, NY 10014-7451
Ph: (212)584-3400
Free: 800-991-2520
Fax: (212)478-4800
Co. E-mail: new.york.regional.office@census.gov
URL: http://www.census.gov/regions/new_york/

60776 ■ U.S. Department of Commerce - Bureau of the Census - Philadelphia Regional Office
833 Chestnut St., 5th Fl., Ste. 504
Philadelphia, PA 19107-4405
Ph: (215)717-1800
Free: 800-262-4236
Fax: (215)717-2588
Co. E-mail: Philadelphia.regional.office@census.gov
URL: http://www.census.gov/regions/philadelphia/

60777 ■ U.S. Department of Commerce - Bureau of the Census - Seattle Regional Office
601 Union St., Ste. 3800
Seattle, WA 98101-1074
Ph: (206)381-6200
Free: 800-233-3308
Fax: (206)381-6310
Co. E-mail: seattle.regional.office@census.gov
URL: http://www.census.gov/regions/seattle/

60778 ■ U.S. Department of Commerce - Bureau of Economic Analysis - Florida Department of Commerce
107 E. Gaines St.
315 Collins Bldg.
Tallahassee, FL 32399-2000
Ph: (904)487-2971
Fax: (904)487-3014

60779 ■ U.S. Department of Commerce - California Department of Finance - State Census Data Center
915 L St.
Sacramento, CA 95814
Ph: (916)445-3878
URL: http://www.dof.ca.gov/HTML/DEMOGRAP/SDC/SDC-Products.asp
Contact: Linda Gage, Director

60780 ■ U.S. Department of Commerce - California Department of Finance - State Census Data Center
915 L St.
Sacramento, CA 95814
Ph: (916)445-3878
URL: http://www.dof.ca.gov/research/demographic/
    state_census_data_center/

60781 ■ U.S. Department of Commerce - Camden Computing Services - Office of Information Technology - Rutgers University
227 Penn St.
Business and Science Bldg., Rm. 126
Camden, NJ 08102
Ph: (856)225-6274
Co. E-mail: help@camden.rutgers.edu
URL: http://rucs.camden.rutgers.edu

60782 ■ U.S. Department of Commerce - Capital Region Council of Governments
241 Main St.
Hartford, CT 06106-5310
Ph: (860)522-2217
Free: 800-522-2217
Fax: (860)724-1274
Co. E-mail: info@crcog.org
URL: http://www.crcog.org

60783 ■ U.S. Department of Commerce - Capital Region Council of Governments
241 Main St.
Hartford, CT 06106-5310
Ph: (860)522-2217
Free: 800-522-2217
Fax: (860)724-1274
Co. E-mail: info@crcog.org
URL: http://www.crcog.org

60784 ■ U.S. Department of Commerce - Center for Business and Economic Research - University of Alabama
Box 870221
Tuscaloosa, AL 35487-0221
Ph: (205)348-6191
Fax: (205)348-2951
Co. E-mail: uacber@cba.ua.edu
URL: http://cber.cba.ua.edu/

60785 ■ U.S. Department of Commerce - Center for Business and Economic Research - University of Alabama
Box 870221
Tuscaloosa, AL 35487-0221
Ph: (205)348-6191
Fax: (205)348-2951
Co. E-mail: uacber@cba.ua.edu
URL: http://cber.cba.ua.edu/

60786 ■ U.S. Department of Commerce - Center for Economic and Management Research - Michael F. Price College of Business - University of Oklahoma
Adams Hall
307 W. Brooks, Ste. 4
Norman, OK 73019
Ph: (405)325-2931
Fax: (405)325-7688
Co. E-mail: rdauffen@ou.edu
URL: http://price.ou.edu/cemr/index.aspx

60787 ■ U.S. Department of Commerce - Center for Economic and Management Research - Michael F. Price College of Business - University of Oklahoma
Adams Hall
307 W. Brooks, Ste. 4
Norman, OK 73019
Ph: (405)325-2931
Fax: (405)325-7688
Co. E-mail: rdauffen@ou.edu
URL: http://price.ou.edu/cemr.html

60788 ■ U.S. Department of Commerce - Center for Geographic Information and Analysis - Office of State Planning
301 N. Wilmington St., Ste. 700
Raleigh, NC 27601-2825

Ph: (919)733-2090
Fax: (919)715-0725
Co. E-mail: dataq@its.nc.gov
URL: http://www.cgia.state.nc.us

60789 ■ U.S. Department of Commerce - Center for Geographic Information and Analysis - Office of State Planning
333 Six Forks Rd.
Raleigh, NC 27609
Ph: (919)754-2090
Fax: (919)715-8551
Co. E-mail: dataq@its.nc.gov
URL: http://www.cgia.state.nc.us

60790 ■ U.S. Department of Commerce - Center for Public Affairs Research - Nebraska State Data Center - University of Nebraska at Omaha
University of Nebraska at Omaha
6001 Dodge St., EAB 106
Omaha, NE 68182
Ph: (402)554-2134
Fax: (402)595-2366
Co. E-mail: jdeicher@mail.unomaha.edu
URL: http://www.unomaha.edu/cpar/nsdc.php

60791 ■ U.S. Department of Commerce - Center for Public Affairs Research - Nebraska State Data Center - University of Nebraska at Omaha
6001 Dodge St., EAB 106
Omaha, NE 68182
Ph: (402)554-2134
Fax: (402)595-2366
Co. E-mail: mkiper@unomaha.edu
URL: http://www.unomaha.edu/cpar/

60792 ■ U.S. Department of Commerce - Central Washington University - Department of Sociology - Applied Social Data Center
400 E. University Way
Ellensburg, WA 98926-7545
Ph: (509)963-1111
Fax: (509)963-1308
URL: http://www.cwu.edu

60793 ■ U.S. Department of Commerce - Central Washington University - Department of Sociology - Applied Social Data Center
400 E. University Way
Ellensburg, WA 98926-7545
Ph: (509)963-1111
Fax: (509)963-1308
URL: http://www.cwu.edu/~asdc/home.html

60794 ■ U.S. Department of Commerce - Chicago Area Geographic Information Study - University of Illinois at Chicago
1007 W. Harrison St., Rm. 2102
Chicago, IL 60607-7138
Ph: (312)996-6367
Fax: (312)996-6343
URL: http://www.uic.edu/UI-Service/programs/UIC12.
    html

60795 ■ U.S. Department of Commerce - Chicago Area Geographic Information Study - University of Illinois at Chicago
1007 W. Harrison St., Rm. 2102
M/C 92
Chicago, IL 60607-7138
Ph: (312)996-6367
Fax: (312)996-6343
Co. E-mail: jbash@uic.edu
URL: http://www.uops.uillinois.edu/ui-service/display.
    asp?ProgID=172

60796 ■ U.S. Department of Commerce - Cleveland State University - Northern Ohio Data and Information Service - Maxine Goodman Levin College of Urban Affairs
2121 Euclid Ave., UR 335
Cleveland, OH 44115-2214
Ph: (216)687-2135
URL: http://www.urban.csuohio.edu

60797 ■ U.S. Department of Commerce - Cleveland State University - Northern Ohio Data and Information Service - Maxine Goodman Levin College of Urban Affairs
2121 Euclid Ave., UR 335
Cleveland, OH 44115-2214
Ph: (216)687-2135
Co. E-mail: c.eucker@csuohio.edu
URL: http://www.urban.csuohio.edu

60798 ■ U.S. Department of Commerce - Colorado Department of Local Affairs - Division of Local Government
1313 Sherman St., Ste. 521
Denver, CO 80203
Ph: (303)866-2156
Fax: (303)866-4819
Co. E-mail: dola.helpdesk@state.co.us
URL: http://www.dola.colorado.gov/dlg/index.html

60799 ■ U.S. Department of Commerce - Colorado Department of Local Affairs - Division of Local Government
1313 Sherman St., Ste. 521
Denver, CO 80203
Ph: (303)866-2156
Fax: (303)866-4819
Co. E-mail: dlg.helpdesk@state.co.us
URL: http://www.colorado.gov/cs/Satellite/DOLA-
    Main/CBON/1251590375285

60800 ■ U.S. Department of Commerce - Colorado State University - Agricultural and Resource Economics
B-320 Clark Bldg.
Ft. Collins, CO 80523
Ph: (303)491-6325
Fax: (303)491-2067
Co. E-mail: cas_dare@mail.colostate.edu
URL: http://dare.agsci.colostate.edu

60801 ■ U.S. Department of Commerce - Colorado State University - Agricultural and Resource Economics
B-320 Clark Bldg.
Ft. Collins, CO 80523
Ph: (970)491-6325
Fax: (970)491-2067
Co. E-mail: cas_dare@mail.colostate.edu
URL: http://dare.agsci.colostate.edu

60802 ■ U.S. Department of Commerce - Colorado State University Libraries - Morgan Library
1201 Center Ave. Mall
1019 Campus Delivery
Ft. Collins, CO 80523-1019
Ph: (303)491-1880
URL: http://lib.colostate.edu

60803 ■ U.S. Department of Commerce - Colorado State University Libraries - Morgan Library
501 University Ave.
1019 Campus Delivery
Ft. Collins, CO 80523-1019
Ph: (970)491-1880
URL: http://lib.colostate.edu

60804 ■ U.S. Department of Commerce - Connecticut Department of Economic and Community Development - Research and Planning
505 Hudson St.
Hartford, CT 06106-7106
Ph: (860)270-8000
Co. E-mail: decd@ct.us
URL: http://www.ct.gov/ecd/cwp/view.
    asp?a=11095Q=249626

60805 ■ U.S. Department of Commerce - Connecticut Department of Economic and Community Development - Research, Planning, and Information Systems
505 Hudson St.
Hartford, CT 06106-7106

Ph: (860)270-8000
Co. E-mail: decd@ct.us
URL: http://www.ct.gov/ecd/cwp/view.
asp?a=11095Q=249626

**60806 ■ U.S. Department of Commerce -
Connecticut Office of Policy and Management
- Policy Development and Planning Division -
Budget and Financial Management Division -
Office of Finance**
450 Capitol Ave.
Hartford, CT 06106-1379
Ph: (860)418-6200
Fax: (860)418-6487
Co. E-mail: OPMwebmaster@po.state.ct.us
URL: http://opm.state.ct.us

**60807 ■ U.S. Department of Commerce -
Connecticut Office of Policy and Management
- Policy Development and Planning Division -
Budget and Financial Management Division -
Office of Finance**
450 Capitol Ave.
Hartford, CT 06106-1379
Ph: (860)418-6200
Fax: (860)418-6487
Co. E-mail: OPMwebmaster@po.state.ct.us
URL: http://www.ct.gov/opm/site/default.asp

**60808 ■ U.S. Department of Commerce -
Connecticut State Library - Government
Information and References Services**
231 Capitol Ave.
Hartford, CT 06106
Ph: (860)757-6570
Free: 866-886-4478
Fax: (860)757-6569
Co. E-mail: isref@cslib.org
URL: http://www.cslib.org/gis.htm

**60809 ■ U.S. Department of Commerce -
Connecticut State Library - Government
Information and References Services**
231 Capitol Ave.
Hartford, CT 06106
Ph: (860)757-6570
Free: 866-886-4478
Fax: (860)757-6569
URL: http://www.cslib.org/gis.htm

**60810 ■ U.S. Department of Commerce -
Cornell University (CISER) - Cornell Institute
for Social and Economic Research Data
Archive**
391 Pine Tree Rd.
Ithaca, NY 14850-2820
Ph: (607)255-4801
Fax: (607)255-9353
Co. E-mail: ciser@cornell.edu
URL: http://www.ciser.cornell.edu

**60811 ■ U.S. Department of Commerce -
Cornell University (CISER) - Cornell Institute
for Social and Economic Research Data
Archive**
391 Pine Tree Rd.
Ithaca, NY 14850-2820
Ph: (607)255-4801
Fax: (607)255-9353
Co. E-mail: ciser@cornell.edu
URL: http://www.ciser.cornell.edu

**60812 ■ U.S. Department of Commerce -
Delaware Economic Development Office
(DEDO)**
99 Kings Hwy.
Dover, DE 19903
Ph: (302)739-4271
Fax: (302)739-5749
Co. E-mail: bernice.whaley@state.de.us
URL: http://www.state.de.us/dedo/default.shtml

**60813 ■ U.S. Department of Commerce -
Delaware Economic Development Office
(DEDO)**
99 Kings Hwy.
Dover, DE 19901
Ph: (302)739-4271

Fax: (302)739-5749
URL: http://dedo.delaware.gov/

**60814 ■ U.S. Department of Commerce -
Department of Administration - Demographic
Services Center**
101 E. Wilson St., 10th Fl.
Madison, WI 53708-8944
Ph: (608)266-1927
Fax: (608)267-6917
Co. E-mail: doaweb@doa.state.wi.us
URL: http://www.doa.state.wi.us/

**60815 ■ U.S. Department of Commerce -
Department of Administration - Demographic
Services Center**
101 E. Wilson St., 9th Fl.
Madison, WI 53703
Ph: (608)266-1927
Fax: (608)267-6917
Co. E-mail: doaweb@doa.state.wi.us
URL: http://www.doa.state.wi.us/section_detail.
asp?linkcatid=11&linkid=64&locid=9

**60816 ■ U.S. Department of Commerce -
Department of Administration and
Information - Economic Analysis Division**
2800 Central Ave.
Cheyenne, WY 82002-0060
Ph: (307)777-7504
Fax: (307)632-1819
Co. E-mail: ai-ead-info@wyo.gov
URL: http://eadiv.state.wy.us
Description: Provide customers with quality and
timely research, data, and analysis.

**60817 ■ U.S. Department of Commerce -
Department of Administration and
Information - Economic Analysis Division**
2800 Central Ave.
Cheyenne, WY 82002-0060
Ph: (307)777-7504
Fax: (307)632-1819
Co. E-mail: ai-ead-info@wyo.gov
URL: http://eadiv.state.wy.us
Description: Provide customers with quality and
timely research, data, and analysis.

**60818 ■ U.S. Department of Commerce -
Department of Commerce and Economic
Opportunity - Springfield Office**
620 E. Adams St.
Springfield, IL 62701
Ph: (217)782-7500
URL: http://www.commerce.state.il.us

**60819 ■ U.S. Department of Commerce -
Department of Employment Security - LMEA**
PO Box 9046
Olympia, WA 98507
Ph: (360)902-9500
URL: http://www.esd.wa.gov/

**60820 ■ U.S. Department of Commerce -
Departmento de Educacion**
PO Box 190759
San Juan, PR 00919-0759
Ph: (787)759-2000
Fax: (787)250-0275
Co. E-mail: nieves_c@de.gobierno.pr
URL: http://www.de.gobierno.pr

**60821 ■ U.S. Department of Commerce -
Departmento de Educacion**
Calle Cesar Gonzales
San Juan, PR 00917
Ph: (787)759-2000
Fax: (787)250-0275
URL: http://www.de.gobierno.pr

**60822 ■ U.S. Department of Commerce -
Economic Development Administration**
Herbert Clark Hoover Bldg.
1401 Constitution Ave., NW
Washington, DC 20230
Ph: (202)482-5081
URL: http://www.eda.gov

**60823 ■ U.S. Department of Commerce -
Economic Development Administration**
Herbert Clark Hoover Bldg.
1401 Constitution Ave. NW, Ste. 7800
Washington, DC 20230
Ph: (202)482-5081
Co. E-mail: webmaster@eda.gov
URL: http://www.eda.gov

**60824 ■ U.S. Department of Commerce -
Employment Security Department - LMEA**
PO Box 9046
Olympia, WA 98507
Ph: (360)902-9500
URL: http://www.esd.wa.gov/

**60825 ■ U.S. Department of Commerce -
Enoch Pratt Free Library - State Library
Resource Center**
400 Cathedral St.
Baltimore, MD 21201-4484
Ph: (410)396-5430
Fax: (410)396-1441
URL: http://www.epfl.net/slrc/index.html

**60826 ■ U.S. Department of Commerce -
Enoch Pratt Free Library - State Library
Resource Center**
400 Cathedral St.
Baltimore, MD 21201-4484
Ph: (410)396-5430
Fax: (410)396-1441
URL: http://www.prattlibrary.org/locations/central/

**60827 ■ U.S. Department of Commerce -
Florida Agency for Workforce Innovation -
Labor Market Statistics - State Census Data
Center**
107 E. Madison St.
MSC G-020
Tallahassee, FL 32399-4111
Ph: (850)245-7205
Free: 866-537-3615
Fax: (850)921-1048
Co. E-mail: info@labormarketinfo.com
URL: http://www.labormarketinfo.com/library/census.
htm

**60828 ■ U.S. Department of Commerce -
Florida Department of Commerce - Bureau of
Economic Analysis**
107 E. Gaines St.
315 Collins Bldg.
Tallahassee, FL 32399-2000
Ph: (904)487-2971
Fax: (904)487-3014

**60829 ■ U.S. Department of Commerce -
Florida Department of Economic Opportunity
- Labor Market Information - Florida Census
Data Center**
107 E. Madison St.
Tallahassee, FL 32399
Ph: (850)245-7205
Free: 866-537-3615
Fax: (850)921-1048
URL: http://www.floridajobs.org/labor-market-
information/data-center/florida-census-data-center

**60830 ■ U.S. Department of Commerce -
Florida State University - Center for
Demography and Population Health - College
of Social Sciences**
601 Bellamy Bldg.
113 Collegiate Loop
Tallahassee, FL 32306-2240
Ph: (850)644-1762
Fax: (850)644-8818
Co. E-mail: popctr@fsu.edu
URL: http://www.fsu.edu/

**60831 ■ U.S. Department of Commerce -
Florida State University - Center for
Demography and Population Health - College
of Social Sciences**
601 Bellamy Bldg.
113 Collegiate Loop
Tallahassee, FL 32306-2240

Ph: (850)644-1762
Fax: (850)644-8818
Co. E-mail: popctr@fsu.edu
URL: http://www.fsu.edu/~popctr/

60832 ■ U.S. Department of Commerce - Geographic Resources Center - University of Missouri--Columbia
Stewart Hall, Rm. 104
Columbia, MO 65211-0001
Ph: (573)882-1404
Co. E-mail: haithcoatt@missouri.edu
URL: http://www.grc.missouri.edu

60833 ■ U.S. Department of Commerce - Geographic Resources Center - University of Missouri--Columbia
Stewart Hall
Columbia, MO 65211
Ph: (573)882-1404
Fax: (573)884-4239
Co. E-mail: msdismail@missouri.edu
URL: http://www.grc.missouri.edu

60834 ■ U.S. Department of Commerce - Georgia Department of Community Affairs - Office of Planning and Quality Growth
60 Executive Park South, NE
Atlanta, GA 30329
Ph: (404)679-4940
Free: 800-359-4663
Fax: (404)679-0589
URL: http://www.dca.state.ga.us/main/About/
structure.asp

60835 ■ U.S. Department of Commerce - Georgia Department of Community Affairs, Office of Planning and Quality Growth
60 Executive Park South NE
Atlanta, GA 30329
Ph: (404)679-4940
Free: 800-359-4663
Fax: (404)679-0563
URL: http://www.dca.state.ga.us/economic/Develop-
mentTools/programs/downloads/OZbrochure.pdf

60836 ■ U.S. Department of Commerce - Georgia Institute of Technology - Georgia Tech Library - Government Information Department
704 Cherry St.
Atlanta, GA 30332-0900
Ph: (404)894-4529
Free: 888-225-7804
Fax: (404)894-3005
URL: http://www.library.gatech.edu

60837 ■ U.S. Department of Commerce - Georgia Institute of Technology - Georgia Tech Library - Government Information Department
704 Cherry St.
Atlanta, GA 30332-0900
Ph: (404)894-4530
Free: 888-225-7804
Fax: (404)894-3005
URL: http://www.library.gatech.edu

60838 ■ U.S. Department of Commerce - Georgia Office of Planning and Budget - Division of Operational Support and Development
270 Washington St. SW
Atlanta, GA 30334
Ph: (404)656-3820
Fax: (404)656-3828
URL: http://www.opb.state.ga.us

60839 ■ U.S. Department of Commerce - Georgia Office of Planning and Budget - Division of Operational Support and Development
270 Washington St. SW, 8th Fl.
Atlanta, GA 30334
Ph: (404)656-3820
Fax: (404)656-3828
URL: http://www.opb.state.ga.us

60840 ■ U.S. Department of Commerce - Governor's Office of Policy and Management
702 Capitol Ave.
Capitol Annex, Rm. 284
Frankfort, KY 40601
Ph: (502)564-7300
Fax: (502)564-6684
URL: http://www.osbd.ky.gov/contactus/gopm.htm

60841 ■ U.S. Department of Commerce - Governor's Office of Policy and Management
702 Capitol Ave., Rm. 284
Capitol Annex
Frankfort, KY 40601
Ph: (502)564-7300
Fax: (502)564-6684
URL: http://www.osbd.ky.gov/contactus/gopm.htm

60842 ■ U.S. Department of Commerce - Guam Department of Commerce
102 M St.
Tiyan, GU 96931
Ph: (671)475-0321
Fax: (671)646-9031

60843 ■ U.S. Department of Commerce - Guam Department of Commerce
102 M St.
Tiyan, GU 96931

60844 ■ U.S. Department of Commerce - Hawaii Department of Budget and Finance - Information and Communication Services Division
1151 Punchbowl St., B-20
Honolulu, HI 96813-3007
Ph: (808)568-1940
Fax: (808)586-2337
Co. E-mail: dave.e.dewitt@hawaii.gov
URL: http://hawaii.gov/budget/

60845 ■ U.S. Department of Commerce - Hawaii Department of Budget and Finance - Information and Communication Services Division
1151 Punchbowl St., B-20
Honolulu, HI 96813-3007
Ph: (808)568-1940
Fax: (808)586-2337
Co. E-mail: dave.e.dewitt@hawaii.gov
URL: http://hawaii.gov/budget/

60846 ■ U.S. Department of Commerce - Hawaii Department of Business, Economic Development, and Tourism - Hawaii State Data Center
250 S. Hotel St., 4th Fl.
Honolulu, HI 96804
Ph: (808)586-2493
Fax: (808)586-8449
Co. E-mail: jnakamot@dbedt.hawaii.gov
URL: http://hawaii.gov/dbedt

60847 ■ U.S. Department of Commerce - Hawaii Department of Business, Economic Development, and Tourism - Hawaii State Data Center
250 S. Hotel St., 4th Fl.
Honolulu, HI 96813
Ph: (808)586-2493
Fax: (808)586-8449
URL: http://hawaii.gov/dbedt

60848 ■ U.S. Department of Commerce - Headwaters Regional Development Commission
403 4th St. NW, Ste. 310
Bemidji, MN 56619-0906
Ph: (218)444-4732
Fax: (218)444-4722
Co. E-mail: hrdc@hrdc.org
URL: http://www.hrdc.org

60849 ■ U.S. Department of Commerce - Headwaters Regional Development Commission
403 4th St. NW, Ste. 310
Bemidji, MN 56619-0906

Ph: (218)444-4732
Fax: (218)444-4722
Co. E-mail: hrdc@hrdc.org
URL: http://www.hrdc.org

60850 ■ U.S. Department of Commerce - Idaho Commission for Libraries
325 W. State St.
Boise, ID 83702
Ph: (208)334-2150
Fax: (208)334-4016
URL: http://libraries.idaho.gov/

60851 ■ U.S. Department of Commerce - Idaho Commission for Libraries
325 W. State St.
Boise, ID 83702
Ph: (208)334-2150
Fax: (208)334-4016
URL: http://libraries.idaho.gov/

60852 ■ U.S. Department of Commerce - Idaho Department of Commerce
700 W. State St.
Boise, ID 83702-5868
Ph: (208)334-2470
Free: 800-842-5858
Fax: (208)334-2631
Co. E-mail: megan.ronk@commerce.idaho.gov
URL: http://commerce.idaho.gov/
URL(s): www.visitid.org/.

60853 ■ U.S. Department of Commerce - Idaho State University - Business and Technology Center
1651 Alviin Ricken Dr.
Pocatello, ID 83201
Ph: (208)282-3600
Fax: (208)282-5960
URL: http://www.isu.edu/respark/

60854 ■ U.S. Department of Commerce - Idaho State University - Center for Business Research and Services
Campus Box 8044
Pocatello, ID 83209
Ph: (208)236-3050
URL: http://www.isu.edu

60855 ■ U.S. Department of Commerce - Illinois Bureau of the Budget - Office of Management and Budget
108 Statehouse
Springfield, IL 62706
Ph: (217)782-4520
Fax: (217)524-1514
Co. E-mail: GOMB@illinois.gov
URL: http://www.state.il.us/budget

60856 ■ U.S. Department of Commerce - Illinois Bureau of the Budget - Office of Management and Budget
401 S. Spring
603 Stratton
Springfield, IL 62706
Ph: (217)782-4520
Fax: (217)524-1514
Co. E-mail: GOMB@illinois.gov
URL: http://www.state.il.us/budget

60857 ■ U.S. Department of Commerce - Illinois Department of Commerce and Economic Opportunity - Springfield Office
500 E. Monroe St.
Springfield, IL 62701-1643
Ph: (217)782-7500
Free: 877-221-4403
URL: http://www.commerce.state.il.us/dceo/

60858 ■ U.S. Department of Commerce - Illinois State University - Census and Data User Services - Applied Social Research Unit
Campus Box 4950
Normal, IL 61790-4950
Ph: (309)438-7771
Fax: (309)438-2898
Co. E-mail: asru@ilstu.edu
URL: http://www.cadus.ilstu.edu/publicdata.htm

60859 ■ U.S. Department of Commerce - Illinois State University - Census and Data User Services - Applied Social Research Unit
Campus Box 4950
Normal, IL 61790-4950
Ph: (309)438-5326
Fax: (309)438-7198
Co. E-mail: asru@ilstu.edu
URL: http://www.asru.ilstu.edu/

60860 ■ U.S. Department of Commerce - Indiana Business Research Center (IBRC) - Research at Indiana University
100 S. College Ave., Ste. 240
Bloomington, IN 47404
Ph: (812)855-5507
Fax: (812)855-7763
Co. E-mail: ibrc@iupui.edu
URL: http://www.research.iu.edu/centers/ibrc.html

60861 ■ U.S. Department of Commerce - Indiana Business Research Center (IBRC) - Research at Indiana University
100 S. College Ave., Ste. 240
Bloomington, IN 47404
Ph: (812)855-5507
Fax: (812)855-7763
Co. E-mail: ibrc@iupui.edu
URL: http://www.ibrc.indiana.edu/

60862 ■ U.S. Department of Commerce - Indiana Department of Workforce Development - Research and Analysis
10 N. Senate Ave., SE211
Indianapolis, IN 46204
Ph: (317)233-2697
Co. E-mail: lmidata@dwd.in.gov
URL: http://www.hoosierdata.in.gov/
URL(s): www.census.gov/sdc/insdc.html.

60863 ■ U.S. Department of Commerce - Indiana Economic Development Corporation - Research Division and Technology
1 N. Capitol, Ste. 700
Indianapolis, IN 46204
Ph: (317)232-8959
Fax: (317)232-4146
Co. E-mail: iedc@iedc.in.gov
URL: http://www.census.gov/sdc/www/insdc.html

60864 ■ U.S. Department of Commerce - Indiana State Data Center - Indiana State Library
140 N. Senate Ave.
Indianapolis, IN 46204
Ph: (317)232-3733
Fax: (317)232-3728
Co. E-mail: kspringer@library.in.gov
URL: http://www.in.gov/library/isdc.htm

60865 ■ U.S. Department of Commerce - Indiana State Data Center - Indiana State Library
140 N. Senate Ave.
Indianapolis, IN 46204-2296
Ph: (317)232-3733
Fax: (317)232-3728
Co. E-mail: kspringer@library.in.gov
URL: http://www.in.gov/library/isdc.htm

60866 ■ U.S. Department of Commerce - Indiana University - Indiana Business Research Center
777 Indiana Ave., Ste. 210
Indianapolis, IN 46202-5151
Ph: (317)274-2979
Fax: (317)278-3400
Co. E-mail: ibrc@iupui.edu
URL: http://www.ibrc.indiana.edu/

60867 ■ U.S. Department of Commerce - Indiana University - Indiana Business Research Center
777 Indiana Ave., Ste. 210
Indianapolis, IN 46202-5151
Ph: (317)274-2979

Fax: (317)278-3400
Co. E-mail: ibrc@iupui.edu
URL: http://www.ibrc.indiana.edu/

60868 ■ U.S. Department of Commerce - Iowa Department of Education - Census Data Center
Grimes State Office Bldg.
Des Moines, IA 50319-0147
Ph: (515)281-4730
Co. E-mail: steve.boal@edu.state.ia.us

60869 ■ U.S. Department of Commerce - Iowa Department of Education - Census Data Center
Ola Babcock Miller Bldg.
Des Moines, IA 50319-0233
Free: 800-248-4483
Fax: (515)242-6543
Co. E-mail: census@lib.state.ia.us
URL: http://www.iowadatacenter.org

60870 ■ U.S. Department of Commerce - Iowa State University - Iowa Community Indicators Program (ICIP)
17 East Hall
Ames, IA 50010-1070
Ph: (515)294-9903
Fax: (515)294-0592
Co. E-mail: icip@iastate.edu
URL: http://www.icip.iastate.edu/

60871 ■ U.S. Department of Commerce - Iowa State University - Regional Economics and Community Analysis Program (ReCAP)
17 East Hall
Ames, IA 50010-1070
Ph: (515)294-9903
Fax: (515)294-0592
Co. E-mail: recap@iastate.edu
URL: http://www.recap.iastate.edu/

60872 ■ U.S. Department of Commerce - Junta de Planificacion - Oficina del Censo
Centro Gubernamental Minillas
San Juan, PR 00940-1119
Ph: (787)723-6200
Fax: (787)268-0506
URL: http://www.censo.gobierno.pr

60873 ■ U.S. Department of Commerce - Junta de Planificacion - Oficina del Censo
Centro Gubernamental Roberto Sanchez Vilella
Ave. De Diego, Pda. 22, Santurce Edificio Norte
Piso 15, Oficina 1501
San Juan, PR 00940-1119
Ph: (787)723-6200
Fax: (787)268-0506
URL: http://www.censo.gobierno.pr

60874 ■ U.S. Department of Commerce - Kansas Division of the Budget
900 SW Jackson, Ste. 504
Topeka, KS 66612
Ph: (785)296-2436
Fax: (785)296-0231
Co. E-mail: budget.info@budget.ks.gov
URL: http://budget.ks.gov/

60875 ■ U.S. Department of Commerce - Kansas Division of the Budget
900 SW Jackson, Ste. 504
Topeka, KS 66612
Ph: (785)296-2436
Fax: (785)296-0231
Co. E-mail: budget.info@budget.ks.gov
URL: http://budget.ks.gov/

60876 ■ U.S. Department of Commerce - Kansas State University - Department of Sociology, Anthropology and Social Work - Kansas Population Center
255 Waters Hall
Manhattan, KS 66506
Ph: (785)532-4959
Fax: (785)532-6978
Co. E-mail: kpopcenter@ksu.edu
URL: http://www.ksu.edu/sasw/kpc/

60877 ■ U.S. Department of Commerce - Kentucky Department for Libraries and Archives - State Library Division
300 Coffee Tree Rd.
Frankfort, KY 40601-0537
Ph: (502)564-8300
Free: 800-928-7000
URL: http://www.kdla.ky.gov

60878 ■ U.S. Department of Commerce - Kentucky Department for Libraries and Archives - State Library Division
300 Coffee Tree Rd.
Frankfort, KY 40602-0537
Ph: (502)564-8300
Free: 800-928-7000
URL: http://www.kdla.ky.gov

60879 ■ U.S. Department of Commerce - L. William Seidman Research Institute - W.P. Carey School of Business
PO Box 874011
Tempe, AZ 85287-4011
Ph: (480)965-5362
Fax: (480)965-5458
Co. E-mail: wpcareyseid@asu.edu
URL: http://wpcarey.asu.edu/seid/

60880 ■ U.S. Department of Commerce - L. William Seidman Research Institute - W.P. Carey School of Business
PO Box 874011
Tempe, AZ 85287-4011
Ph: (480)965-5362
Fax: (480)965-5458
Co. E-mail: wpcareyseid@asu.edu
URL: http://wpcarey.asu.edu/seid/

60881 ■ U.S. Department of Commerce - The Library of Michigan - Government Documents Service
702 W. Kalamazoo St.
Lansing, MI 48909
Ph: (517)373-2971
Co. E-mail: govdoc@michigan.gov
URL: http://www.michigan.gov/hal/0,1607,7-160-17449_18637---,00.html

60882 ■ U.S. Department of Commerce - The Library of Michigan - Government Documents Service
702 W. Kalamazoo St.
Lansing, MI 48915
Ph: (517)373-2971
Fax: (517)373-9438
Co. E-mail: librarian@michigan.gov
URL: http://michigan.gov/libraryofmichigan/0,2351,7-160-50206_18637-53073--,00.html

60883 ■ U.S. Department of Commerce - Library of Virginia - Collection Management Division
800 E. Broad St.
Richmond, VA 23219-8000
Ph: (804)692-3600
Fax: (804)692-3603
Co. E-mail: recman@lva.lib.va.us
URL: http://www.lva.lib.va.us

60884 ■ U.S. Department of Commerce - Library of Virginia - Records Management Division
800 E. Broad St.
Richmond, VA 23219-8000
Ph: (804)692-3600
Fax: (804)692-3603
Co. E-mail: recman@lva.lib.va.us
URL: http://www.lva.lib.va.us

60885 ■ U.S. Department of Commerce - Maine Department of Labor - Center for Workforce Research and Information
45 Commerce Dr.
State House Station 118
Augusta, ME 04333-0118
Ph: (207)623-7900

Fax: (207)287-2947
Co. E-mail: mdol@maine.gov
URL: http://www.maine.gov/labor

**60886 ■ U.S. Department of Commerce -
Maine Department of Labor - Center for
Workforce Research and Information**
54 State House Station
Augusta, ME 04333-0118
Ph: (207)623-7900
Fax: (207)287-2947
Co. E-mail: mdol@maine.gov
URL: http://www.maine.gov/labor

**60887 ■ U.S. Department of Commerce -
Maine State Library**
64 State House Station
Augusta, ME 04333-0064
Ph: (207)287-5600
Fax: (207)287-5624
Co. E-mail: reference.desk@maine.gov
URL: http://www.state.me.us/msl

**60888 ■ U.S. Department of Commerce -
Maine State Library**
64 State House Station
Augusta, ME 04333-0064
Ph: (207)287-5600
Fax: (207)287-5615
URL: http://www.state.me.us/msl

**60889 ■ U.S. Department of Commerce -
Maine State Planning Office - Census
Information Office**
38 State House Station
Augusta, ME 04333-0038
Ph: (207)287-1475
Fax: (207)287-6489
URL: http://www.maine.gov/spo/economics/census/
Description: A network of organizations (libraries,
planning organizations, university departments, and
agencies of state government) that makes US
Census data products available to the Maine public.
The Program also provides assistance in the use of
these products.

**60890 ■ U.S. Department of Commerce -
Maine State Planning Office - Census State
Data Center**
38 State House Station
Augusta, ME 04333-0038
Ph: (207)287-1475
Fax: (207)287-6489
URL: http://www.maine.gov/spo/economics/census/
Description: A network of organizations (libraries,
planning organizations, university departments, and
agencies of state government) that makes US
Census data products available to the Maine public.
The Program also provides assistance in the use of
these products.

**60891 ■ U.S. Department of Commerce -
Maryland Department of Planning (MDP)**
301 W Preston St., Ste. 1101
Baltimore, MD 21201-2305
Ph: (410)767-4500
Free: 877-634-6361
Fax: (410)767-4480
Co. E-mail: servicedesk@doit.state.md.us
URL: http://www.mdp.state.md.us
Contact: Ted Cozmo, Director
E-mail: tcozmo@mdp.state.md.us
Description: Description: Publishes a directory of
state, county, local and regional planning agencies in
Maryland concerned with planning. Also publishes a
directory of programs, grants, loans and services
available to state and local agencies and to the
general public. Does not accept unsolicited manu-
scripts. **Publications:** *Directory of Planning Agencies
and Maryland APA Members* (Irregular); *Directory of
Planning Agencies and Maryland APA Members* (Irregular); *The Red Book: Catalog of State Assistance
Programs.* **Telecommunication Services:** aratner@
mdp.state.md.us.

**60892 ■ U.S. Department of Commerce -
Massachusetts Institute for Social and
Economic Research (MISER)**
McCormack Building
1 Ashburton Pl., Rm. 1004
Boston, MA 02133-0219
Ph: (617)727-4537
Fax: (617)727-4660
Co. E-mail: miser@miser.umass.edu
URL: http://www.umass.edu/miser

**60893 ■ U.S. Department of Commerce -
Massachusetts Institute for Social and
Economic Research (MISER)**
McCormack Bldg.
1 Ashburton Pl., Rm. 1004
Boston, MA 02108
Ph: (617)727-4537
Fax: (617)727-4660
Co. E-mail: miser@miser.umass.edu
URL: http://www.umass.edu/miser

**60894 ■ U.S. Department of Commerce -
Mayor's Office of Planning - Data Services
Division**
801 North Capitol St., NE, Ste. 4000
Washington, DC 20002
Ph: (202)442-7600
Fax: (202)442-7637
Co. E-mail: planning@dc.gov
URL: http://planning.dc.gov/planning/cwp/

**60895 ■ U.S. Department of Commerce -
Mayor's Office of Planning - Data Services
Division**
1100 4th St. SW, Ste. E650
Washington, DC 20024
Ph: (202)442-7600
Fax: (202)442-7638
Co. E-mail: planning@dc.gov
URL: http://planning.dc.gov/DC/Planning

**60896 ■ U.S. Department of Commerce -
Metropolitan Council Research - Metropolitan
Council Data Center**
390 Robert St. North
St. Paul, MN 55101-1805
Ph: (651)602-1140
Fax: (651)602-1464
Co. E-mail: data.center@metc.state.mn.us
URL: http://www.metrocouncil.org

**60897 ■ U.S. Department of Commerce -
Metropolitan Council Research - Metropolitan
Council Data Center**
390 Robert St. N.
St. Paul, MN 55101-1805
Ph: (651)602-1140
Fax: (651)602-1464
Co. E-mail: data.center@metc.state.mn.us
URL: http://stats.metc.state.mn.us/stats/census.aspx

**60898 ■ U.S. Department of Commerce -
Metropolitan Washington Council of
Governments**
777 N. Capitol St. NE, Ste. 300
Washington, DC 20002
Ph: (202)962-3200
Fax: (202)962-3201
URL: http://www.mwcog.org

**60899 ■ U.S. Department of Commerce -
Metropolitan Washington Council of
Governments**
777 N. Capitol St. NE, Ste. 300
Washington, DC 20002
Ph: (202)962-3200
Fax: (202)962-3201
URL: http://www.mwcog.org

**60900 ■ U.S. Department of Commerce -
Michigan Department of Technology,
Management, and Budget - Center for Shared
Solutions and Technology Partnerships -
Michigan Information Center**
111 S. Capitol Ave.
Romney Bldg., 10th Fl.
Lansing, MI 48933

Ph: (517)373-7910
Fax: (517)373-2939
Co. E-mail: swansone@michigan.gov
URL: http://www.michigan.gov/dmb

**60901 ■ U.S. Department of Commerce -
Michigan Department of Technology,
Management and Budget - Demographic
Research and Statistics - Michigan
Information Center**
320 S.Walnut St.
Lansing, MI 48909
Ph: (517)373-7910
Fax: (517)373-2939
Co. E-mail: dtmb@michigan.gov
URL: http://www.michigan.gov/dmb

**60902 ■ U.S. Department of Commerce -
Minnesota Department of Administration -
State Demographic Center**
300 Centennial Office
658 Cedar St., Rm. 300
St. Paul, MN 55155-1603
Ph: (612)296-2557
Fax: (612)296-3698
Co. E-mail: demography.helpline@state.mn.us
URL: http://www.demography.state.mn.us/

**60903 ■ U.S. Department of Commerce -
Minnesota Department of Administration -
State Demographic Center**
Centennial Office Bldg.
658 Cedar St., Rm. 300
St. Paul, MN 55155-1603
Ph: (651)201-2474
Co. E-mail: demography.helpline@state.mn.us
URL: http://www.demography.state.mn.us

**60904 ■ U.S. Department of Commerce -
Minnesota Department of Education -
Education Resource Center—Minnesota
Department of Children, Families & Learning**
1500 Hwy. 36 W.
Roseville, MN 55113-4266
Ph: (651)582-8200
Free: 800-657-3757
Fax: (612)296-6684
Co. E-mail: education@state.mn.us
URL: http://www.education.state.mn.us
Contact: Brenda Cassellius, Commissioner
Publications: *Education and Community Services
Directory* (Annual). **Telecommunication Services:**
mde.commissioner@state.mn.us.

**60905 ■ U.S. Department of Commerce -
Minority Business Development Agency
(MBDA)—Department of Commerce**
Herbert Clark Hoover Bldg., Rm. 5053
1401 Constitution Ave. NW
Washington, DC 20230
Ph: (202)482-5061
Free: 888-324-1551
URL: http://www.mbda.gov
Description: The Minority Business Development
Agency is the only federal agency specifically created to establish policies and programs to develop
the U.S. minority business community. The agency's
goal is to increase opportunities for racial and ethnic
minorities to participate in the free enterprise system
through the formation and development of competitive minority-owned and managed firms, with emphasis on private sector involvement and entrepreneurial
self-reliance. To accomplish this goal, the agency
coordinates the federal government's plans, programs, and operations that affect or may contribute
to the establishment, preservation, and strengthening
of minority business enterprise. The MBDA also
promotes the mobilization of activities and resources
of state and local governments, business and trade
associations, universities, foundations, professional
organizations, and other groups towards the growth
of minority business enterprise, as well as facilitates
the coordination of the efforts of these groups with
those of federal departments and agencies. In addition, the MBDA acts as a center for the development,
collection, summarization, and dissemination of
information that will be helpful to persons and
organizations throughout the United States in under-

taking or promoting the establishment and successful operation of minority business enterprises. The agency also provides financial assistance to public and private organizations so that they may render technical and management assistance to minority business enterprises and defray all or part of the costs of pilot or demonstration projects conducted by public or private agencies or organizations that are designed to overcome the special problems of minority business enterprises. The MBDA sponsors a network of approximately 100 Minority Business Development Centers, located throughout the country in areas with the largest minority populations. The mission of the centers is to increase the formation of minority-owned firms, to expand existing minority-owned enterprises, and to minimize minority business failures. Counselors at each center provide management, marketing, and technical assistance to minority individuals wishing to start, expand, or improve their businesses. Socially or economically disadvantaged individuals eligible for assistance include, but are not limited to, Blacks, Hispanics, Native Americans, Eskimos, Aleuts, Asian Pacific Americans, Asian Indians, and Hasidic Jews. General referral assistance is provided free of charge to minority entrepreneurs seeking management, marketing, procurement, and financial assistance from federal, state, and local agencies, private institutions, and other sources. For a nominal fee counselors provide assistance to eligible individuals and firms in such areas as accounting, inventory control, bid estimating, bonding, personnel management, contract negotiations, and marketing. Each minority business development center develops and maintains a listing of existing minority-owned firms for inclusion in the agency's PROFILE National Minority Data Base. The PROFILE system is used by government and private industry purchasing officials to identify minority vendors qualified to supply the goods and services they need. Minority business owners wishing to register their firms in the PROFILE system may do so at no charge at any minority business development center. Counselors at the centers also identify both private and public sector sources of financing for minority-owned firms. They assist minority entrepreneurs with the preparation of financial packages and plans for submission to lenders for the purpose of financing business ventures. The centers cannot make or underwrite loans because the MBDA has no loan-making authority. In addition, center personnel match minority-owned firms with new business opportunities in domestic and foreign markets. They maintain contact with major corporations to identify business opportunities for minority-owned enterprises, and they utilize other federal, state, and local government agencies to identify contract opportunities and sources of financing to expand the minority business community. Center personnel also determine constraints to minority business development at the federal, state, and local levels and make recommendations for improvement. The centers are funded on a competitive basis. Applicants for the operation of these centers may be individuals, nonprofit organizations, private firms, state and local governments, Native American tribes, or educational institutions. The maximum federal funding of each center represents not more than 85 percent of the total cost of the project. Each center is expected to provide the other 15 percent.

60906 ■ U.S. Department of Commerce - Minority Business Development Agency
Herbert Clark Hoover Bldg., Rm. 5053
1401 Constitution Ave. NW
Washington, DC 20230
Ph: (202)482-2332
Free: 888-324-1551
URL: http://www.mbda.gov
Description: The Minority Business Development Agency is the only federal agency specifically created to establish policies and programs to develop the U.S. minority business community. The agency's goal is to increase opportunities for racial and ethnic minorities to participate in the free enterprise system through the formation and development of competitive minority-owned and managed firms, with emphasis on private sector involvement and entrepreneurial self-reliance. To accomplish this goal, the agency coordinates the federal government's plans, pro-

grams, and operations that affect or may contribute to the establishment, preservation, and strengthening of minority business enterprise. The MBDA also promotes the mobilization of activities and resources of state and local governments, business and trade associations, universities, foundations, professional organizations, and other groups towards the growth of minority business enterprise, as well as facilitates the coordination of the efforts of these groups with those of federal departments and agencies. In addition, the MBDA acts as a center for the development, collection, summarization, and dissemination of information that will be helpful to persons and organizations throughout the United States in undertaking or promoting the establishment and successful operation of minority business enterprises. The agency also provides financial assistance to public and private organizations so that they may render technical and management assistance to minority business enterprises and defray all or part of the costs of pilot or demonstration projects conducted by public or private agencies or organizations that are designed to overcome the special problems of minority business enterprises. The MBDA sponsors a network of approximately 100 Minority Business Development Centers, located throughout the country in areas with the largest minority populations. The mission of the centers is to increase the formation of minority-owned firms, to expand existing minority-owned enterprises, and to minimize minority business failures. Counselors at each center provide management, marketing, and technical assistance to minority individuals wishing to start, expand, or improve their businesses. Socially or economically disadvantaged individuals eligible for assistance include, but are not limited to, Blacks, Hispanics, Native Americans, Eskimos, Aleuts, Asian Pacific Americans, Asian Indians, and Hasidic Jews. General referral assistance is provided free of charge to minority entrepreneurs seeking management, marketing, procurement, and financial assistance from federal, state, and local agencies, private institutions, and other sources. For a nominal fee counselors provide assistance to eligible individuals and firms in such areas as accounting, inventory control, bid estimating, bonding, personnel management, contract negotiations, and marketing. Each minority business development center develops and maintains a listing of existing minority-owned firms for inclusion in the agency's PROFILE National Minority Data Base. The PROFILE system is used by government and private industry purchasing officials to identify minority vendors qualified to supply the goods and services they need. Minority business owners wishing to register their firms in the PROFILE system may do so at no charge at any minority business development center. Counselors at the centers also identify both private and public sector sources of financing for minority-owned firms. They assist minority entrepreneurs with the preparation of financial packages and plans for submission to lenders for the purpose of financing business ventures. The centers cannot make or underwrite loans because the MBDA has no loan-making authority. In addition, center personnel match minority-owned firms with new business opportunities in domestic and foreign markets. They maintain contact with major corporations to identify business opportunities for minority-owned enterprises, and they utilize other federal, state, and local government agencies to identify contract opportunities and sources of financing to expand the minority business community. Center personnel also determine constraints to minority business development at the federal, state, and local levels and make recommendations for improvement. The centers are funded on a competitive basis. Applicants for the operation of these centers may be individuals, nonprofit organizations, private firms, state and local governments, Native American tribes, or educational institutions. The maximum federal funding of each center represents not more than 85 percent of the total cost of the project. Each center is expected to provide the other 15 percent.

60907 ■ U.S. Department of Commerce - Minority Business Development Agency - Atlanta Regional Office
401 W. Peachtree St., NW, Ste. 1715
Atlanta, GA 30308-3516

Ph: (404)730-3300
Fax: (404)730-3313
Co. E-mail: aro-info@mbda.gov
URL: http://www.mbda.gov/
Description: Serves Alabama, Florida, Georgia, Kentucky, Mississippi, North Carolina, South Carolina, and Tennessee.

60908 ■ U.S. Department of Commerce - Minority Business Development Agency - Atlanta Regional Office
401 W. Peachtree St., NW, Ste. 1715
Atlanta, GA 30308-3516
Ph: (404)730-3300
Fax: (404)730-3313
Co. E-mail: aro-info@mbda.gov
URL: http://www.mbda.gov/main/offices
Description: Serves Alabama, Florida, Georgia, Kentucky, Mississippi, North Carolina, South Carolina, and Tennessee.

60909 ■ U.S. Department of Commerce - Minority Business Development Agency - Boston Regional Office
10 Causeway St., Ste. 418
Boston, MA 02222
Ph: (617)565-6850
Fax: (617)565-8897
URL: http://www.mbda.gov

60910 ■ U.S. Department of Commerce - Minority Business Development Agency - California Native American Business Enterprise Center
11138 Valley Mall, Ste. 200
El Monte, CA 91731
Ph: (626)442-3701
Fax: (626)442-7115
Co. E-mail: feaster@ncaied.org
URL: http://www.mbda.gov

60911 ■ U.S. Department of Commerce - Minority Business Development Agency - Chicago Regional Office
55 E. Monroe St., Ste. 2810
Chicago, IL 60603
Ph: (312)353-0182
Fax: (312)353-0191
Co. E-mail: cro-info@mbda.gov
URL: http://www.mbda.gov/
Description: Serves Illinois, Indiana, Iowa, Kansas, Michigan, Minnesota, Missouri, Nebraska, Ohio, and Wisconsin.

60912 ■ U.S. Department of Commerce - Minority Business Development Agency - Chicago Regional Office
55 E. Monroe St., Ste. 2810
Chicago, IL 60603
Ph: (312)353-0182
Fax: (312)353-0191
Co. E-mail: cro-info@mbda.gov
URL: http://www.mbda.gov/main/offices
Description: Serves Illinois, Indiana, Iowa, Kansas, Michigan, Minnesota, Missouri, Nebraska, Ohio, and Wisconsin.

60913 ■ U.S. Department of Commerce - Minority Business Development Agency - Dallas Regional Office
1100 Commerce St., Rm. 726
Dallas, TX 75242
Ph: (214)767-8001
Fax: (214)767-0613
Co. E-mail: dro-info@mbda.gov
URL: http://www.mbda.gov/
Description: Serves Arkansas, Colorado, Louisiana, Montana, New Mexico, North Dakota, Oklahoma, South Dakota, Texas, Utah, and Wyoming.

60914 ■ U.S. Department of Commerce - Minority Business Development Agency - Dallas Regional Office
1100 Commerce St., Rm. 726
Dallas, TX 75242
Ph: (214)767-8001

Fax: (214)767-0613
Co. E-mail: dro-info@mbda.gov
URL: http://www.mbda.gov/main/offices
Description: Serves Arkansas, Colorado, Louisiana, Montana, New Mexico, North Dakota, Oklahoma, South Dakota, Texas, Utah, and Wyoming.

60915 ■ U.S. Department of Commerce - Minority Business Development Agency District Office (Boston, Massachusetts)
100 Huntington Ave., Copley Plc.
Boston, MA 02116
Ph: (617)986-6366
Co. E-mail: info@bostonmbdacenter.com
URL: http://www.mbda.gov/businesscenters/boston

60916 ■ U.S. Department of Commerce - Minority Business Development Agency District Office (Miami, Florida) - Atlanta Regional Enterprise Center - Miami (Florida) Business Center
970 SW 1st St., Ste. 405-406
Miami, FL 33130
Ph: (786)316-0888
Co. E-mail: jorge@mbdabusinesscenterfl.org
URL: http://www.mbda.gov/main/offices

60917 ■ U.S. Department of Commerce - Minority Business Development Agency District Office (Los Angeles, California) - Native American Business Enterprise Center
11138 Valley Mall, Ste. 200
El Monte, CA 91731
Ph: (626)442-3701
Fax: (626)442-7115
Co. E-mail: curtis.feaster@ncaied.org
URL: http://www.mbda.gov/main/offices

60918 ■ U.S. Department of Commerce - Minority Business Development Agency District Office (Philadelphia, Pennsylvania) - Philadelphia Regional Enterprise Center
4548 Market St.
Philadelphia, PA 19139
Ph: (215)895-4046
Co. E-mail: jsanders@mbc-pa.com
URL: http://www.mbda.gov/main/offices

60919 ■ U.S. Department of Commerce - Minority Business Development Agency - Miami Regional Enterprise Center
Claude Plaza Federal Bldg., Ste. 1314
51 SW 1st Ave.
Miami, FL 33130
Ph: (305)536-5054
Fax: (305)530-7068
Co. E-mail: jiglesias@mbecflorida.org
URL: http://www.mbda.gov

60920 ■ U.S. Department of Commerce - Minority Business Development Agency - New York Regional Office
26 Federal Plz., Rm. 3270
New York, NY 10278
Ph: (212)264-3262
Fax: (212)264-0725
Co. E-mail: nyro-info@mbda.gov
URL: http://www.mbda.gov/
Description: Serves Connecticut, Maine, Massachusetts, New Hampshire, New Jersey, New York, Puerto Rico, Rhode Island, Vermont, and the Virgin Islands.

60921 ■ U.S. Department of Commerce - Minority Business Development Agency - New York Regional Office
26 Federal Plz., Rm. 3720
New York, NY 10278
Ph: (212)264-3262
Fax: (212)264-0725
Co. E-mail: nyro-info@mbda.gov
URL: http://www.mbda.gov/main/offices
Description: Serves Connecticut, Maine, Massachusetts, New Hampshire, New Jersey, New York, Puerto Rico, Rhode Island, Vermont, and the Virgin Islands.

60922 ■ U.S. Department of Commerce - Minority Business Development Agency - Philadelphia Regional Enterprise Center
William J. Green, Jr. Federal Bldg.
600 Arch St., Ste. 10128
Philadelphia, PA 19106
Ph: (215)861-3597
Fax: (215)861-3595
Co. E-mail: jhill@pa-mbec.com
URL: http://www.mbda.gov

60923 ■ U.S. Department of Commerce - Minority Business Development Agency - San Francisco Regional Office
221 Main St., Rm. 1280
San Francisco, CA 94105
Ph: (415)744-3001
Fax: (415)744-3061
Co. E-mail: sfro-info@mbda.gov
URL: http://www.mbda.gov/
Description: Serves Alaska, American Samoa, Arizona, California, Hawaii, Idaho, Nevada, Oregon, and Washington.

60924 ■ U.S. Department of Commerce - Minority Business Development Agency - San Francisco Regional Office
221 Main St., Rm. 1280
San Francisco, CA 94105
Ph: (415)744-3001
Fax: (415)744-3061
Co. E-mail: sfro-info@mbda.gov
URL: http://www.mbda.gov/main/offices
Description: Serves Alaska, American Samoa, Arizona, California, Hawaii, Idaho, Nevada, Oregon, and Washington.

60925 ■ U.S. Department of Commerce - Minority Business Development Agency - Washington DC, Regional Office
64 New York Ave., NE
Ste. 3152
Washington, DC 20002
Ph: (202)671-1552
Fax: (202)671-3073
Co. E-mail: erice@dcmbec.org
URL: http://www.mbda.gov
Description: Serves Delaware, the District of Columbia, Maryland, Pennsylvania, Virginia, and West Virginia.

60926 ■ U.S. Department of Commerce - Minority Business Development Agency - Washington, DC, Regional Office
64 New York Ave. NE
Ste. 3152
Washington, DC 20002
Co. E-mail: ojackson@dcmbec.org
URL: http://www.mbda.gov
Description: Serves Delaware, the District of Columbia, Maryland, Pennsylvania, Virginia, and West Virginia.

60927 ■ U.S. Department of Commerce - Mississippi Department of Economic and Community Development - Industry Resource Bureau - Mississippi Development Authority
1200 Walter Sillas Bldg.
Jackson, MS 39205
Ph: (601)359-3449
Fax: (601)359-2832
Co. E-mail: dtate@mississippi.org
URL: http://www.mississippi.org/content.aspx?url=/page/about

60928 ■ U.S. Department of Commerce - Mississippi Development Authority
Woolfolk Bldg., Ste. B 01, 501 N West St.
Jackson, MS 39201
Ph: (601)359-3449
Free: 800-340-3323
Fax: (601)359-2832
Co. E-mail: eibus@mississippi.org
URL: http://www.mississippi.org
Contact: Brent Christensen, Executive Director
URL(s): www.visitmississippi.org/. **Description:** Provides assistance to the state's businesses and industries, including loans and loan guarantees to

small businesses, and an outreach program. **Telecommunication Services:** tinquiry@mississippi.org; state@mississippi.org.

60929 ■ U.S. Department of Commerce - Missouri Small Business and Technology Development Centers
University of Missouri-Columbia
W1026 Lafferre Hall
410 S. Sixth St.
Columbia, MO 65211
Ph: (573)882-7096
Fax: (314)884-4297
Co. E-mail: businesscenter@missouri.edu
URL: http://www.missouribusiness.net/sbdc/index.asp

60930 ■ U.S. Department of Commerce - Missouri Small Business and Technology Development Centers
University of Missouri-Columbia
410 S. Sixth St.
200 Engineering N.
Columbia, MO 65211
Ph: (573)884-1555
Co. E-mail: businesscenter@missouri.edu
URL: http://www.missouribusiness.net/sbdc/index.asp

60931 ■ U.S. Department of Commerce - Missouri State Library - Library Development
600 W. Main St.
Jefferson City, MO 65101
Ph: (573)526-7648
Free: 800-325-0131
Fax: (573)751-3612
Co. E-mail: mostlib@sos.mo.gov
URL: http://www.sos.mo.gov/library/development/

60932 ■ U.S. Department of Commerce - Missouri State Library - Library Development
600 W. Main St.
Jefferson City, MO 65101
Ph: (573)526-7648
Free: 800-325-0131
Fax: (573)751-3612
Co. E-mail: mostlib@sos.mo.gov
URL: http://www.sos.mo.gov/library/development/

60933 ■ U.S. Department of Commerce - Missouri State Office of Administration
124 Capitol Bldg.
Jefferson City, MO 65102-0809
Ph: (573)751-9318
Fax: (573)526-4811
Co. E-mail: matt.hesser@oa.mo.us
URL: http://www.census.gov/sdc/www/mosdc.html

60934 ■ U.S. Department of Commerce - Missouri State Office of Administration
124 State Capitol Bldg.
Jefferson City, MO 65101
Ph: (573)751-9318
Fax: (573)526-4811
Co. E-mail: matt.hesser@oa.mo.us
URL: http://oa.mo.gov

60935 ■ U.S. Department of Commerce - Missouri State Office of Social and Economic Data Analysis - University of Missouri--Columbia
602 Clark Hall
Columbia, MO 65211
Ph: (573)882-7396
Fax: (573)884-4635
URL: http://www.oseda.missouri.edu/

60936 ■ U.S. Department of Commerce - Missouri State Office of Social and Economic Data Analysis - University of Missouri--Columbia
602 Clark Hall
Columbia, MO 65211
Ph: (573)882-7396
Fax: (573)884-4635
URL: http://www.oseda.missouri.edu

60937 ■ U.S. Department of Commerce - Montana Department of Commerce - Census and Economic Information Center
301 S. Park Ave.
Helena, MT 59620-0505
Ph: (406)841-2740
Fax: (406)841-2731
URL: http://www.commerce.mt.gov

60938 ■ U.S. Department of Commerce - Montana Department of Commerce - Census and Economic Information Center
301 S. Park Ave.
Helena, MT 59620-0505
Ph: (406)841-2740
Fax: (406)841-2731
URL: http://ceic.mt.gov

60939 ■ U.S. Department of Commerce - Montana Department of Labor and Industry - Research and Analysis Bureau - Employment Policy Division
PO Box 1728
Helena, MT 59624
Ph: (406)444-2430
Free: 800-541-3904
Fax: (406)444-2638
Co. E-mail: webmasterrad@mt.gov
URL: http://www.ourfactsyourfuture.org/

60940 ■ U.S. Department of Commerce - Montana State Library - Digital Library Division
1515 E. 6th Ave.
Helena, MT 59620-1800
Ph: (406)444-3115
Fax: (406)444-5612
Co. E-mail: mslreference@mt.gov
URL: http://msl.mt.gov/

60941 ■ U.S. Department of Commerce - Montana State Library - Digital Library Division
1515 E. 6th Ave.
Helena, MT 59620-1800
Ph: (406)444-3115
Fax: (406)444-5612
Co. E-mail: mslreference@mt.gov
URL: http://msl.mt.gov

60942 ■ U.S. Department of Commerce - Nebraska Department of Administrative Services - The Central Data Processing Division
301 Centennial Mall S., Lower level
Lincoln, NE 68509-5045
Ph: (402)471-4855
Co. E-mail: aicjerry@vmhost.cdp.state.ne.us
URL: http://www.census.gov/sdc/www/nesdc.html

60943 ■ U.S. Department of Commerce - Nebraska Department of Labor
550 S. 16th St.
Lincoln, NE 68508
Ph: (402)471-9000
Fax: (402)471-9867
Co. E-mail: ndol.AdministrativeOffice@nebraska.gov
URL: http://www.dol.nebraska.gov
Contact: Phillip A. Baker, Administrator
Telecommunication Services: lmi_ne@dol.state.ne.us.

60944 ■ U.S. Department of Commerce - Nebraska Department of Natural Resources
301 Centennial Mall S.
Lincoln, NE 68509-4676
Ph: (402)471-2363
Fax: (402)471-2900
URL: http://www.dnr.state.ne.us/

60945 ■ U.S. Department of Commerce - Nebraska Department of Natural Resources
301 Centennial Mall S.
Lincoln, NE 68509-4676
Ph: (402)471-2363
Fax: (402)471-2900
URL: http://www.dnr.state.ne.us

60946 ■ U.S. Department of Commerce - Nebraska Governor's Policy Research and Energy Office
State Capitol, Rm. 1319
Lincoln, NE 68509-4601
Ph: (402)471-2414
URL: http://www.census.gov/sdc/www/nesdc.html

60947 ■ U.S. Department of Commerce - Nebraska Library Commission - Federal Document Librarian
The Atrium
1200 North St., Ste. 120
Lincoln, NE 68508-2023
Ph: (402)471-2045
Fax: (402)471-2083
URL: http://www.nlc.state.ne.us

60948 ■ U.S. Department of Commerce - Nebraska Library Commission - Federal Document Librarian
The Atrium
1200 North St., Ste. 120
Lincoln, NE 68508-2023
Ph: (402)471-2045
Fax: (402)471-2083
Co. E-mail: lori.sailors@nebraska.gov
URL: http://www.nlc.state.ne.us

60949 ■ U.S. Department of Commerce - Nebraska Policy Research Office
State Capitol, Rm. 1319
Lincoln, NE 68509-4601
Ph: (402)471-2414
Co. E-mail: lhill@pro.state.ne.us
URL: http://www.census.gov/sdc/www/nesdc.html

60950 ■ U.S. Department of Commerce - Neighborhood Info DC
1825 K St., Ste. 1100
Washington, DC 20006
Ph: (202)261-5760
Co. E-mail: info@neighborhoodinfodc.org
URL: http://www.neighborhoodinfodc.org

60951 ■ U.S. Department of Commerce - NeighborhoodInfo DC
1825 K St., Ste. 1100
Washington, DC 20006
Ph: (202)261-5760
Co. E-mail: info@neighborhoodinfodc.org
URL: http://www.neighborhoodinfodc.org/

60952 ■ U.S. Department of Commerce - Nelson A. Rockefeller Institute of Government
411 State St.
Albany, NY 12203-1003
Ph: (518)443-5522
Fax: (518)443-5788
Co. E-mail: info@rockinst.org
URL: http://www.rockinst.org/

60953 ■ U.S. Department of Commerce - The Nelson A. Rockefeller Institute of Government
411 State St.
Albany, NY 12203-1003
Ph: (518)443-5522
Fax: (518)443-5788
Co. E-mail: cooperm@rockinst.org
URL: http://www.rockinst.org

60954 ■ U.S. Department of Commerce - Nevada State Library - Department of Cultural Affairs
716 N. Carson St., Ste. B
Carson City, NV 89701
Ph: (775)687-8393
Fax: (775)684-5446
Co. E-mail: nslref@nevadaculture.org
URL: http://nevadaculture.org

60955 ■ U.S. Department of Commerce - Nevada State Library - Department of Tourism and Cultural Affairs
716 N. Carson St., Ste. B
Carson City, NV 89701
Ph: (775)687-8393

Fax: (775)684-5446
URL: http://nevadaculture.org

60956 ■ U.S. Department of Commerce - New Hampshire Office of Energy and Planning
4 Chenell Dr.
Concord, NH 03301-8501
Ph: (603)271-2155
Fax: (603)271-2615
Co. E-mail: OEPinfo@nh.gov
URL: http://nh.gov/oep/index.htm

60957 ■ U.S. Department of Commerce - New Hampshire Office of Energy and Planning
Johnson Hall
107 Pleasant St., 3rd Fl.
Concord, NH 03301
Ph: (603)271-2155
Fax: (603)271-2615
Co. E-mail: OEPinfo@nh.gov
URL: http://nh.gov/oep/index.htm

60958 ■ U.S. Department of Commerce - New Hampshire State Library
20 Park St.
Concord, NH 03301
Ph: (603)271-2397
Free: 800-462-1726
Fax: (603)271-6826
Co. E-mail: myork@library.state.nh.us
URL: http://www.nh.gov/nhsl/

60959 ■ U.S. Department of Commerce - New Hampshire State Library
20 Park St.
Concord, NH 03301
Ph: (603)271-2397
Free: 800-462-1726
Fax: (603)271-6826
Co. E-mail: myork@library.state.nh.us
URL: http://www.nh.gov/nhsl/

60960 ■ U.S. Department of Commerce - New Jersey State Data Center - New Jersey Department of Labor Market and Demographic Research
PO Box 388
Trenton, NJ 08625-0388
Ph: (609)984-2595
Fax: (609)984-6833
Co. E-mail: leonard.preston@dol.state.nj.us
URL: http://lwd.dol.state.nj.us/labor/lpa/content/njsdc_index.html

60961 ■ U.S. Department of Commerce - New Jersey State Data Center - New Jersey Department of Labor and Workforce Development - Department of Labor Market and Demographic Research
PO Box 388
Trenton, NJ 08625-0388
Ph: (609)984-2595
Fax: (609)984-6833
Co. E-mail: lpreston@dol.state.nj.us
URL: http://lwd.dol.state.nj.us/labor/lpa/content/njsdc_index.html

60962 ■ U.S. Department of Commerce - New Jersey State Library - U.S. Documents Office
185 W. State St.
Trenton, NJ 08625-0520
Ph: (609)292-6259
Fax: (609)984-7900
URL: http://www.njstatelib.org/

60963 ■ U.S. Department of Commerce - New Jersey State Library - U.S. Documents Office
185 W. State St.
Trenton, NJ 08625-0520
Ph: (609)278-2640
Fax: (609)278-2646
Co. E-mail: ttaylor@njstatelib.org
URL: http://slic.njstatelib.org/Collections_and_Services/US_Documents.php

60964 ■ U.S. Department of Commerce - New Mexico Economic Development Department - New Mexico State Data Center
1100 St. Francis Dr., Ste. 1060
Santa Fe, NM 87505
Ph: (505)827-0300
Free: 800-374-3061
Fax: (505)827-0328
Co. E-mail: edd.info@state.nm.us
URL: http://www.edd.state.nm.us/

60965 ■ U.S. Department of Commerce - New Mexico Economic Development Department - New Mexico State Data Center
1100 St. Francis Dr., Ste. 1060
Santa Fe, NM 87505
Ph: (505)827-0300
Free: 800-374-3061
Fax: (505)827-0328
Co. E-mail: edd.info@state.nm.us
URL: http://www.edd.state.nm.us/

60966 ■ U.S. Department of Commerce - New Mexico State Library
1209 Camino Carlos Rey
Santa Fe, NM 87505
Ph: (505)476-9717
Fax: (505)476-9703
Co. E-mail: laurie.canepa@state.nm.us
URL: http://www.nmstatelibrary.org/

60967 ■ U.S. Department of Commerce - New Mexico State Library
1209 Camino Carlos Rey
Santa Fe, NM 87507-5166
Ph: (505)476-9700
Fax: (505)476-9703
Co. E-mail: devon.skeele@state.nm.us
URL: http://www.nmstatelibrary.org/

60968 ■ U.S. Department of Commerce - New Mexico State University - Department of Economics/3CQ
Box 30001
Las Cruces, NM 88003-0001
Ph: (505)646-4905
Fax: (505)646-1915
Co. E-mail: kbrook@nmsu.edu
URL: http://www.census.gov/sdc/www/nmsdc.html

60969 ■ U.S. Department of Commerce - New Mexico State University - Department of Economics/3CQ
Box 30001
Las Cruces, NM 88003-0001
Ph: (505)646-4905
Fax: (505)646-1915
Co. E-mail: kbrook@nmsu.edu
URL: http://www.census.gov/sdc/nmsdc.html

60970 ■ U.S. Department of Commerce - New York Department of Economic Development - Division of Policy and Research
1 Commerce Plz., Rm. 905
99 Washington Ave.
Albany, NY 12245
Ph: (518)474-1141
Fax: (518)473-9748
URL: http://www.dos.state.ny.us

60971 ■ U.S. Department of Commerce - New York Department of State - Division of Policy and Research
1 Commerce Plz.
99 Washington Ave.
Albany, NY 12231
URL: http://www.dos.state.ny.us

60972 ■ U.S. Department of Commerce - New York State Library - Office of Cultural Education
Madison Ave.
Albany, NY 12230
Ph: (518)474-5976
Fax: (518)474-2718
Co. E-mail: OCEWEB@mail.nysed.gov
URL: http://www.oce.nysed.gov/

60973 ■ U.S. Department of Commerce - New York State Library - Office of Cultural Education (OCE)
222 Madison Ave.
Albany, NY 12230
Ph: (518)474-5355
Fax: (518)474-5786
Co. E-mail: OCEWEB@mail.nysed.gov
URL: http://www.oce.nysed.gov/

60974 ■ U.S. Department of Commerce - North Carolina Office of State Budget and Management
116 W. Jones St.
Raleigh, NC 27603-8005
Ph: (919)807-4700
Fax: (919)733-0640
Co. E-mail: OSBM@osbm.nc.gov
URL: http://www.osbm.state.nc.us/osbm

60975 ■ U.S. Department of Commerce - North Carolina Office of State Budget and Management
116 W. Jones St.
Raleigh, NC 27603-8005
Ph: (919)807-4700
Fax: (919)733-0640
Co. E-mail: joel.sigmon@osbm.nc.gov
URL: http://www.osbm.state.nc.us

60976 ■ U.S. Department of Commerce - North Dakota Department of Commerce - North Dakota Division of Community Services - Office of Intergovernmental Assistance
1600 E. Century Ave., Ste. 2
Bismarck, ND 58505-2057
Ph: (701)328-5300
Co. E-mail: ccmail.jboyd@nd.us
URL: http://www.census.gov/sdc/ndsdc.html

60977 ■ U.S. Department of Commerce - North Dakota Department of Commerce - North Dakota State Data Center
Dept. 8000
Fargo, ND 58108-6050
Ph: (701)328-5300
Fax: (701)231-9730
URL: http://www.ndsu.edu/sdc/index.htm

60978 ■ U.S. Department of Commerce - North Dakota State Library
604 E. Blvd. Ave., Dept. 250
Capitol Grounds
Bismarck, ND 58505-0800
Ph: (701)328-4622
Free: 800-472-2104
Fax: (701)328-2040
Co. E-mail: statelib@nd.gov
URL: http://www.library.nd.gov/

60979 ■ U.S. Department of Commerce - North Dakota State Library
604 E. Blvd. Ave.
Capitol Grounds
Bismarck, ND 58505-0800
Ph: (701)328-4622
Free: 800-472-2104
Fax: (701)328-2040
Co. E-mail: statelib@nd.gov
URL: http://www.library.nd.gov/

60980 ■ U.S. Department of Commerce - North Dakota State University - North Dakota State Data Center
Dept. 8000
Fargo, ND 58108-6050
Ph: (701)231-7980
Fax: (701)231-9730
Co. E-mail: Richard.rathge@ndsu.edu
URL: http://www.ndsu.edu/sdc/index.htm

60981 ■ U.S. Department of Commerce - Northeastern Illinois Planning Commission - Data Research and Forecasting
Sears Tower
233 S. Wacker, Ste. 800
Chicago, IL 60606

60982 ■ U.S. Department of Commerce - Northern Arizona University - W.A. Franke College of Business
PO Box 15066
Flagstaff, AZ 86011
Ph: (502)523-3657
Fax: (502)523-7331
URL: http://www.franke.nau.edu/

60983 ■ U.S. Department of Commerce - Northern Arizona University - W.A. Franke College of Business
PO Box 15066
Flagstaff, AZ 86011
Ph: (928)523-3657
Fax: (928)523-7331
Co. E-mail: fcboas@nau.edu
URL: http://www.franke.nau.edu

60984 ■ U.S. Department of Commerce - Northern Illinois University - The Regional Development Institute (RDI) - Center for Governmental Studies
148 N. 3rd St.
De Kalb, IL 60115
Ph: (815)753-1907
Fax: (815)753-2305
Co. E-mail: drobinson@niu.org
URL: http://www.cgsniu.org

60985 ■ U.S. Department of Commerce - Northern Illinois University - The Regional Development Institute (RDI) - Center for Governmental Studies
148 N. 3rd St.
De Kalb, IL 60115-2828
Ph: (815)753-1907
Fax: (815)753-7278
Co. E-mail: drobinson@niu.org
URL: http://www.cgsniu.org

60986 ■ U.S. Department of Commerce - Office of Business Liaison
Herbert Clark Hoover Bldg., Rm. 5062
1401 Constitution Ave., NW
Washington, DC 20230
Ph: (202)482-1360
Fax: (202)482-4054
Co. E-mail: businessliaison@doc.gov
URL: http://www.osec.doc.gov/obl
Description: The Department of Commerce's Office of Business Liaison seeks to develop and promote a cooperative working relationship and to assure effective communication between the department and the business community, including small businesses. The office serves as the focal point for all of the department's agencies to contact the business community. It informs the business community of department and administration resources, policies, and programs, as well as informs department and administration officials about business community interests and issues. In addition, the office promotes business involvement in departmental policymaking and program development. The office also provides business assistance to individuals and firms that need help dealing with the federal government. The Business Assistance Program provides professional staff members to give guidance on the many federal programs; to answer inquiries concerning government policies, programs, and services; and to provide information and published materials on a variety of business topics.

60987 ■ U.S. Department of Commerce - Office of Business Liaison
1401 Constitution Ave. NW
Washington, DC 20230
Ph: (202)482-1360
Fax: (202)482-4054
Co. E-mail: businessliaison@doc.gov
URL: http://www.osec.doc.gov/obl
Description: The Department of Commerce's Office of Business Liaison seeks to develop and promote a cooperative working relationship and to assure effective communication between the department and the business community, including small businesses. The office serves as the focal point for all of the department's agencies to contact the business community.

It informs the business community of department and administration resources, policies, and programs, as well as informs department and administration officials about business community interests and issues. In addition, the office promotes business involvement in departmental policymaking and program development. The office also provides business assistance to individuals and firms that need help dealing with the federal government. The Business Assistance Program provides professional staff members to give guidance on the many federal programs; to answer inquiries concerning government policies, programs, and services; and to provide information and published materials on a variety of business topics.

60988 ■ U.S. Department of Commerce - Office of Economic Analysis - Department of Administrative Services
155 Cottage St. NE, U20
Salem, OR 97301-3966
Ph: (503)378-3405
Fax: (503)373-7643
Co. E-mail: OEA.info@state.or.us
URL: http://www.oea.das.state.or.us/DAS/OEA/index.shtml
Description: Provides objective forecasts of the state's economy, revenue, population,corrections population, and Youth Authority population. These forecasts are used to enable the governor, the legislature, state agencies, and the public to achieve their goals.

60989 ■ U.S. Department of Commerce - Office of Economic Analysis - Department of Administrative Services
155 Cottage St. NE, U20
Salem, OR 97301-3966
Ph: (503)378-3405
Fax: (503)373-7643
Co. E-mail: OEA.info@state.or.us
URL: http://www.oea.das.state.or.us/DAS/OEA/index.shtml
Description: Provides objective forecasts of the state's economy, revenue, population,corrections population, and Youth Authority population. These forecasts are used to enable the governor, the legislature, state agencies, and the public to achieve their goals.

60990 ■ U.S. Department of Commerce - Office of Financial Management - Forecasting Division
210 11th Ave.
Olympia, WA 98504-3113
Ph: (360)902-0599
Co. E-mail: ofm.forecasting@ofm.wa.gov
URL: http://www.ofm.wa.gov/

60991 ■ U.S. Department of Commerce - Office of Intergovernmental Assistance - North Dakota Division of Community Services - North Dakota Department of Commerce
1600 E. Century Ave., Ste. 2
Bismarck, ND 58505-2057
Ph: (701)328-5300
Co. E-mail: jboyd@nd.gov
URL: http://www.census.gov/sdc/ndsdc.html

60992 ■ U.S. Department of Commerce - Office of Real Property Services
16 Sheridan Ave.
Albany, NY 12210
Ph: (518)473-6758
Co. E-mail: bill.godell@orps.state.ny.us
URL: http://www.census.gov/sdc/nysdc.html

60993 ■ U.S. Department of Commerce - Office of Real Property Tax Services (ORPTS) - Department of Taxation and Finance
WA Harriman State Campus
Bldg. 8, 6th Fl.
Albany, NY 12227
Ph: (518)486-4403
Fax: (518)435-8593
Co. E-mail: orpts.northern@tax.ny.gov
URL: http://www.tax.ny.gov/about/orpts/albany.htm

60994 ■ U.S. Department of Commerce - Office of Small and Disadvantaged Business Utilization
Herbert Clark Hoover Bldg., Rm. 6411
14th St. & Constitution Ave. NW
Washington, DC 20230
Ph: (202)482-1472
Fax: (202)482-0501
Co. E-mail: ldesmukes@doc.gov
URL: http://www.osec.doc.gov/osdbu/

60995 ■ U.S. Department of Commerce - Office of Small and Disadvantaged Business Utilization
Herbert Clark Hoover Bldg., Rm. 6411
14th St. & Constitution Ave. NW
Washington, DC 20230
Ph: (202)482-1472
Fax: (202)482-0501
Co. E-mail: OSDBU@doc.gov
URL: http://www.osec.doc.gov/osdbu/

60996 ■ U.S. Department of Commerce - Ohio Department of Development - Office of Policy Research and Strategic Planning
77 S. High St., 27th Fl.
Columbus, OH 43215-6130
Ph: (614)466-2116
Fax: (614)466-9697
URL: http://www.development.ohio.gov/research/

60997 ■ U.S. Department of Commerce - Ohio Occupational Information Coordinating Commission - Ohio Department of Job and Family Services - Bureau of Labor Market Information
145 S. Front St.
Columbus, OH 43215
Ph: (614)752-9494
Co. E-mail: contactLMI@jfs.ohio.gov
URL: http://www.census.gov/clo/www/dc/sdclist.asc

60998 ■ U.S. Department of Commerce - Ohio Occupational Information Coordinating Commission - Ohio Department of Job and Family Services - Bureau of Labor Market Information
4020 E. 5th Ave.
Columbus, OH 43219
Ph: (614)752-9494
Fax: (614)752-9621
Co. E-mail: contactLMI@jfs.ohio.gov
URL: http://ohiolmi.com

60999 ■ U.S. Department of Commerce - Ohio State University Library - Census Data Center
126 Main Library
1858 Neil Avenue Mall
Columbus, OH 43210-1286
Ph: (614)292-6154
Fax: (614)292-7859
URL: http://library.osu.edu/

61000 ■ U.S. Department of Commerce - Ohio State University Library - Census Data Center
126 Main Library
1858 Neil Avenue Mall
Columbus, OH 43210-1286
Ph: (614)292-6785
Fax: (614)292-7859
URL: http://library.osu.edu/

61001 ■ U.S. Department of Commerce - Oklahoma Census Data Center - Oklahoma Department of Commerce
900 N. Stiles Ave.
Oklahoma, OK 73104-3234
Ph: (405)815-5186
Free: 800-879-6552
Fax: (405)605-2807
Co. E-mail: deidre_myers@okcommerce.gov
URL: http://www.okcommerce.gov/data
Description: As the state data center, Commerce receives a constant flow of U.S. Census Bureau statistics and data pertaining specifically to Oklahoma and organized into county and city subcategories.

Commerce also regularly received information from the Bureau of Economic Analysis, the Bureau of Labor Statistics, the U.S. Department of Agriculture, and the Oklahoma Employment Security Commission.

61002 ■ U.S. Department of Commerce - Oklahoma Census Data Center - Oklahoma Department of Commerce
900 N. Stiles Ave.
Oklahoma, OK 73104-3234
Ph: (405)815-5182
Fax: (405)605-2982
Co. E-mail: steven_barker@okcommerce.gov
URL: http://www.census.gov/sdc/oksdc.html
Description: As the state data center, Commerce receives a constant flow of U.S. Census Bureau statistics and data pertaining specifically to Oklahoma and organized into county and city subcategories. Commerce also regularly received information from the Bureau of Economic Analysis, the Bureau of Labor Statistics, the U.S. Department of Agriculture, and the Oklahoma Employment Security Commission.

61003 ■ U.S. Department of Commerce - Oklahoma Department of Libraries - U.S. Government Information Division
200 NE 18th St.
Oklahoma City, OK 73105-3298
Ph: (405)522-3335
Fax: (405)525-7804
Co. E-mail: sbeleu@oltn.odl.state.ok.us
URL: http://www.odl.state.ok.us/usinfo/

61004 ■ U.S. Department of Commerce - Oklahoma Department of Libraries - U.S. Government Information Division
200 NE 18th St.
Oklahoma City, OK 73105-3298
Ph: (405)522-3335
Fax: (405)525-7804
Co. E-mail: sbeleu@oltn.odl.state.ok.us
URL: http://www.odl.state.ok.us/usinfo/

61005 ■ U.S. Department of Commerce - Oregon Geographic Information Systems - Oregon Geospatial Enterprise Office (GEO)
955 Center St. NE, Room 470
Salem, OR 97310
Ph: (503)378-2166
Co. E-mail: gis@gis.state.or.us
URL: http://www.oregon.gov/DAS/EISPD/GEO/ogic/ogicplan.shtml
Description: The Geospatial Enterprise (GEO) provides GIS coordination for state agencies.

61006 ■ U.S. Department of Commerce - Oregon Geographic Information Systems - Oregon Geospatial Enterprise Office (GEO)
955 Center St. NE, Room 470
Salem, OR 97310
Ph: (503)378-2166
Co. E-mail: gis@gis.state.or.us
URL: http://www.oregon.gov/DAS/EISPD/GEO/ogic/ogicplan.shtml
Description: The Geospatial Enterprise (GEO) provides GIS coordination for state agencies.

61007 ■ U.S. Department of Commerce - Oregon Housing and Community Services Department
725 Summer St. NE, Ste. B
Salem, OR 97301-1266
Ph: (503)986-2000
Fax: (503)986-2020
Co. E-mail: info@hcs.state.or.us
URL: http://www.ohcs.oregon.gov
Description: Provide leadership that enables Oregonians to gain housing, become self-sufficient and achieve prosperity.

61008 ■ U.S. Department of Commerce - Oregon Housing and Community Services Department
725 Summer St. NE, Ste. B
Salem, OR 97301-1266
Ph: (503)986-2000

Fax: (503)986-2020
Co. E-mail: info@hcs.state.or.us
URL: http://www.ohcs.oregon.gov
Description: Provide leadership that enables Oregonians to gain housing, become self-sufficient and achieve prosperity.

61009 ■ U.S. Department of Commerce - Oregon State Library
250 Winter St. NE
Salem, OR 97310-0640
Ph: (503)378-5020
Co. E-mail: library.help@state.or.us
URL: http://www.census.gov/sdc/orsdc.html

61010 ■ U.S. Department of Commerce - Oregon State Library
250 Winter St. NE
Salem, OR 97310-0640
Ph: (503)378-5020
Fax: (503)585-8059
Co. E-mail: alice.laviolette@state.or.us
URL: http://www.census.gov/sdc/orsdc.html

61011 ■ U.S. Department of Commerce - Penn State University at Harrisburg - Pennsylvania State Data Center - Institute of State and Regional Affairs
777 W. Harrisburg Pke.
Middletown, PA 17057-4898
Ph: (717)948-6336
Fax: (717)948-6754
Co. E-mail: pasdc@psu.edu
URL: http://www.census.gov/sdc/pasdc.html

61012 ■ U.S. Department of Commerce - Pennsylvania Bureau of State Library
Forum Bldg., Rm. 219
333 Market St.
Harrisburg, PA 17105
Ph: (717)787-2327
Fax: (717)772-2683
Co. E-mail: alubrecht@state.pa.us
URL: http://www.census.gov/sdc/pasdc.html

61013 ■ U.S. Department of Commerce - Pennsylvania State Data Center - Penn State University at Harrisburg - Institute of State and Regional Affairs
777 W. Harrisburg Pke.
Middletown, PA 17057-4898
Ph: (717)948-6336
Fax: (717)948-6754
Co. E-mail: sdc3@psu.edu
URL: http://www.census.gov/sdc/pasdc.html

61014 ■ U.S. Department of Commerce - Pennsylvania State Data Center - State Capital Office
Forum Bldg., Rm. 357
Harrisburg, PA 17120
Ph: (717)772-2683
Fax: (717)772-2683
Co. E-mail: PASDC-SCO@psu.edu
URL: http://www.pasdc.edu

61015 ■ U.S. Department of Commerce - Pennsylvania State Data Center - State Capital Office
Forum Bldg., Rm. 357
Harrisburg, PA 17120
Ph: (717)772-2710
Fax: (717)772-2683
Co. E-mail: jrm55@psu.edu
URL: http://www.census.gov/sdc/pasdc.html

61016 ■ U.S. Department of Commerce - Pennsylvania State Library
Forum Bldg., Rm. 219
333 Market St.
Harrisburg, PA 17101
Ph: (717)787-2327
Fax: (717)772-2683
Co. E-mail: khale@state.pa.us
URL: http://www.census.gov/sdc/pasdc.html

61017 ■ U.S. Department of Commerce - Portland State University - Population Research Center
PO Box 751
Portland, OR 97207-0751
Ph: (503)725-3922
Free: 800-547-8887
Fax: (503)725-5162
Co. E-mail: askPRC@pdx.edu
URL: http://www.pdx.edu/prc/
Description: The Population Research Center (PRC) is an interdisciplinary public service, research, and training unit for population-related data and research for the State of Oregon.

61018 ■ U.S. Department of Commerce - Portland State University - Population Research Center - College of Urban and Public Affairs
PO Box 751
Portland, OR 97207-0751
Ph: (503)725-3922
Free: 800-547-8887
Fax: (503)725-5162
Co. E-mail: askPRC@pdx.edu
URL: http://www.pdx.edu/prc/
Description: The Population Research Center (PRC) is an interdisciplinary public service, research, and training unit for population-related data and research for the State of Oregon.

61019 ■ U.S. Department of Commerce - Princeton University - Firestone Library - Social Science Reference Center - Data and Statistical Services
1 Washington Rd.
Princeton, NJ 08544
Ph: (609)258-3211
Fax: (609)258-4105
Co. E-mail: bordelon@princeton.edu
URL: http://www.census.gov/sdc/njsdc.html

61020 ■ U.S. Department of Commerce - Princeton University - Firestone Library - Social Science Reference Center - Data and Statistical Services
1 Washington Rd.
Princeton, NJ 08544
Ph: (609)258-3211
Fax: (609)258-4105
Co. E-mail: bordelon@princeton.edu
URL: http://www.census.gov/sdc/njsdc.html

61021 ■ U.S. Department of Commerce - Puget Sound Regional Council
1011 Western Ave., Ste. 500
Seattle, WA 98104-1035
Ph: (206)464-7090
Fax: (206)587-4825
Co. E-mail: info@psrc.org
URL: http://www.psrc.org/
Description: The Puget Sound Regional Council works with local government, business, and citizens to build a common vision for the region's future, expressed through three connected major activities: VISION 2040, the region's growth strategy, Destination 2030, the region's comprehensive long-range transportation plan; and Prosperity Partnership, which develops and advances the region's economic strategy.

61022 ■ U.S. Department of Commerce - Puget Sound Regional Council
1011 Western Ave., Ste. 500
Seattle, WA 98104-1035
Ph: (206)464-7090
Fax: (206)587-4825
Co. E-mail: info@psrc.org
URL: http://www.psrc.org/
Description: The Puget Sound Regional Council works with local government, business, and citizens to build a common vision for the region's future, expressed through three connected major activities: VISION 2040, the region's growth strategy, Destination 2030, the region's comprehensive long-range transportation plan; and Prosperity Partnership, which develops and advances the region's economic strategy.

61023 ■ U.S. Department of Commerce - Recinto Universitario De Mayaguez - Universidad de Puerto Rico
PO Box 9000
Mayaguez, PR 00681-5000
Ph: (787)832-4040
URL: http://www.uprm.edu/

61024 ■ U.S. Department of Commerce - Recinto Universitario De Mayaguez - Universidad de Puerto Rico
PO Box 9000
Mayaguez, PR 00681-9000
Ph: (787)832-4040
URL: http://www.uprm.edu/

61025 ■ U.S. Department of Commerce - Regional Research and Development Services - Southern Illinois University at Edwardsville
PO Box 1456
Edwardsville, IL 62026-1456
Ph: (618)650-2000
Free: 800-447-SIUE

61026 ■ U.S. Department of Commerce - Research and Analysis Bureau - Employment Policy Division - Montana Department of Labor and Industry
840 Helena Ave.
Helena, MT 59601
Ph: (406)444-2430
Free: 800-541-3904
Fax: (406)444-2638
Co. E-mail: webmasterrad@mt.gov
URL: http://www.ourfactsyourfuture.org/

61027 ■ U.S. Department of Commerce - Rhode Island Department of Elementary and Secondary Education
255 Westminster St.
Providence, RI 02903
Ph: (401)222-4600
Free: 800-745-6575
Fax: (401)222-6178
Co. E-mail: hayley.jamroz@ride.ri.gov
URL: http://www.ride.ri.gov/
Contact: Kenneth G. Swanson, Manager
E-mail: kenneth.swanson@ride.ri.gov
Description: Description: Publishes educational materials for schools and colleges. **Founded:** 1973. **Publications:** *Rhode Island Educational Directory* (Annual). **Telecommunication Services:** rid03249@ride.ri.net.

61028 ■ U.S. Department of Commerce - Rhode Island Department of Health - Center for Health Data and Analysis
3 Capitol Hill
Providence, RI 02908
Ph: (401)222-5960
URL: http://www.health.ri.gov/programs/health-dataandanalysis/

61029 ■ U.S. Department of Commerce - Rhode Island Department of Health - Office of Health Statistics
3 Capitol Hill
Providence, RI 02908
Ph: (401)222-2550
Fax: (401)273-4350
Co. E-mail: jbuechner@doh.state.ri.us
URL: http://www.census.gov/sdc/risdc.html

61030 ■ U.S. Department of Commerce - Rhode Island Economic Development Corporation
315 Iron Horse Way, Ste. 101
Providence, RI 02908
Ph: (401)278-9100
Fax: (401)273-8270
Co. E-mail: info@riedc.com
URL: http://www.riedc.com/

61031 ■ U.S. Department of Commerce - Rhode Island Economic Development Corp. (RIEDC)
315 Iron Horse Way, Ste. 101
Providence, RI 02908
Ph: (401)278-9100
Free: 800-250-7384
Fax: (401)273-8270
Co. E-mail: info@riedc.com
URL: http://www.riedc.com
Contact: J. Michael Saul, Executive Director
URL(s): www.visitrhodeisland.com/. **Description:** Provides site and building information to businesses expanding or relocating within the state. Also provides employee relocation assistance for out-of-state companies moving to Rhode Island. **Telecommunication Services:** visitrhodeisland@riedc.com.

61032 ■ U.S. Department of Commerce - Rhode Island Office of Library and Information Services - Rhode Island Department of Administration
One Capitol Hill
Providence, RI 02908-5803
Ph: (401)574-9300
Fax: (401)574-9320
URL: http://www.olis.ri.gov/

61033 ■ U.S. Department of Commerce - Rhode Island Office of Library and Information Services - Rhode Island Department of Administration
One Capitol Hill, 4th Fl.
Providence, RI 02908-5803
Ph: (401)574-9300
Fax: (401)574-9320
Co. E-mail: webmaster@olis.ri.gov
URL: http://www.olis.ri.gov

61034 ■ U.S. Department of Commerce - Rhode Island State Department of Revenue - Division of Municipal Finance
1 Capitol Hill, 4th Fl.
Providence, RI 02908-5873
Ph: (401)222-7701
Fax: (401)222-4195
Co. E-mail: peders@budget.state.ri.us
URL: http://www.muni-info.ri.gov

61035 ■ U.S. Department of Commerce - Rhode Island State Department of Revenue - Division of Municipal Finance
1 Capitol Hill, 1st Fl.
Providence, RI 02908-5873
Ph: (401)574-9900
Fax: (401)574-9912
Co. E-mail: susanne.greschner@dor.ri.gov
URL: http://www.muni-info.ri.gov

61036 ■ U.S. Department of Commerce - Rutgers University - Camden Computing Services
227 Penn St.
Camden, NJ 08102
Ph: (856)225-6274
Co. E-mail: help@camden.rutgers.edu
URL: http://rucs.camden.rutgers.edu

61037 ■ U.S. Department of Commerce - Rutgers University - Edward J. Bloustein School of Planning and Public Policy - Rutgers Regional Report / State Data Center
33 Livingston Ave.
New Brunswick, NJ 08901
Ph: (732)932-5475
Fax: (732)932-1771
Co. E-mail: ejb@policy.rutgers.edu
URL: http://www.policy.rutgers.edu/news/reports.html
Description: The Rutgers Regional Report is a Coordinating Agency of the New Jersey State Data Center (New Jersey Department of Labor and Workforce Development) Network. It produces the quarterly SITAR-Rutgers Regional Report as well as a more extensive Rutgers Regional Report series.

61038 ■ U.S. Department of Commerce - Rutgers University - Rutgers Regional Report / State Data Center - Edward J. Bloustein School of Planning and Public Policy
303 George St., Ste. 300
New Brunswick, NJ 08901
Ph: (848)932-2828
Fax: (732)932-2253
Co. E-mail: wirving@rci.rutgers.edu
URL: http://policy.rutgers.edu/centers/rrr.php
Description: The Rutgers Regional Report is a Coordinating Agency of the New Jersey State Data Center (New Jersey Department of Labor and Workforce Development) Network. It produces the quarterly SITAR-Rutgers Regional Report as well as a more extensive Rutgers Regional Report series.

61039 ■ U.S. Department of Commerce - Sacramento Area COG
1415 L St., Ste. 300
Sacramento, CA 95814
Ph: (916)321-9000
Fax: (916)321-9551
Co. E-mail: sacog@sacog.org
URL: http://www.sacog.org
Description: The Sacramento Area Council of Governments (SACOG) provides transportation planning and funding for the region, and serves as a forum for the study and resolution of regional issues.

61040 ■ U.S. Department of Commerce - Sacramento Area Council of Governments (SACOG)
1415 L St., Ste. 300
Sacramento, CA 95814
Ph: (916)321-9000
Fax: (916)321-9551
Co. E-mail: infocenter@sacog.org
URL: http://www.sacog.org
Description: The Sacramento Area Council of Governments (SACOG) provides transportation planning and funding for the region, and serves as a forum for the study and resolution of regional issues.

61041 ■ U.S. Department of Commerce - Sacramento State Census Data Center - Department of Finance
915 L St., 8th Fl.
Sacramento, CA 95814-3706
Ph: (916)323-4086
Fax: (916)327-0222
Co. E-mail: ficalpop@dof.ca.gov
URL: http://www.census.gov/sdc/casdc.html
Description: Through a year-long process, the Department of Finance prepares, explains and administers California's annual financial plan, the California Budget.

61042 ■ U.S. Department of Commerce - San Diego Association of Governments
401 B St., Ste. 800
San Diego, CA 92101-3585
Ph: (619)699-1900
Fax: (619)699-1905
Co. E-mail: webmaster@sandag.org
URL: http://www.sandag.org/
Description: The San Diego Association of Governments (SANDAG) builds consensus, makes strategic plans, obtains and allocates resources, plans, engineers, and builds public transportation, and provides information on a broad range of topics pertinent to the region's quality of life.

61043 ■ U.S. Department of Commerce - San Diego Association of Governments
401 B St., Ste. 800
San Diego, CA 92101-3585
Ph: (619)699-1900
Fax: (619)699-1905
Co. E-mail: webmaster@sandag.org
URL: http://www.sandag.org/
Description: The San Diego Association of Governments (SANDAG) builds consensus, makes strategic plans, obtains and allocates resources, plans, engineers, and builds public transportation, and provides information on a broad range of topics pertinent to the region's quality of life.

61044 ■ U.S. Department of Commerce - South Carolina State Budget and Control Board - Office of Research and Statistical Services
1201 Main St., Suite 715
Box 27
Columbia, SC 29201
Ph: (803)734-2320
Fax: (803)734-2117
URL: http://www.bcb.sc.gov/BCB/BCB-index.phtm
Description: Institution that is unique to South Carolina and provides a broad array of services to other parts of the public sector as well as administrative and regulatory functions.

61045 ■ U.S. Department of Commerce - South Carolina State Budget and Control Board - Office of Research and Statistics
1000 Assembly St., Rm. 425
Columbia, SC 29201
Ph: (803)734-2320
Fax: (803)734-2117
URL: http://ors.sc.gov
Description: Institution that is unique to South Carolina and provides a broad array of services to other parts of the public sector as well as administrative and regulatory functions.

61046 ■ U.S. Department of Commerce - South Carolina State Library
PO Box 11469
Columbia, SC 29211
Ph: (803)734-8666
Co. E-mail: reference@statelibrary.sc.gov
URL: http://www.statelibrary.sc.gov/

61047 ■ U.S. Department of Commerce - South Carolina State Library
PO Box 11469
Columbia, SC 29211
Ph: (803)734-8666
Co. E-mail: reference@statelibrary.sc.gov
URL: http://www.statelibrary.sc.gov/

61048 ■ U.S. Department of Commerce - South Dakota Department of Health - Director of Administration
600 E. Capitol Ave.
Pierre, SD 57501-2536
Ph: (605)773-3361
URL: http://doh.sd.gov/
Description: The mission of the South Dakota Department of Health is to prevent disease and promote health, ensure access to needed, high-quality health care, and to efficiently manage public health resources.

61049 ■ U.S. Department of Commerce - South Dakota Department of Health - Director of Administration
600 E. Capitol Ave.
Pierre, SD 57501-2536
Ph: (605)773-3361
URL: http://doh.sd.gov/
Description: The mission of the South Dakota Department of Health is to prevent disease and promote health, ensure access to needed, high-quality health care, and to efficiently manage public health resources.

61050 ■ U.S. Department of Commerce - South Dakota Department of Labor - Labor Market Information Center
PO Box 4730
Aberdeen, SD 57402-4730
Ph: (605)626-2314
Fax: (605)626-2322
URL: http://dlr.sd.gov/lmic/

61051 ■ U.S. Department of Commerce - South Dakota Department of Labor and Regulation - Labor Market Information Center
PO Box 4730
Aberdeen, SD 57402-4730
Ph: (605)626-2314
Fax: (605)626-2322
Co. E-mail: merle.aske@state.sd.us
URL: http://www.state.sd.us/dol/lmic/index.htm

61052 ■ U.S. Department of Commerce - South Dakota State Library - Documents Department
800 Governors Dr.
Pierre, SD 57501-2294
Ph: (605)773-3131
Free: 800-423-6665
Fax: (605)773-6962
Co. E-mail: library@state.sd.us
URL: http://www.sdstatelibrary.com/

61053 ■ U.S. Department of Commerce - South Dakota State Library - Documents Department
800 Governors Dr.
Pierre, SD 57501-2294
Ph: (605)773-3131
Free: 800-423-6665
Fax: (605)773-6962
URL: http://library.sd.gov

61054 ■ U.S. Department of Commerce - South Dakota State University - Department of Sociology and Rural Studies
Scobey Hall, Rm. 226
Box 504
Brookings, SD 57007-1296
Ph: (605)688-4132
Fax: (605)688-6354
Co. E-mail: jacobsen@sdstate.edu
URL: http://sdstate.edu/Academics/

61055 ■ U.S. Department of Commerce - South Dakota State University - Sociology and Rural Studies
Scobey Hall, Rm. 224
Box 504
Brookings, SD 57007
Ph: (605)688-4132
Fax: (605)688-6354
URL: http://www.sdstate.edu/soc/index.cfm

61056 ■ U.S. Department of Commerce - Southern California Association of Governments
818 W. 7th St., 12th Fl.
Los Angeles, CA 90017
Ph: (213)236-1800
Fax: (213)236-1825
Co. E-mail: webmaster@scag.ca.gov
URL: http://www.scag.ca.gov
Description: The Association of Governments is mandated by the federal government to research and draw up plans for transportation, growth management, hazardous waste management, and air quality. Additional mandates exist at the state level.

61057 ■ U.S. Department of Commerce - Southern California Association of Governments
818 W. 7th St., 12th Fl.
Los Angeles, CA 90017
Ph: (213)236-1800
Fax: (213)236-1825
Co. E-mail: webmaster@scag.ca.gov
URL: http://www.scag.ca.gov
Description: The Association of Governments is mandated by the federal government to research and draw up plans for transportation, growth management, hazardous waste management, and air quality. Additional mandates exist at the state level.

61058 ■ U.S. Department of Commerce - Southern Illinois University at Edwardsville - Regional Research and Development Services
PO Box 1456
Edwardsville, IL 62026-1456
Ph: (618)650-2000
Free: 800-447-SIUE
URL: http://www.siue.edu/

61059 ■ U.S. Department of Commerce - State Census Data Center - California Department of Finance
915 L St., Ste. 1260
Sacramento, CA 95814-3706
Ph: (916)445-3274

Fax: (916)323-9584
Co. E-mail: administrative.officer@dof.ca.gov
URL: http://www.dof.ca.gov
Description: Through a year-long process, the Department of Finance prepares, explains and administers California's annual financial plan, the California Budget.

61060 ■ U.S. Department of Commerce - State Library of Florida
R.A. Gray Bldg.
500 S. Bronough St.
Tallahassee, FL 32399-0250
Ph: (850)245-6600
Fax: (850)487-6242
Co. E-mail: info@dos.state.fl.us
URL: http://dlis.dos.state.fl.us/

61061 ■ U.S. Department of Commerce - State Library of Florida
R.A. Gray Bldg.
500 S. Bronough St.
Tallahassee, FL 32399-0250
Ph: (850)245-6600
Fax: (850)245-6651
URL: http://dlis.dos.state.fl.us/Library

61062 ■ U.S. Department of Commerce - State Library of Iowa
1112 E. Grand Ave.
Des Moines, IA 50319-0233
Ph: (515)281-4105
Free: 800-248-4483
Fax: (515)281-6191
Co. E-mail: is@libraryofiowa.org
URL: http://www.statelibraryofiowa.org

61063 ■ U.S. Department of Commerce - State Library of Iowa
1112 E. Grand Ave.
Des Moines, IA 50319-0233
Ph: (515)281-4105
Free: 800-248-4483
Fax: (515)281-6191
Co. E-mail: is@libraryofiowa.org
URL: http://www.statelibraryofiowa.org

61064 ■ U.S. Department of Commerce - State Library of Kansas
State Capitol Bldg., Rm. 169-W
300 SW 10th Ave.
Topeka, KS 66612-1593
Ph: (785)296-3296
Free: 800-432-3919
Fax: (785)368-7291
Co. E-mail: infodesk@kslib.info
URL: http://skyways.lib.ks.us/KSL/

61065 ■ U.S. Department of Commerce - State Library of Kansas
State Capitol Bldg., Rm. 169-W
300 SW 10th Ave.
Topeka, KS 66612-1593
Ph: (785)296-3296
Free: 800-432-3919
Fax: (785)368-7291
Co. E-mail: infodesk@library.ks.gov
URL: http://www.kslib.info

61066 ■ U.S. Department of Commerce - State Library of North Carolina Division of State Library
State Library Bldg.
109 E. Jones St.
Raleigh, NC 27601-2807
Ph: (919)807-7430
Fax: (919)733-5679
URL: http://statelibrary.dcr.state.nc.us

61067 ■ U.S. Department of Commerce - State Library of North Carolina - Division of State Library
109 E. Jones St.
Raleigh, NC 27601-2807
Ph: (919)807-7430
Fax: (919)733-5679
URL: http://statelibrary.ncdcr.gov/units.html

61068 ■ U.S. Department of Commerce - State Library of Ohio
274 E. 1st Ave., Ste. 100
Columbus, OH 43201
Ph: (614)644-7061
Free: 800-686-1532
Fax: (614)752-9178
URL: http://www.library.ohio.gov/

61069 ■ U.S. Department of Commerce - State Library of Ohio
274 E. 1st Ave., Ste. 100
Columbus, OH 43201
Ph: (614)644-7061
Free: 800-686-1532
Fax: (614)752-9178
URL: http://www.library.ohio.gov/

61070 ■ U.S. Department of Commerce - Tennessee Department of Economic and Community Development - Research Division
312 Rosa L. Parks Ave., 11th Fl.
Nashville, TN 37243
Ph: (615)741-1912
Co. E-mail: ECD.Communications.Office@tn.gov
URL: http://www.tnecd.gov/

61071 ■ U.S. Department of Commerce - Tennessee Department of Economic and Community Development - Research Division
312 Rosa L. Parks Ave., 11th Fl.
Nashville, TN 37243
Ph: (615)741-1888
Co. E-mail: ECD.communications.office@tn.gov
URL: http://www.tn.gov/ecd/

61072 ■ U.S. Department of Commerce - Texas A&M University System - Department of Sociology
311 Academic Bldg.
College Station, TX 77840-4351
Ph: (979)845-5133
Fax: (979)862-4057
Co. E-mail: virgilm@tamu.edu
URL: http://sociweb.tamu.edu/compute.php

61073 ■ U.S. Department of Commerce - Texas A&M University System - Department of Sociology
311 Academic Bldg.
College Station, TX 77840-4351
Ph: (979)845-5133
Fax: (979)862-4057
Co. E-mail: virgilm@tamu.edu
URL: http://sociweb.tamu.edu/compute.php

61074 ■ U.S. Department of Commerce - Texas Department of Commerce - State Data Center
9th and Congress Sts.
Austin, TX 78701
Ph: (512)936-0223

61075 ■ U.S. Department of Commerce - Texas Natural Resources Information System (TNRIS)
Stephen F. Austin State Bldg.
1700 N. Congress Ave., Rm. B40
Austin, TX 78701-3231
Ph: (512)463-8337
Fax: (512)463-7274
URL: http://www.tnris.state.tx.us

61076 ■ U.S. Department of Commerce - Texas Natural Resources Information System (TNRIS)
Stephen F. Austin State Bldg.
1700 N. Congress Ave., Rm. B40
Austin, TX 78701-3231
Ph: (512)463-8337
Fax: (512)463-7274
URL: http://www.tnris.state.tx.us

61077 ■ U.S. Department of Commerce - Texas State Data Center
9th and Congress Sts.
Austin, TX 78701

Ph: (512)936-0223
Co. E-mail: txsdc@utsa.edu
URL: http://www.tdoc.tex.gov

61078 ■ U.S. Department of Commerce - Texas State Library and Archives Commission
1201 Brazos
Austin, TX 78711-2927
Ph: (512)463-5455
Fax: (512)463-5436
Co. E-mail: info@tsl.state.tx.us
URL: http://www.tsl.state.tx.us

61079 ■ U.S. Department of Commerce - Texas State Library and Archives Commission
1201 Brazos
Austin, TX 78711-2927
Ph: (512)463-5455
Fax: (512)463-5436
Co. E-mail: info@tsl.state.tx.us
URL: http://www.tsl.state.tx.us

61080 ■ U.S. Department of Commerce - U.S. Census Bureau
4600 Silver Hill Rd.
Washington, DC 20233
Ph: (301)763-4636
Free: 800-923-8282
URL: http://www.census.gov/

Description: The Census Bureau gathers and disseminates a wide variety of statistics about the people and economy of the United States. It is the principal source in the federal government for business information relating to manufacturers, retail trade, wholesale trade, construction trade, and services. These data are generated both from the regular five-year census programs and from annual, quarterly, and monthly survey programs. Data concerning the number of establishments, production, value added by manufacture, shipments, receipts, employees, payrolls--as well as other general and specific business statistics--are compiled and published periodically. Small business owners interested in learning more about the statistics available from the Census Bureau and how to use them may obtain a set of introductory materials and order forms by contacting Customer Services. Other information may be obtained from Census Bureau regional. In addition, the Census Bureau sponsors a state data center program, which provides (for a fee) local access to the bureau's computer products in all states, the District of Columbia, Puerto Rico, Guam, and the U.S. Virgin Islands.

61081 ■ U.S. Department of Commerce - U.S. Census Bureau
395 Hudson St., Ste. 800
New York, NY 10014-7451
Ph: (212)584-3400
Free: 800-991-2520
Fax: (212)478-4800
Co. E-mail: new.york.regional.office@census.gov
URL: http://www.census.gov/regions/new_york/

61082 ■ U.S. Department of Commerce - U.S. Census Bureau - Atlanta Regional Office
101 Marietta St. NW, Ste. 3200
Atlanta, GA 30303-2700
Ph: (404)730-3832
Free: 800-424-6974
Fax: (404)730-3835
Co. E-mail: Atlanta.regional.office@census.gov
URL: http://www.census.gov/regions/atlanta/

61083 ■ U.S. Department of Commerce - U.S. Census Bureau - Boston Regional Office
4 Copley Pl., Ste. 301
Boston, MA 02117-9108
Ph: (617)424-4501
Free: 800-562-5721
Fax: (617)424-0547
Co. E-mail: boston.regional.office@census.gov
URL: http://www.census.gov/regions/boston/

61084 ■ U.S. Department of Commerce - U.S. Census Bureau - Charlotte Regional Office
901 Center Park Dr., Ste. 106
Charlotte, NC 28217-2935
Ph: (704)424-6400
Free: 800-331-7360
Fax: (704)424-6944
Co. E-mail: charlotte.regional.office@census.gov
URL: http://www.census.gov/regions/charlotte/

61085 ■ U.S. Department of Commerce - U.S. Census Bureau - Chicago Regional Office
1111 W. 22nd St., Ste. 400
Oak Brook, IL 60523-1918
Ph: (630)288-9200
Free: 800-865-6384
Fax: (630)288-9288
Co. E-mail: Chicago.regional.office@census.gov
URL: http://www.census.gov/regions/chicago/

61086 ■ U.S. Department of Commerce - U.S. Census Bureau - Dallas Regional Office
8585 N. Stemmons Fwy., Ste. 800 S
Dallas, TX 75247-3836
Ph: (214)653-4400
Free: 800-835-9752
Fax: (214)253-4419
Co. E-mail: daro.census@census.gov
URL: http://www.census.gov/regions/dallas/

61087 ■ U.S. Department of Commerce - U.S. Census Bureau - Denver Regional Office
6900 W. Jefferson Ave., Ste. 100
Denver, CO 80235-2032
Ph: (303)264-0202
Free: 800-852-6159
Fax: (303)969-6777
Co. E-mail: Denver.regional.office@census.gov
URL: http://www.census.gov/regions/denver/

61088 ■ U.S. Department of Commerce - U.S. Census Bureau - Detroit Regional Office
1395 Brewery Park Blvd., Ste. 100
Detroit, MI 48207
Ph: (313)259-0056
Free: 800-432-1495
Fax: (313)259-5045
Co. E-mail: Detroit.regional.office@census.gov
URL: http://www.census.gov/regions/detroit/

61089 ■ U.S. Department of Commerce - U.S. Census Bureau - Kansas City Regional Office
1211 N. 8th St.
Kansas City, KS 66101-2129
Ph: (913)551-6728
Free: 800-728-4748
Fax: (913)551-6789
Co. E-mail: kansas.city.regional.office@census.gov
URL: http://www.census.gov/regions/kansas_city/

61090 ■ U.S. Department of Commerce - U.S. Census Bureau - Los Angeles Regional Office
15350 Sherman Way, Ste. 400
Van Nuys, CA 91406-4224
Ph: (818)267-1700
Free: 800-992-3530
Fax: (818)904-6429
Co. E-mail: los.angeles.regional.office@census.gov
URL: http://www.census.gov/regions/los_angeles/

61091 ■ U.S. Department of Commerce - U.S. Census Bureau - Philadelphia Regional Office
833 Chestnut St., Ste. 504
Philadelphia, PA 19107
Ph: (215)717-1800
Free: 800-262-4236
Fax: (215)717-2588
Co. E-mail: Philadelphia.regional.office@census.gov
URL: http://www.census.gov/regions/philadelphia/

61092 ■ U.S. Department of Commerce - U.S. Census Bureau - Seattle Regional Office
601 Union St., Ste. 3800
Seattle, WA 98101-1074
Ph: (206)381-6200
Free: 800-233-3308

Fax: (206)381-6310
Co. E-mail: seattle.regional.office@census.gov
URL: http://www.census.gov/regions/seattle/

61093 ■ U.S. Department of Commerce - United Way of Rhode Island
50 Valley St.
Providence, RI 02909-2459
Ph: (401)444-0600
Fax: (401)444-0635
Co. E-mail: info@uwri.org
URL: http://www.uwri.org/

61094 ■ U.S. Department of Commerce - United Way of Rhode Island
50 Valley St.
Providence, RI 02909-2459
Ph: (401)444-0600
Fax: (401)444-0635
Co. E-mail: info@uwri.org
URL: http://www.uwri.org/

61095 ■ U.S. Department of Commerce - University of Alabama - Center for Business and Economic Research
Box 870221
Tuscaloosa, AL 35487-0221
Ph: (205)348-6191
Fax: (205)348-2951
Co. E-mail: uacber@cba.ua.edu
URL: http://cber.cba.ua.edu/

61096 ■ U.S. Department of Commerce - University of Alabama - Center for Business and Economic Research
Box 870221
Tuscaloosa, AL 35487-0221
Ph: (205)348-6191
Fax: (205)348-2951
Co. E-mail: uacber@cba.ua.edu
URL: http://cber.cba.ua.edu/

61097 ■ U.S. Department of Commerce - The University of Arizona - Economic and Business Research Center - Eller College of Management
McClelland Hall, Rm. 103
1130 Helen St.
Tucson, AZ 85721-0108
Ph: (520)621-2155
Fax: (520)621-2150
Co. E-mail: ebrlib@eller.arizona.edu
URL: http://ebr.eller.arizona.edu

61098 ■ U.S. Department of Commerce - The University of Arizona - Economic and Business Research Program - Eller College of Management
McClelland Hall, Rm. 103
1130 Helen St.
Tucson, AZ 85721-0108
Ph: (520)621-2155
Fax: (520)621-2150
Co. E-mail: ebrlib@eller.arizona.edu
URL: http://ebr.eller.arizona.edu

61099 ■ U.S. Department of Commerce - University of Arkansas at Little Rock - Census State Data Center
2801 S. University Ave.
Little Rock, AR 72204-1099
Ph: (501)569-8530
Fax: (501)569-8538
Co. E-mail: pnpoche@ualr.edu
URL: http://www.aiea.ualr.edu/csdc.html

61100 ■ U.S. Department of Commerce - University of Arkansas - Little Rock - Institute for Economic Advancement - Census State Data Center
2801 S. University Ave.
Little Rock, AR 72204
Ph: (501)569-8530
Fax: (501)569-8538
Co. E-mail: pnpoche@ualr.edu
URL: http://www.aiea.ualr.edu/census/censusdata/default.html

61101 ■ U.S. Department of Commerce - University of California, Berkeley - UC DATA
2538 Channing Way, Ste. 5100
Berkeley, CA 94720-5100
Ph: (510)642-6571
Fax: (510)643-8292
Co. E-mail: ucdata@berkeley.edu
URL: http://ucdata.berkeley.edu:7101/

61102 ■ U.S. Department of Commerce - University of California, Berkeley - UC Data Survey Research Center
2538 Channing Way, Ste. 5100
Berkeley, CA 94720-5100
Ph: (510)642-6571
Fax: (510)643-8292
Co. E-mail: jons@berkeley.edu
URL: http://ucdata.berkeley.edu

61103 ■ U.S. Department of Commerce - University of Cincinnati - Southwest Ohio Regional Data Center - Institute for Policy Research
Edwards Center I, Ste. 3110
Cincinnati, OH 45221-0132
Ph: (513)556-5028
Fax: (513)556-9023
Co. E-mail: kim.downing@uc.edu
URL: http://www.ipr.uc.edu

61104 ■ U.S. Department of Commerce - University of Cincinnati - Southwest Ohio Regional Data Center - Institute for Policy Research
Edwards Center I, Ste. 3110
Cincinnati, OH 45221-0132
Ph: (513)556-5028
Fax: (513)556-9023
Co. E-mail: kim.downing@us.edu
URL: http://www.ipr.uc.edu

61105 ■ U.S. Department of Commerce - University of Colorado at Boulder - Business Research Division - Graduate School of Business Administration
UCB 419
Boulder, CO 80309-0419
Ph: (303)492-8227
Co. E-mail: BRDinfo@colorado.edu
URL: http://leeds.colorado.edu/

61106 ■ U.S. Department of Commerce - University of Colorado at Boulder - Leeds School of Business - Business Research Division - Graduate School of Business Administration
Koelbel S350
Boulder, CO 80309
Ph: (303)492-3307
Fax: (303)492-3620
Co. E-mail: BRDinfo@colorado.edu
URL: http://leeds.colorado.edu

61107 ■ U.S. Department of Commerce - University of Delaware - School of Public Policy and Administration
184 Graham Hall
Newark, DE 19716
Ph: (302)831-1687
Fax: (302)831-3296
Co. E-mail: sppa@udel.edu
URL: http://www.udel.edu/suapp/

61108 ■ U.S. Department of Commerce - University of Delaware - School of Public Policy and Administration
184 Graham Hall
Newark, DE 19716
Ph: (302)831-1687
Fax: (302)831-3296
Co. E-mail: sppa@udel.edu
URL: http://www.udel.edu/suapp/

61109 ■ U.S. Department of Commerce - University of Georgia Libraries - Government Documents Department
2nd Fl.
Athens, GA 30602-1641

Ph: (706)542-3251
URL: http://www.libs.uga.edu/govdocs/index.html

61110 ■ U.S. Department of Commerce - University of Georgia Libraries - Government Documents Department
320 S. Jackson St.
Athens, GA 30602-1641
Ph: (706)542-3251
Co. E-mail: stuggle@uga.edu
URL: http://www.libs.uga.edu/govdocs/index.html

61111 ■ U.S. Department of Commerce - University of Iowa - Iowa Social Science Research Center
345 Schaeffer Hall
Iowa City, IA 52242-1409
Ph: (319)335-2371
URL: http://www.uiowa.edu

61112 ■ U.S. Department of Commerce - University of Iowa - Iowa Social Science Research Center
310 S. Grand Ave.
Iowa City, IA 52242
Ph: (319)335-6800
URL: http://ppc.uiowa.edu/isrc

61113 ■ U.S. Department of Commerce - University of Kansas - Institute for Policy and Social Research
1541 Lilac Ln.
607 Blake Hall
Lawrence, KS 66045-3129
Ph: (785)864-3701
Fax: (785)864-3683
Co. E-mail: ipsr@ku.edu
URL: http://www.ipsr.ku.edu/

61114 ■ U.S. Department of Commerce - University of Kansas - Institute for Policy and Social Research
1541 Lilac Ln.
607 Blake Hall
Lawrence, KS 66045-3129
Ph: (785)864-3701
Fax: (785)864-3683
Co. E-mail: ipsr@ku.edu
URL: http://www.ipsr.ku.edu/

61115 ■ U.S. Department of Commerce - University of Louisville - Department of Urban and Public Affairs - Urban Studies Institute
426 W. Bloom St.
Louisville, KY 40208
Ph: (502)852-7906
Fax: (502)852-4558
Co. E-mail: upa@louisville.edu
URL: http://louisville.edu/upa

61116 ■ U.S. Department of Commerce - University of Louisville - School of Urban and Public Affairs - Urban Studies Institute
426 W. Bloom St.
Louisville, KY 40208
Ph: (502)852-7906
Fax: (502)852-4558
Co. E-mail: upa@louisville.edu
URL: http://supa.louisville.edu/

61117 ■ U.S. Department of Commerce - University of Maryland - Department of Computer Science
A.V. Williams Bldg.
College Park, MD 20742
Ph: (301)405-2662
Fax: (301)405-6707
URL: http://www.cs.umd.edu

61118 ■ U.S. Department of Commerce - University of Maryland - Department of Computer Science
A.V. Williams Bldg.
College Park, MD 20742
Ph: (301)405-2662
Fax: (301)405-6707
URL: http://www.cs.umd.edu

61119 ■ U.S. Department of Commerce - University of Massachusetts at Amherst - Massachusetts Institute for Social and Economic Research
128 Thompson Hall
Amherst, MA 01003-7515
Ph: (413)545-3460
Fax: (413)545-3686
Co. E-mail: jgaviglio@donahue.umassp.edu
URL: http://www.umass.edu/miser

61120 ■ U.S. Department of Commerce - University of Massachusetts at Amherst - Massachusetts Institute for Social and Economic Research
128 Thompson Hall
Amherst, MA 01003-7515
Ph: (413)545-3460
Fax: (413)545-3686
Co. E-mail: jgaviglio@donahue.umassp.edu
URL: http://www.umass.edu/miser

61121 ■ U.S. Department of Commerce - The University of Mississippi - State Data Center of Mississippi - Center for Population Studies
301 Leavell Hall
University, MS 38677
Ph: (662)915-7288
Fax: (662)915-7736
Co. E-mail: saholley@olemiss.edu
URL: http://www.olemiss.edu/depts/sdc/

61122 ■ U.S. Department of Commerce - The University of Mississippi - State Data Center of Mississippi - Center for Population Studies
301 Leavell Hall
University, MS 38677
Ph: (662)915-7288
Fax: (662)915-7736
Co. E-mail: lcwoo@olemiss.edu
URL: http://www.olemiss.edu/depts/sdc/

61123 ■ U.S. Department of Commerce - University of Missouri-Kansas City - Center for Economic Information
5211 Rockhill Rd.
Haag Hall 210
Kansas City, MO 64110
Ph: (816)235-2832
Fax: (816)235-2834
Co. E-mail: eatonp@umkc.edu
URL: http://cei.umkc.edu/

61124 ■ U.S. Department of Commerce - University of Missouri-Kansas City - Center for Economic Information
5211 Rockhill Rd.
Haag Hall 210
Kansas City, MO 64110
Ph: (816)235-2832
Fax: (816)235-2834
Co. E-mail: eatonp@umkc.edu
URL: http://cei.umkc.edu/

61125 ■ U.S. Department of Commerce - University of Montana - Bureau of Business Administration
Gallagher Business Bldg.
32 Campus Dr.
Missoula, MT 59812
Ph: (406)243-4831
Fax: (406)243-2086
URL: http://www.business.umt.edu

61126 ■ U.S. Department of Commerce - University of Montana - Bureau of Business and Economic Research
Gallagher Business Bldg.
32 Campus Dr., Rm. 6840
Missoula, MT 59812-6840
Ph: (406)243-4831
Fax: (406)243-2086
URL: http://www.bber.umt.edu

61127 ■ U.S. Department of Commerce - University of New Hampshire - Office of Biometrics
Pettee Hall
Durham, NH 03824

61128 ■ U.S. Department of Commerce - University of New Hampshire - Office of Biometrics
105 Main St.
Durham, NH 03824
Ph: (603)862-1990
Co. E-mail: chris.neefus@unh.edu
URL: http://departments.unh.edu

61129 ■ U.S. Department of Commerce - University of New Mexico - Bureau of Business and Economic Research - Business and Industrial Data Center
1919 Las Lomas NE
Albuquerque, NM 87106
Ph: (505)277-6626
Fax: (505)277-2773
Co. E-mail: dbinfo@unm.edu
URL: http://bber.unm.edu/

61130 ■ U.S. Department of Commerce - University of New Mexico - Bureau of Business and Economic Research - Data Bank
1919 Las Lomas NE
1 University of New Mexico
Albuquerque, NM 87131-0001
Ph: (505)277-6626
Fax: (505)277-2773
Co. E-mail: dbinfo@unm.edu
URL: http://bber.unm.edu/

61131 ■ U.S. Department of Commerce - University of North Carolina - Odum Institute for Research in Social Science
Manning Hall
Campus Box 3355
Chapel Hill, NC 27599-3355
Ph: (919)962-3061
Co. E-mail: abb@unc.edu
URL: http://www.irss.unc.edu/odum/jsp/home.jsp

61132 ■ U.S. Department of Commerce - University of North Carolina - Odum Institute for Research in Social Science
Manning Hall
Campus Box 3355
Chapel Hill, NC 27599-3355
Ph: (919)962-3061
URL: http://www.odum.unc.edu/odum/home2.jsp

61133 ■ U.S. Department of Commerce - University of North Dakota - Department of Geography
O'Kelly and Ireland Rm. 152
221 Centennial Dr. Stop 9020
Grand Forks, ND 58202-9020
Ph: (701)777-4246
Fax: (701)777-6195
URL: http://www.und.edu/dept/Geog/mainpage.htm

61134 ■ U.S. Department of Commerce - University of North Dakota - Department of Geography
O'Kelly Hall, Rm. 152
221 Centennial Dr. Stop 9020
Grand Forks, ND 58202-9020
Ph: (701)777-4246
Fax: (701)777-6195
URL: http://arts-sciences.und.edu/geography/

61135 ■ U.S. Department of Commerce - University of Northern Colorado - Library Government Publics
Campus Box 48
Greeley, CO 80639
Ph: (970)351-2671
Co. E-mail: library.reference@unco.edu
URL: http://www.unco.edu/library/

61136 ■ U.S. Department of Commerce - University of Northern Colorado - Library Government Publics
Campus Box 48
Greeley, CO 80639
Ph: (970)351-2671
Co. E-mail: library.reference@unco.edu
URL: http://www.unco.edu/library/

61137 ■ U.S. Department of Commerce - University of Northern Iowa - Center for Social and Behavioral Research
2304 College St.
Cedar Falls, IA 50614-0402
Ph: (319)273-2105
Fax: (319)273-3104
Co. E-mail: Sharon.Cory@uni.edu
URL: http://www.uni.edu/csbr/

61138 ■ U.S. Department of Commerce - University of Northern Iowa - Center for Social and Behavioral Research
2304 College St.
Cedar Falls, IA 50614-0402
Ph: (319)273-2105
Fax: (319)273-3104
Co. E-mail: Sharon.Cory@uni.edu
URL: http://www.uni.edu/csbr/

61139 ■ U.S. Department of Commerce - University of Oregon Library - Document Center
1299 University of Oregon
Eugene, OR 97403-1299
Ph: (503)346-3070
Fax: (503)346-3094
Co. E-mail: govdocs@uoregon.edu
URL: http://libweb.uoregon.edu/govdocs/index.html

61140 ■ U.S. Department of Commerce - University of Oregon Library - Documents Center
1299 University of Oregon
Eugene, OR 97403-1299
Ph: (541)346-1970
Co. E-mail: govdocs@uoregon.edu
URL: http://library.uoregon.edu/govdocs/index.html

61141 ■ U.S. Department of Commerce - University of South Dakota - Beacom School of Business - Business Research Bureau
Beacom Hall
414 E. Clark St.
Vermillion, SD 57069
Ph: (605)677-5455
Fax: (605)677-5058
Co. E-mail: business@usd.edu
URL: http://www.usd.edu/business/

61142 ■ U.S. Department of Commerce - University of South Dakota - School of Business - Business Research Bureau
Beacom Hall
414 E. Clark St.
Vermillion, SD 57069
Ph: (605)677-5455
Fax: (605)677-5058
Co. E-mail: business@usd.edu
URL: http://www.usd.edu/business/

61143 ■ U.S. Department of Commerce - University of Southern Maine - Maine State Data Center - Center for Business and Economic Research
96 Falmouth St.
Portland, ME 04104-9300
Ph: (207)780-4187
Fax: (207)780-4046
Co. E-mail: usmcber@maine.maine.edu
URL: http://www.usm.maine.edu/cber/

61144 ■ U.S. Department of Commerce - University of Southern Maine - Maine State Data Center - Center for Business and Economic Research
118 Bedford St.
Portland, ME 04104-9300
Ph: (207)780-4187

Fax: (207)780-4017
Co. E-mail: usmcber@usm.maine.edu
URL: http://www.usm.maine.edu/mcber/

61145 ■ U.S. Department of Commerce - University of Tennessee - Center for Business and Economic Research - College of Business Administration
Stokely Management Ctr., Fl. 7
916 Volunteer Blvd.
Knoxville, TN 37996-0570
Ph: (423)974-5441
Fax: (865)974-3100
Co. E-mail: vickiec@utk.edu
URL: http://cber.bus.utk.edu/

61146 ■ U.S. Department of Commerce - University of Tennessee - College of Business Administration - Center for Business and Economic Research
Stokely Management Ctr.
916 Volunteer Blvd.
Knoxville, TN 37996-0570
Ph: (423)974-5441
Fax: (865)974-3100
Co. E-mail: vickiec@utk.edu
URL: http://cber.bus.utk.edu/

61147 ■ U.S. Department of Commerce - University of Utah - Bureau of Economic and Business Research
1645 E. Campus Ctr. Dr., Rm. 401
Salt Lake City, UT 84112-9302
Ph: (801)581-6333
Fax: (801)581-3354
Co. E-mail: bureau@business.utah.edu
URL: http://www.bebr.utah.edu

61148 ■ U.S. Department of Commerce - University of Utah - Bureau of Economic and Business Research
1635 E. Campus Ctr. Dr., Rm. 401
Salt Lake City, UT 84112-9302
Ph: (801)581-6333
Fax: (801)581-3354
Co. E-mail: bureau@business.utah.edu
URL: http://www.bebr.utah.edu

61149 ■ U.S. Department of Commerce - University of Vermont - Center for Rural Studies
206 Morrill Hall
146 University Place
Burlington, VT 05405
Ph: (802)656-3021
Fax: (802)656-1423
Co. E-mail: crs@uvm.edu
URL: http://www.uvm.edu/crs/

61150 ■ U.S. Department of Commerce - University of Vermont - Center for Rural Studies
206 Morrill Hall
146 University Place
Burlington, VT 05405
Ph: (802)656-3021
Fax: (802)656-1423
Co. E-mail: crs@uvm.edu
URL: http://www.uvm.edu/crs/

61151 ■ U.S. Department of Commerce - University of the Virgin Islands - Eastern Caribbean Center
2 John Brewer's Bay
St. Thomas, VI 00802
Ph: (340)693-1027
Fax: (340)693-1025
Co. E-mail: fmills@uvi.edu
URL: http://www.uvi.edu

Description: To conduct scientific research and associated training, technology transfer and information dissemination, that is responsive to the social, economic and environmental needs of the USVI and applicable to the small islands of he Eastern Caribbean.

61152 ■ U.S. Department of Commerce - University of the Virgin Islands - Eastern Caribbean Center
2 John Brewer's Bay
St. Thomas, VI 00802-9990
Ph: (340)693-1027
Fax: (340)693-1025
Co. E-mail: fmills@uvi.edu
URL: http://www.uvi.edu
URL(s): www.census.gov/sdc/visdc.html. **Description:** To conduct scientific research and associated training, technology transfer and information dissemination, that is responsive to the social, economic and environmental needs of the USVI and applicable to the small islands of he Eastern Caribbean.

61153 ■ U.S. Department of Commerce - University of Virginia - Weldon Cooper Center for Public Service
2400 Old Ivy Rd., Rm. 220
Charlottesville, VA 22903-4206
Ph: (804)982-5522
Fax: (434)982-5524
Co. E-mail: coopercenter@virginia.edu
URL: http://www.coopercenter.org/

61154 ■ U.S. Department of Commerce - University of Virginia - Weldon Cooper Center for Public Service
2400 Old Ivy Rd., Rm. 220
Charlottesville, VA 22904-4206
Ph: (434)982-5522
Fax: (434)982-5524
Co. E-mail: coopercenter@virginia.edu
URL: http://www.coopercenter.org/

61155 ■ U.S. Department of Commerce - University of Washington (CSSCR) - Center for Social Science Computation and Research
611 Condon Hall
Seattle, WA 98195
Ph: (206)543-8110
Fax: (206)543-2062
Co. E-mail: csscr@u.washington.edu
URL: http://www.artsci.washington.edu/deptdetails.asp?ID=84

61156 ■ U.S. Department of Commerce - University of Washington - CSSCR
611 Condon Hall
Seattle, WA 98195
Ph: (206)543-8110
Fax: (206)543-2062
Co. E-mail: csscr@u.washington.edu
URL: http://julius.csscr.washington.edu/

61157 ■ U.S. Department of Commerce - University of Wisconsin - Madison - Applied Population Laboratory - Department of Community and Environmental Sociology
350 Agricultural Hall
1450 Linden Dr.
Madison, WI 53706
Ph: (608)262-1510
Fax: (608)262-6022
Co. E-mail: contact@dces.wisc.edu
URL: http://www.dces.wisc.edu

61158 ■ U.S. Department of Commerce - University of Wisconsin - Madison - Department of Community and Environmental Sociology - Applied Population Laboratory
350 Agricultural Hall
1450 Linden Dr.
Madison, WI 53706
Ph: (608)262-1510
Fax: (608)262-6022
Co. E-mail: contact@dces.wisc.edu
URL: http://www.drs.wisc.edu/

61159 ■ U.S. Department of Commerce - University of Wyoming - Survey Research Center
WYSAC, Dept. 3925
1000 E. University Ave.
Laramie, WY 82071
Ph: (307)766-2189

Fax: (307)766-2759
Co. E-mail: wysac@uwyo.edu
URL: http://wysac.uwyo.edu/Department.aspx?DeptId=4

61160 ■ U.S. Department of Commerce - University of Wyoming - Wyoming Survey and Analysis Center - Survey Research Center
WYSAC, Dept. 3925
1000 E. University Ave.
Laramie, WY 82071
Ph: (307)766-2189
Fax: (307)766-2759
Co. E-mail: wysac@uwyo.edu
URL: http://wysac.uwyo.edu/Department.aspx?DeptId=4

61161 ■ U.S. Department of Commerce - Urban Information Center - University of Missouri--St. Louis
8001 Natural Bridge Rd.
St. Louis, MO 63121-4499
Ph: (314)516-6014
Fax: (314)516-6274
Co. E-mail: john@oseda.missouri.edu
URL: http://www.oseda.missouri.edu

61162 ■ U.S. Department of Commerce - Urban Information Center - University of Missouri--St. Louis
8001 Natural Bridge Rd.
St. Louis, MO 63121-4401
Ph: (314)516-6014
Fax: (314)516-6274
Co. E-mail: john@oseda.missouri.edu
URL: http://www.oseda.missouri.edu

61163 ■ U.S. Department of Commerce - Utah Governor's Office of Economic Development
324 S. State St., Ste. 500
Salt Lake City, UT 84111
Ph: (801)538-8700
Free: 877-488-3233
Fax: (801)538-8888
URL: http://goed.utah.gov/

61164 ■ U.S. Department of Commerce - Utah Governor's Office of Planning and Budget
Utah State Capital, Ste. 150
Salt Lake City, UT 84114-2210
Ph: (801)538-1027
Free: 800-705-2464
Fax: (801)538-1547
URL: http://www.governor.utah.gov/gopb/
Description: Provides leadership for the initiatives of the Governor and meets customer information, budgeting, planning, strategy, and issue coordination needs by providing accurate and timely data, impartial analyses, and objective recommendations.

61165 ■ U.S. Department of Commerce - Utah Office of Economic Development
324 S. State St., Ste. 500
Salt Lake City, UT 84111
Ph: (801)538-8700
Free: 877-488-3233
Fax: (801)538-8888
URL: http://goed.utah.gov/
URL(s): www.utah.gov/governor/offices/index.html.

61166 ■ U.S. Department of Commerce - Utah Office of Planning and Budget
Utah State Capital, Ste. 150
Salt Lake City, UT 84114-2210
Ph: (801)538-1027
Free: 800-705-2464
Fax: (801)538-1547
URL: http://www.governor.utah.gov/gopb/
Description: Provides leadership for the initiatives of the Governor and meets customer information, budgeting, planning, strategy, and issue coordination needs by providing accurate and timely data, impartial analyses, and objective recommendations.

61167 ■ U.S. Department of Commerce - Vermont Department of Libraries
109 State St.
Pavilion Office Building
Montpelier, VT 05609-0601
Ph: (802)828-3261
Fax: (802)828-2199
URL: http://info.libraries.vermont.gov/

61168 ■ U.S. Department of Commerce - Vermont Department of Libraries
109 State St.
Pavilion Office Building
Montpelier, VT 05609-0601
Ph: (802)828-3261
Fax: (802)828-2199
URL: http://libraries.vermont.gov/

61169 ■ U.S. Department of Commerce - Vermont Department of Tourism and Marketing
National Life Bldg., 6th Fl.
Montpelier, VT 05620-0501
Ph: (802)828-3237
Free: 800-VER-MONT
Co. E-mail: info@VermontVacation.com
URL: http://www.travel-vermont.com/
URL(s): www.vermontvacation.com/.

61170 ■ U.S. Department of Commerce - Vermont Office of Policy Research and Coordination
Pavilion Office Bldg.
109 State St.
Montpelier, VT 05609
Ph: (802)828-3261
Co. E-mail: sybil@dol.state.vt.us
URL: http://www.dol.state.vt.us

61171 ■ U.S. Department of Commerce - Vermont Travel Department
1 National Life Bldg., 6th Fl.
Montpelier, VT 05620-0501
Ph: (802)828-3237
Co. E-mail: info@VermontVacation.com
URL: http://www.vermontvacation.com/

61172 ■ U.S. Department of Commerce - Virgin Islands Department of Economic Development
PO Box 6400
St. Thomas, VI 00804
Ph: (340)774-8784
Fax: (340)774-4390
URL: http://www.visitusvi.com/official_business

61173 ■ U.S. Department of Commerce - Virgin Islands Economic Development Authority
Charlotte Amalie
St. Thomas, VI 00801
Ph: (340)774-8784
URL: http://www.auber.org/docs/apc.htm

61174 ■ U.S. Department of Commerce - Virginia Employment Commission
703 E. Main St.
Richmond, VA 23219
Ph: (804)786-1485
Fax: (804)371-0412
URL: http://www.vec.state.va.us

61175 ■ U.S. Department of Commerce - Virginia Employment Commission
703 E. Main St.
Richmond, VA 23219
Ph: (804)786-1485
Fax: (804)371-0412
URL: http://www.vec.virginia.gov/

61176 ■ U.S. Department of Commerce - Washington State Library - Federal Depository Program
Point Plaza E.
6880 Capitol Blvd. S
Olympia, WA 98504-2460

Ph: (360)753-5221
Co. E-mail: askalibrarian@sos.wa.gov
URL: http://www.sos.wa.gov/library/FederalDeposito-
ryProgram.aspx

**61177 ■ U.S. Department of Commerce -
Washington State Library - Federal
Depository Program**
Point Plaza E.
6880 Capitol Blvd. Se
Tumwater, WA 98501-5513
Ph: (360)753-5221
Co. E-mail: askalibrarian@sos.wa.gov
URL: http://www.sos.wa.gov/library/FederalDeposito-
ryProgram.aspx

**61178 ■ U.S. Department of Commerce -
Washington State Office of Financial
Management - Forecasting Division**
PO Box 43113
Olympia, WA 98504-3113
Ph: (360)902-0555
Co. E-mail: ofm.forecasting@ofm.wa.gov
URL: http://www.ofm.wa.gov/forecasting/

**61179 ■ U.S. Department of Commerce -
Washington State Office of Financial
Management - Forecasting Division**
210 11th Ave.
Olympia, WA 98504-3113
Ph: (360)902-0555
Co. E-mail: ofm.forecasting@ofm.wa.gov
URL: http://www.ofm.wa.gov/

**61180 ■ U.S. Department of Commerce -
Washington State Office of Financial
Management - Forecasting Division**
PO Box 43113
Olympia, WA 98504-3113
Ph: (360)902-0599
Co. E-mail: ofm.forecasting@ofm.wa.gov
URL: http://www.ofm.wa.gov/forecasting/

**61181 ■ U.S. Department of Commerce -
Washington State University - School of
Economics Sciences**
Hulbert Hall 101
Pullman, WA 99164-6210
Ph: (509)335-5555
Fax: (509)335-1173
Co. E-mail: dkbishop@wsu.edu
URL: http://www.ses.wsu.edu

**61182 ■ U.S. Department of Commerce -
Washington State University - School of
Economics Sciences**
Hulbert Hall 101
Pullman, WA 99164-6210
Ph: (509)335-5555
Fax: (509)335-1173
Co. E-mail: dkbishop@wsu.edu
URL: http://www.ses.wsu.edu

**61183 ■ U.S. Department of Commerce -
Wayne State University - Center for Urban
Studies**
5700 Cass Ave., Rm. 2207 A/AB
Detroit, MI 48202
Ph: (313)577-2208
Fax: (313)577-1274
Co. E-mail: CUSInfo@wayne.edu
URL: http://www.cus.wayne.edu/

**61184 ■ U.S. Department of Commerce -
Wayne State University - MIMIC/Center for
Urban Studies**
5700 Cass Ave., Rm. 2207 A/AB
Detroit, MI 48202
Ph: (313)577-2208
Fax: (313)577-1274
Co. E-mail: CUSInfo@wayne.edu
URL: http://www.cus.wayne.edu/

**61185 ■ U.S. Department of Commerce -
West Virginia Development Office - Research
and Strategic Planning Division**
Capitol Complex
Bldg. 6, Rm. 620
Charleston, WV 25305-0311
Ph: (304)558-2234
Free: 800-982-3386
Fax: (304)558-0449
Co. E-mail: mark.r.julian@wv.gov
URL: http://www.wvcommerce.org/info/aboutcom-
merce/developmentoffice/services.aspx

**61186 ■ U.S. Department of Commerce -
West Virginia Development Office - Research
and Strategic Planning Group**
Capitol Complex
Bldg. 6, Rm. 553
1900 Kanawha Blvd.
Charleston, WV 25305-0311
Ph: (304)558-2234
Free: 800-982-3386
Fax: (304)558-0449
URL: http://www.wvlc.wvnet.edu

**61187 ■ U.S. Department of Commerce -
West Virginia State Library Commission -
Reference Library**
1900 Kanawha Blvd. E.
Charleston, WV 25305
Ph: (304)558-2041
Free: 800-642-9021
Fax: (304)293-2044
Co. E-mail: web_one@wvlc.lib.wv.us
URL: http://librarycommission.lib.wv.us/

**61188 ■ U.S. Department of Commerce -
West Virginia State Library Commission -
Reference Library**
1900 Kanawha Blvd. E.
Charleston, WV 25305
Ph: (304)558-2041
Free: 800-642-9021
Fax: (304)293-2044
URL: http://www.librarycommission.wv.gov/

**61189 ■ U.S. Department of Commerce -
West Virginia University Health Science
Center - Office of Health Services Research**
2267 Health Sciences S.
Morgantown, WV 26506-9104
Ph: (304)293-7206
Fax: (304)293-7038
Co. E-mail: jodonnell@hsc.wvu.edu
URL: http://www.hsc.wvu.edu/ResOff/ContactUs/

**61190 ■ U.S. Department of Commerce -
West Virginia University Health Sciences
Center - Office of Health Services Research**
2267 Health Sciences S.
Morgantown, WV 26506-9104
Ph: (304)293-7206
Fax: (304)293-7038
URL: http://www.hsc.wvu.edu

**61191 ■ U.S. Department of Commerce -
Western Washington University -
Demographic Research Laboratory -
Department of Sociology**
Arntzen Hall 501
Bellingham, WA 98225-9081
Ph: (360)650-3176
Fax: (360)650-7295
Co. E-mail: lucky.tedrow@wwu.edu
URL: http://www.wwu.edu/depts/socad/OSR.html

**61192 ■ U.S. Department of Commerce -
Western Washington University -
Demographic Research Laboratory -
Department of Sociology**
Arntzen Hall 501
Bellingham, WA 98225-9081
Ph: (360)650-3176
Fax: (360)650-7295
Co. E-mail: lucky.tedrow@wwu.edu
URL: http://www.wwu.edu/soc/bios/tedrow.shtml

**61193 ■ U.S. Department of Commerce -
Wichita State University - Center for
Economic Development and Business
Research**
Devlin Hall, 2nd Fl.
1845 Fairmount
Wichita, KS 67260-0121
Ph: (316)978-3225
Fax: (316)978-3950
Co. E-mail: cedbr@wichita.edu
URL: http://webs.wichita.edu/?u=cedbr

**61194 ■ U.S. Department of Commerce -
Wichita State University - Center for
Economic Development and Business
Research**
Devlin Hall, 2nd Fl.
1845 Fairmount
Wichita, KS 67260-0121
Ph: (316)978-3225
Fax: (316)978-3950
Co. E-mail: cedbr@wichita.edu
URL: http://webs.wichita.edu/?u=cedbr

61195 ■ University of Alaska Anchorage
3211 Providence Dr.
Anchorage, AK 99508
Ph: (907)786-1800
URL: http://www.uaa.alaska.edu/
Publications: *Alaska Quarterly Review: A Literary
Magazine of Consequence.* **Awards:** UAA Elaine At-
wood Scholarships; UAA Mark A. Beltz Scholarships;
Chugach Gem & Mineral Society Scholarships; UAA
Jan & Glenn Fredericks Scholarships; UAA Ardell
French Memorial Scholarships; UAA Ken Gray Endow-
ment Scholarships; Lenore & George Hedla Account-
ing Scholarships; Killam Fellowships Program; UAA
Chris L. Kleinke Scholarships; UAA Kris Knudson
Memorial Scholarships; Arlene Kuhner Memorial
Scholarships; UAA Paul G. Landis Scholarships; UAA
Diane Olsen Memorial Scholarships; UAA April Re-
lyea Scholarships; UAA Jack & Martha Roderick
Scholarships; UAA Brown Schoenheit Memorial
Scholarships; Sheri Stears Education Scholarships;
Sturgulewski Family Scholarships; UAA Accounting
Club Scholarships; UAA Alaska Kidney Foundation
Scholarships; UAA Alumni Association Scholarships;
UAA Emi Chance Memorial Scholarships; UAA GCI,
Inc. Scholarships; UAA Pignalberi Public Policy
Scholarships; UAA Quanterra Scholarships; UAA
RRANN Program Scholarships; UAA Wells Fargo
Career Scholarships; UAA Melissa J. Wolf Scholar-
ships; UAA Dr. Jon Baker Memorial Scholarships;
UAA Michael Baring-Gould Memorial Scholarships;
UAA Pat Brakke Political Science Scholarships; UAA
Edward Rollin Clinton Memorial for Music; UAA
Governor William A. Egan Scholarships; Alaska Com-
munity Foundation Sven E. & Lorraine Eriksson
Scholarships; UAA Michael D. Ford Memorial Schol-
arships; UAA Muriel Hannah Scholarships in Art;
Providence Alaska Medical Center Auxiliary Scholar-
ships; UAA Eveline Schuster Memorial Award/
Scholarships; Lillian Smith Scholarship for Teaching
Students; UAA Anchorage Daily News Journalism
Scholarships; UAA College of Business & Public
Policy Scholarships; UAA Friends of the Performing
Arts Scholarships; UAA Kimura Scholarship Fund Il-
lustration Scholarships; UAA Kimura Scholarship
Fund Photography Scholarships.

U.S. DEPARTMENT OF DEFENSE

*The following list of supply centers is arranged
alphabetically.*

**61196 ■ Ballistic Missile Defense
Organization**
5700 18th St., Bldg. 245
Fort Belvoir, VA 22060-5573
Co. E-mail: mda.info@mda.mil
URL: http://www.mda.mil

**61197 ■ Defense Contract Administration,
Services, and Management Area Operations**

(Phoenix, Arizona)
The Monroe School Bldg.
215 N. 7th St.
Phoenix, AZ 85034-1012
Ph: (602)379-6170
Fax: (602)379-6409
URL: http://www.dtic.dla.mil/defenselink/

61198 ■ Defense Contract Administration, Services, and Management Area Operations (Phoenix, Arizona)
The Monroe School Bldg.
215 N. 7th St.
Phoenix, AZ 85034-1012
Ph: (602)379-6170
Fax: (602)379-6409
URL: http://www.dtic.dla.mil/defenselink/

61199 ■ Defense Contract Management Agency (Atlanta, Georgia)
805 Walker St.
Marietta, GA 30060-2789
Ph: (770)494-3271
URL: http://www.dcma.mil/CMO/LM_Marietta/contact.cfm

61200 ■ Defense Contract Management Agency (Baltimore, Maryland)
217 E. Redwood St., Ste. 1800
Baltimore, MD 21202-5299
Ph: (410)962-9800
Fax: (410)962-3299

61201 ■ Defense Contract Management Agency (Boston, Massachusetts)
495 Summer St.
Boston, MA 02210-2138
Ph: (617)753-4006
Co. E-mail: casboston@dcma.mil
URL: http://www.dcma.mil/CMO/Boston/contact.cfm

61202 ■ Defense Contract Management Agency (Chicago, Illinois)
10601 W. Higgins Rd., Bldg. 4
Chicago, IL 60666-0911
Ph: (224)625-8201
URL: http://www.dcma.mil/CMO/Chicago/contact.cfm

61203 ■ Defense Contract Management Agency (Clearwater, Florida)
Gasden Bldg., Ste. 200
9549 Kroger Blvd.
St. Petersburg, FL 33702-2455
Ph: (727)258-9511
URL: http://www.dcma.mil/CMO/St_Petersburg/contact.cfm

61204 ■ Defense Contract Management Agency (Dallas, Texas)
1200 Main St., Rm. 640
Dallas, TX 75202-4399
Ph: (214)670-9201
Free: 800-255-8574
URL: http://www.dcma.mil/CMO/Dallas/contact.cfm

61205 ■ Defense Contract Management Agency (Denver, Colorado)
Orchard Pl. 2
5975 Greenwood Plaza Blvd., Ste. 200
Englewood, CO 80111-4751
Ph: (303)220-4005
Fax: (303)220-4125

61206 ■ Defense Contract Management Agency (Denver, Colorado)
Orchard Pl. 2
5975 Greenwood Plaza Blvd., Ste. 200
Englewood, CO 80111-4751
Co. E-mail: dcmadenverseniorstaff@dcma.mil

61207 ■ Defense Contract Management Agency (Detroit, Michigan)
905 McNamara Federal Bldg.
477 Michigan Ave., Rm. 515
Detroit, MI 48226
Ph: (313)226-6075
Fax: (313)226-4769

61208 ■ Defense Contract Management Agency (East Hartford, Connecticut)
130 Darlin St.
East Hartford, CT 06108-3234
Ph: (860)291-7702
Fax: (860)291-7905
Co. E-mail: dcmahartfordseniorleaders@dcma.mil

61209 ■ Defense Contract Management Agency (East Hartford, Connecticut)
130 Darlin St.
East Hartford, CT 06108-3234
Ph: (860)291-7702
Fax: (860)291-7905
Co. E-mail: dcmahartfordseniorleaders@dcma.mil
URL: http://www.dcma.mil/CMO/Hartford/contact.cfm

61210 ■ Defense Contract Management Agency (Garden City, New York)
605 Stewart Ave.
Garden City, NY 11530-4761
Ph: (516)228-5722
Fax: (516)228-5938
Co. E-mail: bvc2251@dcrb.dla.mil

61211 ■ Defense Contract Management Agency (Garden City, New York)
605 Stewart Ave.
Garden City, NY 11530-4761
Ph: (516)228-5715
Co. E-mail: dvc2251@dcrb.dla.mil
URL: http://www.dcma.mil/CMO/Garden_City/contact.cfm

61212 ■ Defense Contract Management Agency (Indianapolis, Indianna)
8899 E. 56th St.
Indianapolis, IN 46249-5701
Ph: (317)510-2016
Fax: (317)510-2348
Co. E-mail: indygid@dcma.mil

61213 ■ Defense Contract Management Agency (Indianapolis, Indianna)
8899 E. 56th St.
Indianapolis, IN 46249-5701
Co. E-mail: indygid@dcma.mil

61214 ■ Defense Contract Management Agency (Orlando, Florida)
3555 Maguire Blvd.
Orlando, FL 32803-3726
Ph: (407)228-5115
Fax: (407)228-5312

61215 ■ Defense Contract Management Agency (Orlando, Florida)
3555 Maguire Blvd.
Orlando, FL 32803-3726
Ph: (407)228-5248
Co. E-mail: dcmaorlando@dcma.mil
URL: http://www.dcma.mil/cmo/Orlando/contact.cfm

61216 ■ Defense Contract Management Agency (Orlando, Florida)
1425 Troutman Blvd., NE
Palm Bay, FL 32905-4102
Ph: (407)228-5248
URL: http://www.dcma.mil/CMO/Orlando/contact.cfm

61217 ■ Defense Contract Management Agency (Philadelphia, Pennsylvania)
2800 S. 20th St.
Philadelphia, PA 19101-7478
Ph: (215)737-5818
Fax: (215)737-7046

61218 ■ Defense Contract Management Agency (Philadelphia, Pennsylvania)
2800 S. 20th St.
Philadelphia, PA 19101-7478
Ph: (215)737-3402
URL: http://www.dcma.mil/CMO/Philadelphia/contact.cfm

61219 ■ Defense Contract Management Agency (Pittsburgh, Pennsylvania)
1612 William S. Moorehead Federal Bldg.
1000 Liberty Ave.
Pittsburgh, PA 15222-4190
Ph: (412)644-5926
Fax: (412)644-5907

61220 ■ Defense Contract Management Agency (St. Louis, Missouri)
1222 Spruce St.
St. Louis, MO 63103-2812
Ph: (314)232-2731
Free: 800-797-8375
URL: http://www.dcma.mil/CMO/Boeing_St_Louis/contact.cfm

61221 ■ Defense Contract Management Agency (San Antonio, Texas)
615 E. Houston St.
San Antonio, TX 78294-1040
Ph: (210)472-4667
Fax: (210)472-4667

61222 ■ Defense Contract Management Agency (San Diego, California)
7675 Dagget St., Ste. 200
San Diego, CA 92111-2241
Ph: (858)495-7411
URL: http://www.dcma.mil/CMO/San_Diego/contact.cfm

61223 ■ Defense Contract Management Agency (San Diego, Texas)
7675 Dagget St., Ste. 200
San Diego, CA 92111-2241
Ph: (858)495-7401
Fax: (858)-495-7660

61224 ■ Defense Contract Management Agency (Santa Ana, California)
34 Civic Center Plz.
Santa Ana, CA 92712-2700
URL: http://www.dcma.mil/CMO/Santa_Ana/contact.cfm

61225 ■ Defense Contract Management Agency (Springfield, New Jersey)
955 S. Springfield Ave.
Springfield, NJ 07081-3170
Ph: (973)724-8201
URL: http://www.dcma.mil/CMO/Springfield/contact.cfm

61226 ■ Defense Contract Management Agency (Stratford, Connecticut)
550 Main St.
Stratford, CT 06497-7574
Ph: (203)385-4418
Fax: (203)385-4418

61227 ■ Defense Contract Management Agency (Stratford, Connecticut)
550 Main St.
Stratford, CT 06497-7574
Ph: (203)386-6766
URL: http://www.dcma.mil/CMO/Sikorsky_Aircraft/contact.cfm

61228 ■ Defense Contract Management Agency (Sunnyvale, California)
1265 Borregas Ave.
Sunnyvale, CA 94089
Ph: (408)541-7042
Fax: (408)541-7084

61229 ■ Defense Contract Management Agency (Syracuse, New York)
615 Erie Blvd. W., Ste. 300
Syracuse, NY 13204-2408
Ph: (315)423-8588
URL: http://www.dcma.mil/cmo/Syracuse/contact.cfm

61230 ■ Defense Contract Management Agency (Twin Cities, Minnesota)
3001 Metro Dr., Ste. 200
Bloomington, MN 55425-1573
Ph: (612)814-4100
Fax: (612)814-4154

61231 ■ Defense Contract Management Agency (Wichita, Kansas)
271 W. 3rd St., N., Ste. 6000
401 N. Market, Ste. B-34
Wichita, KS 67202-1212
Ph: (316)299-7201
URL: http://www.dcma.mil/CMO/Wichita/contact.cfm

61232 ■ Defense Contract Management Agency - Aircraft Program - Management Office
805 Walker St.
Marietta, GA 30060-2789
Ph: (770)590-6197
Fax: (770)590-6551

61233 ■ Defense Contract Management Agency (Baltimore, Maryland) - Baltimore Office
217 E. Redwood St., Ste. 1800
Baltimore, MD 21202-5299
Ph: (410)962-9800
Fax: (410)962-3299
Co. E-mail: gtd@dcma.mil
URL: http://www.dcma.mil/cmo/Baltimore/contact.cfm

61234 ■ Defense Contract Management Agency District Headquarters (Boston, Massachusetts)
495 Summer St., 8th Fl.
Boston, MA 02210-2184
Ph: (617)753-4006
Free: 800-321-1861
URL: http://www.dcma.mil/CMO/Boston/contact.cfm

61235 ■ Defense Contract Management Area Operations (Detroit, Michigan)
905 McNamara Federal Bldg.
477 Michigan Ave., Rm. 515
Detroit, MI 48226
Ph: (586)365-0589
URL: http://www.dcma.mil/CMO/Detroit/contact.cfm

61236 ■ Defense Contract Management Area Operations (Grand Rapids, Michigan)
Riverview Center Bldg.
678 Front St. NW
Grand Rapids, MI 49504-5352
Co. E-mail: dcm_detroit@dcma.mil

61237 ■ Defense Contract Management Area Operations (Grand Rapids, Michigan)
Riverview Center Bldg.
678 Front St. NW
Grand Rapids, MI 49504-5352
Ph: (616)233-4601
Fax: (616)233-4630
Co. E-mail: dcm_detroit@dcma.mil

61238 ■ Defense Contract Management Area Operations (Pittsburgh, Pennsylvania)
1612 William S. Moorehead Federal Bldg.
1000 Liberty Ave.
Pittsburgh, PA 15222-4190

61239 ■ Defense Contract Management Area Operations (Reading, Pennsylvania)
1125 Berkshire Blvd., Ste. 160
Wyomissing, PA 19610-1249

61240 ■ Defense Contract Management Area Operations (Reading, Pennsylvania)
1125 Berkshire Blvd., Ste. 160
Wyomissing, PA 19610-1249
Ph: (610)320-5012
Fax: (610)320-5075

61241 ■ Defense Contract Management Area Operations (San Antonio, Texas)
615 E. Houston St.
San Antonio, TX 78294-1040
Co. E-mail: contract@dcma.mil

61242 ■ Defense Contract Management Area Operations (San Francisco, California)
1265 Borregas Ave.
Sunnyvale, CA 94089
Ph: (408)541-7042

Fax: (408)541-7084
Co. E-mail: jfosbery@dcmdw.dla.mil

61243 ■ Defense Contract Management Area Operations (Springfield, New Jersey)
955 S. Springfield Ave.
Springfield, NJ 07081-3170

61244 ■ Defense Contract Management Area Operations (Syracuse, New York)
615 Erie Blvd. W., Ste. 300
Syracuse, NY 13204-2408
Ph: (315)448-7817
Co. E-mail: Syracuse_cas_poc@dcma.mil

61245 ■ Defense Contract Management Area Operations (Van Nuys, California)
6230 Van Nuys Blvd.
Van Nuys, CA 91401-2713
Ph: (818)756-4444
Fax: (818)904-6532
Co. E-mail: romeo_allas@vnyao.dcmdw.dla.mil

61246 ■ Defense Contract Management Area Operations (Van Nuys, California)
6230 Van Nuys Blvd.
Van Nuys, CA 91401-2713
Ph: (818)756-4444
Fax: (818)904-6532
Co. E-mail: romeo_allas@vnyao.dcmdw.dla.mil

61247 ■ Defense Contract Management Area Operations, Twin Cities
3001 Metro Dr., Ste. 200
Bloomington, MN 55425-1573
Ph: (612)814-4100
Fax: (612)814-4154
Co. E-mail: omurry@gt-link.dcmdc.dla.mil

61248 ■ Defense Contract Management Center
1910 Third Ave. N., Ste. 201
Birmingham, AL 35203-3502
Ph: (205)716-7402
Fax: (205)716-7836

61249 ■ Defense Contract Management Center
1910 Third Ave. N., Ste. 201
Birmingham, AL 35203-3502

61250 ■ Defense Contract Management Center - Aircraft Program - Management Office
805 Walker St.
Marietta, GA 30060-2789
Ph: (770)590-6197
Fax: (770)590-6551

61251 ■ Defense Contract Management Command (Atlanta, Georgia)
805 Walker St.
Marietta, GA 30060-2789
Ph: (770)590-6197
Fax: (770)590-6551

61252 ■ Defense Contract Management Command (Boston-Manchester)
2 Wall St.
Manchester, NH 03101-1518
Ph: (603)621-0413
Fax: (603)621-4835
Co. E-mail: casboston@dcma.mil

61253 ■ Defense Contract Management Command (Boston, Massachusetts)
495 Summer St.
Boston, MA 02210-2138
Ph: (617)753-4006
Fax: (617)753-4005
Co. E-mail: casboston@dcma.mil

61254 ■ Defense Contract Management Command (Buffalo, New York)
Thaddeus J. Dulski Federal Bldg., Rm. 1103
111 W. Huron St.
Buffalo, NY 14202-2392
Ph: (716)551-4761
Fax: (716)551-4531

61255 ■ Defense Contract Management Command (Buffalo, New York)
Thaddeus J. Dulski Federal Bldg., Rm. 1103
111 W. Huron St.
Buffalo, NY 14202-2392
Ph: (716)551-4761
Fax: (716)551-4531

61256 ■ Defense Contract Management Command (Chicago, Illinois)
10601 W. Higgins Rd., Bldg. 4
Chicago, IL 60666-0911
Ph: (773)825-6800
Free: 800-637-3848
Fax: (773)825-5424
URL: http://www.dcmdc.hq.dla.mil

61257 ■ Defense Contract Management Command (Cleveland, Ohio)
555 E. 88th St.
Bratenahl, OH 44108-1068

61258 ■ Defense Contract Management Command (Cleveland, Ohio)
555 E. 88th St.
Bratenahl, OH 44108-1068

61259 ■ Defense Contract Management Command (Dallas, Texas)
1200 Main St., Rm. 640
Dallas, TX 75202-4399
Ph: (214)670-9205
Free: 800-255-8574
Fax: (214)573-2185

61260 ■ Defense Contract Management Command (Dayton, Ohio)
Area C, Bldg. 30
1725 Van Patton Dr.
Wright Patterson AFB, OH 45433-5302
Ph: (937)656-3104
Fax: (937)656-3228

61261 ■ Defense Contract Management Command (Dayton, Ohio)
Area C, Bldg. 30
1725 Van Patton Dr.
Wright Patterson AFB, OH 45433-5302

61262 ■ Defense Contract Management Command (Louisville Kentucky)
120 Rochester Dr.
Louisville, KY 40214-2681
Ph: (502)364-6492

61263 ■ Defense Contract Management Command (Louisville, Kentucky)
120 Rochester Dr.
Louisville, KY 40214-2681
Ph: (502)364-6492

61264 ■ Defense Contract Management Command (Orlando, Florida)
1425 Troutman Blvd., NE
Palm Bay, FL 32905-4102
Ph: (407)727-4367
Fax: (407)729-3334

61265 ■ Defense Contract Management Command (St. Louis, Missouri)
1222 Spruce St.
St. Louis, MO 63103-2812
Ph: (314)331-5431
Free: 800-797-8375
Fax: (314)331-5800

61266 ■ Defense Contract Management Command (St. Petersburg, Florida)
Gasden Bldg., Ste. 200
9549 Kroger Blvd.
St. Petersburg, FL 33702-2455
Ph: (813)579-3100
Fax: (813)579-3106

61267 ■ Defense Contract Management Command (Santa Ana, California)
34 Civic Center Plz.
Santa Ana, CA 92712-2700
Ph: (714)836-2912

Fax: (714)836-2358

61268 ■ Defense Contract Management Command (Seattle, Washington)
3009 112th Ave., NE, Ste. 200
Bellevue, WA 98004-8019
Ph: (206)889-7317
Fax: (206)889-7252

61269 ■ Defense Contract Management Command (Seattle, Washington)
3009 112th Ave., NE, Ste. 200
Bellevue, WA 98004-8019

61270 ■ Defense Contract Management Command (South Bend, Indiana)
244 S. Olive St.
South Bend, IN 46619-7726
Ph: (219)429-7726
Fax: (219)236-8118

61271 ■ Defense Contract Management Command (South Bend, Indiana)
244 S. Olive St.
South Bend, IN 46619-7726

61272 ■ Defense Contract Management Command (Staten Island, New York)
Ft. Wadsworth
Staten Island, NY 10305
Ph: (718)390-1016
Fax: (718)390-1020

61273 ■ Defense Contract Management Command (Staten Island, New York)
Ft. Wadsworth
Staten Island, NY 10305
Ph: (718)390-1016
Fax: (718)390-1020

61274 ■ Defense Contract Management Command (Wichita, Kansas)
271 W. 3rd St., N., Ste. 6000
401 N. Market, Ste. B-34
Wichita, KS 67202-1212
Ph: (316)299-7219
Fax: (316)299-7302

61275 ■ Defense Contract Management Command, Boston-Manchester
2 Wall St.
Manchester, NH 03101-1518
Ph: (603)621-0413
Fax: (603)621-4835
Co. E-mail: casboston@dcma.mil

61276 ■ Defense Contract Management District Headquarters (Boston, Massachusetts)
495 Summer St., 8th Fl.
Boston, MA 02210-2184
Ph: (617)753-4317
Free: 800-321-1861
Fax: (617)753-3174

61277 ■ Defense Information Systems Agency
PO Box 4502
Arlington, VA 22204-4502
Ph: (703)607-6515
Fax: (703)607-4344
URL: http://www.disa.mil

61278 ■ Defense Information Systems Agency
PO Box 4502
Arlington, VA 22204-4502
Ph: (703)607-6515
Fax: (703)607-4344
Co. E-mail: bergerr@ncr.disa.mil
URL: http://www.disa.mil

61279 ■ Defense Information Systems Agency (DISA) - Office of Small Business Programs
PO Box 4502
Arlington, VA 22204-4502
Ph: (703)607-6436

Fax: (703)607-4173
Co. E-mail: disasmallbusinessoffice@disa.mil
URL: http://www.acq.osd.mil/osbp/offices/index.shtml

61280 ■ Defense Information Systems Agency (DISA) - Office of Small and Disadvantaged Business Utilization
701 S. Courthouse Rd., D04 RM. 1108B
Arlington, VA 22204-2199
Ph: (703)607-6436
Fax: (703)607-4173
Co. E-mail: disasmallbusinessoffice@disa.mil

61281 ■ Defense Plant Representative Office (Great Neck, New York)
Defense Logistics Agency
Northeast DPRO
c/o Unisys Corp.
365 Lakerville Rd.
Great Neck, NY 11020-1696
Ph: (516)574-2987
Fax: (516)228-5938

61282 ■ Defense Plant Representative Office (Great Neck, New York)
Defense Logistics Agency
Northeast DPRO
c/o Unisys Corp.
365 Lakerville Rd.
Great Neck, NY 11020-1696

61283 ■ Defense Plant Representative Office (Los Angeles, California)
Hughes Aircraft Co.
Los Angeles, CA 90009-2463

61284 ■ Defense Plant Representative Office (Los Angeles, California)
Hughes Aircraft Co.
Los Angeles, CA 90009-2463

61285 ■ Defense Plant Representative Office (Marietta, Georgia)
c/o Lockheed Georgia Co.
86 S. Cobb Dr.
Marietta, GA 30063-0567

61286 ■ Defense Plant Representative Office (Marietta, Georgia)
c/o Lockheed Georgia Co.
86 S. Cobb Dr.
Marietta, GA 30063-0567

61287 ■ Defense Plant Representative Office (Tucson, Arizona)
Hughes Aircraft Co.
Missile Systems Group
Tucson, AZ 85734-1337
Fax: (602)794-3275

61288 ■ Defense Plant Representative Office (Tucson, Arizona)
Hughes Aircraft Co.
Missile Systems Group
Tucson, AZ 85734-1337

61289 ■ Defense Plant Representative Office (West Palm Beach, Florida)
Pratt & Whitney Aircraft Group
Government Engine and Space Propulsion Division
West Palm Beach, FL 33410-9600

61290 ■ Defense Plant Representative Office, West Palm Beach, Florida
Pratt & Whitney Aircraft Group
Government Engine and Space Propulsion Division
West Palm Beach, FL 33410-9600

61291 ■ Defense Threat Reduction Agency - Office of Small and Disadvantaged Business Utilization
8725 John J. Kingman Rd.
Fort Belvoir, VA 22310-3398
Ph: (703)767-4799
Co. E-mail: dtra.publicaffairs@dtra.mil
URL: http://www.dtra.mil/

61292 ■ Defense Threat Reduction Agency - Office of Small and Disadvantaged Business Utilization
8725 John J. Kingman Rd., Stop 6201
Fort Belvoir, VA 22060-6201
Ph: (703)767-4799
Co. E-mail: ato.andoh@dtra.mil
URL: http://www.dtra.mil/business/officeSBP.aspx

61293 ■ Department of Defense - Defense Logistics Agency - Defense Construction Supply Center
3990 E. Broad St.
Columbus, OH 43218-3990
Ph: (614)692-3131
Free: 877-352-2255
Co. E-mail: dlacontactcenter@dla.mil
URL: http://www.landandmaritime.dla.mil/

61294 ■ Department of Defense - Defense Logistics Agency - Defense Electronics Supply Center
1507 Wilmington Pke.
Dayton, OH 45444-5000
Fax: (513)296-5038

61295 ■ Department of Defense - Defense Logistics Agency - Defense Electronics Supply Center
1507 Wilmington Pke.
Dayton, OH 45444-5000

61296 ■ Department of Defense - Defense Logistics Agency - Defense General Supply Center
8000 Jefferson Davis Hwy.
Richmond, VA 23297-5100
Ph: (804)279-3861
URL: http://www.dscr.dla.mil

61297 ■ Department of Defense - Defense Logistics Agency - Defense General Supply Center
8000 Jefferson Davis Hwy.
Richmond, VA 23297-5100
Ph: (804)279-3861
URL: http://www.aviation.dla.mil/

61298 ■ Department of Defense - Defense Logistics Agency - Defense Industrial Supply Center
700 Robbins Ave.
Philadelphia, PA 19111-5092

61299 ■ Department of Defense - Defense Logistics Agency - Defense Supply Center (Columbus, Ohio)
3990 E. Broad St.
Columbus, OH 43218-3990
Ph: (614)692-3131
Free: 877-352-2255
Co. E-mail: dlacontactcenter@dla.mil
URL: http://www.dscc.dla.mil

61300 ■ Department of Defense - Defense Logistics Agency - Defense Supply Center Philadelphia
2800 S. 20th St.
Philadelphia, PA 19101
Free: 800-523-0705
Fax: (215)737-7116

61301 ■ Department of Defense - Defense Logistics Agency - Troop Support
700 Robbins Ave.
Philadelphia, PA 19111-5092
Ph: (215)697-2747
Fax: (215)697-3465
URL: http://www.dscp.dla.mil/

61302 ■ Missile Defense Agency - Office of Small Business Programs - U.S. Department of Defense
7100 Defense Pentagon
Washington, DC 20301-7100
Ph: (703)697-6634
Co. E-mail: missiledefenseagencyoutreach@mda.mil
URL: http://www.mda.mil

61303 ■ Naval Technical Representative Office (Laurel, Maryland)
Johns Hopkins Rd.
Laurel, MD 20723-6090
Fax: (301)953-6370

61304 ■ Naval Technical Representative Office (Laurel, Maryland)
Johns Hopkins Rd.
Laurel, MD 20723-6090

61305 ■ Office of Civil Rights - Office of Small and Disadvantaged Business Utilization - U.S. Department of Education
Potomac Center Plaza, Rm. 7050
550 12th St. SW
Washington, DC 20202
Ph: (202)245-6300
URL: http://www.ed.gov/about/offices/list/ods/osdbu.html

61306 ■ Office of the Secretary of the Army - Office of Small Business Programs
106 Army Pentagon, Rm. 3B514
Washington, DC 20310-0106
Ph: (703)697-2868
Fax: (703)693-3898
URL: http://www.sellingtoarmy.info

61307 ■ Office of the Secretary of the Army - Office of Small Business Programs
106 Army Pentagon, Rm. 3B514
Washington, DC 20310-0106
Ph: (703)697-2868
Fax: (703)693-3898
Co. E-mail: suellen.jeffress@us.army.mil
URL: http://www.sellingtoarmy.info

61308 ■ Office of the Secretary of the Navy - Office of Small Business Programs
720 Kennon St. SE, Bldg. 36, Rm. 207
Washington, DC 20374-5015
Ph: (202)685-6485
Fax: (202)685-6865
Co. E-mail: OSBP.info@navy.mil
URL: http://www.donhq.navy.mil/OSBP/about/staff.html

61309 ■ Office of the Under Secretary of the Navy - Office of Small Business Programs
720 Kennon St. SE, Bldg. 36, Rm. 207
Washington, DC 20374-5015
Ph: (202)685-6485
Fax: (202)685-6865
Co. E-mail: OSBP.info@navy.mil
URL: http://www.hq.navy.mil/sadbu

61310 ■ U.S. Department of Defense (DOD) - Office of Small Business Programs
Crystal Gateway N., Ste. 406, W. Tower
201 12th St. S.
Washington, DC 20003-1427
Ph: (703)604-0157
Fax: (703)604-0025
Co. E-mail: OSBPinfo@osd.mil
URL: http://www.acq.osd.mil/sadbu

Description: One of the primary objectives of the Department of Defense (DOD) is to acquire weapons and materials that fully meet qualitative, quantitative, and delivery requirements at the lowest overall cost. Maximum emphasis is placed on full and free competition to achieve this objective, with equal opportunity to all interested, qualified suppliers to compete for defense contracts. The Department of Defense's military departments and defense agencies have contracting offices located throughout the United States. Each department and agency has an office of the director of small and disadvantaged business utilization. They also have small business specialists at each of their procurement and contract administration offices to assist small and disadvantaged businesses, women-owned businesses, minority-owned businesses, and firms to market their products and services with the DOD. These specialists can provide information and guidance on defense procurement procedures, placement on the solicitation mailing lists, and identification of both prime and subcontract opportunities.

61311 ■ U.S. Department of Defense - Office of Small Business Programs
4800 Mark Center Dr., Ste. 15G13
Alexandria, VA 22350
Ph: (571)372-6191
Fax: (571)371-6195
Co. E-mail: OSBPinfo@osd.mil
URL: http://www.acq.osd.mil/osbp/

Description: One of the primary objectives of the Department of Defense (DOD) is to acquire weapons and materials that fully meet qualitative, quantitative, and delivery requirements at the lowest overall cost. Maximum emphasis is placed on full and free competition to achieve this objective, with equal opportunity to all interested, qualified suppliers to compete for defense contracts. The Department of Defense's military departments and defense agencies have contracting offices located throughout the United States. Each department and agency has an office of the director of small and disadvantaged business utilization. They also have small business specialists at each of their procurement and contract administration offices to assist small and disadvantaged businesses, women-owned businesses, minority-owned businesses, and firms to market their products and services with the DOD. These specialists can provide information and guidance on defense procurement procedures, placement on the solicitation mailing lists, and identification of both prime and subcontract opportunities.

U.S. DEPARTMENT OF EDUCATION

61312 ■ U.S. Department of Education - Assistant Secretary for Educational Research and Improvement - Small Business Innovation Research Program Coordinator
555 New Jersey Ave., NW, Rm. 608D
Washington, DC 20208-5544
Ph: (202)208-1983
Fax: (202)219-2030
URL: http://www.ed.gov/programs/sbir/index.html

61313 ■ U.S. Department of Education - Assistant Secretary for Educational Research and Improvement - Small Business Innovation Research Program Coordinator
555 New Jersey Ave. NW, Rm. 608D
Washington, DC 20208-5544
Ph: (202)208-1983
Fax: (202)219-2030
Co. E-mail: Edward.metz@ed.gov
URL: http://www.ed.gov/programs/sbir/index.html

61314 ■ U.S. Department of Education - Office for Civil Rights - Office of Small and Disadvantaged Business Utilization
Potomac Center Plaza
550 12th St. SW, Rm. 7050
Washington, DC 20202
Ph: (202)245-6300
Co. E-mail: beatrice.pacheco@ost.dot.gov
URL: http://www.ed.gov/about/offices/list/ods/osdbu.html

61315 ■ U.S. Department of Education - Office of Small and Disadvantaged Business Utilization
Potomac Center Plaza, Rm. 7050
550 12th St. SW
Washington, DC 20202
Ph: (202)245-6300
Fax: (202)245-7304
URL: http://www.ed.gov/about/offices/list/ods/osdbu.html

Description: The Department of Education solicits proposals for the following services and materials: management consulting; program evaluation or surveys; computer-based projects; student testing materials; plus other professional services. In addition, federal funds may be used by schools, state agencies, and other recipients for the purchase of audiovisual and other types of equipment. Inquiries should be made to the applicable organization. The department also provides various publications to aid small businesses in their dealings. These publica-

tions include A Guide to U.S. Department of Education Programs. This annual guide provides the information necessary to begin the process of applying for funding from individual federal education programs. Another publication is Doing Business With the Department of Education. This guide is designed to provide business firms, small businesses, small disadvantaged businesses, and small disadvantaged subcontractors with basic information on contracting opportunities with the Department of Education. A 'Forecast of Contract Opportunities' is also available listing upcoming contracts, which is distributed by the OSDBU office.

61316 ■ U.S. Department of Education - Office of Small and Disadvantaged Business Utilization
Potomac Center Plaza
550 12th St. SW, Rm. 7050
Washington, DC 20202
Ph: (202)245-6300
Fax: (202)245-7304
URL: http://www.ed.gov/about/offices/list/ods/osdbu.html

Description: The Department of Education solicits proposals for the following services and materials: management consulting; program evaluation or surveys; computer-based projects; student testing materials; plus other professional services. In addition, federal funds may be used by schools, state agencies, and other recipients for the purchase of audiovisual and other types of equipment. Inquiries should be made to the applicable organization. The department also provides various publications to aid small businesses in their dealings. These publications include A Guide to U.S. Department of Education Programs. This annual guide provides the information necessary to begin the process of applying for funding from individual federal education programs. Another publication is Doing Business With the Department of Education. This guide is designed to provide business firms, small businesses, small disadvantaged businesses, and small disadvantaged subcontractors with basic information on contracting opportunities with the Department of Education. A 'Forecast of Contract Opportunities' is also available listing upcoming contracts, which is distributed by the OSDBU office.

61317 ■ University of Delaware
33 Smith Hall
Newark, DE 19716
Ph: (302)831-2792
Fax: (302)831-4205
Co. E-mail: www@udel.edu
URL: http://www.udel.edu

61318 ■ University of Delaware
33 Smith Hall
Newark, DE 19716
Ph: (302)831-2792
Fax: (302)831-4205
Co. E-mail: www@udel.edu
URL: http://www.udel.edu

U.S. DEPARTMENT OF ENERGY

The following power administration offices are arranged alphabetically.

61319 ■ U.S. Department of Energy - Alaska Power Administration
PO Box 101020
Anchorage, AK 99510-1020
Ph: (907)338-6100
URL: http://www.ahfc.state.ak.us/energy/energy.cfm

61320 ■ U.S. Department of Energy - Alaska Power Administration
4300 Boniface Pkwy.
Anchorage, AK 99504
Ph: (907)338-6100
Fax: (907)338-9218
URL: http://www.ahfc.us/about/office_locations.cfm

61321 ■ U.S. Department of Energy - Albuquerque Operations Office
PO Box 5400
Albuquerque, NM 87185-5400
Ph: (505)845-4665
Co. E-mail: fbaca@doeal.gov
URL: http://www.doeal.gov/ofcfo/default.htm

61322 ■ U.S. Department of Energy - Amarillo Field Office
801 S. Fillmore St., Ste. 500
Amarillo, TX 79101-3545

61323 ■ U.S. Department of Energy - Argonne Area Office
9800 S. Cass Ave.
Argonne, IL 60439
Ph: (630)252-2000
Fax: (630)252-5274
URL: http://www.anl.gov/index.html

61324 ■ U.S. Department of Energy - Argonne Area Office
9800 S. Cass Ave.
Argonne, IL 60439
Ph: (630)252-2000
Fax: (630)252-5274
URL: http://www.anl.gov/index.html

61325 ■ U.S. Department of Energy - Argonne National Laboratory (West) - Idaho Operations Office
1955 N. Freemont Ave.
Idaho Falls, ID 83415
Ph: (208)533-7341
URL: http://www.inl.gov

61326 ■ U.S. Department of Energy - Argonne National Laboratory (West) - Idaho Operations Office
1955 N. Freemont Ave.
Idaho Falls, ID 83415
Ph: (208)533-7341
URL: http://www.inl.gov

61327 ■ U.S. Department of Energy - Atlanta Support Office
75 Spring St., Ste. 200
Atlanta, GA 30308-3308
Ph: (404)562-0556
Free: 877--3472839
Fax: (404)562-0538

61328 ■ U.S. Department of Energy - Atlanta Support Office
75 Spring St., Ste. 200
Atlanta, GA 30308-3308

61329 ■ U.S. Department of Energy - Bettis Atomic Power Laboratory
c/o Bechtel Bettis, Inc.
814 Pittsburgh McKeesport Blvd.
West Mifflin, PA 15122-2849
Ph: (412)476-6000
Free: 800-296-5002
URL: http://www.bettislab.com

61330 ■ U.S. Department of Energy - Bettis Atomic Power Laboratory
c/o Bechtel Bettis, Inc.
814 Pittsburgh McKeesport Blvd.
West Mifflin, PA 15122-2849
Ph: (412)476-6000
Free: 800-296-5002
URL: http://www.bettislab.com

61331 ■ U.S. Department of Energy - Bonneville Power Administration
905 NE 11th Ave.
Portland, OR 97208-3621
Ph: (503)230-3000
Free: 800-282-3713
Fax: (501)230-3285
URL: http://www.bpa.gov

61332 ■ U.S. Department of Energy - Bonneville Power Administration
905 NE 11th Ave.
Portland, OR 97232

Ph: (503)230-3000
Free: 800-282-3713
Fax: (501)230-3285
URL: http://www.bpa.gov

61333 ■ U.S. Department of Energy - Boston Regional Office
John F. Kennedy Federal Bldg., Ste. 675
Boston, MA 02203-0002
Fax: (617)565-9723

61334 ■ U.S. Department of Energy - Boston Regional Office
John F. Kennedy Federal Bldg., Ste. 675
Boston, MA 02203-0002
Ph: (617)565-9712
Fax: (617)565-9723

61335 ■ U.S. Department of Energy - Brookhaven Area Office
PO Box 5000
Upton, NY 11973-5000
Ph: (631)344-8000
URL: http://www.bnl.gov/world/

61336 ■ U.S. Department of Energy - Brookhaven National Laboratory
53 Bell Ave., Bldg. 464
Upton, NY 11973
Ph: (631)344-3427
URL: http://www.ch.doe.gov/

61337 ■ U.S. Department of Energy - Carlsbad Field Office
4021 National Parks Highway
Carlsbad, NM 88220
Ph: (505)887-6544
Free: 800-336-9477
Fax: (505)885-9264
URL: http://www.wipp.energy.gov/

61338 ■ U.S. Department of Energy - Carlsbad Field Office - Waste Isolation Pilot Plant
4021 National Parks Highway
Carlsbad, NM 88220
Ph: (505)887-6544
Free: 800-336-9477
Fax: (505)885-9264
URL: http://www.wipp.energy.gov/

61339 ■ U.S. Department of Energy - Chicago Operations Office
9700 S. Cass Ave.
Argonne, IL 60439
Ph: (630)252-2000
Fax: (630)252-2527
URL: http://www.anl.gov

61340 ■ U.S. Department of Energy - Chicago Operations Office
9700 S. Cass Ave.
Argonne, IL 60439
Ph: (630)252-2000
Fax: (630)252-2527
URL: http://www.anl.gov

61341 ■ U.S. Department of Energy - Chicago Regional Office
9800 S. Cass Ave.
Argonne, IL 60439
Ph: (630)252-2110
Fax: (312)886-8561
Co. E-mail: webmaster@ch.doe.gov
URL: http://www.ch.doe.gov/

61342 ■ U.S. Department of Energy - Chicago Regional Office
9800 S. Cass Ave.
Argonne, IL 60439
Ph: (630)252-2110
URL: http://www.ch.doe.gov/

61343 ■ U.S. Department of Energy - Denver Regional Office
1617 Cole Blvd.
Golden, CO 80401-3305
Ph: (303)275-4700
Fax: (303)275-4830

61344 ■ U.S. Department of Energy - Denver Regional Office
1617 Cole Blvd.
Mail Stop 1521
Golden, CO 80401

61345 ■ U.S. Department of Energy - Energy Efficiency and Renewable Energy - Golden Field Office
1617 Cole Blvd.
Mail Stop 1501
Golden, CO 80401
Ph: (303)275-4700
Fax: (303)275-4788
URL: http://www.eere.energy.gov/golden/

61346 ■ U.S. Department of Energy - Energy Efficiency and Renewable Energy - Golden Field Office
1617 Cole Blvd.
Mail Stop 1501
Golden, CO 80401
Ph: (720)356-1800
Fax: (720)356-1750
URL: http://www.eere.energy.gov/golden/

61347 ■ U.S. Department of Energy - Fermi National Accelerator Laboratory
PO Box 500
Batavia, IL 60510-5011
Ph: (630)840-3000
URL: http://www.fnal.gov/

61348 ■ U.S. Department of Energy - Fermi Site Office
PO Box 500
Batavia, IL 60510-5011
Ph: (630)840-3000
Fax: (630)840-4343
URL: http://www.fnal.gov/

61349 ■ U.S. Department of Energy, Headquarters (DOE) - Office of Small and Disadvantaged Business Utilization
1000 Independence Ave. SW, Rm. 5B-148
Washington, DC 20585
Ph: (202)586-7377
Fax: (202)586-5488
Co. E-mail: Small.Business@hq.doe.gov
URL: http://smallbusiness.doe.gov/
Description: The Department of Energy purchases a wide variety of materials, equipment, supplies, and support services at each DOE buying office. Small business/disadvantaged business specialists are located at DOE offices throughout the United States to assist small business owners in procurement matters. DOE also administers--together with the National Bureau of Standards--the Energy-Related Inventions Program, a comprehensive program for research and development of all potentially beneficial energy sources and utilization technologies. The program calls for particular attention to be paid to individual inventors and small companies seeking direct grants (for information on this program call (301)975-5500).

61350 ■ U.S. Department of Energy, Headquarters - Office of Small and Disadvantaged Business Utilization
1000 Independence Ave. SW, Rm. 5B-148
Washington, DC 20585
Ph: (202)586-7377
Fax: (202)586-5488
Co. E-mail: Small.Business@hq.doe.gov
URL: http://smallbusiness.doe.gov/
Description: The Department of Energy purchases a wide variety of materials, equipment, supplies, and support services at each DOE buying office. Small business/disadvantaged business specialists are located at DOE offices throughout the United States to assist small business owners in procurement matters. DOE also administers--together with the National Bureau of Standards--the Energy-Related Inventions Program, a comprehensive program for research and development of all potentially beneficial energy sources and utilization technologies. The program calls for particular attention to be paid to individual inventors and small companies seeking direct grants (for information on this program call (301)975-5500).

61351 ■ U.S. Department of Energy - Idaho Operations Office
1955 Fremont Ave.
Idaho Falls, ID 83415
Ph: (208)526-1322
Fax: (208)526-5406
URL: http://www.id.doe.gov/index.htm

61352 ■ U.S. Department of Energy - Idaho Operations Office
1955 Fremont Ave.
Idaho Falls, ID 83415
Ph: (208)526-1322
Fax: (208)526-5406
URL: http://www.id.doe.gov/

61353 ■ U.S. Department of Energy - Kirtland Area Office
PO Box 5400
Albuquerque, NM 87185-5400
Ph: (505)845-5542
Fax: (505)845-4710

61354 ■ U.S. Department of Energy - Los Alamos Area Office
528 35th St.
Los Alamos, NM 87544
Fax: (505)667-9998

61355 ■ U.S. Department of Energy - Los Alamos Area Office
3747 W. Jemez Rd.
Los Alamos, NM 87544
Ph: (505)667-6691
URL: http://www.doeal.gov/laso/default.aspx

61356 ■ U.S. Department of Energy (NETL-MGN) - National Energy Technology Laboratory
3610 Collins Ferry Rd.
Morgantown, WV 26507-0880
Ph: (304)285-4764
Free: 800-553-4403
Co. E-mail: anna@netl.doe.gov
URL: http://www.netl.doe.gov

61357 ■ U.S. Department of Energy (NETL-MGN) - National Energy Technology Laboratory
3610 Collins Ferry Rd.
Morgantown, WV 26507-0880
Ph: (304)285-4764
Free: 800-553-4403
Co. E-mail: anna@netl.doe.gov
URL: http://www.netl.doe.gov

61358 ■ U.S. Department of Energy - National Nuclear Security Administration Service Center
PO Box 5400
Albuquerque, NM 87185-5400
Ph: (505)845-4665
URL: http://www.doeal.gov/ofcfo/default.htm

61359 ■ U.S. Department of Energy - Nevada Operations Office
PO Box 98518
Las Vegas, NV 89193-8518
Ph: (702)295-3521
URL: http://www.nv.doe.gov/default.htm

61360 ■ U.S. Department of Energy - Nevada Operations Office
PO Box 98518
Las Vegas, NV 89193-8518
Ph: (702)295-3521
URL: http://www.nv.doe.gov/default.htm

61361 ■ U.S. Department of Energy - Oak Ridge National Laboratory
200 Administration Rd.
Oak Ridge, TN 37831
Ph: (865)576-0885
Free: 800-382-6938
Fax: (865)576-1665
URL: http://www.oakridge.doe.gov

61362 ■ U.S. Department of Energy - Oak Ridge Operations Office
200 Administration Rd.
Oak Ridge, TN 37830
Ph: (865)576-0885
Free: 800-382-6938
Fax: (865)576-1665
URL: http://www.oakridge.doe.gov

61363 ■ U.S. Department of Energy - Office of Kansas City Site Operations
2000 E. 9th St.
Kansas City, MO 64131-6159
Ph: (816)997-2000
Fax: (816)997-4094
Co. E-mail: Customer_Inquiry@kcp.com
URL: http://www.honeywell.com/sites/kcp/

61364 ■ U.S. Department of Energy - Office of Kansas City Site Operations
2000 E. 9th St.
Kansas City, MO 64131-6159
Ph: (816)997-2000
Fax: (816)997-7259
Co. E-mail: Customer_feedback@kcp.com
URL: http://honeywell.com/sites/aero-kcp/About-Us/
  Pages/contact-us.aspx

61365 ■ U.S. Department of Energy - Philadelphia Regional Support Office
1880 John F. Kennedy Blvd., Ste. 501
Philadelphia, PA 19102
Fax: (215)264-2272

61366 ■ U.S. Department of Energy - Philadelphia Regional Support Office
1880 John F. Kennedy Blvd., Ste. 501
Philadelphia, PA 19102
Ph: (215)264-0691
Fax: (215)264-2272

61367 ■ U.S. Department of Energy - Pinellas Area Office
PO Box 2900
Largo, FL 33779
Fax: (813)545-6287

61368 ■ U.S. Department of Energy - Pinellas Area Office
PO Box 2900
Largo, FL 33779
Ph: (813)541-8196
Fax: (813)545-6287

61369 ■ U.S. Department of Energy - Pittsburgh Energy Technology Center
626 Cochran Mill Rd.
Pittsburgh, PA 15236-0940
Ph: (412)386-4687
Fax: (412)386-4604
URL: http://www.netl.doe.gov

61370 ■ U.S. Department of Energy - Pittsburgh Energy Technology Center
626 Cochran Mill Rd.
Jefferson Hills, PA 15025
Ph: (412)386-4984
Fax: (412)386-4604
URL: http://www.netl.doe.gov

61371 ■ U.S. Department of Energy - Pittsburgh Naval Reactors (PNR)
PO Box 109
West Mifflin, PA 15122-0109
Ph: (412)476-7240
Fax: (412)476-7310
Co. E-mail: bullianj@bettis.gov
URL: http://management.energy.gov/contact_us/
  1203.htm

61372 ■ U.S. Department of Energy - Pittsburgh Naval Reactors (PNR)
PO Box 109
West Mifflin, PA 15122-0109
Ph: (412)476-7240
Fax: (412)476-7310
Co. E-mail: bullianj@bettis.gov
URL: http://management.energy.gov/contact_us/
  1203.htm

61373 ■ U.S. Department of Energy - Princeton Area Office
PO Box 102
Princeton, NJ 08542
Ph: (609)243-3700
Fax: (609)243-2032
URL: http://www-pg.pppl.gov/index.html

61374 ■ U.S. Department of Energy - Princeton Plasma Physics Laboratory
PO Box 102
Princeton, NJ 08542
Ph: (609)243-3700
Fax: (609)243-2032
Co. E-mail: pppl_info@pppl.gov
URL: http://www.ch.doe.gov/

61375 ■ U.S. Department of Energy - Richland Operations Office - Office of Organizational Effectiveness and Communications
825 Jadwin Ave.
Mail Stop A7-75
Richland, WA 99352
Ph: (509)376-7501
Fax: (509)376-1563
Co. E-mail: webmaster@rl.gov
URL: http://www.hanford.gov/rl/

61376 ■ U.S. Department of Energy - Richland Operations Office - Office of Organizational Effectiveness and Communications
825 Jadwin Ave., Ste. 1
Richland, WA 99352
Ph: (509)376-7411
Fax: (509)376-1563
Co. E-mail: webmaster@rl.gov
URL: http://www.hanford.gov/

61377 ■ U.S. Department of Energy - Sandia National Laboratories
PO Box 5400
Albuquerque, NM 87185-5400
Ph: (505)845-5542
Fax: (505)845-4710

61378 ■ U.S. Department of Energy - Savannah River Operations Office
PO Box A
Aiken, SC 29802
Ph: (803)952-7697
Co. E-mail: james-r.giusti@srs.gov
URL: http://sro.srs.gov/index.html

61379 ■ U.S. Department of Energy - Savannah River Operations Office
PO Box A
Aiken, SC 29802
Ph: (803)952-7697
Co. E-mail: DOE-SROEA@srs.gov
URL: http://sro.srs.gov

61380 ■ U.S. Department of Energy - Schenectady Naval Reactors Office
PO Box 1069
Schenectady, NY 12301-1069
Ph: (518)395-6397
Fax: (518)395-6078
URL: http://management.energy.gov/contact_us/
  1204.htm

61381 ■ U.S. Department of Energy - Schenectady Naval Reactors Office
PO Box 1069
Schenectady, NY 12301-1069
Ph: (518)395-6397
Fax: (518)395-6078
URL: http://management.energy.gov/contact_us/
  1204.htm

61382 ■ U.S. Department of Energy - SouthEastern Power Administration (SEPA)
1166 Athens Tech Rd.
Elberton, GA 30635-6711
Ph: (708)213-3800

Fax: (706)213-3884
Co. E-mail: info2@sepa.doe.gov
URL: http://www.sepa.doe.gov

61383 ■ U.S. Department of Energy - Southeastern Power Administration
1166 Athens Tech Rd.
Elberton, GA 30635-6711
Ph: (708)213-3800
Fax: (706)213-3884
Co. E-mail: info@sepa.doe.gov
URL: http://www.sepa.doe.gov

61384 ■ U.S. Department of Energy - Southwestern Power Administration
1 W. 3rd St.
Tulsa, OK 74103-3502
Ph: (918)595-6600
Fax: (918)595-6656
Co. E-mail: info@swpa.gov
URL: http://www.swpa.gov

61385 ■ U.S. Department of Energy - Southwestern Power Administration
1 W. 3rd St.
Tulsa, OK 74103-3502
Ph: (918)595-6600
Fax: (918)595-6656
Co. E-mail: info@swpa.gov
URL: http://www.swpa.gov

61386 ■ U.S. Department of Energy - Western Area Power Administration
PO Box 281213
Lakewood, CO 80228-8213
Ph: (720)962-7000
Fax: (720)962-7200
Co. E-mail: corpcomm@wapa.gov
URL: http://www.wapa.gov

61387 ■ U.S. Department of Energy - Western Area Power Administration
PO Box 281213
Lakewood, CO 80228-8213
Ph: (720)962-7000
Fax: (720)962-7200
Co. E-mail: corpcomm@wapa.gov
URL: http://www.wapa.gov

61388 ■ U.S. Department of the Interior - Bureau of Land Management - Amarillo Field Office
801 S. Fillmore St., Ste. 500
Amarillo, TX 79101-3545
Ph: (806)356-1000
Fax: (806)356-1041

61389 ■ Waste Isolation Pilot Plant
Carlsbad Field Office
4021 National Parks Hwy.
Carlsbad, NM 88220
Free: 800-336-9477
Co. E-mail: infocntr@wipp.ws
URL: http://www.wipp.energy.gov/

U.S. DEPARTMENT OF HEALTH AND HUMAN SERVICES

The following HHS offices are arranged by region.

61390 ■ Health Resources and Services Administration - Grants and Procurement Management Division - Contracts Policies and Operations
Parklawn Bldg., Rm. 13A-03
5600 Fishers Ln.
Rockville, MD 20857-0001
Ph: (301)443-1433
Free: 877-464-4772
Co. E-mail: CallCenter@hrsa.gov
URL: http://www.hrsa.gov/grants/

61391 ■ Health Resources and Services Administration (HRSA) - Office of Equal Opportunity and Civil Rights
Parklawn Bldg., 14A-27
5600 Fishers Ln.
Rockville, MD 20857
Ph: (301)443-5636
Fax: (301)443-7898
Co. E-mail: ask@hrsa.gov
URL: http://www.hrsa.gov/

61392 ■ Health Resources and Services Administration (HRSA) - Office of Equal Opportunity and Civil Rights
Parklawn Bldg., 14A-27
5600 Fishers Ln.
Rockville, MD 20857
Ph: (301)443-5636
Fax: (301)443-7898
Co. E-mail: alinkins@hrsa.gov
URL: http://www.hrsa.gov/

61393 ■ National Institutes of Health - Division of Contracts and Grants - Small and Disadvantaged Business Utilization Specialist
9000 Rockville Pke.
Bethesda, MD 20892
Ph: (301)496-4000
Co. E-mail: nihinfo@od.nih.gov
URL: http://www.dhhs.gov/osdbu/

61394 ■ National Institutes of Health - Division of Contracts and Grants - Small and Disadvantaged Business Utilization Specialist
9000 Rockville Pke.
Bethesda, MD 20892
Ph: (301)496-4000
Co. E-mail: nihinfo@od.nih.gov
URL: http://www.dhhs.gov/osdbu/

61395 ■ U.S. Department of Health and Human Services - Division of Grants and Contracts - Small Business Specialist
1 Choke Cherry Rd., Rm. L-1053
Rockville, MD 20857
Ph: (240)276-1017
Fax: (240)276-1232
Co. E-mail: debra.stidham@samhsa.hhs.gov
URL: http://www.dhhs.gov/osdbu/

61396 ■ U.S. Department of Health and Human Services - Equal Employment Opportunity Office
200 Independence Ave. SW
Washington, DC 20201
Ph: (202)690-6555
Co. E-mail: bonita.white@hhs.gov
URL: http://www.hhs.gov/odme/eeo/

61397 ■ U.S. Department of Health and Human Services - Office for Civil Rights - Equal Employment Opportunity/Affirmation Action Coordinator
HHH Bldg., Rm. 509F
200 Independence Ave., SW
Washington, DC 20201
Ph: (202)619-0257
Free: 800-368-1019
Co. E-mail: ocrmail@hhs.gov
URL: http://www.hhs.gov/ocr/

61398 ■ U.S. Department of Health and Human Services - Office for Civil Rights - Equal Employment Opportunity/Affirmation Action Coordinator
HHH Bldg., Rm. 509F
200 Independence Ave., SW
Washington, DC 20201
Ph: (202)619-0257
Free: 800-368-1019
Co. E-mail: ocrmail@hhs.gov
URL: http://www.hhs.gov/ocr/

61399 ■ U.S. Department of Health and Human Services (HHS) - Office of Small and Disadvantaged Business Utilization
Hubert H. Humphrey Bldg., Rm. 360G
200 Independence Ave., SW
Washington, DC 20201
Ph: (202)690-7235
Fax: (202)260-4872
Co. E-mail: debbie.ridgely@hhs.gov
URL: http://www.hhs.gov/osdbu/
Description: The procurement policy of the Department of Health and Human Services seeks to stimulate competition among potential contractors and to make awards on a competitive basis to the fullest degree consistent with quality, efficiency, and economy. It is the department's policy that small businesses, disadvantaged businesses, women-owned businesses, and labor-surplus area concerns receive a fair and equitable share of the contracts awarded. Procurement assistance is available from the HHS's Office of Small and Disadvantaged Business Utilization and from the small business specialists at each HHS regional office.

61400 ■ U.S. Department of Health and Human Services - Office of Small and Disadvantaged Business Utilization
Hubert H. Humphrey Bldg., Rm. 360G
200 Independence Ave., SW
Washington, DC 20201
Ph: (202)690-7235
Fax: (202)260-4872
Co. E-mail: debbie.ridgely@hhs.gov
URL: http://www.hhs.gov/osdbu/
Description: The procurement policy of the Department of Health and Human Services seeks to stimulate competition among potential contractors and to make awards on a competitive basis to the fullest degree consistent with quality, efficiency, and economy. It is the department's policy that small businesses, disadvantaged businesses, women-owned businesses, and labor-surplus area concerns receive a fair and equitable share of the contracts awarded. Procurement assistance is available from the HHS's Office of Small and Disadvantaged Business Utilization and from the small business specialists at each HHS regional office.

61401 ■ U.S. Department of Health and Human Services - Program Support Center - Small and Disadvantaged Business Utilization Specialist - Division of Acquisitions Services
Parklawn Bldg., Rm. 5C-26
5600 Fishers Ln.
Rockville, MD 20857
Ph: (301)443-1715
Fax: (301)443-7593
Co. E-mail: anita.allen@psc.hhs.gov
URL: http://www.hhs.gov

61402 ■ U.S. Department of Health and Human Services, Region 1
John F. Kennedy Federal Bldg., Rm. 2100
Government Center
Boston, MA 02203
Ph: (617)565-1500
Fax: (617)565-1491
Co. E-mail: christie.hager@hhs.gov
URL: http://www.hhs.gov/about/regions/index.html#r1
Description: Serves Connecticut, Maine, Massachusetts, New Hampshire, Rhode Island, and Vermont.

61403 ■ U.S. Department of Health and Human Services, Region 1
John F. Kennedy Federal Bldg., Rm. 2100
Government Center
Boston, MA 02203
Ph: (617)565-1500
Fax: (617)565-1491
Co. E-mail: Brian.Golden@hhs.gov
URL: http://www.hhs.gov/about/regions/index.html#r1
Description: Serves Connecticut, Maine, Massachusetts, New Hampshire, Rhode Island, and Vermont.

61404 ■ U.S. Department of Health and Human Services, Region 2
Jacob K. Javits Federal Bldg., Rm. 3835
26 Federal Plz.
New York, NY 10278
Ph: (212)264-4600
Fax: (212)264-3620
Co. E-mail: jaime.torres@hhs.gov
URL: http://www.hhs.gov/about/regions/index.html#r2
Description: Serves New Jersey, New York, Puerto Rico, and the Virgin Islands.

61405 ■ U.S. Department of Health and Human Services, Region 2
Jacob K. Javits Federal Bldg., Rm. 3835
26 Federal Plz.
New York, NY 10278
Ph: (212)264-4600
Fax: (212)264-3620
Co. E-mail: Deborah.Konopko@hhs.gov
URL: http://www.hhs.gov/about/regions/index.html#r2
Description: Serves New Jersey, New York, Puerto Rico, and the Virgin Islands.

61406 ■ U.S. Department of Health and Human Services, Region 3
Public Ledger Bldg., Ste. 436
150 S. independence Mall W.
Philadelphia, PA 19106-3499
Ph: (215)861-4633
Fax: (215)861-4625
Co. E-mail: joanne.grossi@hhs.gov
URL: http://www.hhs.gov/about/regions/index.html#r3
Description: Serves Delaware, the District of Columbia, Maryland, Pennsylvania, Virginia, and West Virginia.

61407 ■ U.S. Department of Health and Human Services, Region 3
Public Ledger Bldg., Ste. 436
150 S. independence Mall W.
Philadelphia, PA 19106-3499
Ph: (215)861-4633
Fax: (215)861-4625
Co. E-mail: gordon.woodrow@hhs.gov
URL: http://www.hhs.gov/about/regions/index.html#r3
Description: Serves Delaware, the District of Columbia, Maryland, Pennsylvania, Virginia, and West Virginia.

61408 ■ U.S. Department of Health and Human Services, Region 4
Sam Nunn Atlanta Federal Ctr., Rm. 5B95
61 Forsyth St., SW
Atlanta, GA 30303-8909
Ph: (404)562-7888
Fax: (404)562-7899
Co. E-mail: anton.gunn@hhs.gov
URL: http://www.hhs.gov/about/regions/index.html#r4
Description: Serves Alabama, Florida, Georgia, Kentucky, Mississippi, North Carolina, South Carolina, and Tennessee.

61409 ■ U.S. Department of Health and Human Services, Region 4
Sam Nunn Atlanta Federal Ctr., Rm. 5B95
61 Forsyth St., SW
Atlanta, GA 30303-8909
Ph: (404)562-7888
Fax: (404)562-7899
Co. E-mail: chris.downing@hhs.gov
URL: http://www.hhs.gov/about/regions/index.html#r4
Description: Serves Alabama, Florida, Georgia, Kentucky, Mississippi, North Carolina, South Carolina, and Tennessee.

61410 ■ U.S. Department of Health and Human Services, Region 5
233 N. Michigan Ave., Ste. 1300
Chicago, IL 60601
Ph: (312)353-5160
Fax: (312)353-4144
Co. E-mail: cristal.thomas@hhs.gov
URL: http://www.hhs.gov/about/regions/index.html#r5
Description: Serves Illinois, Indiana, Michigan, Minnesota, Ohio, and Wisconsin.

61411 ■ U.S. Department of Health and Human Services, Region 5
233 N. Michigan Ave., Ste. 1300
Chicago, IL 60601
Ph: (312)353-5160
Fax: (312)353-4144
Co. E-mail: Maureen.Lydon@hhs.gov
URL: http://www.hhs.gov/about/regions/index.html#r5
Description: Serves Illinois, Indiana, Michigan, Minnesota, Ohio, and Wisconsin.

61412 ■ U.S. Department of Health and Human Services, Region 6
1301 Young St., Ste. 1124
Dallas, TX 75202
Ph: (214)767-3301
Fax: (214)767-3617
URL: http://www.hhs.gov/about/regions/index.html#r6
Description: Serves Arkansas, Louisiana, New Mexico, Oklahoma, and Texas.

61413 ■ U.S. Department of Health and Human Services, Region 6
1301 Young St., Ste. 1124
Dallas, TX 75202
Ph: (214)767-3301
Fax: (214)767-3617
Co. E-mail: michael.garcia@hhs.gov
URL: http://www.hhs.gov/about/regions/index.html#r6
Description: Serves Arkansas, Louisiana, New Mexico, Oklahoma, and Texas.

61414 ■ U.S. Department of Health and Human Services, Region 7
Bolling Federal Bldg., Rm. S1801
601 E. 12th St.
Kansas City, MO 64106
Ph: (816)426-2821
Fax: (816)426-2178
Co. E-mail: judy.baker@hhs.gov
URL: http://www.hhs.gov/about/regions/index.html#r7
Description: Serves Iowa, Kansas, Missouri, and Nebraska.

61415 ■ U.S. Department of Health and Human Services, Region 7
Bolling Federal Bldg., Rm. S1801
601 E. 12th St.
Kansas City, MO 64106
Ph: (816)426-2821
Fax: (816)426-2178
Co. E-mail: Fred.Schuster@hhs.gov
URL: http://www.hhs.gov/about/regions/index.html#r7
Description: Serves Iowa, Kansas, Missouri, and Nebraska.

61416 ■ U.S. Department of Health and Human Services, Region 8
Byron G. Rogers Federal Office Bldg.
1961 Stout St., Rm. 1076
Denver, CO 80294-3538
Ph: (303)844-3372
Fax: (303)844-4545
Co. E-mail: joe.nunez@hhs.gov
URL: http://www.hhs.gov/about/regions/index.html#r8
Description: Serves Colorado, Montana, North Dakota, South Dakota, Utah, and Wyoming.

61417 ■ U.S. Department of Health and Human Services, Region 8
Byron G. Rogers Federal Office Bldg.
1961 Stout St., Rm. 1076
Denver, CO 80294-3538
Ph: (303)844-3372
Fax: (303)844-4545
Co. E-mail: joe.nunez@hhs.gov
URL: http://www.hhs.gov/about/regions/index.html#r8
Description: Serves Colorado, Montana, North Dakota, South Dakota, Utah, and Wyoming.

61418 ■ U.S. Department of Health and Human Services, Region 9
Federal Office Bldg., Ste. 5-100
90 7th St.
San Francisco, CA 94103
Ph: (415)437-8500

Fax: (415)536-8505
Co. E-mail: herb.schultz@hhs.gov
URL: http://www.hhs.gov/about/regions/index.html#r9
Description: Serves Arizona, California, Guam, Hawaii, Nevada, and the Trust Territory of the Pacific Islands.

61419 ■ U.S. Department of Health and Human Services, Region 9
Federal Office Bldg., Ste. 5-100
90 7th St.
San Francisco, CA 94103
Ph: (415)437-8500
Fax: (415)536-8505
Co. E-mail: Thomas.Lorentzen@hhs.gov
URL: http://www.hhs.gov/about/regions/index.html#r9
Description: Serves Arizona, California, Guam, Hawaii, Nevada, and the Trust Territory of the Pacific Islands.

61420 ■ U.S. Department of Health and Human Services, Region 10
Blanchard Plaza Bldg., Rm. 1036
2201 6th Ave.
Mail Stop-01
Seattle, WA 98121-1831
Ph: (206)615-2010
Fax: (206)615-2087
Co. E-mail: susan.johnson@hhs.gov
URL: http://www.hhs.gov/about/regions/index.html#r10
Description: Serves Alaska, Idaho, Oregon, and Washington.

61421 ■ U.S. Department of Health and Human Services, Region 10
Blanchard Plaza Bldg., Rm. 1036
2201 6th Ave.
Mail Stop-01
Seattle, WA 98121-1831
Ph: (206)615-2010
Fax: (206)615-2087
Co. E-mail: james.whitfield@hhs.gov
URL: http://www.hhs.gov/about/regions/index.html#r10
Description: Serves Alaska, Idaho, Oregon, and Washington.

61422 ■ U.S. Food and Drug Administration - Division of Contracts and Grants Management - Office of Management
5600 Fishers Ln., Rm. 12-07
Rockville, MD 20857
Ph: (301)827-2906
Free: 800-216-7331
URL: http://www.fda.gov/

61423 ■ U.S. Food and Drug Administration - Division of Contracts and Grants Management - Small and Disadvantaged Business Utilization Specialist
12420 Parklawn Dr., Ste. 3-30
Rockville, MD 20857
Ph: (301)443-6890

61424 ■ U.S. Food and Drug Administration - Office of Acquisitions and Grants Services - Office of Regional Operations
5600 Fishers Ln., Rm. 12-07
Rockville, MD 20857
Ph: (301)827-2906
Free: 800-216-7331
URL: http://www.fda.gov/

61425 ■ U.S. Food and Drug Administration - Office of Acquisitions and Grants Services - Office of Small Disadvantaged Business Utilization Specialist
12420 Parklawn Dr., Ste. 3-30
Rockville, MD 20857
Ph: (301)443-6890
Co. E-mail: anita.allen@psc.hhs.gov

61426 ■ U.S. Food and Drug Administration - Office of Small Business, Scientific, and Trade Affairs
5630 Fishers Ln., Rm. 2115, FHA-500
Rockville, MD 20857

Ph: (301)827-1994
Fax: (301)827-7039
Co. E-mail: Douglas.smith@fda.gov
URL: http://www.fda.gov/oc/ofacs/fdasbo/default.html

61427 ■ U.S. Food and Drug Administration - Office of Small Business, Scientific, and Trade Affairs
5630 Fishers Ln., Rm. 2115, FHA-500
Rockville, MD 20857
Ph: (301)827-1994
Fax: (301)827-7039
Co. E-mail: Douglas.smith@fda.gov
URL: http://www.fda.gov/oc/ofacs/fdasbo/default.html

61428 ■ U.S. Health Care Financing Administration - Equal Employment Opportunity Office
200 Independence Ave. SW
Washington, DC 20201
Ph: (202)690-6555
Co. E-mail: bonita.white@hhs.gov
URL: http://www.hhs.gov/odme/eeo/

61429 ■ U.S. Health Resources Services Administration - Grants and Procurement Management Division - Contracts Policies and Operations
Parklawn Bldg., Rm. 13A-03
5600 Fishers Ln.
Rockville, MD 20857-0001
Ph: (301)443-1433
Free: 877-464-4772
Co. E-mail: CallCenter@hrsa.gov
URL: http://www.hrsa.gov/grants/

61430 ■ U.S. Public Health Service - Administrative Services Center - Small and Disadvantaged Business Utilization Specialist - Division of Acquisitions Management
Parklawn Bldg., Rm. 5C-26
5600 Fishers Ln.
Rockville, MD 20857
Ph: (301)443-1715
Fax: (301)443-7593
Co. E-mail: anita.allen@psc.hhs.gov
URL: http://www.hhs.gov

61431 ■ U.S. Public Health Service - Division of Grants and Contracts - PHS Small Business Specialist
1 Choke Cherry Rd., Rm. L-1053
Rockville, MD 20857
Ph: (240)276-1017
Fax: (240)276-1232
Co. E-mail: debra.peters@samhsa.hhs.gov
URL: http://www.dhhs.gov/osdbu/

61432 ■ U.S. Social Security Administration - Office of Acquisitions and Grants - Small and Disadvantaged Business Utilization Specialist
1st Fl., Rear Entrance
7111 Security Blvd.
Baltimore, MD 21244
Free: 800-772-1213
URL: http://www.ssa.gov/oag/osdbu/osdbu.htm

61433 ■ U.S. Social Security Administration - Office of Acquisitions and Grants - Small and Disadvantaged Business Utilization Specialist
1st Fl., Rear Entrance
7111 Security Blvd.
Baltimore, MD 21244
Free: 800-772-1213
URL: http://www.ssa.gov/oag/osdbu/osdbu.htm

U.S. DEPARTMENT OF HOUSING AND URBAN DEVELOPMENT

The following HUD offices are arranged by region.

61434 ■ U.S. Department of Housing and Urban Development - Deputy Assistant Secretary for Economic Development -

Grants Management Division
451 7th Ave., SW, Rm. 7136
Washington, DC 20410
Ph: (202)708-4091
Fax: (202)401-2231
Co. E-mail: Otto_V_Banks@hud.gov
URL: http://www.hud.gov/grants/index.cfm

61435 ■ U.S. Department of Housing and Urban Development - Deputy Assistant Secretary for Economic Development - Grants Management Division
451 7th Ave., SW, Rm. 7136
Washington, DC 20410
Ph: (202)708-4091
Fax: (202)401-2231
Co. E-mail: Otto_V_Banks@hud.gov
URL: http://www.hud.gov/grants/index.cfm

61436 ■ U.S. Department of Housing and Urban Development - Office of the Chief Procurement Officer
451 7th St., SW, Rm. 5278
Washington, DC 20410
Ph: (202)708-3477
Fax: (202)708-5607
URL: http://www.hud.gov/offices/cpo/

61437 ■ U.S. Department of Housing and Urban Development - Office of the Chief Procurement Officer
451 7th St., SW, Rm. 5278
Washington, DC 20410
Ph: (202)708-3477
Fax: (202)708-5607
Co. E-mail: David_R._Williamson@hud.gov
URL: http://www.hud.gov/offices/cpo/

61438 ■ U.S. Department of Housing and Urban Development - Office of Departmental Operations and Coordination
451 7th St., SW, Rm. 2124
Mail Stop I
Washington, DC 20410
Ph: (202)708-2806
Fax: (202)401-8848
URL: http://www.hud.gov/directory/dirodoc.cfm

61439 ■ U.S. Department of Housing and Urban Development - Office of Departmental Operations and Coordination
451 7th St., SW, Rm. 2124
Mail Stop I
Washington, DC 20410
Ph: (202)708-2806
Fax: (202)401-8848
URL: http://www.hud.gov/directory/dirodoc.cfm

61440 ■ U.S. Department of Housing and Urban Development - Office of Healthy Homes and Lead Hazard Control
451 7th St., SW
Washington, DC 20410
Ph: (202)708-1112
Fax: (202)708-1455
URL: http://www.hud.gov/offices/lead

61441 ■ U.S. Department of Housing and Urban Development - Office of Healthy Homes and Lead Hazard Control
451 7th St., SW
Washington, DC 20410
Ph: (202)708-1112
Fax: (202)708-1455
URL: http://www.hud.gov/offices/lead

61442 ■ U.S. Department of Housing and Urban Development - Office of Security and Emergency Planning
451 7th St., SW, Rm. 6186
Mail Stop AG
Washington, DC 20410
Ph: (202)708-4022
Fax: (202)401-8354
URL: http://www.hud.gov/offices/adm/osa/osep.cfm

61443 ■ U.S. Department of Housing and Urban Development - Office of Security and Emergency Planning
451 7th St., SW, Rm. 6186
Mail Stop AG
Washington, DC 20410
Ph: (202)708-4022
Fax: (202)401-8354
URL: http://www.hud.gov/offices/adm/osa/osep.cfm

61444 ■ U.S. Department of Housing and Urban Development (HUD) - Office of Small and Disadvantaged Business Utilization
451 7th St., SW, Rm. 3130
Washington, DC 20410
Ph: (202)708-1428
Fax: (202)708-7642
Co. E-mail: arnette_s._mcgill@hud.gov
URL: http://www.hud.gov/smallbusiness
Description: The Department of Housing and Urban Development purchases supplies and services to repair and provide housing management services for the properties it acquires, as well as to fulfill its logistical, administrative, and programmatic requirements. Private contractors, including small and disadvantaged firms, are awarded contracts based on bids that they submit to appropriate HUD offices or area managers. HUD encourages and facilitates the participation of small business firms, minority business firms, and firms located in labor-surplus areas. Activities are carried out through a network of field offices. HUD also encourages small business firms to participate in its research and demonstration programs, as the majority of competitively awarded contracts and assistance agreements have been granted to small businesses.

61445 ■ U.S. Department of Housing and Urban Development - Office of Small and Disadvantaged Business Utilization
451 7th St., SW, Rm. 3130
Washington, DC 20410
Ph: (202)708-1428
Fax: (202)708-7642
Co. E-mail: valerie_t._hayes@hud.gov
URL: http://www.hud.gov/smallbusiness
Description: The Department of Housing and Urban Development purchases supplies and services to repair and provide housing management services for the properties it acquires, as well as to fulfill its logistical, administrative, and programmatic requirements. Private contractors, including small and disadvantaged firms, are awarded contracts based on bids that they submit to appropriate HUD offices or area managers. HUD encourages and facilitates the participation of small business firms, minority business firms, and firms located in labor-surplus areas. Activities are carried out through a network of field offices. HUD also encourages small business firms to participate in its research and demonstration programs, as the majority of competitively awarded contracts and assistance agreements have been granted to small businesses.

61446 ■ U.S. Department of Housing and Urban Development, Region 1
Thomas P. O'Neill, Jr. Federal Bldg.
10 Causeway St., Rm. 370
Boston, MA 02222-1092
Ph: (617)994-8380
Fax: (617)565-6878
URL: http://www.hud.gov/offices/oig/locations/oigreg-1.cfm
Description: Administers field offices in Connecticut, Maine, Massachusetts, New Hampshire, Rhode Island, and Vermont.

61447 ■ U.S. Department of Housing and Urban Development, Region 1
Thomas P. O'Neill, Jr. Federal Bldg.
10 Causeway St., Rm. 370
Boston, MA 02222-1092
Ph: (617)994-8380
Fax: (617)565-6878
URL: http://www.hud.gov/offices/oig/locations/oigreg-1.cfm
Description: Administers field offices in Connecticut, Maine, Massachusetts, New Hampshire, Rhode Island, and Vermont.

61448 ■ U.S. Department of Housing and Urban Development, Region 2
26 Federal Plz., Ste. 3430
New York, NY 10278-0068
Ph: (212)264-4174
Fax: (212)264-1400
URL: http://www.hud.gov/offices/oig/locations/oigreg-2.cfm
Description: Administers field offices in New Jersey and New York.

61449 ■ U.S. Department of Housing and Urban Development, Region 2
26 Federal Plz., Ste. 3430
New York, NY 10278-0068
Ph: (212)264-4174
Fax: (212)264-1400
URL: http://www.hud.gov/offices/oig/locations/oigreg-2.cfm
Description: Administers field offices in New Jersey and New York.

61450 ■ U.S. Department of Housing and Urban Development, Region 3
The Wanamaker Bldg.
100 Penn Square E., 10th Fl.
Philadelphia, PA 19107-3380
Ph: (215)656-3401
Fax: (215)656-3409
URL: http://www.hud.gov/offices/oig/locations/oigreg-3.cfm
Description: Administers field offices in Delaware, the District of Columbia, Maryland, Pennsylvania, Virginia, and West Virginia.

61451 ■ U.S. Department of Housing and Urban Development, Region 3
The Wanamaker Bldg.
100 Penn Square E., 10th Fl.
Philadelphia, PA 19107-3380
Ph: (215)656-3401
Fax: (215)656-3409
URL: http://www.hud.gov/offices/oig/locations/oigreg-3.cfm
Description: Administers field offices in Delaware, the District of Columbia, Maryland, Pennsylvania, Virginia, and West Virginia.

61452 ■ U.S. Department of Housing and Urban Development, Region 4
Richard B. Russell Federal Bldg.
75 Spring St., SW, Rm. 330
Atlanta, GA 30303-2806
Ph: (404)331-5001
Fax: (404)331-2382
URL: http://www.hud.gov/offices/oig/locations/oigreg-4.cfm
Description: Administers field offices in Alabama, Florida, Georgia, Kentucky, Mississippi, North Carolina, Puerto Rico, South Carolina, Tennessee, and the Virgin Islands.

61453 ■ U.S. Department of Housing and Urban Development, Region 4
Richard B. Russell Federal Bldg.
75 Spring St., SW, Rm. 330
Atlanta, GA 30303-2806
Ph: (404)331-5001
Fax: (404)331-2382
URL: http://www.hud.gov/offices/oig/locations/oigreg-4.cfm
Description: Administers field offices in Alabama, Florida, Georgia, Kentucky, Mississippi, North Carolina, Puerto Rico, South Carolina, Tennessee, and the Virgin Islands.

61454 ■ U.S. Department of Housing and Urban Development, Region 5
Metcalfe Federal Bldg., Rm. 2646
77 W. Jackson Blvd.
Chicago, IL 60604-3507
Ph: (312)353-7832
Fax: (312)886-8866
URL: http://www.hud.gov/offices/oig/locations/oigreg-5.cfm
Description: Administers field offices in Illinois, Indiana, Michigan, Minnesota, Ohio, and Wisconsin.

61455 ■ U.S. Department of Housing and Urban Development, Region 5
Metcalfe Federal Bldg., Rm. 2646
77 W. Jackson Blvd.
Chicago, IL 60604-3507
Ph: (312)353-7832
Fax: (312)886-8866
URL: http://www.hud.gov/offices/oig/locations/oigreg-5.cfm
Description: Administers field offices in Illinois, Indiana, Michigan, Minnesota, Ohio, and Wisconsin.

61456 ■ U.S. Department of Housing and Urban Development, Region 6
Fritz G. Lanham Federal Bldg.
819 Taylor St., Ste. 13A09
Ft. Worth, TX 76102-6195
Ph: (817)978-9309
Fax: (817)978-9316
URL: http://www.hud.gov/offices/oig/locations/oigreg-6.cfm
Description: Administers field offices in Arkansas, Louisiana, New Mexico, Oklahoma, and Texas.

61457 ■ U.S. Department of Housing and Urban Development, Region 6
Fritz G. Lanham Federal Bldg.
819 Taylor St., Ste. 13A09
Ft. Worth, TX 76102-6195
Ph: (817)978-9309
Fax: (817)978-9316
URL: http://www.hud.gov/offices/oig/locations/oigreg-6.cfm
Description: Administers field offices in Arkansas, Louisiana, New Mexico, Oklahoma, and Texas.

61458 ■ U.S. Department of Housing and Urban Development, Region 7
Gateway Tower II, 5th Fl.
400 State Ave.
Kansas City, KS 66101-2406
Ph: (913)551-5870
Fax: (913)551-5877
URL: http://www.hud.gov/offices/oig/locations/oigreg-7.cfm
Description: Administers field offices in Iowa, Kansas, Missouri, and Nebraska.

61459 ■ U.S. Department of Housing and Urban Development, Region 7
Gateway Tower II, 5th Fl.
400 State Ave.
Kansas City, KS 66101-2406
Ph: (913)551-5870
Fax: (913)551-5877
URL: http://www.hud.gov/offices/oig/locations/oigreg-7.cfm
Description: Administers field offices in Iowa, Kansas, Missouri, and Nebraska.

61460 ■ U.S. Department of Housing and Urban Development, Region 8
1670 Broadway
UMB Plaza, 24th Fl.
Denver, CO 80202
Ph: (303)672-5452
Fax: (303)672-5006
URL: http://www.hud.gov
Description: Administers field offices in Colorado, Montana, North Dakota, South Dakota, Utah, and Wyoming.

61461 ■ U.S. Department of Housing and Urban Development, Region 8
1670 Broadway
UMB Plaza, 24th Fl.
Denver, CO 80202
Ph: (303)672-5452
Fax: (303)672-5006
URL: http://www.hud.gov
Description: Administers field offices in Colorado, Montana, North Dakota, South Dakota, Utah, and Wyoming.

61462 ■ U.S. Department of Housing and Urban Development, Region 9
611 W. 6th St., Ste. 1160
Los Angeles, CA 90017
Ph: (213)894-8016
Fax: (213)894-8115
URL: http://www.hud.gov/offices/oig/locations/oigreg-9.cfm
Description: Administers field offices in the American Samoa, Arizona, California, Guam, Hawaii, and Nevada.

61463 ■ U.S. Department of Housing and Urban Development, Region 9
611 W. 6th St., Ste. 1160
Los Angeles, CA 90017
Ph: (213)894-8016
Fax: (213)894-8115
URL: http://www.hud.gov/offices/oig/locations/oigreg-9.cfm
Description: Administers field offices in the American Samoa, Arizona, California, Guam, Hawaii, and Nevada.

61464 ■ U.S. Department of Housing and Urban Development, Region 10
909 1st Ave., Rm. 126
Seattle, WA 98104-1000
Ph: (206)220-5360
Fax: (206)220-5162
URL: http://www.hud.gov
Description: Administers field offices in Alaska, Idaho, Oregon, and Washington.

61465 ■ U.S. Department of Housing and Urban Development, Region 10
909 1st Ave., Rm. 126
Seattle, WA 98104-1000
Ph: (206)220-5360
Fax: (206)220-5162
URL: http://www.hud.gov
Description: Administers field offices in Alaska, Idaho, Oregon, and Washington.

U.S. DEPARTMENT OF THE INTERIOR

The offices following the main office of the U.S. Fish and Wildlife Service (Washington, DC) are arranged by region.

61466 ■ Bureau of Indian Affairs - Business Utilization and Development Specialist - Aberdeen Area Office
115 4th Ave. SE
Aberdeen, SD 57401
Ph: (605)226-7343
Fax: (605)228-7446
URL: http://www.bia.gov/

61467 ■ Bureau of Indian Affairs - Business Utilization and Development Specialist - Aberdeen Area Office
115 4th Ave. SE
Aberdeen, SD 57401
Ph: (605)226-7343
Fax: (605)228-7446
URL: http://www.bia.gov/

61468 ■ Bureau of Indian Affairs - Business Utilization and Development Specialist - Albuquerque Area Office
1001 Indian School Road, NW
Albuquerque, NM 87125-6567
Ph: (505)346-7590
Fax: (505)346-7517
URL: http://www.bia.gov/

61469 ■ Bureau of Indian Affairs - Business Utilization and Development Specialist - Albuquerque Area Office
1001 Indian School Road, NW
Albuquerque, NM 87125-6567
Ph: (505)346-7590
Fax: (505)346-7517
URL: http://www.bia.gov/

61470 ■ Bureau of Indian Affairs - Business Utilization and Development Specialist - Anadarko Area Office
WCD Office Complex
Anadarko, OK 73005
Ph: (405)247-6673
Fax: (405)247-2242
URL: http://www.bia.gov/

61471 ■ Bureau of Indian Affairs - Business Utilization and Development Specialist - Anadarko Area Office
WCD Office Complex
Anadarko, OK 73005
Ph: (405)247-6673
Fax: (405)247-2242
URL: http://www.bia.gov/

61472 ■ Bureau of Indian Affairs - Business Utilization and Development Specialist - Billings Area Office
316 N. 26th St.
Billings, MT 59101
Ph: (406)247-7943
Fax: (406)247-7976
URL: http://www.bia.gov/

61473 ■ Bureau of Indian Affairs - Business Utilization and Development Specialist - Billings Area Office
316 N. 26th St.
Billings, MT 59101
Ph: (406)247-7943
Fax: (406)247-7976
URL: http://www.bia.gov/

61474 ■ Bureau of Indian Affairs - Business Utilization and Development Specialist - Eastern Area Office
545 Marriott Dr., Ste. 700
Nashville, TN 37214
Ph: (615)564-6700
Fax: (615)564-6701
URL: http://www.bia.gov/

61475 ■ Bureau of Indian Affairs - Business Utilization and Development Specialist - Eastern Area Office
545 Marriott Dr., Ste. 700
Nashville, TN 37214
Ph: (615)564-6700
Fax: (615)564-6701
URL: http://www.bia.gov/

61476 ■ Bureau of Indian Affairs - Business Utilization and Development Specialist - Juneau Area Office
709 W. 9th St.
Juneau, AK 99802-5520
Ph: (907)586-7177
Free: 800-645-8397
Fax: (907)586-7252
URL: http://www.bia.gov/

61477 ■ Bureau of Indian Affairs - Business Utilization and Development Specialist - Juneau Area Office
709 W. 9th St.
Juneau, AK 99802-5520
Ph: (907)586-7177
Free: 800-645-8397
Fax: (907)586-7252
URL: http://www.bia.gov/

61478 ■ Bureau of Indian Affairs - Business Utilization and Development Specialist - Minneapolis Area Office
1 Federal Dr., Rm. 550
Minneapolis, MN 55111-4007
Ph: (612)713-4400
Fax: (612)713-4401
URL: http://www.bia.gov/

61479 ■ Bureau of Indian Affairs - Business Utilization and Development Specialist - Minneapolis Area Office
1 Federal Dr., Rm. 550
Minneapolis, MN 55111-4007

Ph: (612)713-4400
Fax: (612)713-4401
URL: http://www.bia.gov/

61480 ■ Bureau of Indian Affairs - Business Utilization and Development Specialist - Muskogee Area Office
3100 W. Peak Blvd.
Muskogee, OK 74402-8002
Ph: (918)781-4600
Fax: (918)781-4604
URL: http://www.bia.gov/

61481 ■ Bureau of Indian Affairs - Business Utilization and Development Specialist - Muskogee Area Office
3100 W. Peak Blvd.
Muskogee, OK 74402-8002
Ph: (918)781-4600
Fax: (918)781-4604
URL: http://www.bia.gov/

61482 ■ Bureau of Indian Affairs - Business Utilization and Development Specialist - Navajo Area Office
PO Box 1060
Gallup, NM 87305
Ph: (505)863-8314
Fax: (505)863-8324
URL: http://www.bia.gov/

61483 ■ Bureau of Indian Affairs - Business Utilization and Development Specialist - Navajo Area Office
PO Box 1060
Gallup, NM 87305
Ph: (505)863-8314
Fax: (505)863-8324
URL: http://www.bia.gov/

61484 ■ Bureau of Indian Affairs - Business Utilization and Development Specialist - Phoenix Area Office
2600 N. Central Ave.
4th Fl. Mailroom
Phoenix, AZ 85004-3050
Ph: (602)379-6600
Fax: (602)379-4413
URL: http://www.bia.gov/

61485 ■ Bureau of Indian Affairs - Business Utilization and Development Specialist - Phoenix Area Office
2600 N. Central Ave.
4th Fl. Mailroom
Phoenix, AZ 85004-3050
Ph: (602)379-6600
Fax: (602)379-4413
URL: http://www.bia.gov/

61486 ■ Bureau of Indian Affairs - Business Utilization and Development Specialist - Portland Area Office
Federal Bldg.
911 NE 11th Ave.
Portland, OR 97232
Ph: (503)231-6702
Fax: (503)231-2201
URL: http://www.bia.gov/

61487 ■ Bureau of Indian Affairs - Business Utilization and Development Specialist - Portland Area Office
Federal Bldg.
911 NE 11th Ave.
Portland, OR 97232
Ph: (503)231-6702
Fax: (503)231-2201
URL: http://www.bia.gov/

61488 ■ Bureau of Indian Affairs - Business Utilization and Development Specialist - Sacramento Area Office
2800 Cottage Way
Sacramento, CA 95825
Ph: (916)978-6000
Fax: (916)978-6099

61489 ■ Bureau of Indian Affairs - Business Utilization and Development Specialist - Sacramento Area Office
2800 Cottage Way
Sacramento, CA 95825
Ph: (916)978-6000
Fax: (916)978-6099

61490 ■ Bureau of Land Management - Alaska State Office
222 W. 7th Ave.
Anchorage, AK 99513-7504
Ph: (907)271-5960
Fax: (907)271-3684
Co. E-mail: AK_AKSO_Public_Room@blm.gov
URL: http://www.ak.blm.gov

61491 ■ Bureau of Land Management - Arizona State Office
One N. Central Ave., Ste. 800
Phoenix, AZ 85004-4427
Ph: (602)417-9200
Fax: (602)417-9556
URL: http://www.blm.gov/az/st/en.html

61492 ■ Bureau of Land Management - Business Utilization and Development Specialist - Branch of Procurement Management
1620 L St. NW, Rm. 1075
Washington, DC 20240
Ph: (202)785-6586
Fax: (202)452-5141
Co. E-mail: Barbara_Gains@blm.gov
URL: http://www.blm.gov

61493 ■ Bureau of Land Management - Business Utilization and Development Specialist - Division of Procurement Management
14015 NE Airport Way
Portland, OR 97230
Ph: (503)255-5115

61494 ■ Bureau of Land Management - California State Office
2800 Cottage Way, Ste. W-1623
Sacramento, CA 95825-1886
Ph: (916)978-4400
Fax: (916)978-4416
URL: http://www.blm.gov/ca/st/en.html

61495 ■ Bureau of Land Management - Colorado State Office
2850 Youngfield St.
Lakewood, CO 80215
Ph: (303)239-3600
URL: http://www.co.blm.gov/

61496 ■ Bureau of Land Management - Eastern States Office
7450 Boston Blvd.
Springfield, VA 22153-3121
Ph: (703)440-1600
URL: http://www.blm.gov/es/st/en.html

61497 ■ Bureau of Land Management - Idaho State Office
1387 S. Vinnell Way
Boise, ID 83709-1657
Ph: (208)373-4000
Fax: (208)373-3899
Co. E-mail: id_so_information@blm.gov
URL: http://www.blm.gov/id/st/en.html

61498 ■ Bureau of Land Management - Montana State Office
5001 Southgate Dr.
Billings, MT 59101
Ph: (406)896-5000
Fax: (406)896-5229
Co. E-mail: MT_SO_Information@blm.gov
URL: http://www.blm.gov/mt/st/en.html

61499 ■ Bureau of Land Management - Nevada State Office
1340 Financial Blvd.
Reno, NV 89502-0006

Ph: (705)861-6400
URL: http://www.blm.gov/nv/st/en.html

61500 ■ Bureau of Land Management - New Mexico State Office
PO Box 27115
Santa Fe, NM 87502-0115
Ph: (505)954-2000
Co. E-mail: nm_comments@nm.blm.gov
URL: http://www.blm.gov/nm/st/en.html

61501 ■ Bureau of Land Management - Oregon State Office
333 SW 1st Ave.
Portland, OR 97204
Ph: (503)808-6001
Fax: (503)808-6308
Co. E-mail: ORwaland@blm.gov
URL: http://www.blm.gov/or/st/en.html

61502 ■ Bureau of Land Management - Utah State Office
440 W. 200 S., Ste. 500
Salt Lake City, UT 84145-0155
Ph: (801)539-4133
Fax: (801)539-4013
Co. E-mail: utsomail@blm.gov
URL: http://www.blm.gov/ut/st/en.html

61503 ■ Bureau of Land Management - Wyoming State Office
5353 Yellowstone Rd.
Cheyenne, WY 82009
Ph: (307)775-6256
Fax: (307)775-6129
Co. E-mail: state_office_wymail@blm.gov
URL: http://www.blm.gov/wy/st/en.html

61504 ■ Bureau of Ocean Energy Management, Regulation and Enforcement - Alaska OCS
3801 Centerpoint Dr., Ste. 500
Anchorage, AK 99503-5820
Ph: (907)334-5200
Free: 800-764-2627
Fax: (907)334-5202
URL: http://www.mms.gov/alaska

61505 ■ Bureau of Ocean Energy Management, Regulation and Enforcement - Business Utilization and Development Specialist - Division of Procurement and Contracts
381 Elden St.
Herndon, VA 2070-4817
Ph: (703)787-1370
Fax: (703)787-1009

61506 ■ Bureau of Ocean Energy Management, Regulation and Enforcement - Business Utilization and Development Specialist - Western ASC Procurement and Contracts
12600 W. Colfax Ave., Ste. C-200
Lakewood, CO 80255-0165
Ph: (303)231-3937
Fax: (303)231-3908
Co. E-mail: Theresa.velasquez@mms.gov
URL: http://www.mms.gov

61507 ■ Bureau of Ocean Energy Management, Regulation and Enforcement - Pacific OCS Region
770 Paseo Camarillo, 2nd Fl.
Camarillo, CA 93010
Ph: (805)389-7533
Free: 800-672-2627
Co. E-mail: john.romero@mms.gov
URL: http://www.mms.gov/omm/pacific/index.htm

61508 ■ Bureau of Reclamation - Business Utilization and Development Specialist - Acquisition and Assistance Management Services
Denver Federal Ctr.
6th and Kipling, Bldg. 56
Denver, CO 80225-0007
Ph: (303)445-2445

Fax: (303)445-6410
URL: http://www.usbr.gov/mso/aamd/index.html

61509 ■ Bureau of Reclamation - Business Utilization and Development Specialist - Administrative Service Center
PO Box 25007
Denver, CO 80225
Ph: (303)969-7235

61510 ■ Bureau of Reclamation - Business Utilization and Development Specialist - Denver Office
Denver Federal Center
Denver, CO 80225-0007
Ph: (303)445-2442
Fax: (303)236-6345
Co. E-mail: rbrackett@usbr.gov

61511 ■ Bureau of Reclamation - Business Utilization and Development Specialist - Great Plains Region
PO Box 30137
Billings, MT 59107-0137
Ph: (406)247-7300
Fax: (406)247-7338
URL: http://www.usbr.gov/gp/

61512 ■ Bureau of Reclamation - Business Utilization and Development Specialist - Lower Colorado Region
PO Box 61470
Boulder City, NV 89006-1470
Ph: (702)293-8411
Fax: (702)293-8333
URL: http://www.usbr.gov/lc/

61513 ■ Bureau of Reclamation - Business Utilization and Development Specialist - Mid-Pacific Region
Federal Office Bldg.
2800 Cottage Way
Sacramento, CA 95825-1898
Ph: (916)978-5183
Fax: (916)978-5182
Co. E-mail: rdesmet@usbr.gov
URL: http://www.usbr.gov/mp/

61514 ■ Bureau of Reclamation - Business Utilization and Development Specialist - Pacific Northwest Region
1150 N. Curtis Rd., Ste. 100
Boise, ID 83706-1234
Ph: (208)378-5103
Fax: (208)378-5108
Co. E-mail: sfraser@usbr.gov
URL: http://www.usbr.gov/pn/

61515 ■ Bureau of Reclamation - Business Utilization and Development Specialist - Phoenix Area Office
6150 W. Thunderbird Rd.
Glendale, AZ 85306-4001
Ph: (623)773-6214
Fax: (623)773-6485
Co. E-mail: pcox@usbr.gov
URL: http://www.usbr.gov/lc/phoenix/

61516 ■ Bureau of Reclamation - Business Utilization and Development Specialist - Upper Colorado Region
125 S. State St., Rm. 6107
Salt Lake City, UT 84138-1102
Ph: (801)524-3675
Fax: (801)524-3857
Co. E-mail: khapp@usbr.gov
URL: http://www.usbr.gov/uc/

61517 ■ Interior Service Center - Business Utilization and Development Specialist - Branch of Acquisitions, Fiscal and Property Services
1849 C St. NW
Washington, DC 20240
Ph: (202)208-3100

61518 ■ Interior Service Center - Business Utilization and Development Specialist - Branch of Acquisitions, Fiscal and Property Services
1849 C St. NW
Washington, DC 20240
Ph: (202)208-3100

61519 ■ Minerals Management Service - Alaska OCS
3801 Centerpoint Dr., Ste. 500
Anchorage, AK 99503-5820
Ph: (907)334-5200
Free: 800-764-2627
Fax: (907)334-5202
URL: http://www.mms.gov/alaska

61520 ■ Minerals Management Service - Business Utilization and Development Specialist - Division of Procurement and Contracts
381 Elden St.
Herndon, VA 2070-4817
Ph: (703)787-1370
Fax: (703)787-1009
Co. E-mail: nicolette.nye@mms.gov

61521 ■ Minerals Management Service - Business Utilization and Development Specialist - Western ASC Procurement and Contracts
12600 W. Colfax Ave., Ste. C-200
Lakewood, CO 80255-0165
Ph: (303)231-3937
Fax: (303)231-3908
Co. E-mail: Theresa.velasquez@mms.gov
URL: http://www.mms.gov

61522 ■ Minerals Management Service - Pacific Region OCS
770 Paseo Camarillo, 2nd Fl.
Camarillo, CA 93010
Ph: (805)389-7533
Free: 800-672-2627
Co. E-mail: john.romero@mms.gov
URL: http://www.mms.gov/omm/pacific/index.htm

61523 ■ National Park Service - Business Utilization and Development Specialist - Alaska Region
240 W. 5th Ave.
Anchorage, AK 99501
Ph: (907)644-3510
URL: http://www.nps.gov/akso/

61524 ■ National Park Service - Business Utilization and Development Specialist - Alaska Region
240 W. 5th Ave.
Anchorage, AK 99501
Ph: (907)644-3510
URL: http://www.nps.gov/akso/

61525 ■ National Park Service - Business Utilization and Development Specialist - Business and Economic Development Program
1849 C St., NW, Org. Code 2604
Washington, DC 20240
Ph: (202)208-4747
Fax: (202)219-0910
Co. E-mail: waso_public_affairs@npa.gov
URL: http://www.npa.gov

61526 ■ National Park Service - Business Utilization and Development Specialist - Intermountain Region
12795 Alameda Pkwy.
Denver, CO 80225-0287
Ph: (303)969-2500
Fax: (303)969-2785
URL: http://www.nps.gov/legacy/regions.html

61527 ■ National Park Service - Business Utilization and Development Specialist - Intermountain Region
12795 Alameda Pkwy.
Denver, CO 80225-0287

Ph: (303)969-2500
Fax: (303)969-2785
URL: http://www.nps.gov/legacy/regions.html

61528 ■ National Park Service - Business Utilization and Development Specialist - Midwest Region
601 Riverfront Dr.
Omaha, NE 68102
Ph: (402)661-1736
URL: http://www.nps.gov/legacy/regions.html

61529 ■ National Park Service - Business Utilization and Development Specialist - Midwest Region
601 Riverfront Dr.
Omaha, NE 68102
Ph: (402)661-1736
URL: http://www.nps.gov/legacy/regions.html

61530 ■ National Park Service - Business Utilization and Development Specialist - Minority Business and Economic Development Program
1849 C St., NW, Org. Code 2604
Washington, DC 20240
Ph: (202)208-4747
Fax: (202)219-0910
Co. E-mail: waso_public_affairs@npa.gov
URL: http://www.npa.gov

61531 ■ National Park Service - Business Utilization and Development Specialist - National Capitol Region
1100 Ohio Dr., SW
Washington, DC 20242
Ph: (202)619-7222
URL: http://www.nps.gov/legacy/regions.html

61532 ■ National Park Service - Business Utilization and Development Specialist - National Capitol Region
1100 Ohio Dr., SW
Washington, DC 20242
Ph: (202)619-7222
URL: http://www.nps.gov/legacy/regions.html

61533 ■ National Park Service - Business Utilization and Development Specialist - Northeast Region
U.S. Custom House
200 Chestnut St., 5th Fl.
Philadelphia, PA 19106
Ph: (215)597-7013
URL: http://www.nps.gov/legacy/regions.html

61534 ■ National Park Service - Business Utilization and Development Specialist - Northeast Region
U.S. Custom House
200 Chestnut St., 5th Fl.
Philadelphia, PA 19106
Ph: (215)597-7013
URL: http://www.nps.gov/legacy/regions.html

61535 ■ National Park Service - Business Utilization and Development Specialist - Outdoor Recreation Information Center
222 Yale Ave. N.
Seattle, WA 98109
Ph: (206)470-4060
URL: http://www.nps.gov/ccso/oric.htm

61536 ■ National Park Service - Business Utilization and Development Specialist - Pacific Northwest Region
222 Yale Ave. N.
Seattle, WA 98109
Ph: (206)470-4060
URL: http://www.nps.gov/ccso/oric.htm

61537 ■ National Park Service - Business Utilization and Development Specialist - Pacific West Region
1 Jackson Center
1111 Jackson St., Ste. 700
Oakland, CA 94607

Ph: (510)817-1300
URL: http://www.nps.gov/legacy/regions.html

61538 ■ National Park Service - Business Utilization and Development Specialist - Pacific West Region
1 Jackson Center
1111 Jackson St., Ste. 700
Oakland, CA 94607
Ph: (510)817-1300
URL: http://www.nps.gov/legacy/regions.html

61539 ■ National Park Service - Business Utilization and Development Specialist - Southeast Region
100 Alabama St., SW
1924 Bldg.
Atlanta, GA 30303
Ph: (404)507-5600
URL: http://www.nps.gov/legacy/regions.html

61540 ■ National Park Service - Business Utilization and Development Specialist - Southeast Region
100 Alabama St., SW
1924 Bldg.
Atlanta, GA 30303
Ph: (404)507-5600
URL: http://www.nps.gov/legacy/regions.html

61541 ■ Office of Aircraft Services - Business Utilization and Development Specialist - Division of Contracting
4405 Lear Ct.
Anchorage, AK 99502-1032
Ph: (907)271-5021
Fax: (907)271-4788
URL: http://amd.nbc.gov/akro/index.htm

61542 ■ Office of Aircraft Services - Business Utilization and Development Specialist - Division of Contracting
4405 Lear Ct.
Anchorage, AK 99502-1032
Ph: (907)271-5021
Fax: (907)271-4788
URL: http://amd.nbc.gov/akro/index.htm

61543 ■ Office of Aircraft Services - Business Utilization and Development Specialist - Division of Contracting - Aviation Management Directorate
University Plaza, Ste. 300
960 Broadway Ave.
Boise, ID 83706
Ph: (208)334-9310
Fax: (208)334-9303
URL: http://amd.nbc.gov/west/

61544 ■ Office of Aircraft Services - Business Utilization and Development Specialist - Division of Contracting - Aviation Management Directorate
University Plaza, Ste. 300
960 Broadway Ave.
Boise, ID 83706
Ph: (208)334-9310
Fax: (208)334-9303
URL: http://amd.nbc.gov/west/

61545 ■ Office of Surface Mining Reclamation and Enforcement - Appalachian Regional Office
3 Parkway Center
Pittsburgh, PA 15220
Ph: (412)937-2828
Co. E-mail: kbernhard@osmre.gov
URL: http://www.arcc.osmre.gov

61546 ■ Office of Surface Mining Reclamation and Enforcement - Appalachian Regional Office
3 Parkway Center
Pittsburgh, PA 15220
Ph: (412)937-2828
Co. E-mail: kbernhard@osmre.gov
URL: http://www.arcc.osmre.gov

61547 ■ Office of Surface Mining Reclamation and Enforcement - Mid-Continent Regional Office
William J. Beatty Federal Bldg.
501 Belle St., 2nd Fl.
Alton, IL 62002
Ph: (618)463-6460
Fax: (618)463-6470
Co. E-mail: pdege@osmre.gov
URL: http://www.mcrcc.osmre.gov

61548 ■ Office of Surface Mining Reclamation and Enforcement - Mid-Continent Regional Office
William J. Beatty Federal Bldg.
501 Belle St., 2nd Fl.
Alton, IL 62002
Ph: (618)463-6460
Fax: (618)463-6470
Co. E-mail: ebarchender@osmre.gov
URL: http://www.mcrcc.osmre.gov

61549 ■ Office of Surface Mining Reclamation and Enforcement - Western Regional Office
1999 Broadway, Ste. 3320
Denver, CO 80201-4667
Ph: (303)293-5000
Co. E-mail: aklein@osmre.gov
URL: http://www.wrcc.osmre.gov

61550 ■ Office of Surface Mining Reclamation and Enforcement - Western Regional Office
1999 Broadway, Ste. 3320
Denver, CO 80201-4667
Ph: (303)293-5000
Co. E-mail: aklein@osmre.gov
URL: http://www.wrcc.osmre.gov

61551 ■ U.S. Department of the Interior - Bureau of Land Management - Alaska State Office
222 W. 7th Ave.
Anchorage, AK 99513-7504
Ph: (907)271-5960
Fax: (907)271-3684
Co. E-mail: AK_AKSO_Public_Room@blm.gov
URL: http://www.ak.blm.gov

61552 ■ U.S. Department of the Interior - Bureau of Land Management - Arizona State Office
One N. Central Ave., Ste. 800
Phoenix, AZ 85004-4427
Ph: (602)417-9200
Fax: (602)417-9556
URL: http://www.blm.gov/az/st/en.html

61553 ■ U.S. Department of the Interior - Bureau of Land Management - Business Utilization and Development Specialist - Branch of Procurement Management
1620 L St. NW, Rm. 1075
Washington, DC 20240
Ph: (202)785-6586
Fax: (202)452-5141
Co. E-mail: Barbara_Gains@blm.gov
URL: http://www.blm.gov

61554 ■ U.S. Department of the Interior - Bureau of Land Management - Business Utilization and Development Specialist - Division of Procurement Management
14015 NE Airport Way
Portland, OR 97230
Ph: (503)255-5115

61555 ■ U.S. Department of the Interior - Bureau of Land Management - California State Office
2800 Cottage Way, Ste. W-1623
Sacramento, CA 95825-1886
Ph: (916)978-4400
Fax: (916)978-4416
URL: http://www.blm.gov/ca/st/en.html

61556 ■ U.S. Department of the Interior - Bureau of Land Management - Colorado State Office
2850 Youngfield St.
Lakewood, CO 80215
Ph: (303)239-3600
URL: http://www.co.blm.gov/

61557 ■ U.S. Department of the Interior - Bureau of Land Management - Eastern States Office
7450 Boston Blvd.
Springfield, VA 22153-3121
Ph: (703)440-1600
Co. E-mail: es_general_web@blm.gov
URL: http://www.blm.gov/es/st/en.html

61558 ■ U.S. Department of the Interior - Bureau of Land Management - Idaho State Office
1387 S. Vinnell Way
Boise, ID 83709-1657
Ph: (208)373-4000
Fax: (208)373-3899
Co. E-mail: id_so_information@blm.gov
URL: http://www.blm.gov/id/st/en.html

61559 ■ U.S. Department of the Interior - Bureau of Land Management - Montana State Office
5001 Southgate Dr.
Billings, MT 59101
Ph: (406)896-5000
Fax: (406)896-5229
Co. E-mail: MT_SO_Information@blm.gov
URL: http://www.blm.gov/mt/st/en.html

61560 ■ U.S. Department of the Interior - Bureau of Land Management - Nevada State Office
1340 Financial Blvd.
Reno, NV 89502-0006
Ph: (705)861-6400
URL: http://www.blm.gov/nv/st/en.html

61561 ■ U.S. Department of the Interior - Bureau of Land Management - New Mexico State Office
PO Box 27115
Santa Fe, NM 87502-0115
Ph: (505)954-2000
Co. E-mail: nm_comments@nm.blm.gov
URL: http://www.blm.gov/nm/st/en.html

61562 ■ U.S. Department of the Interior - Bureau of Land Management - Oregon State Office
333 SW 1st Ave.
Portland, OR 97204
Ph: (503)808-6001
Fax: (503)808-6308
Co. E-mail: ORwaland@blm.gov
URL: http://www.blm.gov/or/st/en.html

61563 ■ U.S. Department of the Interior - Bureau of Land Management - Utah State Office
440 W. 200 S., Ste. 500
Salt Lake City, UT 84145-0155
Ph: (801)539-4133
Fax: (801)539-4013
Co. E-mail: utsomail@blm.gov
URL: http://www.blm.gov/ut/st/en.html

61564 ■ U.S. Department of the Interior - Bureau of Land Management - Wyoming State Office
5353 Yellowstone Rd.
Cheyenne, WY 82009
Ph: (307)775-6256
Fax: (307)775-6129
Co. E-mail: state_office_wymail@blm.gov
URL: http://www.blm.gov/wy/st/en.html

61565 ■ U.S. Department of the Interior - Bureau of Reclamation - Business Utilization and Development Specialist - Acquisition and

Assistance Management Services
Denver Federal Ctr.
6th and Kipling, Bldg. 56
Denver, CO 80225-0007
Ph: (303)445-2445
Fax: (303)445-6410
URL: http://www.usbr.gov/mso/aamd/index.html

61566 ■ U.S. Department of the Interior - Bureau of Reclamation - Business Utilization and Development Specialist - Administrative Service Center
PO Box 25007
Denver, CO 80225
Ph: (303)969-7235

61567 ■ U.S. Department of the Interior - Bureau of Reclamation - Business Utilization and Development Specialist - Denver Office
Denver Federal Center
Denver, CO 80225-0007
Ph: (303)445-2442
Fax: (303)236-6345
Co. E-mail: rbrackett@usbr.gov

61568 ■ U.S. Department of the Interior - Bureau of Reclamation - Business Utilization and Development Specialist - Great Plains Region
PO Box 30137
Billings, MT 59107-0137
Ph: (406)247-7300
Fax: (406)247-7338
URL: http://www.usbr.gov/gp/

61569 ■ U.S. Department of the Interior - Bureau of Reclamation - Business Utilization and Development Specialist - Lower Colorado Region
PO Box 61470
Boulder City, NV 89006-1470
Ph: (702)293-8411
Fax: (702)293-8333
URL: http://www.usbr.gov/lc/

61570 ■ U.S. Department of the Interior - Bureau of Reclamation - Business Utilization and Development Specialist - Mid-Pacific Region
Federal Office Bldg.
2800 Cottage Way
Sacramento, CA 95825-1898
Ph: (916)978-5183
Fax: (916)978-5182
URL: http://www.usbr.gov/mp/

61571 ■ U.S. Department of the Interior - Bureau of Reclamation - Business Utilization and Development Specialist - Pacific Northwest Region
1150 N. Curtis Rd., Ste. 100
Boise, ID 83706-1234
Ph: (208)378-5103
Fax: (208)378-5108
Co. E-mail: pninfo@usbr.gov
URL: http://www.usbr.gov/pn/

61572 ■ U.S. Department of the Interior - Bureau of Reclamation - Business Utilization and Development Specialist - Phoenix Area Office
6150 W. Thunderbird Rd.
Glendale, AZ 85306-4001
Ph: (623)773-6214
Fax: (623)773-6485
Co. E-mail: pcox@usbr.gov
URL: http://www.usbr.gov/lc/phoenix/

61573 ■ U.S. Department of the Interior - Bureau of Reclamation - Business Utilization and Development Specialist - Upper Colorado Region
125 S. State St., Rm. 6107
Salt Lake City, UT 84138-1102
Ph: (801)524-3675
Fax: (801)524-3857
URL: http://www.usbr.gov/uc/

61574 ■ U.S. Department of the Interior - Office of Small and Disadvantaged Business Utilization
1849 C St. NW
Washington, DC 20240
Ph: (202)208-3493
Free: 877-375-9927
URL: http://www.doi.gov/osdbu/

Description: The Department of the Interior's Small and Disadvantaged Business Program provides counseling and advice to small, women-owned, and minority-owned businesses on opportunities in the department. The program helps the bureaus and offices of the department in their efforts to increase contracting opportunities for such businesses. (This applies to direct contracting and subcontracting opportunities as well as to the Small Business Administration's programs.) For instance, the department's Bureau of Land Management sets aside certain commodities and services for procurement from small businesses. This bureau also conducts a lottery to allow the public the opportunity to purchase land. The Bureau of Indian Affairs provides technical assistance to Native American and tribal businesses on reservations for the establishment of enterprises, the preparation of economic development plans, the development of educational and residential facilities, and related undertakings. Furthermore, the department provides various publications that assist small business and small and disadvantaged business concerns with contracting opportunities. The Department of the Interior also hosts an annual Small Business Procurement Fair, which provides contact between the department's acquisition officials and small businesses.

61575 ■ U.S. Department of the Interior - Office of Small and Disadvantaged Business Utilization
1851 Constitution Ave. NW
Washington, DC 20240
Ph: (202)208-3493
Free: 877-375-9927
Fax: (202)208-7444
URL: http://www.doi.gov/pmb/osdbu/index.cfm

Description: The Department of the Interior's Small and Disadvantaged Business Program provides counseling and advice to small, women-owned, and minority-owned businesses on opportunities in the department. The program helps the bureaus and offices of the department in their efforts to increase contracting opportunities for such businesses. (This applies to direct contracting and subcontracting opportunities as well as to the Small Business Administration's programs.) For instance, the department's Bureau of Land Management sets aside certain commodities and services for procurement from small businesses. This bureau also conducts a lottery to allow the public the opportunity to purchase land. The Bureau of Indian Affairs provides technical assistance to Native American and tribal businesses on reservations for the establishment of enterprises, the preparation of economic development plans, the development of educational and residential facilities, and related undertakings. Furthermore, the department provides various publications that assist small business and small and disadvantaged business concerns with contracting opportunities. The Department of the Interior also hosts an annual Small Business Procurement Fair, which provides contact between the department's acquisition officials and small businesses.

61576 ■ U.S. Department of the Interior - Office of the Solicitor
1849 C St., NW, Rm. 6415
Washington, DC 20240
Ph: (202)208-4423
Fax: (202)208-5584
Co. E-mail: jason.earwood@sol.doi.gov
URL: http://www.doi.gov/solicitor/

61577 ■ U.S. Department of the Interior - Office of the Solicitor
1849 C St., NW, Rm. 6415
Washington, DC 20240
Ph: (202)208-4423

Fax: (202)208-5584
URL: http://www.doi.gov/solicitor/

61578 ■ U.S. Fish and Wildlife Service - Budget and Administration Division - Region 5 - Northeast Regional Office
300 Westgate Center Dr.
Hadley, MA 01035-9587
Ph: (413)253-8300
Fax: (413)253-8308
Co. E-mail: northeast@fws.gov
URL: http://www.fws.gov/northeast

61579 ■ U.S. Fish and Wildlife Service - Budget and Administration Division - Region 5 - Northeast Regional Office
300 Westgate Center Dr.
Hadley, MA 01035-9589
Ph: (413)253-8200
Fax: (413)253-8308
Co. E-mail: northeast@fws.gov
URL: http://www.fws.gov/northeast

61580 ■ U.S. Fish and Wildlife Service - Business Utilization and Development Specialist - Division of Contracting and General Services
1875 Century Blvd., Ste. 310
Atlanta, GA 30345-3319
Ph: (404)679-4055
Fax: (404)679-4057
Co. E-mail: southeast@fws.gov
URL: http://www.fws.gov/southeast

61581 ■ U.S. Fish and Wildlife Service - Business Utilization and Development Specialist - Division of Contracting and General Services
Denver Federal Center
Denver, CO 80228-0486
Ph: (303)236-5412
Fax: (303)236-4791
URL: http://www.fws.gov/offices/directory/

61582 ■ U.S. Fish and Wildlife Service - Business Utilization and Development Specialist - Division of Contracting and General Services
1875 Century Blvd., Ste. 400
Atlanta, GA 30345
Ph: (404)679-4000
Fax: (404)679-4006
Co. E-mail: southeast@fws.gov
URL: http://www.fws.gov/southeast

61583 ■ U.S. Fish and Wildlife Service - Business Utilization and Development Specialist - Division of Contracting and General Services
134 Union Blvd.
Lakewood, CO 80228-1807
Ph: (303)236-5412
Fax: (303)236-4791
URL: http://www.fws.gov/offices/directory/OfficeDetail.cfm?OrgCode=60181

61584 ■ U.S. Fish and Wildlife Service - Contracting & General Services Chief - Alaska Region
605 W. 4th Ave., Rm. G-61
Anchorage, AK 99501
Ph: (907)271-2888
Free: 800-272-4174
Fax: (907)271-2786
Co. E-mail: ak_fisheries@fws.gov
URL: http://alaska.fws.gov/fisheries/fieldoffice/
   anchorage/

61585 ■ U.S. Fish and Wildlife Service - Contracting & General Services Chief - Alaska Region
605 W. 4th Ave., Rm. G-61
Anchorage, AK 99501
Ph: (907)271-2888
Free: 800-272-4174

Fax: (907)271-2786
Co. E-mail: ak_fisheries@fws.gov
URL: http://alaska.fws.gov/fisheries/fieldoffice/
   anchorage/

61586 ■ U.S. Fish and Wildlife Service - Contracting & General Services Chief - Region 4
1875 Century Blvd., Ste. 380
Atlanta, GA 30345
Ph: (404)679-7057
Fax: (404)679-7065
URL: http://www.fws.gov/southeast

61587 ■ U.S. Fish and Wildlife Service - Contracting & General Services Chief - Region 4
1875 Century Blvd., Ste. 400
Atlanta, GA 30345
Ph: (404)679-4000
Fax: (404)679-4006
URL: http://www.fws.gov/southeast

61588 ■ U.S. Fish and Wildlife Service - Contracting & General Services Officer - Region 2
500 Gold Ave. SW, Rm. 5222
Albuquerque, NM 87103-1306
Ph: (505)248-6911
URL: http://www.fws.gov/southwest

61589 ■ U.S. Fish and Wildlife Service - Contracting & General Services Officer - Region 2
500 Gold Ave. SW, Rm. 5222
Albuquerque, NM 87102
Ph: (505)248-6911
Co. E-mail: rdtuggle@fws.gov
URL: http://www.fws.gov/southwest

61590 ■ U.S. Fish and Wildlife Service - Contracting Officer - Region 6
134 Union Blvd.
Lakewood, CO 80228
Ph: (303)236-7905
Fax: (303)236-3815
Co. E-mail: mountainprairie@fws.gov
URL: http://www.fws.gov/mountain-prairie/

61591 ■ U.S. Fish and Wildlife Service - Contracting Officer - Region 6
134 Union Blvd.
Lakewood, CO 80228
Ph: (303)236-7905
Fax: (303)236-3815
Co. E-mail: mountainprairie@fws.gov
URL: http://www.fws.gov/mountain-prairie/

61592 ■ U.S. Fish and Wildlife Service - Contracting & Procurement Officer - Region 3
Bishop Henry Whipple Federal Bldg.
1 Federal Dr.
Ft. Snelling, MN 55111-4056
Ph: (612)713-5360
Fax: (612)713-5280
Co. E-mail: midwestnews@fws.gov
URL: http://www.fws.gov/midwest

61593 ■ U.S. Fish and Wildlife Service - Contracting & Procurement Officer - Region 3
Bishop Henry Whipple Federal Bldg.
1 Federal Dr.
Ft. Snelling, MN 55111-4056
Ph: (612)713-5360
Fax: (612)713-5280
Co. E-mail: midwestnews@fws.gov
URL: http://www.fws.gov/midwest

61594 ■ U.S. Fish and Wildlife Service - Policy, Management and Budget - Alaska Region
1011 E. Tudor Rd.
Mail Stop 171
Anchorage, AK 99503
Ph: (907)786-3309
Fax: (907)786-3495
Co. E-mail: ak_admin@fws.gov
URL: http://alaska.fws.gov/

61595 ■ U.S. Fish and Wildlife Service - Policy, Management and Budget - Alaska Region
605 W. 4th Ave., Rm. G-61
Anchorage, AK 99501
Ph: (907)271-2888
Fax: (907)271-2786
Co. E-mail: ak_admin@fws.gov
URL: http://alaska.fws.gov/

61596 ■ U.S. Fish and Wildlife Service - Policy, Management and Budget - Great Lakes, Big Rivers Region
BHW Federal Bldg.
1 Federal Dr.
Ft. Snelling, MN 55111-4056
Ph: (612)713-5360
Fax: (612)713-5280
Co. E-mail: midwestnews@fws.gov
URL: http://www.fws.gov/midwest/

61597 ■ U.S. Fish and Wildlife Service - Policy, Management and Budget - Midwest Region
BHW Federal Bldg.
1 Federal Dr.
Ft. Snelling, MN 55111-4056
Ph: (612)713-5360
Fax: (612)713-5280
Co. E-mail: midwestnews@fws.gov
URL: http://www.fws.gov/midwest/

61598 ■ U.S. Fish and Wildlife Service - Policy, Management and Budget - Mountain Prairie Region
134 Union Blvd.
Lakewood, CO 80228
Ph: (303)236-7905
Fax: (303)236-3815
URL: http://www.fws.gov/mountain-prairie/

61599 ■ U.S. Fish and Wildlife Service - Policy, Management and Budget - Mountain Prairie Region
134 Union Blvd.
Lakewood, CO 80228
Ph: (303)236-7905
Fax: (303)236-3815
Co. E-mail: mountainprairie@fws.gov
URL: http://www.fws.gov/mountain-prairie/

61600 ■ U.S. Fish and Wildlife Service - Policy, Management and Budget - Northeast Regional Office
300 Westgate Center Dr.
Hadley, MA 01035-9589
Ph: (413)253-8300
Fax: (413)253-8308
Co. E-mail: northeast@fws.gov
URL: http://www.fws.gov/northeast

61601 ■ U.S. Fish and Wildlife Service - Policy, Management and Budget - Northeast Regional Office
300 Westgate Center Dr.
Hadley, MA 01035-9587
Ph: (413)253-8300
Fax: (413)253-8308
Co. E-mail: northeast@fws.gov
URL: http://www.fws.gov/northeast

61602 ■ U.S. Fish and Wildlife Service - Policy, Management and Budget - Pacific Region
Eastside Federal Complex
911 NE 11th Ave.
Portland, OR 97232-4181
Ph: (503)231-6120
Fax: (503)872-2716
URL: http://www.fws.gov/pacific/

61603 ■ U.S. Fish and Wildlife Service - Policy, Management and Budget - Pacific Region
Eastside Federal Complex
911 NE 11th Ave.
Portland, OR 97232-4181
Ph: (503)231-6120

Fax: (503)872-2716
URL: http://www.fws.gov/pacific/

61604 ■ U.S. Fish and Wildlife Service - Policy, Management and Budget - Southeast Region
1875 Century Blvd., Ste. 400
Atlanta, GA 30345
Ph: (404)679-4000
Fax: (404)679-4006
Co. E-mail: southeast@fws.gov
URL: http://www.fws.gov/southeast

61605 ■ U.S. Fish and Wildlife Service - Policy, Management and Budget - Southeast Region
1875 Century Blvd., Ste. 400
Atlanta, GA 30345
Ph: (404)679-4000
Fax: (404)679-4006
Co. E-mail: southeast@fws.gov
URL: http://www.fws.gov/southeast

61606 ■ U.S. Fish and Wildlife Service - Policy, Management and Budget - Southwest Region
PO Box 1306
Albuquerque, NM 87103-1306
Ph: (505)248-6911
Co. E-mail: RDTuggle@fws.gov
URL: http://www.fws.gov/southwest/

61607 ■ U.S. Fish and Wildlife Service - Policy, Management and Budget - Southwest Region
PO Box 1306
Albuquerque, NM 87103-1306
Ph: (505)248-6911
Co. E-mail: RDTuggle@fws.gov
URL: http://www.fws.gov/southwest/

61608 ■ U.S. Fish and Wildlife Service - Procurement Assistant - Region 1
911 NE 11th Ave.
Portland, OR 97232-4181
Ph: (503)231-6120
Fax: (503)231-2122
URL: http://www.fws.gov/pacific/

61609 ■ U.S. Fish and Wildlife Service - Procurement Assistant - Region 1
911 NE 11th Ave.
Portland, OR 97232-4181
Ph: (503)231-6120
Fax: (503)231-2122
URL: http://www.fws.gov/pacific/

61610 ■ U.S. Geological Survey - Business Utilization and Development Specialist
345 Middlefield Rd.
Mail Stop 285
Menlo Park, CA 94025
Ph: (650)853-8300
URL: http://menlocampus.wr.usgs.gov/

61611 ■ U.S. Geological Survey - Business Utilization and Development Specialist
12201 Sunrise Valley Dr.
Mail Stop 205P
Reston, VA 22092
Ph: (703)648-7346
Fax: (703)648-7901
Co. E-mail: rhelleman@usgs.gov
URL: http://www.usgs.gov

61612 ■ U.S. Geological Survey - Business Utilization and Development Specialist
12201 Sunrise Valley Dr.
Mail Stop 205P
Reston, VA 20192
Ph: (703)648-5953
URL: http://www.usgs.gov/ask/index.php

61613 ■ U.S. Geological Survey - Business Utilization and Development Specialist
345 Middlefield Rd.
Mail Stop 285
Menlo Park, CA 94025

Ph: (650)853-8300
URL: http://www.usgs.gov/contact_us/?state=CA

61614 ■ U.S. Geological Survey - Business Utilization and Development Specialist - Central Region
Denver Federal Center, Bldg. 810
Mail Stop 150
Denver, CO 80225-0046
Ph: (303)202-4740
Fax: (303)202-4742
URL: http://www.cr.usgs.gov/

61615 ■ U.S. Geological Survey - Business Utilization and Development Specialist - Central Region
Denver Federal Center, Bldg. 810
Mail Stop 150
Denver, CO 80225-0046
Ph: (303)202-4200
URL: http://www.cr.usgs.gov/

U.S. DEPARTMENT OF JUSTICE

The following Department of Justice divisions are arranged alphabetically by office or agency name.

61616 ■ Federal Bureau of Prisons - Acquisition Offices Administration Division
320 1st St. NW, Rm. 600
Washington, DC 20534
Ph: (202)307-3067
Fax: (202)514-4418
Co. E-mail: info@bop.gov
URL: http://www.bop.gov/

61617 ■ Federal Bureau of Prisons - National Contracts and Policy Section
320 1st St. NW, Rm. 600
Washington, DC 20534
Ph: (202)307-3067
Fax: (202)514-4418
Co. E-mail: info@bop.gov
URL: http://www.bop.gov/business/offices.jsp

61618 ■ Justice Management Division - Procurement Services Staff
2 Constitution Sq.
145 North St. NE, Ste. 8E.300
Washington, DC 20002
Ph: (202)307-2000
Fax: (202)307-1931
Co. E-mail: askdoj@usdoj.gov
URL: http://www.justice.gov/jmd/pss/profile.html

61619 ■ Office of Justice Programs - Information Systems Division
810 7th St., NW
Washington, DC 20531
Ph: (202)307-0703
Fax: (202)307-0086
Co. E-mail: ask.ocfo@usdoj.gov
URL: http://www.ojp.usdoj.gov/

61620 ■ Office of Justice Programs - Information Systems Division
810 7th St. NW
Washington, DC 20531
Ph: (202)307-0703
Fax: (202)307-0086
Co. E-mail: ask.oc@usdoj.gov
URL: http://www.ojp.usdoj.gov/

61621 ■ U.S. Citizenship and Immigration Services - Human Resources and Administrative Services Division - Procurement Policy and Evaluation
425 Eye St. NW, Rm. 2208
Washington, DC 20536
Ph: (202)305-1270
Fax: (202)616-2414
URL: http://www.uscis.gov/portal/site/uscis

61622 ■ U.S. Department of Justice - Federal Bureau of Investigation - Seattle Field Office
1110 3rd Ave.
Seattle, WA 98101-2904

Ph: (206)622-0460
Co. E-mail: seattle.fbi@ic.fbi.gov
URL: http://seattle.fbi.gov/

61623 ■ U.S. Department of Justice - Federal Bureau of Investigation - Seattle Field Office
1110 3rd Ave.
Seattle, WA 98101-2904
Ph: (206)622-0460
Co. E-mail: seattle.fbi@ic.fbi.gov
URL: http://seattle.fbi.gov/

61624 ■ U.S. Department of Justice - Justice Management Division - Procurement Services Staff
1331 Pennsylvania Ave. NW, Rm. 1000
Washington, DC 20530
Ph: (202)307-2000
Fax: (202)307-1931
Co. E-mail: askdoj@usdoj.gov
URL: http://www.justice.gov/jmd/pss/profile.html

61625 ■ U.S. Department of Justice - Office of Small and Disadvantaged Business Utilization
National Place Bldg., Rm. 1010
1331 Pennsylvania Ave. NW
Washington, DC 20530
Ph: (202)616-0521
Free: 800-345-3712
Fax: (202)616-1717
URL: http://www.usdoj.gov/jmd/osdbu/index.html

Description: The Department of Justice's Office of Small and Disadvantaged Business Utilization develops and implements appropriate outreach programs aimed at heightening the awareness of the small business community to the contracting opportunities available within the department. Outreach efforts include activities such as sponsoring small business fairs and procurement conferences, and participating in trade group seminars, conventions, and other forums that promote the utilization of small businesses as contractors. The office also provides counseling and advice to inquiring small businesses regarding their possible eligibility for special consideration under preferential purchasing programs that the department employs.

61626 ■ U.S. Department of Justice - Office of Small and Disadvantaged Business Utilization
950 Pennsylvania Ave. NW
Washington, DC 20530-0001
Ph: (202)616-0521
Free: 800-345-3712
Fax: (202)616-1717
URL: http://www.justice.gov/jmd/osdbu/index.html

Description: The Department of Justice's Office of Small and Disadvantaged Business Utilization develops and implements appropriate outreach programs aimed at heightening the awareness of the small business community to the contracting opportunities available within the department. Outreach efforts include activities such as sponsoring small business fairs and procurement conferences, and participating in trade group seminars, conventions, and other forums that promote the utilization of small businesses as contractors. The office also provides counseling and advice to inquiring small businesses regarding their possible eligibility for special consideration under preferential purchasing programs that the department employs.

61627 ■ U.S. Drug Enforcement Administration - Office of Acquisition and Relocation Management
2401 Jefferson Davis Hwy.
Alexandria, VA 22301
Ph: (202)307-4921
Free: 800-882-9539
Fax: (202)307-4877
Co. E-mail: dea.small.business.hotline@usdoj.gov
URL: http://www.usdoj.gov/dea/index.htm

61628 ■ U.S. Drug Enforcement Administration - Office of Acquisition and Relocation Management
800 K St. NW, Ste. 500
Washington, DC 20001
Ph: (202)307-8500
Co. E-mail: dea.small.business.hotline@usdoj.gov
URL: http://www.justice.gov/dea/resource-center/doing-business.shtml

61629 ■ U.S. Federal Bureau of Investigation - Administrative Services Division - Property Procurement and Management
935 Pennsylvania Ave. NW, Rm. 6863
Washington, DC 20535
Ph: (202)324-4930
Fax: (202)324-0570
URL: http://www.fbi.gov/business/business.htm

61630 ■ U.S. Federal Bureau of Investigation - Administrative Services Division - Property Procurement and Management
935 Pennsylvania Ave. NW, Rm. 6863
Washington, DC 20535
Ph: (202)324-4930
Fax: (202)324-0570

61631 ■ U.S. Federal Prisons Industries/ UNICOR - Procurement Division
400 1st St. NW, 7th Fl.
Washington, DC 20534
Ph: (202)305-7365
Co. E-mail: frohlich@central.unicor.gov
URL: http://www.unicor.gov/

61632 ■ U.S. Federal Prisons Industries/ UNICOR - Procurement Division
400 1st St. NW, 7th Fl.
Washington, DC 20534
Ph: (202)305-7304
Fax: (202)305-7365
Co. E-mail: lisbeth.day@usdoj.gov
URL: http://www.unicor.gov/

61633 ■ U.S. Immigration and Naturalization Service - Human Resources and Administrative Services Division - Procurement Policy and Evaluation
425 Eye St. NW, Rm. 2208
Washington, DC 20536
Ph: (202)305-1270
Fax: (202)616-2414
URL: http://www.uscis.gov/portal/site/uscis

61634 ■ U.S. Marshals Service - Procurement Policy and Oversight Team
United States Marshals Service Headquarters, CS-3
Arlington, VA 20530-1000
Ph: (202)307-9227
URL: http://www.usmarshals.gov/

61635 ■ U.S. Marshals Service - Procurement Policy and Oversight Team
United States Marshals Service Headquarters, CS-3
Arlington, VA 20530-1000
Ph: (202)307-9227
URL: http://www.usmarshals.gov/business/glance.htm

U.S. DEPARTMENT OF LABOR

61636 ■ Department of Labor - Labor Market Information - Research and Statistics Division
1001 N. 23rd St.
Baton Rouge, LA 70804
Ph: (225)342-9192
Fax: (225)342-9192
Co. E-mail: oois@lwc.la.gov
URL: http://www.laworks.net

61637 ■ Department of Labor - Louisianan Workforce Commission - Media Relations
PO Box 94094
Baton Rouge, LA 70804
Ph: (225)342-3035
Fax: (225)342-3743
URL: http://www.laworks.net

61638 ■ Department of Labor - Media Relations
PO Box 94094
Baton Rouge, LA 70804
Ph: (225)342-3035
Fax: (225)342-3743
URL: http://www.laworks.net

61639 ■ Department of Labor - Office of Management & Finance - Tax Accounting/ Adjustments Unit
PO Box 94100
Baton Rouge, LA 70804-9100
Ph: (225)342-2955
Fax: (225)342-5822
URL: http://www.laworks.net

61640 ■ Department of Labor - Office of Management & Finance - Tax Accounting/ Adjustments Unit
PO Box 94100
Baton Rouge, LA 70804-9100
Ph: (225)342-2955
Fax: (225)342-5822
URL: http://www.laworks.net

61641 ■ Department of Labor - Office of Occupational and Labor Market Information
19 W. Lea Blvd.
Wilmington, DE 19802
Ph: (302)761-8060
Co. E-mail: George.Sharpley@state.de.us
URL: http://www.delawareworks.com/oolmi/welcome.shtml
Description: Provides information regarding employment levels, unemployment rates, wages and earnings, employment projections, jobs, training resources, and careers.

61642 ■ Department of Labor - Office of Occupational and Labor Market Information
19 W. Lea Blvd.
Wilmington, DE 19802
Ph: (302)761-8069
Free: 800-452-1589
Fax: (302)761-6598
Co. E-mail: George Sharpley@state.de.us
URL: http://www.delawareworks.com/oolmi/welcome.shtml
Description: Provides information regarding employment levels, unemployment rates, wages and earnings, employment projections, jobs, training resources, and careers.

61643 ■ Department of Labor - Workforce Information and Analysis
Courtland Bldg., Rm. 300
148 International Blvd. NE
Atlanta, GA 30303
Ph: (404)232-3875
Fax: (404)232-2683
URL: http://www.dol.state.ga.us/em/get_labor_market_information.htm
Description: Collects, analyzes, and publishes a wide array of information about the state's labor market to provide a snapshot of Georgia's economy, job market, businesses, and its workforce.

61644 ■ Florida Agency of Economic Opportunity - Labor Market Statistics - State Census Data Center
107 E. Madison St.
MSC G-020
Tallahassee, FL 32399-4111
Ph: (850)245-7205
Free: 866-537-3615
Co. E-mail: info@labormarketinfo.com
URL: http://www.floridajobs.org/labor-market-information

61645 ■ Florida Department of Economic Opportunity - Labor Market Statistics - State Census Data Center
107 E. Madison St.
MSC G-020
Tallahassee, FL 32399-4111
Ph: (850)245-7205

Free: 866-537-3615
Co. E-mail: info@labormarketinfo.com
URL: http://www.floridajobs.org/labor-market-information/data-center/florida-census-data-center

61646 ■ Georgia Department of Labor - Labor Market Information
Courtland Bldg., Rm. 300
148 International Blvd., NE
Atlanta, GA 30303
Ph: (404)232-3875
Fax: (404)232-2683
URL: http://www.dol.state.ga.us/em/get_labor_market_information.htm
Description: Collects, analyzes, and publishes a wide array of information about the state's labor market to provide a snapshot of Georgia's economy, job market, businesses, and its workforce.

61647 ■ Louisiana Workforce Commission - Labor Market Information - Research and Statistics Division
1001 N. 23rd St.
Baton Rouge, LA 70804
Ph: (225)342-9192
Fax: (225)342-7960
Co. E-mail: oois@lwc.la.gov
URL: http://www.laworks.net

61648 ■ U.S. Department of Labor - Bureau of Labor Statistics
Postal Square Bldg.
2 Massachusetts Ave., NE
Washington, DC 20212-0001
Ph: (202)691-5200
URL: http://www.bls.gov/
Description: The Bureau of Labor Statistics is the principal fact-finding agency for the Federal Government in the broad field of labor economics and statistics.

61649 ■ U.S. Department of Labor - Occupational Safety and Health Administration (OSHA)
200 Constitution Ave. NW, Rm. S2315
Washington, DC 20210
Ph: (202)693-2000
Free: 800-321-6742
Fax: (202)693-1659
URL: http://www.osha.gov

61650 ■ U.S. Department of Labor - Occupational Safety and Health Administration (OSHA) - Office of Communications
200 Constitution Ave., NW, Rm. 3476
Washington, DC 20210
Ph: (202)693-1999
URL: http://www.osha.gov

61651 ■ U.S. Department of Labor - Occupational Safety and Health Administration (OSHA) - Office of Communications
200 Constitution Ave. NW, Rm. N-3647
Washington, DC 20210
Ph: (202)693-1999
URL: http://www.osha.gov/as/opa/media_contact.html

61652 ■ U.S. Department of Labor - Occupational Safety and Health Administration (OSHA) - Office of Small Business Assistance - Directorate of Cooperative and State Programs
200 Constitution Ave., NW, Rm. N-3660
Washington, DC 20210
Ph: (202)693-2220
URL: http://www.osha.gov/dcsp/osba/index.html

61653 ■ U.S. Department of Labor - Office of Small and Disadvantaged Business Utilization
Frances Perkins Bldg.
200 Constitution Ave. NW, Rm. N-6432
Washington, DC 20210

Ph: (202)693-7297
Co. E-mail: osbdu@dol.gov
URL: http://www.dol.gov/oasam/programs/osdbu/
Description: Emphasizes development of small and disadvantaged business utilization in contract and grant activities, promotes interaction with Historically Black Colleges and Universities and Hispanic and other minority colleges and universities, and has management oversight responsibility for Department of Labor advisory committees. The department fully supports the federal government's Small and Disadvantaged Business Utilization Program created to give small, disadvantaged, and women-owned businesses maximum opportunity to participate in government contracting and grant activities for supplies and services (including research, evaluation, maintenance, repairs, and construction).

61654 ■ U.S. Department of Labor - Office of Small and Disadvantaged Business Utilization
Frances Perkins Bldg.
200 Constitution Ave. NW, Rm. N-6432
Washington, DC 20210
Ph: (202)693-7297
Free: 866-487-2365
Co. E-mail: osbdu@dol.gov
URL: http://www.dol.gov/oasam/programs/osdbu/
Description: Emphasizes development of small and disadvantaged business utilization in contract and grant activities, promotes interaction with Historically Black Colleges and Universities and Hispanic and other minority colleges and universities, and has management oversight responsibility for Department of Labor advisory committees. The department fully supports the federal government's Small and Disadvantaged Business Utilization Program created to give small, disadvantaged, and women-owned businesses maximum opportunity to participate in government contracting and grant activities for supplies and services (including research, evaluation, maintenance, repairs, and construction).

61655 ■ U.S. Department of Labor - Patent and Trademark Office - Board of Patent Appeals and Inferences
Mail Stop 8
Alexandria, VA 22313-1450
Ph: (571)272-9797
Fax: (571)273-0053
URL: http://www.uspto.gov/patents/announce/patent_
appeal_final_decision.jsp

61656 ■ U.S. Department of Labor - Patent and Trademark Office - Office of the Chief Communications Officer
PO Box 1450
Alexandria, VA 22313-1450
Ph: (517)272-8400
Free: 800-786-9199
Fax: (517)272-0340
URL: http://www.uspto.gov/about/offices/opa/index.
jsp
Description: The Patent and Trademark Office examines applications for patents and trademarks to determine whether an invention is patentable or if a trademark may be registered. Patents and trademarks, because of the legal rights they represent, are important to small businesses competing against larger or more established businesses. The Patent and Trademark Office maintains the Public Search Room for use by individuals wishing to identify new products, find solutions to problems, or check patents in a field of technology. The Patent and Trademark Office's Trademark Search Room is also open to the public. In addition, the office sponsors a system of Patent Depository Libraries, which brings collections of U.S. patents to within one hour commuting time of 45 percent of the U.S. population. An automated system known as CASSIS (Classification and Search Support Information System) is available in most of the libraries. CASSIS provides free, online access to the Patent and Trademark Office's classification databases to assist users in their patent searches.

61657 ■ U.S. Department of Labor - Patent and Trademark Office - Office of Enforcement
Madison Bldg., 10th Fl. W.
600 Dulany St.
Alexandria, VA 22313-1450

Ph: (571)272-9300
Fax: (571)273-0085
URL: http://www.uspto.gov

61658 ■ U.S. Department of Labor - Patent and Trademark Office - Office of Enrollment and Discipline
Mail Stop OED
Alexandria, VA 22313-1450
Ph: (571)272-4097
Fax: (571)273-0074
URL: http://www.uspto.gov/ip/boards/oed/index.jsp

61659 ■ U.S. Department of Labor - Patent and Trademark Office - Office of Initial Patent Examination
PO Box 1450
Alexandria, VA 22313-1450
Ph: (571)272-4000
Fax: (571)273-8300
URL: http://www.uspto.gov/about/offices/patents/
index.jsp

61660 ■ U.S. Department of Labor - Patent and Trademark Office - Office of Patent and Cooperation Operations (PCT)
PO Box 1450
Alexandria, VA 22313-1450
URL: http://www.uspto.gov

61661 ■ U.S. Department of Labor - Patent and Trademark Office - Office of Patent Publication
PO Box 1450
Alexandria, VA 22313-1450
Ph: (571)272-4200
Free: 888-786-0101
Fax: (571)273-8300
Co. E-mail: Pubscustomerservice@uspto.gov
URL: http://www.uspto.gov/web/patents/pubs/

61662 ■ U.S. Department of Labor - Patent and Trademark Office - Office of Petitions
PO Box 1450
Alexandria, VA 22313-1450
Ph: (571)272-3282
Fax: (571)273-0025
URL: http://www.uspto.gov/web/offices/pac/dapp/peti-
tionsmain.html

61663 ■ U.S. Department of Labor - Patent and Trademark Office - Office of Policy and External Affairs
PO Box 1450
Alexandria, VA 22313-1450
Ph: (571)272-9300
URL: http://www.uspto.gov/ip/global/index.jsp

61664 ■ U.S. Department of Labor - Patent and Trademark Office - Office of Procurement
Madison W. Bldg.
600 Dulany St.
Alexandria, VA 22313-1450
Ph: (571)272-6575
Fax: (571)273-0464
Co. E-mail: procurementhelp@uspto.gov
URL: http://www.uspto.gov/web/offices/ac/comp/proc/
Telecommunication Services: kate.kudrewicz@
uspto.gov.

61665 ■ U.S. Department of Labor - U.S. Bureau of Labor Statistics
Postal Square Bldg.
2 Massachusetts Ave. NE
Washington, DC 20212-0001
Ph: (202)691-5200
URL: http://www.bls.gov/
Description: The Bureau of Labor Statistics is the principal fact-finding agency for the Federal Government in the broad field of labor economics and statistics.

61666 ■ U.S. Department of Labor - United States Patent and Trademark Office - Board of Patent Appeals and Interferences
Mail Stop 8
Alexandria, VA 22313-1450
Ph: (571)272-9797

Fax: (571)273-0053
URL: http://www.uspto.gov/web/offices/dcom/bpai/
index.html

61667 ■ U.S. Department of Labor - United States Patent and Trademark Office - Office of Administrator for Policy and External Affairs
PO Box 1450
Alexandria, VA 22313-1450
Ph: (571)272-9300
URL: http://www.uspto.gov/web/offices/dcom/olia/

61668 ■ U.S. Department of Labor - United States Patent and Trademark Office - Office of Enforcement
Madison Bldg., 10th Fl. W.
600 Dulany St.
Alexandria, VA 22313-1450
Ph: (571)272-9300
URL: http://www.uspto.gov

61669 ■ U.S. Department of Labor - United States Patent and Trademark Office - Office of Enrollment and Discipline
Mail Stop OED
Alexandria, VA 22313-1450
Ph: (571)272-4097
Fax: (571)273-0074
URL: http://www.uspto.gov/ip/boards/oed/index.jsp

61670 ■ U.S. Department of Labor - United States Patent and Trademark Office - Office of Initial Patent Examination (OIPE)
PO Box 1450
Alexandria, VA 22313-1450
Ph: (571)272-4000
Fax: (571)273-8300
URL: http://www.uspto.gov

61671 ■ U.S. Department of Labor - United States Patent and Trademark Office - Office of Patent Cooperation Treaty (PCT)
PO Box 1450
Alexandria, VA 22313-1450
Ph: (703)308-9290
Fax: (703)305-3230
URL: http://www.uspto.gov

61672 ■ U.S. Department of Labor - United States Patent and Trademark Office - Office of Patent Publication
PO Box 1450
Alexandria, VA 22313-1450
Ph: (571)272-4200
Free: 888-786-0101
Fax: (571)273-8300
Co. E-mail: Pubscustomerservice@uspto.gov
URL: http://www.uspto.gov/web/patents/pubs/

61673 ■ U.S. Department of Labor - United States Patent and Trademark Office - Office of Petitions
PO Box 1450
Alexandria, VA 22313-1450
Ph: (571)272-3282
Fax: (571)273-0025
URL: http://www.uspto.gov/web/offices/pac/dapp/peti-
tionsmain.html

61674 ■ U.S. Department of Labor - United States Patent and Trademark Office - Office of Procurement
Madison W. Bldg.
600 Dulany St.
Alexandria, VA 22313-1450
Ph: (571)272-6575
Fax: (571)273-0464
Co. E-mail: jennifer.passaro@uspto.gov
URL: http://www.uspto.gov/web/offices/ac/comp/proc/

61675 ■ U.S. Department of Labor - United States Patent and Trademark Office - Office of Public Affairs
PO Box 1450
Alexandria, VA 22313-1450
Ph: (517)272-8400
Free: 800-786-9199

Fax: (517)272-0340

URL: http://www.uspto.gov/web/offices/ac/ahrpa/opa/opahome.htm

Description: The Patent and Trademark Office examines applications for patents and trademarks to determine whether an invention is patentable or if a trademark may be registered. Patents and trademarks, because of the legal rights they represent, are important to small businesses competing against larger or more established businesses. The Patent and Trademark Office maintains the Public Search Room for use by individuals wishing to identify new products, find solutions to problems, or check patents in a field of technology. The Patent and Trademark Office's Trademark Search Room is also open to the public. In addition, the office sponsors a system of Patent Depository Libraries, which brings collections of U.S. patents to within one hour commuting time of 45 percent of the U.S. population. An automated system known as CASSIS (Classification and Search Support Information System) is available in most of the libraries. CASSIS provides free, online access to the Patent and Trademark Office's classification databases to assist users in their patent searches.

U.S. DEPARTMENT OF STATE

61676 ■ **U.S. Department of State - Bureau of Diplomatic Security - Office of Foreign Missions**
3507 International Pl., NW
2201 C St.
Washington, DC 20522-3302
Ph: (202)895-3594
Co. E-mail: OFMinfo@state.gov
URL: http://www.state.gov/ofm/

Description: The Office of Foreign Missions (OFM) provides the legal foundation to facilitate secure and efficient operations of U.S. missions abroad, and of foreign missions and International organizations in the United States.

61677 ■ **U.S. Department of State - Bureau of Diplomatic Security - Office of Foreign Missions**
2201 C St. NW, Rm. 2236
Washington, DC 20520
Ph: (202)895-3500
Co. E-mail: OFMinfo@state.gov
URL: http://www.state.gov/ofm/

Description: The Office of Foreign Missions (OFM) provides the legal foundation to facilitate secure and efficient operations of U.S. missions abroad, and of foreign missions and International organizations in the United States.

61678 ■ **U.S. Department of State - Office of Civil Rights**
Harry S. Truman Bldg., Rm. 7428
2201 C St., NW
Washington, DC 20520
Ph: (202)647-9294
Fax: (202)647-4969
Co. E-mail: socr_direct@state.gov
URL: http://www.state.gov/s/ocr/

61679 ■ **U.S. Department of State - Office of Civil Rights**
Harry S. Truman Bldg., Rm. 7428
2201 C St., NW
Washington, DC 20520
Ph: (202)647-9294
Fax: (202)647-4969
Co. E-mail: socr_direct@state.gov
URL: http://www.state.gov/s/ocr/

61680 ■ **U.S. Department of State - Office of the Inspector General**
2201 C Street, NW, Rm. 8100, SA-3
Washington, DC 20520
Ph: (202)647-0340
Fax: (202)647-6047
Co. E-mail: oighotline@state.gov
URL: http://oig.state.gov

61681 ■ **U.S. Department of State - Office of the Inspector General**
2201 C Street NW, Rm. 8100, SA-3
Washington, DC 20520-0308
Ph: (202)647-3320
Free: 800-409-9926
Co. E-mail: oighotline@state.gov
URL: http://oig.state.gov

61682 ■ **U.S. Department of State - Office of Small and Disadvantaged Business Utilization**
2201 C St., NW, SA-6, Rm. L500
Washington, DC 20522
Ph: (703)875-6822
Fax: (703)875-6825
URL: http://www.state.gov/m/a/sdbu/

Description: The Department of State actively seeks qualified small businesses, minority-owned businesses, and women-owned businesses for participation in contract work generated in the course of day-to-day operations. The mission of the State Department--the making and conduct of foreign policy--does not require a large procurement support program on the magnitude of many federal agencies. However in 1995, the Department spent approximately $1 billion in goods and services in support of that mission. Of that amount, the fifteen domestic procurement offices spent $750 million. The contract spectrum of the domestic procurement pattern includes some minor research and development; office and household furniture and furnishings; transportation, warehousing and packing/shipping services; information technology supplies and services; training; translation and interpreting services (personal services contracts only); building construction, renovation/rehabilitation and architect/engineer services; and security support services, among other things. The Department of State embassies, consulates and Regional Procurement & Support Offices worldwide spent the remaining $400 million.

61683 ■ **U.S. Department of State - Office of Small and Disadvantaged Business Utilization**
2201 C St. NW, SA-6, Rm. L500
Washington, DC 20522
Ph: (703)875-6822
Fax: (703)875-6825
URL: http://www.state.gov/s/dmr/sdbu/index.htm

Description: The Department of State actively seeks qualified small businesses, minority-owned businesses, and women-owned businesses for participation in contract work generated in the course of day-to-day operations. The mission of the State Department--the making and conduct of foreign policy--does not require a large procurement support program on the magnitude of many federal agencies. However in 1995, the Department spent approximately $1 billion in goods and services in support of that mission. Of that amount, the fifteen domestic procurement offices spent $750 million. The contract spectrum of the domestic procurement pattern includes some minor research and development; office and household furniture and furnishings; transportation, warehousing and packing/shipping services; information technology supplies and services; training; translation and interpreting services (personal services contracts only); building construction, renovation/rehabilitation and architect/engineer services; and security support services, among other things. The Department of State embassies, consulates and Regional Procurement & Support Offices worldwide spent the remaining $400 million.

U.S. DEPARTMENT OF TRANSPORTATION

The following Department of Transportation offices are arranged alphabetically by agency name.

61684 ■ **U.S. Department of Transportation - Coast Guard - Acquisition Directorate - Minority Business Program**
2100 2nd St., SW
Washington, DC 20593
Ph: (202)267-2499

Fax: (202)267-4158
Co. E-mail: acquisitionweb@uscg.mil
URL: http://osdbu.dot.gov/

61685 ■ **U.S. Department of Transportation - Coast Guard - Procurement Management Division - Minority Business Program**
2100 2nd St., SW
Washington, DC 20593
Ph: (202)267-2499
Fax: (202)267-4158
URL: http://osdbu.dot.gov/

61686 ■ **U.S. Department of Transportation - Federal Aviation Administration - Small Business Innovative Research (SBIR)**
800 Independence Ave. SW, Rm. 715
Washington, DC 20591
Ph: (202)267-8881
Co. E-mail: inez.williams@faa.gov
URL: http://www.tc.faa.gov/technologytransfer/sbir/

61687 ■ **U.S. Department of Transportation - Federal Aviation Administration - Small Business Utilization Office**
800 Independence Ave. SW, Rm. 715
Washington, DC 20591
Ph: (202)267-8881
Co. E-mail: inez.williams@faa.gov
URL: http://www.faa.gov/about/office_org/regions_centers/mmac/acquisition/small_business/

61688 ■ **U.S. Department of Transportation - Federal Highway Administration - Central Federal Lands Highway Division**
12300 W. Dakota Ave.
Lakewood, CO 80228-2583
Ph: (720)963-3500
Free: 888-739-1055
Fax: (720)963-3379
URL: http://www.cflhd.gov

61689 ■ **U.S. Department of Transportation - Federal Highway Administration - Central Federal Lands Highway Division**
12300 W. Dakota Ave.
Lakewood, CO 80228-2583
Ph: (720)963-3500
Free: 888-739-1055
Fax: (720)963-3379
Co. E-mail: kpease@fhwa.dot.gov
URL: http://www.cflhd.gov

61690 ■ **U.S. Department of Transportation - Federal Highway Administration - Eastern Federal Lands Highway Division - Small and Disadvantaged Business Utilization Liaison**
Loudoun Technical Center
21400 Ridge Top Cir.
Sterling, VA 20166-6511
Ph: (703)404-6201
Free: 800-892-8776
Fax: (703)285-0011
URL: http://www.efl.fhwa.dot.gov

61691 ■ **U.S. Department of Transportation - Federal Highway Administration - Eastern Federal Lands Highway Division - Small and Disadvantaged Business Utilization Liaison**
Loudoun Technical Center
21400 Ridge Top Cir.
Sterling, VA 20166-6511
Ph: (703)404-6201
Free: 800-892-8776
Fax: (703)285-0011
URL: http://www.efl.fhwa.dot.gov

61692 ■ **U.S. Department of Transportation - Federal Highway Administration - Federal Lands Highway Division**
1200 New Jersey Ave., SE
Washington, DC 20590
Ph: (202)366-9494
Fax: (202)366-7495
URL: http://flh.fhwa.dot.gov/

61693 ■ U.S. Department of Transportation - Federal Highway Administration - Federal Lands Highway Division
1200 New Jersey Ave. SE
Washington, DC 20590
Ph: (202)366-9494
Fax: (202)366-7495
URL: http://flh.fhwa.dot.gov/

61694 ■ U.S. Department of Transportation - Federal Highway Administration - Small Business Specialist
1200 New Jersey Ave., SE, Rm. W36-320
Washington, DC 20590
Ph: (202)366-4205
Free: 800-532-1169
Fax: (202)366-7538
Co. E-mail: frank.waltos@fhwa.dot.gov
URL: http://www.fhwa.dot.gov/

61695 ■ U.S. Department of Transportation - Federal Highway Administration - Small Business Specialist
1200 New Jersey Ave. SE
Washington, DC 20590
Ph: (202)366-4205
Free: 800-532-1169
Fax: (202)366-7538
Co. E-mail: frank.waltos@dot.gov
URL: http://www.osdbu.dot.gov/procurement/specialists.cfm

61696 ■ U.S. Department of Transportation - Federal Highway Administration - Western Federal Lands Highway Division
610 E. 5th St.
Vancouver, WA 98661-3801
Ph: (360)619-7700
URL: http://www.wfl.fha.dot.gov

61697 ■ U.S. Department of Transportation - Federal Highway Administration - Western Federal Lands Highway Division
610 E. 5th St.
Vancouver, WA 98661-3801
Ph: (360)619-7700
URL: http://www.wfl.fha.dot.gov

61698 ■ U.S. Department of Transportation - Federal Railroad Administration - Small Business Specialist
1200 New Jersey Ave., SE, Rm. W34-304
Washington, DC 20590
Ph: (202)493-6131
Co. E-mail: frapa@dot.gov
URL: http://www.fra.dot.gov/

61699 ■ U.S. Department of Transportation - Federal Railroad Administration - Small Business Specialist
1200 New Jersey Ave. SE
Washington, DC 20590
Ph: (202)493-6131
Fax: (202)493-6171
Co. E-mail: dana.hicks@dot.gov
URL: http://www.fra.dot.gov/
URL(s): www.osdbu.dot.gov/procurement/specialists.cfm.

61700 ■ U.S. Department of Transportation - Federal Transit Administration - Small Business Specialist
1200 New Jersey Ave., SE
Rm. C42-318
Washington, DC 20590
Ph: (202)366-2502
Co. E-mail: ledra.post@dot.gov
URL: http://www.fta.dot.gov/civilrights/civil_rights_5089.html

61701 ■ U.S. Department of Transportation - Federal Transit Administration - Small Business Specialist
1200 New Jersey Ave. SE
Washington, DC 20590
Ph: (202)366-4980

Fax: (202)366-3808
Co. E-mail: ledra.post@fta.dot.gov
URL: http://www.fta.dot.gov/civilrights/civil_rights_5089.html

61702 ■ U.S. Department of Transportation - John A. Volpe National Transportation Center - Office of Management Services - Contracts and Small Business Programs Branch
55 Broadway
Cambridge, MA 02142-1093
Ph: (617)494-2051
Fax: (617)494-2370
Co. E-mail: leisa.moniz@dot.gov
URL: http://www.volpe.dot.gov/sbir/index.html

61703 ■ U.S. Department of Transportation - John A. Volpe National Transportation Systems Center - Research and Innovative Technology Administration - Contracts and Small Business Branch
55 Broadway
Cambridge, MA 02142-1093
Ph: (617)494-2000
URL: http://www.volpe.dot.gov/

61704 ■ U.S. Department of Transportation - Maritime Administration - Small Business Specialist - Office of Acquisition
1200 New Jersey Ave. SE
Room W26-421
Washington, DC 20590
Ph: (202)366-2802
Fax: (202)366-3889
Co. E-mail: rita.thomas@.dot.gov
URL: http://voa.marad.dot.gov/

61705 ■ U.S. Department of Transportation - Maritime Administration - Small Business Specialist - Virtual Office of Acquisition
1200 New Jersey Ave., SE
Room W26-421
Washington, DC 20590
Ph: (202)366-2802
Fax: (202)366-3889
Co. E-mail: rita.thomas@.dot.gov
URL: http://voa.marad.dot.gov/

61706 ■ U.S. Department of Transportation - National Highway Traffic Safety Administration - Office of Small and Disadvantaged Business Utilization - Procurement Assistance Division
West Bldg.
1200 New Jersey Ave., SE, Rm. W56-485
Washington, DC 20590
Ph: (202)366-1169
Fax: (202)366-7228
URL: http://osdbu.dot.gov/documents/Cont_DOT/CWD-7-09.cfm

61707 ■ U.S. Department of Transportation (DOT) - Office of Small and Disadvantaged Business Utilization
1200 New Jersey Ave., SE, W56-485
Washington, DC 20590
Ph: (202)366-1930
Free: 800-532-1169
Fax: (202)366-7228
URL: http://osdbu.dot.gov/
Description: The DOT's Office of Small and Disadvantaged Business Utilization provides policy direction for minority, women-owned, and small and disadvantaged business enterprise participation in direct procurement and federal financial assistance activities. It also is responsible for conducting programs directed at encouraging, promoting, and assisting disadvantaged business enterprises in securing contracts, subcontracts, and projects generated by these activities. The office schedules presentations for firms to present their capabilities to the procurement and program staff and monitors all procurement activities for disadvantaged business enterprises by the department, its grantees, and recipients nationwide. All proposed procurements are reviewed for the participation of small business. When possible, specific procurements are set aside exclusively for small business competition.

61708 ■ U.S. Department of Transportation - Office of Small and Disadvantaged Business Utilization
1200 New Jersey Ave., SE, W56-485
Washington, DC 20590
Ph: (202)366-1930
Free: 800-532-1169
Fax: (202)366-7228
URL: http://osdbu.dot.gov/
Description: The DOT's Office of Small and Disadvantaged Business Utilization provides policy direction for minority, women-owned, and small and disadvantaged business enterprise participation in direct procurement and federal financial assistance activities. It also is responsible for conducting programs directed at encouraging, promoting, and assisting disadvantaged business enterprises in securing contracts, subcontracts, and projects generated by these activities. The office schedules presentations for firms to present their capabilities to the procurement and program staff and monitors all procurement activities for disadvantaged business enterprises by the department, its grantees, and recipients nationwide. All proposed procurements are reviewed for the participation of small business. When possible, specific procurements are set aside exclusively for small business competition.

61709 ■ U.S. Department of Transportation - Office of Small and Disadvantaged Business Utilization - Procurement Assistance Division
West Bldg.
1200 New Jersey Ave., SE, Rm. W51-125
Washington, DC 20590
Ph: (202)366-9564
Fax: (202)366-9555
Co. E-mail: jerry.franco@dot.gov
URL: http://www.nhtsa.dot.gov/

61710 ■ U.S. Department of Transportation - Pipeline and Hazardous Materials Safety Administration
1200 New Jersey Ave., SE
East Bldg., 2nd Fl.
Washington, DC 20590
Ph: (202)366-4433
Fax: (202)366-3666
Co. E-mail: patricia.klinger@dot.gov
URL: http://www.phmsa.dot.gov

61711 ■ U.S. Department of Transportation - Pipeline and Hazardous Materials Safety Administration
1200 New Jersey Ave. SE
East Bldg., 2nd Fl.
Washington, DC 20590
Ph: (202)366-4433
Fax: (202)366-3666
Co. E-mail: patricia.klinger@dot.gov
URL: http://www.phmsa.dot.gov

61712 ■ U.S. Department of Transportation - Research and Innovative Technology Administration (RITA)
1200 New Jersey Ave., SE
Washington, DC 20590
Ph: (202)366-3492
Free: 800-853-1351
Fax: (202)366-3759
Co. E-mail: ritainfo@dot.gov
URL: http://www.rita.dot.gov

61713 ■ U.S. Department of Transportation - Research and Innovative Technology Administration (RITA)
1200 New Jersey Ave. SE
Washington, DC 20590
Ph: (202)366-3492
Free: 800-853-1351
Fax: (202)366-3759
Co. E-mail: ritainfo@dot.gov
URL: http://www.rita.dot.gov

61714 ■ U.S. Department of Transportation - Research and Special Programs Administration - Office of Contracts and

Administration
400 7th St. SW, Rm. 8321
Washington, DC 20590
Ph: (202)366-5513
Fax: (202)366-7974
URL: http://www.rspa.dot.gov/

61715 ■ U.S. Department of Transportation - Research and Special Programs Administration - Office of Contracts and Administration
400 7th St. SW, Rm. 8321
Washington, DC 20590
Ph: (202)366-5513
Fax: (202)366-7974

61716 ■ U.S. Department of Transportation - St. Lawrence Seaway Development Corporation - Office of the Associate Administrator
180 Andrews St.
Massena, NY 13662-0520
Ph: (315)764-3200
Fax: (315)764-3235
Co. E-mail: Research@sls.dot.gov
URL: http://www.seaway.dot.gov/

61717 ■ U.S. Department of Transportation - St. Lawrence Seaway Development Corporation - Office of the Associate Administrator
180 Andrews St.
Massena, NY 13662-0520
Ph: (315)764-3200
Fax: (315)764-3235
Co. E-mail: info@sls.dot.gov
URL: http://www.seaway.dot.gov/

61718 ■ U.S. Department of Transportation - Transportation Safety Institute - Operations Support Division
6500 S. MacArthur Blvd.
Oklahoma City, OK 73125-5050
Ph: (405)954-6441
Fax: (405)954-3521
URL: http://www.tsi.dot.gov

61719 ■ U.S. Department of Transportation - Transportation Safety Institute - Operations Support Division
6500 S. MacArthur Blvd.
Oklahoma City, OK 73125-5050
Ph: (405)954-6441
Fax: (405)954-3521
Co. E-mail: operations.support@tsi.jccbi.gov
URL: http://www.tsi.dot.gov

U.S. DEPARTMENT OF THE TREASURY

The following Treasury Department Regional Financial Centers are arranged alphabetically by city.

61720 ■ U.S. Department of Homeland Security - Federal Law Enforcement Training Center
Glynco Facility
1131 Chapel Crossing Rd.
Glynco, GA 31524
Ph: (912)267-2100
Fax: (912)267-2071
URL: http://www.fletc.gov
Contact: Susan Smallwood, Specialist

61721 ■ U.S. Department of Homeland Security - Federal Law Enforcement Training Center
Artesia Facility
1300 W. Richey Ave.
Artesia, NM 88210
Ph: (505)748-8000
URL: http://www.fletc.gov/about-fletc/locations/artesia

61722 ■ U.S. Department of Homeland Security - U.S. Customs and Border Protection
1300 Pennsylvania Ave., NW
Washington, DC 20229
Ph: (202)344-2990
Fax: (202)344-2950
URL: http://www.customs.gov/
Contact: William Bickelman, Specialist

61723 ■ U.S. Department of Homeland Security - U.S. Customs and Border Protection
1300 Pennsylvania Ave. NW
Washington, DC 20229
Ph: (703)526-4200
URL: http://www.cbp.gov/xp/cgov/home.xml

61724 ■ U.S. Department of Homeland Security - U.S. Secret Service - Procurement Division
Procurement Division
245 Murray Dr., Bldg. 410
Washington, DC 20223
Ph: (202)406-6940
URL: http://www.secretservice.gov/
Contact: Andy Anderson, Specialist

61725 ■ U.S. Department of Homeland Security - U.S. Secret Service - Procurement Division
245 Murray Dr., Bldg. 410
Washington, DC 20223
Ph: (202)406-6940
URL: http://www.secretservice.gov/

61726 ■ U.S. Department of the Treasury - Acquisition Management
Liberty Ctr., Rm. 110
401 14th St., SW
Washington, DC 20227
URL: http://www.ustreas.gov/offices/management/dcfo/procurement/bcpo.shtml

61727 ■ U.S. Department of the Treasury - Acquisition Management
Liberty Ctr., Rm. 110
401 14th St., SW
Washington, DC 20227
URL: http://www.ustreas.gov/offices/management/dcfo/procurement/bcpo.shtml

61728 ■ U.S. Department of the Treasury - Acquisition and Procurement Office
650 Massachusetts Ave., NW, Rm. 5000
Washington, DC 20226
URL: http://www.ustreas.gov/offices/management/dcfo/procurement/bcpo.shtml

61729 ■ U.S. Department of the Treasury - Acquisition and Procurement Office
650 Massachusetts Ave., NW, Rm. 5000
Washington, DC 20226
URL: http://www.treasury.gov/about/organizational-structure/offices/Pages/Office-of-the-Procurement-Executive.aspx

61730 ■ U.S. Department of the Treasury - Acquisition Services Division
250 E St., SW, 4th Fl.
Washington, DC 20219
URL: http://www.ustreas.gov/offices/management/dcfo/procurement/bcpo.shtml

61731 ■ U.S. Department of the Treasury - Acquisition Services Division
250 E St., SW, 4th Fl.
Washington, DC 20219

61732 ■ U.S. Department of the Treasury - Austin Financial Center
PO Box 149058
Austin, TX 78714-9058
Ph: (512)342-7300
Fax: (512)342-7228
Co. E-mail: afc.help@fms.treas.gov
URL: http://fms.treas.gov/afc/index.html

61733 ■ U.S. Department of the Treasury - Austin Financial Center
PO Box 149058
Austin, TX 78714-9058
Ph: (512)342-7300
Fax: (512)342-7228
Co. E-mail: afc.help@fms.treas.gov

61734 ■ U.S. Department of the Treasury - Birmingham Financial Center
190 Vulcan Rd.
Birmingham, AL 35201-2451
Fax: (205)912-6114

61735 ■ U.S. Department of the Treasury - Birmingham Financial Center
190 Vulcan Rd.
Birmingham, AL 35201-2451
Ph: (205)912-6207
Fax: (205)912-6114

61736 ■ U.S. Department of the Treasury (TTB) - Bureau of Alcohol and Tobacco Tax and Trade
1310 G St. NW, Ste. 300
Washington, DC 20220
Ph: (202)453-2000
Fax: (202)927-5611
Co. E-mail: ttbquestions@ttb.treas.gov
URL: http://www.ttb.gov
Contact: Jackie Barber, Specialist

61737 ■ U.S. Department of the Treasury (TTB) - Bureau of Alcohol, Tobacco Tax and Trade (TTB)
1310 G St. NW, Box 12
Washington, DC 20005
Ph: (202)453-2000
Fax: (202)927-5611
Co. E-mail: ttbinternetquestions@ttb.gov
URL: http://www.ttb.gov

61738 ■ U.S. Department of the Treasury - Bureau of Engraving and Printing
14th & C Sts., SW
Washington, DC 20228
Ph: (202)874-8888
Free: 877-874-4114
Fax: (202)874-3135
URL: http://www.moneyfactory.gov/
Contact: Dennis Milsten, Specialist

61739 ■ U.S. Department of the Treasury - Bureau of Engraving and Printing
14th & C Sts. SW
Washington, DC 20228
Free: 877-874-4114
Fax: (202)874-3135
URL: http://www.moneyfactory.gov/

61740 ■ U.S. Department of the Treasury - Bureau of Engraving & Printing - Office of Acquisitions
14th & C Sts., SW, Rm. 705A
Washington, DC 20228
URL: http://www.ustreas.gov/offices/management/dcfo/procurement/bcpo.shtml

61741 ■ U.S. Department of the Treasury - Bureau of Engraving & Printing - Office of Acquisitions
14th & C Sts. SW
Washington, DC 20228
Free: 877-874-4114
URL: http://www.moneyfactory.gov/acquisitions.html

61742 ■ U.S. Department of the Treasury - Bureau of the Public Debt
PO Box 7015
Parkersburg, WV 26106-7015
Ph: (304)480-5151
Fax: (304)480-8445
URL: http://www.publicdebt.treas.gov/
Contact: Jeff Stephenson, Specialist

61743 ■ U.S. Department of the Treasury - Bureau of the Public Debt
200 3rd St., UNB 4th Fl.
Parkersburg, WV 26106-1328
URL: http://www.ustreas.gov/offices/management/
dcfo/procurement/bcpo.shtml

61744 ■ U.S. Department of the Treasury - Bureau of the Public Debt
PO Box 7015
Parkersburg, WV 26106-7015
Ph: (304)480-5151
Fax: (304)480-8445
URL: http://www.publicdebt.treas.gov/

61745 ■ U.S. Department of the Treasury - Bureau of the Public Debt
799 9th St.
Parkersburg, WV 20239-0001
Free: 800-722-2678
URL: http://www.publicdebt.treas.gov/

61746 ■ U.S. Department of the Treasury - Chicago Financial Center
PO Box 8670
Chicago, IL 60680-8670
Ph: (312)353-5622
Fax: (312)353-3183

61747 ■ U.S. Department of the Treasury - Comptroller of the Currency - Large Banks Office
Independence Square
250 E. St., SW
Washington, DC 20219-0001
Ph: (202)874-4610
Free: 800-613-6743
Fax: (202)874-4950
URL: http://www.occ.treas.gov
Contact: Karen Waters, Specialist

61748 ■ U.S. Department of the Treasury - Comptroller of the Currency - Large Banks Office
Independence Square
250 E. St., SW
Washington, DC 20219-0001
Ph: (202)874-4610
Free: 800-613-6743
Fax: (202)874-4950
URL: http://www.occ.treas.gov

61749 ■ U.S. Department of the Treasury - Departmental Offices - Procurement Services Division
1425 New York Ave., NW, Ste. 2100
Washington, DC 20220
Fax: (202)622-2243
Contact: Renee Fitzgerald, Specialist

61750 ■ U.S. Department of the Treasury - Departmental Offices - Procurement Services Division
1425 New York Ave., NW, Ste. 2100
Washington, DC 20220

61751 ■ U.S. Department of the Treasury - Federal Law Enforcement Training Center
Charleston Facility
2000 Bainbridge Ave.
Charleston, SC 29405-2607
Ph: (843)566-8551
Fax: (843)566-7704
Co. E-mail: FLETC-Charleston@dhs.gov
URL: http://www.fletc.gov/about-fletc/locations/
charleston

61752 ■ U.S. Department of the Treasury - Federal Law Enforcement Training Center
Cheltenham Facility
9000 Commo Rd.
Cheltenham, MD 20588-4000
Ph: (301)868-5830
Fax: (301)868-6549
Co. E-mail: fletc-webmasterche@dhs.gov
URL: http://www.fletc.gov/about-fletc/locations/chel-
tenham

61753 ■ U.S. Department of the Treasury - Federal Law Enforcement Training Center
Washington Office
555 Eleventh St., NW, Ste. 400
Washington, DC 20004
Ph: (202)233-0260
Fax: (202)233-0258
Co. E-mail: FLETC-WashingtonOffice@dhs.gov
URL: http://www.fletc.gov/about-fletc/locations/wash-
ingtonDC/

61754 ■ U.S. Department of the Treasury - Financial Crimes Enforcement Network
2070 Chain Bridge Rd.
Vienna, VA 22182
URL: http://www.ustreas.gov/offices/management/
dcfo/procurement/bcpo.shtml

61755 ■ U.S. Department of the Treasury - Financial Crimes Enforcement Network
2070 Chain Bridge Rd.
Vienna, VA 22182
Ph: (703)905-3591
URL: http://www.fincen.gov/

61756 ■ U.S. Department of the Treasury - Financial Management Service
Liberty Center Bldg.
401 14th St. SW
Washington, DC 20227
Ph: (202)874-9560
Fax: (202)874-9629
URL: http://fms.treas.gov/
Contact: Wendi Smith, Specialist

61757 ■ U.S. Department of the Treasury - Financial Management Service
Liberty Center Bldg.
401 14th St. SW
Washington, DC 20227
Ph: (202)874-6950
Fax: (202)874-9629
URL: http://fms.treas.gov/

61758 ■ U.S. Department of the Treasury - Internal Revenue Service
Constellation Centre, Rm. 700
6009 Oxon Hill Rd.
Oxon Hill, MD 20745
Ph: (202)283-1610
Fax: (202)283-1533
Co. E-mail: awssproccustomerservice@irs.gov
URL: http://www.irs.gov/opportunities/procurement/
article/0,,id=125136,00.html
Contact: Jodie Paustian, Specialist

61759 ■ U.S. Department of the Treasury - Internal Revenue Service
Constellation Centre
6009 Oxon Hill Rd., Rm. 700
Oxon Hill, MD 20745
Ph: (202)283-1610
Fax: (202)283-1533
Co. E-mail: joe.gregory@irs.gov
URL: http://www.irs.gov/uac/Office-of-Procurement

61760 ■ U.S. Department of the Treasury - Internal Revenue Service - Detroit Computing Center
500 Woodward Ave.
Detroit, MI 48226
Ph: (313)628-3722
Fax: (313)234-2180
Contact: Wenda Hollenbeck, Specialist

61761 ■ U.S. Department of the Treasury - Internal Revenue Service - Detroit Computing Center
500 Woodward Ave.
Detroit, MI 48226
Ph: (313)628-3722
URL: http://www.irs.gov/uac/Contact-My-Local-Office-
in-Michigan

61762 ■ U.S. Department of the Treasury - Internal Revenue Service - Martinsburg Computing Center
250 Murall Dr.
Mail Stop 223
Kearneysville, WV 25430
Fax: (304)264-7008
Contact: Linda Miller, Specialist

61763 ■ U.S. Department of the Treasury - Internal Revenue Service - Martinsburg Computing Center
250 Murall Dr.
Mail Stop 223
Kearneysville, WV 25430
Ph: (304)264-5589
Fax: (304)264-7008

61764 ■ U.S. Department of the Treasury - Internal Revenue Service - Mid-States Area
4050 Alpha Rd.
1800 MSRO, 9th Flr.
Dallas, TX 75244-4203
Ph: (972)308-1990
Fax: (972)308-1928
Co. E-mail: Zach.Rich@irs.gov
Contact: Marguerite Overs, Specialist
Description: Serves Oklahoma, Texas, Arkansas, Kansas, Missouri, Illinois, Nebraska, Iowa, Wisconsin, Minnesota, North Dakota, and South Dakota. This office also supports the IRS Service Centers in Austin, TX, Kansas City, MO, and Ogden, UT.

61765 ■ U.S. Department of the Treasury - Internal Revenue Service - Mid-States Region
4050 Alpha Rd.
1800 MSRO, 9th Flr.
Dallas, TX 75244-4203
Ph: (972)308-1990
Fax: (972)308-1928
Co. E-mail: Zach.Rich@irs.gov
URL: http://www.irs.gov/uac/Office-of-Procurement
Description: Serves Oklahoma, Texas, Arkansas, Kansas, Missouri, Illinois, Nebraska, Iowa, Wisconsin, Minnesota, North Dakota, and South Dakota. This office also supports the IRS Service Centers in Austin, TX, Kansas City, MO, and Ogden, UT.

61766 ■ U.S. Department of the Treasury - Internal Revenue Service - Northeast Area
290 Broadway
New York, NY 10007-1867
Ph: (212)436-1481
Fax: (212)436-1442
Co. E-mail: Deborah.E.Foster@irs.gov
Contact: Deborah Foster, Specialist
Description: Serves Maine, Massachusetts, New Hampshire, Vermont, Rhode Island, Connecticut, New York, New Jersey, Pennsylvania, Ohio, and Michigan. This office also supports the IRS Service Centers in Andover, MA, Brookhaven, NY, and Philadelphia, PA.

61767 ■ U.S. Department of the Treasury - Internal Revenue Service - Northeast Region
290 Broadway
New York, NY 10007-1867
Ph: (212)436-1481
Fax: (212)436-1849
Co. E-mail: Deborah.E.Foster@irs.gov
URL: http://www.treasury.gov/resource-center/sb-
programs/Pages/contacts-small-biz-specialists.aspx
Description: Serves Maine, Massachusetts, New Hampshire, Vermont, Rhode Island, Connecticut, New York, New Jersey, Pennsylvania, Ohio, and Michigan. This office also supports the IRS Service Centers in Andover, MA, Brookhaven, NY, and Philadelphia, PA.

61768 ■ U.S. Department of the Treasury - Internal Revenue Service - Southeast Area
2888 Woodcock Blvd., Ste. 300
Atlanta, GA 30341
Ph: (404)338-9204

Fax: (404)338-9203
Co. E-mail: Lori.Aviles@irs.gov
Contact: Peggie Lynch, Specialist
Description: Serves Delaware, District of Columbia, Maryland, Virginia, West Virginia, Indiana, Kentucky, Tennessee, South Carolina, Georgia, Alabama, Louisiana, Mississippi, North Carolina, and Florida. This office also supports the IRS Service Centers in Atlanta, GA, Memphis, TN, and Covington, KY (Cincinnati).

61769 ■ U.S. Department of the Treasury - Internal Revenue Service - Southeast Region
2888 Woodcock Blvd., Ste. 300
Atlanta, GA 30341
Ph: (404)338-9204
Fax: (404)338-9221
Co. E-mail: Lori.Aviles@irs.gov
URL: http://www.treasury.gov/resource-center/sb-programs/Pages/contacts-small-biz-specialists.aspx
Description: Serves Delaware, District of Columbia, Maryland, Virginia, West Virginia, Indiana, Kentucky, Tennessee, South Carolina, Georgia, Alabama, Louisiana, Mississippi, North Carolina, and Florida. This office also supports the IRS Service Centers in Atlanta, GA, Memphis, TN, and Covington, KY (Cincinnati).

61770 ■ U.S. Department of the Treasury - Internal Revenue Service - Western Area
1301 Clay St., Ste. 810S
Oakland, CA 94612
Ph: (510)637-2149
Fax: (510)637-2110
Co. E-mail: Cathy.Handy@irs.gov
Contact: Jan Janson, Specialist
Description: Serves Montana, Idaho, Washington, Oregon, Wyoming, Colorado, Utah, Nevada, California, Arizona, New Mexico, Alaska, and Hawaii. This office also supports the IRS Service Center in Fresno, CA.

61771 ■ U.S. Department of the Treasury - Internal Revenue Service - Western Region
1301 Clay St., Ste. 810 S.
Oakland, CA 94612
Ph: (510)637-2149
Fax: (510)637-2110
Co. E-mail: Cathy.Handy@irs.gov
URL: http://www.treasury.gov/about/organizational-structure/offices/Mgt/Pages/dcfo-osdbu-how-to-part4-index.aspx
Description: Serves Montana, Idaho, Washington, Oregon, Wyoming, Colorado, Utah, Nevada, California, Arizona, New Mexico, Alaska, and Hawaii. This office also supports the IRS Service Center in Fresno, CA.

61772 ■ U.S. Department of the Treasury - Kansas City Financial Center
PO Box 12599-0599
Kansas City, KS 64116-0599
Ph: (816)414-2100
Fax: (816)414-2111
URL: http://fms.treas.gov/kfc/index.html

61773 ■ U.S. Department of the Treasury - Kansas City Financial Center
PO Box 12599-0599
Kansas City, KS 64116-0599
Ph: (816)414-2100
Fax: (816)414-2111
URL: http://fms.treas.gov/kfc/index.html

61774 ■ U.S. Department of the Treasury - Office of the Comptroller of the Currency - Central District - Chicago Field Office
1 Financial Pl.
440 S. LaSalle St., Ste. 2700
Chicago, IL 60605
Ph: (312)360-8800
Fax: (312)435-0951
URL: http://www.occ.treas.gov/about/who-we-are/district-and-field-offices/central-district-info.html
Description: Serves Ohio, Illinois, Indiana, Michigan, and Wisconsin.

61775 ■ U.S. Department of the Treasury - Office of the Comptroller of the Currency - Northeastern District - Jersey City Field Office
Harborside Financial Center Plz. Five, Ste. 1600
Jersey City, NJ 07311
Ph: (201)413-7333
Fax: (201)413-5842
URL: http://www.occ.treas.gov/about/who-we-are/district-and-field-offices/index-organization.html
Description: Serves Connecticut, Delaware, Massachusetts, Maine, New Hampshire, New Jersey, New York, Pennsylvania, Rhode Island, Vermont, and West Virginia.

61776 ■ U.S. Department of the Treasury - Office of the Comptroller of the Currency - Northeastern District - Washington D.C. Field Office
395 E. St. SW, Ste. 850
Washington, DC 20024
Ph: (202)874-9504
Fax: (202)874-5876
URL: http://www.occ.treas.gov/about/who-we-are/district-and-field-offices/northeastern-district-info.html
Description: Serves Connecticut, Delaware, Massachusetts, Maine, New Hampshire, New Jersey, New York, Pennsylvania, Rhode Island, Vermont, and West Virginia.

61777 ■ U.S. Department of the Treasury - Office of the Comptroller of the Currency - Southern District - Dallas Field Office
225 E. John Carpenter Fwy., Ste. 500
Irving, TX 75062-2326
Ph: (972)277-9500
Fax: (972)277-9501
URL: http://www.occ.treas.gov/about/who-we-are/district-and-field-offices/southern-district-info.html
Description: Serves Arkansas, Iowa, Kansas, Louisiana, Minnesota, Missouri, Mississippi, North Dakota, Nebraska, New Mexico, Oklahoma, South Dakota, and Texas.

61778 ■ U.S. Department of the Treasury - Office of the Comptroller of the Currency - Southern Region - Atlanta Field Office
1475 Peachtree St., NE
Atlanta, GA 30309-3019
Ph: (404)974-9620
Fax: (404)978-9800
URL: http://www.occ.treas.gov/about/who-we-are/district-and-field-offices/southern-district-info.html
Description: Serves Alabama, Florida, Georgia, Kentucky, Maryland, North Carolina, South Carolina, Tennessee, Virginia, District of Columbia, Puerto Rico, and Virgin Islands.

61779 ■ U.S. Department of the Treasury - Office of the Comptroller of the Currency - West District - Santa Ana Field Office
1551 N. Tustin Ave., Ste. 1050
Santa Ana, CA 92705-8661
Ph: (714)796-4700
Fax: (714)796-4710
URL: http://www.occ.treas.gov/about/who-we-are/district-and-field-offices/western-district-info.html
Description: Serves Alaska, Arizona, California, Colorado, Hawaii, Idaho, Montana, North Dakota, New Mexico, Oregon, South Dakota, Utah, Washington, Wyoming, Guam, and Northern Mariana Islands.

61780 ■ U.S. Department of the Treasury - Office of Comptroller of the Currency - West Region
225 E. John Carpenter Freeway, Ste. 500
Irving, TX 75062-2326
Ph: (972)277-9500
Fax: (972)277-9501
URL: http://www.occ.treas.gov/about/who-we-are/district-and-field-offices/southern-district-info.html
Description: Serves Alaska, Arizona, California, Colorado, Hawaii, Idaho, Montana, North Dakota, New Mexico, Oregon, South Dakota, Utah, Washington, Wyoming, Guam, and Northern Mariana Islands.

61781 ■ U.S. Department of the Treasury - Office of Small and Disadvantaged Business Utilization
1500 Pennsylvania Ave., NW
655 15th St., Rm. 6099
Washington, DC 20220
Ph: (202)622-0530
Fax: (202)622-4963
Co. E-mail: TreasuryOSDBU@do.treas.gov
URL: http://www.ustreas.gov/sba
Description: The mission of the Department of the Treasury includes formulating and recommending financial, tax, and fiscal policies; serving as the financial agent for the U.S. government; enforcing various federal laws; protecting the President and Vice President of the United States; and manufacturing coins and currency. The accomplishment of this mission requires the procurement of a wide variety of commercial goods and services at an annual expenditure of approximately two billion dollars. Contracting authority has been delegated to the various bureaus of the department, and each conducts the procurement transactions necessary to carry out its respective program. The department's procurement efforts include a commitment to increase contract awards to small, minority, and women-owned business firms.

61782 ■ U.S. Department of the Treasury - Office of Small and Disadvantaged Business Utilization
1500 Pennsylvania Ave. NW
655 15th St./6W525
Washington, DC 20220
Ph: (202)622-0530
Fax: (202)622-4963
URL: http://www.treasury.gov/about/organizational-structure/offices/Mgt/Pages/dcfo-osdbu-contacts-osdbu.aspx
Description: The mission of the Department of the Treasury includes formulating and recommending financial, tax, and fiscal policies; serving as the financial agent for the U.S. government; enforcing various federal laws; protecting the President & Vice President of the United States; and manufacturing coins and currency. The accomplishment of this mission requires the procurement of a wide variety of commercial goods and services at an annual expenditure of approximately two billion dollars. Contracting authority has been delegated to the various bureaus of the department, and each conducts the procurement transactions necessary to carry out its respective program. The department's procurement efforts include a commitment to increase contract awards to small, minority, and women-owned business firms.

61783 ■ U.S. Department of the Treasury - Office of Thrift Supervision
1700 G St. NW
Washington, DC 20552
Ph: (202)906-6000
Fax: (202)906-5748
Co. E-mail: webmaster@ots.treas.gov
URL: http://www.ots.treas.gov/
Contact: Doug Mason, Specialist

61784 ■ U.S. Department of the Treasury - Office of Thrift Supervision
1700 G St., NW, 3rd Fl.
Washington, DC 20552
URL: http://www.ustreas.gov/offices/management/dcfo/procurement/bcpo.shtml

61785 ■ U.S. Department of the Treasury - Office of Thrift Supervision
1700 G St., NW, 3rd Fl.
Washington, DC 20552

61786 ■ U.S. Department of the Treasury - Office of Thrift Supervision - Central Region
Chicago Regional Office
One S. Wacker Dr., Ste. 2000
Chicago, IL 60606
Ph: (312)917-5000

Fax: (312)917-5001
URL: http://www.ots.treas.gov/?p=Central
Description: Serves Ohio, Illinois, Indiana, Michigan, Wisconsin, Minnesota, Iowa, Nebraska, North Dakota, and South Dakota.

61787 ■ U.S. Department of the Treasury - Office of Thrift Supervision - Northeast Region
Jersey City Regional Office
Harborside Financial Center Plz. Five, Ste. 1600
Jersey City, NJ 07311
Ph: (201)413-1000
Fax: (201)413-7543
URL: http://www.ots.treas.gov/?p=Northeast
Description: Serves Connecticut, Delaware, Massachusetts, Maine, New Hampshire, New Jersey, New York, Pennsylvania, Rhode Island, Vermont, and West Virginia.

61788 ■ U.S. Department of the Treasury - Office of Thrift Supervision - Southeast Region
Atlanta Regional Office
1475 Peachtree St., NE
Atlanta, GA 30309
Ph: (404)888-0771
Fax: (404)888-5634
URL: http://www.ots.treas.gov/?p=Southeast
Description: Serves Alabama, Florida, Georgia, Kentucky, Maryland, North Carolina, South Carolina, Tennessee, Virginia, District of Columbia, Puerto Rico, and Virgin Islands.

61789 ■ U.S. Department of the Treasury - Office of Thrift Supervision - West Region
Pacific Plaza
San Francisco Regional Office
2001 Junipero Serra Blvd., Ste. 650
Daly City, CA 94014-1976
Ph: (650)746-7000
Fax: (650)746-7001
URL: http://www.ots.treas.gov/
Description: Serves Alaska, Arizona, California, Colorado, Hawaii, Idaho, Montana, North Dakota, New Mexico, Oregon, South Dakota, Utah, Washington, Wyoming, Guam, and Northern Mariana Islands.

61790 ■ U.S. Department of the Treasury - Office of Thrift Supervision - West Region
Southern California Area Office
Bentall Executive Ctr.
1551 N. Tustin Ave., Ste. 1050
Santa Ana, CA 92705-8635
Ph: (714)796-4700
Fax: (714)796-4710
URL: http://www.ots.treas.gov/
Description: Serves Alaska, Arizona, California, Colorado, Hawaii, Idaho, Montana, North Dakota, New Mexico, Oregon, South Dakota, Utah, Washington, Wyoming, Guam, and Northern Mariana Islands.

61791 ■ U.S. Department of the Treasury - Office of Thrift Supervision - West Region
Pacific Plaza
San Francisco Regional Office
2001 Junipero Serra Blvd., Ste. 650
Daly City, CA 94014-1976
Ph: (650)746-7000
Fax: (650)746-7001
Description: Serves Alaska, Arizona, California, Colorado, Hawaii, Idaho, Montana, North Dakota, New Mexico, Oregon, South Dakota, Utah, Washington, Wyoming, Guam, and Northern Mariana Islands.

61792 ■ U.S. Department of the Treasury - Office of Thrift Supervision - Western Region
225 E. John Carpenter Freeway, Ste. 500
Dallas/Ft. Worth, TX 75261-9027
Ph: (972)277-9500
Fax: (972)277-9501
URL: http://www.ots.treas.gov/?p=Western
Description: Serves Alaska, Arizona, California, Colorado, Hawaii, Idaho, Montana, North Dakota, New Mexico, Oregon, South Dakota, Utah, Washington, Wyoming, Guam, and Northern Mariana Islands.

61793 ■ U.S. Department of the Treasury - Philadelphia Financial Center
PO Box 51317
Philadelphia, PA 19115-6317
Ph: (215)516-8000
Fax: (215)516-8010
Co. E-mail: philly@fms.treas.gov
URL: http://fms.treas.gov/pfc/

61794 ■ U.S. Department of the Treasury - Philadelphia Financial Center
PO Box 51317
Philadelphia, PA 19115-6317
Ph: (215)516-8154
Fax: (215)516-8010
Co. E-mail: philly@fms.treas.gov
URL: http://fms.treas.gov/pfc/

61795 ■ U.S. Department of the Treasury - Procurement A.P.
IRS National Office, Rm. 3113
1111 Constitution Ave., NW
Washington, DC 20224
URL: http://www.ustreas.gov/offices/management/dcfo/procurement/bcpo.shtml

61796 ■ U.S. Department of the Treasury - Procurement A.P.
IRS National Office, Rm. 3113
1111 Constitution Ave., NW
Washington, DC 20224

61797 ■ U.S. Department of the Treasury - San Francisco Financial Center
PO Box 24700
Oakland, CA 94623-1700
Ph: (510)594-7300
Fax: (510)594-7341
Co. E-mail: sfc@fms.treas.gov
URL: http://fms.treas.gov/sfc/index.html

61798 ■ U.S. Department of the Treasury - San Francisco Financial Center
PO Box 24700
Oakland, CA 94623-1700
Ph: (510)594-7300
Fax: (510)594-7341
Co. E-mail: sfc@fms.treas.gov
URL: http://fms.treas.gov/sfc/index.html

61799 ■ U.S. Department of the Treasury - U.S. Customs Service - Field Procurement Services
6026 Lakeside Blvd.
Indianapolis, IN 46278
Fax: (317)298-1344
Contact: Lee Sullivan, Specialist

61800 ■ U.S. Department of the Treasury - U.S. Customs Service - Field Procurement Services
6026 Lakeside Blvd.
Indianapolis, IN 46278

61801 ■ U.S. Department of the Treasury - U.S. Mint
801 9th St., NW
Washington, DC 20220-0001
Ph: (202)898-6468
Free: 800-872-6468
Fax: (202)354-6299
URL: http://www.usmint.gov/
Contact: Caroline Bennington, Specialist

61802 ■ U.S. Department of the Treasury - U.S. Mint
801 9th St. NW
Washington, DC 20220-0001
Ph: (202)756-6468
Free: 800-872-6468
Fax: (202)756-6200
URL: http://www.usmint.gov/

U.S. DEPARTMENT OF VETERANS AFFAIRS

61803 ■ U.S. Department of Veterans Affairs - Office of Small and Disadvantaged Business Utilization
810 Vermont Ave., NW
Washington, DC 20420
Ph: (202)461-4300
Free: 800-949-8387
Fax: (202)461-4301
Co. E-mail: OSDBU@mail.va.gov
URL: http://www.va.gov/OSDBU/

61804 ■ U.S. Department of Veterans Affairs - Office of Small and Disadvantaged Business Utilization
810 Vermont Ave. NW
Washington, DC 20420
Ph: (202)461-4300
Free: 800-949-8387
Fax: (202)461-4301
Co. E-mail: OSDBU@va.gov
URL: http://www.va.gov/OSDBU/

61805 ■ U.S. Department of Veterans Affairs - Public Health and Environmental Hazards
810 Vermont Ave., NW, Rm. 870
Washington, DC 20420
Ph: (202)461-1000
Fax: (202)273-9079

61806 ■ U.S. Department of Veterans Affairs - Public Health and Environmental Hazards
810 Vermont Ave. NW, Rm. 870
Washington, DC 20420
Ph: (202)461-1000
Fax: (202)273-9079
URL: http://www.publichealth.va.gov/

U.S. INFORMATION AGENCY

61807 ■ U.S. Printing Office - General Procurement Division - Office of Small and Disadvantaged Business Utilization
732 N. Capitol St., NW, Rm. A332
Stop MMG
Washington, DC 20401
Ph: (202)512-0526
Fax: (202)512-0975

61808 ■ U.S. Printing Office - General Procurement Division - Office of Small and Disadvantaged Business Utilization
732 N. Capitol St., NW, Rm. A332
Stop MMG
Washington, DC 20401

U.S. NUCLEAR REGULATORY COMMISSION

61809 ■ U.S. Nuclear Regulatory Commission - Office of Small and Disadvantaged Business Utilization/Civil Rights
11555 Rockville Pike
Rockville, MD 20852-2738
Ph: (301)415-7380
Free: 800-368-5642
URL: http://www.nrc.gov/
Description: The Nuclear Regulatory Commission's Office of Small and Disadvantaged Business Utilization offers small businesses information and guidance on procurement procedures, how to be placed on a bidder's mailing list, and identification of both prime and subcontracting opportunities.

61810 ■ U.S. Nuclear Regulatory Commission - Office of Small and Disadvantaged Business Utilization/Civil Rights
11555 Rockville Pike
Rockville, MD 20852-2738
Ph: (301)415-7380

Free: 800-368-5642
URL: http://www.nrc.gov/about-nrc/civil-rights.html
Description: The Nuclear Regulatory Commission's Office of Small and Disadvantaged Business Utilization offers small businesses information and guidance on procurement procedures, how to be placed on a bidder's mailing list, and identification of both prime and subcontracting opportunities.

61811 ■ U.S. Nuclear Regulatory Commission, Region 1 - King of Prussia Regional Office
475 Allendale Rd.
King of Prussia, PA 19406-1415
Ph: (610)337-5000
Free: 800-432-1156
URL: http://www.nrc.gov
Description: Serves Connecticut, Delaware, Maine, Maryland, Massachusetts, New Hampshire, New Jersey, New York, Pennsylvania, Rhode Island, Vermont, and Washington.

61812 ■ U.S. Nuclear Regulatory Commission, Region 1 - King of Prussia Regional Office
2100 Renaissance Blvd., Ste. 100
King of Prussia, PA 19406-2713
Ph: (610)337-5000
Free: 800-432-1156
URL: http://www.nrc.gov
Description: Serves Connecticut, Delaware, Maine, Maryland, Massachusetts, New Hampshire, New Jersey, New York, Pennsylvania, Rhode Island, Vermont, and Washington.

61813 ■ U.S. Nuclear Regulatory Commission, Region 2 - Atlanta Regional Office
Sam Nunn Atlanta Federal Ctr., 23 T85
61 Forsyth St., SW
Atlanta, GA 30303-8931
Ph: (404)562-4400
Free: 800-577-8510
URL: http://www.nrc.gov
Description: Serves Alabama, Florida, Georgia, Kentucky, Mississippi, North Carolina, Puerto Rico, South Carolina, Tennessee, Virginia, Virgin Islands, and West Virginia.

61814 ■ U.S. Nuclear Regulatory Commission, Region 2 - Atlanta Regional Office
Marquis One Tower
245 Peachtree Ctr. Ave. NW, Ste. 1200
Atlanta, GA 30303
Ph: (404)997-4400
Free: 800-577-8510
URL: http://www.nrc.gov/about-nrc/organization/rii-funcdesc.html
Description: Serves Alabama, Florida, Georgia, Kentucky, Mississippi, North Carolina, Puerto Rico, South Carolina, Tennessee, Virginia, Virgin Islands, and West Virginia.

61815 ■ U.S. Nuclear Regulatory Commission, Region 3 - Lisle Regional Office
2443 Warrenville Rd., St. 210
Lisle, IL 30532-4352
Ph: (630)829-9500
Free: 800-522-3025
Fax: (630)515-1078
URL: http://www.nrc.gov
Description: Serves Illinois, Indiana, Iowa, Michigan, Minnesota, Missouri, Ohio, and Wisconsin.

61816 ■ U.S. Nuclear Regulatory Commission, Region 3 - Lisle Regional Office
2443 Warrenville Rd., St. 210
Lisle, IL 60532-4352
Ph: (630)829-9500
Free: 800-522-3025
Fax: (630)515-1078
URL: http://www.nrc.gov/info-finder/region-state/region3.html
Description: Serves Illinois, Indiana, Iowa, Michigan, Minnesota, Missouri, Ohio, and Wisconsin.

61817 ■ U.S. Nuclear Regulatory Commission, Region 4 - Arlington Regional Office
Texas Health Resources Tower
612 E. Lamar Blvd., Ste. 400
Arlington, TX 76011-4125
Ph: (817)860-8100
Free: 800-952-9677
URL: http://www.nrc.gov
Description: Serves Alaska, Arizona, Arkansas, California, Colorado, Hawaii, Idaho, Kansas, Louisiana, Montana, Nebraska, Nevada, New Mexico, North Dakota, Oklahoma, Oregon, South Dakota, Texas, Utah, Washington, and Wyoming.

61818 ■ U.S. Nuclear Regulatory Commission, Region 4 - Arlington Regional Office
1600 E. Lamar Blvd., Ste. 400
Arlington, TX 76011-4511
Ph: (817)860-8100
Free: 800-952-9677
URL: http://www.nrc.gov/info-finder/region-state/region4.html
Description: Serves Alaska, Arizona, Arkansas, California, Colorado, Hawaii, Idaho, Kansas, Louisiana, Montana, Nebraska, Nevada, New Mexico, North Dakota, Oklahoma, Oregon, South Dakota, Texas, Utah, Washington, and Wyoming.

U.S. POSTAL SERVICE

61819 ■ U.S. Postal Service - Administrative Operations - Information Technology Division
2111 Wilson Blvd., Ste. 500
Arlington, VA 22201
Ph: (703)248-3701
URL: http://www.usps.gov

61820 ■ U.S. Postal Service - Administrative Operations - Information Technology Division
2111 Wilson Blvd., Ste. 500
Arlington, VA 22201
URL: http://www.usps.gov

61821 ■ U.S. Postal Service - Chicago Service Center
233 S. Wacker Dr., Ste. Ll1a
Chicago, IL 60606-9997
Ph: (312)424-3488
Fax: (312)424-3170
URL: http://www.usps.gov

61822 ■ U.S. Postal Service - Chicago Service Center
233 S. Wacker Dr., Ste. Ll1a
Chicago, IL 60606-9997
URL: http://www.usps.gov

61823 ■ U.S. Postal Service - Environmental and MRO Category Management Center
7800 N. Stemmons Fwy., Ste. 700
Dallas, TX 75247-4223
Co. E-mail: cmc.Environmental@usps.gov
URL: http://www.usps.gov
Description: Serves Arizona, Louisiana, Oklahoma, and Texas.

61824 ■ U.S. Postal Service - Environmental and MRO Category Management Centers
7800 N. Stemmons Fwy., Ste. 700
Dallas, TX 75247-4223
Co. E-mail: cmc.Environmental@usps.gov
URL: http://www.usps.gov
Description: Serves Arizona, Louisiana, Oklahoma, and Texas.

61825 ■ U.S. Postal Service - Field Operations - East
2 Gateway Ctr., 9th Fl., Rm. 3100
Newark, NJ 07173-0001
Ph: (610)668-4544
URL: http://www.usps.gov

61826 ■ U.S. Postal Service - Field Operations - East
2 Gateway Ctr., 9th Fl., Rm. 3100
Newark, NJ 07173-0001

Ph: (610)668-4544
URL: http://www.usps.gov

61827 ■ U.S. Postal Service - Field Operations - South
1 Church Cir., Rm. 208
Annapolis, MD 21404-0426
Ph: (410)267-1081
URL: http://www.usps.gov

61828 ■ U.S. Postal Service - Field Operations - South
1 Church Cir., Rm. 208
Annapolis, MD 21404-0426
URL: http://www.usps.gov

61829 ■ U.S. Postal Service - Field Operations - West
1 Church Cir., Rm. 208
Annapolis, MD 21404-0426
Free: 800-275-8777
URL: http://www.usps.gov

61830 ■ U.S. Postal Service - Field Operations - West
1 Church Cir., Rm. 208
Annapolis, MD 21404-0426
Free: 800-275-8777
URL: http://www.usps.gov

61831 ■ U.S. Postal Service - General Counsel - Business Services
475 L'Enfant Plz. W., SW, Rm. 6015
Washington, DC 20260-0010
Ph: (202)268-2802
Co. E-mail: james.g.schlett@usps.gov
URL: http://www.usps.gov

61832 ■ U.S. Postal Service - General Counsel - Business Services
475 L'Enfant Plz. W., SW, Rm. 6015
Washington, DC 20260-0010
URL: http://www.usps.gov

61833 ■ U.S. Postal Service - Intelligent Mail
475 L'Enfant Plz., SW, Rm. 2100
Washington, DC 20260-0010
Ph: (202)268-6200
Fax: (202)268-4492
URL: http://www.usps.gov

61834 ■ U.S. Postal Service - Intelligent Mail and Address Quality
475 L'Enfant Plz., SW, Rm. 2100
Washington, DC 20260-0010
Fax: (202)268-4492
Co. E-mail: incsc@email.usps.gov
URL: http://www.usps.gov

61835 ■ U.S. Postal Service - Investigations and Security - Dangerous Mail Investigations and Homeland Security
475 L'Enfant Plz. W., SW, Rm. 3301
Washington, DC 20260-0010

61836 ■ U.S. Postal Service - Investigations and Security - Dangerous Mail Investigations and Homeland Security
475 L'Enfant Plz. W., SW, Rm. 3301
Washington, DC 20260-0010
Ph: (202)268-4432

61837 ■ U.S. Postal Service - Memphis Purchasing Service Center
225 N. Humphreys Blvd.
Memphis, TN 38166-6260
Ph: (901)747-7530
Fax: (901)747-7492
URL: http://www.usps.gov

61838 ■ U.S. Postal Service - Memphis Purchasing Service Center
225 N. Humphreys Blvd.
Memphis, TN 38166-6260
Ph: (901)747-7530
Fax: (901)747-7492
URL: http://www.usps.gov

61839 ■ U.S. Postal Service - Office of the Inspector General
1735 N. Lynn St.
Arlington, VA 22209-2020
Ph: (703)248-2300
Free: 888-877-7644
Fax: (866)756-6741
Co. E-mail: hotline@uspsoig.gov
URL: http://www.uspsoig.gov

61840 ■ U.S. Postal Service - Office of the Inspector General
1735 N. Lynn St.
Arlington, VA 22209-2020
Ph: (703)248-2100
Co. E-mail: hotline@uspsoig.gov
URL: http://www.uspsoig.gov

61841 ■ U.S. Postal Service - Office of Operations
475 L'Enfant Plz. W., SW, Rm. 3010
Washington, DC 20260-0010
Ph: (202)268-5425
URL: http://www.usps.gov

61842 ■ U.S. Postal Service - Office of Operations
475 L'Enfant Plz. W., SW, Rm. 3010
Washington, DC 20260-0010
Ph: (202)268-5425
URL: http://www.usps.gov

61843 ■ U.S. Postal Service - Office of Small and Disadvantaged Business Utilization
475 L'Enfant Plz. SW, Rm. 4320
Washington, DC 20260-4320
Ph: (202)268-4633
Fax: (202)268-7288
URL: http://www.usps.gov/
Description: The Postal Service's Office of Small and Disadvantaged Business Utilization offers small businesses information and guidance on procurement procedures, how to be placed on a bidder's mailing list, and identification of both prime and subcontracting opportunities.

61844 ■ U.S. Postal Service - Office of Small and Disadvantaged Business Utilization
475 L'Enfant Plz. SW, Rm. 4320
Washington, DC 20260-4320
Ph: (202)268-4633
Fax: (202)268-7288
URL: http://www.usps.gov/
Description: The Postal Service's Office of Small and Disadvantaged Business Utilization offers small businesses information and guidance on procurement procedures, how to be placed on a bidder's mailing list, and identification of both prime and subcontracting opportunities.

61845 ■ U.S. Postal Service - San Francisco Purchasing Service Center
395 Oyster Point Blvd., Ste. 205
San Francisco, CA 94080-1996
Fax: (650)615-7293
URL: http://www.usps.gov
Description: Serves California and Hawaii.

61846 ■ U.S. Postal Service - United States Postal Inspection Service
222 S. Riverside Plz., Ste. 1250
Chicago, IL 60606-6100
Free: 877-876-2455
URL: https:postalinspectors.uspis.gov/

61847 ■ U.S. Postal Service - United States Postal Inspection Service
433 W. Harrison St., Rm. 50190
Chicago, IL 60669-2201
Free: 877-876-2455
URL: https://postalinspectors.uspis.gov/

61848 ■ U.S. Postal Service - Windsor Purchasing Service Center E
8 Griffin Rd., N.
Windsor, CT 06095-1572
Ph: (860)285-7126
Fax: (860)285-7272
Co. E-mail: pete.l.dolder@usps.gov
URL: http://www.usps.gov

61849 ■ U.S. Postal Service - Windsor Purchasing Service Center E
8 Griffin Rd., N.
Windsor, CT 06095-1572
Co. E-mail: pete.l.dolder@usps.gov
URL: http://www.usps.gov

U.S. SMALL BUSINESS ADMINISTRATION

The following field offices are arranged alphabetically by state.

61850 ■ U.S. Small Business Administration - Albuquerque District Office
625 Silver Ave. SW, Ste. 320
Albuquerque, NM 87102
Ph: (505)249-8225
Fax: (505)248-8246
URL: http://www.sba.gov/localresources/district/nm/index.html

61851 ■ U.S. Small Business Administration - Albuquerque District Office
500 Gold SW, Rm. 11301
Albuquerque, NM 87102
Ph: (505)248-8225
Fax: (505)248-8245
URL: http://www.sba.gov/about-offices-content/2/3132

61852 ■ U.S. Small Business Administration - Anchorage District Office
510 L St., Ste. 310
Anchorage, AK 99501
Ph: (907)271-4022
Fax: (907)271-4545
URL: http://www.sba.gov/localresources/district/ak/index.html

61853 ■ U.S. Small Business Administration - Anchorage District Office
420 L St., Ste. 300
Anchorage, AK 99501
Ph: (907)271-4022
Fax: (907)271-4545
Co. E-mail: karen.forsland@sba.gov
URL: http://www.sba.gov/about-offices-content/2/2821#

61854 ■ U.S. Small Business Administration, Area 1
360 Rainbow Blvd. S, 3rd Fl.
Niagara Falls, NY 14303-1192
Ph: (716)282-4612
Free: 800-659-2955
Fax: (716)282-1472
Description: Covers regions one and two.

61855 ■ U.S. Small Business Administration, Area 1
Niagara Center
130 S. Elmwood Ave., Ste. 540
Buffalo, NY 14202
Ph: (716)551-4301
Free: 800-659-2955
Fax: (716)551-4418
URL: http://www.sba.gov/about-offices-content/2/3134
Description: Covers regions one and two.

61856 ■ U.S. Small Business Administration, Area 3
4400 Amon Carter Blvd., Ste. 102
Ft. Worth, TX 76155
Ph: (817)885-7600
Free: 800-366-6303
Fax: (817)885-7621
Description: Covers regions six and seven.

61857 ■ U.S. Small Business Administration, Area 6
4300 Amon Carter Blvd., Ste. 108
Ft. Worth, TX 76155
Ph: (817)684-5581

Fax: (817)684-5588
URL: http://www.sba.gov/about-offices-content/3/3075
Description: Covers regions six and seven.

61858 ■ U.S. Small Business Administration - Arizona District Office
2828 N. Central Ave., Ste. 800
Phoenix, AZ 85004-1093
Ph: (602)745-7200
Fax: (602)745-7210
URL: http://www.sba.gov/localresources/district/az/index.html

61859 ■ U.S. Small Business Administration - Arkansas District Office
2120 Riverfront Dr., Ste. 250
Little Rock, AR 72202-1796
Ph: (501)324-7379
Fax: (501)324-7394
URL: http://www.sba.gov/localresources/district/ar/index.html

61860 ■ U.S. Small Business Administration - Associate Deputy Administrator for Economic Development
740 15th St., NW, Ste. 300
Washington, DC 20005-3544
Co. E-mail: joseph.loddo@sba.gov
URL: http://www.sba.gov/localresources/district/dc/index.html

61861 ■ U.S. Small Business Administration - Associate Deputy Administrator for Government Contracting and Minority Enterprise Development
740 15th St. NW, Ste. 300
Washington, DC 20005-3544
Ph: (202)272-0345
URL: http://www.sba.gov/about-offices-content/2/3106

61862 ■ U.S. Small Business Administration - Atlanta District Office
233 Peachtree St., Ste. 1900
Atlanta, GA 30303
Ph: (404)331-0100
Fax: (404)331-0101
URL: http://www.sba.gov/localresources/district/ga/index.html

61863 ■ U.S. Small Business Administration - Atlanta District Office
233 Peachtree St. NE, Ste. 1900
Atlanta, GA 30303
Ph: (404)331-0100
Fax: (404)331-0101
URL: http://www.sba.gov/about-offices-content/2/3110

61864 ■ U.S. Small Business Administration - Augusta District Office
Edmund S. Muskie Federal Bldg.
68 Sewall St., Rm. 512
Augusta, ME 04330
Ph: (207)622-8551
Fax: (207)622-8277
URL: http://www.sba.gov/about-offices-content/2/3163

61865 ■ U.S. Small Business Administration - Baltimore District Office
City Crescent Bldg., 6th Fl.
10 S. Howard St.
Baltimore, MD 21201
Ph: (410)962-6195
Fax: (410)962-1805
URL: http://www.sba.gov/localresources/district/md/index.html

61866 ■ U.S. Small Business Administration - Baltimore District Office
City Crescent Bldg., 6th Fl.
10 S. Howard St.
Baltimore, MD 21201
Ph: (410)962-6195

Fax: (410)962-1805
URL: http://www.sba.gov/about-offices-content/2/
3120

61867 ■ U.S. Small Business Administration -
Birmingham District Office
801 Tom Martin Dr., Ste. 201
Birmingham, AL 35211
Ph: (205)290-7101
Fax: (205)290-7404
URL: http://www.sba.gov/localresources/district/al/
index.html

61868 ■ U.S. Small Business Administration -
Birmingham District Office
801 Tom Martin Dr., Ste. 201
Birmingham, AL 35211
Ph: (205)290-7101
Fax: (205)290-7404
URL: http://www.sba.gov/about-offices-content/2/
2822

61869 ■ U.S. Small Business Administration -
Boise District Office
380 E. Parkcenter Blvd., Ste. 330
Boise, ID 83706
Ph: (208)334-1696
Fax: (208)334-9353
URL: http://www.sba.gov/localresources/district/id/
index.html

61870 ■ U.S. Small Business Administration -
Boise District Office
Boise District Office
380 E. Parkcenter Blvd., Ste. 330
Boise, ID 83706
Ph: (208)334-1696
Fax: (208)334-9353
URL: http://www.sba.gov/id/

61871 ■ U.S. Small Business Administration -
Boise District Office
380 E. Parkcenter Blvd., Ste. 330
Boise, ID 83706
Ph: (208)334-1696
Fax: (208)334-9353
URL: http://www.sba.gov/about-offices-content/2/
3115

61872 ■ U.S. Small Business Administration -
Boston District Office
Federal Bldg.
10 Causeway St., Rm. 265
Boston, MA 02222
Ph: (617)565-5590
Fax: (617)565-5598
URL: http://www.sba.gov/ma

61873 ■ U.S. Small Business Administration -
Boston District Office
Massachusetts District Office
Thomas P. I'Neill Federal Bldg.
10 Causeway St., Rm. 265
Boston, MA 02222
Ph: (617)565-5590
Fax: (617)565-5598
URL: http://www.sba.gov/ma/

61874 ■ U.S. Small Business Administration -
Boston District Office
Federal Bldg.
10 Causeway St., Rm. 265
Boston, MA 02222
Ph: (617)565-5590
Fax: (617)565-5598
URL: http://www.sba.gov/about-offices-content/2/
3162

61875 ■ U.S. Small Business Administration -
Buffalo District Office
Niagara Center
130 S. Elmwood Ave., Ste 540
Buffalo, NY 14202
Ph: (716)551-4301
Fax: (716)551-4418
Co. E-mail: sba@buffalo.com
URL: http://www.sba.gov/ny/buffalo/index.html

61876 ■ U.S. Small Business Administration -
Buffalo District Office
Niagara Center
130 S. Elmwood Ave., Ste 540
Buffalo, NY 14202
Ph: (716)551-4301
Fax: (716)551-4418
Co. E-mail: sba@buffalo.com
URL: http://www.sba.gov/about-offices-content/2/
3134

61877 ■ U.S. Small Business Administration -
Buffalo District Office - Rochester Branch
Office
Federal Bldg., Rm. 410
100 State St.
Rochester, NY 14614
Ph: (585)263-6700
Fax: (585)263-3146

61878 ■ U.S. Small Business Administration -
Business Information Center (Atlanta,
Georgia)
Georgia District Office
Harris Tower
233 Peachtree St. NE, Ste. 1900
Atlanta, GA 30303
Ph: (404)331-0100
Fax: (404)331-0101
URL: http://www.sba.gov/about-offices-content/2/
3110

61879 ■ U.S. Small Business Administration -
Business Information Center (Boise, Idaho)
Boise District Office
380 E. Parkcenter Blvd., Ste. 330
Boise, ID 83706
Ph: (208)334-1696
Fax: (208)334-9353
URL: http://www.sba.gov/about-offices-content/2/
3115

61880 ■ U.S. Small Business Administration -
Business Information Center (Boston,
Massachusetts)
10 Causeway St., Rm. 265
Boston, MA 02222
Ph: (617)565-5590
Fax: (617)565-5598
URL: http://www.sba.gov/about-offices-content/2/
3162

61881 ■ U.S. Small Business Administration -
Business Information Center (Chicago,
Illinois)
Chicago District Office
500 W. Madison St., Ste. 1150
Chicago, IL 60661-2511
Ph: (312)353-4528
Fax: (312)886-5688
URL: http://www.sba.gov/about-offices-content/2/
3161

61882 ■ U.S. Small Business Administration -
Business Information Center (Denver,
Colorado)
721 19th St., Ste. 426
Denver, CO 80202-2599
Ph: (303)844-2607
Fax: (303)844-6490
URL: http://www.sba.gov/about-offices-content/2/
3104

61883 ■ U.S. Small Business Administration -
Business Information Center (East Randolph,
Vermont)
Vermont Technical College
Hartness Library
Randolph Center, VT 05061-0500
Ph: (802)728-1000
Free: 800-442-8821
Fax: (802)728-1390
URL: http://www.vtc.edu
Contact: Ms. Jane U. Bartlett, Director

61884 ■ U.S. Small Business Administration -
Business Information Center (East Randolph,
Vermonth)
Vermont Technical College
Hartness Library
Randolph Center, VT 05061-0500
Ph: (802)728-1000
Free: 800-442-8821
Fax: (802)728-1390
URL: http://www.vtc.edu
URL(s): www.sba.gov/sites/default/files/files/re-
sourceguide_3156.pdf.

61885 ■ U.S. Small Business Administration -
Business Information Center (Houston,
Texas)
Houston District Office
8701 S. Gessner Dr., Ste. 1200
Houston, TX 77074
Ph: (713)773-6500
Fax: (713)773-6550
URL: http://www.sba.gov/about-offices-content/2/
3151

61886 ■ U.S. Small Business Administration -
Business Information Center (Kansas City,
Missouri)
1000 Walnut, Ste. 500
Kansas City, MO 64106
Ph: (816)426-4900
URL: http://www.sba.gov/localresources/district/mo/
kansas/

61887 ■ U.S. Small Business Administration -
Business Information Center (Los Angeles,
California)
Los Angeles District Office
330 N. Brand, Ste. 1200
Glendale, CA 91203
Ph: (818)552-3201
URL: http://www.sba.gov/about-offices-content/2/
3099

61888 ■ U.S. Small Business Administration -
Business Information Center (Omaha,
Nebraska)
10675 Bedford Ave., Ste. 100
Omaha, NE 68134
Ph: (402)221-4691
Fax: (402)221-3680
URL: http://www.sba.gov/about-offices-content/2/
3129

61889 ■ U.S. Small Business Administration -
Business Information Center (Providence,
Rhode Island)
380 Westminster Mall, Rm. 511
Providence, RI 02903
Ph: (401)528-4561
Fax: (401)528-4539
Co. E-mail: faith.white@sba.gov
URL: http://www.sba.gov/about-offices-content/2/
3144

61890 ■ U.S. Small Business Administration -
Business Information Center (St. Louis,
Missouri)
1222 Spruce St., Ste. 10.103
St. Louis, MO 63103
Ph: (314)539-6600
Fax: (314)539-3785
URL: http://www.sba.gov/about-offices-content/2/
3124

61891 ■ U.S. Small Business Administration -
Business Information Center (San Diego,
California)
San Diego District Office
550 W. C St., Ste. 550
San Diego, CA 92101
Ph: (619)557-7250
Fax: (619)557-5894
Co. E-mail: ruben.garcia@sba.gov
URL: http://www.sba.gov/about-offices-content/2/
3101

61892 ■ U.S. Small Business Administration - Business Information Center (Seattle, Washington)
Seattle District Office
2401 4th Ave., Ste. 450
Seattle, WA 98121
Ph: (206)553-7310
URL: http://www.sba.gov/about-offices-content/2/3157

61893 ■ U.S. Small Business Administration - Business Information Center (Warm Springs, Oregon)
601 SW Second Ave., Ste. 950
Portland, OR 97204-3192
Ph: (503)326-2682
Fax: (503)326-2808
URL: http://www.sba.gov/about-offices-content/2/3140

61894 ■ U.S. Small Business Administration - Business Information Center (Washington, Distict of Columbia)
Washington Metropolitan Area District Office
740 15th St. NW, Ste. 300
Washington, DC 20005-3544
Ph: (202)272-0345
URL: http://www.sba.gov/about-offices-content/2/3106

61895 ■ U.S. Small Business Administration - Casper District Office
Federal Bldg., Rm. 4001
100 E. B St.
Casper, WY 82602-5013
Ph: (307)261-6500
Free: 800-776-9144
Fax: (307)261-6535
URL: http://www.sba.gov/wy

61896 ■ U.S. Small Business Administration - Casper District Office
Federal Bldg., Rm. 4001
100 E. B St.
Casper, WY 82602-5013
Ph: (307)261-6500
Free: 800-776-9144
Fax: (307)261-6535
Co. E-mail: Steven.despain@sba.gov
URL: http://www.sba.gov/wy

61897 ■ U.S. Small Business Administration - Cedar Rapids District Office
2750 1st Ave. NE, Ste. 350
Cedar Rapids, IA 52402-4831
Ph: (319)362-6405
Fax: (319)362-7861
URL: http://www.sba.gov/localresources/district/ia/cedar/index.html

61898 ■ U.S. Small Business Administration - Cedar Rapids District Office
2750 1st Ave. NE, Ste. 350
Cedar Rapids, IA 52402-4831
Ph: (319)362-6405
Fax: (319)362-7861
URL: http://www.sba.gov/about-offices-content/2/3114

61899 ■ U.S. Small Business Administration - Charleston Branch Office
405 Capitol St., Ste. 412
Charleston, WV 26301
Ph: (304)347-5220
Fax: (304)347-5350
URL: http://www.sba.gov/wv/

61900 ■ U.S. Small Business Administration - Charleston Branch Office
405 Capitol St., Ste. 412
Charleston, WV 25301
Ph: (304)347-5220
Fax: (304)347-5350
URL: http://www.sba.gov/about-offices-content/2/3159

61901 ■ U.S. Small Business Administration - Charlotte District Office
6302 Fairview Rd., Ste. 300
Charlotte, NC 28210-2227
Ph: (704)344-6563
Free: 800-827-5722
Fax: (704)344-6769
URL: http://www.sba.gov/about-offices-content/2/3127

61902 ■ U.S. Small Business Administration - Chicago District Office
Chicago District Office
500 W. Madison St., Ste. 1150
Chicago, IL 60661-2511
Ph: (312)353-4528
Fax: (312)886-5688
URL: http://www.sba.gov/il

61903 ■ U.S. Small Business Administration - Chicago Regional Office
Illinois District Office
500 W. Madison, Ste. 1150
Chicago, IL 60661-2511
Ph: (312)353-4528
Fax: (312)886-5688
URL: http://www.sba.gov/localresources/district/il/index.html

61904 ■ U.S. Small Business Administration - Chicago Regional Office
Illinois District Office
500 W. Madison, Ste. 1150
Chicago, IL 60661-2511
Ph: (312)353-4528
Fax: (312)886-5688
URL: http://www.sba.gov/about-offices-content/2/3161

61905 ■ U.S. Small Business Administration - Clarksburg District Office
320 W. Pike St., Ste. 330
Clarksburg, WV 26301
Ph: (304)623-5631
Fax: (304)623-0023
Co. E-mail: wvinfo@sba.gov
URL: http://www.sba.gov/wv

61906 ■ U.S. Small Business Administration - Clarksburg District Office
320 W. Pike St., Ste. 330
Clarksburg, WV 26301
Ph: (304)623-5631
Fax: (304)623-0023
Co. E-mail: wvinfo@sba.gov
URL: http://www.sba.gov/about-offices-content/2/3159

61907 ■ U.S. Small Business Administration - Cleveland District Office
Ohio District Office
1350 Euclid Ave., Ste. 211
Cleveland, OH 44115
Ph: (216)522-4180
Fax: (216)522-2038
URL: http://www.sba.gov/localresources/district/oh/cleveland/

61908 ■ U.S. Small Business Administration - Cleveland District Office
1350 Euclid Ave., Ste. 211
Cleveland, OH 44115
Ph: (216)522-4180
Fax: (216)522-2038
URL: http://www.sba.gov/about-offices-content/2/3137

61909 ■ U.S. Small Business Administration - Columbia District Office
South Carolina District Office
1835 Assembly St., Rm. 1425
Columbia, SC 29201
Ph: (803)765-5377
Fax: (803)765-5962
URL: http://www.sba.gov/localresources/district/sc/index.html

61910 ■ U.S. Small Business Administration - Columbia District Office
South Carolina District Office
1835 Assembly St., Rm. 1425
Columbia, SC 29201
Ph: (803)765-5377
Fax: (803)765-5962
URL: http://www.sba.gov/about-offices-content/2/3145

61911 ■ U.S. Small Business Administration - Columbus District Office
401 N. Front St., Ste. 200
Columbus, OH 43215
Ph: (614)469-6860
URL: http://www.sba.gov/localresources/district/oh/columbus/

61912 ■ U.S. Small Business Administration - Columbus District Office
401 N. Front St., Ste. 200
Columbus, OH 43215
Ph: (614)469-6860
URL: http://www.sba.gov/about-offices-content/2/3138

61913 ■ U.S. Small Business Administration - Concord District Office
New Hampshire District Office
55 Pleasant St., Ste. 3101
Concord, NH 03301
Ph: (603)225-1400
Fax: (603)225-1409
Co. E-mail: witmer.jones@sba.gov
URL: http://www.sba.gov/about-offices-content/2/3130

61914 ■ U.S. Small Business Administration - Confederated Tribes of the Grand Ronde Community - Business Information Center
9615 Grand Ronde Rd.
Grand Ronde, OR 97347
Ph: (503)879-5211
Free: 800-422-0232
Fax: (503)879-2117
Co. E-mail: info@grandronde.org
URL: http://www.grandronde.org

61915 ■ U.S. Small Business Administration - Confederated Tribes of the Grand Ronde Community - Business Information Center
9615 Grand Ronde Rd.
Grand Ronde, OR 97347
Ph: (503)879-5211
Free: 800-422-0232
Fax: (503)879-2117
Co. E-mail: info@grandronde.org
URL: http://www.grandronde.org

61916 ■ U.S. Small Business Administration - Connecticut District Office
330 Main St., 2nd Fl.
Hartford, CT 06106
Ph: (860)240-4700
Fax: (860)240-4659
URL: http://www.sba.gov/localresources/district/ct/index.html

61917 ■ U.S. Small Business Administration - Corpus Christi Branch Office
3649 Leopard St., Ste. 411
Corpus Christi, TX 78408
Ph: (361)879-0017
Fax: (361)879-0764
URL: http://www.sba.gov/about-offices-content/2/3150

61918 ■ U.S. Small Business Administration - Dallas District Office
4300 Amon Carter Blvd., Ste. 114
Ft. Worth, TX 76155
Ph: (817)684-5500
Fax: (817)684-5516
URL: http://www.sba.gov/about-offices-content/2/3148

61919 ■ U.S. Small Business Administration - Dallas/Fort Worth District Office
4300 Amon Carter Blvd., Ste. 114
Ft. Worth, TX 76155
Ph: (817)684-5500
Fax: (817)684-5516
URL: http://www.sba.gov/localresources/district/tx/
dallas/

61920 ■ U.S. Small Business Administration - Dallas/Fort Worth District Office
4300 Amon Carter Blvd., Ste. 114
Ft. Worth, TX 76155
Ph: (817)684-5500
Fax: (817)684-5516
URL: http://www.sba.gov/localresources/district/tx/
dallas/index.html

61921 ■ U.S. Small Business Administration - Dallas/Fort Worth District Office
4300 Amon Carter Blvd., Ste. 114
Ft. Worth, TX 76155
Ph: (817)684-5500
Fax: (817)684-5516
URL: http://www.sba.gov/about-offices-content/2/
3148

61922 ■ U.S. Small Business Administration - Delaware Branch Office
1007 N. Orange St., Ste. 1120
Wilmington, DE 19801-1232
Ph: (302)573-6294
Fax: (302)573-6060
URL: http://www.sba.gov/localresources/district/de/
index.html

61923 ■ U.S. Small Business Administration - Denver District Office
721 19th St., Ste. 426
Denver, CO 80202-2517
Ph: (303)844-2607
Fax: (303)844-6468
URL: http://www.sba.gov/localresources/district/co/
index.html

61924 ■ U.S. Small Business Administration - Denver District Office
721 19th St., Ste. 426
Denver, CO 80202-2599
Ph: (303)844-2607
Fax: (303)844-6490
URL: http://www.sba.gov/co

61925 ■ U.S. Small Business Administration - Denver District Office
721 19th St., Ste. 426
Denver, CO 80202-2517
Ph: (303)844-2607
Fax: (303)844-6468
URL: http://www.sba.gov/about-offices-content/2/
3104

61926 ■ U.S. Small Business Administration - Des Moines District Office
210 Walnut St., Rm. 749
Des Moines, IA 50309-4106
Ph: (515)284-4422
Fax: (515)284-4572
URL: http://www.sba.gov/localresources/district/ia/
desmo/

61927 ■ U.S. Small Business Administration - Des Moines Office
210 Walnut St., Rm. 749
Des Moines, IA 50309-4106
Ph: (515)284-4422
Fax: (515)284-4572
URL: http://www.sba.gov/about-offices-content/2/
3114

61928 ■ U.S. Small Business Administration - Detroit District Office
McNamara Federal Bldg.
477 Michigan Ave., Ste. 515
Detroit, MI 48226
Ph: (313)226-6075

Fax: (313)226-4769
Co. E-mail: richard.temkin@sba.gov
URL: http://www.sba.gov/about-offices-content/2/
3121

61929 ■ U.S. Small Business Administration - Disaster Assistance Customer Service Center
130 S. Elmwood Ave.
Buffalo, NY 14202
Ph: (716)843-4100
Free: 800-659-2955
Fax: (716)848-4281
Co. E-mail: disastercustomerservice@sba.gov
URL: http://www.sba.gov/about-offices-content/2/
2817/news/6712

61930 ■ U.S. Small Business Administration - Disaster Assistance Processing & Disbursement Center
14925 Kingsport Rd.
Ft. Worth, TX 76155
Ph: (817)868-2300
Free: 800-366-6303
Fax: (817)684-5616
URL: http://www.sba.gov/localresources/disasterof-
fices/dapdc/index.html

61931 ■ U.S. Small Business Administration - Disaster Assistance Processing & Disbursement Center
14925 Kingsport Rd.
Ft. Worth, TX 76155
Ph: (817)868-2300
Free: 800-366-6303
Fax: (817)684-5616
URL: http://www.sba.gov/about-offices-content/4/
2819

61932 ■ U.S. Small Business Administration - Disaster Field Offices - Field Operations Center - East
101 Marietta St. NW, Ste. 700
Atlanta, GA 30303-2725
Ph: (404)331-0333
Free: 800-659-2955
Fax: (404)331-0273
URL: http://www.sba.gov/about-offices-content/3/
2818
Description: Covers regions three, four, and five.

61933 ■ U.S. Small Business Administration - Disaster Field Offices - Field Operations Center - West
PO Box 419004
Sacramento, CA 95841-9004
Ph: (916)735-1500
Free: 800-488-5323
Description: Covers regions 6-10.

61934 ■ U.S. Small Business Administration - Disaster Field Offices - Field Operations Center - West
PO Box 419004
Sacramento, CA 95841-9004
Ph: (916)735-1500
Free: 800-488-5323
URL: http://www.sba.gov/about-offices-content/2/
2820
Description: Covers regions eight, nine, and ten.

61935 ■ U.S. Small Business Administration - Disaster Field Operations Center - East
101 Marietta St., NW, Ste. 700
Atlanta, GA 30303-2725
Ph: (404)331-0333
Free: 800-659-2955
Fax: (404)331-0273
URL: http://www.sba.gov/localresources/disasterof-
fices/foceast/index.html
Description: Covers regions 1-5.

61936 ■ U.S. Small Business Administration - Disaster Field Operations Center - West
PO Box 419004
Sacramento, CA 95841-9004
Ph: (916)735-1500
Free: 800-488-5323

Fax: (916)735-1683
URL: http://www.sba.gov/localresources/disasterof-
fices/focwest/index.html

61937 ■ U.S. Small Business Administration - Disaster Office - Customer Service Center
130 S. Elmwood Ave., Ste. 516
Buffalo, NY 14202
Ph: (716)843-4100
Free: 800-659-2955
Fax: (716)848-4281
Co. E-mail: disastercustomerservice@sba.gov
URL: http://www.sba.gov/localresources/disasterof-
fices/dacsc/index.html

61938 ■ U.S. Small Business Administration - El Paso District Office
211 N. Florence St., 2nd Fl., Ste. 201
El Paso, TX 79901
Ph: (915)834-4600
Fax: (915)834-4689
URL: http://www.sba.gov/tx/elpaso/

61939 ■ U.S. Small Business Administration - El Paso District Office
211 N. Florence St., 2nd Fl., Ste. 201
El Paso, TX 79901
Ph: (915)834-4600
Fax: (915)834-4689
URL: http://www.sba.gov/about-offices-content/2/
3149

61940 ■ U.S. Small Business Administration - Elmira Branch Office
333 E. Water St., 4th Fl.
Elmira, NY 14901
Ph: (607)734-8130
Fax: (607)733-4656
URL: http://www.sba.gov/localresources/district/ny/
syracuse/index.html

61941 ■ U.S. Small Business Administration - Elmira Branch Office
333 E. Water St., 4th Fl.
Elmira, NY 14901
Ph: (607)734-8130
Fax: (607)733-4656
URL: http://www.sba.gov/about-offices-content/2/
3136

61942 ■ U.S. Small Business Administration - Fargo District Office
657 2nd Ave. N., Rm. 218
Fargo, ND 58108-3086
Ph: (701)239-5131
Fax: (701)239-5645
Co. E-mail: north.dakota@sba.gov
URL: http://www.sba.gov/localresources/district/nd/
index.html

61943 ■ U.S. Small Business Administration - Fargo District Office
657 2nd Ave. N., Rm. 218
Fargo, ND 58108-3086
Ph: (701)239-5131
Fax: (701)239-5645
Co. E-mail: north.dakota@sba.gov
URL: http://www.sba.gov/about-offices-content/2/
3128

61944 ■ U.S. Small Business Administration - Field Operations Center - West
PO Box 419004
Sacramento, CA 95841-9004
Ph: (916)735-1500
Free: 800-488-5323
Fax: (916)735-1683
URL: http://www.sba.gov/localresources/disasterof-
fices/focwest/index.html

61945 ■ U.S. Small Business Administration - Fresno District Office
2719 N. Air Fresno Dr., Ste. 200
Fresno, CA 93727
Ph: (559)487-5791
Fax: (559)487-5636
URL: http://www.sba.gov/localresources/district/ca/
fresno/index.html

61946 ■ U.S. Small Business Administration - Fresno District Office
801 R St., Ste. 201
Fresno, CA 93721
Ph: (559)487-5791
Fax: (559)487-5636
URL: http://www.sba.gov/about-offices-content/2/3098

61947 ■ U.S. Small Business Administration - Georgia District Office
Georgia District Office
Harris Tower
233 Peachtree St., NE, Ste. 1900
Atlanta, GA 30303
Ph: (404)331-0100
Fax: (404)331-0101
URL: http://www.sba.gov/localresources/district/ga/index.html

61948 ■ U.S. Small Business Administration - Gulfport Branch Office
Gulf Coast Business Technology Center
Hancock Bank Plz.
2510 14th St., Ste. 103
Gulfport, MS 39532
Ph: (228)863-4449
Fax: (228)864-0179
URL: http://www.sba.gov/localresources/district/ms/index.html

61949 ■ U.S. Small Business Administration - Gulfport Branch Office
Gulf Coast Business Technology Center
Hancock Bank Plz.
2510 14th St., Ste. 103
Gulfport, MS 39501
Ph: (228)863-4449
Fax: (228)864-0179
URL: http://www.sba.gov/about-offices-content/2/3125

61950 ■ U.S. Small Business Administration - Harlingen District Office
222 E. Van Buren, Ste. 500
Harlingen, TX 78550
Ph: (956)427-8533
Fax: (956)427-8537
URL: http://www.sba.gov/localresources/district/tx/harlingen/index.html

61951 ■ U.S. Small Business Administration - Harlingen District Office
222 E. Van Buren, Ste. 500
Harlingen, TX 78550
Ph: (956)427-8533
Fax: (956)427-8537
URL: http://www.sba.gov/about-offices-content/2/3150

61952 ■ U.S. Small Business Administration - Hartford District Office
330 Main St., 2nd Fl.
Hartford, CT 06106
Ph: (860)240-4700
Fax: (860)240-4659
URL: http://www.sba.gov/about-offices-content/2/3105

61953 ■ U.S. Small Business Administration - Hawaii District Office
300 Ala Moana Blvd., Rm. 2-235
Honolulu, HI 96850
Ph: (808)541-2990
Fax: (808)541-2976
URL: http://www.sba.gov/localresources/district/hi/index.html

61954 ■ U.S. Small Business Administration - Helena District Office
Montana District Office
10 W. 15th St., Ste. 1100
Helena, MT 59626
Ph: (406)441-1081
Fax: (406)441-1090
URL: http://www.sba.gov/about-offices-content/2/3126

61955 ■ U.S. Small Business Administration - Honolulu District Office
500 Ala Moana Blvd., Rm. 1-306
Honolulu, HI 96850
Ph: (808)541-2990
Fax: (808)541-2976
URL: http://www.sba.gov/localresources/district/hi/index.html

61956 ■ U.S. Small Business Administration - Houston District Office
8701 S. Gessner Dr., Ste. 1200
Houston, TX 77074
Ph: (713)773-6500
Fax: (713)773-6550
URL: http://www.sba.gov/localresources/district/tx/hous/

61957 ■ U.S. Small Business Administration - Houston District Office
Houston District Office
8701 S. Gessner Dr., Ste. 1200
Houston, TX 77074
Ph: (713)773-6500
Fax: (713)773-6550
URL: http://www.sba.gov/localresources/district/tx/hous/

61958 ■ U.S. Small Business Administration - Houston District Office
8701 S. Gessner Dr., Ste. 1200
Houston, TX 77074
Ph: (713)773-6500
Fax: (713)773-6550
URL: http://www.sba.gov/about-offices-content/2/3151

61959 ■ U.S. Small Business Administration - Indiana District Office
Indiana District Office
8500 Keystone Crossing, Ste. 400
Indianapolis, IN 46240
Ph: (317)226-7272
Fax: (317)226-7259
Co. E-mail: indiana@sba.gov
URL: http://www.sba.gov/localresources/district/in/index.html

61960 ■ U.S. Small Business Administration - Indianapolis District Office
Indiana District Office
8500 Keystone Crossing, Ste. 400
Indianapolis, IN 46240
Ph: (317)226-7272
Fax: (317)226-7259
Co. E-mail: indiana@sba.gov
URL: http://www.sba.gov/about-offices-content/2/3116

61961 ■ U.S. Small Business Administration - Jackson District Office
Regions Plaza
210 E. Capitol St., Ste. 900
Jackson, MS 39201
Ph: (601)965-4378
Fax: (601)965-5629
URL: http://www.sba.gov/localresources/district/ms/index.html

61962 ■ U.S. Small Business Administration - Jackson District Office
Regions Plaza
210 E. Capitol St., Ste. 900
Jackson, MS 39201
Ph: (601)965-4378
Fax: (601)965-5629
URL: http://www.sba.gov/about-offices-content/2/3125

61963 ■ U.S. Small Business Administration - Jacksonville District Office
7825 Baymeadows Way, Ste. 100B
Jacksonville, FL 32256-7504
Ph: (904)443-1900
Fax: (904)443-1980
URL: http://www.sba.gov/localresources/district/fl/north/index.html

61964 ■ U.S. Small Business Administration - Jacksonville District Office
7825 Baymeadows Way, Ste. 100B
Jacksonville, FL 32256-7504
Ph: (904)443-1900
Fax: (904)443-1980
URL: http://www.sba.gov/about-offices-content/2/3108

61965 ■ U.S. Small Business Administration - Kansas City District Office
1000 Walnut, Ste. 500
Kansas City, MO 64106
Ph: (816)426-4900
URL: http://www.sba.gov/localresources/district/mo/index.html

61966 ■ U.S. Small Business Administration - Kansas City District Office
1000 Walnut, Ste. 500
Kansas City, MO 64106
Ph: (816)426-4900
URL: http://www.sba.gov/localresources/district/mo/kansas/

61967 ■ U.S. Small Business Administration - Kansas City District Office
1000 Walnut, Ste. 500
Kansas City, MO 64106
Ph: (816)426-4900
URL: http://www.sba.gov/about-offices-content/2/3123

61968 ■ U.S. Small Business Administration - Kentucky District Office
600 Dr. Martin Luther King Jr. Pl., Rm. 188
Louisville, KY 40202-2254
Ph: (502)582-5971
Fax: (502)582-5009
URL: http://www.sba.gov/localresources/district/ky/index.html

61969 ■ U.S. Small Business Administration - The Klamath Tribes - Business Information Center
501 Chiloquin Blvd.
Chiloquin, OR 97624
Ph: (541)783-2219
Free: 800-524-9787
Fax: (541)783-2029
URL: http://www.klamathtribes.org

61970 ■ U.S. Small Business Administration - The Klamath Tribes - Business Information Center
501 Chiloquin Blvd.
Chiloquin, OR 97624
Ph: (541)783-2219
Free: 800-524-9787
Fax: (541)783-2029
URL: http://www.klamathtribes.org

61971 ■ U.S. Small Business Administration - Las Vegas District Office
Nevada District Office
400 S. 4th St., Ste. 250
Las Vegas, NV 89101
Ph: (702)388-6611
Fax: (702)388-6469
URL: http://www.sba.gov/about-offices-content/2/3133

61972 ■ U.S. Small Business Administration - Little Rock District Office
2120 Riverfront Dr., Ste. 250
Little Rock, AR 72202-1796
Ph: (501)324-7379
Fax: (501)324-7394
URL: http://www.sba.gov/about-offices-content/2/3096

61973 ■ U.S. Small Business Administration - Los Angeles District Office
330 N. Brand Blvd., Ste. 1200
Glendale, CA 91203
Ph: (818)552-3215
URL: http://www.sba.gov/localresources/district/ca/la/index.html

61974 ■ U.S. Small Business Administration - Los Angeles District Office
Los Angeles District Office
330 N. Brand, Ste. 1200
Glendale, CA 91203
Ph: (818)552-3215
URL: http://www.sba.gov/localresources/district/ca/la/
index.html

61975 ■ U.S. Small Business Administration - Los Angeles District Office
330 N. Brand Blvd., Ste. 1200
Glendale, CA 91203
Ph: (818)552-3201
URL: http://www.sba.gov/about-offices-content/2/
3099

61976 ■ U.S. Small Business Administration - Louisville District Office
600 Dr. Martin Luther King Jr. Pl., Rm. 188
Louisville, KY 40202-2254
Ph: (502)582-5971
Fax: (502)582-5009
URL: http://www.sba.gov/about-offices-content/2/
3118

61977 ■ U.S. Small Business Administration - Lower Rio Grande Valley District Office - Corpus Christi Branch Office
3649 Leopard St., Ste. 411
Corpus Christi, TX 78408
Ph: (361)879-0017
Fax: (361)879-0764
URL: http://www.sba.gov/localresources/district/tx/
harlingen/

61978 ■ U.S. Small Business Administration - Lubbock District Office
1205 Texas Ave., Rm. 408
Lubbock, TX 79401-2693
Ph: (806)472-7462
Fax: (806)472-7487
URL: http://www.sba.gov/localresources/district/tx/
lubbock/

61979 ■ U.S. Small Business Administration - Lubbock District Office
1205 Texas Ave., Rm. 408
Lubbock, TX 79401-2693
Ph: (806)472-7462
Fax: (806)472-7487
Co. E-mail: Herbert.johnston@sba.gov
URL: http://www.sba.gov/about-offices-content/2/
3152

61980 ■ U.S. Small Business Administration - Madison District Office
740 Regent St., Ste. 100
Madison, WI 53715
Ph: (608)441-5263
Fax: (608)441-5541
URL: http://www.sba.gov/about-offices-content/2/
3158

61981 ■ U.S. Small Business Administration - Maine District Office
Edmund S. Muskie Federal Bldg. , Rm. 512
68 Sewall St.
Augusta, ME 04330
Ph: (207)622-8551
URL: http://www.sba.gov/localresources/district/me/
index.html

61982 ■ U.S. Small Business Administration - Marshall Post of Duty
505 E. Travis, Rm. 103
Marshall, TX 75670
Ph: (903)935-5257
Fax: (903)935-1248

61983 ■ U.S. Small Business Administration - Marshall Post of Duty
505 E. Travis, Rm. 103
Marshall, TX 75670

61984 ■ U.S. Small Business Administration - Melville Branch Office
35 Pinelawn Rd., Ste. 207W
Melville, NY 11747

Ph: (631)454-0750
Fax: (202)481-4286
Co. E-mail: malinda.chen@sba.gov
URL: http://www.sba.gov/aboutsba/sbaprograms/gc/
contacts/gc_cmr.html

61985 ■ U.S. Small Business Administration - Melville Branch Office
35 Pinelawn Rd., Ste. 207W
Melville, NY 11747

61986 ■ U.S. Small Business Administration - Miami District Office
100 S. Biscayne Blvd., 7th Fl.
Miami, FL 33131
Ph: (305)536-5521
Fax: (305)536-5058
URL: http://www.sba.gov/localresources/district/fl/
south/index.html

61987 ■ U.S. Small Business Administration - Miami District Office
100 S. Biscayne Blvd., 7th Fl.
Miami, FL 33131
Ph: (305)536-5521
Fax: (305)536-5058
Co. E-mail: Francisco.Marrero@sba.gov
URL: http://www.sba.gov/about-offices-content/2/
3109

61988 ■ U.S. Small Business Administration - Michigan District Office
McNamara Federal Bldg.
477 Michigan Ave., Ste. 515
Detroit, MI 48226
Ph: (313)226-6075
Fax: (313)226-4769
URL: http://www.sba.gov/localresources/district/mi/
index.html

61989 ■ U.S. Small Business Administration - Minneapolis District Office
Butler Sq.
100 N. Sixth St., Ste. 210-C
Minneapolis, MN 55403
Ph: (612)370-2324
Fax: (202)481-0139
URL: http://www.sba.gov/about-offices-content/2/
3122

61990 ■ U.S. Small Business Administration - Minnesota District Office
Butler Sq.
100 N. Sixth St., Ste. 210-C
Minneapolis, MN 55403
Ph: (612)370-2324
Fax: (612)370-2303
URL: http://www.sba.gov/localresources/district/mn/
index.html

61991 ■ U.S. Small Business Administration - Montana District Office
Montana District Office
10 W. 15th St., Ste. 1100
Helena, MT 59626
Ph: (406)441-1081
Fax: (406)441-1090
URL: http://www.sba.gov/localresources/district/mt/
index.html

61992 ■ U.S. Small Business Administration - Montpelier District Office
87 State St., Rm. 205
Montpelier, VT 05601-0605
Ph: (802)828-4422
Fax: (802)828-4485
URL: http://www.sba.gov/about-offices-content/2/
3156

61993 ■ U.S. Small Business Administration - Nashville District Office
Tennessee District Office
50 Vantage Way, Ste. 201
Nashville, TN 37228-1500
Ph: (615)736-5881
Fax: (615)736-7232
URL: http://www.sba.gov/localresources/district/tn/
index.html

61994 ■ U.S. Small Business Administration - Nashville District Office
Small Business Resource Center
3401 W. End Ave., Ste. 110
Nashville, TN 37203-1609
Ph: (615)749-4088
Free: 800-342-8217
Fax: (615)749-3685

61995 ■ U.S. Small Business Administration - Nashville District Office
Tennessee District Office
50 Vantage Way, Ste. 201
Nashville, TN 37228-1500
Ph: (615)736-5881
Fax: (615)736-7232
Co. E-mail: w.smith@sba.gov
URL: http://www.sba.gov/about-offices-content/2/
3147

61996 ■ U.S. Small Business Administration - Nebraska District Office
10675 Bedford Ave., Ste. 100
Omaha, NE 68134
Ph: (402)221-4691
Fax: (402)221-3680
URL: http://www.sba.gov/ne

61997 ■ U.S. Small Business Administration - Nevada District Office
Nevada District Office
400 S. 4th St., Ste. 250
Las Vegas, NV 89101
Ph: (702)388-6611
Fax: (702)388-6469
URL: http://www.sba.gov/localresources/district/nv/
index.html

61998 ■ U.S. Small Business Administration - New Hampshire District Office - Concord District Office
New Hampshire District Office
JC Cleveland Federal Bldg.
55 Pleasant St., Ste. 3101
Concord, NH 03301
Ph: (603)225-1400
Fax: (603)225-1409
URL: http://www.sba.gov/localresources/district/nh/

61999 ■ U.S. Small Business Administration - New Jersey District Office
New Jersey District Office
2 Gateway Center, 15th Fl.
Newark, NJ 07102
Ph: (973)645-2434
Fax: (973)645-6265
URL: http://www.sba.gov/localresources/district/nj/
index.html

62000 ■ U.S. Small Business Administration - New York District Office
Jacob K. Javits Federal Bldg.
26 Federal Plz., Ste. 3100
New York, NY 10278
Ph: (212)264-4354
Fax: (212)264-4963
URL: http://www.sba.gov/localresources/district/ny/
ny/

62001 ■ U.S. Small Business Administration - New York District Office
Jacob K. Javits Federal Bldg.
26 Federal Plz., Ste. 3100
New York, NY 10278
Ph: (212)264-4354
Fax: (212)264-4963
URL: http://www.sba.gov/about-offices-content/2/
3135

62002 ■ U.S. Small Business Administration - Newark District Office
New Jersey District Office
2 Gateway Center, Ste. 1501
Newark, NJ 07102
Ph: (973)645-2434
Fax: (973)645-6265
URL: http://www.sba.gov/about-offices-content/2/
3131

62003 ■ U.S. Small Business Administration - North Carolina District Office - Charlotte District Office
6302 Fairview Rd., Ste. 300
Charlotte, NC 28210-2227
Ph: (704)344-6563
Free: 800-827-5722
Fax: (704)344-6769
URL: http://www.sba.gov/nc

62004 ■ U.S. Small Business Administration - North Texas U.S. Export Assistance Center (Grapevine, Texas)
1450 Hughes Rd., Ste. 220
Grapevine, TX 76051
Ph: (817)310-3749
Fax: (817)310-3757
URL: http://www.sba.gov/aboutsba/sbaprograms/
internationaltrade/useac/
Description: Serves Oklahoma, Texas, Louisiana, and Arkansas.

62005 ■ U.S. Small Business Administration - North Texas U.S. Export Assistance Center (Grapevine, Texas)
4300 Amon Carter Blvd., Ste. 114
Ft. Worth, TX 76155
Ph: (817)310-3749
Fax: (817)310-3757
Co. E-mail: Richard.schultze@sba.gov
URL: http://export.gov/texas/northtexas/contactus/
index.asp
Description: Serves Oklahoma, Texas, Louisiana, and Arkansas.

62006 ■ U.S. Small Business Administration - Office of 8(a) Business Development
409 3rd St. SW
Washington, DC 20416
Ph: (202)205-5852
Fax: (202)205-7064
URL: http://www.sba.gov/aboutsba/sbaprograms/
8abd/index.html

62007 ■ U.S. Small Business Administration - Office of 8(a) Business Development
409 3rd St. SW, Ste. 8800
Washington, DC 20416
Ph: (202)205-5852
Fax: (202)205-7259
Co. E-mail: 8abd@sba.gov
URL: http://www.sba.gov/content/8a-business-
development

62008 ■ U.S. Small Business Administration - Office of Advocacy
409 Third St., SW, 7th Fl.
Washington, DC 20416
Ph: (202)205-6533
Fax: (202)206-6928
Co. E-mail: advocacy@sba.gov
URL: http://www.sba.gov/advo/

62009 ■ U.S. Small Business Administration - Office of Advocacy
409 3rd St. SW
Washington, DC 20416
Ph: (202)205-6533
Fax: (202)206-6928
Co. E-mail: advocacy@sba.gov
URL: http://www.sba.gov/advocacy

62010 ■ U.S. Small Business Administration - Office of Advocacy - Research and Statistics - Office of Economic Research
409 Third St., 7th Fl.
Washington, DC 20416
Ph: (202)205-6533
Fax: (202)206-6928
Co. E-mail: advocacy@sba.gov
URL: http://www.sba.gov/advo/research/

62011 ■ U.S. Small Business Administration - Office of Business and Community Initiatives - Office of Entrepreneurial Development
409 3rd St. SW, Ste. 7000
Washington, DC 20416
Ph: (202)205-6605

Free: 800-877-8339
Fax: (202)205-6802
URL: http://www.sba.gov/aboutsba/sbaprograms/
obci/index.html

62012 ■ U.S. Small Business Administration - Office of Business and Community Initiatives - Office of Entrepreneurial Development
409 3rd St. SW, Ste. 6200
Washington, DC 20416
Ph: (202)205-6239
Free: 800-877-8339
Fax: (202)205-6903
URL: http://www.sba.gov/about-offices-content/1/
2463

62013 ■ U.S. Small Business Administration - Office of Communications and Public Liaison
409 3rd St. SW
Washington, DC 20416
Ph: (202)205-6740
Fax: (202)205-6901

62014 ■ U.S. Small Business Administration - Office of Communications and Public Liaison
409 3rd St. SW, Ste. 7450
Washington, DC 20416
Ph: (202)205-6740
Fax: (202)205-6913
URL(s): www.sba.gov/about-offices-content/1/2460.

62015 ■ U.S. Small Business Administration - Office of Financial Assistance - Office of Loan Programs
740 15th St. NW, 3rd Fl.
Washington, DC 20005-3544
Ph: (202)272-0345
Fax: (202)272-0344
URL: http://www.sba.gov/services/financialassis-
tance/index.html

62016 ■ U.S. Small Business Administration - Office of Financial Assistance - Office of Loan Programs
409 3rd St. SW, Ste. 8300
Washington, DC 20416
Ph: (202)205-6490
Fax: (202)205-7722
URL: http://www.sba.gov/about-offices-content/1/
2888/about-us

62017 ■ U.S. Small Business Administration - Office of Government Contracting
409 3rd St., SW
Washington, DC 20416
Ph: (202)205-6618
Fax: (202)205-6390
URL: http://www.sba.gov/gc

62018 ■ U.S. Small Business Administration - Office of Government Contracting
409 3rd St. SW
Washington, DC 20416
Ph: (202)205-6618
Fax: (202)205-6390
Co. E-mail: sizestandards@sba.gov
URL: http://www.sba.gov/contracting

62019 ■ U.S. Small Business Administration - Office of the Inspector General
409 Third St., SW
Washington, DC 20416
Free: 800-767-0385
Fax: (202)205-7064
Co. E-mail: OIG@sba.gov
URL: http://www.sba.gov/ig/

62020 ■ U.S. Small Business Administration - Office of the Inspector General
409 3rd St. SW
Washington, DC 20416
Free: 800-767-0385
Fax: (202)205-7064
Co. E-mail: OIG@sba.gov
URL: http://www.sba.gov/office-of-inspector-general

62021 ■ U.S. Small Business Administration - Office of International Trade
6501 Sylvan Rd.
Citrus Heights, CA 95610
Ph: (916)735-1708
Fax: (202)741-6851
URL: http://www.sba.gov/aboutsba/sbaprograms/
internationaltrade/index.html

62022 ■ U.S. Small Business Administration - Office of International Trade
409 3rd St. SW, Ste. 8500
Washington, DC 20416
Ph: (202)205-6720
Fax: (202)205-7722
URL: http://www.sba.gov/aboutsba/sbaprograms/
internationaltrade/index.html

62023 ■ U.S. Small Business Administration - Office of Minority Enterprise Development - Division of 8(a) Program Certification and Eligibility
409 3rd St. SW
Washington, DC 20416
Ph: (202)619-0628
Free: 800-827-5722
URL: http://www.sba.gov/aboutsba/sbaprograms/
8abd/index.html

62024 ■ U.S. Small Business Administration - Office of Minority Enterprise Development - Division of 8(a) Program Certification and Eligibility
409 3rd St. SW
Washington, DC 20416
Free: 800-827-5722
URL: http://www.sba.gov/content/8a-business-
development

62025 ■ U.S. Small Business Administration - Office of the National Ombudsman
409 3rd St., SW
MC2120
Washington, DC 20416-0005
Ph: (202)205-2417
Free: 888-734-3247
Fax: (202)481-5719
Co. E-mail: ombudsman@sba.gov
URL: http://www.sba.gov/aboutsba/sbaprograms/
ombudsman/index.html

62026 ■ U.S. Small Business Administration - Office of the National Ombudsman
409 3rd St. SW, Ste. 7125
Washington, DC 20416
Free: 888-734-3247
Fax: (202)481-5719
Co. E-mail: ombudsman@sba.gov
URL: http://www.sba.gov/ombudsman

62027 ■ U.S. Small Business Administration - Office of Native American Affairs
409 Third St., SW, Sixth Fl.
Washington, DC 20415
Ph: (202)205-7364
URL: http://www.sba.gov/aboutsba/sbaprograms/naa/
index.html
Description: Ensures that American Indians, Native Alaskans and Native Hawaiians seeking to create, develop and expand small businesses have full access to the necessary business development and expansion tools available through the Agency's entrepreneurial development, lending and procurement programs.

62028 ■ U.S. Small Business Administration - Office of Native American Affairs
409 3rd St. SW, Ste. 6700
Washington, DC 20416
Ph: (202)205-7364
Fax: (202)205-6139
URL: http://www.sba.gov/about-offices-content/1/
2960
Description: Ensures that American Indians, Native Alaskans and Native Hawaiians seeking to create, develop and expand small businesses have full access to the necessary business development and

expansion tools available through the Agency's entrepreneurial development, lending and procurement programs.

62029 ■ U.S. Small Business Administration (SBA) - Office of Small Business Development Centers

409 3rd St. SW, 6th Fl.
Washington, DC 20416
URL: http://www.sba.gov/aboutsba/sbaprograms/sbdc/index.html

Description: Although other federal agencies also provide some services to small business, the SBA's primary duties are to aid, counsel, assist, and protect the interests of small business. It ensures that small business concerns receive a fair portion of government purchases, contracts, and subcontracts, as well as fair portions of the sales of government property. The SBA grants loans to small business concerns, to state and local development companies, and to the victims of floods, other catastrophes, or certain types of economic injuries. The administration also licenses, regulates, and grants loans to small business investment companies (SBICs). A small business must meet SBA size standards to be eligible for its loans, procurement assistance, and other services. Interested small business owners should contact the nearest SBA field offices for current standards since they vary by industry and are subject to change. The SBA administers a variety of loan programs for eligible small business concerns that cannot borrow money on reasonable terms from conventional lenders without government assistance. Most of the SBA's loans are made by private lenders and then guaranteed by the SBA, which can guarantee loans up to 90 percent for a maximum of $500,000. In addition to these regular business loans, the SBA offers a variety of special loan programs, including local development company loans that are offered to groups of local citizens. The SBA licenses and regulates small business investment companies (SBICs) which provide venture capital to small businesses. SBA field officers provide counseling and other services to small business owners seeking to do business with the federal government. Procurement specialists at district offices assist in identifying the government agencies that are prospective customers, in instructing small businesses about inclusion on bidders' lists, and in obtaining drawings and specifications for specific contracts. The SBA seeks to increase small business' share of procurement through the activities of its network of procurement center representatives (PCRs), stationed at or in liaison with all federal military and civilian installations with major buying programs. The SBA's procurement assistance program sets aside suitable government purchases for competitive award to small business concerns and provides an appeal procedure when the ability of a low-bidding small firm to perform a contract is questioned. The SBA also develops subcontracting opportunities, designating the amounts to be subcontracted to small business concerns by prime contractors undertaking major federal projects. The SBA administers the Small Business Innovation Research Program, which fosters participation by small businesses in federal research and development; and provides counseling and information to small businesses through a network of resource programs. The SBA also sponsors the Small Business Development Center (SBDC) Program in conjunction with the educational community, state and local governments, the federal government, and the private sector. In each state there is one "lead" organization that sponsors each SBDC and from which a statewide director manages the program. SBDCs seek to further economic development by providing management and technical assistance to existing and prospective small businesses. The lead organizations coordinate the activities performed on behalf of small business through the participation and establishment of SBDC subcenters and satellite locations. The SBA also offers export counseling and training through its Office of International Trade or small businesses wishing to export products and materials. The SBA is authorized, under Section 8 (a) of the Small Business Act, to enter into contracts with other federal agencies for goods and services and then to subcontract the work to firms owned by socially and economically disadvantaged persons. The firms must be approved to

participate in the 8(a) program by the SBA. In addition, the SBA also is authorized, under Section 7(j) of the act, to provide management and technical assistance to SBA clients and small businesses in areas of high unemployment. This program allows the SBA to contract with qualified individuals, state and local governments, educational institutions, Native American tribes, and other nonprofit institutions. The SBA seeks to increase the strength, profitability, and visibility of women-owned businesses by enhancing their access to existing government and private sector resources. Specific efforts include assisting women business owners in surviving business crises; providing SBA personnel with the appropriate skills to respond to the needs of women business owners; increasing federal marketing opportunities; negotiating an annual goal for procurement from women business owners for each federal department and agency; and collecting and analyzing data about women-owned businesses. The SBA's Office of Advocacy attempts to evaluate the impact of legislative proposals and other public policy issues on small business and represents its views before Congress, federal agencies, and state and local governments. The chief counsel also coordinates and conducts applied economic research on a wide range of small business issues, as well as serves as a source of information about the federal government for small business. The office's activities are supported by advocates located at each of the ten SBA regional offices. The SBA also publishes a variety of pamphlets and booklets about its programs and services.

62030 ■ U.S. Small Business Administration - Office of Small Business Development Centers

409 3rd St. SW, Ste. 6400
Washington, DC 20416
Ph: (202)205-6766
Fax: (202)205-7727
URL: http://www.sba.gov/about-offices-content/1/700

Description: Although other federal agencies also provide some services to small business, the SBA's primary duties are to aid, counsel, assist, and protect the interests of small business. It ensures that small business concerns receive a fair portion of government purchases, contracts, and subcontracts, as well as fair portions of the sales of government property. The SBA grants loans to small business concerns, to state and local development companies, and to the victims of floods, other catastrophes, or certain types of economic injuries. The administration also licenses, regulates, and grants loans to small business investment companies (SBICs). A small business must meet SBA size standards to be eligible for its loans, procurement assistance, and other services. Interested small business owners should contact the nearest SBA field offices for current standards since they vary by industry and are subject to change. The SBA administers a variety of loan programs for eligible small business concerns that cannot borrow money on reasonable terms from conventional lenders without government assistance. Most of the SBA's loans are made by private lenders and then guaranteed by the SBA, which can guarantee loans up to 90 percent for a maximum of $500,000. In addition to these regular business loans, the SBA offers a variety of special loan programs, including local development company loans that are offered to groups of local citizens. The SBA licenses and regulates small business investment companies (SBICs) which provide venture capital to small businesses. SBA field officers provide counseling and other services to small business owners seeking to do business with the federal government. Procurement specialists at district offices assist in identifying the government agencies that are prospective customers, in instructing small businesses about inclusion on bidders' lists, and in obtaining drawings and specifications for specific contracts. The SBA seeks to increase small business' share of procurement through the activities of its network of procurement center representatives (PCRs), stationed at or in liaison with all federal military and civilian installations with major buying programs. The SBA's procurement assistance program sets aside suitable government purchases for competitive award to small business concerns and provides an appeal procedure when the ability of a low-bidding small firm to perform a contract is

questioned. The SBA also develops subcontracting opportunities, designating the amounts to be subcontracted to small business concerns by prime contractors undertaking major federal projects. The SBA administers the Small Business Innovation Research Program, which fosters participation by small businesses in federal research and development; and provides counseling and information to small businesses through a network of resource programs. The SBA also sponsors the Small Business Development Center (SBDC) Program in conjunction with the educational community, state and local governments, the federal government, and the private sector. In each state there is one "lead" organization that sponsors each SBDC and from which a statewide director manages the program. SBDCs seek to further economic development by providing management and technical assistance to existing and prospective small businesses. The lead organizations coordinate the activities performed on behalf of small business through the participation and establishment of SBDC subcenters and satellite locations. The SBA also offers export counseling and training through its Office of International Trade or small businesses wishing to export products and materials. The SBA is authorized, under Section 8 (a) of the Small Business Act, to enter into contracts with other federal agencies for goods and services and then to subcontract the work to firms owned by socially and economically disadvantaged persons. The firms must be approved to participate in the 8(a) program by the SBA. In addition, the SBA also is authorized, under Section 7(j) of the act, to provide management and technical assistance to SBA clients and small businesses in areas of high unemployment. This program allows the SBA to contract with qualified individuals, state and local governments, educational institutions, Native American tribes, and other nonprofit institutions. The SBA seeks to increase the strength, profitability, and visibility of women-owned businesses by enhancing their access to existing government and private sector resources. Specific efforts include assisting women business owners in surviving business crises; providing SBA personnel with the appropriate skills to respond to the needs of women business owners; increasing federal marketing opportunities; negotiating an annual goal for procurement from women business owners for each federal department and agency; and collecting and analyzing data about women-owned businesses. The SBA's Office of Advocacy attempts to evaluate the impact of legislative proposals and other public policy issues on small business and represents its views before Congress, federal agencies, and state and local governments. The chief counsel also coordinates and conducts applied economic research on a wide range of small business issues, as well as serves as a source of information about the federal government for small business. The office's activities are supported by advocates located at each of the ten SBA regional offices. The SBA also publishes a variety of pamphlets and booklets about its programs and services.

62031 ■ U.S. Small Business Administration - Office of Women's Business Ownership Entrepreneurial Development

409 3rd St. SW, 6th Fl.
Washington, DC 20416
Ph: (202)205-6673
Fax: (202)205-7287
Co. E-mail: owbo@sba.gov
URL: http://www.sba.gov/womeninbusiness

62032 ■ U.S. Small Business Administration - Office of Women's Business Ownership Entrepreneurial Development

409 3rd St. SW, Ste. 6600
Washington, DC 20416
Ph: (202)205-6673
Fax: (202)205-7287
Co. E-mail: owbo@sba.gov
URL: http://www.sba.gov/about-offices-content/1/2895

62033 ■ U.S. Small Business Administration - Oklahoma City District Office

Federal Bldg.
301 NW 6th St.
Oklahoma City, OK 73102

Ph: (405)609-8000
URL: http://www.sba.gov/localresources/district/ok/
index.html

62034 ■ U.S. Small Business Administration - Oklahoma City District Office
Federal Bldg.
301 NW 6th St.
Oklahoma City, OK 73102
Ph: (405)609-8000
URL: http://www.sba.gov/about-offices-content/2/
3139

62035 ■ U.S. Small Business Administration - Omaha District Office
10675 Bedford Ave., Ste. 100
Omaha, NE 68134
Ph: (402)221-4691
Fax: (402)221-3680
URL: http://www.sba.gov/localresources/district/ne/
index.html

62036 ■ U.S. Small Business Administration - Omaha District Office
10675 Bedford Ave., Ste. 100
Omaha, NE 68134
Ph: (402)221-4691
Fax: (402)221-3680
URL: http://www.sba.gov/about-offices-content/2/
3129

62037 ■ U.S. Small Business Administration - Philadelphia District Office
1150 First Ave., Ste. 1001
King of Prussia, PA 19406
Ph: (610)382-3062
URL: http://www.sba.gov/localresources/district/pa/
phil/

62038 ■ U.S. Small Business Administration - Philadelphia District Office
1150 First Ave., Ste. 1001
Parkview Tower
King of Prussia, PA 19406
Ph: (610)382-3062
URL: http://www.sba.gov/about-offices-content/2/
3141

62039 ■ U.S. Small Business Administration - Phoenix District Office
2828 N. Central Ave., Ste. 800
Phoenix, AZ 85004-1093
Ph: (602)745-7200
Fax: (602)745-7210
URL: http://www.sba.gov/about-offices-content/2/
3097

62040 ■ U.S. Small Business Administration - Pittsburgh District Office
411 7th Ave., Ste. 1450
Pittsburgh, PA 15219
Ph: (412)395-6560
Fax: (412)395-6562
URL: http://www.sba.gov/localresources/district/pa/
pitt/

62041 ■ U.S. Small Business Administration - Pittsburgh District Office
411 7th Ave., Ste. 1450
Pittsburgh, PA 15219
Ph: (412)395-6560
Fax: (412)395-6562
Co. E-mail: carl.knoblock@sba.gov
URL: http://www.sba.gov/about-offices-content/2/
3142

62042 ■ U.S. Small Business Administration - Portland District Office
601 SW 2nd Ave., Ste. 950
Portland, OR 97204-3192
Ph: (503)326-2682
Fax: (503)326-2808
URL: http://www.sba.gov/localresources/district/or/
index.html

62043 ■ U.S. Small Business Administration - Portland District Office
601 SW Second Ave., Ste. 950
Portland, OR 97204-3192

Ph: (503)326-2682
Fax: (503)326-2808
URL: http://www.sba.gov/localresources/district/or/

62044 ■ U.S. Small Business Administration - Portland District Office
601 SW 2nd Ave., Ste. 950
Portland, OR 97204-3192
Ph: (503)326-2682
Fax: (503)326-2808
Co. E-mail: harry.dewolf@sba.gov
URL: http://www.sba.gov/about-offices-content/2/
3140

62045 ■ U.S. Small Business Administration - Providence District Office
380 Westminster St., Ste. 511
Providence, RI 02903
Ph: (401)528-4561
Fax: (401)528-4539
URL: http://www.sba.gov/localresources/district/ri/
index.html

62046 ■ U.S. Small Business Administration - Providence District Office
380 Westminster St., Ste. 511
Providence, RI 02903
Ph: (401)528-4561
Fax: (401)528-4539
URL: http://www.sba.gov/about-offices-content/2/
3144

62047 ■ U.S. Small Business Administration - Puerto Rico and U.S. Virgin Islands District Office
Citibank Tower, Ste. 200
252 Ponce de Leon Ave.
San Juan, PR 00918
Ph: (787)766-5572
Free: 800-669-8049
Fax: (787)766-5309
URL: http://www.sba.gov/localresources/district/pr/
index.html

62048 ■ U.S. Small Business Administration - Puerto Rico and U.S. Virgin Islands District Office
273 Ponce de Leon Ave.
Plaza Scotiabank, Ste. 510
San Juan, PR 00917
Ph: (787)766-5572
Free: 800-669-8049
Fax: (787)766-5309
Co. E-mail: Francisco.marrero@sba.gov
URL: http://www.sba.gov/about-offices-content/2/
3143

62049 ■ U.S. Small Business Administration, Region 1
10 Causeway St., Ste. 812
Boston, MA 02222-1093
Ph: (617)565-8416
Fax: (617)565-8420
URL: http://www.sba.gov/localresources/regionalof-
fices/region1/index.html
Description: Serves Connecticut, Maine, Mas-
sachusetts, New Hampshire, Rhode Island, and
Vermont.

62050 ■ U.S. Small Business Administration, Region 1
10 Causeway St., Ste. 265A
Boston, MA 02222
Ph: (617)565-8416
Fax: (617)565-8420
URL: http://www.sba.gov/about-offices-content/3/
3070
Description: Serves Connecticut, Maine, Mas-
sachusetts, New Hampshire, Rhode Island, and
Vermont.

62051 ■ U.S. Small Business Administration, Region 2
26 Federal Plz., Ste. 3108
New York, NY 10278
Ph: (212)264-1450

Fax: (212)264-0038
URL: http://www.sba.gov/region2/index.html
Description: Serves New Jersey, New York, Puerto
Rico, and the Virgin Islands.

62052 ■ U.S. Small Business Administration, Region 2
26 Federal Plz., Ste. 3108
New York, NY 10278
Ph: (212)264-1450
Fax: (212)264-0038
URL: http://www.sba.gov/about-offices-content/3/
3071
Description: Serves New Jersey, New York, Puerto
Rico, and the Virgin Islands.

62053 ■ U.S. Small Business Administration, Region 3
1150 First Ave. Ste. 1001
King of Prussia, PA 19406
Ph: (610)382-3092
URL: http://www.sba.gov/localresources/regionalof-
fices/region3/index.html
Description: Serves Delaware, the District of Colum-
bia, Maryland, Pennsylvania, Virginia, and West
Virginia.

62054 ■ U.S. Small Business Administration, Region 3
1150 First Ave. Ste. 1001
King of Prussia, PA 19406
Ph: (610)382-3092
URL: http://www.sba.gov/about-offices-content/3/
3072
Description: Serves Delaware, the District of Colum-
bia, Maryland, Pennsylvania, Virginia, and West
Virginia.

62055 ■ U.S. Small Business Administration, Region 4
233 Peachtree St. NE, Ste. 1800
Atlanta, GA 30303
Ph: (404)331-4999
Fax: (404)331-2354
URL: http://www.sba.gov/region4/index.html
Description: Serves Alabama, Florida, Georgia,
Kentucky, Mississippi, North Carolina, South Carolina,
and Tennessee.

62056 ■ U.S. Small Business Administration, Region 4
233 Peachtree St. NE, Ste. 1800
Atlanta, GA 30303
Ph: (404)331-4999
Fax: (404)331-2354
URL: http://www.sba.gov/about-offices-content/3/
3073
Description: Serves Alabama, Florida, Georgia,
Kentucky, Mississippi, North Carolina, South Carolina,
and Tennessee.

62057 ■ U.S. Small Business Administration, Region 5
Citicorp Ctr., Ste. 1150
500 W. Madison St.
Chicago, IL 60606-2511
Ph: (312)353-0357
Fax: (312)353-3426
URL: http://www.sba.gov/region5/index.html
Description: Serves Illinois, Indiana, Michigan, Min-
nesota, Ohio, and Wisconsin.

62058 ■ U.S. Small Business Administration, Region 5
500 W. Madison St., Ste. 1150
Chicago, IL 60661
Ph: (312)353-0357
Fax: (312)353-3426
URL: http://www.sba.gov/about-offices-content/3/
3074
Description: Serves Illinois, Indiana, Michigan, Min-
nesota, Ohio, and Wisconsin.

62059 ■ U.S. Small Business Administration, Region 6
Dallas Regional Office
4300 Amon Carter Blvd., Ste. 108
Ft. Worth, TX 76155
Ph: (817)684-5581

Fax: (817)684-5588
URL: http://www.sba.gov/region6/index.html
Description: Serves Arkansas, Louisiana, New Mexico, Oklahoma, and Texas.

62060 ■ U.S. Small Business Administration, Region 6
Dallas Regional Office
4300 Amon Carter Blvd., Ste. 108
Ft. Worth, TX 76155
Ph: (817)684-5581
Fax: (817)684-5588
URL: http://www.sba.gov/about-offices-content/3/3075
Description: Serves Arkansas, Louisiana, New Mexico, Oklahoma, and Texas.

62061 ■ U.S. Small Business Administration, Region 7
Kansas City Regional Office
1000 Walnut, Ste. 530
Kansas City, MO 64106
Ph: (816)426-4840
Fax: (816)426-4848
URL: http://www.sba.gov/region7/index.html
Description: Serves Iowa, Kansas, Missouri, and Nebraska.

62062 ■ U.S. Small Business Administration, Region 7
Kansas City Regional Office
1000 Walnut, Ste. 530
Kansas City, MO 64106
Ph: (816)426-4840
Fax: (816)426-4848
URL: http://www.sba.gov/about-offices-content/3/3076
Description: Serves Iowa, Kansas, Missouri, and Nebraska.

62063 ■ U.S. Small Business Administration, Region 8
Denver regional Office
721 19th St., Ste. 400
Denver, CO 80202-2599
Ph: (303)844-0500
Fax: (303)844-0506
URL: http://www.sba.gov/region8/index.html
Description: Serves Colorado, Montana, North Dakota, South Dakota, Utah, and Wyoming.

62064 ■ U.S. Small Business Administration, Region 8
Denver Regional Office
721 19th St., Ste. 400
Denver, CO 80202-2599
Ph: (303)844-0500
Fax: (303)844-0506
URL: http://www.sba.gov/about-offices-content/3/3077
Description: Serves Colorado, Montana, North Dakota, South Dakota, Utah, and Wyoming.

62065 ■ U.S. Small Business Administration, Region 9
Los Angeles Regional Office
330 N. Brand Blvd., Ste. 1270
Glendale, CA 91203-2304
Ph: (818)552-3434
Fax: (818)552-3440
URL: http://www.sba.gov/region9/index.html
Description: Serves American Samoa, Arizona, California, Guam, Hawaii, Nevada, and the Trust Territory of the Pacific Islands.

62066 ■ U.S. Small Business Administration, Region 9
455 Market St., Ste. 600
San Francisco, CA 94105
Ph: (818)552-3434
Fax: (818)552-3440
URL: http://www.sba.gov/about-offices-content/3/3078
Description: Serves American Samoa, Arizona, California, Guam, Hawaii, Nevada, and the Trust Territory of the Pacific Islands.

62067 ■ U.S. Small Business Administration, Region 10
Seattle Regional Office
2401 4th Ave., Ste. 400
Seattle, WA 98121
Ph: (206)553-5676
Fax: (206)553-4155
URL: http://www.sba.gov/region10/index.html
Description: Serves Alaska, Idaho, Oregon, and Washington.

62068 ■ U.S. Small Business Administration, Region 10
Seattle Regional Office
2401 4th Ave., Ste. 400
Seattle, WA 98121
Ph: (206)553-5676
Fax: (206)553-4155
URL: http://www.sba.gov/about-offices-content/3/3079
Description: Serves Alaska, Idaho, Oregon, and Washington.

62069 ■ U.S. Small Business Administration - Research and Statistics - Office of Economic Research
409 3rd St. SW
Washington, DC 20416
Ph: (202)205-6533
Fax: (202)206-6928
URL: http://www.sba.gov/advo/research/

62070 ■ U.S. Small Business Administration - Rhode Island District Office
380 Westminster Mall, Rm. 511
Providence, RI 02903
Ph: (401)528-4561
Fax: (401)528-4539
URL: http://www.sba.gov/ri

62071 ■ U.S. Small Business Administration - Richmond District Office
Federal Bldg.
400 N. 8th St., Ste. 1150
Richmond, VA 23219-4829
Ph: (804)771-2400
Fax: (804)771-2764
Co. E-mail: richmond.va@sba.gov
URL: http://www.sba.gov/va

62072 ■ U.S. Small Business Administration - Richmond District Office
Federal Bldg.
400 N. 8th St., Ste. 1150
Richmond, VA 23219-4829
Ph: (804)771-2400
Fax: (804)771-2764
Co. E-mail: Richmond.va@sba.gov
URL: http://www.sba.gov/about-offices-content/2/3155

62073 ■ U.S. Small Business Administration - Rochester Office
100 State St., Rm. 410
Rochester, NY 14614
Ph: (585)263-6700
Fax: (585)263-3146
URL: http://www.sba.gov/about-offices-content/2/3134

62074 ■ U.S. Small Business Administration - Sacramento Branch Office
650 Capitol Mall, Ste. 7-500
Sacramento, CA 95814
Ph: (916)930-3700
Fax: (916)930-3737
URL: http://www.sba.gov/localresources/district/ca/sacr/index.html

62075 ■ U.S. Small Business Administration - Sacramento Branch Office
6501 Sylvan Rd., Ste. 100
Citrus Heights, CA 95610
Ph: (916)735-1700
Fax: (916)735-1719
URL: http://www.sba.gov/about-offices-content/2/3100

62076 ■ U.S. Small Business Administration - St. Croix Post of Duty
Almeric L. Christian Federal Bldg. & U.S. Court House
3013 Estate Golden Rock, Room 167
St. Croix, VI 00830
Ph: (340)778-5380
Free: 800-669-8049
URL: http://www.sba.gov/localresources/district/pr/index.html

62077 ■ U.S. Small Business Administration - St. Croix Post of Duty
Almeric L. Christian Federal Bldg. & U.S. Court House
3013 Estate Golden Rock, Room 167
St. Croix, VI 00830
Ph: (340)718-5381
Free: 800-669-8049
URL: http://www.sba.gov/about-offices-content/2/3143

62078 ■ U.S. Small Business Administration - St. Louis District Office
200 N. Broadway, Ste. 1500
St. Louis, MO 63102
Ph: (314)539-6600
Fax: (314)539-3785
URL: http://www.sba.gov/localresources/district/mo/stlouis/index.html

62079 ■ U.S. Small Business Administration - St. Louis District Office
200 N. Broadway, Ste. 1500
St. Louis, MO 63102
Ph: (314)539-6600
Fax: (314)539-3785
URL: http://www.sba.gov/mo

62080 ■ U.S. Small Business Administration - St. Louis District Office
1222 Spruce St., Ste. 10.103
St. Louis, MO 63103
Ph: (314)539-6600
Fax: (314)539-3785
URL: http://www.sba.gov/about-offices-content/2/3124

62081 ■ U.S. Small Business Administration - St. Thomas Post of Duty
3800 Crown Bay
Virgin Islands Maritime Bldg.
St. Thomas, VI 00802
Ph: (340)774-8530
Fax: (340)776-2312

62082 ■ U.S. Small Business Administration - St. Thomas Post of Duty
3800 Crown Bay
Virgin Islands Maritime Bldg.
St. Thomas, VI 00802
Fax: (340)776-2312

62083 ■ U.S. Small Business Administration - Salt Lake City District Office
125 S. State St., Rm. 2227
Salt Lake City, UT 84138-1195
Ph: (801)524-3209
Fax: (801)524-4160
URL: http://www.sba.gov/localresources/district/ut/index.html

62084 ■ U.S. Small Business Administration - Salt Lake City District Office
125 S. State St., Rm. 2227
Salt Lake City, UT 84138-1195
Ph: (801)524-3209
Fax: (801)524-4160
Co. E-mail: Stanley.nakano@sba.gov
URL: http://www.sba.gov/about-offices-content/2/3154

62085 ■ U.S. Small Business Administration - San Antonio District Office
17319 San Pedro, Ste. 200
San Antonio, TX 78232-1411
Ph: (210)403-5900

Fax: (210)403-5936
URL: http://www.sba.gov/localresources/district/tx/
sanantonio/

62086 ■ U.S. Small Business Administration -
San Antonio District Office
615 E. Houston St., Ste. 298
San Antonio, TX 78205
Ph: (210)403-5900
Fax: (210)403-5936
Co. E-mail: sado.email@sba.gov
URL: http://www.sba.gov/about-offices-content/2/
3153

62087 ■ U.S. Small Business Administration -
San Diego District Office
550 W. C St., Ste. 550
San Diego, CA 92101
Ph: (619)557-7250
Fax: (619)727-4883
URL: http://www.sba.gov/localresources/district/ca/
sandiego/

62088 ■ U.S. Small Business Administration -
San Diego District Office
San Diego District Office
550 W. C St., Ste. 550
San Diego, CA 92101
Ph: (619)557-7250
Fax: (619)727-4883
URL: http://www.sba.gov/ca/sandiego

62089 ■ U.S. Small Business Administration -
San Diego District Office
550 W. C St., Ste. 550
San Diego, CA 92101
Ph: (619)557-7250
Fax: (619)557-5894
URL: http://www.sba.gov/about-offices-content/2/
3101

62090 ■ U.S. Small Business Administration -
San Francisco District Office
455 Market St., 6th Fl.
San Francisco, CA 94105-2420
Ph: (415)744-6820
Fax: (415)744-6812
URL: http://www.sba.gov/localresources/district/ca/sf/

62091 ■ U.S. Small Business Administration -
San Francisco District Office
455 Market St., Ste. 600
San Francisco, CA 94105-2420
Ph: (415)744-6820
Fax: (415)744-6812
URL: http://www.sba.gov/about-offices-content/2/
3102

62092 ■ U.S. Small Business Administration -
Santa Ana District Office
200 W. Santa Ana Blvd., Ste. 700
Santa Ana, CA 92701
Ph: (714)550-7420
Fax: (714)550-0191
URL: http://www.sba.gov/localresources/district/ca/
santa/index.html

62093 ■ U.S. Small Business Administration -
Santa Ana District Office
200 W. Santa Ana Blvd., Ste. 700
Santa Ana, CA 92701
Ph: (714)550-7420
Fax: (714)550-7409
Co. E-mail: adalberto.quijada@sba.gov
URL: http://www.sba.gov/about-offices-content/2/
3103

62094 ■ U.S. Small Business Administration -
SBA/Greater El Paso Chamber of Commerce -
Business Information Center
10 Civic Center Plz.
El Paso, TX 79901
Ph: (915)534-0500
Fax: (915)534-0510
Co. E-mail: gepccreceptionist@elpaso.org
URL: http://www.elpaso.org/

62095 ■ U.S. Small Business Administration -
SBA/Greater El Paso Chamber of Commerce -
Business Information Center
10 Civic Center Plz.
El Paso, TX 79901
Ph: (915)534-0500
Fax: (915)534-0510
Co. E-mail: gepccreceptionist@elpaso.org
URL: http://www.elpaso.org/

62096 ■ U.S. Small Business Administration -
SBA/NationsBank/MBDA/BellSouth/College of
Charleston - Business Information Center
Small Business Resource Center
284 King St.
Charleston, SC 29401
Ph: (843)853-3900
Fax: (843)853-2529

62097 ■ U.S. Small Business Administration -
SBA/NationsBank/MBDA/BellSouth/College of
Charleston - Business Information Center
Small Business Resource Center
284 King St.
Charleston, SC 29401

62098 ■ U.S. Small Business Administration -
SBA/NationsBank/MBDA - Business
Information Center (Nashville, Tennessee)
Small Business Resource Center
3401 W. End Ave., Ste. 110
Nashville, TN 37203-1609

62099 ■ U.S. Small Business Administration -
Seattle District Office
2401 4th Ave., Ste. 450
Seattle, WA 98121
Ph: (206)553-7310
URL: http://www.sba.gov/wa/seattle/index.html

62100 ■ U.S. Small Business Administration -
Seattle District Office
Seattle District Office
2401 4th Ave., Ste. 450
Seattle, WA 98121
Ph: (206)553-7310
URL: http://www.sba.gov/wa/seattle/index.html

62101 ■ U.S. Small Business Administration -
Seattle District Office
2401 4th Ave., Ste. 450
Seattle, WA 98121
Ph: (206)553-7310
URL: http://www.sba.gov/about-offices-content/2/
3157

62102 ■ U.S. Small Business Administration -
Sioux Falls District Office
South Dakota District Office
2329 N. Career Ave., Ste. 105
Sioux Falls, SD 57107
Ph: (605)330-4243
Fax: (605)330-4215
URL: http://www.sba.gov/about-offices-content/2/
3146

62103 ■ U.S. Small Business Administration -
South Dakota District Office
South Dakota District Office
2329 N. Career Ave., Ste. 105
Sioux Falls, SD 57107
Ph: (605)330-4243
Fax: (605)330-4215
URL: http://www.sba.gov/localresources/district/sd/
index.html

62104 ■ U.S. Small Business Administration -
Space and Naval Warfare Systems
4301 Pacific Hwy.
San Diego, CA 92110-3127
Ph: (619)727-4868
Fax: (202)481-4152
Co. E-mail: linda.coakley@sba.gov

62105 ■ U.S. Small Business Administration -
Space and Naval Warfare Systems
4301 Pacific Hwy.
San Diego, CA 92110-3127
Ph: (619)727-4868

Fax: (202)481-4152
Co. E-mail: linda.coakley@sba.gov

62106 ■ U.S. Small Business Administration -
Spokane Branch Office
801 W. Riverside, Ste. 200
Spokane, WA 99201
Ph: (509)353-2800
Fax: (509)747-0077
URL: http://www.sba.gov/wa/spokane/

62107 ■ U.S. Small Business Administration -
Spokane Regional Chamber of Commerce -
Business Information Center - Spokane
Branch Office
801 W. Riverside, Ste. 444
Spokane, WA 99201
Ph: (509)353-2800
Fax: (509)747-0077
URL: http://www.sba.gov/about-offices-content/2/
3157

62108 ■ U.S. Small Business Administration -
Spokane, WA Branch Office
Spokane Branch Office
801 W. Riverside Ave., Ste. 200
Spokane, WA 99201
Ph: (509)353-2800
URL: http://www.sba.gov/wa/spokane/
Description: Serving Eastern Washington and
Northern Idaho.

62109 ■ U.S. Small Business Administration -
Spokane, WA Branch Office
801 W. Riverside Ave., Ste. 444
Spokane, WA 99201
Ph: (509)353-2800
URL: http://www.sba.gov/about-offices-content/2/
3157
Description: Serving Eastern Washington and
Northern Idaho.

62110 ■ U.S. Small Business Administration -
Springfield, IL, Branch Office
511 W. Capitol St., Ste. 302
Springfield, IL 62704
Ph: (217)492-4416
Fax: (217)492-4867

62111 ■ U.S. Small Business Administration -
Springfield, IL, Branch Office
3330 Ginger Creek Rd., Ste. B
Springfield, IL 62711
Ph: (217)793-5020
Fax: (217)793-5025
URL: http://www.sba.gov/about-offices-content/2/
3161

62112 ■ U.S. Small Business Administration -
Springfield, MA, Branch Office
STCC Technology Park
One Federal St., Bldg. 101-R
Springfield, MA 01105
Ph: (413)785-0484
Fax: (413)785-0267

62113 ■ U.S. Small Business Administration -
Springfield, MA, Branch Office
STCC Technology Park
One Federal St., Bldg. 101-R
Springfield, MA 01105
Ph: (413)785-0484
Fax: (413)785-0267
Co. E-mail: robert.nelson@sba.gov
URL: http://www.sba.gov/about-offices-content/2/
3162

62114 ■ U.S. Small Business Administration -
Springfield, MO, Branch Office
830 E. Primrose, Ste. 102
Springfield, MO 65807
Ph: (417)890-8501
URL: http://www.sba.gov/localresources/district/mo/
kansas/index.html

62115 ■ U.S. Small Business Administration -
Springfield, MO, Branch Office
830 E. Primrose, Ste. 101
Springfield, MO 65807

Ph: (417)890-8501
URL: http://www.sba.gov/about-offices-content/2/3123

62116 ■ U.S. Small Business Administration - Sunbelt U.S. Export Assistance Center (Miami, Florida)
5835 Blue Lagoon Dr., Ste. 203
Miami, FL 33132
Ph: (305)526-7425
Fax: (305)526-7434
Co. E-mail: mary.hernandez@sba.gov
URL: http://www.sba.gov/aboutsba/sbaprograms/internationaltrade/useac/
Description: Serves Florida.

62117 ■ U.S. Small Business Administration - Syracuse District Office
401 S. Salina St., 5th Fl.
Syracuse, NY 13202-2415
Ph: (315)471-9393
Fax: (315)471-9288
URL: http://www.sba.gov/localresources/district/ny/syracuse/

62118 ■ U.S. Small Business Administration - Syracuse District Office
224 Harrison St., 5th Fl.
Syracuse, NY 13202
Ph: (315)471-9393
Fax: (315)471-9288
URL: http://www.sba.gov/about-offices-content/2/3136

62119 ■ U.S. Small Business Administration - U.S. Export Assistance Center (Atlanta, Georgia)
75 5th St., NW Ste. 1055
Atlanta, GA 30308
Ph: (404)897-6089
Fax: (404)897-6085
Co. E-mail: raymond.gibeau@sba.gov
URL: http://www.sba.gov/aboutsba/sbaprograms/internationaltrade/useac/
URL(s): www.sba.gov/content/us-export-assistance-centers. **Description:** Serves Georgia, Alabama, Kentucky, Tennessee, Mississippi. **Telecommunication Services:** sandro.murtas@sba.gov.

62120 ■ U.S. Small Business Administration - U.S. Export Assistance Center (Baltimore, Maryland)
300 W. Pratt St., Ste. 300
Baltimore, MD 21201
Ph: (202)205-6426
Fax: (202)205-7272
URL: http://www.sba.gov/aboutsba/sbaprograms/internationaltrade/useac/
Description: Serves Maryland, Virginia, West Virginia, and District of Columbia.

62121 ■ U.S. Small Business Administration - U.S. Export Assistance Center (Baltimore, Maryland)
300 W. Pratt St., Ste. 300
Baltimore, MD 21201
Ph: (202)205-6426
Fax: (202)205-7272
Co. E-mail: patrick.tunison@sba.gov
URL: http://archive.sba.gov/aboutsba/sbaprograms/internationaltrade/useac/index.html
Description: Serves Maryland, Virginia, West Virginia, and District of Columbia.

62122 ■ U.S. Small Business Administration - U.S. Export Assistance Center (Boston, Massachusetts)
SBA
JFK Federal Bldg., Ste. 1826A
55 New Sudbury St.
Boston, MA 02203
Ph: (617)565-4305

Fax: (617)565-4313
Co. E-mail: john.joyce@mail.doc.gov
URL: http://www.sba.gov/aboutsba/sbaprograms/internationaltrade/useac/
Description: Serves Maine, Vermont, New Hampshire, Massachusetts, Connecticut, and Rhode Island.

62123 ■ U.S. Small Business Administration - U.S. Export Assistance Center (Boston, Massachusetts)
JFK Federal Bldg., Ste. 1826A
55 New Sudbury St.
Boston, MA 02203
Ph: (617)565-4305
Fax: (617)565-4313
Co. E-mail: john.joyce@sba.gov
URL: http://www.sba.gov/content/us-export-assistance-centers
Description: Serves Maine, Vermont, New Hampshire, Massachusetts, Connecticut, and Rhode Island.

62124 ■ U.S. Small Business Administration - U.S. Export Assistance Center (Chicago, Illinois)
200 Adams St., Ste. 2450
Chicago, IL 60606
Ph: (312)353-8065
Fax: (312)353-8098
Co. E-mail: john.nevell@sba.gov
URL: http://www.sba.gov/aboutsba/sbaprograms/internationaltrade/useac/
Description: Serves Wisconsin, Illinois, and Indiana.

62125 ■ U.S. Small Business Administration - U.S. Export Assistance Center (Chicago, Illinois)
200 W. Adams St., Ste. 2450
Chicago, IL 60606
Ph: (312)353-8065
Fax: (202)481-2281
Co. E-mail: john.nevell@sba.gov
URL: http://www.sba.gov/content/us-export-assistance-centers
Description: Serves Wisconsin, Illinois, and Indiana.

62126 ■ U.S. Small Business Administration - U.S. Export Assistance Center (Cleveland, Ohio)
600 Superior Ave. E., Ste. 700
Cleveland, OH 44114
Ph: (216)522-4731
Fax: (216)522-2235
Co. E-mail: patrick.hayes@sba.gov
URL: http://www.sba.gov/aboutsba/sbaprograms/internationaltrade/useac/

62127 ■ U.S. Small Business Administration - U.S. Export Assistance Center (Cleveland, Ohio)
600 Superior Ave., Ste. 700
Cleveland, OH 44114
Ph: (216)522-4731
Fax: (216)522-2235
Co. E-mail: patrick.hayes@sba.gov
URL: http://www.sba.gov/content/us-export-assistance-centers

62128 ■ U.S. Small Business Administration - U.S. Export Assistance Center (Denver, Colorado)
1625 Broadway Ave., Ste. 680
Denver, CO 80202
Ph: (303)844-6623
Fax: (303)844-5651
Co. E-mail: dennis.chrisbaum@.sba.gov
URL: http://www.sba.gov/aboutsba/sbaprograms/internationaltrade/useac/
Description: Serves Wyoming, Utah, Colorado, and New Mexico.

62129 ■ U.S. Small Business Administration - U.S. Export Assistance Center (Denver, Colorado)
1625 Broadway Ave., Ste. 680
Denver, CO 80202
Ph: (303)844-6623

Fax: (202)481-0540
Co. E-mail: bryson.patterson@.sba.gov
URL: http://www.sba.gov/content/us-export-assistance-centers
Description: Serves Wyoming, Utah, Colorado, and New Mexico.

62130 ■ U.S. Small Business Administration - U.S. Export Assistance Center (Detroit, Michigan)
8109 E. Jefferson, Ste. 110
Detroit, MI 48214
Ph: (313)226-3670
Fax: (313)226-3657
Co. E-mail: john.ogara@sba.gov
URL: http://www.sba.gov/aboutsba/sbaprograms/internationaltrade/useac/
Description: Serves Michigan.

62131 ■ U.S. Small Business Administration - U.S. Export Assistance Center (Detroit, Michigan)
8109 E. Jefferson, Ste. 110
Detroit, MI 48214
Ph: (313)320-1226
Co. E-mail: john.ogara@sba.gov
URL: http://www.sba.gov/content/us-export-assistance-centers
Description: Serves Michigan.

62132 ■ U.S. Small Business Administration - U.S. Export Assistance Center (Miami, Florida)
5835 Blue Lagoon Dr., Ste. 203
Miami, FL 33132
Ph: (305)526-7425
Fax: (202)481-4471
Co. E-mail: mary.hernandez@sba.gov
URL: http://www.sba.gov/content/us-export-assistance-centers
Description: Serves Florida.

62133 ■ U.S. Small Business Administration - U.S. Export Assistance Center (New York, New York)
33 Whitehall St., 22nd Fl.
New York, NY 10004
Ph: (212)809-2645
Fax: (212)809-2687
Co. E-mail: toni.corsini@mail.doc.gov
URL: http://www.sba.gov/aboutsba/sbaprograms/internationaltrade/useac/

62134 ■ U.S. Small Business Administration - U.S. Export Assistance Center (New York, New York)
33 Whitehall St., 22nd Fl.
New York, NY 10004
Ph: (212)809-2645
Fax: (212)809-2687
Co. E-mail: toni.corsini@trade.gov
URL: http://www.sba.gov/content/us-export-assistance-centers

62135 ■ U.S. Small Business Administration - U.S. Export Assistance Center (Newport Beach, California)
3300 Irvine Ave., Ste. 305
Newport Beach, CA 92660-3198
Ph: (949)660-1688
Fax: (949)660-1338
Co. E-mail: martin.selander@sba.gov
URL: http://www.sba.gov/aboutsba/sbaprograms/internationaltrade/useac/
Description: Serves Southern California, Nevada, Arizona, and Hawaii.

62136 ■ U.S. Small Business Administration - U.S. Export Assistance Center (Newport Beach, California)
3300 Irvine Ave., Ste. 305
Newport Beach, CA 92660-3198
Ph: (949)660-1688

Fax: (949)660-1338
Co. E-mail: martin.selander@sba.gov
URL: http://archive.sba.gov/aboutsba/sbaprograms/
internationaltrade/useac/index.html
Description: Serves Southern California, Nevada,
Arizona, and Hawaii.

**62137 ■ U.S. Small Business Administration -
U.S. Export Assistance Center (Philadelphia,
Pennsylvania)**
The Curtis Center
601 Walnut St., Ste. 580 W.
Philadelphia, PA 19106
Ph: (215)597-6110
Fax: (215)597-6123
Co. E-mail: robert.elsas@mail.doc.gov
URL: http://www.sba.gov/aboutsba/sbaprograms/
internationaltrade/useac/

**62138 ■ U.S. Small Business Administration -
U.S. Export Assistance Center (Philadelphia,
Pennsylvania)**
The Curtis Center
601 Walnut St., Ste. 580 W.
Philadelphia, PA 19106
Ph: (215)597-6110
Fax: (202)481-5216
Co. E-mail: Robert.elsas@trade.gov
URL: http://www.sba.gov/content/us-export-
assistance-centers

**62139 ■ U.S. Small Business Administration -
U.S. Export Assistance Center (St. Louis,
Missouri)**
8235 Forsyth Blvd., Ste. 520
St. Louis, MO 63105
Ph: (314)425-3304
Fax: (314)425-3381
Co. E-mail: john.blum@mail.doc.gov
URL: http://www.sba.gov/aboutsba/sbaprograms/
internationaltrade/useac/
Description: Serves South Dakota, Nebraska, Iowa,
Kansas, and Missouri.

**62140 ■ U.S. Small Business Administration -
U.S. Export Assistance Center (St. Louis,
Missouri)**
8235 Forsyth Blvd., Ste. 520
St. Louis, MO 63105
Ph: (314)425-3304
Fax: (314)425-3381
Co. E-mail: john.blum@trade.gov
URL: http://www.sba.gov/content/us-export-
assistance-centers
Description: Serves South Dakota, Nebraska, Iowa,
Kansas, and Missouri.

**62141 ■ U.S. Small Business Administration -
U.S. Export Assistance Center (Seattle,
Washington)**
2601 4th Ave., Ste. 320
Seattle, WA 98121
Ph: (206)553-0051
Fax: (206)553-7253
Co. E-mail: pru.balatero@mail.doc.gov
URL: http://www.sba.gov/aboutsba/sbaprograms/
internationaltrade/useac/

**62142 ■ U.S. Small Business Administration -
U.S. Export Assistance Center (Seattle,
Washington)**
2001 6th Ave., Ste. 2610
Seattle, WA 98121
Ph: (206)553-0051
Fax: (206)553-7253
Co. E-mail: pru.balatero@trade.gov
URL: http://www.sba.gov/content/us-export-
assistance-centers

**62143 ■ U.S. Small Business Administration -
Vermont District Office**
Vermont District Office
87 State St., Rm. 205
Montpelier, VT 05601-0605
Ph: (802)828-4422
Fax: (802)828-4485
URL: http://www.sba.gov/vt/

**62144 ■ U.S. Small Business Administration -
Washington DC, District Office**
740 15th St. NW, Ste. 300
Washington, DC 20005-3544
Ph: (202)272-0345
Fax: (202)272-0344
URL: http://www.sba.gov/localresources/district/dc/
index.html

**62145 ■ U.S. Small Business Administration -
Washington, DC, District Office**
740 15th St. NW, Ste. 300
Washington, DC 20005-3544
Ph: (202)272-0345
Fax: (202)272-0344
URL: http://www.sba.gov/about-offices-content/2/
3106

**62146 ■ U.S. Small Business Administration -
Washington D.C. District Office - Associate
Deputy Administrator for Economic
Development**
740 15th St., NW, Ste. 300
Washington, DC 20005-3544
Ph: (202)205-0345
Co. E-mail: joseph.loddo@sba.gov
URL: http://www.sba.gov/localresources/district/dc/
index.html

**62147 ■ U.S. Small Business Administration -
Washington D.C. District Office - Associate
Deputy Administrator for Government
Contracting and Minority Enterprise
Development**
740 15th St., NW, Ste. 300
Washington, DC 20005-3544
Ph: (202)205-0345
URL: http://www.sba.gov/localresources/district/dc/
index.html

**62148 ■ U.S. Small Business Administration -
Washington D.C. District Office - Business
Information Center (Washington, District of
Columbia)**
Washington Metropolitan Area District Office
740 15th St. NW, Ste. 300
Washington, DC 20005-3544
Ph: (202)272-0345
URL: http://www.sba.gov/localresources/district/dc/
index.html

**62149 ■ U.S. Small Business Administration -
West Palm Beach Post of Duty - South
Florida District Office**
1320 S. Dixie Hwy., 501
Coral Gables, FL 33146-2911
Ph: (305)536-5521
Fax: (305)536-5058

**62150 ■ U.S. Small Business Administration -
West Palm Beach Post of Duty - South
Florida District Office**
1320 S. Dixie Hwy., 501
Coral Gables, FL 33146-2911
Ph: (305)536-5521
Fax: (305)536-5058

**62151 ■ U.S. Small Business Administration -
Wichita District Office**
271 W. 3rd St. N., Ste. 2500
Wichita, KS 67202
Ph: (316)269-6616
Fax: (316)269-6499
URL: http://www.sba.gov/localresources/district/ks/
index.html

**62152 ■ U.S. Small Business Administration -
Wichita District Office**
271 W. 3rd St. N., Ste. 2500
Wichita, KS 67202
Ph: (316)269-6566
Fax: (316)269-6499
URL: http://www.sba.gov/about-offices-content/2/
3117

**62153 ■ U.S. Small Business Administration -
Wilkes-Barre Branch Office**
7 N. Wilkes-Barre Blvd., Ste. 407
Wilkes Barre, PA 18702
Ph: (570)826-6497
Fax: (570)826-6287

**62154 ■ U.S. Small Business Administration -
Wilkes-Barre Branch Office**
7 N. Wilkes-Barre Blvd., Ste. 407
Wilkes Barre, PA 18702

**62155 ■ U.S. Small Business Administration -
Wilmington Branch Office**
1007 N. Orange St., Ste. 1120
Wilmington, DE 19801-1232
Ph: (302)573-6294
Fax: (302)573-6060
URL: http://www.sba.gov/about-offices-content/2/
3107

**62156 ■ U.S. Small Business Administration -
Wisconsin District Office**
Wisconsin District Office
740 Regent St., Ste. 100
Madison, WI 53715
Ph: (608)441-5263
Fax: (608)441-5541
URL: http://www.sba.gov/wi/

**62157 ■ U.S. Small Business Administration -
WVHTC Foundation - Business Information
Center**
1000 Technology Dr., Ste. 1000
Fairmont, WV 26554
Ph: (304)366-2577
Fax: (304)366-2699
Co. E-mail: info@wvhtf.org
URL: http://www.wvhtf.org/

**62158 ■ U.S. Small Business Administration -
WVHTC Foundation - Business Information
Center**
1000 Technology Dr., Ste. 1000
Fairmont, WV 26554
Ph: (304)366-2577
Free: 877-363-5482
Fax: (304)366-2699
Co. E-mail: info@wvhtf.org
URL: http://www.wvhtf.org/

HEADQUARTERS

**62159 ■ Agency for International
Development (AID) - Office of Small and
Disadvantaged Business Utilization - Minority
Resource Center**
Ronald Reagan Bldg.
1300 Pennsylvania Ave., NW, Ste. 5.8C
Washington, DC 20523
Ph: (202)712-1500
Fax: (202)216-3065
Co. E-mail: osdbu@usaid.gov
URL: http://www.usaid.gov/business/small_business/
Description: A small business advocacy and advisory
office with the responsibility for ensuring that these
enterprises receive access to USAID programs. The
office maintains the USAID Consultant Registry
Information System (ACRIS) and publishes The
Guide to Doing Business with the Agency for Interna-
tional Development.

**62160 ■ Environmental Protection Agency
(EPA) - Office of Small Business Programs**
1200 Pennsylvania Ave. NW
Mail Code 1230T
Washington, DC 20460
Ph: (202)566-2075
URL: http://www.epa.gov/osdbu
Description: The Environmental Protection Agency's
Office of Small and Disadvantaged Business Utilization performs the following duties: provides a convenient way for small businesses to access the EPA;
facilitates communication between small businesses
and the EPA; helps small businesses understand and
comply with environmental regulations; investigates
and resolves individual small business disputes with
the EPA; and works with EPA personnel to increase

their understanding of small businesses in the development and enforcement of environmental regulations. Provides procurement information as it regards to small businesses, small and disadvantaged businesses, minority-owned businesses, and women-owned businesses.

62161 ■ Executive Office of the President - Office of Management and Budget - Office of Federal Procurement Policy
725 17th St. NW
Washington, DC 20503
Ph: (202)395-3080
Fax: (202)395-3888
URL: http://www.whitehouse.gov/omb/

62162 ■ Export-Import Bank of the United States
811 Vermont Ave. NW
Washington, DC 20571
Ph: (202)565-3946
Free: 800-565-3946
Fax: (202)565-3931
URL: http://www.exim.gov/
Description: The Export-Import Bank of the United States assists in financing and in facilitating the export sales of U.S. goods and services. Programs directed at small businesses include pre-export guarantees to assist small and medium-sized businesses in obtaining working capital from financial entities for export-related activities such as inventory purchases or the manufacture of goods; a small business insurance policy, that assists in providing risk protection on export receivables for companies just beginning to export or with limited export volumes; and loan and guarantee programs that enable U.S. banks to offer medium-term, fixed-rate export loans to finance the sales of products and services produced or performed by small businesses. Nonfinancial assistance includes the operation of the Eximbank Hotline (800-565-EXIM). Through this service, Eximbank International Business Development Division is available to assist more business owners in developing competitive export financing plans, answer questions regarding Eximbank financing programs, and explain how to apply for Eximbank assistance, where to locate credit insurance, or how to make maximum use of complementary export programs offered by other U.S. government agencies. In addition, Eximbank offers monthly seminars in Washington, D.C., to help firms new to exporting understand the programs available from the federal government.

62163 ■ Federal Communications Commission (FCC) - Office of Communications Business Opportunities
445 12th St. SW
Washington, DC 20554
Ph: (202)418-0990
Free: 888-225-5322
Fax: (866)418-0235
Co. E-mail: OCBOinfo@fcc.gov
URL: http://www.fcc.gov/ocbo

62164 ■ Federal Trade Commission (FTC) - Procurement and General Services Division
600 Pennsylvania Ave. NW
Washington, DC 20580
Ph: (202)326-2258
Fax: (202)326-2502
URL: http://www.ftc.gov/os/ar97/manage.shtm
Description: The Federal Trade Commission works to preserve a free marketplace by acting as the advocate of consumers and by resisting efforts of any one group to profit at the expense of the general public. The FTC maintains three bureaus and ten regional offices through which to carry out its responsibilities: the Bureau of Competition seeks to prevent business practices that restrain competition by investigating alleged violations, by recommending enforcement action when appropriate, and by participating in an advocacy program; the Bureau of Consumer Protection helps to preserve competition by prohibiting deceptive claims or practices that interfere with the public's ability to make informed purchasing decisions; and the Bureau of Economics offers support to these activities by ensuring that the FTC's actions are based on sound economic prin-

ciples. FTC regional offices conduct investigations and litigations, offer advice, recommend cases, provide outreach services, sponsor conferences, and coordinate activities with local, state, and regional authorities.

62165 ■ International Trade Administration (ITA) - Office of Public Affairs
Herbert Clark Hoover Bldg., Rm. 3416
1401 Constitution Ave., NW
Washington, DC 20230
Ph: (202)482-3809
Free: 800-872-8723
Fax: (202)482-4821
Co. E-mail: public_affairs@ita.doc.gov
URL: http://trade.gov/press/index.asp
Description: The International Trade Administration's domestic and overseas programs are designed to stimulate the expansion of U.S. exports. Major programs include export counseling and assistance; promotion of U.S. products abroad; coordination and conduct of overseas trade missions; support for the Export Trading Company formation; and management of federal participation in international expositions held in the United States. The ITA gathers, analyzes, and disseminates commercially usable trade and marketing information, including advice on marketing opportunities abroad; information about government assistance available for expanding trade with other nations; location of needed materials and resources; and advice on international trade policy and tariff questions. The ITA operates a network of 48 U.S. and foreign Commercial Service district offices through which to carry out its programs. The ITA's information services, market research, and overseas promotion programs provide opportunities to introduce products abroad at small costs. The ITA, with its variety of low-cost marketing aids, also may assist small firms in locating overseas outlets for their products, namely agents, distributors, licensees, buyers, and suppliers.

62166 ■ National Aeronautics and Space Administration (NASA) - Office of Small Business Programs
NASA Headquarters, Rm. 2K39
300 E. St., SW
Washington, DC 20546-0001
Ph: (202)358-2088
Fax: (202)358-3261
Co. E-mail: smallbusiness@nasa.gov
URL: http://osdbu.nasa.gov
Description: The development and management of the National Aeronautics and Space Administration's programs to assist small businesses are administered by its Office of Small and Disadvantaged Business Utilization. Services include individual counseling sessions for business owners seeking advice on how to best pursue contracting opportunities at NASA. NASA's procurement program is decentralized, with procurements planned and accomplished by field installations that also maintain small and minority business specialists. NASA's Technology Utilization Program provides information and other assistance to small business owners seeking to apply the results of NASA research and development projects to new commercial products or processes.

62167 ■ National Credit Union Administration - Office of Small and Disadvantaged Business Utilization
1775 Duke St.
Alexandria, VA 22314-3428
Ph: (703)518-6300
Fax: (703)518-6661
URL: http://www.ncua.gov
Description: The National Credit Union Administration's Office of Small and Disadvantaged Business Utilization offers small businesses information and guidance on procurement procedures, how to be placed on a bidder's mailing list, and identification of both prime and subcontracting opportunities.

62168 ■ National Science Foundation - Office of Small and Disadvantaged Business Utilization
4201 Wilson Blvd., Rm. 550 S
Arlington, VA 22203
Ph: (703)292-7082

Fax: (703)292-9056
Co. E-mail: dsenich@nsf.gov
URL: http://www.nsf.gov/
Description: The National Science Foundation's Office of Small and Disadvantaged Business Utilization offers small businesses information and guidance on procurement procedures, how to be placed on a bidder's mailing list, and identification of both prime and subcontracting opportunities.

62169 ■ Securities and Exchange Commission (SEC) - Office of Small Business Policy - Small Business Ombudsman
100 F St., NE
Washington, DC 20549-0310
Ph: (202)551-3460
Co. E-mail: smallbusiness@sec.gov
URL: http://www.sec.gov/info/smallbus/reachsec.htm
Contact: William E. Toomey, Deputy Chief
Description: The Security and Exchange Commission's responsibilities under the securities laws are to protect investors and to ensure that capital markets operate in a fair and orderly manner. Nevertheless, the SEC believes that its regulations should not have the effect of inadvertently impairing capital formation by small businesses. Therefore the SEC has taken a number of steps to facilitate capital-raising by small businesses and to reduce undue regulatory burdens arising. from the federal securities laws. The SEC is in a continuous process of examining other ways to further aid in accomplishing these goals. The SEC's Office of Small Business Policy, for example, directs the commission's small business rulemaking initiatives. It also reviews and comments on the impact of SEC rule proposals on smaller issuers and serves as a liaison with Congressional committees, government agencies, and other groups concerned with small business.

62170 ■ Tennessee Valley Authority (TVA) - Minority Economic and Small Business Development
PO Box 292409
Nashville, TN 37229-2409
Ph: (615)232-6225
Co. E-mail: econdev@tva.com
URL: http://www.tvaed.com/bus_serv.htm
Description: The Tennessee Valley Authority maintains agency-wide Minority Economic Development initiatives that assist small minority and women-owned businesses (SMWOBs) that seek TVA business opportunities, as well as, the entire business community of the Valley. TVA's Economic Development organization provides capital, technical, and managerial assistance for SMWOBs, start-ups, retention and expansions. Assistance takes the form of revolving loan funds, public/private partnerships that administer training programs, and in-house technical assistance. Through its Procurement organizations, TVA encourages minority participation in prime and subcontracting opportunities. Its policy is to promote the full participation of SMWOBs in all of its procurement and contracting activities. Further, priority shall be given to fostering the economic development of the Valley through use of products and services of such firms located in the Valley region. TVA's commitment is to maximize participation through the development of mutually beneficial business relationships with these firms consistent with achieving the best value to TVA.

62171 ■ U.S. Department of Agriculture (USDA) - Office of Small and Disadvantaged Business Utilization
1400 Independence Ave., SW
South Bldg., Rm. 1085
Washington, DC 20250
Ph: (202)720-7117
Fax: (202)720-3001
URL: http://www.usda.gov/osdbu
Description: The USDA's Office of Small and Disadvantaged Business Utilization offers information and other services to minority-owned, women-owned, and small and disadvantaged businesses to assist them in increasing and maintaining their participation in the department's procurement and other program opportunities. The department has 18 major procurement offices, and an additional 260 offices across the

country that offer procurement assistance to the small business community. These services are provided to increase the overall viability and competitiveness of businesses as part of maintaining an economically strong national industrial and commercial base. Emphasis is given to assisting firms that can contribute to revitalizing the nation's rural communities, improving the private agricultural sector's foreign trade competitiveness, and/or increasing the federal government's productivity. The department procures approximately $2 billion in products and services each year, $1 billion of which is awarded to minority-owned, women-owned, and small and disadvantaged businesses.

62172 ■ U.S. Department of Commerce - Minority Business Development Agency (MBDA)—Department of Commerce

Herbert Clark Hoover Bldg., Rm. 5053
1401 Constitution Ave. NW
Washington, DC 20230
Ph: (202)482-5061
Free: 888-324-1551
URL: http://www.mbda.gov

Description: The Minority Business Development Agency is the only federal agency specifically created to establish policies and programs to develop the U.S. minority business community. The agency's goal is to increase opportunities for racial and ethnic minorities to participate in the free enterprise system through the formation and development of competitive minority-owned and managed firms, with emphasis on private sector involvement and entrepreneurial self-reliance. To accomplish this goal, the agency coordinates the federal government's plans, programs, and operations that affect or may contribute to the establishment, preservation, and strengthening of minority business enterprise. The MBDA also promotes the mobilization of activities and resources of state and local governments, business and trade associations, universities, foundations, professional organizations, and other groups towards the growth of minority business enterprise, as well as facilitates the coordination of the efforts of these groups with those of federal departments and agencies. In addition, the MBDA acts as a center for the development, collection, summarization, and dissemination of information that will be helpful to persons and organizations throughout the United States in undertaking or promoting the establishment and successful operation of minority business enterprises. The agency also provides financial assistance to public and private organizations so that they may render technical and management assistance to minority business enterprises and defray all or part of the costs of pilot or demonstration projects conducted by public or private agencies or organizations that are designed to overcome the special problems of minority business enterprises. The MBDA sponsors a network of approximately 100 Minority Business Development Centers, located throughout the country in areas with the largest minority populations. The mission of the centers is to increase the formation of minority-owned firms, to expand existing minority-owned enterprises, and to minimize minority business failures. Counselors at each center provide management, marketing, and technical assistance to minority individuals wishing to start, expand, or improve their businesses. Socially or economically disadvantaged individuals eligible for assistance include, but are not limited to, Blacks, Hispanics, Native Americans, Eskimos, Aleuts, Asian Pacific Americans, Asian Indians, and Hasidic Jews. General referral assistance is provided free of charge to minority entrepreneurs seeking management, marketing, procurement, and financial assistance from federal, state, and local agencies, private institutions, and other sources. For a nominal fee counselors provide assistance to eligible individuals and firms in such areas as accounting, inventory control, bid estimating, bonding, personnel management, contract negotiations, and marketing. Each minority business development center develops and maintains a listing of existing minority-owned firms for inclusion in the agency's PROFILE National Minority Data Base. The PROFILE system is used by government and private industry purchasing officials to identify minority vendors qualified to supply the goods and services they need. Minority business owners wishing to register their firms in the PROFILE system may do so at no charge at any minority business development center. Counselors at the centers also identify both private and public sector sources of financing for minority-owned firms. They assist minority entrepreneurs with the preparation of financial packages and plans for submission to lenders for the purpose of financing business ventures. The centers cannot make or underwrite loans because the MBDA has no loan-making authority. In addition, center personnel match minority-owned firms with new business opportunities in domestic and foreign markets. They maintain contact with major corporations to identify business opportunities for minority-owned enterprises, and they utilize other federal, state, and local government agencies to identify contract opportunities and sources of financing to expand the minority business community. Center personnel also determine constraints to minority business development at the federal, state, and local levels and make recommendations for improvement. The centers are funded on a competitive basis. Applicants for the operation of these centers may be individuals, nonprofit organizations, private firms, state and local governments, Native American tribes, or educational institutions. The maximum federal funding of each center represents not more than 85 percent of the total cost of the project. Each center is expected to provide the other 15 percent.

62173 ■ U.S. Department of Commerce - Office of Small and Disadvantaged Business Utilization

Herbert Clark Hoover Bldg., Rm. 6411
14th St. & Constitution Ave. NW
Washington, DC 20230
Ph: (202)482-1472
Fax: (202)482-0501
Co. E-mail: ldesmukes@doc.gov
URL: http://www.osec.doc.gov/osdbu

62174 ■ U.S. Department of Commerce - U.S. Census Bureau

4600 Silver Hill Rd.
Washington, DC 20233
Ph: (301)763-4636
Free: 800-923-8282
URL: http://www.census.gov/

Description: The Census Bureau gathers and disseminates a wide variety of statistics about the people and economy of the United States. It is the principal source in the federal government for business information relating to manufacturers, retail trade, wholesale trade, construction trade, and services. These data are generated both from the regular five-year census programs and from annual, quarterly, and monthly survey programs. Data concerning the number of establishments, production, value added by manufacture, shipments, receipts, employees, payrolls--as well as other general and specific business statistics--are compiled and published periodically. Small business owners interested in learning more about the statistics available from the Census Bureau and how to use them may obtain a set of introductory materials and order forms by contacting Customer Services. Other information may be obtained from Census Bureau regional. In addition, the Census Bureau sponsors a state data center program, which provides (for a fee) local access to the bureau's computer products in all states, the District of Columbia, Puerto Rico, Guam, and the U.S. Virgin Islands.

62175 ■ U.S. Department of Defense (DOD) - Office of Small Business Programs

Crystal Gateway N., Ste. 406, W. Tower
201 12th St. S.
Washington, DC 20003-1427
Ph: (703)604-0157
Fax: (703)604-0025
Co. E-mail: OSBPinfo@osd.mil
URL: http://www.acq.osd.mil/sadbu

Description: One of the primary objectives of the Department of Defense (DOD) is to acquire weapons and materials that fully meet qualitative, quantitative, and delivery requirements at the lowest overall cost. Maximum emphasis is placed on full and free competition to achieve this objective, with equal opportunity to all interested, qualified suppliers to compete for defense contracts. The Department of Defense's military departments and defense agencies have contracting offices located throughout the United States. Each department and agency has an office of the director of small and disadvantaged business utilization. They also have small business specialists at each of their procurement and contract administration offices to assist small and disadvantaged businesses, women-owned businesses, minority-owned businesses, and firms to market their products and services with the DOD. These specialists can provide information and guidance on defense procurement procedures, placement on the solicitation mailing lists, and identification of both prime and subcontract opportunities.

62176 ■ U.S. Department of Education - Office of Small and Disadvantaged Business Utilization

Potomac Center Plaza, Rm. 7050
550 12th St. SW
Washington, DC 20202
Ph: (202)245-6300
Fax: (202)245-7304
URL: http://www.ed.gov/about/offices/list/ods/osdbu.html

Description: The Department of Education solicits proposals for the following services and materials: management consultating; program evaluation or surveys; computer-based projects; student testing materials; plus other professional services. In addition, federal funds may be used by schools, state agencies, and other recipients for the purchase of audiovisual and other types of equipment. Inquiries should be made to the applicable organization. The department also provides various publications to aid small businesses in their dealings. These publications include A Guide to U.S. Department of Education Programs. This annual guide provides the information necessary to begin the process of applying for funding from individual federal education programs. Another publication is Doing Business With the Department of Education. This guide is designed to provide business firms, small businesses, small disadvantaged businesses, and small disadvantaged subcontractors with basic information on contracting opportunities with the Department of Education. A 'Forecast of Contract Opportunities' is also available listing upcoming contracts, which is distributed by the OSDBU office.

62177 ■ U.S. Department of Energy, Headquarters (DOE) - Office of Small and Disadvantaged Business Utilization

1000 Independence Ave. SW, Rm. 5B-148
Washington, DC 20585
Ph: (202)586-7377
Fax: (202)586-5488
Co. E-mail: Small.Business@hq.doe.gov
URL: http://smallbusiness.doe.gov/

Description: The Department of Energy purchases a wide variety of materials, equipment, supplies, and support services at each DOE buying office. Small business/disadvantaged business specialists are located at DOE offices throughout the United States to assist small business owners in procurement matters. DOE also administers--together with the National Bureau of Standards--the Energy-Related Inventions Program, a comprehensive program for research and development of all potentially beneficial energy sources and utilization technologies. The program calls for particular attention to be paid to individual inventors and small companies seeking direct grants (for information on this program call (301)975-5500).

62178 ■ U.S. Department of Health and Human Services (HHS) - Office of Small and Disadvantaged Business Utilization

Hubert H. Humphrey Bldg., Rm. 360G
200 Independence Ave., SW
Washington, DC 20201
Ph: (202)690-7235
Fax: (202)260-4872
Co. E-mail: debbie.ridgely@hhs.gov
URL: http://www.hhs.gov/osdbu/

Description: The procurement policy of the Department of Health and Human Services seeks to stimulate competition among potential contractors and to make awards on a competitive basis to the fullest degree consistent with quality, efficiency, and economy. It is the department's policy that small businesses, disadvantaged businesses, women-owned businesses, and labor-surplus area concerns receive a fair and equitable share of the contracts awarded. Procurement assistance is available from the HHS's Office of Small and Disadvantaged Business Utilization and from the small business specialists at each HHS regional office.

62179 ■ U.S. Department of Housing and Urban Development (HUD) - Office of Small and Disadvantaged Business Utilization
451 7th St., SW, Rm. 3130
Washington, DC 20410
Ph: (202)708-1428
Fax: (202)708-7642
Co. E-mail: arnette_s._mcgill@hud.gov
URL: http://www.hud.gov/smallbusiness
Description: The Department of Housing and Urban Development purchases supplies and services to repair and provide housing management services for the properties it acquires, as well as to fulfill its logistical, administrative, and programmatic requirements. Private contractors, including small and disadvantaged firms, are awarded contracts based on bids that they submit to appropriate HUD offices or area managers. HUD encourages and facilitates the participation of small business firms, minority business firms, and firms located in labor-surplus areas. Activities are carried out through a network of field offices. HUD also encourages small business firms to participate in its research and demonstration programs, as the majority of competitively awarded contracts and assistance agreements have been granted to small businesses.

62180 ■ U.S. Department of the Interior - Office of Small and Disadvantaged Business Utilization
1849 C St. NW
Washington, DC 20240
Ph: (202)208-3493
Free: 877-375-9927
URL: http://www.doi.gov/osdbu/
Description: The Department of the Interior's Small and Disadvantaged Business Program provides counseling and advice to small, women-owned, and minority-owned businesses on opportunities in the department. The program helps the bureaus and offices of the department in their efforts to increase contracting opportunities for such businesses. (This applies to direct contracting and subcontracting opportunities as well as to the Small Business Administration's programs.) For instance, the department's Bureau of Land Management sets aside certain commodities and services for procurement from small businesses. This bureau also conducts a lottery to allow the public the opportunity to purchase land. The Bureau of Indian Affairs provides technical assistance to Native American and tribal businesses on reservations for the establishment of enterprises, the preparation of economic development plans, the development of educational and residential facilities, and related undertakings. Furthermore, the department provides various publications that assist small business and small and disadvantaged business concerns with contracting opportunities. The Department of the Interior also hosts an annual Small Business Procurement Fair, which provides contact between the department's acquisition officials and small businesses.

62181 ■ U.S. Department of Justice - Office of Small and Disadvantaged Business Utilization
National Place Bldg., Rm. 1010
1331 Pennsylvania Ave. NW
Washington, DC 20530
Ph: (202)616-0521
Free: 800-345-3712
Fax: (202)616-1717
URL: http://www.usdoj.gov/jmd/osdbu/index.html
Description: The Department of Justice's Office of Small and Disadvantaged Business Utilization develops and implements appropriate outreach programs aimed at heightening the awareness of the small business community to the contracting opportunities

available within the department. Outreach efforts include activities such as sponsoring small business fairs and procurement conferences, and participating in trade group seminars, conventions, and other forums that promote the utilization of small businesses as contractors. The office also provides counseling and advice to inquiring small businesses regarding their possible eligibility for special consideration under preferential purchasing programs that the department employs.

62182 ■ U.S. Department of Labor - Office of Small and Disadvantaged Business Utilization
Frances Perkins Bldg.
200 Constitution Ave. NW, Rm. N-6432
Washington, DC 20210
Ph: (202)693-7297
Co. E-mail: osbdu@dol.gov
URL: http://www.dol.gov/oasam/programs/osdbu/
Description: Emphasizes development of small and disadvantaged business utilization in contract and grant activities, promotes interaction with Historically Black Colleges and Universities and Hispanic and other minority colleges and universities, and has management oversight responsibility for Department of Labor advisory committees. The department fully supports the federal government's Small and Disadvantaged Business Utilization Program created to give small, disadvantaged, and women-owned businesses maximum opportunity to participate in government contracting and grant activities for supplies and services (including research, evaluation, maintenance, repairs, and construction).

62183 ■ U.S. Department of Labor - United States Patent and Trademark Office - Office of Public Affairs
PO Box 1450
Alexandria, VA 22313-1450
Ph: (517)272-8400
Free: 800-786-9199
Fax: (517)272-0340
URL: http://www.uspto.gov/web/offices/ac/ahrpa/opa/opahome.htm
Description: The Patent and Trademark Office examines applications for patents and trademarks to determine whether an invention is patentable or if a trademark may be registered. Patents and trademarks, because of the legal rights they represent, are important to small businesses competing against larger or more established businesses. The Patent and Trademark Office maintains the Public Search Room for use by individuals wishing to identify new products, find solutions to problems, or check patents in a field of technology. The Patent and Trademark Office's Trademark Search Room is also open to the public. In addition, the office sponsors a system of Patent Depository Libraries, which brings collections of U.S. patents to within one hour commuting time of 45 percent of the U.S. population. An automated system known as CASSIS (Classification and Search Support Information System) is available in most of the libraries. CASSIS provides free, online access to the Patent and Trademark Office's classification databases to assist users in their patent searches.

62184 ■ U.S. Department of State - Office of Small and Disadvantaged Business Utilization
2201 C St., NW, SA-6, Rm. L500
Washington, DC 20522
Ph: (703)875-6822
Fax: (703)875-6825
URL: http://www.state.gov/m/a/sdbu/
Description: The Department of State actively seeks qualified small businesses, minority-owned businesses, and women-owned businesses for participation in contract work generated in the course of day-to-day operations. The mission of the State Department--the making and conduct of foreign policy--does not require a large procurement support program on the magnitude of many federal agencies. However in 1995, the Department spent approximately $1 billion in goods and services in support of that mission. Of that amount, the fifteen domestic procurement offices spent $750 million. The contract spectrum of the domestic procurement pattern includes some minor research and development; of-

fice and household furniture and furnishings; transportation, warehousing and packing/shipping services; information technology supplies and services; training; translation and interpreting services (personal services contracts only); building construction, renovation/rehabilitation and architect/engineer services; and security support services, among other things. The Department of State embassies, consulates and Regional Procurement & Support Offices worldwide spent the remaining $400 million.

62185 ■ U.S. Department of Transportation (DOT) - Office of Small and Disadvantaged Business Utilization
1200 New Jersey Ave., SE, W56-485
Washington, DC 20590
Ph: (202)366-1930
Free: 800-532-1169
Fax: (202)366-7228
URL: http://osdbu.dot.gov/
Description: The DOT's Office of Small and Disadvantaged Business Utilization provides policy direction for minority, women-owned, and small and disadvantaged business enterprise participation in direct procurement and federal financial assistance activities. It also is responsible for conducting programs directed at encouraging, promoting, and assisting disadvantaged business enterprises in securing contracts, subcontracts, and projects generated by these activities. The office schedules presentations for firms to present their capabilities to the procurement and program staff and monitors all procurement activities for disadvantaged business enterprises by the department, its grantees, and recipients nationwide. All proposed procurements are reviewed for the participation of small business. When possible, specific procurements are set aside exclusively for small business competition.

62186 ■ U.S. Department of the Treasury - Office of Small and Disadvantaged Business Utilization
1500 Pennsylvania Ave., NW
655 15th St., Rm. 6099
Washington, DC 20220
Ph: (202)622-0530
Fax: (202)622-4963
Co. E-mail: TreasuryOSDBU@do.treas.gov
URL: http://www.ustreas.gov/sba
Description: The mission of the Department of the Treasury includes formulating and recommending financial, tax, and fiscal policies; serving as the financial agent for the U.S. government; enforcing various federal laws; protecting the President and Vice President of the United States; and manufacturing coins and currency. The accomplishment of this mission requires the procurement of a wide variety of commercial goods and services at an annual expenditure of approximately two billion dollars. Contracting authority has been delegated to the various bureaus of the department, and each conducts the procurement transactions necessary to carry out its respective program. The department's procurement efforts include a commitment to increase contract awards to small, minority, and women-owned business firms.

62187 ■ U.S. General Services Administration (GSA) - Office of Small Business Utilization
Regional Office Bldg.
7th and D. Sts. SW
Washington, DC 20407-0002
Ph: (202)501-1021
Free: 800-0ED-IGSA
Fax: (202)208-5938
Co. E-mail: small.business@gsa.gov
URL: http://www.gsa.gov/
Description: The General Services Administration (GSA), the Federal government's purchasing agent, real estate developer, telecommunications manager, and computer overseer, contracts for over $10 billion worth of commodities and services each year. The GSA's Office of Enterprise Development (OED) develops and oversees GSA procurement preference programs for small, disadvantaged and women-owned businesses. In addition to other pamphlets, the OED publishes four major publications to assist businesses in their marketing efforts: Doing Business with GSA, GSA Small Purchases, GSA Subcontract-

ing Directory (published semiannually), and Forecast of GSA Contracting Opportunities (published annually). Information about upcoming contracting opportunities is placed on GSA's Electronic Bulletin Board. GSA operates Business Service Centers (BSCs) in 11 major metropolitan areas throughout the country. The BSCs implement GSA procurement preference programs by providing assistance, information and counseling to small businesses interested in pursuing Federal Government contracts. Counselors at the BSCs help small businesses understand GSA contracting procedures and locate GSA buyers for their products or services. The BSCs are also involved in monitoring local GSA contracting programs to insure that small, disadvantaged and women-owned businesses are given access to contracts and subcontracts and to find ways to expand their participation. As part of GSA's program, the BSCs sponsor breakfasts and networking seminars to give small businesses an opportunity to meet contracting personnel and each other.

62188 ■ U.S. Nuclear Regulatory Commission - Office of Small and Disadvantaged Business Utilization/Civil Rights

11555 Rockville Pike
Rockville, MD 20852-2738
Ph: (301)415-7380
Free: 800-368-5642
URL: http://www.nrc.gov/

Description: The Nuclear Regulatory Commission's Office of Small and Disadvantaged Business Utilization offers small businesses information and guidance on procurement procedures, how to be placed on a bidder's mailing list, and identification of both prime and subcontracting opportunities.

62189 ■ U.S. Office of Personnel Management - Office of Small and Disadvantaged Business Utilization - Contracting Division

Theodore Roosevelt Federal Bldg.
1900 E. St., NW
Washington, DC 20415-1000
Ph: (202)606-0583
Fax: (202)606-1464
Co. E-mail: stvanree@opm.gov
URL: http://opm.gov/

Description: The Office of Personnel Management's Office of Small and Disadvantaged Business Utilization offers small businesses information and guidance on procurement procedures, how to be placed on a bidder's mailing list, and identification of both prime and subcontracting opportunities.

62190 ■ U.S. Postal Service - Office of Small and Disadvantaged Business Utilization

475 L'Enfant Plz. SW, Rm. 4320
Washington, DC 20260-4320
Ph: (202)268-4633

Fax: (202)268-7288
URL: http://www.usps.gov/

Description: The Postal Service's Office of Small and Disadvantaged Business Utilization offers small businesses information and guidance on procurement procedures, how to be placed on a bidder's mailing list, and identification of both prime and subcontracting opportunities.

62191 ■ U.S. Small Business Administration (SBA) - Office of Small Business Development Centers

409 3rd St. SW, 6th Fl.
Washington, DC 20416
URL: http://www.sba.gov/aboutsba/sbaprograms/sbdc/index.html

Description: Although other federal agencies also provide some services to small business, the SBA's primary duties are to aid, counsel, assist, and protect the interests of small business. It ensures that small business concerns receive a fair portion of government purchases, contracts, and subcontracts, as well as fair portions of the sales of government property. The SBA grants loans to small business concerns, to state and local development companies, and to the victims of floods, other catastrophes, or certain types of economic injuries. The administration also licenses, regulates, and grants loans to small business investment companies (SBICs). A small business must meet SBA size standards to be eligible for its loans, procurement assistance, and other services. Interested small business owners should contact the nearest SBA field offices for current standards since they vary by industry and are subject to change. The SBA administers a variety of loan programs for eligible small business concerns that cannot borrow money on reasonable terms from conventional lenders without government assistance. Most of the SBA's loans are made by private lenders and then guaranteed by the SBA, which can guarantee loans up to 90 percent for a maximum of $500,000. In addition to these regular business loans, the SBA offers a variety of special loan programs, including local development company loans that are offered to groups of local citizens. The SBA licenses and regulates small business investment companies (SBICs) which provide venture capital to small businesses. SBA field officers provide counseling and other services to small business owners seeking to do business with the federal government. Procurement specialists at district offices assist in identifying the government agencies that are prospective customers, in instructing small businesses about inclusion on bidders' lists, and in obtaining drawings and specifications for specific contracts. The SBA seeks to increase small business' share of procurement through the activities of its network of procurement center representatives (PCRs), stationed at or in liaison with all federal military and civilian installations with major buying programs. The SBA's procurement assistance program sets aside suitable government purchases for competitive award to small business concerns and

provides an appeal procedure when the ability of a low-bidding small firm to perform a contract is questioned. The SBA also develops subcontracting opportunities, designating the amounts to be subcontracted to small business concerns by prime contractors undertaking major federal projects. The SBA administers the Small Business Innovation Research Program, which fosters participation by small businesses in federal research and development; and provides counseling and information to small businesses through a network of resource programs. The SBA also sponsors the Small Business Development Center (SBDC) Program in conjunction with the educational community, state and local governments, the federal government, and the private sector. In each state there is one "lead" organization that sponsors each SBDC and from which a statewide director manages the program. SBDCs seek to further economic development by providing management and technical assistance to existing and prospective small businesses. The lead organizations coordinate the activities performed on behalf of small business through the participation and establishment of SBDC subcenters and satellite locations. The SBA also offers export counseling and training through its Office of International Trade or small businesses wishing to export products and materials. The SBA is authorized, under Section 8 (a) of the Small Business Act, to enter into contracts with other federal agencies for goods and services and then to subcontract the work to firms owned by socially and economically disadvantaged persons. The firms must be approved to participate in the 8(a) program by the SBA. In addition, the SBA also is authorized, under Section 7(j) of the act, to provide management and technical assistance to SBA clients and small businesses in areas of high unemployment. This program allows the SBA to contract with qualified individuals, state and local governments, educational institutions, Native American tribes, and other nonprofit institutions. The SBA seeks to increase the strength, profitability, and visibility of women-owned businesses by enhancing their access to existing government and private sector resources. Specific efforts include assisting women business owners in surviving business crises; providing SBA personnel with the appropriate skills to respond to the needs of women business owners; increasing federal marketing opportunities; negotiating an annual goal for procurement from women business owners for each federal department and agency; and collecting and analyzing data about women-owned businesses. The SBA's Office of Advocacy attempts to evaluate the impact of legislative proposals and other public policy issues on small business and represents its views before Congress, federal agencies, and state and local governments. The chief counsel also coordinates and conducts applied economic research on a wide range of small business issues, as well as serves as a source of information about the federal government for small business. The office's activities are supported by advocates located at each of the ten SBA regional offices. The SBA also publishes a variety of pamphlets and booklets about its programs and services.

This index provides an alphabetical listing of all organizations, products, services, and other activities covered in the Descriptive Listings section of this directory. Citations include organization, product, or service name, followed by book entry number(s). Entry numbers appear in boldface type if the reference is to the organization for which information is provided and in lightface type if the reference is to a former or alternate name included within the text of a cited entry.

Accent [55995]

Accent on Design - A Division of the New York International Gift Fair [9581], [9615], [10433], [11570]

Accent on Design - A Division of the San Francisco International Gift Fair [10434], [11571]

Accent on Design West: A Division of the San Francisco International Gift Fair [10434], [11571]

Accept Report [47843]

Access [53564]

Access DeKalb [50888]

Access to Finance [8053], [31186], [33500]

Access Management Corp. [42301]

ACCESS Payroll / Warren Computer Center [15468]

Access Venture Partners [49613]

Accessible Home Health Care [10569]

Accessible Web Design: Complying with Section 508 [44992]

Accessories [7855]

Accessory Allure [7856], [10156]

Accident Investigation: A Tool for Effective Prevention [47487]

The Accidental Entrepreneur: Practical Wisdom for People Who Never Expected to Work for Themselves [29322], [32341]

The Accidental Entrepreneur: The 50 Things I Wish Someone Had Told Me About Starting a Business [29323], [31187], [32342], [36954], [39628], [43372]

The Accidental Millionaire: How to Succeed in Life Without Really Trying [15844], [15902], [29460]

The Accidental Startup: How to Realize Your True Potential by Becoming Your Own Boss [29324], [32343]

Acclaim [47200]

Accommodations Directory [55074]

Accommodations Guide to Siesta Key [49929]

"According to the Chinese Zodiac, 2009 is the Year of the Ox" in Canadian Business (Vol. 81, December 8, 2008, No. 21, pp. 74) [26874], [36328]

Accordionists and Teachers Guild--Bulletin [14629]

"The Accountability Lens: A New Way to View Management Issues" in Business Horizons (September-October 2007, pp. 405) [30898], [37772]

The Accountant as a Business Advisor [192]

"Accountants Get the Hook" in Canadian Business (Vol. 80, October 22, 2007, No. 21, pp. 19) [57], [21343], [23710], [30899]

Accountants Global Network (AGN) [9], [21313]

Accountants, Inc. [242], [19712]

Accountant's Relief [258], [19738]

Accounting & Tax Database® [252], [19731]

Accounting & Auditing Update: Implementation of Recent Developments [193]

Accounting and Finance Benchmarking Consortium [10], [8024]

Accounting and Finance for Non-Financial Managers [31992]

Accounting and Finance for Your Small Business [58], [21344], [31188]

Accounting Library [194]

Accounting Perspective [11]

The Accounting Review [167]

Accounting Systems [204]

Accounting's New Guidelines: From GAAP to IFRS (Onsite) [21324]

ACCRA Research in Review [27900]

Accreditation Council on Optometric Education (ACOE) [20903]

Accredited Gemologists Association (AGA) [13247]

Accrediting Commission for Cosmetology Education - National Accrediting Commission for Cosmetology Schools - Cosmetology Accrediting Commission [10062]

"Accrual vs. Cash Accounting, Explained" in Business Owner (Vol. 35, July-August 2011, No. 4, pp. 13) [59], [2264], [19605], [21345], [31189]

ACCS - Advanced Cisco Campus Switching (Onsite) [27982]

Accuitive Medical Ventures LLC / AMV Partners [50646]

Accutips [40544], [42678]

AccuTrak Inventory Specialists [37227]

ACDI/VOCA [21486]

"ACE Agrees to Pay Out $266 Million to Investors" in Globe & Mail (February 17, 2006, pp. B1) [8054], [12000], [44237]

"ACE Aims High With Spinoff of Repair Unit" in Globe & Mail (January 31, 2007, pp. B15) [25007], [41318], [44128]

ACE America's Cash Express [3877]

"ACE Back in Unfriendly Skies" in Globe & Mail (February 14, 2006, pp. B17) [8055], [12001], [22675]

Ace DuraFlo Systems LLC [16296]

"Ace Every Introduction" in Women Entrepreneur (September 10, 2008) [22260], [32509], [39629], [47220]

ACEI Exchange [3945]

ACF Equity Atlantic, Inc. [59912]

ACFA Bulletin [1023]

ACFN - The ATM Franchise Business [44602]

Achieve Management Inc. [205]

Achieve Success by Prospecting with Phillip Wexler [43704]

"Achieve Tampa Bay Thrown a Lifeline in Proposed Merger" in Tampa Bay Business Journal (Vol. 30, January 22, 2010, No. 5, pp. 1) [12002], [34181], [41717]

The Achievement Challenge [30356]

Achiever [56453]

Achieving Excellence in Customer Service (Onsite) [26361]

"Achieving Greatness" in Black Enterprise (Vol. 38, January 2008, No. 6, pp. 50) [2763], [22676], [25823], [34753], [37773]

Achieving Leadership Success Through People (Onsite) [37572]

Achieving Planned Innovation: A Proven System for Creating Successful New Products and Services [1970], [4935], [14544], [34182], [34754], [35690], [36955], [38886], [40983], [44238]

"Achieving Sustained Competitive Advantage: A Family Capital Theory" in Family Business Review (Vol. 19, June 2006, No. 2, pp. 135) [25408], [31019]

ACIN Camden Center for Entrepreneurship in Technology [54869]

"Acing the Test" in Contractor (Vol. 57, January 2010, No. 1, pp. 32) [6875], [7087], [7448], [18675], [19072], [30468]

K.B. Ackerman Co. (KBA) [16659]

ACM Electronic Graduate Assistantship Directory [4855], [18911]

Glenn Acomb Associates Inc. [1298]

acorn [57645]

The Acorn [48199]

Acorn Campus [49155]

Acorn Ventures, Inc. [49156]

Acoustic Guitar Magazine [14630], [14743], [14791]

ACP Update [2075]

"Acquisition of a Uranium Exploration Project, Laguiche Basin, Opinaca Area, Quebec" in Canadian Corporate News (May 16, 2007) [25008], [41718]

Acquisition/Divestiture Weekly Report--Current Transaction in Review Section [42271]

Acquisition/Divestiture Weekly Report--Detailed Summaries Section [42271]

"Acsys Interactive Announces Crowdsourcing Comes to the Hospital Industry" in Internet Wire (August 23, 2010) [34183], [39630], [40984]

ACTA Voyage [20123], [20502]

Action! [56955]

ACTION [55996]

Action [48200]; [49930]; [50429]; [53122]; [55570]

Action Bulletin [47618]

Action Consulting Association [26819], [44788]

Action CTIC Action [20462]

Action for Enterprise (AFE) [26819], [44788]

Action Line Newsletter [53826]

Action News [50889]; [56454]

Action Newsletter [7873]

Action Report [50890]; [57921]; [59086]

Action Update [59475]

ActionCoach [2987]

Actionline [54663]

"Actions to Implement Three Potent Post-Crisis Strategies" in Strategy & Leadership (Vol. 38, September-October 2010, No. 5) [22677], [26875], [37774]

"Actiontec and Verizon Team Up for a Smarter Home" in Ecology,Environment & Conservation Business (November 9, 2010) [3676], [7088], [7449], [18386], [30469], [44239]

Activant [5699]

"Active Duty" in Crain's Cleveland Business (Vol. 28, November 26, 2007, No. 47, pp. 3) [28113], [34184], [35261], [45857]

Active Green + Ross [1633]

"Active Sales" in Green Industry Pro (Vol. 23, September 2011) [9770], [13380], [13468], [26876], [39631], [43373], [44240]

Active Server Pages I [21032]

Active Voice [59476]; [6770], [46795]

Activities of Daily Living [15099]; [15100]

Activities Guide [54547]

Activity Guidelines [49443]

Acton Area Chamber of Commerce [52931]

Acton Chamber of Commerce [48201]

Actor's Garage [14584]

"ACTRA Phones It In" in Canadian Business (Vol. 80, January 15, 2007, No. 2, pp. 8) [7901], [16704], [19900], [46835]

Acu-Yoga for Flexibility [15991]

Warren Acuff [41463]

Acuity Ventures LLC [49157]

Acupuncture Foundation of Canada Institute (AFCI) [14809], [16059]

Ad Campaigns That Work [657], [42681]

Ad Complaints Report [337]

"Ad Firms Stew Over Lost Car Biz; Diversifying Business Is Uphill Battle" in Crain's Detroit Business (Vol. 23, July 30, 2007, No. 31) [370], [14851], [38887], [39632]

Ada Area Chamber of Commerce [56455]

Ada Chamber of Commerce [56455]

ADA: Commonsense Compliance [26676]

The ADA Maze: What You Can Do [26677]

ADA: Understanding the Law [26678]

Adam & Eve Stores [43286]

Adam Market Research Inc. [14032]

Adams-Blake Company Inc. [49386]

Adams Capital Management Inc. [57277]

Adams County Chamber of Commerce [55997]

Adams County Chamber of Commerce Newsletter [59477]

Adams County Chamber of Commerce and Tourism (ACCC&T) [59478]

Adams County Genealogical Society Library [9481]

Adams County Visitors Guide [59479]

Adams Jobs Almanac [6956]

The Danielle Adams Publishing Co. [57349]

Adams-Blake Publishing [49386]

Adams-Friendship Chamber of Commerce [59478]

Adapso [44991]

ADAPSO (Computer Software and SErvices Industry Association) [44991]

ADAPSO, the Computer Software and Services Industry Association [44991]

"Adapt or Die" in Black Enterprise (Vol. 38, July 2008, No. 12, pp. 27) [24216], [26727], [26877], [29461], [37775], [38888], [40698], [42746]

Adayana Healthcare Group [21758]

"Add Aquatics to Boost Business" in Pet Product News (Vol. 64, December 2010, No. 12, pp. 20) [1231], [15749], [22678], [42937], [43374]

Addictions Foundation of Manitoba - William Potoroka Memorial Library [46097]

Addison Chamber of Commerce and Industry (ACCI) [50891]

Addison Chamber of Commerce - Addison Industrial Association [50891]

Addison Community Directory [50892]

Addison County Annual Guide & Map [58733]

Addison County Chamber of Commerce (ACCOC) [58734]

Address Book for Germanic Genealogy [9434]

Adel-Cook County Chamber of Commerce [50430]

Adel Partners Chamber of Commerce [51810]

ADG Group [25927], [32005]

"Adidas' Brand Ambitions" in Business Journal Portland (Vol. 27, December 10, 2010, No. 41, pp. 1) [18752], [19315], [22679], [36329], [39633], [42365]

Adirondack Regional Business Incubator [55477]

Adirondack Regional Chamber of Commerce (ARCC) [55075]

Adirondacks-Speculator Region Chamber of Commerce [55076]

Adirondacks-Spectacular Region Chamber of Commerce [55076]

Adjust Your Set: The Static Is Real [26679]

"Adler Blanchard & Freeman Reports New SmartKeeper Bookkeeping Service" in Professional Services Close-Up (March 24, 2011) [60], [2265], [19606], [21346]

Adler Pollock & Sheehan Law Library [7757]

ADM Flash [14017], [40545]

Administration publique du Canada [42398]

Administrative Professionals Retreat [28968]

Adobe Acrobat 9 for Legal Professionals [44993]

Adobe Acrobat I (Onsite) [27983]

Adobe Acrobat II (Onsite) [44994]

Adobe Acrobat Section 508 Accessibility (Onsite) [33480], [44995]

Adobe After Effects I (Onsite) [27984]

Adobe After Effects II (Onsite) [44996]

Adobe Bridge [44997]

Adobe Captivate 3 [22153], [44998]

Adobe ColdFusion I [21033]

Adobe ColdFusion II (Onsite) [44999]

Adobe Creative Suite 5 Bootcamp Training (Onsite) [45000]

Adobe Director I [27985]

Adobe Director II [27986]

Adobe Dreamweaver I (Onsite) [21034]

Adobe Dreamweaver II (Onsite) [21035]

Adobe Dreamweaver III (Onsite) [21036]

Adobe Fireworks I [21037]
Adobe Fireworks II [45001]
Adobe Flash I (Onsite) [27987]
Adobe Flash II (Onsite) [27988]
Adobe Flash III (Onsite) [45002]
Adobe Flash Media Server [45003]
Adobe Flex I - Developing Rich Internet Client Applications [45004]
Adobe Flex II - Data and Communications [45005]
Adobe Flex III - Building Dashboard Applications [45006]
Adobe FrameMaker I (Onsite) [27989]; [45007]
Adobe FrameMaker II (Onsite) [27990]
Adobe FrameMaker III: Structured [45008]
Adobe GoLive [21038]
Adobe Illustrator I (Onsite) [27991]
Adobe Illustrator II (Onsite) [27992]
Adobe Illustrator III (Onsite) [27993]
Adobe InDesign CS4 Master Class for Designers Training (Onsite) [27994]; [45009]
Adobe InDesign I (Onsite) [27995]
Adobe InDesign II (Onsite) [27996]
Adobe InDesign III (Onsite) [45010]
Adobe InDesign with InCopy for Workgroups Training (Onsite) [27997]; [45011]
Adobe InDesign IV (Onsite) [45012]
Adobe InDesign for Long Documents I (Onsite) [45013]
Adobe InDesign for Long Documents II (Onsite) [45014]
Adobe InDesign for Long Documents III (Onsite) [45015]
Adobe Lightroom Photo Workflow [45016]
Adobe Photoshop for Beginners (Onsite) [45017]
Adobe Photoshop Channels and Masks (Onsite) [45018]
Adobe Photoshop Digital Mastery I (Onsite) [45019]
Adobe Photoshop Digital Painting (Onsite) [45020]
Adobe Photoshop Extended [45021]
Adobe Photoshop I (Onsite) [27998]
Adobe Photoshop II (Onsite) [27999]
Adobe Photoshop III: Tips and Tricks (Onsite) [28000]
Adobe Premiere I (Onsite) [28001]
Adoption Resource Book [34185], [41319]
ADR Institute of Canada (ADR Canada) [14157]
Adult Day Care in America: Summary of a National Survey [306]
Adult Day Care: Findings From a National Survey [307]
Adult Day Services Letter [308], [10545]
Adult Learning Video? You've Got to Be Kidding! [4770], [28409]
"AdvacePierre Heats Up" in Business Courier (Vol. 27, October 29, 2010, No. 26, pp. 1) [9908], [12003], [22680], [35262], [38889], [41719]
AdvaMed [14182], [14310]
"Advance America Closing All Pa. Stores" in American Banker (Vol. 172, December 20, 2007, No. 244, pp. 11) [8056], [37290]
Advance Directives and the Elderly: Making Decisions about Treatment Limitations [15101]
Advance Grower Solutions I Nursery/Greenhouse Accounting Software [13445]; [9839]
Advance Realty [17130]
Advanced Auditing for In-Charge Auditors (Onsite) [31155]
Advanced Benefits & Human Resources [13786], [22032], [25928], [36004], [38645]
Advanced Collection Strategies (Onsite) [31156]
Advanced Communication Designs Inc. [22653]
Advanced Computer Consulting Inc. [5048]
Advanced Copyediting (Onsite) [22547]
Advanced Cost Accounting (Onsite) [31157]
Advanced Critical Thinking Applications Workshop (Onsite) [24966]
Advanced Diversity Strategies (Onsite) [35658]
Advanced Editing [22154]
Advanced Electric Motor/Generator/Actuator Design and Analysis for Automotive Applications (Onsite) [38872]
Advanced Employee Complaint Handling (Onsite) [35659]
Advanced Grammar Roundtable (Onsite) [28002]
Advanced Hazardous Waste Management (Onsite) [30444], [33481]
Advanced Issues in EEO Law [35660]
Advanced Issues in Employee Relations [28969], [37573]
Advanced IT Audit School (Onsite) [37574]
Advanced Leadership Communication Strategies (Onsite) [22155]
Advanced Maintenance [44603]
Advanced Manufacturing Technology [34755]
Advanced Materials Partners, Inc. [49768]
Advanced Medical Technology Association (AdvaMed) [14182], [14310]
Advanced Medical Technology Association--Directory [14189]
Advanced Network Consulting (ANC) [41464], [41567]
Advanced PC Configuration, Troubleshooting and Data Recovery: Hands-On (Onsite) [28003]

Advanced Progressions for Across the Floor [6391]
Advanced Sales Management (Onsite) [43350]
Advanced Section 1031 Exchanges (Onsite) [23675]
Advanced Selling for Dummies [28537], [39634], [43375]
Advanced Shiatsu Massage [14147]
Advanced Skills for the EMT [934]
Advanced Technology Development Center [50670]
Advanced Technology Ventures (ATV) [53000]
Advanced Technology Ventures (Palo Alto) [49158]
Advanced Training for Microsoft Excel (Onsite) [45022]
Advanced Training for Your Retriever [15697]
Advanced Walleye Systems I [1702]
Advanced Walleye Systems II [1703]
Advanced Walleye Systems III [1704]
Advanced Walleye Trolling Tactics [1705]
Advanced Writing and Editing for Government Proposals [22548], [33393]
Advances [34483]
"Advances in Pump Technology - Part Two" in Contractor (Vol. 57, February 2010, No. 2, pp. 22) [6876], [11034], [16217], [25723], [36330]
"Advancing the Ball" in Inside Healthcare (Vol. 6, December 2010, No. 7, pp. 31) [291], [1420], [10526], [15063], [22681], [35263], [35691], [40985]
Advancing Canadian Entrepreneurship (ACE) [29439]
Advancing Research on Minority Entrepreneurship [22682], [29325], [40671], [43376]
Advantage [50893]
The Advantage [54240]
Advantage Cash Advance [3878]
The Advantage Group Inc. [25929], [26614]
Advantage Steel [5160]
"Advantage Tutoring Center" in Bellingham Business Journal (Vol. February 2010, pp. 16) [20728], [28114], [31020]
AdvantageNews [52826]
Advent International Corp. [53001]
Advent International Corp. (New York) [49159]
Advent Management International Ltd. [13787]
Advent-Morro Equity Partners [59866]
Adventa Global Intermediaries [2860], [13823], [25991], [32023], [36913], [38707], [44933]
Adventure Cycling Association [1963]
Adventure Cyclist [1974]
Adventure Learning Associates [25279], [29232]
Adventure Learning Associates Inc. [25279], [29232]
Adventure Travel Trade Association (ATTA) [20124], [20503]
The Adventures of Elmer and Friends: Freedom Rocks [3952]
The Adventures of Elmer and Friends: Pirate Island [3953]
The Adventures of Elmer and Friends: The Magic Map [3954]
The Adventures of Elmer and Friends: Treasure Beyond Measure [3955]
"Adventures at Hydronicahh" in Contractor (Vol. 56, November 2009, No. 11, pp. 36) [780], [7090], [7451], [19074], [30471]
"Adventures at Hydronicahh" in Contractor (Vol. 56, October 2009, No. 10, pp. 42) [781], [7091], [7452], [19075], [30472]
"Adventures at Hydronicahh" in Contractor (Vol. 56, September 2009, No. 9, pp. 52) [779], [5212], [7089], [7450], [19073], [30470]
Advertiser & Agency Red Books Plus [42693]
"Advertisers Don't Party With CBS's Swingers" in Advertising Age (Vol. 79, July 7, 2008, No. 26, pp. 1) [371], [19901], [39635]
"Advertisers Hooked on Horns, their Playground" in Austin Business JournalInc. (Vol. 28, July 25, 2008, No. 19, pp. A1) [372], [1266], [5213], [19399], [39636]
Advertising Age [681]
Advertising Age--Agencies Ranked by Gross Income Issue [373]
Advertising Agency Production Club of New York [4432]
Advertising Brochure [54664]
Advertising Club of New York (ACNY) [338], [42564]
Advertising Compliance Service [650]
Advertising Council (AC) [339], [42565]
Advertising Federation of America - Associated Advertising Clubs of the World [344], [42570]
Advertising and Marketing International Network (AMIN) [340], [39554], [42566]
"Advertising May Take a Big Hit in Southwest/AirTran Merger" in Baltimore Business Journal (Vol. 28, October 1, 2010, No. 21, pp. 1) [374], [3163], [8057], [12004], [15517], [19902], [24818], [41720]
Advertising Men's League of New York [338], [42564]
Advertising Photographers of America [346], [15834]
Advertising Production Club of New York (APC) [4432]
Advertising Red Books™ [682]
Advertising Research Foundation (ARF) [42567]

Advertising Research Foundation Information Center [685], [14064]
Advertising Research (Onsite) [28004]; [39572]
Advertising the Small Business [42682]
Advertising Standards Canada (ASC) [341]
Advertising: The Hidden Language [658], [42683]
Advertising Tricks Without the Gimmicks [659], [42684]
Advertising Women of New York (AWNY) [342], [42568]
Advisor [1959], [19862], [20959], [56903]
Advisor Media Inc. [49387]
Advisor Voice [8025]
Advisory Management Services Inc. [13788], [25930], [29233], [38646]
ADVOCAP, Inc. - Business Development Center [59781]
Advocate [48202]; [49444]; [58842]; [58843]
The Advocate [56456]; [57922]
ADVOCIS (TFAAC) [8026]
Adweek/New England [651]
A.E. Roberts Co. [22033], [36255]
AEC-ST [5620]
AECB News [2076]
Aegis Communications Inc. [25931], [40574]
AEP Associates Inc. [2562]
Aero-Colours Inc. [1600]
AERO Library. [19133]
Aerobics and Fitness [15984]
"Aeronautics Seeking New HQ Site" in The Business Journal-Milwaukee (Vol. 25, September 5, 2008, No. 50, pp. 1) [24217], [24712], [38890], [44633]
Aerospace Industries Association of America [720]
Aerospace Research Applications Center [60509]; [60510]
Aerowest Restroom Deodorizing Service [2642]
Aesthetics International Association Library [10108]
"AF Expands in New Green Building in Gothenburg" in Ecology,Environment & Conservation Business (September 24, 2011, pp. 2) [7092], [7453], [17752], [25824], [30473], [36331]
AFCOM [4751]
Affaires Etrangeres et Commerce International Canada - Bibliotheque. [36928]
Affiliated Car Rental LC [17830]
Affiliated Chambers of Commerce of Greater Springfield (ACCGS) [52827]
Affiliated Chambers of Greater Springfield [52827]
Affiliated Warehouse Companies (AWC) [16637]
Affinity Capital Management [53773]
Affirmative Action Plan Workshop (Onsite) [35661]
Affirmative Action Register [19158]; [19185], [35532], [40925]
"Affordable Again" in The Business Journal-Serving Greater Tampa Bay (Vol. 28, July 18, 2008, No. 30, pp. 1) [16507], [16806], [17183], [24713], [26878]
"Affordable Financing for Acquisitions" in Franchising World (Vol. 42, September 2010, No. 9, pp. 47) [32121], [33139], [37291], [41363], [41721]
"Affordable Housing on the Rise" in Philadelphia Business Journal (Vol. 28, October 23, 2009, No. 36, pp. 1) [5214], [16807], [26879], [33140]
Affton Business Connection [53954]
Affton Chamber of Commerce [53955]
AFL-CIO - SEIU - District 925 [20817]
AFM Library. [46097]
"Africa Rising" in Harvard Business Review (Vol. 86, September 2008, No. 9, pp. 36) [375], [2110], [2362], [11035], [36332], [39637]
African American Chamber of Commerce of Oregon (AACCO) [56699]
African-American Chamber of Commerce of Philadelphia [56956]
African American Chamber of Commerce of Westchester and Rockland Counties (AACCWR) [55077]
African Medical and Research Foundation, U.S.A. (AMREF USA) [34643]
African-American Chamber of Commerce [55077]
AFS Editorials [8993]
"After Price Cuts, Competition GPS Makers Lose Direction" in Brandweek (Vol. 49, April 21, 2008, No. 16, pp. 16) [3677], [5730], [8058], [12005], [25409], [25724], [31190], [34756], [38891], [39638]
"After the Storm: Following a Tragic Loss, the Chambers Family Is Starting To See the Light" in Black Enterprise (November 2007) [23711], [31021]
Aftermarket Insider [1572]
Afton Area Chamber of Commerce [59845]
A.G. Edwards & Sons [54175]
Ag Equipment Power [21507]
"Ag Firms Harvest Revenue Growth" in The Business Journal-Serving Metropolitan Kansas City (Vol. 26, July 18, 2008, No. 45, pp. 1) [8059], [12006], [21508], [22683], [31191]
"Ag Officials Employ Preventive Pest Control" in Yakima Herald-Republic (June 24, 2011) [11036], [15624], [21509]

Alabama Procurement Technical Assistance Center - University of Alabama [47757]
Alabama Small Business Development Consortium [47758]
Alabama Small Business Development Consortium, Lead Office (ASBDC) [47602]
Alabama State House of Representatives - Bill Status Office [47766]
Alabama State House of Representatives - House Commerce Committee [47767]
Alabama State University Small Business Development Center [47603]
Alachua Chamber of Commerce [49931]
Alamance County Area Chamber of Commerce [55571]
Alamance County Chamber of Commerce [55571]
Alameda Chamber of Commerce [48204]
Alameda County Library - Business Library [3052], [3126]
Alameda County Small Business Development Center [48132]
Alameda Small Business Development Center [48133]
Alamo Chamber of Commerce [57924]
Alamo City Black Chamber of Commerce [57925]
Alamogordo Chamber of Commerce [54921]
Alamogordo Small Business Development Center [54893]
Alamosa County Chamber of Commerce (ACCC) [49445]
Alan D. Biller & Associates Inc. [8909]
Alarm Installer and Dealer [3313], [18518]
Alaska AVHRR Data [9837]
Alaska Business Monthly [47828]
Alaska Department of Commerce, Community, and Economic Development [47775]
Alaska Industrial Directory [38894]
Alaska Marine Safety Education Association Library [13973]
Alaska Minority Business Development Center - Tanana Chief Conference, Inc. [47825]
Alaska Small Business Development Center - Central Region [47770]
Alaska Small Business Development Center - Great North Region [47771]
Alaska Small Business Development Center - South Central Region [47772]
Alaska Small Business Development Center - South West Region [47773]
Alaska Small Business Development Center - Southeast Region [47774]
Alaska State Chamber of Commerce (ASCC) [47777]
Albany Area Chamber of Commerce (AACC) [56700]
Albany Area Chamber of Commerce, Georgia [50432]
Albany Center for Economic Success [55478]
Albany Chamber of Commerce [48205]
Albany Chamber of Commerce (ACC) [53566]; [57926]
Albany-Colonie Regional Chamber of Commerce [55079]
Albany Historical Society, Inc. - Library/Special Collections [21792]
Albany Medical College - Schaffer Library of Health Sciences [1441]
"Albany Molecular on Hiring Spree as Big Pharma Slashes Work Force" in *Business Review, Albany New York* (December 28, 2007) [6957], [34187], [35265], [41660]
Albany Park Chamber of Commerce [50896]
Albany Small Business Development Center [55012]
Albee-Campbell L.L.C. [39517]
Albemarie County Chamber of Commerce [58890]
Albert Lea - Freeborn County Chamber of Commerce (ALFCCOC) [53567]
"Albert Schultz" in *Canadian Business* (Vol. 83, August 17, 2010, No. 13-14, pp. 71) [29008], [29462], [37780], [39643]
Alberta Agriculture and Food - Crop Diversification Centre South - Branch Library [21793]
Alberta Agriculture, Food and Rural Development - Business Management Innovations Branch Library [21794]
Alberta Agriculture and Rural Development - Crop Diversification Centre South (CDCS) [10381]
Alberta Band Association - Music Lending Library [14764]
"Alberta: Help Wanted, Badly" in *Globe & Mail* (March 11, 2006, pp. B5) [26884], [32513]
Alberta Land Surveyor's Association Library [19537]
Alberta Securities Commission Library [13227], [24164], [32326]
Alberta Securities Commission - Resource Centre. [13227], [24164], [32326]
"Alberta Slashes Tax Rate to Ten Percent" in *Globe & Mail* (March 23, 2006, pp. B2) [32514], [46139]
"Alberta Star Begins Phase 2 Drilling On Its Eldorado & Contact Lake IOCG & Uranium Projects" in *Canadian Corporate News* (May 16, 2007) [33503], [41320], [42748], [46985]

"Alberta Warns Ottawa On Taxes" in *Globe & Mail* (March 9, 2007, pp. B1) [26885], [46140]
"Alberta's Runaway Train" in *Canadian Business* (Vol. 80, December 25, 2006, No. 1, pp. 17) [12011], [22689], [26886], [38895]
Albion Chamber of Commerce (ACC) [54355]
Albion Economic Development Corp. [53497]
Albuquerque SBDC [54996]
Albuquerque Small Business Development Center [54894]
Albuquerque Technical-Vocational Institute [55003]
"Alcan Statement on Water Rights Could Encourage Bid" in *Globe & Mail* (April 25, 2007, pp. B5) [32515], [33504]
Alcatel Network Systems, Inc. - Library [20967]
ALCO Capital Group Inc. [42304]
Alcohol, Health and Research World [34486]
Alcohol Research Group - Library [46099]
Alcohol Research and Health [34486]
Alcoholics Anonymous World Services, Inc. [46059]
Alden and Associates Marketing Research [40575]
Aldrich & Cox Inc. (A & C) [22034]
Ale Street News [2471]
Aledo Area Chamber of Commerce [50897]
Alert! [14018]
Alert [48206]
Alexander Associates [41466]
Alexander City Chamber of Commerce (ACCC) [47620]
Alexander City - Lake Martin Area Chamber of Commerce - Alexander City Area Chamber of Commerce [47620]
Alexander County Chamber of Commerce (ACCC) [55572]
Alexander Technique International (ATI) [14810]
Alexandria Bay Chamber of Commerce [55080]
Alexandria Business Guide [58844]
Alexandria Chamber of Commerce (ACC) [58845]
Alexandria Lakes Area Chamber of Commerce (AACC) [53568]
Alexandria Lakes Area Visitor Guide [53569]
Alexandria - Monroe Chamber of Commerce (ACC) [51514]
Alexandria Small Business Development Center [58794]
Alexandria Technical College [53794]
Alfred University - Center for Glass Research (CGR) [9647]
Alger County Chamber of Commerce [53123]
Algoma Area Chamber of Commerce (AACC) [59480]
"Algoma Resolves Hedge Fund Fight" in *Globe & Mail* (March 8, 2006, pp. B1) [8062], [12012], [44129]
"Algoma Shares Soar on Growing Sale Rumors" in *Globe & Mail* (February 13, 2007, pp. B1) [8063], [12013], [22690], [38896]
Algona Area Chamber of Commerce (AACC) [51811]
Algonquin - Lake in the Hills Chamber of Commerce [50898]
Alhambra Chamber of Commerce [48207]
Alice Business Today [57927]
Alice Chamber of Commerce (ACC) [57928]
Aliceville Area Chamber of Commerce (AACC) [47621]
Alimansky Capital Group Inc. [47116]
Alimansky Capital Group, Inc. [55391]
Alive [34487]
Jay Alix & Associates [29299]
AlixPartners [29299]
All About Credit [6191], [6230], [26133]
All About Folsom Business [48208]
All About Honeymoons [20628]
"All About The Benjamins" in *Canadian Business* (Vol. 81, September 29, 2008, No. 16, pp. 92) [5217], [11038], [11612], [12014], [17186], [23714], [24793], [34760], [36335], [41728]
All America Karate Federation [14077]
All American Ice Cream & Frozen Yogurt Shops [10942]
A All Animal Control [2644]
"All Bubbles Must Burst" in *Canadian Business* (Vol. 83, August 17, 2010, No. 13-14, pp. 12) [14378], [16810], [17187], [33505]
"All Bundled Up" in *Entrepreneur* (Vol. 35, November 2007, No. 11, pp. 104) [379], [39644], [44247]
"All Eyes On Iris" in *Canadian Business* (Vol. 81, July 22, 2008, No. 12-13, pp. 20) [8064], [12015], [25013], [31193], [33506], [45268]
"All Fired Up!" in *Small Business Opportunities* (November 2008) [16122], [17880], [24222], [25014], [28116], [32122]
"All For One, None for All?" in *Canadian Business* (Vol. 83, October 12, 2010, No. 17, pp. 60) [11039], [25412], [33507], [36336], [41729]
All Handwriting Services L.L.C. [10116]
"All In Good Fun" in *Entrepreneur* (Vol. 36, May 2008, No. 5, pp. 22) [22261], [25015], [29009], [29463], [37781]

"All In The Family" in *Canadian Business* (Vol. 79, September 25, 2006, No. 19, pp. 75) [22691], [31022], [32516]
"All Indicators in Michigan Innovation Index Drop in 4Q" in *Crain's Detroit Business* (Vol. 25, June 22, 2009, No. 25, pp. 9) [22692], [26887], [33143], [36956], [37292], [43318], [46986]
All the Money in the World: How the Forbes 400 Make and Spend - Their Fortunes [12016], [31194]
All Nations Flag Co., Inc. [4422]
All Night Auto [18635]
"All Options Open On Chrysler: Magna" in *Globe & Mail* (February 28, 2007, pp. B3) [24223], [25016], [25413], [38897]
"All Revved Up" in *Barron's* (Vol. 90, September 13, 2010, No. 37, pp. 18) [1547], [8065], [12017], [22693]
All Seasons Tree Service Inc. [13504]
"All-Star Advice 2010" in *Black Enterprise* (Vol. 41, October 2010, No. 3, pp. 97) [6273], [8066], [11305], [12018], [16811], [17188], [26134], [36105], [46141]
All Star Franchising, LLC [6603]
"All Those Applications, and Phone Users Just Want to Talk" in *Advertising Age* (Vol. 79, August 11, 2008, No. 31, pp. 18) [3494], [3680], [11613], [18855], [22262], [32123], [34761]
"All the Trimmings" in *Green Industry Pro* (Vol. 23, March 2011, No. 3, pp. 29) [9771], [13351], [13381], [13469], [44248]
All Tune and Lube [16671], [18636]
All You Need Is a Good Idea!: How to Create Marketing Messages that Actually Get Results [380], [39645]
All You Need to Know About Cigars! [20104]
ALLDATA® Online [706]
Allegan Area Chamber of Commerce (AACC) [53124]
Allegany County Chamber of Commerce (ACCC) [52669]
Allegany County Map [52670]
Alleghany Business Directory [55573]
Alleghany County Chamber of Commerce (ACCC) [55574]
Alleghany Highlands Chamber of Commerce (AHCC) [58846]
Allegheny Valley Chamber of Commerce [56957]
Allegis Capital LLC / Media Technology Ventures [49161]
Allegra Marketing [22544]
Allegra Partners / Lawrence, Smith & Horey [55392]
Charles J. Allen and Associates [38647], [40576]
Allen Business Investments (ABI) [2721], [2807]
Allen Chamber of Commerce [57929]
Allen County Business Directory [55998]
Allen County Public Library - Business and Technology Department [42912]
Allen Economic Development Group [56391]
John E. Allen, Inc. - Motion Picture Archives [14587]
"Allen Tate Expanding to Research Triangle Park: Firm Expects Raleigh Market to Grow Faster" in *Charlotte Observer* (January 31, 2007) [16812], [17189], [22694], [44635]
Allentown-Lehigh County Chamber of Commerce [57096]
Allergy/Asthma Information Association (AAIA) [916]
Alleviating Stress Associated with Nursing Home Admission [15103]
"AllHipHop.com's Founders Thought a Weeklong Event Would Raise the Company" in *Inc.* (February 2008, pp. 48-51) [14731], [22695], [28538], [42448], [42599]
Alliance [55999]
Alliance for Amesbury [52828]
Alliance of Area Business Publications (AABP) [15479], [49388]
Alliance Area Chamber of Commerce (AACC) [56000]
"Alliance Atlantis Takes a Cheekier Attitude to Life" in *Globe & Mail* (March 5, 2007, pp. B5) [381], [19903], [39646]
Alliance of Canadian Cinema, Television and Radio Artists (ACTRA) [16686], [19877]
Alliance Canadienne du Camionnage [20650]
Alliance Chamber of Commerce (AACC) [54356]
Alliance for Children and Television - Resource Library [20015]
Alliance for Community Media Library [3210]
Alliance Cost Containment LLC [2988]
Alliance Des Arts Mediatiques Independants [7885]
Alliance E-Newsletter [56701]
"Alliance to End Hunger to Hold Press Conference on Fasting, Prayer and Budget Cuts" in *Food & Beverage Close-Up* (March 28, 2011) [9146], [9238], [45858]
The Alliance Management Group Inc. [2808], [13789], [25932], [38648]
Alliance Management International Ltd. [2809], [13790], [22647], [25933], [38649]
Alliance Membership Directory [57646]
Alliance News [56702]
Alliance Newsletter [52829]

American Association for Laboratory Accreditation (A2LA) [14257]

American Association for Laboratory Animal Science Conference & Exhibits [14291]

The American Association of Language Specialists (TAALS) [20463]

American Association of Managing General Agents (AAMGA) [11264]

American Association of Meat Processors (AAMP) [3136]

American Association of Nutritional Consultants (AANC) [15148]

American Association of Occupational Health Nurses Library [1442]

American Association of Advertising Agencies - Research Services [345], [42571]

American Association of Clinical Laboratory Supervisors and Administrators [14267]

American Association of Counseling and Development [3338]

American Association of Equipment Lessors [17748]

American Association of Fundraising Counsel [9234]

American Association of Homes and Services for the Aging [15054]

American Association of Homes for the Aging [15054]

American Association of Industrial Editors - International Council of Industrial Editors [22151], [22546]

American Association of Minority Enterprise Small Business Investment Companies [40685], [46980]

American Association of Nurserymen [9758], [13345]

American Association of Nursing Homes [15044], [34100]

American Association of Professional Bridal Consultants [2487]

American Association of School Photographers [15898]

American Association of University Instructors in Accounting [13]

American Association of University Teachers of Insurance [11268]

American Association of Pharmacy Technicians (AAPT) [6621]

American Association of Radon Scientists and Technologists (AARST) [16775]

American Audiology Society [10332]

American Auditory Society (AAS) [10332]

American Automobile Association Research Library [6605], [15005]

American Automotive Leasing Association (AALA) [1616], [14835]

"American Axle Sues to Force Steelmaker to Resume Suspended Parts Shipment' in Crain's Detroit Business (Vol. 25, June 15, 2009) [1548], [23715], [38900]

American Bakers Association (ABA) [1679], [1744]

American Ballet Competition [6371]

American Banker Financial Publications [2736], [8929], [13192], [14533]

American Banker News Service [2736], [8929], [13192], [14533]

American Bar Association Legal Guide for Small Business: Everything You Need to Know About Small Business [23716], [31195], [32345], [35693], [37293], [44130]

American Beauty Association [1893], [10066]

American Bee Journal [1947]

American Beekeeping Federation (ABF) [1940]

American Beekeeping Federation Convention [1954]

American Beekeeping Federation--News Letter [1948]

American Beverage Association Information Center [5113], [18297]

American Beverage Institute (ABI) [2441]

American Beverage Licensees (ABL) [13566]

American Big Businesses Directory [38901]

American Board of Bioanalysis (ABB) [14258]

American Board of Funeral Service Education (ABFSE) [9315]

American Board of Bioanalysts [14258]

American Board of Opticianry [20920]

American Board on Counseling Services - American Board on Professional Standards in Vocational Counseling [3342]

American Board on Professional Standards in Vocational Counseling [3342]

American Board of Opticianry (ABO) [20905]

American Boarding Kennels Association [15671], [15812]

American Boat Builders and Repairers Association (ABBRA) [13921]

American Boat and Yacht Council (ABYC) [13922]

American Boat and Yacht Council--Membership List [13935]

American Book Producers Association (ABPA) [2077], [6771]

American Book Publishers Council [2079]

American Booksellers Association (ABA) [2078], [2350], [55521]

American Booksellers Association Convention and Trade Exhibit [2402]

American Booksellers Association Information Service Center [2221], [2409]

American Border Leicester Association (ABLA) [993]

American Bowling Congress - United States Seniors Bowling Association [2432]

American Brahmousin Council (ABC) [994], [21491]

American Breweriana Association (ABA) [2442]

American Business Communication Association - American Business Writing Association [22150], [22545]

American Business Law Association [45258]

American Business Management Series [38613]

American Business Media (ABM) [15480]

American Business Press [15480]

American Business Publishing [301]

American Business Sales Series [43705]

American Business Women's Association (ABWA) [47202]

American Camp Association Library [3275]

American Camping Association [3243]

American Camping Association. [3275]

American Camping Association Conference & Exhibits [3272]

American-Canadian Genealogical Society Library [9482]

American Casino Guide [9410]

American Cat Fanciers Association (ACFA) [995]

American Cemetery Association [9321]

American Ceramic Society Bulletin [6001]

American Chain of Warehouses (ACWI) [16638]

American Chain of Warehouses--Membership Directory [16648]

American Chambers of Commerce Abroad [36340]

American Chapter, International Real Estate Federation [16783]

American Cheese Society (ACS) [19204]

"American Chemistry Council Launches Flagship Blog" in Ecology,Environment & Conservation Business (October 29, 2011, pp. 5) [7099], [7460], [18388], [25416], [28539], [30480], [33509], [35694], [36957]

American Choral Directors Association National Conference [14657], [14755]

American Christmas Tree Journal [4052]

American City and County [42396]

American Clinical Laboratory Association (ACLA) [14259]

American Coatings Association (ACA) [15366], [15384]

American Coin-Op [6745]

American Collectors Association [6272]

American Collectors Associations--Membership Roster [6272]

American College of Apothecaries (ACA) [6622]

American College of Apothecaries - Research and Education Resource Center [34644]

American College of Health Care Administrators (ACHCA) [1418], [15043]

American College of Health Care Administrators - ACHCA Information Center [327], [15122]

American College of Nursing Home Administrators [1418], [15043]

American Commercial Collectors Association [6267]

American Compensation Association [25370]

American Conference of Pharmaceutical Faculties [6620]

American Congress on Surveying and Mapping (ACSM) [19500]

American Conservatory of Music - Robert R. McCormick Memorial Library [14667]

American Convention of Meat Processors [3153]

American Council for Construction Education (ACCE) [5161]

American Council on Exercise [15937]

American Council of Life Insurers (ACLI) [11265]

American Council on Public Relations [16579], [42446]

American Counseling Association (ACA) [3338]

American Countertrade Association [36294]

American Court and Commercial Newspapers (ACCN) [15481]

American Craft [6120]

American Craft Council (ACC) [5956], [6091]

American Craft Council Library [6072], [6165]

American Craft--News Section [5965]

American Crafts Council [5956], [6091]

American Craftsmen's Council [5956], [6091]

American Culinary Federation (ACF) [5830]

American Custom Gunmakers Guild (ACGG) [10023]

American Cut Crystal Corp. [14033]

American Cutlery Manufacturers Association--Annual Membership Directory [10387]

American Dance Guild (ADG) [6365]

American Dance Therapy Association (ADTA) [6366]

American Defense Institute (ADI) [44088]

The American Demand for Office Furniture and Anticipated Trends [15282]

American Dental Trade Association [14184]

American Dietetic Association [15147]

American Dietetic Association - Knowledge Center [10263], [10324], [15209], [21291]

American Disc Jockey Association (ADJA) [6554]

American Documentation Institute [11222]

American Down Association [2022], [10385], [11527]

American Driver and Safety Education Association [6594]

American Driver Education Association [6594]

American Driver and Traffic Safety Education Association (ADTSEA) [6594]

American Driving Society (ADS) [10595]

American Driving Society Inc. [10595]

American Drycleaner: The Industry's Number One Magazine [6746]

American Economic Development Council [26849]

American Economic Development Council - Council for Urban Economic Development - American Industrial Development Council [26849]

American Edged Products Manufacturers Association--Annual Membership Directory [10387]

American Educational Publishers Institute [2079]

American Electrology Association (AEA) [10051]

American Electrolysis Association [10051]

American English Academy (AEA) [2813], [22514], [22648], [25936], [28429]

American English College [2813], [22514], [22648], [25936], [28429]

American Enterprise Institute (AEI) [34096]

The American Entrepreneur Today [30357]

American Federation for Clinical Research [14305]

American Federation for Medical Research (AFMR) [14305]

American Federation of Teachers Library [20750]

American Film Institute - Louis B. Mayer Library [3211], [14588], [20900]

American Financial Services Association (AFSA) [6225]

American Firms, Subsidiaries and Affiliates Operating in Foreign Countries [36469]

American Fisheries Society (AFS) [8993]

American Fisheries Society Annual Meeting [9030]

American Fitness [15984]

American Floorcovering Alliance (AFA) [9053], [11524]

American Floorcovering Association [9059]

American Floral Art School - Floral Library [9131], [18805]

American Forensic Engineers [2563], [47513]

American Formalwear Association [4191]

American Foundation for Management Research [13757], [37556]

American Foundation for Pharmaceutical Education (AFPE) [6623]

American Franchise Consultants [2992], [26113]

American Franchisee Association (AFA) [32114]

American Fraternal Insurance Company - Mutual Benefit and Aid Society [21860]

American-French Genealogical Society Library [9483]

American Fur Industry [9351], [9355]

American Furniture Manufacturers Association [10445]

American Gaming Association (AGA) [9376]

The American Gardener: The Magazine of the American Horticultural Society [9799]

American Gem Trade Association (AGTA) [13248]

American Hair Loss Council (AHLC) [10052]

American Handwriting Analysis Foundation (AHAF) [10111]

American Hardware Manufacturers Association (AHMA) [10120]

American Harp Society National Conference [14658]

American Hatpin Society [1110], [4328], [13249]

American Hatter [10155]

American Health and Beauty Aids Institute (AHBAI) [1888], [10060]

American Health Care Association (AHCA) [15044], [34100]

American Health Care Association Annual Convention and Exposition [15109]

American Health Care Association Journal [34584]

American Health Care Association - Mark A. Jerstad Information Resource Center [15044], [34100]

American Health Information Management Association (AHIMA) [14248]

American Health Information Management Association - FORE Library [14345]

American Hellenic Institute (AHI) [36273]

American Herb Association (AHA) [10358]

American Herb Association - Library [10370]

American Herbal Products Association (AHPA) [10359]

American Highway Freight Association [20649]

American Hockey Magazine [18810]

American Home Business Association (AHBA) [35588]

American Home Furnishings Alliance (AHFA) [10445]

American Home Laundry Manufacturers Association [1182]

American Home Lighting Association [6925]

American Reflexology Certification Board (ARCB) **[14811]**
American Reiki Master Association (ARMA) **[14812]**
American Rental Association (ARA) **[17746]**
American Rental Association Annual Convention and Rental Trade Show **[17827]**
American Resource Recovery Ltd. [10179]
American Restaurant Institute [9144], [17869]
American Restoration Services **[2645]**
The American Review of Public Administration **[42397]**
American Rifleman **[1244]**
American Risk and Insurance Association (ARIA) **[11268]**
American River College **[49365]**
American River Ventures **[49167]**
American Roofing Consultants Inc. **[2564]**
American Running Association **[15938]**
American Saddlebred Museum - Library **[10623]**
American Salers **[1024]**
American School Band Directors' Association (ASBDA) **[14726]**
American School Health Association National School Health Conference **[34613]**, **[46742]**
American Seed Research Foundation (ASRF) **[21818]**
American Seed Trade Association (ASTA) **[9759]**, **[13346]**
American Senior Benefits Association (ASBA) **[33476]**
American Seniors Housing Association (ASHA) **[15047]**
American Sewing Guild (ASG) **[6092]**, **[18718]**
American Small Business Association [33476]
American Small Businesses Association [33476]
American Society of Agricultural Consultants (ASAC) **[21492]**
American Society for the Alexander Technique (AMSAT) **[6367]**
American Society of Appraisers (ASA) **[1205]**
American Society of Appraisers - International Appraisal Conference **[1223]**
American Society of Artists (ASA) **[5957]**
American Society of Artists, Inc. - Resource Center **[6073]**, **[6167]**
American Society of Association Executives (ASAE) **[1454]**
American Society of Association Executives - The Center for Association Leadership - Knowledge Center **[1477]**
American Society of Baking **[1745]**
American Society of Baking - Information Service and Library **[1699]**, **[1824]**
American Society of Bariatric Physicians (ASBP) **[21276]**
American Society of Civil Engineers (ASCE) - Architectural Engineering Institute (AEI) **[14095]**
American Society for Clinical Laboratory Science (ASCLS) **[14261]**
American Society for Clinical Pathology (ASCP) **[14262]**
American Society of Consultant Pharmacists (ASCP) **[6625]**
American Society of Consultant Pharmacists Annual Meeting and Exhibition **[6692]**
American Society of Consulting Arborists (ASCA) **[13364]**
American Society of Consulting Arborists--Membership Directory **[13382]**
American Society for Industrial Security [18372]
American Society for Industrial Security--Annual Membership Directory [18391]
American Society for Medical Technology [14261]
American Society for Training and Development [4752], [27971], [35651]
American Society for Training and Development-- Consultant Directory [28363]
American Society of Furniture Designers (ASFD) **[9357]**
American Society of Furniture Designers--Membership Directory **[9358]**
American Society of Hand Therapists (ASHT) **[14138]**
American Society of Health-System Pharmacists (ASHP) **[6626]**
American Society Heating and Air-Conditioning Engineers - American Society of Refrigerating Engineers [762]
American Society of Heating, Refrigerating and Air-Conditioning Engineers (ASHRAE) **[762]**
American Society of Heating, Refrigerating and Air-Conditioning Engineers Research Program (ASHRAE) **[914]**
American Society for Indexing (ASI) **[1]**
American Society for Information Science and Technology (ASIS&T) **[11222]**
American Society of Inventors (ASI) **[36948]**
American Society of Journalists and Authors (ASJA) **[6772]**
American Society of Journalists and Authors--Directory **[6816]**
American Society of Journalists and Authors Newsletter **[6832]**

American Society of Landscape Architects (ASLA) **[13365]**
American Society of Landscape Architects Annual Meeting and Expo **[13428]**
American Society of Landscape Architects - Professional Practice Library **[13447]**
American Society of Magazine Editors (ASME) **[15482]**
American Society of Media Photographers Inc. (Society of Magazine Photographers) **[15483]**, **[15836]**
American Society of Media Photographers--Membership Directory **[15845]**
American Society of Bakery Engineers [1745]
American Society of Clinical Laboratory Technicians [14261]
American Society of Clinical Pathologists [14284]
American Society of Clinical Pathologists [14262]
American Society of CLU and ChFC [11301]
American Society of Corporate Secretaries [20820]
American Society of Heating, Refrigerating, and Air Conditioning Engineers, Inc. [762]
American Society of Hospital Pharmacists [6626]
American Society of Indexers [1]
American Society of Indexers, Inc. [1]
American Society of Inspectors of Plumbing and Sanitary Engineering [16210]
American Society of Insurance Management [11300]
American Society of Journalists and Authors--Directory of Professional Writers [6816]
American Society of Landscape Architects Foundation [13372]; [13461]
American Society of Magazine Photographers-- Membership Directory [15845]
American Society of Medical Technologists [14261]
American Society of Pension Actuaries [21850]
American Society of Piano Technicians [14789]
American Society of Real Estate Counselors [16782]
American Society of Refrigerating Engineers [762]
American Society of Superintendents of Training Schools for Nurses [10525]
American Society of Technical Appraisers [1205]
American Society of Tool and Manufacturing Engineers [13693]
American Society of Tool Engineers [13693]
American Society of Traffic and Transportation [16639]
American Society of Training Directors [4752], [27971], [35651]
American Society of Pension Professionals and Actuaries (ASPPA) **[21850]**
American Society for Pharmacy Law (ASPL) **[6627]**
American Society of Photographers (ASP) **[15837]**
American Society of Plumbing Engineers (ASPE) **[16209]**
American Society of Professional Estimators (ASPE) **[5163]**
American Society of Professional Estimators-- Membership Directory and Buyers' Guide **[5218]**
American Society for Public Administration (ASPA) **[42359]**
American Society for Quality Press (ASQ) **[59794]**
American Society of Sanitary Engineering (ASSE) **[16210]**
American Society Training and Development Buyer's Guide and Consultant Directory **[28106]**
American Society for Training and Development - Information Center **[3053]**, **[13902]**, **[28483]**, **[36076]**
American Society of Transportation and Logistics (AST&L) **[16639]**
American Society of Travel Agents (ASTA) **[20504]**
American Society of Wedding Professionals (ASWP) **[2486]**
American Society of Women Accountants (ASWA) **[16]**
American Society of Women Accountants--Membership Directory **[61]**
American Solar Energy Society (ASES) **[19067]**
American Sports Builders Association (ASBA) **[5164]**, **[15939]**, **[20050]**
American Staffing Association (ASA) **[6948]**, **[20023]**
American Stamp Dealers Association (ASDA) **[4333]**
American Steamship and Tourist Agents Association [20504]
American String Teachers Association (ASTA) **[14602]**
American Subcontractors Association (ASA) **[15385]**, **[18311]**
American Suffolk Horse Association Library **[10624]**
American Supply Association (ASA) **[16211]**
American Supply Association--Membership Directory: Resource Guide **[785]**, **[16284]**
American Suzuki Journal **[14632]**
American Taxation Association [13]
American Taxation Association (ATA) **[17]**, **[19592]**, **[46132]**
American Taxation Association - American Accounting Association [13]

American Technical Education Association National Conference on Technical Education **[44078]**, **[46743]**
American Television Society [16696], [19887]
American Tennis Association (ATA) **[20051]**
American Title Association [16779]
American Tool, Die & Stamping News **[13723]**
American Topical Association, Americana Unit (AU) **[21452]**, **[41467]**
American Town Mailer **[667]**
American Trade Association Executives [1454]
American Transit Association [19798]
American Translators Association (ATA) **[20464]**
American Translators Association Annual Conference **[20485]**
American Translators Association--Membership Directory **[20472]**
American Transportation Research Institute (ATRI) **[20725]**
American Truck Historical Society - Zoe James Memorial Library **[20723]**
American Trucker--Badger Edition: Serving Upper Peninsula of Michigan, Wisconsin **[20697]**
American Trucker--Buckeye Edition: Serving Ohio **[20698]**
American Trucker--Central States Edition: Serving Iowa, Kansas, Nebraska, Western Missouri **[20699]**
American Trucker--Illinois Edition: Serving Eastern Missouri, Illinois **[20700]**
American Trucker--South Central Edition: Serving Arkansas, Louisiana, Oklahoma, Texas **[20701]**
American Trucking Association Management Conference & Exhibition **[20715]**
American Trucking Associations (ATA) **[20649]**
American Typecasting Fellowship Newsletter **[20808]**
American University - National Center for Health Fitness (NCHF) **[14255]**
American-Uzbekistan Chamber of Commerce (AUCC) **[36276]**
American Veterinary Medical Association (AVMA) **[1047]**
American Veterinary Medical Association Annual Convention **[1083]**
American Veterinary Medical Association--Directory and Resource Manual: AVMA Membership Directory and Resource Manual **[1055]**
American Viewpoint Inc. [46031]
American Walnut Manufacturers Association (AWMA) **[13635]**
American Warehouse Association [16641]
American Warehousemen's Association [16641]
American Waste Industries Inc. [10179]
American Waste Processing Ltd. **[10179]**
American Waterpark Association [968]
American Wholesale Marketers Association (AWMA) **[3277]**, **[20084]**
American Wholesalers and Distributors Directory **[26730]**, **[47170]**
American Window Cleaner Magazine: TheVoice of the Professional Window Cleaner **[2632]**
American Window Covering Manufacturers Association [2024], [11537]
American Woman's Society of Certified Public Accountants (AWSCPA) **[18]**
American Yachtmen's Association [3863], [13923]
American Youth Horse Council (AYHC) **[10598]**
Americana Philatelic News **[4358]**
AmeriCandy Retail Interactive Kiosk (AIRK) **[3300]**
"The Americans Are Coming" in The Economist (Vol. 390, January 3, 2009, No. 8612, pp. 44) **[20473]**, **[22263]**, **[25827]**, **[28117]**, **[36341]**
The Americans with Disabilities Act: New Access to the Workplace **[26680]**
Americans for Better Care [15052]
Americans With Disabilities Act (ADA) **[26650]**
AmeriCare Franchise Ltd. **[668]**
America's Choice/Canada's Choice **[40658]**
Americas Consulting Group Inc. **[36911]**
America's Corporate Families **[32519]**
America's Little Switzerland **[59482]**
Americas MLM Consultants [58606]
America's Pharmacist: The Voice of the Community Pharmacists **[6674]**
Americas Project Management Services [36911]
"Americhem to Shutter Maryland Operation" in Crain's Cleveland Business (Vol. 28, October 29, 2007, No. 43, pp. 14) **[22697]**, **[24225]**, **[38902]**
Americus-Sumter County Chamber of Commerce **[50434]**
Ameriflex Benefits Corp. [22035]
AmeriFlex Financial Services [22035]
Amerimark Capital Corp. **[58546]**
Amerispec Home Inspection Service **[2578]**
AmeriSpec Inspection Service **[2579]**
Ameriwest Business Consultants Inc. (ABCI) **[24652]**, **[25281]**

Ames Chamber of Commerce (ACC) [51814]
Amgen Inc. [49168]
Amgen, Inc. - Amgen Libraries [6708]
Amherst Area Chamber of Commerce [52830]
Amherst Chamber of Commerce [55082]
Amherst County Chamber of Commerce (ACCC) [58848]
Amherst County Guidebook [58849]
"Amid Recession, Companies Still Value Supplier Diversity Programs" in Hispanic Business (July-August 2009, pp. 34) [5219], [26889], [38903], [40701], [42938], [45270]
Amidzad, LLC [49169]
"Amit Wadhwaney" in Canadian Business (Vol. 80, March 12, 2007, No. 6, pp. 22) [8067], [12020], [29468]
Amory-North Monroe Chamber of Commerce and Development Council [53884]
Amoskeag Business Incubator [54629]
"Amount Md. Pays to Unemployed Dips to Lowest Level Since '08" in Baltimore Business Journal (Vol. 28, November 12, 2010, No. 27) [21864], [33144], [35695], [45271]
Ampersand Ventures [53002]
Amphora [3220]
"Ampm Focus Has BP Working Overtime; New Convenience-Store Brand Comes to Chicago" in Crain's Chicago Business (April 28, 2008) [382], [5795], [11041], [32125], [36342], [39652], [42601]
AMS - Knowledge Center Library [5064]
AMS Newsletter [14633]
AmSpirit Business Connections [3096]
AMT--Member Product Directory [13698]
"AMT's Partner Program Enables New Security Business Models" in Internet Wire (August 12, 2010) [3495], [4841], [18389], [18856], [40987], [45084]
Amusement Industry Manufacturers and Suppliers International (AIMS) [964]
Amusement and Music Operators Association Convention [958]
The Amusement and Theme Parks Industry Market [978]
Anaconda Chamber of Commerce (ACOC) [54241]
Anacortes Chamber of Commerce (ACC) [59087]
The Anacortes Communicator [59088]
Anadarko Chamber of Commerce [56459]
Anago Franchising, Inc. [2646]
Anaheim Business Advocate [48214]
Anaheim Chamber of Commerce [48215]
Anahuac Area Chamber of Commerce [57933]
"An Analysis of Three Labor Unions' Outreach to Brazilian Immigrant Workers in Boston" in WorkingUSA (Vol. 11, June 2008, No. 2) [40858], [46838]
"Analyst Questions CanWest Papers' Viability" in Globe & Mail (January 14, 2006, pp. B3) [15518], [24226], [25017]
"Analysts: Intel Site May Be Last Major U.S.-Built Fab" in Business Journal-Serving Phoenix and the Valley of the Sun (Oct. 19, 2007) [5220], [34763], [38904], [45272]
"Analysts: More Mergers for the Region's Hospitals" in Boston Business Journal (Vol. 30, October 15, 2010, No. 36, pp. 1) [12021], [25292], [33510], [34188], [41733], [45273]
"Analysts Not Fazed By Constellation's Halt to New Nuclear Plants" in Baltimore Business Journal (Vol. 28, October 22, 2010, No. 24) [5221], [8068], [12022], [25018]
"Analysts Not Too Sad Over Gemunder" in Business Courier (Vol. 27, August 6, 2010, No. 14, pp. 1) [6642], [15064], [37784]
Analytical Consulting Services [10180]
Analytical Solutions [41468]
"Analyzing the Analytics" in Entrepreneur (Vol. 37, October 2009, No. 10, pp. 42) [11614], [15306], [21045], [22698], [28540], [44808]
Analyzing Our Time Usage [46546]
Anamosa Area Chamber of Commerce [51815]
The Anatomical Record: Advances in Integrative Anatomy and Evolutionary Biology [43995]
"The Anatomy of a High Potential" in Business Strategy Review (Vol. 21, Autumn 2010, No. 3, pp. 52) [25417], [29011], [35696], [37785], [25418], [29012], [35697]
Anatomy of a Leveraged Buyout [2719]
"Anatomy of a Rumor" in Entrepreneur (Vol. 37, September 2009, No. 9, pp. 18) [29013], [37786]
"ANATURALCONCEPT" in Crain's Cleveland Business (Vol. 30, June 22, 2009, No. 24, pp. 1) [7100], [7461], [29469], [30481], [38905]
Ancestry [9452]
Anchor Bay Chamber of Commerce (ABCC) [53125]
Anchor News [52831]
Anchor Point Brochure/Visitor Guide [47778]
Anchor Point Chamber of Commerce (APCOC) [47779]
Anchorage Chamber of Commerce (ACC) [47780]

"And In This Briefcase" in Mergers & Acquisitions: The Dealmaker's Journal (March 1, 2008) [8069], [12023], [20308], [26890], [41734], [46589]
"And the Money Comes Rolling In" in Inc. (Vol. 31, January-February 2009, No. 1, pp. 62) [5091], [29470]
"And The Winner Is.." in Canadian Business (Vol. 81, March 3, 2008, No. 3, pp. 21) [11042], [18390], [26891], [33511], [36343]
A & W Restaurants, Inc. [18068]
Andersen Horticultural Library's Source List of Plants and Seeds [9772]
Anderson Area Chamber of Commerce [56001]
Anderson Area Chamber of Commerce (AACOC) [57428]
Anderson Area Medical Center Library [6709], [15123]
Anderson County Chamber of Commerce [52259]
Anderson County Chamber of Commerce (ACCC) [57647]
Larry J. Anderson Insurance [21453], [22142]
Anderson, Kill & Olick - Library [36264]
Richard I. Anderson [4670]
Anderson/Roethle Inc. [13791], [25937], [38651], [39518], [40577]
Anderson Valley Chamber of Commerce [48216]
Andover Area Chamber of Commerce and Convention and Visitors' Bureau [52040]
Andover Area Chamber of Commerce [52040]
Andrew Harper's Hideaway Report [20593]
Andrew Smash [10943], [18069]
Andrews Chamber of Commerce [55575]
Andrews & Kurth L.L.P. Library [7393]
Androscoggin County Chamber of Commerce [52556]
Andy OnCall [5683]
Angel Crafts Video Vol. 1 [6146]
Angel Financing: How to Find and Invest in Private Equity [29326], [37266], [41360], [46957]
Angel Fire Chamber of Commerce [54922]
"Angel Investing 2009" in Inc. (Vol. 31, January-February 2009, No. 1, pp. 83) [37294], [41364], [46987]
"Angel Investments Tripled in 2009" in Austin Business JournalInc. (Vol. 29, January 8, 2010, No. 44, pp. 1) [3496], [18857], [37295], [42749], [43319], [43792], [45085], [46988]
"Angel Investors Across State Collaborate" in Austin Business Journal (Vol. 31, May 20, 2011, No. 11, pp. 1) [32346], [37296], [41365], [41735]
Angelina College Small Business Development Center [57837]
Angelina County Chamber of Commerce [58291]
Angelo State University Small Business Development Center [57838]
Angels Ice Cream and Hot Dog Franchise [10944]
"Angels for the Jobless; Church Volunteer Groups Give Career Guidance" in Crain's Detroit Business (Vol. 24, March 31, 2008, No. 13) [28118], [32520], [43378]
Angier Chamber of Commerce (ACC) [55576]
"Angiotech to Buy Top Medical Devices Company" in Globe & Mail (February 1, 2006, pp. B1) [6643], [41736], [43793]
Angiuli Katkin & Gentile, LLP [24115]
Angola Area Chamber of Commerce (AACC) [51515]
Angwin Community Council [48217]
Anheuser-Busch Companies, Inc. - Corporate Library [1885], [2479]
Animal Health Institute (AHI) [1048]
Animal Medical Center Library [1093]
Animal News [1070]
Animal Spirits: How Human Psychology Drives the Economy, and Why it Matters for Global Capitalism [26892], [36344]
"Anja Carroll; Media Director-McDonald's USA" in Advertising Age (Vol. 79, November 17, 2008, No. 34, pp. 6) [383], [17881], [29471], [37787], [39653]
Ankeny Area Chamber of Commerce [51816]
"Ann Alexander; Senior Attorney, Natural Resources Defense Council" in Crain's Chicago Business (Vol. 31, May 5, 2008, No. 18) [23717], [30482], [33512], [36345], [37788], [38906], [44249]
Ann Arbor Area Chamber of Commerce [53126]
Ann Arbor Business-to-Business [53127]
Ann Arbor Consulting Associates Inc. [26615]
"Ann Arbor Google's Growth Dips" in Crain's Detroit Business (Vol. 25, June 8, 2009, No. 23, pp. 3) [22699], [28541], [34764]
Ann Arbor SPARK Regional Incubator Network [53499]
Ann Arbor/Ypsilanti Regional Chamber [53500]
Ann Welsh Communications Inc. [22515]
Anna Maria Island Chamber of Commerce [49932]
Anna Maria Island Vacation Guide [49933]
Anna-Jonesboro Area Chamber of Commerce [51340]
Annals & Magazine of Natural History [44048]
Annandale Chamber of Commerce (ACC) [58850]
Annandale Chamber of Commerce Newsletter [58851]

Annandale Community Directory [58852]
Annapolis and Anne Arundel County Chamber of Commerce [52671]
"Annapolis Seeks City Market Vendors" in Boston Business Journal (Vol. 29, June 10, 2011, No. 5, pp. 3) [1267], [13313], [33401]
Anne Arundel Small Business Development Center [52650]
Anne Arundel Trade Council [52671]
Annie's Plastic Canvas Magazine [6121]
Anniston SCORE [47614]
Annual Allegheny Sport, Travel and Outdoor Show [19366], [20207]
Annual Area Resource Guide and Directory [57361]
Annual Business Directory [48218]; [51516]
Annual Business and Pleasure Guide [52557]
Annual Dickens Christmas Show [4045], [6037], [6153]
Annual Dickens Christmas Show and Festivals Week [4045], [6037], [6153]
Annual Directory [49934]
Annual Directory and Economic Data Book [55577]
Annual Directory and Guidebook [52832]
Annual Employment by Industry [3397]
"The Annual Entitlement Lecture: Trustees of Medicare and Social Security Issue Another Dismal Report" in Barron's (March 31, 2008) [8070], [11306], [12024], [21865], [31196], [33145], [34189], [36106], [46143]
Annual Fact Book [347]
Annual Hotel, Motel, and Restaurant Supply Show of the Southeast [10779], [18037]
Annual Meeting of the American Academy of Ophthalmology [20942]
Annual NAIW Convention - National Association of Insurance Women International [11479], [47439]
Annual Reading Sport, Travel and Outdoor Show [19367], [20619]
Annual Register of Grant Support: A Directory of Funding Sources, 45th Edition [9240]
Annual Report [52430]
Annual Review [7874]
Annual Rockford RV, Camping and Travel Show [17677], [19368], [20620]
Annual Roster [14263]
Annual Spring New Products Show [13959]
Annual Trade Show Directory [20309], [46590]
Annual World Fishing and Outdoor Exposition [1731], [19392]
Anoka Area Chamber of Commerce (AACC) [53570]
Anonymous Hero [936]
"Another Baby Step" in Canadian Business (Vol. 81, March 31, 2008, No. 5, pp. 32) [22100], [26893], [33513], [42750], [46144]
"Another California Firm On Way" in Austin Business Journal (Vol. 31, May 6, 2011, No. 9, pp. 1) [10990], [16583], [16813], [17190], [24716], [28542], [44637]
"Another Determinant of Entrepreneurship" in International Journal of Entrepreneurship and Small Business (Vol. 10, July 6, 2010) [29472], [36346], [40859]
"Another Man's Pain" in Canadian Business (Vol. 80, October 22, 2007, No. 21, pp. 33) [12025], [16814], [17191], [26894]
Another Meeting [46547]
Anshen + Allen [41571]
Anson County [55578]
Anson County Chamber of Commerce (ACCC) [55579]
"Answers About Commercial Wind Farms Could Come from Downstate" in Erie Times-News (September 27, 2011) [7101], [7462], [30483]
Antares Capital Corp. [47118]
Antelope Highlands Chamber of Commerce [48219]
Antelope Valley Board of Trade (AVBOT) [48220]
Antelope Valley Business News [48221]
Antelope Valley Chambers of Commerce - Rosamond [48222]
Anthem Capital Management LLC [52768]
"Anthem Leading the Way in Social Tech Revolution" in Inside Business (Vol. 13, September-October 2011, No. 5, pp. 1B3) [11307], [28543], [36107], [39654]
Anthem Venture Partners [49170]
Anthony Chamber of Commerce (ACC) [52041]
Anthony Curtis' Las Vegas Advisor [9411]
Anthropological Literature Database [9478]
Anti-Lock Brake Systems Explained [18627]
Anticipation: Rx for Crisis Management [38614]
Antioch Chamber of Commerce [48223]
Antioch Chamber of Commerce and Industry (ACCI) [50901]
Antiquarian Booksellers Association of America (ABAA) [2351]
Antiquarian Booksellers' Association of Canada (ABAC) [1111], [2352]
Antique and Decorative Arts League [1113]

Antique Automobile Club of America - AACA Library & Research Center, Inc. [14559]

Antique Boat Museum, Inc. - Lou Smith Library and Marion Clayton Link Archives [13974]

Antique Bottle and Glass Collector [1130], [4410], [6122]

Antique Trader Weekly: America's Weekly Antiques & Collectibles Marketplace [1131]

Antique Wireless Association Library/Museum [19876]

Antiques and Collecting Hobbies [1133], [4411]

Antiques and the Arts Weekly [1132]

Antiques & Collecting Magazine [1133], [4411]

Antitrust Law: Economic Theory and Common Law Evolution [23718], [26895]

Antitrust & Trade Regulation Report [36921]

Lou Antonelli [3389]

"Antwerpen Takes on Chrysler Financial Over Foreclosure Sales" in Baltimore Business Journal (Vol. 28, July 30, 2010, No. 12, pp. 1) [1491], [14379], [14852], [16815], [17193], [17753], [23719], [31197]

"Anybody Out There?" in Canadian Business (Vol. 81, July 21 2008, No. 11, pp. 31) [5120], [34765], [44250]

"Anything Could Happen" in Inc. (March 2008, pp. 116-123) [11615], [28544], [29473], [34766]

"Anytime Access" in Crain's Cleveland Business (Vol. 28, October 22, 2007, No. 42, pp. 17) [22264], [25419], [34767]

Anytime Fitness [16015]

Anza Valley Chamber of Commerce [48224]

AOA News [20936]

Aon Corp. [22036]

Aon Hewitt [22036]

AOPA Aviation Summit - Aircraft Owners and Pilots Association [738]

A.P. Designs [11575], [41572]

APA: The Engineered Wood Association [13636]

APA--The Engineered Wood Association--Management Journal [13668]

Apache Junction Chamber of Commerce (AJCC) [47847]

Apalachicola Bay Area of Franklin County [49935]

Apalachicola Bay Chamber of Commerce (ABCC) [49936]

Apalachicola Times [49937]

"Apartment Ambitions" in The Business Journal-Portland (Vol. 25, August 8, 2008, No. 22, pp. 1) [16508], [16816], [17193], [26896]

Apartment Association of Metro Denver Seminar and Trade Show [16559]

Apartment For Rent [1164]

Apartment Management Magazine [1162]

"Apartment Market Down, Not Out" in Crain's Detroit Business (Vol. 24, October 6, 2008, No. 40, pp. 9) [12026], [14380], [16509], [16817], [17194], [26135], [26897], [37297]

Apartment Owner/Builder [1162]

"Apartment Tower in River North Fetches More Than $90 Million" in Crain's Chicago Business (Vol. 34, October 24, 2011, No. 42, pp. 17) [8071], [12027], [16818], [17195], [17754], [44131]

ApEx [3476], [9178], [10307], [10780], [18038], [46744]

Apex Associates Inc. [13792], [25938], [38652]

Apex Chamber of Commerce [55580]

Apex Innovations Inc. [13792], [25938], [38652]

Apex Venture Partners [51392]

Apiary Inspectors of America (AIA) [1941]

Apogee Solutions Corp. [21767]

Apollo Beach Chamber of Commerce [49938]

Apopka Area Chamber of Commerce [49939]

"App Time: Smartphone Applications Aren't Just for Fun and Games Anymore" in Inc. (Volume 32, December 2010, No. 10, pp. 116) [384], [3681], [34768], [39655], [44251], [45274]

Appalachia-Science in the Public Interest Library [7394]

Appalachian Center for Economic Networks (ACEnet) [56392]

"Apparel" in Retail Merchandiser (Vol. 51, July-August 2011, No. 4, pp. 14) [4085], [4194], [7814], [18753], [45275]

"Apparel Apparatchic at Kmart" in Barron's (Vol. 88, March 17, 2008, No. 11, pp. 16) [385], [4195], [11616], [21046], [26373], [42939]

Apparel News South [3901], [4292]

AppendX [1292], [5571]

Appian Ventures [49615]

Apple Auto Glass Limited [9641]

Apple Blossom [50435]

"An Apple a Day" in Entrepreneur (Vol. 36, February 2008, No. 2, pp. 19) [11308], [21866], [34190], [36108]

Apple DVD Studio Pro I (Onsite) [45025]

Apple Final Cut Pro Bootcamp (Onsite) [45026]

Apple Final Cut Pro I (Onsite) [45027]

Apple Final Cut Pro II (Onsite) [45028]

Apple II Repair, Maintenance and Expansion [4807]

Apple Motion I (Onsite) [45029]

Apple Valley Chamber of Commerce [48225]; [53571]

Applebee's Neighborhood Grill & Bar [18070]

Applegate Inc. [10945]

"Apples, Decoded: WSU Scientist Unraveling the Fruit's Genetics" in Puget Sound Business Journal (Vol. 29, September 5, 2008, No. 20) [21516], [33402], [42751], [43794]

Appleton Chamber of Commerce [59578]

Appliance--Appliance Industry Purchasing Section Issue [884], [1186], [5731]

Appliance Design [1200]

Appliance Manufacturer [1200]

Appliance Parts Distributors Association (APDA) [1181]

Appliance Parts Jobbers Association [1181]

Appliance: Serving the Appliance Industry Worldwide [1201]

The Application of Good Design [4533]

Application Systems Development Audit and Security [34731]

Applications of Marketing Research (Onsite) [39574]; [39575]

Applied Arts Magazine [4526], [15851]

Applied Engineering in Agriculture [43996]

Applied Fire Protection Engineering Inc. [2565]

The Applied Management Series [30358]

Applied Materials Ventures [49171]

Applied Personnel Research (APR) [26698]

"Applying to Colleges? Consultants Can Demystify the Process" in Palm Beach Post (September 3, 2011) [25828], [28119]

"Applying Continuous Process Improvement for Managing Customer Loyalty" in Agency Sales Magazine (Vol. 39, November 2009, No. 10) [26374], [37789], [39657]

Applying Diversity Management to Innovation, Decision Making, Complex Problem Solving and Business Results (Onsite) [35662]

Appomattox County Chamber of Commerce (ACCC) [58853]

Appraisal Institute [1206]

Appraisal Institute Annual Meeting [1224]

Appraisal Institute Magazine [1220]

Appraisal Institute - Y.T. and Louise Lee Lum Library [1230]

The Appraiser [1218]

Appraiser 4 Jewelry [47140]

Appraisers Association of America (AAA) [1112], [1207]

Appraisers Association of America--Membership Directory [1121], [1213]

The Appraisers Standard [1219], [2560]

"Apprenticeship: Earn While You Learn" in Occupational Outlook Quarterly (Vol. 54, Fall 2010, No. 3, pp. 24) [28120], [35266], [35698], [46839]

"Apps For Anybody With an Idea" in Advertising Age (Vol. 79, October 20, 2008, No. 39, pp. 29) [3497], [3682], [11617], [18858], [34769], [45086]

APQC (APQC) [46475]

Apricot Lane [7864]

April Product Purchasing Maxi-Directory [13305]

"Aptitudes for Apps" in Boston Business Journal (Vol. 31, July 1, 2011, No. 23, pp. 3) [3683], [4938], [28545], [40988], [44986], [46989]

Aptos Chamber of Commerce [48226]

AQUA--Buyers' Guide Issue [19546]

AQUA Magazine: The Business Magazine for Spa and Pool Professionals [19548]

Aquaculture Magazine [9026]

Aquarian Alternatives [14817]

"Aquarium's Solar Demonstration Project Exceeds Expectations" in Contractor (Vol. 57, February 2010, No. 2, pp. 1) [7102], [7463], [19077], [30484]

Aquatic Control Inc. [9031]

Aquatic Exercise Association (AEA) [15940]

"Aquatic Medications Engender Good Health" in Pet Product News (Vol. 64, November 2010, No. 11, pp. 47) [1232], [15750], [28121], [38907], [42940]

Aquatic Research Institute [9040]

"Aquila HQ Hits the Market" in The Business Journal-Serving Metropolitan Kansas City (Vol. 26, July 25, 2008, No. 46, pp. 1) [16510], [16819], [17196], [44638]

Aquinas Group L.L.P. [42306]

ARA Fredericton Appraisal Associates Ltd. [17590]

Arab Chamber of Commerce [47622]

Arabian Horse Owners Foundation - W.R. Brown Memorial Library [10625]

Arabian Horse Trust Library [10626]

"Aramark Rolls Out Ballpark Food Truck" in Nation's Restaurant News (Vol. 45, August 8, 2011, No. 16, pp. 4) [9147], [17882]

Aransas Pass Chamber of Commerce [57934]

Arapahoe Chamber of Commerce [54358]

"Arario Gallery Opens First American Space" in Art Business News (Vol. 34, November 2007, No. 11, pp. 14) [1342], [5966], [36347]

Arbitration and Mediation Institute of Canada [14157]

Arbitration Journal [14167]

Arbor Partners, LLC [53477]

The Arboretum at Flagstaff - Transition Zone Horticultural Institute Library [13448]

Arboretum Ventures [53478]

Arboriculture Consultant [13405]

Arby's [18071]

ARC Analytics L.L.C. [206]

Arc Flash Protection & Electrical Safety 70E [24969], [28007]

Arc Flash Protection & Electrical Safety 70E (In-House Training) [6867]

The Arc News [34490]

Arcade Area Chamber of Commerce [55083]

Arcadia Academy of Music [14665]

Arcadia Chamber of Commerce (ACC) [48227]

Arcata Chamber of Commerce (AACC) [48228]

ARCC Regional Report [55084]

"Arcelor Bid Wins Dofasco Board's Blessing" in Globe & Mail (January 17, 2006, pp. B1) [32521], [41737]

Arch Venture Partners [51393]

Archadeck [3435]

Archbold Area Chamber of Commerce [56002]

Archdale-Trinity Chamber of Commerce (ATCC) [55581]

Archery Lane Operators Association [1239]

Archery Range and Retailers Organization (ARRO) [1239]

The Architect [55582]

Architects' Guide to Glass, Metal & Glazing [5572], [9638]

Architectural Alliance [41573]

Architectural Consultants Ltd. [2566]

Architectural Designs [3423], [5573]

Architectural Digest [11554]

Architectural Glass and Metal Contractors Association (AGMCA) [5165]

Architectural Lighting: The Lighting Specifiers Magazine [6934]

Architectural Research Consultants Inc. (ARC) [44752]

Architectural Woodwork Institute (AWI) [3413]

Architecture, Building Codes & Inspection [2567]

Archives of Environmental & Occupational Health: An International Journal [34491]

Archives of Environmental Health [34491]

Archtectural Lighting Consultation and Design [41629]

Arcola Chamber of Commerce [50902]

"Arctic IT Honored" in Alaska Business Monthly (Vol. 27, October 2011, No. 10, pp. 10) [3498], [4637], [18859], [45087]

ardea consulting [7373]

"Ardesta Venture-Capital Fund Folds" in Crain's Detroit Business (Vol. 24, September 22, 2008, No. 38, pp. 24) [26898], [43795], [46990]

ARDITO Information & Research Inc. [25717], [34077], [42307]

Ardmore Chamber of Commerce (ACOC) [56460]

Ardmore SCORE [56445]

Ardmoreport [56461]

"Are EO Programs Right for Your Business?" in Contractor (Vol. 56, October 2009, No. 10, pp. 49) [18676], [33514], [45861]

Are Government Purchasing Policies Failing Small Business?: Congressional Hearing [23720], [32522], [33403], [33515]

"Are Movie Theaters Doomed?" in Business Horizons (November-December 2007, pp. 491) [14566], [20882], [25420], [45276]

"Are Offline Pushes Important to E-Commerce?" in DM News (Vol. 31, September 14, 2009, No. 23, pp. 10) [386], [11618], [28546], [39658]

"Are Prepaid Legal Services Worthwhile?" in Contractor (Vol. 56, December 2009, No. 12, pp. 31) [11309], [21867], [36109]

Are the Rich Necessary? Great Economic Arguments and How They Reflect Our Personal Values [12028], [26899], [31198]

"Are There Material Benefits To Social Diversity?" in Hispanic Business (Vol. 30, September 2008, No. 9, pp. 10) [28122], [32523], [33146], [35267], [37790], [45862]

"Are We There Yet?" in Business Courier (Vol. 24, April 4, 2008, No. 52, pp. 1) [5222], [12029], [17197], [26136], [37298]

"Are You Ignoring Trends That Could Shake Up Your Business?" in Harvard Business Review (Vol. 88, July-August 2010, No. 7-8, pp. 124) [22700], [39659], [45277]

"Are You Looking for an Environmentally Friendly Dry Cleaner?" in Inc. (Vol. 30, December 2008, No. 12, pp. 34) [4196], [6740], [7103], [7464], [17883], [25293], [30485], [42941]

"Are You Overinsured? Some Policies May Not Offer Much Additional Benefit" in Black Enterprise (Vol. 38, March 2008, No. 8, pp. 126) [11310], [36110]

Ashland Area Chamber of Commerce (AACC) **[56003]**; **[59483]**
Ashland Chamber of Commerce **[52043]**; **[56704]**
Ashland Chamber News **[56705]**
Ashland Chamber of Commerce [54359]
Ashland Group L.P. **[9292]**, **[16613]**
Ashland Small Business Development Center - Kentucky **[52218]**
Ashtabula Area Chamber of Commerce (AACC) **[56004]**
"Asia Breathes a Sigh of Relief" in Business Week (September 22, 2008, No. 4100, pp. 32) **[8074]**, **[12033]**, **[14381]**, **[26137]**, **[26905]**, **[31202]**, **[36352]**, **[37301]**
Asia Pacific Foundation of Canada (APFC) [26820]
Asiafit **[19369]**
ASIAN **[49139]**
Asian American Hotel Owners Association (AAHOA) **[10643]**
Asian American Writers' Workshop (AAWW) **[6773]**
Asian Chamber of Commerce **[47854]**
Asian Chao/Maki of Japan/Chao Cajun **[18072]**
"The Asian Decade" in Hawaii Business (Vol. 53, January 2008, No. 7, pp. 19) **[12034]**, **[17198]**, **[36353]**, **[41741]**, **[44639]**, **[45865]**
Asian Godfathers: Money and Power in Hong Kong and Southeast Asia **[26906]**, **[36354]**
Asian, Inc. [49139]
Asian SUNews **[47855]**
Asian Women in Business (AWIB) **[40676]**, **[47203]**
ASIS International **[18372]**
ASIS International--Annual Membership Directory **[18391]**
Ask Dr. Jim about Cats **[15790]**
Ask Dr. Jim about Dogs **[15698]**, **[15791]**
"Ask Inc" in Inc. (February 2008, pp. 52) **[25829]**, **[43380]**
"Ask Inc." in Inc. (December 2007, pp. 83-84) **[16820]**, **[17199]**, **[35270]**, **[37232]**, **[40860]**
"Ask Inc." in Inc. (January 2008, pp. 60) **[22580]**, **[28553]**
"Ask Inc." in Inc. (January 2008, pp. 61) **[5971]**, **[6100]**, **[39664]**
"Ask Inc." in Inc. (November 2007, pp. 69) **[35699]**, **[37796]**
"Ask Inc." in Inc. (November 2007, pp. 70) **[25294]**, **[44132]**
"Ask Inc." in Inc. (October 2007, pp. 73-74) **[5092]**, **[19505]**, **[28552]**, **[39662]**, **[40960]**, **[42752]**, **[45280]**
"Ask Inc." in Inc. (October 2007, pp. 74) **[388]**, **[4400]**, **[39663]**
Ask NELMA Newsletter **[13669]**
Ask for the Order. . .and Get It! **[8875]**, **[13151]**, **[43706]**
Ask for the Order. . .and Get It!?Revised **[43707]**
ASMP Book [15845]
ASMP Bulletin **[15906]**
Asociacion Mondial de Radios Communautarias [16702]
Asotin Chamber of Commerce **[59090]**
ASP-America's Swimming Pool Co. **[19556]**
Aspen Chamber Resort Association (ACRA) **[49447]**
Asphalt and Vinyl Asbestos Tile Institute [9057]
Asphalt Association [1994]
The Asphalt Contractor **[2009]**
Asphalt Emulsion Manufacturers Association-- Membership Directory **[1997]**
Asphalt Institute (AI) **[1994]**
Asphalt Institute Research Library **[2011]**
Asphalt Paving Technologists **[1998]**
Asphalt Recycling & Reclaiming Association-- Membership Directory **[1999]**
Asphalt Roofing Industry Bureau [18312]
Asphalt Roofing Manufacturers Association (ARMA) **[18312]**
Asphalt Tile Institute [9057]
ASP.NET with VB.NET and C I (Onsite) **[45030]**
ASP.NET with VB.NET and C II **[45031]**
ASP.NET with VB.NET C III **[45032]**
Assabet Valley Chamber of Commerce **[52835]**
Assertive Communication - Essential Skills for Successful Women (Onsite) **[22156]**
Assertive Management (Onsite) **[28972]**, **[37580]**
Assertiveness Skills: Communicating with Authority and Impact (Onsite) **[37581]**
Assertiveness Skills: Communicating With Authority and Impact (Onsite) **[22157]**
Assertiveness Skills for Managers and Supervisors (Onsite) **[37582]**
Assertiveness Training for Managers (Onsite) **[37583]**
Assertiveness Training for Managers (Onsite) (Canada) **[22158]**
Assertiveness Training (Onsite) **[28008]**
Assertiveness Training for Women in Business (Canada) **[22159]**
Assertiveness Training for Women in Business (Onsite) **[22160]**

Assessment & Intervention: The Confused Elderly **[313]**
Asset Development Two (AD2) **[26616]**
Asset Management Company Venture Capital **[49172]**
Assets Protection Inc. (API) **[29300]**
Assist-2-Sell **[17131]**
Assisted Living Facilities Association of America [286], [1419], [15048]
Assisted Living Federation of America (ALFA) **[286]**, **[1419]**, **[15048]**
Associated Advertising Clubs of the World [344], [42570]
Associated Bakers of America [1749]
Associated Bakers of America - Retail and Wholesale [1749]
Associated Bodywork and Massage Professionals (ABMP) **[14139]**
Associated Builders and Contractors (ABC) **[5166]**
Associated Builders and Contractors (ABC) - National Mechanical Contractors Council (NMCC) **[5167]**
Associated Business Publications [15480]
Associated Business Writers of America [6798]
Associated Camera Clubs of America [15839], [15896]
Associated Coffee Industries of America [4313], [9692]
Associated Court and Commercial Newspapers [15481]
Associated Credit Bureaus [6265]
Associated Credit Bureaus Inc. [6265]
Associated Designers of Canada (ADC) **[4434]**
Associated Enterprises Ltd. **[13793]**
Associated Equipment Distributors--Membership Directory **[26732]**
Associated General Contractors of America (AGC) **[5168]**
Associated General Contractors of America - James L. Allhands Memorial Library **[5700]**
Associated Independent Electrical Contractors of America **[6862]**
Associated Industries of Maine [52609]
Associated Institutes for Lath and Plaster [14101]
Associated Landscape Contractors of America and Professional Lawn Care Association of America [13377]
Associated Locksmiths of America (ALOA) **[13612]**
Associated Locksmiths of America Inc. [13612]
Associated Management Services Inc. (AMSI) **[13794]**
Associated Management Systems Inc. **[2722]**, **[42309]**
Associated Manufacturers of Electrical and Supplies [6865]
Associated Manufacturers of Toilet Articles [1892], [2033], [5884]
Associated Marketers **[2723]**, **[42310]**
Associated Medical Services (AMS) **[34101]**
Associated Pipe Organ Builders of America (APOBA) **[14785]**
Associated Press Broadcast (APB) **[16687]**, **[19878]**
Associated Press Broadcasters Association [16687], [19878]
Associated Press Radio-Television Association [16687], [19878]
Associated Professional Massage Therapists and Allied Health Practitioners International - Associated Professional Massage Therapists and Bodyworkers [14139]
Associated Professional Massage Therapists and Bodyworkers [14139]
Associated Retail Bakers of America [1749]
Associated Retail Confectioners of North America [3281]
Associated Retail Confectioners of the U.S. [3281]
Associated Schools of Construction (ASC) **[5169]**
Associated Specialty Contractors (ASC) **[763]**, **[5170]**
Associated Stenotypists of America - National Shorthand Reporters Association [20819]
Associated Telephone Answering Exchanges [19863], [20960]
Associated Telephone Exchanges [19863], [20960]
Associated Warehouses--Directory of Services **[16649]**
Associated Writing Programs [6775]
Associated Writing Programs Catalogue of Writing Programs [6817]
Association **[1455]**
Association for Accounting Administration (AAA) **[19]**
Association for the Advancement of Medical Instrumentation (AAMI) **[14183]**
Association for the Advancement of Medical Instrumentation Annual Conference and Expo **[14238]**
Association for the Advancement of Medical Instrumentation--Membership Directory **[14190]**
The Association Agenda **[1456]**
Association des Aides Familiales du Quebec (AAFQ) **[46796]**
Association of Alternate Postal Systems (AAPS) **[4593]**
Association of Alternative Newsweeklies (AAN) **[15484]**
Association of American Publishers (AAP) **[2079]**
Association of American University Presses (AAUP) **[2080]**
Association of American University Presses--Directory **[2112]**

Association of Applied IPM Ecologists (AAIE) **[15621]**
Association of Authors' Representatives (AAR) **[13606]**
Association of Automotive Aftermarket Distributors/Parts Plus (AAAD) **[1538]**
Association for Behavioral Health and Wellness (ABHW) **[34102]**
Association of Bridal Consultants **[2487]**
Association for Business Communication (ABC) **[22150]**, **[22545]**
Association for Business Communication Annual Convention **[22512]**
Association for the Calligraphic Arts (ACA) **[3215]**
Association of Canadian Publishers (ACP) **[2081]**
Association of Canadian Search, Employment and Staffing Services (ACSESS) **[3339]**
Association of Canadian Travel Agencies (ACTA) **[20125]**, **[20505]**
Association Canadienne Des Industries De La Musique [14729]
Association Canadienne D'Alarme Incendie [18373]
Association Canadienne d'Articles de Sport [19305]
Association Canadienne d'Auto Distribution [20849]
Association Canadienne de Dermatologie [34110]
Association Canadienne de Distribution de Radiodiffusion [18334]
Association Canadienne de Gerance de Tirage [15491]
Association canadienne de gerontologie [34105]
Association Canadienne de Gestion Environnementale [2596], [6562]
Association Canadienne de la Boulangerie [1746]
Association Canadienne de la Construction [5171]
Association Canadienne de la Franchise [32115]
Association canadienne de la medecine du travail et de l'environnement [34155]
Association canadienne de la paie [15452], [21314]
Association Canadienne de l'enseigne [361]
Association Canadienne de l'industrie des Plastiques [38864]
Association Canadienne de Photographes et Illustrateurs de Publicite [4437], [15838]
Association Canadienne de Protection Medicale [34119]
Association Canadienne De Sante Publique [34124]
Association Canadienne de Soins et Services a Domicile [10517]
Association Canadienne de Traitement d'Images et de Reconnaissance des Formes [4631], [4834]
Association Canadienne d'Equitation Therapeutique [10600]
Association Canadienne des Agences de Voyages [20125], [20505]
Association Canadienne des Aliements de Sante [10209], [10274], [15151]
Association Canadienne des Compagnies d'Assurance Mutuelles [11269]
Association Canadienne des Compagnies d'Assurances de Personnes [11274]
Association Canadienne des Cosmetiques, Produits de Toilette et Parfums [5876]
Association Canadienne des employes professionels [46800]
Association Canadienne des Enterprises de Messagerie [14349]
Association Canadienne des Entrepreneurs en Couverture [18313]
Association Canadienne des Entreprises Familiales [29440], [31013], [44791]
Association Canadienne des Femmes Cadres et Entrepreneurs [47205]
Association Canadienne des Foires et Expositions [965]
Association canadienne des importateurs et exportateurs [26846]
Association Canadienne des Importateurs Reglementes [26828]
Association Canadienne des Industries du Recyclage [17686]
Association canadienne des infirmieres en oncologie [10516]
Association canadienne des infirmieres et infirmiers en sante communautaire [34135]
Association Canadienne des Inspecteurs de Biens Immobiliers [2552]
Association Canadienne des Journaux [15495]
Association Canadienne des Medecins Veterinaires [1051]
Association Canadienne des Optometristes [20913]
Association Canadienne des Pilotes de Ligne Internationale [711]
Association Canadienne des Professeurs de Comptabilite [22]
Association Canadienne des Professionnels de l'Insolvabilite et de la reorganisation [8027]

Association Canadienne des Radiodiffuseurs [16689], [19884]

Association Canadienne des Relations Industrielles [46802]

Association Canadienne des Resources Hydriques [30417]

Association Canadienne des Restaurateurs et des Services Alimentaires [3458], [5097], [6433], [9138], [10275], [17861]

Association canadienne des reviseurs [6788], [46813]

Association canadienne des soins de sante [34113]

Association Canadienne des Telecommunications Sans Fil [3668]

Association Canadienne des Therapeutes du Sport [16066]

Association Canadienne D'etudes Cinematographiques [7883]

Association Canadienne du Camionnage d'Entreprise [20664]

Association Canadienne du Capital de Risque et d'Investissement [46972]

Association Canadienne du Comptables d'Assurance [26]

Association Canadienne du Marketing [350]

Association Canadienne du Vehicule Recreatif [17661]

Association Canadienne pour la Sante Mentale [34120]

Association canadienne sur la qualite de l'eau [30414]

Association Candienne des Pepinieristes et des Paysagistes [9760], [13367]

Association of Career Firms North America (ACFI) **[6949]**

Association of Catholic Publishers (ACP) **[2082]**

Association of Chartered Accountants in the United States (ACAUS) **[20]**

Association for Childhood Education International (ACEI) **[3922]**

Association for Childhood Education International Annual International Conference & Exhibition **[4006]**

Association for Computing Machinery **[4657]**, **[4803]**, **[11944]**

Association for Conflict Resolution (ACR) **[14159]**

Association of Consulting Engineering Companies - Canada (ACEC) **[2751]**

Association for Consumer Trends (ACT) **[45259]**

Association for Corporate Growth - Toronto Chapter (ACG) **[2752]**, **[22659]**, **[37557]**

Association de la Librairie Ancienne du Canada [1111], [2352]

Association de L'Industrie Touristique du Canada [20134], [20524]

Association des assureurs-vie du Canada [8026]

Association des biens Immobiliers du Canada [16790], [17166]

Association des Camps du Canada [3245]

Association des courtiers d'assurances du Canada [11285]

Association des Designers Canadiens [4434]

Association des Eleveurs Ayrshire du Canada [997]

Association des Fonderies Canadiennes [13688]

Association des Ingenieurs-Conseils du Canada [2751]

Association des manufacturiers de vetements pour hommes [4082]

Association des Opticiens du Canada [20926]

Association des Produits Forestiers du Canada [38867]

Association des Psychiatres du Canada [34123]

Association des Traducteurs et Interpretes Judiciaires [20465]

Association des Traducteurs et Traductrices Literariness du Canada [20469]

Association des Transports du Canada [19803]

Association of Destination Management Executives (ADME) **[20506]**

Association d'information sur l'allergie et l'asthme [916]

Association Directory **[51818]**

Association of Directory Marketing (ADM) **[39557]**

Association for Enterprise Information (AFEI) **[32484]**

Association of Executive Search Consultants (AESC) **[6950]**

Association Feline Canadienne [1000]

Association of Food Industries (AFI) **[17857]**

Association for Business Communication Annual Symposium [22512]

Association for Childhood Education Annual International Study Conference & Exhibition [4006]

Association for Computer Educators [4634], [4755]

Association for Computer Operations Management [4751]

Association for Convention Operations Management [20296]

Association for Data Center, Networking and Enterprise Systems [4751]

Association for Enterprise Integration [32484]

Association for Interactive Media [19879]

Association for Investment Management and Research [11969]

Association For Manufacturing Technology [13687]

Association for Professional Broadcasting Education [19882]

Association for Public Broadcasting [19880]

Association for School, College and University Staffing-- Directory of Membership/Subject Field Index [19161]

Association for Suppliers of Printing and Publishing Technologies - National Printing Equipment Association - Association for Suppliers of Printing and Publishing and Converting Technologies - National Printing Equipment and Supply Association [16348]

Association for the Export of Canadian Books [2098]

Association for the Management of Organization Design [37566]

Association of Forensic Document Examiners (AFDE) **[10112]**

Association of Free Community Papers (AFCP) **[42573]**

Association of Fund-Raising Distributors and Suppliers (AFRDS) **[9231]**

Association of Fundraising Professionals (AFP) **[9232]**

Association of Golf Merchandisers (AGM) **[9649]**, **[19303]**

Association of Gospel Rescue Missions Library **[34640]**

Association for Healthcare Documentation Integrity (AHDI) **[14342]**

Association of Home Appliance Manufacturers (AHAM) **[1182]**

Association of Home-Based Women Entrepreneurs (HBWE) **[2814]**, **[13795]**, **[25939]**, **[30373]**, **[47440]**

Association of Image Consultants International (AICI) **[10988]**

Association of Independent Commercial Producers (AICP) **[42574]**

Association of Independent Consultants (AIC) **[2753]**, **[25815]**

Association of Independent Manufacturers'/Representatives (AIM/R) **[16212]**

Association for Information Media and Equipment (AIME) **[7875]**

Association for Interactive Marketing (AIM) **[19879]**

Association of International Photography Art Dealers (AIPAD) **[1338]**

Association Internationale du Film d'Animation [7887]

Association for Investment Management & Research-- Membership Directory **[12035]**

Association of Jewish Aging Services **[15049]**

Association of Knitwear Designers (AKD) **[4078]**

Association Law and Policy **[24100]**

Association of Legal Court Interpreters and Translators (ALCIT) **[20465]**

Association Management Companies Institute [1453]

Association Management Companies Institute--Directory **[1460]**

Association of Management Consulting Firms (AMCF) **[13758]**, **[25816]**

Association Management--Convention Center & Convention Bureau Directory [1461], **[20316]**

Association Management--Convention Hall & CVB Directory Issue [1461], [20316]

Association of Manpower Franchise Owners (AMFO) **[20024]**

Association Meeting Trends **[1466]**

Association Meetings: The Independent Voice of the Association Industry [1468], **[20448]**

Association of Moving Image Archivists (AMIA) [7876]

Association of National Advertisers (ANA) **[348]**, **[42575]**

Association nationale des distributeurs aux petites surfaces alimentaires [26725]

Association Nationale des Enterprises en Recrutement et Placement de Personnel [3339]

Association Nationale des Industries de la Neige [18822]

Association News **[1469]**

Association of Accounting Administrators [19]

Association of Accredited Cosmetology Schools Annual Convention and Exhibition [1910], [5907]

Association of American Stock Exchange Firms [11977]

Association of Applied Insect Ecologists [15621]

Association of Area Business Publications [15479], [49388]

Association of Automotive Aftermarket Distributors [1538]

Association of Better Business Bureaus [24792]

Association of Business Publishers [15480]

Association of Canadian Venture Capital Companies [46972]

Association of Career Management Consulting Firms International [6949]

Association of Casualty Accountants and Statisticians [11302]

Association of Casualty and Surety Companies [11267]

Association of Certified Public Accountant Examiners [44]

Association of College Professors of Textiles and Clothing--Membership Directory [4118]

Association of Commerce and Industry [53192]

Association of Commercial Finance Companies of New York [37286], [46975]

Association of Commercial Records Centers [4688]

Association of Consulting Engineers of Canada [2751]

Association of Cooking Schools [5831]

Association of Credit Card Investigators [6268]

Association of Data Processing Service Organizations [44991]

Association of Direct Marketing Agencies [13740], [39559]

Association of Equipment Lessors [17748]

Association of Executive Recruiting Consultants [6950]

Association of Fashion and Image Consultants [10988]

Association of Food Distributors [17857]

Association of Fund Raisers and Direct Sellers [9231]

Association of Governmental Appraisers [1205]

Association of Graphic Arts Consultants [15511], [16350]

Association of Hospital Superintendents of U.S. and Canada [10515], [15045]

Association of Image Consultants [10988]

Association of Independent Optical Wholesalers [20929]

Association of Industry Manufacturers Representatives [16212]

Association of Manufacturers of Confectionary and Chocolate - Pennsylvania Manufacturing Confectioner's Association [3280]

Association of Media Producers [7886], [20881]

Association of Municipal Recycling Coordinators [7054], [17694], [30426]

Association of Nutrition and Food Service Professionals [15154]

Association of Outplacement Consulting Firms [6949]

Association of Outplacement Consulting Firms International [6949]

Association of Private Postal Systems [4593]

Association of Professional Placement Agencies and Consultants [3339]

Association of Promotion Marketing Agencies Worldwide [43347]

Association of Publishers' Representatives [42583]

Association of Sales and Marketing Companies [9902]

Association of Specialists in Cleaning and Restoration Annual Convention and Exhibition [6361]

Association of Telemessaging Services, International [19863], [20960]

Association of the Institute for Certification of Computing Professionals [4836]

Association of Vacation Home Rental Managers [16505]

Association of Visual Communicators [7888]

Association of Visual Science Librarians [20911]

Association of Women Business Owners [47211]

Association Pharmaciens Du Canada [6629]

Association of Pool and Spa Professionals (APSP) **[19541]**

Association Pour La Prevention Des Infections A l'hopital et dans La Communaute [34136]

Association of Professional Computer Consultants (APCC) **[4629]**, **[25817]**

Association of Professional Landscape Designers (APLD) **[13347]**, **[13366]**

Association of Professional Recruiters of Canada (APRC) **[7778]**

Association of Professional Researchers for Advancement (APRA) **[9233]**

Association of Progressive Rental Organizations (APRO) **[17747]**

Association of Progressive Rental Organizations Annual Convention and Trade Show (APRO) **[17828]**

Association of Proposal Management Professionals (APMP) **[6504]**, **[25818]**

Association of Public Television Stations (APTS) **[19880]**

Association of Regulatory Boards of Optometry (ARBO) **[20909]**

Association for Research on Nonprofit Organizations and Voluntary Action Conference (ACNOVA) **[34614]**, **[46745]**

Association of Retail Travel Agents (ARTA) **[20507]**

Association of Schools and Colleges of Optometry (ASCO) **[20910]**

Association of Sewing and Design Professionals (ASDP) **[4079]**

Association of Small Business Development Centers (ASBDC) **[44789]**

Association of Talent Agents (ATA) **[13607]**, **[19564]**

Association of Teachers of Technical Writing (ATTW) **[6774]**

Association for Technology in Music Instruction (ATMI) **[14603]**

Association of TeleServices International (ATSI) **[19863]**, **[20960]**

Association to Advance Collegiate Schools of Business [27970]

Association of Tongue Depressors - Library **[14337]**

Association/L'Association MASTER INDEX

Association of Travel Marketing Executives (ATME) **[20508]**
Association Trends **[1470]**
Association of University Interior Designers (AUID) **[11525]**
Association of Vision Science Librarians (AVSL) **[20911]**
Association of Visual Language Interpreters of Canada (AVLIC) **[20466]**
Association of the Wall and Ceiling Industries International (AWCI) **[14096]**
Association of the Wall and Ceiling Industries International--Buyer's Guide **[14109]**
Association for Wedding Professionals International (AFWPI) **[2488]**
Association for Women in Computing (AWC) **[4830]**
Association of Writers and Writing Programs (AWP) **[6775]**
Association/L'Association des editeurs de magazines canadiens [15504]
"Associations" in MarketingMagazine (Vol. 115, September 27, 2010, No. 13, pp. 76) **[39665]**
Associations Canada **[1476]**
Associations Canada: Directory of Associations in Canada [1476]
Associations Plus **[46573]**
Assumption Area Chamber of Commerce **[52432]**
ASTD **[4752]**, **[27971]**, **[35651]**
"Asterand Eyes Jump to Ann Arbor; TechTown Tenant" in Crain's Detroit Business (Vol. 25, June 22, 2009) **[17755]**, **[28124]**, **[34772]**, **[42753]**, **[43796]**, **[44640]**
ASTM Phase I & Phase II Environmental Site Assessment Processes (Onsite) **[30445]**, **[33482]**
Astoria-Warrenton Area Chamber of Commerce (AWACC) **[56706]**
"Astral Fine-Tunes Details of Standard Purchase" in Globe & Mail (February 26, 2007, pp. B1) **[34773]**, **[41742]**
"Astral Media Set to Broadcast Coast to Coast" in Globe & Mail (February 24, 2007, pp. B5) **[19905]**, **[41743]**, **[44252]**
AstraZeneca Pharmaceuticals LP Library and Information Services **[6710]**
Astrological Research Library of Canada **[14830]**
"ASU Explores Russian Partnership" in The Business Journal - Serving Phoenix and the Valley of the Sun (Vol. 28, September 5, 2008) **[28125]**, **[41744]**, **[43797]**
Asynchronous Learning Networks **[27972]**
"At 5-Year Mark, News 9 Makes Presence Felt in Competition for Ad Dollars" in Business Review, Albany New York (October 5, 2007) **[389]**, **[3164]**, **[3684]**, **[19906]**, **[22703]**, **[39666]**, **[41745]**
AT Associates (ATA) **[4538]**
"At the Drugstore, the Nurse Will See You Now" in Globe & Mail (April 13, 2007, pp. B1) **[6645]**, **[25422]**, **[35271]**
At a Glance **[13250]**
At-Home Dad **[35627]**
At the Lake **[51819]**
AT & T Middletown Technical Library **[4678]**
"At This Bakery, Interns' Hope Rises Along With the Bread" in Chicago Tribune (October 31, 2008) **[1750]**, **[28126]**, **[35272]**, **[45866]**
At the Wheel **[6599]**
"At Wine Kiosk, Show ID, Face Camera, Swipe Card and Blow" in Pittsburgh Post-Gazette (November 28, 2010) **[6192]**, **[13314]**, **[18392]**, **[19210]**, **[40991]**
At Work **[53572]**; **[55588]**; **[55891]**; **[57648]**
"At Your Career Crossroads" in Women In Business (Vol. 61, December 2009, No. 6, pp. 26) **[29016]**, **[32526]**, **[35273]**
"At Your Service: Corporate Concierges Come in Three Varieties" in Incentive (August 25, 2008) **[5121]**, **[21868]**, **[35700]**
ATA Directory of Translators and Interpreters **[20475]**
ATA Distribution Center [715], [9230]
ATA Translation Services Directory [20475]
"AT&T To Acquire Black Telecom Firm" in Black Enterprise (Vol. 38, January 2008, No. 6, pp. 24) **[3685]**, **[6958]**, **[7781]**, **[20027]**, **[40703]**, **[41746]**
"AT&T Wins Networking Deal from GM Worth $1 Billion" in Globe & Mail (February 22, 2007, pp. B14) **[38910]**, **[44253]**
Atascadero Chamber of Commerce **[48233]**
Atchison Area Chamber of Commerce (AACC) **[52044]**
Atchison County Kansas Genealogical Society - Collection **[9484]**
ATHENA Foundation [50905]
ATHENA International **[50905]**
Athena Technology Ventures **[49173]**
The ATHENAIAN **[50906]**
Athenian Ventures / Ohio Valley Venture Fund **[56360]**
Athens Area Chamber of Commerce **[57649]**
Athens Area Chamber of Commerce (AACC) **[50437]**
Athens Business **[57650]**
Athens Chamber of Commerce **[57938]**
Athens Magazine **[57939]**
"Athletes Face Wins and Losses After Pro Sport" in The Business Journal - Serving Phoenix and the Valley of the Sun (Vol. 29, September 19, 2008, No. 3, pp. 1) **[16821]**, **[17200]**, **[26907]**, **[44809]**, **[45281]**, **[45867]**
The Athlete's Foot **[18779]**
"Athletes' Performance Building $10 Million Facility In ASU Park" in The Business Journal - Serving Phoenix and the Valley of the Sun (Vol. 28, August 8, 2008, No. 49, pp. 1) **[5225]**, **[17201]**, **[19318]**, **[19401]**, **[22704]**
Athletic Business--Buyers Guide Issue **[15960]**
Athletic Business--Professional Directory Section **[19402]**
Athletic Equipment Managers Association (AEMA) **[19304]**
The Athletic Footwear Market **[18774]**
Athletic Goods Manufacturers Association [19312]
Athletic Purchasing & Facilities Buyers Guide [15960]
"ATI Now Ready to Pounce on Biotech" in Austin Business Journalinc. (Vol. 28, August 22, 2008, No. 23, pp. 1) **[22705]**, **[28127]**, **[33147]**, **[34714]**, **[42754]**, **[43798]**, **[46958]**
Atir Natural Nail Care Clinic **[14799]**
Atiyah's Accidents, Compensation and the Law **[23721]**, **[26908]**, **[35701]**
Atlanta Area Chamber of Commerce **[53129]**
Atlanta Area Chamber of Commerce (AACC) **[57940]**
Atlanta Boat Show **[13960]**
Atlanta Botanical Garden - Sheffield Botanical Library **[9841]**
Atlanta Bread Company, Intl. **[1798]**
Atlanta Business Chronicle **[47768]**
Atlanta-Fulton Public Library - Learning and Career Center **[10347]**
Atlanta International Gift and Home Furnishing Market **[6038]**
Atlanta JobBank: The Job Hunter's Guide to Georgia **[19168]**
Atlanta Magazine **[50684]**
The Atlanta Small Business Monthly **[50685]**
Atlanta Urban League - Entrepreneurship Center **[50643]**
Atlanta-Fulton Public Library - Learning Center Library. [10347]
Atlantic Area Chamber of Commerce (AACC) **[51820]**
Atlantic Boating & Fishing Almanac [3867]
Atlantic Boating Almanac **[3867]**
Atlantic Cape Community College - William Spangler Library **[5847]**
Atlantic Capital Corporation **[53004]**
Atlantic City Free Public Library - Alfred M. Heston Collection **[9418]**
Atlantic City Pool and Spa Show **[19550]**
Atlantic City Regional Chamber of Commerce **[54668]**
Atlantic City Sub Shops Inc. **[6453]**
Atlantic Coast Boat Builders and Repairers Association [13921]
Atlantic Coast Exposition - Showcasing the Vending and Food Service Industry **[4320]**, **[20878]**
Atlantic Craft Trade Show **[6039]**, **[6154]**
Atlantic Institute for Market Studies (AIMS) **[27926]**
Atlantic Management Company Inc. **[42311]**
Atlantic Mower Parts **[10151]**
Atlantic Provinces Economic Council (APEC) **[27927]**
Atlantic Provinces Reports (APR) **[24132]**, **[37229]**
Atlantic Salmon **[8995]**
Atlantic Salmon Federation (ASF) **[8996]**
Atlantic Windshield Repair, Inc. **[9642]**
"Atlantis-Resistant Figures on the Up" in Farmer's Weekly (March 28, 2008, No. 320) **[21518]**, **[43799]**
Atlas Venture **[53005]**
"Atlific Adds Management of 4 Hotels to Its Portfolio in Fort McMurray" in Canadian Corporate News (May 16, 2007) **[10663]**, **[28554]**, **[37797]**, **[39667]**, **[41747]**
ATMI International Newsletter **[14634]**
Atmore Area Chamber of Commerce (AACC) **[47623]**
Atoka County Chamber of Commerce **[56463]**
Atoka Industrial Incubator - Atoka Kiamichi Area Vo-Tech/ Atoka Campus **[56638]**
"ATS Secures Investment From Goldman Sachs" in The Business Journal - Serving Phoenix and the Valley of the Sun (Vol. 29, September 26, 2008, No. 4, pp. 1) **[8075]**, **[12036]**, **[22706]**, **[31203]**, **[38911]**, **[46993]**
ATS-Chester Engineers [7374]
ATS-Chester Engineers Inc. [7374]
"Attend To Your Corporate Housekeeping" in Women Entrepreneur (December 4, 2008) **[2266]**, **[8076]**, **[23722]**, **[24230]**, **[26138]**, **[31204]**, **[32527]**, **[33516]**, **[43320]**, **[45282]**
"Attending to the Needs of the Too Busy" in New York Times (Vol. 158, October 1, 2008, No. 54450, pp. 7) **[5122]**, **[29476]**
"Attention, Please" in Entrepreneur (Vol. 36, April 2008, No. 4, pp. 52) **[390]**, **[11619]**, **[21047]**, **[28555]**, **[29477]**, **[34774]**, **[39668]**, **[44133]**
"Attention, Shoppers Take a Deep Breath: Why It Pays to Help Customers Relax" in Inc. (Vol. 33, November 2011, No. 9, pp. 26) **[26375]**, **[42942]**
"Attivio Brings Order to Data" in Information Today (Vol. 26, February 2009, No. 2, pp. 14) **[3500]**, **[4691]**, **[18861]**, **[34775]**, **[45089]**
"Attorney Covers Climate in Copenhagen" in Houston Business Journal (Vol. 40, December 25, 2009, No. 33, pp. 1) **[7106]**, **[7467]**, **[23723]**, **[30488]**
Attorney Guide **[48234]**
"Attorney Guides Biotech Company in $6 Million Initial Public Offering" in Miami Daily Business Review (March 26, 2008) **[12037]**, **[23724]**, **[34192]**, **[41748]**, **[42755]**, **[43800]**, **[46994]**
"Attorney Internet Marketing Services Launched by SEO Advantage at SEOLegal.com" in Internet Wire (October 5, 2009) **[11620]**, **[21048]**, **[22267]**, **[23725]**, **[39669]**
"Attorney Panel Tackles Contract Questions" in Agency Sales Magazine (Vol. 39, September-October 2009, No. 9, pp. 8) **[20317]**, **[23726]**, **[38912]**, **[46598]**
"Attract More Online Customers: Make Your Website Work Harder for You" in Black Enterprise (Vol. 37, November 2006, No. 4, pp. 66) **[11621]**, **[15307]**, **[21049]**, **[28556]**, **[45283]**
Attracting Investors: A Marketing Approach to Finding Funds for Your Business **[29478]**, **[39670]**, **[46995]**
"Attracting Veteran-Franchisees To Your System" in Franchising World (Vol. 42, November 2010, No. 11, pp. 53) **[32127]**, **[45284]**, **[45868]**
Atwater Chamber of Commerce **[48235]**
Atwood Chamber of Commerce (ACC) **[52045]**
AtWork HelpingHands Services **[10570]**
AtWork Medical Services **[20041]**
AtWork Personnel Services **[19193]**
Au Bas de l'Echelle [4444]
Au Gres Chamber of Commerce **[53130]**
Au Pair in America (APIA) **[14800]**
"Au Revoir Or Goodbye?" in Barron's (Vol. 88, July 14, 2008, No. 28, pp. 5) **[8077]**, **[12038]**, **[14382]**, **[16822]**, **[26139]**, **[26909]**, **[31205]**, **[33517]**, **[36355]**, **[37302]**
Aub bas de l'echelle...pas pour toujours **[4435]**
Auburn Advantage **[47624]**
Auburn Area Chamber of Commerce **[53131]**; **[59091]**
Auburn Area Chamber of Commerce (AACC) **[48236]**
Auburn Chamber of Commerce (ACC) **[47625]**; **[51517]**; **[54360]**
Auburn Journal **[48237]**
Auburn SCORE **[55040]**
Auburn Small Business Development Center **[59049]**
Auburn University - Alabama Agricultural Experiment Station - Department of Fisheries and Allied Aquacultures **[9041]**
Auburn University - Alabama Agricultural Experiment Station - Ornamental Horticulture Research Center **[9885]**
Auburn University - Center for Governmental Services (CGS) **[19774]**
Auburn University - Charles Allen Cary Veterinary Medical Library **[1094]**
Auburn University - International Center for Aquaculture and Aquatic Environments (ICAAE) **[1238]**
Auburn University - International Center for Aquaculture and Aquatic Environments Library **[9034]**
Auburn University at Montgomery - Center for Business (CBED) **[3055]**
Auburn University - National Center for Asphalt Technology (NCAT) **[2017]**
Auburn University Small Business Development Center **[47604]**
Auburn Works **[59092]**
Auburndale Chamber of Commerce [49942]
Auburndale-Mainstreet Chamber of Commerce **[49942]**
"Auction Company Grows with Much Smaller Sites" in Automotive News (Vol. 86, October 31, 2011, No. 6488, pp. 23) **[1479]**, **[5137]**, **[14853]**, **[22707]**, **[31024]**
Auction Marketing Institute [1488], [7775]
"Auction-Rate Cash Frees Up" in The Business Journal-Portland (Vol. 25, August 15, 2008, No. 23, pp. 1) **[1492]**, **[8078]**, **[12039]**, **[24231]**, **[31206]**, **[34776]**
Auction it Today Inc. **[11956]**
The Auctioneer **[1534]**
Auctioneer--Directory Issue **[1493]**
"Auctions and Bidding: a Guide for Computer Scientists" in ACM Computing Surveys (Vol. 43, Summer 2011, No. 2, pp. 10) **[1494]**, **[4638]**, **[4842]**, **[21050]**, **[25725]**, **[26910]**, **[28557]**, **[42756]**, **[43801]**
Audatex Collision Estimating Database **[18669]**
Audio Engineering Society [17630]
Audio Engineering Society Inc. (AES) **[17630]**
Audiotex News **[6550]**
Audiotex Update **[20964]**
Audit Bureau of Circulations (ABC) **[15485]**
Auditing: A Journal of Practice & Theory **[168]**
Auditing Business Application Systems (Onsite) **[34732]**, **[45033]**

3454 Small Business Sourcebook • 30th Edition

Auditing the Manufacturing Process (Onsite) **[24970]**
Auditing Networked Computers (Onsite) **[34733]**
Auditing Outsourced Operations (Onsite) **[41658]**
Auditing and Securing Oracle Databases (Onsite) **[34734]**
August Capital **[49174]**
Augusta Chamber of Commerce [52606]
The Augusta Chronicle **[50438]**
Augusta Metro Chamber of Commerce **[50439]**
Auntie Anne's Inc. **[19274]**
Aurora Area Chamber and Development (AACD) **[54361]**
Aurora Chamber of Commerce **[49448]**; **[53957]**; **[56005]**; **[56707]**
Aurora Funds, Inc. **[55853]**
Aurora Management Partners Inc. **[2815]**, **[13796]**, **[25940]**, **[32006]**, **[38653]**, **[41286]**, **[44918]**
Aussie Pet Mobile [15677]
Aussie Pet Mobile Inc. **[15677]**
"Aussie Rules" in Canadian Business (Vol. 79, Winter 2006, No. 24, pp. 45) **[41749]**, **[44254]**
Austin Area Chamber of Commerce **[53573]**
"Austin to Buy $1.1B of Wind Power from Two" in Austin Business Journal (Vol. 31, August 19, 2011, No. 24, pp. A1) **[7107]**, **[7468]**, **[30489]**
Austin Chamber of Commerce [58181]
"Austin Energy May Build $2.3B Biomass Plant" in Austin Business JournalInc. (Vol. 28, July 25, 2008, No. 19, pp. A1) **[7108]**, **[7469]**, **[17705]**, **[25295]**, **[30490]**
Austin Grill **[18073]**
"Austin Homes are Overpriced, Study Says" in Austin Business JournalInc. (Vol. 29, January 1, 2010, No. 43, pp. 1) **[5226]**, **[16823]**, **[17202]**
"Austin to Make it Easier for Stores to Just Pop In" in Austin Business Journal (Vol. 31, August 19, 2011, No. 24, pp. A1) **[33518]**, **[42943]**, **[44098]**
"Austin Ponders Annexing F1 Racetrack" in Austin Business Journal (Vol. 31, July 8, 2011, No. 18, pp. 1) **[5227]**, **[33519]**, **[44641]**, **[46146]**
Austin SCORE **[57884]**
Austin Technology Incubator (IC2-ATI) **[58590]**
Austin Ventures **[58547]**
"Austin Ventures: Is It a VC Firm?" in Austin Business Journal (Vol. 31, June 17, 2011, No. 15, pp. 1) **[12040]**, **[33520]**, **[46996]**
"Austin on Verge of Losing 7,500 Jobs" in Austin Business Journal (Vol. 31, May 6, 2011, No. 9, pp. 1) **[26911]**, **[33521]**, **[35702]**
Austin Womens Chamber of Commerce of Texas [58527]
"Austin's GMP Growth Top in Nation" in Austin Business JournalInc. (Vol. 29, January 8, 2010, No. 44, pp. 1) **[18801]**, **[22708]**, **[32528]**
Austins Steaks and Saloon Inc. [18275]
Australian/American Chamber of Commerce - Hawaii **[50698]**
"Australian Firm Buys Off Sands Engineering Company for $1 Billion" in Globe & Mail (February 8, 2007, pp. B3) **[22709]**, **[25021]**, **[41750]**
Australian Trade Commission (AUSTRADE) **[36277]**
Austrian Information **[20595]**
Austrian Trade Commission (ATC) **[36278]**
Austrian Trade Commissions in the United States and Canada [36279]
Austrian Trade Commissions in the United States (ATCUSC) **[36279]**
Authenticity: What Consumers Really Want **[391]**, **[26376]**, **[39671]**
Authors and Publishers Association (APA) **[2083]**
Authorship **[6833]**
Authorware 7 | Macro Media **[8019]**
Auto Appraisal Network Inc. **[1226]**
"Auto Bankruptcies Could Weaken Defense" in Crain's Detroit Business (Vol. 25, June 8, 2009, No. 23, pp. 1) **[1549]**, **[14854]**, **[18393]**, **[33404]**, **[38913]**
Auto Buyer Alert **[14986]**
Auto Collision Repair Information System [18669]
Auto Detailing **[1613]**
Auto International Association (AIA) **[1539]**
Auto Laundry News: The Voice of the Car Care Industry Since 1953 **[3331]**
The Auto Parts Report **[699]**
"Auto Repair Business Owner Sentenced" in Ventura County Star (November 20, 2010) **[18595]**, **[23727]**
"Auto Sector's Outlook Dims, Survey Finds" in Globe & Mail (January 4, 2006, pp. B4) **[26912]**, **[38914]**
Auto Service Excellence [18586]
"Auto Show Aims to Electrify" in Crain's Detroit Business (Vol. 26, January 11, 2010, No. 2, pp. 1) **[14855]**, **[20318]**, **[26913]**, **[30491]**, **[36960]**, **[38915]**, **[46599]**
"Auto Show Taps Moms" in Marketing to Women (Vol. 21, April 2008, No. 4, pp. 3) **[11622]**, **[14856]**, **[21051]**, **[39672]**, **[41751]**
"Auto Supplier Stock Battered In Wake Of Wall Street Woes" in Crain's Detroit Business (Vol. 24, September 29, 2008, No. 39, pp. 4) **[8079]**, **[12041]**, **[26733]**, **[26914]**, **[31207]**, **[33148]**, **[33522]**, **[38916]**, **[45285]**

Auto Suppliers Benchmarking Association (ASBA) **[1540]**, **[24200]**
Auto Suppliers Benchmarking Consortium [1540], [24200]
AutoInc. **[700]**
"Autoline Goes West" in Michigan Vue (Vol. 13, July-August 2008, No. 4, pp. 6) **[7903]**, **[14857]**, **[19907]**, **[38917]**
"Automaker Foundations Run Leaner" in Crain's Detroit Business (Vol. 26, January 11, 2010, No. 2, pp. 1) **[24232]**, **[25022]**, **[30492]**, **[38918]**, **[39673]**, **[45869]**
Automate Your Business Plan 2009 **[24707]**
Automated Sciences Group, Inc. - Library **[3663]**
Automated Storage/Retrieval Systems (AS/RS) **[4685]**
Automatic Merchandiser--Blue Book Buyer's Guide Issue **[4315]**, **[20852]**
Automatic Merchandiser: The Monthly Management Magazine for Vending and OCS Professionals **[4318]**, **[20877]**
Automating the Office **[41564]**
Automotive Cooling Journal [18613]
Automotive Engineering Directory and Catalog File [698]
Automotive Engineering--Roster Issue [698]
Automotive Engineering--SAE Membership Directory [698]
Automotive Fleet **[1627]**
Automotive Fleet and Leasing Association (AFLA) **[1617]**
Automotive Fleet and Leasing Association--Forum **[1628]**
Automotive Glazing Materials (Onsite) **[33483]**, **[38873]**
Automotive Industries **[14975]**
Automotive Lighting (Onsite) **[33484]**, **[38874]**
Automotive Litigation Reporter **[701]**
Automotive Maintenance Solutions **[18637]**
Automotive Market Research Council (AMRC) **[1656]**
Automotive News **[14976]**; **[14999]**
Automotive Oil Change Association (AOCA) **[16667]**
Automotive Parts Rebuilders Association Convention and Exposition **[1582]**
Automotive Plastics Newsletter **[1573]**, **[1591]**, **[39496]**
Automotive Rebuilder [18614]
Automotive Repair Database [706]
Automotive Service Association (ASA) **[696]**, **[1541]**, **[18579]**
Automotive Service Association Library **[18671]**
Automotive Service Association-Baton Rouge [696], [1541], [18579]
Automotive Service Councils [696], [1541], [18579]
"Automotive Trouble" in Canadian Business (Vol. 82, April 27, 2009, No. 7, pp. 11) **[14858]**, **[26915]**, **[33149]**, **[33523]**, **[38919]**
Automotive Warehouse Distributors Association **[1542]**
Automotive Warehouse Distributors Association-- Membership Directory **[1550]**
AutoNet/Autobase [15000]
AutoSite Pro **[15000]**
AutoWeek **[14977]**
"Autumn Rat Control Essential for Poultry Units" in Poultry World (Vol. 165, September 2011, No. 9, pp. 32) **[15625]**, **[21519]**
"Auxilium Drug's New Use: Putting Squeeze On Cellulite" in Philadelphia Business Journal (Vol. 30, September 16, 2011, No. 31, pp. 1) **[6646]**, **[36961]**, **[40992]**, **[42757]**, **[44134]**
"Auxis Introduces Services for Government Contracting" in Entertainment Close-Up (December 22, 2010) **[13765]**, **[33150]**, **[41661]**, **[44255]**
"AV Concept Expands Into Green Energy Storage" in Wireless News (January 25, 2010) **[26734]**, **[30493]**, **[36356]**, **[38920]**, **[41752]**
AV Video [8004]
AV Video & Multimedia Producer **[8004]**
Ava Area Chamber of Commerce (AACC) **[53958]**
Available Properties Listing Guide **[48238]**
Available Site Location Guide **[50907]**
Avalon Chamber of Commerce **[54669]**
The Avant Gardener **[9801]**, **[13491]**
Avante **[15941]**
"Avanti Hosts Users Conference" in American Printer (Vol. 128, July 1, 2011, No. 7) **[4454]**, **[4939]**, **[16355]**, **[20319]**, **[20758]**, **[46600]**
AvData Air Carrier File **[743]**
Avery Architectural Index [9369]
Avery Architectural Periodicals Index [9369]
Avery Business Development Services **[47119]**
Avery, Cooper & Co. **[207]**, **[21454]**, **[38654]**
Avery Index to Architectural Periodicals [9369]
"AVG Introduces Security Software Suite for SMBs 551179" in eWeek (October 12, 2010) **[3501]**, **[18394]**, **[18862]**, **[28558]**, **[45090]**
AVI Capital LP **[49175]**
Aviation Daily **[744]**
Aviation Industry Expo **[739]**
Aviation Medical Bulletin **[736]**

Aviation Monthly **[737]**
AVITAS Inc. **[741]**
AVLIC News **[20467]**
AVMA Members' Magazine **[1071]**
"Avnet Inc.'s Expansion Fueled By Mergers and Acquisitions" in The Business Journal - Serving Phoenix and the Valley of the Sun (Vol. 28, September 12, 2008, No. 53, pp. 1) **[22710]**, **[24233]**, **[25023]**, **[41753]**
"Avoid a Tablet Generation Gap" in American Printer (Vol. 128, July 1, 2011, No. 7) **[4455]**, **[16356]**, **[20759]**
"Avoiding Invention Scams" in Black Enterprise (Vol. 37, January 2007, No. 6, pp. 46) **[24794]**, **[36962]**, **[39674]**, **[40993]**, **[42758]**, **[44120]**
Avon: Building the World's Premier Company for Women **[2034]**, **[5885]**, **[47225]**
Avon Chamber of Commerce (ACOC) **[49655]**
Avon Lake - Avon Chamber of Commerce [56247]
Avon Park Chamber of Commerce (APCC) **[49943]**
Avon Products, Inc. Research Library **[1916]**, **[2067]**, **[5918]**
"AVT Featured on TD Waterhouse Market News Website and in Vending Times Magazine" in Benzinga.com (August 17, 2011) **[20853]**, **[42602]**
"AVT Launches New ExpressPay Vending Systems" in Benzinga.com (July 13, 2011) **[20854]**, **[45286]**
"avVaa World Health Care Products Rolls Out Internet Marketing Program" in Health and Beauty Close-Up (September 18, 2009) **[392]**, **[1894]**, **[11623]**, **[21052]**, **[26735]**, **[37798]**, **[39675]**, **[43381]**
"Awaiting a Call from Deutsche Telekom" in Barron's (Vol. 90, September 6, 2010, No. 36, pp. M5) **[3686]**, **[12042]**, **[22711]**, **[25423]**, **[36357]**
Awakening the Entrepreneur Within: How Ordinary People Can Create Extraordinary Companies **[29329]**, **[32349]**
Award Magazine: Architecture, Construction, Interior Design **[11556]**
"Award Win Highlights Slingsby's Green Credentials" in Ecology, Environment & Conservation Business (August 20, 2011, pp. 3) **[7109]**, **[7470]**, **[9595]**, **[9889]**, **[30494]**
Awards Express **[19493]**
Aware **[49449]**
Awareness and Info Allergie **[917]**
AWDA Leadership Directory [1550]
Aweida Venture Partners **[49616]**
Awesomely Simple: Essential Business Strategies for Turning Ideas Into Action **[22268]**, **[22712]**, **[25024]**, **[26377]**, **[29479]**
AWI Directory of Services [16649]
AWP Job List **[6834]**
The AWP Official Guide to Writing Programs **[6817]**
AWSCPA Newsletter **[169]**
The Axelrod Group Inc. **[29235]**
Axiom Venture Partners, L.P. **[49769]**
Axon Group [36046]
Axon Group - Library [36046]
Axxon Capital **[53006]**
Ayden Chamber of Commerce **[55589]**
Ayer Directory of Publications **[4065]**, [15533]
Ayrshire Breeders' Association of Canada (ABAC) **[997]**
Azen and Associates [40583], [42545]
Azen Bitner Pierson [40583], [42545]
Azle Area Chamber of Commerce (AACC) **[57941]**
Azpco Arizona Pizza Co. **[16136]**
Aztec Chamber of Commerce **[54923]**
Aztec Etchings **[54924]**
Azure Magazine **[1293]**, **[1361]**
Azusa Chamber of Commerce **[48239]**
Azusa Factbook **[48240]**
The Azusan **[48241]**

B

"B. Jannetta" in Ice Cream Reporter (Vol. 21, August 20, 2008, No. 9, pp. 8) **[10846]**, **[31025]**
"B-N Pawn Shop Auctions Off Jimmy Hoffa's Rifle" in Pantagraph (September 14, 2010) **[1495]**, **[15443]**
B2B **[48242]**
"B2B Commercial Collection Agency Accounts Fall" in Managing Credit, Receivables & Collections (November 2010, No. 10-11, pp. 9) **[6274]**, **[26140]**, **[26916]**, **[36358]**
Babcock Demon Incubator **[55864]**
Babies 'N' Bells Inc. **[16432]**
"BABs in Bond Land" in Barron's (Vol. 89, July 6, 2009, No. 27, pp. 14) **[5228]**, **[8080]**, **[12043]**, **[26917]**, **[31208]**, **[33151]**, **[46147]**
Babson College - Arthur M. Blank Center for Entrepreneurship **[42358]**
Babson College - Center for Entrepreneurial Studies [42358]
Baby Boot Camp **[16016]**
Baby Massage **[1666]**

"Bankruptcies Soar As Market Takes a Tumble" in The Business Journal - Serving Phoenix and the Valley of the Sun (Vol. 28, August 22, 2008, No. 51, pp. 1) [23736], [26933]

"Bankruptcies Swell" in The Business Journal-Portland (Vol. 25, July 4, 2008, No. 17, pp. 1) [14387], [23737], [26148], [26934], [37311]

"Bankruptcy Blowback" in Business Week (September 22, 2008, No. 4100, pp. 36) [8100], [12061], [14388], [23738], [26149], [26935], [31229], [33157], [33533], [37312], [45294]

"Bankruptcy Claims Brooke, Gives Franchisees Hope" in The Business Journal-Serving Metropolitan Kansas City (October 31, 2008) [11313], [23739], [24237], [32130], [36963]

Bankruptcy Law Reporter™ [24133]

Bankruptcy for Small Business [23740], [31230], [32532]

Bankruptcy for Small Business, 2E: Know Your Legal Rights and Recover from Mistakes and Start Over Successfully [23741], [31231]

"Banks Beef Up Deposits, But Lending Lags" in Baltimore Business Journal (Vol. 28, October 29, 2010, No. 25, pp. 1) [31232], [37313]

"Banks Could Greet Tenants in One Year" in Business Courier (Vol. 26, October 16, 2009, No. 25, pp. 1) [5231], [17757], [41757], [42945]

Banks County Chamber of Commerce (BCCC) [50442]

"Banks Deposit Reassurance, Calm Customers" in The Business Journal-Serving Greater Tampa Bay (Vol. 28, August 22, 2008) [26381], [28129], [31233], [39680], [42450], [42603]

"Banks Fall Short in Online Services for Savvy Traders" in Barron's (Vol. 88, March 17, 2008, No. 11, pp. 35) [8101], [11625], [12062], [21054], [28562], [31234], [34779], [44259]

"Banks Find Borrowers Off the Beaten Path" in Boston Business Journal (Vol. 30, December 3, 2010, No. 45, pp. 1) [31235], [37314]

"Banks Fret About Gist Of Bailout" in The Business Journal-Serving Metropolitan Kansas City (Vol. 27, September 26, 2008, No. 2) [12063], [21870], [26936], [31236], [33158], [37805], [42451]

"Banks Lower Rates on CDs, Deposits" in Baltimore Business Journal (Vol. 27, January 1, 2010, No. 35, pp. 1) [26937], [31237], [33534], [45295]

"Banks, Retailers Squabble Over Fees" in Baltimore Business Journal (Vol. 28, June 18, 2010, No. 6, pp. 1) [6275], [26150], [31238], [33535], [42946]

"Banks Seeing Demand for Home Equity Loans Slowing" in Crain's Cleveland Business (Vol. 28, December 3, 2007, No. 48, pp. 1) [8103], [12064], [14389], [26151], [31239], [37315]

BANKSCOPE [8931]

Banning Chamber of Commerce [48245]

Banning Mail Pouch [48246]

Banquet Managers Guild [3462]

BAPTurnkey [208]

Bar-B-Cutie [18077]

Bar Harbor Chamber of Commerce (BHCC) [52561]

"Bar Hopping: Your Numbers At a Glance" in Inc. (January 2008, pp. 44-45) [62], [3503], [13989], [18864], [21347], [35703], [39681], [42760], [45092]

The Bar Register of Preeminent Lawyers™ [24134]

Baraboo Area Chamber of Commerce (BCC) [59486]

Barada Associates Inc. [35541]

Barb Gordon Graphic Design [6537]

"Barbara West" in Crain's Cleveland Business (Vol. 30, June 29, 2009, No. 25, pp. 14) [34196], [37806], [47228]

"Barbarians Set Bar Low With Lowly Canadian Telco" in Globe & Mail (March 31, 2007, pp. B1) [8104], [12065], [41758], [44260]

Barberton Community Development Corp. [56393]

Bare Bones [49656]

"Bargain Hunting In Vietnam" in Barron's (Vol. 88, July 14, 2008, No. 28, pp. M6) [8105], [12066], [22720], [26938], [31240], [36363]

Bargaining With Vendors and Suppliers (Onsite) [22161]

Barger & Wolen Newsletter [11455]

Andrew Barile Consulting Corporation Inc. [47120]

"Bark and Bite" in Canadian Business (Vol. 81, March 31, 2008, No. 5, pp. 20) [25425], [33536], [34780], [36364], [38924]

Bark Busters [15708]

Bark Busters Home Dog Training [15709]

"Bark Up The Right Tree" in Small Business Opportunities (Winter 2009) [15674], [15815], [22721], [24238], [25028], [26939], [32131]

Barker & Associates [26617], [36006], [40579]

Jess Barker, Document Research/Retrieval L.L.C. [14762], [17653]

Barnard's Retail Trend Report [43271]

Frank Barnes & Associates [984]

"Barnes Shakes Up Sara Lee Exec Suite" in Crain's Chicago Business (Vol. 31, April 21, 2008, No. 16, pp. 1) [24239], [37807], [38925]

Barnesville Area Chamber of Commerce [56007]

Barnesville Area Chamber of Commerce and Development Council [56007]

Barnesville-Lamar County Chamber of Commerce [50443]

Melvin E. Barnette & Associates Inc. [2816], [38656]

Barnie's Coffee & Tea Co., Inc. [9724]

"Barred Collection Agency Sued by Colorado AG" in Collections & Credit Risk (Vol. 15, August 1, 2010, No. 7, pp. 7) [6276], [23742], [26152], [26655], [33537]

"Barriers to Small Business Creations in Canada" in International Journal of Entrepreneurship and Small Business (Vol. , pp.) [29483], [32350]

Barrington Area Chamber of Commerce (BACC) [50908]

Barrington Partners [49177]

Barron's Guide to Graduate Business Schools [28130]

"Barron's Lipper Fund Listings" in Barron's (Vol. 89, July 13, 2009, No. 28, pp. 19) [8106], [12067], [31241]

Barron's Online [8932], [13194], [14534]

Barron's: The Dow Jones Business and Financial Weekly [2707], [13110]

Barrow County Chamber of Commerce (BCCC) [50444]

Barrowvision Newsletter [50445]

Barry County Area Chamber of Commerce (BACC) [53134]

Barry Page Consulting [14295]

"Bars, Restaurants to Offer Prix Fixe Menus, Space to Race Patrons" in Boston Business Journal (Vol. 29, July 22, 2011, No. 11, pp. 1) [1831], [17884], [19404]

Barson Marketing Inc. [40580]

Barstow Area Chamber of Commerce [48247]

Laban/Bartenieff Institute of Movement Studies Inc. (LIMS) [6426]

"Bartering, Browsing, Borrowing to Save" in Reading Eagle (July 20, 2010) [21836], [41759]

"Bartering is Local Club's Stock in Trade" in Pueblo Chieftain (September 6, 2010) [21837], [26940]

"Bartering Makes a Return in Hard Times" in Atlanta Journal-Constitution (October 2, 2010, pp. A15) [21838], [26941], [41760], [45296]

"Bartering Takes Businesses Back to Basics: Broker's Exchange Helps Members to Reach New Customers" in Buffalo News (July 9, 2010) [2698], [21839], [22722], [39682], [41761]

"Bartering Trades on Talents" in Reading Eagle (June 20, 2010) [21840], [22723], [26942], [41762], [44261], [45297]

Bartlesville Regional Chamber of Commerce (BRCC) [56464]

Bartlett Arboretum and Gardens - Horticulture Resource Library [9842]

Bartlett Area Chamber of Commerce (BACC) [57651]

Bartlett Chamber of Commerce [50909]

Bartlett Business and Chamber of Commerce Directory [50910]

Barton Area Chamber of Commerce [58737]

Barton County Chamber of Commerce [53959]

Barton County Historical Society [9485]

Bartow Board of Trade [50105]

Bartow Chamber News [49946]

Basalt Chamber of Commerce [49450]

Baseball Card Collector [4418]

BaseCamp Ventures [54841]

"Basel3 Quick Fix Actually Neither" in Canadian Business (Vol. 83, October 12, 2010, No. 17, pp. 19) [22724], [26943], [31242], [33538], [37316]

BASELINE In Production Credits [8018], [20014], [20899]

Baseline Selling [43383]

BaselineFT's In Production Database [8018], [20014], [20899]

"BASF Launches $4.9 Billion Bid for Rival Engelhard" in Globe & Mail (January 4, 2006, pp. B7) [8107], [12068], [24240], [25426], [41763]

Basic Accounting Video Series [195]

Basic Electricity for Auto Mechanics [18628]

Basic Electricity for the Non Electrician (Onsite) [24971], [28009]

Basic Electricity for the Non Electrician (Onsite) (In-House Training) [2607]

Basic Masonry [14118]

Basic Problem Solving Techniques (Onsite) [28010], [28973]

Basic Real Estate Investing [17573]

Basic Screen Printing [18360]

Basic Steps for Better Business Writing [22641]

Basic Techniques in Practical Chemistry [28410]

Basics of Commercial Contracting (Onsite) [28011]

Basics of Government Contract Administration (Onsite) [22550], [33394]

The Basics of Human Resource Law (Onsite) [23676]

Basics of Successful Investing [8876]

Basics of Time Management Workshop (Onsite) [46485]

Basin Business [56710]

"Baskin-Robbins" in Ice Cream Reporter (Vol. 23, November 20, 2010, No. 12, pp. 7) [10847], [40995]

"Baskin-Robbins" in Ice Cream Reporter (Vol. 23, September 20, 2010, No. 10, pp. 6) [10848], [40996]

"Baskin-Robbins Expanding in China and U.S." in Ice Cream Reporter (Vol. 21, August 20, 2008, No. 9, pp. 1) [10849], [22725], [36365]

"Baskin-Robbins Expanding to South Texas" in Ice Cream Reporter (Vol. 23, July 20, 2010, No. 8, pp. 4) [10850], [22726], [32132]

Baskin-Robbins Ice Cream [10947]

"Baskin-Robbins: New in U.S., Old in Japan" in Ice Cream Reporter (Vol. 23, August 20, 2010, No. 9, pp. 2) [10851], [22727], [32133], [36366]

"Baskin-Robbins Reopens in New Orleans" in Ice Cream Reporter (Vol. 23, September 20, 2010, No. 10, pp. 3) [10852], [22728]

"Baskin-Robbins Tests New Upscale Concept" in Ice Cream Reporter (Vol. 21, September 20, 2008, No. 10, pp. 1) [10853], [17885], [22729]

Bass & Co. [5082]

Bass Lake Chamber of Commerce [48248]

Bass Tackle: How to Buy & Save [1706]

Bastrop Chamber of Commerce (BCC) [57946]

Bastyr University Library [14831], [15211]

Batavia Business [50911]

Batavia Chamber of Commerce (BCC) [50912]

Batavia Industrial Center [55479]

Bates International Motor Home Rental Systems, Inc. [1634]

Batesville [48006]

Batesville Area Chamber of Commerce [51518]

Batesville Area Chamber of Commerce (BACC) [48007]

Bath Area Chamber of Commerce [52631]

Bath-Brunswick Region Map [52562]

Bath County Chamber of Commerce [58856]

Bath Fitter [10507]

"Battelle Given Keys to Group" in Business First-Columbus (October 12, 2007, pp. 1) [16512]

Batter Up Kids Culinary Center [5846]

"Battered Loblaw Makes Deep Job Cuts" in Globe & Mail (January 23, 2007) [9912], [25029]

"Battered U.S. Auto Makers in Grip of Deeper Sales Slump" in Globe & Mail (April 4, 2007, pp. B1) [8108], [12069], [14860], [38926]

Batteries Plus [1588]

Batterson Cross Zakin, LLC (BCZ) [51394]

Battery Ventures, L.P. [53007]

Battle Creek Area Chamber of Commerce (BCACC) [53135]

Battle Creek Chamber of Commerce Self-Employment Program [53501]

Battle Ground Chamber of Commerce (BGCC) [59095]

Battle Ground--North Clark County Directory [59096]

"Battle of the Titans" in Canadian Business (Vol. 81, March 17, 2008, No. 4, pp. 15) [8109], [12070], [25427], [31243], [33539], [41764]

"Battling Back from Betrayal" in Harvard Business Review (Vol. 88, December 2010, No. 12, pp. 130) [63], [2267], [17706], [21348], [22730], [23743], [30900], [35274], [35704], [36367], [37185], [37808]

Battling Big Box: How Nimble Niche Companies Can Outmaneuver Giant Companies [25030], [25428], [26382], [29017], [29484], [31244]

Bauder College Library [1675], [4167]

Baudette-Lake of the Woods Chamber of Commerce [53574]

Bavier, Bulger & Goodyear Inc. [26812]

Baxley-Appling County Chamber of Commerce [50446]

"Baxter Baker Wins in Hot Finale of 'Cupcake Wars'" in Fort Mill Times (September 13, 2011) [1751], [3165], [31026], [47229]

Baxter Springs Chamber of Commerce [52047]

Baxter Woodman Consulting Engineers [10181]

Baxter & Woodman Inc. [10181]

Bay Area Business Journal [53136]

Bay Area Chamber of Commerce (BACC) [53137]; [56711]

Bay Area Chamber Handbook [53138]

Bay Area Independent Publishers Association (BAIPA) [2084], [6776]

Bay Area Printmakers - California Society of Etchers [4436]

Bay Biz [49947]

Bay Biz Magazine [49948]

Bay Business Journal [59487]

Bay County Chamber of Commerce (BCCC) [49949]

Bay County SCORE [49909]

Bay County Small Business Incubator [50366]

Bay Meadows Racetrack - William P. Kyne Memorial Thoroughbred Racing Library [10627]

Bay Minette Chamber of Commerce [47719]

Bay Partners [49178]

Bay Tree Publishing [49390]

Bayer Center for Nonprofit Management (BCNM) [38657]

"Bayer Job Cuts to Hit Canada" in Globe & Mail (March 3, 2007, pp. B7) [24241], [38927]

BayerDiag, a Bayer Company Library [14065], [14338]

Bayfield Chamber of Commerce [59488]

Baylor College of Medicine - Center for Medical Ethics and Health Policy [34645]

Baylor University - Center for Business and Economic Research [27929]

Baylor University - Center for Private Enterprise [30379]

Baylor University - Crouch Fine Arts Library [14670]

Baymont Inn & Suites [10798]

Bayou La Batre Chamber of Commerce (BLBCC) [47626]

The Baysider [49950]

Baytown Chamber of Commerce (BCC) [57947]

"BayTSP, NTT Data Corp. Enter Into Reseller Pact to Market Online IP Monitoring" in Professional Services Close-Up (Sept. 11, 2009) [3504], [11626], [18865], [28563], [36368], [39683], [43384], [45093]

Bayview Chamber of Commerce [50737]

BB Views [54469]

BBB Alert [50884]

BBB Broadcaster [57423]

The BBB Bulletin [52035]

BBB Business and Consumer Brochures [57424]

BBB Central Florida Times [49923]

BBB Connections [53561]

BBB Consumer Guide [49651]

BBB Consumer Resource Guide and Membership Directory [49809]

"BBB Hires Marketing Firm to Attract More Businesses" in Baltimore Business Journal (Vol. 27, January 1, 2010, No. 35, pp. 1) [18537], [20320], [28564], [39684], [42452], [46601]

"BBB Reworks Logo, Grading System" in Crain's Cleveland Business (Vol. 28, October 8, 2007, No. 40, pp. 5) [39685], [42453], [42604]

BBB Rules of Arbitration [49842]

BBB Rules of Mediation [49843]

BBB Wise Giving Alliance [24792]

BBIA enews [1983], [2435]

BBLM Architects [41575]

"BC Forest Safety Council Unveils Supervisor Course to Respond to Industry Demands" in Canadian Corporate News (May 14, 2007) [28131], [37809], [47453]

BC Innovation Council [32485]

BCA-Credit Information [16688], [19881]

"BCE Mulls Radical Changes With Industry Under Pressure" in Globe & Mail (March 30, 2007, pp. B1) [22731], [24242], [25031], [41765]

"BCE Wireless Growth Flags in Fourth Quarter" in Globe & Mail (February 8, 2007, pp. B5) [3687], [22732], [34781]

"BCE's Aliant Trust Spinoff Valued at About $8.5 Billion" in Globe & Mail (March 8, 2006, pp. B1) [8110], [12071], [44262]

BCM Technologies, Inc. [58548]

BD Ventures / Becton, Dickinson and Co. [54842]

BDA [46083]

"BDC Launches New Online Business Advice Centre" in Internet Wire (July 13, 2010) [2766], [8111], [12072], [25831], [28565], [29485], [31245], [32351]

BDPA Information Technology Thought Leaders [4831]

"Be a Better Manager: Live Abroad" in Harvard Business Review (Vol. 88, September 2010, No. 9, pp. 24) [29486], [36369], [37810], [40861], [40997]

Be a Brilliant Business Writer: Write Well, Write Fast, and Whip the Competition [6818], [22269], [22581], [25429], [29018]

Be the Elephant: Build a Bigger, Better Business [22733], [29487], [32352], [37811], [43385]

Be the Hero: Three Powerful Ways to Overcome Challenges in Work and In Life [29488], [37812]

"Be Innovative in Other Ways" in Green Industry Pro (Vol. 23, March 2011, No. 3, pp. 4) [9773], [13383], [13470], [26383], [36964], [39686], [44263]

"Be Proactive - Closely Review Contracts" in Contractor (Vol. 56, July 2009, No. 7, pp. 19) [788], [5232], [6877], [16218], [18677], [23744]

Be a Professional Gemmologist [13251]

"Be Safe: CSE Requires a Series of Steps" in Contractor (Vol. 56, October 2009, No. 10, pp. 40) [16219], [47454]

Be Safe, Not Sorry [6441]

"Be Wary of Dual-Flush Conversion Kits" in Contractor (Vol. 56, September 2009, No. 9, pp. 66) [789], [5233], [7111], [18678], [30498]

"Be Wary of Legal Advice on Internet, Lawyers Warn" in Crain's Detroit Business (Vol. 24, September 22, 2008, No. 38, pp. 16) [11627], [21055], [23745], [45298]

Be Your Own Boss [29330], [32353]

Be Your Own Boss: Start a Business [46054]

The Beach Biz [49951]

Beach Business [48249]; [49952]

Franklin F. Beach & Co. [22037]

Beach Waves [49953]

Beachwood Business Development Center [56394]

Beachwood Chamber of Commerce (BCC) [56008]

The Beacon [51519]

Beacon Management - Management Consultants [2817], [13798], [24653], [25942], [30374], [32007], [38658]

Beacon Partners Inc. [49770]

Beacon Technology Ventures [53008]

Bead and Button [6123]

BEAEMPM [3397]

Beall Investigation Bureau Inc. [29301]

"Beam My Data Up" in Canadian Business (Vol. 80, February 12, 2007, No. 4, pp. 42) [4692], [4843], [44264]

BeamPines Inc. [36007]

Bean Association [17857]

Beans: Four Principles for Running a Business in Good Times or Bad [9696], [22734], [32533]

"The Bear Arrives - With Bargain Hunters" in Barron's (Vol. 88, July 7, 2008, No. 27, pp. M3) [8112], [12073], [19212], [21520], [22735], [26944], [31246]

Bear Creek Venture Partners [59326]

Bear Lake Rendezvous Chamber of Commerce (BLRCC) [58628]

"Bear Market Tough On Investors" in The Business Journal-Milwaukee (Vol. 25, July 4, 2008, No. 41, pp. A1) [8113], [12074], [26945], [31247]

Bear River Chamber of Commerce [58629]

Bear River Valley Chamber of Commerce (BRVCC) [58629]

Bear Tracks [59489]

Bear Valley Review [48250]

The Bearclaw Coffee Company [9725]

BearCom Building Services [6569]

Beardstown Chamber of Commerce (BCC) [50913]

"The Bear's Back" in Barron's (Vol. 88, July 7, 2008, No. 27, pp. 17) [8114], [12075], [26946], [31248]

"Beat the Buck: Bartering Tips from In-The-Know Authors" in (June 23, 2010) [21841], [31249], [41766]

Beat the Taxman 2006: Easy Ways to Save Tax in Your Small Business [19607], [46149]

Beat the Taxman 2007: Easy Ways to Save Tax in Your Small Business, 2007 Edition For the 2006 Tax Year [19608], [46150]

Beat the Taxman: Easy Ways to Tax Save in Your Small Business [2268], [19609], [21349], [46151]

Beatrice Area Chamber of Commerce (BCC) [54362]

Beatty Chamber of Commerce [54471]

Beaufort Area Small Business Development Center [57401]

Beaufort Regional Chamber of Commerce [57429]

Beaumont Chamber of Commerce [48251]

Beaumont Chamber of Commerce (BCC) [57948]

"Beaumont Outsources Purchasing as Route to Supply Cost Savings" in Crain's Detroit Business (Vol. 25, June 1, 2009, No. 22) [14312], [31250], [41662]

"The Beauty of Banking's Big Ugly" in Barron's (Vol. 89, July 27, 2009, No. 30, pp. 31) [8115], [12076], [26947], [31251], [37317]

Beauty Fair [2062], [4160], [5908], [7858], [10084]

The Beauty Industry Report [10077]

Beauty Supply Outlet [1911]

Beaver County Chamber of Commerce [56961]

Beaver Dam Area Chamber of Commerce (BDACC) [59490]

Beaver Street Enterprise Center [50367]

Beaver Valley Chamber of Commerce [58630]

Beaverbrook Art Gallery Library [1381]

Beaverhead Chamber of Commerce [54243]

Beaverhead County, Montana [54244]

Beaverton Area Chamber of Commerce (BACC) [56712]

"Because 10 Million Zumba Lovers Can't Be Wrong" in Inc. (Volume 32, December 2010, No. 10, pp. 106) [15961], [29489], [41767]

"Because He Is Always On the Accelerator: Jay Rogers: Local Motors, Chandler, Arizona" in Inc. (Volume 32, December 2010, No. 10) [14861], [38928]

"Because He Is Still Growing: Horst Rechelbacher: Intelligent Nutrients Minneapolis" in Inc. (Volume 32, December 2010, No. 10) [10069], [10364], [21521], [29490]

"Because Kids Need To Be Heard: Tina Wells: Buzz Marketing Group: Voorhees, New Jersey" in Inc. (Volume 32, December 2010) [2114], [13990], [39687], [47230]

Don L. Beck Associates Inc. [38659]

Beck Powell & Parsons Inc. [41576]

Becker College [53086]

Beckett and Raeder Inc. [1300]

Beckley - Raleigh County Chamber of Commerce (BRCCC) [59387]

"Become A Brand" in Women Entrepreneur (September 14, 2008) [22736], [29491], [39688], [45872], [47231]

Become a World Class Assistant (Onsite) [37584]

Become Your Own Boss in 12 Months: A Month-by-Month Guide to a Business that Works [24175], [32354]

Becoming a Personal Trainer for Dummies [14135], [15146], [15931], [21275], [23665], [24176]

Becoming a Publications Manager [6507]

Bed and Breakfast Guide [55087]

"Bedbugs Are Here, But Help Is At Hand" in Register-Guard (June 26, 2011) [15626]

"Bedding a Leader in Kohl's Q1 Gains" in Home Textiles Today (Vol. 31, May 24, 2011, No. 13, pp. 1) [10388], [10456], [22737], [42947]

Bedford-Alleghenies SCORE [56932]

Bedford Area Chamber of Commerce [51520]

Bedford Area Chamber of Commerce (BACC) [58857]

Bedford Associates Inc. [8908], [13178]

Bedford Banner [52836]

Bedford Capital Corp. [55396]

Bedford Chamber of Commerce [52837]

Bedford Chamber of Commerce (BCC) [51821]; [56009]

Bedford Chamber of Commerce [58857]

Bedford County Chamber of Commerce [56962]

Bedford Heights Chamber of Commerce (BHCC) [56010]

Bedford Hills Chamber of Commerce [55088]

Bee Biology and Systematics Laboratory - Library [1955]

Bee Breeding: The Search for the Perfect Honeybee [1953]

Bee County Chamber of Commerce [57949]

Bee Culture--Who's Who in Apiculture Issue: The Magazine of American Beekeeping [1944]

Beech Mountain Area Chamber of Commerce [55590]

Beech-Nut Nutrition Corporation Library [15212]

Beecher Chamber of Commerce [50914]

Beecken Petty O'Keefe & Company [51395]

Beef O'Bradys Family Sports Pubs [18078]

Beehive Co-op LLC [43287]

Beeline Learning Solutions (BLS) [2818], [4903], [22516], [22649], [25943], [28430]

Beer Associates [18047]

Beer Cans and Brewery Collectibles [4412]

"Beer Drinkers Wanted More. The Brewer Had No Room to Expand. How Could It Keep the Taps Flowing?" in Inc. (October 2007, pp. 65-66) [2450], [22738], [29492]

Beer Institute [2443]

"Beer Sales 'Foament' a Dispute" in Philadelphia Business Journal (Vol. 28, October 9, 2009, No. 34, pp. 1) [2451], [9913], [23746], [26736], [42948]

"Beer Stocks Rally on Anheuser, InBev Report" in Globe & Mail (February 16, 2007, pp. B3) [1832], [12077], [13570], [22739], [38929]

Beer-Wells Real Estate Services Inc. [16562]

The Beermat Entrepreneur: Turn Your Good Idea Into a Great Business [22740], [29331], [32355], [37268]

Beewall & Company L.L.C. [22517]

BeeWall Diversity [22517]

Before & After: How to Design Cool Stuff [4527]

"Before Signing a Lease" in Business Owner (Vol. 35, September-October 2011, No. 5, pp. 14) [17205], [17758], [44644]

"Before You Hit Send: Crafting Workplace E-Mails to Avoid Mishaps" in Black Enterprise (Vol. 38, January 2008, No. 6, pp. 85) [22582], [28566]

Beginning Bodybuilding [15993]

Beginning Training for Your Retriever [15699]

Behavioral Research in Accounting [170]

Behind the Cloud [26384], [28567], [34782], [39689], [43386], [44121], [44265], [45299]

"Behind the Numbers: When It Comes to Earnings, Look for Quality, Not Just Quantity" in Black Enterprise (July 2008, pp. 35) [8116], [12078], [22741], [31252]

"Behind the Scenes: Companies At the Heart of Everyday Life" in Inc. (February 2008, pp. 26-27) [3505], [9060], [18395], [18866], [24823], [38930], [45094]

"Behind the Scenes: Companies at the Heart of Everyday Life" in Inc. (March 2008, pp. 34-35) [5234], [33405]

Behind the Scenes [41356]

Beijing International Jewellery Fair [13289]

"Being all a-Twitter" in Canadian Business (Vol. 81, December 8, 2008, No. 21, pp. 22) [393], [3506], [11628], [18867], [28568], [39690], [43387], [45095]

"Being Big By Design" in Canadian Business (Vol. 82, April 27, 2009, No. 7, pp. 39) [12079], [22742], [25430], [34783], [41768], [42761], [43803]

"Being Emotional During Decision Making-Good or Bad?" in Academy of Management Journal (Vol. 50, No. 4, August 2007) [29493], [37813]

Being Self-Employed: How to Run a Business Out of Your Home, Claim Travel and Depreciation and Earn a Good Income Well into Your 70s or 80s [24824], [32534], [35596], [46152]

Belen Chamber of Commerce [54925]

Belfast Area Chamber of Commerce [52563]

Belfast Booklet [52564]

Belgrade Chamber of Commerce (BCC) [54245]

Belgrade Montana, Community Profile and Chamber News [54246]

Belhaven Community Chamber of Commerce [55591]

"The Believer" in Inc. (December 2007, pp. 130-138) [11046], [19213], [21522], [45873], [47232]

The Believer [49954]

Bell County Chamber of Commerce [52261]

Bell Gardens Association of Merchants and Commerce (BGAMC) [48252]

Bell Gardens Chamber of Commerce [48252]

Bell Industries Technology Solutions Group [41469], [41577]

Bell Springs Publishing [49391]

Bell Techlogics [41469], [41577]

"The Bell Tolls for Thee" in Canadian Business (Vol. 81, March 3, 2008, No. 3, pp. 36) [28132], [34784], [35275], [44266]

Bellacino's Pizza & Grinders Inc. [16137]

Bellaire Area Chamber of Commerce [53139]; [56011]

Bellaire/Southwest Houston Chamber of Commerce [58204]

Bellbrook - Sugarcreek Area Chamber of Commerce (BSACoC) [56012]

Belle Glade Chamber of Commerce [49955]

Belle Plaine Area Chamber of Commerce [52048]

Bellefonte Area Chamber of Commerce [56963]

Bellefonte Intervalley Area Chamber of Commerce (BIACC) [56963]

Belleview-South Marion Chamber of Commerce [49956]

Belleville Area Chamber of Commerce (BCC) [53140]

Belleville Chamber of Commerce [52049]

Belleville Economic Progress [51120]

Bellevue Area Chamber of Commerce (BCC) [51822]

Bellevue Chamber of Commerce [57652]; [59097]

"Bellingham Boatbuilder Norstar Yachts Maintains Family Tradition" in Bellingham Business Journal (Vol. February 2010, pp. 12) [13936], [24719], [31027], [38931]

Bellingham Small Business Development Center [59050]

Bellingham/Whatcom Chamber of Commerce and Industry (B/WCCI) [59098]

Bellows Falls Area Chamber of Commerce [58754]

Bellville Chamber of Commerce [57950]

Bellydance! Fast Moves [6393]

Bellydance! Slow Moves [6394]

Belmar Chamber of Commerce [54670]

Belmond Area Chamber of Commerce (BACC) [51823]

"Belmont Annexation Approved" in Charlotte Observer (February 7, 2007) [5235], [33540]

Belmont-Central Chamber of Commerce [50915]

Belmont Chamber of Commerce (BCC) [48253]

Beloit Area Chamber of Commerce (BACC) [52050]

Belpre Area Chamber of Commerce (BACC) [56013]

Belron Canada Inc. [9643], [13895]

Belton Area Chamber of Commerce [57951]

Belton Chamber of Commerce (BCOC) [53960]

"Beltway Monitor" in Mergers & Acquisitions: The Dealmaker's Journal (March 1, 2008) [12080], [33541], [36370], [41769]

Belvidere Area Chamber of Commerce (BACC) [50916]

Belvidere Chamber of Commerce [50916]

Belzoni - Humphreys Development Foundation (BHDF) [53828]

Bemidji Area Chamber of Commerce (BACC) [53575]

Ben Craig Center Incubator & Accelerator [55865]

Ben Franklin: America's Original Entrepreneur, Franklin's Autobiography Adapted for Modern Times [29494], [32535]

Ben Franklin Technology Partners [57278]; [57329]

"Ben & Jerry" in Ice Cream Reporter (Vol. 21, August 20, 2008, No. 9, pp. 7) [10854], [39691]

Ben and Jerry's [10948]

"Ben & Jerry's Changing Some 'All Natural' Labels" in Ice Cream Reporter (Vol. 23, October 20, 2010, No. 11, pp. 1) [10215], [10855]

"Ben & Jerry's Introduces 'Green' Freezer" in Ice Cream Reporter (Vol. 21, October 20, 2008, No. 11, pp. 1) [7472], [10856]

Benaroya Capital Company [59327]

Benaroya Research Institute at Virginia Mason (BRI) [34646]

Benchmark Advisors [2819], [13799], [25944], [32008], [38660]

Benchmark Capital [49179]

The Benchmark Co. [16750], [20001]

Benchmark Consulting Group Inc. [2819], [13799], [25944], [32008], [38660]

"Benchmark Makes Granduca Entrance" in Houston Business Journal (Vol. 40, January 8, 2010, No. 35, pp. 2) [10664], [13766], [22743], [44122], [44267]

Benchmark Market Research [16750], [20001]

Benchmarking the Canadian Business Presence in East Asia [11047], [36371]

The Benchmarking Network Inc. [26618]

Bend Area Chamber of Commerce [56714]

Bend Chamber Business [56713]

Bend Chamber of Commerce (BCC) [56714]

The Benefit Capital Companies Inc. (BCC) [54523]

Benefit Communications Inc. (BCI) [22038]

Benefit Partners [22039], [36008]

Benefit Partners Inc. [22039], [36008]

Benefit Sources & Solutions (BSS) [22040]

"Benefits of Bartering" in Mail Tribune (November 22, 2010) [21842], [41770]

Benefits & Compensation Digest [25384]

Benefits Dynamics Inc. (BDI) [22041], [36009]

Benefits Law Journal [22007]

Benefits Quarterly [22008]

Benetech Inc. [22042]

Benham REO Group [17132]

Benicia Chamber of Commerce and Visitors' Center [48254]

Benicia Chamber of Commerce [48254]

Benihana [18079]

D.R. Bennett & Associates [26699]

Jacalyn E. S. Bennett & Co. [42313]

Bennington Area Chamber of Commerce [58738]

Bennington Area Guide [58739]

Bennington County Industrial Corp. [58790]

Bensinger, Du Pont & Associates [46083]

Benson Area Chamber of Commerce (BACC) [55592]

Benson Chamber of Commerce [47857]

Benson - San Pedro Valley Chamber of Commerce [47857]

Bentley College - Center for Business Ethics (CBE) [46030]

Benton Area Chamber of Commerce [48008]

Benton City Chamber of Commerce [59099]

Benton County/Camden Chamber of Commerce [57653]

Benton-West City Area Chamber of Commerce (BACC) [50917]

Bentonville-Bella Vista Chamber of Commerce [48009]

Benzie County Chamber of Commerce (BCCC) [53141]

Berea Chamber of Commerce [56014]

Beresford Chamber of Commerce (BCC) [57563]

Bergen Community College [54878]

Bergen County Economic Development Book [54671]

Bergen Small Business Development Center [54636]

Dr. John A. Berger and Associates [26700]

Berkeley Business Advocate [48255]

Berkeley Chamber of Commerce [48256]; [57430]

Berkeley County Chamber of Commerce [57430]

Berkeley International Capital Corp. [49180]

Berkeley Richmond Jewish Community Center [48256]

Berkeley Springs Chamber of Commerce [59388]

Berkeley Springs - Morgan County Chamber of Commerce (BSMCCC) [59388]

Berklee College of Music - Stan Getz Library [14671]

Linda Berkowitz [10565]

Berks Deaf & Hard of Hearing Services Library [10348]

Berkshire Botanical Garden - Horticulture Library [9843]

Berkshire Chamber of Commerce [52838]

Berkshires Capital Investors [53009]

Berkshires Chamber of Commerce [52839]

Berlin Chamber of Commerce (BCC) [49657]; [59491]

Bermuda Now [20193]

Berne Chamber of Commerce (BCC) [51521]

Bernie Shaeffer's Option Advisor [13111]

"Bernier Open to Telecom Changes" in Globe & Mail (March 22, 2006, pp. B1) [33542], [34785], [44268]

Bernstein Global Wealth Management. [13228]

Burt Bernstein Insurance Litigation Consultants [47121]

Berrien County Chamber of Commerce [50585]

Berrybrook Farm Franchising Inc. [10257]

Bert Dohmen's Wellington Letter [13112]

"Bertha's Birth Stirs Juice" in Barron's (Vol. 88, July 14, 2008, No. 28, pp. M11) [8117], [9914], [12081], [21523], [26948], [31253]

Berthel Fisher & Company Planning, Inc. [51999]

Berthoud Area Chamber of Commerce [49451]

Berwick Area Chamber of Commerce (BACC) [56964]

Ken Berwitz Marketing Research (KBMR) [14034]

Bessemer Area Today [47627]

Bessemer Area Wage/Salary Research 2000 [47628]

Bessemer Business Incubation System [47760]

Bessemer Venture Partners (Cambridge) [53010]

Bessemer Venture Partners (Larchmont) [55397]

Bessemer Venture Partners (Menlo Park) [49181]

"The Best Advice I Ever Got" in Harvard Business Review (Vol. 86, September 2008, No. 9, pp. 29) [3935], [29495], [45874]

Best in Bar Harbor Guide Book [52565]

"Best Buy's CEO On Learning to Love Social Media" in Harvard Business Review (Vol. 88, December 2010, No. 12, pp. 43) [5733], [15309], [28569], [39692], [42605], [42949]

"Best Cash Flow Generators" in Canadian Business (Vol. 81, Summer 2008, No. 9, pp. 73) [8118], [12082], [22744], [31254]

"Best Cash Flow Generators" in Canadian Business (Vol. 82, Summer 2009, No. 8, pp. 40) [12083], [24825], [31255]

"Best Companies for Diversity" in Black Enterprise (Vol. 38, July 2008, No. 12, pp. 12) [32536], [35276], [37814], [40705]

Best Coupon Book [669]

"Best Defensive Stocks" in Canadian Business (Vol. 81, Summer 2008, No. 9, pp. 67) [8119], [12084], [22745], [31256]

BEST Employers Association (BEA) [44790]

"The Best Execs in Canada" in Canadian Business (Vol. 79, October 9, 2006, No. 20, pp. 68) [29496], [32537], [37815]

"The Best Five-Month Run Since 1938" in Barron's (Vol. 89, August 3, 2009, No. 31, pp. M3) [8120], [12085], [19909], [31257]

"Best Foot Forward" in Canadian Business (Vol. 80, October 22, 2007, No. 21, pp. 115) [2767], [25832], [28133]

The Best of Golf in Paradise [19358]

"Best Growth Stocks" in Canadian Business (Vol. 81, Summer 2008, No. 9, pp. 61) [8121], [12086], [22746], [24243], [25032], [26949], [31258], [36372], [41771]

"Best Growth Stocks" in Canadian Business (Vol. 82, Summer 2009, No. 8, pp. 28) [6647], [8122], [12087], [22747], [31259], [36965], [41772]

Best Holiday Trav-L-Park Association (BHTPA) [3244]

"Best In Show" in Pet Product News (Vol. 64, November 2010, No. 11, pp. 20) [1056], [14808], [15751], [26385]

"Best Income Trust" in Canadian Business (Vol. 81, Summer 2008, No. 9, pp. 69) [8123], [12088], [14390], [16827], [17206], [22748], [31260]

"Best Income Trusts" in Canadian Business (Vol. 82, Summer 2009, No. 8, pp. 36) [12089], [46153]

"Best Managed Companies (Canada)" in Canadian Business (Vol. 82, Summer 2009, No. 8, pp. 38) [3507], [4693], [12091], [18868], [22750], [37817], [45096]

"Best Managed Companies" in Canadian Business (Vol. 81, Summer 2008, No. 9, pp. 71) [8124], [12090], [22749], [31261], [37816]

"The Best Option for All" in American Executive (Vol. 7, September 2009, No. 5, pp. 170) [6231], [6277], [21871], [24244], [26153]

Best Places to Stay in New England [1923]

"Best Practices Award-Winning Teams 2010-2011" in Women In Business (Vol. 63, Fall 2011, No. 3, pp. 19) [47233]

"Best Practices: Developing a Rewards Program" in Franchising World (Vol. 42, September 2010, No. 9, pp. 13) [21872], [32134]

Best Practices in Java Programming: Hands-On (Onsite) [28012]

"Best Practices: Just Say No" in Entrepreneur (Vol. 35, October 2007, No. 10, pp. 107) [26386]

Best Practices for Managing Inventories and Cycle Counts (Onsite) [37180]

Best Practices for the Multi-project Manager (Onsite) [37585]

Best Southwest Small Business Development Center [57839]

"Best Turnaround Stocks" in Canadian Business (Vol. 81, Summer 2008, No. 9, pp. 65) [8125], [12092], [22751], [26154], [26950], [31262], [37318], [38932]

"Best Turnaround Stocks" in Canadian Business (Vol. 82, Summer 2009, No. 8, pp. 32) [8126], [12093], [13352], [21524], [36373]

"Best Value Stocks" in Canadian Business (Vol. 81, Summer 2008, No. 9, pp. 63) [8127], [12094], [22752], [26951], [31263]

"Best Value Stocks" in Canadian Business (Vol. 82, Summer 2009, No. 8, pp. 30) [8128], [12095], [15519], [26952], [31264], [43388]

"The Best and Worst Economic Times" in Agency Sales Magazine (Vol. 39, December 2009, No. 11, pp. 22) [26387], [26953], [38933], [43389]

Best's Key Rating Guide [11314]

Best's Review [11456]; [11456]

Best's Statement File - Life/Health - United States [2737]

Best's Statement File - Property/Casualty - United States [2738], [11488], [13195]

BestWeek Life/Health Edition [11457]

BestWeek Property/Casualty Editions [11458]

"Bet on China" in Canadian Business (Vol. 80, November 5, 2007, No. 22, pp. 30) [3688], [12096], [26954], [36374]

"Bet on the Subcontinent" in Canadian Business (Vol. 81, April 14, 2008, No. 6, pp. 27) [8129], [12097], [26955], [31265], [36375]

"BETC Backers Plot Future" in Business Journal Portland (Vol. 27, December 10, 2010, No. 41, pp. 1) [7112], [7473], [30499], [33159], [33543], [35277], [35705], [38934], [46154]

Bethany Chamber of Commerce [56559]

Bethany-Fenwick Area Chamber of Commerce [49811]

Bethel Area Chamber of Commerce (BACC) [52566]

Bethel Chamber of Commerce [49658]

Bethel Island Chamber of Commerce [48257]

"Bethesda Stepping Out" in Business Courier (Vol. 27, October 15, 2010, No. 24, pp. 1) [9241], [33544], [34197], [45875]

Bethesda-Chevy Chase Chamber of Commerce [52715]

Bethlehem Chamber of Commerce [54550]; [55089]

Bettendorf Chamber of Commerce (BCC) [51824]

Better Bottom Lines [38661], [40581]

Better Business Bureau [51510]

Better Business Bureau (BBB) [48188]; [48189]

Better Business Bureau of Abilene [57904]

Better Business Bureau of Acadiana [52425]

Better Business Bureau of Akron [55986]

Better Business Bureau of Alaska [47776]

Better Business Bureau of Amarillo, Texas [57905]

Better Business Bureau of Arkansas [48001]

Better Business Bureau of Asheville/Western North Carolina [55565]

Better Business Bureau, Austin [57906]

Better Business Bureau, Birmingham [47615]

Better Business Bureau of Brazos Valley [57907]

Better Business Bureau, Buffalo [55066]

Better Business Bureau, Catawba and Lincoln Counties [55568]

Better Business Bureau of Central California [48190]

Better Business Bureau of Central East Texas [57908]

Better Business Bureau of Central and Eastern Iowa [51809]

Better Business Bureau of Central and Eastern Kentucky [52254]

Better Business Bureau of Central Florida [49924]

Better Business Bureau of Central Georgia [50425]

Better Business Bureau of Central Illinois [50885]

Better Business Bureau of Central Indiana [51510]

Better Business Bureau of Central Louisiana [52426]

Better Business Bureau of Central New England (BBB) [52824]

Better Business Bureau Central and Northern Alberta [59874]

Better Business Bureau, Central/Northern Arizona [47841]

Better Business Bureau of Central Ohio [55987]

Better Business Bureau of Central Oklahoma [56450]

Better Business Bureau of Central South Carolina and Charleston [57425]

Better Business Bureau of Central and South Central Texas [57909]

Better Business Bureau of Central Virginia [58839]

Better Business Bureau, Chattanooga [57640]

Better Business Bureau of Chicago and Northern Illinois [50886]

Better Business Bureau, Cleveland [55988]

Better Business Bureau of the Coastal Bend [57910]

Better Business Bureau of Coastal Carolina [57426]

Better Business Bureau, Connecticut [49652]

Better Business Bureau of Dayton/Miami Valley [55989]

Better Business Bureau of Delaware [49810]

Better Business Bureau of Denver [49439]

Better Business Bureau of Detroit and Eastern Michigan [53118]

Better Business Bureau of Eastern Idaho and Western Wyoming [50735]

Better Business Bureau of Eastern Missouri and Southern Illinois [53950]

Better Business Bureau of Eastern North Carolina [55566]

Better Business Bureau Education Foundation of the Heart of Texas I [57909]

Better Business Bureau, Fairbanks [47776]

Better Business Bureau Four Corners [54919]

Better Business Bureau of Greater East Tennessee [57641]

Better Business Bureau of Greater Hampton Roads [58840]

Better Business Bureau of Greater Kansas City [53951]

Better Business Bureau of Greater Maryland [52667]

Better Business Bureau of Greater Toronto Area (GTA) [59916]

Better Business Bureau of Hawaii [50697]

Better Business Bureau of the Inland Northwest [59084]

Better Business Bureau of Kansas [52036]

Better Business Bureau - Louisville [52255]

Better Business Bureau - Louisville, Southern Indiana and Western Kentucky [52255]

Better Business Bureau of Mahoning Valley [55990]

Better Business Bureau of Mainland British Columbia [59880]

Better Business Bureau of Manitoba [59901]

Better Business Bureau of the Maritime Provinces Inc. [59911]

Better Business Bureau of Metro Atlanta, Athens and Northeast Georgia [50426]

Better Business Bureau of Metropolitan Dallas [57911]

Better Business Bureau of Metropolitan Houston [57912]

Better Business Bureau of Metropolitan New York [55067]

Better Business Bureau of the Mid-South [57642]

Better Business Bureau of Middle Tennessee (BBBN) [57643]

Better Business Bureau of Mississippi [53825]

Better Business Bureau of the Mountain States [49440]

Better Business Bureau of New Hampshire [54546]

Better Business Bureau of New Jersey (BBB) [54661]

Better Business Bureau of New Jersey Consumer Guide [54662]

Better Business Bureau of New Mexico and Southwestern Colorado [54918]

Better Business Bureau of Newfoundland and Labrador [59908]

Better Business Bureau of North Alabama [47616]

Better Business Bureau of North Central Texas [57913]

Better Business Bureau of Northeast California [48191]

Better Business Bureau of Northeast Florida [49925]

Better Business Bureau of Northeast Kansas [52037]

Better Business Bureau of Northeast Louisiana [52427]

Better Business Bureau of Northern Indiana [51511]

Better Business Bureau of Northwest Florida [49926]

Better Business Bureau of Northwest North Carolina [55567]

Better Business Bureau, Northwest Ohio and Southeastern Michigan [55991]

Better Business Bureau of Coastal Empire [50427]

Better Business Bureau of Greenville [57427]

Better Business Bureau of Lexington [52254]

Better Business Bureau of Metropolitan Atlanta [50426]

Better Business Bureau of Northeastern Indiana [51511]

Better Business Bureau of Northern Connecticut [49652]

Better Business Bureau of Oregon/Southwest Washington [56698]

Better Business Bureau of Santa Clara Valley [48194]

Better Business Bureau of South Jersey [54661]

Better Business Bureau of South-East Connecticut [49652]

Better Business Bureau of Southwest Idaho [50736]

Better Business Bureau of St. Paul [53562]

Better Business Bureau of Stockton [48188]

Better Business Bureau of the Pike's Peak Region [49441]

Better Business Bureau of Western Connecticut [49652]

Better Business Bureau of Oregon and Western Washington [56698]

Better Business Bureau, Oregon/Western Washington [59085]

Better Business Bureau of Ottawa [59917]

Better Business Bureau, Phoenix [47841]

Better Business Bureau of Quebec [59959]

Better Business Bureau, Rochester (BBB) [55068]

Better Business Bureau of San Angelo [57914]

Better Business Bureau, San Antonio [57915]

Better Business Bureau of San Diego [48192]

Better Business Bureau of San Mateo County [48193]

Better Business Bureau of Saskatchewan [59967]

Better Business Bureau serving Columbus and Central Ohio [55987]

Better Business Bureau Serving Eastern Massachusetts, Maine and Vermont [52825]

Better Business Bureau Serving Eastern Washington and North Idaho [59084]

Better Business Bureau Serving Eastern Washington, North Idaho and Montana [59084]

Better Business Bureau Serving Four Corners and Western Slope [54919]

Better Business Bureau Serving Metropolitan Washington, DC and Eastern Pennsylvania [49844]

Better Business Bureau Serving Minnesota and North Dakota [53562]

Better Business Bureau Serving Upstate South Carolina [57427]

Better Business Bureau (Shreveport, Louisiana) [52424]

Better Business Bureau of Silicon Valley [48194]

Better Business Bureau of South Alabama [47617]

Better Business Bureau of South Central Louisiana [52428]

Better Business Bureau of South Central Ontario [59918]

Better Business Bureau of South Texas [57916]

Better Business Bureau Southeast Atlantic [50427]

Better Business Bureau of Southeast Texas [57917]

Better Business Bureau of Southern Alberta [59875]

Better Business Bureau of Southern Colorado [49441]

Better Business Bureau of Southern Nevada [54470]

Better Business Bureau of Southern Piedmont [55568]

Better Business Bureau of the Southland [48195]

Better Business Bureau of Southwest Idaho and Eastern Oregon [50736]

Better Business Bureau of Southwest Louisiana [52429]

Better Business Bureau of Southwest Missouri [53952]

Better Business Bureau of Tri-Counties [48196]

Better Business Bureau of Tucson [47842]

Better Business Bureau of Utah [58627]

Better Business Bureau of Vancouver Island [59881]

Better Business Bureau of West Central Ohio [55992]

Better Business Bureau of West Florida [49927]

Better Business Bureau of West Georgia - East Alabama [50428]

Better Business Bureau of Western Michigan (BBB WMI) [53119]

Better Business Bureau of Western Ontario [59919]

Better Business Bureau of Western Pennsylvania [56954]

Better Business Bureau of Western Virginia [58841]

Better Business Bureau, Wichita Falls [57913]

Better Business Bureau of Windsor and South Western Ontario [59920]

Better Business Bureau of Wisconsin [59474]

Better Business Bureau Wise Giving Alliance [24792]

"Better Business: Get Ready (Marketing Strategies for Better Sales Performance)" in Entrepreneur (Vol. 35, October 2007, No. 10) [39693], [43390]

Better Business Grammar [22642]

Better Business Traveling [24951]

Better Business Writing [22654]

"Better Card Collecting" in Canadian Business (Vol. 80, January 15, 2007, No. 2, pp. 66) [22753], [28134], [29497]

Better Homes Realty, Inc. [17133]

Better Investing [2708]

"Better Made's Better Idea: Diversify Despite Rising Costs" in Crain's Detroit Business (Vol. 24, September 22, 2008, No. 38, pp. 18) [9915], [22754], [24245], [25033], [26956], [38935], [40998], [43391]

Better Nutrition for Today's Living [15173]

Better Nutrition Magazine [15173]

Better Pages [53563]

Better Productivity Is Not By Chance—Dr. Robert Lorher [29198]

Better Roads--Annual Winter Maintenance Equipment & Materials Issue: Federal State County Township Road & Municipalities [2007]

"Better ROI Or Your Money Back, Says Buzz Agency" in Advertising Age (Vol. 79, July 14, 2008, No. 7, pp. 1) [394], [39694], [42454], [42606]

A Better Solution, Inc. [10571]

"Better Than New" in Bellingham Business Journal (Vol. February 2010, pp. 16) [395], [4199], [7816], [31028], [39695], [42950]

Better Vision Institute (BVI) [20912]

Betterway [56421]

Betterway Books [56421]

Betterway Publications, Inc. [56421]

"Betting Big, Winning Big" in Barron's (Vol. 88, March 17, 2008, No. 11, pp. 49) [8130], [12098], [31266]

"Betting on the Glitz" in Canadian Business (Vol. 79, October 9, 2006, No. 20, pp. 104) [22755], [25034], [42951]

"Betting on a Happy Ending" in Barron's (Vol. 88, July 7, 2008, No. 27, pp. 14) [8131], [12099], [19910], [31267]

"Betting On Slots" in Baltimore Business Journal (Vol. 28, November 19, 2010, No. 28, pp. 1) [9384], [44645]

"Betting On Volatile Materials" in Barron's (Vol. 88, July 14, 2008, No. 28, pp. M11) [8132], [11048], [12100], [26957], [31268], [36376], [38936]

Between the Issues [7024], [30413]

Between Rounds Bakery Sandwich Cafe [1690]

Beulah Chamber of Commerce (BCC) [55892]

BEV Capital / Brand Equity Ventures [49771]

Beverage & Food Dynamics [13601]

"Beverage Brand Vies To Be the Latest Purple Prince" in Brandweek (Vol. 49, April 21, 2008, No. 16, pp. 20) [10216], [10280], [21525], [29498], [38937], [39696], [40999]

Beverage Dynamics: Wine, Beer & Spirits for Retail Decision Makers [13601]

Beverage Industry--Annual Manual Issue [1833], [13571], [19252]

Beverage Marketing Directory [1867], [13572], [19214]

Beverage Network (BN) [1828], [17858]

Beverage World [13602]

Beverage World--Buyers Guide Issue [1834], [13598]
Beveridge & Diamond, P.C. Library [7395]
Beverly Chamber of Commerce [52840]
Beverly Foundation (BF) [15050]
Beverly Hills Chamber of Commerce [48258]
Beverly Hills Public Library - Fine Arts Division [6417]
Beverly Hyman and Associates [22531]
Bevinco [1879], [13604], [37228]
"Beware of Bad Blade Rentals" in Rental Product News
(Vol. 33, June 2011) [17759]
"Beware this Chinese Export" in Barron's (Vol. 90,
August 30, 2010, No. 35, pp. 21) [8133], [11049],
[12101], [36377], [41773]
"Beware of E15" in Rental Product News (Vol. 33,
October 2011) [7113], [7474], [17760], [30500],
[33545]
"Beware the Ides of March" in Canadian Business (Vol.
81, April 14, 2008, No. 6, pp. 13) [8134], [12102],
[14391], [26155], [31269], [37319]
Beware the Naked Man Who Offers You His Shirt
[40966], [43277], [43710]
"Beware of Rotting Money" in Barron's (Vol. 89, July 13,
2009, No. 28, pp. 31) [8135], [12103], [26958],
[31270], [33546]
Bexley Area Chamber of Commerce (BACC) [56015]
"Beyond Auto; Staffing Firm Malace Grabs Revenue
Jump" in Crain's Detroit Business (Vol. 26, January 18,
2010, No. 3, pp. 3) [6959], [22756], [24246], [35706],
[38938]
Beyond Booked Solid: Your Business, Your Life, Your
Way-It's All Inside [22757], [26388], [44269]
Beyond Buzz: The Next Generation of Word-of-Mouth
Marketing [39697], [42607]
"Beyond Grits: The Many Varieties of Southern Cuisine"
in Women In Business (Vol. 62, June 2010, No. 2, pp.
14) [5834], [17886]
"Beyond Microsoft and Yahoo!: Some M&A Prospects" in
Barron's (Vol. 88, March 17, 2008, No. 11, pp. 39)
[3508], [8136], [12104], [18869], [31271], [34786],
[41774], [45097]
Beyond Protection [15994]
"Beyond the RAZR's Edge" in Canadian Business (Vol.
79, November 6, 2006, No. 22, pp. 15) [3689],
[34787], [41000]
Beyond Routine [6395]
Beyond Start-Up: Management Lessons for Growing
Companies [38616], [44904]
"Beyond YouTube: New Uses for Video, Online and Off"
in Inc. (October 2007, pp. 53-54) [3509], [7904],
[18870], [20883], [28570], [39698], [45098], [45300]
"Beyond Zipcar: Collaborate Consumption" in Harvard
Business Review (Vol. 88, October 2010, No. 10, pp.
30) [37186], [41775]
BGP - Configuring BGP on Cisco Routers (Onsite)
[34735]
Bi-Annual Member Directory [53142]
BIA Financial Network Inc. [28960], [40582]
BIA/Kelsey [28960], [40582]
BIA's Radio Yearbook [16739]
BIA's Television Yearbook [19991]
Bibliography of the History of Art (BHA) [1375]
Bibliotheque Canadienne de l'Agriculture - Lennoxville.
[21796]
Bick International Library [4388]
Bicycle Federation of America [1968]
Bicycle Product Suppliers Association (BPSA) [1964]
Bicycle Stamps Club (BSC) [4334]
Bicycle Wholesale Distributors Association [1964]
Bicycling [1975]
Biddeford-Saco Chamber of Commerce and Industry
(BSCCI) [52567]
Biennial Guide [49957]
"The Big 50" in Canadian Business (Vol. 81, Summer
2008, No. 9, pp. 125) [8137], [12105], [22758],
[31272]
Big Apple Bagels [1691], [18080]
Big Bear Chamber of Commerce (BBCC) [48259]
Big Bend Community College [59353]
Big Bend Small Business Development Center [57840]
The Big Book of Small Business: You Don't Have to Run
Your Business by the Seat of Your Pants [29499],
[32538]
Big-Box Swindle: The True Cost of Mega-Retailers and
the Fight for America's Independent Businesses
[26959], [30501], [42952], [45301], [45876], [46842]
Big Boy Family Restaurant [18081]
"Big Boys Drawn Back to Play in Oil Sands" in Globe &
Mail (March 7, 2006, pp. B2) [38939], [41776]
"Big Bucks In Pet-ty Cash" in Small Business Opportuni-
ties (Fall 2008) [15716], [44756]
Big Businesses Directory [38901]
The Big Catfish Connection [1707]
The Big Catfish Connection II [1708]

The Big Comfy Couch: Are You Ready for School?
[3961]
The Big Comfy Couch: Be Nice, Snicklefritz! [3962]
The Big Comfy Couch: Dustbunny Dreams [3963]
"A Big Dream That 'Was Going Nowhere" in Globe &
Mail (February 4, 2006, pp. B4) [24247], [25035],
[41001]
"Big Energy Deals Power OptiSolar's Local Growth" in
Sacramento Business Journal (Vol. 25, August 22,
2008, No. 25, pp. 1) [7114], [19078], [22759], [30502]
"Big Energy Ideas for Our Times" in Canadian Business
(Vol. 83, August 17, 2010, No. 13-14, pp. 49) [7115],
[7475], [30503]
Big Fish Ontario [1709]
"Big Gains Brewing at Anheuser-Busch InBev" in Bar-
ron's (Vol. 90, August 30, 2010, No. 35, pp. 34) [1835],
[2452], [8138], [12106], [41777]
Big I Show/International Automotive Aftermarket Show
[1598]
Big Kids Baseball Cards [4419]
Big Lake Chamber of Commerce [47781]; [57952]
"Big Losses Mount for Hospitals" in Baltimore Business
Journal (Vol. 27, October 23, 2009, No. 24, pp. 1)
[12107], [26960], [31273], [34198]
Big O Tires [18638], [20081]
The Big Payback: The History of the Business of Hip-
Hop [14732], [17639], [29500], [40862], [41778],
[42953], [47171]
"Big Paychecks for Hospital CEOs" in Sacramento Busi-
ness Journal (Vol. 28, April 8, 2011, No. 6, pp. 1)
[34199], [35707], [37818]
"The Big Picture" in Canadian Business (Vol. 79, Winter
2006, No. 24, pp. 142) [5734], [34788]
"The BIG Picture" in Crain's Cleveland Business (Vol. 30,
June 22, 2009, No. 24, pp. 12) [28135], [29501]
Big Picture Framing [16327]
Big Rapids Chamber of Commerce [53374]
The Big Rich: The Rise and Fall of the Greatest Texas
Oil Fortunes [12108], [29502]
"Big Sell-Off At Sunwest" in The Business Journal-
Portland (Vol. 25, July 25, 2008, No. 20, pp. 1) [292],
[1421], [12109], [24248], [26156], [44135], [44270]
"Big Shoes to Fill for New United Way Chairman" in
Business Courier (Vol. 27, June 25, 2010, No. 8, pp. 4)
[9242], [37819], [45877]
Big Sky Business Journal [54333]
Big Sky Economic Development Authority [54222]
"Big Spenders" in Hawaii Business (Vol. 53, November
2007, No. 5, pp. 28) [10665], [41779]
Big Spring Area Chamber of Commerce (BSACC)
[57953]
The Big Squeeze: Tough Times for the American Work-
ers [23747], [26961], [31274]
Big Stone Lake Area Chamber of Commerce (BSLACC)
[53576]
The Big Switch [3510], [4940], [18871], [25431],
[26962], [28571], [34789], [41392], [45099], [45302]
The Big Switch: Rewiring the World, From Edison to
Google [4694], [28572], [34790], [45303]
Big and Tall Men's Apparel Needs Show [4297]
Big Town Hero [1692], [6455]
"Big Trouble at Sony Ericsson" in Barron's (Vol. 88,
March 24, 2008, No. 12, pp. M9) [3690], [8139],
[12110], [31275], [41780], [43392], [44271], [46155]
Big Vision, Small Business [24249], [25036], [25833],
[26389], [29019], [29503], [32539], [47234]
Big Walleye Presentations [1710]
Big Water Catfish [1711]
Big Yellow: Yellow Pages on the Web [683], [19859]
Biga & Associates, Inc. [26114]
Bigfork Area Chamber of Commerce (BACC) [54247]
"A Bigger Deal" in Crain's Cleveland Business (Vol. 28,
November 12, 2007, No. 45, pp. 1) [64], [2269],
[19610], [21350], [22760], [24250], [25037], [41781]
"Bigger is Definitely Not Better When It Comes to Cool-
ing" in Indoor Comfort Marketing (Vol. 70, May 2011,
No. 5, pp. 49) [790], [7116], [7476], [30504], [45304]
Bigger Isn't Always Better [22761], [32540]
"A Bigger Slice; Buscemi's Adds Licensees, Profits" in
Crain's Detroit Business (Vol. 23, October 15, 2007,
No. 42, pp. 3) [16123], [17887]
"Bigger TIF Makes Development Inroads" in The Busi-
ness Journal-Serving Metropolitan Kansas City (Vol.
26, July 11, 2008, No. 44) [5236], [17207], [22762],
[24826], [33160], [33547], [46156], [46997]
"Biggest Loser' Adds Bit of Muscle to Local Economy" in
Crain's Detroit Business (Vol. 26, January 4, 2010, No.
1, pp. 1) [15962], [19911], [26963], [44812]
"Biggest UM Landlords" in Crain's Detroit Business (Vol.
25, June 15, 2009, No. 24, pp. 1) [17208], [17761],
[28136]
Bighorn Area Chamber of Commerce [59562]
Bijan International Inc. [36010]

Bildor [1163]
"Bill Kaneko" in Hawaii Business (Vol. 53, December
2007, No. 6, pp. 32) [16828], [17209], [20139],
[20533], [26964], [33548], [42366], [45305]
"Bill Lee's Auto Repair Business Chugs Along Despite
Life's Obstacles" in Bradenton Herald (August 22,
2010) [18596], [26965], [29504], [44272]
Bill Sandy Co. [28450]
Billboard Connection [670]
Billboard's International Talent and Touring Guide
[19566]
Alan Biller and Associates [8909]
Billiard Basics [1985]
Billiard and Bowling Institute of America (BBIA) [1981],
[2427]
Billiard Congress of America (BCA) [1982]
Billiard Congress of America Trade Expo [1990]
Billiards for All Age Groups [1986]
Billiards Digest [1984]
Billings Area Chamber of Commerce [54248]
Billings SCORE [54231]
Billings Small Business Development Center [54212]
"Billion-Dollar Impact" in Business First Buffalo
(November 9, 2007, pp. 1) [32541], [45305]
Billions of Entrepreneurs: How China and India Are
Reshaping Their Futures and Yours [29505], [36378]
"Bills Raise Blues Debate; An Unfair Edge or Level Play-
ing Field?" in Crain's Detroit Business (Vol. 24, January
21, 2008, No. 3) [11315], [21873], [33549], [36113],
[46157]
"Bills Would Regulate Mortgage Loan Officers" in Crain's
Detroit Business (Vol. 24, February 25, 2008, No. 8,
pp. 9) [14392], [16829], [17210], [23748], [33550]
Biloxi Chamber of Commerce (BCC) [53829]
"BIM and LPS Improve Project Management" in Contrac-
tor (Vol. 57, January 2010, No. 1, pp. 56) [5237],
[37820]
"BIM: The Risks You Need to Watch Out For" in Contrac-
tor (Vol. 57, February 2010, No. 2, pp. 28) [23749],
[37821]
"BIM and You: Know Its Benefits and Risks" in Contrac-
tor (Vol. 57, January 2010, No. 1, pp. 46) [5238],
[6878], [16220], [18679], [23750]
BIN Number Directory of All Visa/Mastercard Issuing
Banks [6193]
Binders' Guild (BG) [2235]
Binding Industries Association International (BIA) [2236]
Binding Industries of America [2236]
Binghamton Small Business Development Center
[55013]
The Bingo Bugle Newspaper [15601]
Bio-Integral Resource Center (BIRC) [15658]
Bio-Technical Resources L.P. (BTR) [2478], [2820],
[25945], [44080]
BioAdvance [57279]
BioChem Technology Inc. [2821], [25946], [44081]
Biochemistry and Cell Biology [43997]
Biochimie et Biologie Cellulaire [43997]
"Biodiesel Poised to Regain Growth" in Farm Industry
News (January 21, 2011) [7117], [7477], [21526],
[22763], [30505], [41002], [45306], [46158]
Biogen Idec Innovation Incubator [53079]
Biographical Dictionaries Master Index [9435]
Biography and Genealogy Master Index: A Consolidated
Index to Biographical Sketches in Current and
Retrospective Biographical Dictionaries [9435]
"Bioheat - Alternative for Fueling Equipment" in Indoor
Comfort Marketing (Vol. 70, May 2011, No. 5, pp. 14)
[791], [7118], [7478], [30506], [39699], [45307]
Biological Control [15635]
Biomedical Instrumentation & Technology: Association for
the Advancement of Medical Instrumentation [14222]
Biomedical Management Resources (BMR) [24654],
[38662], [42314], [44919]
Biomedical Products [14224], [43999]
Biomedical Safety & Standards [14223]
Biomedical Science Consulting Co. [2822], [3060],
[13800], [25947], [34617]
Biomedical Technology Today [14222]
BioPed Footcare Centres [14241]
Biopolymers [43998]
BioQUEST Library [7383]
BioSciCon Inc. [2822], [3060], [13800], [25947], [34617]
Bioscience Technology: Tools and Techniques for Life
Science Researchers [14224], [43999]
Biospherics Inc. [28965], [47150]
Biospherics Research Inc. [28965], [47150]
BIOSTART [56395]
Bio-Technical Resources [2478], [2820], [25945], [44080]
Bio-Technical Resources Inc. [2478], [2820], [25945],
[44080]
BioTechniques [44000]
Biotechnology Advances: Research Reviews and Patent
Abstracts [44001]

Biotechnology & Bioengineering [44002]

"Biotechnology Wants a Lead Role" in Business North Carolina (Vol. 28, March 2008, No. 3, pp. 14) [34200], [34791], [42762], [43804]

"Biotechs Are Using Back Door to Go Public" in Boston Business Journal (Vol. 31, May 27, 2011, No. 18, pp. 1) [12111], [34792], [41782], [45308]

"Biovail Hits SAC With $4.6 Billion Suit" in Globe & Mail (February 23, 2006, pp. B1) [12112], [23751], [30901]

BioVentures [48127]

BioVentures Investors [53011]

Birch Bay Chamber of Commerce [59100]

Birch Run Area Chamber of Commerce [53143]

Birchfield Jacobs Foodsystems Inc. [2823], [10313], [25948]

Birchmere Ventures [57280]

"Birdcage Optimization" in Pet Product News (Vol. 64, November 2010, No. 11, pp. 54) [15717], [38940], [42954], [45309]

Birenbaum & Associates [46084]

Birmingham-Bloomfield Chamber of Commerce (BBCC) [53144]

Birmingham Botanical Gardens - Library [9844], [13449]

Birmingham Business Alliance (BBA) [47629]

Birmingham Business Resource Center [47748]

Birmingham Home and Garden Show [9824]

Birmingham Magazine [47630]

Birmingham Regional International Business Directory [47631]

Birminghamchamber.com Newsletter [47632]

Birth Defects Research Part B: Developmental and Reproductive Toxicology [44003]

Birthflowers.com, Inc. [13437]

Birthing the Elephant: A Woman's Go-For-It Guide to Overcoming the Big Challenges of Launching a Business [25834], [47185]

Birthing the Elephant: The Woman's Go-for-It! Guide to Overcoming the Big Challenges of Launching a Business [10991], [16584], [29332], [47186]

Bisbee Business to Business [47858]

Bisbee Chamber of Commerce and Visitor Center (BCCVC) [47859]

Bisbee Chamber of Commerce [47859]

Bishop Area Chamber of Commerce and Visitors Bureau [48260]

Bishop Chamber Bulletin [48261]

Bishop Chamber of Commerce (BCC) [57954]

Bishop Chamber of Commerce [48260]

Bismarck Area Chamber of Commerce [55893]

Bismarck-Mandan Chamber of Commerce (BMCC) [55893]

Bitner Gary Public Relations Inc. [40583], [42545]

Bitner Goodman [40583], [42545]

Bitner Laurenti and Pierson [40583], [42545]

Bitner.com [40583], [42545]

"Bits 'n' Pieces: Shelter Gives Out Pet Food to Keep Animals At Home" in Columbian (January 19, 2009) [15752], [45879]

Bitter Root Valley Chamber of Commerce [54249]

Bitterroot Business News [54250]

Bitterroot SCORE [54232]

Bixby Metro Chamber of Commerce [56465]

Bixler Consulting Group (BCG) [11014]

"Biz Assesses 'Textgate' Fallout; Conventions, Smaller Deals Affected" in Crain's Detroit Business (Vol. 24, March 31, 2008) [20321], [26966], [34793], [36091], [36379], [38941], [44646], [46602]

Biz Buzz [48262]

"Biz Pays Tribute: Franchise Helps Owners Grieve and Honor Their Beloved Pets" in Small Business Opportunities (November 2007) [15690], [32084]

"Biz U: Cool for School" in Entrepreneur (Vol. 35, October 2007, No. 10, pp. 144) [28137], [34794], [47579]

Biz2Biz [59101]

BizBest Media Corp. [49392]

BizConnect [58858]

Bizline [48263]

BizLink [49659]

BizTech Center [56396]

BizVoice [51522]

BJ Chagnon Corp. [6545]

"BK Franchisees Lose Sleep Over Late-Night Rule" in Advertising Age (Vol. 79, August 11, 2008, No. 31, pp. 1) [17888], [23752], [32135], [39700], [46159]

"BK Menu Gives Casual Dining Reason to Worry" in Advertising Age (Vol. 79, November 17, 2008, No. 43, pp. 12) [17889], [22764], [25432], [25726], [32136], [39701], [41003]

BKR International (BKR) [21]

Black Belt Magazine: World's Leading Magazine of Martial Arts [14088]

Black Book, Inc. [1643], [15003]

Black Book Photography [4456]

Black Business Association of Los Angeles [48264]

Black Chamber of Commerce of Greater Kansas City (BCCGKC) [53961]

Black Chamber of Commerce [53961]

Black Data Processing Associates (BDPA) [4831]

"Black Diamond Holdings Corp. Receives SEC Approval" in Canadian Corporate News (May 16, 2007) [12113], [13573], [26737], [36380], [38942], [39702], [41783]

Black Eagle Consulting 2000 Inc. [661]

Black Eagle Executive Search [661]

Black Enterprise [40832]

"Black Gold" in Canadian Business (Vol. 79, August 14, 2006, No. 16-17, pp. 57) [35278], [36935], [37822], [38943], [44273]

Black Hawk College - Quad-Cities Campus [51457]

Black Hills Business Development Center [57613]

"Black Lotus Brewing Co." in Crain's Detroit Business (Vol. 23, October 1, 2007, No. 40, pp. 13) [2453], [29506]

Black Mountain-Swannanoa Chamber of Commerce [55593]

"Black Network Shifts Gears: Struggling Channel To Focus On Broadband TV" in Black Enterprise (Vol. 38, November 2007, No. 4, pp. 34) [3166], [19912]

"Black On Black Business: Moorehead Buys Hank Aaron's Toyota Dealership" in Black Enterprise (Vol. 38, February 2008, No. 7, pp. 28) [14862], [22765], [25296], [40706], [44136]

The Black Swan [29507], [32542]

Black Tennis Magazine: Tennis [20063]

Blackford Associates [38663], [39519]

Blackman Kallick [51466]

Blackman Kallick Bartelstein L.L.P. [51466]

Blackmon Roberts Group Inc. [22518], [28431]

"Blacks Go Broadband: High Speed Internet Adoption Grows Among African Americans" in Black Enterprise (Vol. 38, February 2008) [11629], [19506], [22766], [28573], [34795]

"Black's Truth: Will a Prison Stay Change the Way Conrad Black Operates?" in Canadian Business (Vol. 81, March 31, 2008, No. 5) [23753], [24795], [37823]

Blacksburg Regional Chamber of Commerce [58965]

Blackstone Chamber of Commerce (BCC) [58859]

"Blackstone Set to Sell Stake" in Globe & Mail (March 17, 2007, pp. B6) [8140], [12114], [24251], [25038], [41784]

Blackstone Valley Chamber of Commerce (BVCC) [52841]

Blackstone Valley Chamber of Commerce [57385]

"Blackstone's Outlook Still Tough" in Barron's (Vol. 88, March 17, 2008, No. 11, pp. 19) [8141], [12115], [31276], [41785]

"Blackwater is LEED Golden for Port of Portland Building" in Contractor (Vol. 56, October 2009, No. 10, pp. 3) [7119], [7479], [20973], [30507]

Blackwell Area Chamber of Commerce [56466]

Blaine Community Chamber of Commerce [59102]

The Blaine Group Inc. [44209]

Blair Area Chamber of Commerce (BACC) [54363]

Blair Business Mirror [56965]

Blair County Chamber of Commerce [56966]

Blairsville - Union County Chamber of Commerce (BUCCC) [50447]

Blakely-Early County Chamber of Commerce [50448]

Blanchard Training & Development Inc. [29256]

Blanco Chamber of Commerce [57955]

Blanding Chamber of Commerce (BCC) [58631]

Blanding Small Business Development Center [58611]

Blankinship & Associates Inc. [13801], [25949], [36011], [38664]

Blanton-Peale Institute [34647]

"Blast Blame" in The Business Journal-Milwaukee (Vol. 25, September 5, 2008, No. 50, pp. 1) [23754], [38944], [47455]

"Blast from the Past" in Entrepreneur (Vol. 35, November 2007, No. 11, pp. 48) [29020], [29508], [36966]

"A Bleak Earnings View" in Barron's (Vol. 88, March 10, 2008, No. 10, pp. 15) [8142], [12116], [22767], [26967], [31277]

Blendz Franchise System, Inc. [6456]

Blenz Coffee [4321], [18082], [19275]

Blimpie Subs & Salads [18083]

Blind Brokers Network [21302]

Blind Man of America [2026]

The Blind Side [19405]

Blinn College Small Business Development Center [57841]

Blissfield Area Chamber of Commerce [53145]

Blissymbolics Communication International (BCI) [4832]

BLM Architects [41574]

Bloch Consulting Group [29236]

Block Drug Company - Research and Development Library [6711]

"Block Plans Office Park Along K-10 Corridor" in The Business Journal-Serving Metropolitan Kansas City (Vol. 27, October 3, 2008) [5239], [16513], [16830], [17211], [24252], [26968], [37824]

"Block Pulls Plug On Riverside Deal" in The Business Journal-Serving Metropolitan Kansas City (Vol. 27, October 10, 2008, No. 4) [5240], [16831], [17212], [26969]

"Blockbuster Launches Internet Movie Downloads to Compete Against Netflix, Others" in Chicago Tribune (December 3, 2008) [11630], [20884], [22768], [25433], [26390], [34796], [44274]

BlockDATA® [8933], [13196], [14535]

"Blog Buzz Heralds Arrival of IPhone 2.0" in Advertising Age (Vol. 79, June 9, 2008, No. 40, pp. 8) [3511], [3691], [11631], [18872], [22270], [32137], [34797]

"Blood Bank" in Canadian Business (Vol. 80, February 12, 2007, No. 4, pp. 36) [24253], [43805], [44275]

Blood Center of Southeastern Wisconsin. [14303]

"Blood Diamonds are Forever" in Canadian Business (Vol. 83, August 17, 2010, No. 13-14, pp. 59) [23755], [30902], [36381]

BloodCenter of Wisconsin - Benz Oil Library [14303]

Bloodstock Research Information Services, Inc. Library [1036], [10628]

"Bloody Monday for Bear?" in Barron's (Vol. 88, March 17, 2008, No. 11, pp. M14) [8143], [12117], [31278]

Daniel Bloom and Associates Inc. (DBAI) [24783], [28432], [34078]

Bloomberg BusinessWeek [33095]

"Bloomberg Law Upgraded Its Online Legal Research Platform" in Information Today (Vol. 28, September 2011, No. 8, pp. 28) [23756], [28574], [36967], [42763], [43806]

Bloomer Chamber of Commerce [59492]

Bloomfield Chamber of Commerce [54926]

Bloomfield Chamber of Commerce (BCC) [49660]

Bloomfield Chamber of Commerce [54817]

Bloomingdale Chamber of Commerce [50918]

Bloomsburg Area Chamber of Commerce [57040]

Blount County Chamber of Commerce [57654]

Blount-Oneonta Chamber of Commerce [47633]

Blowing Rock Chamber of Commerce (BRCC) [55594]

"Blue Bell Breaks Ground in South Carolina" in Ice Cream Reporter (Vol. 23, August 20, 2010, No. 9, pp. 3) [10857], [22769], [26738]

"Blue Bell Touts Non-Shrinkage" in Ice Cream Reporter (Vol. 21, July 20, 2008, No. 8, pp. 1) [396], [10858], [39703]

Blue Chip Cookies [1693], [1799]

Blue Chip Venture Company [56361]

"Blue-Collar Broker" in Boston Business Journal (Vol. 31, July 15, 2011, No. 25, pp. 1) [8144], [12118]

"Blue Cross Confronts Baby Blues" in Marketing to Women (Vol. 21, March 2008, No. 3, pp. 3) [11316], [34201], [36114], [39704], [45880]

"Blue Cross to Put Kiosk in Mall" in News & Observer (November 9, 2010) [11317], [13315], [34202], [36115], [39705], [41004]

Blue Garnet Associates L.L.C. [25282], [38665]

Blue Hill Partners, LLC [57281]

Blue Hill Peninsula Chamber of Commerce [52568]

"Blue Hill Tavern to Host Baltimore's First Cupcake Camp" in Daily Record (August 10, 2011) [1752], [39706], [45310]

Blue Island Area Chamber of Commerce and Industry [50919]

Blue Mountain Community College Small Business Development Center [56670]

Blue Ocean Strategy: How to Create Uncontested Market Space and Make Competition Irrelevant [24254], [25434]

Blue Ribbon Coalition [17660]

Blue Ridge Community College Small Business Development Center (BRCC SBDC) [58795]

Blue Rock Capital [49833]

The Blue Seal [18611]

Blue Sky Creamery [10949]

Blue Springs Chamber of Commerce [53962]

Blue Suit [24689], [28445]

"Blue Tractor Barbeque and Brewery, Cafe Havana" in Crain's Detroit Business (Vol. 23, October 1, 2007, No. 40, pp. 15) [9697], [17890]

BlueCar Partners [55398]

Bluefish Ventures [55399]

Bluegrass Community & Technical College - Learning Resource Center [41526]

Bluegrass Small Business Development Center [52219]

Blueprint Books [49393]

Blueprint Fundraising and Communications [47122]

"Blueprint for Profit: Family-Run Lumberyard Sets Sites On Sales of $100 Million a Year" in Small Business Opportunities (Jan. 2008) [13651], [25435], [32138]

MASTER INDEX Boots

Master Index

Blueprint Ventures **[49182]**
BlueRibbon Coalition (BRC) **[17660]**
"Blues Asking Price Out of Their League" in Saint Louis Business Journal (Vol. 32, September 23, 2011, No. 4, pp. 1) **[19406]**, **[25727]**
Blue's Clues: Arts and Crafts **[3964]**
Blue's Clues: Story Time **[3965]**
"Blues at the Toy Fair: Industry Reeling From Recalls, Lower Sales Volumes" in Crain's New York Business (February 18, 2008) **[18396]**, **[20234]**, **[33551]**, **[36382]**, **[38945]**, **[42955]**
Bluestar Ventures LP **[51396]**
Bluestream Ventures **[53774]**
Bluff Business Bulletin **[53963]**
Bluffton Chamber of Commerce [51737]
Blumberg Capital Ventures **[49183]**
Myron I. Blumenfeld & Associates (MIBA) **[26808]**
Bob Bly Copywriter [662], [6857]
Blytheville Area Chamber of Commerce [48059]
Blytheville-Gosnell Area Chamber of Commerce [48059]
BMA Annual Marketing Forum **[8902]**, **[32000]**, **[46747]**
BMA Private Wealth Sales Management Workshop, an ABA Program **[8903]**, **[32001]**, **[46748]**
BMO Nesbitt Burns Library **[13230]**
BMR Bathmaster Reglazing Ltd. **[16305]**
BMV Archives: Butterick, McCall's, Vogue - Patterns Archives **[5933]**
"BMW Makes Bet on Carbon Maker" in Wall Street Journal Eastern Edition (November 19 , 2011, pp. B3) **[12119]**, **[14863]**, **[36383]**, **[38946]**, **[41005]**, **[41786]**
"BMW Revs Up for a Rebound" in Barron's (Vol. 89, July 13, 2009, No. 28, pp. M7) **[8145]**, **[12120]**, **[14864]**, **[31279]**, **[38947]**, **[43393]**
BNA Estate and Gift Tax Planner **[259]**, **[19739]**
BNA Fixed Asset Management System **[260]**
BNA Health Care Daily [34636]
BNA Income Tax Planner **[261]**, **[19740]**
BNA Library **[47534]**
BNA Pension & Benefits Reporter **[22009]**, **[25385]**
BNA Pensions & Benefits Daily [22085]
BNA Securities Law Daily [8951], [13218], [14539]
BNA's Employee Relations Weekly; BNA's Human Resources Report [36075], [46947]
BNA's Patent, Trademark & Copyright Journal [37173]
BNA's Patent, Trademark & Copyright Journal **[37151]**
BNA's Weekly Tax Report [257], [19737]
"Boar Market: Penny-Wise Consumers Favoring Pork" in Crain's Chicago Business (Vol. 31, April 14, 2008, No. 15, pp. 4) **[8146]**, **[12121]**, **[29509]**, **[31280]**
The Board Book: An Insider's Guide for Directors and Trustees **[30903]**, **[32543]**, **[37825]**
Board for Certification of Genealogists (BCG) **[9424]**
Board of Cooperative Educational Services - Adult and Continuing Education **[55499]**
Board of Hospitals and Homes of The Methodist Church [34173]
Board of Schools of Medical Technology [14270]
Board of Schools of the ASCP [14270]
Board of Trade Association [52952]
"The Board Shorts Executive" in Hawaii Business (Vol. 53, January 2008, No. 7, pp. 33) **[19407]**, **[24255]**, **[26970]**, **[35279]**, **[37826]**
"Board This Powertrain" in Barron's (Vol. 89, July 27, 2009, No. 30, pp. 30) **[8147]**, **[12122]**, **[30508]**, **[31281]**, **[34203]**
Boardwalk Fresh Burgers & Fries **[18084]**
Boat America Corp. [3863], [13923]
Boat Manufacturers Association [13931]
Boat Owners Association of the United States (BOAT US) **[3863]**, **[13923]**
"Boat Sales Sputter as Cash-Strapped Buyers Drift Away" in Puget Sound Business Journal (Vol. 29, August 15, 2008, No. 17, pp. 1) **[13937]**, **[26971]**
Boating Industry Associations [13931]
Boating Magazine **[13948]**
Boating Writers International (BWI) **[6777]**
BoatUS [3863], [13923]
Boaz Chamber of Commerce (BCC) **[47634]**
Boaz Vision **[47635]**
"Bob Johnson Opens Car Dealership: Plans To Provide a Bridge To Create More Minority Owners" in Black Enterprise (December 2007) **[14865]**, **[40707]**
Bob Pike's Train-the-Trainer Boot Camp (Onsite) **[35663]**
Bob Rizzo's Dance New York: Jazz **[6396]**
Bob Rizzo's Dance New York: Lyrical **[6397]**
Bob Rizzo's Dance New York: Tap **[6398]**
Boca Grande Area Chamber of Commerce **[49958]**
Boca Raton Annual **[49959]**
Boca Raton West Chamber of Commerce [50106]
BOCES Putnam/Northern Westchester - BOCES Professional Library **[4035]**
Samuel E. Bodily Associates **[8910]**, **[32009]**, **[47123]**
Body Language **[1574]**
Body Soul Magazine: The Journal for Holistic Living **[14818]**
BodyShop Business: The Magazine that Delivers the Collision Repair Industry **[18612]**
Boeing Company - Integrated Defense Systems - Business Information Center **[753]**
"Boeing Earns Its Wings With Strong Quarter" in Crain's Chicago Business (Vol. 31, April 28, 2008, No. 17, pp. 4) **[8148]**, **[12123]**, **[31282]**, **[38948]**
"Boeing Scores $21.7 Billion Order in Indonesia" in Wall Street Journal Eastern Edition (November 18 , 2011, pp. B6) **[24827]**, **[33161]**, **[36384]**, **[38949]**
"Boeing's Next Flight May Well Be to the South" in Puget Sound Business Journal (Vol. 29, November 21, 2008, No. 31, pp.) **[23757]**, **[24720]**, **[38950]**, **[44647]**, **[46843]**
"BofA Cutting 70 Charlotte Tech Jobs" in Charlotte Observer (January 31, 2007) **[8149]**, **[22770]**, **[34798]**, **[35708]**
"BofA Goes for Small Business" in Austin Business Journal (Vol. 31, July 22, 2011, No. 20, pp. A1) **[31283]**, **[37320]**
"BofA May Part With U.S. Trust" in Boston Business Journal (Vol. 31, May 20, 2011, No. 17, pp. 1) **[8150]**, **[12124]**, **[31284]**, **[44137]**
"BofA Will Reach the Top with Countrywide Deal" in Business North Carolina (Vol. 28, March 2008, No. 3, pp. 36) **[8151]**, **[12125]**, **[14393]**, **[41787]**
Bogalusa Chamber of Commerce **[52433]**
Boice Dunham Group **[2724]**
Boiler Operation, Maintenance & Safety (Onsite) **[24972]**, **[28013]**
Boiler Operation, Maintenance and Safety (Onsite) (In-House Training) **[2608]**
Boise Area Chamber of Commerce [50739]
"Boise-based Highway 12 Invests in Crowdsourcing Platform" in Idaho Business Review (September 24, 2010) **[28575]**, **[39707]**, **[41006]**, **[46998]**
Boise City Area Chamber of Commerce [56492]
Boise City Chamber of Commerce [56492]
Boise Metro Business Today **[50738]**
Boise Metro Chamber of Commerce **[50739]**
Boise Sports and RV Show [17680]
Bojangles' Chicken 'n Biscuits **[1800]**, **[18085]**
Bold Endeavors: How Our Government Built America, and Why It Must Rebuild Now **[33162]**, **[33552]**
"Bold Goals Will Require Time" in Contractor (Vol. 56, October 2009, No. 10, pp. S2) **[792]**, **[7480]**, **[19079]**, **[28138]**, **[30509]**
Bolingbrook Area Chamber of Commerce **[50920]**
Bolingbrook Chamber of Commerce and Industry [50920]
Bolivar Area Chamber of Commerce (BACC) **[53964]**
Bolivar Area Chamber of Commerce Visitor's Guide and Membership Directory **[53965]**
Bolivar Peninsula Chamber of Commerce (BPCC) **[57956]**
Bologna Children's Book Fair - Fiera Del Libro Per Ragazzi **[2200]**, **[6944]**
C. Clint Bolte & Associates **[2824]**, **[13802]**, **[16429]**, **[25950]**, **[38666]**, **[41287]**, **[41697]**
BOMA. [17613]
"Bombardier Wins Chinese Rail Deal" in Globe & Mail (March 20, 2006, pp. B1) **[32544]**, **[44276]**
Bon Appetit: America's Food and Entertaining Magazine **[5842]**
"Bon-Ton Halves Q1 Losses, Show Operating Profit" in Home Textiles Today (Vol. 31, May 24, 2011, No. 13, pp. 7) **[10389]**, **[10457]**
"Bon Voyager" in Entrepreneur (Vol. 36, April 2008, No. 4, pp. 58) **[3692]**, **[5735]**, **[34799]**, **[41007]**
Bonaventure Capital **[47750]**
The Bond Buyer Online **[8934]**, **[13197]**
"Bond Hill Cinema Site To See New Life" in Business Courier (Vol. 27, October 29, 2010, No. 26, pp. 1) **[5241]**, **[15041]**, **[24721]**, **[28139]**, **[40863]**, **[42956]**, **[44648]**
The Bond Market Association - Fixed Income Summit Expo on E-Commerce & Technology **[8904]**, **[13176]**, **[14525]**
"Bond OK Could Bring Back the Housing Battle?" in Charlotte Business Journal (Vol. 25, November 5, 2010, No. 33, pp. 1) **[5242]**, **[16832]**, **[17213]**
Bond's Franchise Guide 2007 **[32119]**; **[32139]**
Bond's Franchise Guide 2009 **[23699]**, **[25835]**, **[32120]**
Bonds - the Other Market **[12126]**, **[31285]**
Bonds: Types, Terminology & Principles **[13152]**
"Bonds v. Stocks: Who's Right About Recession?" in Barron's (Vol. 90, August 23, 2010, No. 34, pp. M3) **[8152]**, **[12127]**, **[26972]**, **[31286]**, **[41788]**
Boneheads Grilled Fish & Piri Piri Chicken **[18086]**
Bonham Area Chamber of Commerce and Economic Development (BACC) **[57957]**
Bonita Springs Area Chamber of Commerce (BSACC) **[49960]**
Bonner Business Center (BBC) **[50812]**
Bonner Springs/Edwardsville Area Chamber of Commerce **[52051]**
Bonney Lake Chamber of Commerce **[59103]**
Bonsall Chamber of Commerce **[48265]**
Bonus Building Care **[2647]**
Book and Periodical Development Council [2087], [15487]
Book for Business **[51523]**
Book Club of California - Albert Sperisen Library **[2249]**
Book Dealers Dropship Directory **[2115]**, **[2363]**
Book Dealers World **[2393]**
The Book of Entrepreneurs' Wisdom **[29510]**, **[32545]**
Book Fairs: An Exhibiting Guide for Publishers **[2116]**
The Book of Hard Choices: Making the Right Decisions at Work without Losing Your Self-Respect **[29511]**, **[37827]**
Book Industry Study Group (BISG) **[2085]**, **[2353]**
Book Industry Trends **[2176]**, **[2244]**, **[2391]**
"Book of Lists 2010" in Philadelphia Business Journal (Vol. 28, December 25, 2009, No. 45, pp. 1) **[65]**, **[10666]**, **[12128]**, **[16833]**, **[17214]**, **[17891]**, **[21351]**, **[23758]**, **[26973]**, **[31287]**, **[32546]**, **[34204]**, **[34800]**, **[39708]**, **[43394]**
Book Manufacturers' Institute (BMI) **[2086]**, **[2237]**
Book Marketing Update **[2181]**
"The Book On Indigo" in Canadian Business (Vol. 81, July 22, 2008, No. 12-13, pp. 29) **[2117]**, **[2364]**, **[8153]**, **[12129]**, **[14733]**, **[22771]**, **[31288]**
Book and Periodical Council (BPC) **[2087]**, **[15487]**
Book Publishers Directory [2154], [2385], [6828]
"Book Publishing is Growing" in Information Today (Vol. 28, October 2011, No. 9, pp. 10) **[2118]**, **[2365]**, **[22772]**
Book Review Index Online (BRI) **[2218]**
"Book Smart" in Hawaii Business (Vol. 53, December 2007, No. 6, pp. 39) **[22271]**, **[28140]**, **[37828]**, **[44813]**
BookEasy [54892]
BookExpo America **[2402]**
Bookhaven Press L.L.C. **[57350]**
"Bookkeeping Service Opens First Sacramento Franchise" in Sacramento Bee (April 13, 2011) **[66]**, **[2270]**, **[19611]**, **[21352]**, **[32140]**, **[44277]**
Bookman's Price Index: A Guide to the Values of Rare and Other Out of Print Books **[4406]**
Books on Canada **[2088]**
Books Master File [2220], [2407]
Books in Print **[2119]**, **[2366]**
Books in Print ON DISC™ - Canadian Edition **[2404]**
Bookselling This Week **[2394]**
BooksInPrint.com® Professional (BIP) **[2219]**, **[2405]**, **[44087]**
Bookstore Journal [2395]
The Bookwoman **[2182]**
"Boom and Bust in the Book Biz" in Canadian Business (Vol. 83, August 17, 2010, No. 13-14, pp. 16) **[2367]**, **[6942]**, **[15310]**, **[28576]**, **[41789]**, **[42957]**, **[43395]**
BOOM: Marketing to the Ultimate Power Consumer-The Baby-Boomer Woman **[397]**, **[39709]**
"Boom has Tech Grads Mulling Their Options" in Globe & Mail (March 14, 2006, pp. B1) **[11632]**, **[21056]**, **[22773]**, **[34801]**, **[35280]**
Boomtown Gazette **[49961]**
Boone Area Chamber of Commerce **[51825]**; **[55595]**
Boone County Chamber of Commerce (BCCC) **[51524]**
Boone Hospital Center Medical Library **[10590]**
Boone's Landscaping L.L.C. [13432]
Boone's Landscaping Nursery Corp. **[13432]**
Booneville Area Chamber of Commerce (BACC) **[53830]**
Booneville Development Corporation - South Logan County Chamber of Commerce **[48010]**
Boonton-Mountain Lakes Chamber of Commerce [54826]
Boonville Area Chamber of Commerce **[55090]**
Boonville Chamber of Commerce [55090]
Booster Juice **[10258]**
"Boosting Corporate Entrepreneurship Through HRM Practices" in Human Resource Management (Vol. 49, July-August 2010, No. 4) **[21874]**, **[28141]**, **[29021]**, **[29512]**, **[35709]**, **[36385]**
"Boosting Strategy With An Online Community" in Business Strategy Review (Vol. 21, Spring 2010, No. 1, pp. 40) **[28577]**, **[29022]**, **[35710]**
"Boosting Worried Customers' Confidence" in Gallup Management Journal (November 8, 2011) **[26391]**, **[26974]**, **[43396]**
"Boosting Your Merchant Management Services With Wireless Technology" in Franchising World (Vol. 42, August 2010, No. 8, pp. 27) **[3693]**, **[6278]**, **[26157]**, **[28578]**, **[32141]**, **[34802]**, **[43397]**
Boothbay Harbor Region Chamber of Commerce **[52569]**
"Boots Treat Street Rolls Out Trolley Dash App on Androis and iPhone OS" in Entertainment Close-Up (October 24, 2011) **[940]**, **[1496]**, **[3694]**, **[34803]**, **[42958]**

Small Business Sourcebook • 30th Edition 3463

Booz Allen Hamilton - Research Services and Information Center **[21795]**
"Booze Makers Battle Over Turkey Day" in Advertising Age (Vol. 78, October 29, 2007, No. 43, pp. 4) **[1836], [13574], [19215], [39710]**
"Border Boletin: UA to Take Lie-Detector Kiosk to Poland" in Arizona Daily Star (September 14, 2010) **[13316], [18397], [23759], [24828], [34804], [36386], [40864], [41790], [42764], [43807]**
Border Security Expo **[6040]**
"Borders Previews New Web Site" in Crain's Detroit Business (Vol. 23, October 8, 2007, No. 41, pp. 4) **[2368], [11633], [21057], [28579]**
Borger Chamber of Commerce **[57958]**
"Boring Bonds Gain Pizzazz as Investors Flock to Debt Issues" in Baltimore Business Journal (Vol. 28, June 11, 2010, No. 5, pp. 1) **[6279], [8154], [9243], [12130], [26158]**
"Born of Culture of Innovation" in Canadian Business (Vol. 81, October 27, 2008, No. 18, pp. 98) **[36968], [42765], [43808]**
Bornhofen & Associates [29302], [31001]
Frederick A. Bornhofen & Associates **[29302], [31001]**
Boron Chamber of Commerce **[48266]**
Borough of Cresson Chamber of Commerce [57054]
Borrego Springs Chamber of Commerce (BSCC) **[48267]**
"Borrow For Tomorrow" in Canadian Business (Vol. 80, October 8, 2007, No. 20, pp. 193) **[26975], [33553]**
Borrowing Brilliance: The Six Steps to Business Innovation by Building on the Ideas of Others **[36969], [41008], [42766], [43809]**
Borvin Beverage **[19276]**
Bo's Lasting Lessons **[29513], [37829]**
Boscobel Chamber of Commerce **[59493]**
Marion R. Boslaugh **[41470]**
Bosley & Associates [22519]
The Bosley Group **[22519]**
Boss of You: Everything a Woman Needs to Know to Start, Run, and Maintain Her Own Business **[32356], [47235]**
Bossier Chamber of Commerce **[52434]**
Boston Architectural Center - Alfred Shaw and Edward Durell Stone Library **[5701], [19137]**
Boston Bartenders School of America **[1880], [34629]**
Boston Biomedical Research Institute (BBRI) **[16101]**
Boston Business Journal **[53091]**
Boston Capital Ventures **[53012]**
Boston College - Center for Corporate Citizenship **[42703]**
Boston College - Center for Corporate Community Relations [42703]
Boston College - Center on Wealth and Philanthropy (CWP) **[42420]**
Boston College - Social Welfare Research Institute [42420]
Boston Consulting Group - Chicago Information and Research Group **[3128]**
Boston Consulting Group Inc. (BCG) **[17579]**
Boston Financial Consulting Group [17579]
Boston Financial & Equity Corporation **[53013]**
Boston Gift Show **[9582], [9616], [15035]**
"Boston Globe" in Ice Cream Reporter (Vol. 21, August 20, 2008, No. 9, pp. 7) **[10859], [13317], [33554]**
"Boston Hedge Fund Pours Money Into Real Estate Projects" in Charlotte Business Journal (Vol. 25, December 3, 2010, No. 37, pp. 1) **[8155], [12131], [16834], [17215], [31289]**
Boston JobBank: The Job Hunter's Guide to the Bay State **[19169]**
Boston Millennia Partners **[53014]**
Boston Pizza International Inc. **[18087]**
"Boston Printer Celebrates 60th Anniversary" in American Printer (Vol. 128, August 1, 2011, No. 8) **[4457], [16358], [20760], [31029]**
Boston Public Library - Kirstein Business Branch **[40661], [44965]**
"Boston Scientific Makes Formal Offer for Guidant, Possibly Thwarting J&J" in Globe & Mail (January 9, 2006, pp. B6) **[25436], [41791]**
Boston University - Center for Law, Business and Technology **[24174]**
Boston University - Corporate Education Center Library **[4909], [19054]**
Boston University - Entrepreneurial Management Institute [30380]
Boston University - Frederick S. Pardee Management Library **[38837]**
Boston University - Institute for Technology Entrepreneurship and Commercialization (ITEC) **[30380]**
Boston University - Morin Center for Banking and Financial Law **[8967]**
Boston University - Multimedia Communications Laboratory (MCL) **[4749]**
Boston University - Neuromuscular Research Center (NMRC) **[16102]**
Boston University - Neuromuscular Research Center - Muscle Fatigue Laboratory **[16103]**
The Boston's Gourmet Pizza **[16138], [18088]**
Botetourt County Chamber of Commerce (BCCC) **[58860]**
"Both Eyes on the Prize" in Canadian Business (Vol. 83, September 14, 2010, No. 15, pp. 42) **[21875], [25371], [33555], [35711], [37830]**
Bottin Touristique du Quebec **[20534]**
The Bottled Water Market **[2418]**
Bottled Water Reporter **[2419]**
"Bottler Will Regain Its Pop" in Barron's (Vol. 88, March 17, 2008, No. 11, pp. 56) **[8156], [11050], [12132], [21527], [22774], [31290], [36387], [38951]**
"Bottom-Fishing and Speed-Dating in India" in Barron's (Vol. 88, March 24, 2008, No. 12, pp. M12) **[8157], [11051], [12133], [20322], [22775], [26976], [31291], [36388], [46603]**
"The Bottom Line" in Retail Merchandiser (Vol. 51, July-August 2011, No. 4, pp. 60) **[4087], [7817], [13560], [42959]**
Bottom Line **[54927]**
The Bottom Line **[53577]; [55091]; [55092]**
"The Bottom Line: Did CN Push Too Hard?" in Globe & Mail (February 23, 2007, pp. B1) **[32547], [46844]**
Bottom Line Service System **[18294]**
Bottom-Line Training: Performance-Based Results **[29023], [29514], [37831]**
"Bottom's Up" in Barron's (Vol. 88, July 14, 2008, No. 28, pp. 25) **[14394], [16835], [17216], [26977]**
"Bottoms Up!" in Entrepreneur (Vol. 36, April 2008, No. 4, pp. 128) **[11634], [13575], [15311], [21058], [23760], [26392], [28580], [29515], [39711], [43398], [44757]**
Boulder Chamber of Commerce **[49452]**
Boulder City Chamber of Commerce **[54472]**
Boulder Junction Chamber of Commerce **[59494]**
Boulder Small Business Development Center **[49414]**
Boulder Small Business Development Center (Longmont, Colorado) **[49415]**
Boulder Ventures, Ltd. **[52769]**
Bound Brook Area Chamber of Commerce **[54672]**
"Bountiful Barrels: Where to Find $140 Trillion" in Barron's (Vol. 88, July 14, 2008, No. 28, pp. 40) **[8158], [11052], [12134], [22776], [31292], [36389], [44278]**
"Bountiful Exterminator Indicted for Unlawful Pesticide Use" in Standard-Examiner (February 3, 2011) **[15627], [23761]**
Bourbannais Chamber of Commerce [50921]
Bourbon Institute [1829]
Bourget Research Group **[40584]**
Bouse Chamber of Commerce **[47860]**
"Bovie Medical Makes Electrosurgical Strike" in The Business Journal-Serving Greater Tampa Bay (Vol. 28, August 22, 2008, No. 35) **[14191], [24256], [24722], [41009]**
Bow & Arrow [1245]
Bow and Arrow Hunting: America's Bow Hunting Authority **[1245]**
Law Offices of David Bow Woo **[24107]**
Bowdens International Directory **[3167]**
Bowdens Media Directory [3167]
Bowes & Co. **[17580]**
Bowie Chamber of Commerce (BCC) **[57959]**
Bowie Decimal Systems **[209]**
Bowker's Annual Library and Book Trade Almanac [2146], [2381], [15550]
Bowker's Complete Video Directory **[20885]**
Bowl Expo [2439]
Bowlers Journal **[2436]**
Bowling-Golfing News **[2437]**
Bowling Green **[52262]**
Bowling Green Area Chamber of Commerce **[52263]**
Bowling Green Chamber of Commerce **[53966]**
Bowling Green Community College of Western Kentucky University **[52400]**
Bowling Green State University - Music Library and Sound Recordings Archives **[17657]**
Bowling Green-Warren County Chamber of Commerce [52263]
Bowling Proprietors' Association of America (BPAA) **[2428]**
Bowling Proprietors' Association of Canada (BPAC) **[2429]**
Bowling Writers Association of America (BWAA) **[6778]**
Bowling Writers Association of America and National Women Bowling Writers Association [6778]
Bowman Area Chamber of Commerce **[55894]**
Bowman R&C Projects **[14035]**
The Bowser Directory of Small Stocks **[13113]**
"Boxing, Tech Giants Team to Help Teens" in Hispanic Business (January-February 2009, pp. 44) **[941], [7905], [15846], [34805], [45881]**
Boxoffice Magazine: The Business Magazine of The Global Motion Picture Industry **[14579]**
The Boyd Company Inc. **[24784]**
Lisa Boyd Consulting L.L.C. **[38667]**
"Boyd's Pawn Shop Looks More Like a Mini-Mall With Plenty For Sale" in The Hawk Eye (January 2, 2011) **[15444], [17707]**
Boyne Area City Chamber of Commerce **[53146]**
Boynton Beach Business Monthly **[49962]**
Bozeman Area Chamber of Commerce (BACC) **[54251]**
Bozeman Small Business Development Center **[54213]**
Bozeman Visitor Guide **[54252]**
BPT Consulting Associates Ltd. **[2825], [3061], [13803], [23653], [24655], [25358], [25951], [38668], [44920]**
BPW Canada [47206]
"Brace for the Bill" in Boston Business Journal (Vol. 27, December 28, 2007, No. 48, pp. 1) **[33556], [34205]**
Bracewell & Patterson Library **[7396]**
"Bracing for a Bear of a Week" in Barron's (Vol. 88, March 17, 2008, No. 11, pp. 24) **[8159], [12135], [26159], [26978], [31293], [37321]**
"Bracing for Impact" in Playthings (Vol. 106, September 1, 2008, No. 8, pp. 15) **[18398], [24257]**
"Bracing for More Layoffs" in Sacramento Business Journal (Vol. 28, September 30, 2011, No. 31, pp. 1) **[26979], [35712]**
"Brad Wall" in Canadian Business (Vol. 82, April 27, 2009, No. 7, pp. 9) **[22777], [26980], [28142], [33163], [35281], [35713]**
Bradford Area Chamber of Commerce (BACC) **[56967]**
Bradford Regional Chamber of Commerce [50243]
Bradford's Directory of Marketing Research Agencies and Management Consultants of the United States and the World [13991], [37832], [39712]
Bradford's International Directory of Marketing Research Agencies **[13991], [37832], [39712]**
Bradley Association of Commerce and Industry [50921]
Bradley-Bourbonnais Chamber of Commerce (BBCC) **[50921]**
Bradley County Chamber of Commerce **[48011]**
Chip Bradley Management Advisor **[38669]**
Bradley University - Center for Business and Economic Research (CBER) **[45842]**
Bradley University - Center for Executive and Professional Development (CEPD) **[38855]**
Bradley University - Urban Affairs Institute [45842]
Brady Center to Prevent Gun Violence Library **[10041]**
Brady Chamber of Commerce [57960]
Brady - McCulloch County Chamber of Commerce **[57960]**
Brag!: The Art of Tooting Your Own Horn Without Blowing It **[29516], [32548]**
Brain-Based Time Management **[46486]**
Brain, Behavior, and Immunity **[44004]**
Brainerd Lakes Area Chambers of Commerce **[53578]**
Braintree Business Development Center **[56397]**
Brake Masters **[18639]**
Brakeley Inc. - Library **[9305]**
Branch County Area Chamber of Commerce **[53147]**
Branches and Twigs Genealogical Society - Collection **[9486]**
"Branching Out" in Canadian Business (Vol. 79, July 17, 2006, No. 14-15, pp. 41) **[22778], [26160], [39713]**
Branchline Income Tax Services **[41471]**
Branchline Services [41471]
"Brand Imaging" in Small Business Opportunities (November 2010) **[10992], [16585], [39714], [42455], [42608]**
"Brand Police Keep the Lines Distinct at GM" in Automotive News (Vol. 86, October 31, 2011, No. 6488, pp. 3) **[14866], [39715]**
Brandeis University - Bigel Institute for Health Policy [34648]
Brandeis University - Center for Health Policy Analysis and Research [34648]
Brandeis University - Center for Human Resources [13310]
Brandeis University - Center for Youth Development [13310]
Brandeis University - Center for Youth and Communities (CYC) **[13310]**
Brandeis University - Center for Youth and Communities - Library **[19198]**
Brandeis University - Health Policy Center [34648]
Brandeis University - Schneider Institutes for Health Policy (SIHP) **[34648]**
"Branding Specialist" in Black Enterprise (Vol. 38, July 2008, No. 12, pp. 1) **[19913], [29517], [39716]**
"Branding Your Way" in Canadian Business (Vol. 80, February 12, 2007, No. 4, pp. 31) **[398], [11635], [34806], [39717], [42456], [45311]**
Brandon Area Chamber of Commerce (BACC) **[58740]**
Brandon Area Directory **[49963]**

3464 Small Business Sourcebook • 30th Edition

Broadsword Solutions Corp. [4904]

Broadview Heights Chamber of Commerce (BHCC) [56020]

BroadVision Inc. [25283], [38671]

"Broadway Casino Climbing Hills to Get to Gambling" in Business Courier (Vol. 26, January 1, 2010, No. 37, pp. 1) [9385], [33558]

Broadway-Timberville Chamber of Commerce (BTCC) [58862]

Brochure and Business Directory/Recreation Guide [54551]

Brockport Small Business Development Center [55014]

Brodhead Chamber of Commerce [59496]

Broken Arrow Chamber of Commerce [56467]

Broken Bow Chamber of Commerce [54365]; [56468]

Broker Management Council (BMC) [2695], [17859]

Brokerage Yacht Show [13970]

"Brokerages Seek a Foothold in Local Real Estate Market" in Charlotte Business Journal (Vol. 25, October 15, 2010, No. 30, pp. 1) [16837], [17219], [44650]

Bronnercom Inc. [28962]

Bronx Chamber of Commerce [55094]

Bronx Small Business Development Center [55015]

Bronxville Chamber of Commerce [55095]

Brook Venture Partners [53015]

Brookdale Community College [54879]

"Brooke Agents Claim Mistreatment" in The Business Journal-Serving Metropolitan Kansas City (Vol. 27, October 24, 2008, No. 7, pp. 1) [8162], [11318], [12140], [23765], [26161], [31295], [32144], [36971]

Brookfield Area Chamber of Commerce [53968]

Brookfield Chamber of Commerce [50925]

Brookfield Chamber of Commerce [59589]

"Brookfield Eyes 'New World'" in Globe & Mail (February 6, 2007, pp. B1) [5244], [38956], [41799]

Brookgreen Gardens Library [9845]

Brookhaven - Lincoln County Chamber of Commerce [53831]

Brookings Area Chamber of Commerce and Convention Bureau [57564]

Brookings Area Chamber of Commerce [57564]

Brookings-Harbor Chamber of Commerce [56715]

Brookings Harbor Light [56716]

Brookline Business Report [52842]

Brookline Chamber of Commerce (BCC) [52843]

Brooklyn Area Chamber of Commerce [59497]

Brooklyn Botanic Garden Library [9846]

Brooklyn Chamber of Commerce [55096]

Brooklyn Historical Society Library [9489]

Brooklyn - Irish Hills Chamber of Commerce [53148]

Brooklyn Museum - Library [4168]

Brooklyn Public Library - Business Library [266], [19747]

Brooklyn SCORE [55041]

Brooks Institute - Library [15885], [15927]

Brooks Institute of Photography - Library. [15885], [15927]

Brookville Area Chamber of Commerce (BACC) [56971]

Broome Chamber [55213]

Broome County Chamber of Commerce [55213]

Broome County Industrial Development Agency [55480]

Broome County Public Library - J. Donald Ahearn Business Resource Center [33103]

Broomfield Chamber of Commerce [49454]

The Broomfielder [49455]

Brown Associates Inc. [36012]

"Brown At Center of Local CleanTech Lobbying Efforts" in Boston Business Journal (Vol. 30, October 15, 2010, No. 36, pp. 1) [7120], [7481], [30510], [33559], [34808]

Brown & Caldwell Library [10191]

George Brown College of Applied Arts & Technology - Archives [4169], [7866]

Brown County Chamber of Commerce [51526]

Brown County Genealogy Society Library [9490]

Brown Forum for Enterprise [57356]

Brown University - Center for Environmental Studies [10192]

Brown University - Center for Environmental Studies (CES) [17742]

Brown University - Center for Gerontology and Health Care Research [334]

John Brown University - Music Library [14672], [14766]

Brown University - Orwig Music Library [14673]

Brown University - Watson Institute for International Studies [34649]

The Browning Group [14037]

Brownsburg Chamber of Commerce (BCoC) [51527]

Brownsville Chamber of Commerce (BCC) [57964]

Brownsville Minority Business Development Center - Management Assistance Services [58531]

Brownwood Area Chamber of Commerce (BCC) [57965]

BRS [24657], [45248]

Bruegger's [1695]

Brunswick Area Chamber of Commerce (BACC) [56021]

Brunswick Bulletin [55598]

Brunswick Chamber of Commerce [56021]

Brunswick County Chamber of Commerce [55599]

Brunswick-Golden Isles Chamber of Commerce (BGICC) [50449]

Brunswick-Golden Isles Today [50450]

Brush Area Chamber of Commerce [49456]

Brush Chamber of Commerce [49456]

Brush Valley Buyer's Guide [56972]

Brush Valley Regional Chamber of Commerce [56973]

Bruster's Real Ice Cream [10951]

Bruster's Real Ice Cream Inc. [10951]

Bryan Area Chamber of Commerce [56022]

"Bryan Berg" in Hawaii Business (Vol. 53, March 2008, No. 9, pp. 28) [26987], [32552], [44815]

Bryant Business Chronicle [48013]

Bryant Chamber of Commerce (BCC) [48014]

Bryant and Stratton Business Institute - Henrietta Campus [55500]

Bryant and Stratton Business Institute - Parma Campus [56408]

Bryant and Stratton Business Institute - Syracuse Campus [55501]

Bryant and Stratton College - Buffalo Campus [55502]

Bryant and Stratton College - Virginia Beach Campus [59034]

BSpudly Enterprises Inc. [47126]

BTA Solutions [5078]

BtoB [28967], [33096], [40660]

BUC Book--The Statistically Authenticated Used Boat Price Guide [13938]

BUC Used Boat Price Guide [13938]

BUCCC Monthly News [50451]

Buchanan Area Chamber of Commerce (BACC) [53149]

Bucher, Willis and Ratliff Consulting Engineers, Planners [19552]

Bucher, Willis and Ratliff Consulting Engineers, Planners and Architects [19552]

Bucher, Willis and Ratliff Corp. [19552]

Larry W. Buck & Associates Inc. [22043]

"Buck-ing the Trend?" in Baltimore Business Journal (Vol. 28, August 13, 2010, No. 14, pp. 1) [19319], [19408], [20855]

"The Buck Stops Here" in Canadian Business (Vol. 81, November 10, 2008, No. 19, pp. 25) [10993], [16586], [29525], [37836], [39726], [42610]

Buck or Two Plus! [43289]

Buckeye Valley Chamber of Commerce [47861]

Buckhannon SCORE [59381]

Buckingham Chamber of Commerce [58863]

Buckley Chamber of Commerce [59108]

Bucknell University Small Business Development Center [56904]

Buckner Chamber of Commerce [53969]

Buck's Pizza [16140]

Bucksport Bay Area Chamber of Commerce [52570]

Bucksport Chamber of Commerce [52570]

Bucyrus Area Chamber of Commerce (BACC) [56023]

Buda Area Chamber of Commerce (BACC) [57966]

Budd Lake Chamber of Commerce [54775]

Budget Blinds [2027]

Budget Brake & Muffler Distributors Ltd [1635]

"Budget Cuts Afflict Health Department" in Business Courier (Vol. 24, November 23, 2008, No. 32, pp. 1) [26988], [34206]

"Budget Strategically to Stay on Course" in Entrepreneur (August 28, 2008) [22101], [24261], [25040], [37837]

"Budget Woes Endanger E-Prep Progress" in Crain's Cleveland Business (Vol. 30, June 22, 2009, No. 24, pp. 6) [28145], [29526], [33164]

Budgeting [22140]

Budgeting for Publications [21327]

Buena Park Area Chamber of Commerce [48275]

Buena Park Business Journal [48276]

Buena Park Map [48277]

Buena Venture Associates, L.P. [58549]

Buena Vista Area Chamber of Commerce [49457]

Buffalo Area Chamber of Commerce [53970]

Buffalo Area Chamber of Commerce (BACC) [53579]

Buffalo Chamber of Commerce [56469]; [57967]

Buffalo Chamber of Commerce [59805]

Buffalo & Erie County Public Library - Business, Science & Technology [21477], [23661], [36265]

Buffalo Grove Area Chamber of Commerce [50926]

Buffalo Grove Chamber of Commerce [50926]

Buffalo Home and Garden Show [9825]

Buffalo Niagara Partnership [55097]

Buffalo Philly's - Wings, Cheesesteaks N' More [18089]

Buffalo State College Small Business Development Center [55016]

Buffalo Wild Wings Grill & Bar [18090]

Buffalo Wings & Rings [18091]

Buffalo, Wyoming Chamber of Commerce [59805]

The Bugle Call [52052]

Buhl Chamber of Commerce [50740]

"Buhler Versatile Launches Next Generation of Equipment" in Farm Industry News (November 23, 2011) [21530], [36395], [38957]

"Buick Prices Verano Below Rival Luxury Compacts" in Automotive News (Vol. 86, October 31, 2011, No. 6488, pp. 10) [14867], [25728], [38958]

W.A. Buie Consulting Services [41472]

"Build a Better Bonus" in Canadian Business (Vol. 80, January 15, 2007, No. 2, pp. 65) [21876], [29026]

Builder & Contractor [5583]

Builder & Contractor--Associated Builders and Contractors Membership Directory Issue [5211]

"Builder Comes Back Home" in Houston Business Journal (Vol. 40, September 18, 2009, No. 19, pp. 1A) [5156], [16838]

Builder: The Magazine of the National Association of Home Builders [5574]

"Builder's Bankruptcy Fans Fears" in Crain's Cleveland Business (Vol. 28, October 22, 2007, No. 42, pp. 1) [5245], [16839], [17220], [26989]

"Builder's Comeback Highlights Uptick in Demand for New Homes" in Boston Business Journal (Vol. 29, June 3, 2011, No. 4, pp. 1) [5246], [16840]

Builders Hardware Manufacturers Association (BHMA) [10121]

Builders Home and Garden Show [9826], [13502]

"Builders Land Rutenberg Deal" in Charlotte Observer (February 2, 2007) [5247], [31031], [32145]

Builders St. Charles Home Show [9826], [13502]

The Builders' Show [5621]

"Builders, Unions Aim to Cut Costs; Pushing Changes to Regain Share of Residential Market; Seek Council's Help" in Crain's New York Business [5248], [12141], [21877], [25438], [25729], [33560], [46846]

"Building Alexian Brothers' Clinical Reputation" in Crain's Chicago Business (Vol. 31, May 5, 2008, No. 18, pp. 6) [24262], [29527], [34207], [37838]

Building Applications with Microsoft Access 2007: Hands-On (Onsite) [28014]

"Building a Better Twitter Brand: My Foray Into Social Analytics" in Inc. (Vol. , pp.) [21059], [28585], [39727]

Building Better Work Relationships: New Techniques for Results-oriented Communication (Onsite) [28974]

Building Blocks for Team Performance [29199]

Building Bridges [55896]

Building Business & Apartment Management [1163]

Building a Business the Buddhist Way [25041], [29528], [32553]

"Building a Business: Directbuild Helps Clients Build Their Own Home" in Small Business Opportunities (Winter 2007) [5157], [32085]

Building Buzz to Beat the Big Boys [15313], [25439], [39728], [42960], [44280]; [25440], [39729], [42961]

"Building Confidence" in Black Enterprise (Vol. 38, January 2008, No. 6, pp. 50) [12142], [39730], [42457], [42611]

Building Conservation Associates Inc. [1301]

Building and Construction Trades Department - Canadian Office [46797]

Building Cost Analysis [1229]

Building Design Service [15256]

Building a Dream: A Canadian Guide to Starting Your Own Business [24177], [25297], [32086], [32359], [37269], [44138]

Building Dreams [3432]

Building High Performing Teams [29200]

"Building His Dream" in Business Courier (Vol. 24, January 25, 2008, No. 42, pp. 1) [22787], [24263], [29529], [34809], [41800]

Building Owners and Managers Association International Annual Convention and The Office Building Show [16560]

Building Owners and Managers Association International Library [17613]

"Building Portfolios for a World of 2.5 Percent Gains" in Barron's (Vol. 88, July 7, 2008, No. 27, pp. L9) [8163], [12143], [17221], [21531], [26990], [31296]

Building a Positive, Motivated and Cooperative Team (Onsite) [37586]

Building Products Digest [10143], [13670]

Building a Profitable Consulting Practice Series [2804], [11012], [13783], [16611]

Building Service Contractors Association International (BSCAI) [2595]

Building Standards [5575]

Building Stone Institute (BSI) [14098]

Building a Strategy Focused Organization (Onsite) [24973]

Building a Successful Business Analysis Work Plan [37587]

Building a Successful Business Analysis Work Plan: Effective Project Management Skills for Business Analysts (Onsite) **[37588]**

"Building Targeted for Marriott in Violation" in Business Journal-Milwaukee (Vol. 28, December 24, 2010, No. 12, pp. A1) **[5249]**, **[10667]**, **[18399]**, **[33561]**

Building the Trans-National Team **[36908]**

Building Wealth in China: 36 True Stories of Chinese Millionaires and How They Made Their Fortunes **[11056]**, **[29530]**, **[36396]**

Building XML Web Services with Java- Hands-On (Onsite) **[30386]**

Building XML Web Services with .NET: Hands-On (Onsite) **[30387]**

"Building Your Business: A Strong Web Presence Is a Must" in Black Enterprise (Vol. 38, December 2007, No. 5, pp. 74) **[21060]**, **[22788]**, **[28586]**, **[42962]**, **[43400]**

BuildingStars Inc. **[2648]**

Built to Last: Successful Habits of Visionary Companies **[29531]**, **[32554]**

Bulk Barn Foods Limited **[19277]**

Bulk Transporter **[20702]**

Bull Shoals Dam Chamber of Commerce [48015]

Bull Shoals Lake - White River Chamber of Commerce **[48015]**

Bull Shoals Lake - White River Visitor's Guide **[48016]**

Bulldog Reporter Business Media I Media Pro **[16604]**

Bulletin **[49968]**; **[56024]**; **[57918]**

The Bulletin **[1747]**; **[52844]**; **[59109]**

Bulletin of Experimental Treatments for AIDS: Bulletin of Experimental Treatments for AIDS (BETA) **[14282]**, **[34492]**

Bullhead Area Chamber of Commerce **[47862]**

Bullitt County Chamber of Commerce **[52264]**

Bullitt-Hutchins Inc. **[2725]**

Bullock County Chamber of Commerce [47740]

Jack J. Bulloff Consulting and Expert Witness Services **[4539]**

Bulverde/Spring Branch Area Chamber of Commerce (BSBACOC) **[57968]**

"Bumpy Ride Ahead for United" in Crain's Chicago Business (Vol. 31, May 5, 2008, No. 18, pp. 3) **[24264]**, **[26991]**, **[41801]**, **[44281]**

Bunker Hill Community College **[53087]**

Burbank Business Journal **[48278]**

Burbank Chamber of Commerce **[48279]**

"Burdened by Debt, Borders Group Suspends Dividends, May Be Sold" in Crain's Detroit Business (Vol. 24, March 24, 2008, No. 12) **[2369]**, **[24265]**, **[26162]**, **[37323]**

Bureau D'Assurance du Canada [11286]

Bureau de la Television du Canada - Bibliotheque. [694]

Bureau de Traduction du Nouveau-Brunswick Bibliotheque. [20494]

Bureau of Indian Affairs - Business Utilization and Development Specialist - Aberdeen Area Office **[61466]**; **[61467]**

Bureau of Indian Affairs - Business Utilization and Development Specialist - Albuquerque Area Office **[61468]**; **[61469]**

Bureau of Indian Affairs - Business Utilization and Development Specialist - Anadarko Area Office **[61470]**; **[61471]**

Bureau of Indian Affairs - Business Utilization and Development Specialist - Billings Area Office **[61472]**; **[61473]**

Bureau of Indian Affairs - Business Utilization and Development Specialist - Eastern Area Office **[61474]**; **[61475]**

Bureau of Indian Affairs - Business Utilization and Development Specialist - Juneau Area Office **[61476]**; **[61477]**

Bureau of Indian Affairs - Business Utilization and Development Specialist - Minneapolis Area Office **[61478]**; **[61479]**

Bureau of Indian Affairs - Business Utilization and Development Specialist - Muskogee Area Office **[61480]**; **[61481]**

Bureau of Indian Affairs - Business Utilization and Development Specialist - Navajo Area Office **[61482]**; **[61483]**

Bureau of Indian Affairs - Business Utilization and Development Specialist - Phoenix Area Office **[61484]**; **[61485]**

Bureau of Indian Affairs - Business Utilization and Development Specialist - Portland Area Office **[61486]**; **[61487]**

Bureau of Indian Affairs - Business Utilization and Development Specialist - Sacramento Area Office **[61488]**; **[61489]**

Bureau of Land Management - Alaska State Office **[61490]**

Bureau of Land Management - Arizona State Office **[61491]**

Bureau of Land Management - Business Utilization and Development Specialist - Branch of Procurement Management **[61492]**

Bureau of Land Management - Business Utilization and Development Specialist - Division of Procurement Management **[61493]**

Bureau of Land Management - California State Office **[61494]**

Bureau of Land Management - Colorado State Office **[61495]**

Bureau of Land Management - Eastern States Office **[61496]**

Bureau of Land Management - Idaho State Office **[61497]**

Bureau of Land Management - Montana State Office **[61498]**

Bureau of Land Management - Nevada State Office **[61499]**

Bureau of Land Management - New Mexico State Office **[61500]**

Bureau of Land Management - Oregon State Office **[61501]**

Bureau of Land Management - Utah State Office **[61502]**

Bureau of Land Management - Wyoming State Office **[61503]**

Bureau of Ocean Energy Management, Regulation and Enforcement - Alaska OCS **[61504]**

Bureau of Ocean Energy Management, Regulation and Enforcement - Business Utilization and Development Specialist - Division of Procurement and Contracts **[61505]**

Bureau of Ocean Energy Management, Regulation and Enforcement - Business Utilization and Development Specialist - Western ASC Procurement and Contracts **[61506]**

Bureau of Ocean Energy Management, Regulation and Enforcement - Pacific OCS Region **[61507]**

Bureau of Maps and Surveys. [19539]

Bureau of Reclamation - Business Utilization and Development Specialist - Acquisition and Assistance Management Services **[61508]**

Bureau of Reclamation - Business Utilization and Development Specialist - Administrative Service Center **[61509]**

Bureau of Reclamation - Business Utilization and Development Specialist - Denver Office **[61510]**

Bureau of Reclamation - Business Utilization and Development Specialist - Great Plains Region **[61511]**

Bureau of Reclamation - Business Utilization and Development Specialist - Lower Colorado Region **[61512]**

Bureau of Reclamation - Business Utilization and Development Specialist - Mid-Pacific Region **[61513]**

Bureau of Reclamation - Business Utilization and Development Specialist - Pacific Northwest Region **[61514]**

Bureau of Reclamation - Business Utilization and Development Specialist - Phoenix Area Office **[61515]**

Bureau of Reclamation - Business Utilization and Development Specialist - Upper Colorado Region **[61516]**

"Burger Heirs' Long-Bottled Fight Plays Out" in Business Courier (Vol. 24, January 11, 2008, No. 40, pp. 1) **[17892]**, **[23766]**

Burger King [18092]

Burger King Corp. **[18092]**

"Burger Market Sizzling with Newcomers" in Boston Business Journal (Vol. 29, June 10, 2011, No. 5, pp. 1) **[6438]**, **[17893]**, **[22789]**, **[45312]**

Sarah G. Burger **[15111]**

Burkburnett Chamber of Commerce (BCC) **[57969]**

M.W. Burke & Associates Inc. **[16660]**

Burke County Chamber of Commerce **[55600]**

Burkesville Cumberland County Chamber of Commerce **[52265]**

Burkesville-Cumberland County Chamber of Commerce [52265]

Burleson Area Chamber of Commerce (BACC) **[57970]**

Burleson County Chamber of Commerce - Caldwell Office (BCCC) **[57971]**

Burley Chamber of Commerce [50785]

Burlingame Business **[48280]**

Burlingame Chamber of Commerce **[48281]**

Burlington Area Chamber of Commerce (BACC) **[59498]**

Burlington Chamber of Commerce (BCC) **[59110]**

Burlington County Chamber of Commerce (BCCC) **[54677]**

Burlington County College **[54880]**

Burlington, Discover the Treasures **[59499]**

Burlington SCORE **[51792]**

Burlington/West Burlington Area Chamber of Commerce (BWBCC) **[51827]**

"Burned Investors Fire Back" in Canadian Business (Vol. 80, April 23, 2007, No. 9, pp. 12) **[12144]**, **[23767]**

"Burner Handles Everything From #2 to B100" in Indoor Comfort Marketing (Vol. 70, May 2011, No. 5, pp. 24) **[793]**, **[7121]**, **[7482]**, **[30511]**, **[41012]**, **[45313]**

Burnet Chamber of Commerce **[57972]**

Burney Basin Chamber of Commerce [48282]

Burney Chamber of Commerce **[48282]**

"A Burning Issue: Lives Are at Stake Every Day" in Contractor (Vol. 56, October 2009, No. 10, pp. 29) **[5250]**, **[16221]**, **[36972]**

"Burning Issues: Four of Today's Hottest Energy Topics" in Canadian Business (Vol. 83, August 17, 2010, No. 13-14, pp. 45) **[7122]**, **[7483]**, **[14868]**, **[30512]**

Steve Burns Inc. **[211]**

Burns Innovation Group Inc. **[47127]**

Burns Public Relations Services Inc. **[42546]**

Burnsville Chamber of Commerce (BCC) **[53580]**

Burrelle's New Jersey Media Directory **[3168]**

Burrill & Company **[49185]**

"Burritos New Bag for Shopping Developer" in Houston Business Journal (Vol. 40, December 4, 2009, No. 30, pp. 4A) **[17222]**, **[17894]**, **[32146]**, **[42963]**

Burson-Marsteller Knowledge Center **[16634]**, **[42695]**

Burt Hill Inc. **[41578]**

Burt Hill Kosar Rittelmann Associates [41578]

Burt Hill Kosar Rittelmann Associates Library **[19138]**

Burton Barr Central Library - Vehicle and Appliance Repair Collection. [1615]

"Burton Group Answers Industry Need for Practical Data Center Advice" in Canadian Corporate News (May 14, 2007) **[4639]**, **[4695]**, **[4844]**, **[44282]**

Burwell Chamber of Commerce **[54366]**

Bus Ride **[19816]**

Buset & Partners Library **[11496]**, **[17153]**, **[17614]**

Bushnell Chamber of Commerce **[50927]**

Business **[48283]**; **[48284]**; **[48285]**; **[48286]**; **[49663]**; **[49969]**; **[49970]**; **[50452]**; **[50453]**; **[50928]**; **[52675]**; **[52845]**; **[55601]**; **[57973]**

"The Business of Activism" in Entrepreneur (Vol. 37, September 2009, No. 9, pp. 43) **[7123]**, **[7484]**, **[19080]**, **[30513]**, **[36092]**, **[41802]**

The Business Advantage **[52053]**

Business Advisor **[53150]**

The Business Advisor **[56025]**

The Business Advisor **[212]**, **[19708]**

Business Advocate **[48287]**; **[52054]**; **[52676]**; **[53581]**; **[54928]**; **[55602]**; **[59111]**

The Business Advocate **[47863]**; **[48288]**; **[50929]**

Business Agenda **[58864]**

Business Alameda Style **[48289]**

Business America **[1227]**, **[2728]**

Business Analysis Essentials (Onsite) **[37589]**, **[45034]**

Business and Professional Chamber of Commerce of McCloud [48769]

Business and Professional Software Database **[4746]**, **[4788]**, **[5062]**, **[41525]**, **[45255]**

Business Asia **[33069]**

Business Barometer **[53971]**; **[56026]**; **[57974]**

Business Basics in Hawaii: Secrets of Starting Your Own Business in Our State **[50724]**

Business Beacon **[48290]**; **[53151]**

Business Beat **[49971]**; **[49972]**; **[50930]**; **[52256]**; **[53152]**; **[56717]**; **[56718]**; **[59500]**

Business for Beginners, Canadian Edition: A Simple Step-By-Step Guide to Starting a Small Business **[29532]**, **[32360]**

Business Black Belt: Develop the Strength, Flexibility and Agility to Run Your Company **[8164]**, **[25836]**, **[28146]**, **[29533]**, **[31297]**, **[35717]**, **[37839]**, **[39731]**, **[43401]**

Business Books International **[49799]**

Business Bridge **[49812]**

Business Brief **[53582]**

Business in Brief **[50454]**

The Business Brief **[56974]**

Business Briefs **[48291]**

Business Broadcast **[56027]**

Business Brokers Hawaii L.L.C. (BBH) **[42315]**, **[44210]**

Business in Broward **[50379]**

Business Browser North America **[36922]**

Business Browser U.S. [36922]

Business Builder **[50455]**

Business Bulletin **[48292]**; **[50456]**; **[50931]**; **[51528]**

The Business Bulletin **[52266]**

Business to Business **[48293]**; **[51529]**; **[53153]**; **[53154]**; **[53972]**; **[55098]**; **[55099]**; **[59501]**

Business to Business Buyers Guide **[58742]**

Business to Business Journal **[53155]**

Business to Business News **[52846]**

The Business Buzz **[54929]**

Business Bylines **[47864]**; **[48294]**

Business Calendar **[52847]**

Business Call **[52267]**

"C.A. Bancorp Inc. (TSX:BKP) Announces First Quarter 2007 Financial Results" in Canadian Corporate News (May 16, 2007) **[8168]**, **[12146]**, **[31302]**
CAA News **[1362]**
"Cabela's Repays Incentives as Sales Lag" in Business Journal-Milwaukee (Vol. 28, November 19, 2010, No. 7, pp. A1) **[19320]**, **[33166]**, **[35284]**, **[37324]**, **[46169]**
"Caber Engineering Helps to Reduce Canada's Carbon Footprint" in Ecology,Environment & Conservation Business (July 16, 2011, pp. 7) **[7124]**, **[7485]**, **[30515]**
Cable Ad Ventures Corp. **[20002]**
Cable and Telecommunications: A Marketing Society [3157], [19885]
Cable Area Chamber of Commerce **[59509]**
Cable Fax [3201], [19994]
Cable Online [3201], [19994]
Cable Television Administration and Marketing Society [3157], [19885]
Cable TV Advertising Bureau - Cable Advertising Conference [3208], [46750]
Cable TV Facts **[3169]**
Cable Yellow Pages **[3201]**, **[19994]**
Cabletelevision Advertising Bureau (CAB) **[19883]**
Cabletelevision Advertising Bureau - Cable Advertising Conference **[3208]**, **[46750]**
Caboose on the Loose **[51836]**
Cabot Chamber of Commerce **[48019]**
Cache Chamber of Commerce (CCC) **[58639]**
Cactus Car Wash **[3334]**
Caddott Chamber **[59510]**
Cadillac Area Business Magazine **[53173]**
Cadillac Area Chamber of Commerce (CACC) **[53174]**
"Cadillac Tower Largest to Start in a Decade" in Globe & Mail (March 28, 2006, pp. B5) **[5252]**, **[22797]**, **[24275]**
Cadiz-Trigg County Chamber of Commerce **[52271]**
Cadott Area Chamber of Commerce **[59511]**
Cadwalader, Wickersham & Taft Library **[926]**, **[7397]**
Cafe Ala Carte **[4322]**, **[9726]**
Cafe Depot/Coffee Depot **[9727]**
Cafe Fondue Franchise Systems Inc. **[18093]**, **[19278]**
Caffino [9728]
Caffino Inc. **[9728]**
CAG Newsletter **[34103]**
Cahokia Area Chamber of Commerce **[50948]**
Cairo Chamber of Commerce **[55113]**
Caixa Geral do Depositos SA - Mediateca e Centro de Informacao Europeia **[267]**, **[19748]**
CAJ Media **[6780]**, **[15488]**
Cake Decorating for All Occasions **[1788]**
"Cal-ISO Plans $125 Million Facility" in Sacramento Business Journal (Vol. 25, August 1, 2008, No. 22, pp. 1) **[5253]**, **[17226]**, **[24723]**, **[33167]**
Calabasas Chamber of Commerce **[48369]**
Calabasas Post **[48370]**
Calais Regional Chamber of Commerce [52626]
Calaveras County Chamber of Commerce **[48371]**
Calaveras County Small Business Development Center **[48140]**
Calcutta Area Chamber of Commerce **[56041]**
Caldwell Area Chamber of Commerce (CACC) **[52059]**
Caldwell Chamber of Commerce (CCC) **[50747]**
Caldwell Chamber of Commerce [57971]
Caldwell Community College and Technical Institute - Small Business Center **[55870]**
Caldwell County Chamber of Commerce (CCCC) **[55616]**
"Calendar" in Crain's Detroit Business (Vol. 24, April 14, 2008, No. 15, pp. 25) **[18543]**, **[20329]**, **[27010]**, **[29554]**, **[30516]**, **[46175]**, **[46610]**
"Calendar" in Crain's Detroit Business (Vol. 24, April 7, 2008, No. 14, pp. 27) **[18542]**, **[20328]**, **[27009]**, **[29553]**, **[40711]**, **[46174]**, **[46609]**
"Calendar" in Crain's Detroit Business (Vol. 24, March 10, 2008, No. 10, pp. 21) **[18538]**, **[20324]**, **[27005]**, **[29549]**, **[46170]**, **[46605]**, **[47238]**
"Calendar" in Crain's Detroit Business (Vol. 24, March 17, 2008, No. 11, pp. 20) **[18539]**, **[20325]**, **[27006]**, **[29550]**, **[46171]**, **[46606]**, **[47239]**
"Calendar" in Crain's Detroit Business (Vol. 24, March 24, 2008, No. 12, pp. 25) **[18540]**, **[20326]**, **[27007]**, **[29551]**, **[46172]**, **[46607]**, **[47240]**
"Calendar" in Crain's Detroit Business (Vol. 24, March 31, 2008, No. 13, pp. 1) **[18541]**, **[20327]**, **[27008]**, **[29552]**, **[40710]**, **[46173]**, **[46608]**
"Calendar" in Crain's Detroit Business (Vol. 24, October 6, 2008, No. 40, pp. 22) **[16843]**, **[17227]**, **[18545]**, **[20331]**, **[27012]**, **[29556]**, **[38962]**, **[39745]**, **[46177]**, **[46612]**, **[47242]**
"Calendar" in Crain's Detroit Business (Vol. 24, September 22, 2008, No. 38, pp. 17) **[18544]**, **[20330]**, **[27011]**, **[29555]**, **[46176]**, **[46611]**, **[47241]**
"Calendar" in Crain's Detroit Business (Vol. 26, January 11, 2010, No. 2, pp. 16) **[4459]**, **[11057]**, **[20332]**, **[27013]**, **[36398]**, **[46613]**
"Calendar" in Crain's Detroit Business (Vol. 26, January 18, 2010, No. 3, pp. 16) **[11058]**, **[20333]**, **[27014]**, **[36399]**, **[39746]**, **[46614]**
Calendar of Community Events **[48372]**
Calendar with Directory **[53175]**
Calendar of Events **[47876]**; **[48020]**; **[49460]**; **[51837]**; **[53979]**; **[55114]**; **[56732]**; **[56994]**; **[58743]**
Calendar of Events - Information Directory **[56995]**
CALEXICO California, City Directory and Tourist Guide **[48373]**
Calexico Chamber of Commerce (CCC) **[48374]**
"Calgary East" in Canadian Business (Vol. 80, January 15, 2007, No. 2, pp. 13) **[27015]**, **[32573]**
Calhoun City Chamber of Commerce (CCCC) **[53833]**
Calhoun County Chamber of Commerce (CCCC) **[57433]**
Calhoun County Chamber of Commerce (CCCOC) **[49984]**
Caliche Ltd. **[47514]**
Caliente Chamber of Commerce **[54476]**
California Apparel News **[3902]**
California Association of Homes and Services for the Aging Annual Meeting and Exhibition **[1440]**
California Association of Homes and Services for the Aging Annual Meeting [1440]
California Association of Pet Professionals [1236], [15747]
California Builder & Engineer **[5576]**
California Career Conference [3388]
California Chamber Advocate **[48375]**
California Chamber of Commerce **[53980]**
California Chamber of Commerce (CCC) **[48376]**
California Chamber of Commerce, Southern California Office **[48377]**
California Closet Company **[15268]**, **[15285]**, **[16490]**, **[41653]**
California College of the Arts Libraries - Meyer Library **[4564]**, **[6074]**, **[6168]**
"California Company Suing City's Lupin Over its Generic Diabetes Drug" in Baltimore Business Journal (Vol. 27, January 1, 2010) **[23776]**, **[34210]**, **[36400]**, **[36973]**, **[38963]**, **[42769]**, **[43812]**
California Corporation Formation Package and Minute Book **[49379]**
California Council Against Health Fraud [34153]
California Culinary Academy Library **[5848]**, **[10325]**, **[10827]**, **[15213]**, **[18299]**
California Department of Conservation - Division of Recycling - Resource Center **[10193]**, **[17737]**
California Department of Housing and Community Development - Housing Resource Center **[16573]**
California Department of Pesticide Regulation Library **[15653]**
California Dietetic Association Meeting **[15193]**, **[21282]**
California Employer Advisor **[49375]**
California Environmental Protection Agency Library **[927]**
California Farm Equipment Show [21757]
California Federal Bank - Technical Library. [5065]
California Federation of Legal Secretaries [20818]
California Film Commission - Location Resource Center Library **[8020]**
California Garden **[9109]**, **[9803]**, **[13406]**
California Gift Show **[9583]**, **[9617]**
California Grape Grower [19266]
California Institute for Rural Studies (CIRS) **[21820]**
California Integrated Waste Management Board Library **[17738]**
California Israel Chamber of Commerce (CICC) **[48378]**
California Job Journal **[19170]**
California Labor and Employment ALERT Newsletter **[24102]**, **[49376]**
California Labor and Employment Law Quarterly **[49377]**
California Land Surveyors Association Conference **[19534]**
California Native American Business Center - National Center for American Indian Enterprise **[49140]**
California Optometric Association OptoWest **[20943]**
California Optometric Association Spring Optica & Congress [20943]
California Polytechnic State University - Robert F. Kennedy Library - Government Documents and Map Department - Diablo Canyon Power Plant Depository Library **[3130]**
California Procurement Technical Assistance Center - The Federal Technology Center (The FTC) **[49349]**
California Procurement Technical Assistance Center - Federal Technology Center Procurement Technical Assistance Center **[49350]**
California Procurement Technical Assistance Center - Los Angeles County Office of Small Business **[49351]**
California Procurement Technical Assistance Center - Pacific American Indian Development (PAID) - Procurement Technical Assistance Center **[49352]**
California Procurement Technical Assistance Center - Riverside Community College District **[49353]**
California Procurement Technical Assistance Center - San Diego Contracting Opportunities Center **[49354]**
California Public Health Foundation [14307]
California Quivers **[13336]**
California Real Estate Journal **[17553]**
California Real Estate Services Division Library **[5702]**
California Society of Printmakers (CSP) **[4436]**
California Special Education Alert **[25923]**, **[28403]**
California State Department of Motor Vehicles - Licensing Operations Division - Research and Development Branch - Traffic Safety Research Library **[1645]**, **[6606]**, **[13546]**, **[19821]**
California State Polytechnic University, Pomona - Apparel Technology and Research Center (ATRC) **[39530]**
California State Polytechnic University, Pomona - Center for Regenerative Studies [19144]
California State Polytechnic University, Pomona - John T. Lyle Center for Regenerative Studies **[19144]**
California State Polytechnic University - W.K. Kellogg Arabian Horse Library **[10629]**
California State University, Fresno - Center for Agricultural Business (CAB) **[21821]**
California State University, Long Beach - Graduate Center for Public Policy and Administration (GCPPA) **[42421]**
California State University, Los Angeles - Edmund G. "Pat" Brown Institute of Public Affairs **[34650]**
California State University Press **[49395]**
California Technology Ventures, LLC **[49187]**
California University of Pennsylvania - Louis L. Manderino Library - Special Collections **[1143]**, **[1382]**, **[14674]**, **[14767]**
California Vehicle Leasing Association [1620]
California.Calm, A Guide to San Benito County **[48379]**
"Calista Sells Rural Newspapers" in Alaska Business Monthly (Vol. 27, October 2011, No. 10, pp. 8) **[15520]**, **[16360]**, **[25299]**, **[44141]**
Calistoga Chamber of Commerce (CCC) **[48380]**
Call Center Solutions Buyer's Guide & Directory Issue [19847]
"A Call for Common Sense with WaterSense" in Contractor (Vol. 56, July 2009, No. 7, pp. 42) **[1187]**, **[16223]**
"A Call to Make SOX More Elastic" in Canadian Business (Vol. 80, February 12, 2007, No. 4, pp. 14) **[32574]**, **[33570]**
Call Me Ted **[408]**, **[3170]**, **[29557]**, **[39747]**
"Call of Prepaid Heard by More" in Chicago Tribune (November 26, 2008) **[3699]**, **[27016]**, **[44286]**, **[45321]**
"Call Them Gorgeous" in Entrepreneur (Vol. 35, October 2007, No. 10, pp. 54) **[3700]**, **[34814]**
"Calling All Recruiters: Agent HR Puts Staffing Agents In Charge" in Black Enterprise (Vol. 38, December 2007, No. 5, pp. 72) **[6960]**, **[7782]**, **[20028]**, **[27017]**, **[35720]**, **[43408]**
"Calling An Audible" in The Business Journal-Milwaukee (Vol. 25, August 1, 2008, No. 45, pp. A1) **[14567]**, **[19409]**, **[27018]**, **[39748]**
Calmac Manufacturing Corp. **[900]**
Calmas Associates **[31140]**
CALMideas **[46798]**
"Calming Customers" in The Business Journal-Portland (Vol. 25, August 29, 2008, No. 25, pp. 1) **[8169]**, **[12147]**, **[24276]**, **[25042]**, **[26397]**, **[31303]**, **[42459]**
Calorie Control Commentary **[21280]**
CALTRUX **[20703]**
Calvert Chamber of Commerce **[57991]**
Calvert County Chamber of Commerce (CCCC) **[52685]**
Calvert Social Venture Partners, L.P. **[59011]**
CAM Expo [5624]
CAMA Parade [3906]
Camara de Comercio Latina de los EEUU [36304]
Camara En Accion **[59860]**
Camarillo Chamber of Commerce **[48381]**
Camarro Research **[40586]**
Camas-Washougal Chamber of Commerce (CWCC) **[59120]**
"Cambodia Calls" in Barron's (Vol. 89, July 27, 2009, No. 30, pp. M7) **[8170]**, **[11059]**, **[12148]**, **[31304]**, **[36401]**
Cambria Chamber of Commerce **[48382]**
The Cambria Group **[49188]**
Cambrian Ventures, Inc. **[49189]**
Cambridge Area Chamber of Commerce **[53587]**
Cambridge Area Chamber of Commerce (CCC) **[56042]**
Cambridge Chamber of Commerce **[54368]**; **[59512]**
Cambridge Chamber of Commerce (CCC) **[52854]**
Cambridge Public Library - Audio-Visual Department **[14675]**
Cambridge Quarterly of Healthcare Ethics **[34495]**
Cambridge Samsung Partners LLC **[53016]**
Cambridge Seven Associates Inc. (C7A) **[41579]**
Cambridge Strategic Management Group Inc. [2919], [38763]

3470 Small Business Sourcebook • 30th Edition

Cambridge Ventures, L.P. **[51750]**
CambridgeLight Partners **[53017]**
Camden Area Chamber of Commerce (CACC) **[55115]**
Camden County Chamber of Commerce **[50462]**
Camden County Regional Chamber of Commerce **[54683]**
Camdenton Area Chamber of Commerce (CACC) **[53981]**
Camelot Therapeutic Horsemanship - Camelot Library **[10630]**
Camelot Venture Group **[53479]**
Camera de Comercio Espana - Estados Unidos [36312]
Cameron Chamber of Commerce **[53982]**; **[57992]**
Camilla Chamber of Commerce **[50463]**
Camille's Sidewalk Cafe **[5108]**, **[6457]**
CAMM News **[39497]**
Camp Bow Wow **[15678]**
Camp County Chamber of Commerce **[57993]**
Camp Dresser & McKee. [20996]
Camp Horsemanship Association [10601]
Camp Verde Chamber of Commerce (CVCC) **[47877]**
"Campaign Not Stirred by Wind Issue in Roanoke County" in Roanoke Times (September 18, 2011) **[7125]**, **[7486]**, **[30517]**
Campaign Solutions **[16614]**
"Campaigner Survey: 46 Percent of Small Businesses Use Email Marketing" in Wireless News (November 21, 2009) **[11640]**, **[22584]**, **[22798]**, **[28590]**, **[39749]**, **[45322]**
Campbell Chamber of Commerce (CCC) **[48383]**
Campbell Connection **[48384]**
Campbell County Chamber of Commerce **[57662]**; **[59808]**
Campbell Mithun Library & Information Services **[42696]**
Campbell Soup Company Research Information Center **[15214]**
Campbellsville - Taylor County Chamber of Commerce **[52272]**
Campgroundata **[3267]**
Camping Magazine **[3268]**
Camping Magazine--Buyer's Guide Issue **[3253]**
The Campus CEO: The Student Entrepreneur's Guide to Launching a Multi-Million Dollar Business **[28148]**, **[29335]**
CampVentures **[49190]**
CAMUS International **[38863]**
"Can America Invent Its Way Back?" in Business Week (September 22, 2008, No. 4100, pp. 52) **[22799]**, **[27019]**, **[32575]**, **[34815]**, **[36974]**, **[41015]**, **[42770]**, **[43813]**, **[44818]**
"Can Avenue be Fashionable Again? Livernois Merchants, City Want Revival" in Crain's Detroit Business (March 10, 2008) **[4204]**, **[17228]**, **[27020]**, **[33168]**, **[42969]**
"Can a Brazilian SUV Take On the Jeep Wrangler?" in Business Week (September 22, 2008, No. 4100, pp. 50) **[11060]**, **[14870]**, **[22800]**, **[25444]**, **[36402]**, **[38964]**, **[41016]**
"Can Brewer Make Cheap Seats Pay?" in Globe & Mail (January 7, 2006, pp. B4) **[22801]**, **[24277]**, **[25043]**
Can Clean **[6360]**
"Can He Win the Patent Game?" in Globe & Mail (February 20, 2006, pp. B1) **[23777]**, **[29558]**, **[36975]**, **[37852]**
"Can HOAs Stop You From Going Green?" in Contractor (Vol. 56, July 2009, No. 7, pp. 39) **[5254]**, **[7487]**, **[19081]**, **[45323]**
"Can the State Afford a Big Time College Football Program?" in Hawaii Business (Vol. 53, March 2008, No. 9, pp. 26) **[19321]**, **[19410]**, **[27021]**, **[32576]**
"Can This Duo be Saved? Renovating 2 Tallest Edifices Downtown Will Be Costly, Owner Says" in Charlotte Observer (February 4, 2007) **[1269]**, **[22802]**
"Can Turfway Park Stay in the Race?" in Business Courier (Vol. 26, January 8, 2010, No. 38, pp. 1) **[9386]**, **[10616]**, **[21537]**, **[33571]**
"Can We Talk?" in Canadian Business (Vol. 79, September 11, 2006, No. 18, pp. 131) **[22274]**, **[32577]**
"Can You Hear Me Now?" in Harvard Business Review (Vol. 86, July-August 2008, No. 8, pp. 23) **[22275]**, **[29028]**, **[32578]**, **[37853]**
"Can You Hear Them Now?" in Hawaii Business (Vol. 54, August 2008, No. 2, pp. 48) **[3701]**, **[22803]**, **[34816]**, **[43409]**, **[44287]**
"Can You Say $1 Million? A Language-Learning Start-Up Is Hoping That Investors Can" in Inc. (Vol. 33, November 2011, No. 9, pp. 116) **[20461]**, **[21062]**, **[27958]**, **[37325]**, **[41367]**
"Can Your Business Still Land a Loan?" in Entrepreneur (Vol. 37, August 2009, No. 8, pp. 62) **[26163]**, **[37326]**
Canaan Partners (Menlo Park) **[49191]**
Canaan Partners (Westport) **[49772]**
Canada Agriculture and Agri-Food - Dairy and Swine Research and Development Centre Lennoxville - Canadian Agriculture Library **[21796]**

Canada Bread Company, Limited **[1696]**
Canada Business and Investment Opportunities Yearbook **[11061]**, **[12149]**
The Canada Co. **[21771]**
Canada-Czech Republic Chamber of Commerce (CCRCC) **[26823]**
Canada Department of Foreign Affairs and International Trade - Main Library **[36928]**
Canada Earth Energy Association [7039]
Canada EarthSaver **[7025]**, **[17685]**
Canada-Finland Chamber of Commerce (CFCC) **[26824]**
Canada Fitness Survey [16057]
Canada Hippique [10602]
Canada-India Business Council (C-IBC) **[26825]**
Canada Industrial Innovation Centre [29441]
Canada Investment and Business Guide **[11062]**, **[12150]**
Canada Manitoba Business Service Centre **[59890]**
Canada Manitoba Business Service Centre - Business Start Program **[59891]**
Canada Manitoba Business Service Centre - Manitoba Marketing Network, Inc. **[59892]**
Canada Manitoba Business Service Centre - One-on-One Business Counseling **[59893]**
Canada Manitoba Business Service Centre - Reference Library **[59894]**
Canada/Manitoba Business Services Centre - Importing/Exporting **[59895]**
Canada National Committee of the International Association on Water Pollution Research and Control - Canada Association on Water Pollution Research and Control [30414]
Canada National Research Council - CISTI Institute for Research in Construction Branch **[5703]**
"Canada Nears European Trade Treaty" in Globe & Mail (February 5, 2007, pp. B1) **[27022]**, **[33572]**, **[36403]**
"Canada, Not China, Is Partner In Our Economic Prosperity" in Crain's Chicago Business (Vol. 31, April 14, 2008, No. 15, pp. 14) **[11063]**, **[22804]**, **[27023]**, **[36404]**
Canada Numismatica **[4402]**
Canada Office of the Auditor General Knowledge Centre Library **[268]**
Canada Pakistan Bulletin **[26826]**
Canada-Pakistan Business Council (CPBC) **[26827]**
Canada Public Works & Government Services - Consulting and Audit Canada Information Centre **[3131]**
Canada School of Public Service Library **[38839]**
"Canada Tomorrow" in Canadian Business (Vol. 80, October 8, 2007, No. 20, pp. 14) **[27024]**, **[28149]**, **[29559]**, **[34817]**, **[45324]**
"Canada Tops Again in G7: Study" in Globe & Mail (March 22, 2006, pp. B8) **[27025]**, **[32579]**
Canada-United States Business Association (CUSBA) **[36284]**
"Canada Wins Second NAFTA Decision on Softwood Tariffs" in Globe & Mail (March 18, 2006, pp. B2) **[33573]**, **[36405]**, **[46118]**
"Canada's Clean Energy Advantages Offer a Bright Future" in Canadian Business (Vol. 83, August 17, 2010, No. 13-14, pp. 38) **[7126]**, **[7488]**, **[30518]**, **[33574]**, **[34818]**
"Canada's Largest Bakery Officially Opened Today" in Ecology,Environment & Conservation Business (October 15, 2011, pp. 7) **[1754]**, **[5255]**, **[7127]**, **[7489]**, **[30519]**
"Canada's New Government Introduces Amendments to Deny Work Permits to Foreign Strippers" in Canadian Corporate News (May 16, 2007) **[1837]**, **[33575]**
"Canada's Oil Rush" in Canadian Business (Vol. 81, October 13, 2008, No. 17, pp. 58) **[22805]**, **[45325]**
"Canada's Uber-Wealthy" in Canadian Business (Vol. 80, Winter 2007, No. 24, pp. 16) **[27026]**, **[29560]**
Canada's Venture Capital and Private Equity Association (CVCA) **[46972]**
Canadian Aboriginal and Minority Supplier Council **[59921]**
Canadian Academic Accounting Association (CAAA) **[22]**
Canadian Academy of Periodontology (CAP) **[34104]**
Canadian Academy of Recording Arts and Sciences (CARAS) **[17631]**
Canadian Academy of Sport Medicine (CASM) **[16064]**
Canadian Accounting Education and Research News **[23]**
Canadian Accredited Independent Schools (CAIS) **[27973]**
Canadian Administrative Housekeepers' Association **[2596]**, **[6562]**
Canadian Advertising Research Foundation (CARF) **[349]**
Canadian Aerophilatelic Society (CAS) **[4335]**
Canadian Aerophilatelist **[4336]**
Canadian-American Business Council (CABC) **[36285]**

Canadian Angus Association [2752], [22659], [37557]
Canadian Apparel Directory **[4205]**, **[13562]**
Canadian Apparel Manufacturer--Buyers' Guide Issue [4205], [13562]
Canadian Arctic Multimedia Information Kit **[1339]**
Canadian Association of Aquarium Clubs (CAOAC) **[1234]**
Canadian Association of Broadcasters (CAB) **[16689]**, **[19884]**
Canadian Association of Chemical Distributors (CACD) **[26719]**
Canadian Association of Environmental Management (CAEM) **[2596]**, **[6562]**
Canadian Association of Fairs and Exhibitions (CAFE) **[965]**
Canadian Association of Family Enterprise (CAFE) **[29440]**, **[31013]**, **[44791]**
Canadian Association for Distance Education [27976]
Canadian Association for Health, Physical Education and Recreation [15953]
Canadian Association of Gerontology (CAG) **[34105]**
Canadian Association of Home and Property Inspectors (CAHPI) **[2552]**
Canadian Association for Information Science (CAIS) **[11224]**
Canadian Association of Insolvency and Restructuring Professionals (CAIRP) **[8027]**
Canadian Association of International Development Consultants (CAIDC) **[2754]**, **[25819]**
Canadian Association of Journalists (CAJ) **[6781]**, **[15489]**
Canadian Association of Labour Media (CALM) **[46799]**
Canadian Association of Mutual Insurance Companies (CAMIC) **[11269]**
Canadian Association of Numismatic Dealers (CAND) **[4337]**
Canadian Association of Nurses in Oncology (CANO) **[10516]**
Canadian Association of Financial Planners [8026]
Canadian Association of Home Inspectors [2552]
Canadian Association of Importers and Exporters [26846]
Canadian Association of Importers and Exporters Inc. [26846]
Canadian Association of Independent Schools [27973]
Canadian Association of Insurance and Financial Advisors [8026]
Canadian Association of Insurance and Financial Advisors (CAIFA) [8026]
Canadian Association of Landscape Architecture [13368]
Canadian Association of Message Exchanges [1960], [19864], [20961]
Canadian Association of Rehabilitation Personnel [16075]
Canadian Association of Rehabilitation Professionals [16075]
Canadian Association of Optometrists (CAO) **[20913]**
Canadian Association of Photographers and Illustrators in Communications (CAPIC) **[4437]**, **[15838]**
Canadian Association of Physical Medicine and Rehabilitation (CAPM&R) **[16065]**
Canadian Association of Professional Employees (CAPE) **[46800]**
Canadian Association of Professional Speakers (CAPS) **[47132]**
Canadian Association of Recycling Industries (CARI) **[17686]**
Canadian Association of Regulated Importers (CARI) **[26828]**
Canadian Association for School Health (CASH) **[34106]**
Canadian Association of Token Collectors (CATC) **[4403]**
Canadian Association on Water Quality (CAWQ) **[30414]**
Canadian Association of Women Executives and Entrepreneurs (CAWEE) **[47205]**
Canadian Athletic Therapists Association (CATA) **[16066]**
Canadian Auto Workers (CAW) **[46801]**
Canadian Automatic Merchandising Association (CAMA) **[20849]**
Canadian Automobile Dealers Association (CADA) **[14837]**
Canadian Automotive Repair and Service Council (CARS) **[18580]**
Canadian Ayrshire Review **[999]**
The Canadian Badge Maker Ltd. **[3098]**
"Canadian Banks Too Timid in China, Beijing Tells Flaherty" in Globe & Mail (January 22, 2007, pp. B1) **[8171]**, **[12151]**
Canadian Biosystems Engineering **[21493]**
Canadian Board of Marine Underwriters (CBMU) **[11270]**
The Canadian Book of Charities: The Guide to Intelligent Giving **[8040]**
Canadian Bookbinders & Book Artists Guild Library **[2250]**
Canadian Bookseller **[2354]**
Canadian Booksellers Association (CBA) **[2355]**

Canadian MASTER INDEX

Canadian Broadcast Distribution Association (CBDA) **[18334]**
Canadian Broadcasting Corporation - Reference Library/Image Research Library **[16763]**
Canadian Business Aircraft Operators [717]
Canadian Business Aviation Association (CBAA) **[717]**
Canadian Business Press (CBP) **[15490]**
Canadian Business Resource Centre (CBRC) **[2829]**
Canadian Call Management Association (CAM-X) **[1960]**, **[19864]**, **[20961]**
Canadian Camping Association (CCA) **[3245]**
Canadian Cancer Society (CCS) **[34107]**
Canadian Cardiovascular Society (CCS) **[34108]**
Canadian Carpet Institute (CCI) **[20823]**
Canadian Carwash Association (CCA) **[3325]**
Canadian Cat Association (CCA) **[1000]**
Canadian Centre for Architecture (CCA) **[1256]**
Canadian Centre for Fisheries Innovation (CCFI) **[9042]**
Canadian Chamber of Commerce **[26829]**
Canadian Children's Book Centre (CCBC) **[2089]**
Canadian Children's Book News **[2090]**
Canadian Circulation Management Association (CCMA) **[15491]**
Canadian Cleaner and Launderer [6751]
Canadian Coast Guard Library **[13975]**
Canadian Coin News **[4360]**
Canadian College of Health Leaders **[34109]**
Canadian College of Health Service Executives [34109]
Canadian Committee on Irrigation and Drainage [30417]
Canadian Community Newspapers Association (CCNA) **[15492]**
Canadian Construction Association (CCA) **[5171]**
Canadian Consulting Agrologists Association (CCAA) **[21494]**
Canadian Consulting Engineer **[2755]**
Canadian Contractor **[15493]**
Canadian Cooperative Wool Growers Magazine: Livestock Supply Catalogue **[9352]**
Canadian Copyright Institute (CCI) **[2091]**, **[6782]**, **[15494]**
Canadian Cosmetic, Toiletry and Fragrance Association (CCTFA) **[5876]**
Canadian Council for Aboriginal Business (CCAB) **[26830]**
Canadian Council of Chief Executives (CCCE) **[26831]**
Canadian Council of Land Surveyors [19502]
Canadian Courier and Messenger Association [14349]
Canadian Courier and Logistics Association (CCLA) **[14349]**
Canadian Craft and Hobby Association (CCHA) **[6093]**
Canadian Craft Trade **[6094]**
Canadian Crafts Council [6178]
Canadian Crafts Federation (CCF) **[6178]**
Canadian Credit Institute Educational Foundation (CCIEF) **[8028]**
Canadian Decorating Products Association [11535], [15387]
Canadian Dermatology Association (CDA) **[34110]**
Canadian Direct Marketing Association [350]
Canadian Disc Jockey Association (CDJA) **[6555]**, **[16690]**
Canadian Entrepreneurship and Small Business Management **[29561]**, **[36406]**, **[37854]**
Canadian Environmental Defence Fund [7048]
Canadian Environmental Law and Research Foundation [7029]
Canadian Environmental Law Association (CELA) **[7026]**
Canadian Environmental Law Research Foundation [7029]
Canadian Environmental Network (CEN) **[7027]**, **[17687]**, **[30415]**
Canadian Environmental Network News **[7028]**, **[17688]**, **[30416]**
Canadian Equestrian Federation [10602]
Canadian Family Camping Federation (CFCF) **[3246]**
Canadian Family Physician **[34111]**
Canadian Federation of Business and Professional Women's Clubs (CFBPWC) **[47206]**
Canadian Federation of Independent Business (CFIB) **[26832]**, **[32486]**, **[35589]**, **[44792]**
Canadian Federation of Independent Business Research Library **[30378]**
Canadian Federation of Independent Grocers (CFIG) **[9898]**
Canadian Federation of Music Teachers' Associations (CFMTA) **[14604]**
Canadian Federation of University Women (CFUW) **[27974]**
Canadian Film and Television Production Association [7878]
Canadian Fire Alarm Association (CFAA) **[18373]**
Canadian Fishery Consultants Ltd. (CFCL) **[9032]**
Canadian Fitness and Lifestyle Research Institute (CFLRI) **[15942]**; **[16057]**
Canadian Foodservice Industry Operations Report **[3457]**, **[5096]**, **[6432]**, **[9137]**, **[10273]**, **[17860]**
Canadian Foundation for Dietetic Research (CFDR) **[15150]**
Canadian Foundry Association (CFA) **[13688]**
Canadian Franchise Association (CFA) **[32115]**
Canadian Fur Trade Development Institute [9350], [9354]
Canadian Gemmological Association **[13252]**
Canadian Gemmologist **[13253]**
Canadian German Chamber of Industry and Commerce (CGCIC) **[26833]**
Canadian German Headlines **[26834]**
Canadian Golf Hall of Fame Library and Archives **[9685]**
Canadian Good Roads Association [19803]
Canadian Grain Commission Library **[21797]**
Canadian Grocer: The Voice of Grocer Industry in Canada **[9995]**
Canadian Health Coalition (CHC) **[34112]**
Canadian Health Food Association (CHFA) **[10209]**, **[10274]**, **[15151]**
Canadian Healthcare Association (CHA) **[34113]**
Canadian Home Builders' Association (CHBA) **[5172]**
Canadian Home Builders' Association - Saskatchewan Library **[5704]**
Canadian Home Care Association (CHCA) **[10517]**
The Canadian Home Inspector **[2553]**
Canadian Hospital Association [34113]
"Canadian Hydronics Businesses Promote 'Beautiful Heat'" in Indoor Comfort Marketing (Vol. 70, September 2011, No. 9, pp. 20) **[794]**, **[7128]**, **[7490]**, **[30520]**, **[36407]**, **[39750]**, **[45326]**
Canadian Image Processing and Pattern Recognition Society (CIPPRS) **[4631]**, **[4834]**
Canadian Importers Association [26846]
Canadian Independent Adjuster **[11271]**
Canadian Independent Adjusters' Association (CIAA) **[11272]**
Canadian Independent Adjusters' Claims Manual **[11273]**
Canadian Independent Film Caucus [7882]
Canadian Independent Music Association (CIMA) **[17632]**
Canadian Independent Record Production Association [17632]
Canadian Industrial Relations Association (CIRA) **[46802]**
Canadian Innovation Centre **[29441]**
Canadian Innovation Centre (CIC) **[41309]**
Canadian Insolvency Foundation [8027]
Canadian Institute of Chartered Accountants (CICA) **[24]**, **[2257]**, **[19593]**
Canadian Institute for Environmental Law and Policy (CIELAP) **[7029]**
Canadian Institute of Financial Planning (CIFP) **[8029]**
Canadian Institute of Gemmology (CIG) **[13254]**
Canadian Institute of Management (CIM) **[37559]**
Canadian Institute of Public and Private Real Estate Companies [16790], [17166]
Canadian Institute of Plumbing and Heating **[10122]**
Canadian Institute of Plumbing and Heating Pipeline **[10123]**
Canadian Institute of Professional Home Inspectors (CIPHI) **[2554]**
Canadian Institute of Quantity Surveyors (CIQS) **[25]**, **[2258]**
Canadian Institute of Resources Law (CIRL) **[7030]**
Canadian Institute of Steel Construction (CISC) **[5173]**
Canadian Institute of Travel Counsellors (CITC) **[20510]**
Canadian Insurance Accountants Association (CIAA) **[26]**
Canadian International Trade Tribunal Library **[36929]**
Canadian Investor Relations Institute (CIRI) **[8030]**
Canadian Jewellers Association (CJA) **[13255]**
Canadian Journal on Aging **[34114]**
The Canadian Journal of Cardiology **[34115]**
Canadian Journal of Chemistry **[44005]**
Canadian Journal of Dietetic Practice and Research **[15152]**; **[34496]**
Canadian Journal of Film Studies **[7877]**
Canadian Journal of Infection Control **[34116]**
Canadian Journal of Information and Library Science **[11225]**
Canadian Journal of Learning and Technology **[27975]**
Canadian Journal of Medical Laboratory Science **[14264]**
Canadian Journal of Ophthalmology **[20914]**
Canadian Journal of Psychiatry **[34117]**
Canadian Journal of Public Health **[34497]**
Canadian Journal of Respiratory Therapy: Leadership through Advocacy, Service and Unity for Respiratory Therapists in Canada **[34498]**
Canadian Journal of Veterinary Research **[1049]**
Canadian Kendo Federation (CKF) **[14079]**
Canadian Kennel Club (CKC) **[1001]**
Canadian Labour Congress (CLC) **[26835]**, **[46803]**
Canadian Labour Congress Library **[46949]**
Canadian Law List **[24135]**
Canadian Learning Journal **[35652]**
Canadian Library Handbook [11231]
Canadian Library Yearbook [11231]
Canadian Life and Health Insurance Association (CLHIA) **[11274]**
Canadian Long Distance Riding Association (CaLDRA) **[10599]**
Canadian Luggage, Leathergoods, Handbags and Accessories Show **[13632]**
Canadian Magazine Publishers Association [15504]
Canadian Magazine Publishers Association CMPA [15504]
Canadian Management Centre (CMC) **[37560]**
Canadian Management Centre's 5-Day "MBA"(Canada) (Onsite) **[37592]**
Canadian Manager **[37561]**
"Canadian Market Data" in MarketingMagazine (Vol. 115, September 27, 2010, No. 13, pp. 6) **[409]**, **[39751]**
Canadian Marketing Association (CMA) **[350]**
Canadian Meat Council (CMC) **[3138]**
Canadian Media Guild (CMG) **[46804]**
Canadian Media Production Association (CMPA) **[7878]**
Canadian Medical Association (CMA) **[34118]**
Canadian Medical Protective Association (CMPA) **[34119]**
Canadian Mental Health Association (CMHA) **[34120]**
Canadian MoneySaver **[19684]**
Canadian Motion Picture Distribution Association [7892]
Canadian Multinationals and International Finance **[12152]**, **[31305]**, **[36408]**
Canadian Museum of Contemporary Photography - Research Resources **[15886]**
The Canadian Music Teacher **[14605]**
The Canadian Music Teacher: Canada Music Week Edition **[14606]**
Canadian National Committee for Mental Hygiene [34120]
Canadian National Exhibition (CNE) **[20293]**
Canadian Netherlands Business and Professional Association (CNBPA) **[26836]**
Canadian Network for Innovation in Education (CNIE) **[27976]**
Canadian Network of Toxicology Centres (CNTC) **[7031]**
Canadian Newspaper Association (CNA) **[15495]**
Canadian Numismatic Association Convention **[4383]**
Canadian Numismatic Association Library **[4389]**
Canadian Numismatic Research Society (CNRS) **[4338]**
Canadian Nursery Landscape Association (CNLA) **[9760]**, **[13367]**
Canadian Nursery Trades Association [9760], [13367]
Canadian Nurses Foundation (CNF) **[10518]**
Canadian Nutrition Society (CNS) **[15153]**
Canadian Oncology Nursing Journal **[10519]**
Canadian Ophthalmological Society (COS) **[20915]**
Canadian Ornamental Plant Foundation (COPF) **[9089]**
Canadian Paediatric Society (CPS) **[34121]**
Canadian Pain Society (CPS) **[34122]**
Canadian Paperworks Union [46809]
Canadian Parks and Wilderness Society (CPAWS) **[7032]**
Canadian Patent Reporter Plus (CPR) **[37168]**
"Canadian Patients Give Detroit Hospitals a Boost" in Crain's Detroit Business (Vol. 24, April 14, 2008, No. 15, pp. 10) **[22806]**, **[34211]**, **[36409]**
Canadian Payroll Association (CPA) **[15452]**, **[21314]**
Canadian Pharmaceutical Journal **[6628]**
Canadian Pharmacists Association (CPhA) **[6629]**
The Canadian Philatelist **[4339]**
Canadian Physical Education Association - Canadian Association for Health, Physical Education, Recreation and Dance [15953]
Canadian Pizza Magazine **[9169]**, **[16132]**, **[32271]**
Canadian Plastics Industry Association (CPIA) **[38864]**
Canadian Pool & Spa Marketing [19549]
Canadian Pool Players Association **[16298]**
Canadian Professional Gemmology Course **[13256]**
Canadian Professional Sales Association (CPSA) **[43343]**
Canadian Professional Sales Association - Sales Resource Centre **[43776]**
Canadian Property Valuation **[1220]**
Canadian Psychiatric Association (CPA) **[34123]**
Canadian Public Administration **[42398]**
Canadian Public Health Association (CPHA) **[34124]**
Canadian Public Personnel Management Association [35656]
Canadian Public Relations Society (CPRS) **[16578]**
Canadian Publishers' Council (CPC) **[2092]**
Canadian Pulp and Paper Association [38867]
Canadian Real Estate Association (CREA) **[16781]**
Canadian Real Estate Association Annual Conference and Trade Show **[1167]**, **[46751]**
Canadian Recording Industry Association [17634]

3472 Small Business Sourcebook • 30th Edition

Centerville Area Chamber of Commerce [51842]
Centerville Chamber of Commerce [58000]
Cen-Tex Hispanic Chamber of Commerce of Waco [57999]
Central Arizona College Small Business Development Center [47831]
Central Arkansas Manufacturing Directory [48023]
Central Baldwin Chamber of Commerce (CBCC) [47638]
Central Bark Doggy Day Care [15820]
Central Bradford County Chamber of Commerce (CBCCC) [56998]
Central Bucks Chamber of Commerce (CBCC) [56999]
Central California Hispanic Chamber of Commerce (CCHCC) [48402]
Central California Small Business Development Center - Fresno [48141]
Central California Small Business Development Center - Visalia [48142]
Central Chester County Chamber of Commerce [57075]
Central City Area Chamber of Commerce [54369]
Central Coast SCORE [48182]
Central Coast Small Business Development Center [48143]
Central Committee on Lumber Standards [13634]
Central Connecticut State University - Connecticut Small Business Development Center (CSBDC) [45843]
Central Delaware Chamber of Commerce (CDCC) [49813]
Central Delaware Info Book [49814]
Central Fairfax Chamber of Commerce (CFCC) [58870]
Central Fayette Chamber of Business and Industry [57076]
Central Hillsborough county Chamber of Commerce [50137]
Central Indiana Better Business Bureau [51512]
Central Indiana Small Business Development Center [51473]
Central Institute for the Deaf - Speech, Hearing and Education Library [10349]
Central Iowa SCORE [51794]
Central Jersey SCORE [54652]
Central Lake Chamber of Commerce [53179]
Central Lakes College [53795]
Central Lakes College Small Business Development Center [53531]
Central Louisiana Business Incubator [52525]
Central Louisiana Chamber of Commerce [52437]
Central Macomb County Chamber of Commerce (CMCCC) [53180]
Central Massachusetts Small Business Development Center [52803]
Central Michigan University Research Corporation [53502]
Central Minnesota Small Business Development Center [53532]
Central Oklahoma Business and Job Development Corp. - Center for Business, Technology, Research and Development [56639]
Central Oklahoma Technology Center [56650]
Central Oregon SCORE [56694]
Central Park Restaurants [18097]
Central Pasco Chamber of Commerce [49987]
Central Pennsylvania Chamber of Commerce [57000]
Central Pennsylvania College [57343]
Central Point Area Chamber of Commerce [56737]
Central Point Chamber of Commerce [56737]
Central Rhode Island Chamber of Commerce [57365]
Central State University - International Center for Water Resources Management (ICWRM) [21007]
Central Supply Association [16211]
Central Utah SCORE [58622]
Central Valley Business Incubator [49356]
Central Valley SCORE [48183]
Central Vermont Chamber of Commerce [58744]
Central Virginia Procurement Technical Assistance Center [59022]
Central Virginia Small Business Development Center [58796]
Central Washington SCORE [59075], [59123]
Central Whidbey Chamber of Commerce (CWCC) [59124]
Centrale des Syndicats du Quebec [46815]
Centralia Area Chamber of Commerce (CACC) [53987]
Centralia-Chehalis Chamber of Commerce [59125]
Centre for Addiction and Mental Health Library [46100]
Centre Canadien d'Architecture [1256]
Centre d'étude des niveaux de vie [27931]
Centre d'Action Écologique [17745]
Centre de Recherches pour le Développement International [34663]
Centre for Investigative Journalism [6781], [15489]
Centre Harbor-Moultonboro Chamber of Commerce [54608]

Centre International pour l'Entreprise Privée [33390]
Centre for the Study of Living Standards (CSLS) [27931]
CENTREX Hotel & Restaurant Tradeshow [10782]
"Centrue Sets Down New Roots in St. Louis; Bank Looks to Expand in Exurbs of Chicago" in Crain's Chicago Business (May 5, 2008) [8178], [12162], [22814], [24725], [31311], [37330], [41817]
"Cents and Sensibility" in Playthings (Vol. 107, January 1, 2009, No. 1, pp. 19) [11066], [18402], [20235], [36414], [38974], [45332]
Centum Financial Group Inc. [14530]
"Centurion Signs Egypt Deal With Shell" in Globe & Mail (March 21, 2006, pp. B5) [38975], [41818]
Century 21 Canada Limited Partnership [17135]
Century Business Services Inc. [214], [2833], [13807], [21456], [25959], [32011], [38678]
Century City Chamber of Commerce [48403]
Century Publishing [48597]
Century Small Business Solutions [3654], [19043]
CEO Advisors [2837], [25964], [44921]; [50348]
"CEO Forecast" in Hispanic Business (January-February 2009, pp. 34, 36) [7139], [7501], [27042], [29572], [30532], [33408], [34218], [34827], [37862], [40713]
"CEO Pay: Best Bang for Buck" in Philadelphia Business Journal (Vol. 30, September 30, 2011, No. 33, pp. 1) [21880], [35723], [37863]
"CEO Pay: The Details" in Crain's Detroit Business (Vol. 25, June 22, 2009, No. 25, pp.) [12163], [21881], [35724], [37864]
CEO Report [49988]
CEO Report Update [49989]
"CEO Tapped for Perrier, Poland Springs" in Black Enterprise (Vol. 38, February 2008, No. 7, pp. 30) [2413], [37865]
CEO Venture Fund [57282]
"CEOs Decry Budget Taxation Change" in Globe & Mail (April 2, 2007, pp. B1) [36415], [37866], [46185]
"CEOs Divided About Census" in Canadian Business (Vol. 83, August 10, 2010, No. 13-14, pp. 20) [23785], [33587], [37867]
"CEOs Gone Wild" in Canadian Business (Vol. 79, August 14, 2006, No. 16-17, pp. 15) [12164], [37868], [38976]
"The CEO's New Armor" in Conde Nast Portfolio (Vol. 2, June 2008, No. 6, pp. 56) [23786], [33588], [37869]
"CEOs Split on Migrant Workers" in Canadian Business (Vol. 83, September 14, 2010, No. 15, pp. 23) [33589], [35293], [35725], [37870], [40868]
"CEOs With a Functional Background in Operations" in Human Resource Management (Vol. 49, September-October 2010, No. 5) [35726], [37871]
"CEOs With Headsets" in Harvard Business Review (Vol. 88, September 2010, No. 9, pp. 21) [25372], [37872]
Ceramic Arts & Crafts [6015], [6132]
Ceramic Distributors of America - Ceramic Arts Federation International - Model Industry Association - National Ceramic Teachers Association - National Ceramic Manufacturers Association - National Ceramic Dealers Association - Hobby Industry Association of America [4342], [6095]
Ceramics Corridor Innovation Center [55483]
Ceramics Monthly [6002], [6124]
Cercles des Jeunes Naturalistes [7076]
The Cereal Bowl [18098]
Cereal Chemistry [44006]
Ceres Chamber of Commerce (CCC) [48404]
Ceres Directory and Fact Book [48405]
Ceridian Corp. [53787]
"Cerner Works the Business Circuit" in Business Journal-Serving Metropolitan Kansas City (Vol. 26, October 5, 2007, No. 4, pp. 1) [3515], [4696], [5076], [11322], [18877], [34219], [36119], [41819], [45103]
Cerritos Chamber of Commerce (CCOC) [48406]
Certapro Painters [2649], [15403]
"Certification Experts Germanischer Lloyd Wind Energy Assist NaiKun's Offshore Wind Project" in Canadian Corporate News (May 14, 2007) [25840], [30533], [34828], [37873], [44291]
Certified Coin Dealer Newsletter [4362]
Certified Ethical Hacker (Onsite) [28017]
"Certified Financial Planner Board of Standards Reacts to Jobs Program" in Professional Services Close-Up (September 14, 2011) [8179], [12165]
Certified Housekeeping Consultants [10789]
Certified Management Accountants of Canada [53]
"Certified Technicians can Increase Bottom Line" in Contractor (Vol. 56, September 2009, No. 9, pp. 37) [796], [26399], [44292]
Certigard [1537]
Certirestore Certified Furniture Restoration [9363]
"C'est Bon" in Canadian Business (Vol. 79, September 25, 2006, No. 19, pp. 39) [27043], [32589]
CEX - Canadian Environmental Exposition [16290]

The CF Apartment Reporter [17106], [17554]
CFA Institute [11969]
CFA Research Foundation [8971]
CFAL. [14670]
CFI Group USA L.L.C. [25965], [29238], [36015], [38683]
C.F.M.A. Building Profits: The Magazine for Construction Financial Professionals [5578]
CFO & Controller Alert [171], [31985]
CFO Today Inc. [243], [2327], [19714]
CFPC-Liaison Newsletter [34130]
"CGB Purchases Illinois Grain-Fertilizer Firm" in Farm Industry News (December 2, 2011) [12166], [21541], [25302]
"CGG Home Fashions to Show Hand-Loomed Textiles" in Home Textiles Today (Vol. 31, May 24, 2011, No. 13, pp. 4) [10390], [10458]
CGW Southeast Partners / Cravey, Green & Wahlen Inc. [50649]
CH2M Hill Companies Ltd. [10182]
CH2M Hill, Inc. Technical Library [10194]
CH2M Hill [10182]
CH2M Hill Ltd. [10182]
CHA - Certified Horsemanship Association [10601]
CHA Consulting [17582]
CHA Guide to Canadian Healthcare Facilities [34131]
CHA Winter Convention and Trade Show [6041], [6155], [20284]
CHA-Association for Horsemanship Safety and Education [10601]
Chabot College [49366]
Chadron Area Chamber of Commerce [54370]
Chadron - Dawes County Area Chamber of Commerce (CDCCC) [54370]
Chadron State College - Nebraska Business Development Center (NBDC) [24708]
Chaffee Chamber of Commerce (CCC) [53988]
Chagrin Valley [56047]
Chagrin Valley Chamber of Commerce (CVCC) [56048]
Chain of Blame: How Wall Street Caused the Mortgage and Credit Crisis [6194], [6232], [6280], [12167], [14396], [26164], [37331]
Chain Drug Marketing Association (CDMA) [6630]
Challenge Healthcare Corp. [22062], [46087]
"Challenges Await Quad in Going Public" in Milwaukee Business Journal (Vol. 27, January 29, 2010, No. 18, pp. A1) [4461], [12168], [16361], [25450], [37874], [41820]
"The Challenges of Commercial Work" in Indoor Comfort Marketing (Vol. 70, May 2011, No. 5, pp. 14) [797], [22815]
"Challenges, Responses and Available Resources" in Journal of Small Business and Entrepreneurship (Vol. 23, Winter 2010, No. 1) [27044], [29573], [37875], [44652]
Chama Chamber of Commerce [54934]
Chama Valley Chamber of Commerce [54934]
Chamber [52438]; [55125]
The Chamber [47785]; [48024]; [48407]; [50468]; [52690]; [53590]; [55124]; [59126]
Chamber Action [48408]; [48409]; [51843]; [52274]; [55126]; [55622]
Chamber Advantage [51541]; [53989]
The Chamber Advantage [48410]; [54371]; [54554]; [57567]
Chamber Advantage Newsletter [53591]
Chamber Advocate [48411]
The Chamber Advocate [50469]
Chamber Affairs [51844]
Chamber Annual Business and Community Directory [48412]
Chamber Beacon [59516]
Chamber Bits [58871]
Chamber Biz [49990]
Chamber Briefings [52275]
Chamber Bullet [52575]
Chamber Bulletin [49991]; [52061]; [52857]
The Chamber Bulletin [56049]
Chamber Business [48413]; [51542]; [54479]; [58872]; [59517]
Chamber Business and Community Guide [50957]
Chamber Business Directory [48025]; [54480]; [56738]; [58873]
Chamber of Business and Industry of Centre County [57333]
Chamber of Business and Industry of Centre County (CBICC) [57001]
Chamber Business Journal [48414]
Chamber Business Line [53990]
Chamber Business Monthly [59127]
Chamber Business News [54255]
The Chamber Business Report [58001]
Chamber Business Update [55623]

Chatham County United Chamber of Commerce and Travel and Tourism Office [55658]

The Chatham Group Inc. (CG) [14038]

Chatsworth Chamber of Commerce [48455]

Chatsworth-Murray County Chamber of Commerce [50495]

Chatsworth - Porter Ranch Chamber of Commerce [48455]

Chattanooga Area Chamber of Commerce [57679]

"Chattanooga at a Glance" in Women In Business (Vol. 62, June 2010, No. 2, pp. 29) [20337], [46618], [47245]

Chattanooga/Hamilton County Business Development Center [57824]

Chattanooga Procurement Technical Assistance Center - Center for Industrial Services (CIS) [57815]

Chattanooga State Community College [57829]

Chatter [51019]

Chatters Salon [1912], [10087]

Chattooga County Chamber of Commerce [50496]

Chaucer News [52452]

Chautauqua County Chamber of Commerce (CCCC) [55160]

Chautauqua Region SCORE [55042]

"Cheap Deposits Fuel Bank Profits" in Boston Business Journal (Vol. 31, July 29, 2011, No. 27, pp. 1) [27048], [31315]

Cheap: The High Cost of Discount Culture [25732], [42972]

"Cheap Thrills: Where to Look When You're Craving a Low-Price Wine" in Chicago Tribune (January 12, 2009) [13576], [19216], [22819], [27049], [43416]

"Cheap Ticket" in Entrepreneur (Vol. 35, November 2007, No. 11, pp. 126) [32088]

Cheatham County Chamber of Commerce [57680]

Cheba Hut Roasted Subs [6459]

Cheboygan Area Chamber of Commerce (CACC) [53208]

Cheboygan Area Chamber of Commerce Membership Directory and Buying Guide [53209]

"Check Provider Says It Plans to Close Call Center in Charlotte" in Charlotte Observer (February 6, 2007) [8181], [44293]

Checkers / Ralley's [18101]

The Checklist Manifesto: How to Get Things Right [24284], [29575], [37878]

CheckMark Software Inc. [216], [3655], [19044], [21457], [45249]

Checotah Chamber of Commerce [56487]

Chedd's Gourmet Grilled Cheese [6460]

Cheeburger Cheeburger Restaurants, Inc. [18102]

Cheektowaga Chamber of Commerce (CCC) [55161]

Cheekwood Botanical Gardens Library [9847]

Cheers: The Beverage Magazine for Full Service Restaurants and Bars [1869]

Cheese 101 [19267]

Cheese Classics of America [19268]

The Cheese Market [19253]

The Cheese Reporter [19257]

"Cheese Spread Whips Up a Brand New Bowl" in Brandweek (Vol. 49, April 21, 2008, No. 16, pp. 17) [414], [9917], [21542], [25453], [26743], [38981], [39764], [41020]

Chef Institutional [10297]

Chef: The Food Magazine for Professionals [10297]

Chehalem Valley Chamber of Commerce [56758]

Chelsea Area Chamber of Commerce [53210]

"Chelsea Community Hospital to Merge with St. Joseph Mercy Health" in Crain's Detroit Business (Vol. 24, March 24, 2008, No. 12) [24285], [34221], [41824]

Chem-Dry Carpet Drapery & Upholstery Cleaning [20833]

Chem-Dry Carpet and Upholstery Cleaning [20834]

ChemDry Canada Ltd. [20835], [44604]

"Chemed's Vitas Aims to Acquire" in Business Courier (Vol. 27, July 9, 2010, No. 10, pp. 1) [9246], [10529], [12171], [15065], [34222], [41825]

Chemeketa Community College Small Business Development Center [56671]

Chemeketa Community College - Training and Economic Development Center [56891]

The Chemical Educator [28404]

Chemical Engineering Research and Design (ChERD) [44007]

Chemical and Petroleum Engineering [44008]

Chemical Waste Transportation Institute [10163]

Chemical Week Price Report [10170]

Chemistri Information Center. [691]

CHEMSAFE [47489]

Chemstation International Inc. [2650]

"ChemSW Software Development Services Available for Outsourcing" in Information Today (Vol. 26, February 2009, No. 2, pp. 30) [3516], [4845], [5032], [18878], [37187], [41664], [45104]

Chemtura Corporation Library [19557]

Chemung County Chamber of Commerce [55162]

Chemung Valley SCORE [55043]

The Chemunicator [26720]

Cheney Chamber of Commerce [52076]

Cheney Chamber of Commerce [59314]

Chernoff Diamond & Company L.L.C. [22045]

Cherokee Chamber of Commerce [51862]

Cherokee Chamber of Commerce (CCC) [55659]

Cherokee County Chamber of Commerce [50497]; [57448]

Cherokee County Chamber of Commerce (CCCC) [55660]

Cherokee County Chamber of Commerce (CCCoC) [47659]

Cherokee County Directory [55661]

Cherokee County Genealogical-Historical Society Library [9492]

Cherokee Group Tour Manual [55662]

Cherokee Official Vacation Map and Directory [55663]

Cherokee Visitor Center Newsletter [55664]

Cherry County Historical Society [9493]

Cherry Hill Regional Chamber of Commerce - Greater Cherry Hill Chamber of Commerce [54683]

Cherry Tree Investments, Inc. [53775]

Cherryville Chamber of Commerce EDC [55665]

Chesaning Chamber of Commerce (CCC) [53211]

Chesapeake Bay Maritime Museum - Howard I. Chapelle Memorial Library [13976]

"Chesapeake Beach Resort and Spa Announces Dream Waterfront Wedding Giveaway" in Benzinga.com (October 29, 2011) [2494], [39765]

Cheshire Chamber of Commerce (CCC) [49684]

"Chesley Fighting Ky. Disbarment" in Business Courier (Vol. 27, September 10, 2010, No. 19, pp. 1) [23789], [30909], [33592]

Chester Chamber of Commerce [51020]

Chester County Chamber of Business and Industry (CCCBI) [57032]

Chester County Chamber of Commerce (CCCC) [57449]

Chester Engineers Inc. [7374]

Chester/Lake Almanor Chamber of Commerce [48456]

Chesterfield Chamber of Commerce (CCC) [54013]

Chesterfield County Chamber of Commerce [58891]

Chesterland Chamber of Commerce (CCC) [56087]

Chester's International, LLC [18103]

Chesterton and Duneland Chamber of Commerce (DCC) [51571]

Chetek Area Chamber of Commerce [59539]

Chetek Chamber of Commerce [59539]

Chetopa Chamber of Commerce [52077]

Diego Chevere & Co. [42319]

M.H. Chew & Associates Corporate Library [7399], [7726]

"Chew On This: Soul Fans to 'Chew' Games' First Play" in Philadelphia Business Journal (Vol. 30, September 30, 2011, No. 33, pp. 3) [19411], [39766], [41826]

Chewelah Chamber of Commerce (CCoC) [59150]

Cheyenne Business Weekly [59814]

Cheyenne County Chamber of Commerce (CCCC) [54380]

Cheyenne - Roger Mills Chamber of Commerce and Tourism [56488]

Chi Kung the Healing Workout [15995]

Chicago Apparel News [3903]

Chicago Area Gay and Lesbian Chamber of Commerce [51021]

"Chicago Botanic Garden Builds Green Research Facility" in Contractor (Vol. 56, December 2009, No. 12, pp. 5) [7504], [16225], [19082], [30536], [43820]

Chicago Chinatown Chamber of Commerce [51022]

Chicago Design Show [9077], [11572]

Chicago-Edison Electrical & Lighting [41583]

Chicago Home and Garden [9804], [11558]

Chicago JobBank: The Job Hunter's Guide to Metro Chicago [19172]

Chicago Minority Business Opportunity Center [51386]

Chicago Minority Supplier Development Council [51387]

Chicago Negro Chamber of Commerce [51054]

Chicago Park District - Garfield Park Conservatory [9133], [9848], [13450]

Chicago Public Library Central Library - Business/Science/Technology Division [3399], [37174], [38841], [40663], [41527], [44968]

Chicago Public Library - Visual & Performing Arts Division - Music Information Center [4628], [14678], [14768]

"Chicago Public School District Builds Green" in Contractor (Vol. 56, October 2009, No. 10, pp. 5) [799], [918], [5258], [6880], [30537]

Chicago SCORES [50867]

Chicago Southland Enterprise Center [51443]

Chicago State University - Office of Continuing Education [51458]

Chicago Technology Park Corp. [51444]

Chicagoland [14239], [14327]

Chicagoland Chamber of Commerce (CCoC) [51023]

Chickamauga Chamber of Commerce - Lafayette Chamber of Commerce - Rossville Chamber of Commerce [50631]

Chickasha Chamber of Commerce [56489]

Chicken Connection Franchise Corp. [18104]

Chicken Delight [16141], [18105]

Chico Business [48457]

Chico Chamber of Commerce [48458]

Chico SCORE [48184]

Chicopee Chamber of Commerce [52871]

"Chief Boo Boo Officer" in Marketing to Women (Vol. 21, February 2008, No. 2, pp. 1) [415], [34223], [39767], [43821]

Chief Culture Officer: How to Create a Living, Breathing Corporation [4092], [4207], [25841], [37879], [45335]

"Chiefs Hope Renovations Score Big With Sponsors" in The Business Journal-Serving Greater Kansas City (Vol. 26, July 11, 2008) [19322], [19412], [22820], [39768]

Child Care Bridges [3947]

Child Care Plus [3948]

"Child-Care Policy and the Labor Supply of Mothers with Young Children" in University of Chicago Press (Vol. 26, July 2008, No. 3) [3936], [23790], [45336]

Child Health Investment Company, LLC [52205]

Child Safety [3966]

Child Welfare: Journal of Policy, Practice, and Program [3949]

Child Welfare League of America (CWLA) [3923]

Child and Youth Services [34503]

Childersburg Chamber of Commerce (CCC) [47660]

Children's Book Insider [6835]

Children's Books in Print [2122], [2371]

Children's Defense Fund (CDF) [3924]

Children's Defense Fund of the Washington Research Project [3924]

"Children's Hospital to Build in New Berlin" in The Business Journal-Milwaukee (Vol. 25, August 1, 2008, No. 45, pp. A1) [5259], [16516], [17234]

"Children's Hospital to Grow" in Austin Business Journal (Vol. 31, July 22, 2011, No. 20, pp. A1) [5260], [22821], [34224]

Children's Lighthouse Franchise Co. [1672], [4009], [10508]

Children's Orchard [3915], [4303]

"Children's Products Maker Not the New Kid on the Block" in Crain's Cleveland Business (Vol. 28, November 26, 2007, No. 47, pp. 3) [22822], [24286], [25048], [25454], [26744], [38982]

The Children's Psychological Trauma Center [2841], [25969], [34619]

Children's Voice [34504]

ChildrensBooksInPrint.com™ [2406]

Childress Chamber of Commerce [58049]

Child's Play: The World of Learning [3967]

Chilean and American Chamber of Commerce of Greater Philadelphia (CACCGP) [57033]

Chilled Water Systems (Onsite) [24974], [28018]

Chillicothe Area Chamber of Commerce (CACC) [54014]

Chillicothe Chamber of Commerce (CCOC) [51024]

Chillicothe Ross Chamber of Commerce (CRCC) [56088]

Chilson's Management Controls Inc. [21766]

Chilton Chamber of Commerce [59540]

Chilton County Chamber of Commerce (CCCC) [47661]

Chimney Sweep Guild [4043]

Frederick Chin [40589]

"The China Connection" in Crain's Chicago Business (Vol. 31, March 24, 2008, No. 12, pp. 26) [27050], [28156], [28592], [36421]

China International Footwear Fair [18778]

The China Painter [6003]

"China Pegs Surplus at $101.9 Billion" in Globe & Mail (January 12, 2006, pp. B1) [27051], [36422]

"The China Syndrome" in Canadian Business (Vol. 79, July 17, 2006, No. 14-15, pp. 25) [22823], [32591], [41665]

"The China Tax" in Forbes (Vol. 180, October 1, 2007, No. 6, pp. 35) [20236], [36423], [46187]

"China Trade Deficit Costs California Jobs" in Sacramento Business Journal (Vol. 25, August 8, 2008, No. 23, pp. 1) [11069], [27052], [36424]

"China Vs. the World: Whose Technology Is It?" in Harvard Business Review (Vol. 88, December 2010, No. 12, pp. 94) [11070], [23791], [33593], [34829], [36425], [41827]

"China Wind Power Generates Stronger First Quarter Results" in Marketwire Canada (September 28, 2011) [7142], [7505], [30538]

"China's Dagong Show" in Canadian Business (Vol. 83, August 17, 2010, No. 13-14, pp. 15) [6281], [26166], [27053], [36426]

China's Rational Entrepreneurs: The Development of the New Private Business Sector [29576], [32592], [36427]

"China's Transition to Green Energy Systems" in Energy Policy (Vol. 39, October 2011, No. 10, pp. 5909-5919) [7143], [7506], [19083], [30539], [33594], [36428]

"China's ZTE in Hunt for Partners" in Globe & Mail (February 27, 2006, pp. B1) [22824], [24287], [41828]

Chinatown Chamber of Commerce [51022]

Chincoteague Chamber of Commerce (CCC) [58892]

Chinese for Affirmative Action [35534]

Chinese Ethnic Business [36429], [40715], [40869]

Chinese Ethnic Business: Global and Local Perspectives [27054], [33595], [36430], [40870]

"Chinese Fund Loans $33.5 Million to Prestolite" in Crain's Detroit Business (Vol. 26, January 18, 2010, No. 3, pp. 1) [11071], [14879], [26745], [36431], [37334], [38983], [41021]

"Chinese Solar Panel Manufacturer Scopes Out Austin" in Austin Business JournalInc. (Vol. 29, October 30, 2009, No. 34, pp. 1) [5261], [7144], [7507], [19084], [25455], [30540], [36432], [38984], [44653]

Chino Valley Area Chamber of Commerce [47885]

Chino Valley Chamber of Commerce [48459]

The Chino Valley Connection [47886]

"Chino Valley Ranches: a Family of Farmers" in Retail Merchandiser (Vol. 51, September-October 2011, No. 5, pp. 79) [21543], [30910], [31036]

Chip Chats [6004]

CHIP - The Child ID Program [4010]

Chippewa Falls Area Chamber of Commerce [59541]

"The Chips Are In" in Business Journal-Portland (Vol. 24, November 2, 2007, No. 35, pp. 1) [34830], [47001]

Chisholm Area Chamber of Commerce (CACC) [53618]

Chisholm Private Capital Partners [56616]

CHL Medical Partners / Collinson, Howe, and Lennox [49774]

Chloride Chamber of Commerce (CCC) [47887]

Chocolate Chocolate Chocolate Co. [10953]

Choctaw Chamber of Commerce [56490]

"Choice Bits" in Crain's Cleveland Business (Vol. 30, June 29, 2009, No. 25, pp. 19) [17895], [25733], [29577]

Choice Hotels Canada Inc. [10799]

Choice Hotels International [10800]

Choice Voice [59815]

Choices [26682], [40927]

Choices: How to Control Internal Shrink [29297]

Choose Your Weapon [10037]

Choosing Careers [3373]

Choosing a Job [3374]

Choosing the Right Legal Form of Business: The Complete Guide to Becoming a Sole Proprietor, Partnership, LLC, or Corporation [23792], [36082], [43322], [46041]

"Choosing Strategies For Change" in Harvard Business Review (Vol. 86, July-August 2008, No. 8, pp. 130) [24288], [25049], [32593], [37880]

"Chopping Option Added to Calmer Corn Head Kits" in Farm Industry News (January 16, 2011) [21544], [41022]

Chouteau Chamber of Commerce [56491]

Chow! A Nutrition Curriculum [15182]

CHRIE Member Directory & Resource Guide [10679], [17902]

"Chris Curtis Preaches the Gospel of Internet Success" in Black Enterprise (Vol. 38, March 2008, No. 8, pp. 56) [11645], [21065], [22825], [28593]

Chris Frings & Associates [46085]

"Christ Hospital to Expand" in Business Courier (Vol. 27, June 25, 2010, No. 8, pp. 3) [5262], [22826], [34225], [35296], [42973]

Christian Booksellers Association [2356]

Christian Booksellers Association International Convention [2403]

Christian Camp & Conference Journal [3269]

Christian Camping International/USA [3247]

Christmas in Cape May [54698]

Christmas Decor Inc. [4049], [4059]

Christmas Gift and Hobby Show [4046], [6043], [6156]

Christmas Trees: World's Leading Christmas Tree Magazine [4053]

Chronicle [48460]

Chronicle Newsletter [52872]

The Chronicle of Philanthropy: The Newspaper of the Non-Profit World [9287]

Chrysalis Ventures [52392]

"Chrysler Unions Set Up Roadblocks to Private Equity" in Globe & Mail (March 20, 2007, pp. B3) [38985], [46853]

Chuck Spicer's Coastline [50034]

"Chuck's Big Chance" in Barron's (Vol. 89, July 13, 2009, No. 28, pp. L3) [8182], [12172], [31316], [41023]

Chugiak-Eagle River Business & Service Directory [47789]

Chugiak-Eagle River Chamber of Commerce [47790]

Chula Vista Chamber of Commerce [48461]

Kelley Chunn & Associates (KCA) [40590], [42547]

Church of Jesus Christ of Latter-Day Saints - Cleveland, Ohio Stake Family History Center [9494]

Church of Jesus Christ of Latter-day Saints - Valley Forge, Pennsylvania Stake - Family History Center [9495]

Churchill County Chamber of Commerce [54493]

Churchill County Nevada Small Business Development Center [54456]

Church's Chicken [18106]

Churro; Navajosa [1012]

John Chute & Associates [22046]

"Chuy's Gears Up to Serve Atlants, Other Untapped Cities" in Austin Business Journal (Vol. 31, June 17, 2011, No. 15, pp. 1) [17896], [22827], [24726], [44654]

Chyten Educational Services [20741]

"CIBC Spends $1.1 Billion on Caribbean Expansion" in Globe & Mail (March 14, 2006, pp. B1) [8183], [12173], [22828], [24289], [41829]

Cicero Chamber of Commerce and Industry [51025]

CiCi's Pizza [16142], [18107]

Cigar Aficionado [20092]

Cigars 101 [20106]

CIGNA Corporation Philadelphia Research Library [47536]

Cimarron Chamber of Commerce [52078]; [54945]

Cimarron County Chamber of Commerce (CCCC) [56492]

Cincinnati Better Business Bureau [55993]

Cincinnati Golf Show [9678]

Cincinnati Home and Garden Show [9827]

Cincinnati Travel, Sports, and Boat Show [1727], [13961], [19370]

Cincinnati U.S.A. Business Connections Directory [56089]

Cincinnati USA Regional Chamber [56149]

Cincinnati Wedding [2532]

"Cincinnati's Senior Moment" in Business Courier (Vol. 27, June 11, 2010, No. 6, pp. 1) [5263], [45337]

Cincy Business Magazine: The Magazine for Business Professionals [33077]

"Cineplex Sees Past the Big Picture" in Globe & Mail (February 8, 2007, pp. B9) [942], [7911], [22829], [25050]

Cinescope [14560]

Cini-Little International Inc. [3480], [10790], [18048]

Cinnzeo [1732], [1802]

Circle Chamber of Commerce and Agriculture [54260]

Circle K [5824]

Circleville - Pickaway Chamber of Commerce [56090]

Cisco Chamber of Commerce (CCC) [58050]

Cisco Network Design Solutions for Small-Medium Businesses [3703], [4798], [4846], [4942], [5033], [11646], [26401], [41394]

Cisco Networking Introduction: Hands-On (Onsite) [30389]

CISM Journal ACSGC [19530]

CIT Group / Venture Capital [54844]

"Citadel Hires Three Lehman Execs" in Chicago Tribune (October 2, 2008) [8184], [12174], [24290], [25051], [25456], [31317], [35297], [37881]

"Citi Ruling Could Chill SEC, Street Legal Pacts" in Wall Street Journal Eastern Edition (November 29, 2011, pp. C1) [8185], [12175], [14397], [23793], [30911], [31318]

CitiBank Technical Library [5065]

Cities from the Arabian Desert: The Building of Jubail and Yanbu in Saudi Arabia [32594], [33596], [36433], [45338]

Cities on the Move: Alabaster/Pelham/Helena [47662]

"Cities Work to Attract Small Biz" in Crain's Detroit Business (Vol. 25, June 8, 2009, No. 23, pp. 20) [24727], [44655]

"Citigroup Moves to Buy Japan's Nikko" in Globe & Mail (March 7, 2007, pp. B12) [8186], [12176], [41830]

Citizen's Association [51070]

Citizens Budget Commission (CBC) [42424]

Citizens for Tax Justice (CTJ) [19777]

"Citizens Unveils Mobile App for Business Customers" in New Hampshire Business Review (Vol. 33, March 25, 2011, No. 6, pp. 27) [3704], [8187], [26167], [31319]

Citrus County Chamber of Commerce [50035]

Citrus County Chamber of Commerce, Crystal River [50036]

Citrus Heights Chamber of Commerce [48462]

City of Batesville/Independence County Maps [48033]

"City Board Tweaks Internet Cafe Ordinance" in Ocala Star-Banner (July 19, 2011) [9700], [17897], [33597], City of Cleveland - Office of Equal Opportunities [56358]

City College of City University of New York - Art Visual Resources Library [1327], [11583]

City College of San Francisco - Department - Culinary Arts and Hospitality Studies Alice Statler Library [3485], [5850], [10326], [10828], [18301]

"City Consults Executives on Police Hire" in Business Courier (Vol. 27, August 27, 2010, No. 17, pp. 1) [33598], [35298], [35727], [37882], [42370]

City of Corpus Christi Economic Development Division [58532]

"City Council Committee Votes Against Establishing Small and Minority Business Fund" in Commercial Appeal (November 10, 2010) [33171], [40716]

City and County Map [53619]

City/County Maps [47663]

"City, County May Kill VC Tax" in Business Journal-Portland (Vol. 24, October 12, 2007, No. 33, pp. 1) [24728], [46188], [47002]

City Directory [50037]; [51026]

City of Eden [58051]

"City Eyeing Tax Breaks for Arena" in Boston Business Journal (Vol. 29, June 3, 2011, No. 4, pp. 1) [5264], [10670], [19413], [33172], [37335], [46189]

The City Haller [54015]

"City Hopes Casino Will Be $333M Jackpot" in Business First Buffalo (October 5, 2007, pp. 1) [9390], [10671], [17898]

City of Industry News [48463]

City of Jackson Economic Development Division - Equal Business Opportunity [53913]

City Kitchen [3481]

City Looks [10088]

City Map [48464]; [48465]; [48466]; [53620]; [58052]

City Map/Business and Tourist Directory [48467]

City of Oilton Council [56493]

"City a Pawn in Airlines' Chess Game" in Business Courier (Vol. 24, January 18, 2008, No. 41, pp. 1) [24834], [27055], [41831], [44294]

"City Plans Downtown Congestion Fees" in Crain's Chicago Business (Vol. 31, May 5, 2008, No. 18, pp. 12) [24835], [33173]

City Publications [672]

City and Regional Magazine Association (CRMA) [15497]

City of Ridgeland Chamber of Commerce [53841]

"City Seeks More Minorities" in Austin Business JournalInc. (Vol. 28, November 7, 2008, No. 34, pp. A1) [5265], [33409], [40717], [44295], [47246]

"City Sets Yamhill Makeover" in The Business Journal-Portland (Vol. 25, July 4, 2008, No. 17, pp. 1) [5266], [16849], [17235], [27056], [33174], [44821]

"City Slickers" in Canadian Business (Vol. 81, March 31, 2008, No. 5, pp. 36) [4462], [5974], [11072], [27057], [29578], [36434], [39769], [42614]

City of South Houston Chamber of Commerce (CSHCC) [58053]

"City Struggles to Iron Out Tangled Transportation" in Crain's New York Business (Vol. 24, January 14, 2008, No. 2, pp. 33) [5267], [24291], [24836], [32595]

City Wide Maintenance Franchise Co. [2651]

City Wok [18108]

"City Wooing Red Roof Inn for Return of Corporate HQ" in Business First-Columbus (October 19, 2007, pp. A1) [10672], [24729], [44656]

CityArt Magazine: A Contemporary Review of the Visual Arts [1363], [1411], [6005]

Citylife [58054]

CityLine [48468]

"CityLink Project On Hold" in Business Courier (Vol. 24, November 9, 2008, No. 30, pp. 3) [5268], [17236], [23794], [24292], [33599]

"City's Hilton Hotel Still Losing Money" in Baltimore Business Journal (Vol. 28, October 15, 2010, No. 23, pp. 1) [10673], [46619]

"City's New Energy Audits to Spawn 'Fantastic' Market" in Austin Business JournalInc. (Vol. 28, November 14, 2008, No. 35, pp. 1) [7145], [7508], [30541], [33600]

"City's Streetcar Utility Estimate Way Off Mark" in Business Courier (Vol27, November 19, 2010, No. 29., pp. 1) [19807], [33175], [42371], [44657]

Civic Club and Organizational Directory [53842]

Civic and Organization Guide [51572]

"Civil Council Almost On Board With Light Rail Plan" in The Business Journal-Serving Metropolitan Kansas City (September 5, 2008) [5269], [24293], [24837], [25052]

Civil Engineering News [5577], [19529]

CJO [20916]

CKO Kickboxing [16018]

CLA Member Journal [6747]

Clackamas Community College Small Business Development Center [56672]

Claes Fornell International [25965], [29238], [36015], [38683]

Claiborne Chamber of Commerce [52453]
Claiborne County Chamber of Commerce (CCCC)
[57681]
CLAIMS® Citation Database [37169]
Clairol Research Library [2068], [5919], [10109]
Clairvest Group Inc. [59923]
Clallam Bay - Sekiu Chamber of Commerce [59151]
Clapp and Mayne Library [14067]
Clare Area Chamber of Commerce [53212]
Claremont Consulting Group [2842], [13812], [25970],
[38686], [45250]
Claremore Chamber of Commerce [56494]
Clarence Chamber of Commerce [55163]
Clarendon Chamber of Commerce (CCC) [48034]
Clarendon County Chamber of Commerce (CCCC)
[57450]
Clarinda Association of Business and Industry [51863]
Clarinda Chamber of Commerce (CABI) [51863]
The Clarion [48469]
Clarion Area Chamber of Business and Industry [57034]
Clarion Capital Corp. [56363]
Clarion University Small Business Development Center
[56905]
Claritas Demographics [1173], [27917]
Claritas Update Demographics [1173], [27917]
Clark Consulting International Inc. [21772]
CLark County Chamber of Commerce [51719]
Clark University - George Perkins Marsh Institute -
Center for Technology, Environment, and Development
(CENTED) [7739]
Clarkdale Chamber of Commerce [47888]
Clarke County Chamber of Commerce [53843]
Clarkesville-Habersham County Library [9496]
Clarkesville Lake Country Chamber of Commerce
[58893]
Clarksburg Area Chamber of Commerce [59407]
Clarksdale - Coahoma County Chamber of Commerce
and Industry Foundation (CCCCCIF) [53844]
Clarkston Area Chamber of Commerce [53213]
Clarkston Chamber of Commerce (CCC) [59152]
Clarksville Area Chamber of Commerce [57682]
Clarksville Chamber of Commerce [58405]
Clarksville-Johnson County Chamber of Commerce
[48035]
"Clash of the Titans" in Canadian Business (Vol. 80,
March 12, 2007, No. 6, pp. 27) [8188], [12177],
[25457], [34831], [36978]
"A Class Act" in Hawaii Business (Vol. 53, March 2008,
No. 9, pp. 25) [11647], [15522], [21066], [28157],
[44759]
Class Action Litigation Report® [24137]
"Class Management" in Canadian Business (Vol. 80,
April 23, 2007, No. 9, pp. 64) [28158], [29031],
[37883]
A Classic Guide to Custom Deli Trays [6443]
*"The Classless Workplace: The Digerati and the New
Spirit of Technocapitalism"* in WorkingUSA (Vol. 11,
June 2008, No. 2, pp. 181) [29579], [30912], [32596],
[35728]
*The Classroom Collection, Vol. 2: Basic Daylight
Exposure and Equivalent Exposures* [15865]
*The Classroom Collection, Vol. 3: Metering and
Exposure Controls* [15866]
*The Classroom Collection, Vol. 4: Advanced Camera
Techniques* [15867]
*The Classroom Collection, Vol. 5: Black and White
Techniques* [15868]
*The Classroom Collection, Vol. 6: Careers in
Photography* [15869]
Clatskanie Chamber of Commerce [56759]
Clatskanie Chamber Newsletter [56760]
Clatsop Community College Small Business Develop-
ment Center [56673]
Claude Travis & Associates [20722]
Clavier [14636]
Claxton-Evans County Chamber of Commerce [50498]
Clay Center Area Chamber of Commerce [52079]
Clay County Chamber of Commerce [55666]
Clay County Chamber of Commerce (CCCC) [50038]
Clay County Chamber of Commerce, Alabama [47664]
Clay County Partnership Chamber of Commerce [57683]
"Clay Riddell" in Canadian Business (Vol. 80, February
12, 2007, No. 4, pp. 86) [29580], [37884], [38986]
Claymore Engineering [47516]
Clayton Chamber of Commerce (CCC) [54016]; [55667]
Clayton Chamber of Commerce [55073]
Clayton County Chamber of Commerce [50499]
Clayton/Curtis/Cottrell [2843], [24663], [25971], [32014],
[40591], [44924]
Clayton State University Small Business Development
Center [50389]
Clayton-Union County Chamber of Commerce [54946]
Clayton Vacation Guide [55164]

C.L.C. Fax-Press [26837], [46808]
Cle Elum-Roslyn Chamber of Commerce (CECC)
[59153]
*"Clean Bathrooms Are Big Key to Convenience Store's
Success"* in Marketing to Women (Vol. 23, January
2010, No. 1, pp. 3) [5797], [22830], [39770]
Clean Cut Lawn and Garden Services [13516]
Clean Energy Incubator [58592]
Clean First Time, Inc. [13896]
Clean, Fresh & Friendly [6444], [43712]
Clean & Happy Windows [2652]
Clean Living Specialists [2653]
Clean Show - World Educational Congress for Launder-
ing and Drycleaning [6753]
"Clean-Tech Focus Sparks Growth" in Philadelphia Busi-
ness Journal (Vol. 28, January 15, 2010, No. 48, pp. 1)
[7146], [7509], [22831], [27058], [30542], [41832]
*"Clean Wind Energy Tower Transitions from R&D Stage
Company"* in Professional Services Close-Up
(September 30, 2011) [5270], [7147], [7510], [25842],
[30543], [42775], [43822]
"Cleaner and Greener" in Canadian Business (Vol. 80,
February 12, 2007, No. 4, pp. 45) [30544], [33176],
[43823]
The Cleaning Authority [2654], [6570]
Cleaning Business Magazine [2638], [6568], [20831],
[59361]
Cleaning Consultant Services Inc. [2655], [6571],
[13897]
Cleaning Consultant Services Inc. (CCS) [2638], [6568],
[20831], [59361]
Cleaning Management Institute (CMI) [2597]
Cleaning & Restoration [6358], [20827]
"Cleaning Up" in Small Business Opportunities (Get Rich
At Home 2010) [3324], [31037], [32089]
Cleaning Up Toxics [30877]
Cleannet USA, Inc. [2656]
"Cleanup to Polish Plating Company's Bottom Line" in
Crain's Cleveland Business (Vol. 28, October 29, 2007,
No. 43, pp. 4) [24294], [33177], [37336], [38987]
Clear Business, Technical, and E-mail Writing [22560]
Clear Lake Area Chamber of Commerce (CLACC)
[51864]
Clear Lake Chamber of Commerce [48470]
Clear Lake Chamber Newsletter [48471]
Clear Light Books [26809]
Clear Light Publishers [26809]
"ClearEdge Hums Along" in Business Journal Portland
(Vol. 26, December 18, 2009, No. 41, pp. 1) [22832],
[35299], [47003]
Clearfield Chamber of Commerce [57035]
Clearstone Venture Partners / Idealab! Capital Partners
[49194]
Clearwater Regional Chamber of Commerce [50039]
Cleburne Chamber of Commerce [58055]
Clements Lockeford Chamber of Commerce (CLCC)
[48472]
Mark Clements Research Inc. [14039]
Clemson Area Chamber of Commerce [57451]
Clemson Area Small Business Development Center
[57403]
Clemson University - College of Health, Education & Hu-
man Development Learning Resource Center [15124]
Clermont Area Chamber of Commerce [50297]
Clermont County Chamber of Commerce (CCC) [56091]
Cleveland Area Chamber of Commerce [56495]
Cleveland-Bolivar County Chamber of Commerce
(CBCCC) [53845]
Cleveland Botanical Garden - Eleanor Squire Library
[9849], [10372], [13451]
Cleveland/Bradley Chamber of Commerce [57684]
Cleveland Chamber of Commerce [59542]
Cleveland County Chamber of Commerce [55668]
Cleveland County Chamber of Commerce (Kings
Mountain, North Carolina) [55669]
Cleveland FES Center (FESC) [16107]
Cleveland Health Sciences Library [15215]
Cleveland Institute of Art - Jessica R. Gund Memorial
Library [4565], [6075]
Cleveland Institute of Music - Robinson Music Library
[14679]
Cleveland Public Library - Cleveland Research Center
(CRC) [40667]
Cleveland Public Library - Literature Department [2222],
[6860], [20812]
Cleveland Public Library - Science and Technology
Department [1037]
Cleveland Sport, Travel & Outdoor Show [1728], [3871]
The Clevelander-Growth Association [56416]
Clevenger Associates [10791], [18049]
Clevenger Frable Lavalle Inc. [10791], [18049]
Clewiston Chamber of Commerce [50040]
Clewiston Chamber of Commerce Newsletter [50041]

"Click Here to Book" in Caterer & Hotelkeeper (October
28, 2011, No. 288) [10674], [21067], [28594], [43417]
*"A Click In the Right Direction: Website Teaches Youth
Financial Literacy"* in Black Enterprise (Vol. 38,
December 2007, No. 5) [12178], [21068], [28595],
[31320], [43824]
*"ClickFuel Launches New Products to Help Small and
Mid-Sized Businesses Bolster Their Brand Online"* in
Internet Wire (Dec. 3, 2009) [3518], [11649], [18880],
[39772], [41025], [45106]
*"ClickFuel Launches New Products to Help Small and
Mid-Sized Businesses Bolster Their Brand Online"* in
Internet Wire (Dec. 3,2009) [3517], [11648], [18879],
[39771], [41024], [45105]
*"ClickFuel Unveils Internet Marketing Tools for Small
Businesses"* in Internet Wire (October 19, 2009)
[3519], [11650], [18881], [22833], [28596], [39773],
[45107], [45339]
*Clicking Through: A Survival Guide for Bringing Your
Company Online* [11651], [21069], [23795], [28597],
[36979]
"Clicks For Cash: Earning More From Your Website" in
Inc. (December 2007, pp. 64-65) [416], [21070],
[28598], [39774]
*"Clicks From Round the World: Simplifying International
E-Commerce"* in Inc. (Volume 32, December 2010, No.
10, pp. 146) [22834], [28599], [36435]
ClieNT Server News [5042]
Clifton Chamber of Commerce [58056]
Clifton Chamber of Commerce and the Passaic Valley
Chamber of Commerce [54782]
Clifton Springs Area Chamber of Commerce (CSCOC)
[55165]
Clifton-Passaic Regional Chamber of Commerce [54782]
"Climate Law Could Dig into our Coal-Dusted Pockets" in
Business Courier (Vol. 26, November 20, 2009, No. 30,
pp. 1) [7148], [7511], [23796], [30545], [33601]
*"Climate Right Systems Provides Pre-Assembled Equip-
ment Packages"* in Contractor (Vol. 56, July 2009, No.
7, pp. 1) [800], [16226], [18680], [22835]
Climatic Test Techniques (Onsite) [30446]
"Climbing the Wall of Worry, Two Steps at a Time" in
Barron's (Vol. 89, July 13, 2009, No. 28, pp. L16)
[8189], [12179], [31321]
*"Clinic to Use Medical Summit to Pump Up Cardiology
Center"* in Crain's Cleveland Business (Vol. 28,
October 1, 2007, No. 39, pp. 6) [20338], [24730],
[34226], [39775], [46620]
Clinical Chemistry News [34505]
*Clinical Gerontologist: The Journal of Aging and Mental
Health* [309], [15091]
Clinical and Investigative Medicine [34132]
Clinical Journal of Sport Medicine [16068]
Clinical Laboratory Management Association (CLMA)
[14267]
Clinical Laboratory Management Review [34506]
Clinical Laboratory News [34505]
Clinical and Laboratory Standards Institute (CLSI)
[14268]
Clinical Leadership and Management Review: CLMR
[34506]
Clinical Pharmacology™ [6702]
Clinical Practice Guidelines [34133]
Clintar Groundskeeping Services [2657], [13438],
[13517]
Clinton [54017]
Clinton Area Chamber of Commerce [55670]
Clinton Area Chamber of Commerce [51865]; [54018]
Clinton Area Chamber of Commerce (CACC) [51027]
Clinton Chamber of Commerce [48036]; [49685];
[56496]
Clinton Chamber of Commerce (CCC) [53846]; [55166]
Clinton Chamber of Commerce [51027]
Clinton Connection [56497]
Clinton County Chamber of Commerce (CCCC) [51573]
Clinton County Chamber of Commerce [53430]; [57036];
[57647]
Clinton County Economic Partnership (CCEP) [57036]
Clinton-Sampson Chamber of Commerce (CACC)
[55671]
Clintonville Area Chamber of Commerce [59543]
CLIX [4011]
CLMA/ASCP Annual Conference and Exhibition [Thin-
kLab] [14293]
"Clock Ticking for Hotel Berry" in Sacramento Business
Journal (Vol. 25, July 25, 2008, No. 21, pp. 1) [5271],
[17237], [33178], [46190]
"Clock Ticks On Columbia Sussex Debt" in Business
Courier (Vol. 27, July 30, 2010, No. 13, pp. 1) [6282],
[10675], [26168], [31322], [37337]
Cloquet Area Chamber of Commerce [53621]
Close Up [57685]
"Closed Minds and Open Skies" in Barron's (Vol. 88,
March 10, 2008, No. 10, pp. 50) [11073], [27059],
[36436], [38988], [41666]

Closer Look [57575]
Closet Factory [16491]
Closets by Design Franchising [16492]
Closets & Storage Concepts [16493]
"Closing the Marketing Capabilities Gap" in *Journal of Marketing* (Vol. 75, July 2011, No. 4, pp. 183) [39776], [45340]
"Closures Pop Cork on Wine Bar Sector Consolidation" in *Houston Business Journal* (Vol. 40, January 22, 2010, No. 37, pp. A2) [1838], [19217], [25458], [41833]
Cloth by the Yard [4153]
Clothes Mentor [7865]
Clothes That Fit [4154]
"Clothier Delays Opening" in *The Business Journal-Serving Metropolitan Kansas City* (Vol. 27, November 14, 2008, No. 10, pp. 1) [4208], [24295], [25053], [27060], [42974]
Clothing Around the World [4155]
Clothing and Fashion: A History [4156]
Clothing Manufacturers Association--News Bulletin [4146]
Cloudcroft Chamber of Commerce (CCC) [54947]
"Clouds in the Forecast" in *Information Today* (Vol. 28, September 2011, No. 8, pp. 10) [3520], [4697], [4943], [18882], [45108], [45341]
"Cloudy Future for VMware?" in *Barron's* (Vol. 90, September 13, 2010, No. 37, pp. 21) [4698], [4847], [12180], [25459], [28600]
"Cloudy Skies" in *Canadian Business* (Vol. 81, October 27, 2008, No. 18, pp. 101) [7149], [7512], [30546], [33602]
Clough Harbor & Associates Library [20997]
Cloverdale Area Chamber of Commerce (CACC) [51574]
Cloverdale Chamber of Commerce [48473]
Clovis Chamber of Commerce and Economic Development [54948]
Clovis - Curry County Chamber of Commerce [54948]
Clovis Directory and Visitor Guide [48474]
Clovis District Chamber of Commerce [48475]
Clovis Small Business Development Center [54896]
Clown Club of America [15410]
Clowns of America International (COAI) [15410]
Clowns of America [15410]
Club 50 Fitness [16019]
Club Canin Canadien [1001]
Club List [56092]
Club and Organizations Directory [55672]
Club Scientific [28454]
Club Z! In-Home Tutoring [20742]
Clubs and Associations [55673]
Clubs and Civic Organizations [53214]
Clubs and Organization [57037]
Clubs and Organization Listings [55167]
Clubs and Organizations [57038]; [58057]; [58058]
Clubs and Organizations Directory [48476]; [52454]; [53215]; [57039]; [58059]
Clubs and Organizations List [55168]
Clued In [26402], [43418]
"Cluster Truck Events Updates on Curbside Dining Sweeps in Las Vegas" in *Food & Beverage Close-Up* (November 4, 2011) [9148], [17899]
"Clusters Last Stand?" in *Canadian Electronics* (Vol. 23, February 2008, No. 1, pp. 6) [5737], [20339], [33603], [34832], [36980], [46621]
CM Advisor [5579]
C.M. Co. St. Maps & Guide [54699]
CM Equity Partners, L.P. [55402]
Cm It Solutions [4811]
CM News [14114]
CMA Management Magazine [29]
CMA Ontario - Member Services Centre [269], [13231], [13903], [19749]
The CMA Today: Professional Medical Assistant [34507]
CMC Inc. [21766]
CMC's Course on Financial Analysis (Onsite) (Canada) [21328]
CMD Group [5629]
CMEA Capital / Chemicals & Materials Enterprise Association [49195]
CMIT Solutions [4778], [35636]
"The CMO of Consequence" in *Business Strategy Review* (Vol. 21, Autumn 2010, No. 3, pp. 42) [37885], [39777], [42776], [43825]
"CMO Nicholson Exits Pepsi as Share Declines" in *Advertising Age* (Vol. 79, July 7, 2008, No. 26, pp. 4) [417], [12181], [37886], [38989], [39778]
CMP Books [49396]
"CMS Products and Aveco Team for Business Security Product Solutions" in *Wireless News* (November 11, 2009) [4699], [4799], [18403], [41834]
CMX - CIPHEX National Tradeshow and Learning Forum [16290]

"CN Aims for Regional Pacts to Halt Labor Row" in *Globe & Mail* (April 17, 2007, pp. B2) [41321], [46854]
"CN 'Extremely Optimistic' After Record Profit" in *Globe & Mail* (January 24, 2007, pp. B3) [12182], [31323], [41322]
The CN Journal [4340]
"CN Profit a Boon for Top Brass" in *Globe & Mail* (March 23, 2007, pp. B5) [22836], [37887]
"CN Rail Strike Ends With Fragile Truce" in *Globe & Mail* (February 26, 2007, pp. B1) [32597], [46855]
"CN to Webcast 2007 Analyst Meeting in Toronto May 23-24" in *Canadian Corporate News* (May 16, 2007) [11652], [12183], [25054], [34833], [37888]
CNA Members' Bulletin [15498]
Cnez Nous, At Home [10521]
"CNinsure Offers Safety in Numbers" in *Barron's* (Vol. 90, September 13, 2010, No. 37, pp. 29) [8190], [11324], [12184], [22837], [36121], [36437]
CNLA Newsbrief [9761], [13369]
CNQ Market Data Feed [8938], [13201]
"CO2 Emissions Embodied in China-US Trade" in *Energy Policy* (Vol. 39, October 2011, No. 10, pp. 5980-5987) [7150], [7513], [30547], [33604], [36438]
Coach Curry's Quarterback Clinic: Developing the Quarterback [19359]
Coachella Valley SCORE [48185]
Coachella Valley Small Business Development Center [48145]
Coaching: A Strategic Tool for Effective Leadership (Onsite) (Canada) [37593]
Coaching for Business Results: A Hands-On Practical Workshop (Onsite) [37594]
Coaching and Counseling for Outstanding Job Performance (Onsite) [37595]
Coaching, Mentoring & Team-Building Skills (Onsite) [37596]
Coaching Skills: Developing a Better Employee [29201]
Coaching and Teambuilding Skills for Managers and Supervisors (Onsite) [28976]
Coaching for Top Performance [29202]
CoachMeFit [16020]
The Coach's 10 Commandments of Positive Athletic Parenting [19360]
Coahoma County Business Development Center [53925]
Coahoma County Chamber of Commerce [53844]
Coahoma County Industrial Foundation [53844]
Coalition Canadienne de la Sante [34112]
Coalition for Common Sense in Government Procurement [33391]
Coalition for Jobs, Peace, and Freedom in the Americas [2937], [26066], [42414]
Coalition for Scenic Beauty - National Coalition to Preserve Scenic Beauty [42588]
Coalition for Government Procurement (CGP) [33391]
Coalition of Service Industries (CSI) [44232]
Coast Commerce [47665]
Coastal Carolina SCORE [55550]
Coastal Chamber of Commerce [54591]
"Coastal Luxury Management Reports Los Angeles Food and Wine Tickets On Sale" in *Food & Beverage Close-Up* (August 24, 2011) [1501], [9149], [9247]
Coastal Training Technologies Corp. [26701]
Coastlines [50042]; [52873]
Cobb Chamber of Commerce [50500]
Cobscook Bay Area Chamber of Commerce (CBACC) [52583]
Coby Chamber Communicator [52080]
"Coca-Cola Bottler Up for Sale: CEO J. Bruce Llewellyn Seeks Retirement" in *Black Enterprise* (Vol. 37, December 2006, No. 5, pp. 31) [9918], [25460], [36083], [38990], [40718], [44144]
Coca-Cola Company - The INFOSOURCE [1886], [2426], [9192]
"Coca-Cola Looks Ready to Pause" in *Barron's* (Vol. 88, March 10, 2008, No. 10, pp. 18) [8191], [12185], [21545], [22838], [31324], [38991]
Cocciardi & Associates Inc. [47517]
Cochise College Small Business Development Center [47832]
BJ Cockrell Real Estate Appraisal & Consulting [38687]
Cocktails Magazine [1870], [2472]
Cocoa Beach Area Chamber of Commerce (CBACC) [50043]
Coconino Community College Small Business Development Center [47833]
Coconut Grove Chamber of Commerce [50044]
"The Code-Cracker" in *Business Courier* (Vol. 24, January 11, 2008, No. 40, pp. 1) [38992], [41026], [43826]
Code of Federal Regulations: Title 13: Business Credit and Assistance [27061], [31325], [32598], [33179], [33605]
"Code Name: Investors: Go From Golden Idea to Agent of Invention" in *Black Enterprise* (Vol. 41, November 2010, No. 4, pp. 78) [10129], [29581], [36981]

Cody Country Chamber of Commerce (CCCC) [59816]
Coeur d'Alene Area Chamber of Commerce (CDACC) [50755]
Coffee Association of Canada (CAC) [9691]
Coffee Beanery [4323], [9729]
Coffee News [9730], [15026]
Coffee Perks [9180]
Coffee Time Donuts Inc. [1803], [6461], [9731]
Coffey County Chamber of Commerce [52081]
Coffeyville Chamber of Commerce (CCC) [52082]
Coffeyville Community College [52213]
"Cogeco Profit Jumps 47 Percent in First Quarter" in *Globe & Mail* (January 13, 2006, pp. B3) [8192], [12186], [22839]
Cognetics Corp. [3656]
Cogswell College Library [47537]
Cogswell Polytechnical College. [47537]
John Alan Cohan [19709], [24664], [32015]
Cohasset Chamber of Commerce [52874]
Cohen & Associates [36912]
Jonathan Cohen and Associates, Architects and Planners (JC&A) [1302]
"Coherent Laying Off 144 As It Prepares To Shut Auburn Plant" in *Sacramento Business Journal* (Vol. 25, August 1, 2008, No. 22, pp. 1) [12187], [16850], [17238], [22840], [46856]
Cohn Consulting Corp. (CCC) [41475], [41584]
The Coin Dealer Newsletter [4363]
Coin Laundries - Road to Financial Independence: A Complete Guide to Starting and Operating Profitable Self-Service Laundries [6735], [32366]
Coin Laundry Association (CLA) [6736]
Coin Laundry Association Supplier Directory [6741]
Coin Prices: Complete Guide to U.S Coin Values [4364]
Coin World: World's 1 Publication for Coin Collectors [4365]
The COINfidential Report [4366], [13115], [31986]
Coins Magazine [4367]
Coit Cleaning and Restoration Services [924], [2028], [20836]
Cokato Chamber of Commerce (CCC) [53622]
Colbert/Ball Tax Service [19715]
Colburn & Guyette Consulting Partners Inc. [6755]
Colby Area Chamber of Commerce [52083]
Colby College - Bixler Art and Music Library [1384]
Colby - Thomas County Chamber of Commerce [52083]
The Cold Call [8878], [13153], [43713]
Cold Spring - Garrison Area Chamber of Commerce [55169]
"Cold Stone Creamery" in *Ice Cream Reporter* (Vol. 22, January 20, 2009, No. 2, pp. 8) [10862], [22841], [32148], [36439]
"Cold Stone Creamery" in *Ice Cream Reporter* (Vol. 23, November 20, 2010, No. 12, pp. 6) [10863], [37889]
Cold Stone Creamery [10954]
"Cold Stone Creamery Offers New Eight-Layer Ice Cream Cakes" in *Ice Cream Reporter* (Vol. 23, October 20, 2010, No. 11, pp. 2) [1755], [10864], [41027]
"Cold Stone in Licensing Agreement with Turin Chocolates" in *Ice Cream Reporter* (Vol. 22, December 20, 2008, No. 1, pp. 2) [3284], [10865], [41028], [41835]
"Cold-Storage Cargo Facility a Late Bloomer" in *Houston Business Journal* (Vol. 40, August 28, 2009, No. 16, pp. 1A) [9100], [9203], [16650], [17765]
Coldspring Chamber of Commerce [58060]
Coldspring/San Jacinto County Chamber of Commerce (CCC) [58060]
Coldwater - Branch County Chamber of Commerce [53147]
Coldwater Chamber of Commerce (CCC) [52084]
Coldwell Banker Commercial United Realty Services [17584]
Monte G. Cole & Associates [7375]
Cole Financial Service Inc. [29240], [36016]
Cole Financial Services Inc. [29240], [36016]
Cole & Goyette Architects & Planners Inc. [41585]
Cole, Warren and Long Inc. (CWL) [42320]
Coleman Chamber of Commerce [58061]
Coleman County Chamber of Commerce, Agriculture and Tourist Bureau [58061]
Coleman County Chamber of Commerce and Agriculture [58061]
Coleman Foundation [46974]
Coleman Swenson Booth Inc. / Coleman Swenson Hoffman Booth [57809]
Colfax Area Chamber of Commerce [48477]
Colfax Chamber of Commerce [51866]
Colgate Palmolive Company Technology Information Center [2069], [5920]
Collaborative Leadership Skills for Managers (Onsite) [37597]
"Collateral Damage" in *Business Courier* (Vol. 26, October 16, 2009, No. 25, pp. 1) [5272], [23797], [33606], [35729], [46857]

Congestion MASTER INDEX

"Congestion Relief" in Canadian Business (Vol. 80, February 12, 2007, No. 4, pp. 31) **[24839]**, **[34838]**, **[42778]**
Congoleum Corporation Technical Research Library **[9087]**
"Congratulations to the 2010 Top Ten Business Women of ABWA" in Women In Business (Vol. 61, August-September 2009, No. 4, pp. 12) **[29593]**, **[32611]**, **[47251]**
"Congratulations to the 2012 Top Ten Business Women of ABWA" in Women In Business (Vol. 63, Fall 2011, No. 3, pp. 14) **[37897]**, **[47252]**
Congres du travail du Canada [26835], [46803]
"Congress Ponders Annuity Trusts" in National Underwriter Life & Health (Vol. 114, June 21, 2010, No. 12, pp. 10) **[33182]**, **[45350]**, **[46195]**
Congress Report **[15943]**
Congress on Research in Dance (CORD) **[6427]**
"Congress Targets Ad Tracking" in Inc. (Vol. 33, November 2011, No. 9, pp. 30) **[422]**, **[33621]**
Conifer Chamber of Commerce **[49481]**
ConnDOT Library and Information Center **[1646]**, **[6607]**, **[13547]**, **[19822]**
Conneaut Area Chamber of Commerce (CACC) **[56106]**
"Connect the Thoughts" in Canadian Business (Vol. 81, October 27, 2008, No. 18, pp. 8) **[8205]**, **[12199]**
Connected International Meeting Professionals Association (CIMPA) **[18531]**
Connected Planet: Intelligence for the Broadband Economy **[3843]**
Connecticut Business and Industry Association (CBIA) **[49688]**
Connecticut Center for Advanced Technology **[49793]**
Connecticut Craft Show **[6044]**
Connecticut Economic Resource Center **[49647]**
Connecticut Enterprise Center **[49794]**
Connecticut Food Association Convention **[10009]**
Connecticut Innovations, Inc. **[49775]**
Connecticut Judicial Branch - Putnam Law Library **[7758]**
Connecticut Procurement Technical Assistance Center - Outreach Office **[49787]**
Connecticut Procurement Technical Assistance Center - Small Business Development Procurement Center **[49788]**
Connecticut Small Business Development Center - Eastern Connecticut State University **[49644]**
Connecticut Small Business Development Center - Southern Connecticut State University **[49645]**
Connecticut Small Business Development Center - Western Connecticut State University **[49646]**
Connecticut Society of Certified Public Accountants - Education and Research Foundation **[2341]**
Connecticut Society of Genealogist Library **[9499]**
Connecticut State Library - History and Genealogy Unit **[9500]**
"Connecting the Dots Between Wellness and Elder Care" in Benefits and Compensation Digest (Vol. 47, August 2010, No. 8, pp. 18) **[293]**, **[1422]**, **[10530]**, **[11325]**, **[15066]**, **[21883]**, **[34231]**, **[35742]**, **[36122]**
Connecting Point **[47669]**
The Connecting Source **[58081]**
Connecting—Grades K-8 **[3969]**
Connection **[51051]**; **[51584]**; **[53231]**; **[53233]**; **[53625]**; **[57046]**; **[58083]**; **[58084]**; **[59158]**
The Connection **[48498]**; **[53232]**; **[53624]**; **[58082]**
The Connection Key: Seven Ways the World's Most Successful Entrepreneurs Trounce the Competition and How You Can, Too **[22852]**, **[25475]**, **[29594]**
CONNECTIONS **[17108]**
Connections **[26840]**; **[50701]**; **[50702]**; **[51871]**; **[53626]**; **[53850]**; **[54025]**; **[54026]**; **[55176]**; **[56107]**; **[57047]**; **[57048]**; **[57049]**; **[57370]**; **[57453]**; **[58085]**; **[58898]**; **[59159]**
"Connections: United We Gab" in Entrepreneur (Vol. 35, October 2007, No. 10, pp. 60) **[3706]**, **[11655]**, **[28603]**, **[34839]**
Connector **[7035]**, **[17689]**, **[30421]**
The Connector **[51052]**; **[57454]**
"Connectors for Space, Mil/Aero and Medical Applications" in Canadian Electronics (Vol. 23, June-July 2008, No. 4, pp. 13) **[34840]**, **[36983]**, **[41032]**, **[43828]**, **[47457]**
"Connie Ozan; Founder, Design Director, Twist Creative, 37" in Crain's Cleveland Business (Vol. 28, November 19, 2007, No. 46) **[423]**, **[25055]**, **[29595]**, **[31038]**, **[39793]**
Conor Environmental Services Inc. **[25718]**, **[40593]**
Conquering Information Chaos in the Growing Business: IBM Solutions for Managing Information in an On Demand World **[11229]**, **[37234]**
"Conquering Your Fear of Fees" in Entrepreneur (Vol. 37, October 2009, No. 10, pp. 86) **[8206]**, **[12200]**, **[31338]**, **[44300]**
Conrad Area Chamber of Commerce (CACC) **[54263]**
Conrad Chamber of Commerce [54263]
Conroe Chamber of Commerce - Greater Conroe Chamber of Commerce [58186]
Consad Research Corporation Library **[47538]**
Conseil Économique Des Provinces De L'Atlantique [27927]
Conseil Canadien de la Fourrure [9350], [9354]
Conseil Canadien des Chefs d'Enterprise [26831]
Conseil Canadien du Compost [30419]
Conseil Canadien pour le Commerce Autochtone [26830]
Conseil de Commerce Canada-Inde [26825]
Conseil des traducteurs, terminologues et interpretes du Canada [20468]
Conseil des Viandes du Canada [3138]
Consensus, National Futures & Financial Weekly **[13116]**
"The Consequences of Tardiness" in Modern Machine Shop (Vol. 84, August 2011, No. 3, pp. 34) **[13699]**, **[29034]**, **[35743]**, **[37898]**
Conservatoire de Musique de Quebec - Bibliotheque **[14681]**, **[14769]**
"Consignment Shop Closes Without Warning to Customers, Landlord" in Sun Journal (June 30, 2010) **[4094]**, **[4210]**, **[5139]**, **[7821]**
"Consignment Shop Offers Children's Clothes, Products" in Frederick News-Post (August 19, 2010) **[1659]**, **[2372]**, **[3888]**, **[4095]**, **[4211]**, **[5140]**, **[7822]**, **[20237]**
Consistent Tennis Wins **[20065]**
Consolidated Canadian Market Data Feed [8938], [13201]
Consolidated Fine Housekeeping [10789]
Consortium House Co. **[42321]**
Construction Briefings **[5580]**
Construction Canada **[2556]**, **[5176]**
"Construction Companies Think Smaller, Find Niches as Projects Become Fewer" in Crain's Detroit Business (March 10, 2008) **[5278]**, **[25476]**, **[25736]**
Construction Computing Solutions Inc. **[11954]**, **[21269]**
Construction Consultants Library **[18333]**
Construction Contracting **[5201]**
Construction Contracts Law Report **[5581]**
Construction Directions **[14120]**
Construction Division Newsletter **[5582]**
The Construction Economist **[31]**, **[2259]**
Construction Executive: The Magazine for the Business of Construction **[5583]**
Construction Experts Inc. (CEI) **[5631]**
Construction Financial Management Association (CFMA) **[5177]**
"Construction Firms Support NAACP Plan" in Business Courier (Vol. 27, September 24, 2010, No. 21, pp. 1) **[19218]**, **[33412]**, **[40721]**, **[40872]**, **[41842]**
Construction Industry CPAs/Consultants Association (CICPAC) **[32]**, **[21316]**
Construction Interface Services Inc. **[5632]**
Construction Labor Report™ **[5697]**, **[46946]**
Construction Litigation Reporter **[5584]**
Construction Management Association of America (CMAA) **[5178]**
Construction Owners Association of America (COAA) **[5179]**
Construction Reports: Housing Starts (C20) **[5585]**
Construction Specifications Canada (CSC) **[2557]**, **[5180]**
Construction Specifications Institute (CSI) **[5181]**
Construction Specifications Institute--Newsdigest **[5586]**
The Construction Specifier: Solutions for the Construction Industry **[2561]**, **[5587]**
Construction Systems Technology **[5617]**
Construction Testing Inc. (CTI) **[5633]**
Constructive Leisure **[3393]**
Constructor: The Construction Management Magazine **[5588]**
Construire **[5589]**
Consultant Dieticians Special Interest Group [15155]
Consultant Dietitians in Health Care Facilities [15155]
The Consultant Pharmacist **[6676]**
Consultants and Consulting Organizations Directory **[7154]**, **[13767]**, **[25843]**
Consultants National Resource Center (CNRC) **[2847]**, **[25975]**
Consultants News **[4659]**, **[13777]**
Consultative Selling Skills Training (Onsite) **[39577]**
Consulting, Appraisals & Studies Ltd. **[17586]**, **[27913]**
Consulting & Conciliation Service (CCS) **[2848]**, **[13814]**, **[14170]**, **[25976]**, **[36017]**, **[38690]**
The Consulting Exchange **[2849]**, **[3064]**, **[13815]**, **[25977]**, **[38691]**
"Consulting Firm Goes Shopping" in Crain's Chicago Business (Vol. 31, April 28, 2008, No. 17, pp. 45) **[11326]**, **[21884]**, **[25844]**, **[34232]**, **[36123]**, **[37899]**, **[41843]**
The Consulting Firm Inc. **[42322]**
Consulting Partners Inc. [2818], [4903], [22516], [22649], [25943], [28430]
The Consulting Source Inc. **[25978]**
Consumer Behavior **[26404]**, **[39794]**, **[42977]**, **[43423]**
Consumer Buying Power™ **[1204]**, **[4307]**, **[10019]**, **[10262]**
Consumer Credit Industry Association (CCIA) **[11276]**
Consumer Data Industry Association (CDIA) **[6265]**
"Consumer Electronics: Brick and Mortar Vs. Online" in Retail Merchandiser (Vol. 51, September-October 2011, No. 5, pp. 15) **[3707]**, **[5738]**, **[21072]**, **[28604]**
Consumer Electronics Vision **[1575]**, **[3312]**
Consumer Guide **[48198]**
Consumer InSite<svs> **[324]**, **[1641]**, **[6070]**, **[15119]**
Consumer Products Division of the National Electrical Manufacturers Association [1182]
Consumer Protection Report **[24810]**
Consumer Research Corp. **[14040]**
Consumer Resource Digest **[57919]**
The Consumer Resource Guide **[50887]**
Consumer Science Business Professionals [45259]
Consumer Trends Forum International [45259]
"Consumer Trust in E-Commerce Web Sites: a Meta-Study" in ACM Computing Surveys (Vol. 43, Fall 2011, No. 3, pp. 14) **[4640]**, **[4848]**, **[18405]**, **[28605]**
Consumer-Facts [1204], [4307], [10019], [10262]
"Consumers Finding It Harder to Get and Keep Credit" in Chicago Tribune (January 10, 2009) **[8207]**, **[12201]**, **[26178]**, **[27081]**, **[31339]**, **[37344]**
Consumers' Guide to Timesharing and Resort Report **[10646]**
"Consumers Like Green, But Not Mandates" in Business Journal-Milwaukee (Vol. 28, December 10, 2010, No. 10, pp. A1) **[1189]**, **[7155]**, **[7516]**, **[14881]**, **[30553]**, **[45351]**
"Consumers Seek to Redo Rate Structure: Smaller Biz Paid Big Rates" in Crain's Detroit Business (Vol. 25, June 22, 2009) **[25737]**, **[31340]**
"Consumers Who Saw a Food Truck This Summer" in Nation's Restaurant News (Vol. 45, September 26, 2011, No. 20, pp. 8) **[9150]**, **[45352]**
ConTACt **[50053]**
Contact **[43344]**
Contact Lens Manufacturers Association (CLMA) **[20918]**
Contact Lens Manufacturers Association--Member Directory **[20931]**
"Contec Innovations Inc.: MovieSet.com First to Mobilize Content Using BUZmob" in Canadian Corporate News (May 16, 2007) **[11656]**, **[18884]**, **[21073]**, **[34841]**
Contempo Nails **[14798]**
Contemporary A Cappella News **[14637]**
Contemporary Accounting Research **[33]**
Contemporary Crafts Museum & Gallery. [6078], [6174], [15040]
Contemporary Long Term Care **[15092]**, **[34508]**
Contemporary Women Poets **[6813]**
Content Delivery and Storage Association (CDSA) **[7879]**, **[17633]**
Content Rich: Writing Your Way to Wealth on the Web **[21074]**, **[28606]**, **[36984]**, **[39795]**, **[43424]**
"Contest Produce Ad Designs on a Dime" in San Diego Business Journal (Vol. 31, August 23, 2010, No. 31, pp. 1) **[424]**, **[4595]**, **[28607]**, **[39796]**, **[41033]**
Contex Analytical Inc. **[10157]**
Continental Advertising Agency Network [340], [39554], [42566]
Continental Appraisal Co. **[17587]**
Continental Association of CPA Firms [12]
Continental Association of Funeral and Memorial Societies--Directory of Member Societies [9330]
Contingency Planning and Disaster Recovery: A Small Business Guide **[4700]**, **[11230]**, **[18406]**, **[24299]**
"Contingent Offers: Weighing the Risk" in Crain's Chicago Business (Vol. 31, April 21, 2008, No. 16, pp. 48) **[14400]**, **[16857]**, **[17246]**
Continuity **[7880]**
Continuous Quality Improvement in Health Care **[34603]**
Continuous Quality Improvement in Long-Term Care **[34604]**
"Continuously Monitoring Workers' Comp Can Limit Costs" in Crain's Cleveland Business (Vol. 28, October 8, 2007, No. 40, pp. 21) **[11327]**, **[24300]**, **[36124]**
"ContiTech Celebrates 100 Years" in American Printer (Vol. 128, July 1, 2011, No. 7) **[4463]**, **[16362]**, **[20762]**, **[38998]**
Contours Express **[16021]**
Contra Costa Small Business Development Center (CCSBDC) **[48147]**
Contract Design [11559]
"Contract Design as a Firm Capability" in Academy of Management Review (October 2007, pp. 1060) **[23803]**, **[37900]**, **[41667]**
Contract Furnishings Forum [41531]

3486 Small Business Sourcebook • 30th Edition

Corporate Design [15255]
Corporate Directions [46446]
"Corporate Diversity Driving Profits" in Hispanic Business (Vol. 30, September 2008, No. 9, pp. 12) [25058], [32617], [35308], [37904], [45354], [45893]
"Corporate Elite Face Steep Challenges" in Hispanic Business (January-February 2008, pp. 20, 22, 24, 26, 28, 30, 32) [3708], [37905], [40725]
"Corporate Elite Show Resilience" in The Business Journal-Serving Greater Tampa Bay (Vol. 28, August 1, 2008, No. 32, pp. 1) [8216], [12212], [14402], [17251], [27092], [31347], [41847]
Corporate Entrepreneurship & Innovation [25478], [29603], [32618]
Corporate Entrepreneurship: Top Managers and New Business Creation [22856], [29604], [37906]
"Corporate Etiquette: The Art of Apology" in Canadian Business (Vol. 80, January 29, 2007, No. 3, pp. 62) [29036], [29605], [32619]
Corporate Expressions International Inc. [40594]
Corporate Facility Services Inc. (CFS) [5634]
Corporate Financial Management: Emerging Trends and Recent Developments [8880], [31994]
Corporate Governance Library® [38834]
Corporate Governance Library/Manual/Report [38834]
"Corporate Governance Reforms in China and India: Challenges and Opportunities" in Business Horizons (January-February 2008) [36446], [37907]
Corporate Growth Assistance Ltd. [42324]
Corporate Growth Report [42271]
Corporate Impact [38694]
Corporate & Incentive Travel [20449], [20596]
Corporate Law Daily™ [24139]
Corporate Meetings & Incentives: The Senior Executives Guide to Decision Making [20597], [24953]
"Corporate Park Retrofits for Water Savings" in Contractor (Vol. 56, October 2009, No. 10, pp. 5) [5285], [16231], [18683], [20974], [30556]
Corporate Radar: Tracking the Forces That Are Shaping Your Business [18408], [30557], [32620]
Corporate Real Estate Executive [17556]; [17556]
Corporate Report [34137]
Corporate Report-Wisconsin [59786]
"Corporate Responsibility" in Professional Services Close-Up (July 2, 2010) [7157], [7518], [9249], [29037], [29606], [30558], [30913], [31348], [33183], [35745], [37908], [45894]
"Corporate Social Responsibility: A Process Model of Sensemaking" in Academy of Management Review (January 2008, pp. 122) [37909], [45895]
Corporate Technology Directory [33099]
"Corporate Training" in Hawaii Business (Vol. 53, October 2007, No. 4, pp. 46) [15964], [37910], [41848]
Corporate Writer and Editor [22496]
"Corporation, Be Good! The Story of Corporate Social Responsibility" in Business and Society (December 2007, pp. 479-485) [27093], [45896]
Corporation des associations de detaillants d'automobiles [14837]
Corporation for Enterprise Development (CFED) [26841], [30405]
Corporation for National and Community Service - Department of AmeriCorps [59983]; [59984]
Corporation for National and Community Service - Field Liaison [59985]; [59986]
Corporation for National and Community Service - Office of Learn and Serve [59987]; [59988]
Corporation for National and Community Service (CNCS) - Office of Procurement [59989]; [59990]
Corporation for National and Community Service - Office of Public Affairs [59991]; [59992]
Corporation: Small Business Start-Up Kit [32370], [46034]
"Corporex in Battle With Hedge Fund" in Business Courier (Vol. 24, December 21, 2008, No. 36, pp. 1) [16862], [23807], [41849]
"Corporex Checks Into Hotel Niche" in Business Courier (Vol. 24, October 12, 2008, No. 26, pp. 1) [5286], [10677], [12213], [41850]
The CorpTech Directory of Technology Companies [33099]
Corpus Christi Area Hispanic Chamber of Commerce [58088]
Corpus Christi Minority Business Development Center [58533]
Correspondent [58089]
Corridor Chamber Membership Directory [52705]
Corridor Chamber News [52706]
Corrosion: The Journal of Science and Engineering [44012]
Corry Area Chamber of Commerce [57050]
Corset and Brassiere Association of America [3887], [13557]

Corsicana/Navarro County Chamber of Commerce [58090]
Corte Madera Chamber of Commerce [48503]
Cortez Area Chamber of Commerce (CACC) [49482]
Cortland County Chamber of Commerce [55180]
"Corus Eases Off Ailing Condo Market; Office Developers Get Majority of 1Q Loans" in Crain's Chicago Business (April 28, 2008) [5287], [8217], [10678], [12214], [17252], [31349], [37347]
Corvallis-Benton Chamber Coalition [56766]
"COSE: More Small Companies Offering Wellness Plans" in Crain's Cleveland Business (Vol. 28, December 3, 2007, No. 48, pp. 22) [34236], [45355]
"COSE Turns On To Electricity Market" in Crain's Cleveland Business (Vol. 30, June 22, 2009, No. 24, pp. 4) [25740], [31350], [41851]
Coshocton Area Chamber of Commerce [56109]
Coshocton Chamber of Commerce [56109]
Coshocton County Chamber of Commerce [56109]
Cosmetic Career Women [5878]
Cosmetic Executive Women (CEW) [5878]
Cosmetic Industry Buyers and Suppliers (CIBS) [1889], [2031], [5879]
Cosmetic Ingredient Review (CIR) [5880]
Cosmetic and Personal Services [5905]
Cosmetic, Toiletry and Fragrance Association [1892], [2033], [5884]
Cosmetics & Toiletries--Cosmetic Materials Directory Issue [2036]
Cosmetics & Toiletries--Cosmetic Bench Reference [2036]
Cosmetics & Toiletries: The International Magazine of Cosmetic Technology [1908], [2058], [5900]
CosmoConnection [51053]
Cosmopolitan Chamber of Commerce (CCC) [51054]
"Cost of Business Banking May Soon Go Up" in Baltimore Business Journal (Vol. 28, October 29, 2010, No. 25, pp. 1) [6196], [6289], [26182], [31351]
"Cost Cuts Lead Dealers to Record Profits" in Globe & Mail (March 24, 2006, pp. B3) [8218], [12215], [22857]
Cost Cutters Family Hair Care [10090]
"The Cost of Energy" in Canadian Business (Vol. 83, August 17, 2010, No. 13-14, pp. 39) [7158], [7519], [30559]
"Cost of Home Purchase Loans are Higher for Hispanics" in Hispanic Business (October 2007, pp. 88) [14403], [16863]
"Cost of Md. Health Plan Not Known" in Baltimore Business Journal (Vol. 28, September 3, 2010, No. 17, pp. 1) [11329], [25479], [25741], [31352], [34237], [36126]
"Cost Remains Top Factor In Considering Green Technology" in Canadian Sailings (June 30, 2008) [7520], [11077], [25846], [30560], [36447], [43829]
Costa Mesa Chamber of Commerce [48504]
CoStaff Services L.L.C. [36019]
Milton Costello, Consulting Engineer [19553]
Costilla County Chamber of Commerce [49483]
Costume Society of America (CSA) [5927]
Cotati Chamber of Commerce (CCC) [48505]
Cotati Promotion Club [48505]
COTC Technologies Inc. [4671], [5051], [13818], [25981]
COTC-TrenzSoft [4671], [5051], [13818], [25981]
Morton Cotlar [38695]
Cottage Grove Area Chamber of Commerce [53628]; [56767]
CottageCare Canada [6572]
CottageCare, Inc. [6573]
Cotter Chamber of Commerce [48040]
Cotton Production [4157], [18739]
Cottonwood Chamber of Commerce [47892], [48506]
Cottonwood/Verde Valley Chamber of Commerce [47892]
Coudersport Area Chamber of Commerce [57051]
"Could This Be Your Next Office Building?" in Austin Business Journal (Vol. 31, May 13, 2011, No. 10, pp. A1) [5288], [7159], [7521], [9205], [30561], [44660], [45897]
"Could UNCC Be Home to Future Med School Here?" in Charlotte Business Journal (Vol. 25, July 23, 2010, No. 18, pp. 1) [28167], [34238], [44661]
Coulee City Chamber of Commerce [59160]
Council for Advancement and Support of Education Information Center [9306]
Council of the Americas (CoA) [36287]
Council Bluffs Area Chamber of Commerce (CBACC) [51872]
Council Bluffs Chamber of Commerce [51872]
Council Bluffs SCORE [51795]
Council Chamber of Commerce [50757]
Council of Dedicated Merchants Chamber of Commerce (CDM) [55181]
Council of Development Finance Agencies (CDFA) [26842], [46976]

Council of the District of Columbia [49857]
Council on Employee Benefits (CEB) [21851], [25365]
Council for Entrepreneurial Development [55540]
Council for Ethical Leadership (CEE) [30895]
Council of Fashion Designers of America (CFDA) [4080]
Council for Ethics in Economics [30895]
Council for Inter-American Cooperation [11023]
Council for Latin America [36287]
Council for Urban Economic Development [27377]
Council on Foreign Relations (CFR) [42426]
Council on Foundations Resource Center [9307]
Council on Hotel, Restaurant and Institutional Education--Member Directory and Resource Guide [10679], [17902]
Council of Insurance Agents and Brokers [11277]
Council for Interior Design Accreditation (CIDA) [11526]
Council of International Investigators (CII) [16452]
Council for International Tax Education (CITE) [11019], [36288]
Council of Better Business Bureaus Foundation [24792]
Council of Industrial Development Bond Issuers [26842], [46976]
Council of Mechanical Specialty Contracting Industries [763], [5170]
Council of Sales Promotion Agencies [43347]
Council on Employee Benefit Plans [21851], [25365]
Council on Hotel, Restaurant and Institutional Education - National Council on Hotel and Restaurant Education [5832], [10653]
Council on Optometric Education [20903]
Council on the Safe Transportation of Hazardous Articles [10161]
"Council Power Shift Could Benefit Business" in Business Courier (Vol. 26, November 6, 2009, No. 28, pp. 1) [7160], [7522], [18409], [27094], [30562], [33628], [46196]
Council of Protocol Executives (COPE) [20295]
Council of Real Estate Brokerage Managers (CRB) [14369]
Council for Research in Music Education (CRME) [14723]
Council on Safe Transportation of Hazardous Articles (COSTHA) [10161]
"Councilman May Revive Labor Bill" in Baltimore Business Journal (Vol. 28, August 13, 2010, No. 14, pp. 1) [5289], [17253], [33629], [42372], [46862]
Counseling Today [3364]
The Counsellor [20651]
The Counselor [16605], [34509]
CounselorConnect [42594]
Counselors of Real Estate (CRE) [16782]
"Count Out The Consumer" in Barron's (Vol. 88, July 7, 2008, No. 27, pp. 10) [21553], [26183], [27095], [44302]
"Countdown" in Canadian Business (Vol. 81, March 3, 2008, No. 3, pp. 27) [8219], [12216], [27096], [31353], [33630], [45356]
The Counter [18111]
"A Counter Offer" in Inc. (February 2008, pp.) [10392], [10460], [15316], [25306], [42980], [44147]
"Counter Service" in Nation's Restaurant News (Vol. 45, September 26, 2011, No. 20, pp. 8) [9151], [17903], [45357]
"Counter Service: We Gear Up Some Food Truck Stats" in Nation's Restaurant News (Vol. 45, August 8, 2011, No. 16, pp. 6) [9152], [45358]
Counterman: Dedicated to Successful Parts Distribution [1576], [43698]
"Counting on Cornhole: Popular Bean Bag Game Brings Crowds to Bars" in Boston Business Journal (Vol. 29, July 15, 2011, No. 10, pp. 1) [1839], [20238], [39804], [43429]
"Counting Crabs: Supply Dips, Putting Crimp on Memorial Day Feast" in Boston Business Journal (Vol. 29, June 3, 2011, No. 4, pp. 1) [8980], [9016], [17904]
"Counting on Engagement at Ernst and Young" in Workforce Management (Vol. 88, November 16, 2009, No. 12, pp. 25) [22858], [25847], [27097], [29038], [46863]
Country Business: The Magazine for Today's Independent Gift Retailers [9610]
Country Dance and Song Society of America - Country Dance Society of America [6369]
Country Dance and Song Society (CDSS) [6369]
Country Dance and Song Society Newsletter [6387]
Country Home [1135], [1364], [1412], [4528], [6006], [6125], [9805], [11560], [13407]
Country Inns & Suites by Carlson [10801]
Country Kitchen International [18112]
Country Radio Broadcasters (CRB) [16691]
Country Sampler [11561]
Country Sampler Calendar of Events [58899]
Country Squire Inc. [25360]
Country Studies in Entrepreneurship: A Historical Perspective [29607], [36448]

Current [3868]
The Current [48517]
Current Blackjack News [9412]
Current Housing Reports: H-130, Market Absorption of Apartments [5591]
Currents [48518]; [50058]; [7037]
Curtis Institute of Music - Milton L. Rock Resource Center [14682]
Curves [21284]
Cushing Chamber of Commerce and Industry [56502]
Cushing Chamber of Commerce [56502]
Custer Area Chamber of Commerce and Visitors Bureau [57577]
Custer County Chamber of Commerce [49489]; [57577]
Custer County Merchants and Chamber of Commerce [49489]
"Custom Fit" in Canadian Business (Vol. 80, November 19, 2007, No. 23, pp. 42) [35313], [35752], [37919]
Custom Forestry Inc. [21773]
Custom Payroll [15471]
The Custom Tailor [19561]
Custom Tailors and Designers Association (CTDA) [4081]
Customer Care Classic Moments [26587]
Customer Expectations [26588]
Customer Focused Telephone Techniques (Onsite) [22178]
Customer Inter@ctions Buyer's Guide & Directory Issue [19847]
"The Customer Is Right Even If He's Wrong" in Contractor (Vol. 57, February 2010, No. 2, pp. 12) [6882], [16233], [18684], [26408], [42464]
"Customer Loyalty: Making Your Program Excel" in Franchising World (Vol. 42, August 2010, No. 8, pp. 47) [22867], [26409], [32156]
"Customer OKs on Press" in American Printer (Vol. 128, August 1, 2011, No. 8) [4466], [16364], [20764], [26410]
Customer Perspectives [14043], [40596]
"Customer Preferences Control Skid Steer Choices" in Rental Product News (Vol. 33, June 2011) [17768], [26411]
Customer-Responsive Selling [43715]
"Customer Retention is Proportionate to Employee Retention" in Green Industry Pro (Vol. 23, September 2011) [9774], [13384], [13471], [26412], [29043], [37920], [44306]
Customer Retention/Service Quality [26589]
Customer Satisfaction and Loyalty Research (Onsite) [26363], [39579]
Customer Service 101 [43716]
Customer Service Advantage [26582]
"Customer Service Center Will Rise in Indian Land" in Charlotte Observer (February 4, 2007) [5294], [13700], [26413]
Customer Service or Else [26590]
Customer Service Excellence: How to Win and Keep Customers (Onsite) [26364]
Customer Service: It's Good Business & It's Everybody's Business [26591]
Customer Service That Wows! (Onsite) [26365]
"Customers Turned Off? Not at Best Buy" in Barron's (Vol. 88, March 24, 2008, No. 12, pp. 29) [5740], [8229], [12228], [22868], [31366], [34846]
"Customized Before Custom Was Cool" in Green Industry Pro (July 2011) [7162], [7524], [9775], [13385], [13472], [29612], [30564], [44307]
Cut Bank Area Chamber of Commerce [54265]
"Cut Energy Waste" in Inc. (Vol. 31, January-February 2009, No. 1, pp. 42) [3522], [7163], [7525], [18885], [30565], [45110]
Cute Little Store: Between the Entrepreneurial Dream and Business Reality [22869], [26414], [29044], [29342], [42917]
Cutten Associates Lighting Design [41588]
Cutter IT Journal [19028]
Cuttin' Hoss Chatter [19486]
"Cutting Credit Card Processing Costs" in Hawaii Business (Vol. 53, March 2008, No. 9, pp. 56) [22870], [26193], [32625]
Cutting Edge [49689]
"Cutting Health Care Costs: the 3-Legged Stool" in HR Specialist (Vol. 8, September 2010, No. 9, pp. 1) [11333], [21889], [35753], [36130]
Cutting Horse Chatter: Official Publication of the National Cutting Horse Assn [19486]
Cutting Tool Engineering--Superabrasives Directory Issue [13701]
Cutting Tool Engineering--Diamond Superabrasives Directory Issue [13701]
Cutting Tool Manufacturers Association [13696]
Cutting Tool Manufacturers of America [13696]
Cuyahoga Community College [56409]

Cuyahoga Falls Chamber of Commerce (CFCC) [56112]
CVMA Directory [1053]
CVO Update [1073]
"CVRD Inco Strike Shuts Sudbury Mines" in Globe & Mail (April 2, 2007, pp. B1) [8230], [12229], [46865]
"The CW" in Brandweek (Vol. 49, April 21, 2008, No. 16, pp. SR8) [428], [7914], [19924], [37921], [39816], [41855], [43435]
CW Group, Inc. [55404]
CWB Custom Woodworking Business: Environmental Studies [3425], [6011]
CWB NET [13690]
CWC Communicator [47429]
CWI: Credit Professionals [6226], [6266]
CWTA Membership - Products and Services Directory [3671]
Cy-Fair Houston Chamber of Commerce [58095]
Cy-Fair Houston Chamber of Commerce Quarterly News Magazine [58096]
"Cyber Thanksgiving Online Shopping a Growing Tradition" in Marketing Weekly News (December 12, 2009, pp. 137) [11662], [15317], [21078], [28616], [39817], [42983], [43436]
Cybertary [3099], [28455]
"Cyberwise" in Black Enterprise (Vol. 40, July 2010, No. 12, pp. 48) [46504]
"Cyberwise" in Black Enterprise (Vol. 41, December 2010, No. 5, pp. 50) [3710], [4945], [28617], [34847], [41041], [41396]
"Cyberwise" in Black Enterprise (Vol. 41, September 2010, No. 2, pp. 49) [2699], [15318], [28618], [44148]
Cycle Jobbers Association [1964]
Cycle News [14552]
Cycle World [14553]
Cycles [6748]
"Cyclicals, Your Day Is Coming" in Barron's (Vol. 89, July 27, 2009, No. 30, pp. 24) [8231], [12230], [31367], [39008]
Cyclists' Yellow Pages [1971]
Cylburn Arboretum Association Library [9851]
Cynthiana-Harrison County Chamber of Commerce [52299]
Cypress Chamber of Commerce [48519]
Cypress College [49367]
Cytoskeleton [44013]
Czechoslovak Genealogical Society [9425]
Czechoslovak Genealogical Society International (CGSI) [9425]

D

D & B Consultants Directory [13768]
D & B Principal International Businesses: The World Marketing Directory [11080], [36455]
D Bellavance Agency [53096]
The Da Vinci Group [16616]
DacEasy Inc. [218], [3657], [19047], [21459], [45251]
DacEasy Payroll / Sage Software SB, Inc. [15472]
"Daddy's Home! Fathers Stay Home To Watch the Kids and Build Businesses To Suit Their Values" in Black Enterprise (October 2007) [35599], [45370]
Dade County Chamber of Commerce [50510]
Dadeville Area Chamber of Commerce [47671]
"D.A.G. Sues to Stay on Job" in Business Courier (Vol. 24, November 9, 2008, No. 30, pp. 4) [5295], [23814]
Dahlonega Lumpkin County Chamber of Commerce [50511]
Dahlonega-Lumpkin County Chamber of Commerce [50511]
Daily Brief Services [15029], [15605]
Daily Business Review [50380]
Daily Commerce: Serving the Southern California Real Estate Investor [17557]
Daily Labor Report® (DLR) [14171]
Daily Labor Report [46938]
Daily News Record [3905], [4148], [4293]
"Daily Newspapers" in MarketingMagazine (Vol. 115, September 27, 2010, No. 13, pp. 32) [15527], [39818]
Daily Pilot [48520]
The Daily Record [17558]
Daily Tax Report [250], [19726]
The Daily Times [57692]
"DaimlerChrysler Bears Down on Smart" in Globe & Mail (March 27, 2006, pp. B11) [24310], [39009]
Daingerfield Chamber of Commerce (DCC) [58097]
Dairy and Food Industries Supply Association [10841]
Dairy and Ice Cream Machinery and Supplies Association [10841]
Dairy-Deli-Bake Digest [1685]
Dairy-Deli-Bake Seminar and Expo [1688], [1796], [6449], [19271]
Dairy Industries Supply Association [10841]
Dairy Management, Inc. (DMI) [10840]

Dairy Management Inc. Information Resources [15216]
"Dairy Queen Aims to Blitz Blizzberry" in Ice Cream Reporter (Vol. 23, August 20, 2010, No. 9, pp. 1) [10867], [23815]
Dairy Queen Canada Inc. [10956]
"Dairy Queen Ends Effort Against Yogubliz" in Ice Cream Reporter (Vol. 23, November 20, 2010, No. 12, pp. 1) [10868], [25485]
Dairy-Deli-Bake [1688], [1796], [6449], [19271]
Dairy-Deli-Bakery Seminar and Expo [1688], [1796], [6449], [19271]
Daito-Ryu Revelations [14092]
Daito-Ryu Secrets [14093]
Dakota County Regional Chamber of Commerce [53630]
Dakotas-Montana Medical Directory [34242]
Dale Hollow-Clay County Chamber of Commerce [57683]
Dale System Inc. [29303]
"Daley's Efforts to Ease Traffic Woes Fall Short" in Crain's Chicago Business (Vol. 31, May 5, 2008, No. 18, pp. 18) [24840], [27112], [33188], [33637], [46199]
Dalhart Area Chamber of Commerce (DACC) [58098]
Dalhousie University - Population Health Research Unit (PHRU) [34652]
Dallas Apparel News [3904], [4147]
Dallas Area [56770]
Dallas Area Chamber of Commerce [56771]
Dallas Black Chamber of Commerce (DBCC) [58099]
Dallas/Ft. Worth JobBank: The Job Hunter's Guide to the Dallas-Fort Worth Metroplex [19173]
Dallas/Fort Worth Minority Business Enterprise Center [58534]
Dallas Market Center--Permanent Directory [10418]
Dallas Men's and Boys' Apparel Market [3908]
Dallas Northeast Chamber of Commerce [58100]
Dallas Small Business Development Center [57845]
Dalton Directory [57351]
Dalton Floor Covering Market Association [9053], [11524]
Dalton-Whitfield Chamber of Commerce [50512]
Dalton-Whitfield SCORE [50409]
Daly City Business Center [49358]
Daly City - Colma Chamber of Commerce [48521]
Leo A. Daly Company Library [11587]
Damariscotta Region Chamber of Commerce (DRCC) [52585]
Damas & Associates [32277]
D-Amp Publications [57350]
"Dana Anderson's Celebrity Rules for Digital Marketing" in Advertising Age (Vol. 81, December 6, 2010, No. 43, pp. 4) [429], [39819]
"Danaher to Acquire Tectronix" in Canadian Electronics (Vol. 22, November-December 2007, No. 7, pp. 1) [12231], [34848], [39010], [41856]
Danbury Chamber of Commerce [49704]
Danbury Difference [49690]
Dance Affiliates [6371]
Dance Educators of America (DEA) [6372]
Dance Films Association, Inc. [6418]
Dance International [6388]
Dance Magazine [6389]
Dance Magazine College Guide [6381]
Dance Notation Bureau (DNB) [6373]
Dance Teachers Guild [6365]
Dances for Drill and Dance Teams [6400]
Dancing in Hollywood: A Guide for the Professional Dancer [6401]
Dancing a Miracle [15996]
"Dancing With Giants: Acquisition and Survival of the Family Firm" in Family Business Review (Vol. 19, December 2006, No. 4, pp. 289) [12232], [19219], [31041], [41857]
D'Angelo Grilled Sandwiches [18115]
"Danger, Will Robinson!" in Business Owner (Vol. 35, July-August 2011, No. 4, pp. 3) [24311], [32626]
Dangerous Goods Advisory Council (DGAC) [10162]
Dangerous Goods Council Inc. (DGC) [10183]
Daniels County Chamber of Commerce and Agriculture [54266]
Danish American Chamber of Commerce (DACC) [36289]
Danish American Trade Council [36289]
Danish Luncheon Club of New York [36289]
Dansville Chamber of Commerce (DCC) [55183]
DANTH Inc. [1305]
Danville Area Chamber of Commerce (DACC) [48522]
Danville Area Chamber of Commerce and Visitor Center [58902]
Danville Boyle County [52300]
Danville-Boyle County Chamber of Commerce [52301]
Danville Pittsylvania County Chamber of Commerce [58902]
D'Arcy Masius Benton & Bowles Information Center [42697]
Dare Mighty Things [38697]

Dare to Prepare - How to Win Before You Begin [24312], [29613], [32627]

Dargan Burns Public Relations Services [42546]

Darien Chamber of Commerce (DCC) [49691]; [51058]

Darien Chamber of Commerce and Industry [51058]

Darien-McIntosh Chamber of Commerce [50513]

"*Dark Horse Murphy Means Business In Gubernatorial Race*" in Baltimore Business Journal (Vol. 28, June 25, 2010, No. 7, pp. 1) [32628], [42374]

Darke County Chamber of Commerce [56113]

Darke County Genealogy Library. [9502]

Darke County Historical Society Library [9502]

"*Darkness Falling..*" in Barron's (Vol. 89, July 20, 2009, No. 29, pp. 13) [8232], [12233], [27113], [31368], [36456]

Darkroom & Creative Camera Techniques [15908]

Darlington Chamber of Commerce [59551]

DART: British Columbia Statute Service [24141]

DART: Western Decisions [24142]

Dartmouth College - Center for Evaluative Clinical Sciences [34653]

Dartmouth College - Dartmouth Institute for Health Policy and Clinical Practice [34653]

Dartmouth Regional Technology Center [54630]

Charles Darwin University - Palmerston Campus Library [33106]

Data Analysis for EEO Professionals (Onsite) [23680]

Data Analysis for Marketing Research: The Fundamentals (Onsite) [39580]

Data Associates [15645], [21785]

The DATA BASE for Advances in Information Systems [11233]

Data Base Alert [11234], [11945]

"*Data Center Plan Bearing Fruit From Apple, Spec Center*" in Charlotte Business Journal (Vol. 25, October 15, 2010, No. 30, pp. 1) [4702], [4849], [5296], [22871]

Data Concepts [41480]

Data Conversion Laboratory [3658]

"*Data Dispel Some Notions About Value of Stock Buybacks*" in Crain's Cleveland Business (Vol. 28, November 19, 2007, No. 46, pp. 9) [8233], [12234], [31369]

Data Doctors [4815], [5022]

Data Driven Investing: Professional Edition [12235], [30917], [31370]

"*The Data Drivers*" in Canadian Business (Vol. 81, September 15, 2008, No. 14-15, pp. 1) [1503], [3711], [25062], [25307], [25486], [25743], [33638], [34849], [44308]

"*Data Firm Growth 'Opportunistic*'" in Tampa Bay Business Journal (Vol. 30, January 29, 2010, No. 6, pp. 1) [4703], [4850], [22872], [44309]

"*Data Security is No. 1 Compliance Concern*" in HRMagazine (Vol. 53, October 2008, No. 10, pp. 32) [4704], [18411]

Database Design for Web Development [30390]

Database Publishing [47913]

Datamation: The Emerging Technologies Magazine for Today's IS [4887], [19029]

"*Datebook*" in Crain's Chicago Business (Vol. 31, April 28, 2008, No. 17, pp. 18) [18554], [20351], [27116], [29616], [46202], [46632], [47261]

"*Datebook*" in Crain's Chicago Business (Vol. 31, March 24, 2008, No. 12, pp. 18) [18552], [20349], [27114], [29614], [35314], [46200], [46630], [47259]

"*Datebook*" in Crain's Chicago Business (Vol. 31, March 31, 2008, No. 13, pp. 1) [18553], [20350], [27115], [29615], [35315], [46201], [46631], [47260]

Dateline [50059]; [51059]

Dateline Cullman [47672]

"*Dating Games*" in Canadian Business (Vol. 79, September 25, 2006, No. 19, pp. 23) [8234], [12236], [24796], [30918]

DatLine [11235]

"*Datran Media Executives to Lead Industry Debates Across Q1 Conferences*" in Internet Wire (January 22, 2010) [430], [11663], [20352], [26746], [28619], [39820], [46633]

Dauphin Capital Partners [55405]

Davenport Chamber of Commerce [56503]

Davenport Chamber of Commerce (DCC) [59162]

Davenport University - Thomas F. Reed, Jr. Memorial Library [14346], [20216], [20640]

DavenportOne [51876]

David Armstrong Paints [1369]

"*David Azriell*" in Canadian Business (Vol. 82, April 27, 2009, No. 7, pp. 54) [12237], [27117]

David City Area Chamber of Commerce [54367]

David Hall's Inside View [4371]

David Herson Associates [26622]

"*David Low*" in Hawaii Business (Vol. 53, October 2007, No. 4, pp. 38) [25487], [29617], [34243], [37922]

"*David Maus Debuting New Dealership*" in Orlando Business Journal (Vol. 26, February 5, 2010, No. 36, pp. 1) [14833], [35316], [41858]

"*David Robinson Column*" in Buffalo News (October 2, 2011) [7164], [7526], [30566]

"*David Saunders Q&A*" in Canadian Business (Vol. 80, October 22, 2007, No. 21, pp. 11) [28168], [32629]

James W. Davidson Company Inc. [42325], [44213]

Davie-Cooper City Chamber of Commerce [50060]

Davie County Chamber of Commerce [55677]

Davis Area Chamber of Commerce & Visitor Center [48523]

Davis Area Chamber of Commerce [48523]

J.M. Davis Arms & Historical Museum - Charles R. Suydam Library [10042]

Davis Chamber of Commerce [48523]; [56504]; [58648]

Davis Chamber Viewpoint [48524]

Davis Consultants Library [2248], [4542]

Davis, Tuttle Venture Partners, L.P. / DTVP (Tulsa) [56617]

The Davlin Report [21728], [30871]

Dawes Arboretum Library [9852]

Dawntreader Ventures [55406]

Dawson County Chamber of Commerce [50514]

Dawson Springs Chamber of Commerce [52302]

"*Day Care for Affluent Drawing a Crowd*" in Business First Columbus (Vol. 24, August 15, 2008, No. 52, pp. 1) [3937], [28169], [32157]

Day Care Center Directory [53852]

"*Day-Care Center Owner to Argue Against Liquor Store Opening Nearby*" in Chicago Tribune (March 13, 2008) [3938], [13577], [23816], [28170]

Day Care Grows Up [3970], [14804]

Day in the Career Series [6988]

A Day to Cherish Wedding Videos [3100], [15876]

Diane Day Designs [14798]

"*A Day Late and a Dollar Short*" in Indoor Comfort Marketing (Vol. 70, March 2011, No. 3, pp. 30) [803], [7165], [7527], [12238], [30567], [39821], [45371]

"*Daycare Dollars*" in Small Business Opportunities (Winter 2009) [3939], [22873], [32158], [44310]

Days Inn Worldwide, Inc. [10802]

Days Inns-Canada [2995]

Days of Reckoning [38618]

Daytime Broadcasters Association [16697], [19889]

Dayton Area Chamber of Commerce [54488]; [56114]

Dayton Area Chamber of Commerce Economic Development Division [56114]

Dayton Auto Show [703]

Dayton Chamber of Commerce [57693]

Dayton Chamber of Commerce (DCC) [59163]

Daytona Beach Area Chamber of Commerce [50061]

Daytona Beach - Halifax Area Chamber of Commerce (DBHACC) [50061]

Dazbog Coffee [9734]

DBA Books [53096]

DBCC Update [58101]

DC Press [50385]

"*DCAA-Compliant Accounting Solution Provider Intros Redesign of Website at sympaq.com*" in Entertainment Close-Up (April 18, 2011) [21079], [33417], [39822]

DCL [3658]

DCLNews [2687], [3649], [4660], [4763], [5012], [19030]

D.C.W. Research Associates International [40940]

DDB Chicago Library [686]

DDB Worldwide Information Center [687]

DDL OMNI [22525]

DDL OMNI Engineering [22525]

De Anza College [49368]

De Baca County Chamber of Commerce [54957]

De Bellas & Co. [2856], [13179]

De Dutch Pannekoek House Restaurants [18116]

De Forest Area Chamber of Commerce [59552]

De Leon Chamber of Commerce and Agriculture [58102]

DE Micro Enterprise Program - Retail Incubator Program [49835]

De Novo Ventures [49200]

De Queen/Sevier County Chamber of Commerce [48043]

De Villiers Inc. [49799]

De Witt Chamber of Commerce [51877]

De Witt Chamber of Commerce and Development Company [51877]

Deaconess Hospital Health Science Library [1444]

Dead on Arrival: How the Anti-Business Backlash is Destroying Entrepreneurship in America and What We Can Still Do About It! [29618], [32630], [33639]

Deadwood Chamber of Commerce and Visitors' Bureau [57578]

Deadwood-Lead Area Chamber of Commerce [57578]

Deaf Smith County Chamber of Commerce [58103]

"*Deal Braces Cramer for Growth Run*" in The Business Journal-Serving Metropolitan Kansas City (Vol. 26, July 4, 2008, No. 43, pp. 1) [8235], [12239], [22874], [26747], [31371], [41859]

"*Deal Made for Pontiac Home of Film Studio*" in Crain's Detroit Business (Vol. 25, June 1, 2009, No. 22, pp. 3) [7915], [28171], [44663]

"*Deal or No Deal?*" in Canadian Business (Vol. 80, January 15, 2007, No. 2, pp. 38) [8236], [12240]

"*The Deal - Rhymes With Steal - Of A Lifetime*" in Barron's (Vol. 88, March 24, 2008, No. 12, pp. 24) [8237], [12241], [31372], [37357], [41860]

"*Deal With Tribes Revives Revenue Stream*" in Crain's Detroit Business (Vol. 24, March 24, 2008, No. 12, pp. 6) [9392], [23817], [27118], [33640], [41042]

"*Dealer Gets a Lift with Acquisitions at Year's End*" in Crain's Detroit Business (Vol. 26, January 11, 2010, No. 2, pp. 3) [14883], [20676], [22875], [35317], [39011], [41861]

Dealernews: The Voice Of The Powersports Industry [14554]

"*Dealers Fight To Steer Course*" in The Business Journal-Serving Metropolitan Kansas City (Vol. 27, November 7, 2008, No. 9, pp. 1) [14884], [26194], [37358], [43437]

"*Dealers Trying Not to Fold*" in Business First Columbus (Vol. 25, December 5, 2008, No. 15, pp. A1) [14885], [27119], [41862], [43438], [45372]

Dealing with Competing Demands (Canada) [28021]

Dealing with Difficult People Volume Two [29203], [38619]

Dealing with Difficult Prospects [43717]

Dealing with the Irate Customer [26592]

Dealing with the Tough Stuff: Practical Wisdom for Running a Values-Driven Business [32631]

"*Dealing With Dangers Abroad*" in Financial Executive (Vol. 23, December 2007, No. 10, pp. 32) [18412], [20240], [35631], [36457], [39012]

"*Deals Still Get Done at Drake's Coq d'Or*" in Crain's Chicago Business (Vol. 31, November 17, 2008, No. 46, pp. 35) [1841], [10681], [17907], [22284], [24313], [25063], [32632], [39823]

Dean College [53088]

"*The Dean of Design*" in Canadian Business (Vol. 79, November 6, 2006, No. 22, pp. 42) [25488], [26415], [32633]

"*Dean Foods*" in Ice Cream Reporter (Vol. 23, November 20, 2010, No. 12, pp. 8) [8238], [10869], [12242], [21555], [25489], [25744]

"*Dean Foods*" in Ice Cream Reporter (Vol. 23, September 20, 2010, No. 10, pp. 8) [10870], [37190], [37923], [42781], [43832]

Dean Fowler Associates Inc. [31141]

W. Dean Productions [42549]

Wayne Dean Public Relations [42549]

"*Dear Customer: Managing E-Mail Campaigns*" in Inc. (March 2008, pp. 58-59) [431], [3523], [15319], [18886], [28620], [39824], [43439], [44311], [45111]

"*Dear Diary, Arbitron is Dumping You*" in Business Courier (Vol. 26, September 25, 2009, No. 22, pp. 1) [5741], [16709], [34850]

Dearborn Business Journal [53236]

Dearborn Chamber of Commerce [53237]

Dearborn County Chamber of Commerce (DCC) [51587]

Dearborn Trade Publishing Inc. [51467]

Lille D'Easum Library - SPEC Library [7400]

"*Death of the PC*" in Canadian Business (Vol. 83, October 12, 2010, No. 17, pp. 44) [3712], [4946], [25490], [41043], [41397], [45373]

"*Death Spiral*" in Business Journal Serving Greater Tampa Bay (Vol. 30, October 29, 2010, No. 45, pp. 1) [6293], [12243], [26195], [33642], [37359], [41863]

Death Valley Chamber of Commerce [48525]

Debbie Allen International [47994]

Debits and Credits: How Accounting Really Works [21329]

"*Debt Buyers Industry Rankings*" in Collections and Credit Risk (Vol. 14, September 1, 2009, No. 8, pp. 19) [6239], [6294], [22876], [26196]

"*Debt-Collection Agency to Lay Off 368 in Hampton Center*" in Virginian-Pilot (December 4, 2010) [6295], [26197], [35318], [35754], [41668], [44312]

"*The Debt Mountain in Mid-Collapse*" in Canadian Business (Vol. 83, October 12, 2010, No. 17, pp. 28) [10682], [16869], [17255]

Debut Computer Services [4816]

"*Debut Year Brings Success for Bike-Trail Boosters*" in Business Courier (Vol. 24, January 4, 2008, No. 39, pp. 4) [24841], [27120]

"*Debutante NYSE Soars 20 Percent*" in Globe & Mail (March 9, 2006, pp. B1) [8239], [12244], [22877]

Decatur Chamber of Commerce (DCC) [51588]; [58104]

Decatur Chamber of Commerce [47673]

Decatur County Area Chamber of Commerce (DCACC) [52087]

Decatur County Chamber of Commerce [57694]

Decatur Genealogical Society Library [9503]

Decatur Morgan County Chamber of Commerce (DCC) **[47673]**

"December 19 Is a Great Day to be Terrible" in Internet Wire (December 15, 2009) **[5801]**, **[22878]**, **[24314]**, **[39825]**

"A Decent Proposal" in Hawaii Business (Vol. 53, March 2008, No. 9, pp. 52) **[5978]**, **[22879]**, **[39013]**

Dechert LLP Library **[13233]**

"Decision CEO Cool to Acquisitions" in Globe & Mail (April 19, 2007, pp. B6) **[8240]**, **[12245]**, **[41323]**

The Decision Group (TDG) **[38698]**

Decision Making: How to Make Better, Faster, Smarter Decisions **[30361]**

Deck Renewal Systems USA **[6362]**

Deck the Walls **[11578]**, **[16328]**

"Decline in Assets Is Costly for Advisers" in The Business Journal-Serving Metropolitan Kansas City (Vol. 27, October 24, 2008) **[8241]**, **[12246]**, **[24315]**, **[25064]**, **[27121]**, **[31373]**, **[36458]**

"Decoding Demand Opportunities" in Business Strategy Review (Vol. 21, Spring 2010, No. 1, pp. 64) **[13993]**, **[39826]**

Decor & You, Inc. **[11579]**

Decorah Area Chamber of Commerce (DACC) **[51878]**

"Decorated Marine Sues Contractor" in Wall Street Journal Eastern Edition (November 29, 2011, pp. A4) **[5297]**, **[23818]**, **[33418]**, **[35319]**

Decorating Elves **[3101]**

Decorating Registry **[15370]**, **[15400]**

Decorating Retailer [15380], [18803]

Decorating Retailer--Buyers Guide Issue [15370], [15400]

Decorative Arts Digest [6021]

Decorative Arts Painting [6021]

"Dedge Rejects Inflation Concerns" in Globe & Mail (January 26, 2007, pp. B3) **[27122]**, **[32634]**

Deduct It! Lower Your Small Business Taxes **[19617]**, **[46203]**

Deduct It!: Lower Your Small Business Taxes **[73]**, **[2275]**, **[19618]**, **[21358]**, **[46204]**

"Deep in the Heart of Drought" in Green Industry Pro (Vol. 23, October 2011) **[9776]**, **[13386]**, **[13473]**, **[44313]**

"Deep Thoughts: Getting Employees to Think Better Requires a Bit of Creative Thinking Itself" in Canadian Business (March 17, 2008) **[25065]**, **[28172]**, **[29045]**, **[44824]**

Deer Isle - Stonington Chamber of Commerce **[52586]**

Deer Isle-Stonington Historical Society Library **[13977]**

Deer Lodge Demographics **[54267]**

Deer Lodge Visitor's Guide **[54268]**

Deer Park Area Chamber of Commerce **[59164]**

Deer Park Chamber of Commerce **[59164]**

Deer Park Chamber of Commerce (DPCC) **[58105]**

Deer Show Previews [19487]

Deer and Turkey Show Previews **[19487]**

"Deere to Open Technology Center in Germany" in Chicago Tribune (September 3, 2008) **[21556]**, **[22880]**, **[24316]**, **[36459]**, **[39014]**, **[43833]**

Deerfield, Bannockburn, Riverwoods Chamber of Commerce (DBRCC) **[51060]**

Deerfield Chamber of Commerce [51060]

Defending Windows Networks (Onsite) **[28022]**

"Defense Budge Ax May Not Come Down So Hard On the Region" in Baltimore Business Journal (Vol. 28, August 20, 2010, No. 15, pp. 1) **[18413]**, **[33189]**, **[33643]**

Defense Contract Administration, Services, and Management Area Operations (Phoenix, Arizona) **[61197]**; **[61198]**

Defense Contract Management Agency - Aircraft Program - Management Office **[61232]**

Defense Contract Management Agency (Atlanta, Georgia) **[61199]**

Defense Contract Management Agency (Baltimore, Maryland) **[61200]**

Defense Contract Management Agency (Baltimore, Maryland) - Baltimore Office **[61233]**

Defense Contract Management Agency (Boston, Massachusetts) **[61201]**

Defense Contract Management Agency (Chicago, Illinois) **[61202]**

Defense Contract Management Agency (Clearwater, Florida) **[61203]**

Defense Contract Management Agency (Dallas, Texas) **[61204]**

Defense Contract Management Agency (Denver, Colorado) **[61205]**; **[61206]**

Defense Contract Management Agency (Detroit, Michigan) **[61207]**

Defense Contract Management Agency District Headquarters (Boston, Massachusetts) **[61234]**

Defense Contract Management Agency (East Hartford, Connecticut) **[61208]**; **[61209]**

Defense Contract Management Agency (Garden City, New York) **[61210]**; **[61211]**

Defense Contract Management Agency (Indianapolis, Indianna) **[61212]**; **[61213]**

Defense Contract Management Agency (Orlando, Florida) **[61214]**; **[61215]**; **[61216]**

Defense Contract Management Agency (Philadelphia, Pennsylvania) **[61217]**; **[61218]**

Defense Contract Management Agency (Pittsburgh, Pennsylvania) **[61219]**

Defense Contract Management Agency (St. Louis, Missouri) **[61220]**

Defense Contract Management Agency (San Antonio, Texas) **[61221]**

Defense Contract Management Agency (San Diego, California) **[61222]**

Defense Contract Management Agency (San Diego, Texas) **[61223]**

Defense Contract Management Agency (Santa Ana, California) **[61224]**

Defense Contract Management Agency (Springfield, New Jersey) **[61225]**

Defense Contract Management Agency (Stratford, Connecticut) **[61226]**; **[61227]**

Defense Contract Management Agency (Sunnyvale, California) **[61228]**

Defense Contract Management Agency (Syracuse, New York) **[61229]**

Defense Contract Management Agency (Twin Cities, Minnesota) **[61230]**

Defense Contract Management Agency (Wichita, Kansas) **[61231]**

Defense Contract Management Area Operations (Detroit, Michigan) **[61235]**

Defense Contract Management Area Operations (Grand Rapids, Michigan) **[61236]**; **[61237]**

Defense Contract Management Area Operations (Pittsburgh, Pennsylvania) **[61238]**

Defense Contract Management Area Operations (Reading, Pennsylvania) **[61239]**; **[61240]**

Defense Contract Management Area Operations (San Antonio, Texas) **[61241]**

Defense Contract Management Area Operations (San Francisco, California) **[61242]**

Defense Contract Management Area Operations (Springfield, New Jersey) **[61243]**

Defense Contract Management Area Operations (Syracuse, New York) **[61244]**

Defense Contract Management Area Operations, Twin Cities **[61247]**

Defense Contract Management Area Operations (Van Nuys, California) **[61245]**; **[61246]**

Defense Contract Management Center **[61248]**; **[61249]**

Defense Contract Management Center - Aircraft Program - Management Office **[61250]**

Defense Contract Management Command (Atlanta, Georgia) **[61251]**

Defense Contract Management Command (Boston-Manchester) **[61252]**

Defense Contract Management Command, Boston-Manchester **[61275]**

Defense Contract Management Command (Boston, Massachusetts) **[61253]**

Defense Contract Management Command (Buffalo, New York) **[61254]**; **[61255]**

Defense Contract Management Command (Chicago, Illinois) **[61256]**

Defense Contract Management Command (Cleveland, Ohio) **[61257]**; **[61258]**

Defense Contract Management Command (Dallas, Texas) **[61259]**

Defense Contract Management Command (Dayton, Ohio) **[61260]**; **[61261]**

Defense Contract Management Command (Louisville Kentucky) **[61262]**

Defense Contract Management Command (Louisville, Kentucky) **[61263]**

Defense Contract Management Command (Orlando, Florida) **[61264]**

Defense Contract Management Command (St. Louis, Missouri) **[61265]**

Defense Contract Management Command (St. Petersburg, Florida) **[61266]**

Defense Contract Management Command (Santa Ana, California) **[61267]**

Defense Contract Management Command (Seattle, Washington) **[61268]**; **[61269]**

Defense Contract Management Command (South Bend, Indiana) **[61270]**; **[61271]**

Defense Contract Management Command (Staten Island, New York) **[61272]**; **[61273]**

Defense Contract Management Command (Wichita, Kansas) **[61274]**

Defense Contract Management District Headquarters (Boston, Massachusetts) **[61276]**

"Defense Contractor May Expand Locally; BAE Systems Ramps Up Vehicle Prototypes" in Crain's Detroit Business (March 24, 2008) **[22881]**, **[25491]**, **[39015]**, **[41044]**, **[42782]**, **[43834]**

Defense Finance & Accounting Service - Denver Center - Learning Center **[2329]**

Defense Information Systems Agency **[61277]**; **[61278]**

Defense Information Systems Agency (DISA) - Office of Small Business Programs **[61279]**

Defense Information Systems Agency (DISA) - Office of Small and Disadvantaged Business Utilization **[61280]**

Defense Plant Representative Office (Great Neck, New York) **[61281]**; **[61282]**

Defense Plant Representative Office (Los Angeles, California) **[61283]**; **[61284]**

Defense Plant Representative Office (Marietta, Georgia) **[61285]**; **[61286]**

Defense Plant Representative Office (Tucson, Arizona) **[61287]**; **[61288]**

Defense Plant Representative Office (West Palm Beach, Florida) **[61289]**

Defense Plant Representative Office, West Palm Beach, Florida **[61290]**

Defense Procurement Technical Assistance Center - New Jersey Institute of Technology **[54861]**

Defense Procurement Technical Assistance Center - New Jersey Institute of Technology - Atlantic Cape Community College - Satellite Office **[54862]**

Defense Procurement Technical Assistance Center - New Jersey Institute of Technology - Business & Career Development Center - Satellite Office **[54863]**

Defense Procurement Technical Assistance Center - New Jersey Institute of Technology - New Jersey Commerce & Economic Growth Commission - Satellite Office **[54864]**

Defense Supply Center Philadelphia **[57305]**

Defense Threat Reduction Agency - Office of Small and Disadvantaged Business Utilization **[61291]**; **[61292]**

Defensive Driving Techniques **[6600]**

"Defensive Training" in Crain's Detroit Business (Vol. 24, September 22, 2008, No. 38, pp. 11) **[23819]**, **[28173]**, **[37924]**, **[46866]**

"Defer Tax with Installment Sale Election" in Business Owner (Vol. 35, September-October 2011, No. 5, pp. 12) **[19619]**, **[44149]**, **[46205]**

Defiance Area Chamber of Commerce **[56115]**

The Definitive Drucker: The Final Word from the Father of Modern Management **[29620]**, **[37925]**

Defta Partners **[49201]**

"Defying Gravity?" in Canadian Business (Vol. 81, October 13, 2008, No. 17, pp. 17) **[24842]**, **[27123]**, **[45374]**

DEI Franchise Systems **[35638]**, **[43773]**

DEI Sales Training Systems **[43774]**

Aaron Deitsch, F.S.A. **[22051]**

"Deja Vu" in Canadian Business (Vol. 81, July 22, 2008, No. 12-13, pp. 38) **[25066]**, **[29621]**, **[37926]**, **[39016]**

DeKalb Chamber of Commerce (DCOC) **[51061]**

DeKalb Chamber Membership Guide **[51062]**

DeKalb County Map **[51063]**

Del Mar College Small Business Development Center **[57846]**

Del Mar Regional Chamber of Commerce **[48958]**

Del Norte Chamber of Commerce (DNCC) **[49490]**

Del Rio Chamber of Commerce (DRCC) **[58106]**

Del Technology Inc. **[38699]**, **[41481]**

Delafield Chamber of Commerce (DCC) **[59553]**

DeLand Area Chamber of Commerce (DACC) **[50062]**

DeLand Data **[50063]**

Delano Area Chamber of Commerce **[53631]**

Delano Chamber of Commerce **[48526]**

Delavan - Delavan Lake Area Chamber of Commerce **[59554]**

Delaware Area Chamber of Commerce (DACC) **[56116]**

Delaware Coast Vacationland **[49817]**

Delaware County Chamber of Commerce **[55184]**

Delaware County Chamber of Commerce (DCCC) **[57056]**

Delaware County Chamber of Commerce **[56116]**

Delaware County Community College **[57345]**

"Delaware Diaper Maker Wanting To Expand Less Than a Year After Move" in Business First-Columbus (December 7, 2007, pp. A6) **[1660]**, **[24733]**, **[33190]**, **[35320]**, **[39017]**

Delaware Directory of Commerce and Industry **[49818]**

Delaware Economic Development Office - Business Finance Section **[49808]**

Delaware Membership Directory & Business Resource Guide [49818]

Delaware Procurement Technical Assistance Center - Delaware Small Business Development Center Network **[49834]**

Delco MASTER INDEX

Delaware Senate Committee on Small Business **[49837]**
Delaware Small Business Development Center - Lead Office (DSBDC) **[49803]**
Delaware State Chamber Business Journal **[49819]**
Delaware State Chamber of Commerce Inc. (DSCC) **[49820]**
Delaware State Chamber of Commerce [49820]
Delaware State Chamber of Commerce Membership Directory & Business Resource Guide [49818]
Delaware State Museums Division of Historical and Cultural Affairs - Johnson Victrola Museum **[17658]**
Delaware Technology Park **[49836]**
Delaware Valley College of Science and Agriculture - Joseph Krauskopf Memorial Library **[21799]**
Delco Chamber of Commerce Membership Directory **[57057]**
Delegating Responsibility **[38620]**
Deli Meats 101 **[6445]**
Deli Meats & Poultry: Classic Tastes for Today's Consumer **[6446]**
"Delinquent Properties on the Rise" in Business Courier (Vol. 27, June 11, 2010, No. 6, pp. 1) **[6296]**, **[14407]**, **[17256]**, **[26198]**, **[37360]**
Delivering Knock Your Socks Off Service, 4th Edition **[32635]**, **[44314]**
Delivering Successful Presentations **[18574]**
Delohery Associates **[38700]**
Deloitte Services LLP Information Center **[2330]**
Deloitte Services LLP - Research Center. [2330]
Deloitte & Touche - Library **[270]**, **[19750]**
Deloitte & Touche - Library and Information Center **[2331]**
Deloitte & Touche - Research Center **[2332]**
Deloitte & Touche - Toronto North Library **[19751]**
Delphi Ventures **[49202]**
Delphos Area Chamber of Commerce (DACC) **[56117]**
Delta Alpha Publishing Ltd. **[53528]**
Delta Area Chamber of Commerce **[49491]**
Delta Area Chamber of Commerce (DACC) **[58649]**
Delta Chamber of Commerce **[56118]**
Delta Chamber of Commerce (DCC) **[47792]**
Delta Consulting Group [57835]
Delta County Area Chamber of Commerce **[53238]**
Delta County Chamber of Commerce (DCCC) **[58107]**
Delta Junction Chamber of Commerce **[47793]**
Delta Junction Visitor Guide **[47794]**
"Delta Looks at Downtown Departure" in Business Courier (Vol. 27, October 1, 2010, No. 22, pp. 1) **[17769]**, **[24734]**, **[24843]**, **[35321]**, **[35755]**, **[44664]**
Delta Properties **[53503]**
Delta Systems **[29244]**
"Deltona to Get First Movie Theater, Shopping Center" in Orlando Business Journal (Vol. 26, December 4, 2009, No. 26, pp. 1) **[5298]**, **[14568]**, **[42984]**
D.E.M. Allen & Associates Ltd. **[16751]**, **[20003]**
DeMers Programming Media Consultants **[16752]**, **[20004]**
Deming-Luna County Chamber of Commerce **[54949]**
Deming-Luna Chamber of Commerce [54949]
Democracy Data & Communications L.L.C. **[9293]**, **[16617]**
Democratization Without Representation: The Politics of Small Industry in Mexico **[33644]**, **[36460]**
Demographic Journal **[48044]**
Demographic Packet **[57058]**
Demographics **[57457]**
Demographics About Cleburne **[58108]**
Demokratizatsiya: The Journal of Post-Soviet Democratization **[42399]**
A Demon of Our Own Design: Markets, Hedge Funds, and the Perils of Financial Innovation **[8242]**, **[12247]**, **[33645]**
Demopolis Area Chamber of Commerce (DACC) **[47674]**
Demotte Chamber of Commerce (DCC) **[51589]**
"Demystifying Demotion" in Business Horizons (November-December 2007, pp. 455) **[29046]**, **[37927]**
"Denali Asks Consumers to Name Next Moose Tracks Flavor" in Ice Cream Reporter (Vol. 23, August 20, 2010, No. 9, pp. 4) **[10871]**, **[39827]**
Denali Chamber of Commerce **[47795]**
Denham Springs-Livingston Parish Chamber of Commerce [52465]
Denison Area Chamber of Commerce (DACC) **[58109]**
Denison Consulting **[38701]**
Dennis G. Glore Inc. (DGG) **[985]**
Dennis Township Chamber of Commerce **[54706]**
Denny's, Inc. **[18117]**
Dent Clinic Canada 2000, Inc. **[18642]**
Dent Doctor **[18643]**
Dental Economics **[14225]**
Dental Manufacturers of America [14184]
Dental Trade Alliance (DTA) **[14184]**
Dentaletter **[14226]**, **[34510]**, **[42901]**
DentalWare **[1091]**
The Dentist Choice, Inc. **[15202]**, **[34632]**
Denton Chamber of Commerce (DCC) **[58110]**
Denton County Small Business Development Center **[57847]**
Denver Apparel and Accessory Market **[1667]**, **[3909]**, **[4298]**, **[13563]**
Denver Botanic Gardens - Helen Fowler Library **[9853]**
The Denver Business Journal **[49636]**
The Denver Enterprise Center **[49623]**
Denver Hispanic Chamber of Commerce **[49492]**
Denver JobBank: The Job Hunter's Guide to Colorado **[19174]**
Denver JobBank [19174]
Denver Merchandise Mart Directory **[3900]**
Denver Metro Chamber of Commerce **[49493]**
Denver Metro Chamber of Commerce - Small Business Development Center **[49437]**
Denver Metro Small Business Development Center **[49417]**
"Denver Will Put Up Fight for MillerCoors HQ" in Business Journal-Milwaukee (Vol. 25, October 19, 2007, No. 3, pp. A1) **[2456]**, **[41864]**, **[44665]**
Denville Chamber of Commerce (DCOC) **[54707]**
dEpagnier Furniture **[41589]**
Departement des Metiers de la Construction - Bureau Canadien [46797]
Department of Administrative Services - Office of Small and Minority Business Division **[50660]**
"Department of Agriculture" in Ice Cream Reporter (Vol. 23, November 20, 2010, No. 12, pp. 8) **[10872]**, **[21557]**, **[27124]**, **[33646]**
Department of Central Services - Purchasing Division **[56618]**
Department of Defense - Defense Logistics Agency - Defense Construction Supply Center **[61293]**
Department of Defense - Defense Logistics Agency - Defense Electronics Supply Center **[61294]**; **[61295]**
Department of Defense - Defense Logistics Agency - Defense General Supply Center **[61296]**; **[61297]**
Department of Defense - Defense Logistics Agency - Defense Industrial Supply Center **[61298]**
Department of Defense - Defense Logistics Agency - Defense Supply Center (Columbus, Ohio) **[61299]**
Department of Defense - Defense Logistics Agency - Defense Supply Center Philadelphia **[61300]**
Department of Defense - Defense Logistics Agency - Troop Support **[61301]**
Department of Economic & Community Development - Office of Business and Industry Development **[49648]**
Department of Labor - Labor Market Information - Research and Statistics Division **[61636]**
Department of Labor - Louisianan Workforce Commission - Media Relations **[61637]**
Department of Labor - Media Relations **[61638]**
Department of Labor - Office of Management & Finance - Tax Accounting/Adjustments Unit **[61639]**; **[61640]**
Department of Labor - Office of Occupational and Labor Market Information **[61641]**; **[61642]**
Department of Labor - Workforce Information and Analysis **[61643]**
The Department of Labor's Overtime Regulations Effect on Small Business: Congressional Hearing **[33647]**, **[35756]**
Department of Business Education of the National Education Association [27981]
Department of Commerce [60905], [62172]
"DePaul To Train Hotel Leaders" in Chicago Tribune (September 22, 2008) **[10683]**, **[20143]**, **[20537]**, **[28174]**
Deploying Intrusion Detection Systems: Hands-On (Onsite) **[28023]**, **[34738]**
Deploying Microsoft Windows Vista Business Desktops (Onsite) **[45038]**
Deploying Virtual Server and Workstation Technology: Hands-On (Onsite) **[28024]**
Deposit Chamber of Commerce **[55185]**
Deposit Growth Strategies **[8862]**, **[31987]**
The Depot Connection **[58111]**
Depot Signal **[51590]**
Derby Chamber of Commerce (DCC) **[52088]**
Dermott Area Chamber of Commerce (DACC) **[48045]**
Dermott Chamber of Commerce [48045]
Des Moines Area Community College - Urban Campus **[52009]**
Des Moines Art Center Library **[4566]**
Des Plaines Chamber of Commerce and Industry **[51064]**
"Descartes Launches Ocean Shipment Management Suite" in Canadian Corporate News (May 16, 2007) **[18887]**, **[41045]**, **[44315]**
"Describing the Entrepreneurial Profile" in International Journal of Entrepreneurship and Small Business (Vol. 11, November 1, 2010) **[29622]**, **[42783]**
Desert Hot Springs Chamber of Commerce **[48527]**
Desert Moon Fresh Mexican Grill **[1733]**, **[19281]**
Deshler Chamber of Commerce **[56119]**
"Design program in Athletic Footwear" in Occupational Outlook Quarterly (Vol. 55, Fall 2011, No. 3, pp. 21) **[3348]**, **[4096]**, **[18754]**, **[19323]**, **[28175]**
"Design Center Shows Quality of Digital Paper" in American Printer (Vol. 128, June 1, 2011, No. 6) **[4467]**, **[16365]**, **[20765]**, **[45112]**
Design Collective Architecture Inc. [41590]
Design Collective Inc. (Columbus, Ohio) **[41590]**
Design Cost Data: Cost Estimating Magazine for Design and Construction **[5592]**
Design Financial Inc. **[47135]**
Design Journal Perspective [11531], [15241]
Design and Launch an Online Travel Business in a Week **[15290]**, **[20120]**, **[20499]**, **[21080]**, **[26199]**
Design and Launch Your eCommerce Business in a Week **[11664]**, **[21019]**, **[28507]**
Design and Launch Your Online Boutique in a Week **[432]**, **[4185]**, **[7810]**, **[15291]**, **[26416]**, **[28508]**, **[39828]**, **[42918]**, **[43339]**
Design Library. [16763]
Design Management Institute (DMI) **[21274]**
Design & Manufacturing Midwest **[39513]**
Design and Page Layout Skills (Onsite) **[42593]**
Design for Presentations **[18535]**
Design for Print **[6508]**
"Design Programs for HVAC Sizing Solutions" in Contractor (Vol. 57, January 2010, No. 1, pp. 44) **[804]**, **[3524]**, **[5299]**, **[18888]**, **[30568]**, **[34851]**, **[45113]**
Design Reviews for Effective Product Development (Onsite) **[24201]**
"The Design of Tax Policy in Canada" in Canadian Journal of Economics (Vol. 44, November 2011, No. 4, pp. 1184) **[36461]**, **[46206]**
"The Design of Things to Come" in Business Horizons (Vol. 51, January-February 2008, No. 1, pp. 74) **[29623]**, **[36990]**, **[39829]**, **[41046]**
Design Your Own Effective Employee Handbook: How to Make the Most of Your Staff with Companion CD-ROM **[29047]**, **[37928]**
Design Your Own Home **[11580]**
"Designer is Walking Ad for TIBI Line" in Charlotte Observer (February 5, 2007) **[433]**, **[4097]**, **[4213]**, **[39830]**
The Designer's Guide to Marketing and Pricing: How to Win Clients and What to Charge Them **[4098]**, **[25745]**, **[39831]**
"Designers' Hats Foretell a Big Comeback Next Fall" in Charlotte Observer (February 8, 2007) **[4099]**, **[7824]**
Designing and Building Great Web Pages: Hands-On (Onsite) **[28025]**, **[45039]**
Designing for Diversity **[22179]**
The Designing Editor **[6810]**
Designing Effective Questionnaires: A Step By Step Workshop (Onsite) **[39581]**
Designing Effective Questionnaires: A Step by Step Workshop (Onsite) **[39582]**
"Designing Events Updates Online Suite" in Wireless News (October 25, 2009) **[2769]**, **[11665]**, **[20353]**, **[21081]**, **[37929]**, **[39832]**, **[41669]**, **[46634]**
"Designing Solutions Around Customer Network Identity Goals" in Journal of Marketing (Vol. 75, March 2011, No. 2, pp. 36) **[26417]**, **[39833]**
Designing Websites for Every Audience **[11666]**, **[21082]**, **[28621]**
"Desk-Bound No More" in Charlotte Business Journal (Vol. 25, August 13, 2010, No. 21, pp. 1) **[21890]**, **[29048]**, **[46505]**
"Deskside Story: As the Latest Buzzword Suggests, PR Firms Are Happy To Drop By" in Inc. (December 2007, pp. 70, 73) **[10994]**, **[16587]**, **[39834]**, **[43440]**
Desktop Design 1: Basic Electronic Graphic Techniques **[6532]**
Desktop Design 2: Creative Design with PostScript Drawing Software **[6533]**
Desktop Design 3: Creative Design with Page-Layout Software **[6534]**
Desloge Chamber of Commerce **[54031]**
"Desmarais Makes Move into U.S." in Globe & Mail (February 2, 2007, pp. B1) **[25067]**, **[41865]**
Desmond-Fish Library **[9036]**
DeSoto Chamber of Commerce (DCC) **[58112]**
DeSoto County Chamber of Commerce **[50064]**
"Despite Economic Upheaval Generation Y is Still Feeling Green: RSA Canada Survey" in CNW Group (October 28, 2010) **[7166]**, **[7528]**, **[27125]**, **[30569]**, **[45375]**
"Despite Gloom, Auto Sales Saw Gains in 2005" in Globe & Mail (January 5, 2006, pp. B1) **[14886]**, **[27126]**, **[39018]**

3494 Small Business Sourcebook • 30th Edition

DirectBuild **MASTER INDEX**

Direct Link **[18522]**
Direct Mail Advertising Association [13740], [39559]
Direct Mail/Marketing Association [13740], [39559]
"Direct Marketing" in MarketingMagazine (Vol. 115, September 27, 2010, No. 13, pp. 74) **[435]**, **[39837]**
Direct Marketing Association (DMA) **[13740]**, **[39559]**
Direct Marketing Association Annual Conference & Exhibition **[13751]**
Direct Marketing Association Catalog Council [13739]
Direct Marketing Association Library & Resource Center **[13754]**
Direct Marketing Computer Association [13740], [39559]
Direct Marketing List Source **[13741]**
Direct Marketing Sales Source [4596]
"Direct Recovery Associates Debt Collection Agency Beats Industry Record" in Internet Wire (June 24, 2010) **[6298]**, **[23824]**, **[26202]**, **[36467]**
"Direct Recovery Associates, Inc. Debt Collection Agency Founder Featured in China Daily" in Internet Wire (November 9, 2010) **[6299]**, **[26203]**, **[36468]**
Direct Selling Association **[43345]**
Direct Selling Education Foundation (DSEF) **[43346]**
DirectBuild **[2996]**
DirectBuy **[43290]**
Direction for Business **[54383]**
DIRECTIONS **[48530]**
Directions **[51592]**; **[53854]**; **[56120]**; **[56121]**; **[56505]**
Directions Ltd. **[38703]**
"Director Elections Campaign Pays Off" in Globe & Mail (March 9, 2006, pp. B1) **[32638]**, **[33652]**
The Director: Official Publication of the National Funeral Directors Association **[9340]**
Directors Guild of America--Directory of Members **[7916]**
Directors Guild of Canada (DGC) **[7881]**
Directory of American Agriculture **[21559]**
Directory of American Firms Operating in Foreign Countries **[36469]**
Directory of Apparel Specialty Stores **[3889]**, **[4214]**
Directory of the Association of Machinery and Equipment Appraisers **[1214]**
Directory of Automotive Aftermarket Suppliers **[1552]**
Directory/Business Profile Booklet **[51593]**
Directory of Businesses **[48531]**; **[58115]**
Directory of Businesses and Services **[55678]**
Directory and Buyer's Guide **[56506]**
Directory of Canadian Chartered Accountants **[37]**, **[2260]**, **[19596]**
The Directory of Canadian Recruiters **[3346]**
Directory of Catholic Charities USA Directories **[34245]**
Directory of Certified Unitary Air-Conditioners, Unitary Air-Source Heat Pumps and Sound-Rated Outdoor Unitary Equipment **[805]**
Directory of Chain Restaurant Operators **[17908]**
Directory of Chamber Members **[53633]**
Directory of Clubs & Organizations **[57059]**
Directory of Clubs and Organizations **[51594]**
Directory of Community **[51595]**
Directory and Community Guide **[51067]**
Directory of Computer & Consumer Electronics Retailers **[18337]**
Directory of Contract Staffing Firms **[19156]**
Directory of Department Stores **[42987]**
Directory of Drug Store & HBC Chains **[6652]**
Directory of Executive and Professional Recruiters: 2009-2010 **[7784]**
Directory of Family Associations **[9436]**
Directory of Festivals, Schools and Workshops **[14621]**
Directory of Firms, Products, and Services **[53241]**
Directory of Florida Industries **[50067]**
Directory of Foodservice Distributors **[3466]**, [9920], **[18017]**
Directory of Freight Forwarders and Custom House Brokers **[9206]**
Directory of Global Professional Accounting and Business Certifications **[76]**, **[2277]**, **[19621]**, **[21359]**
Directory of High Volume Independent Restaurants **[10282]**
Directory of Home Center Operators & Hardware Chains **[10130]**, **[13652]**, **[15371]**
Directory of Home Furnishings Retailers **[10461]**
Directory of Human Services and Self Help Support Groups--Maricopa County **[34246]**
Directory of International and Regional Organizations Conducting Standards-Related Activities **[14272]**
Directory of Libraries in Canada **[11231]**
Directory of Listed Plumbing Products **[16234]**
The Directory of Mail Order Catalogs **[13742]**
Directory of Major Mailers **[4596]**
Directory of Manufacturers and Industrial Suppliers **[58116]**
Directory of Manufactures, Community Profile, Membership Directory **[58117]**
Directory of Manufacturing **[48047]**
Directory and Map **[53634]**
Directory of Members **[51068]**; **[56122]**; **[59856]**
Directory of Nationally Certified Teachers **[14622]**
Directory and New Resident Guide **[54033]**
Directory of Bonded Collectors [6272]
Directory of Business Writers [6827]
Directory of Catholic Charities Diocesan Agencies and Organizations [34245]
Directory of Chamber Music Workshops, Schools & Festivals [14621]
Directory of Contract Service Firms [19156]
Directory of Convenience Stores [5816]
Directory of Diocesan Agencies of Catholic Charities and NCCC Member Institutions in the United States, Puerto Rico [34245]
Directory of Executive Recruiters [7784]
Directory of Festivals and Workshops [14621]
Directory of Government Prime Contractors [33430]
Directory of Government Production Prime Contractors [33430]
Directory of Human Service Agencies in Rhode Island [34420]
Directory of Human Services--Maricopa County [34246]
Directory of Marketing Services and Membership Roster [39651]
Directory of Plumbing Research Recommendations [16234]
Directory of Primes [33413]
Directory of Professional Genealogists and Related Services [9437]
Directory of Summer Chamber Music Workshops, Schools & Festivals [14621]
Directory of U.S.-Based Agencies Involved in International Health [34282]
Directory of Waste Equipment Manufacturers and Distributors [10168]
Directory of Ontario Lumber and Building Materials, Hardware and Home Improvement Retailers **[10124]**
Directory of Operating Small Business Investment Companies **[47007]**
Directory and Planning Calendar **[53242]**
Directory of Private Accredited Career Schools and Colleges of Technology **[55]**, **[729]**, **[778]**, **[2241]**, **[2617]**, **[3417]**, **[3934]**, **[4449]**, **[4797]**, **[4840]**, **[4933]**, **[5202]**, **[6874]**, **[7014]**, **[7896]**, **[9099]**, **[9769]**, **[10025]**, **[10054]**, **[10068]**, **[10614]**, **[10657]**, **[11030]**, **[11538]**, **[13269]**, **[13615]**, **[13697]**, **[13934]**, **[14108]**, **[14271]**, **[14363]**, **[14790]**, **[14796]**, **[14802]**, **[15012]**, **[15390]**, **[15673]**, **[15693]**, **[15901]**, **[16216]**, **[16353]**, **[16461]**, **[16793]**, **[17638]**, **[17874]**, **[18385]**, **[18593]**, **[19504]**, **[19559]**, **[19834]**, **[19872]**, **[19896]**, **[20136]**, **[20528]**, **[20669]**, **[20821]**, **[20825]**, **[20930]**, **[21309]**, **[42933]**
Directory of Products and Services **[58118]**
Directory of Professional Genealogists **[9437]**
Directory of Real Estate Development & Related Education Programs **[17167]**
Directory of Small Press--Magazine Editors and Publishers **[2124]**, **[15528]**
Directory of SRCC Certified Collectors and Solar Water Heating Systems Ratings **[19085]**
Directory of Supermarket, Grocery & Convenience Store Chains **[5802]**, **[9921]**
Directory of Venture Capital: 2nd Edition **[47008]**
Directory of Venture Capital and Private Equity Firms **[44825]**
The Directory of Venture Capital and Private Equity Firms: 2009 **[8254]**, **[12259]**, **[47009]**
"Dirty Work Required" in Workforce Management (Vol. 88, November 16, 2009, No. 12, pp. 34) **[27136]**, **[29049]**, **[32639]**, **[37937]**, **[46867]**
Disa Conus - Defense Information Systems Agency **[51426]**
Disability Income Concepts Inc. (DIC) **[47136]**
Disabled Businesspersons Association (DBA) **[40680]**
"Disappearing Act" in Globe & Mail (April 21, 2007, pp. B1) **[8255]**, **[12260]**
Disaster Kleenup Int'l. **[6363]**
Disaster Recovery Planning: Ensuring Business Continuity (Onsite) **[24202]**; **[34741]**
Disciple's Directory, Inc. **[15027]**, **[16435]**
Discipline: A Matter of Judgment **[29205]**, **[38621]**
"Discount Beers Take Fizz Out Of Molson" in Globe & Mail (February 10, 2006, pp. B3) **[1842]**, **[8256]**, **[12261]**, **[13578]**, **[39025]**
Discount Imaging Franchise Corporation **[3102]**
"Discount Shopping: Holiday Shopping Meets Social Media" in Employee Benefit News (Vol. 25, December 1, 2011, No. 15) **[21891]**, **[29050]**, **[42988]**, **[44099]**
Discount Sport Nutrition **[15203]**, **[43291]**
Discover **[47894]**
Discover Baytown **[58119]**
Discover Cannon Falls **[53635]**
Discover the Chamber **[51880]**
Discover Expo [18741]
Discover Gilroy **[48532]**
Discover Mid-America **[1136]**, **[6128]**
Discover Our Spirit **[50068]**
Discover Wayzata **[53636]**
"Discover the Wedding Location of Your Dreams" in Benzinga.com (December 24, 2011) **[2497]**, **[10685]**
DISCOVERY **[44015]**
Discovery **[52089]**
Discovery Capital **[59882]**
"Discovery Communications" in Workforce Management (Vol. 88, December 14, 2009, No. 13, pp. 17) **[11336]**, **[21892]**, **[34247]**, **[36133]**
Discovery Line **[58120]**
"Discovery Networks" in Brandweek (Vol. 49, April 21, 2008, No. 16, pp. SR9) **[436]**, **[7917]**, **[19926]**, **[22889]**, **[37938]**, **[39838]**, **[43441]**
"Discrete Wavelet Transform-Based Time Series Analysis and Mining" in ACM Computing Surveys (Vol. 43, Summer 2011, No. 2, pp. 6) **[4641]**, **[4705]**, **[4851]**
Disease Concept of Alcoholism/EAP **[46074]**
"Disney-ABC Domestic Television Distribution" in Brandweek (Vol. 49, April 21, 2008, No. 16, pp. SR13) **[437]**, **[7918]**, **[19927]**, **[37939]**, **[39839]**, **[43442]**
"Disney Has High Hopes for Duffy" in Canadian Business (Vol. 83, October 12, 2010, No. 17, pp. 14) **[20242]**, **[25496]**, **[36470]**, **[41048]**
Disney Presents Bill Nye the Science Guy Sampler III **[28416]**
Walt Disney World - Global Business Technology Strategy Library **[4681]**, **[4827]**, **[4911]**, **[5027]**, **[36077]**
"The Display Group Is Super-Sized" in Michigan Vue (Vol. 13, July-August 2008, No. 4, pp. 34) **[7919]**, **[17772]**, **[20357]**, **[22890]**, **[33192]**, **[33653]**, **[39840]**, **[46207]**, **[46638]**
Dispute Resolution Journal **[14167]**
Distilled Spirits Council of the United States Inc. [1829]
Distilled Spirits Council of the United States (DISCUS) **[1829]**
Distilled Spirits Council of the U.S. Library **[1887]**, **[13605]**
Distilled Spirits Institute [1829]
The Distinct Advantage (Onsite) **[43352]**
Distinctly Denton **[58121]**
Distribution Assistance **[39520]**
Distribution Business Management Association (DBMA) **[26721]**
Distribution Center Management **[26804]**
Distribution Channels [3296], [20093]
Distribution Channels Buying Guide & AWMA Membership Directory **[3285]**
Distribution and LTL Carriers Association (DLTLCA) **[20653]**
Distribution Research and Education Foundation [26726], [47169]
Distributorless Ignition **[18629]**
District of Columbia Chamber of Commerce (DCCC) **[49846]**
District of Columbia Office of the Deputy Mayor - Planning and Economic Development **[49841]**
District of Columbia Public Library - Business, Economics and Vocations Division **[2333]**, **[19200]**
District of Columbia Public Library - Technology and Science Division **[1095]**, **[4682]**, **[21272]**
District of Columbia Small Business Development Center at University of District of Columbia (DC SBDC) **[49839]**
Dittrick Medical History Center **[10373]**
Richard Ditzler **[219]**
Divas Doing Business: What the Guidebooks Don't Tell You About Being A Woman Entrepreneur **[29631]**, **[47263]**
Diversified Health Resources Inc. **[2859]**, **[15112]**, **[25988]**, **[34620]**
Diversity Awareness (Onsite) **[40854]**
The Diversity Code: Unlocking the Secrets to Making Differences Work in the Real World **[23825]**, **[33654]**, **[35759]**, **[37940]**, **[40874]**
"Diversity Elite Scorecard" in Hispanic Business (September 2007, pp. 72-74, 76, 78, 80, 82, 84) **[3715]**, **[40875]**
Diversity Information Resources (DIR) **[40681]**
"Diversity Knocks" in Canadian Business (Vol. 83, October 12, 2010, No. 17, pp. 62) **[36471]**, **[40876]**
"Diversity Stock Indexes" in Hispanic Business (September 2007, pp. 28) **[12262]**
Diversity Train-the-Trainer (Onsite) **[28030]**, **[40855]**
"DiversityStockIndexes" in Hispanic Business (October 2007, pp. 68) **[12263]**, **[40729]**
DiversityWorks **[26702]**, **[36021]**
Dividend Record **[2741]**, **[8940]**, **[13204]**
Dividends **[50516]**; **[54570]**
"Dividing to Conquer" in Barron's (Vol. 88, March 31, 2008, No. 13, pp. 22) **[8257]**, **[12264]**, **[21560]**, **[24318]**, **[25068]**, **[31382]**, **[36472]**, **[39841]**

3496 **Small Business Sourcebook • 30th Edition**

"Don't Quit When The Road Gets Bumpy" in Women Entrepreneur (November 25, 2008) [24324], [25070], [26207], [27148], [29642], [32646], [47266]

"Don't Shoot the Messenger: A Wake-Up Call For Academics" in Academy of Management Journal (Vol. 50, No. 5, October 2007, pp. 1020) [28179], [37948]

"Don't Touch My Laptop, If You Please Mr. Customs Man" in Canadian Electronics (Vol. 23, June-July 2008, No. 4, pp. 6) [3526], [18890], [24847], [32647], [34858], [45114]

"Don't Try This Offshore" in Harvard Business Review (Vol. 86, September 2008, No. 9, pp. 39) [11082], [21897], [24325], [25071], [41670]

"Don't Tweak Your Supply Chain - Rethink It End to End" in Harvard Business Review (Vol. 88, October 2010, No. 10, pp. 62) [4216], [36478], [37191]

DoodyCalls [44606]

Dooley's [1883], [1992]

Dooly County Chamber of Commerce [50518]

"The Doomsday Scenario" in Conde Nast Portfolio (Vol. 2, June 2008, No. 6, pp. 91) [14888], [26748], [27149], [39027]

Door County Chamber of Commerce [59557]

Door and Hardware Institute Annual Convention and Exposition [10147]

Door-To-Door Dry Cleaning [6757]

Doorways [58904]

Dorchester Chamber of Commerce [52708]

Dorland's Medical Directory [34255]

Dorland's Medical Directory: Eastern Pennsylvania and Southern New Jersey [34255]

Dorland's Medical Directory for the Delaware Valley [34255]

Dorland's Physicians Directory and Resource Guide [34255]

Dorn & Associates Inc. [21460], [22052], [28439], [36023], [38705], [42327]

Dorset Capital [49207]

Dorsey & Whitney, LLP [32301]

Dot Edu Ventures [49208]

DOT Hazardous Materials Training (Onsite) [30450], [33486]

Dothan Area Chamber of Commerce [47675]

"Dots Sings To New Tune With Its Radio Station" in Crain's Cleveland Business (Vol. 30, June 15, 2009, No. 23, pp. 7) [4217], [15320], [16710], [21084], [28627], [39845], [41051], [42991]

"Double Duty" in Black Enterprise (Vol. 38, February 2008, No. 7, pp. 56) [3718], [41399]

Double or Nothing: How Two Friends Risked It All to Buy One of Las Vegas' Legendary Casinos [9393], [11671], [20145], [20539], [28628], [29643]

Doubleday Broadway Publishing Group [55523]

Doubleday Publishing Group [55523]

"Doubletree Finds a Niche for Giving Back" in Hotel and Motel Management (Vol. 225, July 2010, No. 8, pp. 6) [10686], [20146], [20540], [24848], [45905]

"Doubtful Donors" in Canadian Business (Vol. 81, December 8, 2008, No. 21, pp. 8) [27150], [45906]

Douglas Area Chamber of Commerce [59817]

Douglas - Coffee County Chamber of Commerce [50519]

Douglas County Chamber of Commerce [50520]

Douglass Chamber of Commerce [52092]

Dove Cleaners & Cadet Cleaners [6758]

Dover Area Chamber of Commerce [54708]

Dover Chamber of Commerce [54577]

Dover Small Business Development Center [49804]

"Dow AgroSciences Buys Wheat Breeding Firm in Pacific Northwest" in Farm Industry News (July 29, 2011) [21562], [25308], [42784], [43837]

"Dow Champions Innovative Energy Solutions for Auto Industry at NAIAS" in Business of Global Warming (January 25, 2010, pp. 7) [7170], [7532], [20358], [30575], [36479], [39028], [41872], [46639]

Dow Jones Business and Financial Weekly [8932], [13194], [14534]

"Dow Jones Gives Apple-Loving Sales Professionals a Boost" in Information Today (Vol. 26, February 2009, No. 2, pp. 30) [3719], [8272], [12279], [41873], [43446]

Dow Jones News/Retrieval [54886]

Dow Jones Reuters Business Interactive L.L.C. [54886]

Dow Theory Forecasts [2711]

Dowagiac Event and Festival [53243]

Dowagiac Tourist Guide [53244]

"Down by the Bay" in Canadian Business (Vol. 81, December 8, 2008, No. 21, pp. 15) [22896], [26419], [42992], [43447]

"Down on the Boardwalk" in Retail Merchandiser (Vol. 51, September-October 2011, No. 5, pp. 56) [20244], [39846], [42466]

Down to Business [57060]

"Down Mexico Way" in Canadian Business (Vol. 79, September 25, 2006, No. 19, pp. 27) [27151], [36480]

"Down a 'Peg" in Canadian Business (Vol. 79, September 25, 2006, No. 19, pp. 41) [27152], [32648]

"Down the Tracks, a Whistle Is a Blowin" in Barron's (Vol. 89, July 27, 2009, No. 30, pp. 36) [11083], [27153], [33197], [33663]

"Down to the Wire for Your Taxes" in Women In Business (Vol. 63, Spring 2011, No. 1, pp. 22) [19623], [46210]

Downeast Maine SCORE [52546]

Downer & Company [53022]

Downers Grove Area Chamber of Commerce and Industry [51071]

Downey Business [48534]

Downey Chamber of Commerce (DCC) [48535]

Downingtown Area Chamber of Commerce [57061]

Downingtown-Thorndale Regional Chamber of Commerce [57061]

"The Downside of Self-Management" in Academy of Management Journal (August 2007) [26420], [37949]

Downtime Inc. [41474], [41582]

"Downtown Bank Got High Marks for Irwin Purchase, Is Looking For More" in Business Courier (Vol. 27, September 3, 2010, No. 18, pp. 1) [8273], [12280], [25309], [41391], [41874]

"Downtown Detroit Needs More Retail" in Crain's Detroit Business (Vol. 24, March 10, 2008, No. 10, pp. 9) [27154], [42993], [44666]

"Downtown Evens Tenant Ledger" in The Business Journal-Serving Metropolitan Kansas City (Vol. 26, July 11, 2008, No. 44, pp. 1) [14412], [16522], [16880], [17270], [24736], [25498]

Downtown Idea Exchange [1294]

"Downtown Light Rail Plans Up in the Air" in Business Journal Serving Greater Tampa Bay (Vol. 30, October 22, 2010, No. 44, pp. 1) [2003], [5311]

Downtown Merchant Directory [50070]

"Downtown Retail Site Sold to ATCO" in Austin Business JournalInc. (Vol. 29, November 20, 2009, No. 37, pp. 1) [12281], [17271], [42994], [44667]

"Downtowns Must Court Young, CEOs for Cities President Says" in Crain's Detroit Business (Vol. 24, October 6, 2008, No. 40, pp. 18) [20359], [28180], [35323], [37950], [46640]

"Downturn Tests HCL's Pledge to Employees" in Workforce Management (Vol. 88, November 16, 2009, No. 12, pp. 23) [27155], [29055], [34859], [35761], [37951], [46868]

Antoinette Doyle Consulting [47137]

"Doyle: Domino's New Pizza Seasoned with Straight Talk" in Crain's Detroit Business (Vol. 26, January 11, 2010, No. 2, pp. 1) [438], [16124], [24326], [25072], [39847]

Doyle & Dulaney [21461]

"Dozens 'Come Alive' in Downtown Chicago" in Green Industry Pro (July 2011) [9777], [13387], [13474], [28181], [39848], [43448], [44320]

DPRA Inc. [21774]

Draft/FCB Worldwide Information Center [688]

"Dragon, but.." in Canadian Business (Vol. 81, December 8, 2008, No. 21, pp. 45) [11084], [36481], [45907]

Dragon Magazine [6130]

Drama Kids International, Inc. [28456]

"Dramatic Results: Making Opera (Yes, Opera) Seem Young and Hip" in Inc. (October 2007, pp. 61-62) [439], [16711], [28629], [37952], [39849], [42616]

Draper & Associates [5635]

Draper, Fisher, Jurvetson / Draper Associates [49209]

Draper International [49210]

Draper Richards L.P. [49211]

Draper Triangle Ventures [57284]

Draperies & Window Coverings--Directory & Buyer's Guide Issue: 2005 [2025]

"Drawn to York County: Less-Expensive Homes, Good Schools Attract Charlotteans" in Charlotte Observer (February 4, 2007) [5312], [16881], [17272], [44668]

"Dream Big! When the Going Gets Tough, Reps Work Harder and Smarter" in Agency Sales Magazine (Vol. 39, July 2009, No. 7, pp. 22) [26421], [27156], [43449]

Dream Dinners Inc. [6185]

The Dream Manager [29056], [29644], [37953], [45908]

"Dream On: California's Budget Fix may not Last for Long." in Barron's (Vol. 89, July 27, 2009, No. 30, pp. 21) [22105], [27157], [33198]

DreamCatcher Interactive Inc. [59943]

"Dreaming in Macau" in Canadian Business (Vol. 81, December 8, 2008, No. 21, pp. 65) [11085], [27158], [36482]

DreamMaker Bath and Kitchen [3437]

Dreams with a Deadline: How to Turn a Strategy for Tomorrow Into a Plan for Today [24327], [29645]

"Dreamy Fortune: Pillow Biz Dreams of Sales Reaching $10 Million a Year" in Small Business Opportunities (Spring 2008) [10394], [10463]

Drennan Communications [40601]

Drennan Literary Agency [40601]

Dresdner RCM Global Investors - Research Library. [13243]

Dresner Capital Resources, Inc. [51399]

"Dress Professionally Cool for Summer" in Women In Business (Vol. 62, June 2010, No. 2, pp. 38) [4218], [47267]

Drew County Chamber of Commerce [48088]

"Dreyer's Grand Ice Cream" in Ice Cream Reporter (Vol. 23, September 20, 2010, No. 10, pp. 8) [10873], [22897], [35324], [39029]

DRI Capital Inc. [59925]

DRI Consulting (DRIC) [3066], [13822], [24667], [25990], [38706]

Dried Fruit Association of New York [17857]

Jordan Driks [37162]

"Drilling Deep and Flying High" in Barron's (Vol. 88, June 30, 2008, No. 26, pp. 34) [8274], [12282], [22898], [31392], [36483], [39030], [44321]

"Drink Up" in Black Enterprise (Vol. 38, March 2008, No. 8, pp. 50) [10219], [10283], [21482]

Drinking Water & Backflow Prevention [20984]

Dripping Springs SCORE [57886]

"Drive Traffic To Your Blog" in Women Entrepreneur (January 13, 2009) [11672], [21085], [22288], [28630], [34860], [39850]

"Driving Home Success: Stamped Asphalt for Driveways and Paths is Hottest New Trend" in Small Business Opportunities (Winter 2007) [5158], [32091]

Driving Innovation: Proven Processes, Tools and Strategies for Growth (Onsite) [37612]

"Driving Passion" in Small Business Opportunities (Spring 2008) [9657], [29646]

Driving School Association of America Annual Conference [6602]

Driving School Association of America International Convention [6602]

Driving With No Brakes: How a Bunch of Hooligans Built the Best Travel Company in the World [20147], [20541], [29647], [37954], [41875]

"Drop in the Bucket Makes a lot of Waves" in Globe & Mail (March 22, 2007, pp. B1) [25746], [30576], [39031]

Drop Shipping Marketing Methods [26805]

Dropkin Consulting [2936], [13868], [26065], [29265], [38782], [44951]

"Dropped Calls" in Canadian Business (Vol. 80, November 5, 2007, No. 22, pp. 34) [3720], [25747], [34861], [36992]

"Drought Takes Toll on Farmers, Restaurants" in Saint Louis Business Journal (Vol. 31, August 12, 2011, No. 51, pp. 1) [17910], [21563]

Drug & Alcohol Treatment Association of Rhode Island - In-Rhodes Library Library [46101]

Drug Discovery/Technology News [6677]

The Drug-Free Workplace [46075]

"Drug-Maker Plans IPO" in Business Courier (Vol. 24, November 23, 2008, No. 32, pp. 1) [8275], [12283], [31393], [41876], [43450]

Drug Resource Guide [50071]

"Drug, Seed Firms Offer Antidote For Inflation" in Crain's Chicago Business (Vol. 31, April 21, 2008, No. 16, pp. 4) [8276], [12284], [27159], [31394]

Drug Testing in the Workplace [46076]

Drug Topics: The Newsmagazine for Pharmacists [6678]

"Drug Trial Halt at YM Sets Stage for Selloff" in Globe & Mail (January 31, 2007, pp. B3) [8277], [12285], [43838]

Drug Wholesalers Association [6634]

Drugs in the Workplace 2: What Every Manager and Supervisor Must Know [46077]

Drumright Chamber of Commerce [56507]

Drury University - F.W. Olin Library - Art & Architecture Slide Library [1386], [15888]

DRY-B-LO International, Inc. [3438]

Dry Cleaning To-Your-Door [6759]

Dry Eye and Tear Research Center [20954]

"Dry Idea" in Entrepreneur (Vol. 36, April 2008, No. 4, pp. 20) [3329], [30577], [41052]

Drycleaners News: The News and Management Magazine [6749]

Drycleaning and Laundry Institute International (DLI) [6737], [6768]

Drycleaning and Laundry Institute International Library [6767]

DSP: Digital Signal Processing (Onsite) [34742]

DSSCourse [4735]

"DST Turns to Banks for Credit" in The Business Journal-Serving Metropolitan Kansas City (Vol. 27, October 3, 2008, No. 3, pp. 1) [3527], [18891], [26208], [27160], [34862], [37955], [44322], [45115]

DTS Language Services Inc. [20486]

Eastern Apicultural Society [1942]

Eastern Apicultural Society of North America (EAS) [1942]

Eastern Arizona College [47989]

Eastern Arizona College Small Business Development Center (EAC SBDC) [47834]

Eastern Dairy Deli Bakery Association--Membership Directory [6439]

Eastern Fishing and Outdoor Exposition [1730], [3872], [19372]

Eastern Idaho Technical College [50822]

Eastern Iowa Small Business Development Center (Davenport, Iowa) [51773]

Eastern Kentucky University Small Business Development Center [52220]

Eastern Laboratory Service Associates [21775]

Eastern Madera County Chamber of Commerce [48830]

Eastern Maumee Bay Chamber of Commerce [56123]

Eastern Monmouth Area Chamber of Commerce (EMACC) [54712]

Eastern Montgomery County Chamber of Commerce (EMCCC) [57064]

Eastern New Mexico University--Roswell [55004]

Eastern Oregon University Small Business Development Center [56675]

Eastern Panhandle Small Business Development Center [59367]

Eastern Perishable Products Association--Membership Directory [6439]

Eastern Plumas Chamber of Commerce [48547]

Eastern Point Consulting Group Inc. [2863], [25994], [26704], [29248], [36024], [40973]

Eastern Shore Chamber of Commerce (ESCC) [47676]

Eastern Shore of Virginia Chamber of Commerce [58906]

Eastern Ski Representatives Association [18817]

Eastern Sports & Outdoor Show [13963], [17678], [19373], [20209], [20621]

Eastern Sports Show/The Harrisburg Show [13963], [17678], [19373], [20209], [20621]

Eastern West Virginia Small Business Development Center [59368]

Eastern Winter Sports Representatives Association (EWSRA) [18817]

Eastgate Regional Council of Government - Mahoning Valley Technical Procurement Center - EDATA [56371]

Eastham Chamber of Commerce [52882]

Eastland Chamber of Commerce [58126]

"Eastland Future Unclear: Local Merchants Say They're OK Amid Closings of 4 More Stores" in *Charlotte Observer* (February 8, 2007) [22907], [42995]

Eastman - Dodge County Chamber of Commerce [50522]

George Eastman House - International Museum of Photography & Film - Richard and Ronay Menschel Library [15928]

Easton Hunt Capital Partners, L.P. [55408]

Eastpointe Area Chamber of Commerce (EACC) [53246]

Eastport Area Chamber of Commerce [52588]

Eastport Partners [55409]

"Easy Answers? Hall No" in *Charlotte Business Journal* (Vol. 25, December 17, 2010, No. 39, pp. 1) [19419], [39854], [42617]

"Easy to be Queasy" in *Canadian Business* (Vol. 81, December 24, 2007, No. 1, pp. 25) [14414], [27163], [36485], [46212]

"The Easy Route" in *Entrepreneur* (Vol. 36, April 2008, No. 4, pp. 60) [5744], [11673], [34863], [41054], [41537]

EasyChair Media LLC [15602]

"easyhome Ltd. Discovers Employee Fraud at an Easyfinancial Kiosk Company" in *Internet Wire* (October 14, 2010) [8280], [12288], [13320], [17776], [23827], [30923], [36486]

"Eat, Drink and Be a Success" in *Entrepreneur* (Vol. 37, August 2009, No. 8, pp. 70) [1843], [17912], [29653]

"Eat Up!" in *Entrepreneur* (Vol. 36, April 2008, No. 4, pp. 104) [17913], [32161]

"Eatery Honored for Top Alaska Pizza" in *Alaska Business Monthly* (Vol. 27, October 2011, No. 10, pp. 10) [16125]

Eating Well Magazine: The Magazine of Food & Health [15174]

Eaton Design Group Inc. [41592]

Eaton - Preble County Chamber of Commerce [56124]

Eatonton-Putnam County Chamber of Commerce [50523]

Eau Claire Area Chamber of Commerce [59559]

"eBay Business Looking Up" in *Zacks* (July 26, 2011) [1505], [12289], [26422], [28634]

eBay Business the Smart Way [1481], [5133], [15292], [21086], [28510], [37193], [43451]

EBay Business Start-up Kit: 100s of Live Links to All the Information and Tools You Need [1482], [2694], [5134], [15293], [28511], [43452]

"EBay Finally Gaining Traction in China" in *San Jose Mercury News* (October 26, 2011) [1506], [11086], [28635], [36487]

EBay Income: How ANYONE of Any Age, Location, and/or Background Can Build a Highly Profitable Online Business with eBay [442], [1483], [6301], [11674], [15294], [19624], [21087], [21361], [24178], [25748], [26209], [28636], [36488], [39855], [42919], [43453], [46213]

"eBay Inc. Completes Acquisition of Zong" in *Benzinga.com* (October 29, 2011) [1507], [3721], [12290], [26210], [28637], [44323]

"eBay Introduces Open Commerce Ecosystem" in *Entertainment Close-Up* (October 24, 2011) [1508], [26211], [28638], [34864], [42996], [45386]

"eBay and Jonathan Adler Team to Launch 'The eBay Inspiration Shop" in *Entertainment Close-Up* (October 25, 2011) [1509], [4101], [28639], [42997], [44101], [44324]

The Ebay Seller's Tax and Legal Answer Book [1510], [2700], [5141], [15321], [28640], [46214]

Ebay the Smart Way: Selling, Burying, and Profiting on the Web's Number One Auction Site [1511], [5142], [15322], [28641], [43454]

EBI Consulting [7376]

Ebony/Jet Guide to Black Excellence: The Entrepreneurs [40838]

EBRI Issue Brief [22010], [25386]

EBRI Notes [22011], [25387]

"EBSCO Adds New Features to EBSCOhost Content Viewer" in *Information Today* (Vol. 26, February 2009, No. 2, pp. 31) [2125], [3529], [4707], [15529], [18893], [45117]

ECA Magazine [5593]

ECentury Capital Partners, L.P. [59012]

ECG Advisors L.L.C. [47138]

Echelon Ventures LLC [53023]

Echo [48548]; [51884]

"Echo Vintage Clothing Fundraiser Set July 24" in *Tri-City Herald* (July 22, 2010) [1122], [4219], [9252]

"Eckerd Sales Spell Relief for Coutu" in *Globe & Mail* (January 18, 2006, pp. B4) [6653], [22908], [42998]

"Eclipse to Hire 50 for Airp;ort Hangar" in *Business Review, Albany New York* (Vol. 34, November 9, 2007, No. 32, pp. 3) [5314], [22909], [35326], [39036]

ECnow.com Inc. [47139]

Eco Barons: The New Heroes of Environmental Activism [7173], [7535], [29654], [30581]

Eco News [7042]

"Eco-Preneuring" in *Small Business Opportunities* (Jan. 2008) [2414], [5887], [20148], [20542], [21565], [39856]

"Eco-Preneuring" in *Small Business Opportunities* (July 2008) [7174], [7536], [20149], [20543], [21566], [22910], [30582], [43840]

"Eco Smart Home Will Showcase Green Technology" in *Contractor* (Vol. 56, September 2009, No. 9, pp. 3) [808], [5315], [7175], [7537], [19088]

Ecojustice Canada [7043]

Ecole des Gardes Forestiers. [7413]

Ecology Action Centre (EAC) [17745]; [7044], [30422]

Ecompanies [49214]

Econo Lube N' Tune [16672], [18646]

Economic Bulletin [48549]

Economic and Community Profile/Directory [59167]

"Economic Crises Calls For Better Marketing Plans" in *Entrepreneur* (October 1, 2008) [443], [24328], [25073], [27164], [39857], [43455]

"Economic Crisis and Accounting Evolution" in *Accounting and Business Research* (Vol. 41, Summer 2011, No. 3, pp. 2159) [78], [2279], [19625], [21362], [27165]; [79], [2280], [19626], [21363], [27166]

Economic and Demographics of Tuscarawas County [56125]

Economic Development [27903]

Economic Development Administration--Annual Report [27167]

Economic Development Corporation of Lea County [54997]

Economic Development Council Newsletter [50079]

Economic Development & Industrial Corporation of Lynn, Massachusetts - Office of Economic Development [53080]

Economic Development Partnership of Monroe County [53884]

Economic Development Promotional Brochure [52883]

Economic Development Research Focus [27904]

"Economic Distance and the Survival of Foreign Direct Investments" in *Academy of Management Journal* (Vol. 50, No. 5, October 2007) [12291], [27168], [36489]

Economic Edge [4529], [6525], [16415]

Economic Focus [50524]

Economic Forecast [54035]

Economic Freedom and the American Dream [27169], [29655], [37960]

"The Economic Loss Rule and Franchise Attorneys" in *Franchise Law Journal* (Vol. 27, Winter 2008, No. 3, pp. 192) [23828], [32162]

"Economic Outlook 2009" in *Hispanic Business* (January-February 2009, pp. 30, 32) [24329], [27170], [45387]

Economic Profile [49500]; [54952]; [55682]; [56773]; [57065]; [59399]

"Economic Prognosis" in *Barron's* (Vol. 89, July 13, 2009, No. 28, pp. 11) [8281], [12292], [27171], [31397]

Economic Research and Development Centre [27939]

Economic Review [52458]; [55189]

"Economic Stimulus Plan Needs Scrutiny" in *Crain's Detroit Business* (Vol. 24, April 7, 2008, No. 14, pp. 8) [24330], [27172]

"Economic Trends for Small Business" in *Small Business Economic Trends* (April 2008, pp. 1) [6199], [6240], [6302], [26212], [27173], [37194], [43456], [45388]

Economic Update [54713]

The Economics of Entrepreneurship [27174], [29656]

The Economics of Integrity [30924], [32654], [41879]

The Economics and Management of Small Business: An International Perspective [27175], [36490], [37961]

"Economics at Play When Allocating Seats to Series" in *Boston Business Journal* (Vol. 27, October 26, 2007, No. 39, pp. 1) [19420], [32655], [39858]

The Economics of Self-Employment and Entrepreneurship [27176], [29657]

The Economics of Small Firms [27177], [32656]

The Economist Intelligence Unit Information Center [11210]

"Economy Forcing Meeting Planners to Think Fast" in *Crain's Cleveland Business* (Vol. 30, June 15, 2009, No. 23, pp. 15) [18555], [20362], [27178], [46643]

"Economy Hammers Local Builders" in *Business Courier* (Vol. 24, February 8, 2008, No. 44, pp. 1) [5316], [16883], [17274]

"Economy Peddles Rent In This Cycle" in *The Business Journal-Serving Metropolitan Kansas City* (Vol. 26, August 8, 2008, No. 48) [14415], [16524], [16884], [17275], [22911], [27179]

"Economy Should Play Big Role When Presidential Spotlight Returns" in *Business First-Columbus* (November 9, 2007, pp. A1) [444], [27180], [42618]

Ecopreneuring: Putting Purpose and the Planet Before Profits [29658], [30583], [37962], [39859], [45389], [45909]

Ecotourism Society [20128]

ECRI Institute [14246]

ECRI Institute Library [14339]

Ed Expo [19845]

"Ed Otto, Director of Biotechnology at RCCC" in *Charlotte Observer* (February 8, 2007) [29659], [42787], [43841]

ED Update [51077]; [58127]

"EDCO Doling Out Capital Along Border" in *Austin Business JournalInc.* (Vol. 28, August 1, 2008, No. 20, pp. 1) [5745], [7021], [7434], [30409], [34715], [41880], [46959]

Edelson Technology Partners [54849]

Eden Chamber of Commerce [55683]

Eden Chamber of Commerce (ECC) [58128]

Eden Prairie Chamber of Commerce (EPC) [53639]

Edenton-Chowan Chamber of Commerce (ECCC) [55684]

"EDF Ventures Dissolves Fund, Begins Anew On Investment" in *Crain's Detroit Business* (Vol. 24, February 25, 2008, No. 8, pp. 14) [37365], [47012]

EDF Ventures / Enterprise Development Fund [53480]

The Edge [59168]

Edgebrook Chamber of Commerce [51078]

Edgebrook-Sauganash Chamber of Commerce [51078]

Edgerton Area Chamber of Commerce (EACC) [59560]

Edgewalkers: People and Organizations That Take Risks, Build Bridges, and Break New Ground [29660], [32657]

"Edible Endeavors" in *Black Enterprise* (March 2008) [3467], [40730], [47268]

Edinboro University - Baron-Forness Library - Special Collections [1387], [14683], [14770]

Edinburg Area Chamber of Commerce (EACC) [58907]

Edinburg Chamber of Commerce [58129]

Edison Chamber of Commerce [54714]

Edison Highlights [54715]

Edison Venture Fund [54850]

Editorial Code and Data Inc. (ECDI) [2203], [6538], [15022]

Editorial Freelancers Association (EFA) [6787]

Editorial Freelancers Association--Membership Directory [6819]

Editorial Services of New England Inc. [2212]

Editorial Skills for Non-Editors (Onsite) [22185]

Eliminating MASTER INDEX

"Eliminating All of Your Estate Tax Burden" in Contractor (Vol. 57, January 2010, No. 1, pp. 48) [7743], [46216]
Charlotte Eliopoulos Considine, PhD [15113]
Elizabeth Area Chamber of Commerce (EACOC) [49501]
Elizabeth Chamber of Commerce [51084]
Elizabeth City Area Chamber of Commerce [55686]
Elizabethton - Carter County Chamber of Commerce [57697]
Elizabethtown-Hardin County Chamber of Commerce [52305]
Elizabethtown-White Lake Area Chamber of Commerce [55687]
Elk Associates Funding Corp. [55410]
Elk City Chamber of Commerce [56512]
Elk Grove Chamber of Commerce [48557]
Elk Rapids Area Chamber of Commerce (ERACC) [53248]
Elk Rapids Chamber of Commerce [53248]
Elk River Area Chamber of Commerce (ERACC) [53640]
Elkader Area Chamber of Commerce (EACC) [51886]
Elkader Chamber of Commerce [51886]
Elkhart Area Recreational Vehicle Directory [51597]
Elkhart County Manufacturers Directory [51598]
Elkhart Lake Area Chamber of Commerce [59561]
Elkhorn Area Chamber of Commerce (EACC) [59562]
Elkins-Randolph County Chamber of Commerce [59425]
Elko Chamber of Commerce [54489]
Elko Directory [54490]
Elko Nevada Small Business Development Center [54457]
Elkton Chamber and Alliance [52710]
Ellensburg Chamber of Commerce (ECC) [59169]
Ellenville Area Chamber of Commerce [55190]
Ellenville - Wawarsing Chamber of Commerce [55190]
Ellianos Coffee Co. [9736]
Ellicottville Chamber of Commerce [55191]
Ellington Chamber of Commerce [54038]
Ellinwood Area Chamber of Commerce [52096]
Elliott Appraisers L.L.C. [47140]
Ellsworth Area Chamber of Commerce [52589]
Ellsworth Area Chamber of Commerce (EACC) [59563]
Ellsworth-Kanopolis Area Chamber of Commerce (EKAC) [52097]
Ellwood City Area Chamber of Commerce [57066]
Elma Chamber of Commerce [59170]
Elmhurst Chamber of Commerce and Industry [51085]
Elmhurst Community [51086]
Eloy Chamber of Commerce (ECC) [47897]
Eloy Living Offers You [47898]
Elrick and Lavidge Library [14068]
Elroy Area Advancement Corporation [59564]
Elsberry Chamber of Commerce (ECC) [54039]
Elsewhere, U.S.A.: How We Got From the Company Man, Family Dinners, and the Affluent Society to the Home Office, BlackBerry Moms, and Economic Anxiety [27188], [34868]
Ely Chamber of Commerce (ECC) [53641]
Ely Nevada Small Business Development Center [54458]
EM Microelectronic-US Inc. [41486]
"Emack & Bolio" in Ice Cream Reporter (Vol. 23, October 20, 2010, No. 11, pp. 8) [10874], [26423], [39864], [43459]
Email Marketing by the Numbers: How to Use the World's Greatest Marketing Tool to Take Any Organization to the Next Level [22918], [28646], [39865]
"Embarq Sale Sets New Tone" in The Business Journal-Serving Metropolitan Kansas City (Vol. 27, October 31, 2008, No. 8, pp. 1) [27189], [41882], [44325]
"Embassy Suites Signs On: Dulski Building Developer Lands Anchor Tenant" in Business First Buffalo (October 26, 2007, pp. 1) [10687], [17277]
Embedded Entrepreneurship: The Institutional Dynamics of Innovation [29663], [36993]
Embrace the Pace [51599]
Embroiderers' Guild of America (EGA) [6096]
Embroiderers' Guild of London, American Branch [6096]
EmbroidMe [43293]
Embroidme [4305]
"EMC Greens Its Machines" in Boston Business Journal (Vol. 31, July 15, 2011, No. 25, pp. 3) [7176], [7539], [30587]
Emedia [3651]
EMediaLive: Practical Solutions Using Optical Disc Technologies, Tools, and Services [3651]
Emerald Alliance L.L.C. [220]
Emerge Memphis [57825]
Emergence Capital Partners, L.L.C. [49217]
"The Emergence of Governance In an Open Source Community" in Academy of Management Journal (Vol. 50, No. 5, October 2007, pp. 1079) [3531], [18896], [37964], [45120]
Emergency Care Research Institute [14246]
Emergency Care Research Institute. [14339]
Emergency Medical Services Magazine--Buyers Guide Issue: The Journal of Emergency Care, Rescue and Transportation [14313]
Emergency Medicine Alert I Practical Summary and Acute Care Report [933]
Emergency Planning and Crisis Management Series [47493]
Emerging Business Online: Global Markets and the Power of B2B Internet Marketing [11677], [21090], [22292], [28647], [36496], [39866], [45394]
"The Emerging Capital Market for Nonprofits" in Harvard Business Review (Vol. 88, October 2010, No. 10, pp. 110) [8285], [9253], [12296], [39867], [47014]
The Emerging Digital Economy: Entrepreneurship, Clusters, and Policy [27190], [29664], [44669], [45395]
The Emerging Markets Century: How a New Breed of World-Class Companies is Overtaking the World [22919], [25502], [27191], [32662], [45396]
"Emerging Tech Fund Strong in 2009" in Austin Business JournalInc. (Vol. 29, December 25, 2009, No. 42, pp. 1) [22920], [33200], [34869], [37366], [47015]
Emerging Technology Centers [52786]
Vince Emery Productions [49399]
Emeryville Chamber of Commerce [48558]
Emily Griffith Opportunity School [49633]
"Eminent Domain Fight Looks Imminent" in The Business Journal-Serving Metropolitan Kansas City (Vol. 26, August 1, 2008, No. 47) [16525], [16886], [17278], [23832], [33422], [33671], [45397]
Emmanuel College - Cardinal Cushing Library [1388], [6712]
Emmetsburg Chamber of Commerce (ECC) [51887]
Riegel and Emory Human Resource Research Center [29289]
Emory University - Center for Lifelong Learning [50680]
"Emotional Brand Attachment and Brand Personality" in Journal of Marketing (Vol. 75, July 2011, No. 4, pp. 35) [39868], [42468], [42619]
Emotional Intelligence for Administrative Professionals (Onsite) [37618]
"Empathy: An Entrepreneur's Killer App" in Women Entrepreneur (February 3, 2009) [27192], [29665], [35327], [37965], [46869]
"The Emperor Strikes Back" in Canadian Business (Vol. 80, March 26, 2007, No. 7, pp. 48) [8286], [12297], [22921], [24332]
Emphasis [51600]
Empire Building Diagnostics Inc. [5636]
Empire Business Brokers [2729]
Empire College - School of Business [49369]
"Empire of Pixels" in Entrepreneur (Vol. 37, September 2009, No. 9, pp. 50) [3532], [18897], [21091], [22293], [29666], [39869], [45121]
Empire State Development [55385]
Empire State Development - Division for Small Business - Procurement Assistance Program [55466]
Empire State Development - Minority and Women's Business Development Division [55385]
"Empire of the Sun" in Canadian Business (Vol. 82, April 27, 2009, No. 7, pp. 42) [12298], [41883]
Employability Skills Video Series [6989]
Employee Benefit Plan Review [22012], [35984]
Employee Benefit Research Institute (EBRI) [19779], [21852], [22053], [25366]
Employee Benefits Cases [22013], [25388]; [22083]
Employee Benefits Infosource™ [22084]
Employee Benefits Management Directions [22014]
Employee Benefits Review [25389]
Employee Benefits of St. Cloud Inc. [22054]
"The Employee Brand: Is Yours an All-Star?" in Business Horizons (September-October 2007, pp. 423) [29058], [39870]
"Employee Called for Jury Duty" in Business Owner (Vol. 35, March-April 2011, No. 2, pp. 14) [23833], [35764]
Employee Development Systems Inc. (EDSI) [29250]
Employee Management for Small Business [29667], [35765], [37966]
"Employee Motivation: A Powerful New Model" in Harvard Business Review (Vol. 86, July-August 2008, No. 8, pp. 78) [21899], [29059], [29668], [32663], [37967]
Employee Relations Law Journal [22015]
Employee Services Management [22016]
Employee Services Management Association (ESM) [22055]
Employee Services Management Association Information Center [22088]
Employee Terminations Law Bulletin [35985]
"Employees Can't Be Punished for Refusing to Work Due to Safety Concerns" in HR Specialist (Vol. 8, September 2010, No. 9, pp. 1) [23834], [35766]
"Employees Change Clothes at Work? Heed New Pay Rules" in HR Specialist (Vol. 8, September 2010, No. 9, pp. 1) [23835], [35767]
"Employer Jobless Tax Could Rise" in Sacramento Business Journal (Vol. 28, May 27, 2011, No. 13, pp. 1) [11344], [33201], [36141], [46217]
Employer Legal Forms Simplified [81], [15456], [19628], [21365], [23836], [35768]
Employers of America (EofA) [44793]
Employers Council on Flexible Compensation (ECFC) [21853], [25367]
Employer's Desk Manual [57458]
Employers Directory [51888]
Employers Group (EG) [46477]
The Employer's Legal Advisor [23837], [33672]
"Employers Plan to Fill Jobs" in Philadelphia Business Journal (Vol. 28, February 5, 2010, No. 51, pp. 1) [22922], [33673], [35328]
"Employers See Workers' Comp Rates Rising" in Sacramento Business Journal (Vol. 28, April 8, 2011, No. 6, pp. 1) [23838], [34261], [45398], [47460]
"Employers Tied in Knots" in Sacramento Business Journal (Vol. 25, August 15, 2008, No. 24, pp. 1) [11345], [33674], [36142], [45399], [46218]
"Employers Waking Up to Effects of Workers' Sleep Problems" in Crain's Cleveland Business (Vol. 28, December 3, 2007, No. 48, pp. 18) [11346], [34262], [36143], [47461]
Employing Bookbinders of American [2086], [2237]
Employment Agencies Protective Association [6954], [20025]
Employment Discrimination Law Update (Onsite) [23681], [26652]
Employment Discrimination Report™ [26715]
Employment Relations Today [22017]
Employment Support Center Library [7011], [29288], [44969]
Emporia Area Chamber of Commerce [52098]
Emporia Chamber of Commerce and Convention and Visitors Bureau [52098]
Emporia - Greensville Chamber of Commerce [58908]
Emporia SCORE [52026]
"Empowered" in Harvard Business Review (Vol. 88, July-August 2010, No. 7-8, pp. 94) [10995], [11678], [16588], [24849], [26424], [28648], [29060], [37968], [42469], [42620]
Empowering Employees to Claim Their Autonomy [29206]
Empowerment: Communicating with Others [29207]
Empowerment: How to Receive Work Assignments [30362]
Empowerment: It's Your Career [6990]
Empowerment: Managing Your Time [46551]
Empowerment: Meeting Change Creatively [29208]
Empowerment: Moving from Criticism to Feedback [30363]
Empowerment: Solving Problems Together [29209]
Empowerment: Team Skills for Meeting Together [29210]
Empowerment: The Attitude Opportunity [38623]
Empowerment: The Employee Development Series [30364], [46552]
Empowerment: Working Effectively with Others [29211]
Empress Chili [18124]
Empress Chinchilla Breeders Cooperative (ECBC) [9349], [9353]
"Empty Office Blues" in Business Journal Portland (Vol. 26, December 4, 2009, No. 39, pp. 1) [17279], [17777], [41884]
EMS Consultants [38713]
EMS Network International [38713]
"EMU, Spark Plan Business Incubator for Ypsilanti" in Crain's Detroit Business (Vol. 23, October 15, 2007, No. 42, pp. 3) [28185], [42788], [43843], [46960]
Enabling Environments for Jobs and Entrepreneurship: The Role of Policy and Law in Small Enterprise Employment [23839], [33675], [47462]
"EnCana Axes Spending on Gas Wells" in Globe & Mail (February 16, 2006, pp. B1) [8287], [12299], [24333], [25074], [39039]
"EnCana Gets Top Dollar for Gas Depot Division" in Globe & Mail (March 7, 2006, pp. B6) [41885], [44326]
"EnCana Surpasses All Canadian Profit Records" in Globe & Mail (February 16, 2007, pp. B5) [22923], [44327]
Encinitas Chamber of Commerce [48559]
Encinitas Chamber and Visitors Center [48559]
Encino Chamber of Commerce [48560]
Encino Chamber of Commerce Envoy [48561]
Encounters [34513]
"Encouraging Study in Critical Languages" in Occupational Outlook Quarterly (Vol. 55, Summer 2011, No. 2, pp. 23) [3349], [18419], [20476], [28186], [33202], [35769]
Encyclopedia of Associations: National Organizations of the U.S. [1462]
The Encyclopedia of Associations and Information Sources for Architects, Designers, and Engineers [1263]

3502 Small Business Sourcebook • 30th Edition

Encyclopedia of Information Systems and Services [4716], [5034], [21129]

Encyclopedia of Small Business [29669], [32664]

Encyclopedia of Sports Business Contacts [19396]

"End of the Beginning" in *Canadian Business* (Vol. 81, November 10, 2008, No. 19, pp. 17) [6200], [6241], [6303], [8288], [12300], [26213], [27193], [33676], [36497]

"The End of Clock-Punching" in *Canadian Business* (Vol. 83, September 14, 2010, No. 15, pp. 96) [2770], [29061], [33677], [35770], [46508]

"End of an Era" in *Barron's* (Vol. 88, July 7, 2008, No. 27, pp. 3) [8289], [12301], [27194], [31402], [35329]

The End of the Line [26595]

"The End of the Line for Line Extensions?" in *Advertising Age* (Vol. 79, July 7, 2008, No. 26, pp. 3) [8290], [9924], [12302], [22924], [31403], [39040], [39871]

The Endeavor [59565]

Endeavor Capital Management [49776]

Endeavor Center [56398]

"Endeca Gears Up for Likely IPO Bid" in *Boston Business Journal* (Vol. 31, July 1, 2011, No. 23, pp. 1) [11679], [12303], [22925], [28649], [41886]

"Ending the Ebola Death Sentence" in *Canadian Business* (Vol. 83, August 17, 2010, No. 13-14, pp. 22) [14192], [14273], [33678], [34263], [34870], [41059], [42789], [43844]

"The Endless Flow of Russell Simmons" in *Entrepreneur* (Vol. 37, September 2009, No. 9, pp. 24) [4220], [19929], [22926], [29670], [40732]

"Endowments for Colleges Hit Hard in '09" in *Milwaukee Business Journal* (Vol. 27, February 12, 2010, No. 20, pp. A1) [9254], [27195], [28187]

Energy Alliance Group [2846], [25974], [38689], [40592], [41290], [44926]

Energy and Chemical Workers Union [46809]

Energy Auditing 101: Identifying Cost Saving Opportunities in Plants & Buildings (Onsite) [30451]

"Energy Consulting Company to Expand" in *Austin Business JournalInc.* (Vol. 28, November 7, 2008, No. 34, pp. A1) [7177], [7540], [22927], [30588]

Energy Design Online [19132]

Energy Design Update [19132]

Energy Detente [7385]

"Energy Efficiency Ordinance Softened" in *Austin Business JournalInc.* (Vol. 28, October 3, 2008, No. 29) [7178], [7541], [16887], [30589], [33679]

Energy Efficient Building Association [5182]

Energy and Environmental Building Association (EEBA) [5182]

Energy & Environmental Management Library [7402]

"Energy Firms Face Stricter Definitions" in *Globe & Mail* (March 26, 2007, pp. B3) [8291], [12304], [33680], [39041]

Energy Insurance Group [19131]

"Energy Is Put to Good Use in Antarctica" in *Contractor* (Vol. 56, July 2009, No. 7, pp. 32) [809], [7179], [30590]

"Energy, MLPs: Pipeline to Profits" in *Barron's* (Vol. 89, July 27, 2009, No. 30, pp. 9) [8292], [12305], [31404], [44328]

"Energy Outfitter Wings Into Houston" in *Houston Business Journal* (Vol. 40, December 4, 2009, No. 30, pp. 2A) [18756], [26750], [37195], [39042]

"Energy Slide Slows Fourth Quarter Profits" in *Globe & Mail* (April 13, 2007, pp. B9) [12306], [32665], [39043]

"Energy Sparks Job Growth" in *The Business Journal-Serving Greater Tampa Bay* (Vol. 28, August 8, 2008, No. 33, pp. 1) [5318], [22928], [24334], [35330], [37969], [44329], [46870]

Enertech Capital /Enertech Capital Partners, L.P. [57285]

enews [49695]

"Enforcer In Fantasyland" in *Crain's New York Business* (Vol. 24, February 25, 2008, No. 8, pp. 10) [18420], [20246], [23840], [27196], [33681], [36498], [36994], [39044]

The Engine of America: The Secrets to Small Business Success from Entrepreneurs Who Have Made It! [22929], [29671]

Engine Builder: Serving Engine Builders and Rebuilders since 1964 [18614]

"Engine of Growth: U.S. Industry Funk hasn't Hurt Cummins or Its Investors" in *Barron's* (Vol. 88, July 14, 2008, No. 28, pp. 43) [6655], [8293], [12307], [22930], [25503], [31405]

Engineered Lighting Products (ELP) [41594]

Engineering and Grading Contractors Association [5183]

Engineering Contractors Association (ECA) [5183]

Engineering Harmonics Inc. [16755], [17654]

Engineering News Record--Top Specialty Contractors Issue [18320]

"Engineering Services Supplier Launches 'Robotic Renaissance'" in *Modern Machine Shop* (Vol. 84, September 2011, No. 4, pp. 46) [13703], [25849], [34871], [39045], [41060]

Engineering and Technical Consultants Inc. [5637]

Englewood Area Chamber of Commerce [50080]

Englewood-Cape Haze Area Chamber of Commerce [50080]

Englewood Chamber of Commerce (ECC) [54716]

English/French EFlash [18377]

Enhanced and Video Podcasts (Onsite) [45046]

Enhancing Your Management Skills (Onsite) [28983], [37619]

Enhancing Your People Skills [22192], [28984]

Enid/Northwest Oklahoma SCORE [56446]

L'Enjeu [7045]

ENLASO Corp. [20487]

Enlightened Leadership: Best Practice Guidelines and Time Tools for Easily Implementing Learning Organizations [28188], [29672], [36995], [37970], [46509]

Enlightened Leadership: Best Practice Guidelines and Timesaving Tools for Easily Implementing Learning Organizations [28189], [29062], [29673], [37971], [46510]

Ennis Area Chamber of Commerce [54269]

Ennis Chamber of Commerce [58133]

Ennis Chamber of Commerce [54269]

E.nopi [28457]

ENR--Top 600 Specialty Contractors Issue [18320]

Enrich! [3365], [24649]

ENT: The Independent Newspaper for Windows NT Enterprise Computing [15585], [19032]

Enterprise [46977]; [48562]; [48563]; [50526]; [53249]; [55192]; [55688]; [58909]; [58910]

The Enterprise [52306]; [54040]

Enterprise Center of Johnson County [52209]

Enterprise Center of Louisiana [52527]

Enterprise Center at Salem State College [53081]

Enterprise Chamber of Commerce [47677]

Enterprise Consulting Inc. [26625]

Enterprise Development Corporation of South Florida [50369]

Enterprise and Endeavor [55689]

Enterprise, Entrepreneurship and Innovation: Concepts, Context and Commercialization [22931], [29674], [32666], [36996]

Enterprise Florida, Inc. - Marketing And Development Division [49907]

The Enterprise Institute [57614]

Enterprise Minnesota - Minnesota Department of Trade and Economic Development Center [53802]

Enterprise North Florida Corporation, Inc. (ENFC) [50370]

Enterprise Partners Venture Capital / EPVC [49218]

Enterprise Planning and Development: Small Business and Enterprise Start-Up Survival and Growth [23666], [29346], [32375], [36997], [37237]

Enterprise and Small Business: Principles, Practice and Policy [29675], [32667]

Enterprise UNB [59907]

Enterprising Women in Urban Zimbabwe: Gender, Microbusiness, and Globalization [5982], [10071], [18721], [29676], [36499], [47269]

Entertainment Merchants Association (EMA) [20880]

Entertainment Operators of America [6378]

Entertainment Software Association (ESA) [18848]

Entertainment and Specialty Projects [17559]

Entree [20602]

Entrees Made Easy [19282]

The Entrepreneur [56126]

"Entrepreneur Column" in *Entrepreneur* (September 24, 2009) [446], [11680], [21092], [22294], [39872], [41887]

Entrepreneur Magazine [11217], [44897]

Entrepreneur Magazine--Franchise 500 Survey Issue [32163]

The Entrepreneur Next Door: Discover the Secrets to Financial Independence [29677], [32668]

"Entrepreneur Says Spirituality Has Been a Key to Her Success" in *Business First Columbus* (Vol. 25, October 17, 2008, No. 8, pp. 1) [10395], [10464], [11540], [29678], [47270]

The Entrepreneur and Small Business Problem Solver [29679], [32669], [37273], [41061]

Entrepreneurial Assistance in Wisconsin: Sources of Management and Technical Support [59787]

The Entrepreneurial Author [2126], [29680]

The Entrepreneurial Culture Network Advantage Within Chinese and Irish Software Firms [3533], [18898], [29681], [36500], [45122]

Entrepreneurial Decision-Making Individuals, Tasks and Cognitions [29682], [37972]

Entrepreneurial Development Center [58593]

Entrepreneurial Finance [22107], [29683], [31406], [43324], [46042]

Entrepreneurial Finance: A Casebook [29684], [31407], [34872]

"Entrepreneurial Human Resource Leadership" in *Human Resource Management* (Vol. 49, July-August 2010, No. 4, pp. 793-804) [29063], [29685], [35771]

The Entrepreneurial Imperative: How America's Economic Miracle Will Reshape the World [27197], [29686]

Entrepreneurial Itch: What No One Tells You About Starting Your Own Business [24180], [29347], [32376]

Entrepreneurial Management [24335], [29348], [32377]

"Entrepreneurial Orientation and Firm Performance" in *Journal of Small Business and Entrepreneurship* (Vol. 23, Winter 2010, No. 1) [24336], [25075], [29687], [36998], [37973], [42790], [43845]

Entrepreneurial Skills: 2nd Edition [29688], [37974]

Entrepreneurial Small Business [29689], [31408], [32670]

Entrepreneurial Strategies [24668], [30376]

Entrepreneurial Strategies: New Technologies and Emerging Markets [22932], [29690], [34873], [36501]

Entrepreneurial Strategy Emerging Businesses in Declining Industries [22933], [29691]

The Entrepreneur's Almanac: Fascinating Figures, Fundamentals and Facts You Need to Run and Grow Your Business [29692]

Entrepreneurs Center [56399]

"Entrepreneurs Conference" in *Black Enterprise* (Vol. 38, February 2008, No. 7, pp. 163) [20363], [29693], [46644]

The Entrepreneur's Edge: Finding Money, Making Money, Keeping Money [29694], [31409], [32378]

The Entrepreneur's Guide to Managing Growth and Handling Crisis [22934], [29850], [29695], [35331], [35772], [37975]

Entrepreneurs' Organization (EO) [44794], [47575]

The Entrepreneurs: Risk Takers [44905]

"Entrepreneurs Save the World" in *Women In Business* (Vol. 61, December 2009, No. 6, pp. 12) [27198], [32671]

"Entrepreneurs: Search Party" in *Business Strategy Review* (Vol. 21, Autumn 2010, No. 3, pp. 30) [24850], [29349], [32379], [37274]

Entrepreneurs Series, Part 1: The Entrepreneurs [37154]

Entrepreneurs Series, Part 2: The Land & Its People [37155]

Entrepreneurs Series, Part 3: Expanding America [37156]

Entrepreneurs Series, Part 4: Made in America [37157]

Entrepreneurs Series, Part 5: Giving 'Em What They Want [37158]

Entrepreneurs Series, Part 6: Instant America [37159]

The Entrepreneur's Source [2730]

Entrepreneurs in the Southern Upcountry: Commercial Culture in Spartanburg, South Carolina, 1845-1880 [29696], [32672]

The Entrepreneur's Strategy Guide: Ten Keys for Achieving Marketplace Leadership [24337], [29697], [37976]

The Entrepreneur's Strategy Guide: Ten Keys for Achieving Marketplace Leadership and Operational Excellence [29698], [32673]

Entrepreneurship [24181], [29350], [37275], [39538]; [24338], [29699], [29700], [32674], [29701], [32675]; [29702], [32676], [29703], [32677]

Entrepreneurship: A Process Perspective [22935], [23841], [24339], [29704], [32678]

Entrepreneurship: A Small Business Approach [29705], [32380]

"Entrepreneurship: As Cool As It Gets" in *Canadian Business* (Vol. 80, January 29, 2007, No. 3, pp. 10) [5319], [17914], [22936], [29706]

Entrepreneurship As Social Change: A Third New Movements in Entrepreneurship Book [29707], [45912]

Entrepreneurship and the Creation of Small Firms Empirical Studies of New Ventures [29351], [32381]

Entrepreneurship and Economic Growth [22937], [25504], [27199], [29708]

Entrepreneurship and Economic Progress [27200], [29709]

Entrepreneurship and the Financial Community Starting Up and Growing New Businesses [22938], [29352], [31151]

Entrepreneurship: Frameworks and Empirical Investigations from Forthcoming Leaders of European Research [29710], [36502], [42737], [43780]

Entrepreneurship: From Opportunity to Action [29711], [32679]

Entrepreneurship, Geography, and American Economic Growth [27201], [29712]

Entrepreneurship and the Growth of Firms [22939], [29713]

Entrepreneurship and How to Establish Your Own Business [29714], [32680]

Entrepreneurship, Innovation and Economic Growth [22940], [27202], [29715], [36999]

Environmental Protection Agency State Superfund Office (Atlanta, Georgia) - Department of Natural Resources - Land Protection Branch - Solid Waste Management Program **[60084]**; **[60085]**
Environmental Protection Agency State Superfund Office (Des Moines, Iowa) - Department of Natural Resources Waste Management - Air Quality Bureau - Water Supply Section **[60086]**; **[60087]**
Environmental Protection Agency State Superfund Office (Madison, Wisconsin) - Department of Natural Resources - Waste and Materials Management **[60088]**
Environmental Protection Agency State Superfund Office (Denver, Colorado) - Department of Public Health and Environment - Hazardous Materials and Waste Management Division **[60089]**; **[60090]**
Environmental Protection Agency State Superfund Office (Sacramento, California) - Department of Toxic Substances Control **[60091]**; **[60092]**
Environmental Protection Agency State Superfund Office (Carson City, Nevada) - Division of Environmental Protection - Department of Conservation and Natural Resources **[60093]**; **[60094]**
Environmental Protection Agency State Superfund Office (Charleston, West Virginia) - Division of Environmental Protection - Office of Waste Management **[60095]**; **[60096]**
Environmental Protection Agency State Superfund Office (Columbus, Ohio) - Division of Environmental Response and Revitalization **[60097]**
Environmental Protection Agency State Superfund Office (Washington, District of Columbia) - Environmental Health Administration - Hazardous Materials, Pesticides and Underground Storage Tank Management **[60098]**; **[60099]**
Environmental Protection Agency State Superfund Office (Santa Fe, New Mexico) - Environmental Improvement Division - Hazardous Waste Bureau **[60100]**; **[60101]**
Environmental Protection Agency State Superfund Office (Barrigada, Guam) - Environmental Protection Agency **[60102]**; **[60103]**
Environmental Protection Agency State Superfund Office (Springfield, Illinois) - Environmental Protection Agency - Bureau of Land - Pollution Prevention **[60104]**; **[60105]**
Environmental Protection Agency State Superfund Office (Columbus, Ohio) - Environmental Protection Agency - Division of Environmental Response and Revitalization **[60106]**
Environmental Protection Agency State Superfund Office (Indianapolis, Indiana) - Indiana Department of Environmental Management - Office of Environmental Response - Office of Land Quality **[60107]**; **[60108]**
Environmental Protection Agency State Superfund Office (Lansing, Michigan) - Michigan Department of Environmental Quality - Waste Management Division **[60109]**; **[60110]**
Environmental Protection Agency State Superfund Office (St. Paul, Minnesota) - Pollution Control Agency - Groundwater & Solid Waste Division **[60111]**; **[60112]**
Environmental Protection Agency State Superfund Office (Austin, Texas) - Water Commission - Hazardous and Solid Waste Division - Superfund and Emergency Response Section **[60113]**
Environmental Quality Management **[17725]**
Environmental Regulations Seminars **[33488]**
Environmental Research Foundation (ERF) **[21009]**
Environmental and Safety Directory **[56127]**
Environmental Sciences & Pollution Management **[7388]**
Environmental Solutions Inc. **[34085]**
Environmental Support Network Inc. **[34086]**, **[47521]**
Environmental Toxicology and Chemistry: An International Journal **[44020]**
The Environmentalist **[7389]**
Environmex/Watermex South China - International Environment & Water Management Technology, Equipment & Control Systems Exhibition **[20992]**
Environnement Jeunesse (ENJEU) **[7049]**
EnviroQuest Inc. [2867]
EnviroSpect, Inc. **[7724]**
Envision **[51889]**
EOC Technology Center **[56651]**
Eola Wine Company Franchising **[43294]**
EOS Partners, L.P. **[55411]**
"EOTech Product Improves Holographic Gun Sights" in Crain's Detroit Business (Vol. 24, February 4, 2008, No. 5, pp. 9) **[10027]**, **[18421]**, **[33423]**, **[34875]**
EP Update **[51087]**
"EPA 'Finalizes' WaterSense for Homes" in Contractor (Vol. 57, January 2010, No. 1, pp. 70) **[5320]**, **[7181]**, **[7543]**, **[16237]**, **[30592]**, **[45400]**
"EPA Grants E15 Waiver for 2001-2006 Vehicles" in Farm Industry News (January 21, 2011) **[7182]**, **[7544]**, **[21568]**, **[30593]**, **[33683]**, **[46219]**
"EPA to Tighten Energy Star Standards for 2011" in Contractor (Vol. 56, September 2009, No. 9, pp. 6) **[810]**, **[5321]**, **[6885]**, **[30594]**
ePartners Inc. **[41487]**, **[41595]**
Epcon Communities **[5686]**
Ephraim Small Business Development Center **[58613]**
Ephrata Area Chamber of Commerce **[57067]**
Ephrata Chamber of Commerce (ECC) **[59172]**
Ephrata Newsletter **[59173]**
Epic Design Technology Inc. [49327]
Epilepsie Canada [34141]
Epilepsy Canada (EC) **[34141]**
Episcopal Church Annual **[34264]**
The Epler Co. **[22056]**, **[25394]**
ePoint! **[50081]**
ePostal News **[5043]**
Epstein, Becker, & Green, PC Law Library **[19752]**
Equal Treatment/Equal Opportunity **[35537]**
Equilibrium **[34514]**
Equine Canada (EC) **[10602]**
Equipment Leasing Association [17748]
Equipment Leasing Association of America [17748]
Equipment Leasing and Finance Association (ELFA) **[17748]**
Equipment Marketing and Distribution Association--Membership Directory **[21569]**
Equipment World's Market Center--Top Bid Auction Directory Section [5322]
Equipment World's Top Bid **[5322]**
Equipro Inc. **[16673]**
"An Equity Fund of Their Own" in Entrepreneur (Vol. 35, October 2007, No. 10, pp. 68) **[12308]**, **[25505]**, **[31410]**, **[45401]**
Equity-South Advisors, LLC / Grubb & Williams Ltd. **[50652]**
Erbert & Gerbert's Subs & Clubs **[6467]**
"eResearch Issues Initiating Report on Aldershot Resources Ltd." in Canadian Corporate News (May 14, 2007) **[22944]**, **[41327]**, **[41888]**, **[43846]**
ErgoKinetics: Safety in Motion **[47494]**
ErgoMetrics Consulting Services Inc. [41596]
Ergometrics Inc. **[41596]**
Ergonomics: Low-Cost, Common-Sense Training Solutions **[47495]**
Ergonomics at Work **[47496]**
Erick Chamber of Commerce **[56513]**
Erico Inc. - Information Resources Center **[13734]**
Erie **[57068]**
Erie Area Chamber of Commerce [57074]
Erie Business and Community Resource Guide **[57069]**
Erie Chamber of Commerce **[49502]**
Erie City/County Map **[57070]**
Erie Community College, City Campus **[55504]**
Erie County Fact Packet **[57071]**
Erie Extra **[57072]**
ERIE Industrial Directory **[57073]**
Erie Insurance Group Corporate Library **[11498]**
Erie Regional Chamber and Growth Partnership **[57074]**
Erin Services Inc. **[961]**, **[986]**, **[2639]**, **[6451]**, **[13433]**, **[16134]**, **[18051]**
ERISA Industry Committee (ERIC) **[21854]**
ERM - West, Inc. Library **[7403]**
Ernst & Young Center for Business Knowledge **[271]**, **[19753]**; **[272]**, **[2334]**, **[19754]**
Ernst & Young Library **[273]**, **[15475]**, **[19755]**
Ernst & Young LLP Center for Business Knowledge **[274]**, **[19756]**
Ernst & Young LLP - Center for Business Knowledge Library **[4912]**
Error Analysis Inc. (EAI) **[41597]**, **[47522]**
ESAPP Financial, LLC **[2997]**, **[3103]**
Escalon Chamber of Commerce **[48564]**
Escape **[15792]**
"Escape the AMT Trap" in Entrepreneur (Vol. 36, February 2008, No. 2, pp. 64) **[46220]**
Escape from Corporate America: A Practical Guide to Creating the Career of Your Dreams **[29356]**, **[32383]**
Escape from Cubicle Nation: From Corporate Prisoner to Thriving Entrepreneur **[29357]**, **[32384]**
Escape to Historic Salamanca **[55193]**
Escapees Magazine **[17671]**
Escondido Chamber of Commerce **[48565]**
"Esencia Estate to Host 'The Esencia Experience for Upscale Wedding Planners'" in Benzinga.com (October 29, 2011) **[2498]**
eShipping **[9227]**
ESM Association [22055]
"ESolar Partners With Penglai on Landmark Solar Thermal Agreement for China" in Business of Global Warming (January 25, 2010, pp. 8) **[7183]**, **[7545]**, **[19090]**, **[30595]**, **[36507]**, **[41889]**
ESOPS: The Ultimate Way to Finance a Company **[41386]**
ESP Psychic Expo [14828]
ESP - Psychic Expo and Psychic, Mystics, and Seers Fair [14828]
Espanola Valley Chamber of Commerce (EVCC) **[54954]**
Espanola Valley Visitors Guide **[54955]**
Esparto District Chamber of Commerce **[48566]**
Espionage Research Institute (ERI) **[38714]**
ESSENCE **[5844]**
The Essential Administrative Professional: The Skills and Know-How to Make You Invaluable (Onsite) **[37620]**
Essential Coaching and Mentoring Skills for Managers, Supervisors and Team Leaders (Onsite) **[37621]**
Essential Facilitation (Onsite) **[37622]**
The Essential Online Solution: The 5-Step Formula for Small Business Success **[21093]**, **[28650]**, **[42999]**
"Essential Releases Record First Quarter Results" in Canadian Corporate News (May 14, 2007) **[8294]**, **[12309]**, **[22945]**, **[31411]**
Essential Skills of Dynamic Public Speaking (Onsite) **[22193]**
Essential Skills for the First-Time Manager or Supervisor (Onsite) **[28985]**
Essential Time Management & Organizational Skills (Onsite) **[46488]**
"Essentially Organic Vending Takes Healthy Snacks to Ohio High School" in Entertainment Close-Up (September 13, 2011) **[10222]**, **[10285]**, **[20859]**, **[28190]**
Essentialnet Solutions [41510], [41630]
Essentials **[50527]**
The Essentials of Cash Flow Forecasting (Onsite) **[31162]**
The Essentials of Collections Law (Onsite) **[23682]**
The Essentials of Communicating With Diplomacy and Professionalism (Onsite) **[22194]**
The Essentials of Communication and Collaboration (Onsite) **[22195]**
Essentials of Entrepreneurship and Small Business Management **[24340]**, **[28651]**, **[29358]**, **[31412]**, **[37552]**, **[39873]**
The Essentials of HR Law 2012 (Onsite) (Canada) **[35666]**
The Essentials of Human Resources Law (Onsite) **[35667]**
The Essentials Of Crystal Reports (Onsite) **[45047]**
The Essentials of OSHA Compliance (Onsite) **[47448]**
Essentials for Personnel and HR Assistants (Onsite) **[35668]**
Essentials of Project Management for the Nonproject Manager (Onsite) **[37623]**
Essex & Drake Fund Raising Counsel **[9294]**
Essex - Middle River Chamber of Commerce [52711]
Essex - Middle River - White Marsh Chamber of Commerce (EMRWMCC) **[52711]**
Essex Woodlands Health Ventures / Woodlands Venture (The Woodlands) **[58555]**
Estacada Chamber of Commerce [56774]
Estacada - Clackamas River Area Chamber of Commerce (ECRACC) **[56774]**
Estate Group **[7777]**
Estate Planners Alert **[31137]**; **[7751]**
Estate Planning **[7755]**
Estate Planning Review **[7752]**
"Estate Tax Problems may Soon Disappear" in Contractor (Vol. 56, September 2009, No. 9, pp. 60) **[7744]**, **[23842]**, **[46221]**
Estates, Gifts, and Trust Journal **[7756]**
Estero **[50082]**
Estero Chamber of Commerce **[50083]**
Estes Park Area Chamber of Commerce [49503]
Estes Park Chamber of Commerce (EPCC) **[49503]**
Estes Park Chamber Resort Association [49503]
Estherville Area Association of Business and Industry [51890]
Estherville Area Chamber of Commerce **[51890]**
Estherville Chamber of Commerce [51890]
Estill Development Alliance (EDA) **[52307]**
Estrada Strategies Franchise Inc. **[28458]**
Estuarine Research Federation Conference **[44079]**, **[46753]**
"Etextbook Space Heats Up" in Information Today (Vol. 28, November 2011, No. 10, pp. 10) **[2127]**, **[3723]**, **[4948]**, **[28191]**, **[28652]**
"Etextbooks: Coming of Age" in Information Today (Vol. 28, September 2011, No. 8, pp. 1) **[2128]**, **[28192]**, **[28653]**
"ETF Process May be Tweaked" in Austin Business JournalInc. (Vol. 28, December 26, 2008, No. 41, pp. 3) **[33203]**, **[34716]**, **[37276]**
"ETF Score Card" in Barron's (Vol. 89, July 13, 2009, No. 28, pp. 51) **[8295]**, **[12310]**, **[31413]**
The Ethical Executive: Becoming Aware of the Root Causes of Unethical Behavior **[30925]**, **[32683]**

Small Business Sourcebook • 30th Edition
3505

Ethical Hacking and Countermeasures: Hands-On - Preventing Network and System Breaches (Onsite) [34743]

Ethics in American Business [31000]

Ethics Centre CA Library [31003]

"Ethics Commission May Hire Collection Agency" in *Tulsa World* (August 21, 2010) [82], [6304], [21366], [23843], [26214], [30926], [31414]

"Ethics and the End of Life" in *Crain's Chicago Business* (Vol. 34, October 24, 2011, No. 42, pp. 31) [14193], [30927], [34265], [34876]

Ethics & Policy [30994]

"The Ethics of Price Discrimination" in *Business Ethics Quarterly* (Vol. 21, October 2011, No. 4, pp. 633) [25749], [26658], [30928]

Ethics Resource Center, Inc. (ERC) [46031]

Ethics Today [30995]

Ethnic and Multicultural Information Exchange [40849]

"Ethnic Businesses Ending Vacancies" in *Business First-Columbus* (Vol. 26, August 20, 2010, No. 51, pp. 1) [17778], [40733], [40878], [43000]

"Ethnic Chambers Seek Combined Facility" in *Business Journal* (Vol. 28, October 8, 2010, No. 18, pp. 1) [40734], [41890]

Ethnic Materials and Information Exchange Round Table [40849]

Ethnic Materials Information Exchange Task Force [40849]

Ethnic NewsWatch: A History™ [15606]

Ethnic Solidarity for Economic Survival: Korean Green-grocers in New York City [9925], [21570], [29724], [31046], [40735], [40879], [43001]

Ethnicity & Mental Health Associates [40941]

"Etiquette, Common Sense Often Lag Behind Smarter Devices" in *Crain's Cleveland Business* (Vol. 28, October 22, 2007, No. 42, pp. 21) [22295], [22588], [28654], [34877]

ETOH, the Alcohol and Alcohol Problems Science Database [46096]

Etowah Area Chamber of Commerce [57698]

etracks Newsletter [17647]

Euclid Chamber of Commerce (ECC) [56128]

Euclidsr Partners [55412]

Eufaula Area Chamber of Commerce [56514]

Eufaula - Barber Chamber of Commerce [47678]

Eufaula - Barbour County Chamber of Commerce [47678]

Eugene Area Chamber of Commerce [56775]

Eunice Chamber of Commerce [52459]

Eureka! [29442]

Eureka Area Chamber of Commerce [54270]

Eureka Chamber of Commerce [54041]

Eureka Chamber of Commerce [48616]

The Eureka Chamber Review [48567]

Eureka, The California Career Information System Library [3400]

Eureka! The Canadian Invention & Innovation Newsletter [37152]

European-American Business Council (EABC) [36290]

European Clinical Laboratory [6013], [34515]

European Congress on Psychiatry [14660], [14757]

"European Stocks on Deck" in *Barron's* (Vol. 89, July 27, 2009, No. 30, pp. M7) [8296], [11088], [12311], [31415], [36508]

European Travel Commission (ETC) [20512], [24814]

European-American Chamber of Commerce in Washington, DC [36290]

"Europe's Meltdown" in *Canadian Business* (Vol. 83, June 15, 2010, No. 10, pp. 76) [8297], [11089], [12312], [36509]

EuroShop - Global Retail Trade Fair [43279]

Eustis Area Chamber of Commerce (ECC) [50084]

Eustis Book [50085]

Eustis Brochure and Membership Directory [50086]

Eutaw Area Chamber of Commerce [47679]

Eva Rosenberg & Associates [54531]

"Evaluate Your Process and Do It Better" in *Modern Machine Shop* (Vol. 84, October 2011, No. 5, pp. 34) [13704], [25506], [39046]

"Evaluating the 1996-2006 Employment Projections" in *Montly Labor Review* (Vol. 133, September 2010, No. 9, pp. 33) [27206], [33684], [35332], [35773]

Evaluation & the Health Professions [34516]

Evangelical Christian Publishers Association (ECPA) [2095]

Evangelical Lutheran Good Samaritan Society - Resource Library [15125]

Evanston Chamber of Commerce [59820]

Evanston Chamber of Commerce (ECC) [51088]

Evanston Community Guide [51089]

Evanston Marketplace [51090]

Evansville Area Chamber of Commerce and Tourism [59566]

Evaporative Cooling Institute (ECI) [764]

Evart Area Chamber of Commerce (EACC) [53250]

Evart Chamber of Commerce [53250]

"Eve in the Sky: A Look at Security Tech from All Angles" in *Bellingham Business Journal* (October 2008, pp. 23) [13616], [18422]

"Even Gold Gets Tarnished When Everyone Wants Cash" in *Globe & Mail* (February 28, 2007, pp. B1) [12313], [27207], [31416]

"Even Money on Recession" in *Barron's* (Vol. 88, March 10, 2008, No. 10, pp. M9) [27208], [32684], [35333]

Event Directory [59174]

Event Service Professionals Association (ESPA) [20296]

"Event Stresses Cross-Border Cooperation" in *Crain's Detroit Business* (Vol. 24, March 31, 2008, No. 13, pp. 5) [11090], [27209], [36510], [39047]

"Events Struggling with Fees" in *Philadelphia Business Journal* (Vol. 28, November 20, 2009, No. 40, pp. 1) [20364], [46645]

eVents Update [59175]

Everest Marketing [2869], [26000], [40603]

Everett Area Chamber of Commerce [59176]

Everett & Co. [2870], [8911], [13826], [26001], [32025]

"Everett Dowling" in *Hawaii Business* (Vol. 54, August 2008, No. 2, pp. 32) [5323], [7184], [17280], [19091], [29725], [30596], [37977], [44330]

Everett Guide [59177]

"Everett Hospice Planned" in *Puget Sound Business Journal* (Vol. 29, September 26, 2008, No. 23, pp. 1) [5324], [34266]

Everglades Area Chamber of Commerce [50087]

Evergreen [49504]

Evergreen Area Chamber of Commerce [49505]

Evergreen/Conecuh Chamber of Commerce [47680]

Evergreen - Conecuh County Area Chamber of Commerce [47680]

Evergreen - Conecuh County Chamber of Commerce [47680]

Evergreen Freedom Foundation (EFF) [34654]

Evergreen Park Chamber of Commerce (EPCC) [51091]

"Every Little Bit Helps" in *Black Enterprise* (Vol. 38, November 2007, No. 4, pp. 102) [447], [2037], [5888], [10055], [14797], [39874]

Every Monday [50088]

"Every Resume Tells a Story" in *Women In Business* (Vol. 62, September 2010, No. 3, pp. 26) [35334], [35774], [47271]

"Every Year, Thousands of People Are Killed By Pathogens In Food. William Hanson Wants To Help" in *Inc.* (November 2007, pp. 46-47) [21571], [45402]

"Everybody Wants To Save the World: But When You Start a Charity Overseas, Good Intentions Often Go Awry" in *Inc.* (December 2007) [36511], [45914]

Everybody's Business [59567]

"Everyone Has a Story Inspired by Chevrolet" in *Automotive News* (Vol. 86, October 31, 2011, No. 6488, pp. S003) [448], [14889], [39048]

"Everyone Out of the Pool" in *Barron's* (Vol. 89, July 20, 2009, No. 29, pp. 18) [8298], [12314], [16888], [17281], [19545], [31417]

Everyone's Backyard [7361]

Everything I Know About Business I Learned at Mc-Donald's: The 7 Leadership Principles that Drive Break Out Success [17915], [24341], [37978]

Everything I Know About Business I Learned from My Mama: A Down-Home Approach to Business and Personal Success [29726], [32685]

Everything is Possible: Life and Business Lessons from a Self-Made Billionaire and the Founder of Slim-Fast [15162], [21279], [29727]

Everything You Always Wanted to Know about Management [29212], [30365], [38624]

Everything You Need to Know to Sell By Owner [16889], [17282]

"Evidence-Based Management and the Marketplace For Ideas" in *Academy of Management Journal* (Vol. 50, No. 5, October 2007, pp. 1009) [35775], [37979]

"Evidence Growing of Commercial Real Estate" in *Boston Business Journal* (Vol. 27, October 5, 2007, No. 36, pp. 1) [16890], [17283]

"EVMS Gets Grant to Train Providers for Elder Care" in *Virginian-Pilot* (October 29, 2010) [297], [1426], [10534], [15071], [28193]

"The Evolution of Carolyn Elman" in *Women In Business* (Vol. 62, September 2010, No. 3, pp. 11) [37980], [47272]

"The Evolution of Corporate Social Responsibility" in *Business Horizons* (November-December 2007, pp. 449) [12315], [29728], [30929], [37981], [45915]

"The Evolution of the Mobile Entrepreneur" in *Entrepreneur* (Vol. 37, August 2009, No. 8, pp. 31) [32686], [34878]

Evos [10317]

"Ex Libris Rosetta Hits the Market" in *Information Today* (Vol. 26, February 2009, No. 2, pp. 30) [2129], [3534], [4708], [18899], [45123]

"Ex-MP? Ex-con? Exactly!" in *Canadian Business* (Vol. 83, October 12, 2010, No. 17, pp. 16) [2130], [7921]

"EX3D to Launch In-Theater Vending Machines for Stylish RealD 3D Glasses" in *Entertainment Close-Up* (August 16, 2011) [14569], [20860]

Exceeding Customer Expectations [2805]

Excelling as A Manager or Supervisor (Onsite) [37624]

Excelling as a Highly Effective Team Leader (Onsite) [37625]

Excelsior Springs Area Chamber of Commerce [54042]

The Exceptional Assistant (Onsite) [28986]

Exceptional Business Writing and Goof-Proof Grammar [22567]

Exceptional Children [20737]

Exceptional Customer Service Leadership [26366]

Exceptional Management Skills (Onsite) [37626]

Exceptional Presentation Training (Onsite) [22196]

Exceptional Selling: How the Best Connect and Win in High Stakes Sales [43460]

Exceptional Service, Exceptional Profit: The Secrets of Building a Five-Star Customer Service Organization [10688], [20886], [22946], [26425], [44331]

The Exchange [48568]; [59178]

Execution: The Discipline of Getting Things Done [29729], [37982]

Executive [54384]

Executive Analytics & Design Inc. [4672]

"The Executive Brain" in *Canadian Business* (Vol. 80, October 22, 2007, No. 21, pp. 41) [29730], [37983], [42791], [43847]

Executive Business Maintenance Franchise [2660], [2731]

Executive Consultants Inc. [42328]

"Executive Decision: Damn the Profit Margins, Sleeman Declares War on Buck-a-Beer Foes" in *Globe & Mail* (January 28, 2006, pp. B3) [1844], [13579], [24342], [25076], [39049]

"Executive Decision: Just What the Doctor Ordered" in *Globe & Mail* (February 11, 2006, pp. B3) [6656], [37984], [39050], [41891], [43848]

"Executive Decision: Lead a Double Life for Geac's Sake" in *Globe & Mail* (January 21, 2006, pp. B4) [22947], [24343], [25077], [39051]

"Executive Decision: To Make Inroads Against RIM, Palm Steals Its Strategy" in *Globe & Mail* (March 25, 2006, pp. B3) [3724], [22948], [24344], [41062], [41892]

Executive Directions International Inc. [36027]

Executive Excellence Publishing (EEP) [58712]

The Executive Group [36028]

"Executive Interview: Arturo Elias" in *Canadian Business* (Vol. 80, January 29, 2007, No. 3, pp. 16) [22949], [39052]

Executive Management Services Inc. [29304]

Executive Office Link [57335]

Executive Office of the President - Office of Management and Budget - Administrator of the Small Business Administration [60114]

Executive Office of the President - Office of Management and Budget - Office of Federal Procurement Policy [60115]; [62161]; [60116]

Executive Office of the President - Office of Management and Budget - Small Business Administration [60117]

Executive Protection Video Catalog [18519]

Executive Quickline [51601]

Executive Recruiter News [7800]

Executive Report [53251]; [53252]

Executive Tans [19576]

"Executive Training" in *Black Enterprise* (Vol. 37, December 2006, No. 5, pp. 70) [24345], [28194]

"Executives Exit at Wal-Mart in China" in *Wall Street Journal Eastern Edition* (October 17, 2011, pp. B3) [33685], [35776], [36512], [37985], [43002]

Executrain Corporation [4781]

The Exempt Organization Tax Review [19686]

Exercise Ball Workout [15998]

Exercise Safety Association (ESA) [15944]

Exer-Safety Association - International Exer-Safety Association [15944]

Exeter Area Chamber of Commerce [54571]

Exeter Board of Trade [48569]

Exeter Capital Partners [55413]

Exeter Chamber of Commerce [48569]

Exhibit Builder [46731]

Exhibit Designers and Producers Association (EDPA) [20297], [46734]

Exhibition Services and Contractors Association [20298]

Existing Industry Resource [50528]

"Exit Strategy" in *Barron's* (Vol. 89, July 6, 2009, No. 27, pp. 3) [22108], [27210], [33204], [35335]

"Exiting Stage Left" in *Baltimore Business Journal* (Vol. 28, June 18, 2010, No. 6, pp. 1) [3176], [7922], [19930], [33205], [44670], [45403]

"Fair Play? China Cheats, Carney Talks and Rankin Walks; Here's the Latest" in Canadian Business (Vol. 81, March 17, 2008, No. 4) [11095], [14891], [23845], [33689], [36520], [37368], [39058], [46227]
"Fair Tax Backers Hope MBT Anger Will Bring Votes" in Crain's Detroit Business (Vol. 24, March 31, 2008, No. 13, pp. 32) [33690], [45410], [46228]
Fairbanks Historical Society [58422]
Fairborn Area Chamber of Commerce (FACC) [56129]
Fairbury Association of Commerce [51092]
Fairbury Chamber of Commerce [51092]; [54386]
Fairchild Tropical Garden Views [13408]
The Fairer Sex? [26684]
"Fairfax Announces Acquisition of William Ashley" in Benzinga.com (August 16, 2011) [2499], [12319], [31047], [44334]
Fairfax County Chamber of Commerce [58911]
Fairfax Partners, LLC [59013]
Fairfax Small Business Development Center [58797]
The Fairfield Advantage [56130]
Fairfield Area Chamber of Commerce (FACC) [51891]
Fairfield Chamber of Commerce [49696]; [56131]
Fairfield Chamber of Commerce (FCC) [58135]
Fairfield Chamber of Commerce [51125]
Fairfield County Chamber of Commerce (FCCC) [57459]
The Fairfield Factor Inc. [14044]
Fairfield Town Map [49697]
Fairmont Area Chamber of Commerce (FACC) [53643]
"Fairness First" in Canadian Business (Vol. 80, April 23, 2007, No. 9, pp. 45) [25373], [45916], [46871]
Fairview Area Chamber of Commerce [57699]
Fairview Chamber of Commerce [56515]
Fairview Heights Chamber of Commerce (FHCOC) [51093]
Fairview Technology Center [57826]
Faith Chamber of Commerce [57579]
Faith Country Development Corp. [57579]
Falcon Fund [49219]
Edgar Falk Communications [40604]
Fall Art Fair/Novi [6044]
Fall Crafts Festival/Gaithersburg [6058]
Fall Crafts Festival/Manassas [6060]
Fall Crafts Festival/Timonium [6064]
Fall is a Favorite Time of Year [59568]
"Fall Fever" in Canadian Business (Vol. 81, October 13, 2008, No. 17, pp. S12) [4102], [4221], [7826]
Fall River Area Chamber of Commerce and Industry Inc. (FRCOC) [52885]
Fall River Area Chamber of Commerce [52885]
Fall River Area Chamber of Commerce and Industry [52885]
"Fall Wardrobe on a Budget" in Women In Business (Vol. 62, September 2010, No. 3, pp. 38) [4222], [47273]
Fall/Winter/Spring Guide [53253]
Fallbrook Chamber of Commerce [48573]
Falling Behind: How Rising Inequality Harms the Middle Class [27218], [32687]
"Falling Local Executive Pay Could Suggest a Trend" in Tampa Bay Business Journal (Vol. 30, January 15, 2010, No. 4, pp. 1) [12320], [21904], [31424], [35779], [37989], [45411]
"Falling Markets' Nastiest Habits" in Barron's (Vol. 88, July 7, 2008, No. 27, pp. 7) [8301], [12321], [27219], [31425]
"Falling Share Prices Will Convince Big Oil Producers to Pay Up to Drill" in Globe & Mail (April 21, 2007, pp. B1) [8302], [12322]
Falls Chamber of Commerce [59569]
Falls City Area Chamber of Commerce (FCACC) [54387]
Falmouth Brochure [52886]
Falmouth Chamber of Commerce [52887]
False Economy: A Surprising Economic History of the World [27220], [36521]
Famaco Publishers L.L.C. [50386]
"Familiar Face Aims to Rebuild Distributor's Once-Strong Local Ties" in Crain's Cleveland Business (December 3, 2007) [24348], [26751], [37990]
"Familiar Fun" in Crain's Cleveland Business (Vol. 28, October 22, 2007, No. 42, pp. 3) [18423], [20247], [22959], [33691], [36522], [39059], [39879], [43004]
A Familiarization of Drivetrain Components (Onsite) [38875]
Family Business [27221], [31048], [37991]
Family Business Advisor [31138]
Family Business Experts [2872], [3067], [13827], [31142], [38715]
Family Business Institute Inc. [2872], [3067], [13827], [31142], [38715]
Family Business Magazine [29443], [31014], [44796]
Family Business Models [31049], [37992]
"Family Business Research" in International Journal of Entrepreneurship and Small Business (Vol. 12, December 3, 2010, No. 1) [31050], [42792], [43849], [45412]

Family Campers and RVers (FCRV) [3248]
"Family Dynamics and Family Business Financial Performance: Spousal Commitment" in Family Business Review (Vol. 19, March 2006) [31009]
Family Enterpriser [29444], [31015], [44797]
"Family Feud: Pawn Shop Empire Stalls with Transition to Second Generation" in Billings Gazette (December 19, 2010) [15447], [24349], [31051]
Family Financial Centers [3881]
Family Findings [9453]
"Family Firm Performance: Further Evidence" in Family Business Review (Vol. 19, June 2006, No. 2, pp. 103) [25507], [31052]
"Family Governance and Firm Performance: Agency, Stewardship, and Capabilities" in Family Business Review (Vol. 19, March 2006) [31053], [37993]
Family Law Reporter® [24145]
Family Limited Partnership Deskbook [23846], [24350], [31054], [37369], [41898], [46229]
Family Limited Partnerships Deskbook: Forming and Funding FLPs and Other Closely Held Business Entities [31055], [41899], [46230]
A Family Matter: A Guide to Operating Your Personal Estate [12323], [31426], [46231]
"Family Matters: Founding Family Firms and Corporate Political Activity" in Business and Society (December 2007, pp. 395-428) [12324], [31056], [45917]
"Family Matters: Founding Family Firms and Corporate Political Activity" in Business and Society (Vol. 46, December 2007, No. 4) [31057], [32688]
Family Resource Center on Disabilities (FRCD) [2873], [26003], [34622]
"The Family-Run Business" in Small Business Opportunities (Get Rich At Home 2010) [24351], [31058]
"Family Takes Wind Turbine Companies to Court Over Gag Clauses on Health Effects of Turbines" in CNW Group (September 12, 2011) [7185], [7546], [23847], [30598], [34269]
"Family Throne" in Hawaii Business (Vol. 53, March 2008, No. 9, pp. 51) [20677], [22960], [31059], [44335]
"The Family Tools" in Canadian Business (Vol. 80, March 26, 2007, No. 7, pp. 14) [29735], [31060]
Family Tree Maker® [9479]
Family Wars [31061]
"A Family's Fortune" in Canadian Business (Vol. 80, Winter 2007, No. 24, pp. 103) [16712], [19560], [21845], [31062]
Famous Famiglia [16146]
Famous Sam's, Inc. [18126]
Fancy Food [3297], [18025]
Fancy Food & Culinary Products [3297], [18025]
Fandom Directory [4408]
"Fannie and Freddie: How They'll Change" in Business Week (September 22, 2008, No. 4100, pp. 30) [8303], [12325], [14417], [26216], [27222], [31427], [33207], [33692], [33700]
Fannin County Chamber of Commerce [50529]
Fanning, Fanning & Associates Inc. [902], [5639]
Fannin-Polk Chamber of Commerce [50529]
Fantastic Flagler [50089]
Fantastic Sams [10091]
Far East Capital Corp. [49220]
"Far Out: Satellite Radio Finds New Way to Tally Listeners" in Globe & Mail (March 14, 2007, pp. B14) [449], [16713], [34881], [39880]
Fard Engineers Inc. [5640]
Fargo Chamber of Commerce [55901]
Fargo Small Business Development Center - University of North Dakota [55935]
Faribault Area Chamber of Commerce and Tourism (FACC) [53644]
"Farm Aid" in Canadian Business (Vol. 80, November 5, 2007, No. 22, pp. 123) [21573], [33208]
Farm Bureau News [21729]
Farm Chemicals Handbook [15628]
Farm Credit Administration - Office of Equal Employment Opportunity [60144]
Farm Credit Administration - Office of Equal Employment Opportunity and Inclusion [60145]
Farm Credit Administration - Office of Inspector General [60146]; [60147]
Farm Credit Administration - Office of Management Services [60148]; [60149]
Farm Credit Administration (FCA) - Office of Management Services - Office of Procurement [60150]
Farm Credit Administration (FCA) - Office of Procurement [60151]
Farm Industry News [21730]
Farm and Ranch News [21731]
Farm Tax Saver [19687]
Farmer Boys [9181], [18127]
Farmers Branch Chamber of Commerce [58136]

Farmersville Chamber of Commerce (FCC) [58137]
Farmerville Chamber of Commerce [52503]
"Farming Season Starts in December" in Farm Industry News (November 29, 2011) [21574], [44102]
Farmingdale Small Business Development Center [55019]
Farmington Chamber of Commerce [54956]; [55195]
Farmington Chamber of Commerce (FCC) [49698]; [54043]
Farmington/Farmington Hills Chamber of Commerce [53254]
Farmington River Watershed Association - Environmental Research Center [7404]
Farmington Small Business Development Center [54897]
Farmington-Wilton Chamber of Commerce [52593]
Farmville Area Chamber of Commerce [58912]
Farmville Chamber of Commerce (FCC) [58912]
The Farnsworth Group [40605]
Farwell Area Chamber of Commerce (FACC) [53255]
Farwest Nursery Show [9828]
FAS Fixed Asset Programs / Sage Software SB, Inc. [263], [19741]
FASB 95: Statement of Cash Flows [22141]
Fashion Association [3887], [13557]
Fashion Calendar [4103]
The Fashion Designer Survival Guide [4104], [4223]
"Fashion Forward - Frugally" in Entrepreneur (Vol. 37, July 2009, No. 7, pp. 18) [4224], [22961], [29736], [32165]
Fashion Institute of Design & Merchandising - Cyril Magnin Resource and Research Center [1676], [4172], [4309], [10158]
Fashion Institute of Design & Merchandising - Orange County Library [4173], [5935], [10159]
Fashion Institute of Technology - Gladys Marcus Library [1677], [4174], [4310], [5936], [7868], [10160], [11588]
Fashion & Print Directory [4470], [39881]
"Fashionistas Weigh in on the Super-Thin" in Charlotte Observer (February 7, 2007) [4105], [4225], [14365]
Fasken Martineau DuMoulin LLP Toronto Library [7760]
Fast Company's Greatest Hits: Ten Years of the Most Innovative Ideas in Business [29737], [32689], [37003]
"Fast Fact: Quality of Foods, Cost Top Factors in Determining Where to Grocery Shop" in Marketing to Women (Vol. 22, August 2009) [9926], [26427], [39882]
"Fast Fact: Women's Online Habits" in Marketing to Women (Vol. 22, July 2009, No. 7, pp. 1) [11682], [21096], [22300], [39883]
Fast-Fix Jewelry and Watch Repairs [13296]
Fast Food and Multi-Unit Restaurant Business [18018]
"Fast-Forward Fortune" in Small Business Opportunities (July 2010) [7871], [35554], [44223]
"Fast-Release Calcium Could Help Control Club Root" in Farmer's Weekly (March 28, 2008, No. 320) [21575], [33209], [43850]
"Fast Revival Unlikely For Indian 'Net Stocks" in Barron's (Vol. 88, July 7, 2008, No. 27, pp. 12) [8304], [11683], [12326], [31428], [34882], [36523]
Fast Signs [18795]
Fast-teks On-site Computer Services [4818], [40844]
Fast-Track Business Start-Up Kit: California [29360], [30599], [32386], [33693], [35780], [43325], [46043], [46232]
Fast-Track Employer's Kit: California [29738], [32690]
FastBucks [3882]
Faster Cheaper Better [22962], [25508], [25750], [36524]
"Faster and Shorter" in Canadian Business (Vol. 81, October 13, 2008, No. 17, pp. 25) [3726], [22301], [22591], [45413]
Fastframe USA [16329]
Fastline--Bluegrass Truck Edition [4598], [9219]
Fastline--Florida Truck Edition [4599], [9220]
Fastline--Georgia Truck Edition [4600], [9221]
Fastline--Illinois Farm Edition [21732]
Fastline--Indiana Farm Edition [21733]
Fastline--Iowa Farm Edition [21734]
Fastline--Kansas Farm Edition [21735]
Fastline--Kentucky Farm Edition [21736]
Fastline--Mid-Atlantic Farm Edition [21737]
Fastline--Mid-South Farm Edition [21738]
Fastline--Minnesota Farm Edition [21739]
Fastline--Missouri Farm Edition [21740]
Fastline--Nebraska Farm Edition [21741]
Fastline--Northeast Farm Edition [21742]
Fastline--Ohio Farm Edition [21743]
Fastline--Oklahoma Farm Edition [21744]
Fastline--Rocky Mountain Farm Edition [21745]
Fastline--Southeast Farm Edition [21746]
Fastline--Tennessee Farm Edition [21747]
Fastline--Tennessee Truck Edition [4601], [9222]

Fernley Chamber of Commerce **[54491]**
G. Ferrell & Associates **[34087]**
Ferrum College - Blue Ridge Heritage Archive **[6170]**
Fertility Weekly **[34518]**
"Fertilizer for Growth" in Canadian Business (Vol. 83, September 14, 2010, No. 15, pp. 76) **[12332]**, **[21577]**, **[36527]**, **[41901]**
Festival and Events Guide **[50090]**
"Festivals Press on Despite Loss of Sponsors" in Crain's Detroit Business (Vol. 25, June 22, 2009, No. 25, pp. 3) **[27227]**, **[32691]**, **[45918]**
Jeff Fetter Associates **[18052]**
"A Few Points of Contention" in Barron's (Vol. 88, July 14, 2008, No. 28, pp. 3) **[8311]**, **[12333]**, **[21578]**, **[27228]**, **[31432]**, **[33215]**, **[33697]**, **[44336]**
"Fewer Banks Offer Big Gifts to Lure Clients" in Globe & Mail (March 14, 2006, pp. D1) **[8312]**, **[26217]**, **[27229]**, **[31433]**
"Fewer People Dying At Work" in Sacramento Business Journal (Vol. 25, August 29, 2008, No. 26, pp. 1) **[5327]**, **[22964]**, **[27230]**, **[47463]**
FFA Inc. [902], [5639]
FHL Capital Corp. **[47751]**
FIABCI-U.S.A. **[16783]**
Fiber Fuels Institute [30427]
Fibreclean Supplies Ltd. **[2661]**
Fibrenew **[1606]**
Fiction Writer's Guideline **[2183]**, **[6836]**, **[13609]**
Fictionwise Inc. **[54887]**
Fictionwise.com [54887]
Fidelity Investor **[8863]**
Fidelity Management & Research Company - Fixed Income Research Center **[13235]**
Fidelity Polygraph & Investigation Consultants Inc. **[29305]**
Fidelity Ventures **[53025]**
Field Marketing Services Association [42930]
Field Spaniel Society of America (FSSA) **[1006]**
"Fieldbrook Foods Acquired By Private Equity Firm" in Ice Cream Reporter (Vol. 23, October 20, 2010, No. 11, pp. 1) **[10875]**, **[12334]**, **[41902]**
Fierce Conversations **[22302]**, **[29740]**
Fierce Leadership **[29741]**, **[37996]**
Fife Area Chamber of Commerce **[59182]**
Fifteenth Reunion of the International Association for Time Use Research Amsterdam **[2758]**, **[13760]**
Fifth Estate **[7718]**
"Fifth Third CEO Kabat: A World of Difference" in Business Courier (Vol. 26, January 1, 2010, No. 37, pp. 1) **[8313]**, **[12335]**, **[22965]**, **[31434]**, **[33216]**, **[37997]**
"Fifth Third Grapples With Account Snafu" in Business Courier (Vol. 24, December 7, 2008, No. 34, pp. 1) **[14419]**, **[26218]**, **[31435]**, **[41671]**
"Fifth Third Spinoff" in Business Courier (Vol. 27, July 16, 2010, No. 11, pp. 1) **[12336]**, **[16893]**, **[17286]**, **[22966]**, **[31436]**, **[41903]**, **[44337]**, **[44672]**
Fifty-Forty-Ten-News **[55020]**
"Fifty Percent of Global Online Retail Visits Were to Amazon, eBay and Alibaba in June 2011" in Benzinga.com (October 29, 2011) **[1513]**, **[28660]**, **[43006]**, **[45414]**
Figaro's Pizza **[16147]**
"Fight Against Fake" in The Business Journal-Portland (Vol. 25, July 18, 2008, No. 19, pp. 1) **[11097]**, **[19324]**, **[23853]**, **[33217]**, **[36528]**, **[39061]**, **[45415]**
"Fight Ensues Over Irreplaceable Gowns" in Tampa Bay Business Journal (Vol. 30, January 15, 2010, No. 4, pp. 1) **[4106]**, **[6305]**, **[9255]**, **[23854]**, **[26219]**, **[37371]**, **[47016]**
"Fight Over Casino Funds Limits Kitty for MEDC" in Crain's Detroit Business (Vol. 24, January 21, 2008, No. 3, pp. 3) **[9394]**, **[27231]**
"Fighting Detroit" in Baltimore Business Journal (Vol. 27, January 22, 2010, No. 38, pp. 1) **[14892]**, **[23855]**, **[31437]**, **[32166]**, **[33698]**, **[39062]**
"Fighting the Good Fight" in Inc. (Vol. 33, October 2011, No. 8, pp. 8) **[28199]**, **[37998]**
"The File On..Jenne Distributors" in Crain's Cleveland Business (Vol. 28, October 8, 2007, No. 40, pp. 26) **[22303]**, **[22967]**
"The File On..Skoda Minotti" in Crain's Cleveland Business (Vol. 28, October 8, 2007, No. 40, pp. 26) **[83]**, **[8314]**, **[12337]**, **[22968]**, **[29742]**, **[31438]**
Filene Research Institute **[8968]**
"Filling the Business Gap" in Hispanic Business (December 2010) **[27232]**, **[35338]**, **[35781]**, **[40737]**, **[40880]**, **[47277]**
"Filling the Gap" in Canadian Business (Vol. 80, March 12, 2007, No. 6, pp. 62) **[22969]**, **[29743]**, **[43007]**
Fillmore Chamber of Commerce **[48574]**
Film and Tape Directory [7981]
Film and Television Archives Advisory Committee [7876]
Film Comment **[14580]**
"Film Giants Disney, Pixar Talk Marriage" in Globe & Mail (January 19, 2006, pp. B1) **[7923]**, **[24352]**, **[25080]**, **[41904]**
"Film Incentives: A Hit or a Flop?" in Michigan Vue (Vol. 13, July-August 2008, No. 4, pp. 10) **[7924]**, **[25509]**, **[27233]**, **[33218]**, **[33699]**, **[45416]**, **[46234]**
Film Journal International **[14581]**
Film Journal International--Equipment, Concessions & Services Guide **[14571]**
Film Journal--Equipment, Concessions, & Services Guide Issue [14571]
Film Studies Association of Canada (FSAC) **[7883]**
Film & Television Directory: The Production Maker Source **[7897]**
Films and Videos on Photography **[15848]**
Fina A Groomer Inc. [59362]
"The Final Frontier" in Canadian Business (Vol. 80, October 8, 2007, No. 20, pp. 127) **[21579]**, **[27234]**, **[30602]**
"The Final Piece; Lowe's to Fill Last Big Parcel Near Great Lakes Crossing" in Crain's Detroit Business (March 10, 2008) **[1191]**, **[10132]**, **[17287]**, **[17919]**, **[43008]**
"Final Player In Big Mortgage Fraud Operation Gets Jail Time" in Boston Business Journal (Vol. 31, May 27, 2011, No. 18, pp. 3) **[14420]**, **[16894]**, **[17288]**, **[23856]**, **[30932]**
"The Final Say" in Hispanic Business (Vol. 30, March 2008, No. 3, pp. 52) **[12338]**, **[21905]**, **[40738]**, **[47278]**
"Final State Budget Is a Mixed Bag of Key Industries" in The Business Journal - Serving Phoenix and the Valley of the Sun (Vol. 28, July 4, 2008, No. 44, pp. 3) **[16895]**, **[17289]**, **[19092]**, **[21367]**, **[33219]**, **[33700]**, **[45417]**, **[46235]**
"Finalist: BlackEagle Partners L.L.C." in Crain's Detroit Business (Vol. 24, March 24, 2008, No. 12, pp. 12) **[8315]**, **[12339]**, **[26752]**, **[31439]**, **[39063]**, **[41905]**
"Finalist: Private Company, $100M-$1B" in Crain's Detroit Business (Vol. 25, June 22, 2009, No. 25) **[14893]**, **[39064]**
"Finalist: Private Company, Less Than $100M" in Crain's Detroit Business (Vol. 25, June 22, 2009, No. 25) **[14194]**, **[18424]**, **[31063]**; **[22970]**, **[24353]**, **[25851]**, **[34884]**
"Finally, Justice" in Canadian Business (Vol. 82, April 27, 2009, No. 7, pp. 12) **[84]**, **[2282]**, **[12340]**, **[19629]**, **[21368]**, **[23857]**, **[30933]**
"Finally, a Unique Solution to Meet All Wedding Planning Needs" in Benzinga.com (September 29, 2011) **[2500]**
Finance & Accounting: How to Keep Your Books and Manage Your Finances with an MBA, a CPA, or a Ph.D **[85]**, **[2283]**, **[21369]**, **[31440]**
"The Finance Function In A Global Corporation" in Harvard Business Review (Vol. 86, July-August 2008, No. 8, pp. 108) **[86]**, **[8316]**, **[12341]**, **[21370]**, **[31441]**, **[36529]**
Finance for Non-Financial Managers - Improving Financial Literacy (Onsite) **[37630]**
Financial & Accounting Concepts, Statements & Terminology: 2 Day (Onsite) **[31164]**
Financial Analysts Federation [11969]
Financial Analysts Research Foundation [8971]
Financial Aspects **[18345]**
Financial Business Services **[13155]**, **[14524]**
Financial Computer Support Inc. **[8912]**, **[11481]**, **[13180]**
"Financial Education: Boomer's Spending Hurts Retirement" in Employee Benefit News (Vol. 25, November 1, 2011, No. 14, pp. 18) **[8317]**, **[12342]**, **[21906]**, **[31442]**
Financial and Estate Planning **[8864]**, **[19688]**
Financial Executives Research Foundation (FERF) **[2343]**
Financial Management 101: Get a Grip on Your Business Numbers **[87]**, **[450]**, **[21371]**, **[22110]**, **[31443]**, **[32692]**
Financial Management for Data Processing [4837]
Financial Management for the Small Business **[31444]**
Financial Management Solutions Inc. **[32027]**
Financial Management Workshops **[8881]**
Financial Managers Society (FMS) **[8031]**
Financial Managers Society Annual Conference **[8905]**, **[32002]**
Financial Modeling and Forecasting **[31165]**
Financial Planning Association (FPA) **[8032]**
Financial Planning and Management **[8882]**
Financial Product News [2714]
Financial Research Association Inc. (FRA) **[50387]**
Financial Services Review: The Journal of Individual Financial Management **[8865]**, **[31988]**
Financial Solutions Inc. **[16756]**, **[20006]**
Financial Statement Analysis (Onsite) **[31166]**
Financial Studies of the Small Business **[31989]**
Financial Success Strategies for the 1990s **[31995]**
Financial Times Guide to Business Start Up 2007 **[88]**, **[21372]**, **[26429]**, **[29361]**, **[32387]**, **[37999]**
Financial Women International (FWI) **[8033]**
Financial Women's Association of New York (FWA) **[8034]**
Financing Growth: Strategies, Capital Structure, and M and A Transactions **[12343]**, **[22971]**, **[24354]**, **[31445]**, **[41906]**
"Financing for NNSA Plant Is a Work in Progress" in The Business Journal-Serving Metropolitan Kansas City (October 24, 2008) **[5328]**, **[17290]**, **[24355]**, **[26220]**, **[27235]**, **[33701]**, **[37372]**, **[39065]**
Financing Your Business: Get a Grip on Finding the Money **[32693]**, **[37373]**
Financing Your Small Business **[8318]**, **[12344]**, **[37374]**, **[41907]**, **[47017]**
"Financo Panel Lauds Product, Online Marketing" in Home Textiles Today (Vol. 31, January 25, 2010, No. 3, pp. 1) **[11684]**, **[21097]**, **[28661]**, **[39885]**, **[43009]**
Finaventures **[49221]**
"Find Private Money for FutureGen Plant" in Crain's Chicago Business (Vol. 34, September 12, 2011, No. 37, pp. 18) **[7187]**, **[7547]**, **[30603]**, **[37375]**
"Find the Upside to a Down Economy" in Women Entrepreneur (September 30, 2008) **[27236]**, **[29362]**, **[44761]**, **[47187]**
"Find Your Marketing Mojo" in Business Owner (Vol. 35, July-August 2011, No. 4, pp. 14) **[25081]**, **[25510]**, **[39886]**
FINDERBINDER--Arizona: Arizona's Updated Media Directory **[3198]**
FINDERBINDER--Greater Detroit **[3199]**
FINDERBINDER--Oklahoma **[3200]**
FinderBinder/SourceBook Directories **[2216]**
"Finding A Higher Gear" in Harvard Business Review (Vol. 86, July-August 2008, No. 8, pp. 68) **[11098]**, **[22972]**, **[29744]**, **[36530]**, **[38000]**
"Finding Competitive Advantage in Adversity" in Harvard Business Review (Vol. 88, November 2010, No. 11, pp. 102) **[25511]**, **[27237]**, **[41908]**
"Finding Good Bets Down on the Farm" in Crain's Chicago Business (Vol. 31, March 24, 2008, No. 12, pp. 4) **[8319]**, **[12345]**, **[29745]**, **[31446]**
"Finding Life Behind the Numbers" in Crain's Chicago Business (Vol. 31, March 24, 2008, No. 12, pp. 25) **[28200]**, **[36531]**
Finding a Niche: Determining Business Potential **[40566]**, **[44906]**
"Finding Room for Financing" in The Business Journal-Serving Metropolitan Kansas City (Vol. 26, August 1, 2008, No. 47, pp. 1) **[10690]**, **[17291]**, **[20365]**, **[27238]**, **[33220]**, **[46236]**, **[46647]**, **[47018]**
Finding That First Apartment **[1165]**
"Finding the Voice of the Marketplace" in Mergers & Acquisitions: The Dealmaker's Journal (March 1, 2008) **[12346]**, **[24356]**, **[25082]**, **[39887]**, **[41909]**
"Finding a Way to Continue Growing" in Green Industry Pro (Vol. 23, March 2011, No. 3, pp. 31) **[9778]**, **[13388]**, **[13475]**, **[22973]**, **[25512]**, **[44338]**
"Finding Your Place in the World: Global Diversity Has Become a Corporate Catchphrase" in Black Enterprise (November 2007) **[36532]**, **[40881]**
Findlay-Hancock County Chamber of Commerce **[56133]**
Fine Details Inc. **[3335]**
Fine Hardwood Veneer Association/American Walnut Manufacturers Association [13635]
Fine Hardwoods American Walnut Association [13635]
Fine Homebuilding **[5595]**
Fine Woodworking **[3426]**, **[6014]**, **[6131]**
"Finger-Pointing Time" in Barron's (Vol. 88, March 10, 2008, No. 10, pp. 9) **[8320]**, **[12347]**, **[14421]**, **[26221]**, **[27239]**, **[31447]**
Fingerplays and Footplays **[3971]**
Fingerprints **[6790]**
FINIS: Financial Industry Information Service [8930], [13193], [17609]
"Finishing High School Leads to Better Employment Prospects" in Occupational Outlook Quarterly (Vol. 55, Summer 2011, No. 2, pp. 36) **[3350]**, **[28201]**
"Finishing Touches: the Fashion Statement is in the Detail" in Black Enterprise (Vol. 37, January 2007, No. 6, pp. 106) **[4226]**, **[7827]**, **[29746]**, **[32694]**, **[43010]**
Wayne Finkelman Research Library at Western Costume Company **[5937]**
Finnegan, Henderson, Farabow, Garrett and Dunner Library **[37175]**
Finney County Genealogical Society Library **[9504]**
Finnish American Chamber of Commerce (FACC) **[36292]**
"FinOvation 2009" in Farm Industry News (Vol. 42, January 1, 2009, No. 1) **[21580]**, **[37006]**, **[41065]**, **[43853]**

3510 Small Business Sourcebook • 30th Edition

Fiorello H. LaGuardia Community College of the City University of New York - Division of Adult and Continuing Education - Center for Corporate Education [55505]

"Fire Destroys Surplus Store, Sets Off Live Rounds Near Jacksonville NAS" in Florida Times-Union (December 5, 2010) [10028], [43011]

"Fire Destroys Veterans' Kiosk" in Houston Chronicle (November 24, 2010, pp. 14) [13321], [45919]

Fired Arts & Crafts: The Bible of the Ceramic Hobbyists Since 1955 [6015], [6132]

"Firefighter Wins ABC's American Inventor" in Hispanic Business (September 2007, pp. 94) [36944], [41361], [44096]

Firelands Historical Society Library [9505]

Firemark Investments [38717]

The Firkin Group of Pubs [9182], [18129]

"Firm Restricts Cellphone Use While Driving" in Globe & Mail (January 30, 2006, pp. B3) [3727], [33702]

"Firm Stays In the 'Family'; After Owner's Death, Employees Buy Company" in Crain's Detroit Business (Vol. 24, January 28, 2008) [15278], [31064], [41401], [41539]

"Firm Takes 'Local' Worldwide" in Hispanic Business (July-August 2007, pp. 48) [1270], [5329], [36533]

"Firms Sue Doracon to Recoup More Than $1M in Unpaid Bills" in Baltimore Business Journal (Vol. 28, July 9, 2010, No. 9, pp. 1) [5330], [6306], [11349], [14111], [17780], [23858], [26222], [36146]

"Firms Upbeat About Future, Survey Shows" in Globe & Mail (January 17, 2006, pp. B4) [35339], [39066]

First Aid on the Job [47498]

"First Airport Location for Paciugo Gelato" in Ice Cream Reporter (Vol. 23, October 20, 2010, No. 11, pp. 2) [10876], [24851]

First Analysis Corp. [51401]

First, Break All the Rules: What the World's Greatest Managers Do Differently [32695], [38001]

First Capital Management Co. LLC / FCG [58556]

First Choice Haircutters [10092]

First Continental Realty Inc. [17587]

First Editions, a Guide to Identification: Statements of Selected North American, British Commonwealth, and Irish Publishers on Their Methods of Designating First Editions [2132]

"First Financial Aiming for Banking Big Leagues" in Business Courier (Vol. 26, December 4, 2009, No. 32, pp. 1) [8321], [12348], [25311], [31448]

First Flight Venture Center [55867]

"First Franchising Census Report Highlights Industry's Economic Role" in Franchising World (Vol. 42, November 2010, No. 11, pp. 41) [27240], [32167], [35782]

First Growth Capital, Inc. [50653]

First Health [22057]

"First Impression of Robotic Farming Systems" in Farm Industry News (September 30, 2011) [21581], [34885], [39067]

"First Mariner's New Ads No Passing Fancy" in Boston Business Journal (Vol. 29, September 16, 2011, No. 19, pp. 1) [451], [31449]

"First the Merger: Then, The Culture Clash. How To Fix the Little Things That Can Tear a Company Apart" in Inc. (January 2008) [452], [1271], [11541], [12349], [18787], [41910]

First Monday [50091]

First Moves: Welcoming a Child to a New Caregiving Setting [3972]

First New England Capital, L.P. [49777]

"First: Package Deal" in Entrepreneur (Vol. 35, October 2007, No. 10, pp. 114) [2038], [39888], [43463]

First-Rate Customer Service [26583]

First Strike Management Consulting Inc. [3068], [13829], [26005], [38718], [44937]

"First Suzlon S97 Turbines Arrive in North America for Installation" in PR Newswire (September 28, 2011) [7188], [7548], [30604], [39068]

"First-Time Homebuyer Credit May Add Some Momentum to Market" in Crain's Cleveland Business (Vol. 30, May 18, 2009, No. 20) [5331], [14422], [16896], [17292], [33221], [46237]

First Tuesday [17110], [17560]

"First U.S. :M-Press Tiger with Inline Screen Printing" in American Printer (Vol. 128, June 1, 2011, No. 6) [4472], [12350], [16368], [20768], [25312], [41911]

"First Venture Reports Proprietary Yeasts Further Reduce Ethyl Carbamate in Sake" in Canadian Corporate News (May 16, 2007) [13580], [30605], [43854]

First Washington Associates Ltd. [36914]

F1RSTMARK HMOs and PPOs [14253]

F1RSTMARK Home Healthcare Agency Directory [10588]

"FirstMerit's Top Executive Turns Around Credit Quality" in Crain's Cleveland Business (Vol. 28, October 15, 2007, No. 41, pp. 3) [8322], [22974], [25083], [26223], [31450], [35340]

"FIS-Metavante Deal Paying Off for Many" in Business Journal-Milwaukee (Vol. 28, December 17, 2010, No. 11, pp. A1) [8323], [9256], [12351], [24738], [25313], [34886], [45920]

Fiscal Agents - Financial Information Service - Research Department - Library [8960]

Fiscal Management Associates L.L.C. [221]

"Fiscally Fit" in Entrepreneur (Vol. 37, October 2009, No. 10, pp. 130) [15966], [22975], [29747], [32168]

Fish Bites [57580]

Fish Window Cleaning [2662]

Fish Wrapper [57581]

Fisheries Museum of the Atlantic Library [9037]

Fisheries of the United States [9017]

Fishers Chamber of Commerce (FCC) [51603]

FishersChamber.Com [51604]

Fishery Bulletin [9027]

Fishing Tackle Retailer [1701]

Fisons Corporation Limited - Information Resources Centre [6713]

Fit Zone For Women [16022]

Fitch Insights [13118]

"Fitness: Dispelling Rocky Mountain Myths Key to Wellness" in Employee Benefit News (Vol. 25, November 1, 2011, No. 14, pp. 12) [28202], [34271], [35783]

"Fitness Made Fun" in Playthings (Vol. 106, September 1, 2008, No. 8, pp. 12) [5125], [15967], [20248]

"Fitter from Twitter" in Boston Business Journal (Vol. 30, December 17, 2010, No. 47, pp. 1) [453], [11685], [15968], [21098], [39889], [45418], [47279]

Fitwize 4 Kids Inc. [16023]

Fitzgerald Valuation Services Inc. [17589]

Fitzsimons BioBusiness Partners [49624]

Fitzsimons Life Science District [49625]

FIU Hospitality Review [10767]

"Five Area Businesses Win State Tax Breaks" in Crain's Detroit Business (Vol. 25, June 22, 2009, No. 25, pp. 9) [33222], [46238]

"Five Distinct Divisions, One Collective Focus" in Green Industry Pro (Vol. 23, October 2011) [9779], [13389], [13476], [39890], [43464], [44339]

The Five Dysfunctions of a Team: A Leadership Fable [29066], [38002]

Five Guys [18130]

"Five Low-Cost Home Based Startups" in Women Entrepreneur (December 16, 2008) [2772], [5117], [11519], [11686], [16897], [21021], [27241], [28662], [29748], [35555], [43340], [44762], [47280]

"Five More Great Books on Entrepreneurship" in Entrepreneur (Vol. 37, July 2009, No. 7, pp. 19) [2133], [29749], [32696], [44828]

"Five New Scientists Bring Danforth Center $16 Million" in Saint Louis Business Journal (Vol. 32, October 7, 2011, No. 6, pp. 1) [28203], [33223], [42794], [43855]

"Five Reasons Why the Gap Fell Out of Fashion" in Globe & Mail (January 27, 2007, pp. B4) [4227], [25513], [39069], [43012]

"Five-Ring Circus" in Entrepreneur (Vol. 35, November 2007, No. 11, pp. 76) [19421], [22976], [23859], [30606], [30934], [34272], [36534]

"Five Steps to the Corner Office" in Canadian Business (Vol. 80, March 12, 2007, No. 6, pp. 36) [29750], [38003]

"Five Steps to an Effective Business Call" in Hawaii Business (Vol. 53, October 2007, No. 4, pp. 64) [22304], [22592], [44829]

"Five Steps to an Effective Meeting" in Hawaii Business (Vol. 53, March 2008, No. 9, pp. 55) [29067], [32697], [38004], [44830]

"Five Steps for Handling Independent Contractors" in Hawaii Business (Vol. 53, January 2008, No. 7, pp. 49) [28204], [32698], [38005], [41672], [44831]

"Five Steps to Killer Business Ideas" in Hawaii Business (Vol. 53, December 2007, No. 6, pp. 135) [24357], [25084], [32699], [44832]

Five Steps to Successful Selling [43720]

"Five Things" in Hawaii Business (Vol. 53, November 2007, No. 5, pp. 20) [22305], [24852], [32700]

"Five Things..For Photo Fun" in Hawaii Business (Vol. 53, October 2007, No. 4, pp. 20) [3232], [5748], [22593], [34887], [41066]

"Five Tips for New Managers" in Hawaii Business (Vol. 53, November 2007, No. 5, pp. 59) [22306], [26430], [32701], [38006]

"Five Ways to Make RTK Pay" in Farm Industry News (March 25, 2011) [21582], [45419]

"Fix-It Career: Jobs in Repair" in Occupational Outlook Quarterly (Vol. 54, Fall 2010, No. 3, pp. 26) [813], [18600], [44340]

Fixed Asset Accounting (Onsite) [21330]

"Fixing Up the Area: Leo Piatz Opens General Repair Business" in The Dickinson Press (November 16, 2010) [21483], [44224]

Flagler Beach Chamber of Commerce [50092]

Flagler County Directory and Shopping Guide [50093]

Flagler County Palm Coast Chamber of Commerce [50094]

Flagship [52888]

Flagship Enterprise Center [51756]

Flagship Ventures [53026]

Flagstaff Chamber of Commerce [47900]

Flagstaff Today [47901]

The Flame Broiler, Inc. [18131]

Flamers Charbroiled [18132]

Flamingo A Friend [44608]

Flat Rate Realty [17137]

Flat River Area Chamber of Commerce [54112]

"Flat or Slight Decline Seen for Nortel 2007 Revenue" in Globe & Mail (March 17, 2007, pp. B3) [25085], [44341]

Flatfooting Workshop [6404]

Flatiron Partners [55415]

Flatonia Chamber of Commerce (FCC) [58138]

Flavour and Fragrance Journal [2059]

The Flaw of Averages: Why We Underestimate Risk in the Face of Uncertainty [89], [7189], [7549], [12352], [21373], [30607], [31451], [33703], [34273]

"A Flawed Yardstick for Banks" in Barron's (Vol. 88, July 14, 2008, No. 28, pp. M6) [8324], [12353], [14423], [26224], [27242], [31452]

"Fledgling Brands May Take the Fall With Steve & Barry's" in Advertising Age (Vol. 79, July 7, 2008, No. 26, pp. 6) [4107], [4228], [19325], [37007], [43013]

Fleet Equipment: The Leading Information Resource for Fleet Equipment Managers [20705]

Fleming County Chamber of Commerce [52308]

Fletcher & Rowley Inc. [16619]

Fletcher Spaght Ventures [53027]

Flett Research Ltd. [2875], [26006], [44083]

Flex [15945]

Flex-Plan Services Inc. (FPS) [22058]

Flexible Benefits [22018]

Flexible Working Time: More Time to Live [35997]

Flexing Your Creative Muscle in the Financial Marketplace [41387]

FLEXO: Converting Technology [16416]

Flexographic Technical Association (FTA) [16338]

Flexographic Technical Journal [16416]

"Flight of Capital?" in Canadian Business (Vol. 80, February 26, 2007, No. 5, pp. 76) [44342]

Flight Safety Foundation [718]

Flight Safety Foundation Library [755]

Flightplan [719]

"Flights of Fancy" in Crain's Chicago Business (Vol. 31, April 21, 2008, No. 16, pp. 27) [24853], [25514], [44343]

"Flint Group Raises Prices" in American Printer (Vol. 128, August 1, 2011, No. 8) [4473], [16369], [20769], [25751]

Flint Ink - Information Resource Center [16448]

FLIP: How to Find, Fix, and Sell Houses for Profit [16898], [17293]

Flippin Chamber of Commerce (FCC) [48051]

Floor Covering Installation Contractors Association (FCICA) [9055]

Floor Covering News [9070]

Floor Covering Weekly [9071]

Floor Covering Weekly--Annual Product Source Guide [9061], [11542]

Floor Covering Weekly--Annual Directory Issue [9061], [11542]

Floor Covering Weekly--Local Product Source Directory Issue [9061], [11542]

Floor Coverings International [9080]

Floor Focus [9072]

Floorguard [16494]

Flor & Associates [23654], [25284], [40608], [41291]

Flora Magazine [9110]

FloraCulture International Magazine [9806]

Floral Design [9117]

"Floral-Design Kiosk Business in Colorado Springs Blossoming" in Colorado Springs Business Journal (September 24, 2010) [9101], [9927], [13322], [29751], [35600], [47281]

Floral Fundamentals [9118]

Florence Area Chamber of Commerce (FACC) [56776]

Florence Area Small Business Development Center [57404]

Florence Chamber of Commerce [49506]

Florence Crittenton Association of American [3923]

Florence-Darlington Technical College [57547]

Florence/Darlington Technical College - SBDC [57545]

Floresville Chamber of Commerce [58139]
Florida A&M University - Frederick S. Humphries Science Research Center Library [14347], [16097]
Florida Agency of Economic Opportunity - Labor Market Statistics - State Census Data Center [61644]
Florida Atlantic Research and Development Authority [50371]
Florida Black Business Investment Board [50343]
Florida Capital Partners [50349]
Florida Chamber of Commerce (FCC) [50095]
Florida Department of Agriculture and Consumer Services - Division of Plant Industry Library [1956]
Florida Department of Economic Opportunity - Labor Market Statistics - State Census Data Center [61645]
Florida Department of Management Services - Division of Purchasing [50356]
Florida Fashion Focus Show [3910], [4299], [7859], [13564]
Florida Furniture and Accessory Market [10500]
Florida International Restaurant & Hotel Expo [10783]
Florida JobBank: The Job Hunter's Guide to the Sunshine State [19176]
Florida Jurisprudence on Westlaw® [24146]
Florida Keys Community College [50375]
Florida Minority Supplier Development Council (FMSDC) [50344]
Florida/NASA Business Incubation Center - Technology Research and Development Authority [50372]
Florida Ophthalmic Institute Library [20950]
Florida Pest Management Association Convention and Exposition [15644]
Florida Pharmacy Association Annual Meeting and Convention [6693]
Florida Procurement Center Representatives [50357]
Florida Procurement Technical Assistance Center - Florida Gulf Coast University [50358]
Florida Procurement Technical Assistance Center - Jacksonville Chamber of Commerce - Small Business Center (SBC) [50359]
Florida Procurement Technical Assistance Center - Palm Beach Community PTAC [50360]
Florida Procurement Technical Assistance Center - Pinellas Park Office - University of South Florida [50361]
Florida Procurement Technical Assistance Center - Tampa Office - University of South Florida [50362]
Florida Procurement Technical Assistance Center - University of Central Florida [50363]
Florida Procurement Technical Assistance Center - University of West Florida [50364]
Florida Procurement Technical Assistance Center - University of West Florida - FWB Branch Office [50365]
Florida RV Supershow [1581], [46755]
Florida Small Business Development Center at Daytona State College [49868]
Florida Small Business Development Center Network (FSBDCN) [49869]
Florida Small Business Development Center at Seminole Community College [49870]
Florida Solar Energy Center Research Library [19139]
Florida State University - Career Center Library [3401]
Florida State University - Center for Personnel and Industrial Relations Research [13311]
Florida State University - Center for Human Resource Management [13311]
Florida State University - Center for Music Research (CMR) [14724]
Florida State University - Florida Center for Public Management (FCPM) [42427]
Florida State University - Panama Branch Library [33108]
Florida State University - Special Collections [10374]
Florida TaxWatch [19780]
Florida Trend [3124]
Florida Tropical Fish Farms Association (FTFFA) [8997]
Florida Veterinary Medical Association Annual Meeting [1084]
Florida-Israel Chamber of Commerce [56959]
"Florida's Bright Upside" in Tampa Bay Business Journal (Vol. 29, November 6, 2009, No. 46, pp. 1) [7190], [7550], [19093], [30608], [39070], [39891]
"Florida's Housing Gloom May Add To Woes of National City" in Crain's Cleveland Business (Vol. 28, October 29, 2007, No. 43, pp. 1) [8325], [12354], [26225], [31453], [41912]
"Florin Car Dealers Drive Plan" in Sacramento Business Journal (Vol. 25, August 22, 2008, No. 25, pp. 1) [14894], [16899], [17294], [26226], [27243], [37376]
Florissant Valley Chamber of Commerce [54051]
Florists' Review Magazine [9111]
Flower Arrangements Made Easy [9119]
"Flower Confidential" in Business Horizons (Vol. 51, January-February 2008, No. 1, pp. 73) [9102]

Flower Confidential: The Good, the Bad, and the Beautiful in the Business of Flowers [9103]
Flower Mound Chamber of Commerce [58140]
The Flower Shop Series [9120]
Flowerama of America [9127]
Flowers Canada (FC) [9094], [9762]
Flowers& [9112]
Floyd Browne Group (FBG) [34088]
Floyd County [52309]
Floyd County Chamber of Commerce [52310]; [58914]
Floyd County Chamber of Commerce [51719]
"Floyd County Considers Wind Farms" in Roanoke Times (September 19, 2011) [7191], [7551], [30609]
"Flu is a Booster for Firms Here" in Philadelphia Business Journal (Vol. 28, September 25, 2009, No. 32, pp. 1) [33424], [37008], [41067], [42795], [43856]
"Flue Vaccines are Going Green" in Canadian Business (Vol. 83, September 14, 2010, No. 15, pp. 24) [7192], [7552], [30610], [34274], [37009], [42796], [43857]
Fluke Venture Partners [59329]
Flushing Area Chamber of Commerce [53257]
Flute for Beginners [14648]
Fluvanna County Chamber of Commerce (FCCC) [58915]
Fly Fishing for Pike [1714]
"Fly Phishing" in Canadian Business (Vol. 80, October 22, 2007, No. 21, pp. 42) [3535], [11687], [18425], [18900], [28663], [45124]
Flying Biscuit [18133]
"Flying High Down Under" in Entrepreneur (Vol. 37, August 2009, No. 8, pp. 16) [24854], [44344]
"Flying High?" in Canadian Business (Vol. 80, April 9, 2007, No. 8, pp. 42) [8326], [12355], [39071]
"Flying the Unfriendly Skies" in Crain's Chicago Business (Vol. 31, April 21, 2008, No. 16, pp. 26) [24855], [36535], [44345], [45420]
Flying Wedge Pizza Co. [16148]
Flywheel Ventures [49222]
FMedia! [16743]
The FMI Show [26807]
FMLA Compliance (Onsite) [35669]
FMN: Financial Management Network [198]
Focal Point Business Coaching [3000]
Focal Points [57460]
FOCUS [50531]; [55196]; [59183]; [59572]; [56134]; [58141]; [58142]; [58143]; [58144]; [58653]; [59785]
The Focus [53646]; [55197]
Focus on Autism and Other Developmental Disabilities [34519]
Focus on Business [48575]; [48576]; [56777]
Focus on the Family (FOTF) [31016]
Focus on Fort Atkinson [59573]
Focus Group Moderator Training (Onsite) [39583]; [39584]
Focus on Autistic Behavior [34519]
Focus on Photography [15870], [15918]
FocusOn [49821]
Fogg Management Consulting [24670]
"Fogg Planning Twinsburg Warehouse Project" in Crain's Cleveland Business (Vol. 28, November 26, 2007, No. 47, pp. 6) [5332], [16900], [17295], [26753]
Foire Commerciale Artisanat Atlantique [6039], [6154]
Foit-Albert Associates [2569]
The FOLEPI Guide [51096]
Foliage Design Systems [16206]
Foliage Locator [50097]
Foliage Plant Production [9822]
Foliage Service by Concepts [16205]
Folio Show [15594]
Folkston/Charlton County Chamber of Commerce [50590]
Follett Software Company Resource Center [19055]
"Follow the ABCs of Buying a Business" in Women Entrepreneur (September 10, 2008) [23860], [24358], [25086], [25314], [28205], [32702]
"Follow the Numbers: It's the Best Way To Spot Problems Before They Become Life-Threatening" in Inc. (January 2008, pp. 63-64) [24183], [43341]
Follow-Up News [32278]
Follow-Up: Proven Methods & Strategies That Will Covert Your Contacts into Closings [43721]
"The Folly of Google's Latest Gambit" in Barron's (Vol. 89, July 13, 2009, No. 28, pp. 23) [3536], [11688], [18901], [41068], [45125]
Folsom Chamber of Commerce [48577]
Folsom Magazine [48578]
Fond du Lac Area Chamber of Commerce [59574]
Fond du Lac Area Association of Commerce (FDLAAC) [59574]
Fondation Asie Pacifique du Canada [26820]
Fondation Canadienne de la Recherche en Dietetique [15150]

Fondation des Infirmieres et Infirmiers du Canada [10518]
Fondation Scolaire de l'Institut Canadien du Credit [8028]
*FONE*Data* [19860]
Russ Fons Public Relations [40609], [42552], [42688]
Fontana Area Chamber of Commerce [48579]
Fontana Chamber of Commerce (FCC) [48579]
Food & Drug Packaging [4603]
"Food Bank to Move, Double in Size" in Austin Business Journal (Vol. 31, July 8, 2011, No. 18, pp. 1) [5333], [45921]
The Food & Beverage International [9996], [19258]
The Food & Beverage Journal [1871], [9997], [18026]
Food & Beverage Packaging: The Information Source for Food and Drug Packagers [4603]
Food Brokers Association [17857]
Food Code - Recommendations of the United States Public Health Service Food and Drug Administration [1939], [10323]
The Food & Drug Letter [5901]
"Food Fight" in Canadian Business (Vol. 79, November 6, 2006, No. 22, pp. 18) [9928], [22977], [25515], [43014]
Food & Fuel Expo [10010]
The Food Industry Advisor [9998]
Food Industry Association Executives (FIAE) [9899]
Food Institute (FI) [9900]
The Food Institute Report [9999]
Food, Lodging and Service Guide [56778]
Food Marketing Institute (FMI) [5790], [9901]
Food Marketing Institute Information Service [9194]
"Food as Nature Intended" in Pet Product News (Vol. 64, November 2010, No. 11, pp. 30) [1059], [15164], [15722], [43015], [45421]
Food Processing Suppliers Association (FPSA) [10841]
Food Service Equipment Industry [17863]
Food Service Industry Video Series: Career Opportunities [9172]
Food Service Industry Video Series: Employee Skills [9173]
Food Service Industry Video Series: Food Preparation [9174]
Food Service Industry Video Series: Management Skills [9175]
Food Service Industry Video Series: Safety and Sanitation [9176]
Food Service Meat Manual [3139]
Food Services [3475], [9177], [18034]
Food Trade News [10000]
"Food-Truck Learnings Travel Indoors" in Nation's Restaurant News (Vol. 45, June 27, 2011, No. 13, pp. 3) [9153], [17920]
"Food & Wine Publisher Tries His Hand at Saber Rattling" in Advertising Age (Vol. 77, December 4, 2006, No. 49, pp. 16) [19221], [21583]
"Foods for Thought" in Pet Product News (Vol. 64, December 2010, No. 12, pp. 16) [1233], [15756], [39072], [41069], [45422]
Foodservice and Lodging Institute [9144], [17869]
Foodservice Consultants Society International-- Membership Directory [3468]
Foodservice Equipment Distributors Association (FEDA) [17863]
Foodservice Facts [3460], [5098], [6434], [9139], [10276], [17864]
Foodservice and Hospitality Magazine: Canada's Hospitality Business Magazine [10300]
Foodservice Organization of Distributors [9904]
Foodservice & Packaging Institute Inc. (FPI) [9140]
Fooling Some of the People All of the Time [8327], [12356], [31454]
Fool's Gold: How the Bold Dream of a Small Tribe at J.P. Morgan Was Corrupted by Wall Street Greed [8328], [12357]
Foot Solutions, Inc. [15615]
Foothill Business [48580]
Foothills Focus [57461]
Footwear Distributors and Retailers of America (FDRA) [18749]
Footwear Industries of America [3887], [13557]
Footwear Retailers of America [18749]
"For $150 Million Mall, Failure to Launch" in Business Courier (Vol. 24, January 25, 2008, No. 42, pp. 1) [16901], [17296], [43016]
"For All It's Worth" in Entrepreneur (Vol. 36, April 2008, No. 4, pp. 46) [7746], [11350], [33704], [36147], [45423], [46239]
"For Apple, It's Showtime Again" in Barron's (Vol. 90, August 30, 2010, No. 35, pp. 29) [3177], [3728], [4952], [19874], [28664], [34888], [41070], [41402], [41540]
"For Baxter, A Lingering PR Problem; Ongoing Focus On Heparin Deaths Ups Heat On CEO" in Crain's Chicago Business (April 21, 2008) [8329], [12358], [23861], [31455], [36536], [39073], [42471]

Founding MASTER INDEX

"Founding Family Acquires Airport Marriott" in Crain's Cleveland Business (Vol. 28, November 5, 2007, No. 44, pp. 3) **[10691]**, **[24364]**, **[25089]**
Fountain Hills Chamber of Commerce **[47903]**
Fountain Valley Chamber of Commerce **[48585]**; **[49509]**
"Four Big Fat Business Plan Lies" in Entrepreneur (December 11, 2008) **[24365]**, **[25090]**, **[32706]**
"The Four Cheapest Plays in Emerging Markets" in Barron's (Vol. 89, July 27, 2009, No. 30, pp. 34) **[8334]**, **[12366]**, **[31462]**, **[36540]**
"Four Exhibition Considerations" in American Printer (Vol. 128, August 1, 2011, No. 8) **[4474]**, **[16370]**, **[20366]**, **[20770]**, **[46648]**
Four Flags Area Chamber of Commerce (FFACC) **[53259]**
"Four Lessons in Adaptive Leadership" in Harvard Business Review (Vol. 88, November 2010, No. 11, pp. 86) **[29764]**, **[38012]**
The Four Routes to Entrepreneurial Success **[29765]**
4Pillars Consulting Group Inc. **[8924]**
4Refuel **[44609]**
Fowler, Anthony & Co. **[2876]**, **[42329]**
Fowlie & Associates **[41598]**
"Fox" in Brandweek (Vol. 49, April 21, 2008, No. 16, pp. SR3) **[454]**, **[7926]**, **[19931]**, **[25519]**, **[38013]**, **[39894]**, **[43468]**
"Fox Cable Entertainment Networks" in Brandweek (Vol. 49, April 21, 2008, No. 16, pp. SR10) **[455]**, **[7927]**, **[19932]**, **[38014]**, **[39895]**, **[43469]**
Fox Cities Business **[59577]**
Fox Cities Chamber of Commerce and Industry (FCCCI) **[59578]**
Fox and Fiddle Corporation **[18134]**
Fox Fire Safety Inc. **[47523]**
Fox Lake Area Chamber of Commerce **[59579]**
Fox Lake Area Chamber of Commerce and Industry (FLACCI) **[51099]**
Fox Lake Chamber of Commerce [59579]
Fox Lake Visitors Guide **[59580]**
Fox Lawson & Associates L.L.C. **[25395]**, **[36029]**
Fox's Pizza Den, Inc. **[16149]**
FPC/F-O-R-T-U-N-E Personnel Consultants **[7804]**
Fragrance and Olfactory Dictionary **[2039]**
"A Framework for Conceptual Contributions in Marketing" in Journal of Marketing (Vol. 75, July 2011, No. 4, pp. 136) **[456]**, **[39896]**
Framework for Excellence (Course on Request) **[37632]**
Framing & Art Centre **[16330]**
Franchise Architects **[32279]**
Franchise Bancorp **[26115]**
Franchise Brokers Network **[32280]**
The Franchise Co., Inc. **[44610]**
Franchise Compliance, Inc. **[3001]**
Franchise Consultants, Inc. **[3002]**
Franchise Consultants International Association Library **[3054]**, **[32327]**
The Franchise Consulting Group **[2877]**
Franchise Development International, LLC **[3003]**, **[26116]**, **[32303]**
Franchise Development & Marketing Group **[3004]**, **[32304]**
Franchise Developments Inc. (FDI) **[3005]**, **[26117]**, **[32281]**, **[32305]**
Franchise Focus **[18615]**
Franchise Foundations **[3006]**, **[26118]**, **[32306]**
Franchise: Freedom or Fantasy **[2773]**, **[13769]**, **[25853]**, **[32092]**
Franchise Handbook **[32170]**
"Franchise Law in China: Law, Regulations, and Guidelines" in Franchise Law Journal (Vol. 27, Summer 2007, No. 1, pp. 57) **[23863]**, **[32171]**, **[36541]**
Franchise Law Team **[24118]**
Franchise Masters Inc. (FMI) **[32282]**
Franchise News **[32272]**
Franchise Recruiters Ltd. **[3007]**, **[3104]**, **[32307]**
Franchise Sales **[3008]**, **[3105]**, **[32308]**
Franchise Search, Inc. **[3009]**, **[3106]**, **[32309]**
Franchise Selection Specialists Inc. **[3010]**
Franchise Specialists, Inc. **[3011]**, **[26119]**, **[32310]**
Franchise Strategies Group, Inc. **[3012]**
FranchiseCanada **[32116]**
"Franchisees Lose Battle Against BK" in Advertising Age (Vol. 79, June 2, 2008, No. 22, pp. 46) **[17923]**, **[23864]**, **[24366]**, **[25091]**, **[25520]**, **[25754]**, **[32172]**, **[39897]**
FranchiseInc! **[3013]**, **[32311]**
FranchiseKnowHow L.L.C. **[3014]**
FranchiseMart / Biz1Brokers **[3015]**, **[32312]**
"Franchises with an Eye on Chicago" in Crain's Chicago Business (Vol. 34, March 14, 2011, No. 11, pp. 20) **[2030]**, **[3918]**, **[6429]**, **[6559]**, **[15364]**, **[15382]**, **[17850]**, **[27960]**, **[32173]**, **[44674]**
Franchises Unlimited Network LLC **[3016]**, **[32313]**
Franchising Conference & Expo **[32276]**
Franchising for Dummies **[29364]**, **[32093]**, **[32389]**
The Franchising Explosion **[32274]**
"Franchising Lures Boomers" in Business Journal-Portland (Vol. 24, November 9, 2007, No. 36, pp. 1) **[12367]**, **[22982]**, **[32174]**, **[45425]**
Franchising World **[32273]**
"Franchising's Green Scene" in Entrepreneur (Vol. 37, August 2009, No. 8, pp. 85) **[7557]**, **[30615]**, **[32175]**
Franchoice, Inc. **[32314]**
Francis Tuttle Technology Center - Rockwell Campus **[56652]**
"Francois Coutu" in Canadian Business (Vol. 80, March 12, 2007, No. 6, pp. 66) **[29766]**
"Francois Joly" in Canadian Business (Vol. 79, September 11, 2006, No. 18, pp. 146) **[12368]**, **[29767]**
Franconia Notch Chamber of Commerce **[54573]**
Franconia-Easton-Sugar Hill Chamber of Commerce [54573]
Francorp Inc. **[3017]**, **[26120]**, **[32283]**, **[32315]**
Frandocs, Experts in Franchising **[3018]**
Frank Hawkins Kenan Institute of Private Enterprise **[55542]**
Frank Lloyd Wright Preservation Trust Research Center **[1332]**
Frankel & Company Information Center **[14069]**
Frankel and Topche P.C. **[21463]**, **[24671]**, **[31143]**, **[32029]**, **[41489]**, **[42330]**
Frankenmuth Chamber of Commerce and Convention and Visitors Bureau **[53260]**
Frankenmuth Chamber of Commerce [53260]
Frankfort Area Chamber of Commerce **[52312]**
Frankfort Area Chamber of Commerce [53261]
Frankfort Business **[51100]**
Frankfort Chamber of Commerce **[51101]**
Frankfort - Elberta Area Chamber of Commerce **[53261]**
Frankfort-Franklin County Chamber of Commerce [52312]
Frankitude **[6468]**, **[13338]**
Franklin Area Chamber of Commerce **[57077]**
Franklin Area Chamber of Commerce (FACC) **[55693]**
Franklin Area Historical Society Library **[9506]**
Franklin Chamber of Commerce (FCC) **[51605]**
Franklin Chamber of Commerce Directory **[51606]**
Franklin Chamber of Commerce [54578]
Franklin County Chamber of Commerce **[47684]**; **[52593]**; **[57703]**
Franklin County Chamber of Commerce (FCCC) **[52889]**; **[55694]**; **[58916]**
Franklin County Regional Chamber of Commerce **[58753]**
Franklin Findings **[47685]**
Franklin Lakes Chamber of Commerce (FLCOC) **[54721]**
Franklin Mint Information Research Center **[4392]**
Franklin Park Chamber of Commerce and Industry [51102]
Franklin Park/Schiller Park Chamber of Commerce **[51102]**
Franklin-Sarrett Publishers L.L.C. (FSP) **[50687]**
Franklin-Simpson County Chamber of Commerce **[52313]**
Franklin-Southampton Area Chamber of Commerce **[58917]**
M. S. Franks & Company Inc. **[8913]**, **[14527]**
Fransurvey.com **[14063]**
Franz Wolf Design and Construction Consultants **[5641]**
The Fraser Institute **[19781]**
"Fraser and Neave Acquires King's Creameries" in Ice Cream Reporter (Vol. 23, November 20, 2010, No. 12, pp. 1) **[10877]**, **[12369]**, **[26754]**, **[39081]**, **[41919]**
Fraser River Panel Annual Report **[8998]**
Frasers Trade Directories Company Ltd. **[59945]**
"Fraud Alleged at Norshield; Investors Out $215 Million" in Globe & Mail (March 8, 2007, pp. B1) **[8335]**, **[12370]**, **[23865]**, **[38015]**
Frazier & Company / Frazier Healthcare and Technology Ventures **[59330]**
Frazier Consulting Service Inc. **[41490]**
FRCH Design Worldwide **[41599]**
"Freak Weather Dampens Intrawest Forecast" in Globe & Mail (February 8, 2006, pp. B3) **[8336]**, **[12371]**, **[44103]**
Freakonomics: A Rogue Economist Explores the Hidden Side of Everything **[27245]**
Fred Astaire Dance Studios, Inc. **[6415]**
"Fred Weber CEO Tom Dunne: Sales Talks Confidential" in Saint Louis Business Journal (Vol. 32, September 23, 2011, No. 4, pp. 1) **[5335]**, **[44152]**
Frederick & Hornsby Inc. [17592]
Frederick Chamber of Commerce and Industry **[56517]**
Frederick County SCORE **[52660]**
Frederick Innovative Technology Center **[52787]**
Fredericksburg Chamber of Commerce **[58155]**
Fredericksburg Regional Chamber of Commerce (FRCC) **[58918]**
Fredericktown Chamber of Commerce (FCC) **[54046]**
Fredericton Appraisal Associates Ltd. **[17590]**
Fredonia Chamber of Commerce **[52100]**
Fredonia Chamber of Commerce (FCC) **[55199]**
Free Energy: The Race to Zero Point **[30878]**
"Free Fall" in Canadian Business (Vol. 79, September 11, 2006, No. 18, pp. 28) **[7928]**, **[22983]**, **[25092]**
Free Library of Philadelphia - Art Department **[4567]**
Free Library of Philadelphia - Social Science & History Department **[2223]**, **[20813]**
Free Lunch: How the Wealthiest Americans Enrich Themselves at Government Expense **[32707]**, **[46242]**
Free Market Foundation **[19782]**
Free Software Foundation (FSF) **[18849]**
"Free Speech Vs. Privacy in Data Mining" in Information Today (Vol. 28, September 2011, No. 8, pp. 22) **[4643]**, **[4711]**, **[23866]**, **[28667]**, **[33708]**, **[39898]**
Free: The Future of a Radical Price **[25755]**, **[39899]**
Free University Network [4757]
"Free Your Mind" in Entrepreneur (Vol. 37, October 2009, No. 10, pp. 24) **[34892]**, **[39900]**, **[43018]**, **[44349]**
"Freedom Center May have New Path" in Business Courier (Vol. 26, October 30, 2009, No. 27, pp. 1) **[9258]**, **[33224]**, **[33709]**
Freedom Chamber of Commerce **[56518]**
"Freeing the Wheels of Commerce" in Hispanic Business (July-August 2007, pp. 50, 52, 54) **[9207]**, **[18427]**, **[20678]**, **[33710]**, **[34893]**, **[36542]**, **[37010]**, **[41920]**
Freelance Editorial Association [6787]
"Freelance Writer Creates L.I. Bridal Blog" in Long Island Business News (September 10, 2010) **[2501]**, **[6511]**, **[6820]**
Freelance Writer's Report **[6837]**
The Freelancer **[6838]**
Freelancing for Journalists **[3178]**, **[6512]**, **[6821]**, **[15532]**, **[16714]**, **[19933]**, **[28668]**
"Freeman Beauty Labs" in Retail Merchandiser (Vol. 51, September-October 2011, No. 5, pp. 74) **[1896]**, **[31067]**
Freeport Area Chamber of Commerce (FACC) **[51103]**
Freeport Merchants Association (FMA) **[52594]**
Freese & Associates Inc. **[2878]**, **[13830]**, **[26007]**, **[38721]**, **[40610]**
Freight Carriers Association of Canada (FCA) **[20654]**
Fremont and Dodge County Convention and Visitors Bureau [54388]
Fremont Area Chamber of Commerce **[51607]**; **[54388]**
Fremont Area Chamber of Commerce (FACC) **[53262]**; **[59581]**
Fremont Business Review **[48586]**
Fremont Chamber of Commerce (FCC) **[48587]**
Fremont Chamber of Commerce Membership Directory and Community Guide **[48588]**
Fremont Chamber of Commerce [53262]
Fremont County Business Development Corporation **[49626]**
French-American Chamber of Commerce **[57078]**
French-American Chamber of Commerce (FACC) **[36293]**
French - American Chamber of Commerce (Chicago, Illinois) **[51104]**
French - American Chamber of Commerce - Dallas/Fort Worth **[58156]**
French - American Chamber of Commerce - Houston Chapter **[58157]**
French - American Chamber of Commerce - Louisiana Chapter **[52461]**
French - American Chamber of Commerce - Michigan Chapter **[53263]**
French-Canadian Genealogical Society of Connecticut, Inc. - French-Canadian Genealogical Library **[9507]**
French Chamber of Commerce in the United States [36293]
French and French-Canadian Family Research **[9439]**
French Lick - West Baden Chamber of Commerce (FLWBCC) **[51608]**
French-American Chamber of Commerce in the United States [36293]
French-American Chamber of Commerce in the United States, Inc. [36293]
French-American Chamber of Commerce Inc. [36293]
Fresh City **[18135]**
Fresh Coat **[16675]**
"Fresh Direct's Crisis" in Crain's New York Business (Vol. 24, January 14, 2008, No. 2, pp. 3) **[9929]**, **[11693]**, **[21102]**, **[22984]**, **[26432]**, **[28669]**, **[33711]**, **[35341]**, **[41921]**, **[46874]**
Fresh Facts **[9113]**
Fresh from the Roaster **[9722]**
FreshBerry Natural Frozen Yogurt **[10958]**
"Freshman Lawmaker Graves Keeping Busy" in Atlanta Journal-Constitution (June 20, 2010, pp. A6) **[33225]**, **[45426]**, **[46243]**

3514 Small Business Sourcebook • 30th Edition

Freshwater Aquarium Basics [15793]
Fresno Business Newsletter [48589]
Max Freund [38722]
Friday Facts [51105]; [53648]; [54047]; [58158]
Friday Fax [55200]
Fridley Chamber of Commerce [53742]
"*Friedland's Next Frontier: Drilling for Oil in Iraq*" in *Globe
& Mail (April 20, 2007, pp. B1)* [41922], [44350]
Leonard R. Friedman Risk Management Inc. (LRF/RM)
[36256], [47524]
Friedman, Rosenwasser & Goldbaum, P.A. [24119]
Friend of the Family Home Services Inc. [22030]
"*Friendly*" in *Ice Cream Reporter (Vol. 21, August 20,
2008, No. 9, pp. 8)* [457], [10878], [39901]
Friendly Computers [4819]
"*Friendly Ice Cream Corporation*" in *Ice Cream Reporter
(Vol. 23, August 20, 2010, No. 9, pp. 8)* [10879],
[28670], [38016], [39902]
*Friendly Persuasion: The Art of Converting Objections
into Sales* [43722]
Friendly's Restaurants Franchise LLC [18136]
Friends of the Earth (FOE) [49860]
Friends and Strangers [3973]
Friends of the Western Philatelic Library [4393]
"*Friends With Money*" in *Canadian Business (Vol. 81,
Summer 2008, No. 9, pp. 22)* [8337], [12372], [31463],
[38017], [41923], [47020]
"*Friends With Money*" in *Entrepreneur (Vol. 37, August
2009, No. 8, pp. 74)* [44763], [46961]
Friendswood Chamber of Commerce [58159]
"*Fries With That?*" in *Canadian Business (Vol. 81,
September 29, 2008, No. 16, pp. 33)* [11099], [17924],
[21587], [22985], [24367], [25093], [32176], [36543],
[37011]
Frio Canyon Chamber of Commerce [58160]
Friona Chamber of Commerce and Agriculture [58161]
Frisch's Restaurants, Inc. [18137]
Frisco Chamber of Commerce (FCC) [58162]
Frisco Flyer [58163]
"*Frito Lay Plans to Spice Up Life With New Chips*" in
Globe & Mail (February 21, 2006, pp. B3) [39082],
[39903], [41071]
"*From American Icon to Global Juggernaut*" in *Automo-
tive News (Vol. 86, October 31, 2011, No. 6488, pp.
S003)* [14898], [36544], [39083]
"*From the Battlefield to the Boardroom*" in *Business
Horizons (Vol. 51, March-April 2008, No. 2, pp. 79)*
[29768], [37239], [38018]
"*From Bikes to Building*" in *Austin Business JournalInc.
(Vol. 29, October 30, 2009, No. 34, pp. 1)* [16907],
[17304], [41924]
"*From Buyout to Busted*" in *Business Week (September
22, 2008, No. 4100, pp. 18)* [8338], [12373], [23867],
[27246], [31464], [33226]
From the Chamber... [57079]
*From Concept To Consumer: How to Turn Ideas Into
Money* [25521], [25756], [26755], [37012], [39904],
[41072]
"*From Craft Biz To Wholesale Giant*" in *Women
Entrepreneur (January 19, 2009)* [5983], [22986],
[24368], [25094], [39905], [43019], [44833], [47172],
[47285]
*From Entrepreneur to Infopreneur: Make Money with
Books, E-Books, and Other Information Products*
[2134], [6513], [18556], [28671], [29769]
"*From Fastenal, a Boost*" in *Barron's (Vol. 89, July 20,
2009, No. 29, pp. M13)* [8339], [12374], [31465]
"*From Fat to Fit*" in *Canadian Business (Vol. 79,
September 25, 2006, No. 19, pp. 100)* [15969],
[22987], [45427]
*From Law School to Law Practice: What Every Associate
Needs to Know—The Set* [6947], [6991], [7801]
"*From Lone Hero to a Culture of Leadership*" in *Harvard
Business Review (Vol. 88, November 2010, No. 11, pp.
146)* [29770], [41925]
"*From Malls to Steel Plants*" in *Crain's Chicago Business
(Vol. 31, April 28, 2008, No. 17, pp. 30)* [5336],
[22988], [36545], [41926]
From Mind to Market: The Patent Process [37160]
"*From OTC Sellers to Surgeons, Healthcare Marketers
Target Women to Achieve Growth*" in *Marketing to
Women (February 2008)* [458], [22989], [34278],
[39906], [41073], [43859]
"*From War Zone to Franchise Zone*" in *Entrepreneur
(Vol. 37, August 2009, No. 8, pp. 104)* [24369],
[25095], [32177], [36546], [44834]
"*Fromm Family Foods Converts Old Feed Mill Into Fac-
tory for Gourmet Pet Food*" in *Wisconsin State Journal
(August 3, 2011)* [15757], [19222], [22990], [31068],
[39084]
The Front Door [52462]
Front Royal - Warren County Chamber of Commerce
[58919]

Frontal Lobe [49400]
Frontenac Company [51402]
Frontier Capital, LLC [55854]
*Frontier West/Great Plains & Mountain Region
Campground Guide* [3254]
Frontiers of Health Services Management [34521]
Frontline Group Communispond Inc. [22523]
"*Frost and Sullivan*" in *Investment Weekly News
(December 19, 2009, pp. 150)* [7929], [18428]
"*Frosted Flakes Goes For Gold*" in *Marketing to Women
(Vol. 21, April 2008, No. 4, pp. 3)* [9930], [21588],
[39907], [41074]
Frostproof Chamber of Commerce [50099]
"*Frozen Dessert Year in Review..*" in *Ice Cream Reporter
(Vol. 22, January 20, 2009, No. 2, pp. 1)* [10880],
[22991]
Frozen Food Factbook and Directory [9956]
Frozen Food Locker Institute [3136]
Frozen Ropes Training Centers [28460]
"*Frozen Yogurt Market Heats Up Again*" in *Houston Busi-
ness Journal (Vol. 40, November 27, 2009, No. 29, pp.
1)* [10881], [22992]
FRR Media [16619]
"*The Frugal Billionaire*" in *Canadian Business (Vol. 79,
Winter 2006, No. 24, pp. 63)* [8340], [11694], [12375],
[21103], [29771]
Fruit & Wine Directory [49510]
Fruita Chamber of Commerce [49511]
FruitFlowers/Incredibly Edible Delites [9591]
Fruitland Chamber of Commerce (FCC) [50759]
Fruits & Passion [2064]
Frullati Cafe & Bakery [6469]
FSC/DISC Tax Association [11019], [36288]
FSC/DISC Tax Club [11019], [36288]
FSMC Inc. [3068], [13829], [26005], [38718], [44937]
"*FSU's OGZEB Is Test Bed for Sustainable Technology*"
in *Contractor (Vol. 56, October 2009, No. 10, pp. 1)*
[6887], [7197], [7558], [19095], [30616], [43860]
Ft. Lee Chamber of Commerce and Industry [54724]
Ft. Pierce/St. Lucie County Chamber of Commerce
[50289]
"*FTC Takes Aim At Foreclosure 'Rescue' Firm*" in *The
Business Journal-Serving Greater Tampa Bay (Vol. 28,
September 19, 2008, No. 39)* [459], [14426], [23868],
[24798], [26433], [33712], [39908], [42472], [42621],
[45428]
Fuchsia Flash [13409]
Fuddruckers, Inc. [1805], [18138]
Fuel Calculation Bulletin [20655]
"*Fuel King: The Most Fuel-Efficient Tractor of the Decade
is the John Deere 8295R*" in *Farm Industry News
(November 10, 2011)* [7198], [7559], [21589], [30617],
[39085]
"*Fuel for Thought*" in *Canadian Business (Vol. 81, April
14, 2008, No. 6, pp. 18)* [14899], [24857], [38019],
[39086], [46244]
"*Fuel for Thought; Canadian Business Leaders on
Energy Policy*" in *Canadian Business (Vol. 81,
September 15, 2008, No. 14-15, pp. 12)* [7199],
[7560], [19096], [27247], [30618], [33713], [39087],
[41328], [44351], [45429]
"*Fueling Business*" in *The Business Journal-Milwaukee
(Vol. 25, July 25, 2008, No. 44, pp. A1)* [39909],
[42622], [45430]
"*Fueling Change*" in *Entrepreneur (Vol. 35, November
2007, No. 11, pp. 46)* [29772], [37013]
*Fugitive Denim: A Moving Story of People and Pants in
the Borderless World of Global Trade* [4108], [4230],
[7829], [11100], [21590], [33714], [36547]
"*Fujifilm Invites Printers to Take the 'Onset Challenge*" in
American Printer (Vol. 128, August 1, 2011, No. 8)
[4475], [16371], [20771]
Fujitsu Consulting [49398]
Fujitsu Microelectronics, Inc. - FMI Library [5028], [5789]
Fulbright & Jaworski L.L.P. Library [13236]
"*Full-Court Press for Apple*" in *Barron's (Vol. 88, March
24, 2008, No. 12, pp. 47)* [8341], [12376], [23869],
[31466], [34894], [37014], [39088]
"*Full Speed Ahead: How to Get the Most Out of Your
Company Vehicles*" in *Entrepreneur (Vol. 37, October
2009, No. 10, pp. 78)* [14900], [15324], [24858]
Full Voice [2879], [3069], [8015], [22527], [26008],
[28440]
Fullerton Business Review [48590]
Fullerton Chamber of Commerce [48591]
Fulton Carroll Center Incubator [51445]
Fulton Chamber of Commerce [51106]
Fulton County Chamber of Commerce and Tourism
[57080]
Fulton County Regional Chamber of Commerce and
Industry (FCRCCI) [55201]
Fulton Pennysaver [15614]
"*Fun And Easy Gold Mines*" in *Small Business Op-
portunities (Fall 2008)* [3919], [7872], [15409], [15425],
[20225], [20729], [27961], [44764]

Fun Bus USA, Inc. - 'Fitness Fun on Wheels' [16024]
FUN Expo [959], [981], [2438], [9679], [14361], [18813],
[19375]
"*Funbrain Launches Preschool Content*" in *Marketing to
Women (Vol. 21, March 2008, No. 3, pp. 3)* [11695],
[21104], [28208], [34895], [39910]
"*Function Over Forms?*" in *Barron's (Vol. 88, June 30,
2008, No. 26, pp. 17)* [90], [8342], [21374], [31467],
[33715]
Functional Gage Design (Onsite) [28036]
Fund for Renewable Energy and the Environment
[19068]
Fundamental Selling Techniques for the New or Prospec-
tive Salesperson Level I (Onsite) [43353]
Fundamentals of Buying and Selling Energy (Onsite)
[33395]
Fundamentals of Carbon Reduction (Onsite) [30452]
Fundamentals of Cost Accounting (Onsite) [21331]
Fundamentals of Employee Benefits (Onsite) [35670]
Fundamentals of Energy Auditing (Onsite) [30453]
Fundamentals of Finance and Accounting for Administra-
tive Professionals (Onsite) [21332]
Fundamentals of Human Resources Management
(Onsite) (Canada) [35671]
Fundamentals of Information Security (Onsite) [34744]
Fundamentals of Marketing: Your Action Plan for Suc-
cess (Onsite) [39585]
Fundamentals of Marketing: Your Action Plan for Suc-
cess (Onsite) (Canada) [39586]
Fundamentals of Project Management (Onsite) [37633]
Fundamentals of Purchasing (Canada) [42707]
Fundamentals of Purchasing for the New Buyer (Onsite)
[42708]
Fundamentals of Successful Project Management
(Onsite) [37634]
"*Funding Drought Stalls Biotech Incubators*" in *Saint
Louis Business Journal (Vol. 31, July 29, 2011, No. 49,
pp. 1)* [5337], [11215], [42797], [43861], [47021]
"*Funds 'Friend' Facebook*" in *Barron's (Vol. 89, July 27,
2009, No. 30, pp. 30)* [8343], [12377], [31468],
[33716], [34896], [39911], [43470]
Funeral and Memorial Societies of America [9330]
Funeral Consumers Alliance [9330]
Funeral Consumers Alliance [9320]
Funeral Consumers Alliance Library [9346]
"*Funeral Directors Get Creative As Boomers Near Great
Beyond*" in *Advertising Age (Vol. 79, October 13, 2008,
No. 38, pp. 30)* [460], [9331], [22993], [27248],
[30619], [39912]
Funeral Directors Management System [9344]
Funeral Home & Cemetery Directory--Buyer's Guide
[9332]
"*Funeral Picketing Laws and Free Speech*" in *Kansas
Law Review (Vol. 55, April 2007, No. 3, pp. 575-627)*
[9333], [23870]
"*Funerals-R-Us: From Funeral Home to Mega-Industry*"
in *(Vol. 28, Summer 2004, No. 2, pp. 11-14)* [9334]
Funk, Funk & More Funk [6405]
"*Funkhouser Wants Region to Get On Board Light Rail*"
in *Business Journal-Serving Metropolitan Kansas City
(November 30, 2007)* [5338], [13537], [19808]
"*Funny Business*" in *Canadian Business (Vol. 82, April
27, 2009, No. 7, pp. 27)* [461], [4953], [5862], [13994],
[34897], [39913], [41403], [43471], [45431]
Fuquay-Varina Area Chamber of Commerce (FVACC)
[55695]
Fuquay - Varina Chamber of Commerce [55695]
Fur Council of Canada [9350], [9354]
Fur Information Council of America (FICA) [9351], [9355]
Furla [43295]
"*Furniture Chain Moving to Harford*" in *Baltimore Busi-
ness Journal (Vol. 27, January 22, 2010, No. 38, pp. 1)*
[10396], [10466], [17782], [26756], [35342], [43020],
[44675]
"*The Furniture Company Wanted to Sell Him Its
Buildings-And Close Down. Should He Buy the
Company, Too?*" in *Inc. (November 2007)* [10467],
[16908], [17305], [25318]
The Furniture Executive [10493]
Furniture Factories Marketing Association of the South
[10446]
Furniture Library Association Library [9372], [11589]
"*Furniture Making May Come Back--Literally*" in *Business
North Carolina (Vol. 28, March 2008, No. 3, pp. 32)*
[2284], [10468], [13653], [36548], [39089], [45432]
Furniture Medic of Canada [9364]
Furniture Medic, L.P. [9365]
Furniture Rental Association of America [10448], [17749]
Furniture Retailer Magazine [10497]
*Furniture Today: The Weekly Business Newspaper of the
Furniture Industry* [10494]
Furniture Transporter [10495]
Furniture World Magazine: Furniture Buyer & Decorator
[10496]

The Future Arrived Yesterday: The Rise of the Protean Corporation and What It Means for You [29773], [32708]

"*Future Autoworkers will Need Broader Skills*" in *Crain's Detroit Business* (Vol. 25, June 8, 2009, No. 23, pp. 13) [14901], [28209], [35784], [39090], [45433]

Future Communications Corp. [3660]

"*Future of Diversity: Cultural Inclusion Is a Business Imperative*" in *Black Enterprise* (Vol. 41, August 2010, No. 1, pp. 75) [36549], [40882], [45434]

Future Economic Trends [27906]

Future Focus [50534]

"*The Future Is Another Country; Higher Education*" in *The Economist* (Vol. 390, January 3, 2009, No. 8612, pp. 43) [20477], [20733], [27249], [28210], [35343], [36550], [45435]

"*The Future of Private Equity*" in *Canadian Business* (Vol. 80, March 26, 2007, No. 7, pp. 19) [8344], [12378], [25522], [27250]

"*The Future of Work*" in *Black Enterprise* (Vol. 41, August 2010, No. 1, pp. 65) [28672], [32709], [34898], [35785], [36551], [39914], [41673], [44352], [45436]

"*The Future of Work*" in *Business Strategy Review* (Vol. 21, Autumn 2010, No. 3, pp. 16) [32710], [34899], [36552], [38020], [42798], [43862], [34900], [35786], [36553], [45437]

Futures [47599]

"*Future's Brighter for Financial Stocks*" in *Barron's* (Vol. 89, July 20, 2009, No. 29, pp. 14) [8345], [12379], [31469]

Futures Expo [8906], [13177]

Futures Magazine [2712]

Futures and Options Expo [8906], [13177]

"*Futures Shock for the CME*" in *Crain's Chicago Business* (Vol. 31, November 10, 2008, No. 45, pp. 8) [8346], [12380], [27251], [31470], [33717], [41927], [45438]

"*Futures of the Street*" in *Barron's* (Vol. 88, June 30, 2008, No. 26, pp. 27) [8347], [12381], [31471]

Fuzziwig's Candy Factory [10959]

FW Consultants Ltd. [26705]

FXC Newsletter [13120]

FYI [51107]; [58164]; [58920]

FYI - Weekly Bulletin [58165]

G

G-51 Capital LLC [58557]

G-Force [46814]

G7 Report Inc.- G7 Books [59946]

"*G20 Young Entrepreneur Alliance Signs Charter Outlining Commitment to Entrepreneurship*" in *Internet Wire* (November 10, 2010) [36554], [47585]

Gabelli Multimedia Partners [55416]

"*Gables Unveils Plan for Downtown Tower*" in *Austin Business JournalInc.* (Vol. 28, August 8, 2008, No. 21, pp. A1) [5339], [16909], [17306], [43021]

Gabriel Venture Partners [49226]

"*Gadget Makers Aim for New Chapter in Reading*" in *Crain's Cleveland Business* (Vol. 28, October 22, 2007, No. 42, pp. 20) [2374], [34901], [41075]

Gadsden County Chamber of Commerce [50100]

Gadsden-Etowah Chamber of Commerce [47648]

Gahanna Area Chamber of Commerce [56136]

"*Gail Lissner; Vice-President, Appraisal Research Counselors*" in *Crain's Chicago Business* (Vol. 31, May 5, 2008, No. 18, pp. 28) [16910], [17307], [22994], [25854], [29774], [38021]

"*Gail Mukaihata Hannemann*" in *Hawaii Business* (Vol. 53, January 2008, No. 7, pp. 24) [24370], [25096], [38022]

Gain: AIGA Journal of Business and Design [4530]

"*Gain the 'Come Alive Outside' Selling Edge*" in *Green Industry Pro* (July 2011) [9781], [13391], [13478], [29069], [39915], [43472], [44353]

Gainesville Area Chamber of Commerce [50101]

Gainesville Technology Enterprise Center [50373]

Gaithersburg-Germantown Chamber of Commerce (GGCC) [52712]

Galax - Carroll - Grayson Chamber of Commerce [58921]

Gale Directory of Publications and Broadcast Media [4065], [15533]

Galena Area Chamber of Commerce [51108]

Galenian [51109]

Galesburg Area Chamber of Commerce [51110]

Galesburg Business and Technology Center [51446]

Galesville Area Chamber of Commerce [59582]

Galion Area Chamber of Commerce (GACC) [56137]

Galion Today [56138]

Gallagher Benefit Services Inc. [22059]

Gallatin Chamber of Commerce [57704]

Gallatin Valley Business [54273]

Gallaudet University Press [49861]

Galleria Chamber of Commerce [58166]

"*Gallery Street Launches ArtCandy*" in *Art Business News* (Vol. 34, November 2007, No. 11, pp. 8) [1349], [4476], [5984], [22995], [26757]

Gallia County Chamber of Commerce [56139]

Gallia County Chamber of Commerce Membership Directory & Community Profile [56140]

"*Gallo Family Vineyards to Raise Funds for Meals On Wheels*" in *Food & Beverage Close-Up* (November 4, 2011) [9154], [9259], [19223]

Galt Area Chamber of Commerce [48592]

Galt District Chamber of Commerce (GCC) [48592]

Galt Today [48593]

"*Galvanizing the Scientific Community*" in *Information Today* (Vol. 26, February 2009, No. 2, pp. 20) [15534], [29775], [34902], [42799], [43863]

Galveston Chamber of Commerce [58167]

Galveston County Small Business Development Center [57849]

GAMA International [11280]

Gamblers Anonymous (GA) [9378]

Gamblers Anonymous International Service Office [9378]

Gamblers Anonymous Publishing Inc. [9378]

"*A Gambling Man: Career Transitions that Put a Vegas Hotshot on Top*" in *Black Enterprise* (Vol. 37, October 2006, No. 3, pp. 89) [10692], [29776], [38023], [41329]

"*Game Changer*" in *Canadian Business* (Vol. 83, June 15, 2010, No. 10, pp. 52) [943], [20249], [38024], [41076], [44676], [47286]

The Game-Changer: How Every Leader Can Drive Everyday Innovation [22307], [29070], [35344], [38025]

The Game-Changer: How You Can Drive Revenue and Profit Growth with Innovation [22996], [37015]

The Game Makers [944], [20250], [37016]

"*Game On*" in *Canadian Business* (Vol. 80, February 12, 2007, No. 4, pp. 15) [18903], [24371], [34903], [41077]

"*Game On! African Americans Get a Shot at $17.9 Billion Video Game Industry*" in *Black Enterprise* (Vol. 38, July 2008, No. 12, pp. 56) [3537], [5749], [18904], [27252], [34904], [40740]

"*Game On at Jordan's New Spot*" in *Crain's Chicago Business* (Vol. 34, October 24, 2011, No. 42, pp. 34) [17925], [19423], [29777]

"*Game On: The Hunt Is On for Nation's Top Keeper*" in *Farmer's Weekly* (March 28, 2008, No. 320) [21591], [25523], [30620]

"*The Game of Operation*" in *Crain's Chicago Business* (Vol. 31, April 28, 2008, No. 17, pp. 26) [14196], [22997], [39091]

"*Game Plan*" in *Canadian Business* (Vol. 79, September 11, 2006, No. 18, pp. 50) [3538], [18905], [24372], [34905]

"*Games Gone Wild: City's Newest Public Company Aims for the Sky*" in *Business Courier* (Vol. 27, September 24, 2010, No. 21, pp. 1) [945], [22998], [43473]

Gamma Investors [57286]

Garage Technology Ventures / Garage.com [49227]

Garagetek [3440], [16495]

Garberville-Redway Area Chamber of Commerce (GRCC) [48594]

Garde Cotiere Canadienne. [13975]

Garden Center Products & Supplies: Professional Purchasing Guide for Garden Centers [9807]

Garden City Area Chamber of Commerce (GCACC) [52101]

Garden City Chamber of Commerce [55202]

Garden City Chamber of Commerce (GCCC) [53264]

Garden Design [13410]

Garden Grove Chamber of Commerce [48595]

Garden Pond Basics [13423]

Garden Railways [6133]

Garden Seed Inventory: 6th Edition [9782]

The Garden Spot of Colorado [49512]

Gardena Chamber News [48596]

Gardena Valley Chamber of Commerce (GVCC) [48597]

Gardena Valley Chamber of Commerce Business Directory [48598]

Gardendale Chamber of Commerce [47686]

The Gardener Inc. [13439]

Gardens for All [9764]

Gardens For All, the National Association for Gardening [9764]

Gardiner Chamber of Commerce [54274]

Gardiner Roberts LLP Library [46471]

Gardner Area Chamber of Commerce [52102]

Gardner Chamber of Commerce [52102]; [52892]

Garfield County Chamber of Commerce [54275]

Garfield Heights Chamber of Commerce (GHCC) [56141]

James A. Garfield Historical Society Library [9508]

Garland Chamber of Commerce [58168]

Garland County SCORE [47997]

Garlic Jim's Famous Gourmet Pizza [16150]

Garner Chamber of Commerce (GCC) [51896]; [55696]

Garnett Area Chamber of Commerce (GACC) [52103]

Garrard County Chamber of Commerce (GCCOC) [52314]

Garrett County Chamber of Commerce [52713]

Garrett Information Enterprise Center [52788]

Garrettsville Area Chamber of Commerce [56142]

Garrettsville - Hiram Area Chamber of Commerce (GHACC) [56142]

Garrettsville: New England Charm Today - We Have it All [56143]

Garrity & Associates [16564]

Gartner IRC [2691], [11961]

Gartner Online [4745]

Gary Bitner Public Relations Inc. [40583], [42545]

Gary Chamber of Commerce (GCC) [51609]

Gary Minority Business Opportunity Center [51743]

"*Gas Glut Pummels Prices*" in *Barron's* (Vol. 89, July 27, 2009, No. 30, pp. M8) [8348], [12382], [31472]

"*Gas Supplies Low Heading Into Summer Season*" in *Globe & Mail* (April 13, 2007, pp. B6) [27253], [39092]

Gasoline and Automotive Service Dealers Association (GASDA) [18581]

Gasoline and Automotive Service Dealers Association-- Bulletin [18616]

Gasoline Merchants [18581]

Gasoline: Specifications, Testing, and Technology (Onsite) [30454]

Gaston County Chamber of Commerce [55697]

Gaston Regional Chamber [55697]

Gate Group USA Inc. [4543]

Gately Consulting [35542]

Gates, Hudson & Associates Inc. [16565]

Gatesville Area Chamber of Commerce and Agribusiness (GCC) [58169]

Gatesville Chamber of Commerce [58169]

Gateway [4632], [25820]

The Gateway [55698]

"*Gateway Delays Start*" in *The Business Journal-Serving Metropolitan Kansas City* (Vol. 27, October 31, 2008, No. 8, pp. 1) [5340], [8349], [12383], [17308], [26228], [31473], [37378], [43022]

Gateway News [52463]

Gateway to Opportunity: Interviewing Job Applicants with Disabilities [26685]

Gateway Publishing Company Ltd. (Pembina, North Dakota) [55943]

Gateway Publishing Company Ltd. (Winnipeg, Manitoba) [59905]

Gateway Regional Chamber of Commerce [54722]

Gateways to Greater Nashua: Business, Lifestyle and Relocation Guide [54574]

Gatlinburg Chamber of Commerce [57705]

"*Gatorade Loses Its Competitive Edge; Upstart Rivals Undercut Its Domination of Game*" in *Crain's Chicago Business* (April 28, 2008) [25524], [39093], [39916]

The Gauge [14019], [16606], [22498], [40547], [42679]

The Gavel [50102]

Gavilan Small Business Development Center [48150]

Gaylord - Otsego County Chamber of Commerce (GOCCC) [53265]

Gaylord/Otsego County Chamber of Commerce Membership Directory and Community Profile [53266]

Gazebo Gazette [58922]

Gazelle Techventures [51751]

"*gdgt: The New Online Home for Gadget Fans*" in *Hispanic Business* (July-August 2009, pp. 15) [3729], [4954], [28673], [34906], [41404]

GE Energy [30883]

"*GE Looking to Extend Hot Streak*" in *Business Courier* (Vol. 24, January 25, 2008, No. 42, pp. 1) [8350], [12384], [22999], [31474], [39094]

"*GE Milestone: 1,000th Wind Turbine Installed in Canada*" in *CNW Group* (October 4, 2011) [7200], [7561], [23000], [30621], [39095]

Gear Technology: The Journal of Gear Manufacturing [44022]

Gebbie Press All-in-One Media Directory [4066]

GEC Consultants Inc. [1878], [2880], [10314], [18053], [26009]

"*GeckoSystems Reduces Sensor Fusion Costs Due to Elder Care Robot Trials*" in *Internet Wire* (December 14, 2010) [299], [1428], [10536], [12385], [14197], [14314], [15073], [34907], [37017], [41078], [41928]

Geeks On The Way [4820]

Gefinor Ventures / Inman Ventures [58558]

Geibel Marketing & Public Relations [40611]

Geisinger Medical Center - Community Health Library [10264], [10327], [14832], [15217]

MASTER INDEX

Get

Master Index

Gelato Amare/ Jazzy Juices **[10960]**
Leon Gelfond & Associates **[2205]**, **[13752]**
The Gem **[48599]**; **[56780]**
Gem County Chamber of Commerce (GCCC) **[50760]**
GEM Health Care Services **[10575]**
Gemini Investors / GMN Investors **[53028]**
Gemmology Canada **[13258]**
Gemological Institute of America - Richard T. Liddicoat Gemological Library and Information Center **[13298]**
Gems & Jewelry Appraising: Techniques of Professional Practice **[1215]**, **[13271]**
Gen X **[32711]**
Gendered Processes: Korean Immigrant Small Business Ownership **[32712]**, **[40883]**
Genealogical Computing **[9454]**
Genealogical Helper--Bureau of Missing Ancestors Section **[9440]**
Genealogical Journal of Jefferson County, New York **[9455]**
Genealogical and Local History Books in Print **[9441]**
Genealogical Periodical Annual Index: Key to the Genealogical Literature **[9442]**
The Genealogist's Address Book **[9443]**
General Agents and Managers Association [11280]
General Agents and Managers Conference of NALU [11280]
General Business Consultants Inc. **[26811]**
General Business Services Corp. **[32284]**, **[46452]**
General Catalyst Partners / General Catalyst Group LLC **[53029]**
"General Clark Stresses Ethanols Role In National Security At Ag Connect" in Farm Industry News (January 11, 2011) **[18429]**, **[21592]**
General Driving Safety **[6601]**
General Electric Company - G.E. Asset Management Information Center **[13237]**
General Engineering Laboratories, Inc. Library **[7406]**, **[7727]**
General Merchandise Distributors Council [26722]
General Mills, Inc. - Betty Crocker Kitchens Library **[15218]**
General Mills, Inc. - Business Information Center **[14070]**
"General Motors Can't Kick Incentives-But They Work" in Advertising Age (Vol. 79, July 7, 2008, No. 26, pp. 3) **[462]**, **[8351]**, **[12386]**, **[14902]**, **[31475]**, **[39096]**, **[39917]**
General Nutrition Centers [15204]
General Nutrition Centers Inc [15204]
General Services Administration - Atlanta Business Service Center **[60287]**
General Services Administration - Auburn Business Service Center **[60288]**
General Services Administration - Boston Business Service Center **[60289]**
General Services Administration - Chicago Business Service Center **[60290]**
General Services Administration - Denver Business Service Center **[60291]**
General Services Administration (FTS) - Federal Technology Service - Office of Regional Services **[60292]**
General Services Administration - Ft. Worth Business Service Center **[60293]**
General Services Administration - Kansas City Business Service Center **[60294]**
General Services Administration - New York Business Service Center **[60295]**
General Services Administration - Office of Electronic Government and Technology **[60296]**
General Services Administration - Office of Global Supply - Logistics Operations Ctr. **[60297]**
General Services Administration - Office of Small Business Utilization - GSA **[60298]**
General Services Administration - Philadelphia Business Service Center - Office of Business and Public Affairs **[60299]**
General Services Administration - San Francisco Business Service Center **[60300]**
General Services Administration - Washington, DC, Business Services Center **[60301]**
"A General's Pep Talk Taught Me That a Leader Can't Lose Sight of What It Means To Be a Grunt" in Inc. (March 2008, pp. 85-86) **[29778]**, **[38026]**
Generation Partners **[49778]**
"Generation Y - An Opportunity for a Fresh Financial Start" in (September 11, 2010, pp. 241) **[8352]**, **[12387]**, **[31476]**
"Generation Y Chooses the Mobile Web" in PR Newswire (November 24, 2010) **[3730]**, **[11696]**, **[28674]**, **[45439]**
"Generation Y Driving Portland Multifamily Market" in Daily Journal of Commerce, Portland (October 29, 2010) **[5341]**, **[16911]**, **[17309]**, **[17783]**, **[45440]**
"Generation Y: Engaging the Invincibles" in Employee Benefit News (Vol. 25, November 1, 2011, No. 14, pp. 22) **[34279]**, **[35787]**
"Generation Y Goes To Work; Management" in The Economist (Vol. 390, January 3, 2009, No. 8612, pp. 48) **[32713]**, **[35345]**, **[38027]**, **[45441]**, **[46875]**
"Generational Savvy" in Hawaii Business (Vol. 54, August 2008, No. 2, pp. 135) **[11351]**, **[23001]**, **[31069]**, **[36148]**
Generators & Emergency Power (Onsite) **[24978]**, **[28037]**
Generators and Emergency Power (Onsite) **[6870]**
Generic Pharmaceutical Association (GPhA) **[6633]**
Generic Pharmaceutical Industry Association [6633]
"Generous Donations Fund Repairs for Benton Trail Kiosk" in Morning Sentinel (December 22, 2010) **[9260]**, **[13323]**
Genesee County Chamber of Commerce **[55203]**
Genesee County Metropolitan Planning Commission **[53481]**
Genesis Business Centers, Ltd. **[53788]**
Genesis Medical Center - Illini Campus - Perlmutter Library of the Health Sciences **[15126]**
Genesis Park LP **[58559]**
Genesis Society Inc. **[55525]**
Genesis Technology Incubator **[48128]**
Genesys Partners, Inc. **[55417]**
"Genetic Counselor" in Occupational Outlook Quarterly (Vol. 55, Summer 2011, No. 2, pp. 34) **[3351]**, **[34280]**
Geneva Area Chamber of Commerce **[55204]**
Geneva Area Chamber of Commerce (GACC) **[56144]**
Geneva Chamber of Commerce (GCC) **[51111]**
Geneva Lake Area Chamber of Commerce (GLACC) **[59583]**
Geneva on the Lake Chamber of Commerce **[56145]**
Genghis Grill - The Mongolian Stir Fry **[18139]**
Gentle Fitness **[16000]**
"Genzyme: Underrated Oversold" in Barron's (Vol. 88, March 24, 2008, No. 12, pp. 58) **[8353]**, **[12388]**, **[23002]**, **[31477]**, **[34908]**
"Geo-Marketing: Site Selection by the Numbers" in Franchising World (Vol. 42, September 2010, No. 9, pp.) **[32094]**, **[39918]**, **[44629]**
GeoCanada [7039]
Geocapital Partners, LLC **[54851]**
Geocosmic Magazine **[14819]**
Geographical Center of North America Chamber of Commerce (GCNACC) **[55911]**
The Geography of Small Firm Innovation **[32714]**, **[34909]**
Geologic Hazards Photos **[7390]**
Geomatica **[19530]**
Geomatrix Productions **[26812]**
Geometres professionnels du Canada [19502]
Geometric Dimensioning and Tolerancing, Level 1 (Onsite) **[22198]**
Geomicrobiology Journal **[44023]**
"George Cohon" in Canadian Business (Vol. 79, November 20, 2006, No. 23, pp. 70) **[27254]**, **[29779]**, **[32178]**, **[44835]**
George Eastman House Interactive Catalog [15883]
George S. May International Co. **[38723]**
George Washington University - Center for International Science and Technology Policy (CISTP) **[42428]**
George West Chamber of Commerce **[58170]**
Georgetown Chamber of Commerce (GCC) **[58171]**
Georgetown County Chamber of Commerce (GCCC) **[57462]**
Georgetown County Chamber of Commerce Quarterly **[57463]**
Georgetown SCORE **[57887]**
Georgetown-Scott County Chamber of Commerce **[52315]**
Georgetown Small Business Development Center **[49805]**
Georgetown University - Maternal and Child Health Library **[4036]**
Georgia Association of Chamber of Commerce Executives (GACCE) **[50535]**
Georgia BioBusiness Center **[50673]**
Georgia Chamber of Commerce **[50536]**
Georgia Department of Community Affairs, Business and Financial Assistance Division **[50407]**
Georgia Department of Economic Development - Entrepreneur and Small Business Office **[50408]**
Georgia Department of Labor - Labor Market Information **[61646]**
Georgia Highlands College - Floyd Campus **[50681]**
Georgia Hispanic Chamber of Commerce (GHCC) **[50537]**
Georgia House of Representatives **[50683]**
Georgia Institute of Technology - Center for Rehabilitation Technology [16109]
Georgia Institute of Technology - Advanced Technology Development Center (ATDC) **[35246]**
Georgia Institute of Technology - Center for Assistive Technology and Environmental Access (CATEA) **[16109]**
Georgia Institute of Technology - Enterprise Innovation Institute **[36932]**
Georgia Minority Business Enterprise Center - Georgia Tech Enterprise Innovation Institute **[50644]**
Georgia Procurement Technical Assistance Center - Georgia Institute of Technology - Enterprise Innovation Institute **[50661]**
Georgia Procurement Technical Assistance Center - Outreach Center **[50662]**; **[50663]**; **[50664]**; **[50665]**; **[50666]**; **[50667]**
Georgia Procurement Technical Assistance Center - UIDA Business Services **[50668]**
Georgia Small Business Development Center - Lead Office **[50390]**
Georgia Southern University - Bureau of Business Research and Economic Development (BBRED) **[27935]**
Georgia Southern University Small Business Development Center **[50391]**
Georgia State University - Center for Insurance Research [34656]
Georgia State University - Center for Risk Management and Insurance Research **[34656]**
Georgia State University - Economic Forecasting Center (EFC) **[27936]**
Georgia State University - Small Business Development Center **[33472]**
Georgia State University Small Business Development Center **[50392]**
Georgia Tech Sports and Performance Newsletter **[34522]**
Georgia Wildlife Federation Conservation Library **[7407]**
GEOTECH EXPO 2013 **[1085]**
Geri-Fit: The First Workout with Weights for Older Adults **[16001]**
German American Chamber of Commerce - Philadelphia (GACC) **[57081]**
German Family Research Made Simple **[9444]**
German-Texan Heritage Society - Charles G. Trenckmann Memorial Library **[9509]**
"German Win Through Sharing" in Canadian Business (Vol. 83, September 14, 2010, No. 15, pp. 16) **[3539]**, **[18906]**, **[27255]**, **[33718]**, **[36555]**, **[37018]**, **[37240]**, **[45126]**
"Germans Win Solar Decathlon - Again" in Contractor (Vol. 56, November 2009, No. 11, pp. 1) **[5342]**, **[7201]**, **[7562]**, **[19097]**, **[30622]**
Germantown Area Chamber of Commerce (GACC) **[57706]**; **[59584]**
Germantown Area Chamber News **[57707]**
Germantown Chamber of Commerce [52712]; [57706]
Germantown Magazine **[57708]**
Gerson Goodson Inc. (GGI) **[2881]**, **[24672]**, **[26010]**
"Get Back To Business Planning Fundamentals" in Entrepreneur (October 24, 2008) **[22111]**, **[24373]**, **[26434]**, **[27256]**, **[38028]**, **[39919]**, **[43474]**, **[46876]**
Get Clients Now!, 2nd Edition: A 28-Day Marketing Program for Professionals, Consultants, and Coaches **[25855]**, **[39920]**
Get the Edge with Time Management/Rick Barrera **[46553]**
"Get Fit On a Dine: Resolve To Be Healthy-and Wealthy-This New Year" in Black Enterprise (Vol. 38, January 2008, No. 6, pp. 86) **[15970]**, **[23871]**
Get in the Game: 8 Elements of Perseverance that Make the Difference **[29780]**, **[32715]**, **[38029]**
"Get on the Green" in Entrepreneur (Vol. 35, November 2007, No. 11, pp. 44) **[9658]**, **[22308]**
"Get Hired Now! A 28-Day Program for Landing the Job You Want" in Black Enterprise (Vol. 37, October 2006, No. 3, pp. 119) **[35346]**, **[40884]**
"Get It While Its Hot" in Canadian Business (Vol. 80, January 15, 2007, No. 2, pp. 49) **[8354]**, **[12389]**
"Get in Line" in Canadian Business (Vol. 79, September 25, 2006, No. 19, pp. 43) **[27257]**, **[32716]**
"Get More Time Off" in Canadian Business (Vol. 80, March 12, 2007, No. 6, pp. 32) **[21907]**, **[32717]**
"Get Off The Rollercoaster" in Michigan Vue (Vol. 13, July-August 2008, No. 4, pp. 19) **[8355]**, **[12390]**, **[24374]**, **[27258]**, **[31478]**
"Get Online or Be Left Behind" in Women In Business (Vol. 61, August-September 2009, No. 4, pp. 33) **[11697]**, **[21105]**, **[22309]**, **[34910]**, **[39921]**
"Get Online Quick in the Office Or in the Field" in Contractor (Vol. 56, October 2009, No. 10, pp. 47) **[814]**, **[5343]**, **[6888]**, **[16240]**, **[21106]**, **[38030]**
"Get Over Your Fear of Change" in Canadian Business (Vol. 83, June 15, 2010, No. 10, pp. 38) **[24375]**, **[27259]**, **[38031]**
"Get Paid and Get Moving" in Entrepreneur (Vol. 37, October 2009, No. 10, pp. 38) **[3731]**, **[26229]**, **[28675]**, **[34911]**, **[44354]**
"Get Personal" in Entrepreneur (Vol. 36, April 2008, No. 4) **[22310]**, **[22594]**, **[26435]**, **[34912]**, **[39922]**, **[42623]**, **[43475]**

Small Business Sourcebook • 30th Edition

3517

Glendive Chamber of Commerce and Agriculture (GCCA) [54278]

Glendora Chamber of Commerce [48605]

Glenns Ferry Chamber of Commerce (GFCC) [50761]

Glenns Ferry Directory [50762]

Glenrock Chamber of Commerce [59821]

Glens Falls Chamber of Commerce [55075]

Glenview Chamber of Commerce [51115]

Glenwood Chamber of Commerce Newsletter [53650]

Glenwood Chamber of Commerce [53651]

Glenwood Lakes Area Chamber of Commerce (GACC) [53651]

GLMV Area Chamber of Commerce [51116]

Global Business Browser [36924]

Global Business Consultants (GBC) [2882], [13831], [26011], [36031], [36915], [38724], [45252]

Global Business Travel Association (GBTA) [24815]

Global Competencies for Diversity Leaders (Onsite) [37636]

Global Custodian [8866]

The Global Dumping Ground: International Traffic in Hazardous Waste [10173]

Global E-Commerce: Impacts of National Environment and Policy [28680], [36558]

Global Economic Crisis: Impact on Small Business [27262], [32722]

"The Global Economy, the Labor Force and Franchising's Future" in *Franchising World* (Vol. 42, September 2010, No. 9, pp. 35) [23008], [27263], [32180], [36560]

Global Electronic Business Research: Opportunities and Directions [28681], [36561], [42801]

"The Global Environment Movement is Bjorn Again" in *Canadian Business* (Vol. 83, September 14, 2010, No. 15, pp. 11) [7206], [7566], [30627], [36562]

"Global Good Time" in *Canadian Business* (Vol. 80, January 15, 2007, No. 2, pp. 53) [8362], [12396]

Global Health Directory [34282]

"Global Imagery in Online Advertisements" in *Business Communication Quarterly* (December 2007, pp. 487) [465], [28682], [36563], [39932]

Global Internet Ventures / GIV Venture Partners [59014]

Global Investment Magazine: The Journal of Money Management, Trading and Global Asset Services [13121]

"Global Market Could Be Silver Lining" in *Hispanic Business* (January-February 2008, pp. 14, 16, 18) [11102], [27264], [36564]

Global Market Development Center (GMDC) [26722]

Global Offset and Countertrade Association (GOCA) [36294]

"Global Pain: Alberta's Gain" in *Canadian Business* (Vol. 79, August 14, 2006, No. 16-17, pp. 60) [27265], [39100], [44361]

Global Pet Foods [15799]

"Global-Preneuring: Tax Ramifications Can Make or Break a Worldwide Enterprise" in *Small Business Opportunities* (May 2008) [36565], [46251]

"Global: Put It on Autopilot" in *Entrepreneur* (Vol. 35, October 2007, No. 10, pp. 110) [3541], [18908], [36566], [37196], [45129]

Global Recruiters Network - GRN [3019]

Global Secure Training [10184]

Global Shop - Tradeshow and Seminars for Visual Merchandiser [21301]

"Global Steel Makers Circle Stelco" in *Globe & Mail* (April 19, 2007, pp. B3) [8363], [12397], [39101], [41933]

"The Global Talent Hunt" in *Business Strategy Review* (Vol. 21, Spring 2010, No. 1, pp. 78) [27266], [35792], [36567], [38039], [45925]

Global Technology Transfer L.L.C. [2883], [13832], [26012], [32030], [38725], [41292], [44938]

Global Voice [36897]

GlobalNET Corp. [41493], [41601]

GlobalNet Partners LP [55418]

GLOBE - International Environmental Industry Trade Fair and Conference [7372], [7720], [17733]

Globe-Miami Regional Chamber of Commerce and Economic Development Corporation [47906]

"Gloria Christiansen: Tennessee's Unselfish Citizen" in *Women In Business* (Vol. 61, December 2009, No. 6, pp. 10) [29794], [45926]

Gloria Jean's [9737]

Gloria Jean's Coffees USA [9737]

Gloria Jean's Gourmet Coffee Corp. [9737]

Gloria Jean's Gourmet Coffees Corp. [9737]

"Glossary of Health Benefit Terms" in *HRMagazine* (Vol. 53, August 2008, No. 8, pp. 78) [21909], [34283], [35793]

Gloucester County Chamber of Commerce (GLOCO) [58924]

Glynn Capital Management [49228]

Glynn Law Offices [38726]

"GM Axing Prices; Kerkorian Calls for Crisis Plan" in *Globe & Mail* (January 11, 2006, pp. B1) [24377], [25098], [39102]

"GM Canada Revved Up Over Camaro" in *Globe & Mail* (February 17, 2006, pp. B4) [39103], [39933], [41084]

"GM-Chrysler Merger Could Cull Dealerships From Coast to Coast" in *Globe & Mail* (February 20, 2007, pp. B17) [14903], [39104], [41934]

"GM-Chrysler Merger: Just a Bigger Mess?" in *Globe & Mail* (February 17, 2007, pp. B3) [14904], [39105], [41935]

"GM Flexes Muscles With New Camaro Concept" in *Globe & Mail* (January 10, 2006, pp. B15) [14905], [39106], [39934]

"GM Is On the Road Again" in *Canadian Business* (Vol. 83, September 14, 2010, No. 15, pp. 14) [14906], [38040], [39107]

"GM Releases 2010 Product Guide, Ends Production of Medium-Duty Trucks" in *Contractor* (Vol. 56, July 2009, No. 7, pp. 5) [14907], [39108]

GMAC Commercial Mortgage Corp. [17583]

GMG Capital Partners, L.P. [55419]

"GMREB/Analysis of the Resale Market-First Quarter 2007: Year Off to a Great Start" in *Canadian Corporate News* (May 14, 2007) [16915], [17313]

"GM's Decision to Boot Dealer Prompts Sale" in *Baltimore Business Journal* (Vol. 27, November 6, 2009, No. 26, pp. 1) [5349], [9931], [14908], [17314], [32181], [39109], [43025]

"GM's Mortgage Unit Deal Brings in $9 Billion" in *Globe & Mail* (March 24, 2006, pp. B3) [14427], [16916], [17315], [41936]

"GM's Volt Woes Cast Shadow on E-Cars" in *Wall Street Journal Eastern Edition* (November 28, 2011, pp. B1) [7207], [7567], [14909], [18430], [30628], [33725], [39110]

GNC Corp. [15204]

GNC Holdings Inc. (GNC) [15204]

Gnossos Software Inc. [41522]

"Go Back to Basics to Maximize Skid Steer ROI" in *Rental Product News* (Vol. 33, October 2011) [17784]

"Go Beyond Local Search With Hyper-Local" in *Women Entrepreneur* (October 30, 2008) [466], [11700], [34915], [39935], [45444]

"Go East" in *Canadian Business* (Vol. 80, February 26, 2007, No. 5, pp. 21) [29795], [38041]

The Go-Giver: A Little Story About a Powerful Business Idea [29796], [32723], [45927]

"Go Green Or Go Home" in *Black Enterprise* (Vol. 41, August 2010, No. 1, pp. 53) [7208], [7568], [27267], [29797], [30629], [40741]

Go Put Your Strengths to Work [29074], [38042]

"Go Team? Why Building a Cohesive Organization Is a Necessary Exercise" in *Black Enterprise* (Vol. 38, February 2008, No. 7, pp. 66) [29075], [38043]

Go Westerly [57376]

Goal Setting [25275]

GOALS Institute [59042]

Goals and Objectives [25276]

Goals: Setting and Achieving Them on Schedule [25277]

Goddard School [4015]

Godfather's Pizza, Inc. [16151]

Godfrey Memorial Library [9510]

Goin' Postal [3107]

"Going for the APEX" in *Women In Business* (Vol. 62, September 2010, No. 3, pp. 28) [28215], [38044], [47289]

Going Bare: Crisis in Insurance [11478], [36254]

"Going to Bat" in *Canadian Business* (Vol. 80, February 26, 2007, No. 5, pp. S7) [37379], [44836]

"Going the Distance" in *Hispanic Business* (July-August 2007, pp. 38-40, 42-43) [11103], [36568]

"Going Dutch" in *Canadian Business* (Vol. 81, October 27, 2008, No. 18, pp. 40) [19840], [27268]

Going to Extremes: How Like Minds Unite and Divide [29798], [32724]

"Going Green, Going Slowly" in *Playthings* (Vol. 106, September 1, 2008, No. 8, pp. 17) [7209], [7569], [20251], [30630], [43026], [45445]

Going Into Business in Mississippi: An Entrepreneur's Handbook [53810]

Going Into Business in Wisconsin: An Entrepreneur's Guide [53811]

Going Our Way [53855]

Going Places [20616]

Going Solo: Developing a Home-Based Consulting Business from the Ground Up [22658], [24186], [25810], [35557], [39540]

"Going Western with a Touch of Style" in *Women In Business* (Vol. 63, Summer 2011, No. 2, pp. 8) [4109], [7830]

Gold Beach Chamber of Commerce [56781]

Gold Beach Chamber of Commerce Annual Business Directory [56782]

Gold Beach-Wedderburn Chamber of Commerce [56781]

Gold Book: Directory of the Wallcovering Industry [15376]

"Gold Handshake" in *Canadian Business* (Vol. 79, September 11, 2006, No. 18, pp. 25) [8364], [12398], [41937]

"Gold Medal" in *Canadian Business* (Vol. 79, October 9, 2006, No. 20, pp. 57) [24378], [25099], [29799], [38045]

"Gold Still Has That Glitter" in *Barron's* (Vol. 89, July 20, 2009, No. 29, pp. M8) [8365], [12399], [13272], [15448], [31486]

"Goldbelt Inc.: Targeting Shareholder Development" in *Alaska Business Monthly* (Vol. 27, October 2011, No. 10, pp. 108) [13654], [16917], [17316], [20151], [20546], [33428]

The Golden 120 Seconds of Every Sales Call: A Fresh Innovative Look at the Sales Process [22315], [43482]

Golden Bear Oil Specialties - QC/R & D Library [2012]

Golden Belt SCORE [52027]

Golden Chick [18140]

Golden Corral Buffet & Grill [18141]

Golden Eagle Business Services Inc. [26626]

Golden Gate University - University Library [3132]

Golden Griddle Family Restaurants [18142]

"A Golden Retirement?" in *Canadian Business* (Vol. 81, December 8, 2008, No. 21, pp. 7) [12400], [21910]

Golden Rule Insurance Co. Library [11499]

"Golden Spoon Accelerates Expansion Here and Abroad" in *Ice Cream Reporter* (Vol. 22, December 20, 2008, No. 1, pp. 2) [10884], [23009], [32182], [36569]

Golden States Financial Directory [37380]

Golden Triangle Chamber of Commerce [48606]

Golden Valley Chamber of Commerce [47907]

"Golden Valley, Fling Hills Plan LNG Plant" in *Alaska Business Monthly* (Vol. 27, October 2011, No. 10, pp. 9) [7210], [7570], [30631]

Goldenrod Area Chamber of Commerce [50104]

Goldey Beacom College - J. Wilbur Hirons Library [4683]

"Goldeye Completes Private Placement" in *Canadian Corporate News* (May 16, 2007) [12401], [41330], [41938]

"Goldfingers" in *Canadian Business* (Vol. 81, Summer 2008, No. 9, pp. 31) [41331], [41939]

Goldhaber Research Associates L.L.C. [14045]

Arnold S. Goldin & Associates Inc. [222], [8914], [13833], [21464], [26013], [38727]

Goldman Associates Inc. (GA) [17591]

Goldore Consulting Inc. [2884], [26014], [29251], [38728], [42729]

Gold's Gym [16025]

Goldstein & Associates [223]

N.R. Goldstein & Associates [2570]

Goldstein N R & Associates [2570]

Joseph Goldsten & Associates Inc. [32031]

Goleta Business Update [48607]

Goleta Magazine [48608]

Goleta Valley Chamber of Commerce (GVCOC) [48609]

Golf Digest [9674]

Golf Etc. [19393]

Golf Magazine [9675]

Golf Magazine--Golf Club Buyers' Guide Issue [9659]

Golf Range Association of America (GRAA) [9650]

Golf USA, Inc. [9683]

GolfAhoy Golf & Cruise Travel Bureau [20213]

Goliad County Chamber of Commerce [58176]

Golub Capital [55420]

Gonzales Chamber of Commerce [48610]

Gonzales Chamber of Commerce (GCC) [58177]

Goochland County Chamber of Commerce [58925]

Obie Good & Associates [39521]

"A Good Book Is Worth a Thousand Blogs" in *Barron's* (Vol. 88, July 14, 2008, No. 28, pp. 42) [2135], [2375], [8366], [12402], [27269], [29804], [31487]

The Good Business Basics Series: The Basics of Entre-preneuring [30366]

"Good for Business: Houston is a Hot Spot for Economic Growth" in *Black Enterprise* (Vol. 37, October 2006, No. 3, pp. 216) [24740], [27270], [34284], [43865], [44678]

Good Capitalism, Bad Capitalism, and the Economics of Growth and Prosperity [23010], [27271]

Good Choices . . . Bad Choices [3974]

"Good Decisions. Bad Outcomes" in *Harvard Business Review* (Vol. 88, December 2010, No. 12, pp. 40) [21911], [29076], [38046]

Good Discipline, Good Kids [3975]

Good Earth Coffee House & Bakery [9738]

"Good Going, Partners: Energy-Asset Firms Do Their Parents Proud" in *Barron's* (Vol. 89, July 27, 2009, No. 30, pp. M8) [8367], [12403], [31488], [44362]

Good to Great [29801], [32725]

Good to Great: Why Some Companies Make the Leap.. and Others Don't [23011], [32726], [38047]

Good Green Guide for Small Businesses: How to Change the Way Your Business Works for the Better [7211], [7571], [30632]

"The Good Guys of ABWA" in Women In Business (Vol. 63, Fall 2011, No. 3, pp. 9) [33726], [47290]

Good Health Bulletin [34523]

Good Money Management [8883]

Good News Travel Fast [55206]

The Good Old Days of Quality Service [26596]

"Good Price, Best Brands" in Retail Merchandiser (Vol. 51, July-August 2011, No. 4, pp. 58) [26439], [31071], [43027]

"Good Questions and the Basics of Selling" in Agency Sales Magazine (Vol. 39, September-October 2009, No. 9, pp. 14) [26440], [42473], [43483]

Good Sam RV Travel Guide and Camping Directory [3255]

"A Good Sign for Commercial Real Estate" in Austin Business JournalInc. (Vol. 29, December 18, 2009, No. 41, pp. 1) [12404], [14428], [16918], [17317], [23012], [27272]

"A Good Step, But There's a Long Way to Go" in Business Week (September 22, 2008, No. 4100, pp. 10) [8368], [12405], [14429], [26231], [27273], [31489], [33228], [33727], [37381]

"Good Things Happen When We Buy Local" in Crain's Detroit Business (Vol. 24, October 6, 2008, No. 40, pp. 7) [8369], [9932], [12406], [21594], [27274], [31490], [32727], [43028], [44363]

"Good Track Record Helps Developer Secure Construction Loan for Offices" in Miami Daily Business Review (March 26, 2008) [5350], [37382]

William Goodbar Agricapital [21762], [42302]

Goodbye Graffiti Inc. [2663]

"Goodbye, Locker Room: Hello, Boardroom" in Inc. (Vol. 33, October 2011, No. 8, pp. 30) [19425], [28216], [29802], [38048]

Goodland Area Chamber of Commerce [52105]

Goodlettsville Area Chamber of Commerce [57712]

Goodlife Publishers [49398]

Goodmans Library [7761]

"GoodNews.com and the Little Cupcake Shoppe Support Calgary Food Bank With Unique $1.00 Deal" in Marketwire Canada (March 9, 2011) [1762], [9261], [41940], [45928]

"Goodwill Haunts Local Companies; Bad Buyouts During Boom Times Producing Big Writedowns" in Crain's Chicago Business (Apr. 28, 2008) [12407], [26232], [27275], [37383], [38049], [41941], [46252]

David Goodwin, PhD [32285]

"Goodyear Extends Exclusive Deal to Supply NASCAR's Tires" in Charlotte Observer (February 4, 2007) [19426], [20071]

"Google Book Search Tosses Magazines Into the Mix" in Information Today (Vol. 26, February 2009, No. 2, pp. 31) [15326], [15535]

"Google Edges into Wireless E-Mail" in Globe & Mail (February 19, 2007, pp. B5) [11701], [18909], [21108], [34916]

"Google, MySpace Deal Hits Snag" in Globe & Mail (February 7, 2007, pp. B11) [467], [11702], [34917], [39936], [41942]

"Google Places a Call to Bargain Hunters" in Advertising Age (Vol. 79, September 29, 2008, No. 36, pp. 13) [3542], [3732], [11703], [18910], [28683], [34918], [39937]

The Google Story: Inside the Hottest Business, Media, and Technology Success of Our Time [11704], [23013], [28684], [34919]

"Google's Next Stop: Below 350?" in Barron's (Vol. 88, March 10, 2008, No. 10, pp. 17) [8370], [11705], [12408], [21109], [28685], [31491], [34920]

"Googly Eyed" in Entrepreneur (Vol. 36, February 2008, No. 2, pp. 48) [4955], [11706], [28686]

Gordian Concepts & Solutions [32032], [38729], [41293], [43281], [46453]

Gordon Chamber of Commerce [54389]

Gordon Cooper Technology Center [56653]

Gordon County Chamber of Commerce (GCCC) [50539]

"Gordon Nixon" in Canadian Business (Vol. 80, November 5, 2007, No. 22, pp. 9) [8371], [25527], [33728], [36570]

"Gordon Nixon Q&A" in Canadian Business (Vol. 80, November 5, 2007, No. 22, pp. 9) [8372], [25528], [33729], [36571]

"Gordon Stollery" in Canadian Business (Vol. 81, December 24, 2007, No. 1, pp. 76) [29367], [32391]

Gordon's Print Prices Database [1377]

Goren & Associates Inc. [36032]

Gorge-US [55699]

Goshen Chamber of Commerce (GCC) [51610], [55207]

Goshen Co. Chamber Action Update [59822]

Goshen County Chamber of Commerce (GCCC) [59823]

Got a Problem? Solve It! [28418]

"Got Skills? (Entrepreneurs' Adeptness In Other Fields)" in Entrepreneur (Vol. 35, October 2007, No. 10, pp. 31) [29803], [32728]

"Got Slogan? Guidelines for Creating Effective Slogans" in Business Horizons (September-October 2007, pp. 415) [468], [39938]

"Got to be Smarter than the Average Bear" in Contractor (Vol. 56, September 2009, No. 9, pp. 82) [5351], [7572], [16241], [18685], [19098], [30633]

Gotcha Covered [21303]

Gothenburg Area Chamber of Commerce [54390]

The Gottesman Libraries at Teachers College [15219]

Gottscheer Heritage and Genealogy Association (GHGA) [9427]

GourMade Franchise [6186]

Gourmet News [19259]

"Gov. Kasich to Put DOD On Short Leash" in Business Courier (Vol. 27, November 26, 2010, No. 30, pp. 1) [7212], [7573], [20152], [20547], [30634], [42377]

Gove Lumber Co. [1307]

Goventure: Live the Life of an Entrepreneur [29804], [32729]

Governing Magazine: The Magazine of States and Localities [42400]

Government Contract Accounting (Onsite) [21333], [33396]

Government Contracts Directory [33429]

Government Contracts & Subcontract Leads Directory [33429]

Government of the District of Columbia - Department of Small and Local Business Development [49847]

Government Employee Relations Report™ [14172]

Government Institutes Div. [58603]

"Government Intervention" in Canadian Business (Vol. 79, November 6, 2006, No. 22, pp. 116) [12409], [27276], [46253]

Government National Mortgage Association, Ginnie Mae - Procurement and Contracts [60263]

Government National Mortgage Association, Ginnie Mae - Procurement Management Division [60264]

Government Officials Guide [57083]

Government Prime Contractors Directory [33430]

Government Proposal Writing Basics [22568], [33397]

Government Recreation and Fitness [34524]

Government Relations [1472]

"Government Says Self-Regulation of Online Privacy is Coming Up Short" in Advertising Age (Vol. 81, December 6, 2010, No. 43, pp. 1) [18431], [28687], [33730]

Government Textbook [58926]

Governors Highway Safety Association (GHSA) [6595]

Governor's Office of Economic Development [57558]

Governor's Small Business Center [50645]

Gowanda Area Chamber of Commerce [55208]

Gowling Lafleur Henderson LLP [24120]

GPD P.C. [904]

Trenna R. Grabowski CPA Ltd. [21776]

"Grace Puma; Senior Vice-President of Strategic Sourcing, United Airlines" in Crain's Chicago Business (May 5, 2008) [24379], [25100], [35350], [38050], [44364], [47464]

Grace Venture Partners [50350]

"A Graceful (and Lucrative) Exit" in Black Enterprise (Vol. 38, November 2007, No. 4, pp. 108) [24380], [29805], [44153]

"Graceful Landing" in Entrepreneur (Vol. 37, November 2009, No. 11, pp. 59) [11707], [21110], [39939], [43484]

Everett L. Gracey [54532]

Gradient Corporation - Information Resource Center [7728]

Graduate Assistantship Directory in Computing [4855], [18911]

Graduate Assistantship Directory in the Computer Sciences [4855], [18911]

Graduate Pain Research Foundation [14246]

Graduate Women in Business [47212]

"Graduates to the TSX in 2008" in Canadian Business (Vol. 81, Summer 2008, No. 9, pp. 79) [8373], [12410], [23014], [31492], [47023]

Graduating Engineer [19184]

Graduating Engineer & Computer Careers [19184]

Grafton Area Chamber of Commerce (GACC) [59586]

Grafton Area Chamber of Commerce (GCC) [55912]

Graham County Chamber of Commerce (GCCC) [47908]

Joseph Grahame [4056]

Grainews [21750]

"Grainger Show Highlights Building Green, Economy" in Contractor (Vol. 57, February 2010, No. 2, pp. 3) [5352], [6889], [7213], [7574], [18686], [20367], [27277], [30635], [46649]

Grampa's Catfish House [18143]

Granada Hills Chamber of Commerce [48611]

Granby Chamber of Commerce (GCC) [49513]; [49702]

"Grand Action Makes Grand Changes in Grand Rapids" in Crain's Detroit Business (Vol. 25, June 1, 2009, No. 22, pp. M012) [20368], [23015], [32730], [46650]

Grand Blanc Chamber of Commerce (GBCC) [53267]

Grand Blanc Community Directory and Buyer's Guide [53268]

"Grand Bohemian Hotel in Orlando, Fla. Takes Lead in Wedding Planning" in Benzinga.com (August 4, 2011) [2502], [10693], [28688], [39940]

Grand Canyon [47909]

Grand Canyon Chamber of Commerce [47910]

Grand Coulee Dam Area Chamber of Commerce (GCDACC) [59186]

Grand Forks Chamber of Commerce (GFCC) [55913]

Grand Island Area Chamber of Commerce (GIACC) [54391]

Grand Island Chamber of Commerce (GICC) [55209]

Grand Junction Area Chamber of Commerce [49514]

Grand Junction SCORE [49438]

Grand Junction Small Business Development Center [49419]

Grand Lake Area Chamber of Commerce [49515]; [56519]

Grand Ledge Area Chamber of Commerce (GLACC) [53269]

"Grand Letdown" in The Business Journal-Milwaukee (Vol. 25, September 12, 2008, No. 51, pp. A1) [16527], [27278], [43029]

Grand Marais Chamber of Commerce [53652]

Grand Prairie Chamber of Commerce [58178]

"Grand Prix Didn't Fill Up City's Hotels" in Boston Business Journal (Vol. 29, September 16, 2011, No. 19, pp. 1) [19427]

Grand Rapids Area Chamber of Commerce (GRACC) [53270]; [53653]

Grand Rapids Public Library - Furniture Design Collection [9373]

Grand Rental Station [17834]

Grand Rivers Chamber of Commerce and Tourism Commission [52317]

Grand Rivers Tourism Commission [52317]

The Grand Solution [59824]

The Grand Strander [57464]

Grand Terrace Area Chamber of Commerce [48612]

Grand Terrace Chamber of Commerce [48612]

Grand Valley State University [53476]

Grand Valley State University - Robert B. Annis Water Resources Institute [21010]

Grand Valley State University - Michigan Small Business and Technology Development Center (MI-SBTDC) [39531]

Grand Valley State University - Water Resources Institute [21010]

A Grande Finale Franchise LLC [9739]

The Grandich Letter [13122]

Grandview Area Chamber of Commerce (GACC) [54048]

Grandview Chamber of Commerce [59187]

Grandville Chamber of Commerce [53271]

Grandy's, [18144]

Granger Chamber of Commerce [59188]

Grangeville Chamber of Commerce (GCC) [50763]

Granite Falls Area Chamber of Commerce (GFACC) [53654]

Granite Falls Area Chamber of Commerce - Convention and Visitors Bureau [53654]

Granite Transformations [3441], [16496]

A. Davis Grant & Co. [11246]

Grant County Chamber of Commerce [48058]; [59401]

Grant County Chamber of Commerce (GCCC) [52106]; [52318]; [56783]

GRANTS [34635]

Grants Pass - Josephine County Chamber of Commerce (GPJCCC) [56784]

Grantsburg Chamber of Commerce [59587]

GrantSelect™ [34635]

Granville County Chamber of Commerce (GCCC) [55700]

Granville Sentinel [15586]

"Grape Expectations" in Canadian Business (Vol. 80, March 12, 2007, No. 6, pp. 55) [1846], [13581], [21595]

"Grape Expectations" in Canadian Business (Vol. 80, Winter 2007, No. 24, pp. 57) [19224], [31072]

The Grapevine [52890]

Grapevine Chamber of Commerce [58179]

Graph Expo and Converting Expo [4535]

Graphic Arts Blue Book [4558]

Graphic Arts Education and Research Foundation (GAERF) [4591]

Graphic Arts Employers of America (GAE) [16339]

Graphic Arts Technology Corp. [4543]

Graphic Arts Union Employers of America [16339]

Graphic Communications Association [16340], [21031]

Graphic Communications World Library [4568], [16449]

Graphic Communicator [4531]

Graphic Design [4439]

Greater Englewood Chamber of Commerce (ECC) **[49519]**
Greater Enid Chamber of Commerce **[56520]**
Greater Eureka Chamber of Commerce **[48616]**
Greater Eureka Springs Chamber of Commerce **[48060]**
Greater Eustis Area Chamber of Commerce [50084]
Greater Fairbanks Chamber of Commerce **[47797]**
Greater Fairfield Area Chamber of Commerce (GFACC) **[51125]**
Greater Fairfield Area Chamber of Commerce News **[51126]**
Greater Fallon Area Chamber of Commerce **[54493]**
Greater Federal Way Chamber of Commerce [59180]
Greater Florence Chamber of Commerce **[57470]**
Greater Fort Kent Area Chamber of Commerce **[52596]**
Greater Fort Lauderdale Chamber of Commerce (GFLCC) **[50114]**
Greater Fort Lee Chamber of Commerce (GFLCOC) **[54724]**
Greater Fort Myers Chamber of Commerce **[50115]**
Greater Fort Walton Beach Chamber of Commerce **[50116]**
Greater Fort Wayne Chamber of Commerce **[51615]**
Greater Franklin Chamber of Commerce **[54578]**
Greater Fresno Area Chamber of Commerce **[48617]**
Greater Ft. Dodge Area Chamber of Commerce [51894]
Greater Gardner Chamber of Commerce (GGCC) **[52892]**
Greater Gary Chamber of Commerce [51609]
Greater Geneva Area Chamber of Commerce **[47688]**
Greater Gibson County Area Chamber of Commerce **[57713]**
Greater Glassboro Chamber of Commerce (GCC) **[54725]**
Greater Glenside Chamber of Commerce (GGCC) **[57092]**
Greater Golden Chamber of Commerce (GGCC) **[49520]**
Greater Golden Chamber of Commerce Network **[49521]**
Greater Goldendale Area Chamber of Commerce **[59193]**
Greater Goleta Valley Chamber of Commerce [48609]
Greater Gonzales Chamber of Commerce [52431]
Greater Gouverneur Chamber of Commerce **[55218]**
Greater Greenbrier Chamber of Commerce [59404]
Greater Greencastle Chamber of Commerce (GGCC) **[51616]**
Greater Greenfield Chamber of Commerce (GGCC) **[51617]**
Greater Greenville **[53287]**
Greater Greenville Chamber of Commerce (GCC) **[57471]**
Greater Greenwich Chamber of Commerce (GGCC) **[55219]**
Greater Greenwood Chamber of Commerce (GGCC) **[51618]**
Greater Greer Chamber of Commerce (GGCC) **[57472]**
Greater Hall Chamber of Commerce (GHCC) **[50541]**
Greater Hamilton Chamber of Commerce (GHCC) **[56152]**
Greater Hammond Community Map **[51619]**
Greater Hammond Transit Map **[51620]**
Greater Hammonton Chamber of Commerce **[54726]**
Greater Hampstead Chamber of Commerce **[55702]**
Greater Harlem Chamber of Commerce (GHCC) **[55220]**
Greater Hartsville Chamber of Commerce **[57473]**
Greater Harvard Area Chamber of Commerce (GHACC) **[51127]**
Greater Hatboro Chamber of Commerce **[57093]**
Greater Havelock Area Chamber of Commerce [55715]
Greater Haverhill Chamber of Commerce **[52893]**
Greater Havre De Grace Chamber of Commerce [52722]
Greater Hawkins Chamber of Commerce [58217]
Greater Hazelton Business and Innovation Center **[57337]**
Greater Hazleton Chamber of Commerce **[57094]**
Greater Healy-Denali Chamber of Commerce **[47795]**
Greater Heights Area Chamber of Commerce **[58191]**
Greater Helen Area Chamber of Commerce **[50542]**
Greater Hendersonville Chamber of Commerce **[55703]**
Greater Hermiston Chamber of Commerce (GHCC) **[56785]**
Greater Hernando County Chamber of Commerce **[50117]**
Greater Hewitt Chamber of Commerce (GHCC) **[58192]**
Greater Hillsboro Area Chamber of Commerce [56790]
Greater Hollywood Chamber of Commerce **[50118]**
Greater Holyoke Chamber of Commerce **[52894]**
Greater Homestead/Florida City Chamber of Commerce (GHFCCC) **[50119]**
Greater Hot Springs Chamber of Commerce (GHSCC) **[48061]**
Greater Houlton Chamber of Commerce (HCC) **[52597]**
Greater Houston Chamber of Commerce [58193]

Greater Houston Partnership (GHP) **[58193]**
Greater Hudson Chamber of Commerce (GHCC) **[54579]**
Greater Huntington Park Area Chamber of Commerce **[48618]**
Greater Indianapolis Chamber of Commerce **[51621]**
Greater International Falls Chamber of Commerce **[53663]**
Greater Irving - Las Colinas Chamber of Commerce **[58194]**
Greater Irwin Area Chamber of Commerce [57188]
Greater Issaquah Chamber of Commerce (GICC) **[59194]**
Greater Jackson Chamber of Commerce (GJCC) **[53288]**
Greater Jackson County Chamber of Commerce (SJCCC) **[47689]**
Greater Johnstown/Cambria County Chamber of Commerce **[57095]**
Greater Kansas City Business **[54049]**
Greater Kansas City Chamber of Commerce **[54050]**
Greater Keene Chamber of Commerce (GKCC) **[54580]**
Greater Keller Chamber of Commerce **[58195]**
Greater Kellogg Chamber of Commerce [50773]
Greater Kenai Chamber of Commerce **[47806]**
Greater Ketchikan Chamber of Commerce (GKCC) **[47798]**
Greater Key West Chamber of Commerce [50182]
Greater Killeen Chamber of Commerce (GKCC) **[58196]**
Greater Kingston Community Chamber of Commerce **[59195]**
Greater Kirkland Chamber of Commerce (GKCC) **[59196]**
Greater Knox Area Chamber of Commerce [51721]
Greater Knoxville Chamber of Commerce [57735]
Greater Knoxville SCORE Chapter 435 **[57632]**
Greater La Porte Chamber of Commerce (GLCC) **[51622]**
Greater Laconia-Weirs Beach Chamber of Commerce and Greater Franklin Chamber of Commerce **[54597]**
Greater Lafayette Chamber of Commerce (GLCC) **[52466]**
Greater Lafayette Chamber of Commerce [51661]
Greater Lake City Chamber of Commerce **[57474]**
Greater Lake Placid Chamber of Commerce [50189]
Greater Lake Stevens Chamber of Commerce (GLSCC) **[59197]**
Greater Lake Worth Chamber of Commerce **[50120]**
Greater Lakeport Chamber of Commerce [48707]
Greater Laporte Chamber of Commerce [51622]
Greater Las Cruces Chamber of Commerce (GLCCC) **[54960]**
Greater Lava Hot Springs Chamber of Commerce **[50777]**
Greater Lawrence Chamber of Commerce [52927]
Greater Lawrence County Area Chamber of Commerce (GLCACC) **[56153]**
Greater Leadville Area Chamber of Commerce [49545]
Greater Lebanon Chamber of Commerce [54599]
Greater Lehigh Valley Chamber of Commerce **[57096]**
Greater Limestone County Chamber of Commerce **[47690]**
Greater Lincolnshire Chamber of Commerce (GLCC) **[51128]**
Greater Little Rock Guest Guide **[48062]**
Greater Liverpool Chamber of Commerce **[55221]**
Greater Logan County Area Chamber of Commerce **[56201]**
Greater Long Branch Chamber of Commerce (GLBCC) **[54727]**
Greater Lorain Chamber of Commerce [56203]
Greater Louisville Inc. - The Metro Chamber of Commerce (GLI) **[52322]**
Greater Louisville Ink **[52323]**
Greater Louisville - The Metro Chamber [52322]
Greater Lowell Chamber of Commerce (GLCC) **[52895]**
Greater Lynchburg Chamber of Commerce [58958]
The Greater Mackinaw Area Chamber of Commerce **[53289]**
Greater Mackinaw Area Chamber of Commerce [53358]
Greater Macon Chamber of Commerce (GMCC) **[50543]**
Greater Madawaska Chamber of Commerce **[52598]**
Greater Madison Area Chamber of Commerce (GMACC) **[57582]**
Greater Madison Chamber of Commerce (GMCC) **[59590]**
Greater Madison SCORE **[51492]**
Greater Mahopac-Carmel Chamber of Commerce **[55222]**
Greater Mahwah Chamber of Commerce [54728]
Greater Manchester Chamber of Commerce (GMCC) **[49705]**; **[54581]**
Greater Mankato Business Accelerator - Chamber of Commerce & Economic Development **[53789]**
Greater Mansfield Area Chamber of Commerce **[57097]**

Greater Maple Valley - Black Diamond Chamber of Commerce **[59198]**
Greater Marathon Chamber of Commerce **[50121]**
Greater Marshall Chamber of Commerce [58302]
Greater Martinsville Chamber of Commerce (MCC) **[51623]**
Greater Marysville - Tulalip Chamber of Commerce **[59199]**
Greater Massena Chamber of Commerce **[55223]**
Greater Mauldin Chamber of Commerce **[57475]**
Greater Mauston Area Chamber of Commerce **[59591]**
Greater Medina Chamber of Commerce **[56154]**
Greater Menomonie Area Chamber of Commerce (GMACC) **[59592]**
Greater Merced Chamber of Commerce **[48619]**
Greater Mercer County Chamber of Commerce [54766]
Greater Meriden Chamber of Commerce (GMCC) **[49706]**
Greater Miami Chamber of Commerce (GMCC) **[50122]**
Greater Miami Chamber of Commerce, Women in Business Group **[50123]**
Greater Miami Chamber Membership Directory **[50124]**
Greater Miami Shores Chamber of Commerce **[50125]**
Greater Millville Chamber of Commerce **[54729]**
Greater Mission Chamber of Commerce **[58197]**
Greater Monmouth Chamber of Commerce (GMCC) **[54730]**
Greater Monticello Chamber of Commerce and Visitors Bureau **[51624]**
Greater Mount Airy Chamber of Commerce **[55704]**
Greater Mulberry Chamber of Commerce (GMCC) **[50126]**
Greater Muscatine Chamber of Commerce and Industry (GMCCI) **[51899]**
Greater Muskogee Area Chamber of Commerce (GMCC) **[56521]**
Greater Nags Head Chamber of Commerce [55792]
Greater Naples Chamber of Commerce (GNCC) **[50127]**
Greater Nashua Chamber of Commerce **[54582]**
Greater Nassau Chamber News **[50128]**
Greater Nassau County Chamber of Commerce **[50129]**
Greater New Braunfels Chamber of Commerce **[58198]**
Greater New Haven Chamber of Commerce (GNHCC) **[49707]**
Greater New Milford Chamber of Commerce (GNMCC) **[49708]**
Greater New York Chamber of Commerce **[55224]**
Greater Newark Chamber of Commerce **[55225]**
Greater Newburyport Chamber of Commerce and Industry **[52896]**
Greater Newport Chamber of Commerce (GNCC) **[56786]**
Greater North Augusta Chamber of Commerce [57508]
Greater North County Chamber of Commerce **[54051]**
Greater North Dakota Association [55923]
Greater North Fulton Chamber of Commerce (GNFCC) **[50544]**
Greater North Highlands Chamber of Commerce - North Highlands Chamber of Commerce [48219]
Greater North Miami Beach Chamber of Commerce **[50130]**
Greater North Syracuse Chamber of Commerce [55309]
Greater Northampton Chamber of Commerce **[52897]**
Greater Northeast Philadelphia Chamber of Commerce (GNPCC) **[57098]**
Greater Norwalk Chamber of Commerce **[49709]**
Greater Oak Harbor Chamber of Commerce (GOHCC) **[59200]**
Greater Ogdensburg Chamber of Commerce **[55226]**
Greater Oklahoma City Chamber of Commerce **[56522]**
Greater Oklahoma City Hispanic Chamber of Commerce **[56523]**
Greater Olean Area Chamber of Commerce (GOACC) **[55227]**
Greater Omaha Chamber of Commerce **[54392]**
Greater Oneida Chamber of Commerce **[55228]**
Greater Orange Area Chamber of Commerce (GOACC) **[58199]**
Greater Orange City Area Chamber of Commerce **[50002]**
Greater Orlando Chamber of Commerce [50257]
Greater Ossining Chamber of Commerce **[55229]**
Greater Ossipee Area Chamber of Commerce (GOACC) **[54583]**
Greater Oswego Chamber of Commerce **[55230]**
Greater Othello Chamber of Commerce **[59201]**
Greater Oviedo Chamber of Commerce Business Library **[44970]**, **[45838]**
Greater Oviedo Chamber of Commerce [50260]
Greater Palatine Chamber of Commerce and Industry **[51275]**
Greater Palm Harbor Area Chamber of Commerce (GPHACC) **[50131]**

"Growing at the Margins" in Business Journal Serving Greater Tampa Bay (Vol. 30, November 5, 2010, No. 46, p. 1) [3733], [14198], [23027]

"Growing Pains" in Canadian Business (Vol. 80, November 19, 2007, No. 23, pp. 41) [29079], [38059]

"Growing Pains" in Canadian Business (Vol. 81, July 22, 2008, No. 12-13, pp. 35) [19225], [21599], [24388], [25105], [31074], [39948]

"Growing Pains" in Crain's Cleveland Business (Vol. 30, June 22, 2009, No. 24, pp. 3) [5356], [27290]

"Growing Strong" in Entrepreneur (Vol. 35, November 2007, No. 11, pp. 36) [94], [6962], [7785], [20062], [21377], [47293]

"Growing Subscriber Base Fuels Roger's Rosy Outlook for 2007" in Globe & Mail (February 16, 2007, pp. B3) [12424], [23028], [44370]

Growing Your Business [23029], [29813]

"Growing Your Business Through BPI Certification" in Indoor Comfort Marketing (Vol. 70, May 2011, No. 5, pp. 12) [817], [23030], [28219]

Growing Your Company [23652]

Grown Up Digital: How the Net Generation Is Changing Your World [11709], [28693], [34924], [45457]

"Growth Back on CIBC's Agenda" in Globe & Mail (March 3, 2006, pp. B1) [8385], [12425], [23031], [31499]

The Growth Coach, Inc. [3020]

"Growth in Fits and Starts" in Canadian Business (Vol. 83, July 20, 2010, No. 11-12, pp. 18) [16922], [17321], [27291], [39119]

"Growth of Free Dailies Dropping" in Globe & Mail (March 24, 2007, pp. B7) [11710], [15536], [21111]

Growth Opportunity Connection - Center for Business Innovation [54192]

Growth Oriented Women Entrepreneurs and Their Businesses: A Global Research Perspective [29814], [36576], [47294]

"Growth Seen Climbing Out of a Trough" in Globe & Mail (March 3, 2007, pp. B5) [27292], [32738]

GrowthWorks [59884]

GRP Partners / Global Retail Partners [49230]

Grundy Center Chamber of Commerce and Development [51902]

Gruver Chamber of Commerce [58208]

GSC Assoc [41494]

GSC Associates Inc. [41494]

GTCR Golder Rauner LLC [51403]

"GTI Licenses TMC to Cannon Boiler Works" in Contractor (Vol. 56, December 2009, No. 12, pp. 6) [37024], [39120]

GTM Co. [59043]

Guadalupe Chamber of Commerce and Visitor Center [48632]

Guadalupe Chamber of Commerce [48632]

Guam Chamber of Commerce [36295], [59857]

Guard-A-Kid [4016]

Guardsman Furniturepro [9366]

Guerilla Marketing Newsletter [40548]

Guerrilla Marketing, 4th Edition: Easy and Inexpensive Strategies for Making Big Profits from Your Small Business [23032], [39949]

Guerrilla Marketing During Tough Times [469], [27293], [39950]

Guerrilla Marketing Goes Green: Winning Strategies to Improve Your Profits and Your Planet [7230], [7593], [30664], [39951]

Guerrilla Marketing for the New Millennium [470], [28694], [39952]

Guerrilla Marketing: Put Your Advertising on Steroids [471], [28695], [39953]

"Guidance On Career Guidance for Offender Reentry" in Occupational Outlook Quarterly (Vol. 54, Fall 2010, No. 3, pp. 24) [35354], [35797]

Guide [52898], [7884]

The Guide [49714]; [50148]

Guide to ACA-Accredited Camps [3256]

Guide to the Area's Fifteen Shopping and Professional Centers [48633]

Guide Book [50149]; [52601]; [54735]

Guide Book/Buyers Guide [50150]

The Guide to Burbank [48634]

Guide to Business Information on Central and Eastern Europe [22319]

Guide to Business Information on Russia, the NIS, and the Baltic States [22320]

Guide to Business Permitting and Licensing in Wyoming [59854]

Guide to Calistoga [48635]

Guide to Camel [48636]

"Guide to Carbon Footprinting" in American Printer (Vol. 128, June 1, 2011, No. 6) [2136], [4479], [7231], [7594], [16372], [20772], [30665], [41406]

A Guide to College Programs in Hospitality, Tourism, & Culinary Arts [20153]

Guide to Doing Business in Waterford [56526]

Guide to Downtown Plymouth [52899]

A Guide to Federal Sector Equal Employment Opportunity (EEO) Law and Practice [24147]

Guide to Fluvanna County [58933]

Guide to Government [55241]

The Guide to Graduate Environmental Programs [7078]

Guide to Greater Fort Lauderdale [50151]

Guide to Greater Sarasota [50152]

Guide to Grenada [53859]

Guide to Gridley [48637]

Guide to Hackensack [54736]

Guide to Helena Living and Business [54281]

Guide to Karate-Do [14094]

Guide to the Kennebunks [52602]

Guide to Lake Zurich [51132]

The Guide to Living in Scottsdale [47916]

Guide Map [52900]

A Guide to Merit Systems Protection Board (MSPB) Law and Practice [24148]

Guide to Monadnock Region [54589]

Guide to Palm Beaches [50153]

A Guide to the Project Management Body of Knowledge [32739], [38060]

A Guide to Provincetown [52901]

Guide to the Rio Grande Valley [58209]

Guide to the Seacoast [54590]

Guide to the Shoals [47696]

Guide to Summer Camps and Summer Schools [3257]

Guide to Accredited Camps [3256]

A Guide to College Programs in Hospitality and Tourism [20153]

A Guide to College Programs in Hospitality and Tourism--A Directory of CHRIE Member Colleges and Universities [20153]

Guide to Hospitality and Tourism Education: A Directory of CHRIE Member Colleges and Universities [20153]

Guide to Mortgage Industry Resources on the Internet [14460]

A Guide to Trademarks and Brand Names for the Decorating Products Industry [15370], [15400]

Guidebook [50154]

Guidebook and Directory [57715]

"Guidelines For Family Business Boards of Directors" in Family Business Review (Vol. 19, June 2006, No. 2, pp. 147) [31075], [38061]

Guidelines for Laboratory Safety [14269]

Guidepost [3364]

Guild of American Papercutters (GAP) [5958]

Guild of Book Workers Inc. (GBW) [2239]

Guild of Book Workers Library [2252]

Guild of Book Workers Newsletter [2184], [2245], [3222], [16417]

Guild of Book Workers--Supplies and Services Directory [2137], [2242], [3218]

Guild of Prescription Opticians of America [20925]

Guild of Professional Paperhangers [15386]

Guild Publishing [59795]

Guilde Canadienne des Medias [46804]

Guilderland Chamber of Commerce (GCC) [55242]

Guilford Chamber of Commerce [49715]

Gulf Beaches on Sand Key Chamber of Commerce [50306]

Gulf Breeze Area Chamber of Commerce [50155]

Gulf Breeze Magazine [50156]

Gulf Coast Innovation Center [53926]

Gulf County Chamber of Commerce [50157]

Gun Digest [10031]

Gun & Knife Show Calendar [10032]

Gun List [10031]

The Gun Report [10033]

Gun Safety [10038]

Gun Show Calendar [10032]

Gunnison County Chamber of Commerce (GCCC) [49526]

Guns & Ammo [1246]

Guns Illustrated [1243]

Guntersville Chamber of Commerce [47707]

Gurdon Chamber of Commerce [48066]

Gustine Chamber of Commerce [48638]

Guthrie Center Chamber of Commerce (GCCC) [51903]

Guthrie Chamber of Commerce [56527]

Guthrie Theater Foundation - Staff Reference Library [5938]

"Guts Not Included" in Canadian Business (Vol. 81, March 31, 2008, No. 5, pp. 46) [25532], [28220], [36577], [38062]

The Gutter Guys [39528], [44611]

Guysborough Historical Society Archives [9512]

Gwinnett Chamber of Commerce [50549]

Gwinnett Innovation Park [50674]

Gymboree Play and Music [4017]

H

H & A International [40943]

H&H Investment Solutions [22063]

H2X Canada Hardware & Home Improvement Expo & Conference [10148], [10436], [19376]

"Haagen-Dazs Recruits Shop Owners through Facebook" in Ice Cream Reporter (Vol. 23, November 20, 2010, No. 12, pp. 1) [10885], [28696], [32184]

Haagen-Dazs Shops [10961]

Haas Wheat & Partners L.P. [42331]

Habersham County Chamber of Commerce [50550]

"Habitat, Home Depot Expand Building Programs" in Contractor (Vol. 56, September 2009, No. 9, pp. 16) [5357], [7232], [23033], [30666]

Habitats and Ecosystems: An Encyclopedia of Endangered America [7233], [10165]

Habitual Entrepreneurs [29815]

Hackensack Chamber of Commerce [54738]

Hackensack Commerce [54737]

Hackensack Regional Chamber of Commerce (HRCC) [54738]

"A Hacker in India Hijacked His Website Design and Was Making Good Money Selling It" in Inc. (December 2007, pp. 77-78, 80) [3543], [11711], [18432], [18912], [21112], [30935], [36578], [45130]

Hackettstown Area Living Magazine [54739]

Hagerman Valley Chamber of Commerce (HVCC) [50770]

Hagerstown-Washington County Chamber of Commerce (HWCCC) [52720]

Haight Consulting [26706]

Hailey Chamber of Commerce [50771]

Hailey Chamber News [50772]

"Hain Celestial Acquires Greek Gods Yogurt" in Ice Cream Reporter (Vol. 23, July 20, 2010, No. 8, pp. 1) [10223], [10286], [10886], [12426], [41950]

Haines Chamber of Commerce [47803]

Haines City Chamber of Commerce [50158]

Hair Cut and Style [10078]

Haircut and Style [10078]

Haircutting Basics [10081]

Haircutting with Clippers—Basic Techniques [10082]

Hairshaping [10106]

Halcrow HPA [13971]

Haleyville Area Chamber of Commerce (HCC) [47697]

"Half of Canadian Firms to Boost Marketing Budgets" in Globe & Mail (January 22, 2007, pp. B1) [472], [39954], [42627]

"Half Empty or Half Full" in Crain's Chicago Business (Vol. 31, March 24, 2008, No. 12, pp. 4) [10224], [12427], [21600]

Half Moon Bay - Coastside Chamber of Commerce and Visitors' Bureau (HMBCCCVB) [48639]

Half Moon Bay - Coastside Chamber of Commerce [48639]

"Half a World Away" in Tampa Bay Business Journal (Vol. 30, December 4, 2009, No. 50, pp. 1) [13939], [20369], [33230], [33432], [36579], [46651]

Halifax County Chamber of Commerce (HCCC) [58934]

The Hall Partnership Architects L.L.P. [2571]

Hall Publications [59886]

J.A. Hall Publications [59886]

Hallador Venture Partners [49231]

Hallettsville Chamber of Commerce [58210]

Hallettsville Chamber of Commerce and Agriculture [58210]

Hallmark Cards, Inc. - Business Research Library [9632]

Hallmark Cards, Inc. - Creative Research Library [4569], [9633], [9896]

Halloween Express [5932]

"Halls Give Hospital Drive $11 Million Infusion" in The Business Journal-Serving Metropolitan Kansas City (Vol. 26, July 18, 2008) [9600], [9891], [23034], [29816], [31076], [34285], [38063], [39121], [45933]

The Halo Effect: And the Eight Other Business Delusions That Deceive Managers [29817], [38064]

Halpern, Denny & Co. [53033]

Halstead Architects [1308]

Halstead Chamber of Commerce (HCC) [52111]

Hamburg Area Chamber of Commerce (HCC) [48067]

Hamburg Chamber of Commerce [55243]

Hamburger Mary's Bar & Grille [18148]

Hamden Chamber of Commerce [49716]

Hamilton Bioventures / Hamilton Apex Technology Ventures [49232]

Hamilton Chamber of Commerce (HCC) [58211]

Hamilton City Library - Bluestem Genealogical Society Collection [9513]

Hamilton County Business Center [56400]

Hamilton County Chamber of Commerce (HCCC) [50159]

Hamilton County Chamber of Commerce and Economic Development Commission [51133]

Hamilton/Morrisville Tribune [15587]

Hamilton North Chamber of Commerce [51632]

Hamilton/KSA [43283]
Hammon Chamber of Commerce [51663]
Hammond Chamber of Commerce (HCC) [52471]
Hammonton Business Director [54740]
Hammonton Information Guide [54741]
Hampshire Area Chamber of Commerce (HACC) [51134]
Hampshire Chamber of Commerce [51134]
Hampshire County Chamber of Commerce [59406]
Hampton Area Chamber of Commerce (HACC) [51904]
Hampton Bays Chamber of Commerce (HBCC) [55244]
Hampton Beach Area Chamber of Commerce [54591]
Hampton County Chamber of Commerce [57481]
Hampton Group [25361], [44215]
Hampton Roads Chamber of Commerce [58935]
Hampton Roads Chamber of Commerce - Headquarters
    [58935]
Hampton Roads Virginia Procurement Technical Assistance Center [59023]
Hancock County Chamber of Commerce [52324]
Hancock County Chamber of Commerce (HCCC)
    [53860]
Hancock & Estabrook Law Library [7762]
*"Hand-Held Heaven: Smallcakes Cupcakery" in Tulsa
    World (February 15, 2011)* [1737], [31010], [32095],
    [41951]
Hand and Stone Massage and Facial Spa [14155]
*The Handbook of Financing Growth: Strategies and
    Capital Structure* [23035], [31500]
Handbook of Genealogical Sources [9445]
Handbook of Quality Research in Entrepreneurship
    [29818], [42802]
Handelskammer [58212]
Handgun Fundamentals [10039]
*"Handle with Care" in Entrepreneur (Vol. 35, November
    2007, No. 11, pp. 24)* [41407], [41542]
Handle with Care [47500]
*"Handle With Care" in Hawaii Business (Vol. 53, October
    2007, No. 5, pp. 66)* [95], [2286], [21378], [22112],
    [38065]
*"Handleman Liquidation Leaves Questions For
    Shareholders" in Crain's Detroit Business (Vol. 24,
    October 6, 2008, No. 40, pp. 4)* [12428], [12429],
    [14734], [24389], [25106], [26758], [31501]
The Handler Group Inc. [22529], [22650], [40612]
Handleskammer [53296]
Handling Hazardous Waste [10174]
Handling Objections [43723]
Handling the Sexual Harassment Complaint [26687]
Handling Trademark Registrations under the New Law
    [37161]
*"H&M Offers a Dress for Less" in Canadian Business
    (Vol. 83, September 14, 2010, No. 15, pp. 20)* [4110],
    [4232], [7831], [25759], [27294], [36580], [39122],
    [43033], [45458]
Handmade - A Division of the New York International Gift
    Fair [6049]
Handmade - A Division of the San Francisco
    International Gift Fair [6050], [6183], [46756]
Hands-On Business and Report Writing: The Art of
    Persuasion (Onsite) [22569]
Hands-On PLCs: Operation, Installation, Maintenance
    and Troubleshooting [6871]
Hands-On UNIX and Linux Tools and Utilities (Onsite)
    [28038]
Handweavers Guild of America (HGA) [5959]
Handweavers Guild of America, Inc. [5959]
Handwriting Analysis Research Library [10119]
Handwriting Analyst [10117]
Handy Book for Genealogists [9446]
Handyman Connection [5687], [6918], [16299]
Handyman Matters Franchise Corp. [5688]
Handyman-Network Franchise Systems LLC [3108]
Handypro Handyman Service [5783]
Hanford Chamber of Commerce [48640]
Hanford-Freund & Co. [16567]
Hanford Healy Appraisal Co. [17583]
*"Hank and Ben: Hedgies' BFFs" in Barron's (Vol. 88,
    March 31, 2008, No. 13, pp. 50)* [8387], [12429],
    [27295], [31502]
*"Hank Paulson On the Housing Bailout and What's
    Ahead" in Business Week (September 22, 2008, No.
    4100, pp. 19)* [8388], [12430], [14431], [16923],
    [26237], [27296], [31503], [33231], [33738], [36581],
    [37385], [45459]
Hanley-Wood, LLC Library [689], [2225], [5706],
    [13904], [14130], [15608]
Hannacroix Creek Books Inc. [49800]
Hannibal Area Chamber of Commerce (HCC) [54055]
Hannibal Chamber of Commerce [54055]
Hannoush Jewelers [13297]
Hanover Area Chamber of Commerce (HACC) [54592];
    [57109]
Hanover Area Church Directory [57110]

Hanover Association of Businesses and Chamber of
    Commerce [58936]
Hanover Chamber of Commerce [52902]
Han-Padron Associates [13971]
*"Hansen Mechanical Performs Boiler Upgrade at Brookfield Zoo" in Contractor (Vol. 57, February 2010, No. 2,
    pp. 7)* [6890], [18688], [45934]
Happenings [54394]
*Happy About Joint Venturing: The 8 Critical Factors of
    Success* [29819], [32740], [41952]
A Happy Beginning [8884], [13156], [43724]
*"Happy Blogging" in Black Enterprise (Vol. 38, January
    2008, No. 6, pp. 47)* [11712], [21113], [28697]
Happy & Healthy Products Inc. [10962]
Happy Joes, Inc. [10963], [16153]
*"Happy New Year, Celestica?" in Canadian Business
    (Vol. 80, January 15, 2007, No. 2, pp. 25)* [12431],
    [34925], [39123]
Happy Tails Dog Spa [15682]
*"Happy Trails: RV Franchiser Gives Road Traveling
    Enthusiasts a Lift" in Black Enterprise (Vol. 38, July
    2008, No. 12, pp. 47)* [20154], [20548], [23036],
    [32185], [39955], [40742]
Haralson County Chamber of Commerce [50551]
Harassment Prevention and Appropriate Behaviors in the
    Workplace (Onsite) [23683], [26653]
Harbert Management Corp. [47752]
Harbert Venture Partners LLC [59015]
Harbinger Mezzanine Partners L.P. [47752]
*"A Harbinger?" in The Business Journal-Milwaukee (Vol.
    25, August 29, 2008, No. 49, pp. A1)* [8389], [12432],
    [31504]
Harbor Beach Chamber of Commerce [53297]
Harbor City Chamber of Commerce [48641]
Harbor City - Harbor Gateway Chamber of Commerce
    (HCHGCC) [48641]
Harbor Country Chamber of Commerce [53298]
Harbor County Guide [53299]
Harbor News [50160]
Harbor Springs Chamber of Commerce (HSCC) [53300]
Harbourvest Partners, LLC [53034]
*"Hard Rock on Pike" in Puget Sound Business Journal
    (Vol. 29, September 5, 2008, No. 20, pp. 1)* [3418],
    [5358], [7234], [17926], [30667]
*"Hard Times for Hard Money" in Sacramento Business
    Journal (Vol. 25, July 18, 2008, No. 20, pp. 1)* [5359],
    [17322], [23878], [26238], [37386]
Hardee County Chamber of Commerce (HCCC) [50161]
Hardee's [18149]
Hardeman County Chamber of Commerce [57716]
*"The Harder Side of Sears" in Crain's Chicago Business
    (Vol. 31, March 31, 2008, No. 13, pp. 68)* [41953],
    [43034]
Hardin Area Chamber of Commerce and Agriculture
    (HACC) [54282]
Hardin County Chamber of Commerce [56158]
Hardin-Simmons University - Rupert and Pauline Richardson Library [1389]
Hardin-Simmons University - Smith Music Library
    [14685], [14772]
*"Harding Brews Success at Anheuser-Busch" in Black
    Enterprise (Vol. 37, February 2007, No. 7, pp. 1)*
    [2457], [38066]
Harding & Co. [26020], [28441], [38734], [43762]
Hardscrabble News [55245]
Hardware Manufacturers Statistical Association [10121]
Hardware Merchandising: Solutions for home improvement retailers [10144]
Hardwick Area Chamber of Commerce (HACC) [58755]
Hardwood Manufacturers Association [13637]
Hardwood Plywood Manufacturers Association - Fine
    Hardwood Veneer Association - Southern Plywood
    Manufacturers Association - Hardwood Plywood
    Institute [13638], [13685]
Hardwood Plywood and Veneer Association (HPVA)
    [13638], [13685]
Hardy Stevenson and Associates Ltd. [2889], [4673]
J.H. Hare & Associates Ltd. [21777]
Harford County Chamber of Commerce (HCCC) [52721]
Harford County Maryland Small Business Development
    Center [52652]
Harian Creative Books [2206], [6859]
Harian Creative Enterprises [2206], [6859]
Harker Heights Chamber of Commerce [58213]
Harker Heights SCORE [57888]
HARL. [10119]
*"Harlequin Leads the Way" in Marketing to Women (Vol.
    22, July 2009, No. 7, pp. 1)* [2138], [11713], [21114],
    [22321], [28698], [34926], [39956]
*"Harley-Davidson Moves to Unconventional Marketing
    Plan" in Business Journal-Milwaukee (Vol. 28,
    November 26, 2010, No. 8, pp. A1)* [473], [11714],
    [13995], [14545], [21115], [28699], [39957]

*"Harleysville Eyes Growth After Nationwide Deal" in
    Philadelphia Business Journal (Vol. 30, October 7,
    2011, No. 34, pp. 1)* [11354], [12433], [23037],
    [25320], [36151], [41954], [44154]
Harlingen Area Business [58214]
Harlingen Area Chamber of Commerce (HACC) [58215]
Harlingen Hispanic Chamber of Commerce (HHCOC)
    [58216]
Harmonic Wealth [29368], [32392]
Harmonica Happenings [14746]
Harmony [7051]
Harmony Foundation [7051]
*"Harness the Internet to Boost Equipment Sales" in
    Indoor Comfort Marketing (Vol. 70, July 2011, No. 7,
    pp. 24)* [818], [28700], [39958], [43485]
Harness Racing Museum & Hall of Fame - Peter D.
    Haughton Memorial Library [10631]
*"Harnessing the Wisdom of Crowds" in Entrepreneur
    (Vol. 37, September 2009, No. 9, pp. 74)* [11715],
    [21116], [23038], [26442], [37025]
Harney County Chamber of Commerce (HCCC) [56788]
Harold L. Kestenbaum, Esq. [24121]
Harper County Genealogical Society Library [9514]
Harrington College of Design - Design Library [5707],
    [9374], [11590]
Richard M. Harris Associates [26627]
Harris County Chamber of Commerce [50552]
Harris and Harris Group Inc. [55421]
*"The Harris Teeter Grocery Chain Has Started a New Ice
    Cream Club for Shoppers" in Ice Cream Reporter (Vol.
    21, July 20, 2008)* [9934], [10887], [39959]
Harrisburg Area Chamber of Commerce (HACC) [48068]
Harrisburg Regional Chamber of Commerce [57111]
Harrisburg Regional Industrial Directory [57112]
The Harrisburg Regional News [57113]
Harrison Area Chamber of Commerce [53301]
Harrison Chamber of Commerce [53301]
Harrison Chamber of Commerce (HCC) [48069]
Harrison County Chamber of Commerce [51633]
Harrison County Chamber of Commerce (HCCC)
    [59407]
Harrison Regional Chamber of Commerce (HRCC)
    [56159]
Harrison Regional Chamber of Commerce and Tourism
    Information [56159]
Harrison SCORE [47998]
Harrisonburg-Rockingham Chamber of Commerce
    (HRCC) [58937]
Harrisonville Area Chamber of Commerce (HACC)
    [54056]
Harry W. Lenig Library. [9548]
Hart County Chamber of Commerce [50553]; [52325]
Hart - Silver Lake Mears Chamber of Commerce [53438]
*"Hartco Income Fund Announces the Completion of the
    CompuSmart Strategic Review" in Canadian Corporate
    News (May 14, 2007)* [8390], [12434], [25107],
    [31505], [43035], [44155]
Hartech Inc. [16758]
Hartford Area Chamber of Commerce [59601]
Hartford Area Chamber of Commerce (HACC) [58756]
Hartford Chamber of Commerce [49724]
Hartford Conservatory - Carolyn B. Taylor Library
    [11500], [14686]
Hartford Despatch [24787]
Hartford Despatch International [24787]
The Hartford Financial Services Company - Loss Control
    Library [47541]
Hartington Area Chamber of Commerce [54395]
Hartington Chamber of Commerce [54395]
Hartland Area Chamber of Commerce [59602]
Hartland Matters [59603]
Hartley Chamber of Commerce [51905]
Hartselle Area Chamber of Commerce (HACC) [47698]
Hartselle Chamber of Commerce [47698]
Hartshorne Chamber of Commerce [56528]
Hartsville - Trousdale County Chamber of Commerce
    [57717]
Harvard Management Communication Letter [22499]
Harvard University - Belfer Center for Science and
    International Affairs - Environment and Natural
    Resources Program (ENRP) [7429]
Harvard University - Botany Libraries [9855]
Harvard University - Harvard Negotiation Project (HNP)
    [14178]
Harvard University - Joint Center for Housing Studies
    (JCHS) [1176]
Harvard University - School of Medicine - The Libraries
    of the Massachusetts Eye and Ear Infirmary [14340]
Harvard University - A. Alfred Taubman Center for State
    and Local Government [42429]
Harvest Partners Inc. [55422]
Harvest Partners L.L.C. [55422]
Harvest Ventures Inc. [55422]

Harvey Area Chamber of Commerce [55915]
Harvey's [18150]
Harwich Chamber of Commerce (HCC) [52903]
The Harwood Institute for Public Innovation [16620]
"Has Daylight Savings Time Fuelled Gasoline Consump-
tion" in Globe & Mail (April 14, 2007, pp. B1) [27297],
[33739]
"Has Microsoft Found a Way to Get at Yahoo?" in
Advertising Age (Vol. 79, July 7, 2008, No. 26, pp. 4)
[8391], [11716], [12435], [21117], [24390], [31506],
[34927], [41955]
Haskell Chamber of Commerce [56529]
Haskell County Historical Society [9515]
The Hassayampa Alert [47917]
"Hastily Enacted Regulation Will Not Cure Economic
Crisis" in Crain's Chicago Business (Vol. 31, May 5,
2008, No. 18, pp. 18) [8392], [12436], [14432],
[16924], [17323], [26239], [27298], [31507], [33232],
[33740]
Hastings Area Chamber of Commerce (HACC) [54396]
Hastings Area Chamber of Commerce and Tourism
Bureau [53657]
Hastings Co. [16568]
Hat Life Directory [10155]
Hat Life Yearbook [10155]
Hatboro Online Business Directory [57114]
Hatch [5644]
Hatch Associates [5644]
Hatfield Chamber of Commerce [57115]
Hatfield House Books [52406]
The Hathaway Group Inc. [9295], [16621]
Haus-Garten-Freizeit [2547]
"Haute Flyers" in Canadian Business (Vol. 80, November
19, 2007, No. 23, pp. 68) [4111], [4233], [7832],
[23039]
Havana Area Chamber of Commerce [51135]
The Havana: Cigar of Connoisseurs [20107]
"Have High-Tech Tax Credits Helped or Hurt Hawaii?" in
Hawaii Business (Vol. 53, December 2007, No. 6, pp.
28) [12437], [27299], [33233], [33741], [34928],
[44839], [46256]
"Have I Got a Deal For You" in Canadian Business (Vol.
83, October 12, 2010, No. 17, pp. 65) [12438],
[14911], [23040], [39124]
"Have Tag, Will Travel" in Inc. (Vol. 33, November 2011,
No. 9, pp. 48) [24862], [44371]
Havelock Chamber of Commerce [55715]
Haviland Collectors International Foundation (HCIF)
[4405]
"Having Words with Matt Maroni: Chef-Owner, Gaztro-
Wagon, Chicago" in Nation's Restaurant News (Vol.
45, April 4, 2011, No. 7, pp. 62) [9155], [29820]
Havre Area Chamber of Commerce (HACC) [54283]
Havre de Grace Chamber of Commerce [52722]
Havre Small Business Development Center [54216]
Hawaii Business [50725]
"Hawaii Business 2008 SB Success Awards" in Hawaii
Business (Vol. 53, February 2008, No. 8, pp. 43)
[23041], [25108], [29821], [32741], [43486], [44372],
[44840]
Hawaii Business, Economic Development, and Tourism
Department - Research and Economic Analysis Divi-
sion (READ) [27937]
Hawaii Department of Business, Economic Development,
and Tourism - Strategic Marketing & Support [50694]
Hawaii House Labor and Public Employment Committee
[50721]
Hawaii Industrial Directory [39125]
Hawaii Island Chamber of Commerce (HICC) [50703]
The Hawaii Island Chamber of Commerce Directory &
Guide [50704]
Hawaii Island Portuguese Chamber of Commerce
[50705]
Hawaii Korean Chamber of Commerce (HKCC) [50706]
Hawaii Senate Consumer Protection Committee [50722]
Hawaii Senate Water and Land Use Planning Committee
[50723]
Hawaii Small Business Development Center - Lead Of-
fice [50689]
"Hawaii's Identity Crisis" in Hawaii Business (Vol. 53,
November 2007, No. 5, pp. 10) [8393], [12439],
[27300], [31508], [44841]
"Hawaii's Top Twenty Financial Advisors" in Hawaii Busi-
ness (Vol. 53, February 2008, No. 8, pp. 32) [8394],
[12440], [31509]
Hawarden Area Partnership for Progress (HAPP) [51906]
Hawiian Tropical Plant Sales [41635]
Hawkins Area Chamber of Commerce [58217]
George Hawkins & Associates [18054]
Hawkinsville-Pulaski County Chamber of Commerce
(HPCCC) [50554]
Hawkinsville-Pulaski Chamber of Commerce [50554]
Hawley - Lake Wallenpaupack Chamber of Commerce
[57206]

Haworth College of Business - Western Michigan
University [53482]
Hawthorne Area Chamber of Commerce [50162]
Hawthorne Chamber of Commerce (HCC) [48642]
The Hawthorne Hotline [48643]
Haxtun Chamber of Commerce [49527]
W. Alfred Hayes and Co. [22066]
Claude Hayes & Associates [25285], [38735]
"Hayes Lemmerz Reports Some Good News Despite
Losses" in Crain's Detroit Business (Vol. 24, April 14,
2008, No. 15, pp. 4) [23042], [37387], [39126]
Max S. Hayes Vocational School Library [1614]
Richard Haynes & Associates L.L.C. [29307], [46086]
Hays Area Chamber of Commerce [52112]
Haystack Mountain School of Crafts Library [6076],
[6171], [15039]
Haysville Chamber of Commerce [52113]
Hayward Area Chamber of Commerce (HACC) [59604]
Hayward's Calendar of Events [59605]
Haywood County Chamber of Commerce [55716]
The Hazard Awareness Training Series [47501]
Hazard Management Safety Series [10175]
Hazardous Materials Advisory Committee [10162]
Hazardous Materials Advisory Council [10162]
Hazardous Waste & Hazardous Materials [10171]
Hazardous Waste [10176]
Hazardous Waste Consultant--Directory of Commercial
Hazardous Waste Management Facilities Issue [10166]
Hazardous Waste Management: The Complete Course
[30455], [33489]
Hazardous Waste Management: The Complete Course
(Onsite) [33490]
Hazelden Foundation - Library and Information
Resources. [46102]
Hazelden Library - Library CO-4 [46102]
Hazelden Voice [46069]
Hazen Chamber of Commerce [55916]
Hazleton Area Image [57116]
Haztrain Inc. [10184]
"HB Diversity Stock Index" in Hispanic Business (March
2008, pp. 10) [12441], [40743]
"HBC Enlists IBM to Help Dress Up Its On-Line Shop-
ping" in Globe & Mail (February 7, 2006, pp. B3)
[11717], [38067], [39960], [43036]
"HBC Sells Credit Card Division" in Globe & Mail
(February 8, 2006, pp. B1) [26240], [41956]
"HBC Sets Friday as Deadline to Trump Zucker Takeover
Bid" in Globe & Mail (January 18, 2006, pp. B1)
[24391], [25109], [41957], [43037]
"HBDiversity Stock Index" in Hispanic Business (July-
August 2007, pp. 58) [12442], [40744]
"HBDiversityStockIndex" in Hispanic Business (January-
February 2008, pp. 10) [12443], [40745]
"HBDiversityStockIndex" in Hispanic Business (October
2009, pp. 1) [8395], [12444], [31510], [40746]
"HBMG Targets Federal Contracts from Under Raythe-
on's Wing" in Austin Business JournalInc. (Vol. 29,
January 15, 2010, No. 45, pp. 1) [33433], [34929]
HCRC [32039]
"He Has a Sky-High Outlook on His Business" in
Charlotte Observer (February 4, 2007) [5360], [29822]
"He Said, She Said: Stay Clear of Gossip In the
Workplace With a Mature Attitude" in Black Enterprise
(February 2008) [29080], [38068]
"Head of the Class" in Entrepreneur (Vol. 37, October
2009, No. 10, pp. 59) [28221], [29823], [44842]
"Head of Horse Farmers and Owners Jockey for Sa-
ratoga Pastures, Breeder Awards" in Business Review,
Albany New York (Nov. 23, 2007) [21601], [23043]
"Head West, Young Startup?" in Boston Business Journal
(Vol. 30, October 22, 2010, No. 39, pp. 1) [3666],
[24710], [34719], [44630]
Headland Chamber of Commerce (HCC) [47699]
Headland Ventures, LP / Sterling Payot Capital [49233]
Headquarters for Ghost Investigations [14813]
Heads in Beds [10694], [20155], [20549], [23044],
[39961], [43487]
Heads Up [34142]
"Headwinds From the New Sod Slow Aer Lingus" in Bar-
ron's (Vol. 88, March 10, 2008, No. 10, pp. M6) [474],
[8396], [11106], [12445], [26241], [27301], [31511],
[36582], [39962], [44373]
Healdsburg Area Business [48644]
Healdsburg Chamber of Commerce and Visitors Bureau
[48645]
Healdsburg Chamber of Commerce [48645]
Healdton Chamber of Commerce [56530]
Health Affairs: The Policy Journal of the Health Sphere
[34525]
"Health Alliance Could Sell Group" in Business Courier
(Vol. 27, June 18, 2010, No. 7, pp. 1) [11355], [34286],
[36152], [44156]
Health and Healing Wisdom; PPNF. [10267], [15227]

"Health Care Braces for Federal Cuts" in Boston Busi-
ness Journal (Vol. 29, August 19, 2011, No. 15, pp. 1)
[11356], [33234], [34287], [36153]
"Health Care Checkup" in Business Courier (Vol. 24,
November 16, 2008, No. 31, pp. 1) [26443], [34288]
Health Care Daily Report™ [34636]
"Health Care of the Future" in Business Journal Serving
Greater Tampa Bay (Vol. 30, November 19, 2010, No.
48, pp. 1) [11357], [33235], [33742], [34289], [36154],
[41958]
"Health-Care Highway" in Saint Louis Business Journal
(Vol. 32, October 14, 2011, No. 7, pp. 1) [5361],
[28701], [34290]
Health Care for the Homeless [34607]
"Health Care Leads Sectors Attracting Capital" in
Hispanic Business (March 2008, pp. 14-16, 18) [2139],
[9935], [12446], [15537], [34291], [37388], [40747],
[47026]
"Health Care Leads Sectors Attracting Capital" in
Hispanic Business (Vol. 30, March 2008, No. 3, pp. 14)
[9936], [12447], [17927], [23045], [34292], [34930],
[40748], [41959], [43038]
Health Care Policy Report [34637]
Health Care Valuation Network Inc. [17589]
Health Care for Women International: Official Journal of
the International Council on Women's Health Issues
[34526]
"Health Centers Plan Expansion" in Crain's Detroit Busi-
ness (Vol. 25, June 15, 2009, No. 24, pp. 3) [5362],
[11358], [23046], [33236], [34293], [36155]
Health Devices® Alerts [10345], [14334]
Health Devices International Sourcebase [10346],
[14243], [14299], [14335]
Health Devices Sourcebook [14199], [14315]
Health Devices® Sourcebook [10346], [14243], [14299],
[14335]
Health, Environment, Fitness, Spirituality Nutrition,
Alternative Medicine [14818]
Health Fitness Dynamics Inc. [10792], [16013]
Health Groups in Washington: A Directory [34294]
Health Industries Association - Medical-Surgical
Manufacturers Association [14182], [14310]
Health Industry Distributors Association (HIDA) [14185],
[15053]
Health Industry Manufacturers Association [14182],
[14310]
Health Industry Manufacturers Association--Directory
[14189]
Health Information Resource Center (HIRC) [10210],
[34143]
"Health Insurance Dilemmas" in Hispanic Business
(January-February 2008, pp. 58) [11359], [36156]
Health Insurance Specialists Inc. (HISI) [22060], [36257]
"Health IT Regulations Generate Static Among Providers"
in Philadelphia Business Journal (Vol. 28, January 29,
2010, No. 50, pp. 1) [4712], [4856], [11360], [33743],
[34295], [36157]
"Health Job Shift Looms" in Boston Business Journal
(Vol. 31, June 3, 2011, No. 19, pp. 3) [33744], [34296],
[35798], [45460]
Health Management Systems Inc. [5083]
Health and Medical Care Archive (HMCA) [10587]
"Health Nuts and Bolts" in Entrepreneur (Vol. 36, April
2008, No. 4, pp. 24) [29081], [34297], [38069],
[45461]
Health Occupations Center - Learning Resource Center
[1446]
Health Progress: Official Journal of the Catholic Health
Association of the United States [34527]
Health Providers Guide [48646]
"Health Providers Throw Lifeline to Clinics" in
Sacramento Business Journal (Vol. 25, July 25, 2008,
No. 21, pp. 1) [26242], [34298], [37389]
Health Reference Center [34638]
"Health Reform Could Expand HSA-Based Plans" in
Workforce Management (Vol. 88, December 14, 2009,
No. 13, pp. 6) [11361], [33745], [34299], [36158]
"Health Reform How-To" in Business Courier (Vol. 26,
December 11, 2009, No. 33, pp. 1) [11362], [33746],
[34300], [36159]
Health Research and Educational Trust (HRET) [34657]
Health Research and Educational Trust of New Jersey
[34658]
Health Resources Publishing [301]
Health Resources and Services Administration - Grants
and Procurement Management Division - Contracts
Policies and Operations [61390]
Health Resources and Services Administration (HRSA) -
Office of Equal Opportunity and Civil Rights [61391];
[61392]
Health and Safety Science Abstracts (HSSA) [47531]
Health and Safety Science Abstracts [34528]
Health Science: Living Well Into the Future [34529]

Healthcare MASTER INDEX

Health Services Directory [6661], [10538], [14276]
Health Statistics Group [10515], [15045]
Health Strategy Group Inc. [2890], [24675], [26021], [26628], [41294], [42553], [42902], [44941]
Health Systems Research Inc. [53498]
Health & Wellness InSite<svs> [325], [15120], [15207], [28482], [34639], [37170]
Healthcare Advertising Review: Creative Forum for the People who Plan and Create Healthcare Advertising Programs [34530]
Healthcare Capital Partners [50654]
Healthcare Convention & Exhibitors Association--AIP Alert [20451]
Healthcare Corporate Finance News [11460], [14228], [34531]
Healthcare Distribution Management Association (HDMA) [6634]
HealthCare Distributor [6680]
Healthcare Executive [34532]
"Healthcare: How To Get a Better Deal" in Inc. (November 2007, pp. 34) [11363], [21913], [34301], [36160]
Healthcare Management FORUM [34144]
Healthcare Purchasing News: Business News and Analysis for Purchasing Decision-Makers [34533]
Healthcare Standards Directory [10537]
Healthcare Ventures LLC / Healthcare Investments [54852]
HealthChoice [22061]
Healthscope Inc. [24676]
"HealthTronics Eager to Buy" in Austin Business JournalInc. (Vol. 28, September 12, 2008, No. 26, pp. 1) [12448], [34302], [34931], [41960]
"Healthy Dose of Vitality" in Business Courier (Vol. 24, February 29, 2008, No. 47, pp. 1) [6658], [23047], [34303]
"Healthy Fast Food Acquires Rights to U-Swirl Yogurt" in Ice Cream Reporter (Vol. 21, October 20, 2008, No. 11, pp. 5) [10225], [10287], [10888], [41961]
Healthy Habits Video Series [10306]
Healthy Living Guide [58218]
Healthy Massage Series [14149]
Healy & Associates Inc. [22062], [46087]
HEAR Center (HEAR) [10333]
Hearing Aid Industry Conference [10334], [14186]
Hearing Aid Journal--World Buyers Guide and Directory Issue [10337]
Hearing Aids in Children and Adults [10343]
"Hearing Damage Leads to Settlement" in Register-Guard (August 13, 2011) [15631], [23879], [34304]
Hearing Education Through Auditory Research Foundation [10333]
Hearing Industries Association (HIA) [10334], [14186]
Hearing Journal--Hearing Health Industry World Directory Issue [10337]
Hearing Journal--Hearing Health World Directory Issue [10337]
The Hearing Professional: Official Journal of the International Hearing Society [10339]
Hearne Chamber of Commerce [58219]
Heart-Beat [50163]
The Heart Beat [49528]
Heart of Catskill Association - Catskill Chamber of Commerce [55246]
"Heart Hospitals Analyzed" in Philadelphia Business Journal (Vol. 30, September 2, 2011, No. 29, pp. 1) [14200], [33237], [34305]
The Heart of the Lake, Greers Ferry, Arkansas [48070]
Heart and Lung: The Journal of Acute and Critical Care [34534]
The Heart of Oklahoma Chamber [56531]
Heart of Oklahoma Chamber of Commerce [56532]
Heart of the Rockies Chamber of Commerce (HRCC) [49529]
"Heart Test No Boom for BG Medical" in Boston Business Journal (Vol. 31, June 17, 2011, No. 21, pp. 1) [12449], [14201], [34306], [39127]
Heart of the Valley Chamber of Commerce [59606]
Heartbeat [55717]
The Heartbeat [54284]; [58220]
Heartland Institute [7409]
Heartland Institute (HI) [34659]
Heartland Procurement Technical Assistance Center - Institute for Entrepreneurship and Innovation [54182]
Heartland Procurement Technical Assistance Center - Missouri Southern State University - Central Office [54183]
Heartlines [9456]
HeartMath L.L.C. [40851]
HeartMath organization [40851]
"Heat Brings Out Flavor, Not Visitors to Wineries" in Saint Louis Business Journal (Vol. 31, August 12, 2011, No. 51, pp. 1) [19226]
"The Heat Is On" in Crain's Chicago Business (Vol. 31, April 28, 2008, No. 17, pp. 4) [8397], [12450], [31512], [41962], [44374]
Heating and Piping and Air Conditioning Contractors National Association [771]
Heating and Piping Contractors National Association [771]
Heating/Piping/Air Conditioning Engineering: The Magazine of Mechanical Systems Engineering (HPAC) [889]
Heating-Plumbing-Air Conditioning Magazine (HPAC) [890], [16286]
Heating, Refrigeration and Air Conditioning Institute of Canada (HRAI) [765]
Heating-Plumbing-Air Conditioning Magazine [890], [16286]
"Heat's On, but Glacier Not Retreating" in Globe & Mail (January 26, 2006, pp. B3) [8398], [12451], [41963]
Heavenly Gold Card [9302]
Heaven's Best Carpet & Upholstery Cleaning [20839]
"A Heavy Burden" in Crain's Cleveland Business (Vol. 30, June 8, 2009, No. 22, pp. 13) [27302], [29824], [31513]
Heavy Duty Distribution [18624]
Heavy Duty Representatives Profile Directory [20679]
"Heavy Duty: The Case Against Packing Lightly" in Crain's Chicago Business (Vol. 31, April 21, 2008, No. 16, pp. 29) [24863], [32742], [36583], [38070], [43488], [46512]
Heavy Duty Trucking: The Fleet Business Authority [20706]
Heavy Duty Trucking--Council of Fleet Specialists Equipment Buyer's Guide & Services Directory [20680]
Heavy Equipment Guide [5596], [17824]
"Heavy Industry" in Business North Carolina (Vol. 28, February 2008, No. 2, pp. 54) [5363], [39128]
Heavy Specialized Carriers Conference - Heavy Specialized Carriers Section - Local Cartage National Conference [20666]
Heber Chamber of Commerce [47918]
Heber - Overgaard Chamber of Commerce [47918]
Heber Springs Area Chamber of Commerce (HSACC) [48071]
Heber Springs Chamber of Commerce [48071]
Heber Valley Chamber of Commerce Member Directory [58654]
Heber Valley Chamber of Commerce and Visitor Center (HVCC) [58655]
Heber Valley Chamber of Commerce [58655]
HEC Montreal - Group for Women, Management and Organizations [47444]
HEC Montreal - Groupe de recherche en systèmes d'information [5069]
HEC Montreal - Groupe Femmes, Gestion et Entreprises [47444]
HEC Montreal - Information Systems Research Group [5069]
"Hedge-Fund Titan Cohen Plans Bid for Dodgers" in Wall Street Journal Eastern Edition (November 25 , 2011, pp. C3) [1516], [12452], [19429], [25321]
Heel Quik! & Heel/Sew Quik! [18746], [19563]
Heidelberg Graphics (HG) [2207], [15023], [15597]
Heights-Hillcrest Regional Chamber of Commerce (HRCC) [56160]
Helena Area Chamber of Commerce (HACC) [54285]
Helena Business [54286]
Helena SCORE [54235]
Helena Small Business Development Center [54217]
HELI-EXPO - Helicopter Association International Annual Meeting and Industry Exposition [740]
Helicopter Association International (HAI) [720]
Helicopter Association of America - California Helicopter Association [720]
Hellenic-American Chamber of Commerce [36296]
Hellgate Press [56902]
"Hello, 9000! The Dow's Run Is Far From Over" in Barron's (Vol. 89, July 27, 2009, No. 30, pp. 20) [8399], [12453], [31514]
"Hello, Old Friends" in Business Courier (Vol. 24, October 12, 2008, No. 26, pp. 1) [21602], [24392], [41085]
"Help Customers Choose Full Service Over Discount" in Indoor Comfort Marketing (Vol. 70, September 2011, No. 9, pp. 10) [819], [26444], [39963], [43489], [44105]
Help Desk Institute (HDI) [26359]
"Help Employees Give Away Some Of That Bonus" in Harvard Business Review (Vol. 86, July-August 2008, No. 8, pp. 1) [21914], [29082], [42476], [45935]
"Help, For Some" in Canadian Business (Vol. 81, December 8, 2008, No. 21, pp. 10) [33238], [38071]
"Help for Job Seekers" in Crain's Detroit Business (Vol. 26, January 18, 2010, No. 3, pp. 14) [11718], [22322], [32743], [35356]
"Help for Job Seekers" in Crain's Detroit Business (Vol. 26, January 4, 2010, No. 1, pp. 14) [15538], [27303], [35355], [39964]
Help-U-Sell Real Estate [17138]
"Help Wanted: 100 Hospitals IT Workers" in Business Courier (Vol. 27, October 8, 2010, No. 23, pp. 1) [4713], [4857], [14343], [33239], [34307]
"'Help Wanted' Meets 'Buy It Now': Why More Companies Are Integrating Marketing and Recruiting" in Inc. (November 2007, pp. 50-52) [475], [35357], [39965], [42477], [42628]
"Help in Wings for Aviation, Defense" in Globe & Mail (March 12, 2007, pp. B1) [33240], [39129]
Help Your Child Succeed in School [3977]
"Helping Customers Fight Pet Waste" in Pet Product News (Vol. 64, November 2010, No. 11, pp. 52) [15723], [23048], [28702], [30668], [39130], [39966], [43490], [45462]
"Helping Small Businesses Create Jobs" in America's Intelligence Wire (August 27, 2010) [33241], [45463], [46257]
"Helping Women Grow Their Businesses One Entrepreneur at a Time" in Hispanic Business (July-August 2007, pp. 56-57) [23049], [40749], [47295]
Helping Your Child Succeed in School [28419]
Hemet San Jacinto Valley Chamber of Commerce [48647]
Hemmings Motor News: World's Largest Collector--Car Marketplace Since 1954 [14980]
Hemmler + Camayd Architects [1309]
Hemophilia Ontario News [34535]
Hempire Sales Ltd. [43298]
Hempstead Chamber of Commerce [55247]
Henderson Area Chamber of Commerce [58221]
Henderson Business Resource Center [54527]
Henderson Chamber of Commerce [54494]
Henderson Chamber of Commerce [52326]
Henderson Chester County Chamber of Commerce [57718]
Henderson County Chamber of Commerce [52326]
Henderson County Chamber of Commerce (HCCC) [57719]
Henderson Highlights [52327]
Henderson Nevada Small Business Development Center [54459]
Henderson-Vance County Chamber of Commerce [55718]
Hendersonville Area Chamber of Commerce [57720]
The Hendersonville Information Guide [55719]
Henrietta - Clay County Chamber of Commerce [58222]
Henry Area Chamber of Commerce [51136]
Pamela K. Henry & Associates [36033]
Henry County Chamber of Commerce [50555]; [52328]
"Henry Ford Health Leases Lab Space at TechTown" in Crain's Detroit Business (Vol. 24, March 31, 2008, No. 13, pp. 5) [5364], [34308], [36093], [43867]
"Henry Mintzberg: Still the Zealous Skeptic and Scold" in Strategy and Leadership (Vol. 39, March-April 2011, No. 2, pp. 4) [28222], [38072], [45464]
Henryetta Chamber of Commerce [56533]
Edward M. Hepner & Associates [2891], [3072], [35543], [36034]
Heppner Chamber of Commerce [56789]
Herb Growing and Marketing Network (HGMN) [10360]
Herb Research Foundation (HRF) [10361]; [10382]
Herb Society of America (HSA) [10362]
Herb Society of America--Membership Directory and By-laws [10365]
Herb Society of America, Inc. [10362]
Herbal Green Pages [10366]
Hercules Chamber of Commerce [48648]
Here Come the Regulars: How to Run a Record Label on a Shoestring Budget [17640], [23880], [28703], [29825], [31515], [47586]
Here is Houston [58223]
"Here are the Stocks of the Decade" in Business Courier (Vol. 26, December 18, 2009, No. 34, pp. 1) [8400], [12454], [31516]
"Here's the Deal" in Crain's Cleveland Business (Vol. 30, June 15, 2009, No. 23, pp. 14) [9660], [10695], [17928], [18557], [20370], [46652]
"Here's How Buffett Spent 2007" in Barron's (Vol. 88, March 10, 2008, No. 10, pp. 48) [8401], [11364], [12455], [29826], [31517], [36161]
Herington Chamber of Commerce [52194]
Heritage Commission Corporation Library [9516]
The Heritage Foundation - Asian Studies Center (ASC) [11213]
Heritage Publishing Inc. [58604]
Heritage Rose Foundation (HRF) [9095]
HeritageQuest - Library [9517]
Herkimer County Community College [55506]
Hermann Area Chamber of Commerce (HACC) [54057]

3528 Small Business Sourcebook • 30th Edition

Hispanic Metropolitan Chamber (HMC) [56792]
"Hispanic Representation in Boardrooms Remains Static"
in Hispanic Business (January-February 2008, pp. 36,
38, 40) [32746], [40759]
"Hispanics Take Seats in America's Boardrooms" in
Hispanic Business (January-February 2009, pp. 24, 28)
[29835], [38080], [40760]
Hispano Chamber of Commerce de Las Cruces [54962]
HispanTelligence® [40840]
"Hispantelligence Report" in Hispanic Business (January-
February 2008, pp. 8) [12464], [23059], [40761]
"Hispantelligence Report" in Hispanic Business (January-
February 2009, pp. 10) [27311], [40764], [43041],
[45466]
"Hispantelligence Report" in Hispanic Business (July-
August 2007, pp. 18) [12465], [14913], [39134]
"Hispantelligence Report" in Hispanic Business (July-
August 2009, pp. 8) [8407], [12467], [31523], [40763]
"Hispantelligence Report" in Hispanic Business (March
2008, pp. 8) [12466], [40762]
Hissong Associates Inc. [26630]
Historic Annapolis Foundation Research Center [9571]
Historic Brochure [57117]
Historic Exterior Paint Colors Consulting [1310], [5645],
[15402]
"Historic Glenview Homes Could Be Torn Down" in
Chicago Tribune (September 25, 2008) [1273],
[17326], [24396]
Historic House Colors [1310], [5645], [15402]
Historic Llano [58227]
Historic Port Isabel [58228]
Historic Silver Valley Chamber of Commerce [50773]
Historic Sonora Chamber of Commerce (HSCC) [48654]
"Historic Tax Credit Plan Gains Support" in Baltimore
Business Journal (Vol. 27, January 8, 2010, No. 36,
pp. 1) [1274], [5367], [33243], [33751], [46262]
Historic Walking Tour [48655]
Historical Estacada Walking Tour [56793]
Historical Walking Tour of Ridgway [57118]
Historically Underutilized Business Program - Texas
Comptroller of Public Accounts [58537]
History of Aviation [745]
History of Canadian Business 1867-1914 [23060],
[32747]
"A History of Neglect" in Canadian Business (Vol. 79,
September 11, 2006, No. 18, pp. 21) [12468], [24800],
[33752]
A History of Small Business in America [21603], [27312],
[32748], [39135], [43492], [44379]
"Hit the Books" in Black Enterprise (Vol. 38, July 2008,
No. 12, pp. 42) [2140], [2377], [8408], [12469],
[31524]
"Hit the Books" in Entrepreneur (Vol. 36, April 2008, No.
4, pp. 74) [25533], [28226]
The HIT Center [16026]
"Hit the Green" in Canadian Business (Vol. 79, August
14, 2006, No. 16-17, pp. 73) [9661], [24397], [25111],
[26244]
"Hits and Misses" in Canadian Business (Vol. 80,
December 25, 2006, No. 1, pp. 69) [8409], [12470]
"Hitting Bottom?" in Barron's (Vol. 88, March 24, 2008,
No. 12, pp. 21) [8410], [12471], [27313], [31525],
[33753]
"Hitting the E-Books" in Inc. (Vol. 33, September 2011,
No. 7, pp. 36) [2141], [8227], [28227], [28706]
"Hitting the Green" in Canadian Business (Vol. 81, July
22, 2008, No. 12-13, pp. 34) [9662], [19327], [19431],
[19934], [39969]
Hive Lights [1949]
HLW International L.L.P. [15261]
HMO and Chains Directory [14253]
HMS [5083]
HMS Hawaii Management Partners [50718]
"Ho, Ho, Ho!" in Retail Merchandiser (Vol. 51,
September-October 2011, No. 5, pp. 10) [27314],
[43042], [43493], [44106]
Ho-Lee-Chow [10318]
Ho Math & Chess Learning Centre [28461]
HO2 Partners [58560]
Hobart Chamber of Commerce [51635]; [56534]
Hobart Horizons [51636]
"Hobbies Hold Fast" in Playthings (Vol. 106, November
1, 2008, No. 1, pp. 6) [6106], [20252], [27315]
Hobbs Chamber of Commerce (HCC) [54963]
Hobby Greenhouse Association (HGA) [9763]
Hobby Industries of America Annual Craft, Model, and
Hobby Show [6041], [6155], [20284]
Hobby Industries of America - Hobby Industry Associa-
tion - Model Industry Association - National Ceramic
Manufacturers Association - National Ceramic Dealers
Association - Ceramic Distributors of America -
Ceramic Arts Federation International - Hobby Industry
Association of America - National Ceramic Teachers
Association [4342], [6095]

Hobby Industry Association [4342], [6095]
Hobby Merchandiser [6136]
Hobby Merchandiser Annual Trade Directory [6107]
Hobbytown USA [6162]
Hobe Sound Chamber of Commerce [50166]
Hobo Guide [51907]
Hoffman Estates Chamber of Commerce (HECC)
[51144]
Hogi Yogi [10964]
Hohenwald-Lewis County Tennessee Chamber of Com-
merce [57722]
Hoisington Chamber of Commerce (HCC) [52116]
Hoisington Koegler Group Inc. (HKGI) [1311]
"HOK Sport May Build Own Practice" in The Business
Journal-Serving Metropolitan Kansas City (Vol. 26,
August 29, 2008, No. 51, pp. 1) [5368], [17327],
[19328], [19432], [24398], [25112]
"Hola and Aloha" in Hawaii Business (Vol. 53, December
2007, No. 6, pp. 131) [20156], [20550], [23061],
[25534], [36585]
Hola Amigos Boxed Set [28420]
Hola Amigos: Spanish for Kids [3978]
Holcomb Design [40616], [42689]
Holcomb Gallagher Adams Advertising Inc. [40616],
[42689]
"Hold the IPhone" in Canadian Business (Vol. 80, Janu-
ary 15, 2007, No. 2, pp. 22) [3735], [12472], [39970],
[41089]
"Hold the McJobs: Canada's High-End Employment
Boom" in Globe & Mail (February 17, 2006, pp. B1)
[27316], [35362]
"Hold Your Nose, Say 'Da'" in Canadian Business (Vol.
79, September 11, 2006, No. 18, pp. 151) [8411],
[12473], [27317]
Holden Arboretum - Warren H. Corning Library [9856]
Holden Area Chamber of Commerce [52904]
Holden Chamber of Commerce [54059]
Holden Chamber of Commerce [52904]
Holdenville Chamber of Commerce (HCC) [56535]
Holding Capital Group, Inc. [55423]
Holdrege Area Chamber of Commerce (HACC) [54397]
"Holiday Bloom: Event Designer Collin Abraham
Heightens Glamour With Florals" in Black Enterprise
(Vol. 41, November 2010, No. 4) [9104], [15429]
"Holiday Cheer" in Business Journal-Serving Phoenix &
the Valley of the Sun (Vol. 31, December 3, 2010, No.
13, pp. 1) [35803], [38081], [45467]
Holiday Fair [4047], [6051], [6157]
"Holiday Parties to Take a Hit in Hard Times" in
Philadelphia Business Journal (Vol. 28, November 6,
2009, No. 38, pp. 1) [15412], [15430], [27318]
"Holiday Sales Look Uncertain for Microsoft and PC Sell-
ers" in Puget Sound Business Journal (Vol. 29,
November 28, 2008, No. 32) [3545], [4957], [18914],
[27319], [43043], [45132]
Holiday Showcase [1474]
"Holidays Should Foster Mutual Respect" in Women In
Business (Vol. 61, October-November 2009, No. 5, pp.
33) [22324], [29086], [32749], [38082]
Holistic Management International [7430]
Holland Area Chamber of Commerce (HACC) [53304]
Holland - Springfield Chamber of Commerce [56163]
"Hollander 95 Project Getting Bigger" in Boston Business
Journal (Vol. 29, September 23, 2011, No. 20, pp. 1)
[5369], [14433], [17328], [23062]
"Hollinger Shares Plummet on Reports" in Globe & Mail
(March 10, 2007, pp. B5) [8412], [12474], [31526]
Hollingsworth & Associates [19710], [32037]
Hollister Chamber of Commerce [48951]
"The Hollow Debate" in Canadian Business (Vol. 81,
March 3, 2008, No. 3, pp. 26) [27320], [33754],
[36586], [41966], [45468]
Holly Area Chamber of Commerce [53305]
Holly Hill Chamber of Commerce [50167]
Holly Springs Chamber of Commerce (HSCC) [53863]
Hollywood Business [48656]
Hollywood Business Resource Book [48657]
Hollywood Business Weekly [48658]
Hollywood Chamber of Commerce [48659]
Hollywood Directors and Their Craft [8010]
Hollywood Film Archive Library [14589], [20902]
Hollywood Representation Directory [19568]
Hollywood SCORE [49911]
Holmes County Chamber of Commerce [56164]
H.H. Holmes Testing Laboratories Inc. [5646]
Holt & Co. [2896], [13841], [26026], [32038], [38740],
[44943]
Holt Capital [2896], [13841], [26026], [32038], [38740],
[44943]
Holton Chamber of Commerce [52117]
Holton/Jackson County Chamber of Commerce [52117]
Holtville Chamber of Commerce [48660]
"Holy Wasabi! Sushi Not Just For Parents Anymore" in
Chicago Tribune (March 13, 2008) [5836], [15431],
[17929], [28228], [45469]

Holyoke Chamber of Commerce [49530]
Home-Alyze [2581]
Home-Based Business for Dummies [26245], [31527],
[32393], [35559], [37390], [39971], [46513]
Home-Based Travel Agent, 5th Edition [20121], [20500],
[35560]
Home-Based Working Moms [35628]
"Home Builder, Four Others, Face Sentencing" in Busi-
ness Courier (Vol. 27, November 26, 2010, No. 30, pp.
1) [5370], [14434], [23883], [30937]
Home Builders Network (HBN) [5647]
Home Business News [56422]
The Home Business Report [35629]
Home Business Review [56794]
Home Business Tax Deductions: Keep What You Earn
[19633], [35602], [46263]
Home Care Assistance [10576]
Home Channel News [10145]
Home Cleaning Centers of America [6574]
Home Decorating Combo [10429], [21300]
"Home Depot Eyes Wholesale Spinoff" in Globe & Mail
(February 13, 2007, pp. B13) [23063], [25113],
[43044], [47174]
Home Entertainment Show [6052], [6158], [9584],
[9619], [46757]
Home Fashion Products Association (HFPA) [2022],
[10385], [11527]
Home Furnishings Executive [10497]
Home Furnishings Independents Association (HFIA)
[10447]
Home Furnishings Retailer [10497]
"The Home Game" in Canadian Business (Vol. 80,
October 8, 2007, No. 20, pp. 68) [8413], [27321],
[45470]
The Home Gardener [13495]
The Home Gardener, Revised Edition [13496]
"Home Grown" in Hawaii Business (Vol. 53, November
2007, No. 5, pp. 51) [13302], [28229], [29836],
[37277], [44766]
Home Health Care Management and Practice [10550],
[34536]
Home Health Care Services Quarterly [1437], [10551],
[34537]
Home Health Line [10552]
Home Health Nursing: Nursing Diagnosis in the Home
Health Setting [10561]
Home Healthcare Agency & Chains Directory [10588]
Home Healthcare Nurse: The Journal for the Home Care
and Hospice Professional [10553]
Home Helpers [10577]
"Home Helps Push Macy's to First-Quarter Profit" in
Home Textiles Today (Vol. 31, May 24, 2011, No. 13,
pp. 2) [10397], [10470], [43045]
"A Home of Her Own" in Hawaii Business (Vol. 53,
October 2007, No. 4, pp. 51) [5371], [8414], [12475],
[16927], [23064], [26246], [27322], [31528], [37391],
[45471]
Home Improvement: Decorating [10430]
Home Improvement: Interior Projects [10431]
The Home Improvement Market [10140]
"Home Improvement Marketers Target Women With New
Products, New Campaigns and Plenty of Pink" in
Marketing to Women (March 2008) [10134], [39972],
[43046], [45472]
Home Improvement Retailing [10146], [10427], [10498]
Home Improvement Videos [10432]
Home Instead Inc. [15118]
Home Instead Senior Care [15118]
Home Lighting & Accessories [6935]
Home Lighting & Accessories--Suppliers Directory Issue
[6930]
Home Media Expo [8013]
Home Media Retailing [20895]
"Home Prices Sag" in Crain's Chicago Business (Vol. 31,
April 28, 2008, No. 17, pp. 3) [5372], [14435], [16928],
[17329], [27323]
The Home Shop Machinist [6016]
"Home Shows Signs of Life at Target" in Home Textiles
Today (Vol. 31, May 24, 2011, No. 13, pp. 1) [4234],
[10398], [10471], [43047]
"Home Sits Out Q1 Surge at JCP" in Home Textiles
Today (Vol. 31, May 24, 2011, No. 13, pp. 1) [10399],
[10472], [43048]
"Home Source Debuts Diesel Home Collection" in Home
Textiles Today (Vol. 31, May 24, 2011, No. 13, pp. 1)
[10400], [10473]
"Home Sprinklers Blocked in Texas, Long Beach,
California" in Contractor (Vol. 56, July 2009, No. 7, pp.
1) [5373], [16528], [33755]
Home Staging for Dummies [11543], [16929], [17330]
The Home Star Group [5648]
"Home Sweet Home" in Canadian Business (Vol. 79,
October 9, 2006, No. 20, pp. 22) [11365], [14436],
[36162]

"Home Sweet Home?" in Canadian Business (Vol. 79, September 11, 2006, No. 18, pp. 17) [8415], [12476], [45473]

Home Ventilating Institute (HVI) [766]

Home Ventilating Institute Division of the Air Movement Control Association [766]

Home Video Hits: Great Ideas for Creating Better Home Videos [3241]

Home Video Studio [8016], [35640]

Home Visits: The Nursing Bag [10562]

"Home: Where the Money Is!" in Small Business Opportunities (May 2008) [10512], [32096]

Home Wine and Beer Trade Association [2446]

"Home Work" in Black Enterprise (Vol. 37, October 2006, No. 3, pp. 78) [18307], [35561], [44767]

"Homebuilders Continue to be Our Nemesis" in Contractor (Vol. 56, July 2009, No. 7, pp. 50) [5374], [8416], [12477], [18689], [31529]

Homecare Administrative HORIZONS [310], [10554], [24811], [34538]

Homecare DIRECTION [311], [10555], [14321]

HomeCare Magazine: For Business Leaders in Home Medical Equipment [10556]

HOMECARExpo [10564]

"Homelessness, Hair Care and 12,000 Bottles of Tequila" in Entrepreneur (Vol. 37, July 2009, No. 7, pp. 5) [23065], [29837]

Homemade [6049]

Homemade Money: How to Select, Start, Manage, Market and Multiply the Profits of a Business at Home [35603]

"Homeownership: Still the American Dream?" in Gallup Management Journal (May 5, 2011) [14437], [16930], [27324]

Homer Chamber of Commerce [47804]

Homerville - Clinch County Chamber of Commerce [50556]

Homes 4Sale By Owner Network [17139], [40659]

"A Home's Identity in Black and White" in Crain's Chicago Business (Vol. 31, April 21, 2008, No. 16, pp. 35) [4480], [11719], [16931], [21118], [26445], [45474]

Homes & Land [15603]

Homes Magazine [17111]

"Homes, Not Bars, Stay Well Tended" in Advertising Age (Vol. 79, January 28, 2008, No. 4, pp. 8) [1848], [13583], [17930], [19227], [27325]

"Homes Stall As Owners Resist Major Price Cuts" in Crain's Chicago Business (Vol. 31, April 21, 2008, No. 16, pp. 38) [16932], [17331], [26247], [37392]

The Hometeam Inspection Services, Inc. [2582]

Hometown Happenings [53660]

Hometown Threads [9629], [18743]

"Hometown Value" in Retail Merchandiser (Vol. 51, July-August 2011, No. 4, pp. 50) [9938], [26446], [31077], [43049]

HomeVestors of America, Inc. [17607]

Homewatch CareGivers [320]

Homewood Area Chamber of Commerce (HACC) [51145]

Homewood Chamber of Commerce (HCC) [47700]

Homewood Magazine [47701]

"Homing In On the Future" in Black Enterprise (Vol. 38, October 2007, No. 3, pp. 61) [4958], [5375], [6931], [16933], [18433], [30671], [34937]

Hominy Chamber of Commerce [56536]

Homosassa Springs Area Chamber of Commerce [50035]

"Honcoop Honored as BIAWC's Builder of the Year" in Bellingham Business Journal (Vol. February 2010, pp. 17) [1275], [5376], [29838]

Hondo Area Chamber of Commerce (HACC) [58229]

Hondo Chamber of Commerce [58229]

Honest-1 Auto Care, Inc. [18647]

"Honest Harry" in Hawaii Business (Vol. 53, November 2007, No. 5, pp. 39) [24864], [27326]

"Honesty Doesn't Pay" in Canadian Business (Vol. 79, Winter 2006, No. 24, pp. 28) [8417], [12478]

Honey Grove Chamber of Commerce (HGCC) [58230]

The Honeybaked Ham Co. and Cafe [10018], [18152], [19283]

Honeywell - Federal Manufacturing and Technologies - Technical Information Center [42913]

Honeywell, Inc. - Air Transport Systems Engineering Library [756]

Hong Kong Trade Development Council (HKTDC) [36297]

"Hong Kong's Boom in IPO" in Barron's (Vol. 89, July 13, 2009, No. 28, pp. M7) [8418], [12479], [31530], [36587], [41967]

Honolulu Japanese Chamber of Commerce (HJCC) [50707]

Honolulu Japanese Junior Chamber of Commerce (HJCC) [50708]

Honolulu Minority Business Enterprise Center [50717]

Honolulu Small Business Development Center [50690]

"Honoring Creativity" in Playthings (Vol. 107, January 1, 2009, No. 1, pp. 28) [20226], [29839], [37028], [47297]

The Honors Learning Center [4018]

Hood River County Chamber of Commerce (HRCCC) [56795]

Hooker & Holcombe Inc. [22063]

The Hoosier Genealogist [9457]

Hoosier Heartland Small Business Development Center (HHSBDC) [51475]

Hooters of America, Inc. [9183], [18153]

Hoover Chamber of Commerce [47702]

Hoover Institution [19783]

Hoover Institution on War, Revolution and Peace [19783]

"Hoover's Mobile, MobileSP Now Available" in Information Today (Vol. 26, February 2009, No. 2, pp. 29) [3736], [11720], [25535], [28707], [41409], [43494]

Hoover's Vision [25114], [29840], [32750], [45475]

Hoover's Vision: Original Thinking for Business Success [25115], [29841]

Hope College - Carl Frost Center for Social Science Research [19540]

Hope-Hempstead County Chamber of Commerce (HHCCC) [48072]

"Hopes Grow for Milk Price Increase From Tesco" in Farmer's Weekly (March 28, 2008, No. 320) [9939], [21604]

Hopewell-Prince George Chamber of Commerce (HPGCC) [58939]

Hopkins County Chamber of Commerce (HCCC) [58231]

"Hopkins' Security, Reputation Face Challenges in Wake of Slaying" in Baltimore Business Journal (Vol. 28, August 6, 2010, No. 13) [10996], [16589], [18434], [28230], [42478], [42629], [42804], [43870]

"Hopkins, UMd Worry Reduced NIH Budget Will Impact Research" in Boston Business Journal (Vol. 29, August 19, 2011, No. 15, pp. 1) [25536], [33244], [34311], [42805], [43871]

Hopkinsville-Christian County Chamber of Commerce [52330]

Hopkinsville Small Business Development Center [52221]

Horicon Chamber of Commerce (HCC) [59608]

The Horizon [49531]

"Horizon Acquires Significant Working Interest in High Impact Prospect in Southeast Texas" in Canadian Corporate News (May 14, 2007) [41332], [41968], [44682]

Horizon Consulting Services [24678]

Horizon Lines [50168]

Horizon Ventures [49236]

Horizons [48661], [50169], [51637]

Horn Blower [59609]

The Horn Book Magazine: About Books for Children and Young Adults [2185]

Horn Lake Chamber of Commerce [53864]

Horn Lake Chamber of Commerce [53902]

Hornberger & Associates (H&A) [2897], [26027], [40617], [41297]

Paul Hornsby & Co. [17592]

Horror Writers Association (HWA) [6791]

Horror Writers of America [6791]

Horse Industry Directory [10617]

Horsemanship Safety Association [10594]

Horsemanship, Vol. 1-3 [10621]

Horseshoe Bend Area Chamber of Commerce (HBACC) [48073]

Horticultural Dealers Association [9766], [13350], [13375]

Horticultural Research Institute (HRI) [9886]

Horticultural Society of New York Library [10375], [13452]

Horticulture: The Art and Science of Smart Gardening [9810], [13411]

HortIdeas [9811]

Horton Chamber of Commerce (HCC) [52118]

Horwath International Association [21465], [46454]

Hosiery Association [13558]

"Hospital Errors Made Public" in Sacramento Business Journal (Vol. 25, August 8, 2008, No. 23, pp. 1) [23066], [34312]

"Hospital Fighting for Its Life; Board of St. Anthony Scrambles to Stem Losses" in Crain's Chicago Business (April 28, 2008) [11366], [33245], [34313], [36163], [41969], [44157]

"Hospital to Get $72M Makeover" in Austin Business JournalInc. (Vol. 29, January 15, 2010, No. 45, pp. 1) [1276], [5377], [34314]

Hospital Home Health [10557]

Hospital, Institution and Educational Food Service Society [15154]

"Hospital Jobs" in Baltimore Business Journal (Vol. 28, June 25, 2010, No. 7, pp. 1) [5378], [34315], [35363], [35804]

"Hospital Moves Toward Self-Rule" in Business Courier (Vol. 24, December 7, 2008, No. 34, pp. 1) [34316], [35364]

Hospital News Canada [34539]

"Hospital Pegged for Lakeway" in Austin Business JournalInc. (Vol. 28, August 8, 2008, No. 21, pp. A1) [5379], [34317]

Hospital Progress [34527]

Hospital Purchasing News [34533]

Hospital Research and Educational Trust - Educational Trust of the American Hospital Association [34657]

"Hospital Revenue Healthier in 2009" in Orlando Business Journal (Vol. 26, February 5, 2010, No. 36, pp. 1) [12480], [23067], [31531], [34318]

"Hospital Tax Could be a Separate Bill" in Business Journal-Milwaukee (Vol. 25, October 26, 2007, No. 4, pp. A1) [34319], [46264]

Hospital Telephone Directory: The Quick Reference Information Center of U.S. Hospitals [14188]

Hospital Topics [34540]

Hospitality Design [10768], [11562], [18027]

Hospitality Financial and Technology Professionals (HFTP) [10648]

Hospitality Law [10769]

Hospitality Sales and Marketing Association International (HSMAI) [10649]

Hospitality Sales and Marketing Association International - Research Library [10831]

"Hospitals Face Big Whammy From State Fees" in Business Courier (Vol. 26, October 2, 2009, No. 23, pp. 1) [25761], [32186], [33436], [34320], [46265]

"Hospitals Feel Pain from Slow Economy" in Business Courier (Vol. 27, September 3, 2010, No. 18, pp. 1) [6310], [26248], [27327], [31532], [34321], [37393]

"Hospitals Mandate Shots" in Business Courier (Vol. 27, November 19, 2010, No. 29, pp. 1) [34322], [35805]

"Hospitals See Major Shift To Outpatient Care" in The Business Journal-Milwaukee (Vol. 25, September 12, 2008, No. 51, pp. A1) [11367], [23068], [34323], [36164], [43872], [45476]

"Hospitals Try to Buy Smarter" in Crain's Detroit Business (Vol. 25, June 1, 2009, No. 22, pp. M025) [14202], [14317], [31533], [34324]

"Host Your Dream Wedding at the Minneapolis Marriott Southwest" in Benzinga.com (June 6, 2011) [2503], [10697]

"Hostess Reveals Grand Prize Winner of 'CupCake Jackpot' Promotion" in Entertainment Close-Up (August 19, 2011) [1763], [25537], [39973]

Hostline [10793], [18055]

"Hot Air" in Canadian Business (Vol. 81, July 22, 2008, No. 12-13, pp. 16) [7236], [7596], [30672], [33756], [39136], [45477], [46266]

"Hot Air: On Global Warming and Carbon Tax" in Canadian Business (Vol. 81, October 13, 2008, No. 17, pp. 12) [7237], [7597], [19512], [30673], [33757], [46267]

"Hot-Button Ordinances May Go Up for Review" in Crain's Detroit Business (Vol. 26, January 18, 2010, No. 3, pp. 1) [27328], [33246], [46878]

Hot Deals [56796]

Hot, Flat and Crowded: Why We Need a Green Revolution - and How It Can Renew America [7238], [7598], [30674]

"Hot For All The Wrong Reasons" in Canadian Business (Vol. 81, March 31, 2008, No. 5, pp. 19) [11107], [12481], [27329], [36588], [44380], [47465]

"Hot Kicks, Cool Price" in Black Enterprise (Vol. 37, December 2006, No. 5, pp. 34) [4235], [7833], [18757], [37197], [41090], [43050]

"Hot Market Opportunity" in Small Business Opportunities (January 2011) [14309], [32097]

Hot Prospects [47919]

Hot Spot [59828]

Hot Springs Area Chamber of Commerce (HSACC) [57583]

Hot Springs, Mineral Waters [2420], [20197]

Hot Under the Collar: Dealing with Angry Customers [26597]

Hotchkiss Chamber of Commerce (HCC) [49532]

Hotchkiss Community Chamber of Commerce [49532]

Hotel and Restaurant Employees and Bartenders International Union [10656]

Hotel Brokers International (HBI) [10650]

Hotel Business [10770]

"Hotel Confidential" in Canadian Business (Vol. 80, Winter 2007, No. 24, pp. 91) [10698], [12482]

Hotel Electronic Distribution Association [10651]

Hotel Electronic Distribution Network Association (HEDNA) [10651]

Hotel Employees and Restaurant Employees International Union and Union of Needletrades, Industrial and Textile Employees [10656]

How To Be Your Own Publisher Update [2186], [6526], [6839], [15016], [15588]

How To Change the World [29860], [45939]

"How To Get a Loan the Web 2.0 Way" in Black Enterprise (Vol. 41, December 2010, No. 5, pp. 23) [28719], [37396], [41370], [45485]

How To Go Into Business in Duncanville [58235]

"How To Live To Be 100; John E. Green Co. Grows Through Diversification" in Crain's Detroit Business (February 18, 2008) [23078], [32758], [42482], [42630]

"How To: Manage Your Cash Better" in Inc. (Volume 32, December 2010, No. 10, pp. 69) [99], [2289], [19634], [21382], [31549], [33759]

"How To Turn Your Efforts Into Results" in Green Industry Pro (Vol. 23, September 2011) [9786], [13395], [13482], [29093], [38097], [44387], [46514]

"How-To Workshops Teach Sewing, Styles" in St. Louis Post-Dispatch (September 14, 2010) [18724], [28720], [31078], [45486]

"How to Turn Employee Conflict Into a Positive, Productive Force" in HR Specialist (Vol. 8, September 2010, No. 9, pp. 6) [29094], [35810], [38098]

"How Two Flourishing Exporters Did It" in Hispanic Business (Vol. 30, July-August 2008, No. 7-8, pp. 46) [11112], [23079], [26456], [36597], [39995], [40766], [42483]

"How a Unique Culture Proposition Became a USP" in Business Strategy Review (Vol. 21, Spring 2010, No. 1, pp. 52) [11370], [36167], [43502]

How to Use Crystal Reports (Onsite) [21335]

How to Use the Internet to Advertise, Promote, and Market Your Business or Web Site: With Little or No Money [485], [11729], [15296], [21124], [28721], [31550], [39996], [42922]

How to Use QuickBooks (Onsite) [21336]

How Walmart is Destroying America (And the World): And What You Can Do About It [32759], [43053]

How We Decide [29861], [38099]

How: Why How We Do Anything Means Everything..in Business [29862], [32760]

"How Will You Ever Replace Yourself?" in Canadian Business (Vol. 83, August 17, 2010, No. 13-14, pp. 77) [24405], [28233], [29863]

How to Win Friends and Influence People [29864], [38100]

How to Win Marketing Wars in the 1990s [40968]

How Women Make Money: Inspirational Stories and Practical Advice from Successful Canadian Entrepreneurs [29865], [47306]

How to Work Most Effectively with Your Boss (Onsite) [22208]

How to Work With Difficult, Demanding, and Inconsiderate People (Onsite) [22209]

How to Write a Business Plan [24406], [32761], [24407], [25543], [42807]

How to Write Effective Policies and Procedures (Onsite) [22572]

How to Write a Great Business Plan for Your Small Business in 60 Minutes or Less [24408], [26250], [31551], [32762], [38101], [39997]

How to Write a Killer Marketing Plan (Onsite) [39587]

"How to Write a Report" in Canadian Business (Vol. 80, November 5, 2007, No. 22, pp. 41) [22598], [32763]

"How Yamana CEO First Struck Gold With Desert Sun" in Globe & Mail (February 27, 2006, pp. B3) [38102], [41975]

How You Can Start, Build, Manage, or Turn Around Any Business [30367]

How You Do..What You Do: Create Service Excellence That Wins Clients For Life [25544], [26457]

How Your Chamber Works For You! [53307]

Howard County Chamber of Commerce [52723]

Howard County Small Business Development Center [52653]

Howard High School of Technology - Media Center [3402]

Howard Johnson [10803], [18154]

Howard Johnson Canada Franchise Systems Limited [10804]

Howard University - School of Business Library [2335]

Howe Chamber of Commerce [58236]

Howell Area Chamber of Commerce [53308]

Howell Chamber of Commerce [54742]

Howick Associates [26631]

"Howl-o-ween" in Decatur Daily (October 25, 2011) [9156], [15760], [45940]

"HP Eats Into Rival Dell Sales as Profits Soar" in Globe & Mail (February 21, 2007, pp. B15) [23080], [25545], [34943], [39142]

HPAC Engineering--Info-Dex [823]

HPN [34533]

HR Administration and the Law (Onsite) [35672]

HR Advice.com [36036]

HR Answers Inc. [36037]

The HR Dept. [36038]

HR Northwest Inc. [36037]

HR People and Strategy (HRPS) [35654], [46478]

"HR Tech on the Go" in Workforce Management (Vol. 88, November 16, 2009, No. 12, pp. 1) [3547], [3739], [5750], [18916], [22333], [34944], [38103], [45134]

HRCC Communicator [56165]

HRD Press [53097]

HRD Press Inc. [53097]

HRD in Small Organizations: Research and Practice [32764], [35811]

HRMagazine: On Human Resource Management [35987]

"HSBC Canada Posts 8.8 Percent Profit Gain in 2006" in Globe & Mail (February 20, 2007, pp. B14) [8434], [12501], [23081]

HSMAI Affordable Meetings Exposition and Conference [20458]

HSMAI - Affordable Meetings West [3477], [10784], [40571], [46758]

HSMM - Communications [3853]

"The HST Hornet's Nest" in Canadian Business (Vol. 83, September 14, 2010, No. 15, pp. 17) [27343], [33760], [46275]

HTI/Space Design International [41599]

Huber Heights Chamber of Commerce [56166]

"Huberman Failing to Keep CTA on Track" in Crain's Chicago Business (Vol. 31, April 21, 2008, No. 16, pp. 22) [24869], [38104], [44388], [47466]

Huddle House [18155]

Huddleston, Bolen LLP Law Library [8961], [13239], [19759]

Hudson and Maynard Area Chamber of Commerce [52835]

Hudson Area Chamber of Commerce [53309]

Hudson Area Chamber of Commerce (HACC) [56167]

Hudson Area Chamber of Commerce and Tourism Bureau [59610]

Hudson Chamber of Commerce [52835]; [54579]

Hudson County Business [54743]

Hudson County Chamber of Commerce [54744]

Hudson County Improvement Authority Library [7410]

Hudson Valley Business Journal [55515]

Hudson Valley Center for Innovation [55485]

Hudson Valley Gateway Chamber of Commerce [55249]

Hudson Venture Partners [55424]

Hudson's Grill of America, Inc. [18156]

Hudsonville Area Chamber of Commerce (HACC) [53310]

Hudsonville Area Chamber of Commerce Profile [53311]

Hueytown Chamber of Commerce [47703]

Hug Your Customers [486], [4114], [4238], [7835], [26458], [31552], [35373], [39998]

Huguenot Society of America Library [9519]

Huguenot Society of South Carolina Library [9520]

HuHot Mongolian Grill [18157]

Huiras & Associates International Training [40943]

Hulbert Financial Digest [13123]

"Human Activity Analysis: a Review" in ACM Computing Surveys (Vol. 43, Fall 2011, No. 3, pp. 16) [4644], [4858], [42808], [43875]

"The Human Approach" in Entrepreneur (Vol. 37, September 2009, No. 9, pp. 30) [26459], [43503]

The Human Bean Drive Thru [9740]

"Human Bone Breakthrough" in Houston Business Journal (Vol. 40, January 8, 2010, No. 35, pp. 1) [34326], [34945], [42809], [43876], [47031]

Human Capital Research Corp. (HCRC) [32039]

"Human Capital: When Change Means Terminating an Employee" in Black Enterprise (Vol. 41, November 2010, No. 4, pp. 40) [23888], [26659], [35812]

"The Human Element" in Canadian Business (Vol. 80, April 23, 2007, No. 9, pp. 78) [12502], [35813]

"The Human Factor" in Canadian Business (Vol. 80, October 8, 2007, No. 20, pp. 22) [27344], [32765], [33761], [45487]

Human Factors in Ergonomics and Manufacturing [35988], [38599], [39501]

Human Factors and Ergonomics Society Bulletin [15252]

Human Mutation [44024]

Human Networks Inc. [36039]

Human Resource Development Press Inc. [53097]

Human Resource Executive's Market Resource [35814]

"Human Resource Management: Challenges for Graduate Education" in Business Horizons (Vol. 51, March-April 2008, No. 2, pp. 151) [28234], [35815], [38105]

Human Resource Planning Society [35654], [46478]

Human Resource Solutions Inc. [40944]

Human Resource Specialties Inc. [13842], [26028], [36040], [38741]

Human Resources for Anyone with Newly Assigned HR Responsibilities (Onsite) [35673]

Human Resources Group Ltd. [26707]

Human Resources and the Law (Onsite) [23686], [35674]

Human Resources Management: Ideas and Trends Newsletter [35989]

Human Resources for Professionals Who've Recently Assumed HR Responsibilities (Onsite) [35676]

Human Resources for Professionals who've Recently Assumed HR Responsibilities (Onsite) [35675]

Human Resources Report [36075], [46947]; [46939]; [59611]

Human Resources Research Organization (HumRRO) [13312], [35655]

Human Resources for Small Business Made Easy [32766], [35816]

"Humana: Take Pay Cut or Get Out" in Business Courier (Vol. 24, February 1, 2008, No. 43, pp. 1) [11371], [34327], [36168]

Humane News [1075]

Humanergy Inc. [53529]

Humanics Ergonomics [41603], [47525]

Humanics ErgoSystems Inc. [41603], [47525]

Humanities Full Text™ [6071]

Humble Area Chamber of Commerce [58273]

Humboldt Chamber of Commerce [57723]

Humboldt County Chamber of Commerce [54495]

Humboldt/Dakota City Chamber of Commerce [51908]

Humdinger Books [59042]

Humphreys County Area Chamber of Commerce [57724]

Humpty's Restaurants International Inc. [18158]

The Hungry Heart [15206]

Hungry Howie's Pizza, Inc. [16154]

Hunt-Scanlon Publishing [49801]

Hunter Arts Publishing [49401]

"Hunter and the Hunted" in Canadian Business (Vol. 81, Summer 2008, No. 9, pp. 12) [11730], [14443], [21125], [22334], [22599], [23889], [29095]

Hunter Museum of American Art Library [1146]

Hunterdon County Chamber of Commerce [54745]

Hunterdon Historical Newsletter [9458]

Hunting Lease Lists [58237]

Huntingburg Chamber of Commerce [51638]

Huntington Beach Chamber of Commerce [48662]

Huntington Center Services [20743]

Huntington City and County Map [51639]

Huntington County Chamber of Commerce (HCCC) [51640]

Huntington Regional Area Chamber of Commerce [59408]

Huntington Regional Chamber of Commerce (HRCC) [59408]

Huntington SCORE [59383]

Huntington Township Chamber of Commerce [55250]

"Huntington's Future At a Crossroads" in Crain's Cleveland Business (Vol. 30, June 22, 2009, No. 24, pp. 1) [12503], [23082], [31553]

Huntley Area Chamber of Commerce and Industry [51146]

Huntsville Chamber of Commerce [48074]

Huron Chamber of Commerce (HCC) [56168]

Huron Shores Chamber of Commerce [53312]

Huron Township Business Directory [53313]

Huron Township Chamber of Commerce (HTC of C) [53314]

Huron Valley Area Chamber of Commerce [53315]

Huron Valley Chamber of Commerce (HVCC) [53315]

Hurricane Valley Chamber of Commerce [58656]

Hurst - Euless - Bedford Chamber of Commerce (HEBCC) [58238]

"Husky Proceeds on Heavy-Oil Expansion" in Globe & Mail (March 21, 2006, pp. B1) [23083], [24409], [25117], [39143]

Hutchinson Area Chamber of Commerce, Convention and Visitors Bureau [53661]

Hutchinson/Reno County Chamber of Commerce [52119]

Hutchison Forestry Inc. [4057]

Hutto Chamber of Commerce [58239]

Huxford Genealogical Society, Inc. - Huxford Library [9521]

HVAC Controls & Air Distribution (Onsite) [24980], [28040]

HVAC Controls and Air Distribution (Onsite) [2610]

"HVAC/R Evolution" in Indoor Comfort Marketing (Vol. 70, March 2011, No. 3, pp. 14) [824], [45488]

"Hy-Vee Plans Expansion, Convenience Store in Cedar Rapids" in Gazette (November 26, 2010) [5804], [18601], [43054]

Hyannis Area Chamber of Commerce (HACC) [52905]

"Hyannis Mercedes Franchise Sold" in Cape Cod Times (December 2, 2010) [14915], [32187]

"Hybrid Popularity Pushes Automakers to Add to Offerings" in Crain's Cleveland Business (Vol. 28, November 12, 2007, No. 45, pp. 30) [30678], [39144], [39999], [41097]

Hyde Park Chamber of Commerce [55251]
"Hyde Park Hungry for Expansion at Cap" in Business
First-Columbus (October 12, 2007, pp. A1) [3286],
[17932], [23084], [24741], [43055]
"Hydronicahh - Everything in Modulation" in Contractor
(Vol. 56, December 2009, No. 12, pp. 24) [5383],
[7602], [19102], [30679], [38106]
HyettPalma Inc. [27914]
Beverly Hyman Ph.D. & Associates (BHA) [22531]
"Hype: If You Build It.." in Entrepreneur (Vol. 35, October
2007, No. 10, pp. 138) [32406], [39542]
HYPER-EGG [21777]
The Hysen Group [18056]
"Hyundai Enters Minivan Market" in Globe & Mail
(February 15, 2006, pp. B7) [14916], [39145], [40000]
"Hyundai's Hitting Its Stride" in Barron's (Vol. 89, July 20,
2009, No. 29, pp. M7) [14917], [23085], [39146],
[43504]

I

"I-5 Bridge Funding Unclear" in The Business Journal-
Portland (Vol. 25, July 11, 2008, No. 18, pp. 1)
[24870], [27345], [33762], [47032]
I-94 West Chamber of Commerce [53662]
I Can Do It! Ed Lewis [30368]
I Can Do It! Judi Wineland [20617]
I Can Do It! Stew Leonard [44909]
"I Can Make Your Brain Look Like Mine" in Harvard Busi-
ness Review (Vol. 88, December 2010, No. 12, pp. 32)
[22335], [22600]
I Can't Believe I Get Paid to Do This [29866], [38107]
"I Fought the Law: a Brewery Comes Out on Top" in Inc.
(Vol. 33, November 2011, No. 9, pp. 28) [2458],
[29867]
I-Hatch Ventures, LLC [55425]
"I Have A Business Idea. What Now?" in Women
Entrepreneur (October 15, 2008) [29374], [44768],
[47190]
"I Hear You're Interested In a.." in Inc. (January 2008,
pp. 40-43) [13996], [28722], [40001], [43505]
"I Love L.A." in Canadian Business (Vol. 81, December
8, 2008, No. 21, pp. S22) [1849]
I Love People. . .It's Customers I Can't Stand [26600]
I Love You More Than My Dog [26460], [40002],
[42631]
i9 Sports [19494]
I-15 Diamond Gateway Chamber of Commerce and Ran-
cho Bernardo Chamber of Commerce [48961]
I-93 White Mountain Gateway Chamber of Commerce
[54624]
IAA National & World News [652]
IACCE News [51147]
IAEI News [6910]
IAEM Membership Directory and Buyer's Guide [20374]
IAHI, the Owners' Association [10652]
IAL Auction Newsletter | Auctionier [1535]
"Ian Delaney" in Canadian Business (Vol. 81, Summer
2008, No. 9, pp. 168) [29868], [32767], [38108],
[39147], [43877], [46515]
"Ian Gordon" in Canadian Business (Vol. 81, Summer
2008, No. 9, pp. 10) [8435], [12504], [24410], [31554],
[36598]
IAPMO [767], [19543]
"IAPMO GTC Debates Supplement" in Contractor (Vol.
56, September 2009, No. 9, pp. 3) [7242], [16243],
[18691], [30680]
"IAPMO GTC Finalizes Green Supplement" in Contractor
(Vol. 57, January 2010, No. 1, pp. 1) [7243], [7603],
[16244], [18692], [30681]
"IAPMO GTC Votes to Limit Showers to 2.0-GPM" in
Contractor (Vol. 56, September 2009, No. 9, pp. 1)
[5384], [7244], [16245], [18693], [30682]
IAPMO Research and Testing Inc. [767], [19543]
"IAPMO Seeks Group Participants" in Contractor (Vol.
56, September 2009, No. 9, pp. 37) [825], [18694]
IBA News [1221]
IBAC Update [721], [24816]
IBC Between the Lines [11281]
"IBC Reverses Member Slide" in Philadelphia Business
Journal (Vol. 30, September 23, 2011, No. 32, pp. 1)
[11372], [34328], [36169]
Iberville Chamber of Commerce [52473]
IBIS/Business Information Services International [49402]
IBM Canada, Ltd. - Research Information Centre [41528]
IBM Corporation - Burlington Technical Library [4828],
[4913], [19056]
IBM Corporation - Library/Information Resource Center
[4914], [19057]
IBM on Demand Technology for the Growing Business:
How to Optimize Your Computing Environment for
Today and Tomorrow [4962], [34946], [41410], [45489]
IBM Journal of Research and Development [44025]

IBMI Business Books [49403]
"IBM's Best-Kept Secret" in Canadian Business (Vol. 79,
September 25, 2006, No. 19, pp. 19) [23086], [34947],
[38109]
ICAAE. [9034]
ICAO Journal [722]
I-CAR [18582]
"ICC Works on Prescriptive Green Construction Code" in
Contractor (Vol. 56, October 2009, No. 10, pp. 1)
[5385], [16529], [17338], [30683], [45490]
"An Ice Boost in Revenue; Wings Score With Expanded
Corporate Sales" in Crain's Detroit Business (Vol. 25,
June 1, 2009, No. 22) [487], [19329], [19433],
[23087], [40003], [43506]
Ice Cream and Economics: Ben and Jerry's Homemade
[10940]
Ice Fishing Secrets I [1715]
Ice Skating Institute (ISI) [18806]
Ice Skating Institute of America [18806]
Iceberg Ventures [52393]
ICG Magazine [8006], [15852]
iChange [38670]
"iControl Networks Powers Comcast's XFINITY (Reg)
Home Security Service" in Benzinga.com (June 9,
2011) [3179], [3548], [3740], [11731], [18437],
[18917], [45135]
ICOP, Business Management Consultant [38742]
ICOP Investigations [38742]
ICPA Reporter [46070]
ICS Cleaning Specialist: Information for Today's Floor
Care Professional [9073], [20828]
ICTs and SMEs Antecedents and Consequences of
Technology Adoption [32768], [34948]
iD Ventures America, LLC [49237]
Idabel Chamber of Commerce and Agriculture (ICC)
[56537]
Idabel Chamber of Commerce [56537]
The Idaho Business Review [50827]
Idaho Department of Commerce [50826]
Idaho Department of Commerce - Department of
Economic Development [50732]
Idaho Golf [9676], [19351]
Idaho Innovation Center, Inc. [50816]
Idaho Procurement Technical Assistance Center - Idaho
Department of Commerce [50811]
Idaho Small Business Development Center - Lead Office
[50730]
Idaho Sportsmen's Show [17680], [17680]
Idaho State University - College of Technology [50823]
Idaho State University - Idaho Museum of Natural History
- Stirton-Kelson Library [10376]
Idanta Partners, Ltd. (San Diego) [49238]
IDDBA Legis-Letter [1780], [9170], [10937]
The Idea Book [39562]
"Idea-Generation Program Creates Winning Programs" in
Business Journal-Serving Metropolitan Kansas City
(October 19, 2007) [37034], [39148], [41098]
IDEA Health and Fitness Association [15946]
"Idea Nation" in Canadian Business (Vol. 80, December
25, 2006, No. 1, pp. 57) [27346], [39149]
IDEA Personal Trainer [15985], [15985]
"The Idea That Saved My Company" in Inc. (October
2007, pp. 42) [10709], [38110]
IDEA: The Association for Fitness Professionals - IDEA,
The Health and Fitness Source [15946]
Ideal Image [5914]
Idealab! [49239]
IDEAlliance - International Digital Enterprise Alliance
[16340], [21031]
Ideas To Go Inc. [663]
"Ideas at Work: Sparkling Innovation" in Business
Strategy Review (Vol. 21, Summer 2010, No. 2, pp. 07)
[13997], [36600], [37036], [40005]
"Ideas at Work: Sparkling Innovation" in Business
Strategy Review (Vol. 21, Summer 2010, No. 2, pp. 7)
[36599], [37035], [40004]
"Ideas at Work: The Reality of Costs" in Business
Strategy Review (Vol. 21, Summer 2010, No. 2, pp. 40)
[23088], [24411], [24871], [31555]
"Ideas at Work: Total Communicator" in Business
Strategy Review (Vol. 21, Autumn 2010, No. 3, pp. 10)
[2142], [15540], [22336], [27347], [36601], [38111];
[3741], [15541], [22337], [27348], [36602], [38112]
Ident-A-Kid [44612]
"Identify and Conquer" in Black Enterprise (Vol. 38,
December 2007, No. 5, pp. 76) [2043], [5891],
[23089], [47176], [47587]
"Identity Crisis: The Battle For Your Data" in Canadian
Business (Vol. 81, March 17, 2008, No. 4, pp. 12)
[4859], [8436], [12505], [18438], [24801], [31556]
"Identity Thieves Hit a New Low" in Information Today
(Vol. 26, February 2009, No. 2, pp. 1) [18439],
[23890], [30941]

IDG Ventures (San Francisco) [49240]
iDial Networks Inc. [41493], [41601]
Idyllwild Chamber of Commerce [48663]
I.E. Canada [26846]
I.E. Global [26847]
IE News: Ergonomics [15253]
IEC Quarterly--Directory [6879]
IEEE Computational Science and Engineering [44011]
IEEE Information Center [6921]
IEG Venture Management, Inc. [51405]
"IF Challenges Atlanta's Vending Monopoly" in Benzinga.
com (July 28, 2011) [13324], [20863], [23891]
If Harry Potter Ran General Electric [29869], [38113]
"If Just One Person Applies, Are You Required to Hire
Him?" in HR Specialist (Vol. 8, September 2010, No. 9,
pp. 7) [23892], [33763], [35374], [35817]
"If the Opportunity is There, Move Boldly" in Indoor
Comfort Marketing (Vol. 70, March 2011, No. 3, pp.)
[826], [40006], [43507]
"If You Go Into the Market Today.." in Canadian Business
(Vol. 82, Summer 2009, No. 8, pp. 18) [8437], [12506],
[26251], [27349], [31557], [37397]
If You Have to Cry, Go Outside: And Other Things Your
Mother Never Told You [4115], [10997], [16590],
[22338], [25546], [42484], [42632], [47307]
"IFA-AAG Professional Athlete Franchise Summit Scores"
in Franchising World (Vol. 42, August 2010, No. 8, pp.
56) [20375], [32188], [46656]
IFAC News [175]
IFMA Membership Services Directory [2599]
IFMA News [2600]
IFPA Film and Video Communicators [7888]
iFranchise Group [3021], [24122], [32316]
"IFRS Monopoly: the Pied Piper of Financial Reporting"
in Accounting and Business Research (Vol. 41, Sum-
mer 2011, No. 3, pp. 291) [100], [2290], [19635],
[21383], [23893], [27350], [33764], [36603]
IGA Grocergram [10002]
IGM CorporateWatch [8944], [13209]
The Ignite Group / Ignite Associates, LLC [49241]
IH/M & RS - International Hotel/Motel & Restaurant
Show [10785], [18039]
IHG Owners Association [10652]
iHobby Expo [6159]
IHOP [18119]
IHOP Corp. [18119]
I.H.R. Solutions [2898], [3073], [13843], [26029],
[35244], [36041], [38743]
IHS Adana [19551]
IIMI Information Center [14071]
IIT Research Institute (IITRI) [41310]
ILAMO. [20949]
Ilium Associates Inc. [14047], [40618]
"I'll Be Back: For Entrepreneurs, Retirement Doesn't
Mean Forever" in Inc. (February 2008, pp. 35-36)
[29870], [38114]
"An Ill Wind: Icelandic Bank Failures Chill Atlantic
Canada" in Canadian Business (Vol. 81, November 10,
2008, No. 19, pp. 10) [8438], [8981], [9018], [12507],
[20551], [21608], [27351], [36604], [43056], [45491]
"Ill Winds; Cuba's Economy" in The Economist (Vol. 390,
January 3, 2009, No. 8612, pp. 20) [11113], [12508],
[20158], [20552], [21609], [24412], [27352], [36605]
Illinois Agricultural Association - Illinois Farm Bureau
Information Research Center [21800]
Illinois Association of Chamber of Commerce Executives
(IACCE) [51148]
"Illinois Bets On Recycling Program" in Chicago Tribune
(November 29, 2008) [23090], [30684], [33249],
[35375], [45492]
Illinois CPA Society - Business Research Library. [275],
[19760]
Illinois CPA Society - Information & Research Center
[275], [19760]
Illinois Department of Commerce and Community Affairs
- Entrepreneurship and Small Business Office [50865]
Illinois Department of Commerce and Economic Op-
portunity - Energy and Recycling [50866]
Illinois Early Childhood Intervention Clearinghouse
Library [4037]
"Illinois Farmland Tops $11,000 Per Acre" in Farm
Industry News (June 27, 2011) [16940], [17339],
[21610], [23091]
Illinois Institute of Art/Schaumburg - Learning Resource
Center [4175], [4311], [11592]
Illinois Issues [42401]
Illinois Procurement Technical Assistance Center - Black
Hawk Community College [51427]
Illinois Procurement Technical Assistance Center - Col-
lege of DuPage [51428]
Illinois Procurement Technical Assistance Center - Col-
lege of Lake County [51429]
Illinois Procurement Technical Assistance Center - Illinois
Central College [51430]

Illuminated MASTER INDEX

Illinois Procurement Technical Assistance Center - Illinois Hispanic Chamber of Commerce **[51431]**
Illinois Procurement Technical Assistance Center - John A. Logan Community College - Center for Business & Industry **[51432]**
Illinois Procurement Technical Assistance Center - North Business & Industrial Council (NORBIC) **[51433]**
Illinois Procurement Technical Assistance Center - Rock Valley College **[51434]**
Illinois Procurement Technical Assistance Center - South Suburban College **[51435]**
Illinois Procurement Technical Assistance Center - U.S. General Services Administration (GSA) - Great Lakes (Region 5) **[51436]**
Illinois Procurement Technical Assistance Center - University Entrepreneurship Center **[51437]**
Illinois Procurement Technical Assistance Center at Western Illinois - Quincy Business & Technology Center **[51438]**
Illinois Procurement Technical Assistance Center - Women's Business Development Center **[51439]**
Illinois Quad City Chamber of Commerce **[51149]**
"Illinois Regulators Revoke Collection Agency's License" in Collections & Credit Risk (Vol. 15, August 1, 2010, No. 7, pp. 13) **[6311]**, **[23894]**, **[26252]**, **[33765]**, **[37037]**
"Illinois Residential Building Legislation Includes New HVAC Requirements" in Contractor (Vol. 56, July 2009, No. 7, pp. 3) **[827]**, **[5386]**, **[30685]**, **[33766]**
Illinois Small Business Development Center at Black Hawk College **[50830]**
Illinois Small Business Development Center at Bradley University **[50831]**
Illinois Small Business Development Center at Chicago Community Ventures **[50832]**
Illinois Small Business Development Center at Chicago State University/Greater Southside **[50833]**
Illinois Small Business Development Center at College of DuPage **[50834]**
Illinois Small Business Development Center at College of Lake County **[50835]**
Illinois Small Business Development Center at Danville Area Community College **[50836]**
Illinois Small Business Development Center at Duman Microenterprise Center **[50837]**
Illinois Small Business Development Center at Elgin Community College **[50838]**
Illinois Small Business Development Center at Evanston Technology Innovation Center **[50839]**
Illinois Small Business Development Center at Greater Northwest Chicago Development Corporation **[50840]**
Illinois Small Business Development Center at Harper College **[50841]**
Illinois Small Business Development Center at Highland Community College **[50842]**
Illinois Small Business Development Center at Hull House **[50843]**
Illinois Small Business Development Center at Illinois Eastern Community College **[50844]**
Illinois Small Business Development Center at Illinois State University **[50845]**; **[50846]**
Illinois Small Business Development Center at Illinois Valley Community College **[50847]**
Illinois Small Business Development Center at Industrial Council of Nearwest Chicago **[50848]**
Illinois Small Business Development Center at Joliet Jr. College **[50849]**
Illinois Small Business Development Center at Joseph Center **[50850]**
Illinois Small Business Development Center at Kankakee Community College **[50851]**
Illinois Small Business Development Center at Kaskaskia College **[50852]**
Illinois Small Business Development Center at Lincoln Land Community College **[50853]**
Illinois Small Business Development Center at McHenry County College **[50854]**
Illinois Small Business Development Center at North Business and Industrial Council **[50855]**
Illinois Small Business Development Center at Rend Lake College **[50856]**
Illinois Small Business Development Center at Rock Valley College **[50857]**
Illinois Small Business Development Center at Sauk Valley Community College **[50858]**
Illinois Small Business Development Center at Shawnee Community College **[50859]**
Illinois Small Business Development Center at SIU-E/ East St. Louis **[50860]**
Illinois Small Business Development Center at Southeastern Illinois College **[50861]**
Illinois Small Business Development Center at Southern Illinois University (Edwardsville, Illinois) **[50862]**
Illinois Small Business Development Center at Waubonsee Community College **[50863]**
Illinois Small Business Development Center at Western Illinois University **[50864]**
Illinois State Board of Education - Data Analysis and Progress Reporting Division **[28486]**
Illinois State Chamber of Commerce (ISCC) **[51150]**
Illinois Valley Area Chamber of Commerce and Economic Development (IVAC) **[51151]**
Illuminated Concepts Inc. **[41604]**
I'm on LinkedIn - Now What? (Second Edition): A Guide to Getting the Most Out of LinkedIn **[11732]**, **[21126]**, **[22339]**, **[28723]**, **[41976]**
Image **[51641]**; **[58240]**
Image Booklet **[56169]**
"Image Conscious" in Canadian Business (Vol. 81, March 17, 2008, No. 4, pp. 36) **[3549]**, **[4715]**, **[4860]**, **[11733]**, **[18918]**, **[21127]**, **[34949]**, **[45136]**
Image Sun Tanning Centers **[19577]**
ImageFirst Healthcare Laundry Specialists **[6760]**
Images **[39563]**; **[52474]**; **[53865]**; **[57119]**
Images 4 Kids **[15921]**
Images of Albuquerque **[54964]**
Images of Asheboro/Randolph **[55725]**
IMAGES of Birmingham Bloomfield **[53316]**
Images of Champaign County **[51152]**
Images of Clermont County **[56170]**
Images of Danville and Pittsylvania County **[58940]**
Images Directory **[50557]**
Images of Fairfield County **[56171]**
Images of the Franklin Area **[55726]**
Images of Greater West Chester **[57120]**
Images of the Greater Wichita Area **[52120]**
Images of Greenville Pitt County, NC **[55727]**
Images of Henderson-Henderson County **[52331]**
Images of Jackson County **[55728]**
Images of Jacksonville-Onslow **[55729]**
Images Magazine **[57121]**
Images of Richmond County **[55730]**
Images of Sikeston **[54061]**
Images of Stanley County **[55731]**
Images of Tuscarawas County **[56172]**
Images of Wilkes **[55732]**
Imagine Canada - John Hodgson Library **[9310]**
Imagineria **[3979]**
Imaging News: Guide **[16418]**, **[20809]**
Imaging News Online [16418], [20809]
Imaging World [6529]
Imagining India: The Idea of a Renewed Nation **[34950]**, **[36606]**
Imaginit **[3980]**
"Imax Becomes Toast of Movie Industry" in Globe & Mail (January 10, 2006, pp. B2) **[7931]**, **[23092]**, **[45493]**
"Imax in Play as It Explores Options" in Globe & Mail (March 10, 2006, pp. B3) **[7932]**, **[41977]**, **[44160]**
IMC **[41496]**, **[41605]**
IMC Consulting & Training **[664]**, **[2899]**, **[3074]**, **[13844]**, **[26030]**, **[38744]**, **[40619]**
IMCR Dispute Resolution Center [14161]
IMLS Annual Report [1351]
Immedia Technologies **[7378]**
Immigrant, Inc.: Why Immigrant Entrepreneurs Are Driving the New Economy **[27353]**, **[29871]**, **[40767]**
"Immigrants Trapped in Forex Mess" in Boston Business Journal (Vol. 27, October 5, 2007, No. 36, pp. 1) **[12509]**, **[23895]**
Immigration Digest **[9459]**
"Immigration Issues Frustrate Owners From Overseas" in The Business Journal-Serving Greater Tampa Bay (Vol. 28, August 15, 2008) **[8439]**, **[11114]**, **[12510]**, **[23896]**, **[24872]**, **[31558]**, **[33767]**, **[36607]**, **[45494]**
Immokalee Chamber of Commerce **[50170]**
"iMozi Integrates Esprida LiveControl for Advanced DVD Kiosk Hardware" in Wireless News (December 20, 2010) **[4800]**, **[4861]**, **[13325]**, **[20888]**, **[26461]**, **[36608]**, **[41978]**, **[45137]**
IMPACT **[49717]**
Impact **[4633]**, **[4835]**, **[5031]**; **[52121]**; **[52603]**; **[53317]**; **[54398]**; **[54594]**; **[55733]**; **[57122]**; **[58241]**; **[6681]**
"The Impact of Acquisitions On the Productivity of Inventors at Semiconductor Firms" in Academy of Management Journal (October 2007) **[12511]**, **[34951]**, **[37038]**, **[37243]**, **[41979]**
"The Impact of Brand Quality on Shareholder Wealth" in Journal of Marketing (Vol. 75, September 2011, No. 5, pp. 88) **[8440]**, **[12512]**, **[40007]**
The Impact of Environmental Regulations on Business Transactions **[30881]**
"Impact of Family Relationships On Attitudes of the Second Generation In Family Business" in Family Business Review (September 2006) **[31079]**
The Impact Group L.L.C. **[38745]**
"The Impact of Immigrant Entrepreneurs" in Business Week (February 7, 2007) **[27354]**, **[29872]**, **[40768]**
"The Impact of Incomplete Typeface Logos on Perceptions of the Firms" in Journal of Marketing (Vol. 75, July 2011, No. 4, pp. 86) **[40008]**, **[42633]**
Impact Training Associates Inc. **[26632]**
Impact Venture Partners **[55426]**
Imperial Beach Chamber of Commerce and Visitor's Bureau (IBCC) **[48664]**
Imperial Chamber of Commerce **[54399]**
Imperial Chamber of Commerce (ICC) **[48665]**
Imperial Tobacco Ltd. - Corporate Information Center **[20110]**
Imperial Valley Small Business Development Center at Imperial Valley College **[48151]**
"Implementing Statically Typed Object-Oriented Programming Languages" in ACM Computing Surveys (Vol. 43, Fall 2011, No. 3, pp. 18) **[4645]**, **[4862]**
Import Automotive Parts & Accessories **[1577]**
Import/Export Directory **[57123]**
Import/Export for Dummies **[11115]**, **[23093]**, **[36609]**, **[45495]**
Import/Export Guide **[57124]**
Import/Export Procedures and Documentation (Onsite) **[11028]**
ImportCar: The Complete Import Service Magazine **[1578]**, **[1592]**, **[11205]**
Importers Manual USA: The Single Source Reference Encyclopedia for Importing to the United States **[11116]**, **[36894]**
"Importers Share Safety Liability" in Feedstuffs (Vol. 80, January 21, 2008, No. 3, pp. 19) **[11117]**, **[15761]**, **[18440]**, **[20253]**, **[21611]**, **[33768]**, **[36610]**, **[39150]**, **[41676]**
"Imports Frothing Up Beer Market" in Globe & Mail (February 16, 2006, pp. B4) **[1850]**, **[8441]**, **[12513]**, **[13584]**, **[39151]**
Impressionism and Its Sources **[4559]**
"Impressive Numbers: Companies Experience Substantial Increases in Dollars, Employment" in Hispanic Business (July-August 2007) **[3742]**, **[6963]**, **[7786]**, **[11373]**, **[11734]**, **[14918]**, **[16485]**, **[20029]**, **[23094]**, **[34329]**, **[34952]**, **[36170]**, **[40769]**
The Imprinted Sportswear Show, Atlantic City **[18364]**, **[46759]**
The Imprinted Sportswear Show, Long Beach **[19377]**
The Imprinted Sportswear Show, Orlando **[19378]**
Improve Your Analytical Skills: Making Information Work for You (Onsite) **[24981]**
Improving Editing Skills (Onsite) **[28041]**
Improving Performance of Remote and Virtual Workers (Onsite) **[37650]**
"Improving the USPS" in American Printer (Vol. 128, July 1, 2011, No. 7) **[4482]**, **[16374]**, **[20774]**
Improving Your Communication Skills for Success (Onsite) **[22210]**
Improving Your Managerial Effectiveness (Course on Request) (Canada) **[37651]**
Improving Your Project Management Skills: The Basics for Success (Onsite) **[37652]**
Improving Your Project Management Skills: The Basics for Success (Onsite) (Canada) **[37653]**
"Impulse Buys Find Their Way Into Grocery Cart" in Marketing to Women (Vol. 23, November 2010, No. 11, pp. 6) **[9940]**, **[40009]**
"IMRA's Ultrafast Lasers Bring Precision, profits; Ann Arbor Company Eyes Expansion" in Crain's Detroit Business (March 10, 2008) **[5387]**, **[17340]**, **[23095]**, **[34330]**, **[35376]**, **[39152]**, **[41099]**, **[43878]**
IMS Ayer Directory of Publications [4065], [15533]
IMS Directory of Publications [4065], [15533]
IM=X Pilates Studio **[16027]**
"In Addition, Pinkberry Reports It Is Opening a New Shop in Sunnyvale, CA" in Ice Cream Reporter (Vol. 23, October 20, 2010) **[10890]**, **[23096]**, **[44684]**
"In the Bag?" in Canadian Business (Vol. 81, March 3, 2008, No. 3, pp. 57) **[8442]**, **[12514]**, **[27355]**, **[31559]**, **[34953]**, **[36611]**, **[39153]**
In Brief. . . **[14229]**
In Business for Business **[55252]**
"In China, Railways to Riches" in Barron's (Vol. 88, July 7, 2008, No. 27, pp. M9) **[8443]**, **[11118]**, **[12515]**, **[24873]**, **[31560]**, **[36612]**, **[47033]**
In the Company of Women: Canadian Women Talk About What It Takes to Start and Manage a Successful Business **[29873]**, **[47308]**
"In Control: Tips For Navigating a Buyer's Market" in Black Enterprise (Vol. 38, December 2007, No. 5, pp. 64) **[14444]**, **[16941]**, **[17341]**
"The 'In-Crowd' Online: Professionals Take Networking To New Levels" in Black Enterprise (Vol. 38, January 2008, No. 6, pp. 47) **[22340]**, **[32769]**
In the Driver's Seat **[13543]**, **[19818]**, **[20707]**
"In Everyone's Interests" in Canadian Business (Vol. 80, April 23, 2007, No. 9, pp. 62) **[32770]**, **[46881]**

3536 Small Business Sourcebook • 30th Edition

The Indicator [48667]

"Indigenous Tourism Operators" in International Journal of Entrepreneurship and Small Business (Vol. 10, July 6, 2010, No. 4) [20159], [20553], [27362], [36616], [45498]

Indigo Joe's Sports Pub & Restaurant [18159]

Indigos Fruit Smoothies [10319], [13339]

Indio [48668]

Indio Chamber of Commerce [48669]

The Indispensable Assistant (Onsite) [46490]

Individual Map [48670]

"Indoor Air Quality - a Tribute to Efficiency" in Indoor Comfort Marketing (Vol. 70, August 2011, No. 8, pp. 8) [829], [7246], [7604], [30687], [40013], [45499]

Indoor Tennis Association [15949], [20052]

"Indulgent Parsimony: an Enduring Marketing Approach" in Strategy and Leadership (Vol. 39, March-April 2011, No. 2, pp. 36) [27363], [40014], [43508]

Industrial and Business Directory [51644]

Industrial Computer Control [4773]

Industrial Development Brochure [50558]

Industrial Directory [51153]; [51645]; [51646]; [51647]; [51648]; [51649]; [53320]; [53321]; [53322]; [54063]; [55253]; [55734]; [55735]; [56174]; [57130]; [57131]; [57132]; [57133]; [57134]; [57135]; [57136]; [57137]; [57483]; [57725]; [58941]; [58942]; [58943]

Industrial Directory Labels [57138]

Industrial Directory of Waltham [52907]

"Industrial Evolution" in Entrepreneur (Vol. 35, November 2007, No. 11, pp. 142) [23100], [44390]

Industrial Fabric and Equipment Exposition [18741]

Industrial Fabrics Association International Expo [18741]

Industrial Guide [51650]; [56175]; [57484]; [57485]

Industrial Health Foundation, Inc. Library [47542]

Industrial Hygiene News [34541]

Industrial Laser Solutions [39502]

Industrial List [47704]

Industrial Management Services [39523]

Industrial & Membership Directory [57139]

Industrial Methods Society [37568], [46484]

Industrial Parks Guide [57140]

Industrial Patent Activity in the United States Parts 1 and 2, 1971-1995 [24149], [37171]

Industrial Patent Activity in the United States Parts 1 and 2, 1974-1998 (IPA) [24149], [37171]

Industrial Profile/Directory [55736]

"Industrial RE Market Shows Signs of Health" in Business Courier (Vol. 27, August 20, 2010, No. 16, pp. 1) [16945], [17345], [17789], [23101]

Industrial Relations Bulletin [57726]

Industrial Relations Research Association [46954]

Industrial Reporter [57727]

Industrial Safety [47502]

Industrial Technology Consultants (ITC) [14048]

Industrial Television Society [7890]

"Industrial Vacancies Hit High; Economic Downturn Taking Toll on Area's Demand for Space" in Crain's Chicago Business (Apr. 21, 2008) [16530], [16946], [17346], [27364], [39154]

Industry Business [56176]

Industry Council for Tangible Assets (ICTA) [4345]

Industry Economic Development and Mines - Technology Commercialization Program [59896]

Industry Economic Development - Western Regional Office [59897]

"Industry Escalates Lobbying Efforts For Loan Program" in Crain's Detroit Business (Vol. 24, September 22, 2008, No. 38, pp. 22) [7247], [7605], [26760], [30688], [33776], [37399], [45500]

"Industry Events 2011" in American Printer (Vol. 128, August 1, 2011, No. 8) [4483], [16375], [20376], [20775], [46657]

"Industry/Events 2011" in American Printer (Vol. 128, July 1, 2011, No. 7) [4484], [5751], [16376], [20377], [20776], [46658]

Industry Film Producers Association [7888]

Industry List [55254]

Industry Manufacturers Council (IMC) [48671]

Industry Pulse [3844]

Industry Ventures [53037]

"Industry Vet To Spread Glory's Word" in Business First-Columbus (November 9, 2007, pp. A1) [9942], [40015], [42635]

InfantHouse.com [44613]

Infinisource [22065]

Infinity Capital, L.L.C. [49242]

"Inflation Woes: Secure Your Portfolio Against Rising Prices" in Black Enterprise (Vol. 37, January 2007, No. 6, pp. 40) [8449], [12524], [17347], [31568]

Inflight Food Service Association [9141]

Influence without Authority [29875], [38117]

Influence Skills: Getting Results Without Direct Authority (Onsite) [22213]

Influence Strategies [22214]

Influence: The Psychology of Persuasion [40016], [43509]

"The Influencers" in Entrepreneur (Vol. 36, March 2008, No. 3, pp. 66) [14446], [27365], [36617], [45501]

"Info Junkie" in Crain's Chicago Business (Vol. 34, October 24, 2011, No. 42, pp. 35) [7248], [7606], [9063], [29876], [30689], [40017], [43510]

InfoComm International [7886], [20881]

Infogram [56538]

The Information Advisor [11237]

Information and Telecommunications Technologies Group of Electronic Industries Association [3674], [20962]

Information and Business Directory [48672]

Information Film Producers of America [7888]

Information Industry Directory [4716], [5034], [21129]

Information International [59044]

Information Management [11238]

Information Sources: The IIA Annual Membership Directory [4717], [5035]

Information Standards Quarterly [11239]

Information Storage Industry Consortium (INSIC) [4686]

Information Technology Adviser [4661]

Information Technology Association of Canada (ITAC) [11226]

Information Technology Association of America [44991]

Information Technology Council [20649]

Information Technology Industry Council (ITI) [4931], [15273]

Information Technology Project Management (Onsite) [37654]

Information Technology for the Small Business: How to Make IT Work For Your Company [4718], [4963], [11736], [22342], [22601], [28724], [34957]

Information Technology Ventures [49243]

Information Today [11240], [11946], [11248]

Informe [48673]

The Informer [34542]; [50559]; [55737]; [56177]; [58242]

Inforum [52475]

InfoSource Management Services Inc. [8915], [32040]

InfoWorld: Defining Technology for Business [4890]

Ingleside Chamber of Commerce [58243]

Ingleside Chamber of Commerce Newsletter [58244]

Inglewood/Airport Area Chamber of Commerce (IAACC) [48674]

Inglewood Ventures [49244]

Inglewood/Airport Chamber of Commerce [48674]

Ingot Systems [49327]

Ingram's [54207]

"Ingrian and Channel Management International Sign Distribution Agreement" in Canadian Corporate News (May 16, 2007) [11737], [18919], [26761], [34958], [41984], [44391]

Initiatives Review [47705]

"Injured Workers Caught in the Middle" in Sacramento Business Journal (Vol. 28, June 10, 2011, No. 15, pp. 1) [11374], [33777], [36171], [47467]

"Injury and Illness Data" in Montly Labor Review (Vol. 133, September 2010, No. 9, pp. 147) [34333], [35819]

Ink, Inc. [3223]

Ink Solution & Postal [3109], [17735]

Inkster Chamber of Commerce [53323]

InkTone [3110]

Inland Empire Minority Business Enterprise Center - CHARO Community Development Corp. [49142]

Inland Empire North Small Business Development Center [48152]

Inland Empire Small Business Development Center (IESBDC) [48153]

Inland Seas Education Association (ISEA) [13924]

"Inland Snaps Up Rival REITs" in Crain's Chicago Business (Vol. 31, November 17, 2008, No. 46, pp. 3) [8450], [10711], [12525], [24414], [25119], [25549], [27366], [31569], [41985], [43057]

Inlet Chamber of Commerce [55255]

Inlet Information Office [55255]

Inlet Lamplighter [55256]

"Inmet Selling Nunavut Mining Properties" in Globe & Mail (February 15, 2006, pp. B6) [8451], [12526], [41986], [44161]

Inn Room Visitors Magazine [1937]

"Inn at Saratoga Owners Buy Caribbean Hotel" in Business Review, Albany New York (Vol. 34, November 2, 2007, No. 31, pp. 3) [10712], [17935], [23102]

Inner Circle [3022]

innkeeping [1936]

Innocal Venture Capital [49245]

"InnoCentive Announces Next Generation Crowdsourcing Platform" in Internet Wire (June 15, 2010) [28725], [40018], [41101]

Innov and Entrepren in Biotech [29877], [34959], [37040]

Innovate to Great: Re-Igniting Sustainable Innovation to Win in the Global Economy [27367], [36618], [37041]

"Innovating Globally" in Business Strategy Review (Vol. 21, Spring 2010, No. 1, pp. 24) [23103], [24415], [24874], [36619], [37042], [45941]

"Innovating Low-Cost Business Models" in Strategy and Leadership (Vol. 39, March-April 2011, No. 2, pp. 43) [25768], [36620], [37043], [41102]

"Innovation in 3D: NextFab" in Philadelphia Business Journal (Vol. 28, January 22, 2010, No. 49, pp. 1) [34960], [41103]

The Innovation Advantage [53867]

"Innovation Can Be Imperative for Those in Hands-On Trades" in Crain's Cleveland Business (Vol. 28, November 12, 2007, No. 45) [1278], [5988], [40019], [45502]

Innovation Canada Inc. [59947]

Innovation Connector [51757]

Innovation Depot [47762]

Innovation and Entrepreneurship [27368], [29879], [37045], [29878], [37044], [29880], [37046]

Innovation in Iowa [52014]

Innovation and Its Discontents [25550], [37047], [37244]

Innovation Methodologies in Enterprise Research [32772], [37048], [42811]

Innovation Nation: Canadian Leadership from Java to Jurassic Park [29881], [34961]

Innovation Nation: How America Is Losing Its Innovation Edge, Why It Matters, and How We Can Get It Back [25551], [37049]

Innovation Norway - United States [36298]

Innovation Ontario Corporation Information Centre [47162]

Innovation in Small Construction Firms [5393]

"Innovation Station" in Canadian Business (Vol. 80, October 8, 2007, No. 20, pp. 42) [27369], [28235], [29882], [34962], [37050], [42812]

Innovation Works, Inc. [57287]

"Innovation's Holy Grail" in Harvard Business Review (Vol. 88, July-August 2010, No. 7-8, pp. 132) [24875], [37051]

Innovative Approaches to Global Sustainability [23104], [27370], [32773]

"Innovative Growth" in Small Business Opportunities (March 2008) [23105], [41987]

Innovative Leader [13778], [38600]

Innovative Lease Services, Inc. [47159]

Innovative Scientific Analysis & Computing (ISAac) [2901], [26032], [44084]

"The Innovator: Rob McEwen's Unique Vision of Philanthropy and Business" in Canadian Business (Vol. 81, November 10, 2008, No. 19) [28236], [29883], [42813], [43880], [45942]

"Innovators Critical in Technical Economy" in Crain's Cleveland Business (Vol. 28, November 5, 2007, No. 44, pp. 10) [27371], [28237], [34963], [36621]

INNside Scoop: Everything You Ever Wanted to Know About Bed & Breakfast Inns [1929], [10713]

In-Plant Management Association [16342]

Inprint [58944]

Input - ITAA - Information Technology Association of America - Association of Data Processing Service Organizations - ADAPSO, the Computer Software and Services Industry Association - Adapso - ADAPSO (Computer Software and SErvices Industry Association) [44991]

"The Ins and Outs of Unemployment in Canada, 1976-2008" in Canadian Journal of Economics (Vol. 44, November 2011, No. 4, pp. 1331) [27372], [35377], [35820]

"Insert Grade Coating Improves Tool Live" in Modern Machine Shop (Vol. 84, October 2011, No. 5, pp. 124) [13706], [39155], [41411]

Inside Business [49719]; [53324]

Inside Business Today [2199], [3981], [6992], [10778], [14582], [17126], [18035], [20618], [44912]

Inside Business Today. . .The '90s [44913]

Inside Cal/EPA [7364], [30874]

Inside the Chamber [52476]

Inside Colonie [55257]

The Inside Edge [6792], [15502]

"Inside the Googleplex" in Canadian Business (Vol. 79, November 6, 2006, No. 22, pp. 59) [11545], [15246], [29096]

Inside Gwinnett [50560]

"Inside Intel's Effectiveness System for Web Marketing" in Advertising Age (Vol. 81, January 25, 2010, No. 4, pp. 4) [3550], [11738], [18920], [21130], [40020], [45138]

Inside MBS & ABS [14519]

"Inside the Mind of an Investor: Lessons from Bill Draper" in Inc. (Volume 32, December 2010, No. 10, pp. 140) [37400], [47035]

Inside Missile Defense [33466]

Inside Mortgage Finance [14520]

"Inside the New Nortel" in Canadian Business (Vol. 79, November 6, 2006, No. 22, pp. 93) [24416], [25120], [34964], [35378]

"Inside an Online Bazaar" in Entrepreneur (Vol. 37, September 2009, No. 9, pp. 38) [4485], [5989], [11739], [15329], [21131]

Inside OSHA [47480]

"Inside Out" in Playthings (Vol. 107, January 1, 2009, No. 1, pp. 3) [20254], [37052], [43058]

"The Inside and Outside Scoop on CEO Succession" in Globe & Mail (January 2, 2006, pp. B8) [29884], [32774]

Inside Supply Management: Resources to Create Your Future [42716]

Inside The Chamber [55258]

Inside Tips on Discovering Antiques [1141]

The Inside Track [58657]

inside TRALA [1629]

Inside View [50173]

"Insider" in Canadian Business (Vol. 80, Winter 2007, No. 24, pp.) [4116], [4239], [7836], [15974], [19330]

"Insider" in Canadian Business (Vol. 81, March 3, 2008, No. 3, pp. 96) [8453], [12528], [31571], [36622], [41333]

"Insider" in Canadian Business (Vol. 81, March 31, 2008, No. 5, pp. 76) [8452], [12527], [16947], [23106], [26253], [27373], [31570], [37401]

"Insider" in Canadian Business (Vol. 81, Summer 2008, No. 9, pp. 170) [25863], [27374], [30690], [41334], [45503]

Insider [49533]; [56178]; [58245]; [58659]; [58945]

The Insider [48675]; [58658]; [59212]

The Insider's Guide to Buying and Leasing Automobiles [14988]

Insight [47706]; [48676]; [53325]; [53326]; [55259]; [56179]; [56180]

Insight Center for Community Economic Development [26848]

Insight into Diversity: The EEO Recruitment Publication [19185], [35532], [40925]

INSIGHT Into Diversity [19158]

Insight Venture Partners / Insight Capital Partners [55427]

Insights [48677]; [51154]

Insights: The Corporate & Securities Law Advisor [24103]

InSite [3269]

Insite [5104]

Insites [57141]

"Insitu Looks to Oregon" in Business Journal Portland (Vol. 27, October 29, 2010, No. 35, pp. 1) [27375], [44686]

Insomnia Cookies Franchising LLC [1809], [9184]

INSPEC® Ondisc - Technology [5026], [5787]

Inspect-It 1st LLC [2584]

InspectAmerica Engineering P.C. [2572]

Inspiring Innovation [36942]

Installation & Cleaning Specialist [9073], [20828]

Installation Specialist [9073], [20828]

Installing, Configuring, and Troubleshooting Microsoft SQL Server [28042]

Instant Cashflow: Hundreds of Proven Strategies to Win Customers, Boost Margins and Take More Money Home [23107], [26442], [31572], [40021], [43511]

Instant Imprints [15616]

Instant Income [488], [29885], [40022], [41988], [43512]

Instant Profit: Successful Strategies to Boost Your Margin and Increase the Profitability of Your Business [23108], [31573], [38118], [40023]

Instant Tax Service [19718]

Instantfx Web Services [11957]

Instinct: Tapping Your Entrepreneurial DNA to Achieve Your Business Goals [24417], [29886]

Institut agree de la logistique et des transports Amerique du Nord [19799]

Institut Canadien de Gestion [37559]

Institut canadien de la construction en acier [5173]

Institut Canadien de la Recherche sur la Condition Physique et le Mode de Vie [15942]

Institut Canadien de la Recherche sur la Condition Physique et le mode de vie [16057]

Institut Canadien de Planification Finaniere [8029]

Institut Canadien de Relations avec les Investisseurs [8030]

Institut Canadien des Economistes en Construction [25], [2258]

Institut Canadien des Valeurs Mobilieres [11967]

Institut Canadien du Droit des Ressources [7030]

Institut Canadien du Tapis [20823]

Institut Canadiens des Conseillers en Voyages [20510]

Institut International de l'Ombudsman [14162]

Institut Royal d'Architecture du Canada [1259]

Institute for Agriculture and Trade Policy (IATP) [21823]

Institute of Business Appraisers--Directory [1216]

Institute for Business and Home Safety Library [47543]

Institute for Certification of Computing Professionals (ICCP) [4836]

Institute of Certified Business Counselors (ICBC) [25291]

Institute of Certified Travel Agents [20513]

Institute of Communication Agencies (ICA) [2358]

Institute de la Fondation D'Acupuncture du Canada [14809], [16059]

Institute for the Development of Emotional and Life Skills (IDEALS) [42734]

Institute for a Drug-Free Workplace (IDFW) [46060]

Institute for Entrepreneurial Leadership [54872]

Institute for Food Laws and Regulations - Michigan State University [53504]

Institute for Aerobics Research [16058]

Institute for Certified Investment Management Consultants [11971], [17161]

Institute for the Advancement of Criminal Justice [46065]

Institute for the Cooperative Study of International Seafood Markets [8975], [9000]

Institute for Forensic Imaging (IFI) [28494]

Institute for the Future (IFTF) [41311]

Institute on Global Drug Policy (IGDP) [46061]

Institute of HeartMath (IHM) [40851]

Institute of Internal Auditors - USA International Conference [2324], [19706]

Institute for Local Self-Reliance [17739]

Institute of Management Accountants (IMA) [39]

Institute of Management Accountants Conference [2324]

Institute of Management Accountants, Cost Management Group (CMG) [46479]

Institute of Management Accountants - McLeod Information Center [276]

The Institute for Management Excellence [2902], [3075], [13845], [26033], [38747], [39524], [44944]

Institute for Mediation and Conflict Resolution (IMCR) [14161]

Institute of Museum & Library Services--Annual Report [1351]

Institute of Association Management Companies [1453]

Institute of Association Management Companies-- Directory [1460]

Institute of Association Management Companies-- Referral Directory [1460]

Institute of Biological and Medical Sciences [16101]

Institute of Business Designers [11531], [15241]

Institute of Certified Financial Planners [8032]

Institute of Chartered Financial Analysts [11969]

Institute of Communications and Advertising [2358]

Institute of Museum Services--Annual Report [1351]

Institute of Religion and Health [34647]

Institute of Scrap Iron and Steel [17693]

Institute of Temporary Services [6948], [20023]

Institute for Operations Research and the Management Sciences (INFORMS) [46480]

Institute of Public Administration (IPA) [2903], [26034], [42413]

Institute of Real Estate Management (IREM) [16501], [16784], [51468]

Institute for Research on the Economics of Taxation (IRET) [19784]

Institute of Scrap Recycling Industries (ISRI) [17693]

Institute of Scrap Recycling Industries--Membership Directory [17714]

Institute for SocioEconomic Studies (ISES) [34661]

Institute of Tax Consultants (ITC) [19597]

Institute of Technology and Business Development [49795]

Institute for Traditional Medicine and Preventive Health Care (ITM) [16070]

Institute for Women's Policy Research (IWPR) [34662]

Institutional Food Editorial Council [6795]

Institutional Food Manufacturers Association [9142], [17865]

Institutional Food Manufacturers of America [9142], [17865]

Institutional Food-Service Manufacturers Association [9142], [17865]

Institutional Investor [2713]

"Institutional Logics in the Study of Organizations" in Business Ethics Quarterly (Vol. 21, July 2011, No. 3, pp. 409) [30942], [45943]

The Institutional Real Estate Letter [17112], [17561]

Institutional Venture Partners [49246]

Instructional Design for Participant-Centered Training (Onsite) [35677]

Instructional Design for Trainers (Onsite) [35678]

Instructional Media Services, Inc. [20751]

Instrument Technician Training Program (ITTP) [4774]

Instrumentalist--Buyer's Guide Issue [14623]

Instrumentalist--Directory of Summer Music Camps, Clinics, and Workshops Issue [14624]

Instrumentation, Process Measurement & Control (Onsite) [24982], [28043]

Insulation Contractors Association of America (ICAA) [11255]

Insulation Distributor Contractors National Association [5195], [11256]

Insurance Advertising Conference [11290]

Insurance Brokers Association of Canada (IBAC) [11285]

Insurance Bureau of Canada (IBC) [11286]

Insurance Consumer Affairs Exchange (ICAE) [11287]

Insurance Council of Canada 1998-2000 [11286]

Insurance Daily [11461]

"Insurance Firm Consolidates Offices; Integro Finds the Right Price Downtown" in Crain's New York Business (January 14, 2008) [11375], [24742], [36172]

Insurance Forum [11462]

Insurance Industry Litigation Reporter [11463]

Insurance Information Institute (III) [11288]

Insurance Information Institute Library [11501]

Insurance Institute of America (IIA) [11289]

Insurance Institute for Highway Safety (IIHS) [709]

Insurance Institute of Ontario Library [11502]

Insurance Institute of Southern Alberta Newsletter [11464]

The Insurance Journal of the West [11465]

The Insurance M&A Newsletter [11466]

"Insurance: Marathon Effort" in Canadian Business (Vol. 80, January 29, 2007, No. 3, pp. 11) [11376], [26463], [36173], [42486]

Insurance Marketing and Communications Association (IMCA) [11290]

Insurance Research Council (IRC) [11516]

"An Insurance Roll-Up In Danger of Unraveling" in Barron's (Vol. 88, March 17, 2008, No. 11, pp. 51) [8454], [11377], [12529], [23898], [31574], [36174], [41989], [46277]

The Insurance Tax Review [19689]

Insurance Weekly [11467]

"Insuraprise Growing Fast" in Austin Business Journal (Vol. 31, April 22, 2011, No. 7, pp. 1) [11378], [23109], [35379], [36175], [43513], [44687]

"Insurer Buys Foundation's Uptown HQ" in Charlotte Business Journal (Vol. 25, December 17, 2010, No. 39, pp. 1) [11379], [16948], [24743]

"Insurers No Longer Paying Premium for Advertising" in Brandweek (Vol. 49, April 21, 2008, No. 16, pp. SR3) [489], [11380], [22114], [23110], [24418], [25552], [25769], [27376], [36177], [40024]

"Insurers Warn Brokers" in Sacramento Business Journal (Vol. 25, August 22, 2008, No. 25, pp. 1) [11381], [21920], [34334], [36178]

"Intangible Assets" in Canadian Business (Vol. 79, July 17, 2006, No. 14-15, pp. 17) [8455], [12530], [23111], [25121]

"Integral USA Magazine Sponsors Eco-Fashion in the Park" in Entertainment Close-Up (September 2, 2011) [4117], [15543], [30691]

Integrated Business Information Systems Ltd. [8916], [13182]

Integrated Conservation Resources Inc. (ICR) [1312]

Integrated Development Consulting (IDC) [47142]

Integrated Financial Consultants [32041]

Integrated Marketing Concepts [664], [2899], [3074], [13844], [26030], [38744], [40619]

Integrated Pest Management Reviews [15651]

Integrated Security Technologies (IST) [41497], [41606]

"Integrating Business Core Knowledge through Upper Division Report Composition" in Business Communication Quarterly (December 2007) [16486], [22343], [22602], [28238], [37245], [46516]

Integrating Forms and Databases on the Web (Onsite) [28044]

"Integrating Your Compliance Program" in Franchising World (Vol. 42, November 2010, No. 11, pp. 49) [24419], [32189]

Integration Marketing: How Small Businesses Become Big Businesses and Big Businesses Become Empires [13998], [28726], [40025]

"An Integrative Model of Experiencing and Responding to Mistreatment at Work" in Academy of Management Review (January 2008, pp. 76) [23899], [38119]

"Intel to Buy McAfee Security Business for 768B" in eWeek (August 19, 2010) [3551], [18442], [18921], [25324], [44162], [44392], [45139]

Intel Corporation Library [4684]

"Intel Forges New Strategy With Chinese Fabrication Plant" in Globe & Mail (March 26, 2007, pp. B6) [34965], [39156], [41677]

"Intel Joins Movement to Turn Cube Farms Into Wide-Open Spaces" in Sacramento Business Journal (Vol. 28, May 27, 2011, No. 13, pp. 1) [11546], [15247], [41545], [45504]

MASTER INDEX
International
Master Index

International Data Corp. - IDC Library **[2692]**, **[5086]**, **[11962]**
International Data Corp. Library **[4915]**, **[5087]**
International Desalination and Environmental Association [20970]
International Desalination Association (IDA) **[20970]**
International Development Research Centre (IDRC) **[34663]**
International Directory of Importers--Food and Beverage **[11031]**
International Directory of Importers - Sporting Goods and Toys **[11032]**
International Directory of Little Magazines and Small Presses **[2144]**, **[15544]**
International District Energy Association (IDEA) **[768]**
International District Heating Association - International District Heating and Cooling Association - National District Heating Association [768]
International Documentary Association (IDA) **[7889]**
International Documentary Foundation [7889]
International Drug Strategy Institute [46061]
International Economic Development Council (IEDC) **[26849]**
International Economic Development Council--Membership Directory **[27377]**
The International Ecotourism Society (TIES) **[20128]**
International Employment Hotline **[19178]**
International Entertainment Buyers Association (IEBA) **[19565]**
International Entrepreneurship **[29887]**, **[36626]**, **[42814]**
International Entrepreneurship Education Issues and Newness **[28239]**, **[29888]**, **[36627]**
International Entrepreneurship in Small and Medium Size Enterprises: Orientation, Environment and Strategy **[23113]**, **[25553]**, **[29889]**, **[36628]**
International Entrepreneurship: Starting, Developing, and Managing a Global Venture **[29375]**, **[36270]**
"International ETFs: Your Passport to the World" in Barron's (Vol. 89, July 13, 2009, No. 28, pp. L10) **[8456]**, **[12531]**, **[27378]**, **[31575]**, **[36629]**
International Exer-Safety Association [15944]
International Exhibitors Association--Membership Directory and Product/Service Guide [20433]
International Fabricare Institute [6737]; [6768]
International Fabricare Institute - Library. [6767]
International Facility Management Association (IFMA) **[16502]**
International Facility Management Association - Toronto Chapter **[2601]**
International Falls Area Chamber of Commerce (IFACC) **[53663]**
International Fancy Food and Confection Show/Winter **[3299]**, **[10438]**, **[19272]**
International Federation of Body Building and Fitness (IFBB) **[15948]**
International Federation of Advertising Agencies [357], [42579]
International Federation of Pharmaceutical Wholesalers (IFPW) **[6636]**, **[47167]**
International Fertilizer Development Center - Travis P. Hignett Memorial Library **[21801]**
International Finance Corp. [26850]
International Finance Corporation (IFC) **[26850]**
International Flight Services Association (IFSA) **[9141]**
International Floriculture Industry Short Course and Trade Show [9124], [16203]
International Food Policy Research Institute Library **[21802]**
International Food, Wine and Travel Writers Association (IFWTWA) **[6794]**
International Foodservice Editorial Council (IFEC) **[6795]**
International Foodservice Manufacturers Association (IFMA) **[9142]**, **[17865]**
International Footwear Association [18749]
International Formalwear Association (IFA) **[4191]**
International Foundation of Employee Benefit Plans (IFEBP) **[21855]**, **[25368]**
International Foundation of Employee Benefit Plans Inc. [21855], [25368]
International Foundation for Protection Officers (IFPO) **[16453]**
International Franchise Association (IFA) **[32117]**; **[49863]**
International Franchise Association--Franchise Opportunities Guide **[32190]**
International Franchise Association - Office of Small and Disadvantaged Business Utilization - Minorities in Franchising **[59971]**; **[59972]**
International Franchise Association--Membership Directory: What You Need to Know When You Buy a Franchise [32190]
International Furnishings and Design Association (IFDA) **[2023]**, **[11530]**
International Furniture Rental Association (IFRA) **[10448]**, **[17749]**
International Furniture Transportation and Logistics Council (IFTLC) **[10449]**
International Galapagos Tour Operators Association (IGTOA) **[20129]**, **[20515]**
International Game Fish Association - E.K. Harry Library of Fishes **[1735]**
International Gay and Lesbian Travel Association (IGLTA) **[20516]**
International Gay Rodeo Association (IGRA) **[10605]**, **[19395]**
International Genealogical Index® (IGI) **[9480]**
International Generic Horse Association (IGHA) **[1007]**
International Golf Course Conference and Show **[9680]**
International Golf Federation (IGF) **[9651]**
International Graphoanalysis Society (IGAS) **[10113]**
International Grapho-Analysis Society Inc. [10113]
International Ground Source Heat Pump Association (IGSHPA) **[769]**
International Group of Accounting Firms [50], [21322]
International Group of Agencies and Bureaus [18533]
"International Growth" in Black Enterprise (Vol. 38, July 2008, No. 12, pp. 64) **[2776]**, **[25554]**, **[27379]**, **[28240]**, **[29890]**, **[36630]**
International Growth of Small and Medium Enterprises **[23114]**, **[36631]**, **[37053]**
International Handbook of Entrepreneurship and HRM **[29891]**, **[35825]**
International Handbook of Women and Small Business Entrepreneurship **[29892]**, **[36632]**, **[47311]**
International Hardwood Products Association - Imported Hardwood Plywood Association - Imported Hardwood Products Association - Imported Hardwood Plywood Association of America [13639]
International Hardwood Products Association--Directory [13655]
International Harvester Collectors (IHC) **[4346]**
International Health, Racquet and Sportsclub Association (IHRSA) **[15949]**, **[20052]**
International Hearing Aid Society [10335]
International Hearing Society **[10335]**
International Hearing Society--Directory of Members **[10338]**
International Herb Association (IHA) **[10363]**
International Herb Growers and Marketers Association [10363]
International Home Furnishings Marketing Association [10446]
International Home Furnishings Representatives Association (IHFRA) **[10450]**
International House of Pancakes [18119]
International House of Pancakes [18119]
International Housewares Association (IHA) **[1183]**, **[10386]**
International Imaging Industry Association (I3A) **[15824]**
International Industrial Television Association [7890]
International Inflight Food Service Association [9141]
International Institute of Concern for Public Health (IICPH) **[34145]**
International Institute of Fisheries Economics and Trade (IIFET) **[8975]**, **[9000]**
International Institute for Lath and Plaster (IILP) **[14101]**
International Institute of Conference Management [18531]
International Institute of Convention Management [18531]
International Institute of Trading Mastery Inc. (IITM) **[13183]**
International Interior Design Association (IIDA) **[11531]**, **[15241]**
International Internet Marketing Association (IIMA) **[39564]**
International Jewelry Fair/General Merchandise Show - Fall **[13290]**
International Journal of Adaptive Control and Signal Processing **[44026]**
International Journal on Artificial Intelligence Tools **[44027]**
International Journal of Computer Integrated Manufacturing **[44028]**
International Journal of Computer Simulation **[44029]**
International Journal of Computers and Applications **[4891]**
International Journal of Energy Research **[44030]**
International Journal of Health Planning and Management **[34543]**
International Journal of Health Services **[34544]**
International Journal of Hyperthermia **[44031]**
International Journal of Intelligent Systems **[4892]**, **[5044]**, **[44032]**
International Journal of Cross-Cultural Consumer Behavior [40551]
International Journal of Mini and Microcomputers [4891]
International Journal of Purchasing & Materials Management [42717]
International Journal of Technology Assessment in Health Care **[34545]**
International Journal of Tourism Research **[20604]**
International Jumper Futurity (IJF) **[1008]**, **[10606]**
International Juvenile Product Show **[1668]**
International Kindergarten Union - National Council of Primary Education [3922]
International Labor Rights Forum (ILRF) **[46953]**
International League of Antiquarian Booksellers (ILAB) **[1117]**, **[2359]**
International Licensing Industry Merchandisers' Association (LIMA) **[36949]**
International Literary Market Place: The Directory of the International Book Publishing Industry **[6822]**, **[11232]**, **[13608]**
International Magazine for Family Businesses **[29445]**, **[31017]**, **[44798]**
International Management Tech. Co., LLC (IMTEC) **[3024]**
International Marina Institute (IMI) **[13925]**
International Marketplace Newsletter **[51155]**
International Masonry Institute (IMI) **[5184]**, **[14102]**
International Master Care Janitorial Franchising Inc. **[2664]**
International Mergers and Acquisitions **[3025]**
International Midas Dealers Association (IMDA) **[18583]**
International Midas Dealers Association Annual Conference **[1583]**
"International Monetary Barter Helps Discretionary Industry" in Benzinga.com (January 24, 2011) **[2504]**, **[21846]**
International Music Products Association [14615]
International Nanny Association (INA) **[14801]**
International Newsmedia Marketing Association (INMA) **[15503]**
International Newspaper Marketing Association [15503]
International Newspaper Promotion Association [15503]
"International Nickel Ventures Corporation Reports Results for the First Quarter 2007" in Canadian Corporate News (May 16, 2007) **[8457]**, **[12532]**, **[25122]**, **[41990]**
International Ombudsman Institute (IOI) **[14162]**
International Pacific Salmon Fisheries Commission [9010]
International Paddle Association [15958], [20058]
International Paddle Rackets Association [15958], [20058]
International Paperweight Society (IPS) **[1118]**, **[4347]**
International Personnel Management Association - Canada (IPMA) **[35656]**
International Perspectives in Public Health **[34146]**
International Petroleum Encyclopedia **[16685]**, **[18670]**
International Pharmaceutical Abstracts (IPA) **[6704]**
International Photographer [8006], [15852]
International Physical Fitness Association (IPFA) **[15950]**
International Popcorn Association [5100]
International Premium Cigar and Pipe Retailers (IPCPR) **[20085]**
International Prepress Association [16343]
International Production Planning and Scheduling Association (IPPSA) **[46481]**
International Public Management Association for Human Resources - HR Center **[15476]**
International Publishing Management Association (IPMA) **[16342]**
International Puzzle Features **[55875]**
International Racquet Sports Association [15949], [20052]
International Racquetball Association [15958], [20058]
International Radio and Television Society [16696], [19887]
International Radio and Television Society Foundation Inc. [16696], [19887]
International Radio and Television Society Foundation (IRTS) **[16696]**, **[19887]**
International Real Estate Institute (IREI) **[17160]**
International Reciprocal Trade Association (IRTA) **[21832]**
International Recording Media Association [7879], [17633]
International Repertory of the Literature of Art [1375]
International Reprographic Association (IRgA) **[5861]**
International Reprographic Association Annual Convention and Trade Show **[5867]**
International Reprographic Blueprint Association [5861]
International Research Bureau [16471], [29310]
International Research Centers Directory **[43881]**
International Research Group on Time Budgets and Social Activities [2759], [13761]
International Restaurant & Foodservice Show of New York **[3478]**, **[6450]**, **[10308]**, **[18040]**, **[46761]**

Small Business Sourcebook • 30th Edition
3541

International Sanitary Supply Association (ISSA) [2602]
International Sanitary Supply Association--Membership Directory [6565]
International Security Management Association (ISMA) [18379]
International Shade Tree Conference [13371]
International Shipmasters Association (ISMA) [13926]
International Shipmasters Association of the Great Lakes [13926]
International Sign Association (ISA) [18785]
International Slurry Seal Association [1995]
International Slurry Surfacing Association (ISSA) [1995]
International Society of Appraisers (ISA) [1208]
International Society of Arboriculture (ISA) [13371]
International Society of Arboriculture Annual Conference and Industrial Trade Show [13430]
International Society of Certified Electronics Technicians (ISCET) [4794], [19871]
International Society of Certified Employee Benefit Specialists (ISCEBS) [21856]
International Society of Cleaning Technicians [20824]
International Society for the Study of Ghosts and Apparitions (ISSGA) [14813]
International Society for the Study of Time (ISST) [46482]
International Spa Association (ISPA) [2032], [5881]
International Sport Summit [19490], [46762]
International Sporthorse Registry (ISR) [1009]
International Sports Directory [19397]
International Spotted Horse Registry Association (ISHR) [1010]
International Stamp and Coin Collectors Society - Library. [4388]
International Swimming Hall of Fame - Henning Library [19558]
International Systems Dealers Association [15274]
International Tap Association (ITA) [6376]
International Tape Association [7879], [17633]
International Tape/Disc Association [7879], [17633]
International Tax and Public Finance [8867], [19690]
International Taxicab and Livery Association - Cab Research Bureau - National Association of Taxicab Owners - International Taxicab Association - American Taxicab Association [19802]
International Television Almanac [3180], [19569], [20889]
International Television Association [7890]
International Television and Video Almanac [3180], [19569], [20889]
International Tennis Hall of Fame (ITHOF) [20053]
International Tennis Hall of Fame and Tennis Museum Library [20067]
International Textile & Apparel Association--Membership Directory [4118]
International Tire & Rubber Association Foundation Inc. [20069]
International Tire and Rubber Association [20069]
International Trade Administration (ITA) - Office of Public Affairs [60317], [62165]
International Trade Administration - Office of Public Affairs [60318]
International Trade Administration - U.S. Commercial Service - Export Assistance Center (Anchorage, Alaska) [60319]
International Trade Administration - U.S. Commercial Service - Export Assistance Center (Austin, Texas) [60320]
International Trade Administration - U.S. Commercial Service - Export Assistance Center (Baltimore, Maryland) [60321]
International Trade Administration - U.S. Commercial Service - Export Assistance Center (Birmingham, Alabama) [60322]
International Trade Administration - U.S. Commercial Service - Export Assistance Center (Boise, Idaho) [60323]
International Trade Administration - U.S. Commercial Service - Export Assistance Center (Boston, Massachusetts) [60324]
International Trade Administration - U.S. Commercial Service - Export Assistance Center (Buffalo, New York) [60325]
International Trade Administration - U.S. Commercial Service - Export Assistance Center (Carmel, Indiana) [60326]
International Trade Administration - U.S. Commercial Service - Export Assistance Center (Charleston, South Carolina) [60327]
International Trade Administration - U.S. Commercial Service - Export Assistance Center (Charlotte, North Carolina) [60328]
International Trade Administration - U.S. Commercial Service - Export Assistance Center (Chicago, Illinois) [60329]

International Trade Administration - U.S. Commercial Service - Export Assistance Center (Cincinnati, Ohio) [60330]
International Trade Administration - U.S. Commercial Service - Export Assistance Center (Clearwater, Florida) [60331]
International Trade Administration - U.S. Commercial Service - Export Assistance Center (Cleveland, Ohio) [60332]
International Trade Administration - U.S. Commercial Service - Export Assistance Center (Columbia, South Carolina) [60333]
International Trade Administration - U.S. Commercial Service - Export Assistance Center (Columbus, Ohio) [60334]
International Trade Administration - U.S. Commercial Service - Export Assistance Center (Dallas, Texas) [60335]
International Trade Administration - U.S. Commercial Service - Export Assistance Center (Denver, Colorado) [60336]
International Trade Administration - U.S. Commercial Service - Export Assistance Center (Des Moines, Iowa) [60337]
International Trade Administration - U.S. Commercial Service - Export Assistance Center (Detroit, Michigan) [60338]
International Trade Administration - U.S. Commercial Service - Export Assistance Center (Eugene, Oregon) [60339]
International Trade Administration - U.S. Commercial Service - Export Assistance Center (Ft. Worth, Texas) [60340]
International Trade Administration - U.S. Commercial Service - Export Assistance Center (Gaithersburg, Maryland) [60341]
International Trade Administration - U.S. Commercial Service - Export Assistance Center (Grand Rapids, Michigan) [60342]
International Trade Administration - U.S. Commercial Service - Export Assistance Center (Greensboro, North Carolina) [60343]
International Trade Administration - U.S. Commercial Service - Export Assistance Center (Harrisburg, Pennsylvania) [60344]
International Trade Administration - U.S. Commercial Service - Export Assistance Center (Highland Park, Illinois) [60345]
International Trade Administration - U.S. Commercial Service - Export Assistance Center (Honolulu, Hawaii) [60346]
International Trade Administration - U.S. Commercial Service - Export Assistance Center (Houston, Texas) [60347]
International Trade Administration - U.S. Commercial Service - Export Assistance Center (Jackson, Mississippi) [60348]
International Trade Administration - U.S. Commercial Service - Export Assistance Center (Kansas City, Missouri) [60349]
International Trade Administration - U.S. Commercial Service - Export Assistance Center (Knoxville, Florida) [60350]
International Trade Administration - U.S. Commercial Service - Export Assistance Center (Little Rock) [60351]
International Trade Administration - U.S. Commercial Service - Export Assistance Center (Long Beach) [60352]
International Trade Administration - U.S. Commercial Service - Export Assistance Center (Long Island) [60353]
International Trade Administration - U.S. Commercial Service - Export Assistance Center (Los Angeles, California) [60354]
International Trade Administration - U.S. Commercial Service - Export Assistance Center (Louisville, Kentucky) [60355]
International Trade Administration - U.S. Commercial Service - Export Assistance Center (Memphis, Tennessee) [60356]
International Trade Administration - U.S. Commercial Service - Export Assistance Center (Miami, Florida) [60357]
International Trade Administration - U.S. Commercial Service - Export Assistance Center (Middletown, Connecticut) [60358]
International Trade Administration - U.S. Commercial Service - Export Assistance Center (Milwaukee, Wisconsin) [60359]
International Trade Administration - U.S. Commercial Service - Export Assistance Center (Minneapolis, Minnesota) [60360]

International Trade Administration - U.S. Commercial Service - Export Assistance Center (Monterey, California) [60361]
International Trade Administration - U.S. Commercial Service - Export Assistance Center (Montpelier, Vermont) [60362]
International Trade Administration - U.S. Commercial Service - Export Assistance Center (Nashville, Tennessee) [60363]
International Trade Administration - U.S. Commercial Service - Export Assistance Center (Newark, New Jersey) [60364]
International Trade Administration - U.S. Commercial Service - Export Assistance Center (Newport Beach, California) [60365]
International Trade Administration - U.S. Commercial Service - Export Assistance Center (Novato, California) [60366]
International Trade Administration - U.S. Commercial Service - Export Assistance Center (Oakland, California) [60367]
International Trade Administration - U.S. Commercial Service - Export Assistance Center (Oklahoma City, Oklahoma) [60368]
International Trade Administration - U.S. Commercial Service - Export Assistance Center (Omaha, Nebraska) [60369]
International Trade Administration - U.S. Commercial Service - Export Assistance Center (Orlando, Florida) [60370]
International Trade Administration - U.S. Commercial Service - Export Assistance Center (Philadelphia, Pennsylvania) [60371]
International Trade Administration - U.S. Commercial Service - Export Assistance Center (Phoenix, Arizona) [60372]
International Trade Administration - U.S. Commercial Service - Export Assistance Center (Pittsburgh, Pennsylvania) [60373]
International Trade Administration - U.S. Commercial Service - Export Assistance Center (Pontiac, Michigan) [60374]
International Trade Administration - U.S. Commercial Service - Export Assistance Center (Portland, ME) [60375]
International Trade Administration - U.S. Commercial Service - Export Assistance Center (Portland, Oregon) [60376]
International Trade Administration - U.S. Commercial Service - Export Assistance Center (Portsmouth, New Hampshire) [60377]
International Trade Administration - U.S. Commercial Service - Export Assistance Center (Providence, Rhode Island) [60378]
International Trade Administration - U.S. Commercial Service - Export Assistance Center (Reno, Nevada) [60379]
International Trade Administration - U.S. Commercial Service - Export Assistance Center (Richmond, Virginia) [60380]
International Trade Administration - U.S. Commercial Service - Export Assistance Center (Rochester, New York) [60381]
International Trade Administration - U.S. Commercial Service - Export Assistance Center (Rockford, Illinois) [60382]
International Trade Administration - U.S. Commercial Service - Export Assistance Center (Sacramento, California) [60383]
International Trade Administration - U.S. Commercial Service - Export Assistance Center (St. Louis, Missouri) [60384]
International Trade Administration - U.S. Commercial Service - Export Assistance Center (Salt Lake City, Utah) [60385]
International Trade Administration - U.S. Commercial Service - Export Assistance Center (San Antonio, Texas) [60386]
International Trade Administration - U.S. Commercial Service - Export Assistance Center (San Diego, California) [60387]
International Trade Administration - U.S. Commercial Service - Export Assistance Center (San Francisco, California) [60388]
International Trade Administration - U.S. Commercial Service - Export Assistance Center (San Jose, California) [60389]
International Trade Administration - U.S. Commercial Service - Export Assistance Center (San Juan, Puerto Rico) [60390]
International Trade Administration - U.S. Commercial Service - Export Assistance Center (Santa Clara, California) [60391]

International Trade Administration - U.S. Commercial Service - Export Assistance Center (Santa Fe, New Mexico) [60392]
International Trade Administration - U.S. Commercial Service - Export Assistance Center (Scranton, Pennsylvania) [60393]
International Trade Administration - U.S. Commercial Service - Export Assistance Center (Seattle, Washington) [60394]
International Trade Administration - U.S. Commercial Service - Export Assistance Center (Sioux Falls, South Dakota) [60395]
International Trade Administration - U.S. Commercial Service - Export Assistance Center (Somerset, Kentucky) [60396]
International Trade Administration - U.S. Commercial Service - Export Assistance Center (Spokane, Washington) [60397]
International Trade Administration - U.S. Commercial Service - Export Assistance Center (Tallahassee, Florida) [60398]
International Trade Administration - U.S. Commercial Service - Export Assistance Center (Toledo, Ohio) [60399]
International Trade Administration - U.S. Commercial Service - Export Assistance Center (Trenton, New Jersey) [60400]
International Trade Administration - U.S. Commercial Service - Export Assistance Center (Tulsa, Oklahoma) [60401]
International Trade Administration - U.S. Commercial Service - Export Assistance Center (Westchester, New York) [60402]
International Trade Administration - U.S. Commercial Service - Export Assistance Center (Wheaton, Illinois) [60403]
International Trade Administration - U.S. Commercial Service - Export Assistance Center (Wheeling, West Virgina) [60404]
International Trade Administration - U.S. Commercial Service - Export Assistance Center (Wichita, Kansas) [60405]
International Trade Administration - U.S. Commercial Service - Export Assistance Center (Ypsilanti, Michigan) [60406]
International Trade Administration - U.S. and Foreign Commercial Service - Export Assistance Center (Anchorage, Alaska) [60407]
International Trade Administration - U.S. and Foreign Commercial Service - Export Assistance Center (Austin, Texas) [60408]
International Trade Administration - U.S. and Foreign Commercial Service - Export Assistance Center (Baltimore, Maryland) [60409]
International Trade Administration - U.S. and Foreign Commercial Service - Export Assistance Center (Birmingham, Alabama) [60410]
International Trade Administration - U.S. and Foreign Commercial Service - Export Assistance Center (Boise, Idaho) [60411]
International Trade Administration - U.S. and Foreign Commercial Service - Export Assistance Center (Boston, Massachusetts) [60412]; [60413]; [60414]
International Trade Administration - U.S. and Foreign Commercial Service - Export Assistance Center (Buffalo, New York) [60415]
International Trade Administration - U.S. and Foreign Commercial Service - Export Assistance Center (Carmel, Indiana) [60416]
International Trade Administration - U.S. and Foreign Commercial Service - Export Assistance Center (Charleston, South Carolina) [60417]
International Trade Administration - U.S. and Foreign Commercial Service - Export Assistance Center (Charlotte, North Carolina) [60418]
International Trade Administration - U.S. and Foreign Commercial Service - Export Assistance Center (Chicago, Illinois) [60419]
International Trade Administration - U.S. and Foreign Commercial Service - Export Assistance Center (Cincinnati, Ohio) [60420]
International Trade Administration - U.S. and Foreign Commercial Service - Export Assistance Center (Clearwater, Florida) [60421]
International Trade Administration - U.S. and Foreign Commercial Service - Export Assistance Center (Cleveland, Ohio) [60422]
International Trade Administration - U.S. and Foreign Commercial Service - Export Assistance Center (Columbia, South Carolina) [60423]
International Trade Administration - U.S. and Foreign Commercial Service - Export Assistance Center (Columbus, Ohio) [60424]
International Trade Administration - U.S. and Foreign Commercial Service - Export Assistance Center (Dallas, Texas) [60425]
International Trade Administration - U.S. and Foreign Commercial Service - Export Assistance Center (Denver, Colorado) [60426]
International Trade Administration - U.S. and Foreign Commercial Service - Export Assistance Center (Des Moines, Iowa) [60427]
International Trade Administration - U.S. and Foreign Commercial Service - Export Assistance Center (Detroit, Michigan) [60428]
International Trade Administration - U.S. and Foreign Commercial Service - Export Assistance Center (Eugene, Oregon) [60429]
International Trade Administration - U.S. and Foreign Commercial Service - Export Assistance Center (Ft. Worth, Texas) [60430]
International Trade Administration - U.S. and Foreign Commercial Service - Export Assistance Center (Gaithersburg, Maryland) [60431]
International Trade Administration - U.S. and Foreign Commercial Service - Export Assistance Center (Grand Rapids, Michigan) [60432]
International Trade Administration - U.S. and Foreign Commercial Service - Export Assistance Center (Greensboro, North Carolina) [60433]
International Trade Administration - U.S. and Foreign Commercial Service - Export Assistance Center (Harrisburg, Pennsylvania) [60434]
International Trade Administration - U.S. and Foreign Commercial Service - Export Assistance Center (Highland Park, Illinois) [60435]
International Trade Administration - U.S. and Foreign Commercial Service - Export Assistance Center (Honolulu, Hawaii) [60436]
International Trade Administration - U.S. and Foreign Commercial Service - Export Assistance Center (Houston, Texas) [60437]
International Trade Administration - U.S. and Foreign Commercial Service - Export Assistance Center (Jackson, Mississippi) [60438]
International Trade Administration - U.S. and Foreign Commercial Service - Export Assistance Center (Kansas City, Missouri) [60439]
International Trade Administration - U.S. and Foreign Commercial Service - Export Assistance Center (Knoxville, Tennessee) [60440]
International Trade Administration - U.S. and Foreign Commercial Service - Export Assistance Center (Little Rock) [60441]
International Trade Administration - U.S. and Foreign Commercial Service - Export Assistance Center (Long Beach) [60442]
International Trade Administration - U.S. and Foreign Commercial Service - Export Assistance Center (Long Island) [60443]
International Trade Administration - U.S. and Foreign Commercial Service - Export Assistance Center (Los Angeles (West), California) [60444]
International Trade Administration - U.S. and Foreign Commercial Service - Export Assistance Center (Louisville, Kentucky) [60445]
International Trade Administration - U.S. and Foreign Commercial Service - Export Assistance Center (Memphis, Tennessee) [60446]
International Trade Administration - U.S. and Foreign Commercial Service - Export Assistance Center (Miami, Florida) [60447]
International Trade Administration - U.S. and Foreign Commercial Service - Export Assistance Center (Middletown, Connecticut) [60448]
International Trade Administration - U.S. and Foreign Commercial Service - Export Assistance Center (Milwaukee, Wisconsin) [60449]
International Trade Administration - U.S. and Foreign Commercial Service - Export Assistance Center (Minneapolis, Minnesota) [60450]
International Trade Administration - U.S. and Foreign Commercial Service - Export Assistance Center (Monterey, California) [60451]
International Trade Administration - U.S. and Foreign Commercial Service - Export Assistance Center (Montpelier, Vermont) [60452]
International Trade Administration - U.S. and Foreign Commercial Service - Export Assistance Center (Nashville, Tennessee) [60453]
International Trade Administration - U.S. and Foreign Commercial Service - Export Assistance Center (Newark, New Jersey) [60454]
International Trade Administration - U.S. and Foreign Commercial Service - Export Assistance Center (Newport Beach, California) [60455]
International Trade Administration - U.S. and Foreign Commercial Service - Export Assistance Center (Novato, California) [60456]
International Trade Administration - U.S. and Foreign Commercial Service - Export Assistance Center (Oakland, California) [60457]
International Trade Administration - U.S. and Foreign Commercial Service - Export Assistance Center (Oklahoma City, Oklahoma) [60458]
International Trade Administration - U.S. and Foreign Commercial Service - Export Assistance Center (Omaha, Nebraska) [60459]
International Trade Administration - U.S. and Foreign Commercial Service - Export Assistance Center (Orlando, Florida) [60460]
International Trade Administration - U.S. and Foreign Commercial Service - Export Assistance Center (Philadelphia, Pennsylvania) [60461]
International Trade Administration - U.S. and Foreign Commercial Service - Export Assistance Center (Phoenix, Arizona) [60462]
International Trade Administration - U.S. and Foreign Commercial Service - Export Assistance Center (Pittsburgh, Pennsylvania) [60463]
International Trade Administration - U.S. and Foreign Commercial Service - Export Assistance Center (Pontiac, Michigan) [60464]
International Trade Administration - U.S. and Foreign Commercial Service - Export Assistance Center (Portland, ME) [60465]
International Trade Administration - U.S. and Foreign Commercial Service - Export Assistance Center (Portland, Oregon) [60466]
International Trade Administration - U.S. and Foreign Commercial Service - Export Assistance Center (Portsmouth, New Hampshire) [60467]
International Trade Administration - U.S. and Foreign Commercial Service - Export Assistance Center (Providence, Rhode Island) [60468]
International Trade Administration - U.S. and Foreign Commercial Service - Export Assistance Center (Reno, Nevada) [60469]
International Trade Administration - U.S. and Foreign Commercial Service - Export Assistance Center (Richmond, Virgina) [60470]
International Trade Administration - U.S. and Foreign Commercial Service - Export Assistance Center (Rochester, New York) [60471]
International Trade Administration - U.S. and Foreign Commercial Service - Export Assistance Center (Rockford, Illinois) [60472]
International Trade Administration - U.S. and Foreign Commercial Service - Export Assistance Center (Sacramento, California) [60473]
International Trade Administration - U.S. and Foreign Commercial Service - Export Assistance Center (St. Louis, Missouri) [60474]
International Trade Administration - U.S. and Foreign Commercial Service - Export Assistance Center (Salt Lake City, Utah) [60475]
International Trade Administration - U.S. and Foreign Commercial Service - Export Assistance Center (San Antonio, Texas) [60476]
International Trade Administration - U.S. and Foreign Commercial Service - Export Assistance Center (San Diego, California) [60477]
International Trade Administration - U.S. and Foreign Commercial Service - Export Assistance Center (San Francisco, California) [60478]
International Trade Administration - U.S. and Foreign Commercial Service - Export Assistance Center (San Jose, California) [60479]
International Trade Administration - U.S. and Foreign Commercial Service - Export Assistance Center (San Juan, Puerto Rico) [60480]
International Trade Administration - U.S. and Foreign Commercial Service - Export Assistance Center (Santa Clara, California) [60481]
International Trade Administration - U.S. and Foreign Commercial Service - Export Assistance Center (Santa Fe, New Mexico) [60482]
International Trade Administration - U.S. and Foreign Commercial Service - Export Assistance Center (Scranton, Pennsylvania) [60483]
International Trade Administration - U.S. and Foreign Commercial Service - Export Assistance Center (Seattle, Washington) [60484]
International Trade Administration - U.S. and Foreign Commercial Service - Export Assistance Center (Sioux Falls, South Dakota) [60485]
International Trade Administration - U.S. and Foreign Commercial Service - Export Assistance Center (Somerset, Kentucky) [60486]

Master Index

"It's all Kosher at Downtown Eatery/Bakery" in *AZ Daily Star (July 10, 2008)* [1765], [5838], [17940]

It's in the Mail: Techniques for Collecting Debts [26356]

"It's a New Game: Killerspin Pushes Table Tennis to Extreme Heights" in *Black Enterprise (Vol. 37, October 2006, No. 3, pp. 73)* [7933], [11750], [15332], [15545], [19331], [21136], [28734], [29902], [40040]

"It's New or Improved, But Does It Work?" in *Contractor (Vol. 57, January 2010, No. 1, pp. 22)* [832], [16246], [41110]

"It's Not About the G1; Google Just Wants You to Use the Mobile Web" in *Advertising Age (Vol. 79, September 29, 2008, No. 36, pp. 32)* [3750], [11751], [25126], [25558], [34974]

"It's Not About You" in *Entrepreneur (Vol. 35, November 2007, No. 11, pp. 102)* [22349], [26466], [43517]

"It's Not Easy Being Small" in *Baltimore Business Journal (Vol. 27, October 9, 2009, No. 22, pp. 1)* [5396], [33256], [33438]

"It's Not Easy Investing Green" in *Entrepreneur (Vol. 37, August 2009, No. 8, pp. 64)* [7251], [7609], [30697], [47038]

It's Not Just Courtesy—It's the Law [26689]

It's Not Just Who You Know: Transform Your Life (and Your Organization) by Turning Colleagues and Contacts into Lasting Relationships [22350], [32784], [38128]

"It's Not Perfect; But Illinois a Good Home for Business" in *Crain's Chicago Business (Vol. 34, October 24, 2011, No. 42, pp. 18)* [23124], [32407], [44688], [46282]

"It's Not Rocket Science" in *Hispanic Business (September 2007, pp. 30, 32)* [28243], [40888], [47314]

"It's Not 'Unprofessional' To Gossip At Work" in *Harvard Business Review (Vol. 88, September 2010, No. 9, pp. 28)* [29099], [38129]

It's Not Who You Know - It's Who Knows You!: The Small Business Guide to Raising Your Profits by Raising Your Profile [496], [22351], [23125], [29903], [40041], [42487], [42636], [44123]

It's Our Business [48682]

"It's So You! Consignment Chop Owner Thrilled to See Vision Come to Fruition" in *News-Herald (August 27, 2010)* [4120], [4242], [5145], [7839]

"It's Tea-Riffic! Natural Bottled Tea Satisfies Void In Beverage Market" in *Small Business Opportunities (November 2007)* [9688], [32098]

"It's Time to Take Full Responsibility" in *Harvard Business Review (Vol. 88, October 2010, No. 10, pp. 42)* [2292], [10999], [16592], [19638], [30946], [38130], [42488]

"It's Time To Swim" in *Canadian Business (Vol. 81, March 3, 2008, No. 3, pp. 37)* [11122], [27388], [33257], [36640], [39164], [41678]

"It's Time to Wise Up: Income Trusts" in *Canadian Business (Vol. 79, November 6, 2006, No. 22, pp. 24)* [8468], [12549], [27389], [30947]

"It's What You Know. It's Who You Know. It's China" in *Inc. (Vol. 33, October 2011, No. 8, pp. 80)* [5397], [23126], [36641]

It's Your Business [50562]; [52332]; [52909]; [54748]

It's Your Choice [26601]

It's Your Life!: A Gynecologist's Guide for Taking Control of It [34340]

It's Your Ship [26660], [29100], [29904], [31587], [38131]

"ITT Places Its Bet With Defense Buy; Selling Equipment to Army Pays Off" in *Crain's New York Business (Vol. 24, January 7, 2008)* [23127], [39165], [41996]

The Itty Bitty Guide to Business Travel [20554], [24876]

"Ivernia Mine Closing Could Boost Lead" in *Globe & Mail (April 4, 2007, pp. B5)* [8469], [12550], [33784]

Ivey Publishing [59948]

Ivins, Phillips, Barker Library [22089]

"Ivorydale Looks to Clean Up" in *Business Courier (Vol. 26, January 15, 2010, No. 39, pp. 1)* [2045], [23128], [39166], [41111]

Ivy Software Inc. [59045]

Ivy Tech State College of Indiana - Columbus [51766]

Ivy Tech State College of Indiana - Fort Wayne [51767]

Ivy Tech State College of Indiana - Gary [51768]

"Izod, Loft Outlets Coming To Tanger" in *New Hampshire Business Review (Vol. 33, March 25, 2011, No. 6, pp. 30)* [4243], [7840], [43060]

Izzo's Illegal Burrito [18160]

J

J Ed Turner Co. [17603]

J. K. Lasser's Small Business Taxes 2008: Your Complete Guide to a Better Bottom Line [46283]

J-U-B Engineers Inc. [13972]

"Jack Be Nimble" in *Business Courier (Vol. 24, October 26, 2008, No. 28, pp. 1)* [25559], [34975], [44394]

Jacksboro Chamber of Commerce [58247]

Jackson Area Chamber of Commerce [57729]

Jackson Area Chamber of Commerce (JACC) [53664]; [56183]

Jackson - Beldon Chamber of Commerce (JBCC) [56184]

Jackson Chamber of Commerce (JCOC) [54064]

Jackson Chamber of Commerce [53881]

Jackson Commerce [53869]

Jackson County Area Chamber of Commerce [50563]

Jackson County Chamber of Commerce [50176]

Jackson County Chamber of Commerce (JCCC) [55740]

Jackson County Public Library - Indiana & Jackson County History and Genealogy Collection [9522]

Jackson County Report [55741]

Jackson Enterprise Center [53927]

Jackson Hewitt Tax Service [19719]

Jackson Hole Chamber of Commerce [59829]

C. E. Jackson, Jr. [5651]

Jackson Procurement Technical Assistance Center - Center for Industrial Services (CIS) [57816]

Jackson State University - Bureau of Business and Economic Research [43336]

Jackson State University Small Business Development Center [53811]

Jacksonville Area Chamber of Commerce [51157]

"Jacksonville-based Interline Expanding in Janitorial-Sanitation Market" in *Florida Times-Union (May 10, 2011)* [2623], [23129], [26762], [40042], [44395]

Jacksonville Chamber of Commerce [58248]

Jacksonville Chamber of Commerce and Visitor Center [56798]

Jacksonville Chamber of Commerce [56798]

Jacksonville - Onslow Chamber of Commerce [55742]

Jacksonville Regional Chamber of Commerce [50177]

Jacksonville State University - Center for Economic Development (CED) [27940]

Jacksonville State University Small Business Development Center [47605]

Jacobs Institute of Women's Health (JIWH) [34664]

Jacobs-Schneider Interior Design Inc. [41608]

Jafco Ventures [49249]

Jaffrey Chamber of Commerce (JCC) [54595]

JAGEN UND FISCHEN - International Exhibition for Hunters, Fishermen and Marksmen [1253], [19379], [46763]

Jam Handy Organization [28450]

Jamaica Business Resource Center [60637]; [60638]

Jamaica Business Resource Center - Queens, Nassau, Suffolk Minority Business Enterprise Center [55386]

JAMA--Physician Service Opportunities Overseas Issue [19159]

James B. Sheets, Attorney at Law [24123]

James Madison University Small Business Development Center (JMU SBDC) [58799]

Jamestown Area Chamber of Commerce [55918]

Jamestown Small Business Development Center [55022]

"Jamieson Eyes $175 Million Trust IPO" in *Globe & Mail (March 7, 2006, pp. B1)* [8470], [12551], [24425], [41997]

The Kaleel Jamison Consulting Group Inc. [26708]

Jan and Jeannie Levinson's Startup Guide to Guerilla Marketing: A Simple Battle Plan for Boosting Profits [23130], [39543]

Janbury [5690]

Jancis Robinson's Wine Course [19270]

Janco Associates Inc. [58713]

"J&J Snack Rakes in Sales" in *Philadelphia Business Journal (Vol. 28, September 25, 2009, No. 32, pp. 1)* [9943], [19228], [23131]

Jane Rule. . .Writing [6854]

Jane's Aero-Engines [746]

Jane's Aircraft Upgrades [747]

Jane's Airports and Handling Agents [748]

Jane's Airports and Handling Agents Library [748]

Jane's Helicopter Markets and Systems [749]

Jane's Merchant Ships [7391]

Jane's Unmanned Aerial Vehicles and Targets [750]

Jane's World Airlines [751]

"Janet Froetscher, CEO, United Way of Metropolitan Chicago" in *Crain's Chicago Business (Vol. 31, May 5, 2008, No. 18, pp. 26)* [29905], [38132], [41998], [45946]

Jani-King Canada [6575]

Jani-King International, Inc. [2665]

"Janitorial Equipment and Supplies US Market" in *PR Newswire (October 24, 2011)* [2624], [23132], [41112], [44396]

"Janson: Duke's Dynamo, Regional President Focuses on Economic Development" in *Business Courier (Vol. 27, July 9, 2010, No. 10, pp. 1)* [27390], [41999], [42381]

Jantize America [2666]

Japan Aikido Association U.S.A. [14082]

"Japan-Brand Shortages Will Linger Into '12" in *Automotive News (Vol. 86, October 31, 2011, No. 6488, pp. 1)* [1554], [14919], [39167]

Japan External Trade Organization (JETRO) [36301]

Japan-America Society of Greater Cincinnati - Greater Cincinnati Chamber of Commerce [56149]

Japanese Chamber of Commerce and Industry of New York (JCCINY) [36302]

Japanese Chamber of Commerce of Southern California (JCCSC) [48683]

Japanese Chamber of Commerce of New York [36302]

Jardin Publishing [49404]

Jarlett Consulting [25286]

Jasper Chamber of Commerce (JCC) [51651]

Jasper Chamber of Commerce [58249]

Jasper County Chamber of Commerce (JCCC) [51158]; [57487]

Jasper County Improvement Association [51158]

Jasper Fact Book/Membership Directory [51652]

Jasper Lake Sam Rayburn Area Chamber of Commerce [58249]

Jasper, TX [58250]

JatoTech Ventures [58562]

Java Hut Drive Thru [4324]

Java for Non-Programmers (Onsite) [28049]

JavaScript for Non-Programmers [21040]

"Javo Beverage to Feature On-Demand Coffee System" in *GlobeNewswire (October 20, 2009)* [5806], [20379], [46660]

JAX FAX--Travel Marketing Magazine [20160]

"Jay Berkowitz to Present Making Social Media Money Seminar at Affiliate Summit West" in *Entertainment Close-Up (January 15, 2010)* [11752], [20380], [22352], [40043], [43518], [46661]

Jazz Greats from Louis Armstrong to Duke Ellington [14666]

Jazzin' across the Floor [6407]

J.B. Geller Consulting Inc. [25287]

"J.C. Evans Seeks Bankruptcy Protection" in *Austin Business Journal (Vol. 31, August 12, 2011, No. 23, pp. A1)* [5398], [27391], [31588]

JC Ventures Inc. [32287]

"J.C. Watts First Black John Deere Dealer" in *Black Enterprise (Vol. 37, November 2006, No. 4, pp. 36)* [14920], [23133], [25127], [29906], [40773]

J.D. Byrider [14996]

JDE Construction Management Ltd. [5652]

"JDF Integration: 3 Key Tips" in *American Printer (Vol. 128, August 1, 2011, No. 8)* [4488], [16379], [20779]

JDI Cleaning Systems Inc. [2667]

"Jean Coutu Resuscitates Bottom Line" in *Globe & Mail (January 11, 2006, pp. B5)* [8471], [12552], [23134]

"Jean-Rober's 'oui'" in *Business Courier (Vol. 27, August 6, 2010, No. 14, pp. 1)* [17851], [28244]

"Jeans Draw a Global Following" in *Marketing to Women (Vol. 21, April 2008, No. 4, pp. 6)* [4244], [39168], [40044]

Jefferies Broadview [42332]

Jefferson Area Chamber of Commerce [51914]; [56185]

Jefferson Chamber of Commerce [52478]; [59614]

Jefferson City Area Chamber of Commerce [54065]

Jefferson College - Extended Learning [54203]

Jefferson College of Health Sciences Learning Resource Center [1447]

Jefferson County Chamber of Commerce [50564]; [56186]; [57730]; [59409]

Jefferson County Chamber of Commerce (JCCC) [51159]

Jefferson County Chamber of Commerce [56808]

Jefferson County Job Development Corporation [55486]

Jefferson Parish Economic Development Commission - Business Innovation Center and Technology Incubator [52529]

Jefferson Park Chamber of Commerce [51160]

Jefferson Partners [59927]

Jeffersontown Chamber of Commerce [52333]

Jeffrey Lant Associates Publications [53098]

Jegi Capital, LLC [55429]

Jenkins Group Inc. [53530]

Jenks Chamber of Commerce (JCC) [56540]

"Jennifer Hernandez Helps Developers Transform Contaminated Properties" in *Hispanic Business (Vol. 30, April 2008, No. 4, pp. 32)* [5399], [17352], [23905], [29907], [30698], [33785]

Jennings County Chamber of Commerce [51653]

Jennings County Chamber of Commerce/Economic Development [51653]

Jenny Craig Weight Loss & Management Centres [21286]

Jensen Beach Chamber of Commerce [50178]

Lawrence Jeppson Associates [1373]

Jerome Chamber of Commerce [47920]; [50774]
Jerry's Subs and Pizza [16156], [18161]
Jersey Cape Vacation Guide [54749]
Jersey Caper [54750]
Jersey County Business Association (JCBA) [51161]
Jersey County Chamber of Commerce [51161]
Jersey Mike's Subs [6471]
Jerusalem Venture Partners /JVP [55430]
Jessamine County Chamber of Commerce [52334]
Jessamine Journal [52335]
Jest for the Health of It Services [2906], [26038], [34624]
Jesup Chamber of Commerce [51915]
Jet-Black World's Most Beautiful Driveway's & Parking Lots [18332]
Jet City Pizza [16157]
"Jet Sales Put Bombardier Back in Black" in Globe & Mail (March 30, 2006, pp. B1) [12553], [23135], [39169]
Jewelers of America (JA) [13260]
Jewelers International Showcase [13291]
Jewelers' Security Alliance (JSA) [1209], [13261], [18380]
Jewelers Security Alliance of the U.S. [1209], [13261], [18380]
Jewelers Vigilance Committee (JVC) [13262]
Jewell Chamber of Commerce [52125]
Jewellers Vigilance Canada (JVC) [13263]
Jewellers Vigilance Canada Action Update [13264]
The Jewelry Appraiser [1222], [13285]
Jewelry Industry Council [13265]
Jewelry Information Center (JIC) [13265]
Jewels by Stacy Appraisals [47143]
Jewish Board of Family and Children's Services, Inc. - Child Development Center [4040]
The Jewish Century [29908], [40889]
Jewish Funeral Directors of America (JFDA) [9322]
Jewish Historical Society of New York, Inc. Library [9523]
Jewish Lights Publishing - Longhill Partners Inc. [38768]
JF Robinson Research & Demographics [40621]
Jiffy Lube Canada [16677]
Jiffy Lube Intl., Inc. [16678]
Jim Thorpe Chamber of Commerce [57142]
Jim Thorpe' Visitor's Guide [57143]
Jimmy John's Gourmet Sandwiches [6472]
Jim's Mowing Canada Inc. [13519]
JIS [13291]
JK Lasser's Small Business Taxes 2077: Your Complete Guide to a Better Bottom Line [19639], [46284]
JK&B Capital [51406]
JKM Associates [18058]
J.L. Albright Venture Partners / JLA Ventures [59928]
J.L. Meaher & Associates Inc. [7379]
JLA Consulting [224]
JLA Publications [53098]
JMW Group Inc. [55528]
"Jo-Ann Fabric and Craft Stores Joins ArtFire.com to Of-fer Free Online Craft Marketplace" in Internet Wire (January 26, 2010) [5990], [6109], [15333], [18725], [28735], [42000]
"Jo-Ann Launches Quilt Your Colors Contest to Celebrate National Sewing Month" in Internet Wire (September 10, 2010) [6110], [18726], [40045]
Jo To Go Coffee [1810], [4325]
"Job Corps Center Remains Vacant After Operator is Booted" in Tampa Bay Business Journal (Vol. 30, January 15, 2010, No. 4, pp. 1) [33439], [35828]
Job Finders Employment Service [225]
"Job-Hopping to the Top and Other Career Fallacies" in Harvard Business Review (Vol. 88, July-August 2010, No. 7-8, pp. 154) [35382], [35829]
"Job Losses and Budget Shortfall Adding to Economic Woes" in Sacramento Business Journal (Vol. 25, July 11, 2008, No. 19, pp. 1) [27392], [33786], [35383]
"Job Reviews: Annual Assessments Still the Norm" in HR Specialist (Vol. 8, September 2010, No. 9, pp. 1) [35830], [38133]
"Job Search Made Easy" in Black Enterprise (Vol. 38, January 2008, No. 6, pp. 54) [7788], [38134]
"Job Seeker's Readiness Guide: Unemployment's High and Competition is Tough" in Black Enterprise (Vol. 40, July 2010, No. 12, pp. 83) [25560], [35384], [35831]
"Jobless Rate Climbs Unexpectedly in December" in Globe & Mail (January 7, 2006, pp. B5) [27393], [32785]
"Jobs Boom Ramps Up in March" in Globe & Mail (April 7, 2007, pp. B1) [27394], [32786]
"Jobs Data Show A Slow Leak" in Barron's (Vol. 88, July 7, 2008, No. 27, pp. 34) [23136], [27395], [35385], [38135], [39170]
"Jobs Data Show Wild Card" in Barron's (Vol. 90, September 6, 2010, No. 36, pp. M12) [35386], [35832], [45512]

"Jobs, Export Surge Confirm Recovery" in Globe & Mail (March 10, 2007, pp. B5) [11123], [27396], [32787], [36642]
Jobs for the Future (JFF) [4756]
Jobs In Horticulture Inc. [3394], [9835], [13435]
"The Jobs Man" in Business Courier (Vol. 26, December 25, 2009, No. 35, pp. 1) [6966], [7789], [18558], [29909], [35387], [35833]
Joe Loue Tout Rent All Inc. [17835]
"Joe Wikert, General Manager, O'Reilly Technology Exchange" in Information Today (Vol. 26, February 2009, No. 2, pp. 21) [15546], [25561], [28736], [38136]
Joey's Only Seafood Restaurant [18162]
John Bollinger's Capital Growth Letter [13126]
John F. Kennedy on Leadership: The Lessons and Legacy of a President [29910], [38137]
The John Liner Letter [11468], [36251]
John Pappajohn Entrepreneurial Center [52006]
"John Risley" in Canadian Business (Vol. 80, February 26, 2007, No. 5, pp. 70) [29911], [38138]
John Tyler Community College [59035]
"Johnny Royal of Luthier Society Unveils Archimedes 1.0 Trailer" in Internet Wire (October 22, 2009) [3556], [7934], [11753], [18926], [40046], [45145]
Johnny Tremain [28421]
Johns Hopkins University - Center for Hospital Finance and Management [34665]
Johns Hopkins University - Health Services Research and Development Center [34666]
Carol R. Johnson & Associates, Inc. Library [13453]
Bill Johnson [26633]
Johnson, Butler & Co. (JBC) [42333]
Johnson City Business Magazine [57731]
Johnson City Chamber of Commerce [58251]
Johnson City - Jonesboro - Washington County Chamber of Commerce (JCJWCCC) [57732]
Johnson City/Washington County Area Chamber of Com-merce [57732]
Johnson County Chamber of Commerce (JCCC) [57733]
Johnson County Chamber Newsletter [48076]
Johnson County Chamber of Commerce [48035]
Johnson Creek Area Chamber of Commerce [59615]
Donald Wade Johnson [50388]
Johnson and Johnson - Consumer and Personal Products Worldwide Library [1917], [2070]
Johnson & Johnson Pharmaceutical Research & Development - Hartman Library [6716]
"Johnson Publishing Expands: Moving Into Television and Internet To Extend Brand" in Black Enterprise (October 2007) [3181], [11754], [15547], [19937], [23137], [28737]
Johnson & Wales University - Harborside Culinary Library [3487], [5853], [10832]
Johnson & Wales University (Providence, Rhode Island) [57396]
Johnsonburg Chamber of Commerce [57144]
"Johnson's Taps Online Animation" in Marketing to Women (Vol. 21, April 2008, No. 4, pp. 3) [497], [7935], [11755], [21137], [39171], [40047]
Johnston Associates, Inc. [54853]
Johnston Co. [2907], [13848], [26039], [32043], [38751], [44946]
Johnstown-Alleghenies SCORE [56934]
Johnstown-Milliken Chamber of Commerce [49535]
The Joint Commission Journal on Quality Improvement [34546]
Joint Committee on Mortuary Education [9315]
Joint Directory: Financial Analysts Federation and Institute of Chartered Financial Analysts [12035]
Joint Industry Group (JIG) [11021], [36303]
"Joint Venture Plans Bronzeville Project" in Business Journal-Milwaukee (Vol. 25, October 5, 2007, No. 1, pp. A1) [5400], [17793], [42001]
Joliet Region Chamber of Commerce and Industry [51162]
Jones & Co. [26121], [32317]
Jones County Chamber of Commerce [53870]
Jones County Junior College Small Business Develop-ment Center [53812]
Jones NCTI [3158], [19888]
Jonesboro Regional Chamber of Commerce [48077]
Jon'Ric International Spas [44614]
Joplin Area Chamber of Commerce (JACC) [54066]
The Jordan Edmiston Group Inc. / JEGI Capital [55431]
Joseph J. Walczak, P.C. [24124]
Joseph Newman Innovation Center [54194]
Josephson Institute of Ethics [31005]
Joshua Area Chamber of Commerce (JACC) [58252]
Joshua Tree Chamber of Commerce [48684]
Journal of Accountancy [176]
Journal of Accounting Research [177]

Journal of Advertising Research [653]
Journal of Agromedicine [34547]
Journal of the American Animal Hospital Association [1076]
Journal of the American Board of Family Medicine [34548]
Journal of American College Health [34549]
Journal of the American Medical Association--Physician Service Opportunities Overseas Section [19159]
Journal of the American Oil Chemists' Society [44033]
Journal of the American Pharmacists Association [6682]
Journal of the American Society for Information Science and Technology: The Official Journal of the American Society for Information Science [11241]
Journal of the American Taxation Association (JATA) [178], [19692]
Journal of the American Veterinary Medical Association [1077]
Journal of Andrology [44034]
Journal of Asia-Pacific Business [36901]
Journal of the Association of Nurses in AIDS Care [34550]
Journal of the Audio Engineering Society [17648]
Journal of Behavioral Health Services & Research [34551]
Journal of Biochemical and Molecular Toxicology [44035]
Journal of Bioenergetics and Biomembranes [44036]
Journal of Biological Rhythms [44037]
The Journal of Business Valuation [33082]
Journal of Cellular Biochemistry [44038]
Journal of Chemical Ecology: Official Journal of the International Society of Chemical Ecology [44039]
Journal of Chemical Technology and Biotechnology: International Research in Process, Environmental, and Monitoring Technology [44040]
Journal of Clinical Microbiology [44041]
Journal of Communications Technology and Electronics [44042]
Journal of Compensation and Benefits [22019]
Journal of Construction Accounting and Taxation [5600]
Journal of Culinary Science & Technology [15175]
Journal of Cutaneous Medicine and Surgery [34147]
Journal of Database Management [4736], [4894]
Journal of Deferred Compensation: Nonqualified Plans and Executive Compensation [22020]
Journal of Drug Education [46071]
Journal of East-West Business [36902]
Journal of Economics and Management Strategy [27908], [38601]
Journal of Employee Communication Management / Re-agan Report [22500]
Journal of Employment Counseling [3366], [6983]
Journal of Environmental Engineering [44043]
Journal of Ethnic & Cultural Diversity in Social Work: In-novations in Theory, Research & Practice [34552]
Journal of Film and Video [8007]
Journal of Financial Planning [8868]
Journal of Financial Service Professionals [11469]
Journal of Foodservice Business Research [18029]
The Journal of Futures Markets: Futures, Options, and other Derivative Products [2715]
Journal of Global Marketing [40550]
Journal of Graphoanalysis [10115]
Journal of Health Care Chaplaincy [34553]
Journal of Health Care Finance [34554]
Journal of Health Care for the Poor and Underserved (JHCPU) [34555]
Journal of Health & Social Behavior [34556]
Journal for Healthcare Quality: The Official Journal of the National Association for Healthcare Quality [34557]
Journal of Hospitality Marketing & Management [10774]
Journal of Insurance Regulation [11470]
Journal of Intensive Care Medicine [34558]
Journal of International Consumer Marketing [40551]
Journal of International Food and Agribusiness Marketing [21751]
Journal of Investigative Surgery [44044]
The Journal of Investing [13127]
Journal of IT Financial Management [8869]
Journal of Labelled Compounds and Radiopharmaceuti-cals [44045]
Journal of Management Accounting Research [179]
Journal of Marketing Channels: Distribution Systems, Strategy & Management [40552]
Journal of Marketing Research [14021]
Journal of Materials in Civil Engineering [44046]
Journal of Morphology [44047]
Journal of Music Teacher Education [14639]
Journal of Natural History [44048]
Journal of Neurochemistry: Official Journal of the International Society for Neurochemistry [44049]
Journal of Northwest Atlantic Fishery Science [9001]
Journal of Nuclear Cardiology: Official Journal of the American Society of Nuclear Cardiology [14230], [34559]

Kimble County Chamber of Commerce (KCCC) [58259]
Kimmel & Associates Inc. [10185]
Kinderance International, Inc. [4025]
The Kindess Revolution: The Company-Wide Culture Shift That Inspires Phenomenal Customer Service [26469], [38150]
Kinetic Ventures LLC [52772]
"Kinetico Exec Going Global to Increase Growth Flow" in *Crain's Cleveland Business (Vol. 28, October 1, 2007, No. 39, pp. 5)* [23145], [24430], [36646], [38151], [39180]
KINETIDEX® System [6705], [10589], [14300]
King of Capital [8479], [11386], [12562], [29916], [36183], [41116]
King Chamber of Commerce (KCC) [55744]
King Chamber of Commerce Newsletter [55745]
King City Chamber of Commerce and Agriculture [48692]
King City and Southern Monterey Chamber of Commerce and Agriculture [48692]
"King of the Crib: How Good Samaritan Became Ohio's Baby HQ" in *Business Courier (Vol. 27, June 18, 2010, No. 7, pp. 1)* [1661], [19160], [23146], [25567], [34345]
"King Ink" in *Inc. (November 2007, pp. 98-102, 104, 106, 108)* [19586]
"The King of Kincardine" in *Canadian Business (Vol. 79, October 9, 2006, No. 20, pp. 101)* [12563], [41371], [44403]
The King of Madison Avenue: David Ogilvy and the Making of Modern Advertising [499], [40051]
The King of Vodka: The Story of Pyotr Smirnov and the Upheaval of an Empire [2459], [29917], [39181], [40052]
Kingdom of Callaway Chamber of Commerce (KCCC) [54072]
Kingfisher Chamber of Commerce [56541]
Kingman Area Chamber of Commerce [47921]
Kingman Area Chamber of Commerce (KACC) [52131]
Kingman Area Chamber Report [47922]
Kingman Chamber of Commerce [52131]
Kings County Museum Library [9524]
Kings Mountain Chamber of Commerce [55669]
Kings Park Chamber of Commerce [55262]
Kingsburg District Chamber of Commerce [48693]
Kingsland - Lake LBJ Chamber of Commerce (KCC) [58260]
Kingsport Area Chamber of Commerce [57734]
Kingsport SCORE [57633]
Kingston Chamber of Commerce [59195]
Kingstree Chamber of Commerce [57536]
Kingsville Chamber of Commerce (KCOC) [58261]
Kingwood Center Library [10377]
Kinsley Area Chamber of Commerce [52094]
Kinston-Lenoir County Chamber of Commerce (KLCCC) [55746]
"Kiosk Outfit ecoATM Now Recycling Video Games" in *San Diego Union-Tribune (October 7, 2010)* [948], [13326], [17715]
Kiplinger Washington Editors Inc. [49864]
Kirbyville Centennial Magazine 1995 [58262]
Kirbyville Chamber of Commerce (KCC) [58263]
Kirkland Works [59218]
Dr. Donald Kirkpatrick [46575]
Kirksville Area Chamber of Commerce [54073]
Kirkus Reviews [2189]
Kirkwood Area Chamber of Commerce [54074]
Kirkwood Small Business Development Center (Marion, Iowa) [51778]
Kirlan Venture Capital, Inc. [59331]
"Kirnross Holds Firm on Offer for Bema" in *Globe & Mail (January 20, 2007, pp. B5)* [42006]
Kiss Theory Good Bye: Five Proven Ways to Get Extraordinary Results in Any Company [25866], [32790], [38152]
Kissimmee - Osceola County Chamber of Commerce [50183]
KIT Publishers [59047]
Kitchen Cabinet Manufacturers Association (KCMA) [10451]
Kitchen Capers [3985]
"The Kitchen is Closed; Eateries Forced Out by Soaring Rents, Declining Revenues" in *Crain's New York Business (January 21, 2008)* [16531], [16955], [17358], [17941], [27402]
Kitchen Gardener: Growing and Cooking Great Food [10367]
Kitchen Solvers [3444]
Kitchen Table Entrepreneurs: How Eleven Women Escaped Poverty and Became Their Own Bosses [29918], [47317]
Kitchen Tune-Up & Kitchen Tune-Up Express [3445]
Kittochtinny Historical Society Library [9525]
Klamath Community College Small Business Development Center [56677]

Klamath County Chamber of Commerce (KCCC) [56801]
Kleiner Perkins Caufield & Byers (Menlo Park) [49251]
The Kleper Report on Digital Publishing [6528]
Kline Hawkes & Co. [49252]
KLM Capital Group [49253]
Kluger and Associates Inc. [5084]
KMWorld: Creating and Managing the Knowledge-Based Enterprise [6529]
"A Knack for Entrepreneurship" in *Hispanic Business (January-February 2008, pp. 42, 44-45)* [29919], [40776], [47039]
Knifemakers' Guild (KG) [5961]
"Knight Sold as Industry Struggles" in *Globe & Mail (March 14, 2006, pp. D1)* [15548], [42007]
Knightdale Chamber of Commerce [55747]
Knightdale Chamber of Commerce Map of Knightdale [55748]
Knightdale Chamber of Commerce Membership Directory/Economic Data Booklet [55749]
Knights Inn [10805]
Knights Inn Canada Franchise Systems Limited [10806]
Knightstown Area Chamber of Commerce [51656]
Knightstown Indiana Chamber of Commerce [51656]
Stan Knipe & Associates [43282]
The Knitting Guild Association (TKGA) [5962]
Knock Your Socks Off Selling [25568], [43521]
Knockout Entrepreneur: My Ten Count Strategy for Winning at Business [29920], [32791]
Knopf Doubleday Publishing Group [55523]
"Know the Facts About Natural Gas!" in *Indoor Comfort Marketing (Vol. 70, August 2011, No. 8, pp. 26)* [833], [7252], [7611], [28740], [30702], [45515]
Know-How: The 8 Skills That Separate People Who Perform from Those Who Don't [29921], [38153]
"Know It All Finds Applicants are Stretching the Truth" in *Philadelphia Business Journal (Vol. 28, September 11, 2009, No. 30, pp. 1)* [35388], [35834], [44404]
Know What You're Selling [6447]
Know-Who Based Entrepreneurship from Knowledge Creation to Business Implementation [29922], [37246]
Know Your Basic Finance (Onsite) [31170]
"Know Your Bones: Take Your Bone Health Seriously" in *Women In Business (Vol. 62, June 2010, No. 2, pp. 40)* [34346], [38154], [47318]
Know Your Chamber [52725]
"Know Your Numbers" in *Inc. (Volume 32, December 2010, No. 10, pp. 39)* [103], [2294], [19641], [21387], [31596], [37408], [46285]
"Knowing Is Growing: Five Strategies To Develop You and Your Business" in *Black Enterprise (Vol. 38, November 2007, No. 4, pp. 106)* [23147], [25867], [28246], [29923], [40053]
Knowing the Prospect [8888], [13161], [43729]
"Knowledge Workers" in *Canadian Business (Vol. 79, October 9, 2006, No. 20, pp. 59)* [32792], [38155]
KnowledgePoints Inc. [28463]
Knox County Chamber of Commerce [51657]; [52338]
"Knox County Schools Debate Outsourcing Janitorial Services" in *(March 29, 2011)* [2625], [28247], [41679], [44405]
Knoxville Area Chamber Partnership [57735]
Knoxville Business College - Library. [10836], [44979]
Knoxville Chamber of Commerce and Economic Development [51918]
Knoxville Chamber of Commerce [51918]
Knoxville News Sentinel [57736]
Knoxville Procurement Technical Assistance Center - Center for Industrial Services (CIS) [57817]
Koach Enterprises [32289]
Koch Group Inc. [2910], [13850], [26042], [40624]
Kocham Business Directory [36647]
Kochman Mavrelis Associates Inc. (KMA) [40946]
"Kodak Cuts Deep in Effort to Change Focus" in *Globe & Mail (February 9, 2007, pp. B8)* [15827], [25130], [34980]
"Kodak Offers Cloud-Based Operating Option" in *American Printer (Vol. 128, June 1, 2011, No. 6)* [4490], [16381], [20781], [28741], [42008]
Organization of American Kodaly Educators (OAKE) [14611]
Kodaly Envoy [14641]
Kodaly Society of Canada, Alla Breve [14642]
"Kodiak Bucks Bear Market" in *Austin Business JournalInc. (Vol. 29, December 18, 2009, No. 41, pp. 1)* [5753], [23148], [24745], [27403], [34981], [35389], [44690]
Kodiak Chamber of Commerce (KCC) [47807]
John Michael Kohler Arts Center Resource Center [6172]
"Kohler Building Earns LEED Silver Certification" in *Contractor (Vol. 56, September 2009, No. 9, pp. 12)* [7253], [16247], [30703], [39182]
Kohn Engineering [2573], [5654]
Kohr Bros. Frozen Custard & Smoothie Station [10968]

Kokomo - Howard County Chamber of Commerce (KHCCC) [51658]
Kolache Factory, Inc. [1811]
Komei Inc. [22533]
Kona Kohala Chamber of Commerce (KKCC) [50711]
T. Kondos Associates [41612]
The Konlin Letter [13128]
Kora Management Ltd. [5655]
Korean Trader's Directory [36647]
Kosciusko-Attala Chamber of Commerce (KACC) [53871]
The Kosciusko Business Insights [51659]
"Kosher Ice Cream Features Traditional Jewish Ingredients" in *Ice Cream Reporter (Vol. 23, August 20, 2010, No. 9, pp. 5)* [10892], [41117]
Kostka & Company Inc. [2911], [13851], [26043], [38755]
Kott Koatings, Inc. [16306]
Kountze Chamber of Commerce (KCC) [58264]
Kouts Chamber of Commerce (KCC) [51660]
KPMG LLP Library [2336]
KPMG L.L.P. Resource Centre [2337]
KPMG - Research Centre [277], [2338], [19761]
KPMG Resource Centre [278]
KR Finance and Banking Newsletters [2740], [13203]
Kraft Foods, Inc. - Technical Information Center [15221]
"Kraft Not Alone" in *Crain's Chicago Business (Vol. 30, February 2007, No. 6, pp. 8)* [30948], [40054], [42489], [42637]
"Kraft Taps Cheese Head; Jordan Charged With Fixing Foodmaker's Signature Product" in *Crain's Chicago Business (April 14, 2008)* [21614], [25569], [38156], [39183]
Steven E. Kramer C.P.A. [226]
L.G. Kranick & Associates [42336]
Krantz Marketing Services L.L.C. [40625]
Kremmling Area Chamber of Commerce and Visitor Center [49537]
KressCox Associates [1303]
"Kroger Forges Ahead with Fuel Centers" in *Business Courier (Vol. 26, December 25, 2009, No. 35, pp. 1)* [5403], [9944], [18602]
"Kroger Girds for Invasion of U.K. Chain" in *Business Courier (Vol. 24, November 2, 2008, No. 29, pp. 1)* [9945], [24431], [25570], [36648]
Kroll Zolfo Cooper L.L.C. [241], [2984], [3093], [13894], [21473], [26110]
Charles A. Krueger [21466], [32045]
Krumkill Stables [15196]
The Krystal Co. [18169]
K.T. Analytics Library [19825]
KTB Ventures / KTB Venture Capital [49254]
Kubba Consultants Inc. [2912], [26044], [40626], [41300], [42904]
"Kubicki Juggles Lineup at Vianda" in *Business Courier (Vol. 26, December 11, 2009, No. 33, pp. 1)* [15166], [16956], [17359], [26470], [34347], [40055], [42009]
William E. Kuhn & Associates [2913], [13852], [26045], [29257], [32046], [36045], [38756], [43765]
Kumon Math and Reading Centres [20744]
Kumon North America, Inc. [28464]
Kuna Chamber of Commerce [50776]
"Kuno Creative to Present B2B Social Media Campaign Webinar" in *Entertainment Close-Up (August 25, 2011)* [11761], [20382], [21142], [28742], [40056], [42638], [46663]
Kurt Salmon Associates [43283]
Kurt Salmon Associates Inc. [43283]
Kurt Weill Foundation. [14690], [14774]
Kutler Consultants [26634]
Kutztown University Small Business Development Center (KU SBDC) [56908]
KV Marketing Inc. [10440], [10505]
Kwik Kloset [16498]
Kwik Kopy Business Centers [673], [4554], [5870], [16436]
Kwik-Kopy Printing Canada [16437]
"KXAN Seeks Larger Studio, Office Space" in *Austin Business Journal (Vol. 31, May 27, 2011, No. 12, pp. A1)* [3182], [5404], [14595], [17360], [19938], [24746], [44691]
Kyle Area Chamber of Commerce Business Directory and Guidebook [58265]
Kyle Area Chamber of Commerce and Visitors' Bureau [58266]
Kyle Chamber of Commerce [58266]
Kyocera International, Inc. [49255]
KZF Design Inc. [987]

L

L' Academie Canadienne de Medecine du Sport [16064]
L G Anthony Associates [2914], [10315], [26046]

LandaJob

MASTER INDEX

Land Survey Calculator **[19535]**
"Land Swap Key to Ending Royal Oak Project Impasse" in Crain's Detroit Business (Vol. 25, June 8, 2009, No. 23, pp. 20) **[5406]**, **[15933]**, **[33793]**
LandaJob Advertising Staffing Specialists **[4545]**
Landauer Realty Group Information Center **[17154]**, **[17615]**
Lander Area Chamber of Commerce (LACC) **[59831]**
"Landlord Puts 7 Tops Locations On Market" in Business First Buffalo (November 16, 2007, pp. 1) **[9947]**, **[17363]**
Landmark Partners, Inc. **[49779]**
Landor Assoc [4546]
Landor Associates **[4546]**
The Landplan Collaborative Ltd. **[9126]**
Landscape Architect and Specifier News **[13413]**
Landscape Architecture: The Magazine of the American Society of Landscape Architects **[13414]**
Landscape Architecture Foundation (LAF) **[13372]**; **[13461]**
Landscape Construction & Maintenance [13413]
The Landscape Contractor: Landscape Contracting **[13415]**
Landscape Equipment Safety for the 90s **[13425]**, **[13497]**
Landscape Journal **[13416]**
Landscape Management **[13417]**, **[13492]**
Landscape Tools: Use and Safety **[13426]**, **[13498]**
Landscape Trades: Canada's Premier Horticultural Trade Publication **[9812]**, **[13355]**, **[13418]**
Landscapes/Paysages **[13373]**
Lang Michener LLP Library **[24168]**
Langenwalter Carpet Dyeing **[20841]**
Langley Chamber of Commerce [59226]
Langley South Whidbey Chamber of Commerce **[59226]**
Langston University Small Business Development Center **[56428]**
Language Leaders Franchising LLC **[20493]**, **[28465]**
The Language of Success: Business Writing That Informs, Persuades, and Gets Results **[22356]**, **[22606]**
Languages Inc. **[20488]**
Lansing Regional Chamber of Commerce **[53346]**
Jeffrey Lant Associates Inc. **[9296]**, **[13753]**, **[40627]**, **[42556]**, **[53099]**
Lantis Fireworks & Lasers **[20214]**
"The Lap of Eco-Luxury" in Entrepreneur (Vol. 37, August 2009, No. 8, pp. 38) **[7612]**, **[10715]**, **[30704]**
Lapeer Area Chamber of Commerce (LACC) **[53347]**
Lapels Dry Cleaning **[6761]**
Lapidary Journal--Annual Buyers' Directory Issue **[13274]**
Lapidary Journal--Annual Buyers' Guide Issue [13274]
LaPorte Business Resource Guide **[51665]**
Lappeenrannan teknillinen yliopisto. [38843]
Lappeenranta University of Technology Library **[38843]**
Laramie Area Chamber of Commerce (LACC) **[59832]**
Laredo Chamber of Commerce [58278]
Laredo - Webb County Chamber of Commerce (LWCCC) **[58278]**
"Large Homes can be Energy Efficient Too" in Contractor (Vol. 56, October 2009, No. 10, pp. 5) **[834]**, **[5407]**, **[7254]**, **[7613]**, **[16958]**, **[30705]**
Largest Employers in the Portland/Vancouver Metropolitan Area **[56805]**
Larimer County Small Business Development Center **[49422]**
Larkspur Chamber of Commerce (LCC) **[48713]**
Larned Area Chamber of Commerce (LCC) **[52132]**
Larry Chase's Web Digest for Marketers (WDFM) **[11950]**, **[14022]**, **[40554]**
Larry's Giant Subs **[6473]**
LaRue County Chamber of Commerce **[52339]**
Las Animas - Bent County Chamber of Commerce **[49544]**
Las Cruces Chamber of Commerce [54960]
Las Cruces Small Business Development Center **[54898]**
Las Vegas Chamber of Commerce (LVCC) **[54497]**
Las Vegas Insider **[9413]**
Las Vegas Nevada Small Business Development Center **[54460]**
Las Vegas-San Miguel Chamber of Commerce (LVSMCC) **[54965]**
Las Vegas Small Business Development Center **[54899]**
LaSalle Capital Group, Inc. **[51409]**
"LaSalle Street Firms Cherry-Pick Talent As Wall Street Tanks" in Crain's Chicago Business (Vol. 31, November 17, 2008, No. 46) **[23150]**, **[27408]**, **[35393]**, **[38161]**, **[46889]**
Lassen County Chamber of Commerce (LCCC) **[48714]**
L'Association Canadienne d'Études Fiscales [27], [19594], [19775]
L'Association Canadienne de la Securite [18374]
L'Association canadienne de l'immeuble [16781]
L'Association Canadienne des Distributeurs de Produits Chimiques [26719]
L'Association Canadienne des Experts Independants - Association Canadienne Des Experts Independants [11272]
L'Association Canadienne des Journalistes [6781], [15489]
L'association Canadienne des Professionnels de la Vente [43343]
L'Association canadienne des sciences de l'information [11224]
L'Association Canadienne Marchands Numismatiques [4337]
L'association de l'industrie canadienne de L'enregistrement [17634]
L'Association des architects paysagistes du Canada [13368]
L'Association des Brasseurs du Canada - Association des Brasseurs du Canada [2444]
L'Association internationale de la gestion du personnel - Canada [35656]
"Last Founder Standing" in Conde Nast Portfolio (Vol. 2, June 2008, No. 6, pp. 124) **[2380]**, **[11762]**, **[15334]**, **[21143]**, **[23151]**, **[24435]**, **[25134]**, **[26764]**, **[27409]**, **[28743]**, **[29926]**, **[35394]**, **[38162]**, **[43522]**
"The Last Ingredient?" in Canadian Business (Vol. 81, October 13, 2008, No. 17, pp. 88) **[7937]**, **[12565]**, **[20255]**, **[36650]**, **[42012]**
"Late to Minivan Party, VW Hitches Ride With Daimler" in Globe & Mail (January 6, 2006, pp. B1) **[39184]**, **[42013]**
"A Late Night Run: After-Hours Pediatric Practice Fills Void for Affordable Urgent Care" in Black Enterprise (February 2008) **[34348]**, **[45517]**
Lateral Marketing: New Techniques for Finding Breakthrough Ideas **[500]**, **[40057]**
"Laterooms and Octopus Travel Top Greenlight's Integrated Search Report for the Hotel Sector" in Internet Wire (October 23, 2009) **[10716]**, **[11763]**, **[21144]**, **[40058]**
"The Latest on E-Verify" in Contractor (Vol. 56, September 2009, No. 9, pp. 58) **[835]**, **[5408]**, **[6892]**, **[18697]**, **[33794]**
"Latest Falls, Ontario Hotel Will Be 25-Story Westin" in Business First Buffalo (October 19, 2007, pp. 1) **[5409]**, **[10717]**
The Latest Scoop **[1630]**
"Latest Volley Tries to Press Port Group" in Business Courier (Vol. 26, November 20, 2009, No. 30, pp. 1) **[5410]**, **[14448]**, **[33795]**
Latham Area Chamber of Commerce [55170]
Latham Business and Professional Association [55170]
Lathrop Chamber of Commerce **[48715]**
Lathrop District Chamber of Commerce [48715]
"Lathrop Finds Partner In LA" in The Business Journal-Serving Metropolitan Kansas City (Vol. 27, November 21, 2008, No. 11, pp. 1) **[23152]**, **[23910]**, **[24436]**, **[25135]**, **[38163]**, **[42014]**
Debra F. Latimer Nutrition and Diabetes Associates L.L.C. **[15197]**
William Latimore Associates **[17593]**
Latin American Chamber of Commerce **[51388]**; **[51440]**
"The Latin Beat Goes On" in Barron's (Vol. 88, July 7, 2008, No. 27, pp. L5) **[8480]**, **[12566]**, **[21616]**, **[27410]**, **[31597]**, **[36651]**
Latin Business Association (LBA) **[40682]**
Latin Chamber of Commerce of Nevada **[54498]**
Latin Chamber of Commerce of U.S.A. **[36304]**
Latin Chamber of Commerce [36304]
"LatinWorks Cozies Up to Chevy in Detroit" in Austin Business Journal (Vol. 31, August 12, 2011, No. 23, pp. A1) **[501]**, **[14922]**, **[24748]**, **[40059]**, **[40891]**
Latrobe Area Chamber of Commerce **[57148]**
Latterell Venture Partners **[49257]**
Lauderdale By The Sea Chamber of Commerce (LSCC) **[50193]**
Lauderdale County Chamber of Commerce **[57737]**
"Laugh or Cry?" in Barron's (Vol. 88, March 24, 2008, No. 12, pp. 7) **[5411]**, **[8481]**, **[12567]**, **[14449]**, **[16959]**, **[17364]**, **[26257]**, **[27411]**, **[31598]**, **[37410]**, **[42015]**
Laughing Bear Newsletter **[2190]**
Robert J. Laughlin & Associates **[41615]**
Laughlin Chamber of Commerce **[54499]**
Laughlin Nevada Small Business Development Center **[54461]**
LaunchCyte LLC **[57291]**
Laund-UR-Mutt **[15684]**
Laundry & Cleaning Journal of Canada [6751]
Laundry and Cleaners Allied Trades Association [6739]
Laundry and Dry Cleaners Machinery Manufacturers Association [6739]
Laurel Chamber of Commerce **[54289]**
Laurel Highlands Chamber of Commerce (LHCC) **[57149]**
"Laurent Beaudoin" in Canadian Business (Vol. 80, April 9, 2007, No. 8, pp. 68) **[29927]**, **[32794]**
Laurentian Chamber of Commerce **[53672]**
Laurier Institute **[59949]**
Laurinburg/Scotland County Area Chamber of Commerce (LSCC) **[55753]**
Lava Hot Springs Chamber of Commerce (LHSCC) **[50777]**
Laval University - Centre d'Entrpreneuriat et de PME [44983]
Laval University - Centre for Entrepreneurship and Small Business **[44983]**
"Lavante, Inc. Joins Intersynthesis, Holistic Internet Marketing Company" in Internet Wire (November 5, 2009) **[11764]**, **[21145]**, **[23153]**, **[28744]**, **[40060]**
Laverne Area Chamber of Commerce **[56542]**
Lavonia Chamber of Commerce **[50568]**
"Law Allows Captive Insurance Companies to Form in State" in Crain's Detroit Business (Vol. 24, March 31, 2008, No. 13, pp. 29) **[11388]**, **[33796]**, **[36185]**
The Law Digest **[24151]**
The Law of Equal Employment Opportunity (Onsite) **[46831]**
"Law Firm Jones Day Coming to Boston" in Boston Business Journal (Vol. 30, November 19, 2010, No. 43, pp. 1) **[23911]**, **[24749]**, **[44692]**
"Law Firms Plan Rate Bumps" in Houston Business Journal (Vol. 40, December 25, 2009, No. 33, pp. 1) **[23912]**, **[25772]**
"Law Firms See Improvement in Financing Climate" in Sacramento Business Journal (Vol. 28, October 14, 2011, No. 33, pp. 1) **[14450]**, **[23913]**, **[27412]**, **[37411]**
"Law Firms Troll for Complaints Among Disgruntled Workers" in The Business Journal-Serving Greater Tampa Bay (Vol. 28, July 11, 2008) **[23154]**, **[23914]**, **[27413]**, **[46890]**
Law (in Plain English) for Small Business **[23915]**, **[32795]**
Law Offices of Robert J. Keller P.C. **[2690]**, **[11955]**
Law Offices of Suzanne C. Cummings & Associates, P.C. **[24126]**
"Law Reform, Collective Bargaining, and the Balance of Power: Results of an Empirical Study" in WorkingUSA (June 2008) **[23916]**, **[33797]**, **[46891]**
Law for the Small and Growing Business **[17365]**, **[23155]**, **[23917]**, **[31599]**, **[47468]**
Lawn & Landscape Maintenance [13419], [13493]
Lawn Care for the North American Gardener **[13499]**
Lawn Doctor, Inc. **[13520]**
Lawn and Garden **[13500]**
Lawn & Landscape Magazine **[13419]**, **[13493]**
Lawn Mower Institute [13376], [13467]
Lawns: Planting and Maintenance **[13501]**
Lawrence Chamber of Commerce **[52133]**
Lawrence County Chamber of Commerce **[57150]**; **[57738]**
Lawrence County Chamber of Commerce (LCCC) **[51171]**
Lawrence County Chamber of Commerce, Alabama **[47708]**
Lawrence Financial Group **[49258]**
"Lawrence: Larger than Life Sciences" in Business Journal-Serving Metropolitan Kansas City (Vol. 26, November 2, 2007, No. 8, pp. 1) **[34349]**, **[43887]**
Lawrence Regional Technology Center **[52211]**
Lawrence S. Jeppson & Associates [1373]
Lawrence Siegel-Consultant (LSC) **[5656]**
Lawrence University - Seeley G. Mudd Library - Music Collections **[14688]**, **[14773]**
Lawton Chamber of Commerce [56543]
Lawton - Fort Sill Chamber of Commerce and Industry **[56543]**
Lawton SCORE **[56447]**
Lawyer Locator **[24152]**
"Lawyers Cash In On Alcohol" in Business Journal Portland (Vol. 27, November 19, 2010, No. 38, pp. 1) **[1852]**, **[2460]**, **[13586]**, **[19229]**, **[23918]**, **[33798]**
"Lawyers Lock Up Cops as Clients" in Sacramento Business Journal (Vol. 28, April 8, 2011, No. 6, pp. 1) **[23919]**, **[42382]**, **[45518]**, **[46892]**
"Lawyers Sued Over Lapsed Lacrosse Patent" in Crain's Detroit Business (Vol. 25, June 8, 2009, No. 23, pp. 5) **[19332]**, **[23920]**, **[37059]**, **[37247]**, **[39185]**
"Laying the Groundwork: In Developing Personnel, the Work Takes Place Beforehand" in Black Enterprise (February 2008) **[35395]**, **[35836]**
"Layoffs Continue to Be a Drag on Region's Recovery" in Philadelphia Business Journal (Vol. 28, January 22, 2010, No. 49, pp. 1) **[27414]**, **[35837]**, **[45519]**
Layout Software Basics (Onsite) **[45053]**
Lazard Technology Partners **[55435]**

3552

Small Business Sourcebook • 30th Edition

"Legoland Florida Theme Park Construction to Start in May" in Orlando Business Journal (Vol. 26, January 29, 2010, No. 35, pp. 1) [970], [5413]

"Legoland Plans Could Tumble After State's Modesa Denial" in Business Journal-Serving Metropolitan Kansas City (November 16, 2007) [971], [27422], [33806]

Lehigh Acres Chamber of Commerce (LACC) [50197]

Lehigh University - Institute for Metal Forming (IMF) [13735]

Lehigh University - Small Business Development Center (SBDC) [30381]

Lehigh University Small Business Development Center [56909]

"Lehman's Hail Mary Pass" in Business Week (September 22, 2008, No. 4100, pp. 28) [8486], [12574], [14453], [24439], [25139], [26259], [31604], [37413], [38180]

Lehrer Financial and Economic Advisory Services [17127]

"Leica Beefs Up Steering Options, Steering Display Features" in Farm Industry News (January 10, 2011) [21618], [41120]

"Leinie's Charts National Craft Beer Rollout" in The Business Journal-Milwaukee (Vol. 25, August 29, 2008, No. 49, pp. A1) [13587], [19232], [21619], [40065], [41121]

Leipsic Area Chamber of Commerce [56197]

Leland Chamber of Commerce [53873]

Leland Speakes & Associates [17594]

Leland Speakes Real Estate Inc. [17594]

Lemmen-Holton Cancer Pavilion Library [10265], [10328], [15222], [16050]

Lemmon Chamber of Commerce [57587]

Lemon Tree Family Hair Salon [10094]

Lemont Area Chamber of Commerce [51175]

"Lenders" in The Business Journal - Serving Phoenix and the Valley of the Sun (Vol. 28, July 25, 2008, No. 47, pp. 1) [5414], [8487], [12575], [17370], [23159], [26260], [27423], [31605], [37414], [47041]

"Lenders Capitalize on a Thinning Bulge Bracket" in Mergers & Acquisitions: The Dealmaker's Journal (March 1, 2008) [8488], [12576], [31606], [42018]

"Lenders Get Boost from Low Rates" in Saint Louis Business Journal (Vol. 32, September 9, 2011, No. 2, pp. 1) [14454], [37415]

"Lending Act Touted by Michaud" in Morning Sentinel (June 21, 2010) [33261], [45523], [46289]

"Lending Door Slams" in Puget Sound Business Journal (Vol. 29, October 24, 2008, No. 27, pp. 1) [5415], [8489], [26261], [37416]

"Lending Idea Gets Mixed Review" in Tampa Bay Business Journal (Vol. 29, October 30, 2009, No. 45, pp. 1) [8490], [12577], [33262], [33807], [37417]

"Lending Stays Down at Local Banks" in Business Courier (Vol. 27, October 1, 2010, No. 22, pp. 1) [27424], [31607], [37418], [45524]

Lenexa Chamber of Commerce (LCC) [52136]

Lenhardt Library of the Chicago Botanic Garden [9858]

Lennox Tech Enterprise Center [55487]

Lenny's Sub Shop [6474]

Lenow International Inc. [16469], [18521]

Lenox Chamber of Commerce [52912]

Lenox Library Association - Music Department [14689]

Lentz USA Service Centers [18649]

Weill-Lenya Research Center [14690], [14774]

Leo Burnett Detroit - Information Resource Center [691]

Leon Gottlieb USA/Int'l Franchise/Restaurant Consultants [3028], [26124], [32321]

Leonard Reed's Shim Sham Shimmy [6408]

Leonard's Guide--International Air Cargo Directory [11125]

Leonard's Guide National Warehouse and Distribution Directory [16653]

Leonard's Guide--International Postal, Parcel & Cargo Directory [11125]

Lepercq Capital Management, Inc. / Lepercq de Neuflize & Co., Inc. [55436]

Les Dietetistes du Canada [15156]

Les Franchises Panda Ltee/Panda Franchises Ltd. [18781]

Les Naturalistes [7053]

"Less Malaise in Malaysia" in Barron's (Vol. 88, March 17, 2008, No. 11, pp. M12) [8491], [12578], [31608], [33808]

"Less Than Zero" in Canadian Business (Vol. 80, November 5, 2007, No. 22, pp. 36) [26661], [33809], [35841]

"Lessons From My Father" in Crain's Chicago Business (Vol. 31, November 10, 2008, No. 45, pp. 28) [15549], [27425]

"Lessons Learned from Instructional Design Theory" in Business Communication Quarterly (December 2007, pp. 414) [22358], [28253], [38181]

"Lessons of a Lipstick Queen: Finding and Developing the Great Idea That Can Change Your Life [1898], [2046], [5892], [29939], [47319], [47590]

Lessons in Service From Charlie Trotter [17943], [32800]

"Lessons from Turnaround Leaders" in Strategy and Leadership (Vol. 39, May-June 2011, No. 3, pp. 36-43) [25572], [29107], [29940], [38182]

"Let the Big Fish Eat" in Canadian Business (Vol. 80, March 12, 2007, No. 6, pp. 4) [25573], [42019]

"Let Emerging Market Customers Be Your Teachers" in Harvard Business Review (Vol. 88, December 2010, No. 12, pp. 115) [26472], [36654], [40066], [43067], [43523]

"Let the Insults Fly: Want to Learn What Your Employees Really Think?" in Inc. (Vol. 33, October 2011, No. 8, pp. 36) [29108], [38183]

"Let It Shine: Organization Helps Disadvantaged Girls See Their Worth" in Black Enterprise (Vol. 38, February 2008, No. 7, pp. 142) [3892], [4121], [4245], [7841], [29941], [45949], [47320]

"Let the Light Shine" in Retail Merchandiser (Vol. 51, July-August 2011, No. 4, pp. 74) [1352], [5991]

"Let Markets Decide?" in Canadian Business (Vol. 80, October 8, 2007, No. 20, pp. 67) [27426], [33810]

"Let the Online Games Begin" in Canadian Business (Vol. 80, January 29, 2007, No. 3, pp. 23) [11768], [34984], [40067], [45525]

"Let Us Count the Ways" in Barron's (Vol. 88, July 7, 2008, No. 27, pp. M10) [8492], [12579], [27427], [31609]

Let Us Point You in the Right Direction [51176]

"Let Your Stuff Tell a Story: How to Edit Your Accessories to Showcase Your Personality" in Charlotte Observer (February 8, 2007) [11000], [11548], [15248]

Lethal Logic: Exploding the Myths that Paralyze American Gun Policy [10029], [39192], [40068]

Let's Buy a Company: How to Accelerate Growth Through Acquisitions [12580], [23160], [25325], [42020]

Let's Create for Halloween [3987]

Let's Create for Thanksgiving [3988]

Let's Eat [9185]

Let's Face It USA [34148]

"Let's Go Team: When a Retail Professional Leads by Example, Everyone Benefits" in Black Enterprise (Vol. 41, November 2010, No. 4) [29109], [43068], [43524]

"Let's Put On a Show" in Inc. (November 2007, pp. 127) [20383], [30707], [46664]

Let's Talk Business [48717]

"The Letter of the Law" in Collections and Credit Risk (Vol. 14, November 1, 2009, No. 9, pp. 40) [6244], [6312], [23926], [26262], [27428], [33811]

"Letting the Sunshine In" in Barron's (Vol. 89, July 6, 2009, No. 27, pp. 11) [7256], [19104], [30708], [33263], [33812], [43888]

Levelland Area Chamber of Commerce (LACC) [58279]

Leverage [51177]

The Levison Letter [42542]

R. J. Levulis & Associates [37225]

"Levy Boards: From Unity Comes Farming's Strength" in Farmer's Weekly (March 28, 2008, No. 320) [21620], [33813]

Lewes Chamber of Commerce (LCC) [49824]

Lewes Chamber of Commerce and Visitors Bureau [49824]

Lewis-Clark State College - School of Technology [50824]

Lewis County Chamber of Commerce [55266]

Lewis County Chamber of Commerce Eco. Dev. Zone [55266]

Lewis County Small Business Development Center [59054]

Lewiston Area Chamber of Commerce (LACC) [53349]

Lewiston-Auburn SCORE [52547]

Lewiston Chamber of Commerce (LCC) [50778]

Lewistown Area Chamber of Commerce [54290]

Lewisville Area Chamber of Commerce [58280]

Lexington Area Chamber of Commerce [54405]

Lexington Area Chamber of Commerce (LCC) [54077]

Lexington Business Centre [51759]

Lexington Chamber of Commerce (LCC) [52913]; [57492]

Lexington Concord Battleroad [52914]

Lexington Medical Center - LMC Health Library [6718], [15127]

Lexington-Rockbridge County Chamber of Commerce (LRCCC) [58951]

LEXIS Federal Patent, Trademark, & Copyright Library [37172]

LexisNexis Matthew Bender (Newark, New Jersey) [54888]

LexisNexis Patent & Trademark File History Services [37172]

LexisNexis Technical Library [11963]

LF Leadership [38722]

LF USA Investment, Inc. [49261]

Liaison [34149]

Libby Area Chamber of Commerce (LACC) [54291]

Liberal Area Chamber of Commerce (LACC) [52137]

Liberty Area Chamber of Commerce [54078]

Liberty Business Strategies Ltd. [2915], [26047], [38758], [40628]

Liberty-Casey County Chamber of Commerce [52341]

Liberty County Chamber of Commerce [50569]

Liberty-Dayton Area Chamber of Commerce (LDACC) [58281]

Liberty Tax Service [19722], [3111], [19723]

Liberty Venture Partners, Inc. [57292]

Library Binding Institute (LBI) [2240]

Library and Book Trade Almanac [2146], [2381], [15550]

Library of Congress [60507]; [60508]

Library of Congress - Humanities and Social Sciences Division - Local History & Genealogy Reading Room [9528]

Library of Congress - Motion Picture, Broadcasting & Recorded Sound Division [16765]

Library of Congress - Music Division [14691]

Library of Congress - Prints & Photographs Division [4570]

Library Literature & Information Science Full Text™ [11249], [19197]

The Library at the Mariners' Museum [13978]

Library of Congress Computerized Catalog [2220], [2407]

Licensed Beverage Industries [1829]

Licensed Merchandisers' Association [36949]

Licensing Industry Association [36949]

The LiceSquad Inc. [28467], [35642]

Lieber & Associates [26635]

Liespotting: Proven Techniques to Detect Deception [22359], [29942], [30949], [38184]

"Life After Cod" in Globe & Mail (March 18, 2006, pp. B1) [8982], [9019], [25574], [41335], [43069]

"The Life Changers" in Canadian Business (Vol. 81, October 27, 2008, No. 18, pp. 86) [7938], [28254], [42818], [43889]

The Life Cycle of Entrepreneurial Ventures [29943], [32801]

Life Entrepreneurs [29377], [32410], [37060]

Life Insurance Marketing and Research Association [8036], [11483]

Life Science Business Incubator at Monsanto Place [54195]

"Life Sciences Become State's Growth Powerhouse" in Crain's Detroit Business (Vol. 25, June 1, 2009, No. 22, pp. M008) [23161], [42819], [43890]

"A Life of Spice" in Entrepreneur (Vol. 37, September 2009, No. 9, pp. 46) [15335], [18355], [21148], [23162], [31084]

Life Underwriters Association of Canada - Canadian Institute of Chartered Life Underwriters [8026]

Life Untangled Publishing [59950]

Life in the Valley [58662]

"Lifebank Grants Stock Options" in Canadian Corporate News (May 16, 2007) [12581], [25868], [38185], [43891], [44408]

Lifelines: A Career Profile Study [3378]

Life's a Game So Fix the Odds: How to Be More Persuasive and Influential in Your Personal and Business [22360], [29944]

"Life's Work" in Harvard Business Review (Vol. 88, July-August 2010, No. 7-8, pp. 172) [1192], [29945], [37061], [41122]

"Life's Work: Ben Bradlee" in Harvard Business Review (Vol. 88, September 2010, No. 9, pp. 128) [15551], [23163], [29110], [29946], [30950], [38186]

"Life's Work: Manolo Blahnik" in Harvard Business Review (Vol. 88, December 2010, No. 12, pp. 144) [4122], [7842], [18760], [29947], [31085]

"Life's Work: Oliver Sacks" in Harvard Business Review (Vol. 88, November 2010, No. 11, pp. 152) [22117], [22607], [29948], [34352], [38187]

"Lifesavers" in Black Enterprise (Vol. 41, December 2010, No. 5, pp. 38) [104], [19642], [21388], [31610], [34353]

Lifestyle Media-Relations Reporter / Media Pro [16607]

Lifestyle Sebring [50198]

Lifestyles [50199]; [54753]

"A Lifetime of Giving: Food Bank CEO Fights Hunger One Mouth At a Time" in Black Enterprise (Vol. 41, November 2010, No. 4, pp. 86) [9263], [29949], [45950], [47321]

"A Lifetime of Making Deals" in Crain's Detroit Business (Vol. 24, March 24, 2008, No. 12, pp. 11) [8493], [12582], [29950], [31611], [42021]

"Lifetime Networks" in Brandweek (Vol. 49, April 21, 2008, No. 16, pp. SR10) [505], [7939], [19939], [38188], [40069], [43525]

"Local Dealers Fear Shortages in Car Supply" in Boston Business Journal (Vol. 29, May 13, 2011, No. 1, pp. 1) [1556], [14925], [15372], [15394]

Local Development Corporation of East New York - East Brooklyn Enterprise Center [55488]

Local Enterprises in the Global Economy: Issues of Governance and Upgrading [23169], [27431], [36657], [38192]

"Local Firm Snaps up 91 Area Pizza Huts" in Orlando Business Journal (Vol. 26, January 8, 2010, No. 32, pp. 1) [506], [16128], [25326], [32194], [40073]

"Local Firms Will Feel Impact Of Wall St. Woes" in The Business Journal-Milwaukee (Vol. 25, September 19, 2008, No. 52, pp. A1) [8500], [12591], [26264], [27432], [31617], [37423], [43071], [44410], [45527]

"Local Flavor" in Entrepreneur (Vol. 35, November 2007, No. 11, pp. 110) [9897], [19203], [21484]

"Local Green Technology on Display" in Crain's Detroit Business (Vol. 26, January 18, 2010, No. 3, pp. 1) [14926], [20384], [30715], [39200], [42821], [44693], [46665]

"Local Hospitals Wage Wars on 'Bounce-Backs'" in Business Courier (Vol. 27, July 30, 2010, No. 13, pp. 1) [11391], [33266], [33816], [34355], [36188]

"Local Hotels Brace for Downturn" in Crain's Chicago Business (Vol. 31, March 31, 2008, No. 13, pp. 3) [10721], [22118], [24881], [27433], [44411]

"Local Industrial Vacancies Climb" in Crain's Chicago Business (Vol. 31, November 17, 2008, No. 46, pp. 18) [16532], [16961], [17372], [27434], [39201]

"Local Knowledge" in Hawaii Business (Vol. 53, December 2007, No. 6, pp. 40) [22364], [27435], [32804], [44848]

"Local Lending Tumbles $10 Billion Since '08" in Saint Louis Business Journal (Vol. 31, August 26, 2011, No. 53, pp. 1) [27436], [37424], [45528]

"Local M&A Activity Sputters in 1Q" in Crain's Chicago Business (Vol. 31, April 21, 2008, No. 16, pp. 20) [26265], [27437], [32805], [37425], [42025]

"Local Manufacturers See Tax Proposal Hurting Global Operations" in Crain's Cleveland Business (Vol. 30, May 18, 2009, No. 20) [23928], [33817], [36658], [39202], [41680], [46294]

Local Organizations List [50779]

"Local Outlook: Stronger Growth Ahead" in Montana Business Quarterly (Vol. 49, Spring 2011, No. 1, pp. 10) [23170], [27438]

Local Phone Guide [52915]

"Local Researchers Get Cash Infusion" in Business Courier (Vol. 26, October 9, 2009, No. 24, pp. 1) [28255], [33267], [34356], [42822], [43893]

"Local Shops' Wares Sound Good To Boomers Needing Some Fun" in Crain's Cleveland Business (Vol. 30, May 18, 2009, No. 20, pp. 5) [14546], [39203]

"Local Startup Hits Big Leagues" in Austin Business JournalInc. (Vol. 28, December 19, 2008, No. 40, pp. 1) [3490], [18845], [19436], [25773], [41125], [44987]

"Local TV Hits Media Radar Screen" in Business Courier (Vol. 27, July 2, 2010, No. 9, pp. 1) [3183], [12592], [19940], [42026]

"Locally Based Stocks Escape Worst of Market's Turmoil" in Crain's Detroit Business (Vol. 24, September 22, 2008, No. 38, pp. 4) [8501], [12593], [23171], [27439], [31618], [44412]

"Location, Location" in Black Enterprise (Vol. 38, February 2008, No. 7, pp. 64) [24882], [35843], [36659], [45529]

Lock Haven University Small Business Development Center [56910]

Lock Museum of America (LMA) [13613]

Lock Museum of America Inc. Library [13624]

Lockhart Chamber of Commerce (LCC) [58285]

Lockhart Enterprise [58286]

Lockheed Martin Manassas Library [4917]

Lockheed Martin Orincon Corp. [5055]

Lockport [51185]

Lockport Chamber of Commerce (LCC) [51186]

Lockport Connections [51187]

Lockport Map [51188]

Lodging, Dining and Things To Do [50201]

Lodging Magazine [10722], [10775]

Lodging Magazine--American Hotel and Motel Association Buyers Guide [10722], [10775]

Lodging Magazine--Buyers Guide for Hotels and Motels Issue [10722], [10775]

Lodgings and Accommodations in the Monadnock Region [54604]

Lodi Area Chamber of Commerce [56200]

Lodi Business [48729]

Lodi Chamber of Commerce [48730]

Lodi District Chamber of Commerce [48730]

Loeb & Loeb LLP Law Library [7766]

Loeb Partners Corp. [55437]

Loeb Retail Letter [43272]

"Lofty Ambitions" in Canadian Business (Vol. 80, October 22, 2007, No. 21, pp. 26) [27440], [33818], [36660]

The Log [11291]

Logan County Area Chamber of Commerce (LCCC) [56201]

Logan County Chamber of Commerce [49548]; [52343]; [59410]

Logan County Newsline [52344]

Logan Farms Honey Glazed Hams [3154]

Logan - Hocking Chamber of Commerce [56202]

Logan Small Business Development Center [58615]

Logansport - Cass County Chamber of Commerce [51668]

Logansport SCORE [51494]

The Logic of Life: The Rational Economics of an Irrational World [27441], [32806], [35398], [38193], [40896]

Loma Linda Chamber of Commerce [48731]

Loma Linda Report [48732]

Loma Linda University - Del E. Webb Memorial Library [1449]

Lombard Area Chamber of Commerce and Industry [51189]

Lombard Community Directory [51190]

"Lombard Leaves Starbucks" in Black Enterprise (Vol. 38, July 2008, No. 12, pp. 28) [9705], [23172], [24442], [25141], [40074], [43526]

Lomira Area Chamber of Commerce [59626]

Lomita Chamber of Commerce [48733]

Lompoc Valley Chamber of Commerce and Visitors' Bureau (LVCCVB) [48734]

Lompoc Valley Chamber of Commerce [48734]

London Area Chamber of Commerce [56207]

London-Laurel County Chamber of Commerce [52345]

London SCORE [52242]

Lone Pine Chamber of Commerce (LPCC) [48735]

Lone Star College System Small Business Development Center [57855]

"Long - And Leery" in Barron's (Vol. 88, March 31, 2008, No. 13, pp. 47) [8502], [12594], [23173], [27442], [31619]

Long Beach Area Chamber of Commerce (LBACC) [48736]

Long Beach Business [48737]

Long Beach Chamber of Commerce (LBCC) [55270]

Long Beach City College Small Business Development Center [48155]

Long Beach Public Library - Performing Arts Department [3226]

"The Long Game" in Business Strategy Review (Vol. 21, Summer 2010, No. 2, pp. 36) [24883], [29961]

Long Island Association (LIA) [55271]

Long Island Better Business Bureau [55069]

Long Island Business News [55516]

Long Island Forum for Technology [55489]

Long Island High Technology Incubator [55490]

Long Island Lighting Company Resource Center [10196], [17740]

Long John Silver's [18174]

Long & Levit Library [24170], [36266]

"Long Live Rock" in Inc. (November 2007, pp. 130) [5416], [30716], [31086]

Long Prairie Area Chamber of Commerce (LPACC) [53677]

"A Long Road to Recovery" in Barron's (Vol. 89, July 27, 2009, No. 30, pp. 37) [27443], [33819]

Long & Silverman Publishing Inc. (L&S) [54533]

Long Term Care: Published for the Canadian Long Term care community [15095]

"The Long View: Roberta Bondar on Science and the Need for Education" in Canadian Business (Vol. 81, October 27, 2008, No. 18) [7260], [7618], [28256], [30717]

Longaberger [29962]

Longboat Key Chamber of Commerce (LKCC) [50202]

Longhill Partners Inc. [38768]

Longmont Area Best of Business Directory and Community Guide [49549]

Longmont Area Chamber of Commerce [49550]

Longmont Entrepreneurial Network [49627]

"Longtime Peoria Heights Second-Hand Clothing Shop Closing" in Journal Star (December 18, 2010) [4246], [5146]

Longview Chamber of Commerce [58287]

Longview Partnership [58287]

Longview Small Business Development Center [59055]

Longwood Gardens, Inc. Library [9859]

Longwood University Small Business Development Center - Crater [58800]

Longwood University Small Business Development Center - Danville [58801]

Longwood University Small Business Development Center - Farmville [58802]

Longwood University Small Business Development Center - Martinsville [58803]

Longwood University Small Business Development Center - South Boston [58804]

Longworth Venture Partners, L.P. [53040]

Longy School of Music - Bakalar Music Library [14692]

"A Look Ahead Into 2007" in Canadian Business (Vol. 80, December 25, 2006, No. 1, pp. 40) [12595], [27444], [34988], [39204], [43072], [44413]

"A Look At Three Gas-Less Cars" in Hispanic Business (Vol. 30, September 2008, No. 9, pp. 90) [7261], [7619], [14927], [25577], [30718], [39205]

"Look Before You Lease" in Women Entrepreneur (February 3, 2009) [16533], [23929], [24750], [32807], [44849]

"Look, Leap, and License" in Retail Merchandiser (Vol. 51, July-August 2011, No. 4, pp. 16) [20256], [20385], [36661], [37064], [46666]

"Look, No Hands!" in Inc. (Vol. 33, September 2011, No. 7, pp. 52) [3754], [41417]

Look North [54500]; [54501]

"Look Out, Barbie, Bratz are Back" in Canadian Business (Vol. 83, August 17, 2010, No. 13-14, pp. 18) [20257], [23930], [37065]

"Look Who's Eating Loblaw's Lunch" in Canadian Business (Vol. 80, February 26, 2007, No. 5, pp. 44) [25578], [43073]

"Looking Back" in Entrepreneur (Vol. 36, March 2008, No. 3, pp. 118) [24443], [29963]

"Looking For Financing?" in Hispanic Business (Vol. 30, July-August 2008, No. 7-8, pp. 16) [12596], [21931], [23174], [24444], [25142], [32808], [38194], [42027], [47043]

"Looking For Good Buys" in Black Enterprise (Vol. 38, November 2007, No. 4, pp. 39) [12597], [27445], [43074]

Looking to the Future [53353]

Looking at It from Every Angle [38626]

"Looking Like a Million Bucks" in Entrepreneur (Vol. 37, August 2009, No. 8, pp. 102) [7943], [19574], [19941], [29964]

"Looking Out for the Little Guys" in Black Enterprise (Vol. 38, October 2007, No. 3, pp. 58) [507], [3755], [22365], [26474], [28747], [34989], [40075]

"Looking for a Sales Tax Extension" in Milwaukee Business Journal (Vol. 27, January 29, 2010, No. 18, pp. A1) [19437], [33820], [43075], [46295]

"Looking To Hire Young? Be Careful" in Boston Business Journal (Vol. 30, November 19, 2010, No. 43, pp. 1) [10893], [17944], [26662], [33821], [35399], [35844]

"Looking To Leap?" in Black Enterprise (Vol. 38, January 2008, No. 6, pp. 64) [28748], [29378], [32411]

Looking Up [52480]

Lookout [48738]

Loomis Basin Chamber of Commerce [48739]

Loomsong [6017]

"Loonie Tunes: When Will the Dollar Rise Again?" in Canadian Business (Vol. 81, November 10, 2008, No. 19, pp. 62) [12598], [27446], [31620], [36662]

"Loop 360 Offices Planned" in Austin Business JournalInc. (Vol. 28, December 5, 2008, No. 38, pp. A1) [5417], [8503], [27447]

"Loop Hotel Plan Locks Up Funding" in Crain's Chicago Business (Vol. 31, March 24, 2008, No. 12, pp. 2) [10723], [23175]

Lopez Island Chamber of Commerce [59228]

Lorain County Chamber of Commerce [56203]

Lord Fairfax Small Business Development Center - Culpeper [58805]

Lord Fairfax Small Business Development Center - Fauquier [58806]

Lord Fairfax Small Business Development Center - Middletown [58807]

Lord & Partners Ltd. [3112], [7382]

"The Lords of Ideas" in Business Strategy Review (Vol. 21, Autumn 2010, No. 3, pp. 57) [24884], [29965]; [25143], [38195]

"Lords Should Get Real About Food" in Farmer's Weekly (March 28, 2008, No. 320) [9951], [21622], [33268]

Lorillard Tobacco Company Library [20111]

Loris Chamber of Commerce [57494]

Los Alamitos Area Chamber of Commerce [48740]

Los Alamitos Business [48741]

Los Alamos Chamber of Commerce [54967]

Los Alamos Commerce and Development Corporation (LACDC) [54968]

Los Alamos County Chamber of Commerce [54967]

Los Alamos National Laboratory - Advanced Computing Laboratory (ACL) [4789]

Los Alamos Research Park [54998]

Los Alamos Small Business Development Center [54900]

Los Alomitos Chamber of Commerce [48740]

Los Alomitos/Rossmoor Chamber of Commerce [48740]
Los Altos Chamber of Commerce [48742]
Los Altos Chamber of Commerce Directory [48743]
Los Angeles Advertising Agencies Association [42590]
Los Angeles Area Chamber of Commerce [48744]
Los Angeles Business Journal [48745]
Los Angeles Business Owner Outreach Support and Training (LABOOST) [49361]
Los Angeles County/Harbor-UCLA Medical Center - A.F. Parlow Library of the Health Sciences [1450]
Los Angeles County Museum of Art - Balch Art Research Library [5940]
Los Angeles JobBank: The Job Hunter's Guide to Southern California [19179]
Los Angeles Minority Business Enterprise Center [49143]
Los Angeles Minority Business Opportunity Center - City of Los Angeles [49144]
Los Angeles Public Library - Arts, Music and Recreation Department [6419]
Los Angeles Small Business Development Center Network (LA SBDC) [48156]
Los Angeles Urban League Entrepreneur Center [49145]
Los Banos Business Journal [48746]
Los Banos Chamber of Commerce (LBCC) [48747]
Los Banos Chamber Directory [48748]
Los Cabos Magazine [10776]
Los Fresnos Chamber of Commerce [58288]
Los Gatos Chamber of Commerce [49060]
Los Lunas Small Business Development Center [54901]
Los Osos/Baywood Park Chamber of Commerce [48749]
"Loseley Dairy Ice Cream" in *Ice Cream Reporter* (Vol. 23, November 20, 2010, No. 12, pp. 8) [10229], [10894], [38196], [43527]
"Losing the Top Job - And Winning It Back" in *Harvard Business Review* (Vol. 88, October 2010, No. 10, pp. 136) [17945], [29966], [35400], [35845], [38197]
"Losses Threaten Comp Care's Future Viability" in *The Business Journal-Serving Greater Tampa Bay* (Vol. 28, August 15, 2008, No. 34) [24445], [25144], [34357], [44414], [47044]
"Lost in America" in *Canadian Business* (Vol. 79, October 23, 2006, No. 21, pp. 23) [27448], [32809]
"The Lost Opportunity for a Canadian Steel Giant" in *Globe & Mail* (April 23, 2007, pp. B1) [39206], [42028], [45530]
Loto-Quebec - Centre de Documentation [9419]
"Lots More Mr. Nice Guy" in *Canadian Business* (Vol. 80, October 22, 2007, No. 21, pp. 58) [23176], [29967], [31087], [38198]
"Lots of Qualified Women, But Few Sit on Boards" in *Globe & Mail* (March 2, 2006, pp. B1) [32810], [38199]
"Lotteries Scratch Their Way to Billions" in *Saint Louis Business Journal* (Vol. 31, August 19, 2011, No. 52, pp. 1) [508], [9400], [42383]
Lottery, Parimutuel & Casino Regulation [9414]
"Lotus Starts Slowly, Dodges Subprime Woes" in *Crain's Detroit Business* (Vol. 24, April 14, 2008, No. 15, pp. 3) [8504], [12599], [14456], [24446], [25579], [31621], [37426]
Lou Antonelli Rehabilitation Consultant [3389]
LOU View [53874]
Loudon County Chamber of Commerce (LCCC) [57742]
Loudon County Living Membership Guide [57743]
Loudonville - Mohican Area Chamber of Commerce [56204]
Loudonville - Mohican Area Convention and Visitor's Bureau [56204]
Loudonville-Greater Mohican Area Chamber of Commerce [56204]
Loudoun Chamber Business Directory and Resource Guide [58952]
Loudoun County Chamber of Commerce (LCCC) [58953]
Loudoun County Small Business Development Center [58808]
Loudounclear [58954]
Lougheed Resource Group Inc. (LRG) [988], [17655], [43284]
Louis Navellier's Emerging Growth [13130]
Louis Rukeyser's Wall Street Investment Seminar [13162]
Louisa County Chamber of Commerce [58955]
Louisburg Area Chamber of Commerce [52141]
Louisburg Chamber of Commerce (LCC) [52141]
Louise-Hillje Chamber of Commerce [58289]
Louisiana Business & Technology Center [52530]
Louisiana Emerging Technology Center [52531]
Louisiana Minority Business Opportunity Center [52512]
Louisiana Procurement Technical Assistance Center at Kisatchie-Delta [52516]
Louisiana Procurement Technical Assistance Center at LEDA [52517]
Louisiana Procurement Technical Assistance Center at New Orleans [52518]

Louisiana Procurement Technical Assistance Center at SLEC [52519]
Louisiana Procurement Technical Assistance Center - University of Louisiana - LAPTAC State Administrative Office [52520]
Louisiana Small Business Development Center - Greater New Orleans Region [52408]
Louisiana Small Business Development Center - Lead Office (LSBDC) [52409]
Louisiana Small Business Development Center at Louisiana State University in Shreveport [52410]
Louisiana Small Business Development Center - LSU South Campus [52411]
Louisiana Small Business Development Center at Mc-Neese State University [52412]
Louisiana Small Business Development Center at Northwestern State University [52413]
Louisiana Small Business Development Center at Southeastern Louisiana University [52414]
Louisiana Small Business Development Center at Southern University [52415]
Louisiana Small Business Development Center at University of Louisiana at Lafayette [52416]
Louisiana Tech Enterprise Center [52532]
Louisiana Technology Park [52533]
Louisiana Workforce Commission - Labor Market Information - Research and Statistics Division [61647]
Louisina MBEC [52513]
Louisina Minority Supplier Development Council [52514]
Louisville Area Chamber of Commerce [56205]
Louisville Area Chamber of Commerce [52322]
Louisville Boat, RV & Sportshow [3873], [19382], [20211], [20624]
Louisville Chamber of Commerce [49551]
Louisville Fact Book [52346]
Louisville SCORE [52243]
Louisville Small Business Development Center (LSBDC) [52224]
Louisville Sport, Boat, RV & Vacation Show [3873], [19382], [20211], [20624]
Louisville-Winston County Chamber of Commerce (LWCCC) [53875]
Loup City Chamber of Commerce [54408]
Love County Chamber of Commerce [56545]
"A Love of Likes" in *Boston Business Journal* (Vol. 31, July 8, 2011, No. 24, pp. 1) [28749], [40076], [43528], [45531]
Lovejoy's MarketBrief Hotline [13131]
Lovelady Consulting [6541]
Loveland Area Chamber of Commerce [56206]
Loveland Chamber of Commerce and Visitors Center [49552]
Loveland Info Chamber of Commerce [49553]
Loveland Small Business Development Center [49423]
Lovelock/Pershing County Chamber of Commerce [54502]
Loves Park - Machesney Park Chamber of Commerce [51191]
Lovett Miller & Co. Incorporated [50352]
Lovington Chamber of Commerce [54969]
Low-Budget Online Marketing for Small Business [28750], [40077], [44415]; [28751], [40078], [44416]; [28752], [40079]
Low Risk, High Reward [23177], [29379], [32412]
Low Voltage Safety [6912]
Lowell Area Chamber of Commerce (LACC) [53354]
Lower Bucks County Chamber of Commerce (LBCCC) [57154]
Lower Keys Chamber of Commerce (LKCC) [50203]
"Lower Prices No Shoo-In as Telcos Near Deregulation" in *Globe & Mail* (March 28, 2007, pp. B1) [8505], [12600], [33822], [44417]
Lox of Bagels [1697], [9743]
Loyalist Gazette [9462]
"Loyalty Cards Score Points" in *Crain's Cleveland Business* (Vol. 30, June 8, 2009, No. 22, pp. 1) [23178], [26475], [31622], [43076], [43529]
"Loyalty Pays" in *Entrepreneur* (Vol. 36, February 2008, No. 2, pp. 63) [12601], [24447], [31623], [34990]
Loyola Marymount University Small Business Development Center [48157]
Loyola University Chicago - Center for Ethics and Social Justice [31006]
Loyola University Chicago - School of Continuing and Professional Studies [51459]
LPD Enterprises [6542]
LPD Press & Rio Grande Books [6542]
LRP Publications [36046]
LRP Publications - lrp.com Technology Contacts [36046]
LSA Associates Inc. [44753]
LSC [5656]
LSG Insurance Partners [36047]
LTD Shippers Association (LTD) [26723], [38868]

LTI Ventures Leasing Corp. / Leasing Technologies International, Inc. [49780]
Lubar & Co. [59774]
Lubbock Chamber of Commerce [58290]
Lubbock Small Business Development Center [57856]
Lubepro's International, Inc. [16679]
Lubin Schwartz & Goldman Inc. [36047]
Lucas Area Chamber of Commerce (LACC) [52142]
Lucas Chamber of Commerce [52142]
Lucerne Valley Chamber of Commerce [48750]
Lucille Roberts Fitness Express [16031], [21289]
Lucrative List Building [40080], [43530]
Ludington Area Chamber of Commerce (LACC) [53355]
Lufkin - Angelina County Chamber of Commerce (LACCC) [58291]
"Lufthansa-Cathay Deal Reinforces Outsourcing" in *Globe & Mail* (March 30, 2007, pp. B9) [41336], [41681]
May Toy Lukens [2917], [3078], [13853], [26049], [29259]
Lum, Danzis, Drasco, Positan, & Kleinberg Law Library [7767]
Lumber and Building Materials Association of Ontario (LBMAO) [10125]
The Lumber Co-Operator: The Official Publication of the Northeastern Retail Lumber Association [13671]
"Lumber Rebounds" in *Business Journal Portland* (Vol. 26, December 11, 2009, No. 40, pp. 1) [13656], [23179]
Lumbermen's Association of Texas Convention and Buying Market [13676]
Lumbermen's Association of Texas Convention and Exposition [13676]
Lumbermen's Association of Texas Convention [13676]
Lumbersearch [13679]
Lumberton Area Chamber of Commerce [55758]
Lumberton Area Chamber of Commerce and Visitors Bureau [55758]
Lumina [34150]
The Luminary [48751]
The Luminations Group L.L.C. [41618]
Lumpkin County Chamber of Commerce [50511]
"Lunch Box Maker Gives Back" in *Marketing to Women* (Vol. 23, November 2010, No. 11, pp. 5) [7262], [7620], [30719], [40081], [45532], [45953], [47322]
The Lunch Lady Group Inc. [9186]
"Lundin Deal Leaves Nickel Market Thin" in *Globe & Mail* (April 5, 2007, pp. B4) [8506], [12602], [41337], [42029]
Lundquist, Killeen, Potvin and Bender Inc. [906], [5658], [6917], [16294]
Lupfer & Associates (L&A) [2918], [13854], [26050], [29260], [32290], [38759], [40629]
Luray-Page County Chamber of Commerce [58956]
"Luster Lost" in *Saint Louis Business Journal* (Vol. 32, September 16, 2011, No. 3, pp. 1) [6660], [8507], [11392], [12603], [40082], [42823]
Luverne Area Chamber of Commerce (LCC) [53678]
"Lux Coffees, Breads Push Chains to React" in *Advertising Age* (Vol. 77, June 26, 2006, No. 26, pp. S14) [1767], [9706], [12604], [17946], [40083]
"Luxe Hotels on a Budget" in *Inc.* (Volume 32, December 2010, No. 10, pp. 60) [1519], [10724], [15336], [20555], [24885], [28753]
"Luxe Men Are In Style" in *Brandweek* (Vol. 49, April 21, 2008, No. 16, pp. 12) [4247], [14928], [26476], [40084], [43077]
Luxemburg Chamber of Commerce (LCC) [59627]
Luxury Bath Systems [3113]
"Luxury Still Sells Well" in *Puget Sound Business Journal* (Vol. 29, September 5, 2008, No. 20, pp. 1) [4248], [43078], [44694]
Lynchburg Life/Business Directory [58957]
Lynchburg - Moore County Chamber of Commerce [57744]
Lynchburg Regional Chamber of Commerce (LRCC) [58958]
Lynchburg Small Business Development Center [58809]
Lynden Chamber of Commerce (LCC) [59229]
Lyndon Area Chamber of Commerce [58763]
Lyndon Chamber of Commerce [52143]
Lyndon State College - Continuing Education Department [58793]
Lynn Area Chamber of Commerce (LACC) [52916]
"Lynn Johnson, President: Dowland-Bach" in *Alaska Business Monthly* (Vol. 27, October 2011, No. 10, pp. 11) [26767], [29968], [39207]
Lynwood Chamber of Commerce (LCC) [48752]
Lyons Chamber of Commerce [55272]
Lyons Chamber of Commerce (LCC) [49554]
Lyons Directory [49555]
Lyons Hollis Associates Inc. [42337]
Lyons Solutions L.L.C. [42337]

"Make Money in 2011" in Small Business Opportunities (January 2011) [31624], [32413]
Make More Money by Setting Goals/Rick Barrera [25278]
"Make Relationships Count: CRM Software That Works" in Black Enterprise (Vol. 38, February 2008, No. 7, pp. 60) [3559], [18929], [26477], [43531], [45148]
"Make a Resolution: ADA Training" in HRMagazine (Vol. 54, January 2009, No. 1, pp. 81) [11549], [15249], [33823], [35846], [45954]
Make Sure It's Deductible [19644], [46297]
Make Your Business Survive and Thrive! 100+ Proven Marketing Methods to Help You Beat the Odds [23185], [29975], [32813], [35611], [40092]; [35610], [40091]
Make Your Life Tax Deductible: Easy Techniques to Reduce Your Taxes and Start Building Wealth Immediately [19645], [46298]
"Making Automated Royalty Payments Work for Your Franchise" in Franchising World (Vol. 42, October 2010, No. 10, pp. 30) [6313], [26478], [31625], [32195]
"Making the Cut; Osprey Takes Undervalued Courses to the Leader Board" in Crain's Detroit Business (Vol. 24, April 7, 2008, No. 14) [9666], [17376], [23186], [29976], [42031]
Making Difficult Decisions: How to Be Decisive and Get the Business Done [29977], [38207]
"Making Diverse Teams Click" in Harvard Business Review (Vol. 86, July-August 2008, No. 8, pp. 20) [22367], [29111], [32814], [38208], [46895]
Making Diversity Work [40929]
Making Effective Presentations [18575]
"Making Factory Tours Count" in Playthings (Vol. 107, January 1, 2009, No. 1, pp. 14) [11129], [18446], [20258], [23931], [36666], [39213]
"Making Headlines" in Entrepreneur (Vol. 36, April 2008, No. 4, pp. 126) [40093], [41128], [42640]
Making It Better: How Everyone Can Create a Safer Workplace [47503]
"Making It Click" in Barron's (Vol. 88, March 17, 2008, No. 11, pp. 31) [8511], [11770], [12607], [26479], [28756], [31626]
Making It Live [8889], [13163], [43730]
"Making It Stick" in Business Courier (Vol. 24, November 9, 2008, No. 30, pp. 1) [27451], [33270], [36667]
"Making It Work" in Pet Product News (Vol. 64, December 2010, No. 12, pp. S8) [15167], [15724], [15816], [26480]
"Making It Work" in Retail Merchandiser (Vol. 51, July-August 2011, No. 4, pp. 43) [4123], [4249], [7843], [26481]
Making a Living Without a Job: Winning Ways for Creating Work That You Love [29380], [32414]
Making a Living Without a Job: Winning Ways For Creating Work That You Love, Revised Ed. [29978], [32415]
"Making Money? Child's Play!" in Small Business Opportunities (March 2008) [3920], [32099]
"Making the Most of Milk to Revive a Falling Market" in Farmer's Weekly (March 28, 2008, No. 320) [21623], [28258], [40094]
Making People Your Competitive Advantage [25582], [38209]
"Making Sense of Ambiguous Evidence" in Harvard Business Review (Vol. 86, September 2008, No. 9, pp. 53) [514], [7944], [40095], [42492], [42641]
"Making Social Ventures Work" in Harvard Business Review (Vol. 88, September 2010, No. 9, pp. 66) [32416], [45850]
Making Successful Business Decisions: Getting It Right the First Time (Onsite) [37673]
Making Successful Business Decisions: Getting it Right the First Time (Onsite) [28994], [37674]
"Making the Tough Call: Great Leaders Recognize When Their Values Are On the Line" in Inc. (November 2007, pp. 36, 38) [30951], [38210]
Making the Transition to Management (Onsite) [37675]
Making the Transition from Staff Member to Supervisor (Onsite) [37676]
Making the Transition to Supervising and Managing Others (Onsite) (Online) [37677]
Making a Video Program [8011]
"Making Visitors Out Of Listeners" in Hawaii Business (Vol. 54, July 2008, No. 1, pp. 18) [3756], [16717], [20161], [20480], [20556], [24886], [34994], [40096], [44419]
"Making Waves" in Business Journal Portland (Vol. 27, November 26, 2010, No. 39, pp. 1) [7264], [7622], [28259], [30721], [34995], [37427], [41129], [42824], [43895], [47045]
Making Waves [57497]
"Making Your Mark: Five Steps To Brand Your Success" in Black Enterprise (Vol. 38, November 2007, No. 4, pp. 106) [25869], [32815], [40097]

Malden Chamber of Commerce [52918]
Malden Chamber of Commerce (MCC) [54081]
Malibu Chamber of Commerce [48755]
Malone Chamber of Commerce (MCC) [55273]
Mama Fu's Asian House [18175]
Mama Mio Pregnancy Spa & Imaging Centre [19578]
"The Man Behind Brascan" in Canadian Business (Vol. 79, Winter 2006, No. 24, pp. 64) [23187], [29979], [31627]
Man Hunt [35538]
The Man from OSHA [47504]
"MANAfest Provides Reps with Tools for the Future" in Agency Sales Magazine (Vol. 39, September-October 2009, No. 9, pp. 36) [14547], [20388], [43532], [46669]
Manage Your Time to Build Your Territory [43731], [46557]
Manage Your Writing [22533]
Managed Healthcare Executive: The News Magazine for Health Care Costs and Quality [34564]
Management 21 Inc. [26638]
Management Action Program [38627]
Management Action Programs Inc. [32291]
Management Advisory Associates Inc. [29261]
Management Concepts Inc. [59046]
Management Growth Institute (MGI) [31144], [38760]
Management House Inc. [38761]
Management and Leadership Skills for First-Time Supervisors and Managers (Onsite) [37678]
Management Lessons from Mayo Clinic [34358], [38211]
"Management Matters with Mike Myatt: Are You Creating Growth in a Down Economy?" in Commercial Property News (March 17, 2008) [23188], [27452], [38212]
Management Methods Inc. [38762]
The Management Myth: Why the "Experts" Keep Getting It Wrong [13772], [25870], [38213]
Management Network Group Inc. [2919], [38763]
Management 1 [38628]
Management Recruiters International Inc. [7002], [7805]
Management Report for Nonunion Organizations [13781], [38604]
Management Resource Center Inc. [42341]
Management Resource Partners [2920], [13855], [26051], [32048], [38764], [44948]
Management Rewired: Why Feedback Doesn't Work and Other Surprising Lessons from the Latest Brain Science [29112], [29980], [38214]
Management Services & Development Ltd. [44216]
Management Skills for Administrative Professionals (Onsite) [37679]
Management Skills: Building Performance and Productivity (Onsite) [37680]; [37681]
Management Skills for First-Time Supervisors (Onsite) [37682]
Management Skills for an IT Environment (Onsite) [28995], [37683]
Management Skills for New Supervisors and Managers (Onsite) [37684]
Management Skills for Secretaries, Administrative Assistants, and Support Staff (Onsite) [37685]
The Management of Small and Medium Enterprises [29981], [38215]
Management Strategies [2921], [13856], [24681], [26052], [38765], [40630]
Management Systems Council [20649]
Management Techniques That Work [38629]
Management Technology Associates Ltd. [38766]
Management and Technology Conferences - ASAE Annual Meeting [1475]
Management of Time [46558]
The Management of Work [38630]
"Managerial Rudeness: Bad Attitudes Can Demoralize Your Staff" in Black Enterprise (Vol. 37, January 2007, No. 6, pp. 58) [29113], [38216]
Managerial Skills of the New Supervisors [37686]
Managerial and Team-building Skills for Project Managers [37687]
The Manager's Guide to Rewards: What You Need to Know to Get the Best of-and-from-Your Employees [29114], [38217]
Manager's Legal Bulletin [26673]
"Managers and Their Not-So Rational Decisions" in Business Horizons (Vol. 51, March-April 2008, No. 2, pp. 113) [38218]
"Managers as Visionaries: a Skill That Can Be Learned" in Strategy and Leadership (Vol. 39, September-October 2011, No. 5, pp. 56-58) [24453], [38219], [45535]
Managing Business Growth: Get a Grip on the Numbers That Count [23189], [31628], [38220]
Managing Change: People and Process (Onsite) [37688]
Managing Chaos: Dynamic Time Management, Recall, Reading, and Stress Management Skills for Administrative Professionals (Onsite) [37689]

Managing Chaos: How to set Priorities and Make Decisions Under Pressure (Onsite) [37690]
Managing a Chaos: Tools to Set Priorities and Make Decisions Under Pressure (Onsite) [37691]
Managing Complexity and Change in SMEs Frontiers in European Research [36668], [39214]
Managing Conflict, Difficult People, and Discipline (Onsite) [37692]
"Managing Corporate Social Networks" in Harvard Business Review (Vol. 86, July-August 2008, No. 8, pp. 26) [22368], [22608], [29115], [32816]
Managing Cultural Differences [40930]
Managing for Customer Care [26602]
Managing Difficult and Sensitive Conversations (Onsite) [22219]
Managing Diversity [40931]
Managing a Drug-Free Work Environment [46078]
Managing Economies, Trade and International Business [11130], [23190], [23932], [27453], [36669], [38221], [40098]
Managing the Emerging Company [2806], [24650], [33088]
Managing Emotions under Pressure (Onsite) [22220]
Managing Emotions and Thriving Under Pressure (Onsite) [22221]
Managing Emotions in the Workplace: Strategies for Success (Onsite) [22222]
"Managing the Facebookers; Business" in The Economist (Vol. 390, January 3, 2009, No. 8612, pp. 10) [2779], [11771], [22369], [24454], [25871], [28260], [34996], [35401], [38222], [46896]
Managing Frontline Service [35539]
Managing Health Benefits in Small and Mid-Sized Organizations [11393], [21932], [34359], [36189]
Managing India's Small Industrial Economy: The Catalytic Role of Industrial Counselors and Policy Makers [25872], [27454], [36670]
Managing Information Overload: Techniques for Working Smarter (Onsite) [37693], [46491]
Managing Inventories and Cycle Counts (Onsite) [37183]
Managing Labour in Small Firms [32817], [38223]
Managing Multiple Priorities (Onsite) [46492]
Managing Multiple Priorities, Projects and Deadlines (Onsite) [46494]
Managing Multiple Priorities, Projects, and Deadlines (Onsite) [46493]
Managing Multiple Project, Competing Priorites and Tight Deadlines (Onsite) [37694]
Managing Multiple Projects, Competing Priorities & Tight Deadlines (Onsite) [46495]
Managing Multiple Projects, Objectives and Deadlines (Onsite) [46496]
Managing Multiple Projects and Priorities (Onsite) [37695]
Managing the Older Worker: How to Prepare for the New Organizational Order [29116], [35402], [35847], [37249], [38224], [40897], [45536]
Managing Organizational Transition (Onsite) [37696]
Managing People in Projects (Onsite) [37697]
Managing the Publications Department [2107]
Managing for Results [23191], [29982], [38225]
Managing Sales Stress [43732]
Managing a Small Business Made Easy [26482], [29983], [31629], [32818], [38226]
Managing Stress Productively (Onsite) [28052]
Managing Subcontracts (Onsite) [37698]
Managing for Success: The Latest in Management Thought and Practice from Canada's Premier Business School [28261], [29984], [38227]
Managing Successful Negotiations (Onsite) [22223]
Managing Time [46559]
"Managing in Times of Uncertainty; What Leaders Can Learn From the Tumultuous Past Decade" in Gallup Management Journal (June 1, 2011) [27455], [38228]
Managing Today's IT and Technical Professionals (Onsite) [28996]
Managing in Tough Times (Onsite) [28997], [37699]
Managing Work and Family Inc. [22067]
Managing a World-Class IT Department (Onsite) [37700]
Managing Your Personal Finances [8890]
Managing Your Time [46560]
Manasota SCORE, Chapter 116 [49917]
Manatee Chamber of Commerce [50207]
Mancelona Area Chamber of Commerce [53361]
Manchester Area Chamber of Commerce [51924]; [57746]
Manchester Area Chamber of Commerce (MACC) [53362]
Manchester Chamber of Commerce [50577]
Manchester College - Peace Studies Institute - Program in Conflict Resolution [42735]
Manchester and the Mountains Regional Chamber of Commerce [58764]

Manchu Wok Inc. (Markham, Canada) [18176]
Mancino's, Samuel Italian Eatery [9187], [18177]
Mandalay Associates L.L.C. [28444], [29262]
Mandarin Restaurant Franchise Corp. [18178]
Mandate [26851], [32488], [35590], [44799]
"Mandel Site Favored For UWM Hall" in The Business Journal-Milwaukee (Vol. 25, September 19, 2008, No. 52, pp. A1) [16534], [16965], [17377], [24455], [27456], [28262], [44696], [44850]
"M&I Execs May Get Golden Parachutes" in Business Journal-Milwaukee (Vol. 28, December 31, 2010, No. 14, pp. A3) [8512], [12608], [21933], [25327], [33271], [33824], [35848], [37428], [38229]
M&M/Mars Research Library [3308]
"M&T On the March?" in Baltimore Business Journal (Vol. 28, November 12, 2010, No. 27, pp. 1) [8513], [12609], [23192], [31630], [42032], [44697]
Manhasset Chamber of Commerce (MCC) [55274]
Manhattan Area Chamber of Commerce [52145]; [54295]
Manhattan Beach Chamber of Commerce (MBCC) [48756]
Manhattan Chamber of Commerce [51196]
Manhattan Chamber of Commerce (MCC) [55275]
Manhattan Chamber of Commerce [52145]
The Manhattan Consulting Group Inc. [39525]
Manhattan School of Music - Peter Jay Sharp Library [14693]
Manhattan Small Business Development Center at Pace University [55023]
Manheim Area Chamber of Commerce [57160]
Manistee Area Chamber of Commerce (MACC) [53363]
Manistee County Chamber of Commerce [53363]
Manitoba Beekeeper [1950]
Manitoba Crafts Museum & Library - Gladys Chown Memorial Library [6077], [6173]
Manitoba Department of Labour & Immigration - Workplace Safety and Health Division - Client Resource Centre [47547]
Manitoba Department of Labour - Manitoba Labour Board Library [46951]
Manitoba Genealogical Society Inc. - MGS Resource Center and Library [9530]
Manitoba Industry, Trade and Tourism - Canada Manitoba Business Service Centre - Women's Entrepreneurial Programs [59903]
Manitoba Intergovernmental Affairs and Trade - Community Economic Development Branch - Neighbourhoods Alive! [59898]
Manitoba Intergovernmental Affairs and Trade - Rural Economic Development Initiative (REDI) [59899]
Manitoba Tax Assistance Office [59900]
Manitoba Telecom Services Corporate Library [3859], [6552]
Manitoba Trucking Association Library [20724]
Manitou Springs Chamber of Commerce (MSCC) [49556]
Manitou Springs Chamber of Commerce and Visitors Bureau [49556]
Manitou Ventures, LLC [49265]
Manitowish Waters Chamber of Commerce (MWCC) [59630]
Manitowish Waters Visitor Guide [59631]
Manitowoc/Two Rivers Area Chamber of Commerce [59632]
Mankato Chamber of Commerce (MCC) [52146]
JG Manley and Associates [36048]
"Mann to Lead Builders" in Charlotte Observer (January 31, 2007) [5420], [16966], [17378]
Manners at Work [22510]
Mannes College of Music. [14694]
Mannes College The New School for Music - Harry Scherman Music Library [14694]
Manning Chamber of Commerce [51925]
Manoa Innovation Center (MIC) [50720]
Mansfield Area Chamber of Commerce (MCC) [58293]
Mansfield Chamber Communique [58294]
Mansfield-Richland Area Chamber of Commerce (MRACC) [56209]
Manteca Chamber of Commerce [48757]
Manteca District Chamber of Commerce [48757]
Manteca First [48758]
Manufacturer Directory [53364]; [53877]; [56210]; [59633]
Manufacturer Directory for Muncie-Delaware County [51670]
Manufacturers' Agents Association for the Foodservice Industry (MAFSI) [13908]
Manufacturers' Agents for Foodservice Industry [13908]
Manufacturers' Agents National Association (MANA) [13909]
Manufacturers' Agents National Association--Directory of Manufacturers' Sales Agencies [13915]

Manufacturers' Agents National Association--Directory of Members [13915]
"Manufacturers Become Part of Coalition" in Contractor (Vol. 56, July 2009, No. 7, pp. 40) [837], [30722], [39215], [42033]
Manufacturer's Directory [50573]; [54410]
Manufacturers Directory [51197]; [52919]; [53682]; [55763]; [55764]; [57498]
Manufacturers Directory CD [51671]
Manufacturers Division, National Association of Amusement Parks [964]
Manufacturer's Guide [51198]; [53365]
Manufacturers Guide [50208]
Manufacturer's Mart [39503]
Manufacturers Members of the National Warm Air Heating and Air Conditioning Association [761], [19065]
Manufacturers & Processors Directory [57161]
Manufacturers Representatives of America (MRA) [13910]
Manufacturers Representatives Educational Research Foundation (MRERF) [13911]; [13920]
"Manufacturers Urged to Adapt to Defense" in Crain's Cleveland Business (Vol. 30, June 22, 2009, No. 24, pp. 3) [28263], [33272], [39216]
Manufacturing Advocacy & Growth Network. [4918]
"Manufacturing Behind the Great Wall: What Works, What Doesn't" in Canadian Electronics (Vol. 23, February 2008, No. 1, pp. 6) [5755], [36671], [39217]
Manufacturing and Business Directory [51672]
Manufacturing Confectioner--Directory of Ingredients, Equipment and Packaging [3289]
Manufacturing Confectioner--Directory of Equipment and Supplies [3289]
Manufacturing Control in the Small Plant [39512]
Manufacturing Directory [50574]; [58295]
Manufacturing Jewelers and Silversmiths of America [13266], [38869]
Manufacturing Jewelers and Suppliers of America (MJSA) [13266], [38869]
"Manufacturing Jobs Go Begging in Downturn" in Puget Sound Business Journal (Vol. 29, December 26, 2008, No. 36, pp. 1) [27457], [39218], [45537]
Manufacturing Management Associates [3029], [13898]
"Manufacturing in the Middle Kingdom" in Inc. (December 2007, pp. 54-57) [36672], [39219], [40099], [41130]
Manufacturing Perfumers Association of the United States [1892], [2033], [5884]
Manufacturing Report [59634]
"A Manufacturing Revival" in Boston Business Journal (Vol. 31, May 27, 2011, No. 18, pp. 1) [23193], [35403], [35849], [39220], [45538]
Manufacturing and Technology News [39504]
Manulife Capital Corporation [53042]
Manulife Financial - Canadian Division Law Library [11505]
"Manulife Posts Billion-Dollar Profit" in Globe & Mail (February 14, 2007, pp. B7) [3941], [23194], [36190]
"The Many Hats and Faces of NAOHSM" in Indoor Comfort Marketing (Vol. 70, May 2011, No. 5, pp. 8) [838], [33825], [38230]
"Many Procter Products To Get Price Increase" in Business Courier (Vol. 24, November 16, 2008, No. 31, pp. 1) [39221], [42711]
"Many Retailers Soften Return Policies" in Austin Business JournalInc. (Vol. 28, December 26, 2008, No. 41, pp. 1) [27458], [43082], [45539]
"Many Roads Lead to Value" in Barron's (Vol. 88, March 10, 2008, No. 10, pp. 46) [8514], [12610], [24456], [31631]
"Many Sectors Lost Jobs In Detroit Area" in Crain's Detroit Business (Vol. 24, February 11, 2008, No. 6, pp. 3) [27459], [32819]
Map [48759]; [48760]; [54605]; [58296]
Map Brochure [59635]
Map and Business Guide [49825]
Map of Carmel-Clay [51673]
Map Directory [48762]
Map/Directory [48761]
Map of Gridley [48763]
Map and Guide [52920]
Map of Hammonton, NJ [54757]
Map of Longboat Key, Florida [50209]
Map of Merrimack [54606]
Map and Visitors Guide [49826]; [49827]
Map of York Area [57162]
Maple City Business and Technology Center Incubator - Technology Center Incubator [51449]
The Maple Leaflet [9463]
Maplewood Chamber of Commerce [54758]
Mapping Business Communications (Onsite) [22573]
"Mapping Out a Career" in Occupational Outlook Quarterly (Vol. 54, Fall 2010, No. 3, pp. 12) [35850], [44698], [45540]

"Mapping the Social Internet" in Harvard Business Review (Vol. 88, July-August 2010, No. 7-8, pp. 32) [11772], [28757], [36673]
Maps [48083]
Maquiladona Directory [58297]
Maquoketa Area Chamber of Commerce [51926]
Mara Perez, Ph.D. Development and Planning Services [47144]
Mara Perez, Ph.D. Fund Development and Planning Services [47144]
Marad Fine Art International [1417], [16332]
Marana Chamber of Commerce [47924]
Marana Chamber Newsletter [47925]
Marana Community Profile and Membership Directory [47926]
maranGraphics Inc. [59951]
"The Marathon Club: Building a Bridge to Wealth" in Hispanic Business (March 2008, pp. 24) [29985], [37429], [40779], [47046]
"Marathon Money" in Hawaii Business (Vol. 53, December 2007, No. 6, pp. 127) [19333], [20162], [20557], [23195], [27460], [43083], [43533]
Marble Falls Chamber of Commerce [58298]
Marble Falls - Lake LBJ Chamber of Commerce [58298]
Marble Falls SCORE [57889]
"Marble Slab Creamery" in Ice Cream Reporter (Vol. 23, November 20, 2010, No. 12, pp. 7) [10896], [40100]
Marble Slab Creamery [10972]; [10973]
Marble Slab Creamery Inc. [10973]
Marblehead Chamber of Commerce [52921]
Marblehead Peninsula Chamber of Commerce [56211]
MarbleLife [9082]
E.F. Marburger and Son Inc. [41621]
E.F. Marburger Fine Flooring [41621]
Marceline Chamber of Commerce [54082]
Marcello's Market & Deli Inc. [43299]
Marco [50210]
Marco Island Area Chamber of Commerce [50211]
Marco Island Chamber of Commerce Newsletter [50212]
Marconi Designs [15262], [41622]
Marco's Pizza [16160]
Marengo-Union Chamber of Commerce [51199]
Marfa Chamber of Commerce (MCC) [58299]
Margiloff & Associates [33469], [37164], [42905]
Marianna Chamber of Commerce [50176]
Maricopa Community Colleges at Phoenix Small Business Development Center [47835]
Maricopa County Procurement Technical Assistance Center - APTAN - Bid Source [47984]
Marietta Area Chamber of Commerce [56212]
Marin Self-Publishers Association - Marin Small-Publishers Association [2084], [6776]
Marin Small-Publishers Association [2084], [6776]
Marina Chamber of Commerce [48764]
"Marine Act Amendments Gain Parliamentary Approval" in Canadian Sailings (July 7, 2008) [5421], [11131], [17379], [23196], [26266], [30723], [33826], [36674], [37430], [47469]
Marine Business Journal: The Voice of the Marine Industries [3869]
Marine City Chamber of Commerce [53366]
Marine Engine Manufacturers Association [13931]
Marine Fuels: Specifications, Testing, Purchase & Use [30456]
Marine Museum at Fall River, Inc. Library [13980]
Marine Products Directory [13940]
Marine Retailers Association of America (MRAA) [13927]
Marinette Area Chamber of Commerce [59637]
Marinette Chamber Memo [59636]
Marinette Menominee Area Chamber of Commerce [59637]
Marion Area Chamber of Commerce [56213]
Marion Area Genealogical Society Library [9531]
Marion Chamber of Commerce [48084]; [51200]
Marion Chamber of Commerce (MCC) [57499]
Marion County Chamber of Commerce [57747]; [58300]
Marion County Chamber of Commerce (MCCC) [59411]
Marion County Chamber of Commerce [53878]
Marion County Development Partnership (MCDP) [53878]
Marion County Small Business Incubator [57546]
Marion-Grant County Chamber of Commerce [51674]
Francis Marion University - James A. Rogers Library - Special Collections [10043]
Mariposa County Chamber of Commerce [48765]
Maritime College of Forest Technology Library [7413]
Maritime Register [59862]
Maritz [14052]
Maritz Inc. [14052]
Maritz Travel Company Resource Center [24958]
Mark Twain Lake Chamber of Commerce [54083]
Mark West Area Chamber of Commerce [48766]
"Markel American Insurance Company Announces Wedding and Special Event Insurance for Consumers" in Benzinga.com (February 16, 2011) [2505], [11394], [36191]

Masonry **MASTER INDEX**

Mason Contractors Association of America (MCAA) **[14103]**
Mason Contractors of America Annual Convention: The Masonry Show [14121]
Mason County Area Chamber of Commerce (MCACC) **[59414]**
Mason County Chamber of Commerce **[58304]**
Mason County Chamber of Commerce [59414]
"Mason Fashions Its Future" in Business Courier (Vol. 24, December 7, 2008, No. 34, pp. 1) **[17383]**, **[27468]**
Mason in Motion **[53372]**
Mason in Motion Update **[53373]**
Mason Small Business Development Center **[58810]**
Mason Wells Private Equity / M&I Ventures **[59775]**
Masonry Block Explained **[14119]**
Masonry Heater Association of North America (MHA) **[770]**
Masonry Industry Committee [5184], [14102]
Masonry Research Foundation [5184], [14102]
The Masonry Society (TMS) **[14104]**
"Mass Mailers Try to Lick Rising Postal Rates" in Crain's Detroit Business (Vol. 24, March 10, 2008, No. 10, pp. 6) **[26267]**, **[40120]**
Mass Merchandisers & Off-Price Apparel Buyers **[7844]**
"Mass-Transit Backers: Change in State Funding Needed" in Crain's Detroit Business (Vol. 24, October 6, 2008, No. 40, pp. 19) **[24887]**, **[33831]**, **[45545]**
Massachusetts Biomedical Initiatives **[53083]**
Massachusetts Capital Resource Company **[53043]**
Massachusetts College of Art - Design Research Unit (DRU) **[42704]**
Massachusetts Export Center **[52809]**
Massachusetts Horticultural Society Library **[9860]**
Massachusetts Institute of Technology - Center for Coordination Science [4790]
Massachusetts Institute of Technology - CADLAB **[19061]**
Massachusetts Institute of Technology - Center for Collective Intelligence (CCI) **[4790]**
Massachusetts Institute of Technology - Center for Real Estate (CRE) **[17618]**
Massachusetts Institute of Technology - Center for Technology, Policy and Industrial Development - International Motor Vehicle Program (IMVP) **[28495]**
Massachusetts Institute of Technology - Japan Program **[28496]**
Massachusetts Institute of Technology - Laboratory for Computer Science - Programming Methodology Group (PMG) **[4924]**
Massachusetts Institute of Technology - Media Lab **[20021]**
Massachusetts Institute of Technology - Program on the Pharmaceutical Industry (POPI) **[28497]**
Massachusetts International Auto Show **[704]**
"The Massachusetts Mess: Good Health Care Is Expensive" in Barron's (Vol. 89, July 27, 2009, No. 30, pp. 39) **[11396]**, **[21934]**, **[27469]**, **[34361]**, **[36193]**
Massachusetts Office of Housing and Economic Development **[52810]**
Massachusetts Office of International Trade and Investment **[52811]**
Massachusetts Procurement Technical Assistance Center - University of Massachusetts - Small Business Development Center (SBDC) **[53077]**
Massachusetts Small Business Development Center - Berkshire **[52804]**
Massachusetts Small Business Development Center Network - Western **[52805]**
Massachusetts Small Business Development Center - Northeast **[52806]**
Massachusetts Society for the Prevention of Cruelty to Animals - Angell Memorial Animal Hospital Veterinary Library **[1096]**
Massachusetts Technology Development Corp. (MTDC) **[53044]**
Massachusetts Water Resources Authority Library **[21001]**
Massage: A Career at Your Fingertips **[14145]**
Massage Envy **[14156]**
Massage for Health **[14150]**
"Massage the Message" in Canadian Business (Vol. 79, Winter 2006, No. 24, pp. 137) **[29994]**, **[42494]**
Massage Therapy Journal **[34566]**
MassBay Community College **[53089]**
Massena Chamber of Commerce [55223]
Massey Burch Capital Corp. **[57810]**
Massillon Area Chamber of Commerce (MACC) **[56214]**
MassInnovation, LLC **[53084]**
"Massive Ford Restructuring to Cut 1,200 More Canadian Jobs" in Globe & Mail (January 24, 2006, pp. B1) **[24458]**, **[27470]**, **[39226]**
MASTA notes **[14643]**, **[14748]**
Master Brewers Association of the Americas (MBAA) **[2447]**
Master Brewers Association of America [2447]
Master Care **[2669]**
Master Gardener Series **[13427]**
Master Guide **[15829]**, **[15853]**
"Master of His Domain" in Canadian Business (Vol. 81, December 8, 2008, No. 21, pp. S17) **[5893]**, **[29995]**
The Master Mechanic **[18651]**
Master Organizational Politics, Influence and Alliances (Onsite) **[37701]**
Master Photo Dealers' and Finishers' Association [3231], [15825]
Master Photo Finishers and Dealers Association - National Photographic Dealers Association [3231], [15825]
Mastering Business Growth and Change Made Easy **[23200]**, **[32823]**
Mastering Business Negotiation **[22373]**, **[29996]**
Mastering Business Negotiation: A Working Guide to Making Deals and Resolving Conflict **[22374]**, **[29997]**, **[38233]**
Mastering the Complex Sale (Onsite) **[43354]**
Mastering the Complex Sales: How to Compete and Win When the Stakes Are High! **[25585]**, **[43538]**
Mastering CorelDRAW Newsletter **[21267]**
Mastering Microsoft Excel (Onsite) **[45054]**
Mastering Microsoft Project (Onsite) **[28053]**
Mastering QuickBooks Seminars and QuickBooks Classes (Onsite) **[28054]**
Masters of Sales: Secrets from Top Sales Professionals That Will Transform You Into a World Class Salesman **[22375]**, **[43539]**
Masthead Venture **[53045]**
Matanuska-Susitna College **[47827]**
Matanuska Tradewinds **[47808]**
Matawan - Aberdeen Chamber of Commerce **[54759]**
The Match King: Ivar Kreuger, the Financial Genius Behind a Century of Wall Street Scandals **[8523]**, **[12619]**
"Matchmakers Anticipating Tech Valley Boom" in Business Review, Albany New York (Vol. 34, November 2, 2007, No. 31, pp. 1) **[6967]**, **[7790]**, **[20030]**, **[34998]**
Matco Tools **[10152]**
Materials Advisory Group Inc. **[5660]**
Materials Management in Health Care **[14251]**, **[34567]**
"Maternity Wear Goes Green" in Marketing to Women (Vol. 21, March 2008, No. 3, pp. 3) **[4250]**, **[21626]**, **[39227]**, **[40121]**, **[43090]**
Math Monkey Knowledge Centers **[28470]**
Mathnasium Learning Centers **[20746]**, **[28471]**
Stuart Matlins Associates **[38768]**
Maton Venture **[49267]**
Matrix Management Corp. **[53046]**
Matrix Partners [53046]
Matrix Partners (Palo Alto) **[49268]**
Matson & Associates (M&A) **[9297]**, **[16622]**
Matt Trice [50441]
"Mattel's Got a Monster Holiday Hit, But Will Franchise Have Staying Power?" in Advertising Age (Vol. 81, December 6, 2010, No. 43) **[20259]**, **[23201]**, **[28764]**, **[32197]**, **[43091]**, **[44108]**
"A Matter of Interest" in Canadian Business (Vol. 79, July 17, 2006, No. 14-15, pp. 21) **[23202]**, **[31641]**, **[37432]**
"A Matter of Online Trust" in Entrepreneur (Vol. 37, August 2009, No. 8, pp. 35) **[11774]**, **[21023]**, **[40122]**
"A Matter of Perspective" in Business Journal-Portland (Vol. 24, November 2, 2007, No. 35, pp. 1) **[14457]**, **[16970]**, **[17384]**, **[33832]**
Matteson Area Chamber of Commerce (MACC) **[51202]**
Matthew Bender and Company Inc. [54888]
Matthews Business **[55766]**
Matthews CATV Directory **[3184]**
Matthews Chamber of Commerce (MCC) **[55767]**
Matthews Media Directory **[16719]**, **[19943]**
Mattituck Chamber of Commerce **[55276]**
Mattoon Chamber of Commerce **[51203]**
Maui Chamber of Commerce **[50712]**
Maui Small Business Development Center **[50692]**
Maui Wowi Hawaiian Coffees & Smoothies **[10974]**
Maumee Chamber of Commerce **[56215]**
Maumelle Area Chamber of Commerce (MACC) **[48085]**
"Maurice Strong" in Canadian Business (Vol. 81, December 8, 2008, No. 21, pp. 70) **[32824]**, **[36678]**
Maury Alliance **[57749]**
Maury County Chamber of Commerce [57749]
Mauston Chamber of Commerce [59591]
Max Muscle Sports Nutrition **[43300]**
Max Sacks International (MSI) **[43767]**
Maxdeco Interior Design Inc. **[41625]**
"Maximize Your Marketing Results In a Down Economy" in Franchising World (Vol. 42, November 2010, No. 11, pp. 45) **[27471]**, **[32198]**, **[40123]**
"Maximizing the Success of New Products" in Black Enterprise (Vol. 38, October 2007, No. 3, pp. 70) **[23203]**, **[41134]**
Maximum Marketing, Minimum Dollars: The Top 50 Ways to Grow Your Small Business **[23204]**, **[28765]**, **[40124]**, **[43540]**
Maximum PC **[4662]**, **[5013]**, **[19034]**
Maximum Performance Leadership (Canada) **[37702]**
Maximum Response Marketing **[9298]**, **[40636]**
May George S. International Co. [38723]
"May I Handle That For You?" in Inc. (March 2008, pp. 40, 42) **[106]**, **[15457]**, **[19514]**, **[19646]**, **[21391]**, **[35852]**, **[41682]**, **[44422]**
Maya Collection **[1370]**
Mayeri Research Inc. **[14053]**
"Mayfair Considers Moving Boston Store" in The Business Journal-Milwaukee (Vol. 25, September 5, 2008, No. 50, pp. 1) **[24459]**, **[24751]**
Mayfield Fund **[49269]**
Mayfield-Graves County Chamber of Commerce **[52350]**
Mayo Biomedical Imaging Resource Library **[4919]**
Mayo Medical Ventures **[53779]**
"Mayor Unveils Business Plan" in Boston Business Journal (Vol. 29, September 16, 2011, No. 19, pp. 1) **[27472]**, **[33274]**, **[34999]**, **[35853]**, **[44699]**, **[46300]**
Mayor's Office of Baltimore - Minority & Women-Owned Business Development **[52764]**
Maysville-Mason County Area Chamber of Commerce **[52351]**
Maysville Small Business Development Center **[52225]**
Maysville-Mason County Chamber of Commerce [52351]
Mayville Area Chamber of Commerce (MACC) **[59639]**
Mayville - Chautauqua Area Chamber of Commerce **[55277]**
Maywood Chamber of Commerce (MCC) **[48768]**; **[51204]**
Mazomanie Chamber of Commerce **[59640]**
Mazzio's Italian Eatery **[16161]**
MB Venture Partners, LLC **[57811]**
"MBA Essentials: Real-Life Instruction" in Women In Business (Vol. 61, October-November 2009, No. 5, pp. 28) **[25151]**, **[28266]**, **[29998]**, **[32825]**
"MBA Guide 2008" in Canadian Business (Vol. 81, November 10, 2008, No. 19, pp. 92) **[27473]**, **[28267]**, **[38234]**
MBA In a Day **[107]**, **[19647]**, **[21392]**, **[22376]**, **[27474]**, **[28268]**, **[29999]**, **[30952]**, **[32417]**, **[35854]**, **[38235]**, **[40125]**
"MBA Project Turns on Tastebuds" in The Business Journal - Serving Phoenix and the Valley of the Sun (Vol. 28, August 15, 2008, No. 50) **[17947]**, **[23205]**, **[24460]**, **[25152]**, **[32199]**, **[42035]**
MBA—Management Basics in Action **[38631]**
"MBAs Plus Designers Equals New Life for Business" in Globe & Mail (April 24, 2007, pp. B1) **[23206]**, **[28269]**, **[38236]**
"MBT Add On: Gone by 2012?" in Crain's Detroit Business (Vol. 24, October 6, 2008, No. 40, pp. 1) **[24752]**, **[27475]**, **[32826]**, **[33833]**, **[45546]**
"MBT 'Sticker Shock' Surprises Business; Reaction? 'You Can't Print It,' Owner Says" in Crain's Detroit Business (March 17, 2008) **[32827]**, **[46301]**
MCAA Network Guide [9210]
MCAA Reporter **[893]**, **[16288]**
MCAA's Masonry Showcase & MCAA Annual Convention **[14121]**
McAlester Area Chamber of Commerce and Agriculture (MACCA) **[56547]**
McAlester Chamber of Commerce - SBDC **[56640]**
McAlester Chamber of Commerce and Agriculture [56547]
McAlister's Deli **[6477]**
McAllen Chamber of Commerce **[58305]**
McAllen Convention and Visitors Bureau [58305]
McAllen Memorial Library - McAllen Genealogical Society Collection. [9532]
McAllen Public Library - McAllen Genealogical Society Collection **[9532]**
MCBA Newsletter **[2246]**
McCabe-Henley L.P. [17604]
McCallum & Kudravetz P.C. **[227]**
McCamey Chamber of Commerce **[58306]**
McCann-Erickson Advertising of Canada Ltd. Information Centre **[692]**, **[42701]**
Edward F. McCartan Publishing Consultant **[2210]**
McCarthy Tetrault Library **[24171]**
MCCC Newsletter **[50575]**
"McClatchy Believed Front-Runner in Knight Ridder Sale" in Globe & Mail (March 13, 2006, pp. B6) **[32828]**, **[42036]**
McCleary Community Chamber of Commerce **[59231]**
McCloud Chamber of Commerce **[48769]**
McClure Associates Inc. **[40947]**
McCook Area Chamber of Commerce **[54411]**
McCook Chamber of Commerce [54411]
McCormick County Business League [57501]

3562 **Small Business Sourcebook • 30th Edition**

MASTER INDEX

Meet

Master Index

McCormick County Chamber of Commerce **[57501]**
"McCormick Focuses on Customer, Dealer Service" in Farm Industry News (September 17, 2010) **[21627], [24461], [26484]**
McCown De Leeuw and Co. **[49270]**
McCreary County Chamber of Commerce **[52352]**
McCreight & Company Inc. **[2923], [13858], [24684], [26054], [36049]**
McDargh Communications **[26637]**
McDonald Consulting Group Inc. **[2924], [13859], [24685], [26055], [38769]**
McDonald's Corp. **[18180]**
"McDonald's Founders Fund $80 Million Project" in The Business Journal - Serving Phoenix and the Valley of the Sun (Vol. 28, September 12, 2008, No. 53, pp. 1) **[5423], [17385], [45955]**
McDonald's Restaurants of Canada Ltd. **[18181]**
McDowell Chamber of Commerce **[55768]**
McDowell Community Viewbook **[55769]**
"McD's Dollar-Menu Fixation Sparks Revolt" in Advertising Age (Vol. 79, June 2, 2008, No. 22, pp. 1) **[17948], [27476], [32200], [40126], [45547]**
"McD's Picks a Soda Fight; Takes on 7-Eleven With $1 Pop as Economy Softens" in Crain's Chicago Business (April 14, 2008) **[5808], [17949], [25586], [32201]**
"McD's Tries to Slake Consumer Thirst for Wider Choice of Drinks" in Advertising Age (Vol. 79, June 9, 2008, No. 23, pp. 1) **[17950], [25587], [26485], [32202], [40127], [41135], [42826]**
"McD's Warms Up For Olympics Performance" in Advertising Age (Vol. 79, July 7, 2008, No. 26, pp. 8) **[524], [11775], [17951], [21153], [32203], [40128], [42495], [42643]**
McFadden Golden States Financial Directory [37380]
McFarland Chamber of Commerce **[59641]**
Scott McGarvey Associates **[40637]**
Bruce W. McGee & Associates [24686], [37165], [38770], [41503]
Jerome W. McGee & Associates **[24686], [37165], [38770], [41503]**
McGehee Area Chamber of Commerce [48086]
McGehee Chamber of Commerce **[48086]**
McGhin's Southern Pit Bar-B-Que **[18182]**
McGill University - Centre international d'étude sur le je et les comportements à risque chez les jeunes [9422]
McGill University - Desmarais Global Finance Centre (DGFC) **[8969]**
McGill University - Environmental Engineering Laboratory **[21011]**
McGill University - International Centre for Youth Gambling Problems and High-Risk Behaviors (YGI) **[9422]**
McGill University - McGill Finance Research Centre [8969]
McGohen Dermott Times News **[48087]**
The McGraw-Hill Companies, Inc. - Business Information Center **[2227]**
McGraw-Hill Inc. **[56423]**
McGraw-Hill/Irwin **[51469]**
McGraw-Hill Trade **[55530]**
McGraw-Hill Ventures /McGraw-Hill Capital Corp. **[55438]**
McGregor Chamber of Commerce **[58307]**
McGregor/Marquette Chamber of Commerce (MCC) **[51930]**
McGrow Consulting **[3031], [26127]**
McGruff Safe Kids Total Identification System **[16032]**
McHenry Area Chamber of Commerce (MACC) **[51205]**
"mChip: Claros Diagnostics" in Inc. (Vol. 33, November 2011, No. 9, pp. 42) **[14275], [34362], [43896], [44423]**
"McIntosh Family Sells Car Dealership" in Black Enterprise (Vol. 38, December 2007, No. 5) **[14929], [31089], [44167]**
McKay/Moore Consultants L.L.C. **[5661]**
McKenna Long & Aldridge LLP Law Library **[6720], [7414], [11506]**
McKinleyville Chamber of Commerce **[48770]**
McKinney Chamber of Commerce (MCC) **[58308]**
McKinney Focus **[58309]**
McKinney Living Magazine **[58310]**
McKinney Living Magazine's Relocation & Referral Guide **[58311]**
McKinnon, Allen & Associates Western Ltd. **[21780]**
McKinsey & Company, Inc. - Resource Library **[3134]**
McLean County Chamber of Commerce (MCC) **[51206]**
McLean Watson Capital Inc. **[59929]**
McLennan Small Business Development Center **[57857]**
McLeod Associates Inc. **[5085]**
McMafia: A Journey Through the Global Criminal Underworld **[23936], [47047]**
McMann & Ransford **[2925], [23656]**
McMaster University - Health Sciences Library **[1451]**
McMinnville Area Chamber of Commerce (GMCC) **[56809]**
McMinnville - Warren County Chamber of Commerce **[57750]**
McMullen Valley Chamber of Commerce **[47927]**
MCNC Research and Development **[55868]**
MCNC Ventures LLC **[55856]**
McNeil Consumer and Specialty Pharmaceuticals - Pharmaceutical Research Center **[6721]**
McNeilly Business Center **[57338]**
McPherson Chamber of Commerce **[52148]**
McPherson SCORE **[52028]**
MCR Capital Advisors L.L.P. **[38771]**
McShane Group Inc. **[2926], [13860], [24687], [26056], [32049], [38772]**
James V. McTevia & Associates **[42339]**
"Md. Bankers Say 'Devil Is In the Details' of New $30B Loan Fund" in Baltimore Business Journal (Vol. 28, October 8, 2010, No. 22) **[33275], [37433]**
"Md. Tries to Recoup $73M from Actuary" in Baltimore Business Journal (Vol. 28, June 11, 2010, No. 5, pp. 1) **[21935], [23937], [42384]**
MDA Engineering Inc. **[5662]**
MDT Advisers, Inc. **[53047]**
"Me First!" in Black Enterprise (Vol. 38, December 2007, No. 5, pp. 107) **[30000], [35000]**
Me, MyHome, And I **[17140]**
Me-n-Ed's Pizzerias **[16162]**
Meade Chamber of Commerce (MCC) **[52149]**
"Meadowbrook CEO Sees 20 Percent Growth With New Acquisition" in Crain's Detroit Business (Vol. 24, March 10, 2008, No. 10, pp. 4) **[11397], [12620], [23207], [24462], [36194], [38237], [42037]**
"Meadowbrook To Acquire ProCentury in $272.6 Million Deal" in Crain's Detroit Business (Vol. 24, February 25, 2008, No. 8, pp. 4) **[11398], [12621], [23208], [36195], [42038]**
Meadowlands Regional Chamber of Commerce (MRCC) **[54760]**
Meadowlands/USA **[54761]**
Meadville Area Chamber of Commerce [57163]
Meadville - Western Crawford County Chamber of Commerce **[57163]**
Mealey's Emerging Insurance Disputes **[26674]**
"Meals on Wheels Filling 'Blizzard Bags'" in Tulsa World (November 5, 2011) **[9159], [9264]**
Means Labor Rates for the Construction Industry **[5567]**
"Measure Your Business Plan Results" in Entrepreneur (January 6, 2009) **[24463], [25153], [32829]**
MeasureNet **[2927]**
Measuring Customer Satisfaction **[26648]**
"Measuring the Impact" in Mergers & Acquisitions: The Dealmaker's Journal (March 1, 2008) **[26268], [27477], [37434], [42039]**
Measuring and Maximizing Marketing ROI (Onsite) **[39593]**
"Measuring Success In Family Businesses: The Concept of Configurational Fit" in Family Business Review (Vol. 19, June 2006, No. 2) **[31090], [32830]**
Meat Industry [3148]
Meat & Poultry: The Business Journal of the Meat & Poultry Industry **[3148]**
"MEC, Churchill Downs Saddle Up in Racing Deal" in Globe & Mail (March 6, 2007, pp. B1) **[19944], [40129], [42040], [42644]**
Mechanical Contractors Association of America (MCAA) **[771]**
Mechanical Contractors Association of Canada (MCAC) **[5186]**
Mechanical Design Associates Inc. [5662]
The Mechanics of Modernity in Europe and East Asia: Institutional Origins of Social Change and Stagnation **[27478], [36679]**
Mecosta County Area Chamber of Commerce (MCACC) **[53374]**
"MEDC: Put Venture Funds to Work" in Crain's Detroit Business (Vol. 25, June 22, 2009, No. 25, pp. 1) **[33276], [37435], [38238], [47048]**
Medema Consulting Associates L.L.C. **[38773]**
Medford Area Chamber of Commerce **[59642]**
Medford Chamber of Commerce **[52924]**
Media Communications Association-International (MCA-I) **[7890]**
Media Computing **[2688], [3652], [4663], [4766], [5014], [19035]**
"Media Giant Remakes Itself: Job Cuts Signal Journal Sentinel's Focus on New Products" in Business Journal-Milwaukee (Oct. 12, 2007) **[15552], [25588], [28766], [41136]**
Media Graphics Inc. [46790]
Media Guide **[51931]**
The Media Guys Inc. **[16623]**
"Media Industry Collection Agency Completes Acquisition" in Collections & Credit Risk (Vol. 15, December 1, 2010, No. 11, pp. 22) **[6314], [12622], [15553], [26269], [42041]**
Media, Organizations and Identity **[3185], [11001], [15554], [16593], [16720], [19945], [42496], [42645]**
Media Review Digest: The Only Complete Guide to Reviews of Non-Print Media **[7945]**
"Media Software and Data Services" in MarketingMagazine (Vol. 115, September 27, 2010, No. 13, pp. 78) **[3560], [4719], [4867], [18930], [45149]**
Media Technology Ventures **[49271]**
"Media Terminology" in MarketingMagazine (Vol. 115, September 27, 2010, No. 13, pp. 80) **[28767], [40130]**
Media Venture Partners **[49272]**
"Media Wars" in Canadian Business (Vol. 83, August 17, 2010, No. 13-14, pp. 32) **[6943], [15555], [28768]**
"Medicaid Expansion Could Prompt New Taxes, Program Cuts" in Baltimore Business Journal (Vol. 27, October 23, 2009, No. 24, pp. 1) **[33277], [33834], [34363], [46302]**
"Medicaid Insurers See Growth in Small Business Market" in Boston Business Journal (Vol. 31, July 15, 2011, No. 25, pp. 1) **[11399], [23209], [25775], [36196], [42042], [45548]**
Medical Benefits **[22023]**
Medical College of Wisconsin - Center for the Study of Bioethics **[40955]**
"Medical Connectors: Meeting the Demands of Reliability, Portability, Size and Cost" in Canadian Electronics (February 2008) **[14204], [34364], [35001], [39228]**
Medical Device Register (MDR) **[14336]**
Medical Device Register **[14318]**
Medical Devices, Diagnostics & Instrumentation Reports - The Gray Sheet **[14231]**
Medical Electronics & Equipment News [14233]
Medical and Health Information Directory: A Guide to Organizations, Agencies, Institutions, Programs, Publications, Services, and Other Resources Concerned with Clinical Medicine. . . **[6661], [10538], [14276]**
Medical Imaging Consultants Inc. (MIC) **[2928], [13861], [26057], [38774], [40638], [41302], [42906]**
Medical Imaging: News, Issues, and Trends in Health Technology Management **[14232]**
Medical Laboratory Observer (MLO) **[14286]**
"Medical Market a Healthy Alternative" in Crain's Cleveland Business (Vol. 30, June 1, 2009, No. 21, pp. 3) **[14205], [39229]**
"Medical Office Developers To Merge November 1" in The Business Journal - Serving Phoenix and the Valley of the Sun (Vol. 29, September 26, 2008, No. 4, pp. 1) **[5424], [16971], [17386], [42043]**
Medical Outcomes Management Inc. **[2929], [13862], [26058], [38775]**
"Medical Pot Backers Say Industry Will Survive" in Sacramento Business Journal (Vol. 28, October 14, 2011, No. 33, pp. 1) **[33835], [34365]**
Medical Technology and Practice Patterns Institute, Inc. (MTPPI) **[34671]**
Medical-Surgical Manufacturers Association [14182], [14310]
Medicap Pharmacy **[6698]**
"Medicare Inc." in Canadian Business (Vol. 80, October 8, 2007, No. 20, pp. 160) **[25589], [27479], [34366]**
"Medicare Plans Step Up Battle for Subscribers" in Sacramento Business Journal (Vol. 28, October 21, 2011, No. 34, pp. 1) **[11400], [21936], [34367], [36197]**
Medicare & You Handbook **[34368]**
MEDIchair Ltd. **[14242]**
Medici Effect **[30001], [37068]**
Medicine Lodge Area Chamber of Commerce (MLACC) **[52150]**
Medicine Lodge Chamber of Commerce [52150]
"Medicine Men" in Canadian Business (Vol. 80, February 12, 2007, No. 4, pp. 19) **[525], [10230], [40131]**
Medicine on the Net **[11951], [34568]**
Medicine Shoppe Canada **[6699]**
Medicine Shoppe International, Inc. **[6700]**
Medina Area Chamber of Commerce [55300]; [56154]
Mediphase Venture Partners / EHealth Technology Fund **[53048]**
"The Medium 150" in Canadian Business (Vol. 81, Summer 2008, No. 9, pp. 129) **[8524], [12623], [23210], [31642], [45549]**
Medium Sized Firms and Economics Growth **[12624], [23211], [27480], [30002], [32831]**
Medocino Coast Business Directory **[48771]**
Medventure Associates **[49273]**
Meeker Chamber of Commerce **[49557]**
MEEN Cardiology/Critical Care Technology [14233]
MEEN Diagnostic and Invasive Technology **[14233]**
MEEN Imaging Technology News [14233]
"Meet the Dropouts: the Students Who Chose Start-Ups Over College" in Inc. (Vol. 33, September 2011, No. 7, pp. 32) **[47049], [47591]**
"Meet the Gatekeepers" in Crain's Chicago Business (Vol. 30, February 2007, No. 6, pp. 40) **[12625], [35404]**

Small Business Sourcebook • 30th Edition

3563

MASTER INDEX
Microsoft
Master Index

Meritage Private Equity Funds **[49618]**
Meriwether County Chamber of Commerce (MCCC) **[50577]**
Merkel Chamber of Commerce **[58322]**
"Merkle Lands $75M" in Baltimore Business Journal (Vol. 28, October 15, 2010, No. 23, pp. 1) **[35004]**, **[47051]**
Merle Norman Cosmetics Studio **[5915]**
Merlin 200,000 Mile Shops **[18653]**
Merrill Area Chamber of Commerce (MACC) **[59650]**
Merrill City Directory **[59651]**
"Merrill Lynch in Talks to Buy BlackRock Stake" in Globe & Mail (February 13, 2006, pp. B4) **[8526]**, **[31643]**, **[42049]**
Merrill, Wisconsin, A City of Progress and Promise **[59652]**
Merrillville Chamber of Commerce **[51678]**
Merrimac Associates Inc. **[32051]**
Merrimack Chamber of Commerce **[54609]**
Merrimack Valley Chamber of Commerce (MVCC) **[52927]**
Merritt & Harris Inc. **[17595]**
Merry Maids **[6583]**
Merry Maids of Canada **[6584]**
Mertz Associates Inc. **[42340]**, **[44217]**
Mesa Chamber of Commerce (MCC) **[47928]**
Mesa Chamber Directory **[47929]**
Mesa House Publishing **[58605]**
Mesa Minority/Micro Small Business Development Center (M3SBDC) **[47836]**
Mesalands Community College Small Business Development Center **[54902]**
MESBIC Ventures Holding Co. **[58563]**
Mesirow Private Equity Investments, Inc. **[51412]**
Mesquite Area Chamber of Commerce **[54504]**
Mesquite Chamber of Commerce and Convention and Visitors Bureau (MCCCVB) **[58323]**
Messenger **[47930]**; **[49563]**; **[57380]**
Messenger Courier Association of America (MCAA) **[14351]**
Messenger Courier Association of America--Network Guide and Membership Directory **[9210]**
Meta **[20470]**
Metal Architecture **[5601]**
Metal Building News--Building Systems Product File and Directory Issue [5427]
Metal Construction News--Metal Architecture Building Systems Product File and Directory Issue **[5427]**
Metal Cookware Manufacturers Association [10384]
Metal Cutting Tool Institute [13696]
Metal Stamping [13727]
METALFORM Mexico **[13732]**
Metalforming: Serving the Precision Metalforming Industry **[13727]**
"Metallics Education" in American Printer (Vol. 128, June 1, 2011, No. 6) **[4491]**, **[16382]**, **[20783]**, **[45151]**
Metallurgistes Unis d'Amerique [46829]
Metalworking Digest [13730]
Metcalf & Eddy, Inc. - Harry L. Kinsel Library **[10197]**
Methodist Research Institute (MRI) **[34672]**
"Methodological Fit in Management Field Research" in Academy of Management Review (October 2007, pp. 1155) **[38241]**, **[42829]**
Methods Time Measurements Association for Standards and Research [15242]
"The Metrics of Knowledge: Mechanisms for Preserving the Value of Managerial Knowledge" in Business Horizons (Nov.-Dec. 2007) **[37250]**, **[38242]**
Metro Accounting Services Inc. **[32052]**
Metro Atlanta Chamber of Commerce (MACOC) **[50578]**
Metro Brief **[58324]**
Metro Business **[48784]**
Metro Buyers' Guide **[53880]**
Metro East Chamber of Commerce (MECC) **[53379]**
Metro Guide **[53380]**
Metro North Chamber of Commerce (MNCC) **[49564]**
Metro/Regional Business Incubator **[52534]**
Metro South Chamber of Commerce **[52928]**
Metro Tulsa Chamber of Commerce [56597]
Metro Vocational Technical School **[56660]**
Metro West Magazine **[58325]**
Metrocrest Chamber of Commerce **[58326]**
Metrocrest Membergram **[58327]**
MetroHartford Chamber of Commerce **[49724]**
MetroJackson Chamber of Commerce (MJCC) **[53881]**
Metroline **[54767]**
MetroNorth Chamber of Commerce **[53688]**
MetroNorth Chamber of Commerce - Serving Anoka County and Surrounding Areas [53688]
Metropolis Area Chamber of Commerce, Tourism and Economic Development [51220]
Metropolis Chamber of Commerce **[51220]**
Metropolitan Beaumont **[58328]**
Metropolitan Economic Development Association (MEDA) **[53770]**, **[53784]**
Metropolitan Economic Development Association - Procurement Technical Assistance Center [53770], [53784]
Metropolitan Home **[11566]**
Metropolitan Life Insurance Company - Corporate Information Center & Library **[11507]**
Metropolitan Milwaukee Association of Commerce (MMAC) **[59653]**
Metropolitan Museum of Art - Irene Lewisohn Costume Reference Library **[4176]**, **[5941]**
Metropolitan Venture Partners (METVP) **[55439]**
Metropolitan Washington DC JobBank: The Job Hunter's Guide to Washington DC **[19180]**
MetroWest Business **[52929]**
MetroWest Chamber of Commerce **[52930]**
Metter-Candler Chamber of Commerce **[50579]**
"Mettle Detector" in Canadian Business (Vol. 79, July 17, 2006, No. 14-15, pp. 63) **[8527]**, **[12628]**, **[21937]**, **[25156]**, **[28272]**, **[31644]**
Metuchen Area Chamber of Commerce **[54768]**
Mexia Area Chamber of Commerce **[58329]**
Mexicali Rosa's **[18184]**
"Mexican Companies to Rent Space in TechTown, Chinese Negotiating" in Crain's Detroit Business (Vol. 24, September 29, 2008, No. 39) **[23218]**, **[26770]**, **[27484]**, **[30726]**, **[36094]**, **[36682]**, **[41547]**, **[43898]**
Mexico Area Chamber of Commerce (MACC) **[54088]**
"MF Global Moved Clients' Funds to BNY Mellon" in Wall Street Journal Eastern Edition (November 19 , 2011, pp. B2) **[8528]**, **[12629]**, **[23941]**, **[31645]**
The MFP Report **[39506]**
"MFS Survey: Generation X/Y Perplexed and Conservative about Future Investing" in Wireless News (November 16, 2010) **[8529]**, **[12630]**, **[31646]**
"MFSA Officially Endorses Five-Day USPS Delivery" in American Printer (Vol. 128, August 1, 2011, No. 8) **[4492]**, **[16383]**, **[20784]**
MFV Expositions **[3032]**
MGCCI It's Your Business **[51221]**
MHJ Associates **[38776]**
Mhm Professional Resources Inc. [214], [2833], [13807], [21456], [25959], [32011], [38678]
Mi Kitchen es su Kitchen **[55491]**
MIAC E-News **[14728]**
Miami Area Chamber of Commerce (MACC) **[56549]**
Miami Beach Chamber of Commerce **[50224]**
Miami Beach Visitors Guide **[50225]**
Miami-Dade County Chamber of Commerce **[50226]**
The Miami Home Design & Remodeling Show **[10503]**, **[11574]**
Miami International Boat Show and Strictly Sail **[13967]**
Miami Subs Grill **[6478]**
Miami University - Southwest Ohio Regional Depository **[1153]**
Miami University - Walter Havighurst Special Collections Library **[10378]**
"Miami's 'Big Wheels' Keep Latin America Rolling" in Hispanic Business (July-August 2007, pp. 46-47) **[11134]**, **[20072]**, **[40782]**
"Michael Doesn't Live Here Anymore" in Canadian Business (Vol. 80, October 8, 2007, No. 20, pp. 52) **[27485]**, **[30003]**
Michael Edmond Gray **[52800]**
Michael Porter on Competitive Strategy **[25715]**
Michaels Associates Design Consultants Inc. **[15263]**, **[41626]**
"Michaud Touts Small-Business Credentials" in Bangor Daily News (September 10, 2010) **[33279]**, **[45552]**, **[46304]**
Michel's Baguette Bakery Cafe **[1813]**
Michigan & Great Lakes Food Service Show [10309], [18041], [46768]
Michigan Association for Computer Users in Learning Conference **[4777]**, **[28428]**, **[46766]**
Michigan Biotechnology Institute International **[53507]**
Michigan CFO Associates Inc. **[36051]**
Michigan Chamber of Commerce **[53381]**
Michigan City Area Chamber of Commerce **[51679]**
Michigan Construction & Design Tradeshow **[5624]**
Michigan Economic Development Corp. **[53101]**
Michigan Economic Development Corporation - International Development **[53102]**
Michigan Economic Development Corporation - Office of Small Business Group **[53473]**
Michigan Economic Development Corp. - Office of Women Business Owners Services **[53474]**
Michigan Economic Development Corp. - Small Business Outreach **[53103]**
Michigan Family Forum (MFF) **[34673]**
Michigan Financial Independence Agency - Office of Training and Staff Development - Resource Library **[38844]**
Michigan Florist: A publication of the Michigan Floral Association **[9116]**
Michigan Forward **[53382]**
Michigan Grocers Association Annual Convention and Trade Show **[10011]**
"Michigan Institute of Urology Grows in Expertise, Services" in Crain's Detroit Business (Vol. 24, April 7, 2008, No. 14, pp. 13) **[23219]**, **[34371]**
Michigan Interscholastic Athletic Administrators Mid-Winter Conference **[19491]**, **[46767]**
Michigan Minority Supplier Development Council **[53475]**
Michigan Molecular Institute & Impact Analytical **[53508]**
Michigan Procurement Technical Assistance Center - Business Development Center **[53483]**
Michigan Procurement Technical Assistance Center - Downriver Community Conference **[53484]**
Michigan Procurement Technical Assistance Center - Economic Development Alliance of St. Clair County **[53485]**
Michigan Procurement Technical Assistance Center - Genesee Regional Chamber of Commerce (Region 6) - Satellite Office **[53486]**
Michigan Procurement Technical Assistance Center - Kalamazoo Regional Chamber of Commerce **[53487]**
Michigan Procurement Technical Assistance Center - Macomb Community College PTAC **[53488]**
Michigan Procurement Technical Assistance Center - Macomb Community College (Region 4) - Satellite Office **[53489]**
Michigan Procurement Technical Assistance Center - Muskegon Area First **[53490]**
Michigan Procurement Technical Assistance Center - Northeast Michigan Consortium (Presque Isle Region) **[53491]**
Michigan Procurement Technical Assistance Center - Northwest Michigan Council of Governments **[53492]**
Michigan Procurement Technical Assistance Center, Saginaw Future Satellite Office (Region 5) **[53493]**
Michigan Procurement Technical Assistance Center - West Central Michigan Employment & Training Consortium **[53494]**
Michigan Procurement Technical Assistant Center - Schoolcraft College **[53495]**
Michigan Restaurant Show **[10309]**, **[18041]**, **[46768]**
Michigan Small Business and Technology Development Center **[53476]**
Michigan State University - American Polygraph Association Credibility Assessment Research Center **[16476]**
Michigan State University - Institute for Public Policy and Social Research (IPPSR) **[45845]**
Michigan State University - Michigan State University Horse Teaching and Research Center (HTRC) **[10637]**
Michigan State University - Software Engineering and Network Systems Laboratory (SENS) **[4791]**
Michigan State University - Special Collections Division - Russel B. Nye Popular Culture Collection **[4426]**
Michigan State University - Special Collections Library **[1957]**
Michigan Tech Enterprise SmartZone **[53509]**
Michigan Tooling Association [13695]
Micro Cap et Al **[47145]**
"Micro-Cap Companies" in Canadian Business (Vol. 81, Summer 2008, No. 9, pp. 157) **[8530]**, **[12631]**, **[23220]**, **[31647]**, **[41338]**, **[45553]**
"Micro-Finance Agencies and SMEs" in International Journal of Entrepreneurship and Small Business (Vol. 11, August 3, 2010) **[27486]**, **[31648]**, **[36683]**, **[37437]**, **[42050]**
Micro-Macro International Inc. (MMI) **[21781]**
Microbiology Abstracts Section A: Industrial and Applied Microbiology **[44056]**
The Microbreweries Market **[2468]**
Microbrewers Resource Directory [2461]
Microbrewers Resource Handbook and Directory [2461]
MicroBusiness Enterprise Center **[50676]**
Microfinance **[110]**, **[21395]**, **[31649]**, **[38243]**
Microfranchising: Creating Wealth at the Bottom of the Pyramid **[30004]**, **[32100]**, **[45957]**
"Microlending Seen as Having a Major Impact" in Business Journal Serving Greater Tampa Bay (Vol. 30, November 26, 2010, No. 49, pp. 1) **[33280]**, **[37438]**, **[41373]**
Microprocessor Report **[4664]**, **[4806]**, **[5015]**, **[5045]**
Microscopy Research and Technique **[44057]**
Microsoft Access 2003: A Comprehensive Hands-On Introduction - Building a Foundation for Client/Server Database Applications (Onsite) **[28055]**
Microsoft Access 2007: A Comprehensive Hands-On Introduction (Onsite) **[28056]**
Microsoft Access 2007 - I (Onsite) **[28057]**
Microsoft Access 2007 - II (Onsite) **[28058]**
Microsoft Access: A 2-Day Hands-On Workshop (Onsite) **[45055]**
"Microsoft Clicks Into High Speed" in Hispanic Business (Vol. 30, July-August 2008, No. 7-8, pp. 54) **[3562]**, **[18932]**, **[25157]**, **[35005]**, **[35405]**, **[38244]**, **[40135]**, **[41137]**, **[42498]**, **[44425]**, **[45152]**

Small Business Sourcebook • 30th Edition
3565

Mineola Chamber of Commerce [55283]
Mineral County Chamber of Commerce [54297]; [54505]; [59416]
Mineral Insulation Manufacturers Association [11257]
Mineral Point Chamber of Commerce (MPCCMS) [59655]
Mineral Wells Area Chamber of Commerce [58335]
Minerals Management Service - Alaska OCS [61519]
Minerals Management Service - Business Utilization and Development Specialist - Division of Procurement and Contracts [61520]
Minerals Management Service - Business Utilization and Development Specialist - Western ASC Procurement and Contracts [61521]
Minerals Management Service - Pacific Region OCS [61522]
Minerva Area Chamber of Commerce (MACOC) [56229]
Mini-Cassia Chamber of Commerce [50785]
Mini Cities Inc. [16438]
Mini-Guide Brochure [50227]
Mini Maid [6585]
"Mini Melts" in Ice Cream Reporter (Vol. 23, August 20, 2010, No. 9, pp. 8) [10898], [26771], [38247], [43541]
Mini Melts [10975]
"Mini Melts Offers 'Win an Ice Cream Business' Contest" in Ice Cream Reporter (Vol. 23, October 20, 2010, No. 11, pp. 3) [10899], [40139]
Miniature Donkey Talk: The Talk of the Donkey World [1027], [1078], [15695]
"Minimizing Import Risks" in Canadian Sailings (July 7, 2008) [11135], [21630], [33837], [36685], [39233], [43097], [45556]
"Mining Executive Telfer Pocketed Millions" in Globe & Mail (April 5, 2007, pp. B4) [8533], [12636], [38248]
"Mining Goldman for Insight" in Barron's (Vol. 89, July 20, 2009, No. 29, pp. M8) [8534], [12637], [31656]
miniUPDATE e-mail newsletter [51222]
Minneapolis Area Chamber of Commerce (MACC) [52152]
Minneapolis College of Art and Design Library [4574], [5942]
Minneapolis Community and Technical College - Business Management Program [53797]
Minneapolis Home & Garden Show [9829]
Minneapolis International Motorcycle Show [1584], [14556], [46769]
Minneapolis Regional Chamber of Commerce [53690]
"Minnesota ABC Event Looks at Government Contracting" in Finance and Commerce Daily Newspaper (November 23, 2010) [5430], [20389], [33281], [46670]
Minnesota Airport Directory & Travel Guide [730]
Minnesota Business Views [53691]
Minnesota Chamber of Commerce [53692]
Minnesota Chippewa Tribe - Native American Business Enterprise Center [53771]
Minnesota Department of Employment and Economic Development [53541]
Minnesota Department of Employment and Economic Development - Business and Community Development Division and Trade [53542]
Minnesota Department of Employment and Economic Development - Minnesota Trade Office [53543]
Minnesota Department of Children, Families & Learning [60904]
"Minnesota Farms' Net Worth Grows 10 Percent Each Year for 15 Years" in Farm Industry News (August 22, 2011) [16974], [17390], [21631], [23225]
Minnesota Labor and Industry Department - Research and Statistics Office [23664]
Minnesota Labor and Industry Department - Policy Development, Research and Statistics Unit [23664]
Minnesota Procurement Technical Assistance Center - Metropolitan Economic Development Association (MEDA) [53785]
Minnesota Procurement Technical Assistance Center - Minnesota Project Innovation, Inc. [53786]
Minnesota Small Business Development Center - Northeast [53533]
Minnesota Small Business Development Center - Northwest [53534]
Minnesota Small Business Development Center - South Central [53535]
Minnesota Small Business Development Center - Southeast [53536]
Minnesota Small Business Development Center - West Central [53537]
Minnesota Spring Home and Garden Show [9829]
Minnesota State Community and Technical College - Detroit Lakes [53798]
Minnesota State Community and Technical College - Fergus Falls [53799]
"Minnesota State Park Building Exemplifies Sustainability" in Contractor (Vol. 56, November 2009, No. 11, pp. 5) [839], [6894], [16251], [30727]

Minnesota West Community and Technical College (Pipestone, Minnesota) [53800]
Minnesota's Lake of the Woods Area Vacation Guide [53693]
Minocqua - Arbor Vitae - Woodruff Chamber of Commerce [59656]
"Minor-League Baseball's Sliders Plan Stock Offering" in Crain's Detroit Business (Vol. 25, June 15, 2009, No. 24, pp. 3) [5431], [12638], [19440], [42054]
"Minority Auto Suppliers Get Help Diversifying" in Crain's Detroit Business (Vol. 26, January 11, 2010, No. 2, pp. 3) [26772], [33282], [39234], [40784], [44851]
Minority Business Enterprise Center [50345]
Minority Business Enterprise Center of New Jersey [54838]
Minority Business Entrepreneur [11219], [40835]
Minority Business/Professional Directory [56230]
"Minority Entrepreneurs, Business Advocate of the Year Named" in Daily News (November 1, 2010) [30008], [40785], [45959]
Min/Research Alert [14006]
Min's b2b [16479]
Mint Condition Franchising, Inc. [6586]
Minuteman Press [16439]
Minuteman Press International [16440]
Minutes [54772]
Minutes of Board Meeting [51223]
Minutes and Memorandum [52735]
MIOSHA News [53524]
"MIR Growing With Help From Former Pfizer Workers" in Crain's Detroit Business (Vol. 24, January 28, 2008, No. 4, pp. 33) [23226], [41140], [42830], [43899]
Miracle Ear [10344]
Miracle Method Bath And Kitchen Restoration [10441]
Miramar-Pembroke Pines Regional Chamber of Commerce [50228]
The Mirror Test: How to Breathe New Life Into Your Business [2781], [13773], [23227], [25875], [38249]
MIS Quarterly [4895]
"Misguided" in Canadian Business (Vol. 81, July 22, 2008, No. 12-13, pp. 30) [8535], [12639], [31657], [33838], [45557]
Mishicot Area Growth and Improvement Committee (MAGIC) [59657]
Mishicot Newsletter [59658]
"Mismanaging Pay and Performance" in Business Strategy Review (Vol. 21, Summer 2010, No. 2, pp. 54) [25377], [35858], [38251], [38250]
"Misplaced Trust" in Canadian Business (Vol. 79, October 23, 2006, No. 21, pp. 65) [8536], [12640]
Missile Defense Agency - Office of Small Business Programs - U.S. Department of Defense [61302]
The Missing Class: Portraits of the Near Poor in America [27491], [45558]
"Missing MF Global Funds Could Top $1.2 Billion" in Wall Street Journal Eastern Edition (November 22 , 2011, pp. A1) [8537], [12641], [23944], [30954]
Mission Area Chamber of Commerce [52164]
"Mission to China" in Canadian Business (Vol. 81, December 8, 2008, No. 21, pp. 28) [11136], [36686]
"Mission: Poach California" in Business Journal Portland (Vol. 26, December 11, 2009, No. 40, pp. 1) [23228], [24753], [44701]
"Mission: Recruitment" in HRMagazine (Vol. 54, January 2009, No. 1, pp. 42) [33283], [35406], [35859]
Mission Ventures [49276]
Mississippi Action for Community Education, Inc. (MACE) [53928]
Mississippi Contract Procurement Center, Inc. - Delta Contract Procurement Center, Inc. (DCPC) [53917]
Mississippi Contract Procurement Center, Inc. - Northeast Mississippi Contract Procurement Center, Inc. (NMCPC) [53918]
Mississippi Contract Procurement Center, Inc. - South Mississippi Contract Procurement Center, Inc. (SMCPC) [53919]
Mississippi Contract Procurement Technical Assistance Center, Inc. - East Central Procurement Center (ECCPC) [53920]
Mississippi Contract Procurement Technical Center, Inc. - Central Mississippi Procurement Center, Inc. (CMPC) [53921]
Mississippi Department of Economic and Community Development [53823], [60928]
Mississippi Development Authority - Minority and Small Business Development Division [53915]
Mississippi Enterprise for Technology [53929]
Mississippi Enterprise for Technology - Mississippi Technology Transfer Office [53821]
Mississippi Gulf Coast Chamber of Commerce [53882]
The Mississippi Innovator [53813]
Mississippi Lumber Manufacturers Association Convention and Trade Show [13677]

Mississippi Minority Business Enterprise Center [53916]
Mississippi News Media Directory [15556], [16721], [19947]
Mississippi Procurement Technical Assistance Program - Mississippi Development Authority [53922]
Mississippi Procurement Technical Assistance Program - Mississippi Development Authority - Minority and Small Business Development Division (MSBDD) [53923]
Mississippi Small Business Development Center [53814]
Mississippi Small Business Development Center, Copiah Lincoln Community College (Co-Lin SBDC) [53815]
Mississippi Small Business Development Center at Delta State University [53816]
Mississippi Small Business Development Center - Lead Office (MSBDC) [53817]
Mississippi State University - Agricultural & Forestry Experiment Station - Delta Research and Extension Center [21803]
Mississippi State University - Center for Small Town Research and Design [1334]
Mississippi State University Small Business Development Center (MSU SBDC) [53818]
Mississippi State University - Carl Small Town Center (CSTC) [1334]
Mississippi Technology Alliance [53930]
Mississippi University for Women - Career Services [53822]
Missoula Area Chamber of Commerce [54298]
Missoula Area Chamber of Commerce and Convention and Visitors' Bureau [54298]
Missoula SCORE [54236]
Missoula Small Business Development Center [54219]
Missouri Botanical Garden Annals [9813]
Missouri Botanical Garden Library [9862]
Missouri Chamber of Commerce [54065]
Missouri Department of Economic Development - Division of Business and Community Services [53940]
Missouri Department of Economic Development - Economic Development Office [54205]
Missouri Enterprise [54196]
Missouri Grocers Association Annual Convention and Trade Show [10012]
Missouri Highway and Transportation Department - Division of Materials Library [1649], [6610], [13550], [19826]
Missouri Historical Society Archives - Architecture Collection [5710]
Missouri Municipal Review [42403]
Missouri Procurement Technical Assistance Center - Central Region PTAC - University of Missouri-Columbia [54184]
Missouri Procurement Technical Assistance Center - Eastern Region PTAC - University of Missouri at St. Louis [54185]
Missouri Procurement Technical Assistance Center - Mid-South Region PTAC - Howell County Extension Center - University of Missouri [54186]
Missouri Procurement Technical Assistance Center - South Central Region PTAC - Center for Entrepreneurship and Outreach [54187]
Missouri Procurement Technical Assistance Center - Western Region PTAC - University of Missouri, Kansas City [54188]
"Missouri Public Service Commission Chooses APX" in Wireless News (January 22, 2010) [7265], [30728], [33839]
Missouri Small Business Development Center - Lead Office (MO SBDC) [53934]
Missouri Small Business Development Centers - Chillicothe [53935]
Missouri Small Business Development Centers - Northwest Region [53936]
Missouri Small Business Development Centers - St. Joseph [53937]
Missouri Southern State University - Heartland Procurement Technical Assistance Center - Institute for Procurement Assistance [54189]
Missouri State Genealogical Association Journal [9464]
Missouri Valley Chamber of Commerce (MVCC) [51932]
Missouri Veterinary Medical Association Annual Convention [1086]
Mistake-Free Grammar & Proofreading (Onsite) [22224]; [22574]
Mister Bar-B-Que [18185]
Mr. Boston's Official Video Bartender's Guide [1875]
Mister Softee, Inc. [10976]
Mister Transmission International Limited [18657]
"Mitch D'Olier" in Hawaii Business (Vol. 53, November 2007, No. 5, pp. 27) [13303], [27492], [28275], [32836], [38252]
Mitchell Area Chamber of Commerce [57589]
Mitchell B. Architectural Lighting Consultants [41628]
Mitchell B. Kohn Lighting Design [41628]

Mitchell County [55778]
Mitchell County Chamber of Commerce [55779]
Mitchell J. Kassoff, Esq., Attorney [24128]
Mitchell Technical Institute [57615]
Mitchell, Titus & Co. [19711], [21467], [32054]
Mitchell and Titus L.L.P. [19711], [21467], [32054]
Mitchell/Titus [19711], [21467], [32054]
Mitsui & Co. Venture Partners (MCVP) [55441]
Mitteldeutsche Handwerksmesse: Central German
 Handicrafts Fair [4161], [4300], [7860]
"A Mixed-Bag Quarter" in Barron's (Vol. 88, July 7, 2008,
 No. 27, pp. 19) [8538], [12642], [23229], [27493],
 [31658], [44429]
"Mixing Business and Pleasure On the Green" in Black
 Enterprise (Vol. 41, October 2010, No. 3, pp. 65)
 [7266], [7623], [9668], [30729], [47325]
MJS Lighting Consultants [41629]
MJSA Benchmark [13286]
MLM Consultants [58606]
MMA Cycles Report [13132]
mmmuffins [1814]
MMWR [34570]
MOA Fall Seminar [20945]
Moab Area Chamber of Commerce (MACC) [58665]
Moapa Valley Chamber of Commerce [54506]
Moapa Valley City Map [54507]
Moats Kennedy Inc. [38780]
Mobile Air Conditioning Society [772]
Mobile Area Chamber of Commerce (MACC) [47713]
Mobile Attic Franchising Company [14598], [40846]
Mobile Industrial Caterers' Association [3459]
"Mobile: Juanes Fans Sing for Sprint" in Advertising Age
 (Vol. 79, November 3, 2008, No. 41, pp. 22) [3758],
 [11779], [23230], [35011], [40140], [44430]
"Mobile Marketing Grows With Size of Cell Phone
 Screens" in Crain's Detroit Business (Vol. 24, January
 14, 2008, No. 2, pp. 13) [526], [3759], [23231],
 [35012], [40141]
Mobile Office: The Essential Small Business Guide to
 Office Technology [3760], [4969], [32418], [35013],
 [41419]
"Mobile Presence, in a Flash: DIY Tools for Creating
 Smartphone-Friendly Websites" in Inc. (Vol. 33,
 November 2011, No. 9, pp. 50) [3761], [21156]
Mobile Radio Technology [3848], [40842]
"Mobile Security for Business V5" in SC Magazine (Vol.
 20, August 2009, No. 8, pp. 55) [3762], [18450],
 [22378], [35014], [41141]
"The Mobile Workforce Revolution" in Canadian Business
 (Vol. 81, March 31, 2008, No. 5, pp. 28) [22379],
 [23232], [29117], [46898]
"Mobility: So Happy Together" in Entrepreneur (Vol. 35,
 October 2007, No. 10, pp. 64) [3763], [4970], [5126],
 [11780], [28772], [30009], [35015], [46524]
Mobility: The total relocation magazine [19186]
Mobius Venture Capital / Softbank Venture Capital
 [49277]
Mobridge Chamber of Commerce [57590]
Mocha Delites Inc. [9745]
Mode Accessories International Exposition [7861]
Model Airplane News: The World's Premier R/C Model-
 ing Magazine [6137]
"Model Citizen" in Entrepreneur (Vol. 36, February 2008,
 No. 2, pp. 42) [30010], [30955], [45960]
"A Model Development" in Crain's Cleveland Business
 (Vol. 28, October 1, 2007, No. 39, pp. 12) [5432],
 [16975], [17391], [35016], [35407]
"A Model Machine for Titanium" in Modern Machine Shop
 (Vol. 84, October 2011, No. 5, pp. 84) [13709],
 [39235], [41142]
Model Railroader [6138]
Model Retailer: Resources for Successful Hobby Retail-
 ing [6139]
Modeling, Commercials, & Acting [14366]
Modeling Made Easy [14367]
Modern Art Museum of Fort Worth Library [4575]
Modern Baking [1687]
Modern Brewery Age [1872], [2473], [13603]
Modern Brewery Age Tabloid Edition [2474]
Modern Bride [2533]
"Modern Bride Unveiled Exclusively at JCPenney" in
 Benzinga.com (February 3, 2011) [2508], [13276],
 [43098]
Modern Casting Magazine [13728]
"Modern-Day Midas Hasn't Lost Touch" in Globe & Mail
 (January 19, 2006, pp. B4) [8539], [12643], [24469],
 [25163]
Modern Healthcare: The Weekly Healthcare Business
 News Magazine [10558], [34569]
Modern Purchasing [42722]
Modern Salon [10079]
Modern Tire Dealer--Facts/Directory Issue [20073]
Modern Woodworking [3427], [6019]

Modernistic Cleaning Services [20842]
Modesto Chamber of Commerce [48792]
Modesto Junior Chamber of Commerce [48793]
Modesto Memo [48794]
Modesto Progress [48795]
Modoc County Chamber of Commerce [48212]
"Modular Home Center Opens in Arcadia" in Charlotte
 Observer (February 1, 2007) [5433], [16976], [33840],
 [39236]
Moe's Southwest Grill [18186]; [18187]
"Moet, Rivals Pour More Ad Bucks Into Bubbly" in
 Advertising Age (Vol. 88, September 3, 2007, No. 35,
 pp. 4) [527], [1855], [13591], [19235], [40142]
Mohave Community College Small Business Develop-
 ment Center (MCC SBDC) [47837]
Mohave Valley Chamber of Commerce [47931]
Mohawk Valley Chamber of Commerce [55284]
Mohawk Valley Small Business Development Center
 [55026]
Mohr Davidow Ventures (Menlo Park) [49278]
Mokena Chamber of Commerce [51224]
Molalla Area Chamber of Commerce (MACC) [56813]
Molecular Physics: An International Journal in the Field
 of Chemical Physics [44058]
Molly Maid, Inc. [6587]
Moloka'i Chamber of Commerce [50713]
"Molson Coors Ends Ill-Fated Foray Into Brazil" in Globe
 & Mail (January 17, 2006, pp. B1) [8540], [12644],
 [32837], [42055]
"The Molson Way" in Canadian Business (Vol. 80, April
 9, 2007, No. 8, pp. 36) [23233], [31091]
"Molycorp Funds Wind Energy Technology Company" in
 Manufacturing Close-Up (September 19, 2011) [7267],
 [7624], [12645], [30730], [35017], [37070], [42056],
 [47054]
"Mom of Eight Named Regional Minority Small Business
 Person of the Year" in Daily News (November 8, 2010)
 [40786], [47326]
"Mom Insight on Family, Current Affairs, and the
 Economy" in Marketing to Women (Vol. 23, November
 2010, No. 11, pp. 5) [27494], [40143]
The Mom and Pop Store: How the Unsung Heroes of the
 American Economy Are Surviving and Thriving
 [26488], [27495], [31092], [43099], [45961]
Momence Chamber of Commerce [51225]
Momentum [51680]; [59417]
The Mommy Manifesto: How to Use Our Power to Think
 Big, Break Limitations and Achieve Success [27496],
 [30011], [31659], [47327]
Mommy Millionaire: How I Turned My Kitchen Table Idea
 Into a Million Dollars and How You Can, Too! [20292],
 [29381], [36945], [38860], [39544], [42924], [43342],
 [46963], [47191]
"Moms Are Still Shopping" in Marketing to Women (Vol.
 21, February 2008, No. 2, pp. 1) [15557], [27497],
 [40144], [43100]
"Moms Dis Super Bowl Ads" in Marketing to Women
 (Vol. 21, March 2008, No. 3, pp. 6) [528], [19441],
 [19948], [40145]
"Moms Give More Thought to Nutrition" in Marketing to
 Women (Vol. 21, February 2008, No. 2, pp. 8) [9954],
 [10231], [40146]
"Moms Mull Money" in Marketing to Women (Vol. 21,
 February 2008, No. 2, pp. 6) [8541], [12646], [31660],
 [40147]
"Moms Rely on Coupons, Specials to Lower Grocery
 Bills" in Marketing to Women (Vol. 23, November 2010,
 No. 11, pp. 8) [529], [9955], [40148]
Mon Valley Regional Chamber of Commerce [57175]
Mon-Yough Membership Directory [57176]
"Monaco Pay Cut Draws Attention" in The Business
 Journal-Portland (Vol. 25, August 8, 2008, No. 22, pp.
 1) [21938], [24470], [37204], [38253], [39237]
Monahans Chamber of Commerce (MCC) [58336]
Monart School of The Arts [16033]
Monday Morning Report [57753]
"Monday Organizer: Clean and De-Clutter in 15 Minutes"
 in Tulsa World (June 13, 2011) [11550], [16488],
 [46525]
Monett Chamber of Commerce (MCC) [54089]
Money [2717]
Money in America [31996]
"Money Ball" in Canadian Business (Vol. 80, October 22,
 2007, No. 21, pp. 40) [19442], [27498]
Money Fund Report [13133]
Money Mailer, Inc. [674]
"Money Man" in Canadian Business (Vol. 80, January 15,
 2007, No. 2, pp. 67) [12647], [30012]
Money Matters: A Critical Look at Bank Architecture
 [1257]
"Money Matters: Using Sound Resources, You Can Find
 Capital For Your Business" in Black Enterprise (Vol. 38,
 November 2007, No. 4) [4076], [4187], [7812], [37279]

"Money and the Mayhem" in Canadian Business (Vol. 83,
 September 14, 2010, No. 15, pp. 52) [19443], [23234]
Money Source Financial Services Inc. [22068]
"The Money Train: How Public Projects Shape Our
 Economic Future" in Hawaii Business (Vol. 54,
 September 2008, No. 3, pp. 31) [5434], [17392],
 [24891], [27499], [35408]
The Moneychanger [13134]
"MoneyGram In Pact With Payday Lender" in American
 Banker (Vol. 173, March 7, 2008, No. 46, pp. 6)
 [8542], [37441], [42057]
The MoneyLetter [13135]
MoneySoft Inc. [24690], [45253]
The Monitor [58337]
"Monitor Work Productivity" in Business Owner (Vol. 35,
 July-August 2011, No. 4, pp. 4) [29118], [35860],
 [38254]
MonitorClosely.com [18524]
Monkey Joe's Party And Play [962]
Monmouth Area Chamber of Commerce (MACC) [51226]
Monmouth Commercial Club [51226]
Monmouth-Independence Chamber of Commerce
 (MICC) [56814]
Monmouth/Ocean Small Business Development Center
 [54639]
Monmouth SCORE [54653]
Monona Chamber of Commerce [59659]
"Monopoly Money Madness" in Canadian Business (Vol.
 81, March 17, 2008, No. 4, pp. 9) [23945], [26489],
 [33841], [44431]
Monroe Business Bulletin [49728]
Monroe Chamber of Commerce [59237]
Monroe Chamber of Commerce (MCC) [49729]; [52484]
Monroe Chamber of Commerce and Industry (MCCI)
 [59660]
Monroe Chamber of Commerce and Visitor Information
 Center [59237]
Monroe City Area Chamber of Commerce [54090]
Monroe County Chamber of Commerce [53883];
 [53884]; [57754]
Monroe County Chamber of Commerce (MCCC) [53385]
Monroe County Chamber of Commerce (SOCC) [56231]
Monroe County Chamber of Commerce [50533]
Monroe Messenger [53885]
Monroe-Stroudsburg SCORE [56935]
Monroe-Union County Chamber of Commerce [55820]
Monroeville Area Chamber of Commerce [57177]
Monroeville/Monroe County Chamber of Commerce
 [47714]
Monrovia Chamber of Commerce (MCC) [48796]
Monrovia Insider [48797]
"Monsanto Acquires Targeted-Pest Control Technology
 Start-Up; Terms Not Disclosed" in Benzinga.com (,
 2011) [12648], [15618], [25329], [42831], [43900],
 [44432]
"Monsanto's Next Single-Bag Refuge Product Approved"
 in Farm Industry News (December 5, 2011) [21632],
 [33842], [41143]
Monster Mini Golf [14362]
Mont Clare - Elmwood Park Chamber of Commerce
 [51227]
Montage [7891]
Montague County Small Business Development Center
 [57859]
Montana Business Incubator [54330]
Montana Chamber of Commerce [54299]
Montana Department of Administration - State Procure-
 ment Bureau [54321]
Montana Department of Agriculture - Agriculture Develop-
 ment Division [54223]
Montana Department of Commerce - Business
 Resources Division [54224]
Montana Department of Commerce - Census and
 Economic Information Center [54225]
Montana Department of Commerce - Community
 Development Division [54226]
Montana Department of Commerce - Economic Develop-
 ment Division - Marketing Assistance and Made in
 Montana Program [54227]
Montana Department of Commerce - Montana Science
 and Technology Alliance Division [54228]
Montana Department of Commerce - Trade &
 International Relations Bureau [54229]
Montana Department of Transportation Library [1650],
 [6611], [13551], [19827]
Montana Land Magazine: Features Properties for Sale in
 Montana and Surrounding States [17562]
Montana Magazine [54335]
Montana Mike's Steakhouse [18188]
"Montana Outlook: Stronger Growth Ahead" in Montana
 Business Quarterly (Vol. 49, Spring 2011, No. 1, pp. 7)
 [23235], [27500]
Montana Procurement Technical Assistance Center -
 Government Marketing Assistance Group - Big Sky
 Economic Development Authority [54322]

Montana Procurement Technical Assistance Center - Great Falls Development Authority **[54323]**
Montana Procurement Technical Assistance Center - Kalispell Area Chamber of Commerce **[54324]**
Montana Procurement Technical Assistance Center - Missoula Area Economic Development Corp. (MAEDC) **[54325]**
Montana Procurement Technical Assistance Center - Montana National Center for American Indian Enterprise Development **[54326]**
Montana Procurement Technical Assistance Center - Prospera Business Network **[54327]**
Montana State University, Bozeman - Information Technology Center (ITC) **[19062]**
Montana Tech of the University of Montana - Montana Tech Library **[47548]**
Montana Technology Enterprise Center **[54331]**
"Montana's Manufacturing Industry" in Montana Business Quarterly (Vol. 49, Spring 2011, No. 1, pp. 29) **[13660]**, **[23236]**, **[39238]**
Montcalm Community College **[53519]**
Montclair Chamber of Commerce **[48798]**
Monte Rio Chamber of Commerce (MRCC) **[48799]**
Monte Vista Chamber of Commerce (MVCC) **[49565]**
Monte Vista F.Y.I. **[49566]**
Monteagle Mountain Chamber of Commerce **[57755]**
Montebello Chamber of Commerce **[48800]**
Montello Area Chamber of Commerce (MCC) **[59661]**
Monterey Home Video **[49406]**
Monterey Media Inc. [49406]
Monterey Movie Co. [49406]
Monterey Peninsula Chamber of Commerce (MPCC) **[48801]**
Monterey Peninsula Chamber of Commerce/Visitors and Convention Bureau [48801]
Monterey Soundworks [49406]
Monterey Video [49406]
Montevallo Chamber of Commerce **[47715]**
Montevideo Area Chamber of Commerce **[53694]**
Montgomery Area Chamber of Commerce (MACOC) **[47716]**
Montgomery Area Chamber of Commerce Incubation Program **[47763]**
"Montgomery & Barnes: a Service-Disabled, Veteran-Owned Small Business" in Underground Construction (Vol. 65, October 2010, No. 10) **[2782]**, **[33443]**, **[44433]**
Montgomery City Area Chamber of Commerce **[54091]**
Montgomery County Chamber of Commerce **[55780]**
Montgomery County Chamber of Commerce (MCCC) **[52736]**; **[58965]**
Montgomery County Chamber of Commerce [51585]
Montgomery County Department of Economic Development - Business Innovation Network **[52790]**
The Montgomery County Genealogy Society Library **[9535]**
Montgomery's Inn Museum - Heritage Resource Centre **[9536]**
Monthly Coupons Franchising **[675]**
Monthly Memo **[51681]**
Monthly Minutes **[56232]**
Monthly Networking **[58338]**
Monthly Perspective **[57756]**
Monthly ZNews **[52485]**
Monticello Area Chamber of Commerce (MACC) **[51933]**
Monticello Area Chamber of Commerce and Industry **[53695]**
Monticello Chamber of Commerce **[51228]**; **[58666]**
Monticello Chamber of Commerce [53695]
Monticello Drew County Chamber of Commerce **[48088]**
Monticello-Jasper County Chamber of Commerce **[50582]**
Monticello-Jefferson County Chamber of Commerce **[50229]**
Monticello/Wayne County Chamber of Commerce **[52355]**
Montpelier Area Chamber of Commerce (MACC) **[56233]**
"Montreal Exchange Buoyed by U.S. Takeover Moves" in Globe & Mail (March 16, 2007, pp. B1) **[8543]**, **[12649]**, **[42058]**
Montreal International Auto Show **[705]**
"Montreal Port Head Lands CP Ships Deal" in Globe & Mail (January 5, 2006, pp. B4) **[11137]**, **[36687]**, **[42059]**
Montreal Spring Gift Show **[9621]**
Montrose Chamber of Commerce **[49567]**
Montrose-Verdugo City Chamber of Commerce (MVCCC) **[48802]**
Montville Township Chamber of Commerce **[54773]**
Monument Advisors Inc. **[51753]**
Monument Builders of North America (MBNA) **[9323]**
Monument Builders of Canada - American Historic Monument Society - Monument Builders of America [9323]
Mon-Yough Chamber of Commerce [57212]
"MooBella Adds Two Airports" in Ice Cream Reporter (Vol. 23, November 20, 2010, No. 12, pp. 5) **[10900]**, **[23237]**, **[24892]**
"The Mood of a Nation" in Canadian Business (Vol. 81, April 14, 2008, No. 6, pp. 56) **[8983]**, **[9020]**, **[11138]**, **[21633]**, **[27501]**, **[36688]**, **[39239]**
"The Moody Blues" in Entrepreneur (Vol. 36, April 2008, No. 4, pp. 87) **[11401]**, **[21939]**, **[29119]**, **[34373]**, **[36198]**, **[38255]**
"Moody and Paranoid" in Barron's (Vol. 88, March 10, 2008, No. 10, pp. M14) **[8544]**, **[12650]**, **[27502]**, **[31661]**
"Moooove Over, Sodas: Okaloosa to Get Dairy Vending Machines for Two Schools" in Northwest Florida Daily News (September 27, 2001) **[20865]**, **[28276]**
Moore Business Network **[56552]**
Moore Chamber of Commerce (MCC) **[56553]**
Moore County Chamber of Commerce **[55781]**
Moore New Homeowners [13515]
Moore Norman Technology Center **[56662]**
Moore Stephens North America (MSNA) **[42]**
Mooresville-South Iredell Chamber of Commerce **[55782]**
Jane Moosbruker, Organization Development Consultant **[29264]**
Moose Lake Area Chamber of Commerce **[53696]**
Moosehead Lake Region Chamber of Commerce **[52611]**
"Moosylvania Releases Latest XL Marketing Trends Report" in Wireless News (October 6, 2009) **[530]**, **[3764]**, **[7946]**, **[11781]**, **[35018]**, **[40149]**
Mora Area Chamber of Commerce [53665]
"The Moral Legitimacy of NGOs as Partners of Corporations" in Business Ethics Quarterly (Vol. 21, October 2011, No. 4, pp. 579) **[30956]**, **[44434]**
Morbidity and Mortality Weekly Report: Morbidity and Mortality Weekly Report **[34570]**
"More than Able" in Entrepreneur (Vol. 36, March 2008, No. 3, pp. 81) **[35409]**, **[35861]**
"More Ad Shops Link Payment to Results" in Boston Business Journal (Vol. 30, November 12, 2010, No. 42, pp. 1) **[531]**, **[6315]**, **[26271]**, **[43542]**, **[45559]**
More Awkward Customers **[8891]**, **[13164]**
"More Brides, Grooms Say 'I Do' to Interracial Marriage" in Black Enterprise (Vol. 41, August 2010, No. 1, pp. 36) **[2509]**, **[45560]**
"More Businesses Will Shift Health Costs to Workers" in Business Review, Albany New York (Vol. 34, November 16, 2007, No. 33, pp. 1) **[11402]**, **[15458]**, **[19516]**, **[21940]**, **[34374]**, **[36199]**, **[45561]**
"More Callers Are Cutting Their Landlines" in Chicago Tribune (December 30, 2008) **[3765]**, **[27503]**, **[44435]**, **[45562]**
"More Contractors Unpaid" in Puget Sound Business Journal (Vol. 29, October 3, 2008, No. 24, pp. 1) **[5435]**, **[16977]**, **[37442]**
"More Corporate Welfare?" in Canadian Business (Vol. 80, February 12, 2007, No. 4, pp. 96) **[33284]**, **[46306]**
"More Cuts On the Way At Ag School" in Business First-Columbus (December 14, 2007, pp. A1) **[21634]**, **[28277]**
"More Details Emerge on Maersk Plan" in Charlotte Business Journal (Vol. 25, August 13, 2010, No. 21, pp. 1) **[5436]**, **[10727]**, **[43101]**
"More Gains in the Pipeline" in Barron's (Vol. 89, August 3, 2009, No. 31, pp. M5) **[5437]**, **[8545]**, **[12651]**, **[31662]**
"More Important than Results" in Business Strategy Review (Vol. 21, Summer 2010, No. 2, pp. 81) **[29120]**, **[38256]**; **[29121]**, **[38257]**
"More Jobs Heading to Suburb" in Austin Business JournalInc. (Vol. 29, November 20, 2009, No. 37, pp. 1) **[23238]**, **[33285]**, **[35019]**, **[35410]**, **[35862]**
"More Jobs Moving Out of City" in Business Courier (Vol. 24, March 14, 2008, No. 49, pp. 1) **[8546]**, **[12652]**, **[24754]**, **[31663]**, **[42060]**, **[46307]**
More Knowledge, More Sales **[1789]**
"More Law Partners Jumping Ship" in Boston Business Journal (Vol. 27, October 5, 2007, No. 36, pp. 1) **[23946]**, **[45563]**
"More Leading Retailers Using Omniture Conversion Solutions to Boost Sales and Ecommerce Performance" in Internet Wire (Sept. 22,2009) **[532]**, **[3566]**, **[11782]**, **[18936]**, **[28773]**, **[40150]**, **[43102]**, **[43543]**, **[45158]**; **[533]**, **[3567]**, **[11783]**, **[18937]**, **[28774]**, **[40151]**, **[43103]**, **[43544]**, **[45159]**
"More Manufacturers Scout Military Contracts As Auto Industry Lags" in Crain's Detroit Business (Vol. 24, September 29, 2008, No. 39) **[24471]**, **[25164]**, **[27504]**, **[39240]**
"More Mexican Labor Needed in Oil Patch, Executives Say" in Globe & Mail (February 23, 2007, pp. B1) **[35411]**, **[38258]**
More than News **[58339]**
"More Offices Planned For Percheron Square" in The Business Journal-Milwaukee (Vol. 25, August 22, 2008, No. 48, pp. A1) **[16538]**, **[16978]**, **[17393]**, **[27505]**, **[44702]**, **[44852]**
"More Pain" in Canadian Business (Vol. 81, December 24, 2007, No. 1, pp. 12) **[11139]**, **[25593]**, **[27506]**, **[31664]**, **[39241]**, **[42832]**, **[43901]**
"More Power to Your Presentation" in Business Strategy Review (Vol. 21, Spring 2010, No. 1, pp. 50) **[22380]**, **[30013]**
"More Questions Face Huntington" in Business First-Columbus (December 7, 2007, pp. A3) **[12653]**, **[14459]**, **[42061]**
"More Sales Leads, Please: Or, What Happened When Frontline Selling Started Practicing What It Preaches" in Inc. (November 2007) **[534]**, **[2783]**, **[23239]**, **[25876]**, **[28278]**, **[40152]**, **[43545]**
"More Small Businesses Willing to Fund Employees' Benefits" in Baltimore Business Journal (Vol. 28, June 18, 2010, No. 6, pp. 1) **[11403]**, **[21941]**, **[34375]**, **[35863]**, **[36200]**, **[45564]**
"More SouthPark Shopping" in Charlotte Business Journal (Vol. 25, July 16, 2010, No. 17, pp. 1) **[17953]**, **[23240]**, **[33843]**, **[43104]**
More Space Place **[10509]**
"More Than 1,000 Attend Second WaterSmart" in Contractor (Vol. 56, November 2009, No. 11, pp. 3) **[16252]**, **[20390]**, **[20975]**, **[41144]**, **[46671]**
"More Than a Feeling" in Entrepreneur (Vol. 36, April 2008, No. 4, pp. 10) **[30014]**, **[32838]**
More Than a Gut Feeling 2 **[35540]**
More Than a Pink Cadillac **[5894]**, **[23241]**, **[25165]**, **[26490]**, **[29122]**, **[30015]**, **[35612]**, **[36689]**, **[43546]**, **[47328]**
"More Volunteers Needed to Make a Difference" in Times-News (October 18, 2011) **[9160]**, **[45962]**
Morehead-Rowan County Chamber of Commerce **[52356]**
Morehead Small Business Development Center **[52226]**
Morehead State University **[52401]**
Morehead State University - Water Testing Laboratory (WTL) **[21012]**
Moreno Valley Small Business Development Center **[48159]**
Moresales.ca **[3033]**
Morgan County Regional Technology Center **[52398]**
Morgan Hill Chamber of Commerce (MHCC) **[48803]**
Morgan Parker & Johnson Inc. **[41505]**
Morgantown Area Chamber of Commerce (MACoC) **[59418]**
Morgantown-Butler County Chamber of Commerce **[52357]**
Morgenthaler Ventures (Cleveland) **[56366]**
Moriarty Chamber of Commerce (MCC) **[54972]**
The Morning Sun's **[52153]**
Moroccan American Business Council (MABC) **[36305]**
Morocco Manufacturers National Association [13626]
MORPACE International Library **[14073]**
Morrilton Area Chamber of Commerce (MACC) **[48089]**
Morrilton Chamber of Commerce [48089]
Morris Area Chamber of Commerce **[53697]**
George Morris Centre **[21825]**
Morris County Chamber of Commerce **[54774]**
Morrison Chamber of Commerce **[51229]**
Morristimes **[57757]**
Morristown Area Chamber of Commerce (MACC) **[57758]**
Morristown Magazine **[57759]**
Morrisville Chamber of Commerce **[55783]**
Morrisville Chamber Communicator **[55784]**
Morro Bay Chamber of Commerce (MBCC) **[48804]**
Morrow County Chamber of Commerce and Visitors' Bureau (MCCCVB) **[56234]**
Morrow County Chamber of Commerce [56234]
Mortgage Bankers Association (MBA) **[14370]**, **[16785]**
Mortgage Bankers Association of America [14370], [16785]
Mortgage Banking Magazine: The Magazine of Real Estate Finance **[14521]**
Mortgage Delinquency Rates **[14538]**
Mortgage Industry Directory **[14460]**
Mortgage Insurance Companies of America (MICA) **[14371]**
"Mortgage Mess Continues To Trigger Bids To Ease Crisis" in Business First-Columbus (December 14, 2007, pp. A1) **[12654]**, **[14461]**, **[33844]**
"Mortgage Mess: How To Determine Your Exposure To the Subprime Crisis" in Black Enterprise (Vol. 38, November 2007, No. 4, pp. 46) **[12655]**, **[14462]**, **[16979]**, **[17394]**
"Mortgage Securities Drop Hits Home" in The Business Journal-Serving Metropolitan Kansas City (Vol. 27, October 17, 2008, No. 5) **[8547]**, **[12656]**, **[14463]**, **[16980]**, **[17395]**, **[26272]**, **[27507]**, **[31665]**, **[37443]**

Small Business Sourcebook • 30th Edition

3569

Mukwonago Area Chamber of Commerce [59664]
Mukwonago Chamber of Commerce [59664]
Mulberry Magic [50231]
Muleshoe Chamber of Commerce and Agriculture
[58342]
Muleshoe Chamber of Commerce [58342]
Muleshoe Journal [58343]
Mullaney Publishing Group [58607]
*"Mulroney on the Record" in Canadian Business (Vol. 79,
September 11, 2006, No. 18, pp. 43)* [23948], [27512],
[33845]
Multi-Housing Laundry Association (MLA) [6738]
Multi-Level Marketing International Association (MLMIA)
[39566], [40959]
Multi-Media Publications Inc. (MMP) [59952]
Multi-Menu [15800]
MultiAd® Builder [684]
*"Multichannel Marketing: Mindset and Program Develop-
ment" in Business Horizons (September-October 2007)*
[26492], [40157], [40962]
Multicultural Institute of the International Counseling
Center [40852]
Multicultural Marketing News [40836], [47431]
*Multi-Lingual Directory of Machine Tools & Related
Products* [13698]
*Multimedia InternetSchools: A Practical Journal of
Multimedia, CD-ROM, Online, & Internet in K-12*
[5016], [28405]
Multimedia Schools [5016], [28405]
*The Multinational Enterprise Revisited: The Essential
Buckley and Casson* [23243], [36692]
Multiple Association Management Institute - Institute of
Association Management Companies - International
Association of Association Management Companies
[1453]
Mulvane Chamber of Commerce [52156]
Muncie Chamber of Commerce [51682]
Muncie-Delaware County Chamber of Commerce
(MDCCC) [51682]
Municipal Art Society Newsletter [1296]
Municipal Futures Data-Line® [8947], [13212]
Municipal Market Data-Line® [8948], [13213]
Municipal Waste Association (MWA) [7054], [17694],
[30426]
Municipal World [42404]
Art Munin Consulting [28446]
Munising Visitors Bureau [53123]
Munster Business Handbook [51683]
Munster Chamber of Commerce [51684]
Muppet Sales: Make-a-Buck [29219]
*"Murdock Carrousel Sold" in Charlotte Observer (January
31, 2007)* [25330], [43107], [44170]
The Murdock Group Holding Corp. [36054]
*"Murdock Lifer Mans Main Street Journal" in Advertising
Age (Vol. 79, July 7, 2008, No. 26, pp. 1)* [15558],
[30017], [38262], [40158]
*"The Murky Tale of a Failed Fund" in Globe & Mail
(January 3, 2006, pp. B1)* [12664], [30957]
Murphree Venture Partners [58564]
P. Murphy & Associates Inc. (PMA) [41507]
Murphy Business & Financial Corp. [2732]
Murphy/Jahn Library [5711]
Murphy and Partners, L.P. [55442]
Richard D. Murphy [41508]
Murphysboro Chamber of Commerce [51238]
J. Stewart Murray Agency [21783]
Murray Area Chamber of Commerce (MACC) [58667]
Murray-Calloway County Chamber of Commerce [52359]
Murray-Calloway County Magazine [52360]
Murray Dropkin & Associates [2936], [13868], [26065],
[29265], [38782], [44951]
Murray J Stewart Agency [21783]
Murray/Paducah Small Business Development Center
[52227]
Murray Small Business Development Center [52228]
Murray State University - Bureau of Business and
Economic Research (BBER) [42430]
Murray State University - Waterfield Center for Business
and Governmental Research [42430]
Muscatine Chamber of Commerce and Convention and
Visitor Bureau [51899]
Muscatine SCORE [51797]
*Muscle & Fitness: The Super Fitness & Vigorous Health
Any Age* [15987]
Muscular Development [15988]
Musea [1365]
Musee Canadien de la Photographie Contemporaine.
[15886]
Musee McCord d'histoire Canadienne - Archives and
Documentation Centre [1393]
*"Museum Center to Exhibit New Look" in Business
Courier (Vol. 24, February 22, 2008, No. 46, pp. 1)*
[5438], [17397], [24476]

Museum of the City of New York - Department of Collec-
tions Access [5943]
Museum of Contemporary Craft Library [6078], [6174],
[15040]
Museum of Independent Telephony - Archives Collection
[3860], [19868]
Museum of International Folk Art (MOIFA) [6179]
Museum of Television and Radio. [16771]
Museum of Western Colorado - Loyd Files Research
Library [4427]
Music Canada [17634]
Music Educators Journal [14644]
Music Educators National Conference [14612]
Music Go Round [14763]
Music Inc.: For Progresive Music Retailers [4625],
[14749]
Music Industries Association of Canada (MIAC) [14729]
Music Power [14662], [14758]
Music Publishers' Association of the United States (MPA)
[14613]
Music Supervisors National Conference - Music Educa-
tors National Conference [14612]
Music Teachers National Association (MTNA) [14614]
Music Trades [14645], [14750]
*Music Trades--Purchaser's Guide to the Music Industry
Issue* [14628], [14736]
Musicals Tonight Inc. [14054]
Musicians Hotline [14752], [14792]
Muskego Area Chamber of Commerce [59665]
Muskegon Area Chamber of Commerce [53388]
Muskegon Community College - Hendrik Meijer Library -
Special Collections [7012]
Muskegon Lakeshore Chamber of Commerce [53388]
Muskingum County Business Incubator [56402]
Muskingum Valley Area Chamber of Commerce
(MVACC) [56237]
The Muskogee Chamber Connection [56554]
Must Be Heaven Franchise Corp. [6484]
*"Must Work for Food" in Pet Product News (Vol. 64,
November 2010, No. 11, pp. 24)* [1060], [15168],
[15725], [43108], [45569]
Mustang Chamber of Commerce [56555]
Mustard Cafe [6485]
Mutual Advertising Agency Network [359], [42581]
Mutual Aircraft Conference [11263]
Mutual Fund Activity [13214]
*"Mutual Fund Sales of $23.4 Billion Best Since 2001" in
Globe & Mail (January 5, 2006, pp. B3)* [8555],
[12665]
Mutual Funds, Options, Commodities, & Collectibles
[13165]
Mutual Marine Conference [11263]
*"MV Transportation Winds $133M Contract" in Black
Enterprise (Vol. 38, November 2007, No. 4, pp. 30)*
[13539], [19810], [23244]
MVP Capital Partners [57295]
MVTL Laboratories Inc. [10186]
MW Corp. [29266]
*"My Bad: Sometimes, Even CEOs Have to Say They're
Sorry" in Inc. (October 2007, pp. 37-38)* [30018],
[38263]
*My Big Idea: 30 Successful Entrepreneurs Reveal How
They Found Inspiration* [30019]
My Business Advocate [53389]
My City Daily [15028]
*"My Day" in Business Strategy Review (Vol. 21, Autumn
2010, No. 3, pp. 77)* [30020], [44171], [47329];
[30021], [44172], [47330]
*"My Favorite Tool for Managing Expenses" in Inc.
(Volume 32, December 2010, No. 10, pp. 60)* [112],
[2297], [3768], [19649], [21397], [28777], [31671],
[44437]
*"My Favorite Tool for Organizing Data" in Inc. (Vol. 33,
November 2011, No. 9, pp. 46)* [3568], [3769], [4972],
[18938], [45160]
My First Haircut [10083]
My Gym Children's Fitness Center [16034]
*"My Inglorious Road to Success" in Harvard Business
Review (Vol. 88, July-August 2010, No. 7-8, pp. 38)*
[30022], [38264]
*My Life From Scratch: A Sweet Journey of Starting Over,
One Cake at a Time* [1740], [7949], [17954], [47331]
*My So-Called Freelance Life: How to Survive and Thrive
as a Creative Professional for Hire* [6824], [25877],
[30023], [35613], [47332]
*My Start-Up Life: What a (Very) Young C.E.O. Learned
on His Journey Through Silicon Valley* [30024],
[35023], [47592]
Myrtle Beach Area Chamber of Commerce [57505]
Myrtle Beach Area Small Business Development Center
[57408]
Mystic Chamber of Commerce [49731]
The Mystic Four Seasons Discovery Guide [49732]

Mystic Seaport Museum, Inc. - G.W. Blunt White Library
[13981]
*"The Myth of the Overqualified Worker" in Harvard Busi-
ness Review (Vol. 88, December 2010, No. 12, pp. 30)*
[35413], [35864], [38265]
*"Myths of Deleveraging" in Barron's (Vol. 90, August 23,
2010, No. 34, pp. M14)* [12666], [14465], [16982],
[23245], [27513], [39247], [45570]

N

N-Hance [9084]
N&HC: Perspectives on Community [34575]
NAA Reporter [4054]
NAACLS News [14287]
NAADAC: The Association for Addiction Professionals
(NAADAC) [46062]
NAAPA [1489], [14841]
NAB Show [19997]
NABJ Update [6842]
NACE - Information Center. [3405]
Nicholas J. Naclerio and Associates Inc. [6543]
Nacogdoches County Chamber of Commerce [58344]
NACOMEX Insider [181], [8870], [23651], [31990]
NACS [5821]
Nadasdy Ferenc Museum Library [20642], [24959]
NAEP Bulletin [42718]
NAFA Fleet Management Association (NAFA) [1618]
NAFA Fleet Management Association - FleetED [15007]
NAfME National In-Service Conference [14662], [14758]
NAGMR [1891], [2696], [13912]
NAGMR Consumer Products Broker [1891], [2696],
[13912]
NAGMR Consumer Products Sales Agencies [1891],
[2696], [13912]
NAHC Report [10559]
NAHC's Annual Meeting and Home Care and Hospice
Expo [10564]
NAHWW Newsletter [6843]
NAI McCabe-Henley [17604]
*"Naked Ambitions Put Telus on the Spot" in Globe & Mail
(February 6, 2007, pp. B3)* [3770], [35024]
*"Naked Investing" in Canadian Business (Vol. 80, Janu-
ary 15, 2007, No. 2, pp. 27)* [8556], [12667]
Nalco Company Library [21002]
NAMM International Music Market [14759], [17651]
NAMM PlayBack [14751]
The NAMM Show [14759], [17651]
NAMM - Summer Session [17652]
NAMM - The International Music Products Association
[14615]
Nampa Chamber [50788]
Nampa Chamber of Commerce [50789]
*"Nampa Police Department: Electronic Systems Just One
Tool in Business Security Toolbox" in Idaho Business
Review (October 29, 2010)* [2784], [4648], [18451],
[25878], [33286]
NAMS News Online [19531]
*"Nancy Hughes Anthony" in Canadian Business (Vol. 81,
October 13, 2008, No. 17, pp. 104)* [8557], [12668],
[42064], [47333]
Nando's Flame Grilled Chicken [18195]
Nanny Poppinz Corporate, Inc. [14807]
*"Nanoready?" in Entrepreneur (Vol. 36, May 2008, No. 5,
pp. 20)* [8558], [12669], [31672], [35025], [41149],
[43904], [47056]
*"Nanotech Impact is Smaller Than Hoped For" in Boston
Business Journal (Vol. 27, October 26, 2007, No. 39,
pp. 1)* [19517], [35026], [41150]
Nantucket Island Chamber of Commerce [52933]
Napa Chamber of Commerce (NCC) [48807]
Napa Valley College Small Business Development
Center [48160]
Napa Valley Genealogical & Biographical Society Library
[9537]
Napa Valley Wine Library Association Library [19297]
Naperville Area Chamber of Commerce [51239]
Napier University - Craiglockhart Campus Library
[21479]
Naples Area Chamber of Commerce [50127]
Naples on the Gulf [50232]
NAPM Annual International Purchasing Conference
[42723]
NAPM Insights [42716]
Napoleon Area Chamber of Commerce [56238]
Napoleon - Henry County Chamber of Commerce
[56238]
Nappanee Area Chamber of Commerce [51685]
NAQP News [5865]
Narcotics Anonymous (NA) [46063]
NARD Journal [6674]
Narragansett Chamber of Commerce [57382]
NARSA National Newsletter [18619]

National Association of Accountants [39]
National Association of Alcoholic Beverage Importers [13567]
National Association of Alcoholism and Drug Abuse Counselors [46062]
National Association of Alcoholism Treatment Programs [46064]
National Association of Bank Women [8033]
National Association of Barber Boards [10063]
National Association of Beverage Retailers [13566]
National Association of Boards of Barbers Examiners of America [10063]
National Association of Boards of Examiners of Nursing Home Administrators [15055]
National Association of Brick Distributors [14097]
National Association of Building Service Contractors [2595]
National Association of Business and Educational Radio [1961], [3673]
National Association of Business and Educational Radio and Association of Communications Technicians [1961], [3673]
National Association of Business Coaches [2847], [25975]
National Association of Business Economists [49865]
National Association of Casino and Theme Party Operators [9379], [15426]
National Association of Casualty and Surety Agents [11277]
National Association of Coin Laundry Equipment Operators [6738]
National Association of Computer Consultant Brokers [4635], [4838]
National Association of Computer Consultant Businesses [4635], [4838]
National Association of Computer Database Consultant Businesses [4635], [4838]
National Association of Concessionaires--Membership Directory [5104]
National Association of Corporate and Professional Recruiters [35254]
National Association of Corporation Schools [13757], [37556]
National Association of Cost Accountants [39]
National Association of Cruise Only Agencies [20517]
National Association of Demolition Contractors [5192]
National Association of Direct Sellers [9231]
National Association of Diversified Manufacturers Representatives [1891], [2696], [13912]
National Association of Drug Manufacturers Representatives [1891], [2696], [13912]
National Association of Employment Agencies [6954], [20025]
National Association of Employment Managers [13757], [37556]
National Association of Engine and Boat Manufacturers [13931]
National Association of Exposition Managers [20301]
National Association of Exterminators and Fumigators [15622]
National Association of Fine Art Dealers [1337]
National Association of Fisheries Commissioners [9003]
National Association of Fleet Administrators - Fleet Information Resources Center. [15007]
National Association of Floor Covering Distributors [9056]
National Association of Floor Covering Distributors--Membership Directory [9064]
National Association of Food and Dairy Equipment Manufacturers [10841]
National Association of Food Equipment Manufacturers [17872]
National Association of Foremen - International Management Council of the YMCA [37565]
National Association of Furniture Manufacturers [10445]
National Association of Gambling Regulatory Agencies [9382]
National Association of Governors' Highway Safety Representatives [6595]
National Association of Home Builders [5189]
National Association of Home Builders of the U.S. [5189]
National Association of Hotel Accountants [10648]
National Association of Hotel and Motel Accountants [10648]
National Association of Independent Insurers [11299]
National Association of Independent Lubes [16667]
National Association of Independent Tire Dealers [20069]
National Association of Insurance Agents [11284]
National Association of Insurance Women [11294]
National Association of Jazz Educators [14608]
National Association of Life Underwriters [11293]
National Association of Magazine Publishers [15506]
National Association of Mail Service Pharmacies [6639]
National Association of Marketing Teachers [13983], [39556]

National Association of Master Steam and Hot Water Fitters [771]
National Association of Music Merchants [14615]
National Association of Mutual Insurance Agents [11295]
National Association of Passenger Vessel Owners [3865]
National Association of Pension Consultants and Administrators [33477]
National Association of Periodical Publishers [15506]
National Association of Personnel Consultants [6954], [20025]
National Association of Pet Sitters [15669], [15811]
National Association of Photographic Manufacturers [15824]
National Association of Piano Tuners [14789]
National Association of Popcorn Manufacturers [5100]
National Association of Printers and Lithographers [16346]
National Association of Printing Ink Makers [16345]
National Association of Private Geriatric Care Managers [15057]
National Association of Product Fund Raisers [9231]
National Association of Public Relations Counsel [16579], [42446]
National Association of Public Television Stations [19880]
National Association of Radio and Television Broadcasters [16697], [19889]
National Association of Radio Telephone Systems [1961], [3673]
National Association of Real Estate Boards [16787], [17165]
National Association of Real Estate Exchanges - National Association of Real Estate Boards [16787], [17165]
National Association of Real Estate Investment Funds [17164]
National Association of REALTORS® [16787], [17165]
National Association of Record Merchandisers [4621], [17636]
National Association of Recycling Industries [17693]
National Association of Registered Nursing Homes [15044], [34100]
National Association of Retail Druggists [6638]
National Association of Retail Druggists Convention [6694]
National Association of Retail Grocers of the United States - Cooperative Food Distributors of America [5792], [9905]
National Association of Retail Ice Cream Manufacturers [10842]
National Association of Sales Managers [13757], [37556]
National Association of Securities Commissioners [11976]
National Association of Security and Data Vaults [4688]
National Association of Sewer Service Companies [18673]
National Association of Shellfish Commissioners [9003]
National Association of Shoe Chain Stores [18749]
National Association of Small Business Investment Cos. [32490], [46981]
National Association of State Units on Aging [15058]
National Association of Tanners [13626]
National Association of Tax Practitioners [45], [19598]
National Association of Television and Electronic Servicers of America [4795], [5729]
National Association of Temporary and Staffing Services [6948], [20023]
National Association of Temporary Services [6948], [20023]
National Association of Truck Stop Operators--Membeship Directory [20687]
National Association of Urban Flood Management Agencies [6356]
National Association of Vision Program Consultants [20921]
National Association of Visual Education Dealers [7886], [20881]
National Association of Webmasters [11605]
National Association of Wholesaler-Distributors - Distribution Research and Education Foundation [26815]
National Association of Wholesalers [26724], [47168]
National Association of Women's Yellow Pages [39571], [47217]
National Association of Part-Time and Temporary Employees (NAPTE) **[41700]**
National Association of Personal Financial Advisors (NAPFA) **[8037]**
National Association of Personnel Services (NAPS) **[6954], [20025]**
National Association of Plumbing, Heating, Cooling Contractors (PHCC) **[773], [16213]**
National Association of Postmasters of the United States Convention **[4606]**
National Association Practical Refrigerating Engineers [775]

National Association of Printing Ink Manufacturers (NAPIM) **[16345]**
National Association for Printing Leadership (NAPL) **[16346]**
National Association of Professional Background Screeners (NAPBS) **[16457]**
National Association of Professional Band Instrument Repair Technicians (NAPBIRT) **[14787]**
National Association of Professional Employer Organizations (NAPEO) **[20026]**
National Association of Professional Geriatric Care Managers (NAPGCM) **[15057]**
National Association of Professional Insurance Agents (PIA) **[11295]**
National Association of Professional Insurance Agents Library **[36267]**
National Association of Professional Mortgage Women (NAPMW) **[14373]**
National Association of Professional Pet Sitters (NAPPS) **[15669], [15811]**
National Association of Professional Process Servers **[14352]**
National Association of Publishers' Representatives (NAPR) **[42583]**
National Association of Quick Printers (NAQP) **[4441], [16347]**
National Association Quick Printers [4441], [16347]
National Association of Real Estate Appraisers (NAREA) **[1212]**
National Association of Real Estate Brokers (NAREB) **[14374], [16786]**
National Association of Real Estate Companies (NAREC) **[17163]**
National Association of Real Estate Investment Trusts (NAREIT) **[17164]**
National Association of Realtors (NAR) **[16787], [17165]**
National Association of Realtors - Information Central **[17155]**
National Association of Recording Merchandisers (NARM) **[4621], [17636]**
National Association Recycling Industries [17693]
National Association of Rehabilitation Professionals in the Private Sector Annual Conference **[16089]**
National Association for Retail Marketing Services (NARMS) **[42930]**
National Association of Review Appraisers and Mortgage Underwriters (NARA/MU) **[14375], [16788]**
National Association of Review Appraisers and Mortgage Underwriters Convention - National Conference & Expo **[14526]**
National Association of RV Parks and Campgrounds (National ARVC) **[3250]**
National Association of School Music Dealers (NASMD) **[14616], [14730]**
National Association of Schools of Dance (NASD) **[6377]**
National Association of Schools of Music (NASM) **[14617]**
National Association of Schools of Music--Directory **[14625]**
National Association of Security Companies (NASCO) **[18381]**
National Association for the Self-Employed (NASE) **[44801], [46039]**
National Association of Small Business Investment Companies (NASBIC) **[32490], [46981]**
National Association for the Specialty Food Trade (NASFT) **[10211], [19207]**
National Association of State Boards of Accountancy (NASBA) **[44]**
National Association of State United for Aging and Disabilities (NASUAD) **[15058]**
National Association for the Study and Performance of African-American Music (NASPAAM) **[14618]**
National Association of Tax Professionals (NATP) **[45], [19598]**
National Association of Teachers of Singing (NATS) **[14619]**
National Association of Television Program Executives (NATPE) **[19890]**
National Association of Theatre Owners (NATO) **[14564]**
National Association of Vision Professionals (NAVP) **[20921]**
National Association of Wholesaler-Distributors (NAW) **[26724], [47168]**
National Association of Wholesaler-Distributors - NAW Institute for Distribution Excellence **[26815]**
National Association of Women Artists, Inc. News **[1366]**
National Association of Women Business Owners (NAWBO) **[47211]**
National Association of Women in Construction (NAWIC) **[5190]**
National Association of Women MBAs (NAWMBA) **[47212]**

National Associations of Canoe Liveries and Outfitters [19310]

National Auctioneers Association (NAA) **[1488]**, **[7775]**

National Auctioneers Association National Convention **[1536]**

National Auctioneers Association--Membership Directory [1493]

National Audio-Visual Association [7886], [20881]

National Audubon Society - Aullwood Audubon Center and Farm Library **[7729]**

National Auto and Flat Glass Dealers Association [9636]

National Auto Auction Association (NAAA) **[1489]**, **[14841]**

National Auto Auction Association--Membership Directory **[1520]**

National Auto Body Council (NABC) **[18584]**

National Automatic Laundry and Cleaning Council [6736]

National Automatic Merchandising Association (NAMA) **[20850]**

"National Automatic Merchandising Association Takes Vending on the Road' in Food and Beverage Close-Up (September 6, 2011) **[20866]**, **[35027]**

National Automobile Dealers Association (NADA) **[14842]**

National Automotive Radiator Service Association (NARSA) **[18585]**

National Automotive Radiator Service Association Annual Trade Show and Convention **[18633]**

National Autosound Challenge Association [3310]

National Aviation Trades Association [726]

National Ayurvedic Medical Association (NAMA) **[16071]**

National Ballroom and Entertainment Association (NBEA) **[6378]**

National Ballroom Operators Association [6378]

National Barbecue Association (NBBQA) **[3463]**, **[17867]**

National Beauty and Barber Manufacturers Association [1893], [10066]

National Beauty Culturists' League (NBCL) **[5882]**, **[10064]**

National Beauty Show - HAIRWORLD **[5910]**, **[10085]**

National Beef Council - National Live Stock and Meat Board [3140]

National Beer Wholesalers Association (NBWA) **[13568]**

National Beer Wholesalers Association Convention and Exposition **[2476]**

National Beer Wholesalers' Association of America [13568]

National Better Business Bureau [24792]

National Beverage Marketing Directory [1867], [13572], [19214]

National Bicycle Dealers Association (NBDA) **[1966]**

National Bicycle League (NBL) **[1967]**

National Bituminous Concrete Association [1996]

National Black Chamber of Commerce - Alamo City **[58346]**

National Black Chamber of Commerce, Baton Rouge **[52487]**

National Black Chamber of Commerce, Champaign County **[51241]**

National Black Chamber of Commerce, Collin County **[58347]**

National Black Chamber of Commerce (Corpus Christi, Texas) **[58345]**

National Black Chamber of Commerce (Decatur, Illinois) **[51240]**

National Black Chamber of Commerce, Englewood **[51242]**

National Black Chamber of Commerce, Fort Worth Metropolitan **[58348]**

National Black Chamber of Commerce, Illinois State **[51243]**

National Black Chamber of Commerce, Lake County **[51244]**

National Black Chamber of Commerce, New England **[52935]**

National Black Chamber of Commerce - Oklahoma **[56556]**

National Black Chamber of Commerce, Permian Basin (BCCPB) **[58349]**

National Black Chamber of Commerce, Tri-County **[58350]**

National Black Chamber of Commerce, Wisconsin **[59666]**

National Black Child Development Institute (NBCDI) **[3927]**

National Black Masters of Business Administration Annual Conference and Exposition **[40939]**

National Black MBA Association (NBMBAA) **[27980]**, **[40687]**

National Black MBA Association, Inc. [27980], [40687]

National Black McDonald's Operators Association (NBMOA) **[17868]**

National Black Music Caucus of the Music Educators National Conference [14618]

National Board for Certified Counselors and Affiliates (NBCC) **[3343]**

National Board of Examiners in Optometry (NBEO) **[20922]**

National Board for Certified Counselors [3343]

National Board of Fire Underwriters [11267]

The National Bowling Association (TNBA) **[2430]**

National Bowling Writer's Association [6778]

National Bridal Market **[2548]**

National Brotherhood of Skiers (NBS) **[18819]**

National Building Material Distribution Association-- Membership & Product Directory [13662]

National Building Material Distributors Association [5197]

National Building Material Distributors Association-- Membership & Product Directory [13662]

National Bulk Vendors Association (NBVA) **[20851]**

National Bulletin **[5191]**

National Bureau of Economic Research (NBER) **[19787]**

National Burglar and Fire Alarm Association [18376]

National Bus Trader: The Magazine of Bus Equipment for the United States and Canada **[20200]**

National Bus Traffic Association (NBTA) **[19800]**

National Business Aircraft Association - Corp. Aircraft Owners Association [727]

National Business Association (NBA) **[44802]**

National Business Aviation Association (NBAA) **[727]**

National Business and Disability Council (NBDC) **[6955]**

National Business Education Association (NBEA) **[27981]**

National Business Forms Association [15275]

National Business Incubation Association (NBIA) **[11214]**, **[44803]**

National Business Publications [15480]

National Business Teachers Association [27981]

National Business Travel Association [24815]

National Business Woman [47428]

National Cable and Telecommunications Association (NCTA) **[3159]**, **[19891]**

National Cable Television Association [3159], [19891]

National Cable Television Institute Resource Center **[3213]**

National Campers and Hikers Association [3248]

National Campground Owners Association [3250]

National Candy Wholesalers Association [3277], [20084]

National Capital Area Minority Business Opportunity Center - Performance-Based Solutions Inc. **[59009]**

National Career Development Association (NCDA) **[3344]**

National Catholic Cemetery Conference [9318]

National Cattleman's Beef Association [3140]

"National Cattlemen's Beef Association" in Retail Merchandiser (Vol. 51, September-October 2011, No. 5, pp. 77) **[21637]**, **[43109]**

National Cattlemen's Beef Association (NCBA) **[3140]**

National Cattlemen's Beef Association Library **[3156]**

National Center for Bicycling and Walking (NCBW) **[1968]**

National Center for Assisted Living [15044], [34100]

National Center for Montessori Education and American Montessori Society [3921]

National Center for Research in Vocational Education [13299]

National Center for Manufacturing Sciences (NCMS) **[39532]**

National Center for Policy Analysis (NCPA) **[19788]**

National Center for Public Policy Research (NCPPR) **[2937]**, **[26066]**, **[42414]**

National Center for Technology Planning (NCTP) **[35247]**

National Charities Information Bureau [24792]

National Charities Information Bureau Inc. [24792]

National Chimney Sweep Guild (NCSG) **[4043]**

National Chincoteague Pony Association (NCPA) **[1011]**

National Christmas Tree Association (NCTA) **[4050]**

National Christmas Tree Growers Association [4050]

National Citizens' Coalition for Nursing Home Reform (NCCNHR) **[15059]**

National Citizens Committee for Broadcasting [16319]

National City Chamber of Commerce (NCCC) **[48808]**

National City Equity Partners, LLC **[56367]**

National Clearinghouse for Alcohol and Drug Information Library **[46105]**

National Clearinghouse for Smoking and Health Database [14301], [16047]

The National Clothesline **[6752]**

National Coalition for Campus Children's Centers (NCCCC) **[3928]**

National Coalition for Advanced Manufacturing [38871]

National Coalition for Campus Child Care [3928]

National Coalition for Children's Centers [3928]

National Coffee Association of U.S.A. Inc. [4313], [9692]

National Coffee Association of U.S.A. (NCA) **[4313]**, **[9692]**

National Coffee Service Association [20850]

National College of Appraisal and Property Management **[2612]**

National College of Business and Technology **[52402]**

National College of Natural Medicine Library **[15223]**

National College of Naturopathic Medicine - Library. [15223]

National Commercial Finance Association [37286], [46975]

National Commercial Finance Conference [37286], [46975]

National Committee for Small Business Management Development [32487], [37562], [49862]

National Committee for Women in Public Administration [42362]

National Committee on Aging of National Social Welfare Assembly [289]

National Committee on Planned Giving [9235]

National Committee on Planned Giving Inc. [9235]

National Communication Council for Human Services [16579], [42446]

National Community Pharmacists Association (NCPA) **[6638]**

National Community Pharmacists Association Convention and Exhibition [6694]

National Community Television Association [3159], [19891]

National Concierge Association (NCA) **[5119]**

National Concrete Burial Vault Association (NCBVA) **[9324]**

National Concrete Masonry Association (NCMA) **[14105]**

National Concrete Masonry Association Library **[14132]**

National Concrete Masonry Association - Research and Development Laboratory **[14133]**

National Confectioners Association of the U.S. (NCA) **[3278]**

National Confectionery Sales Association (NCSA) **[3279]**

National Confectionery Sales Association of America [3279]

National Conference on the Advancement of Research (NCAR) **[42915]**

National Conference of CPA Practitioners (NCCPAP) **[46]**

National Conference of Commercial Receivable Companies [37286], [46975]

National Conference of State Liquor Administrators-- Official Directory **[1856]**

National Congress of Inventor Organizations (NCIO) **[37166]**

National Congress of Inventors Organizations [37166]

National Congress of Petroleum Retailers [18589]

National Congress on Surveying and Mapping [19500]

National Consortium for Computer-Based Music Instruction [14603]

National Consumer Finance Association [6225]

National Contact Lens Examiners (NCLE) **[20923]**

National Contract Management Association **[33392]**

National Convenience Store Distributors Association (NACDA) **[26725]**

National Cooperative Bank, Corporate Banking Div. (NCB) **[32293]**

National Coordinating Committee for Multi-employer Plans (NCCMP) **[21857]**

National Cosmetology Association [1893], [10066]

National Costumers Association (NCA) **[5928]**

National Costumers Association Annual Convention **[4162]**, **[5931]**

National Council of Acoustical Consultants--Directory **[41341]**

National Council for Advanced Manufacturing (NACFAM) **[38871]**

National Council Against Health Fraud (NCAHF) **[34153]**

National Council on Aging (NCOA) **[289]**

National Council of Agricultural Employers (NCAE) **[21497]**

National Council of Chain Restaurants (NCCR) **[9144]**, **[17869]**

National Council on Ethics in Human Research (NCEHR) **[30896]**

National Council of Exchangors (NCE) **[16789]**

National Council for Business Education [27981]

National Council for Reliable Health Information [34153]

National Council for US-China Trade [11025]

National Council for Interior Design Qualification (NCIDQ) **[11532]**

National Council of Investigation and Security Services (NCISS) **[16458]**, **[18382]**

National Council of American Importers [11018], [36272]

National Council of Health Centers [15044], [34100]

National Council of State Self-Insurers' Associations [36101]

National Council of the Housing Industry [5188]

National Council on Bioethics in Human Research [30896]

National Council on Compulsive Gambling [9380]

National Council on Problem Gambling (NCPG) **[9380]**

National Council of Self-Insurers (NCSI) **[36101]**

National Labor Relations Board, Region 1 - Boston Regional Office **[60562]**; **[60563]**
National Labor Relations Board, Region 2 - New York Regional Office **[60564]**; **[60565]**
National Labor Relations Board, Region 3 - Buffalo Regional Office **[60566]**; **[60567]**
National Labor Relations Board, Region 4 - Philadelphia Regional Office **[60568]**; **[60569]**
National Labor Relations Board, Region 5 - Baltimore Regional Office **[60570]**
National Labor Relations Board, Region 6 - Pittsburgh Regional Office **[60571]**; **[60572]**
National Labor Relations Board, Region 7 - Detroit Regional Office **[60573]**; **[60574]**
National Labor Relations Board, Region 8 - Cleveland Regional Office **[60575]**; **[60576]**
National Labor Relations Board, Region 9 - Cincinnati Regional Office **[60577]**; **[60578]**
National Labor Relations Board, Region 10 - Atlanta Regional Office **[60579]**; **[60580]**
National Labor Relations Board, Region 11 - Winston-Salem Regional Office **[60581]**; **[60582]**
National Labor Relations Board, Region 12 - Tampa Regional Office **[60583]**; **[60584]**
National Labor Relations Board, Region 13 - Chicago Regional Office **[60585]**; **[60586]**
National Labor Relations Board, Region 14 - St. Louis Regional Office **[60587]**; **[60588]**
National Labor Relations Board, Region 16 - Ft. Worth Regional Office **[60589]**; **[60590]**
National Labor Relations Board, Region 17 - Overland Park Regional Office **[60591]**; **[60592]**
National Labor Relations Board, Region 18 - Minneapolis Regional Office **[60593]**; **[60594]**
National Labor Relations Board, Region 19 - Seattle Regional Office **[60595]**; **[60596]**
National Labor Relations Board, Region 20 - San Francisco Regional Office **[60597]**; **[60598]**
National Labor Relations Board, Region 21 - Los Angeles Regional Office **[60599]**; **[60600]**
National Labor Relations Board, Region 22 - Newark Regional Office **[60601]**; **[60602]**
National Labor Relations Board, Region 24 - Hato Rey Regional Office **[60603]**; **[60604]**
National Labor Relations Board, Region 25 - Indianapolis Regional Office **[60605]**; **[60606]**
National Labor Relations Board, Region 26 - Memphis Regional Office **[60607]**; **[60608]**
National Labor Relations Board, Region 27 - Denver Regional Office **[60609]**; **[60610]**
National Labor Relations Board, Region 28 - Phoenix Regional Office **[60611]**; **[60612]**
National Labor Relations Board, Region 29 - Brooklyn Regional Office **[60613]**; **[60614]**
National Labor Relations Board, Region 30 - Milwaukee Regional Office **[60615]**
National Labor Relations Board, Region 31 - Los Angeles Regional Office **[60616]**; **[60617]**
National Labor Relations Board, Region 32 - Oakland Regional Office **[60618]**; **[60619]**
National Labor Relations Board, Region 34 - Hartford Regional Office **[60620]**; **[60621]**
National Labor Relations, Region 5 - Baltimore Regional Office **[60622]**
National Laundry Allied Trades Association [6739]
The National Law Journal **[24154]**
National League for Nursing Education - National Organization for Public Health Nursing - Joint Committee on Careers in Nursing - National Nursing Accrediting Service - National Committee for the Improvement of Nursing Services - Association of Collegiate Schools of Nursing [10525]
National League for Nursing (NLN) **[10525]**
National Leather and Shoe Finders Association [18745]
National Lighting Bureau (NLB) **[6928]**
National Limousine Association (NLA) **[13533]**
National Live Stock and Meat Board [3140]
National Livestock Dealers Association [1487]
National Locksmith **[13621]**
National Locksmith Suppliers Association [13614]
National Luggage Dealers Association (NLDA) **[13627]**
National Lumber and Building Material Dealers Association (NLBMDA) **[10126]**, **[13641]**
National Management Association (NMA) **[37565]**
National Marine Bankers Association (NMBA) **[13928]**
National Marine Distributors Association (NMDA) **[13929]**
National Marine Electronics Association (NMEA) **[13930]**
National Marine Manufacturers Association (NMMA) **[13931]**
National Marine Representatives Association--Directory **[13941]**
National Mechanical Trade Council [5167]
National Midas Dealers Association [18583]

National Minority Business Council (NMBC) **[40689]**
National Minority Business Directories [40681]
National Minority Business Directories - National Minority Business Campaign - National Buy-Black Campaign [40681]
National Minority Purchasing Council [40690]
National Minority Supplier Development Council (NMSDC) **[40690]**
National Minority Supplier Development Council Inc. [40690]
National Minority and Women-Owned Business Directory **[40789]**
National Mobile Radio System [1961], [3673]
National Mortgage News **[14523]**
National Moving and Storage Association [14593]
National MultiCultural Institute (NMCI) **[40852]**; **[40956]**
National Museum of Roller Skating Archives **[18815]**
The National Needle Arts Association (TNNA) **[6098]**, **[18719]**
National Needlework Association Trade Show [6066]
National Negro Funeral Directors and Morticians Association [9326]
National Nutritional Foods Association [10212]
National Office Machine Dealers Association [15272], [21308]
National Office Machine Dealers Association (NOMDA) [15272], [21308]
National Office Products Association [41531]
National Off-Road Bicycling Association [1969]
National Oil and Acrylic Painters' Society (NOAPS) **[4442]**
National Opera Association--Membership Directory: Opera Journal **[14626]**
National Optometric Association (NOA) **[20924]**
National Outdoor Showmen's Association - International Association of Amusement Parks - National Association of Amusement Parks, Pools and Beaches - National Association of Amusement Parks [966]
National Outerwear and Sportswear Association [3887], [13557]
National Paint and Coatings Association [15366], [15384]
National Paint, Oil and Varnish Association [15366], [15384]
National Park Service - Business Utilization and Development Specialist - Alaska Region **[61523]**; **[61524]**
National Park Service - Business Utilization and Development Specialist - Business and Economic Development Program **[61525]**
National Park Service - Business Utilization and Development Specialist - Intermountain Region **[61526]**; **[61527]**
National Park Service - Business Utilization and Development Specialist - Midwest Region **[61528]**; **[61529]**
National Park Service - Business Utilization and Development Specialist - Minority Business and Economic Development Program **[61530]**
National Park Service - Business Utilization and Development Specialist - National Capitol Region **[61531]**; **[61532]**
National Park Service - Business Utilization and Development Specialist - Northeast Region **[61533]**; **[61534]**
National Park Service - Business Utilization and Development Specialist - Outdoor Recreation Information Center **[61535]**
National Park Service - Business Utilization and Development Specialist - Pacific Northwest Region **[61536]**
National Park Service - Business Utilization and Development Specialist - Pacific West Region **[61537]**; **[61538]**
National Park Service - Business Utilization and Development Specialist - Southeast Region **[61539]**; **[61540]**
National Passenger Traffic Association - National Business Travel Association [24815]
National Pavement Maintenance Exposition and Conference **[2010]**
National Pawnbrokers Association (NPA) **[15442]**
National Pediculosis Association (NPA) **[28447]**
National Personnel Association [13757], [37556]
National Pest Control Association [15622]
National Pest Management Association International (NPMA) **[15622]**
National Pest Management Association Library **[15655]**
National Pesticide Information Retrieval System (NPIRS) **[15652]**
National Pharmaceutical Alliance [6633]
National Piano Manufacturers Association of America [14788]
National Prepared Food Festival **[18043]**

National Press Club - Eric Friedheim Library & News Information Center **[6861]**, **[20017]**
National Printing Equipment Association - Association for Suppliers of Printing and Publishing and Converting Technologies - National Printing Equipment and Supply Association [16348]
National Private Truck Council (NPTC) **[20658]**
National Private Trucking Association [20658]
National Professional Colorists of America [15835]
National Professional Electronics Convention and Trade Show [5782]
National Professional Service Convention and Trade Show **[5782]**
National Property Inspections **[2586]**
National Property Law Digests **[17115]**, **[17563]**
National Property Management Association (NPMA) **[16503]**
National Public Radio Broadcast Library **[16767]**
National Public Records Research Association (NPRRA) **[9432]**
National Publishers Association [15506]
National Purchasing Institute (NPI) **[42706]**
National Quotation Bureau Pink Sheets [8950], [13216]
National Radio Broadcasters Association [16697], [19889]
National Real Estate Investor **[17116]**, **[17564]**
The National Registry **[17148]**, **[17610]**
National Regulatory Research Institute (NRRI) **[16318]**
National Research Council Canada - Institute for Information Technology (IIT) **[5070]**
National Resource Center for Health and Safety in Child Care [3930]
National Resource Center for Health and Safety in Child Care and Early Education (NRC) **[3930]**
National Restaurant Association **[5101]**, **[6437]**, **[10278]**
National Restaurant Association Educational Foundation (NRAEF) **[5833]**, **[9145]**, **[17870]**
National Restaurant Association Information Services and Library **[18304]**
National Restaurant Association - Multi-Unit Architects, Engineers and Construction Officers Executive Study Group (MAECO) **[17871]**
National Restaurant Association - Quality Assurance Executive Study Group **[9197]**
National Restaurant Association Restaurant and Hotel-Motel Show **[10786]**
National Retail Federation (NRF) **[4192]**, **[42931]**
National Retail Furniture Association [10452]
National Retail Grocers Secretaries Association [9899]
National Retail Liquor Package Stores Association - National Licensed Beverage Association - National Association of Beverage Retailers - National Liquor Stores Association [13566]
National Retail Lumber Dealers Association [10126], [13641]
National Retail Merchants Association - Apparel Retailers of America - American Retail Federation [4192], [42931]
National Rifle Association of America **[1241]**
National Rifle Association of America - National Firearms Museum Library **[10044]**
National Rifle Association of America - NRA-ILA Library **[10045]**
National Rifle Association of America - NRA Technical Library **[1255]**
National Roofing Contractors Association (NRCA) **[18314]**
National Roofing Contractors Association--Membership Directory **[18323]**
National Roofing Education Foundation [18315]
National Roofing Foundation (NRF) **[18315]**
The National RV Trade Show **[17683]**
National Safety Council (NSC) **[47445]**
National Safety Council Library **[47549]**
National Safety Management Society **[47446]**
National Sanitary Supply Association **[2602]**
National Sash and Door Jobbers Association **[3415]**
National School Orchestra Association [14602]
National School Supply & Equipment Association Fall Show [19846]
National Science Foundation - Office of Small and Disadvantaged Business Utilization **[60623]**; **[62168]**; **[60624]**
National Science Foundation - Small Business Innovation Research Programs **[60625]**; **[60626]**
National Science Foundation - Small Business Technology Transfer Program **[60627]**; **[60628]**
National Scientific Services **[46089]**
National Security Traders Association [11978]
National Selected Morticians [9327]
National Shade Tree Evaluation [13371]
National Shaving Mug Collectors Association (NSMCA) **[1120]**, **[4348]**

National Shellfisheries Association (NSA) **[9003]**
National Shoe Retailers Association (NSRA) **[18750]**
National Shoe Retailers Association Library **[18784]**
National Shorthand Reporters Association [20819]
National Ski Hall of Fame and Museum - Roland Palmedo National Ski Library. [18843]
National Ski Patrol System (NSP) **[18820]**
National Ski Retailers Asso. [18821], [19308]
National Ski and Snowboard Retailers Association (NSSRA) **[18821]**, **[19308]**
National Small Business Association (NSBA) **[32491]**, **[44804]**; **[49866]**
National Small Business Benefits Association Library **[44972]**
National Small Business United [49866]
National Snow Industries Association (NSIA) **[18822]**
National Society of Accountants (NSA) **[47]**, **[19599]**
National Society of Accountants for Cooperatives (NSAC) **[48]**
National Society of Compliance Professionals (NSCP) **[11974]**
National Society for Graphology (NSG) **[10114]**
National Society of Hispanic MBAs (NSHMBA) **[40691]**
National Society of Architectural Engineers [14095]
National Society of Controllers and Financial Officers of Savings Institutions - Financial Managers Society for Savings Institutions - Society of Savings and Loan Controllers [8031]
National Society of Fund Raisers - National Society of Fund Raising Executives [9232]
National Society of Fund Raising Executives [9232]
National Society of Fund Raising Executives Conference [9291], [46760]
National Society of Public Accountants [47], [19599]
National Society of Sales Training Executives [43348]
National Society of Professional Surveyors (NSPS) **[19501]**
National Society of the Sons of the American Revolution - Genealogy Library **[9538]**
National Society of the Sons of Utah Pioneers Library **[9539]**
National Solid Wastes Management Association (NSWMA) **[10163]**
National Spa and Pool Institute [19541]
National Speakers Association (NSA) **[18534]**, **[18576]**
National Sporting Clays Association (NSCA) **[1242]**
National Sporting Goods Association (NSGA) **[18823]**, **[19309]**
National Staff Development Council (NSDC) **[19150]**
National Staff Leasing Association [20026]
National Stationery Show **[9894]**
National Storage Industry Consortium [4686]
National Swimming Pool Foundation (NSPF) **[19544]**
National Swimming Pool Institute [19541]
National Tank Truck Carrier Directory **[20685]**
National Tank Truck Carriers (NTTC) **[20659]**
National Tank Truck Carriers Inc. [20659]
National Tattoo Association (NTA) **[19585]**
National Tattoo Association Convention **[19589]**
National Tattoo Club of the World [19585]
National Tax Association (NTA) **[49]**, **[19600]**
National Telecommunications Cooperative Association Annual Meeting & Expo **[16317]**
National Tenant Network **[6350]**
National Tennis Association [15949], [20052]
National Tennis Educational Foundation [20053]
National Tennis Foundation and Hall of Fame [20053]
National Thrift and Mortgage News [14523]
National Tile Roofing Manufacturers Association [18319]
National Tire Dealers and Retreaders Association [20069]
National Topical Stamp Show **[4384]**
National Tour Association (NTA) **[20130]**, **[20518]**
National Tour Brokers Association [20130], [20518]
National Towing News **[3322]**
National Trade and Professional Associations of the U.S. **[1463]**
National Training Center of Polygraph Science **[16470]**
National Training Center of Polygraph Science Library **[16474]**
National Training and Simulation Association (NTSA) **[13300]**
National Truck Equipment Association (NTEA) **[1544]**, **[20660]**
National Truck Equipment Association--Market Resource Guide **[20686]**
National Truck Equipment Association - Membership Roster & Product Directory [20686]
National Truck Leasing System (NTLS) **[1619]**
National Truck Rate Report **[20710]**
National Truck Stop Guide [20687]
National Trust Company Reference Library **[7769]**
National Typewriter and Office Machine Dealers Association [15272], [21308]

National Underwriter Life & Health **[11489]**
National Underwriter Property & Casualty **[11490]**
National Used Car Dealers Association [14843]
National Utility Contractors Association (CWC) - Clean Water Council (CWC) **[20971]**
National Vehicle Leasing Association (NVLA) **[1620]**
National Vendors Association [20851]
National Venture Capital Association (NVCA) **[46982]**
National Venture Capital Association--Membership Directory **[47057]**
National Vocational Guidance Association [3344]
National Warm Air Heating and Air Conditioning Association - National Environmental Systems Contractors Association - Air Conditioning and Refrigeration Contractors of America [760]
National Wellness Association--Directory [34377]
National Wellness Institute--Member Directory [34377]
National Wholesale Druggists' Association [6634]
National Wholesale Frozen Food Distributors Association **[9904]**
National Wholesale Furniture Salesmen's Association [10450]
National Women's Business Council (NWBC) **[47213]**
National Women's Sailing Association (NWSA) **[3864]**
National Wood Window & Door Association [3416]
National Woodwork Manufacturers Association - National Door Manufacturers Association - Ponderosa Pine Woodwork Association - National Wood Window and Door Association [3416]
National Writers Association (NWA) **[6798]**
National Writers Club [6798]
National-American Wholesale Lumber Association - National Wholesale Lumber Dealers Association [13642]
NationaLease [1619]
Nations Bank - Business Resource Center **[44973]**
The Nation's Health [34571]
"Nationwide Bank Ready for December Conversion" in *Business First-Columbus (October 12, 2007, pp. A1)* **[8559]**, **[11405]**, **[28778]**, **[36202]**, **[40159]**
Nationwide Franchise Marketing Services **[3035]**, **[32296]**
Native American Economic Development Project - Yankton Sioux Tribe **[57607]**
Native Americans for a Clean Environment - Resource Office Native Americans for a Clean Environment **[7731]**
Native Hawaiian Chamber of Commerce (NHCC) **[50714]**
Native Spirit **[16005]**
"Native Wisdom" in *Canadian Business (Vol. 80, October 8, 2007, No. 20, pp. 121)* **[27514]**, **[28280]**, **[36693]**, **[40898]**
"Nat'l Instruments Connects with Lego" in *Austin Business JournalInc. (Vol. 28, August 22, 2008, No. 23, pp. 1)* **[4973]**, **[20260]**, **[28281]**, **[35028]**, **[36694]**, **[41151]**, **[42066]**
Nat'l Listing of Black Funeral Homes [9337]
NATSO--Membership Directory **[20687]**
"Natural Attraction: Bath and Body Products Maker Delivers Wholesome Goodness" in *Black Enterprise (Vol. 38, November 2007, No. 4)* **[2047]**, **[5895]**, **[39249]**, **[47335]**
"The Natural Environment, Innovation, and Firm Performance" in *Family Business Review (Vol. 19, December 2006, No. 4)* **[31095]**, **[37072]**
Natural Foods Merchandiser: News, Trends and Ideas for the Business of Natural Products/A Penton Publication **[10252]**
Natural Gas Partners (NGP) **[58565]**
Natural Hazards Observer **[6359]**
Natural Hazards Research and Applications Information Center **[6357]**
Natural Products Association (NPA) **[10212]**
Natural Products Expo East **[7721]**, **[10310]**, **[46771]**
Natural Products Expo West **[7722]**
Natural Products Marketing Council (NPMC) **[7055]**, **[7439]**
The Natural Voice **[10213]**, **[10279]**, **[15161]**
Natural Waste Water Treatment **[20991]**
Naturalawn of America **[13521]**
Naturally Nice News **[57762]**
The Nature Conservancy in Maine **[13462]**
The Nature Conservancy - New Jersey Chapter Office **[32328]**
The Nature Conservancy - Ohio Chapter **[10201]**
Nature Stone **[6590]**
Nautilus Aerobics Plus: High Impact Aerobics **[16006]**
Nautilus Aerobics Plus: Low Impact Aerobics **[16007]**
"Nautilus Fights For Its Life" in *Business Journal-Portland (Vol. 24, November 23, 2007, No. 38, pp. 1)* **[12670]**, **[15976]**
Nauvoo Chamber of Commerce **[51245]**

Navajo-Churro Sheep Association (NCSA) **[1012]**
Naval Technical Representative Office (Laurel, Maryland) **[61303]**
Naval Technical Representative Office (Laurel, Maryland) **[61304]**
Navarre Beach Area Chamber of Commerce **[50233]**
Navarro, Kim & Associates **[2939]**, **[3079]**, **[13869]**, **[22651]**, **[26067]**, **[38783]**, **[40948]**
Navarro Small Business Development Center **[57860]**
Navasota Grimes County Chamber of Commerce **[58351]**
"Navigate to Better Direct Response Messaging Through Search Marketing" in *DM News (Vol. 32, January 18, 2010, No. 2, pp. 26)* **[536]**, **[11786]**, **[15337]**, **[28779]**, **[40160]**
Navigating with Marine Electronics: A Guide to DC **[13957]**
Navigating Your Way to Business Success: An Entrepreneur's Journey **[25166]**, **[30028]**, **[33287]**
Navigator **[51246]**; **[52936]**; **[7365]**
The Navigator **[38605]**; **[52737]**; **[56239]**
Navigator Research Group Inc. **[16471]**, **[29310]**
Navigator Technology Ventures / NTV **[53051]**
Navis Pack & Ship Centers **[4608]**
Navis Pack and Ship Centers **[4609]**
"Navistar, Cat Talk Truck Deal" in *Crain's Chicago Business (Vol. 31, March 24, 2008, No. 12, pp. 1)* **[39250]**, **[42067]**
Navy Inventory Control Point **[57306]**
NAW Institute for Distribution Excellence **[26726]**, **[47169]**
NAW Report **[47182]**
"NAWBO Takes the Stage at Press Conference for Small Business Jobs, Credit and Tax Relief Acts" in *Internet Wire (June 17, 2010)* **[33288]**, **[45571]**, **[46308]**, **[47336]**
NAWGA - Productivity Conference and Distribution/ Transportation Exposition [26807]
The NAWIC Image **[5603]**
Nazareth Area Chamber of Commerce **[57179]**
Nazareth Chamber News **[57180]**
Nazem and Co. **[55443]**
"NBC" in *Brandweek (Vol. 49, April 21, 2008, No. 16, pp. SR6)* **[537]**, **[7950]**, **[19951]**, **[24477]**, **[25167]**, **[25595]**, **[38268]**, **[40161]**, **[43548]**
"NBC Universal Cable" in *Brandweek (Vol. 49, April 21, 2008, No. 16, pp. SR11)* **[538]**, **[7951]**, **[19952]**, **[23246]**, **[38269]**, **[40162]**, **[43549]**
"NBC Universal Domestic Television Distribution" in *Brandweek (Vol. 49, April 21, 2008, No. 16, pp. SR13)* **[539]**, **[7952]**, **[19953]**, **[38270]**, **[40163]**, **[43550]**
NBC Universal Information Resource Center **[16768]**
NCCI Community Guide **[51247]**
NCCLS: The Clinical Laboratory Standards Organization - NCCLS - National Committee for Clinical Laboratory Standards [14268]
NCPA Annual Convention and Trade Exposition **[6694]**
NCPA Newsletter **[6684]**
NCPD National Update **[34572]**
NCPG [9235]
NCTI - Resource Center. [3213]
NDSU Research & Technology Park **[55937]**
NEAA News [1219], [2560]
Neal-Schuman Guide to Finding Legal and Regulatory Information on the Internet **[23700]**, **[33495]**
The Neatest Little FundLetter **[8872]**
Nebagamon Community Association **[59667]**
Nebraska Chamber of Commerce and Industry (NCCI) **[54413]**
Nebraska City Chamber of Commerce [54414]
Nebraska City Tourism and Commerce (NCTC) **[54414]**
Nebraska Department of Economic Development - Industrial Training Programs **[54451]**
Nebraska Journal of Economics & Business [8874], [27909], [31991]
Nebraska Ombudsman's Office **[54346]**
Nebraska Procurement Technical Assistance Center - Nebraska Business Development Center - University of Nebraska at Kearney **[54447]**
Nebraska Small Business Development Center - Chadron State College **[54337]**
Nebraska Small Business Development Center - Kearney **[54338]**
Nebraska Small Business Development Center - Lead Office **[54339]**
Nebraska Small Business Development Center - Lincoln **[54340]**
Nebraska Small Business Development Center - Norfolk **[54341]**
Nebraska Small Business Development Center - North Platte **[54342]**
Nebraska Small Business Development Center - Omaha **[54343]**

New England Family Campers Association [3252]
New England Gerontological Association (NEGA) [15061]
New England Historical and Genealogical Register [9467]
New England Hot Dog Company, LLC [18197]
New England Human Resource Group [22069], [36055]
New England International Auto Show [14990]
New England Manufacturers Directory [13913]
New England Rainwear Manufacturers Association [3887], [13557]
New England Real Estate Journal [17565]
New England Wholesalers Association - Lending Library [16303]
New Enterprise Associates (Chevy Chase) [52774]
New Enterprise Associates (Menlo Park) [49281]
"A New Era for Raiders" in Harvard Business Review (Vol. 88, November 2010, No. 11, pp. 34) [32842], [33847]
"New Ethanol Plant Planned In Iowa to Use Corn Stover" in Farm Industry News (June 27, 2011) [21640], [39255], [41156]
"The New Face of Detroit" in Inc. (Vol. 33, October 2011, No. 8, pp. 6) [32419], [44441], [47058]
"The New Face of Social Media" in Hispanic Business (December 2010) [28785], [40172], [40900], [45575]
"New Family Dollar Store Now Open in Hermon" in Bangor Daily News (August 12, 2010) [43112]
"A New FICO Scoring Model: Get Ready For Changes That Could Affect Your Score" in Black Enterprise (Vol. 38, March 2008, No. 8) [6203], [6245], [6316]
"A New Flavor for Second Street: Lamberts Chef Backs New Restaurant" in Austin Business JournalInc. (Vol. 28, January 2, 2009) [1857], [17956], [42076]
"The New Frontier" in Crain's Detroit Business (Vol. 26, January 18, 2010, No. 3, pp. S025) [14931], [39256]
New Glarus Chamber of Commerce [59672]
"New Global Hot Spots: Look Beyond Shanghai for the Next Big Thing" in Inc. (October 2007, pp. 40-41) [36698], [45576]
"The New Guard" in Entrepreneur (Vol. 36, February 2008, No. 2, pp. 46) [3772], [11792], [22386], [28786], [41157]
New Hampshire Business Review [54633]
New Hampshire Department of Resources and Economic Development - Business Resource Center [54540]
New Hampshire Procurement Technical Assistance Center - State of New Hampshire - Economic Development [54627]
New Hampshire Procurement Technical Assistance Center - State of New Hampshire - Office of Business & Industrial Department of Defense [54628]
New Hampshire Small Business Development Center (NHSBDC) [54635]
New Hampshire Small Business Development Center - Lead Office (NHSBDC) [54534]
New Hartford Chamber of Commerce [55288]
"New Health Care Sector" in Hispanic Business (July-August 2009, pp. 10-12) [23251], [34382], [45577]
"New Health Law, Lack of Docs Collide on Cape Cod" in Boston Business Journal (Vol. 27, October 12, 2007, No. 37, pp. 1) [11407], [23952], [33848], [34383], [36204]
"New-Home Sales Grab a Foothold With Q2 Boost" in Sacramento Business Journal (Vol. 25, July 11, 2008, No. 19, pp. 1) [5440], [16985], [17400], [23252]
New Horizons [34574]; [50586]; [57506]; [9814]
New Horizons Computer Learning Centers, Inc. [4782]
New Horizons Venture Capital [59017]
"New Hydronic Heating Technologies Work" in Contractor (Vol. 57, January 2010, No. 1, pp. 58) [842], [5441], [6898], [30739]
"New ICA, Ex-Builder Tangle Over Construction" in Boston Business Journal (Vol. 27, October 12, 2007, No. 37, pp. 1) [5442], [23953]
New Information Systems and Services [4716], [5034], [21129]
The New Innovators: How Canadians are Shaping the Knowledge-Based Economy [27517], [35032], [37074], [41158]
"New Institutional Accounting and IFRS" in Accounting and Business Research (Vol. 41, Summer 2011, No. 3, pp. 309) [115], [2300], [19651], [21399], [36699], [42835], [43908]; [116], [2301], [19652], [21400], [36700]
"New IPhone Also Brings New Way of Mobile Marketing" in Advertising Age (Vol. 79, June 16, 2008, No. 24, pp. 23) [3570], [3773], [11793], [18940], [35033], [40173]
New Jersey Accounting, Business & Technology Show & Conference [203], [2325], [19707]
New Jersey Business [54883]
New Jersey City University Business Development Incubator [54873]

New Jersey City University Small Business Development Center [54640]
New Jersey Commerce Economic Growth and Tourism Commission - International Trade and Protocol [54647]
New Jersey Commerce Economic Growth and Tourism Commission - Office of Marketing [54648]
New Jersey Department of Business and Economic Development [54649], [55034]
New Jersey Department of Commerce and Economic Development - Division of Small, Women, and Minority Business [54839]
New Jersey Department of Transportation Research Library [1651], [6612], [13552], [19828]
New Jersey Division of Revenue - Business Action Center - Small Business Set-Aside [54840]
New Jersey Economic Development Authority - Office of the Business Advocate [54650]
New Jersey Economic Growth & Tourism - Business Services & Urban Programs [54651]
New Jersey Institute of Technology - Center for Architecture and Building Science Research (CABSR) [41655]
New Jersey League of Municipalities Annual Conference [42412], [46772]
New Jersey Monthly [54884]
New Jersey Procurement Technical Assistance Center - Union County Economic Development Corporation (UCEDC) [54865]
New Jersey Small Business Development Center, Rutgers University (Camden, New Jersey) [54641]
New Jersey Technology Council / NJTC Venture Fund [54854]
The New Job Security: The 5 Best Strategies for Taking Control of Your Career [35420], [35867]
"New Jobless Claims Filed in December Soar" in Baltimore Business Journal (Vol. 27, January 29, 2010, No. 39, pp. 1) [27518], [35421], [35868], [45578], [46899]
New Kent Chamber of Commerce (NKCC) [58967]
"A New Kid on the Block" in Barron's (Vol. 88, March 17, 2008, No. 11, pp. 58) [8568], [12680], [26276], [31680], [33290], [37448]
"New King Top the Charts" in The Business Journal-Portland (Vol. 25, August 8, 2008, No. 22, pp. 1) [542], [16722], [23253], [27519], [36701], [40174], [40791]
"New Kittinger Showroom Twice the Size of the Last One" in Business First Buffalo (December 7, 2007, pp. 4) [10405], [10477], [23254], [44706]
"New Law Lets Shareholders Play Hardball With Firms" in Globe & Mail (January 2, 2006, pp. B1) [8569], [12681], [23954], [33849]
"New Leadership Panel Has Advice for Collins" in Business First Buffalo (November 23, 2007, pp. 1) [23255], [27520]
New Lenox Chamber of Commerce [51249]
New Lenox, IL: The Community With the Ability to Grow [51250]
The New Library at New Hampshire Technical Institute, Concord [33109]
"New Life for Old Chemistries" in Farm Industry News (Vol. 42, January 1, 2009, No. 1) [21641], [23256], [37075], [41159], [43909]
"New Life for Porsche's VW Dreams" in Barron's (Vol. 89, July 6, 2009, No. 27, pp. 9) [14932], [39257], [42077]
New Lisbon Area Chamber of Commerce (NLCC) [59673]
New London Area Chamber of Commerce (NLACC) [59674]
New London Area Chamber of Commerce and the Lake Sunapee Business Association [54613]
New London - Lake Sunapee Region Chamber of Commerce [54613]
New Madrid Chamber of Commerce [54096]
The New Market [59243]
The New Marketing Network Inc. [2941], [26069], [41304]
New Member Profile [50235]
New Mexico Clinical Research and Osteoporosis Center [34675]
New Mexico Department of Agriculture, Marketing and Economic Development Division [54911]
New Mexico Department of Environment - NMED Library [47550]
New Mexico Economic Development Department [54912]
New Mexico Junior College - Business Assistance Center [55005]
New Mexico Native American Business Enterprise Center [54992]
New Mexico Procurement Assistance Program - General Services Department [54913]
New Mexico Procurement Technical Assistance Center [54995]

New Mexico State University - Agricultural Experiment Station (AES) [21826]
New Mexico State University - Arrowhead Center [54914]
New Mexico State University - Arts and Sciences Research Center [44089]
New Mexico State University-Grants Small Business Development Center [54903]
New Milford Chamber of Commerce [49708]
New Milford Magazine [49735]
New Milford Visitor's Guide [49736]
"A New Mix of Tenants Settles In" in Crain's New York Business (Vol. 24, January 14, 2008, No. 2, pp. 26) [16539], [16986], [17401], [17957], [24758], [43113], [45579]
"New Money" in Entrepreneur (Vol. 36, February 2008, No. 2, pp. 62) [117], [6204], [6246], [6317], [12682], [21401], [26277], [31681]
"The New Nimble" in Barron's (Vol. 90, August 30, 2010, No. 35, pp. S12) [8571], [12683], [45580]
New One-Family Houses Sold and For Sale [17150], [17612]
New Orleans BioInnovation Center [52535]
New Orleans Gift and Jewelry Show Spring [9586], [9622], [13294]
New Orleans Pizza Canada, Inc. [16163]
"The New Orleans Saints" in Entrepreneur (Vol. 37, August 2009, No. 8, pp. 40) [27521], [30034], [36087], [44770]; [27522], [30035], [36088], [44771]
New Palestine Area Chamber of Commerce (NPACC) [51687]
New Paltz Chamber of Commerce [55289]
"A New Perspective On the Development Model for Family Business" in Family Business Review (Vol. 19, December 2006, No. 4, pp. 317) [24482], [31096]
New Prague Chamber of Commerce (NPCC) [53698]
New Product Research: Laying the Foundation for New Product Success (Onsite) [39594], [40977]
"New Program for Entrepreneurs" in Austin Business JournalInc. (Vol. 29, February 12, 2010, No. 29, pp. 1) [29384], [32420], [33131], [46964]
"New Race Suit at Local Coke Plant" in Business Courier (Vol. 24, February 1, 2008, No. 43, pp. 1) [23955], [39258], [46900]
"A New Reality; There are Some Signs of Hope Amid 2009's Darkness" in Crain's Cleveland Business (Vol. 30, June 29, 2009, No. 25) [23257], [27523]
"New Recession-Proof Internet Marketing Package Allows Businesses to Ramp Up Web Traffic and Profits" in PR Newswire (Jan. 25, 2010) [7954], [11794], [21162], [40175], [45581]; [7955], [11795], [21163], [40176], [45582]
"New Recipes Added to IAMS Naturals Pet Food Line" in MMR (Vol. 28, August 1, 2011, No. 11, pp. 17) [10234], [15768], [19236], [41160]
New Residential Construction Index [17149], [17611]
New Residential Sales [17150], [17612]
New Richmond Area Chamber of Commerce and Visitors Bureau [59675]
New Richmond Area Chamber of Commerce [59675]
"The New Risk Tolerance" in Entrepreneur (Vol. 37, September 2009, No. 9, pp. 66) [8572], [12684], [31682]
New River Valley Development Corporation [59032]
New River Valley Small Business Development Center [58812]
New Rochelle Chamber of Commerce (NRCC) [55290]
The New Role of Regional Management [23258], [36702], [38279], [45583]
"New Rule Rankles In Jersey" in Philadelphia Business Journal (Vol. 30, September 16, 2011, No. 31, pp. 1) [6205], [14468], [23956], [31683], [46309]
New School University - Center for New York City Affairs [34676]
"The New Schools" in Black Enterprise (February 2008) [28286], [38280], [45584]
The New Selling with Service [40569], [43735]
New Smyrna Beach-Edgewater-Oak Hill Chamber of Commerce [50299]
The New Social Entrepreneurship What Awaits Social Entrepreneurship Ventures? [30036], [45964]
"New Sony HD Ads Tout Digital" in Brandweek (Vol. 49, April 21, 2008, No. 16, pp. 5) [543], [11796], [15560], [19955], [35034], [40177], [41161], [42646]
"New Sprint Phone Whets Appetite for Applications" in The Business Journal-Serving Metropolitan Kansas City (Vol. 26, July 25, 2008) [3571], [3774], [18941], [22387], [22612], [23259], [35035], [41162], [44442], [45162]
"New State Rules Require Cranes and Operators to be Certified" in Bellingham Business Journal (Vol. February 2010, pp. 11) [5443], [33851]
"New Stores, New Headquarters in Schenectady for Golub Corporation" in Business Review, Albany New York (November 23, 2007) [5444], [9960], [23260]

The New Superfund—What It Is, How It Does—A Series [10177]

"New Tax Sends Biz Scrambling; Service Levy Will Affect 16,000 Businesses" in Crain's Detroit Business (October 8, 2007) [44443], [46310]

New Technology-Based Firms in the New Millennium, Volume 5 [23261], [35036]

New Technology-Based Firms in the New Millennium, Volume 6 [23957], [33852], [35037], [36703]

"New Technology, Growing Fan Base Fuel Truck Trend" in Nation's Restaurant News (Vol. 45, June 13, 2001, No. 12, pp. 16) [9161], [17958], [23262], [45585]

"New Thinking for a New Financial Order" in Harvard Business Review (Vol. 86, September 2008, No. 9, pp. 26) [8573], [12685], [27524], [31684], [36704]

"New TurnHere Survey Reveals Online Video Trends" in Internet Wire (October 22, 2009) [544], [7956], [11797], [21164], [40178]

New Ulm Area Chamber of Commerce [53699]

New Ulm Visitors Guide [53700]

New or Used? Buying a Firm or Starting Your Own [25356], [44914], [46058]

New Venture Creation: Entrepreneurship for the 21st Century with Online Learning Center Access Card [29385], [32421]

New Venture Partners LLC [54855]

New Ventures Initiative [52007]

New Vista Capital, LLC [49282]

"New Wave" in Entrepreneur (Vol. 36, March 2008, No. 3, pp. 100) [32101]

New Wave [59244]

"New Wave of Business Security Products Ushers in the Kaspersky Anti-Malware Protection System" in Internet Wire (October 26, 2010) [3572], [4722], [18452], [18942], [28787], [45163]

"A New Way to Arrive in Style" in Inc. (Vol. 33, September 2011, No. 7, pp. 54) [14548], [17797], [32206]

"A New Way to Swing" in Canadian Business (Vol. 81, December 8, 2008, No. 21, pp. S8) [9669], [41163]

"A New Way to Tell When to Fold" in Barron's (Vol. 88, July 7, 2008, No. 27, pp. 27) [8574], [11798], [12686], [21165], [28788], [31685], [35038], [44444]

"New Ways to Catch a Thief" in Barron's (Vol. 88, March 10, 2008, No. 10, pp. 37) [8575], [11799], [12687], [24804], [28789], [31686], [35039]

"New Ways To Think About Data Loss: Data Loss Is Costly and Painful" in Franchising World (Vol. 42, August 2010, No. 8, pp. 21) [3775], [4723], [4869], [4975], [18453], [32207], [41421]

New Ways to Work [22070]

New Ways to Work [41701]

New Ways to Work Inc. [22070]

The New Wellness Revolution: Make a Fortune in the Next Trillion Dollar Industry [34384], [45586]

"A New Will to Win" in Harvard Business Review (Vol. 88, September 2010, No. 9, pp. 110) [24483], [38281]

"New Work Order" in Black Enterprise (Vol. 38, March 2008, No. 8, pp. 60) [25378], [30037], [35040], [36705], [38282], [41684]

"A New World" in Canadian Business (Vol. 80, October 8, 2007, No. 20, pp. 136) [27525], [30740]

New World Ventures [51415]

New Writer's Magazine [6844]

"New Year, New Estate Plan" in Hawaii Business (Vol. 53, February 2008, No. 8, pp. 54) [7747], [8576], [21942], [24484], [31687], [32843], [46311]

"New Year's Resolutions: How Three Companies Came Up With Their 2008 Growth Strategies" in Inc. (January 2008, pp. 47-49) [2048], [3776], [10406], [10728], [23263]

"New Yetter Stubble Solution Prevents Tire, Track Damage" in Farm Industry News (November 21, 2011) [21642], [41164]

New York Apparel News [3907], [4149]

New York Assembly Standing Committee on Small Business [55508]

New York Botanical Garden - LuEsther T. Mertz Library [9865]

New York Chamber of Commerce and Industry [55303]

"New York City-Based New Street Realty Advisors has Secured a New Flagship for David's Bridal" in Chain Store Age (August 2008) [2510], [16987], [17402]

New York City Department of Business Services - New York City Procurement Outreach Program [55467]

New York City Partnership and Chamber of Commerce [55303]

"New York Collection Agency's Bribery Case Resolved" in Collections & Credit Risk (Vol. 15, August 1, 2010, No. 7, pp. 19) [6318], [14250], [23958], [26278], [33853], [47339]

New York Customs Brokers Association - Customs Brokers and Forwarders Association of America - Customs Clerks Association of the Port of New York [9199]

New York Department of Economic Development - Division of Minority- and Women-owned Business Development [55035]

New York Department of Economic Development - Division for Small Business - Business Service Ombudsman [55036]

New York Department of Labor - Labor Research Library [19201]

New York Department of State - Office of Fire Prevention and Control - Academy of Fire Science - Library [47551]

"New York Firm Secures Sheffield, Amherst Centers for $26 Million" in Crain's Cleveland Business (Vol. 28, December 3, 2007, No. 48) [17403], [42078], [43114]

New York Genealogical and Biographical Society Library [9541]

New York Grant Co. [47146]

New York International Gift Fair [2063], [5909]

New York Jurisprudence, 2d, LawDesk® CD-ROM ed. [24155]

New York/New England & Eastern Canada Campground Guide [3258]

New York Procurement Center [55468]

New York Procurement Technical Assistance Center [55469]

New York Procurement Technical Assistance Center - Cattaraugus County [55470]

New York Procurement Technical Assistance Center - LaGuardia Community College PTAC [55471]

New York Procurement Technical Assistance Center - Long Island Development Corporation [55472]

New York Procurement Technical Assistance Center - Rochester Business Alliance [55473]

New York Procurement Technical Assistance Center - Rockland Economic Development Corporation [55474]

New York Procurement Technical Assistance Center - South Bronx Overall Economic Development Corporation [55475]

New York Public Interest Research Group (NYPIRG) [19789]

New York Public Library - Mid-Manhattan Library - Accessibility Services [10350]

New York Public Library - Mid-Manhattan Library - General Reference and Advisory Services/Health Information Center [10266], [10329], [15225]

New York Public Library - The Research Libraries - Humanities and Social Sciences Library - Arents Tobacco Collection [10379], [20112]

New York Public Library - The Research Libraries - Jerome Robbins Dance Division [6420]

New York Real Estate Journal [17566]

The New York Review of Books [2398]

New York Senate Standing Committee [55509]

New York Society of Security Analysts Inc. [11975]

New York Society of Security Analysts [11975]

New York State Association of Service Stations [18587]

New York State Association of Service Stations and Repair Shops (NYSASSRS) [18587]

New York State Foundation for Science, Technology and Innovation [55037]

New York State Foundation for Science, Technology and Innovation - Incubators & High Technology Economic Development [55038]

New York State Office of General Services - Minority and Women-Owned Business and Community Relations [55387]

New York State School Music Association Winter Conference [14663], [14760]

New York State Small Business Development Center (NYS SBDC) [55027]

New York State Small Business Development Center - Research Network [44974]

New York State Turf and Landscape Association (NYSTLA) [13349], [13374]

New York University - Berkley Center for Entrepreneurial Studies (BCES) [30382]

New York University - Center for Entrepreneurial Studies [30382]

New York University - Conservation Center [1407]

New York University - Glucksman Institute [13246]

New York University - National Center on Philanthropy and the Law (NCPL) [9314]

New York University - Salomon Center for the Study of Financial Institutions [2344]

New Yorktown Chamber of Commerce [55291]

"New Zealand Natural Co-Branding with Mrs. Fields" in Ice Cream Reporter (Vol. 23, November 20, 2010, No. 12, pp. 2) [1769], [10902], [36706], [42079]

"New Zealand Natural Ice Cream is Opening a Second U.S. Scoop Shop" in Ice Cream Reporter (Vol. 21, October 20, 2008, No. 11, pp. 7) [10235], [10289], [10903], [36707]

Newark Chamber of Commerce [48813]

Newark Public Library - Reference Center [5944]

Newark Public Library - Special Collections Division [2254]

Newark Small Business Development Center [49806]

Newberg Area Chamber of Commerce [56758]

Newberry Area Chamber of Commerce [50236]

Newbury Ventures [49283]

Newcastle Area Chamber of Commerce [59834]

Newcomb Chamber of Commerce [55292]

Newcomer Booklet [51688]

Newcomer's Guide [52488]; [54097]; [55789]; [58968]

Newcomers Guide [53887]; [55790]

Newcomer's Guide and Business Directory [55791]; [57507]

"Newcomers Join Roster of Indoor Sports Venues" in Business Review, Albany New York (Vol. 34, October 12, 2007, No. 28, pp. 1) [5445], [19445], [23264]

Newcomers Welcome Service [21295]

Robert Newell Lighting Design [41631]

Newfound Region Chamber of Commerce [54614]

Newfoundland Department of Industry, Trade and Technology - Registry [44975]

Newfoundland and Labrador Business Service Centre [27920], [40664], [44976]

Newington Chamber of Commerce [49737]

Newport Area Chamber of Commerce (NACC) [54615]

Newport Beach Chamber of Commerce [48814]

Newport Chamber of Commerce [54615]

Newport/Cocke County Chamber of Commerce [57763]

Newport County Chamber of Commerce (NCCC) [57383]

Newport - Oldtown Chamber of Commerce [59245]

News [20661]; [52159]

News Blast [50587]

News Break! [59676]

News in Brief [2558]; [5196]

News Briefs From the Chamber [52160]

News Bulletin [54777]; [57181]

News Capsule [53391]

News Column [59835]

News Exchange [48093]

News In Brief [51937]

News Leakes [53888]

News Letter [51689]

News-N-Views [55922]

News and Notes [56240]

News & Views [48094]; [51252]; [53393]

News and Views [47717]; [47810]; [47932]; [48815]; [48816]; [49573]; [49738]; [49739]; [50237]; [50238]; [50790]; [51251]; [51253]; [52362]; [54778]; [55293]; [55294]; [56241]; [56242]; [56243]; [59246]

News Views [53392]

The News and Views [52161]

News, Views & Issues [51254]

News Vine [9096]; [9765]

News-Voice [52162]

News You Can Use [59419]

NewsAccount [183]

NewsBREAK [50239]

Newsbriefs [20662]; [51255]; [57182]

Newsbyte [53394]

NewsChamber [52363]

Newscope [47718]

NewsEdge™ [3050], [33100]

NewsEdge Live™ [3050], [33100]

NewsFile Collection [15607]

NewsFlash [57183]

Newsgram [56244]

Newsletter & Electronic Publishers Association - Newsletter Publishers Association - Newsletter Association [15009]

Newsletter Association [15009]

Newsletter Communications [15018]

The Newsletter on Newsletters [15019]

Newsletter Publishers Association [15009]

NewsLine [57184]

Newsline [10777]; [14844]; [18514]; [50240]; [51938]; [52364]; [52613]; [53395]; [53701]; [55295]; [56818]; [58356]; [8038]

Newslink [54779]

NewsMonth [51690]

Newsounds, Our Kids Magazine [10341]

Newspaper Abstracts [4074]

Newspaper Advertising Executives Association [15495]

Newspaper Promotion Association [15503]

NewSpring Ventures [57296]

Newswave [59677]

Newton Area Chamber of Commerce and Visitors Bureau [52163]

Newton Area Chamber of Commerce [52163]

Newton Chamber of Commerce (NCC) [53889]

Newton County Chamber of Commerce [58357]

Newton - Needham Chamber of Commerce [52940]

"Nonprofits Hope Employees Dig Deep" in Austin Business JournalInc. (Vol. 28, December 5, 2008, No. 38, pp. A1) **[27539]**, **[45968]**

"Nonprofits May Lose MBE Status in MD" in Boston Business Journal (Vol. 29, September 2, 2011, No. 17, pp. 1) **[9273]**, **[33446]**, **[33860]**, **[40794]**, **[47342]**

"Nonprofits Pressured to Rein in Fundraising Events" in Crain's Detroit Business (Vol. 25, June 15, 2009, No. 24, pp. 1) **[27540]**, **[31692]**, **[45969]**

"Nonstop Round Baler Earns Top International Award for Krone" in Farm Industry News (November 18, 2011) **[21644]**, **[39266]**, **[41169]**

Norco Chamber of Commerce (NCC) **[48818]**

Nordonia Hills Chamber of Commerce **[56245]**

"Nordstrom Points for Richmond Heights" in Saint Louis Business Journal (Vol. 31, August 5, 2011, No. 50, pp. 1) **[43117]**, **[44707]**

Norfolk Area Chamber of Commerce (NACC) **[54415]**

Norfolk Botanical Garden Society - Frederic Heutte Memorial Library **[9866]**

Norfolk Chamber of Commerce [54415]; [54439]

Norfolk Heritage Centre. [9542]

Norfolk Historical Society Archives **[9542]**

Norfolk SCORE **[54347]**

Norman Business Journal **[56557]**

Norman Chamber of Commerce **[56558]**

Normandale Associates Inc. **[17597]**

Normandale Community College **[53801]**

Normes Canadiennes de la Publicite [341]

Noro-Moseley Partners **[50656]**

NORTEL Information Resource Network [21273]

"Nortel Makes Customers Stars in New Campaign" in Brandweek (Vol. 49, April 21, 2008, No. 16, pp. 8) **[547]**, **[19956]**, **[22391]**, **[35048]**, **[38291]**, **[40188]**, **[44448]**, **[45593]**

"Nortel Outlook Shows Recovery Won't Come Quickly" in Globe & Mail (March 20, 2007, pp. B4) **[12695]**, **[44449]**

"Nortel Plays Big to Settle Lawsuits" in Globe & Mail (February 9, 2006, pp. B1) **[8581]**, **[12696]**, **[23962]**

"Nortel Romances Chinese Rival Huawei" in Globe & Mail (February 2, 2006, pp. B1) **[35049]**, **[42082]**

"Nortel Starting From Scratch" in Globe & Mail (February 24, 2006, pp. B3) **[24490]**, **[25175]**

Nortex Press [59915]

Nortext Multimedia Inc. (Iqaluit, Northwest Territories) **[59915]**

Nortext Multimedia Inc. (Ottawa, Ontario) **[59953]**

North American Association of Floor Covering Distributors (NAFCD) **[9056]**

North American Association of Floor Covering Distributors--Membership Directory **[9064]**

North American Association of Food Equipment Manufacturers (NAFEM) **[17872]**

North American Association of Jewish Homes & Housing for the Aging [15049]

North American Association of State and Provincial Lotteries Conference and Trade Show **[9416]**, **[46773]**

North American Benefit Association [21859]

North American Brewers Resource Directory **[2461]**

North American Broadcasters Association (NABA) **[16699]**, **[19892]**

North American Building Material Distribution Association (NBMDA) **[5197]**

North American Building Material Distribution Association--Membership Directory **[13662]**

North American Business Development Co., L.L.C. **[50353]**

North American Family Campers Association (NAFCA) **[3252]**

North American Financial Institutions Directory **[31693]**

North American Flowerbulb Wholesalers Association (NAFWA) **[9766]**, **[13350]**, **[13375]**

North American Gaming Regulators Association (NAGRA) **[9382]**

North American Horsemen's Association (NAHA) **[10608]**

North American Insulation Manufacturers Association (NAIMA) **[11257]**

North American International Auto Show **[14991]**

North American Journal of Aquaculture **[9029]**

North American National Broadcasters Association [16699], [19892]

"North American Pet Health Insurance Market Poised for Growth" in Pet Product News (Vol. 64, December 2010, No. 12, pp. 4) **[11408]**, **[15727]**, **[36206]**, **[43554]**, **[45594]**

North American Radio Archives Library **[16769]**

North American Radio Archives - Tape and Printed Materials Libraries **[16770]**

North American Retail Hardware Association (NRHA) **[10127]**

North American Securities Administrators Association (NASAA) **[11976]**

North American Ski Journalists Association [6799], [15509]

North American Snowsports Journalists Association (NASJA) **[6799]**, **[15509]**

North American Wholesale Lumber Association (NAWLA) **[13642]**

North Atlantic Capital Corporation **[52639]**

North Attleboro and Plainville Chamber of Commerce **[52941]**

North Augusta Chamber of Commerce **[57508]**

North Augusta Lifestyle Guide **[57509]**

North Baldwin Chamber of Commerce (NBCC) **[47719]**

North Bay Area Chamber of Commerce [53853]

North Branch Area Chamber of Commerce **[53703]**

North Bridge Venture Partners (NBVP) **[53053]**

North Canton Area Chamber of Commerce (NCACC) **[56246]**

North Carolina Association of Plumbing, Heating, and Cooling Contractors Annual Trade Show **[896]**, **[16291]**

North Carolina Cherokee Satellite Office - Native American Business Development Center **[55849]**

North Carolina Community College System - Small Business Center Network **[55543]**

North Carolina Department of Administration - Purchase and Contract Division - State Purchasing Office **[55861]**

North Carolina Department of Agriculture and Consumer Services - Sandhills Research Station (SRS) **[13530]**

North Carolina Department of Agriculture and Consumers Services, Marketing Division **[55544]**

North Carolina Department of Commerce - Business/Industry Development Division **[55545]**

North Carolina Department of Labor - Charles H. Livengood, Jr. Memorial Library **[47552]**

North Carolina Department of Transportation, Research and Development Library **[1652]**, **[6613]**, **[13553]**, **[19829]**

The North Carolina Enterprise Fund, L.P. **[55857]**

North Carolina Fair Share (NCFS) **[2943]**, **[26071]**, **[42415]**

North Carolina Institute of Minority Economic Development - NC Minority Business Enterprise Center **[55850]**

North Carolina Medical Society Annual Meeting **[14328]**

North Carolina Rural Economic Development Center **[55546]**

North Carolina RV and Camping Show **[6913]**

North Carolina Small Business Partnership **[55547]**

North Carolina Small Business and Technology Development Center **[55548]**

North Carolina Small Business and Technology Development Center - SBTDC Regional Office **[55862]**; **[55863]**

North Carolina State University - Industrial Extension Service **[55549]**

North Carolina State University - Libraries - D.H. Hill Library Special Collections Research Center **[5713]**

North Carolina State University - Research Stations Division **[21827]**

North Central Connecticut Chamber of Commerce (NCCCC) **[49740]**

North Central Idaho Business Technology Incubator **[50817]**

North Central Iowa Small Business Development Center (Fort Dodge, Iowa) **[51780]**

North Central Kansas SCORE **[52029]**

North Central Massachusetts Chamber of Commerce (NCMCC) **[52942]**

North Central Michigan College **[53520]**

North Central Ohio SCORE **[55972]**

North Central Pennsylvania Regional Planning and Development Commission - Enterprise Development **[57339]**

North Central Regional Aquaculture Center (NCRAC) **[8990]**

North Central Texas College - Corinth Small Business Development Center **[57861]**

North Central Texas Small Business Development Center **[57862]**

North Chamber News **[58359]**

North Channel Area Chamber of Commerce **[58360]**

North Charles Mental Health Research and Training Foundation, Inc. **[46121]**

North Clackamas County Chamber of Commerce **[56819]**

North Coast Chamber of Commerce **[56247]**

North Conway Institute - Resource Center - Alcohol and Drugs **[46106]**

North Country Chamber of Commerce **[54616]**

North Country Small Business Development Center **[55029]**

North County Recreation District Small Business Development Center **[56679]**

North Dade Regional Chamber of Commerce **[50242]**

North Dakota Chamber of Commerce (NDCC) **[55923]**

North Dakota Department of Commerce - Division of Economic Development and Finance **[55885]**

North Dakota Department of Transportation - Materials and Research Division Library **[1653]**, **[6614]**, **[13554]**, **[19830]**

North Dakota Economic Development and Finance Department - Procurement Division **[55936]**

North Dakota Small Business Development Center - Belcourt **[55876]**

North Dakota Small Business Development Center - Bismarck **[55877]**

North Dakota Small Business Development Center - Devils Lake **[55878]**

North Dakota Small Business Development Center - Dickinson **[55879]**

North Dakota Small Business Development Center - Fargo **[55880]**

North Dakota Small Business Development Center - Fort Yates **[55881]**

North Dakota Small Business Development Center - Grand Forks **[55882]**

North Dakota Small Business Development Center - Jamestown **[55883]**

North Dakota Small Business Development Center - Minot **[55884]**

North Dakota/South Dakota Native American Business Enterprise Center **[55934]**

North Dakota State University - Center for Economic Development [27941]

North Dakota State University - Institute for Business and Industry Development (IBID) **[27941]**

North Dakota State University - Upper Great Plains Transportation Institute - North Dakota Local Technical Assistance Program **[55938]**

North Dallas Chamber of Commerce (NDCC) **[58361]**

North East Area Chamber of Commerce (NEACC) **[57185]**

North East Chamber of Commerce **[52738]**

North Essex Chamber of Commerce (NECC) **[54780]**

North Essex Report **[54781]**

North Florida Regional Chamber of Commerce **[50243]**

North Fork Chamber of Commerce **[48819]**

North Fort Myers Chamber of Commerce (NFMCC) **[50244]**

North Fulton Chamber of Commerce [50544]

North Galveston County Chamber of Commerce **[58362]**

North Harris Montgomery Community College Small Business Development Center [57855]

North Haven Gardens Inc. [13510]

North Hennepin Area Chamber of Commerce **[53704]**

North Hill Ventures **[53054]**

North Houston Greenspoint Business **[58363]**

North Houston-Greenspoint Chamber of Commerce **[58364]**

North Houston Greenspoint Chamber of Commerce [58364]

North Idaho Business Journal **[50828]**

North Idaho College - Professional - Technical Education **[50825]**

North Iowa Area Small Business Development Center (Mason City, Iowa) **[51781]**

North Jersey Regional Chamber of Commerce (NJRCC) **[54782]**

North Kingstown Chamber of Commerce **[57384]**

North Las Vegas Chamber of Commerce (NLVCC) **[54509]**

North Las Vegas Resource Directory **[54510]**

North Little Rock Chamber of Commerce (NLRCC) **[48095]**

North Little Rock, Your Metropolitan Home: Industrial and Commercial Location Factors **[48096]**

North Logan Chamber of Commerce [48100]

North Manchester Chamber of Commerce (NMCC) **[51692]**

North Mason Chamber of Commerce **[59247]**

North Mecklenburg Chamber of Commerce and Visitors Bureau [55752]

North Metro Small Business Development Center **[49424]**

North Miami Beach Chamber of Commerce **[50245]**

North Miami Chamber of Commerce [50130]

North Mississippi Enterprise Initiative, Inc. **[53931]**

North Mobile Business **[47720]**

North Monterey County Chamber of Commerce **[48820]**

North Monterey County Chamber Times **[48821]**

North Myrtle Beach Chamber of Commerce **[57510]**

North Olmsted Businessmen's Association [56248]

North Olmsted Chamber of Commerce (NOCC) **[56248]**

North Pacific Anadromous Fish Commission (NPAFC) **[9004]**

North Palm Beach County Chamber of Commerce **[50246]**

North Penn Chamber of Commerce [57198]
North Phoenix Chamber of Commerce **[47934]**
North Platte Area Chamber of Commerce and Development Corporation **[54416]**
North Platte Area Chamber of Commerce and Development Corporation of North Platte [54416]
North Platte Chamber Area News [54417]
North Platte Chamber of Commerce [54416]
North Platte SCORE **[54348]**
North Port Area Chamber of Commerce **[50247]**
North Quabbin Chamber of Commerce **[52943]**
North Sacramento Chamber of Commerce [48822]
North San Antonio Chamber of Commerce (NSACC) **[58365]**
North San Diego Small Business Development Center **[48161]**
North Santiam Chamber of Commerce (NSCC) **[56820]**
North Shelby Chamber of Commerce [47691]
North Shore Business Journal **[52944]**
North Shore Chamber of Commerce **[52945]**
North Silicon Valley Chamber of Commerce [48813]
North Suburban Chamber of Commerce (NSCC) **[52946]**
North Tampa Chamber of Commerce **[50248]**
North Valley Regional Chamber of Commerce (NVRCC) **[48823]**
North Webster Tippecanoe Township Chamber of Commerce **[51693]**
North West SCORE **[54654]**
North York Central Library - Canadiana Department **[9543]**
Northampton Area Chamber of Commerce (NACC) **[57186]**
Northampton Community College (NCC) **[57346]**
Northampton Community College - Paul and Harriett Mack Library **[9348]**
Northampton County Chamber of Commerce **[58969]**
Northbrook Chamber of Commerce and Industry (NCCI) **[51258]**
Northbrook Chamber of Commerce [51258]
NorthCentralMass.com **[52947]**
Northcoast Environmental Center Library **[7415]**
Northcoast Small Business Development Center - Del Norte **[48162]**
Northcoast Small Business Development Center - Humboldt **[48163]**
Northeast Alabama Entrepreneurial System **[47764]**
Northeast Cincinnati Chamber of Commerce **[56249]**
Northeast Floral Expo **[9122]**
Northeast Harbor Port Directory **[52614]**
Northeast Homeland Security Regional Advisory Council (NERAC) **[60542]**
Northeast Indiana Innovation Center **[51760]**
Northeast Indiana Small Business Development Center **[51478]**
Northeast Iowa Small Business Development Center (Dubuque, Iowa) **[51782]**
Northeast Johnson County Chamber of Commerce **[52164]**
Northeast Johnson County Chamber of Commerce and Visitors Bureau [52164]
Northeast Kingdom Chamber of Commerce (NEKCC) **[58767]**
Northeast Mississippi Business Journal **[53890]**
Northeast Ohio Procurement Technical Assistance Center - Lake County Economic Development Center **[56373]**
Northeast Ohio Procurement Technical Assistance Center - Lake Erie College Campus **[56374]**
Northeast Outdoors [3271], [17675], [20206], [20615]
Northeast Sustainable Energy Association Library **[19140]**
Northeast Tarrant Chamber of Commerce **[58366]**
Northeast Technology Center **[56663]**
Northeast Texas Small Business Development Center **[57863]**
Northeastern Connecticut Chamber of Commerce (NCCC) **[49741]**
Northeastern Lumber Manufacturers Association (NELMA) **[13643]**
Northeastern Regional Aquaculture Center (NRAC) **[8991]**
Northeastern State University Small Business Development Center (Broken Arrow, Oklahoma) **[56429]**
Northeastern State University Small Business Development Center (Muskogee, Oklahoma) **[56430]**
Northeastern State University Small Business Development Center (Tahlequah, Oklahoma) **[56431]**
Northeastern University - Center for Particulate Control in Process Equipment [930]
Northeastern University - Center for Nano and Microcontamination Control (CMC) **[930]**
Northern Allegheny County Chamber of Commerce (NACCC) **[57187]**

Northern Anne Arundel County Chamber of Commerce (NAACCC) **[52739]**
Northern Arizona Center for Entrepreneurship and Technology **[47986]**
Northern Arizona Genealogical Society Bulletin **[9469]**
Northern Burlington Regional Chamber of Commerce **[54783]**
Northern California Minority Business Enterprise Center **[49146]**
Northern California Real Estate Journal [17553]
Northern California Small Business Development Center **[48164]**
Northern Dakota County Chamber of Commerce [53630]
Northern Gateway Chamber of Commerce **[54617]**
Northern Katahdin Valley Region Chamber of Commerce (NKVRCC) **[52615]**
"Northern Kentucky Adds 1,355 Jobs in '07" in *Business Courier* (Vol. 24, February 15, 2008, No. 45, pp. 3) [23279], [27541], [35424], [44853]
The Northern Kentucky Business Journal **[52365]**
Northern Kentucky Chamber of Commerce **[52366]**
Northern Kentucky University Small Business Development Center **[52229]**
Northern Monmouth Chamber of Commerce (NMCC) **[54784]**
Northern New Mexico Community College **[55006]**
Northern New Mexico's Lakeside Playground **[54975]**
"Northern Overexposure" in *Canadian Business* (Vol. 79, August 14, 2006, No. 16-17, pp. 36) [7959], [12697], [27542], [32847]
Northern Pike: The Water World **[1716]**
Northern Rhode Island Chamber of Commerce (NRICC) **[57385]**
Northern Virginia Community College **[59037]**
Northfield Area Chamber of Commerce **[53705]**
Northland Pioneer College's Small Business Development Center **[47838]**
Northland Regional Chamber of Commerce (NRCC) **[54099]**
The Northland Voice **[54100]**
Northmont Area Chamber of Commerce (ENCC) **[56250]**
Northridge Chamber of Commerce [48823]
Northridge and Chatsworth Business and Community News **[48824]**
Northrop Grumman Mission Systems - Technology Library **[5068]**
Northshore SCORE **[52417]**
Northville Chamber of Commerce **[53397]**
Northwest Alabama Junior Chamber of Commerce **[47721]**
Northwest Atlantic Fisheries Organization (NAFO) **[9005]**
Northwest Cartoonists Association **[4404]**
Northwest Chamber of Commerce **[54101]**
Northwest Chamber of Commerce (NWC) **[56559]**
Northwest Communities Chamber of Commerce [54101]
Northwest Connecticut SCORE **[49649]**
Northwest Fisheries Association (NWFA) **[8977]**
Northwest Indiana SCORE **[51495]**
Northwest Indiana Small Business Development Center (NWISBDC) **[51479]**
Northwest Iowa Small Business Development Center (Spencer, Iowa) **[51783]**
Northwest LA SCORE **[52418]**
Northwest Louisiana Government Procurement Center - Greater Shreveport Chamber of Commerce **[52521]**
Northwest Macomb Chamber of Commerce [53442]
Northwest Marine Industries [13932]
Northwest Marine Trade Association (NMTA) **[13932]**
Northwest Metro Business Network Book **[49574]**
Northwest Metro Chamber of Commerce [49446]
Northwest Montana SCORE **[54237]**
Northwest Native American Business Enterprise Center **[59323]**
Northwest Network **[56560]**
Northwest Ohio SCORE **[55973]**
Northwest Sportshow **[19384]**
Northwest Texas Small Business Development Center (NWTSBDC) **[57864]**
Northwest Trade Adjustment Assistance Center **[39526]**
Northwest Valley Chamber of Commerce **[47935]**
Northwest Venture Associates, Inc. / Spokane Capital MGMT **[59332]**
"Northwest Washington Fair Building Larger Horse Arena" in *Bellingham Business Journal* (Vol. March 2010, pp. 6) [5454], [10618]
Northwestern Building Products Expo **[10149]**, [13678]
Northwestern Lumber Association (NLA) **[13644]**
Northwestern Lumbermen's Association [13644]
Northwestern Oklahoma State University Small Business Development Center (Alva, Oklahoma) **[56432]**
Northwestern Oklahoma State University Small Business Development Center (Enid, Oklahoma) **[56433]**
Northwestern Scene **[13673]**

Northwestern University - Center for Retail Management **[40669]**
Northwestern University - Dispute Resolution Research Center (DRRC) **[14179]**
Northwestern University - Guthrie Center for Real Estate Research **[17619]**
Northwood Area Chamber of Commerce **[51940]**
Northwood Ventures **[55445]**
Northwoods News **[59678]**
Norton Area Chamber of Commerce (NACC) **[52165]**
"Norvax University Health Insurance Sales Training and Online Marketing Conference" in *Internet Wire* (January 27, 2010) [11409], [11802], [20392], [21166], [36207], [40189], [43555], [46673]
Norwalk Area Chamber of Commerce (NACC) **[51941]**; **[56251]**
Norwalk Chamber of Commerce **[48825]**
Norwalk Chamber News **[48826]**
Norwegian-American Chamber of Commerce (NACC) **[36309]**
Norwegian American Genealogical Center and Naeseth Library **[9544]**
Norwegian-American Historical Association Archives **[9545]**
Norwegian Forest Cat Breed Council **[1013]**
Norwegian Trade Council [36298]
Norwegian Trade Council - United States [36298]
Norwest Equity Partners **[53780]**
Norwest Venture Partners **[49284]**
Norwin Chamber of Commerce **[57188]**
Norwood Park Chamber of Commerce and Industry **[51259]**
Norwood Venture Corp. **[55446]**
Nostradamus Advertising **[6544]**
"Not All Contracts a Good Fit for Fashion Reps" in *Agency Sales Magazine* (Vol. 39, September-October 2009, No. 9, pp. 10) [4126], [4254], [23963], [39267], [43556]
"Not Enough Room" in *Austin Business JournalInc.* (Vol. 29, November 13, 2009, No. 36, pp. A1) [1282], [5455], [10730], [18559], [20393], [20559], [46674]
"Not Enough To Go Around" in *The Business Journal-Milwaukee* (Vol. 25, August 15, 2008, No. 47, pp. A1) [17408], [23964], [26281], [33296], [37451]
"Not In My Backyard" in *Entrepreneur* (Vol. 36, May 2008, No. 5, pp. 42) [8582], [12698], [16992], [17409], [27543], [31694], [36711]
"Not In Our Backyard" in *Canadian Business* (Vol. 80, October 22, 2007, No. 21, pp. 76) [18456], [23965], [33861]
Not by Jeans Alone **[4158]**
"Not Just for Kids: ADHD can be Debilitating for an Employee, and Frustrating for Bosses" in *Canadian Business* (April 14, 2008) [25176], [29129], [34386], [38292]
"Not the Six O'Clock News" in *Canadian Business* (Vol. 80, January 15, 2007, No. 2, pp. 10) [19957], [24491], [25177]
"Not in Your Backyard?" in *Canadian Business* (Vol. 80, March 12, 2007, No. 6, pp. 44) [33447], [41342]
"Not Your Dad's Business Card" in *Small Business Opportunities* (July 2008) [22392], [22613], [32848], [45595]
"Not Your Father's Whiteboard" in *Inc.* (Vol. 33, November 2011, No. 9, pp. 50) [3574], [4976], [18560], [18944], [35050], [41422], [45165]
Notables **[6260]**
Notari Associates **[41632]**
"Note to Leonard: Swim Fast" in *Canadian Business* (Vol. 80, January 15, 2007, No. 2, pp. 29) [32849], [42083]
"Note to Marketers: A Viral Video Has a Life of Its Own" in *Advertising Age* (Vol. 80, October 5, 2009, No. 33, pp. 29) [7960], [11803], [40190]
"Note-Taking App, Supercharged" in *Inc.* (Vol. 33, October 2011, No. 8, pp. 48) [3780], [4977], [41423], [45166]
"Notes on Current Labor Statistics" in *Montly Labor Review* (Vol. 133, September 2010, No. 9, pp. 75) [25379], [25771], [34387], [35872]
"Nothing But Green Skies" in *Inc.* (November 2007, pp. 115-120) [17798], [30745], [31098]
"Nothing But Net: Fran Harris Offers Advice On Winning the Game of Business" in *Black Enterprise* (Vol. 38, March 2008, No. 8, pp. 50) [2786], [25881], [30040], [32850]
Nothing But Noodles **[18198]**
"Nothing Like a Weak Team Or An Unrealistic Schedule To Start a Project Off Right" in *Inc.* (November 2007, pp. 85-87) [3575], [18945], [45167]
"Nothing Plus Nothing" in *Entrepreneur* (Vol. 37, October 2009, No. 10, pp. 25) [11804], [44450]
Notice **[52948]**
Noticias Del Valle **[54976]**

Nouvelles CSN [46816]
Nouvelles CSQ [46817]
Nova Scotia Business, Inc. - Business Services Center [59909]
Nova Scotia Department of Education - Drug Dependency Services Division Library [46107]
Nova Scotia Economic Development [59910]
Novak Biddle Venture Partners, L.P. [52775]
"*NovAtel Inc. Licensed to Sell Galileo Receivers*" in *Canadian Corporate News* (May 14, 2007) [35051], [42084], [44451]
Novato Chamber of Commerce [48827]
"*A Novel Approach to the Market*" in *Agency Sales Magazine* (Vol. 39, December 2009, No. 11, pp. 10) [25600], [26773], [43557]
"*A Novel Fix for the Credit Mess*" in *Barron's* (Vol. 88, March 31, 2008, No. 13, pp. 10) [8583], [12699], [26282], [27544], [31695], [33862], [37452]
Novelists, Inc. (NINC) [6800]
Novi Chamber of Commerce (NCC) [53398]
Novi Chamber of Commerce Newsletter [53399]
"*Novi Eyed for $11 Million, 100-Bed Medilodge*" in *Crain's Detroit Business* (Vol. 25, June 1, 2009, No. 22, pp. M032) [5456], [15075], [34388], [44708]
Novus Glass / Novus Franchising Inc. [9646]
NOVUS L.L.C. [38787]
Novus Ventures [49285]
Now, Discover Your Strengths [29130], [38293]
"*Now Entering A Secure Area*" in *Women Entrepreneur* (January 14, 2009) [18457], [30041], [33297], [45596], [47343]
"*Now in Play, Score Keeps Head Up and Stick on Ice*" in *Globe & Mail* (January 20, 2007, pp. B5) [8584], [12700]
"*Now the Real Work Begins*" in *Baltimore Business Journal* (Vol. 28, October 15, 2010, No. 23, pp. 1) [11410], [33863], [34389], [36208]
"*Now See This*" in *Entrepreneur* (Vol. 36, April 2008, No. 4, pp. 53) [5762], [20394], [35052], [39268], [41170], [46675]
"*Now That's Rich*" in *Canadian Business* (Vol. 80, February 12, 2007, No. 4, pp. 92) [8585], [12701], [30959]
"*Now You See It..*" in *Canadian Business* (Vol. 81, November 10, 2008, No. 19, pp. 20) [8586], [12702], [31696], [36712], [46312]
"*Nowspeed and OneSource to Conduct Webinar*" in *Internet Wire* (December 14, 2009) [548], [11805], [20395], [28792], [40191], [43558], [45597], [46676]
"*Nowspeed's David Reske to Speak at SolidWorks World 2010 in Anaheim*" in *Internet Wire* (January 7, 2010) [549], [11806], [20396], [40192], [46677]
NPAFC Annual Report [9006]
NPAFC Bulletin [9007]
NPAFC Technical Report [9008]
NPES: Association for Suppliers of Printing, Publishing and Converting Technologies [16348]
NPR Broadcast Library. [16767]
NRH Nutrition Consultants Inc. [15199]
NRI Relocation Inc. (NRI) [24788]
NSBE Journal [19187]
NSBE Magazine: National Society of Black Engineers [19187]
NSCA Bulletin [15989]
nSight Inc. [2212]
NSS News Bulletin [1367]
NSSRA Newsletter [19352], [43273]
"*NStar Feels the Heat*" in *Cape Cod Times* (September 30, 2011) [7277], [7635], [12703], [30746], [42085]
The NTC Group [49781]
NU Business Trends [53706]
Nu-Look 1-Hour Cleaners [6763]
"*Nuclear Plans May Stall on Uranium Shortage*" in *Globe & Mail* (March 22, 2007, pp. B4) [12704], [39269], [44452]
Nuclear Power: The Hot Debate [30882]
"*Nuclear Renaissance*" in *Canadian Business* (Vol. 83, August 17, 2010, No. 13-14, pp. 46) [7278], [7636], [30747]
Nudge [30042], [38294]
Nueces Canyon Chamber of Commerce [58367]
The Number Express [3990]
"*Number of Mechanic's Liens Triple Since 2005*" in *The Business Journal - Serving Phoenix and the Valley of the Sun* (Vol. 28, August 22, 2008, No. 51, pp. 1) [8587], [12705], [14472], [16993], [17410], [27545], [31697]
"*Numbers Game*" in *Baltimore Business Journal* (Vol. 27, February 6, 2010, No. 40, pp. 1) [27546], [33298], [33448], [33864], [35425], [35873]
"*The Numbers Speak For Themselves*" in *Barron's* (Vol. 88, July 14, 2008, No. 28, pp. 16) [8588], [12706], [23280], [31698]
Numerical Heat Transfer, Part A: Applications: An International Journal of Computation and Methodology [44060]

"*Numerous Changes Made to Crop Production and Consumption Forecasts*" in *Farm Industry News* (November 9, 2011) [21645], [25178]
Numismatic News [4374]
Numismatica Canada [4349]
Numismatics International (NI) [4350]
Numismatics International Library [4394]
The Numismatist: For Collectors of Coins, Medals, Tokens and Paper Money [4375]
Nurse Next Door Senior Care Services [10578]
Nursery Association Executives [9767]
Nursery Association Executives of North America [9767]
Nursery Association Secretaries [9767]
Nursery and Landscape Association Executives of North America (NLAE) [9767]
Nursery/Landscape Expo [9123], [9830], [16202]
Nursery News [9815]
Nursing & Health Care [34575]
Nursing and Health Care Perspectives [34575]
Nursing Education Perspectives [34575]
"*Nursing Home Group Put on the Block*" in *Globe & Mail* (February 23, 2006, pp. B1) [14446], [24492], [44175]
"*Nurturing Talent for Tomorrow*" in *Restaurants and Institutions* (Vol. 118, September 15, 2008, No. 14, pp. 90) [5840], [17960], [28290]
Nussbaum Center for Entrepreneurship [55869]
Nutley Chamber of Commerce [54785]
Nutri-Lawn [13523]
Nutrition Action Healthletter [10254]
Nutrition for Better Health [15186]
Nutrition: Eat and Be Healthy [15187]
Nutrition Entrepreneurs [15114]
Nutrition Facts: The New Food Label with Supermarket Savvy's Leni Reed [15188]
Nutrition for Optimal Health Association [15149]
Nutrition House Canada Inc. [43302]
Nutrition & Mental Health [34576]
Nutrition Reviews [15178]
Nutrition Today [15179], [34577]
Nutrition for Wellness [15189]
Nutrition for You [15190]
Nutritional Assessment of the Elderly [15191]
"*Nvidia Shares Clobbered After Gloomy Warning*" in *Barron's* (Vol. 88, July 7, 2008, No. 27, pp. 25) [5763], [8589], [12707], [31699], [35053], [39270]
"*Nvidia's Picture Brighter Than Stock Price Indicates*" in *Barron's* (Vol. 88, March 24, 2008, No. 12, pp. 46) [8590], [12708], [27547], [31700], [35054], [39271]
"*N.Y. Group Top Bidder for Last Duke Sites*" in *Crain's Cleveland Business* (Vol. 28, November 19, 2007, No. 46, pp. 1) [16540], [16994], [17411], [42086]
"*N.Y. Investors Reject AnorMed Board Proposal*" in *Globe & Mail* (February 21, 2006, pp. B11) [8591], [12709], [24493]
"*NYC Tops Hub in Tech VC Dollars*" in *Boston Business Journal* (Vol. 31, August 5, 2011, No. 28, pp. 1) [35055], [35426], [47060]
Nyikos Associates Inc. [990]
"*Nymex Dissidents Rattle Sabers*" in *Crain's Chicago Business* (Vol. 31, April 21, 2008, No. 16, pp. 2) [8592], [12710], [31701], [42087]
NYPD Pizza [16164]
NYSE Weekly Stock Buys [13136]
Nyssa Chamber of Commerce and Agriculture [56821]
Nyssa Chamber of Commerce [56821]

O

O & A Marketing News [16670]
OAG Business Travel Planner: The Official Lodging Directory of the American Hotel & Motel Association [20164], [20560]
OAG Flight-Finder Asia Pacific Plus [20201], [20607]
OAG Travel Planner European Edition [20165], [20561]
OAG Travel Planner Hotel & Motel Redbook: European Edition [20165], [20561]
Oak Cliff Chamber of Commerce (OCCC) [58368]
Oak Forest Chamber of Commerce [51260]
Oak Grove Chamber of Commerce [54102]
Oak Harbor Area Chamber of Commerce (OHACC) [56252]
Oak Investment Partners [49782]
Oak Investment Partners (Minneapolis) [53781]
Oak Investment Partners (Palo Alto) [49286]
Oak Lawn Chamber of Commerce [51261]
Oak Leaf [51262]
Oak Park-River Forest Chamber of Commerce (OPRFCC) [51263]
Oak Ridge Chamber of Commerce [57764]
Oak Ridge National Laboratory - Toxicology Information Response Center [6725]
Oakdale Business News [48828]
Oakdale District Chamber of Commerce [48829]

Oakdales Olde Towne Veterinary Hospital [38788]
Oakes Area Chamber of Commerce [55924]
Oakhurst Area Chamber of Commerce (OACC) [48830]
Oakland African-American Chamber of Commerce (OAACC) [48831]
Oakland Business Review [48832]
Oakland Chamber of Commerce [54786]
Oakland Chamber of Commerce [48834]
Oakland Chinatown Chamber of Commerce [48833]
"*Oakland County Hopes Auto Suppliers Can Drive Medical Industry Growth*" in *Crain's Detroit Business* (March 10, 2008) [14207], [26774], [27548], [34390], [39272], [42088]
"*Oakland County to Survey Employers on Needed Skills*" in *Crain's Detroit Business* (Vol. 24, April 14, 2008, No. 15, pp. 30) [28291], [35427]
Oakland Five East Bay Counties Black Chamber of Commerce [48831]
Oakland Metropolitan Chamber of Commerce [48834]
Oakland University - School of Education and Human Services - Educational Resources Laboratory [20752]
Oakley Area Chamber of Commerce [52166]
Oakley Chamber of Commerce [48835]
Oakridge - Westfir Chamber of Commerce [56822]
Oakville Chamber of Commerce [59248]
OAS Staff Association (OASSA) [19151]
Oatman-Goldroad Chamber of Commerce [47936]
"*Obama Plan May Boost Maryland Cyber Security*" in *Boston Business Journal* (Vol. 29, May 20, 2011, No. 2, pp. 1) [11807], [18458], [28793], [33865], [35056]
Ober, Kaler, Grimes & Shriver Library [7771]
OberlKaler. [7771]
Oberlin Area Chamber of Commerce [56253]
"*Oberweis Tests Home Ice Cream Delivery*" in *Ice Cream Reporter* (Vol. 21, November 20, 2008, No. 12, pp. 1) [9162], [10906], [31099]
Obion County Chamber of Commerce [57765]
Object-Oriented Programming (OOP) Boot Camp [45065]
Objection Handling: Overcoming the Hurdles [26603]
M. C. O'Brien Inc. [17598]
Obsessive Branding Disorder: The Illusion of Business and the Business of Illusion [550], [40193]
Ocala-Marion County Chamber of Commerce [50249]
Ocala/The Villages SCORE [49912]
"*OccuLogix Shares Plummet 65 Percent*" in *Globe & Mail* (February 4, 2006, pp. B5) [8593], [12711], [41171], [43914]
Occupational & Environmental Health Consulting Services Inc. [2944], [26072], [34626]
Occupational and Environmental Medical Association of Canada (OEMAC) [34155]
Occupational Hazards [34512], [47479]
Occupational Health & Safety [47481]
Occupational Medicine [34156]
Occupational Outlook Handbook [6968]
Occupational Outlook Quarterly [6985]
Occupational Therapy in Health Care: A Journal of Contemporary Practice [34578]
Occusafe Inc. [30884]
"*OCE Boosts JetStream Productivity*" in *American Printer* (Vol. 128, August 1, 2011, No. 8) [3576], [4495], [16385], [18946], [20786], [45168]
"*Oce Business Services: Discovery Made Easy*" in *Information Today* (Vol. 26, February 2009, No. 2, pp. 31) [3577], [18947], [23966], [44453], [45169]
"*Ocean Choice in Running to Acquire Assets of FPI*" in *Globe & Mail* (March 15, 2007, pp. B9) [32851], [42089]
Ocean City Chamber of Commerce [52740]
Ocean City Hotel, Motel, and Restaurant Trade Exposition [10787]
Ocean City Hotel, Motel, and Restaurant Association Spring Trade Exposition [10787]
Ocean City Regional Chamber of Commerce (OCRCC) [54787]
Ocean City Relocation Information [54788]
Ocean City Visitors Guide [54789]
Ocean County SCORE [54655]
Ocean Grove Chamber of Commerce [54790]
"*Ocean of Opportunity*" in *Hawaii Business* (Vol. 53, October 2007, No. 4, pp. 61) [21646], [39273], [40194], [41172]
Ocean Park Area Chamber of Commerce [59249]
Ocean Pines Area Chamber of Commerce [52741]
Ocean Pines Chamber of Commerce [52741]
Ocean Shores/North Beach Chamber of Commerce [59250]
Ocean Springs Chamber of Commerce (OSCC) [53891]
Oceanic Institute (OI) [9045]
Oceanic Society - Environmental Policy Institute [49860]
Oceanside Chamber of Commerce [55297]
Oceanside Chamber of Commerce (OCC) [48836]

Oceanside Chronicle [48837]
O'Charley's Restaurants [18199]
Ocilla - Irwin Chamber of Commerce [50588]
Oconee County Chamber of Commerce [50589]
Oconee County Chamber of Commerce (OCCC) [57511]
Oconomowoc Area Chamber of Commerce (OACC)
  [59679]
Oconomowoc Talk [59680]
Oconto Falls Area Chamber of Commerce [59681]
"October 2009: Recovery Plods Along" in Hispanic Busi-
  ness (October 2009, pp. 10-11) [8594], [12712],
  [14473], [16995], [17412], [27549], [31702]
Octoclean [2670]
Odessa Chamber of Commerce [54103]; [59251]
Odin Capital Group, LLC [54446]
O'Dwyer's Directory of Public Relations Firms [16594],
  [42500]
Oelwein Area Chamber of Commerce and Area Develop-
  ment [51942]
Oelwein Chamber and Area Development (OCAD)
  [51942]
Oelwein Outlook [51943]
"Of Marks and Men" in Canadian Business (Vol. 80,
  March 12, 2007, No. 6, pp. 59) [23967], [37080]
OFA Short Course [9124], [16203]
O'Fallon Chamber of Commerce (OCC) [51264]; [54104]
O'Fallon Chamber News [51265]
Off the Beaten Path L.L.C. [24956]
Off the Grill Franchising, LLC [9188], [18200]
Off-Ramps and On-Ramps: Keeping Talented Women on
  the Road to Success [32852], [35874], [47344]
"Off the RIM" in Canadian Business (Vol. 80, January 15,
  2007, No. 2, pp. 7) [12713], [18948]
Off the Vine [59252]
"Off the Wall: Keith Collins' Larger-Than-Life Designs" in
  Black Enterprise (Vol. 37, February 2007, No. 7, pp.
  138) [5994], [30043]
"Offer for Sears Canada 'Inadequate'" in Globe & Mail
  (February 10, 2006, pp. B4) [42090], [43118]
Office of Aircraft Services - Business Utilization and
  Development Specialist - Division of Contracting
  [61541]; [61542]
Office of Aircraft Services - Business Utilization and
  Development Specialist - Division of Contracting - Avia-
  tion Management Directorate [61543]; [61544]
Office of Civil Rights - Office of Small and Disadvantaged
  Business Utilization - U.S. Department of Education
  [61305]
"The Office: Do Not Disturb" in Inc. (November 2007, pp.
  144) [30044], [38295]
Office Equipment Manufacturers Institute [4931], [15273]
Office Furniture Dealers Alliance [41531]
Office Furniture Market [15283]
"The Office: Good to Great" in Inc. (October 2007, pp.
  140) [29131], [30045], [38296]
Office of Government Contacting [52783]
Office of the Governor - Economic Development and
  Tourism Division - Economic Information Clearinghouse
  [13985]
Office of the Governor - Legislative Liaison Office
  [52403]
Office of Justice Programs - Information Systems Divi-
  sion [61619]; [61620]
"Office Leasing Gains Ground" in Sacramento Business
  Journal (Vol. 25, July 18, 2008, No. 20, pp. 1) [16996],
  [17413], [23281], [24759], [27550]
"Office Market May Turn Down" in Crain's New York
  Business (Vol. 24, January 14, 2008, No. 2, pp. 26)
  [8595], [12714], [14474], [17414], [27551], [31703]
"Office Party Attire" in Women In Business (Vol. 61,
  October-November 2009, No. 5, pp. 27) [4255],
  [22393], [32853]
Office of Personnel Management - Center for National
  Security - Office of Operations [60629]; [60630]
Office of Personnel Management - Division for Human
  Capital Leadership and Merit System Accountability
  [60631]; [60632]
Office of Personnel Management - Office of Communica-
  tions and Public Liaison [60633]; [60634]
Office of Personnel Management - Office of Small and
  Disadvantaged Business Utilization - Contracting Divi-
  sion [60635]
"Office Pests" in Canadian Business (Vol. 79, October 9,
  2006, No. 20, pp. 122) [32854], [38297]
Office Pride Commercial Cleaning Services [2671]
"Office Retooled" in Canadian Business (Vol. 80, March
  26, 2007, No. 7, pp. 67) [11808], [18949], [35057]
Office Safety and Workplace Ergonomics [47505]
Office of the Secretary of the Army - Office of Small
  Business Programs [61306]; [61307]
Office of the Secretary of the Navy - Office of Small
  Business Programs [61308]
"Office Supplier Won't Wait for Opportunity to Knock" in
  Business Courier (Vol. 24, December 28, 2008, No. 37,
  pp. 2) [25601], [25778], [26496]

Office of Surface Mining Reclamation and Enforcement -
  Appalachian Regional Office [61545]; [61546]
Office of Surface Mining Reclamation and Enforcement -
  Mid-Continent Regional Office [61547]; [61548]
Office of Surface Mining Reclamation and Enforcement -
  Western Regional Office [61549]; [61550]
"Office Tech: A Pretty Little Vista" in Canadian Business
  (Vol. 80, January 29, 2007, No. 3, pp. 61) [18950],
  [41173], [41548]
Office Technology [5078]
"The Office: The Bad and the Ugly" in Inc. (January
  2008, pp. 120) [38298]
Office of the Under Secretary of the Navy - Office of
  Small Business Programs [61309]
The Official American International Toy Fair Directory
  [20261]
Official Boothbay Harbor Region Guide [52616]
Official Buyer's Guide [50250]
Official Buyers Guide to the Southern Market [10475]
Official Export Guide [9212], [11142]
Official Guide [50251]
The Official Guide for GMAT Verbal Review, 2nd Edition
  [28292], [38299]
Official Guide to Lakeview East [51266]
Official Guide to Palm Beach [50252]
Official Guide to Portland [58369]
An Official Guide To Lenox [52949]
Official Guide to Wellington [50253]
Official Hotel & Resort Guide [20562]
Official Hotel Guide [20562]
Official SE Volusia County Map [50254]
Official Summary of Security Transactions and Holdings
  [2718]
Offinger's Handcrafted Marketplace [9623]
Offshore Money Fund Report™ [32076]
Ogallala - Keith County Chamber of Commerce
  (OKCCC) [54418]
Ogden Roemer Wilkerson Architecture [11577]
Ogden SCORE [58623]
Ogden Small Business Development Center [58616]
Ogden/Weber Chamber of Commerce [58668]
OgdenKistler Architecture [11577]
Ogunquit Chamber of Commerce (OCC) [52617]
"Oh, Behave!" in Entrepreneur (Vol. 36, April 2008, No.
  4, pp. 87) [11809], [21167], [22394], [22614]
"Oh, Grow Up!" in Entrepreneur (Vol. 35, October 2007,
  No. 10, pp. 120) [23282], [24189], [29388], [32423]
"OHC Aids Long Island Family" in Indoor Comfort
  Marketing (Vol. 70, May 2011, No. 5, pp. 45) [844],
  [45970]
Ohio Bell - Corporate Information Resource Center
  [3861], [19869]
Ohio Bureau of Workers' Compensation - BWC Library
  [47553]
"Ohio Business Incentives Lag Offerings By Other
  States" in Crain's Cleveland Business (Vol. 30, May 18,
  2009, No. 20, pp. 1) [44709], [46313]
Ohio Center for Prevention Studies - Ohio Safe Schools
  Center [46108]
Ohio Chamber of Commerce (OCC) [56254]
"Ohio Collection Agency Settles Second Lawsuit" in Col-
  lections & Credit Risk (Vol. 15, July 1, 2010, No. 6, pp.
  9) [6319], [23968], [26283], [33866]
"Ohio Commerce Draws Closer to Profitability" in Crain's
  Cleveland Business (Vol. 28, October 29, 2007, No.
  43, pp. 14) [8596], [23283], [24494], [31704], [37453]
Ohio Department of Development - Entrepreneurship and
  Small Business Division [55967]
Ohio Department of Development - Technology and In-
  novation Division [55968]
"Ohio Franchise Buys 21 Jacksonville Area Papa John's"
  in Florida Times-Union (December 20, 2010) [16129],
  [17961], [23284], [32210]
Ohio Genealogical Society - Coshocton County Chapter
  Library [9546]
Ohio Genealogical Society - Perry County, Ohio Chapter
  Library [9547]
Ohio House Economic Development and Small Business
  Committee [56413]
Ohio International Floral Short Course [9124], [16203]
Ohio-Israel Chamber of Commerce (OICC) [56255]
The Ohio JobBank: The Job Hunter's Guide to Ohio
  [7008]
Ohio Jurisprudence on Westlaw® [24156]
Ohio Matters [56256]
Ohio Procurement Technical Assistance Center [56375]
Ohio Procurement Technical Assistance Center - Cincin-
  nati Procurement Outreach Center - Toledo Chamber
  of Commerce [56376]
Ohio Procurement Technical Assistance Center - Kent
  Regional Business Alliance - Kent State University
  [56377]
Ohio Procurement Technical Assistance Center -
  Lawrence Economic Development Corporation -
  Procurement Outreach Center [56378]

Ohio Procurement Technical Assistance Center - Mahon-
  ing Valley Technical Procurement Center - MVEDC
  [56379]
Ohio Procurement Technical Assistance Center - Ohio
  University - Procurement Technical Assistance Program
  [56380]
Ohio Procurement Technical Assistance Center -
  Procurement Technical Assistance Program [56381]
Ohio Procurement Technical Assistance Center - Toledo
  Regional Chamber of Commerce [56382]
Ohio Restaurant Food and Beverage Show [18042]
Ohio Safety Congress and Expo [47511]
Ohio Small Business Development Center at Ashland
  University [55947]
Ohio Small Business Development Center at the Cler-
  mont Chamber of Commerce [55948], [56257]
Ohio Small Business Development Center at Terra Com-
  munity College [55949]
Ohio State Gift Show [9623]
Ohio State Journal on Dispute Resolution [14169]
Ohio State University - Advanced Computing Center for
  the Arts and Design (ACCAD) [4925]
Ohio State University - Agricultural Technical Institute
  (ATI) [9887]
Ohio State University - Career Connection [3406]
Ohio State University - Cartoon Library and Museum
  [4428]
Ohio State University - Cartoon Research Library. [4428]
Ohio State University - Center for Real Estate Education
  and Research [17159]
Ohio State University - C. Wayne Ellett Plant and Pest
  Diagnostic Clinic (CWEPPDC) [16207]
Ohio State University - Engineering Research Center for
  Net Shape Manufacturing (ERC/NSM) [39533]
Ohio State University - Food Industries Center (FIC)
  [15237]
Ohio State University - Laboratory for Pest Control Ap-
  plication Technology (LPCAT) [15661]
Ohio State University - Plant and Pest Diagnostic Clinic
  [16207]
Ohio State University - Water Resources Center (WRC)
  [21013]
Ohio State University - Water Treatment Laboratory
  [21013]
Ohio United Way Legislative Bulletin [56414]
Ohio University Innovation Center - Ohio University
  [56403]
Ohio University - Institute for Local Government
  Administration and Rural Development (ILGARD)
  [42431]
Ohio University Procurement Technical Assistance
  Center - Ohio University Voinovich Center for Leader-
  ship and Public Affairs [56383]
Ohio Veterinary Medical Association/Midwest Veterinary
  Conference [1087]
Ohio Wage and Salary Association [25370]
Ohio Wesleyan University - Kinnison Music Library
  [14698], [14776]
Ohio Wesleyan University - L.A. Beeghly Library -
  Archives/Special Collections [1155]
"Ohio's Reputation Lags Its Business Ranking" in Busi-
  ness Courier (Vol. 24, November 23, 2008, No. 32, pp.
  1) [17415], [27552], [44710], [44854]
Ohlone College [49371]
OIAUS L.L.C. [2946], [26073], [42730]
Oil Butler International, Corp. [16680]
Oil Can Henry's [16681]
"Oil Patch Expects Richer Shell Offer" in Globe & Mail
  (January 3, 2006, pp. B1) [8597], [12715], [23285],
  [42091]
"Oil Picks and Pans" in Canadian Business (Vol. 79,
  August 14, 2006, No. 16-17, pp. 67) [8598], [12716],
  [27553]
"Oil Rich" in Canadian Business (Vol. 79, Winter 2006,
  No. 24, pp. 57) [8984], [9021], [45971]
"Oilheating Delivery Issues" in Indoor Comfort Marketing
  (Vol. 70, September 2011, No. 9, pp. 14) [845],
  [44109]
"The Oilman" in Canadian Business (Vol. 79, Winter
  2006, No. 24, pp. 64) [12717], [30046]
"Oil's Going Down, Down, Down" in Canadian Business
  (Vol. 79, October 9, 2006, No. 20, pp. 148) [8599],
  [12718]
Oilton Chamber of Commerce [56493]
Ojai Valley Chamber Business Journal [48838]
Ojai Valley Chamber of Commerce [48839]
"OK, Bring in the Lawyers" in Crain's Chicago Business
  (Vol. 31, November 17, 2008, No. 46, pp. 26) [14475],
  [16997], [23286], [23969], [26284], [27554], [37454],
  [44454]
"Ok, So Now What?" in Canadian Business (Vol. 79,
  November 6, 2006, No. 22, pp. 113) [8600], [12719],
  [31705]

Okanogan Small Business Development Center [59058]
Okawville Chamber of Commerce [51267]
OKC Action [56561]
Okeechobee Chamber of Commerce [50255]
Okeechobee County Chamber of Commerce [50255]
Okefenokee Chamber of Commerce and Folkston and Charlton County Development Authority [50590]
Okefenokee Chamber of Commerce and Development Authority of the City of Folkston and Charlton County, Georgia [50590]
Okefenokee Chamber of Commerce and Folkston - Charlton County Development Authority [50590]
Okemah Chamber of Commerce [56562]
Oklahoma Bid Assistance Network (OBA) - Moore Norman Technology Center (MNTC) - Business Development Center - Bid Assistance Procurement Center [56619]
Oklahoma Center for the Advancement of Science Technology - Oklahoma Inventor's Assistance Service [56437]
Oklahoma City Chamber of Commerce [56522]
Oklahoma City Minority Business Enterprise and Consultant Center [56612]
Oklahoma City SCORE [56448]
Oklahoma Department of Agriculture, Food and Forestry - Market Development Division [56438]
Oklahoma Department of Career and Technology Education - Bid Assistance Centers [56620]
Oklahoma Department of Career and Technology Education - Oklahoma State Department of Vocational and Technical Education (TIP) - Training for Industry Program [56439]
Oklahoma Department of Commerce - Administration and Central Services [56440]
Oklahoma Department of Commerce - Business Development Division [56441]
Oklahoma Department of Commerce - Export Assistance Program [56442]
Oklahoma Department of Commerce - Global Business Solutions [56443]
Oklahoma Department of Commerce - New and Existing Businesses - Minority-Owned Businesses [56613]
Oklahoma Department of Commerce - Oklahoma Small Business Conference [56669]
Oklahoma Family Policy Council (OFPC) [34677]
Oklahoma Fisheries Research Laboratory Library [9038]
Oklahoma Genealogical Society Quarterly [9470]
Oklahoma Minority Supplier Development Council [56614]
Oklahoma Native American Business Enterprise Center [56615]
Oklahoma Procurement Technical Assistance Center - Eastern Oklahoma County Technology Center [56621]
Oklahoma Procurement Technical Assistance Center - Francis Tuttle Tech Center [56622]
Oklahoma Procurement Technical Assistance Center - Great Plains Technology Center [56623]
Oklahoma Procurement Technical Assistance Center - Oklahoma Bid Assistance Network (OBAN) - Autry Technology Center [56624]
Oklahoma Procurement Technical Assistance Center - Oklahoma Bid Assistance Network (OBA) - Gordon Cooper Tech Center [56625]
Oklahoma Procurement Technical Assistance Center - Oklahoma Bid Assistance Network (OBA) - High Plains Tech Center [56626]
Oklahoma Procurement Technical Assistance Center - Oklahoma Bid Assistance Network (OBA) - Indian Capital Technology Center (ICTC) [56627]
Oklahoma Procurement Technical Assistance Center - Oklahoma Bid Assistance Network (OBA) - Kiamichi Tech Center - Kiamichi District Bid Assistance Center [56628]
Oklahoma Procurement Technical Assistance Center - Oklahoma Bid Assistance Network (OBA) - Mid-America Technology Center [56629]
Oklahoma Procurement Technical Assistance Center - Oklahoma Bid Assistance Network (OBA) - Northeast Technology Center Pryor Campus [56630]
Oklahoma Procurement Technical Assistance Center - Oklahoma Bid Assistance Network (OBA) - Pioneer Tech Center [56631]
Oklahoma Procurement Technical Assistance Center - Oklahoma Bid Assistance Network (OBA) - Red River Technology Center [56632]
Oklahoma Procurement Technical Assistance Center - Oklahoma Bid Assistance Network (OBA) - Southwest Technology Center [56633]
Oklahoma Procurement Technical Assistance Center - Oklahoma Bid Assistance Network (OBA) - Tri-County Technology Center [56634]
Oklahoma Procurement Technical Assistance Center - Oklahoma Bid Assistance Network (OBA) - Tulsa Technology Center [56635]

Oklahoma Procurement Technical Assistance Center - Tribal Government Institute [56636]
Oklahoma State Chamber of Commerce and Industry [56588]
Oklahoma State University - Aquatic Biology Laboratory [21014]
Oklahoma State University - Center for Local Government Technology (CLGT) [42432]
Oklahoma State University - Ecotoxicology and Water Quality Research Laboratory [21014]
Oklahoma State University - Ecotoxicology and Water Quality Research Laboratory Library [21003]
Oklahoma State University - Reservoir Research Center [21014]
Oklahoma State University - Surgical Laser Laboratory [1105]
Okoboji Spirit [51944]
Okolona Area Chamber of Commerce-Main Street Program [53892]
Okolona Chamber of Commerce [53892]
Olathe Business Report [52167]
Olathe Chamber of Commerce (OCC) [52168]
Old Chicago Pizza [1884], [16165]
"Old Ford Plant to Sign New Tenants" in *Business Courier* (Vol. 27, August 13, 2010, No. 15, pp. 1) [16998], [17416], [17799], [26775], [35428], [39274], [44711]
"Old Friends Make Old Buildings Successful Restaurants" in *Crain's Detroit Business* (Vol. 24, February 4, 2008, No. 5, pp. 14) [17962], [42092]
Old Hippy Wood Products Inc. [39529]
Old-House Interiors [11567]
Old House/New House Home Show [1168], [46774]
Old Orchard Beach Chamber of Commerce [52618]
"The Old Railway is on a Roll" in *Globe & Mail* (January 26, 2006, pp. B1) [8601], [12720], [44455]
Old Saybrook Chamber of Commerce [49742]
Old School [18836]
"Old Spice Guy (Feb.-July 2010)" in *Canadian Business* (Vol. 83, August 17, 2010, No. 13-14, pp. 23) [551], [2049], [28794], [40195]
Old-Stuff--Directory of Shops Section [1125], [4409]
Oldenburg Registry N.A. (OLD NA) [1014]
Oldham County Chamber of Commerce [52367]
Oldham County Kentucky [52368]
Oldsmar/Upper Tampa Bay Regional Chamber of Commerce [50256]
Olive Branch Chamber of Commerce (OBCC) [53893]
Olive Oil Association of America [17857]
Olivia Area Chamber of Commerce (OACC) [53707]
Olney Chamber of Commerce [58370]
Olney Chamber of Commerce (OCC) [52742]
"O'Loughlin Cuts $6 Million for Chesterfield Doubletree" in *Saint Louis Business Journal* (Vol. 32, September 2, 2011, No. 1, pp. 1) [10731], [20397], [46678]
G.V. Olsen Associates [21784]
Olson Research Associates Inc. (ORA) [8918]
Olver Incorporated - Library. [20997]
Olympia Small Business Development Center [59059]
Olympic College [59354]
"Olympus is Urged to Revise Board" in *Wall Street Journal Eastern Edition* (November 28, 2011, pp. B3) [118], [3234], [12721], [19653], [21402], [24495], [35875], [36713], [38300], [42093]
Omaha Chamber of Commerce [58371]
Omaha Small Business Network [54449]
Omak Chamber of Commerce [59253]
"O'Malley, Ehrlich, Court Business Vote" in *Baltimore Business Journal* (Vol. 28, October 1, 2010, No. 21, pp. 1) [32855], [33867]
OMB Watcher [22138]
O'Melveny & Myers LLP Library [37176]
"OMERS Joins Bid for U.K. Port Giant" in *Globe & Mail* (March 28, 2006, pp. B1) [24496], [36714], [42094]
"OMERS Labors With Troubles at the Top" in *Globe & Mail* (February 26, 2007, pp. B3) [21944], [38301]
Omex Office Maintenance Experts [2672]
OMI Government Relations Inc. [10187]
OM...IM [49407]
Omninet Capital, LLC [49287]
"Omniplex on the Case" in *Black Enterprise* (Vol. 37, December 2006, No. 5, pp. 38) [25602], [32856], [33868], [44456], [47471]
"Omniture's Next Version of SearchCenter Delivers Landing Page Optimization" in *Internet Wire* (September 24, 2009) [552], [3578], [11810], [18951], [21168], [40196], [45170]
Omohundro Institute of Early American History and Culture - Kellock Library [2228]
Omro Area Chamber of Commerce [59682]
"On Beyond Powerpoint: Presentations Get a Wake-Up Call" in *Inc.* (November 2007, pp. 58-59) [3579], [18561], [18952], [22395], [28293], [28795], [40197], [43559], [45171]

"On the Clock" in *Canadian Business* (Vol. 82, April 27, 2009, No. 7, pp. 28) [6969], [7791], [28294], [35429], [35876], [38302], [45972]
"On the Cutting Edge" in *Inc.* (November 2007, pp. 28) [9637], [44176]
ON DEMAND Digital Printing & Publishing Strategy Conference and Exposition [4669], [6535], [16427], [46775]
"On the Economic Dimensions of Corporate Social Responsibility" in *Business and Society* (December 2007, pp. 457-478) [27555], [45973]
"On the Go: a Busy Executive Is Always Well-Equipped for Travel" in *Black Enterprise* (Vol. 40, July 2010, No. 12, pp. 106) [24896], [43560]
"On the Green: Sheila Johnson Adds $35 Million Golf Resort To Her Expanding Portfolio" in *Black Enterprise* (January 2008) [9670], [10732], [17963], [40795], [47345]
"On Growth Path of Rising Star" in *Boston Business Journal* (Vol. 31, June 24, 2011, No. 22, pp. 3) [7279], [7637], [19107], [23287], [30748], [33299], [37455]
"On the High Road" in *Crain's Cleveland Business* (Vol. 28, October 8, 2007, No. 40, pp. 2) [23288], [24897]
"On Hire Ground" in *Entrepreneur* (Vol. 36, February 2008, No. 2, pp. 19) [2787], [23289], [25882], [35430], [35877]
"On the Itinerary: Your Future" in *Entrepreneur* (Vol. 37, October 2009, No. 10, pp. 92) [11143], [13592], [26776], [36715]
On the Make: Clerks and the Quest for Capital in Nineteenth-Century America [38303], [43119], [45598]
"On Managerial Relevance" in *Journal of Marketing* (Vol. 75, July 2011, No. 4, pp. 211) [38304], [40198]
"On a Mission: Ginch Gonch Wants You to Get Rid of Your Tighty Whities" in *Canadian Business* (Vol. 81, September 29, 2008, No. 16) [4127], [4256], [24497], [25179], [38305], [39275], [40199], [42095]
On the Move [51268]
On Nature [7056]
On Point [48840]
On Point On Line [48841]
"On Policy: Where Talk is Cheap" in *Canadian Business* (Vol. 80, January 29, 2007, No. 3, pp. 19) [33869], [44457]
On-Q Software Inc. [231], [2326], [3080], [19048], [45254]
On the Right Track [53400]
"On a Roll" in *Canadian Business* (Vol. 79, October 9, 2006, No. 20, pp. 51) [24499], [25180], [38306]
"On a Roll" in *Canadian Business* (Vol. 79, Winter 2006, No. 24, pp. 49) [1557], [23290], [24498]
On Tap [2448]
"On tap: More Could Get MEGA Credits; Need to Look Outside State May Be Cut" in *Crain's Detroit Business* (April 7, 2008) [12722], [25603], [27556], [33870], [45599], [46314]
"On Target" in *Canadian Business* (Vol. 81, July 22, 2008, No. 12-13, pp. 45) [5093], [11811], [21169], [40200], [44219], [44458], [45600]
On Target [51694], [53894]
On The Button [4083]
On The Move [57512]
"On Their Own" in *Crain's Cleveland Business* (Vol. 28, November 12, 2007, No. 45, pp. 19) [16077], [30047], [34391], [45601]
"On Their Own: Bronx High School Students Open a Bank Branch" in *Black Enterprise* (Vol. 38, February 2008, No. 7, pp. 42) [8023], [28295], [47573]
"On Track" in *Canadian Business* (Vol. 79, July 17, 2006, No. 14-15, pp. 51) [32857], [38307]
On Track [58970]
On Track Power Window Repair [35644], [44616]
"On the Trail of the Bear" in *Canadian Business* (Vol. 81, March 17, 2008, No. 4, pp. 28) [8602], [12723], [31706]
On the Wealth of Nations: Books That Changed the World [27557], [36716]
"On Your Marks, American Airlines, Now Vote!" in *Benzinga.com* (, 2011) [2511], [15434], [40201], [47346]
Onawa Chamber of Commerce (OCC) [51945]
"Once More Into the Fray" in *Canadian Business* (Vol. 80, December 25, 2006, No. 1, pp. 13) [27558]
Once Upon a Child [5152], [20289]
One 2 One Bodyscapes [16036]
"One Charger, Many Devices: the Skinny on Wireless Power Pads" in *Inc.* (Volume 32, December 2010, No. 10, pp. 58) [3781], [41424]
1-800-Radiator [44617]
100 Fabulous Cocktails [1876]
One Foot Out the Door: How to Combat the Psychological Recession That's Alienating Employees and Hurting American Business [27559], [29132], [35878], [38308]

MASTER INDEX Orange

Master Index

One Hour Heating & Air **[911]**
101 Best Home-Based Success Secrets for Women **[35615]**
"One Hundred Years of Excellence in Business Education: What Have We Learned?" in Business Horizons (January-February 2008) **[28296]**, **[32858]**, **[38309]**, **[45602]**
101 Dalmatians: Pongo and Perdita Sing Along Songs **[3991]**
"One Laptop Per Child Weighs Going For-Profit" in Boston Business Journal (Vol. 31, May 20, 2011, No. 17, pp. 1) **[4978]**, **[9274]**, **[28297]**, **[45974]**
One Liberty Ventures **[53055]**
The One Minute Entrepreneur **[119]**, **[21403]**, **[26285]**, **[26497]**, **[29133]**, **[30048]**, **[31707]**
The One Minute Manager **[30049]**, **[38310]**
"One on One With SEIA's President, CEO" in Contractor (Vol. 57, January 2010, No. 1, pp. 40) **[7280]**, **[7638]**, **[19108]**, **[23291]**, **[30749]**, **[45603]**
"One Paddle, Two Paddle" in Hawaii Business (Vol. 53, October 2007, No. 4, pp. 65) **[4257]**, **[19336]**, **[24500]**, **[25181]**
"One-Pass Tillage" in Farm Industry News (Vol. 42, January 1, 2009, No. 1) **[21647]**, **[41174]**
One Small Step **[38633]**
One Stop Capital Shop (Atlanta) **[60639]**; **[60640]**
One Stop Capital Shop (Baltimore, Maryland) **[60641]**; **[60642]**
One Stop Capital Shop (Bismarck) **[60643]**; **[60644]**
One Stop Capital Shop (Detroit, Michigan) **[60645]**; **[60646]**
One Stop Capital Shop (Edinburg) **[60647]**; **[60648]**
One Stop Capital Shop (Glendale) **[60649]**; **[60650]**
One Stop Capital Shop (Hugo) **[60651]**; **[60652]**
One Stop Capital Shop (Kansas City, Kansas) **[60653]**; **[60654]**
One Stop Capital Shop (Mississippi Mid-Delta) **[60655]**; **[60656]**
One Stop Capital Shop (New York, New York) **[60657]**; **[60658]**
One Stop Capital Shop (Oakland, California) **[60659]**; **[60660]**
One Stop Capital Shop (Philadelphia/Camden) **[60661]**; **[60662]**
One Stop Capital Shop (Roxbury) **[60663]**; **[60664]**
One Stop Capital Shop (Somerset, Kentucky) **[60665]**; **[60666]**
One Stop Capital Shop (Tacoma) **[60667]**
One Stop Capital Shop (Houston, Texas) - U.S. General Store **[60668]**; **[60669]**
"The One Thing That's Holding Back Your Wellness Program" in Employee Benefit News (Vol. 25, December 1, 2011, No. 15, pp. 8) **[34392]**, **[40902]**, **[42837]**, **[43915]**, **[47347]**, **[47472]**
"The One Thing You Must Get Right When Building a Brand" in Harvard Business Review (Vol. 88, December 2010, No. 12, pp. 80) **[553]**, **[15339]**, **[22396]**, **[26498]**, **[28796]**, **[40202]**, **[43561]**
"One-Time Area Trust Executive Finds Trouble in N.H." in The Business Journal-Serving Metropolitan Kansas City (September 12, 2008) **[8603]**, **[12724]**, **[24805]**, **[30960]**, **[31708]**, **[38311]**
"One Workforce - Many Languages" in HRMagazine (Vol. 54, January 2009, No. 1, pp. 32) **[35879]**, **[40903]**
"One World" in American Printer (Vol. 128, August 1, 2011, No. 8) **[4496]**, **[16386]**, **[20398]**, **[20787]**, **[46679]**
OneCoach Int'l. LLC **[3036]**
Oneida Chamber of Commerce [55228]
O'Neill Area Chamber of Commerce **[54419]**
Eugene O'Neill Theater Center - Leibling-Wood Library - Monte Cristo Cottage Collection **[5945]**
Onex Corp. **[59932]**
onFocus Healthcare Inc. **[26638]**
"Online All the Time" in Retail Merchandiser (Vol. 51, July-August 2011, No. 4, pp. 18) **[23292]**, **[27560]**, **[28797]**, **[43120]**, **[43562]**
"Online Book Sales Surpass Bookstores" in Information Today (Vol. 28, September 2011, No. 8, pp. 11) **[2151]**, **[2384]**, **[28798]**, **[43563]**, **[45604]**
"Online Forex Broker Tadawul FX Intros Arabic Website" in Entertainment Close-Up (June 23, 2011) **[12725]**, **[21170]**, **[28799]**
"Online Fortunes" in Small Business Opportunities (Fall 2008) **[4063]**, **[5118]**, **[11144]**, **[11598]**, **[15297]**, **[20122]**, **[20501]**, **[21024]**, **[27962]**, **[28516]**, **[34722]**, **[39545]**, **[42739]**, **[44228]**, **[44772]**
"Online Marketing and Promotion of Canadian Films via Social Media Tools" in CNW Group (January 27, 2010) **[7961]**, **[11812]**, **[21171]**, **[26777]**, **[40203]**
"Online Marketing: Puppy Power: Using a New Tool Called a Widget To Boost Your Brand" in Inc. (November 2007, pp. 55-56) **[554]**, **[28800]**, **[40204]**
Online Marketing and Search Engine Optimization **[28070]**, **[39596]**
"Online Pet Medication Store Supports Free Vaccinations for Cats" in Internet Wire (August 31, 2010) **[1062]**, **[15728]**, **[28801]**, **[45975]**
"Online Postings Really Influence Older Women" in Marketing to Women (Vol. 22, July 2009, No. 7, pp. 8) **[11813]**, **[21172]**, **[22397]**, **[28802]**, **[40205]**
"Online Radio That's Cool, Addictive, Free, and Just Maybe A Lasting Business" in Inc. (October 2007, pp. 100-106, 108) **[16723]**, **[28803]**
Online Research Best Practices and Innovations (Onsite) **[39597]**; **[39598]**
"Online Reverse Auctions: Common Myths Versus Evolving Reality" in Business Horizons (September-October 2007, pp. 373) **[1521]**, **[15340]**, **[28804]**, **[37205]**, **[42096]**
"Online Security Crackdown: Scanning Service Oversees Site Security at David's Bridal" in (Vol. 84, July 2008, No. 7, pp. 46) **[2512]**, **[15341]**, **[18459]**, **[28805]**, **[43121]**
"Online Self-Publishing Services" in Black Enterprise (Vol. 37, November 2006, No. 4, pp. 90) **[2152]**, **[6518]**, **[11814]**, **[21173]**, **[30050]**, **[44125]**
Online Synergy **[34157]**
Online: The Leading Magazine for Information Professionals **[4665]**, **[4737]**, **[4767]**, **[4896]**, **[5017]**, **[5046]**, **[11952]**, **[15360]**, **[21268]**
"Online Tools for Jobseekers" in Occupational Outlook Quarterly (Vol. 55, Fall 2011, No. 3, pp. 20) **[3352]**, **[35431]**, **[35880]**
Online Trading Academy **[28473]**
"Online Training Requires Tools, Accessories" in Contractor (Vol. 56, September 2009, No. 9, pp. 67) **[16254]**, **[28298]**, **[35058]**
Online Training Solutions Inc. **[59363]**
"Online Translation Service Aids Battlefield Troops" in Product News Network (August 30, 2011) **[3782]**, **[20481]**, **[28806]**
"Only in Canada, Eh?" in Canadian Business (Vol. 79, November 6, 2006, No. 22, pp. 17) **[23970]**, **[30961]**
The Only Thing Missing **[50591]**
Onondaga Small Business Development Center **[55030]**
Onondaga Venture Capital Fund, Inc. **[55447]**
Onset Ventures **[49288]**
Ontario Association of Landscape Architects Library **[13455]**
The Ontario Business Journal **[48842]**
Ontario Chamber of Commerce **[48843]**
Ontario Chamber of Commerce (OCC) **[56823]**
"Ontario Keeps Bleeding Jobs as Michelin Closes Tire Plant" in Globe & Mail (February 3, 2006, pp. B1) **[25182]**, **[39276]**
The Ontario Land Surveyor **[19532]**
Ontario Ministry of Community Safety and Correctional Services - Centre of Forensic Sciences **[10046]**
Ontario Ministry of Economic Development and Trade - InfoSource **[27921]**, **[36930]**, **[38846]**
Ontario Nature **[7057]**
Ontario Teachers' Pension Plan Board - Knowledge Centre **[8963]**, **[13241]**
Ontonagon County Chamber of Commerce **[53401]**
Ontonagon County Chamber of Commerce and Tourism Association [53401]
Onward Orangeburg **[57513]**
OOC Inc. **[16166]**
Oogles N Googles **[16037]**
Oologah Area Chamber of Commerce **[56563]**
"OPEC Exposed" in Hawaii Business (Vol. 54, September 2008, No. 3, pp. 2) **[7281]**, **[7639]**, **[11145]**, **[21648]**, **[27561]**, **[30750]**, **[36717]**, **[43916]**
Opelika Chamber of Commerce (OCC) **[47722]**
Opelousas-St. Landry Chamber of Commerce (OSLCC) **[52489]**
Open Door **[54511]**
"Open Enrollment: Staying Healthy During Enrollment Season" in Employee Benefit News (Vol. 25, November 1, 2011, No. 14, pp. 41) **[11411]**, **[21945]**, **[34393]**, **[35881]**, **[36209]**
"The Open Mobile Summit Opens in San Francisco Today: John Donahoe CEO eBay to Keynote" in Benzinga.com (November 2, 2011) **[1522]**, **[20399]**, **[28807]**, **[46680]**
Open Prairie Ventures **[51416]**
"Open Price Agreements: Good Faith Pricing in the Franchise Relationship" in Franchise Law Journal (Vol. 27, Summer 2007, No. 1) **[23971]**, **[32211]**
"Open Skies: Opportunity, Challenge for Airlines" in Crain's Chicago Business (April 21, 2008) **[11146]**, **[24501]**, **[25183]**, **[25604]**, **[25779]**, **[36718]**, **[44459]**
Open Source Solutions for Small Business Problems **[120]**, **[3580]**, **[18953]**, **[21404]**, **[22398]**, **[28808]**, **[45172]**
Open Systems Payroll System **[15473]**
Open Technology Business Center **[56888]**
"Open the Telecom Market" in Canadian Business (Vol. 80, April 23, 2007, No. 9, pp. 80) **[12726]**, **[33871]**, **[44460]**
Opening a Business in Stow **[56258]**
Opening Door **[20519]**
Openworks **[2673]**
Operation Eyesight Universal (OEU) **[34158]**
"Operation Fusion" in Black Enterprise (Vol. 38, November 2007, No. 4, pp. 30) **[12727]**, **[30051]**, **[42097]**
Operation Oswego County **[55492]**
Operations Forum **[20986]**
Opimian, the Wine Society of Canada **[19208]**
Opp and Covington County Area Chamber of Commerce **[47723]**
Opportunities for Study in Hand Bookbinding and Calligraphy [2243]
Opportunity Capital Partners **[49289]**
Opportunity Hot-Line **[56424]**
"Opportunity Knocks" in Small Business Opportunities (September 2008) **[5127]**, **[24760]**, **[32212]**, **[35616]**, **[45605]**
"Opportunity Now Lies at Short End of the Market" in Barron's (Vol. 88, June 30, 2008, No. 26, pp. M9) **[8604]**, **[12728]**, **[26286]**, **[31709]**
"An Opportunity for Patience" in Barron's (Vol. 88, June 30, 2008, No. 26, pp. M5) **[8605]**, **[12729]**, **[25605]**, **[31710]**
The Opposable Mind: How Successful Leaders Win Through Integrative Thinking **[30052]**, **[38312]**
"OPSEU: Developmental Service Workers Picketing Across Ontario to Raise Community Awareness" in Canadian Corporate News (May 16, 2007) **[33300]**, **[45976]**, **[46905]**
Optial Corp. **[2945]**
Optical Laboratories Association [20929]
Optical Wholesalers Association [20929]
Optical Wholesalers National Association [20929]
Opticality Ventures **[55448]**
Opticians Association of America (OAA) **[20925]**
Opticians Association of Canada (OAC) **[20926]**
Optics & Photonics News **[35241]**
"Optima Public Relations Gains Partners" in Alaska Business Monthly (Vol. 27, October 2011, No. 10, pp. 10) **[11002]**, **[16595]**, **[44461]**
"Optimal Awarded US $256 Thousand Contract to Conduct LiDAR Survey for a Major Electric Utility in the Southwest" in Canadian Corporate News **[35059]**, **[43917]**, **[44462]**
"Optimism Index" in Black Enterprise (Vol. 41, September 2010, No. 2, pp. 24) **[14476]**, **[16999]**, **[23293]**, **[27562]**, **[31711]**, **[35882]**, **[45606]**
"Optimize.ca Supplies Free Online Financial Advice" in Entertainment Close-Up (October 9, 2010) **[8606]**, **[12730]**, **[15342]**, **[28809]**, **[31712]**, **[45607]**
The Option Strategist **[13137]**
"Options Abound in Winter Wares" in Pet Product News (Vol. 64, November 2010, No. 11, pp. 1) **[4128]**, **[15769]**, **[39277]**, **[40206]**, **[43122]**, **[43564]**, **[44097]**
Optometric Education **[20941]**
opTrack™ Service **[8949]**, **[13215]**
"Oracle: No Profit of Doom" in Barron's (Vol. 88, March 31, 2008, No. 13, pp. 40) **[8607]**, **[12731]**, **[23294]**, **[31713]**, **[35060]**, **[36719]**
Oracle Primavera [38797]
"Oracle and Tauri Group Honored by Homeland Security and Defense Business Council" in Wireless News (December 15, 2009) **[3581]**, **[18460]**, **[18954]**, **[33872]**, **[45173]**
Oracle Venture Fund **[49290]**
"The Oracle's Endgame; Wrigley Investment Isn't What Many Call a Classic Buffett Play" in Crain's Chicago Business (May 5, 2008) **[3290]**, **[8608]**, **[12732]**, **[39278]**, **[42098]**
Orange Business News **[48844]**
Orange Bytes **[48845]**
Orange Chamber of Commerce **[49743]**
Orange Chamber of Commerce and Visitor Bureau (OCCVB) **[48846]**
Orange City Chamber of Commerce **[51946]**
Orange County Business Council (OCBC) **[48847]**
Orange County Business Journal **[49381]**
Orange County Chamber of Commerce (OCCC) **[58971]**
Orange County Chamber of Commerce Profit Connection **[48848]**
Orange County Chamber of Commerce [48847]
Orange County Hispanic Chamber of Commerce (OCHCC) **[48849]**
Orange County SCORE **[55045]**
Orange County Small Business Development Center **[48165]**

Small Business Sourcebook • 30th Edition 3587

Pacifica MASTER INDEX

Pacific Energy Center - Energy Resource Center **[5714]**
Pacific Foundation for Marine Research [9045]
Pacific Gas and Electric Company. [5714]
Pacific Grove Chamber of Commerce (PGCC) **[48858]**
Pacific Health Research Institute (PHRI) **[34678]**
Pacific Institute for Research and Evaluation. [46109]
Pacific Institute of Gemmology [13254]
Pacific Islands Small Business Development Center Network (PISBDCN) **[59855]**
Pacific Northwest Christmas Tree Association Buy-Sell Directory **[4051]**
Pacific Northwest Partners L.P. **[59334]**
Pacific Palisades Chamber of Commerce **[48859]**
Pacific Relocation Consultants [24789]
Pacific Research Institute (PRI) **[34679]**
Pacific Research Institute for Public Policy [34679]
Pacific Research Institute for Public Policy - Pacific Institute [34679]
Pacific Resource Development Group Inc. **[26710]**
Pacific Salmon Commission (PSC) **[9010]**
Pacific Salmon Commission Annual Report **[9011]**
Pacifica Chamber of Commerce and Visitor Center (PCC) **[48860]**
Pacifica Chamber of Commerce [48860]
Pacifica Fund **[49293]**
Paciugo Gelato **[10977]**
"Pack Mentality" in Crain's Chicago Business (Vol. 31, April 21, 2008, No. 16, pp. 31) **[24900]**, **[35888]**, **[36726]**, **[38322]**, **[46527]**
"Packaging Firm Wraps Up Remake; Overseas Plants Help Firm Fatten Margins" in Crain's New York Business (January 7, 2008) **[8612]**, **[12740]**, **[31719]**, **[39283]**
Packaging and Shipping Specialists **[4610]**
The Packer: The Business Newspaper of the Produce Industry **[10004]**
"Packers Still Want Marketing Deal With Favre" in The Business Journal-Milwaukee (Vol. 25, August 15, 2008, No. 47, pp. A1) **[19337]**, **[19448]**, **[40217]**
"Packing Chic" in Black Enterprise (Vol. 38, February 2008, No. 7, pp. 154) **[13629]**, **[24901]**, **[47349]**
PacRim Venture Partners **[49294]**
Paddlesports Industry Association [19310]
Padgett Business Services **[246]**, **[3115]**, **[19724]**
Padgett Business Services (Oakville, Canada) **[3116]**, **[35646]**
Padows's Hams & Deli **[9189]**
Paducah Area Chamber of Commerce **[52372]**
Page County Chamber of Commerce [58956]
Page-Lake Powell Chamber of Commerce (PLPCC) **[47937]**
"Pagetender LLC Releases Website Design Package for HubSpot Users" in Internet Wire (September 30, 2009) **[11821]**, **[21178]**, **[28812]**, **[40218]**
"Paging Dr. Phil" in Canadian Business (Vol. 79, September 25, 2006, No. 19, pp. 21) **[3584]**, **[18957]**, **[23974]**, **[30963]**, **[35071]**
Pagosa Springs Area Chamber of Commerce (PSACC) **[49576]**
PAHO News **[34162]**
Pahokee Chamber of Commerce **[50261]**
Pahrump Nevada Small Business Development Center **[54463]**
Pahrump Valley Chamber of Commerce **[54512]**
"Paid to Persuade: Careers in Sales" in Occupational Outlook Quarterly (Vol. 55, Summer 2011, No. 2, pp. 24) **[3353]**, **[35889]**, **[43566]**
Paier College of Art, Inc. Library **[4576]**
"Pain Ahead as Profit Pressure Increases" in Crain's Chicago Business (Vol. 31, May 5, 2008, No. 18, pp. 4) **[5461]**, **[8613]**, **[12741]**, **[14939]**, **[17003]**, **[17422]**, **[27579]**, **[31720]**, **[33301]**, **[39284]**, **[46320]**
Pain Research and Management **[34163]**
Painesville Area Chamber of Commerce **[56263]**
Paint and Wallpaper Association of America [11535], [15387]
Paint & Decorating Retailer Magazine **[15380]**, **[18803]**
Paint and Decorating Retailers Association (PDRA) **[11535]**, **[15387]**
The Painted Penguin, LLC **[6068]**
Painting **[6021]**
Painting and Wallcovering Contractor--PDCA Yearbook Issue [15395]
Painting and Decorating Contractors of America (PDCA) **[11536]**, **[15388]**
The Painting Pros **[15406]**
Painting and Wallcovering Contractor--PDCA Roster **[15395]**
Paints and Coatings **[15378]**
Paintsville Small Business Development Center **[52231]**
PaintWorks **[6022]**
Pajaro Valley Chamber of Commerce **[48861]**
Pak Mail **[4611]**, **[7870]**, **[11958]**
Pak Mail Centres Ltd. (Toronto, Canada) **[4612]**
"Palace Adds Marketing Arm; College Sponsorships First Step In New Effort" in Crain's Detroit Business (October 1, 2007) **[19449]**, **[28300]**
Palacios Chamber of Commerce (PCC) **[58374]**
Paladin Consultants L.L.C. **[41511]**
Paladin Partners **[59335]**
Palatine Area Chamber of Commerce (PACC) **[51275]**
Palestine Area Chamber of Commerce **[58375]**
Palestine Chamber of Commerce (PCC) **[51276]**
The Paley Center for Media - Research Services **[16771]**
Palisade Chamber of Commerce (PCC) **[49577]**
Palm Bay Chamber [50214]
Palm Beach Chamber of Commerce **[50262]**
Palm Beach County Resource Center, Inc. **[50346]**
Palm Beach Mega Tan **[19579]**
Palm City Chamber of Commerce **[50263]**
Palm Desert Chamber of Commerce **[48862]**
Palm Springs Chamber of Commerce (PSCC) **[48863]**
Palm Tree Computer Systems **[5023]**
Palmdale Chamber of Commerce **[48864]**
John C. Palmer Associates Inc. **[14240]**
Palmerton Area Chamber of Commerce **[57193]**
Palmetto Business Group Inc. (PBG) **[36058]**
Palmetto Poultry Life **[1028]**
The Palms Tanning Resort **[19580]**
Palms West Chamber of Commerce (PWCC) **[50264]**
Palo Alto Chamber of Commerce (PACC) **[48865]**
Palo Alto Venture Partners / 21VC Oartners **[49295]**
Palomar Ventures **[49296]**
Palomino Horse Breeders of America Library **[10633]**
Palos Hills Chamber of Commerce **[51277]**
Palos Verdes Peninsula Chamber of Commerce **[48866]**
Palouse Chamber of Commerce **[59256]**
Pampa Chamber of Commerce [58200]
The Pampered Chef **[10408]**, **[23307]**, **[30061]**, **[47350]**; **[5841]**, **[17965]**
Pana Chamber of Commerce **[51278]**
Panago Pizza Inc. **[16167]**
Panama City/Bay County Chamber of Commerce [49949]
Panchero's Mexican Grill **[18203]**
Panda Franchises Ltd. **[43303]**
"Panda Security for Business 4.05" in SC Magazine (Vol. 21, July 2010, No. 7, pp. 50) **[3585]**, **[4871]**, **[4980]**, **[18462]**, **[18958]**, **[41425]**, **[45176]**
"P&G to Mine E-Commerce Potential" in Business Courier (Vol. 26, September 18, 2009, No. 21, pp. 1) **[2050]**, **[21179]**, **[28813]**, **[43567]**
"P&G vs. IRS: Split Decision" in Business Courier (Vol. 27, July 16, 2010, No. 11, pp. 1) **[23975]**, **[42840]**, **[43920]**, **[46321]**
"P&G's Iams Finds Itself in a Pet-Food Dogfight" in Advertising Age (Vol. 78, March 5, 2007, No. 10, pp. 6) **[9962]**, **[12742]**, **[15771]**, **[23308]**, **[25608]**, **[40219]**, **[41181]**
"P&L Building Owner Nears Start of $157M Condo Plan" in Business Journal-Serving Metropolitan Kansas City (November 23, 2007) **[1283]**, **[5462]**, **[46322]**
"Panel to Call for Reduced Restraints on Telecom Sector" in Globe & Mail (March 17, 2006, pp. B1) **[33880]**, **[35072]**, **[44467]**
"Panel Calls for 'Fundamental' Change to Telecom Regulation" in Globe & Mail (March 23, 2006, pp. B1) **[33881]**, **[35073]**, **[44468]**
"A Panel Study of Copreneurs In Business" in Family Business Review (Vol. 19, September 2006, No. 3, pp. 193) **[30062]**, **[31102]**
Panel World **[5604]**, **[13674]**
Panel World--Directory and Buyers' Guide Issue **[13663]**
Panfish Patterns **[1717]**
Panhandle Area Council - Business Center for Innovation and Development **[50818]**
Panhandle SCORE **[54238]**
The Panhandler **[9630]**, **[10442]**
Panic! The Story of Modern Financial Insanity **[12743]**, **[27580]**, **[31721]**
The Panigas Group of Companies **[5664]**
Pannell Kerr Forster Library **[20217]**
Panola County Chamber of Commerce (PCCC) **[58376]**
The Pantry Restaurants **[18204]**
Panzerotto Pizza Ltd. **[16168]**
Paola Chamber of Commerce **[52176]**
Paola's Business **[52177]**
Paoli Chamber of Commerce **[51699]**
Paonia Chamber of Commerce (PCC) **[49578]**
Papa and Associates Inc. **[2948]**, **[13873]**, **[26075]**, **[36059]**, **[38791]**
Papa Gino's Pizzeria **[16169]**
Papa John's International, Inc. **[16170]**
Papa Murphy's Take'N'Bake Pizza **[16171]**
"Papal Permit Trumps the Plumbing Codes" in Contractor (Vol. 57, February 2010, No. 2, pp. 20) **[16255]**, **[18702]**, **[33882]**
Papa's Pizza To-Go, Inc. **[16172]**
"Paper Cache" in Playthings (Vol. 106, October 1, 2008, No. 9, pp. 9) **[6112]**, **[20262]**
"Paper a la Carte" in American Printer (Vol. 128, June 1, 2011, No. 6) **[4497]**, **[6519]**, **[16388]**, **[20788]**, **[28814]**
"Paper Choices Made Simple" in American Printer (Vol. 128, June 1, 2011, No. 6) **[4498]**, **[16389]**, **[20789]**
Paper Crafts Magazine: More Project-More Skills-More Fun **[6023]**
Paper Fortunes: Modern Wall Street: Where It's Been and Where It's Going **[8614]**, **[12744]**, **[27581]**, **[31722]**
"Paper Replaces PVC for Gift Cards" in American Printer (Vol. 128, June 1, 2011, No. 6) **[4499]**, **[16390]**, **[20790]**, **[45620]**
"The Paper Shredder" in Business Courier (Vol. 26, September 11, 2009, No. 20, pp. 1) **[3586]**, **[17004]**, **[17423]**, **[18959]**, **[30063]**, **[33883]**, **[45177]**
"Paper Tigers" in Conde Nast Portfolio (Vol. 2, June 2008, No. 6, pp. 84) **[558]**, **[15561]**, **[27582]**, **[40220]**
"Paperless Bookkeeping Program" in Fleet Owner Online (February 15, 2011) **[122]**, **[2302]**, **[3587]**, **[18960]**, **[19654]**, **[20688]**, **[21406]**, **[45178]**, **[46323]**
Papermaking & Bookbinding **[2247]**
Papillion Area Chamber of Commerce [54431]
PAR Enterprises Inc. **[22071]**
Par-T-Perfect Party Planners **[35647]**
"Paradise Lost" in Inc. (February 2008, pp. 102-109) **[30064]**, **[39285]**
Paradise Ridge Chamber of Commerce **[48867]**
Paragould Area Chamber of Commerce [48099]
Paragould Regional Chamber of Commerce **[48099]**
"Paralysis Foundation has Big Plans" in Austin Business JournalInc. (Vol. 29, December 11, 2009, No. 40, pp. 1) **[9275]**, **[33884]**, **[34396]**, **[42841]**, **[43921]**
Paramount Chamber of Commerce (PCC) **[48868]**
Paramount Home Beauty **[40847]**
"Paramount Said to be Working on Sale of Oil Sands Assets" in Globe & Mail (April 24, 2007, pp. B1) **[24506]**, **[25184]**
Parcel Plus **[14357]**
"Parent Firm's Global Reach, Stricter Air Quality Rules Have Stock Smiling" in Crain's Cleveland Business (October 15, 2007) **[11147]**, **[23309]**, **[36727]**, **[39286]**, **[42102]**
Parents Guide to Accredited Camps [3256]
Paris Area Chamber of Commerce **[48100]**
Paris Area Chamber of Commerce (PACC) **[54111]**
Paris Area Chamber of Commerce and Tourism (PACCT) **[51279]**
Paris Area Chamber of Commerce [51279]
Paris-Bourbon County Chamber of Commerce **[52373]**
Paris-Bourbon County Chamber Directory **[52374]**
Paris/Henry County Chamber of Commerce **[57766]**
Paris Small Business Development Center **[57865]**
Parisi Speed School **[28475]**
"A Parisian Vending Machine for Baguettes 24/7" in Benzinga.com () **[20867]**
Park City Chamber of Commerce **[58669]**
Park Falls Area Chamber of Commerce (PFACC) **[59686]**
Park Falls - Gateway to the Good Life **[59687]**
Park Hills - Leadington Chamber of Commerce **[54112]**
Park Rapids Lakes Area Chamber of Commerce (PRACC) **[53710]**
Parke County Chamber of Commerce **[51700]**
Parker Area Chamber of Commerce (PACC) **[47938]**
Glenn M. Parker Associates Inc. **[29270]**
Parker Chamber of Commerce (PCC) **[49579]**
Parker Consultants Inc. **[2949]**, **[13874]**, **[26076]**, **[26639]**, **[29271]**, **[38792]**, **[44952]**
Parker Country Magazine **[49580]**
Parker Country Map **[49581]**
Parker Finch Management **[16571]**
Parker, Smith & Feek, Inc. Library **[11509]**
Glenn Parker Team Building Consultant [29270]
Parking Products & Services Directory: Parking Magazine **[2008]**
Parks Chamber of Commerce [51191]
Parma Area Chamber of Commerce (PACC) **[56264]**
Parmasters Golf Training Centers **[28476]**
Parsippany Area Chamber of Commerce (PACC) **[54791]**
Parsons Chamber of Commerce **[52178]**
Parsons School of Design - Adam & Sophie Gimbel Design Library **[4178]**, **[4577]**, **[6079]**
"Part-Time Assignments" in Black Enterprise (Vol. 37, December 2006, No. 5, pp. 70) **[35436]**, **[38323]**, **[45621]**
"Part-Time Office Space" in Hawaii Business (Vol. 53, December 2007, No. 6, pp. 132) **[16541]**, **[17005]**, **[17424]**, **[44855]**, **[45622]**
Partech International **[49297]**
The Participant **[57194]**

3590 Small Business Sourcebook • 30th Edition

Pellet Fuels Institute (PFI) [30427]
Pembina Institute for Appropriate Development (PIAD) [7058], [30428]
Pendleton Business [56825]
Pendleton Chamber of Commerce (PCC) [56826]
Pendleton Chamber of Commerce Directory [56827]
Pendleton County Chamber of Commerce [59420]
Pendleton Small Business Development Center [56681]
Penfund Partners, Inc. [59933]
Peninsula Business Journal [48875]
Peninsula Chamber of Commerce [56211]
Peninsula Equity Partners [49298]
Penn Foster Career School [4796], [57347]
Penn Hills Chamber of Commerce (PHCC) [57196]
Penn State Small Business Development Center [56911]
Penn Station East Coast Subs [6487]
Pennell Venture Partners, LLC [55450]
"Penney's Buys Wal-Mart Site" in Crain's Chicago Business (Vol. 31, March 31, 2008, No. 13, pp. 13) [23313], [24761], [43125]
Pennridge Chamber of Commerce (PCC) [57197]
PennSuburban Chamber of Commerce [57198]
Pennsylvania Business and Industry Chamber of Commerce [57199]
Pennsylvania Chamber of Business and Industry [57199]
Pennsylvania College of Optometry - Gerard Cottet Library [20952]
Pennsylvania Department of Community and Economic Development, Center for Business Financing - Site Development Division (BID) [56924]
Pennsylvania Department of Community and Economic Development, Center Entrepreneurial Assistance [56925]
Pennsylvania Department of Community and Economic Development - Loans Division [56926]
Pennsylvania Department of Community and Economic Development, Office of International Business Development [56927]
Pennsylvania Department of Community and Economic Development, Pennsylvania Industrial Development Authority [56928]
Pennsylvania Department of Community and Economic Development, Technology Innovation - Ben Franklin Technology Partners [56929]
Pennsylvania Department of General Services - Bureau of Minority and Women's Business Opportunities (BMWBO) [57274]
Pennsylvania Environmental Council Library [10198], [17741]
Pennsylvania Family Institute (PFI) [9423]
Pennsylvania Horticultural Society - McLean Library [9867], [10380]
Pennsylvania Manufacturing Confectioners' Association - Bibliography of Technical Papers Collection. [3309]
Pennsylvania & Maryland Procurement Center [57307]
Pennsylvania Minority Business Development Authority [57275]
Pennsylvania Minority Business Enterprise Center [57276]
Pennsylvania Pike County Magazine [57200]
Pennsylvania Procurement Technical Assistance Center [57308]
Pennsylvania Procurement Technical Assistance Center - Economic Development Council of Northeast Pennsylvania - The Northeastern Pennsylvania Alliance (NEPA) - Enterprise Development District [57309]
Pennsylvania Procurement Technical Assistance Center - Government Agency Coordination Office - California University of Pennsylvania [57310]
Pennsylvania Procurement Technical Assistance Center - Government Agency Coordination Office (GACO) - California University of Pennsylvania [57311]
Pennsylvania Procurement Technical Assistance Center - Government Agency Coordination Office (GACO) - Slippery Rock University [57312]
Pennsylvania Procurement Technical Assistance Center - Indiana University of Pennsylvania - Government Contracting Assistance Program [57313]
Pennsylvania Procurement Technical Assistance Center - Johnstown Area Regional Industries [57314]
Pennsylvania Procurement Technical Assistance Center - North Central Pennsylvania Regional Planning & Development Commission [57315]
Pennsylvania Procurement Technical Assistance Center - Northeastern Pennsylvania Alliance [57316]
Pennsylvania Procurement Technical Assistance Center - Northern Tier Regional Planning & Development Commission [57317]
Pennsylvania Procurement Technical Assistance Center - Northwest Pennsylvania Regional Planning and Development Commission [57318]
Pennsylvania Procurement Technical Assistance Center - SEDA Council of Governments [57319]

Pennsylvania Procurement Technical Assistance Center - Small Business Development Center - Kutztown University [57320]
Pennsylvania Procurement Technical Assistance Center - Small Business Development Center - Lehigh University [57321]
Pennsylvania Procurement Technical Assistance Center - Small Business Development Center - Widener University [57322]
Pennsylvania Procurement Technical Assistance Center - Southwestern Pennsylvania Commission [57323]
Pennsylvania Procurement Technical Assistance Center - Trustees of the University of Pennsylvania State Director's Office - Pennsylvania Small Business Development Centers - The Wharton School [57324]
Pennsylvania Small Business Development Center, Lead Office [56912]
Pennsylvania Small Business Development Centers [45846]
Pennsylvania State University - Center for Research in Conflict and Negotiation (CRCN) [14180]
Pennsylvania State University at Harrisburg - Pennsylvania State Data Center (PaSDC) [11966]
Pennsylvania State University - Institute for the Study of Business Markets (ISBM) [41313]
Pennsylvania State University - Pension and Welfare Research Center [22092]
Pennsylvania State University - Risk Management Research Center (RMRC) [22092]
Pennsylvania State University - Technical Assistance Program [56930]
Penny & Associates Inc. [232], [21468], [32056]
"Penny Chapman" in Canadian Business (Vol. 79, July 17, 2006, No. 14-15, pp. 75) [10908], [30068], [38332]
"Penny Chief Shops For Shares" in Barron's (Vol. 88, July 7, 2008, No. 27, pp. 29) [8618], [12752], [21948], [30069], [31726], [38333], [43126]
Penobscot Bay Regional Chamber of Commerce (PBRCC) [52620]
Pensacola Area Chamber of Commerce [50265]
Pension & Benefits Reporter: Current Reports [22086], [25398]
Pension & Benefits Daily™ [22085]
Pension & Benefits Reporter™ [22086], [25398]
Pension Plan Guide [22024]
Pension Plan Guide--Summary [22025]
"Penske Opens Its First Smart Car Dealership In Bloomfield Hills" in Crain's Detroit Business (Vol. 24, January 21, 2008, No. 3) [14940], [23314]
Pentwater Area Chamber of Commerce [53407]
Pentwater Chamber of Commerce [53407]
Penworth Publishing [58608]
"People/Calendar" in Brandweek (Vol. 49, April 21, 2008, No. 16, pp. 30) [18562], [20400], [40224], [44856], [46682]
People in Management [3379]
"People Often Trust Eloquence More Than Honesty" in Harvard Business Review (Vol. 88, November 2010, No. 11, pp. 36) [22407], [22619], [30964], [33888]
"People and Places" in Entrepreneur (Vol. 36, February 2008, No. 2, pp. 12) [20401], [32869], [46683], [47353]
"The People Puzzle; Re-Training America's Workers" in The Economist (Vol. 390, January 3, 2009, No. 8612, pp. 32) [11416], [19162], [21949], [27589], [28302], [33303], [35438], [36214]
People Who Help: Health Careers [3380]
"The People Who Influence You the Most - Believe In You" in Women In Business (Vol. 62, September 2010, No. 3, pp. 9) [38334], [47354]
People Who Sell Things [3381]
People Who Work in Manufacturing [3382]
"People; E-Commerce, Online Games, Mobile Apps" in Advertising Age (Vol. 80, October 19, 2009, No. 35, pp. 14) [7963], [11824], [15563], [19811], [24510], [25186], [28817], [40225], [43127]
"People; E-Commerce, Online Games, Mobile Apps: This Isn't Your Mom's People" in Advertising Age (Vol. 80, October 19, 2009, No. 35) [7964], [11825], [15564], [19812], [24511], [25187], [28818], [40226], [43128]
People's Medical Society (PMS) [34165]
Peoria Area Chamber of Commerce (PACC) [51281]
Peoria Chamber of Commerce (PCC) [47940]
Peoria NEXT Innovation Center [51450]
Peoria SCORE [50869]
"Pep Talk" in Black Enterprise (Vol. 40, July 2010, No. 12, pp. 104) [29139], [38335]
Pep Talk [52744]
Pepe's Inc. [18205]
Pepe's Mexican Restaurants [18205]
"Pepsi Co. Breaches the Walls of Coke Fortress McDonald's" in Globe & Mail (March 13, 2007, pp. B1) [17967], [39289], [42108]

PepsiCo - The Information Center [15226]
Perceptive Technology Corp. (PTC) [41512], [41634]
Percussion News [14646]
Percussive Arts Society Library [14700]
"The Perfect Fit" in Small Business Opportunities (Fall 2007) [28819], [30070]
"The Perfect Formula to Build Your Brand" in Entrepreneur (Vol. 37, July 2009, No. 7, pp. 70) [26503], [40227], [41185], [44773]
The Perfect Pita [18206]
"A Perfect Predator: Brookfield Asset Management Isn't Brash" in Canadian Business (Vol. 83, July 20, 2010, No. 11-12, pp. 50) [12753], [17011], [17431]
The Perfect Scent: A Year Inside the Perfume Industry in Paris and New York [1899], [2051], [5896], [36730], [39290], [41186]
"Perfecting Customer Services" in Pet Product News (Vol. 64, November 2010, No. 11, pp. 18) [15729], [26504], [28303], [37206], [37252], [43129], [43569]
"Perfecting the Process: Creating a Move Efficient Organization On Your Terms" in Black Enterprise (Vol. 41, October 2010, No. 3) [23315], [24512], [25188], [26505], [30071], [38336]
Perfecting Your Presentation Skills [22230]
A Perfectly Normal Day [46561]
Perfecto's Caffe [1698], [6488]
Performance Consulting Associates Inc. (PCA) [2952], [13876], [24694], [26079], [29273], [38794]
Performance Consulting Group Inc. [2953], [13877], [24695], [26080], [38795], [44954]
Performance Dynamics Group L.L.C. [2954], [26081], [42731]
The Performance Group Inc. [14055]
Performance Group, Ltd. [3039]
Performance Improvement Institute [51451]
Performance Management, Leading Change, and Putting It All Together (Onsite) [37706]
Performance Management: The Road to Excellence [38634]
Performance Measurement Analysis (Onsite) [22231]
Performance Systems Corp. [2980], [26107], [42733]
Performance Technologies Inc. [29274]
Perham Area Chamber of Commerce (PACC) [53713]
Periodical and Book Association of America (PBAA) [2101], [15510]
Peritoneal Dialysis International [34580]
Perkins Chamber of Commerce [56569]
Perkins Restaurant & Bakery [18207]
Perkiomen Valley Chamber of Commerce (PVCC) [57201]
"The Perks of Going Public" in Austin Business Journal (Vol. 31, July 15, 2011, No. 19, pp. A17) [12754], [17800], [47062]
"Perks Still Popular: Jets May be Out, but CEO Benefits Abound" in Crain's Detroit Business (Vol. 25, June 22, 2009) [21950], [35892], [38337]
Perma-Glaze, Inc. Multi-Surface Restoration [16307]
Perma-Jack Co. [5693]
Perquimans County Chamber of Commerce (PCCC) [55793]
Perris Valley Chamber of Commerce [48876]
Perry Area Chamber of Commerce (PACC) [50599]
Perry Chamber of Commerce [51955]
Perry Chamber of Commerce (PCC) [56570]
Perry County Chamber of Commerce [51701]
Perry County Community Profile Magazine [51702]
Perry Historians Library [9548]
"Perry's Goes Organic" in Ice Cream Reporter (Vol. 22, December 20, 2008, No. 1, pp. 1) [10239], [10909], [21651], [31103], [41187]
Perrysburg Area Chamber of Commerce [56265]
Perryton-Ochiltree Chamber of Commerce [58384]
Perryville Chamber of Commerce [44113]
Pershing County Chamber of Commerce [54502]
Personal Achievement Institute [26640]
Personal Achievement Series—Time Management: How to Increase Your Productivity and Get the Results You Want [46562]
Personal Care Product Council [1892], [2033], [5884]
Personal Communications Industry Association [1961], [3673]
Personal Edge [43305]
"Personal File: Dean Williams" in Canadian Business (Vol. 80, April 23, 2007, No. 9, pp. 55) [30072], [32870]
"Personal File: Esther Colwill" in Canadian Business (Vol. 80, April 23, 2007, No. 9, pp. 48) [30073], [38338]
"Personal File: Laura Laing" in Canadian Business (Vol. 80, April 23, 2007, No. 9, pp. 58) [30074], [42501]
"Personal File: Malcolm Smillie" in Canadian Business (Vol. 80, April 23, 2007, No. 9, pp. 44) [30075], [38339], [40228]
Personal Mastery Programs [29276]

Pierpont Community and Technical College Small Business Development Center - Fairmont **[59372]**
Pierre Area Chamber of Commerce **[57591]**
Pierre Small Business Development Center **[57553]**
"Pierre's Ice Cream" in Ice Cream Reporter (Vol. 23, October 20, 2010, No. 11, pp. 8) **[5465]**, **[10910]**, **[39294]**
Piet Mondrian: Mr. Boogie-Woogie Man **[1414]**
Pigeon Chamber of Commerce **[53410]**
Pigeon Forge Chamber of Commerce **[57769]**
Pike County Chamber of Commerce **[51283]**; **[51705]**; **[57204]**
Pike County Chamber of Commerce (PCCC) **[56268]**
Pike County Chamber of Commerce and Economic Development District (PCCCEDD) **[53897]**
Pike County Chamber of Commerce [52385]; [53897]
Pike in the Dead Zone **[1718]**
Pikesville Chamber of Commerce **[52745]**
Pikeville - Bledsoe County Chamber of Commerce **[57770]**
Pikeville Small Business Development Center **[52232]**
Pillar to Post Inc. **[2587]**; **[2588]**
Pilot Consulting Corp. **[29257]**
Pilot Point Chamber of Commerce (PPCC) **[58386]**
Pilot Whalin Inc. [26642]
Pima College's Small Business Development Center **[47839]**
Pima Council on Aging Library **[329]**
Pinball Expo **[960]**
Pinch a Penny Inc. **[6163]**
Pinch-A-Penny [6163]
Pinckneyville Chamber of Commerce **[51284]**
Pine City Area Chamber of Commerce **[53714]**
Pine Mountain Chamber of Commerce **[50600]**
Pinedale Area Chamber of Commerce **[59846]**
"Pinellas Leaders Want First Leg of Light Rail" in The Business Journal-Serving Greater Tampa Bay (Vol. 28, August 8, 2008, No. 33) **[5466]**, **[23320]**, **[24514]**, **[24903]**, **[46325]**
Pinellas Park/Mid-County Chamber of Commerce **[50267]**
Pine-Strawberry Chamber of Commerce [47947]
Pinetop-Lakeside Chamber of Commerce [47941]
Pinetree Advisors Inc. [38643]
"Pink Label: Victoria's Sales Secret" in Advertising Age (Vol. 79, July 7, 2008, No. 26, pp. 4) **[4258]**, **[13561]**, **[40233]**, **[41188]**, **[43132]**
The Pink Sheet **[50268]**; **[6689]**
Pink Sheets **[8950]**, **[13216]**
Pink Slip Power!: Recover and Succeed It's Up To You! **[35894]**, **[38342]**
"Pinkberry" in Ice Cream Reporter (Vol. 23, October 20, 2010, No. 11, pp. 6) **[10911]**, **[41189]**
Pinole Chamber of Commerce (PCC) **[48883]**
Pinon Hills Chamber of Commerce **[48884]**
Pioche Chamber of Commerce **[54513]**
Pioneer **[48885]**
"Pioneer Bank Ready to Expand" in Austin Business JournalInc. (Vol. 28, December 19, 2008, No. 40, pp. 1) **[8620]**, **[23321]**
Pioneer Business Consultants **[24696]**, **[37548]**, **[38796]**, **[46455]**
Pioneer Hi-Bred International, Inc. - Library Resources Group **[21804]**
"A Pioneer of Paying With Plastic" in Crain's Chicago Business (Vol. 31, April 28, 2008, No. 17, pp. 39) **[23322]**, **[26288]**, **[31104]**, **[39295]**
Pioneer Technology Center **[56664]**
Pioneer Technology Center Business Incubator - Incubator **[56642]**
"Pioneer Unveils Drought-Tolerant Hybrids" in Farm Industry News (January 6, 2011) **[21653]**, **[41190]**
Pioneering Management Possibilities (PMP) **[29276]**
"Pioneering Strategies for Entrepreneurial Success" in Business Horizons (Vol. 51, January-February 2008, No. 1, pp. 21) **[22410]**, **[30083]**, **[31729]**, **[37089]**, **[41191]**, **[44473]**
"Pioneers Get All The Perks" in Canadian Business (Vol. 81, March 3, 2008, No. 3, pp. 18) **[23981]**, **[32874]**, **[34403]**, **[35078]**, **[41192]**, **[42109]**, **[44474]**, **[45626]**, **[46326]**
Pip Printing and Document Services **[5871]**, **[16441]**
"Pipe Show Finds a Way for Smokers to Light Up" in Crain's Chicago Business (Vol. 31, April 28, 2008, No. 17, pp. 57) **[20403]**, **[23982]**, **[33892]**, **[36734]**, **[46685]**
"Pipeline Dreams" in Canadian Business (Vol. 80, October 22, 2007, No. 21, pp. 19) **[5467]**, **[33893]**
Pipestone Area Chamber of Commerce (PACC) **[53715]**
Pipestone Chamber of Commerce [53715]
Piqua Area Chamber of Commerce (PACC) **[56269]**
Malcolm Pirnie Virtual Library/LSSI **[21004]**
Pirtek USA **[44619]**
Piscataquis County Chamber of Commerce **[52621]**

Pismo Beach Chamber of Commerce and Visitors' Information Center **[48886]**
Pismo Beach Chamber of Commerce [48886]
Pitch-In Canada (PIC) **[7059]**
"Pitch for SPX Expansion was Full of Energy" in Charlotte Business Journal (Vol. 25, November 19, 2010, No. 35, pp. 1) **[23323]**, **[33305]**, **[35441]**, **[39296]**
Pitney Bowes Information Center **[20968]**
Pitt Greenville Chamber of Commerce **[55714]**
Pitts - Aldrich Associates (PAA) **[36062]**
Pittsburg Area Chamber of Commerce **[52180]**
Pittsburg Chamber of Commerce **[48887]**
Pittsburgh Airport Area Chamber of Commerce (PAACC) **[57205]**
Pittsburgh Gift Show **[9587]**, **[9624]**
Pittsburgh Women's Show **[7862]**, **[46779]**
Pittsford Chamber of Commerce **[55308]**
PivotPoint Press **[51470]**
The Pixar Touch: The Making of a Company **[4501]**, **[7966]**, **[14574]**, **[30084]**
Pizza Delight **[18209]**
Pizza Depot **[16174]**
Pizza Expo **[16133]**
Pizza Factory, Inc. **[16175]**
Pizza Fusion **[16176]**
Pizza Hut Canada **[18210]**
Pizza Inn, Inc. **[16177]**
Pizza Nova Take Out Ltd. **[16178]**
Pizza Patron Inc. **[16179]**
The Pizza Pipeline **[16180]**
Pizza Pit **[16181]**
Pizza Pizza **[16182]**
Pizza Ranch, Inc. **[18211]**
Pizza Schimizza **[16183]**
Pizza Today--Pizza Industry Buyer's Guide Issue **[16131]**
Pizzaville, Inc. **[16184]**
Pizzeria Valdiano **[16185]**
Pizzicato Gourmet Pizza **[16186]**
PJ Materials Consultants Ltd. **[5665]**
PJ's Coffee of New Orleans **[1817]**, **[9747]**
PKF Consulting [17599]
PKF Consulting Corp. **[17599]**
PKF Consulting Library **[10834]**
"A Place to Call Home" in Business Courier (Vol. 24, March 7, 2008, No. 48, pp. 1) **[16542]**, **[17014]**, **[17435]**, **[45981]**
"Place Restrictions on Your Stock Shares" in Business Owner (Vol. 35, July-August 2011, No. 4, pp. 14) **[125]**, **[8621]**, **[12761]**, **[21409]**, **[31730]**
The Place: Southern California's Visitors Guide **[1937]**
"A Place in the Sun" in Canadian Business (Vol. 81, July 22, 2008, No. 12-13, pp. 56) **[8622]**, **[12762]**, **[14479]**, **[17015]**, **[17436]**, **[27592]**, **[31731]**, **[36735]**
Placentia Business Link **[48888]**
Placentia Chamber of Commerce **[48889]**
"Placer Land Sells for $12 Million" in Sacramento Business Journal (Vol. 25, July 25, 2008, No. 21, pp. 1) **[5468]**, **[17016]**, **[17437]**, **[26289]**, **[37458]**
Plainfield Area Chamber of Commerce (PACC) **[51285]**
Plainfield Chamber of Commerce **[51706]**
Plainfield-Central Jersey Chamber of Commerce [52128]
Plains-Paradise Chamber of Commerce (PPCC) **[54301]**
Plainview Chamber of Commerce **[54423]**
Plainview Chamber of Commerce (PCC) **[58387]**
Plainview Convention and Visitors Bureau [58387]
Plainwell Chamber of Commerce (PCC) **[53411]**
Plan of Action **[58388]**
Plan Ahead Events **[15441]**
"Plan B Saloon Opened New Year's Eve" in Bellingham Business Journal (Vol. February 2010, pp. 7) **[1859]**, **[17970]**
"Plan: Put Health Centers in ERs" in Crain's Detroit Business (Vol. 25, June 22, 2009, No. 25, pp. 1) **[32875]**, **[34404]**
Plan Sponsor: Insight on Plan Design & Investment Strategy **[8873]**
"Plan Targets Small Banks" in Business Journal Portland (Vol. 26, December 11, 2009, No. 40, pp. 1) **[31732]**, **[33306]**
"Plan Your Future with My Next Move" in Occupational Outlook Quarterly (Vol. 55, Summer 2011, No. 2, pp. 22) **[3355]**, **[28820]**, **[35442]**, **[35895]**
"Plan Your Next Event at Newport News Marriott at City Center" in Benzinga.com (July 29, 2011) **[2515]**, **[2789]**, **[10734]**, **[20404]**, **[46686]**
"Plan Your Wedding with Cleveland Airport Marriott's Certified Event Planners" in Benzinga.com (February 2, 2011) **[2516]**, **[10735]**, **[15436]**
Planet Beach Franchising Corporation **[19581]**
Planet Clean **[43306]**
Planet Google: One Company's Audacious Plan to Organize Everything We Know **[11828]**, **[24515]**, **[28821]**

PLANET News **[16201]**
Planet Smoothie **[10978]**
Planetary Association for Clean Energy (PACE) **[30429]**
Plank Road Chamber of Commerce **[55309]**
Planners Guide **[55310]**
"Planning Ahead" in Crain's Cleveland Business (Vol. 30, June 15, 2009, No. 23, pp. 12) **[27593]**, **[45982]**
"Planning Ahead: Steven Taylor Mulls a Second Career After Retirement" in Black Enterprise (Vol. 37, November 2006, No. 4, pp. 82) **[8623]**, **[12763]**, **[31733]**
Planning and Developing New Products (Onsite) **[39599]**
Planning a Project and Building Your Project Team **[29220]**
Planning and Visual Education Partnership (PAVE) **[41533]**, **[42932]**
"Planning a Wedding Fit for a Royal? Read This First, Urge Legal and General" in Benzinga.com (April 21, 2011) **[2517]**, **[11417]**, **[36215]**
Planning a Wedding to Remember **[2536]**
Planning Your Future: Resources on Careers and Higher Education **[28305]**
"Planning Your Next Move in Ad Land" in Advertising Age (Vol. 81, January 4, 2009, No. 1, pp. 1) **[560]**, **[11829]**, **[40234]**
Planning Your Wedding, Vol. 1: Selecting Your Formal Wear **[2537]**
Planning Your Wedding, Vol. 2: A Visit to Your Caterer **[2538]**
Planning Your Wedding, Vol. 3: Selecting Your Wedding Cake **[2539]**
Planning Your Wedding, Vol. 4: Selecting Your Photographer **[2540]**
Planning Your Wedding, Vol. 5: Visiting Your Travel Agent **[2541]**
Planning Your Wedding, Vol. 6: Meeting with Your Financial Advisor **[2542]**
Planning Your Wedding, Vol. 7: Visiting with Your Jeweler **[2543]**
Planning Your Wedding, Vol. 8: Meeting with Your Minister **[2544]**
Planning Your Wedding, Vol. 9: Selecting Your Flowers **[2545]**
Planning Your Wedding, Vol. 10: Meeting with Your Bridal Consultant **[2546]**
Plano Chamber of Commerce (PCC) **[58389]**
"Plans for $160M Condo Resort in Wisconsin Dells Moves Forward" in Commercial Property News (March 18, 2008) **[5469]**, **[10736]**, **[17801]**, **[17971]**, **[20168]**, **[20565]**, **[43133]**
"Plans for Coal-Fired Electricity Could Go Up in Smoke" in Globe & Mail (March 5, 2007, pp. B7) **[23983]**, **[30757]**, **[44475]**
Plans and Solutions Inc. **[23657]**, **[24697]**, **[26082]**, **[36919]**, **[42909]**
The Plant Cell **[44062]**
Plant Maintenance and Design Engineering Show/Montreal (PMDS) **[39514]**
Plantation Annual **[50269]**
Planting Fields Arboretum - The Garden Library **[9868]**
Plantkeeper Inc. **[41635]**
Plants & Gardens News **[9818]**
Plantscape Inc. **[13511]**
Plastic Canvas Home & Holiday Magazine [6121]
Plastic Recycling Update **[17726]**
Plat Books **[56270]**
Platemakers Educational and Research Institute [16343]
The Platinum Rule for Small Business Success **[30085]**, **[32876]**
Platoon Fitness **[16038]**
Plato's Closet **[5153]**
Platte City Area Chamber of Commerce-Economic Development Council [54115]
Platte City Chamber of Commerce **[54115]**
Platte County Chamber of Commerce (PCCC) **[59837]**
Platteville Chamber of Commerce **[59693]**
Plattsburg Chamber of Commerce (PCC) **[54116]**
Plattsburgh and Clinton County Chamber of Commerce [55311]
Plattsburgh - North Country Chamber of Commerce **[55311]**
Plattsburgh State University of New York - Technical Assistance Center (TAC) **[27942]**
Plattsburgh State University of New York - Economics and Business Research Institute [27942]
Plattsmouth Chamber of Commerce (PCC) **[54424]**
Platypus Publisher **[59876]**
Play it Again Sports **[5154]**, **[19394]**
"Play By Play: These Video Products Can Add New Life to a Stagnant Website" in Black Enterprise (Vol. 41, December 2010, No. 5) **[561]**, **[3236]**, **[3785]**, **[21182]**, **[25610]**, **[28822]**, **[40235]**, **[41426]**
Play Guitar Overnight—Rock **[14650]**

Portland Metropolitan Chamber of Commerce [56831]
Portland Minority Business Development Center [56877]
Portland Public Library - Art/Audiovisual Department
[14701]
Portland VA Research Foundation, Inc. (PVARF) [34680]
"Portland Wooing Under Armour to West Coast Facility"
in Baltimore Business Journal (Vol. 27, January 29,
2010, No. 39, pp. 1) [4130], [4259], [18761], [19338],
[23331], [24762], [44714]
"Portland's Hilton For Sale" in Business Journal Portland
(Vol. 27, October 22, 2010, No. 34, pp. 1) [10737],
[17439], [25334], [44180]
Portrait [51289]
Portrait of Hendersonville [57772]
Portraitefx Franchising Corp. [15879]
Positive Assertive Management (Onsite) [37712]
Positive Impact Consulting [29277]
"Positive Social Interactions and the Human Body at
Work" in Academy of Management Review (January
2008, pp. 137) [29140], [34405], [42844]
Positive Support Review [58713]
"Positive Transformational Change" in Indoor Comfort
Marketing (Vol. 70, April 2011, No. 4, pp. 30) [852],
[7286], [7644], [30758], [38347], [40241], [45628]
Positively Anadarko [56573]
Positively New Britain [49745]
"Possible Green Light On Transit" in The Business
Journal-Milwaukee (Vol. 25, July 25, 2008, No. 44, pp.
A1) [5472], [24906], [33308]
The Post-American World [27600], [45629]
Post Card and Souvenir Distributors Association [9594],
[9888]
Post Card Distributors Association of North America
[9594], [9888]
Post Falls Chamber of Commerce (PFCC) [50791]
Winfred L. and Elizabeth C. Post Foundation - Post
Memorial Art Reference Library [1156]
"Post-Prison Center Idea Rankles OTR" in Business
Courier (Vol. 26, November 27, 2009, No. 31, pp. 1)
[28308], [33449], [44479], [45983]
Postage Stamp Mega Event Fall [4385]
Postal Bulletin: The Official Source of Updates to Postal
Service Policies and Procedures [4605]
Postal Connections of America [4613], [5872], [16442]
Postal History Society of Canada (PHSC) [4351]
Postalannex+ [4614]
Postcard History Society [4417]
The Posthorn: Journal of the Scandinavian Collectors
Club [4377]
PostNet [4615]
PostNet Canada [15287]
Pot Pourri Accent [10443]
"Potash Sale Must Be Blocked" in Canadian Business
(Vol. 83, October 12, 2010, No. 17, pp. 24) [21655],
[33898], [36740], [38348], [44181]
Poteau Chamber of Commerce [56574]
Poteau Kiamichi Technology Center - Incubator [56643]
Potential [51708]
Potomac Chamber of Commerce (PCC) [52748]
Potosi - Tennyson Area Chamber of Commerce [59699]
Potsdam Chamber of Commerce [55312]
The Potsdam Pages [55313]
Pottstown SCORE No. 594 [56936]
Potty Doctor Plumbing Service [16301]
Potty Training One, Two, Three [3992]
Poughkeepsie Area Chamber of Commerce [55186]
Poulsbo Exchange [59261]
Poultry - U.S. [3143]
POV [7893]
Poway Chamber of Commerce [48900]
Poway Telephone Directory [48901]
"Powder River Reports First Quarter Revenues Over 5
Million" in Canadian Corporate News (May 16, 2007)
[12770], [31739], [39299], [40242], [44480]
Powell Area Chamber of Commerce [56271]
Powell County Chamber of Commerce [54303]
Powell Valley Chamber of Commerce (PVCC) [59838]
Powell's Sweet Shoppe [3303]
"The Power of ABWA" in Women In Business (Vol. 62,
September 2010, No. 3, pp. 36) [28309], [38349],
[47358]
"The Power of Alumni Networks" in Harvard Business
Review (Vol. 88, October 2010, No. 10, pp. 34) [8628],
[12771]
Power Ambition Glory [30089], [38350]
The Power of Body Language [22411], [30090]
"The Power Brokers" in Crain's Chicago Business (Vol.
31, April 28, 2008, No. 17, pp. 41) [23332], [33899],
[44481]
Power Budd LLP Law Library [13242], [19763]
"The Power of Commitment: Mere Motivation Is Often
Not Enough To Achieve Your Goals" in Black
Enterprise (November 2007) [2518], [30091], [47359]

The Power of Connection [48902]
The Power of Customer Service [26605]
"The Power of Diversity: Southern California Utility
Company Tops Elite List" in Hispanic Business
(September 2007, pp. 66, 68, 70) [40906]
Power Excel: Making Better Decisions (Onsite) [28075]
The Power of Full Engagement: Managing Energy, Not
Time, is the Key to High Performance and Personal
Renewal [30092], [38351], [46529]
"The Power of Fun" in Canadian Business (Vol. 79,
November 6, 2006, No. 22, pp. 58) [1284], [17440],
[30093]
"Power In the Boardroom" in Black Enterprise (Vol. 38,
February 2008, No. 7, pp. 112) [12772], [38352],
[40798]
"The Power of Innovation" in Canadian Business (Vol.
81, March 17, 2008, No. 4, pp. 57) [12773], [27601],
[33309], [33900], [42845], [43924], [45630]
Power Interviewing: A Headhunter's Guide to Getting
Hired in the '90s [3383]
The Power of Listening: Unlocking Your Communication
Potential [22234]
The Power of Many: Values for Success in Business and
in Life [30094], [30966]
Power and Motoryacht [13951]
"The Power of Negative Thinking" in Inc. (Volume 32,
December 2010, No. 10, pp. 43) [3591], [18964],
[21183], [28824], [45182]
The Power of Nice: How to Conquer the Business World
with Kindness [565], [22412], [30095], [40243]
"Power Partnerships" in Business Courier (Vol. 27,
October 22, 2010, No. 25, pp. 1) [5473], [9402],
[12774], [23333], [27602], [40799], [42114]
"Power Play" in Harvard Business Review (Vol. 88, July-
August 2010, No. 7-8, pp. 84) [24907], [29141],
[38353], [46530]
The Power of Positive and Effective Communication
[36000]
The Power of a Positive No: How to Say No and Still Get
to Yes [22413], [30096], [38354]
The Power of Pull: How Small Moves, Smartly Made,
Can Set Big Things in Motion [24519], [30097],
[38355]
"Power Ranger" in Inc. (November 2007, pp. 131)
[3592], [18965], [30759], [41428], [45183]
Power Show Ohio [5625]
The Power of Social Innovation: How Civic
Entrepreneurs Ignite Community Networks for Good
[30098], [45631], [45984]
The Power of Social Networking: Using the Whuffie Fac-
tor to Build Your Business [15343], [23334], [28825],
[40244], [42649]
"Power Up" in Entrepreneur (Vol. 35, November 2007,
No. 11, pp. 140) [1484], [2703], [5147], [15298],
[28517], [43572]
Power Up Your Small-Medium Business: A Guide to
Enabling Network Technologies [3786], [4802], [4872],
[4985], [5037], [35079], [41429]
Power2BE Media [49409]
Powerful Communication Skills for Women (Onsite)
[22235]
"Powerlessness Corrupts" in Harvard Business Review
(Vol. 88, July-August 2010, No. 7-8, pp. 36) [29142],
[38356]
"Powers Reels in Pinger" in Business Courier (Vol. 24,
December 21, 2008, No. 36, pp. 1) [40245], [42115],
[42504]
Powhatan Chamber of Commerce [58974]
Poynette Chamber of Commerce [59700]
Poynter Center Newsletter [30998]
PPC's Guide to Choosing Retirement Plans for Small
Businesses [12775], [21953]
PPC's Guide to Compensation Planning for Small Busi-
ness [21954], [32879]
PPC's Guide to Small Business Consulting Engagements
[2790], [22414], [25884]
PPC's Guide to Small Business Consulting Engage-
ments, Vol. 2 [2791], [25885]
PPC's Guide to Small Business Consulting Engage-
ments, Vol. 3 [2792], [25886]
"PPC's Major Commitment to Biofuel Infrastructure" in
Indoor Comfort Marketing (Vol. 70, April 2011, No. 4,
pp. 6) [853], [7287], [7645], [30760], [40246], [45632]
PPC's Small Business Tax Guide [23986], [46328]
PPC's Small Business Tax Guide, Vol. 2 [23987],
[46329]
PR Newswire (PRN) [42694]
The Practical Accountant [185]
Practical Allergy Research Foundation [21009]
"A Practical Approach to Addressing Holdover Ex-
Franchisee Trademark Issues" in Franchise Law
Journal (Vol. 27, Summer 2007, No. 1) [23988],
[32216], [37090]

Practical Conjoint Analysis and Discrete Choice Modeling
(Onsite) [39600]
Practical Construction Law (Onsite) [23692]
Practical Debt Collecting for Small Companies and Trad-
ers [6322], [26292]
A Practical Guide to Controls for IT Professionals
(Onsite) [34747], [37713]
A Practical Guide to the Davis-Bacon Act (Onsite)
[23693]
Practical Marketing Research (Onsite) [39601]
Practical Multivariate Analysis (Onsite) [39602]
The Practical Real Estate Lawyer [17117]
The Practical Tax Lawyer [19695]
Practical Tech for Your Business [3593], [3787], [4986],
[18966], [35080], [41430], [45184]
Practical Welding Today [13729]
Practice Beef Quality Grading II [3149]
Practice Development Counsel [2955], [26083], [42416]
Practice Periodical on Structural Design and Construc-
tion [5606]
"Practice Problems" in Crain's Cleveland Business (Vol.
30, June 22, 2009, No. 24, pp. 9) [23989], [27603]
Practice Retail Cut Identification II [3150]
Practice Retail Cut Identification III [3151]
Practice Retail Cut Identification IV [3152]
The Practicing CPA [186]
Prague Chamber of Commerce [56575]
Prairie Agricultural Machinery Institute (PAMI) [21828]
Prairie Du Chien Area Chamber of Commerce
(PDCACC) [59701]
Prairie Grove Chamber of Commerce [48101]
Prairie View A&M Small Business Development Center
[57866]
"Praise for Tax Cuts" in Canadian Business (Vol. 80,
November 19, 2007, No. 23, pp. 16) [19519], [46330]
Cedric Prange Associates Inc. [16093]
Pratt Area Chamber of Commerce [52181]
Joanne H. Pratt Associates [35635]
Prattville Area Chamber of Commerce [47726]
Praxis Media Inc. [2956], [26084], [42417]
"Pre-Certified LEED Hotel Prototype Reduces Energy
Use, Conserves Water" in Contractor (Vol. 57, January
2010, No. 1, pp. 3) [7288], [10738], [16262], [18704],
[30761]
"Pre-Deal Trades More Common in Canada, Study
Finds" in Globe & Mail (March 23, 2007, pp. B5)
[12776], [42116]
"Pre-K Pressure" in Hawaii Business (Vol. 53, October
2007, No. 4, pp. 32) [20734], [25614], [28310],
[45633]
Pre- and Post-Natal Fitness [16009]
"'Pre-Sale' for Planned Could Mich Tower" in Crain's
Chicago Business (Vol. 31, March 24, 2008, No. 12,
pp. 14) [5474], [10739], [17018], [17441], [37459],
[43137]
Precast/Prestressed Concrete Institute (PCI) [14106]
The Precious and Fashion Jewelry Market [13282]
Precious Prints Baby Art, Inc. [15037]
"A Precious Resource: Investing In the Fate of Fresh
Water" in Black Enterprise (Vol. 38, February 2008, No.
7, pp. 44) [2415], [12777], [45634]
Precision Concrete Cutting [14126]
"Precision Crop Control with Valley Irrigation/CropMetrics
Partnership" in Farm Industry News (January 6, 2011)
[3594], [13354], [18967], [21656], [42117], [45185]
Precision Door Service [44621]
"Precision Fertilizer Spreading Shown at Agritechnica" in
Farm Industry News (November 23, 2011) [21657],
[39300], [41197]
Precision Metalforming Association (PMA) [13692]
Precision Shooting [1247]
Precision Tune Auto Care, Inc. [16682], [18660]
Precision Valley Development Corp. [58791]
Predictable Futures Inc. [47148]
Predictable Results in Unpredictable Times [30099],
[38357]
Predictably Irrational: The Hidden Forces That Shape
Our Decisions [27604], [40247], [45635]
Predictive Maintenance and Condition Monitoring
(Onsite) [24990], [28076]
Preferred Business Directory [57773]
Prejudice: A Lesson to Forget [40933]
Premier Living Guide [51957]
Premiere Guitar [14752], [14792]
PremierGarage [16308]
Prentice Hall Business Publishing (PHBP) [54890]
Prentice Hall Press [54891]
"Prepaid Cards and State Unclaimed Property Laws" in
Franchise Law Journal (Vol. 27, Summer 2007, No. 1,
pp. 23) [6206], [23990], [32217], [43138]
"Prepaid Phones Surge in Bad Economy" in Advertising
Age (Vol. 79, November 17, 2008, No. 43, pp. 6)
[3788], [25615], [25784], [26293], [35081]

Pro Bike [1968]

Pro: Business Strategies for Landscape Contractors [13420], [13494]

Pro-Cuts [10096]

"Pro Livestock Launches Most Comprehensive Virtual Sales Barn for Livestock and Breed Stock" in *Benzinga.com (October 29, 2011)* [1524], [21185], [21666], [28826], [40253]

PRO, President's Resource Organization [3040]

Pro Sound News [17649]

"Pro Teams Shift Ad Budgets; Naming Rights Deals Near $1 Billion" in *Brandweek (Vol. 49, April 21, 2008, No. 16, pp. 18)* [567], [11832], [15567], [16725], [19451], [19962], [22121], [40254]

Pro Windows Small Business Server 2003 [4650], [4724], [4988], [5038], [41432]

ProActive English [3082], [22536], [26085], [28448], [35245], [40951]

The Proactive Leader I: Develop an Effective Agenda, Build Support, and Gain Traction [24991], [37715]

"Probability Processing Chip: Lyric Semiconductor" in *Inc. (Volume 32, December 2010, No. 10, pp. 52)* [4829], [5029], [37092], [41203], [44989]

Probe International (PI) [7061]

ProbeAbilities [7062], [30431]

Problem Solving: A Process for Managers [38636]

Problem Solving and Decision Making (Onsite) [37716]

Process Management: Applying Process Mapping to Analyze and Improve Your Operation (Onsite) (Canada) [37717]

"Procter & Gamble Boosts Bet on Exclusive Brands" in *Business Courier (Vol. 27, July 9, 2010, No. 10, pp. 1)* [1662], [9965], [11150], [23340], [25618], [36743], [41204], [42121], [43139]

"Procter Gambles on Wallpaper; Putting Paint On a Roll" in *Advertising Age (Vol. 77, September 18, 2006, No. 38, pp. 4)* [10410], [10480], [11552], [15250], [15396], [40255], [41205]

"Procurement Benefits" in *Black Enterprise (Vol. 38, February 2008, No. 7, pp. 72)* [33450], [40802]

Procurement Center Representative [49855]

Procurement Technical Assistance Center - Lawrence Economic Development Corporation [56384]

Procurement Technical Assistance Center at Lincoln - Nebraska Business Development Center [54448]

Procurement Technical Assistance Center of Northern Virginia - Mason Enterprise Center [59024]

Procurement Technical Assistance Center of South Central Michigan - Enterprise Group of Jackson, Inc. [53496]

Product Costs: What's In Them [25806]

Product News [17826]

Product Safety & Liability Reporter™ [34092]

Product Safety & Liability Reporter [41284]

Product Strategy: All the Right Moves [24651], [30370]

Production Techniques and Technology [2108]

Production Technology News [13730]

Productive Publications [59955]

"Productivity Data" in *Montly Labor Review (Vol. 133, September 2010, No. 9, pp. 137)* [25381], [35898]

Productivity Press (New York, New York) [55532]

Productivity Press (University Park, Illinois) [51471]

Productivity Software [4667], [13782], [19036]

"Products and Services" in *Canadian Electronics (Vol. 23, August 2008, No. 5, pp. 46)* [5765], [35084], [39304]

Products and Services Guide [54800]

Professional Accountant [51], [2261], [19601]

Professional Alternative Inc. [46090]

Professional Association of Custom Clothiers [4079]

Professional Association of Resume Writers and Career Coaches (PARW/CC) [18308]

Professional Beauty Association [1893], [10066]

Professional Beauty Association (NMC) - Nail Manufacturers Council (NMC) [14795]

Professional Beauty Association (PBA) - National Cosmetology Association [1893], [10066]

Professional Bowlers Association of America (PBA) [2431]

Professional Builder: The Magazine of the Housing and Light Construction Industry [5607]

Professional Carpet Systems, Inc. [20843]

Professional Carwashing & Detailing [1593], [3332]

The Professional Chef: The Business of Doing Business As a Personal Chef [3455], [29391]

Professional Communication: What Message Are You Sending? (Onsite) [22236]

Professional Construction Estimators Association of America (PCEA) [5198]

Professional Convention Management Association (PCMA) [20302]

Professional Counseling Centers Inc. [2957], [26086], [34628]

Professional Currency Dealers Association (PCDA) [4352]

Professional Decorating & Coating Action--PDCA Yearbook [15395]

Professional Design Techniques with Adobe Creative Suite 4 (CS4) [45066]

Professional Engineering Inspections Inc. [2575]

Professional Freelance Writers Directory [6827]

Professional Golfers' Association of America (PGA) [9654]

Professional Grounds Management Society--Membership Directory [3259]

Professional Handlers' Association (PHA) [1015]

Professional Healthcare Associates Inc. [15115]

"Professional Help: Cross That Off Your To-Do List" in *Inc. (November 2007, pp. 89-90, 92)* [3470], [5129], [13540], [15612], [15818], [46532]

Professional House Doctors Inc. [16776]

The Professional Image [11013]

Professional Knitwear Designers Guild [4078]

Professional Landcare Network (PLANET) [13377]

Professional Lawn Care Association of America Annual Conference and Show [13503]

Professional Lawn Tennis Association of United States [20056]

Professional Medical Assistant [34507]

Professional Numismatic Guild [4353]

Professional Numismatists Guild (PNG) [4353]

Professional Paddlesports Association (PPA) [19310]

Professional Photographer: the official magazine of Professional Photographers of America [3240], [15830], [15858], [15912]

Professional Photographer [3240], [15830], [15858], [15912]

Professional Photographers of America (PPA) [15841], [15897]

Professional Photographers of America Inc. [15841], [15897]

Professional Photographers of Ohio Annual Convention [15872]

Professional Picture Framers Association (PPFA) [16322]

Professional Polish, Inc [13442]

Professional Psychological Services (PPS) [28449], [40952]

Professional Publishing Report [2192]

Professional Purchasing [42720]

Professional Putters Association (PPA) [14359]

Professional Racing Organization of America [1969]

Professional Report [17118]; [17567]

Professional Roofing [18328]

Professional School Photographers of America [3231], [15825]

Professional School Photographers Association International (PSPA) [15898]

Professional School Photographers of America [15898]

Professional Services Directory of the American Translators Association [20475]

Professional Services Marketing: How the Best Firms Build Premier Brands [25887], [40256], [44485]

Professional Skaters Association (PSA) [18807]

Professional Skaters Guild of America [18807]

Professional Ski Instructors of America (PSIA) [18824]

Professional Society for Sales and Marketing Training (SMT) [43348]

Professional Stained Glass [6134]

Professional Surveyor [19533]

Professional Surveyors Canada [19502]

Professional and Technical Consultants Association (PATCA) [13762]

Professional and Technical Consultants Association--Directory of Consultants [13774]

Professional Tennis Registry (PTR) [20054]

Professional Tennis Registry - U.S.A. - United States Professional Tennis Registry [20054]

Professional Tool & Equipment News: The Independent Tool Authority [18620]

Professional Truck Driver Institute (PTDI) [20665]

Professional Truck Driver Institute of America [20665]

Professional Turf and Landscape Conference [13349], [13374]

Professional Women in Construction (PWC) [5199]

Professional Women Photographers (PWP) [15842]

Professionals for NonProfits Inc. [233]

Professionels en Produits Promotionnels du Canada [39567]

"Profico Takes Itself Off the Market" in *Globe & Mail (March 14, 2006, pp. B1)* [8632], [12784], [24521], [42122]

"Profile" in *Business Strategy Review (Vol. 21, Summer 2010, No. 2, pp. 86)* [30104], [38361]

Profile [50601]; [54427]

Profile Booklet [59262]

"Profile: Lynda Gratton" in *Business Strategy Review (Vol. 21, Autumn 2010, No. 3, pp. 74)* [37093], [38363]; [47361]; [38362]

Profiles in Human Resources [35814]

Profiles in PDM [26806]

Profiles: The HR Executive's Purchasing Resource [35814]

Profiles: The HR Executive's Purchasing Resource Guide [35814]

Profit Associates Inc. [19049], [29278]

Profit Planning Consultants [31145]

"Profit Predictions Look Too Plump" in *Barron's (Vol. 88, March 31, 2008, No. 13, pp. 37)* [8633], [12785], [23341], [27608], [31742], [32887], [45639]

"Profit Strong Rona to Maintain Acquisition Strategy" in *Globe & Mail (February 22, 2007, pp. B14)* [10138], [23342], [25191], [43140]

Profit-Tell International, Inc. [3117]

"The Profitability of Mobility" in *Entrepreneur (Vol. 37, September 2009, No. 9, pp. 98)* [23343], [32218], [35445], [38364]

Profiting from Diversity: The Business Advantages and the Obstacles to Achieving Diversity [40907], [45640]

Profits Aren't Everything. They're the Only Thing: No-Nonsense Rules from the Ultimate Contrarian and Small Business Guru [23344], [27609], [31743]

Profits for Non-Profits: Running a Successful Gift Shop [9279], [9601]

ProFleet Care Franchising [3118]

Proforma [15288]

Proforma Inc. [15288]

Program of Action [51709]

"Program for Women Entrepreneurs: Tips for Surviving this Economy" in *Crain's Detroit Business (Vol. 25, June 22, 2009, No. 25)* [27610], [30105], [47362]

Program of Work [53718]; [55797]

Programming Boot Camp (Onsite) [28078]

C Programming: Hands-On (Onsite) [28079], [45067]

Programming Microsoft Access 2003: Hands-On - Building Database Applications with Access and VBA (Onsite) [28080]

"Programs Provide Education and Training" in *Contractor (Vol. 56, September 2009, No. 9, pp. 56)* [854], [3596], [7289], [18969], [28313], [45187]

Progress [50272]; [50602]; [53719]; [57207]; [57592]; [58398]; [58399]; [58400]; [58671]; [59839]

The Progress [48903]; [48904]; [54304]

Progress Business Journal [58672]

Progress Corporate Park [35248]

Progress-Driven Entrepreneurs, Private Equity Finance and Regulatory Issues [30106], [31744]

Progress in Tourism and Hospitality Research [20604]

Progress in Photovoltaics: Research and Applications [44063]

Progress Report [53414]

Progress Report and Program of Work [57519]

Progress Times [58401]

Progressing Together [56272]

Progressions [50273]

Progressive Grocer: The Industry's Source for News Analysis and Marketing Tactics [10005]

Progressive Grocer's Directory of Convenience Stores [5816]

Progressive Grocer's Marketing Guidebook: The Comprehensive Source for Grocery, Drug and Mass Merchant Insights [3291], [5811], [9966]

Progressive Grocer's Marketing Guidebook [3291], [5811], [9966]

Progressive Grocer/Supermarket Business Marketing Guidebook [3291], [5811], [9966]

"The Progressive Pet Shop: Showcasing Strays" in *Animals' Agenda (March-April 1993, pp. 34)* [15778], [45988]

Progressive Purchasing [42721]

Progressive Sales [18061]

Project Change Management (Onsite) [37718]

Project Cost Management: Estimating, Budgeting and Earned Value Analysis (Onsite) [21339]

"Project Could Forge Path to Jobs, Growth" in *Business Courier (Vol. 26, September 11, 2009, No. 20, pp. 1)* [5476], [23345], [27611], [35446], [35899]

Project Initiation and Planning (Onsite) [24992]

Project Leadership: Building High-Performance Teams (Onsite) [28999], [37719]

Project Management for Administrative Professionals (Onsite) [37720]

Project Management for Auditors (Onsite) [37721]

Project Management Institute (PMI) [46483]

Project Management: Skills for Success (Onsite) [24204], [37722]

Project Management for Small Business Made Easy [32888], [38365]

Project Management for Software Development - Planning and Managing Successful Projects (Onsite) [37723], [45068]

Project Management for Streaming DVD, and Multimedia [37724]

Project Management: The Human and Technical View (Onsite) [37725]
Project Management for Web Development (Onsite) [37726]
Project Management Workshop (Onsite) [37727]
"Project Managers' Creed: Learn It, Live It" in Contractor (Vol. 56, November 2009, No. 11, pp. 46) [38366], [47475]
The Project Performance Management Workshop: Time, Cost and Budget (Onsite) [37728]
The Project Planning Workshop (Canada) [28081]
Project Quality Management for Project Managers - Delivering Consistent Quality (Onsite) [24205], [24993]
Project Report [21500]
Project Scheduling and Budgeting - Achieving Cost-Effective and Timely Delivery (Onsite) [22098], [24994]
Project Scope and Requirements Management (Onsite) [37729]
Projecting a Positive Professional Image [29000]
Projects in Metal [6018]
"Prominent Hispanic Businessman Signs with Choice Hotels" in Hispanic Business (March 2008, pp. 36) [5477], [10740], [40803]
"Prominent Hispanic Businessman Signs With Choice Hotels" in Hispanic Business (Vol. 30, March 2008, No. 3, pp. 36) [5478], [10741], [40804], [42123]
Promising Practices: Progress Toward the Goals (1998): Lessons from the States [972]
PROMO: Ideas. Connections. Brands [654], [40559]
"Promote Your Business Through New Media" in Business Week (November 5, 2009) [11833], [28827], [40257], [42505]
The Promoter [51958]
"Promoting Academic Programs Using Online Videos" in Business Communication Quarterly (December 2007, pp. 478) [7969], [28314], [28828]
Promoting Perquimans [55798]
Promoting Preservation and Progress [52375]
Promotion Marketing Association--Outlook [40560]
Promotion: Polishing the Apple [660], [42685]
Promotional Products Association International (PPAI) [42586]
Promotional Products Association of Canada [39567]
Promotional Products Business [655]
Promotional Products Professionals of Canada (PPPC) [39567]
"Promotions Create a Path to Better Profit" in Pet Product News (Vol. 64, December 2010, No. 12, pp. 1) [568], [15731], [28829], [40258], [43141], [43575]
promoVantage [39568]
promoXpert [39569]
PROMT® - Predicast's Overview of Markets and Technology [3051]
Proof [40561], [55510]
Proof Collectors Corner [4378]
"Proof That Good Entrepreneurs Can Make Bad Investors" in Inc. (October 2007, pp. 77-78) [12786], [30107], [31745]
Proofs: The Magazine of Dental Sales and Marketing [14234]
"A Proper Welcome" in Canadian Business (Vol. 79, July 17, 2006, No. 14-15, pp. 67) [22622], [29144], [35447]
Property Administration Association [16503]
Property Casualty Insurers Association of America (PCI) [11299]
Property Casualty Insurers Association of America Library [11510]
Property Condition Assessments Featuring E2018 Standard Guide (Onsite) [23694]
Property Damage Appraisers, Inc. [1228]
Property Management Association (PMA) [16504]
Property Management Association--Directory [16544]
Property Management Association of America [16504]
"A Property Rights Analysis of Newly Private Firms" in Business Ethics Quarterly (Vol. 21, July 2011, No. 3, pp. 445) [17787], [30968]
Property Taking Through Eminent Domain: What You Need to Know (Onsite) [23695]
PropertyGuys.com Inc. [17142]
Prophetstown-Lyndon Area Chamber of Commerce [51291]
"Proposal for a Macomb County Visitors Bureau Draws Mixed Reaction" in Crain's Detroit Business (Vol. 24, March 31, 2008, No. 13) [20409], [46691]
"Proposal Ruffles Builders" in Austin Business JournalInc. (Vol. 29, November 20, 2009, No. 37, pp. 1) [855], [5479], [16263], [17023], [17447], [19109], [33905]
"Proposed Accounting Changes Could Complicate Tenant's Leases" in Baltimore Business Journal (Vol. 28, July 2, 2010, No. 8, pp. 1) [127], [2304], [17024], [17803], [19657], [21410], [37462]
"Proposed Law Would Stop REIS Bid for Annexation by Livonia" in Crain's Detroit Business (Vol. 24, March 10, 2008, No. 10, pp. 2) [17025], [17448], [33451], [33906], [42124]

"Proposed Transit Legislation" in Crain's Detroit Business (Vol. 24, October 6, 2008, No. 40, pp. 19) [24909], [33907], [46333]
"Proposed Triangle Redo in Motion" in Crain's Cleveland Business (Vol. 28, October 15, 2007, No. 41, pp. 1) [17026], [17449], [17972], [42125], [43142]
ProQuest Accounting & Tax™ [252], [19731]
Proquest Investments [54857]
"Prosecutors Dish Sordid AIPC Story" in The Business Journal-Serving Metropolitan Kansas City (Vol. 27, September 19, 2008, No. 1) [128], [2305], [21411], [21667], [23994], [24806]
Proshop Retail [9684]
Prosource Wholesale Floorcoverings [9085], [47184]
Prospect Chamber of Commerce [52376]
Prospect Chamber News [52377]
Prospect Street Ventures / Prospect Capital Corporation [55452]
Prospect Venture Partners / Prospect Management LLC [49301]
Prospecting Strategies to Build a Qualified Pipeline (Onsite) [43356]
Prospection [2589]
Prospector [57208]
Prosper Area Chamber of Commerce [58402]
Prosser Chamber of Commerce [59263]
Protape, Inc. Library [280], [11511], [17157], [19765]
Protect Painters [15407]
"Protect Your Assets" in Black Enterprise (Vol. 38, January 2008, No. 6, pp. 38) [16545], [17450], [17804], [36084], [46047]
"Protect Your Trade Secrets" in Business Owner (Vol. 35, July-August 2011, No. 4, pp. 11) [30108], [37253]
Protecting Animals [1079]
"Protecting Company Secrets" in Inc. (February 2008, pp. 38-39) [35448], [35900], [37254]
"Protection, Flexibility Make Single-Member LLCs Attractive" in Crain's Cleveland Business (Vol. 28, November 12, 2007, No. 45) [23995], [33908], [45641]
"Protection One Introduces Home and Business Security iPhone App" in Wireless News (November 13, 2009) [3597], [18465], [18970], [41206], [45188]
Protingent Staffing [20046]
Protocol, LLC. [20879]
"Proud Out Loud" in Canadian Business (Vol. 80, April 23, 2007, No. 9, pp. 52) [29145], [45989]
"Proven Success Pays Off" in Small Business Opportunities (January 2011) [9689], [17852], [32102]
Provide Addict Care Today [46065]
Providence Business News [57397]
Providence Equity Partners, Inc. /Providence Ventures [57393]
Providence Journal Bulletin [57398]
Provider [15078]
Provider: For Long Term Care Professionals [34584]
Provider--LTC Buyers' Guide Issue [15078]
"Providers Ride First Wave of eHealth Dollars" in Boston Business Journal (Vol. 31, June 10, 2011, No. 20, pp. 1) [3598], [14344], [18971], [28830], [33311], [34409], [45189]
"Providing Expertise Required to Develop Microsystems" in Canadian Electronics (Vol. 23, February 2008, No. 1, pp. 6) [3790], [5766], [14942], [35085], [37094], [39305], [41207], [42846], [43926]
"Provinces Tackle E-Waste Problem" in Canadian Electronics (Vol. 23, June-July 2008, No. 4, pp. 1) [5767], [7646], [25888], [33613], [33909], [45642]
Provincetown Chamber of Commerce [52952]
Provo-Orem Chamber of Commerce [58682]
"Prudential Courts Hispanics" in Hispanic Business (March 2008, pp. 38, 40) [35449], [35901], [40805]
Prunedale Chamber of Commerce [48820]
"PRWT Service Acquires Pharmaceutical Plant: Firm Wins Multimillion-Dollar Contract with Merck" in Black Enterprise (March 2008) [12788], [23346], [39306], [40806], [42126]
Pryor Area Chamber of Commerce (PACC) [56576]
PSA Journal [15859], [15913]
PSA/FIM Fixed Income [8904], [13176], [14525]
"PSC Approves $130M TECO Solar Project" in Tampa Bay Business Journal (Vol. 30, December 18, 2009, No. 52, pp. 1) [7290], [7647], [19110], [30764], [33910]
PSI Research [56902]
PSI Research Inc./Hellgate Press [56902]
"Pssst! Buzz About Target" in Barron's (Vol. 89, July 27, 2009, No. 30, pp. 15) [4261], [40259], [43143], [43576]
"Psst..Spread the Word" in Boston Business Journal (Vol. 27, November 23, 2007, No. 43, pp. 1) [569], [40260], [42650], [43577], [45643]
"PSU Launches $90 Million Project" in The Business Journal-Portland (Vol. 25, July 18, 2008, No. 19, pp. 1) [5480], [17451], [27612], [28315], [47066]

Psychoanalytic Dialogues [1175]
Psychoanalytic Social Work [34585]
The Psychology of Entrepreneurship [30109]
PT Magazine [16086], [34586]
PT in Motion [16086], [34586]
PTS PROMT™ [3051]
PubCom/i-Imagery Design [6545]
PubEasy [54892]
Public Accounting Report [187]
Public Administration Abstracts [42406]
Public Administration Review [42407]
Public Affairs Report [42408]
"Public Bathroom Pressure Woes Resolved" in Contractor (Vol. 56, September 2009, No. 9, pp. 44) [5481], [16264], [18705]
Public Broadcasting Management Association [19893]
Public Budgeting and Finance [22139]
Public Citizen - Health Research Group [34681]
"Public Health Care Funding and the Montana Economy" in Montana Business Quarterly (Vol. 49, Spring 2011, No. 1, pp. 23) [11420], [33312], [34410], [36218]
Public Health Institute (PHI) [14307]
Public Human Services Directory [34411]
Public Management [42409]
Public Media Business Association (PMBA) [19893]
"Public Media Works to Launch DVD Kiosk Operations in Toronto, Canada" in Internet Wire (November 15, 2010) [951], [13330], [20892], [23347], [26781], [36744], [42127]
"Public Opinion" in Entrepreneur (Vol. 36, April 2008, No. 4, pp. 28) [8634], [12789], [23348], [31746], [38367], [42128], [47363]
Public Personnel Management [19188]
Public Policy Communications [2958], [26087], [42418]
Public/Private Ventures (P/PV) [42433]
Public Relations Journal--Register Issue [16596], [42506]
Public Relations Register [16596], [42506]
Public Relations Review: A Global Journal of Research and Comment [16608]
Public Relations Society of America (PRSA) [16579], [42446]
Public Relations Student Society of America (PRSSA) [16580]
Public Relations Tactics [16609]
Public Relations Tactics--Member Services Directory--The Blue Book: The PRSA Membership Networking Issue [16596], [42506]
Public Risk Management Association (PRIMA) [35657]
Public Safety and Emergency Preparedness [38867]
Public Sector Consultants Inc. (PSC) [2959], [26088], [42419]
Public Securities Association [11977]
Public Telecommunications Financial Management Association [19893]
Public Welfare Directory [34411]
The Publicity Hound [16610], [40562], [42680]
The Publisher [15512]
Publishers and Distributors of the United States [2155], [18972]
Publishers' Catalogues [2153]
Publishers Directory [2154], [2385], [6828]
Publishers, Distributors, and Wholesalers of the United States [2155], [18972]
Publishers Information Bureau (PIB) [15513]
Publishers Marketing Association [2096]
Publishers of the United States [2155], [18972]
Publishers Weekly--Calendar Roundup Issue [9602]
Publishers Weekly: The International voice for Book Publishing and Bookselling [2193], [2400], [13610]
Publishing & Production Executive [2194], [15021], [15591]
Publishing Executive: Creative, Production and Work Flow at Digital Speed [2194], [15021], [15591]
The Publishing Game: Publish a Book in 30 Days [2156], [6521]
Publishing Poynters [2195]
Publishing Services Inc. [56902]
Publishing Technology [2194], [15021], [15591]
"Publishing Technology Introduces IngentaConnect Mobile" in Information Today (Vol. 26, February 2009, No. 2, pp. 33) [2157], [3599], [3791], [15568], [18973], [45190]
Puckmasters International [19495]
Pueblo Business and Technology Center [49628]
Pueblo Chamber of Commerce [49522]
Pueblo Small Business Development Center [49425]
Puerto Rico Business Review [36905]
Puerto Rico Chamber of Commerce (PRCC) [59863]
Puerto Rico House Standing Committee on Industry and Commerce [59868]
Puerto Rico Minority Business Enterprise Center [59865]
Puerto Rico Procurement Technical Assistance Center - Commonwealth of Puerto Rico [59867]

Puff Pastry Dough [1791]
Pulaski Area Chamber of Commerce [59705]
Pulaski County Chamber of Commerce (PCCC) [58976]
Pulaski - Eastern Shore Chamber of Commerce [55314]
Pullman Chamber of Commerce (PCC) [59264]
Pullman Small Business Development Center [59062]
"Pulp Friction: Spin Off Mills to Boost Wood Products" in
    Globe & Mail (February 18, 2006, pp. B3) [5482],
    [13664], [39307], [42129]
"Pulque with Flavor" in Canadian Business (Vol. , pp.)
    [2416], [11151], [36745]
Pulse [47944]; [54428]
The Pulse [17695]; [50274]; [53720]
Pulse Newsletter [21753]
PulseBeat [48905]
"Pulte May Be Bouncing Back From Stock-Price
    Doldrums" in Crain's Detroit Business (Vol. 23, October
    8, 2007, No. 41, pp. 4) [5483], [12790], [17027],
    [17452]
Pump It Up - The Inflatable Party Zone [4032]
Pump Repair & Maintenance (Onsite) [24995], [28082]
"Pump Up the Profits" in Small Business Opportunities
    (Summer 2010) [15934], [32103]
"Pump Up the Profits: Teaching Small Biz How to Handle
    Fuel and Reduce Costs!" in Small Business Opportuni-
    ties (March 2008) [18577], [20647], [32104]
"Pumping in Africa" in Canadian Business (Vol. 79,
    October 23, 2006, No. 21, pp. 162) [23349], [40261]
Pumping Iron After Fifty [16010]
Pumps and Pump Systems [2613]
Pumps & Pump Systems (Onsite) [28083]
Pumps & Pump Systems: Specification, Installation &
    Operation (Onsite) [24996], [28084]
Pundmann & Company Inc. [25362]
"Punta Gorda Interested in Wi-Fi Internet" in Charlotte
    Observer (February 1, 2007) [11834], [28831], [35086]
Purcell Chamber of Commerce [56532]
Purchase Directory [56273]
Purchase and Sale of Commercial Real Estate [17575]
Purchasing b2b [42722]
The Purchasing Department (TPD) [2960], [19191],
    [26089]
Purchasing Today [42716]
"Purdue Agronomist: Consider Costs Before Tilling" in
    Farm Industry News (November 8, 2011) [21668],
    [24522]
Purdue Research Park [51761]
Purdue University - Center for Customer-Driven Quality
    (CCDQ) [26649]
Purdue University - Center for Food and Agricultural
    Business [21829]
Purdue University - Center for Urban and Industrial Pest
    Management [15662]
Purdue University Libraries--KRAN - Management and
    Economics Library [21805]
Purdue University - Southeast-Purdue Agricultural Center
    (SEPAC) [4060]
Purdue University - Technical Assistance Program
    [51491]
Purified Water Store [2422]
Puroclean - The Paramedics of Property Damage
    [36262]
Purple Cow [30110], [32889]
*Purple Directory: National Listing of African-American
    Funeral Firms* [9337]
*Purple Directory: National Listings of Minority Funeral
    Firms* [9337]
The Pursuit of Happyness [12791], [30111], [32890]
"Push Is On To Build Region's Prospects In Film
    Industry" in Crain's Cleveland Business (Vol. 28,
    November 19, 2007, No. 46, pp. 1) [7970], [27613]
Put-in-Bay Chamber of Commerce (PBCC) [56274]
"Put It In Drive" in Entrepreneur (Vol. 36, April 2008, No.
    4, pp. 31) [14943], [24910], [39308], [41208]
"Put it on MasterCard" in Barron's (Vol. 89, July 27,
    2009, No. 30, pp. 16) [8635], [12792], [26295],
    [27614], [31747]
"Put Power in Your Direct Mail Campaigns" in Contractor
    (Vol. 56, September 2009, No. 9, pp. 64) [570],
    [16265], [40262], [44486]
"Put a Projector in Your Pocket" in Inc. (Vol. 31, January-
    February 2009, No. 1, pp. 42) [3792], [35087], [41433]
Put Your Business on Autopilot: The 7-Step System to
    Create a Business That Works So Well That You Don't
    Have To [30112], [32891]
"Put Your Data to Work in the Marketplace" in Harvard
    Business Review (Vol. 86, September 2008, No. 9, pp.
    34) [4725], [35088], [40263]
"Put Your Heating Cap On.." in Indoor Comfort Marketing
    (Vol. 70, September 2011, No. 9, pp. 26) [856],
    [44487]
Putnam County Chamber of Commerce [50275]
Putnam County Chamber of Commerce (PCCC) [59424]

Putnam Lovell NBF Capital Partners, L.P. [49302]
The Putnam Pages [50603]
Putnam SCORE [55046]
Putney, Twombly, Hall & Hirson LLP Law Library [7772]
Puttin' on Your Lips [5906]
Putting the ADA to Work for You [26692]
"Putting the App in Apple" in Inc. (Vol. 30, November
    2008, No. 11, pp.) [3600], [3793], [18974], [28832],
    [35089], [41434], [45191]
"Putting an End to End-of-Year Reviews" in Inc.
    (December 2007, pp. 58, 61) [35902], [38368]
"Putting 'Extra' in Extra-Silky Shampoo" in Crain's
    Chicago Business (Vol. 31, April 28, 2008, No. 17, pp.
    37) [23350], [39309], [41209], [42847], [43927]
"Putting 'Great' Back Into A&P" in Crain's New York Busi-
    ness (Vol. 24, January 7, 2008, No. 1, pp. 3) [9967],
    [23351], [25619]
"Putting the Service-Profit Chain to Work" in Harvard
    Business Review (Vol. 86, July-August 2008, No. 8, pp.
    118) [23352], [26511], [29146], [44488]
"Putting SogoTrade Through Its Paces" in Barron's (Vol.
    89, July 27, 2009, No. 30, pp. 27) [8636], [12793],
    [28833], [31748]
"Putting Vets to Work" in Business Week (September 22,
    2008, No. 4100, pp. 18) [25889], [35450]
"Putting the World at Your Fingertips" in Barron's (Vol.
    88, July 7, 2008, No. 27, pp. L13) [8637], [12794],
    [27615], [31749], [36746]
"The Puzzle of Our Productivity" in Canadian Business
    (Vol. 83, September 14, 2010, No. 15, pp. 22) [23353],
    [27616], [38369]
PWAContact [6846]
PwC - Toronto - Metro North. [2340]
PWC--PDCA Roster [15395]
PYA GatesMoore [234], [21469], [38798]

Q

"Q&A" in Canadian Business (Vol. 81, July 22, 2008, No.
    12-13, pp. 8) [27617], [30113], [41345], [44489]
"Q&A: David Labistour" in Canadian Business (Vol. 81,
    March 17, 2008, No. 4, pp. 10) [8638], [12795],
    [26512], [30114], [30969], [31750], [39310], [43144]
"Q&A Interview With Perrin Beatty" in Canadian Business
    (Vol. 80, October 8, 2007, No. 20, pp. 13) [11152],
    [27618], [39311]
"Q&A: Joseph Ribkoff" in Canadian Business (Vol. 81,
    March 31, 2008, No. 5, pp. 4) [4262], [24523],
    [25620], [25787], [30115], [39312]
"Q&A Patrick Pichette" in Canadian Business (Vol. 81,
    October 13, 2008, No. 17, pp. 6) [3794], [11835],
    [28834], [31751], [38370]
"Q&A With Devin Ringling: Franchise's Services Go
    Beyond Elder Care" in Gazette (October 2, 2010)
    [6972], [10540], [15613], [16078], [19163], [20033],
    [32220], [34412]
QC Direct [51292]
Qdoba Mexican Grill [18216]
"QR Codes: OK, I Get It Now" in American Printer (Vol.
    128, July 1, 2011, No. 7) [4504], [16395], [20793]
Quaboag Hills Chamber of Commerce [52953]
Quackwatch [34153]
Quad Cities SCORE Newsletter [50870]
Quad City Boat and Vacation Show [3874], [20625]
"Qualcomm Could Win Big as the iPhone 3G Calls" in
    Barron's (Vol. 88, July 4, 2008, No. 28, pp. 30) [3795],
    [8639], [12796], [23354], [31752], [35090], [39313],
    [41210]
Qualified Financial Services Inc. [32041]
Qualitative Health Research [34587]
*Qualitative Research Consultants Association--
    Membership Directory* [14005]
"Quality at Bargain Prices" in Black Enterprise (Vol. 41,
    December 2010, No. 5, pp. 30) [8640], [12797],
    [45644]
Quality Care Advocate [15097]
Quality Center for Business [54999]
Quality Control in Publications [2109]
Quality of Life [47727]; [47728]; [50604]; [51710];
    [52378]; [55125]; [57209]
Quality of Life Book & Membership Directory [56275]
Quality of Life Directory [57210]
Quality of Life Guide [55316]
Quality of Life Magazine [47729]; [54117]
Quality of Life Resource Guide [55317]
Quality Management Journal [38606]
Quality Manager's Alert [38607]
Quality for Project Managers (Onsite) [37730]
Quality Review Bulletin [34546]
"The Quality Revolution" in Canadian Business (Vol. 81,
    November 10, 2008, No. 19, pp. 128) [18466],
    [21669], [41211]
Quality Service: Frontline Commitment [26606]

Quality Service: The Three R's for Managers [26607]
Quality Specialists (QS) [38799]
"Quantivo Empowers Online Media Companies to Im-
    mediately Expand Audiences and Grow Online Profits"
    in Internet Wire (Nov. 18, 2009) [571], [11836],
    [23355], [35091], [40264]
The Quants [8641], [12798], [31753]
QuarkXPress I [28085]
QuarkXPress II [28086]
QuarkXPress III [28087]
"Quarreling Parties Keep Schenectady Redevelopment
    Plan In Limbo" in The Business Review Albany (Vol.
    35, April 4, 2008, No. 53) [8642], [12799], [17453],
    [24524], [31754]
The Quarter Racing Journal [19488]
The Quarterly [2603], [6563]
Quarterly Activities Report [55925]
Quarterly Business Barometer [26856], [32492], [35593],
    [44805]
Quarterly Financial Report (QFR) [2744], [13217]
Quarterly Journal of Finance and Accounting [8874],
    [27909], [31991]
Quarterly Journal of Business & Economics [8874],
    [27909], [31991]
The Quarterly Review of Biology [44064]
Quartz Hill Breeze [48906]
Quartz Hill Chamber of Commerce [48907]
Quartzsite Chamber of Commerce [47945]
"Que Pasa? A Canadian-Cuban Credit Card Crisis" in
    Canadian Business (Vol. 81, March 31, 2008, No. 5,
    pp. 10) [26296], [33911], [36747], [42130]
Quebec Province Communications et Societe - Centre
    de Documentation [3214]
Quebec Writers' Federation (QWF) [6802]
"Quebecor Inc. Takes Hit on Slipping Ad Revenue" in
    Globe & Mail (February 21, 2007, pp. B7) [572],
    [40265]
"Quebecor World Cuts Dividend" in Globe & Mail
    (January 20, 2006, pp. B1) [8643], [12800]
Quechee Chamber of Commerce [58756]
Queen Anne's County Chamber of Commerce (QACCC)
    [52750]
"Queen Bees: All Sting, No Honey" in Business Horizons
    (September-October 2007, pp. 348) [25621], [47364]
Queens Borough Public Library - Information Services
    Division [11964]
Queens Business Consulting (QBC) [2961], [25719],
    [32057]
Queens Executive Development Centre [2961], [25719],
    [32057]
Queen's University at Kingston - Institute of
    Intergovernmental Relations (IIGR) [42434]
Queensborough [55511]
Quest [56577]
Quest for a Healthy Workplace (Course on Request)
    [37731]
Quest for Quality Process Improvement Tools (Course on
    Request) [37732]
"The Quest for the Smart Prosthetic" in Canadian Busi-
    ness (Vol. 83, October 12, 2010, No. 17, pp. 26)
    [33313], [33452], [34413], [37095], [39314], [41212],
    [42848], [43928]
"The Question: Who Do You Think Is the Most
    Genuine?" in Advertising Age (Vol. 79, July 7, 2008,
    No. 26, pp. 4) [4597], [11837], [26513], [39315],
    [40266], [42507]
"A Questionable Chemical Romance" in Barron's (Vol.
    88, July 14, 2008, No. 28, pp. 28) [8644], [12801],
    [27619], [31755], [39316], [42131], [43929]
"Questions to Ask Your Customers Before They Rent a
    Generator" in Rental Product News (Vol. 33, October
    2011) [17805]
Quick Caller Area Air Cargo Directory QC [9213]
"Quick Earnings Revival Unlikely" in Barron's (Vol. 88,
    June 30, 2008, No. 26, pp. 31) [8645], [12802],
    [27620], [31756], [35451]
"A Quick Guide to NATE" in Indoor Comfort Marketing
    (Vol. 70, February 2011, No. 2, pp. 12) [857], [7648],
    [28316], [30765], [40267]
*Quick Printing: The Information Source for Commercial
    Copyshops & Printshops* [5866], [16421]
Quick Topics Newsletter [3298]
QuickBooks All-in-One Desk Reference for Dummies
    [129], [2306], [3601], [18975], [19658], [21412],
    [45192]
*QuickBooks for the New Bean Counter: Business
    Owner's Guide 2006* [130], [1020], [18829], [21413],
    [45193]
QuickBooks Simple Start for Dummies [131], [2307],
    [3602], [18976], [19659], [21414], [45194], [46334]
QuickBooks X on Demand [132], [3603], [18977],
    [21415], [45195]
QuickBooks X for Dummies [133], [3604], [15460],
    [18978], [21416], [22122], [43145], [45196], [46335]

"Ready for a Rally?" in The Economist (Vol. 390, January 3, 2009, No. 8612, pp. 54) [8651], [12813], [14482], [26298], [27624], [31761], [37468]

"Ready To Take Your Business Global?" in Black Enterprise (Vol. 41, August 2010, No. 1, pp. 89) [23361], [25625], [30119], [36750], [40809]

"Ready for the Worst? How to Disaster-Proof Your Business" in Inc. (Vol. 33, September 2011, No. 7, pp. 38) [18467], [24525], [44492]

ReadySoft [59942]

"Real Estate Ambitions" in Black Enterprise (Vol. 37, January 2007, No. 6, pp. 101) [5484], [17029], [17455], [28318], [30120], [42852]

Real Estate Analyzer [17151]

Real Estate Brokerage Council [14369]

Real Estate Brokerage Managers Council [14369]

Real Estate Broker's Insider [17119], [17568]

Real Estate Business [17125], [17570]

"Real Estate Defaults Top $300M" in Business Courier (Vol. 26, January 15, 2010, No. 39, pp. 1) [14483], [17030], [17456], [31762], [37469], [45651]

Real Estate Financing [17576]

Real Estate Forum: America's Premier Business Real Estate Magazine [17120]

"Real Estate Funds Swell Past $350M" in Business Journal Portland (Vol. 27, December 31, 2010, No. 44, pp. 1) [17031], [17457], [45652]

Real Estate Law: Advanced Issues and Answers (Onsite) [23696]

Real Estate Law Report [17121]

Real Estate Loopholes: Secrets of Successful Real Estate Investing [17032], [17458]

Real Estate Magazine [59267]

"Real Estate Market Still in a Slump" in Montana Business Quarterly (Vol. 49, Summer 2011, No. 2, pp. 15) [17033], [17459], [27625], [45653]

The Real Estate Recipe: Make Millions by Buying Small Apartment Properties in Your Spare Time [17034], [17460]

Real Estate Report [57520]

Real Estate Research Institute (RERI) [17620]

Real Estate Software Directory and Catalog [17103]

The Real Estate Success Series [43740]

"Real Estate Vets Take Times In Stride" in The Business Journal-Serving Metropolitan Kansas City (Vol. 26, July 25, 2008, No. 46) [14484], [16546], [17035], [17461], [27626], [33314]

Real Estate Weekly [17122]

"Real Estate Wheeling and Dealing Picks Up" in Business Journal Portland (Vol. 27, October 29, 2010, No. 35, pp. 1) [17036], [17462], [23362], [43578], [46339]

"Real Estate Woes Mount for State's Smaller Banks" in Boston Business Journal (Vol. 27, November 30, 2007, No. 44, pp. 1) [8652], [14485], [17037], [17463], [37470]

"Real Estate's New Reality" in Entrepreneur (Vol. 37, July 2009, No. 7, pp. 32) [12814], [17038], [17464]

"The Real Job of Boards" in Business Strategy Review (Vol. 21, Autumn 2010, No. 3, pp. 36) [32895], [38375]

"Real-Life Coursework for Real-Life Business People" in Women In Business (Vol. 63, Summer 2011, No. 2, pp. 22) [20410], [28319], [38376], [40275], [46692], [47365]

"Real Opportunities: Don't Let Mortgage Mayhem Steer You Away From Sound Investments" in Black Enterprise (December 2007) [10742], [12815], [17039], [17465], [31763]

Real Property Association of Canada (REALpac) [16790], [17166]

Real Resources [17128]

Real Selling: How to Increase Sales in Growing Companies [43741]

"Real-Time Computer-Mediated Communication" in Business Communication Quarterly (December 2007, pp. 466) [22418], [22623], [28320], [28836]

RealEasyBooks, Inc. I RPMW [16665]

"Realities May Blur Vision" in The Business Journal-Serving Metropolitan Kansas City (Vol. 27, September 19, 2008, No. 1, pp. 1) [5485], [14944], [16547], [17040], [17466], [24526], [25193], [27627]

Reality-Based Leadership: Ditch the Drama, Restore Sanity to the Workplace [29148], [30121], [35906], [38377]

Reality Check: The Irreverent Guide to Outsmarting, Outmanaging, and Outmarketing Your Competition [25626], [32896], [38378], [40276]

"The Reality of Fantasy Sports" in Entrepreneur (Vol. 37, September 2009, No. 9, pp. 52) [19455], [45654]

Realstar Hospitality [10813]

Realtor Magazine: The Business tool for Real Estate Professionals [17123], [17569]

Realtors Land Institute [16791]

Realtors Land Institute Newsletter [17124]

"Realtors Signing Out" in The Business Journal-Serving Metropolitan Kansas City (Vol. 27, November 21, 2008, No. 11, pp. 1) [17041], [27628], [33916], [37097], [45655]

Realty [15255]

Realty Direct [14531]

Realty Executives International [17144]

Realty World [2733]

"Reaping Social-Media Rewards" in Canadian Business (Vol. 83, July 20, 2010, No. 11-12, pp. 19) [26516], [28837], [40277]

"Rebels' Cause: Adult Stem Cell" in Austin Business Journal (Vol. 31, June 3, 2011, No. 13, pp. 1) [9281], [28321], [34414], [42136], [42853], [43932], [47071]

Rebok Memorial Library [46110]

"The Rebranding Game: If at First You Pick the Wrong Name, You Can Always Try, Try Again" in Inc. (Vol. 30, December 2008, No. 12) [24527], [40278]

Rebuilding Success [8039]

"Recalls Cause Consumers to Put More Stock in Online Reviews" in Crain's Cleveland Business (Vol. 28, November 12, 2007, No. 45) [11153], [11839], [21186], [36751], [40279], [42508]

Receil it Professional Ceiling Restoration [44622]

"Recent Deals Signal an M&A Resurgence" in Austin Business JournalInc. (Vol. 29, January 22, 2010, No. 46, pp. 1) [12816], [23363], [30122], [35097], [42137]

"Recession Drags Down CEO Pay; Full Impact May Not Have Played Out" in Crain's Detroit Business (Vol. 25, June 22, 2009, No. 25) [21957], [32897], [35907], [38379]

"Recession Fears Power Gold" in Barron's (Vol. 88, March 17, 2008, No. 11, pp. M14) [8653], [12817], [27629], [31764], [33315], [33917]

"Recession Management" in Canadian Business (Vol. 81, March 3, 2008, No. 3, pp. 62) [8654], [12818], [27630], [31765], [35098], [39319]

"The Recession: Problem or Opportunity" in Women In Business (Vol. 61, October-November 2009, No. 5, pp. 34) [27631], [32898], [38380]

"Recession-Proof Your Startup" in Crain's Chicago Business (Vol. 31, November 10, 2008, No. 45, pp. 24) [24528], [26299], [26517], [27632], [30123], [37471], [41378], [44774], [47072]

"Recession Survival Tip: Less Is More" in Women Entrepreneur (December 31, 2008) [24529], [25194], [27633], [46907]

"A Recipe for Change" in Canadian Business (Vol. 80, October 22, 2007, No. 21, pp. 25) [10241], [10292], [17976], [45656]

"Recipe for Disaster?" in Sacramento Business Journal (Vol. 25, July 4, 2008, No. 18, pp. 1) [17977], [21671], [27634], [44493]

Recognition Express [7020]

Recognition Review [7015]

Recording Industry Association of America Reference Library [17659]

Records Retention and Destruction (Onsite) [22575], [33491]

ReCourses Inc. [665], [16626], [25289]

Recovery Communications Inc. [46091]

"Recovery a Ruse?" in Baltimore Business Journal (Vol. 28, August 6, 2010, No. 13, pp. 1) [27635], [43579]

"Recovery on Tap for 2010?" in Orlando Business Journal (Vol. 26, January 1, 2010, No. 31, pp. 1) [3189], [5486], [7973], [11421], [12819], [17042], [17467], [17978], [19339], [19456], [19963], [20566], [23999], [27636], [28322], [34415], [36219], [39320], [43146]

"Recovery2.0: a Work in Progress" in Tampa Bay Business Journal (Vol. 30, December 18, 2009, No. 52, pp. 3) [21187], [28838]

Recreation and Relocation Guide [58673]

Recreation Vehicle Dealers Association of America (RVDA) [17662]

Recreation Vehicle Dealers Association--Membership Directory [17668]

Recreation Vehicle Industry Association (RVIA) [17663]

Recreation Vehicle Industry Association--Membership Directory and Industry Buyer's Guide [17666]

Recreation Vehicle Rental Association (RVRA) [1621], [17664]

Recreational Opportunities and Information in Dillon and Beaverhead County, Montana [54305]

Recreational Vehicle Aftermarket Association (RVAA) [16643]

Recreational Vehicle Institute Inc. - Recreational Vehicle Institute - Recreational Vehicle Division of the Trailer Coach Association [17663]

"Recruiters Look Beyond Backyard to Find Gen Y Workers" in HRMagazine (Vol. 53, November 2008, No. 11, pp. 22) [35454], [35908]

"Recruiting 2.0" in Entrepreneur (Vol. 35, November 2007, No. 11, pp. 100) [28839], [35455], [35909], [45657]

Recruiting, Interviewing and Selecting Employees (Onsite) [35680]

Recruiting Trends [6986]

Rector Chamber of Commerce [48104]

Recycle Rex [7371]

"Recycling 202: How to Take Your Recycling Practices to the Next Level" in Black Enterprise (Vol. 41, September 2010, No. 2, pp. 38) [7292], [7650], [17716], [30768]

Recycling in America: A Reference Handbook [7079], [30458]

Recycling Council of Alberta (RCA) [7063], [17696], [30432]

Recycling Council - Canada [7063], [17696], [30432]

Recycling Today [17728]

Recycling and Waste Management Guide to the Internet [17717], [30769]

Red Bluff-Tehama County Chamber of Commerce [48917]

Red Book--A Directory of the PRSA Counselors Academy [42594]

"Red Diesel Cost Sparks a Move to Home-Grown Fuel" in Farmer's Weekly (March 28, 2008, No. 320) [21672], [30770], [39321]

Red Hook Area Chamber of Commerce [55318]

Red Lodge Area Chamber of Commerce [54306]

The Red Lodge Insider [54307]

"Red Mango Set to Grow in Florida" in Ice Cream Reporter (Vol. 23, September 20, 2010, No. 10, pp. 2) [10242], [10293], [10915], [23364]

Red Oak Chamber of Commerce [51959]

Red Oak Chamber of Commerce ChamberGram [51960]

"Red October" in Canadian Business (Vol. 81, December 8, 2008, No. 21, pp. 61) [12820], [36752]

"Red One and The Rain Chronicles" in Michigan Vue (Vol. 13, July-August 2008, No. 4, pp. 30) [3237], [4506], [7974], [28323], [35099], [42854]

"Red, Pink and More: Cause Marketing Surges as a Prime Tactic to Reach Female Customers" in Marketing to Women (April 2008) [21673], [30771], [40280], [45658]

Red River Chamber of Commerce [54977]

Red River County Chamber of Commerce [58405]

Red River Technology Center [56665]

Red River Visitors Guide [54978]

Red Rock Ventures [49303]

Red Roof Inn [10814]

"Red Tape Ties Detroit Housing Rehab Plan" in Crain's Detroit Business (Vol. 24, September 22, 2008, No. 38, pp. 1) [14486], [16548], [17043], [17468], [24530], [27637], [33316], [44494], [46340], [47073]

"Red Velvet Cupcake Bites" in CandyIndustry (Vol. 176, September 2011, No. 9, pp. RC4) [1770], [41213]

Red Wheel Fundraising [3041]

Red Wing Area Chamber of Commerce (RWACC) [53721]

Redbud Area News [53416]

"Redcorp Ventures Ltd.: Tulsequah Camp Construction Begins" in Canadian Corporate News (May 16, 2007) [5487], [39322], [42138]

Redding Directions [48918]

Redding SCORE [48186]

"Redefining Failure" in Harvard Business Review (Vol. 88, September 2010, No. 9, pp. 34) [32899], [38381]

Redevelopment Authority of the City of Meadville [57340]

Redfield Area Chamber of Commerce [57595]

Redford Township Chamber of Commerce (RTCC) [53417]

Redford Township Directory [53418]

"Rediscovering the Land of Opportunity" in Green Industry Pro (July 2011) [9790], [13398], [13485], [23365], [40281], [43580], [44495]

Redlands Chamber of Commerce [48919]

Redlands Chamber Today [48920]

Redlands Daily Facts [15592]

Redleaf Venture Management [49304]

Redmond Business [59268]

Redmond Chamber of Commerce [56834]

Redmond Technology Press [59364]

Redondo Beach Chamber of Commerce and Visitors Bureau [48921]

Redondo Beach Chamber of Commerce [48921]

"Reds Hit Ratings Homer" in Business Courier (Vol. 27, July 30, 2010, No. 13, pp. 1) [3190], [16729], [19457], [19964]

"Reduce or Repay" in Canadian Business (Vol. 80, November 5, 2007, No. 22, pp. 35) [27638], [30772], [33918]

"Reduce the Risk of Failed Financial Judgments" in Harvard Business Review (Vol. 86, July-August 2008, No. 8, pp. 24) [7893], [8655], [12821], [25892], [31766], [32900], [38382]

"Reducing the Book's Carbon Footpring" in American Printer (Vol. 128, July 1, 2011, No. 7) [2158], [4507], [7293], [7651], [15569], [16396], [20794], [30773]

Redwood Area Chamber and Tourism (RACT) **[53722]**
Redwood Empire Small Business Development Center **[48166]**
Redwood Falls Area Chamber of Commerce [53722]
REED [46793]
Reed Business Information - Frederic G. Melcher Library **[2229]**
Reed City Area Chamber of Commerce (RCACC) **[53419]**
Reed - Sendecke - Krebsbach Inc. **[46793]**
Reedsburg Area Medical Center Medical Library **[15132]**
Reedsport - Winchester Bay Chamber of Commerce **[56835]**
Reference Book for Metalworking Machinery [13708]
"Refi Requests Soar, But New Rules May Mean Fewer Closings" in *The Business Review Albany* (Vol. 35, April 4, 2008, No. 53, pp. 1) **[17044]**, **[26300]**, **[37472]**
Refinishing Furniture with Bob Flexner **[9361]**
Reflections **[51961]**
Reflections of Madison County **[50276]**
Reflexology Association of America (RAA) **[14814]**
"Reform Law Spares Community Banks from FDIC Fee Hike" in *Baltimore Business Journal* (Vol. 28, July 23, 2010, No. 11, pp. 1) **[24000]**, **[31767]**, **[33919]**
"Reform or Perish" in *Canadian Business* (Vol. 82, April 27, 2009, No. 7, pp. 20) **[136]**, **[2309]**, **[19662]**, **[21419]**, **[27639]**, **[33920]**
"Refreshing" in *Canadian Business* (Vol. 79, September 11, 2006, No. 18, pp. 22) **[24531]**, **[25195]**, **[43581]**
Refrigerating Engineers and Technicians Association (RETA) **[775]**
Refrigeration Equipment Manufacturers Association [761], [19065]
Refrigeration Service Engineers Society (RSES) **[776]**
Refrigeration Service Engineers Society Library **[913]**
Regal Nails, Salon & Spa **[10097]**
"Regal Venture Puts Imax Back in the Spotlight" in *Globe & Mail* (March 13, 2007, pp. B5) **[7975]**, **[42139]**
"Regarding Warren" in *Canadian Business* (Vol. 80, November 5, 2007, No. 22, pp. 29) **[12822]**, **[27640]**
ReGENERATION Partners **[31146]**
Regenstrief Institute, Inc. **[34682]**
"Regent's Signal, Once Powerful, Fading From Local Scene" in *Business Courier* (Vol. 27, June 4, 2010, No. 5, pp. 1) **[12823]**, **[16730]**, **[42140]**
Regina Economic Development Authority **[59965]**
"Region to Be Named Innovation Hub" in *Business Courier* (Vol. 27, July 2, 2010, No. 9, pp. 1) **[28324]**, **[33317]**, **[35100]**, **[37098]**, **[39323]**, **[40282]**, **[42855]**, **[43933]**
"Region and City Need Influx of Youth" in *Crain's Detroit Business* (Vol. 24, April 14, 2008, No. 15, pp. 8) **[27641]**, **[32901]**, **[44860]**
"Region Ready to Dig Deeper into Tech Fund" in *Business Courier* (Vol. 26, October 30, 2009, No. 27, pp. 1) **[28325]**, **[33318]**, **[35101]**, **[42856]**, **[43934]**
Regional and Distribution Carriers Conference [20653]
Regional Business Directory **[54979]**
Regional Chamber Alliance (RCA) **[57212]**
Regional Contracting Assistance Center - Ranson **[52784]**
Regional Contracting Assistance Center - Robert C. Byrd Institute - Huntington **[59440]**
Regional Contracting Assistant Center - Princeton **[59441]**
Regional Contracting Assisting Center - Southern West Virginia Community & Technical College **[59442]**
Regional Employment by Industry [3397]
Regional Guide **[55319]**
Regional Newsletter **[4445]**
Regional Reporter **[57213]**
Regional Small Business Center **[55939]**
"Regional Talent Network Unveils Jobs Web Site" in *Crain's Cleveland Business* (Vol. 30, June 1, 2009, No. 21, pp. 11) **[6973]**, **[7793]**, **[20034]**, **[28326]**, **[28840]**, **[35456]**, **[35910]**
Regional Tourist Brochures **[58770]**
Regional Vision **[53420]**
Register of Indexers **[4]**
Regroupement des consultants canadiens en developpement internationale [2754], [25819]
Regular Common Carrier Conference [20653]
"Regulation Papered Over" in *Charlotte Business Journal* (Vol. 25, November 5, 2010, No. 33, pp.) **[14487]**, **[24001]**, **[31768]**, **[33921]**
"Regulators Revoke Mann Bracken's Collection Agency Licenses" in *Collections & Credit Risk* (Vol. 15, September 1, 2010, No. 8, pp. 19) **[6323]**, **[24002]**, **[26301]**, **[33922]**, **[37099]**
Regulatory Spending Soars: An Analysis of the US Budget for 2003 **[34062]**
"Rehab Center Slashes Energy Bills By Going Tankless" in *Contractor* (Vol. 56, December 2009, No. 12, pp. 3) **[859]**, **[16266]**

Rehab Review **[16072]**
"Rehab Will Turn Hospital Into Incubator" in *The Business Journal-Serving Metropolitan Kansas City* (Vol. 26, September 12, 2008) **[16500]**, **[24190]**, **[24962]**, **[27963]**, **[36089]**, **[42141]**, **[43935]**, **[44775]**
Rehabilitation Engineering Center [16107]
Rehabilitation Engineering Institute [16111]
Rehabilitation Institute of Chicago - Sensory Motor Performance Program (SMPP) **[16112]**
Rehabilitation Institute of Michigan (RIM) **[16113]**
Rehabilitation Journal **[16073]**
The Rehmann Group **[42344]**
Rehoboth Beach-Dewey Beach Chamber of Commerce (RBDBCC) **[49829]**
Reid and Riege, PC Library **[19766]**
Reimbursement Advisor **[14252]**
Reinsurance News **[11472]**
"Reinventing the Cheeseburger" in *Inc.* (November 2007, pp. 124-125) **[17979]**, **[30124]**, **[30774]**
"Reinventing Management" in *Harvard Business Review* (Vol. 88, July-August 2010, No. 7-8, pp. 167) **[30125]**, **[38383]**
"Reinventing Marketing to Manage the Environmental Imperative" in *Journal of Marketing* (Vol. 75, July 2011, No. 4, pp. 132) **[7294]**, **[7652]**, **[28841]**, **[30775]**, **[40283]**
"Reinventing Your Rep Training Program" in *Agency Sales Magazine* (Vol. 39, August 2009, No. 8, pp. 40) **[22419]**, **[29149]**, **[39324]**, **[43582]**
"The Reinvention of Management" in *Strategy and Leadership* (Vol. 39, March-April 2011, No. 2, pp. 9) **[25196]**, **[30126]**, **[38384]**
The Reinvestment Fund (TRF) **[57301]**
Reisterstown - Owings Mills - Glyndon Chamber of Commerce (ROMG) **[52751]**
"The REIT Stuff" in *Canadian Business* (Vol. 80, March 26, 2007, No. 7, pp. 72) **[8656]**, **[12824]**, **[17045]**, **[17469]**
"REIT's Decry Foreign Limits on Investment" in *Globe & Mail* (March 29, 2007, pp. B4) **[8657]**, **[12825]**, **[17046]**, **[17470]**, **[33923]**
"The Relationship Between Boards and Planning In Family Businesses" in *Family Business Review* (Vol. 19, March 2006, No. 1, pp. 65) **[24532]**, **[31108]**, **[38385]**
"Relationship "Farming" Tools" in *Agency Sales Magazine* (Vol. 39, August 2009, No. 8, pp. 46) **[22420]**, **[39325]**, **[41553]**, **[42509]**
Relax **[50277]**
Relax the Back Corp. **[14331]**
Relaxing Touch: A Guide to the Healing Art of Massage Therapy **[14151]**
"Religious Revival" in *Canadian Business* (Vol. 81, December 8, 2008, No. 21, pp. 57) **[11154]**, **[36753]**, **[45991]**
Relo Directory **[50278]**
Relocation Guide **[50279]**; **[50280]**; **[53901]**; **[56578]**; **[57214]**
Relocation Guide and Membership Directory **[50281]**
Relocation Packet **[47946]**; **[57215]**; **[57216]**
"Relocation, Relocation, Relocation" in *Conde Nast Portfolio* (Vol. 2, June 2008, No. 6, pp. 36) **[32902]**, **[38386]**
Remarkable Leadership **[30127]**, **[38387]**
Rembrandt Venture Partners **[49305]**
Remedy Intelligent Staffing **[20047]**
Remerica Real Estate **[17145]**
Remgro Recycling Equipment Marketing News **[17729]**
"Remind Managers to Avoid Talk of Employee Longevity" in *HR Specialist* (Vol. 8, September 2010, No. 9, pp. 3) **[26664]**, **[35911]**, **[38388]**
Frederic Remington Area Historical Society Library **[9552]**
Remix: Making Art and Commerce Thrive in the Hybrid Economy **[35102]**, **[37100]**
"Remodeled Stores Help Fabric Retailer Stitch Up Profit Growth" in *Investor's Business Daily* (January 7, 2010, pp. A06) **[6113]**, **[18730]**, **[23366]**, **[28842]**
Remodeling **[5608]**
Remote Control Hobbies **[6164]**
"Remote Control: Working From Wherever" in *Inc.* (February 2008, pp. 46-47) **[3606]**, **[3797]**, **[4990]**, **[18468]**, **[18980]**, **[28843]**, **[35103]**, **[41437]**, **[45198]**
Renaissance Executive Forums, Inc. **[3042]**
Renaissance Leadership **[29279]**
Renaissance Ventures **[59018]**
Renal Center **[16570]**, **[24790]**
Renasant Center for IDEAs - Tupelo/Lee County Regional Business Incubator **[53932]**
Rend Lake College **[51460]**
Renew America [19068]
Renew America Library **[7732]**
Renew the Earth (RTE) **[19068]**
"Renewable Energy Adoption in an Aging Population" in *Energy Policy* (Vol. 39, October 2011, No. 10, pp. 6021-6029) **[7295]**, **[7653]**, **[30776]**, **[33924]**

"Renewable Energy Market Opportunities: Wind Testing" in *PR Newswire* (September 22, 2011) **[7296]**, **[7654]**, **[30777]**, **[42857]**, **[43936]**
"A Renewal in Rentals" in *Barron's* (Vol. 88, March 17, 2008, No. 11, pp. 17) **[5488]**, **[16549]**, **[17047]**, **[17471]**, **[23367]**
"Renewed Vision" in *Hawaii Business* (Vol. 54, August 2008, No. 2, pp. 49) **[303]**, **[15079]**, **[23368]**, **[24533]**, **[34416]**, **[40284]**, **[43583]**
Reno-Sparks Chamber of Commerce **[54514]**
RENOCanada-Bathroom & Kitchen Makeover Specialists **[3448]**
Renovate Before You Innovate: Why Doing the New Thing Might Not Be the Right Thing **[23369]**, **[30128]**
"Renren Partners With Recruit to Launch Social Wedding Services" in *Benzinga.com* (June 7, 2011) **[2519]**, **[15570]**, **[20411]**, **[28844]**, **[36754]**, **[44496]**, **[46693]**
"Renren Partnership With Recruit to Launch Social Wedding Services" in *Benzinga.com* (June 7, 2011) **[2520]**, **[28845]**, **[35912]**, **[36755]**, **[44497]**
Rensselaer County Regional Chamber of Commerce **[55320]**
Rensselaer Incubation Program **[55493]**
Rensselaer Polytechnic Institute - Lighting Research Center (LRC) **[41656]**
Rent-A-Tire Canada, Inc. **[17839]**
Rent A Wreck **[17840]**
Rent-A-Wreck Worldwide Directory **[1624]**
"Rent Check" in *Boston Business Journal* (Vol. 31, July 29, 2011, No. 27, pp. 1) **[17806]**, **[43147]**
Rent 'N Drive **[14997]**, **[17841]**
Rent-n-Roll Custom Wheels and Tires **[20083]**
Rental Age--Who's Who in the Rental Industry Issue [17807]
"Rental Demand Boosts Revenue for Sun Communities Inc." in *Crain's Detroit Business* (Vol. 24, March 24, 2008, No. 12, pp. 4) **[16550]**, **[17048]**, **[17472]**, **[23370]**, **[39326]**
Rental Management: Official Magazine of the American Rental Association **[17825]**
Rental Management--Who's Who in the Rental Industry Issue: Who's Who in the Rental Industry **[17807]**
Rental News-Showcase Issue [17826]
Rental Product News **[17826]**
Rental Relocation Inc. (RRI) **[1172]**, **[2962]**, **[26090]**
"Renters' Review - Secret Shoppers Strike Again" in *Rental Product News* (Vol. 33, June 2011) **[17808]**, **[26518]**
Renton Small Business Development Center **[59063]**
"Rep Contracts: Simple, Clear, Fair" in *Agency Sales Magazine* (Vol. 39, September-October 2009, No. 9, pp. 3) **[27642]**, **[39327]**, **[43584]**
"Rep. Loretta Sanchez Holds a Hearing on Small Business Cyber Security" in *Political/Congressional Transcript Wire* (July 29, 2010) **[18469]**, **[28846]**, **[33925]**, **[37101]**
"Rep Vs. Direct: Always an Interesting Story" in *Agency Sales Magazine* (Vol. 39, July 2009, No. 7, pp. 3) **[39328]**, **[41690]**, **[43585]**
"Rep Vs. Direct: Inside the Mind of One Manufacturer" in *Agency Sales Magazine* (Vol. 39, July 2009, No. 7, pp. 8) **[39329]**
Repairing Furniture with Bob Flexner **[9362]**
Repertoire des Associations du Canada [1476]
Repertoire des bibliotheques canadiennes [11231]
RePlay [957]
RePlay Magazine **[957]**
"Reply! Grows at Unprecedented Rate, Rips Beta Off Its Marketplace" in *Marketing Weekly News* (September 19, 2009, pp. 149) **[573]**, **[1558]**, **[11840]**, **[14945]**, **[17049]**, **[17473]**, **[23371]**, **[27643]**, **[40285]**
The Report **[59709]**
Report from the Chamber **[51711]**
Report to the Community **[48922]**; **[57774]**
Report to Investors **[57596]**
"Report: McD's Pepsi Score Best With Young Hispanics" in *Brandweek* (Vol. 49, April 21, 2008, No. 16, pp. 8) **[17980]**, **[21674]**, **[32223]**, **[39330]**, **[40286]**, **[42510]**, **[42651]**, **[43148]**
A Report to Membership **[50795]**
Reporter **[10128]**; **[58406]**
The Reporter **[50282]**; **[51295]**; **[56278]**; **[56279]**
"Reportlinker Adds Report: Social Networks: Five Consumer Trends for 2009" in *Wireless News* (October 23, 2009) **[574]**, **[11155]**, **[11841]**, **[21188]**, **[36756]**, **[40287]**
"Reportlinker.com Adds Report: GeoWeb and Local Internet Markets: 2008 Edition" in *Entertainment Close-Up* (September 11, 2009) **[11842]**, **[21189]**, **[35104]**, **[40288]**
"Reports of Banks' Revival were Greatly Exaggerated" in *Barron's* (Vol. 88, July 7, 2008, No. 27, pp. L14) **[8658]**, **[12826]**, **[31769]**, **[39331]**, **[41346]**, **[44498]**

The Representative [13917]
Representative Jeff Mursau [59784]
"Reps Continue to Move to International Trade" in Agency Sales Magazine (Vol. 39, September-October 2009, No. 9, pp. 24) [11156], [27644], [36757], [43586]
"Reps Have Needs Too!" in Agency Sales Magazine (Vol. 39, December 2009, No. 11, pp. 16) [26519], [35457], [39332], [43587]
"Reps Vs. Factory Direct Sales Force..Which Way to Go?" in Agency Sales Magazine (Vol. 39, September-October 2009, No. 9, pp. 28) [35458], [39333], [43588], [35459], [39334], [43589]
Reptiles [15789]
Republic Area Chamber of Commerce (RACC) [54120]
"Reputation Warfare" in Harvard Business Review (Vol. 88, December 2010, No. 12, pp. 70) [11003], [16597], [42511]
"RES Stakes Its Claim in Area" in Philadelphia Business Journal (Vol. 28, January 29, 2010, No. 50, pp. 1) [3607], [18981], [24764], [36758], [45199]
Rescuecom [4676]
Research & Development [44065]
Research & Development Directory [42894]
Research Alert [14006]; [14027]; [40563]
Research Applications Inc. (RAI) [38800], [41514]
Research Centers Directory: A Guide to about 13,600 University-Related and Other Nonprofit Research Organizations Established on a Permanent Basis. . . [43937]
Research Communications, Inc. [14006]
The Research File [15955]
"A Research Firm With More Than One Foe" in Globe & Mail (February 24, 2006, pp. B1) [12827], [30970], [32903], [42858]
Research Foundation of CFA Institute [8971]
Research Foundation of Association for CFA Institute [8971]
Research Foundation of Association for Investment Management and Research [8971]
Research Foundation of the Institute of Chartered Financial Analysts [8971]
"Research Highlights Disengaged Workforce" in Work-force Management (Vol. 88, November 16, 2009, No. 12, pp. 22) [27645], [29150], [38389]
Research Institute on Addictions Library [46111]
Research Institute on Aging [15142]
"Research and Market Adds: 2010 US Women's and Children's Clothing Wholesale Report" in Wireless News (November 8, 2009) [3894], [4263], [47179]
"Research and Market Adds Report: Endpoint Security for Business" in Wireless News (October 26, 2009) [18470], [35105]
"Research and Markets Adds: 2011 U.S. Women's & Children's Clothing Wholesale Report" in Health & Beauty Close-Up (October 16, 2010) [3895], [4131], [4264], [7846], [45659], [47180]
"Research and Markets Adds Report: Asian - Internet Market" in Health and Beauty Close-Up (January 19, 2010) [11157], [11843], [28847], [36759], [40289]
"Research and Markets Adds Report: Credit and Collection Practices 2009" in Wireless News (August 12, 2009) [6248], [6324], [26302], [45660]
"Research and Markets Adds Report: Cyprus: Convergence, Broadband and Internet Market" in Wireless News (September 4, 2009) [11844], [27646], [36760], [40290]
"Research and Markets Adds Report: Ghana: Convergence, Broadband and Internet Market" in Wireless News (September 4, 2009) [11845], [25627], [27647], [36761], [40291]
"Research and Markets Adds Report: The U.S. Mobile Web Market" in Entertainment Close-Up (December 10, 2009) [575], [3798], [11846], [22421], [22624], [35106], [40292]
"Research and Markets Adds Report: USA - Internet Market - Analysis, Statistics and Forecasts" in Wireless News (January 15, 2010) [576], [11847], [28848], [40293]
"Research and Markets Adds Report: Vending Machines" in Travel and Leisure Close-Up (October 20, 2011) [14007], [20868]
"Research and Markets: Wedding Statistics and Industry Reports" in Benzinga.com (June 24, 2011) [2521], [45661]
"Research: Mind the Gap" in Business Strategy Review (Vol. 21, Summer 2010, No. 2, pp. 84) [26665], [41691]
Research News [9474]
"Research Note" in International Journal of Globalisation and Small Business (Vol. 4, September 21, 2010, No. 1, pp. 92) [27648], [37255], [38390], [42142], [42859], [43938]
Research Park & Enterprise Works [51453]

"Research in Personnel and Human Resources Management, Vol. 28" in Human Resource Management (Vol. 49, July-August 2010, No. 4) [35913], [38391], [42860]
"Research Reports" in Barron's (Vol. 88, March 10, 2008, No. 10, pp. M13) [8660], [12829], [31771], [42143], [44499]
"Research Reports" in Barron's (Vol. 88, March 24, 2008, No. 12, pp. M10) [8659], [12828], [26303], [31770], [37473], [43939]
"Research Reports" in Barron's (Vol. 89, July 20, 2009, No. 29, pp. M12) [8661], [12830], [31772]
"Research Reports: How Analysts Size Up Companies" in Barron's (Vol. 88, July 14, 2008, No. 28, pp. M13) [1559], [8665], [12834], [18762], [31776], [39335], [44501]
"Research Reports: How Analysts Size Up Companies" in Barron's (Vol. 88, June 30, 2008, No. 26, pp. M11) [8664], [12833], [31775], [34417]
"Research Reports: How Analysts Size Up Companies" in Barron's (Vol. 88, March 17, 2008, No. 11, pp. M13) [8663], [11848], [12832], [21190], [31774], [35108]
"Research Reports: How Analysts Size Up Companies" in Barron's (Vol. 88, March 31, 2008, No. 13, pp. M13) [8662], [12831], [31773], [33926], [35107], [42144], [44500]
"Research Reports: How Analysts Size Up Companies" in Barron's (Vol. 89, July 13, 2009, No. 28, pp. M11) [8666], [12835], [31777]
"Research Reports: How Analysts Size Up Companies" in Barron's (Vol. 89, July 27, 2009, No. 30, pp. M12) [8667], [12836], [31778]
"Research Reports: How Analysts Size Up Companies" in Barron's (Vol. 90, August 23, 2010, No. 34, pp. M13) [8669], [12837], [16731], [42862], [43149], [43940]
"Research Reports: How Analysts Size Up Companies" in Barron's (Vol. 90, September 13, 2010, No. 37, pp. M12) [8668], [42861]
Research Services Directory [42863]
Research Triangle Institute [34683]
Research USA Inc. [14056]
Researching Company Financial Information [14008], [25628]
Reseau canadien de l'environnement [7027], [17687], [30415]
Reseau canadien pour l'innovation en education [27976]
Reservoir Venture Partners [56369]
The Residence Inn by Marriott [10815]
Residential Building Permits [5698]
The Residential Specialist [17125], [17570]
Residential Steep-Slope Roofing Materials Guide [18325]
Resident's Guide to Lincoln Park [51296]
Resilient Floor Covering Institute (RFCI) [9057]
Resilient Tile Institute [9057]
The Resolution [47814]
Resolving Conflict (Onsite) [22237]
Resolving Real Estate Title Defects (Onsite) [23697]
Resort and Commercial Recreation--Membership Directory [10743]
Resort Data Processing [10825]
Resort Hotel Association (RHA) [10654]
Resort Report [10655]
Resort Timesharing Council of Canada [10644]
Resource Associates Corp. [3119]
Resource Directory [4991]
Resource Efficient Agricultural Production - Canada (REAPC) [30433]
Resource and Environmental Management in Canada [30778], [32904]
Resource Guide [48923]; [49747]; [51297]; [58978]
Resource Guide and Business Directory [57387]
Resource Guide for the Town of Hunter [55321]
"Resource Line" in Black Enterprise (Vol. 37, January 2007, No. 6, pp. 6) [11849], [21191], [30129], [44861], [45662]
Resource Recycling: North America's Recycling and Composting Journal [17730]
Resources [7064]
Respectfully Yours: Magda Gerber's Approach to Professional Infant/Toddler Care [3993]
Responding to Conflict: Creating Resolution and Cooperation (Onsite) [29001]
Responding to Conflict: Strategies for Improved Communication (Onsite) [22238]
Responding to Conflict: Strategies for Improved Communication (Onsite) (Canada) [22239]
Responsible Industry for a Sound Environment (RISE) [15623]
"Rest Easy, Retailers" in Pet Product News (Vol. 64, December 2010, No. 12, pp. S1) [15732], [40294], [43150], [45663]
Restaurant and Accommodations Directory [50283]
Restaurant and Hotel Design [10768], [11562], [18027]
Restaurant and Dining Guide [56836]

Restaurant Financial Management System [18296]
Restaurant Hospitality: Ideas for Full Service Restaurants [10302], [18032]
The Restaurant Manager's Handbook: How to Set Up, Operate, and Manage a Financially Successful Food Service Operation [17981], [35460], [38392]
Restaurant Marketing for Owners and Managers [17982], [40295]
Restaurant Publishing [49640]
Restaurant/Motel Design [10768], [11562], [18027]
"Restaurants Dish Up Meal Deals To Attract Customers" in Crain's Detroit Business (Vol. 24, October 6, 2008, No. 40, pp. 1) [17983], [27649], [40296], [42512], [42652], [45664]
"Restaurants Rewrite Menu to Get Financing" in Saint Louis Business Journal (Vol. 31, August 19, 2011, No. 52, pp. 1) [17984], [37474]
"Restaurants Slammed by Economy" in Business Courier (Vol. 24, April 4, 2008, No. 52, pp. 1) [9969], [17985], [27650]
"Restaurants Stewing Over Food Prices" in The Business Journal-Milwaukee (Vol. 25, August 22, 2008, No. 48, pp. A1) [17986], [27651]
"Restaurateurs Follow High-End Apartments Into Kendall Square" in Boston Business Journal (Vol. 31, July 22, 2011, No. 26, pp. 3) [17809], [17987], [44717]
Reston Consulting Group Inc. [20966]
Restoration [1594], [18621]
Restoration Industry Association Annual Convention and Exhibition [6361]
"Restoring Grandeur" in Business Courier (Vol. 26, December 4, 2009, No. 32, pp. 1) [1285], [2794], [5489], [10744], [17050], [17474], [17810], [25893]
"'Resume Mining' Services Can Save Time, Money" in HR Specialist (Vol. 8, September 2010, No. 9, pp. 7) [18309], [35461], [35914], [44502]
Resume Preparation [3384]
Resume Writing (Onsite) [28088]
"Retail in Austin Strong, Will Continue to Be" in Austin Business JournalInc. (Vol. 29, January 22, 2010, No. 46, pp. 1) [6664], [23372], [25894], [43151]
Retail Automobile Sales (Onsite) [43357]
Retail Bakers of America (RBA) [1749]
"Retail Briefs - Dollar Store Opens in Long Leaf Mall" in Star-News (November 5, 2010) [1663], [1900], [6114], [9603], [10139], [13277], [43152]
"Retail Center Pitched" in Business Courier (Vol. 27, June 18, 2010, No. 7, pp. 1) [5490], [17051], [17475], [19340], [43153]
"Retail Center Planned for Canton Site" in Boston Business Journal (Vol. 29, May 20, 2011, No. 2, pp. 1) [5491], [17476], [43154]
Retail Confectioners International (RCI) [3281]
Retail Credit Institute of America [6229]
"Retail Franchises to Start Now" in Entrepreneur (Vol. 37, August 2009, No. 8, pp. 88) [15344], [21192], [23373], [32224], [43155]
"Retail Health Clinics Sprout in Area; Doctors Feel Threat, Have Concerns" in Crain's Detroit Business (April 7, 2008) [25629], [34418]
Retail Info Systems News: Fusing Technology Solutions to Corporate Vision [43274]
Retail Jewelers of America [13260]
"Retail: Loblaw Goes for Broke" in Canadian Business (Vol. 80, January 29, 2007, No. 3, pp. 7) [24534], [25197], [43156]
Retail Management Consultants (RMC) [26642]
Retail Merchant Bakers of America [1749]
"Retail News: Children's Boutique Relocates to Conway" in Sun News (June 4, 2010) [3896], [4132], [4265], [7847], [9604], [16325], [18763], [24765]
Retail Paint and Wallpaper Distributors of America [11535], [15387]
The Retail Revolution: How Wal-Mart Created a Brave New World of Business [27652], [43157]
Retail Safety Consortium [47526]
"Retail Slump Deflates Local Development" in Business Courier (Vol. 24, February 29, 2008, No. 47, pp. 1) [17477], [23374], [27653], [43158]
Retail Tobacco Dealers of America [20085]
Retail Traffic [17571]
"Retail Woes: The Shoe Doesn't Fit for Gerald Loftin's Stock Picks" in Black Enterprise (Vol. 38, July 2008, No. 12, pp. 40) [8670], [12838], [15373], [18764], [31779], [43159], [44503]
"Retailers, City Clash Over Wages" in Baltimore Business Journal (Vol. 28, July 9, 2010, No. 9, pp. 1) [33927], [35915], [42386], [43160]
"Retailers Dig In For Holiday Shopping Push" in Business Review, Albany New York (Vol. 34, November 30, 2007, No. 35, pp. 1) [27654], [43161]
"Retailers Pull Out All Stops to Combat Poor Projections" in Austin Business JournalInc. (Vol. 28, November 21, 2008, No. 36, pp. 1) [577], [27655], [40297], [43162]

"Retailers Report 'Shrinkage' of Inventory on the Rise" in Arkansas Business (Vol. 26, September 28, 2009, No. 39, pp. 17) [18471], [24807], [29294], [43163]

"Retailers Tap into War-Room Creativity of Employees" in Globe & Mail (March 12, 2007, pp. B1) [41214], [43164]

"Retailers, Your Will, and More" in Agency Sales Magazine (Vol. 39, July 2009, No. 7, pp. 46) [7748], [24003], [34419], [43165], [46341]

Retailing Today [43275]

"Rethinking the Organization" in Strategy & Leadership (Vol. 38, September-October 2010, No. 5, pp. 13-19) [22422], [26520], [37102], [38393]

Retire-At-Home Services [10579]

Retire Dollar Smart [12839], [21958], [31780], [46342]

"Retirement Barriers: Lowering Retirement System Barriers for Women" in Employee Benefit News (Vol. 25, December 1, 2011, No. 15) [21959], [35916], [40910]

"Retirement Plan Disclosures: Prepare Now for Fiduciary Rules" in Employee Benefit News (Vol. 25, November 1, 2011, No. 14, pp. 24) [21960], [33928], [35917]

Retirement Plans Report [25391]

"Retiring Baby Boomers and Dissatisfied Gen-Xers Cause..Brain Drain" in Agency Sales Magazine (Vol. 39, November 2009, No. 10) [24535], [29151], [35462], [38394]

The Retort [22502]

Retro Fitness [16039]

The Return of Depression Economics and the Crisis of 2008 [27656], [31781]

"The Return of the Infomercial" in Canadian Business (Vol. 83, September 14, 2010, No. 15, pp. 19) [578], [28849], [40298], [43166]

Return on Investment [31998]; [47731]; [50284]; [57775]; [58407]

Return On Investment [55801]

"Return to Wealth; Bank Strategy" in The Economist (Vol. 390, January 3, 2009, No. 8612, pp. 56) [8671], [12840], [24536], [25198], [26304], [27657], [31782], [37475]

"Rev Up Your Engine" in Small Business Opportunities (Fall 2010) [18578], [32105]

Revay and Associates Ltd. [5666]

"Revel in Riches!" in Small Business Opportunities (May 2008) [16333], [32106], [39546], [42563]

Revelations of Awareness [14822]

"Revelations Derek Johnstone, Head Chef, Greywalls Hotel and Chez Roux" in Caterer & Hotelkeeper (October 28, 2011, No. 288) [3471], [10745]

"ReVenture Plan Appears Close to Landing Key Legislative Deal" in Charlotte Business Journal (Vol. 25, July 9, 2010, No. 16, pp. 1) [5492], [7297], [7655], [30779], [33929]

"Revenue Shortfall Leads to Budget Uncertainty" in Crain's Detroit Business (Vol. 24, March 10, 2008, No. 10, pp. 26) [27658], [46343]

Revere Chamber of Commerce (RCC) [52955]

The Review [54802]

Review of Business Information Systems [33085]

Review of Accounting Information Systems [33085]

The Review of Securities & Commodities Regulation [13138]

Reviews in Medical Virology [44068]

Carol K. Revilock [10567]

"Revisiting Rep Coping Strategies" in Agency Sales Magazine (Vol. 39, December 2009, No. 11, pp. 32) [28327], [39336], [43590]

Revista Panamericana de Salud Publica [34588]

"Revitalizing Real Estate: Couple Sails Through Sea of Housing Woes" in Black Enterprise (Vol. 38, February 2008, No. 7, pp. 50) [14488], [17052], [17478]

Revlon Research Center Library [1919], [2072], [5923]

"Revocable, Irrevocable and Living Trusts" in Business Owner (Vol. 35, September-October 2011, No. 5, pp. 5) [24004]

Revue Canadienne de Chimie [44005]

Revue fiscale canadienne [28], [19595]

Rework [24537], [25199], [26521], [30130]

Rexburg Chamber of Commerce [50796]

Russell Reynolds Associates, Inc. Library [8965]

Reynolds Communication [22537]

Reynolds, Oksanna [22537]

Reynoldsburg Area Chamber of Commerce (RACC) [56280]

The RFA at 25: Needed Improvements for Small Business Regulatory Relief [32905], [33930]

RFE Investment Partners [49784]

Rhinebeck Chamber of Commerce [55322]

Rhinelander Area Chamber of Commerce (RACC) [59710]

Rhino's Press [49411]

Rhode Island Department of Environmental Management - Division of Agriculture and Resource Marketing [57357]

Rhode Island Department of Economic Development [57359], [61031]

Rhode Island Department of Education [61027]

Rhode Island Directory of Human Service Agencies & Government Agencies [34420]

Rhode Island Directory of Human Service Agencies [34420]

Rhode Island Economic Development Corporation [57359], [61031]

Rhode Island Economic Development Corporation - Business Services [57358]

Rhode Island Minority Business Enterprise [57392]

Rhode Island Procurement Technical Assistance Center - Rhode Island Economic Development Corporation [57394]

Rhode Island Small Business Development Center - Lead Office (RISBDC) [57355]

The Rhythm of Success: How an Immigrant Produced His Own American Dream [4622], [17641], [30131], [40810]

Rialto Chamber of Commerce [48924]

Riander [4670]

Riben Nehrah Quarterly [10067]

RIC. [27922], [44980]

"Ric Elis/Dan Feldstein" in Charlotte Business Journal (Vol. 25, December 31, 2010, No. 41, pp. 6) [14009], [15345], [23375], [25335], [28850], [40299]

Arthur L. Rice and Associates [38771]

Rice King [18220]

Rice Lake Area Chamber of Commerce (RLACC) [59711]

Marion S. Rice [21470], [46456]

Mary T. Rice [236]

Rice University - Center for Education [28498]

Rice University - Center for the Study of Languages (CSL) [28499]

Rice University - Computer and Information Technology Institute (CITI) [4792]

Ricerca Biosciences - Information Services [14074]

"The Rich 100" in Canadian Business (Vol. 79, Winter 2006, No. 24, pp. 78) [30132], [32906]

Rich Dad, Poor Dad [12841], [31783]

Rich Dad, Poor Dad: What the Rich Teach Their Kids About Money-That the Poor and Middle Class Do Not! [12842], [31784]

Rich Dad's Increase Your Financial IQ: Get Smarter with Your Money [12843], [31785]

"Rich or Poor, Hospitals Must Work Together" in Crain's Chicago Business (Vol. 31, April 28, 2008, No. 17, pp. 22) [11422], [25630], [33319], [34421], [36220]

"Rich Returns: Media Master" in Entrepreneur (Vol. 35, October 2007, No. 10, pp. 42) [579], [40300], [42513], [42653]

Richardson Chamber of Commerce (RCC) [58408]

"Riches In Recreation" in Small Business Opportunities (March 2011) [15935], [32107]

Riches in Niches: How to Make It Big in a Small Market [23376], [44504]

Richfield Small Business Development Center [58619]

Richland Area Chamber of Commerce/Main Street Partnership (RACC) [59712]

Richland Area Chamber of Commerce [59712]

Richmond Area Chamber of Commerce (RACC) [53421]

Richmond Chamber of Commerce [48925]; [52380]; [54121]

Richmond Chamber News [48926]

Richmond County Chamber of Commerce (RCCC) [55802]

Richmond Magazine [48927]; [52381]

Richmond/Spring Grove Area Chamber of Commerce [51298]

Richmond Sterling Inc. [5667]

Richmond-Wayne County Chamber of Commerce (RWCCC) [51712]

Richwood Area Chamber of Commerce [59426]

Richwood Chamber of Commerce (RCC) [59426]

Ricky's All Day Grill [18221]

Ricky's Candy, Cones And Chaos [3304]

Ridgecrest Chamber of Commerce [48928]

Ridgefield Chamber of Commerce [49748]

Ridges [57776]

Ridgewood Businessman's Association [54803]

Ridgewood Capital Management, LLC [54858]

Ridgewood Chamber of Commerce (RCC) [54803]

Ridgway Area Business Directory [57217]

Ridgway-Elk County Chamber of Commerce [57218]

"Riding the Export Wave: How To Find a Good Distributor Overseas" in Inc. (January 2008, pp. 49) [11158], [33931], [36762]

"Riding High" in Small Business Opportunities (November 2008) [1972], [23377], [30133], [43167]

Riedel Marketing Group (RMG) [6452], [10506], [16135], [18063]

Rifle Area Chamber of Commerce (RACC) [49584]

Rifle Chamber Scope [49585]

Rifle: The Sporting Firearms Journal [1248], [10034]

Riggins Chamber of Commerce [50798]

"Right From the Start" in Small Business Opportunities (July 2010) [23378], [25200], [43591], [44505]

Right at Home [10580]

Right Management Consultants - Corporate Research Center [13905], [20018]

The Right One [5095]

"The Right Remedy: Entrepreneur's Success Is a Matter of Life and Death" in Black Enterprise (Vol. 38, February 2008, No. 7, pp. 46) [25895], [30134], [34422], [42864], [43941], [47366]

"The Right Stuff" in Canadian Business (Vol. 79, October 23, 2006, No. 21, pp. 151) [28328], [30135], [32907]

"The Right Time for REITs" in Barron's (Vol. 88, July 14, 2008, No. 28, pp. 32) [8672], [11850], [12844], [17053], [21193], [27659], [28329], [31786]

Right-to-Know: Working Around Hazardous Substances [47508]

Rights Canada [2102]

"RIM Allegedly Caused 'Substantial Harm'" in Globe & Mail (January 18, 2006, pp. B6) [24005], [42865]

Rim Country Regional Chamber of Commerce [47947]

Rim County Lifestyle & Visitor Guide [47948]

"RIM Gets Smart" in Canadian Business (Vol. 79, October 23, 2006, No. 21, pp. 157) [5768], [41215]

"RIM Opts to Be Little Less Open" in Canadian Business (Vol. 83, October 12, 2010, No. 17, pp. 13) [3799], [26522], [41438]

"RIM Reinforces Claim as Top Dog by Expanding Black-Berry" in Globe & Mail (March 11, 2006, pp. B3) [33320], [35109], [42145], [42866]

"RIM Rocks Out: Billionaire Bosses Sponsor a Free Concert for Deserving Staff" in Canadian Business (Vol. 80, Winter 2007, No. 24) [21961], [29152]

"RIM Says It's Willing to Cut a Check" in Globe & Mail (February 24, 2006, pp. B1) [24006], [37103]

"Rimfire Minerals Corporation: Jake Gold Project-Drilling Planned for 2007" in Canadian Corporate News (May 16, 2007) [41347], [42146], [43942]

"RIM's Options Story Under Fire" in Globe & Mail (March 16, 2007, pp. B1) [12845], [24007]

"RIM's Test of Faith" in Canadian Business (Vol. 80, April 9, 2007, No. 8, pp. 29) [23379], [25631], [37104]

"Ring Ka-Ching" in Canadian Business (Vol. 79, November 6, 2006, No. 22, pp. 106) [11851], [35110], [44506]

Ringling College of Art and Design - Verman Kimbrough Memorial Library [4580], [15889]

Ringling School of Art and Design. [4580], [15889]

Ringwood Chamber of Commerce [54804]

Rinksider [18812]

Rio Grande Valley Chamber of Commerce [58409]

Rio Grande Valley Partnership/Rio Grande Valley Chamber of Commerce [58409]

Rio Linda-Elverta Chamber of Commerce [48929]

Rio Rancho Chamber of Commerce (RRCC) [54980]

Rio Salado Community College [47990]

Rio Vista Chamber of Commerce [48930]

Riordan Lewis & Haden [49306]

Ripley County Chamber of Commerce [51713]; [54122]

Ripon Area Chamber of Commerce (RACC) [59713]

Ripon Chamber of Commerce [48931]

The Ripon Guide [59714]

RISE [15623]

"Rise Interactive, Internet Marketing Agency, Now Offers Custom Google Analytics Installation" in Internet Wire (September 29, 2009) [580], [11852], [40301]

"Rise Interactive, Internet Marketing Agency, Now Offers Social Media Training and Advisory Services" in Internet Wire (Nov. 4, 2009) [11853], [21194], [22423], [28851], [40302]

"Rise in Occupancy Rate Fuels Area Hotel Building Boom" in Crain's Detroit Business (Vol. 24, March 10, 2008, No. 10, pp. 14) [5493], [10746], [17479], [23380]

"The Rise of Pompeii" in Retail Merchandiser (Vol. 51, September-October 2011, No. 5, pp. 13) [14010], [22424], [25896], [40303], [43168], [43592]

"A Rise in Rental Units" in Philadelphia Business Journal (Vol. 30, October 7, 2011, No. 34, pp. 1) [5494], [17054], [17480], [17811], [45665]

"Rising in the East; Research and Development" in The Economist (Vol. 390, January 3, 2009, No. 8612, pp. 47) [11159], [23381], [27660], [35111], [36763], [43943]

The Rising Phoenix [57219]

The Rising Star [59427]

Risk-Based Corrective Action RBCA Applied at Petroleum Release Sites (Onsite) [30457]

Risk-Free Entrepreneur [30136], [39337], [40304], [41216], [41379]

Risk & Insurance Magazine [36252]
Risk and Insurance Management Society (RIMS) [11300]
Risk Management Association (RMA) [37288]
Risk Management (Onsite) [37733]
"Risk Management Starts at the Top" in Business
   Strategy Review (Vol. 21, Spring 2010, No. 1, pp. 18)
   [8673], [12846], [30971], [35918], [38395]
Risk Placement Services [2938], [11484]
The Risk Report [11473]
"Risk and Reward" in Canadian Business (Vol. 81,
   October 13, 2008, No. 17, pp. 21) [8674], [19841],
   [27661], [31787], [36764]
Risk Takers and Innovators, Great Canadian Business
   Ventures Since 1950 [23382], [30137], [32908],
   [35112], [37105]
"Risky Business" in Canadian Business (Vol. 79, October
   23, 2006, No. 21, pp. 153) [2704], [2795], [31788]
Rita's Italian Ice [10979]
"Ritchie Bros. Breaks Record for Internet Sales at Fort
   Worth Site During Multi-Million Dollar Unreserved Auc-
   tion" in Canadian Corporate News [1525], [11854],
   [28852]
Rittman Area Chamber of Commerce [56281]
"Ritz Kapalua Sells 93 Suites for $176M to Fund
   Renovation" in Commercial Property News (March 17,
   2008) [5495], [10747], [15978], [17988]
Ritzville Area Chamber of Commerce [59269]
"Rivals Blow In" in Crain's Cleveland Business (Vol. 30,
   June 1, 2009, No. 21, pp. 1) [5496], [7298], [7656],
   [25632], [30780]
River Biz [56282]
River Capital [50657]
River City SCORE [51798]
River East Corp. [56404]
River Falls Area Chamber of Commerce and Tourism
   Bureau [59715]
River Falls Area Chamber of Commerce [59715]
River Heights Chamber of Commerce (RHCC) [53723]
"River Plan in Disarray" in Business Journal Portland
   (Vol. 26, December 4, 2009, No. 39, pp. 1) [5497],
   [33932], [39338], [44718]
River Valley Chamber of Commerce (RVCC) [52623]
River Valley SCORE [47999]
River Valley Technology Center [52646]
River Valley Voice [52624]
River Walleye Location Secrets [1720]
River Walleye Presentation Secrets [1721]
Riverdale Chamber of Commerce (RCC) [51299]
Riverhead Chamber of Commerce [55323]
Riverside Chamber of Commerce [51300]
Riverside Township Chamber of Commerce [51300]
Riverton Area Chamber of Commerce [59841]
Riverton Chamber of Commerce (RCC) [59841]
RiverVest Venture Partners [54181]
RLG's Eureka Avery Index to Architectural Periodicals
   [9369]
RMA Annual Statement Studies [166], [647], [732],
   [886], [979], [1198], [1570], [1626], [1775], [1868],
   [1904], [1973], [2177], [2392], [2434], [2631], [3238],
   [3330], [3421], [3838], [3943], [4044], [4290], [4525],
   [4883], [5009], [5568], [5780], [5818], [5864], [6118],
   [6672], [6744], [6907], [6980], [8003], [9067], [9108],
   [9218], [9338], [9609], [9797], [9992], [10076],
   [10141], [10251], [10489], [10543], [10764], [11452],
   [13283], [13404], [13542], [13599], [13630], [13666],
   [13721], [13747], [13776], [13946], [14113], [14217],
   [14277], [14550], [14578], [14596], [14741], [14972],
   [15085], [15284], [15379], [15401], [15583], [15634],
   [15828], [15905], [15983], [16285], [16413], [16464],
   [16656], [17104], [17670], [17823], [18019], [18327],
   [18513], [18610], [18776], [18792], [18809], [19026],
   [19350], [19547], [19815], [20039], [20279], [20591],
   [20695], [20807], [20875], [20894], [20934], [39495],
   [43269], [47181]
RMA Information Center [6355]
RMHarris Associates [26627]
RNR Custom Wheels & Tires [20083]
"A Road Map to the New FTC Franchise Rule" in
   Franchise Law Journal (Vol. 27, Fall 2007, No. 2, pp.
   105) [24008], [32225]
"The Road Map for Scotiabank's Asian Expansion" in
   Globe & Mail (April 7, 2007, pp. B3) [23383], [24538],
   [25201]
"Road Map To Riches" in Small Business Opportunities
   (September 2010) [20648], [35579]
The Road from Ruin: How to Revive Capitalism and Put
   American Back on Top [27662], [32909]
Road & Track [14982]
"Road Warriors: How To Survive Business Travel" in
   Crain's Detroit Business (Vol. 24, February 4, 2008,
   No. 5, pp. 11) [24911], [30138]
The Road to Wise Money Management: Planning, Credit,
   and Your First Paycheck [8896]

Roads and Transportation Association of Canada [19803]
"Roadside Attraction" in Hawaii Business (Vol. 53, Janu-
   ary 2008, No. 7, pp. 39) [24539], [25202], [40305],
   [42654]
Roane County Chamber of Commerce (RCCC) [59428]
Roane County Chamber of Commerce, Tennessee
   [57777]
Roanoke Regional Chamber of Commerce (RRCC)
   [58979]
Roanoke Regional Small Business Development Center
   [58815]
Roanoke Valley Chamber of Commerce [55803]
Roanoke Valley Chamber of Commerce [58979]
"Rob McEwen" in Canadian Business (Vol. 80, Winter
   2007, No. 24, pp. 138) [12847], [30139]
"Rob Ritchie" in Canadian Business (Vol. 80, January 15,
   2007, No. 2, pp. 70) [30140], [32910]
Robbinex Inc. [42345]
Robbinsdale Chamber of Commerce [53724]
Robert B. Haas Family Arts Library. [5947]
Robert J. Laughlin [41615]
Robert Morris Associates [37288]
Robert Morris Associates-Association of Bank Loan and
   Credit Officers [37288]
Robert Morris Associates/Association of Lending and
   Credit Risk [37288]
"Robert S. McNamara and the Evolution of Modern
   Management" in Harvard Business Review (Vol. 88,
   December 2010, No. 12, pp. 86) [30141], [38396]
Roberta - Crawford County Chamber of Commerce
   [50608]
Douglas F. Roberts [40641]
Norman A. Robins Consulting [23658]
Robin's Donuts [1818]
Fred J. Robinson & Associates Inc. [13512]
Robotics Online E-Newsletter [35242]
Rochelle Area Chamber of Commerce [51301]
Rochester Area Chamber of Commerce (RACC) [53725]
Rochester Business Alliance, Women's Council [55324]
Rochester Business Journal [55517]
Rochester Civic Garden Center Horticultural Library
   [9870]
Rochester Institute of Technology - Center for Integrated
   Manufacturing Studies (CIMS) [39534]
Rochester Institute of Technology - Melbert B. Cary, Jr.
   Graphic Arts Collection [2255], [3227], [4581], [20815]
Rochester Procurement Technical Assistance Center
   [55476]
Rochester SCORE [55047]
The Rock [55804]
Rock Beach Press [55533]
Rock Falls Chamber of Commerce (RFCC) [51302]
"Rock Festival: High Spirited Conventioneers Celebrate
   Their Good Fortune" in Canadian Business (Vol. 81,
   March 31, 2008, No. 5) [8675], [12848], [20412],
   [31789], [41348], [46694]
"Rock Hall Shifts Advertising to 'Significant Markets' in
   Region" in Crain's Cleveland Business (Vol. 28, July
   23, 2007, No. 29, pp. 6) [581], [20169], [24540],
   [40306]
Rock Hill Area Small Business Development Center
   [57410]
Rock Hill Ventures, Inc. / Hillman Medical Ventures, Inc.
   [57302]
Rock Island County Illinois Genealogical Society - Library
   [9553]
Rock Rapids Community Affairs Corporation [51962]
Rock Springs Chamber of Commerce (RSCC) [59842]
Rock Valley Chamber of Commerce (RVCC) [51963]
Rock Valley College [51461]
Rockbridge Almanac [58980]
Rockdale Chamber of Commerce [58410]
"'Rocket Docket' Leaves Memphis Debtors Behind" in
   Commercial Appeal (November 28, 2009) [6249],
   [6325], [24009], [24541], [26305]
Rocket Ventures [49307]
Rockford Area Chamber of Commerce (RACC) [53422]
Rockford Area Chamber of Commerce [51304]
Rockford Area Chamber of Commerce Business
   Women's Council [51305]
Rockford Area Map [51303]
Rockford Chamber of Commerce [51304]
Rockford Living Magazine [53423]
Rockford Regional Chamber of Commerce Business
   Women's Council [51305]
Rockin'Baja Lobster [18222]
Rockland SCORE [55048]
Rockland-Thomaston Area Chamber of Commerce
   [52620]
Rocklin Area Chamber of Commerce [48932]
Rocklin Chamber of Commerce City Guide and Member-
   ship Directory [48933]
Rockport-Camden-Lincolnville Chamber of Commerce
   [52625]

Rockport Chamber of Commerce [51720]
Rockport-Fulton Chamber of Commerce (RFCC) [58411]
Rockport capital Partners [53059]
Rockton Chamber of Commerce [51306]
Rockville Area Chamber of Commerce [49755]
Rockville Centre Chamber of Commerce (RVCCC)
   [55325]
Rockville Chamber of Commerce (RCC) [52752]
Rockville Innovation Center [52792]
Rockwall Area Chamber of Commerce [58412]
Rockwell City Chamber and Development Association
   [51964]
Rockwell City Chamber and Development [51964]
Rockwell City Chamber of Commerce [51964]
Rockwell's Grill & Bar [18223]
Rocky Hill Chamber of Commerce [49749]
Rocky Mount Area Chamber of Commerce [55805]
Rocky Mountain Chocolate Factory, Inc. [3305]
Rocky Mountain Food Service and Restaurant Expo
   [10311], [10788], [18046], [46788]
Rocky Mountain Hospitality Show [10311], [10788],
   [18046], [46788]
Rocky Mountain Innosphere [49629]
Rocky Mountain Restaurant/Hotel Show [10311], [10788],
   [18046], [46788]
Rocky Mountain Snowmobile & Icefishing Expo [19387],
   [46780]
Rocky Mountain Snowmobile Expo [19387], [46780]
Rocky Mountain Snowmobile Winter Recreation Expo
   [19387], [46780]
Rocky River Chamber of Commerce (RRCC) [56283]
Rocky River Residence Reference Guide [56284]
Rocky Rococo Pizza & Pasta [16187]
Rodale Institute [10383]
Rodale Press Library [9871]
Rodeway Inn [10816]
Guy Rodgers & Associates Inc. [9299], [16627]
Rodney E. Stalley & Associates Inc. [38811], [42348]
Roeder Design [41638]
"Roger Hickel Contracting: Smoothing the Road for Own-
   ers" in Alaska Business Monthly (Vol. 27, October
   2011, No. 10, pp. 114) [5498], [26523], [30142]
"Roger Rechler Played Major Role in Long Island's
   Evolution" in Commercial Property News (March 17,
   2008) [17481], [23384], [30143]
Rogers Area Chamber of Commerce [48105]; [53662]
Rogers Chamber of Commerce [48105]
Rogers City Chamber of Commerce [53424]
Rogers Lowell Area Chamber of Commerce (RACC)
   [48105]
Rogers-Dayton Chamber of Commerce [53662]
Rogue Community College Small Business Development
   Center [56683]
Rogue River Area Chamber of Commerce [56837]
Rogue River Chamber of Commerce [56837]
"Rogue's Gallery" in Canadian Business (Vol. 81,
   November 10, 2008, No. 19, pp. 44) [8676], [12849],
   [14489], [30972], [33933]
Rogues' Gallery: The Secret Story of the Lust, Lies,
   Greed, and Betrayals That Made the Metropolitan
   Museum of Art [1353], [30973]
Rohnert Park Chamber of Commerce [48934]
Rohnert Park Chamber of Commerce Business News
   [48935]
"ROIonline Announces Streaming Video Products" in
   Marketing Weekly News (December 5, 2009, pp. 155)
   [582], [7976], [11855], [21195], [28853], [40307]
"The Role for Canada's Research Universities" in
   Canadian Business (Vol. 81, October 27, 2008, No. 18,
   pp. 84) [28330], [42867], [43944]
"The Role of Human and Financial Capital in the Profit-
   ability and Growth of Women-Owned Small Firms" in
   Journal of Small Business Management [23385],
   [38397], [43169], [44507], [47367]
The Role of the Non-Executive Director in the Small to
   Medium-Sized Business [30144], [38398]
"Roll Your Own" in Business North Carolina (Vol. 28,
   March 2008, No. 3, pp. 66) [20088], [21675], [42147]
Rolla Area Chamber of Commerce [54123]
Rollaway Bay Publications Inc. [49641]
Roller Skating Association Convention and Trade Show
   [18814]
Roller Skating Association International (RSA) [18808]
Roller Skating Operators Association of America [18808]
Roller Skating Rink Operators Association [18808]
Roller Skating Rink Operators Association Convention
   and Trade Show [18814]
Rollerz [18224]
Rolling Hills Publishing [52800]
Rolling Meadows Chamber of Commerce (RMCC)
   [51307]
"The Romance of Good Deeds: a Business With a
   Cause Can Do Good in the World" in Inc. (Volume 32,
   December 2010, No. 10, pp. 47) [30145], [31109],
   [45992]

MASTER INDEX S

Master Index

Romanian-U.S. Business Council **[36310]**
Romanian-U.S. Economic Council [36310]
Romanian-U.S. Working Group [36310]
Rome Area Chamber of Commerce **[55326]**
Romeo-Washington Chamber of Commerce (RWCC) **[53425]**
Romeoville Chamber of Commerce **[51308]**
Rommett Floor-Barre Technique: A Method to Develop and Refine Ballet Technique **[6410]**
"Ron Carpenter" in Crain's Cleveland Business (Vol. 30, June 29, 2009, No. 25, pp. 12) **[14946]**, **[38399]**, **[39339]**
"Ronald Taketa" in Hawaii Business (Vol. 54, September 2008, No. 3, pp. 28) **[583]**, **[3419]**, **[5499]**, **[27663]**, **[35463]**, **[40308]**, **[46908]**
Ronzio Pizza **[18225]**
Roof Coatings Manufacturers Association (RCMA) **[18316]**
Roof Consultants Institute (RCI) **[18317]**
Roof Tile Institute [18319]
Roofer--Single Ply Systems Index Issue [18324]
Roofing Canada **[18318]**
Roofing Contractor **[5609]**, **[11259]**
Roofing Contractor--Single Ply Systems Index Issue **[18324]**
Roofing Materials Science & Technology **[18331]**
Roofing Spec [18328]
Roosevelt County Chamber of Commerce **[54981]**
Roosevelt County - Portales Chamber of Commerce and Economic Development [54981]
Roosters Men's Grooming Centers **[10098]**
"Root, Root, Root for the P.A. Hutchison Co." in American Printer (Vol. 128, August 1, 2011, No. 8) **[4508]**, **[16397]**, **[20795]**, **[31110]**
Rooter-Man **[18716]**
"Rooting for Hispanic Dollars" in Hispanic Business (October 2007, pp. 76, 80) **[19458]**, **[32226]**
Rootstown Area Chamber of Commerce **[56285]**
Ropers Majeski Kohn & Bentley Library **[11512]**
Rosalia Chamber of Commerce **[59270]**
Roscoe-Rockland Chamber of Commerce **[55327]**
Rose & Crangle Ltd. **[2963]**, **[3083]**, **[8919]**, **[13878]**, **[26091]**, **[38801]**, **[44955]**
Benjamin Rose Library **[330]**
The Rose Sheet **[2060]**, **[5903]**
Rose State College - Oklahoma Small Business Development Center - Procurement Center **[56637]**
Rose State College Small Business Development Center **[56434]**
Roseburg Area Chamber of Commerce (RACC) **[56838]**
Roselle Chamber Business News **[51309]**
Roselle Chamber of Commerce and Industry **[51310]**
Rosemead Chamber of Commerce **[48936]**
Rosemead Report **[48937]**
Rosen Numismatic Advisory **[4379]**
Rosenberg Chamber of Commerce [58413]
Rosenberg - Richmond Area Chamber of Commerce **[58413]**
Roser Ventures LLC **[49619]**
Rosetta Stone Associates **[20489]**
Roseville Area Chamber of Commerce [48938]
Roseville Chamber of Commerce **[48938]**
Roseville Insight **[48939]**
"Roseville Investing Big in Downtown" in Sacramento Business Journal (Vol. 28, September 2, 2011, No. 27, pp. 1) **[21676]**, **[44719]**
"Roseville Ob-Gyn Group Grows With Patient Focus, Diverse Services" in Crain's Detroit Business (Vol. 24, April 7, 2008, No. 14) **[23386]**, **[24542]**, **[34423]**
Rosevine Winery **[19285]**
Rosewood Capital, L.P. **[49308]**
"Rosewood Site Faces Big Cleanup" in Baltimore Business Journal (Vol. 27, February 6, 2010, No. 40, pp. 1) **[7299]**, **[7657]**, **[25336]**, **[28331]**, **[30781]**, **[33321]**
Ross County Genealogical Society Library **[9554]**
S L Ross Environmental Research Ltd. Library **[7417]**
Annie Halenbake Ross Library Special Collections **[9555]**
Ross & McBride Library **[46473]**
"Ross Stores Reports Spectacular First Quarter" in Home Textiles Today (Vol. 31, May 24, 2011, No. 13, pp. 2) **[10411]**, **[10481]**, **[43170]**
"Ross: There's Still Money In the Auto Industry" in Crain's Detroit Business (Vol. 24, January 28, 2008, No. 4, pp. 12) **[14947]**, **[39340]**
Ross University - School of Veterinary Medicine - Stanley Mark Dennis Veterinary Library **[1098]**
Roswell Chamber of Commerce **[54982]**
Roswell Magazine **[54983]**
"Roswell Park Researcher Gets $1.5M From M&T" in Business First Buffalo (October 19, 2007, pp. 1) **[42868]**, **[43945]**
Roswell Small Business Development Center **[54904]**
Roswellness **[34589]**
Rotelli Pizza & Pasta Inc. **[16188]**
Rothman Consulting Group Inc. **[19050]**
The Rothschild Image **[11016]**, **[16628]**
Rothschild Strategies Unlimited L.L.C. **[2964]**, **[3084]**, **[13879]**, **[24698]**, **[26092]**, **[38802]**, **[44956]**
The Rottweiler Quarterly **[1029]**
"Rough Headwinds" in Boston Business Journal (Vol. 30, November 12, 2010, No. 42, pp. 1) **[7300]**, **[7658]**, **[30782]**
"Rough Q1 Begs Question: Is the Crocs Craze Over?" in Brandweek (Vol. 49, April 21, 2008, No. 16, pp. 16) **[18765]**, **[25789]**, **[27664]**, **[39341]**, **[40309]**, **[43171]**
Rough and Ready Chamber of Commerce **[48940]**
"Rough and Ready: Putting Rugged Phones to the Test" in Inc. (Vol. 33, November 2011, No. 9, pp. 45) **[3800]**, **[41439]**
"Rough Trade" in Canadian Business (Vol. 79, September 11, 2006, No. 18, pp. 31) **[11160]**, **[27665]**, **[36765]**
Round Lake Area Chamber of Commerce and Industry **[51311]**
Round Rock Chamber of Commerce (RRCC) **[58414]**
Round Rock Reporter **[58415]**
Round Rock SCORE **[57890]**
Round Rock Welcome Packet **[58416]**
Round Valley Chamber of Commerce [47960]
"Roundtable: Functional Foods and Treats" in Pet Product News (Vol. 64, December 2010, No. 12, pp. S1) **[15733]**, **[40310]**, **[43172]**
"Roundtable - The Auto Sector Shifts Gears" in Mergers & Acquisitions: The Dealmaker's Journal (March 1, 2008) **[8677]**, **[12850]**, **[27666]**, **[39342]**, **[42148]**
"Roundy' Pushing Chicago Expansion" in Milwaukee Business Journal (Vol. 27, February 12, 2010, No. 20, pp. A1) **[9970]**, **[23387]**, **[27667]**, **[44720]**
Route 422 Business Advisor **[57220]**
"Route Optimization Impacts the Bottom Line" in Contractor (Vol. 56, November 2009, No. 11, pp. 48) **[860]**, **[3608]**, **[16267]**, **[18982]**, **[24912]**, **[45200]**
Rowan County Chamber of Commerce **[55806]**
Rowland Design Inc. **[41639]**
Rowlett Chamber of Commerce (RCC) **[58417]**
Roxboro Area Chamber of Commerce (RACC) **[55807]**
Roxbury Area Chamber of Commerce (RACC) **[54805]**
"Roy MacDowell Jr." in Boston Business Journal (Vol. 31, June 10, 2011, No. 20, pp. 1) **[17482]**, **[44182]**
Roy Rogers Restaurants **[18226]**
Royal Academy of Dance (RAD) **[6380]**
Royal Academy of Dancing, United States Branch [6380]
Royal Architectural Institute of Canada (RAIC) **[1259]**
Royal Canadian Artillery Museum Library **[10047]**
Royal Canadian Numismatic Association (RCNA) **[4354]**
"Royal Dutch's Grip Firm on Shell" in Globe & Mail (March 19, 2007, pp. B1) **[39343]**, **[42149]**
Royal LePage Real Estate Services **[17608]**
Royal Maid Enterprises **[6591]**
Royal Oak Foundation (ROF) **[1260]**
Royal Philatelic Society of Canada (RPSC) **[4355]**
The Royal Spaniels **[1030]**
Roynat Ventures / Roynat Capital Corp. **[59936]**
Roy-Riverdale Chamber of Commerce [58668]
Royse City Chamber of Commerce **[58418]**
"RPA Preps for Building Radiant Conference, Show" in Contractor (Vol. 57, January 2010, No. 1, pp. 5) **[861]**, **[11423]**, **[20413]**, **[24010]**, **[36221]**, **[46695]**
RRT [34498]
"RS Information Systems Signs Buyout Deal" in Black Enterprise (February 2008) **[12851]**, **[25337]**, **[35113]**, **[42869]**, **[43946]**, **[44183]**
RSA Capital **[53060]**
RSA Data Security Inc. [19051]
RSA Security Inc. [19051]
RSA - The Security Division of EMC **[19051]**
RSVP Publications **[677]**
RSVP: The Directory of Illustration and Design **[4509]**
"RT Seeking Ways to Finance Expansion" in Sacramento Business Journal (Vol. 28, July 29, 2011, No. 22, pp. 1) **[5500]**, **[24913]**, **[33322]**
RTI International **[34683]**
RTKL Associates [41640]
RTKL Associates Inc. **[41640]**
Rubber Chemistry and Technology: Papers on Fundamental Research, Technical Developments and Chemical Engineering on Rubber and Allied Substances **[44069]**
Gary Ruben Inc., Marketing Communications Consultants **[40642]**, **[42557]**
Jan Rubin Associates Inc. **[1317]**
Ruf & Associates L.L.C. **[24113]**
Ruffin's Pet Centres Inc. **[15804]**
Rug News **[9075]**
Ruidoso Valley Chamber of Commerce (RVCC) **[54984]**
"Rule of the Masses: Reinventing Fashion Via Crowdsourcing" in WWD (Vol. 200, July 26, 2010, No. 17, pp. 1) **[4133]**, **[4266]**, **[7848]**, **[23388]**, **[26524]**, **[40311]**, **[41217]**, **[43173]**
"Rule of Thumb" in Entrepreneur (Vol. 36, May 2008, No. 5, pp. 44) **[22425]**, **[24543]**, **[25203]**, **[35114]**
"Rules Will Tighten, Bankers are Told: House Panel Chairman Expects More Regulation" in Charlotte Observer (February 6, 2007) **[8678]**, **[14490]**
"Rumor Has It" in Entrepreneur (Vol. 35, October 2007, No. 10, pp. 30) **[21196]**, **[22426]**, **[24011]**, **[28854]**, **[40312]**, **[41218]**, **[42870]**, **[43947]**
"Rumors Kill Algoma Takeover Talks" in Globe & Mail (March 14, 2007, pp. B14) **[25790]**, **[39344]**, **[42150]**
Runeskriber **[53726]**
"Running the Numbers" in Entrepreneur (Vol. 37, July 2009, No. 7, pp. 87) **[26306]**, **[30146]**, **[32227]**, **[37476]**, **[44721]**, **[47074]**
"Running On Empty" in The Business Journal-Milwaukee (Vol. 25, July 4, 2008, No. 41, pp. A1) **[21962]**, **[24914]**, **[27668]**, **[45666]**, **[46909]**
Running Springs Area Chamber of Commerce **[48941]**
Running Your Small Business on a MAC **[137]**, **[32426]**, **[41389]**
Running Your Small Business on a Mac **[4992]**, **[41440]**
Runzheimer Reports on Travel Management **[24954]**
Rural Builder **[5610]**
The Rural Development Center **[52793]**
Rural Enterprises Inc. **[56644]**
Rural Enterprises of Oklahoma **[60543]**; **[60544]**
Rush County Chamber of Commerce **[51714]**
Rush University - Center for Health Management Studies **[34684]**
Rusk Chamber of Commerce **[58419]**
Rusk County Chamber of Commerce [58221]
Ruskin Chamber of Commerce **[50285]**
The Russ von Hoelscher Direct Response Profit Report **[2196]**
Russell Area Chamber of Commerce (RACC) **[52182]**
Russell County Chamber of Commerce **[52382]**
Russell County Historical Society Library **[9556]**
Russellville Area Chamber of Commerce [48106]
Russellville Chamber of Commerce (RCC) **[48106]**
"Russia Eyes Nuclear Power Co-Operation With Canada" in Globe & Mail (April 2, 2007, pp. B1) **[42151]**, **[44508]**
"Russian Renaissance" in Chicago Tribune (September 22, 2008) **[11161]**, **[19238]**, **[21677]**, **[36766]**, **[39345]**
Russian River Chamber of Commerce and Visitor Center **[48942]**
Russian Telecom Newsletter **[3203]**, **[3846]**, **[34071]**
"Rust Belt No More: The Demise of Manufacturing" in Crain's Chicago Business (Vol. 31, March 31, 2008, No. 13, pp. 52) **[27669]**, **[39346]**
Ruston - Lincoln Chamber of Commerce **[52493]**
Rutgers Camden Technology Campus **[54876]**
Rutgers-Newark Small Business Development Center (RNSBDC) **[54642]**
Rutgers School of Management - New Jersey Small Business Development Centers - New Jersey Procurement Technical Assistance Center **[54866]**
Rutgers University - Center of Alcohol Studies (CAS) **[46123]**
Rutgers University - Institute for Health, Health Care Policy, and Aging Research **[34685]**
Rutgers University - Institute for Health, Health Care Policy, and Aging Research - Division on Aging - AIDS Policy Research Group (ARG) **[34686]**
Rutgers University - Institute of Jazz Studies (IJS) **[14725]**
Rutgers University - National Center for Public Productivity (NCPP) **[42435]**
Rutgers University - Rutgers Center of Alcohol Studies **[46112]**
Rutherford Chamber of Commerce **[54806]**
Rutherford County Chamber of Commerce **[55808]**; **[57778]**
Rutland Region Chamber of Commerce (RRCC) **[58771]**
RV Business (Recreational Vehicle) **[17673]**
RV Business--RV Industry Directory Issue **[17667]**
RVC Directory **[20131]**, **[20521]**
The RVDA Membership Directory and Resource Guide **[17668]**
RWI Ventures **[49309]**
RWorld Franchise Canada Inc. **[16444]**
RWS Group L.L.C. [20487]
Ryan's Pet Food **[15687]**, **[15711]**, **[15805]**
"Ryder's Shock Absorbers Are In Place" in Barron's (Vol. 88, March 24, 2008, No. 12, pp. 19) **[8679]**, **[12852]**, **[20690]**, **[31790]**
Rye City Chamber of Commerce [55328]
Rye Merchants Association **[55328]**
"The Rypple Effect; Performance Management" in The Economist (Vol. 390, January 3, 2009, No. 8612, pp. 48) **[11856]**, **[22427]**, **[22625]**, **[35115]**, **[35464]**, **[38400]**, **[44509]**, **[46910]**

S

S & S Office Solutions Inc. **[41515]**, **[41641]**

Small Business Sourcebook • 30th Edition 3607

S & S Public Relations Inc. [42558]
"S2C Global Installs Its First Mass Production Aquaduct Unit in North America" in Canadian Corporate News (May 16, 2007) [23389], [44510]
"S3 Entertainment Group Partners with WFW International for Film Services in Michigan" in Michigan Vue (July-August 2008) [7977], [26782], [33323], [33934], [42152], [44511], [46344]
"Sabathia Deal Makes Dollars and Sense" in The Business Journal-Milwaukee (Vol. 25, July 11, 2008, No. 42, pp. A1) [19341], [19459], [23390], [40313], [42153], [44112]
Sabetha Chamber of Commerce [52183]
"Sabia Signals a Bold, New Course for BCE" in Globe & Mail (February 2, 2006, pp. B1) [24012], [25204]
Sabinal Chamber of Commerce [58420]
Sabine Parish Chamber of Commerce [52494]
"SABMiller Deal Hit by Tax Ruling" in Wall Street Journal Eastern Edition (November 21 , 2011, pp. B9) [2462], [12853], [36767], [42154], [46345]
Sac City Chamber of Commerce [51851]
SACC In New York [36906]
Sacramento Black Chamber of Commerce (SBCC) [48943]
Sacramento Business Journal [49382]
Sacramento Hispanic [48944]
Sacramento Hispanic Chamber of Commerce (SHCC) [48945]
Sacramento Metro Chamber of Commerce [48946]
Sacramento Valley Better Business Bureau [48191]
Saddle & Bridle Magazine: Oldest Name In Show Horse Magazines [10620]
Saddleback College [49372]
Saderling Ventures [49310]
Sadoff Investment Management [13139]
SAE International (SAE) [18588]
SAE Online Roster [698]
"A Safe Bet" in Entrepreneur (Vol. 35, October 2007, No. 10, pp. 26) [20414], [33453], [46696], [47075]
"Safer Ammonium-Nitrate-Based Fertilizer" in Farm Industry News (Vol. 42, January 1, 2009, No. 1) [21678], [37106], [41219], [43948]
Safety in the Auto Shop [18630]
Safety Compliance Alert [47484]
Safety Harbor Chamber of Commerce [50286]
Safety & Loss Control Associates [46092]
Safety Management Services [34089], [47527]
"Safety Managers Need to Be Safety Experts" in Indoor Comfort Marketing (Vol. 70, May 2011, No. 5, pp. 10) [862], [18472], [38401]
Safety Net [8680], [12854], [31791]
"A Safety Net in Need of Repair" in The Economist (Vol. 390, January 3, 2009, No. 8612, pp. 33) [11424], [21963], [27670], [33324], [35465], [36222]
Safety Orientation for Construction Contractors [5618]
Safety Update [47485]
"Safeway" in Ice Cream Reporter (Vol. 23, September 20, 2010, No. 10, pp. 8) [9971], [10916], [25633], [45667]
Saffire Productions [5053]
Saffire Systems & Development Inc. [5053]
Safford/Graham County Chamber of Commerce [47908]
Sag Harbor Chamber of Commerce [55329]
"Sage Advice" in Canadian Business (Vol. 80, October 22, 2007, No. 21, pp. 70) [30147], [32911], [40314], [45993]
Sage Property & Casualty [11491]
"SAGE Publications Announced a Partnership with Which Medical Device" in Information Today (Vol. 28, November 2011, No. 10, pp. 15) [2159], [2386], [14209], [28332], [42155]
Sage Software Inc. [218], [3657], [19047], [21459], [45251]
Saginaw Area Chamber of Commerce (SACC) [58421]
Saginaw County Chamber of Commerce [53426]
Saginaw County Chamber of Commerce Business Advocate [53427]
Sailing World: The Authority on Performance Sailing [13952]
St. Albans Area Chamber of Commerce [59429]
St. Albans Brochure [58772]
St. Ansgar Chamber of Commerce [51965]
St. Charles Chamber of Commerce [51312]; [54124]
St. Charles County Economic Development Center [54198]
Saint Cinnamon Bake Shoppe [1819]
St. Clair Area Chamber of Commerce [54125]
St. Clair Shores Public Library - Local History Center [9557]
St. Cloud Area Chamber of Commerce (SCACC) [53727]
St. Cloud Greater Osceola County Chamber of Commerce [50287]
St. Cloud State University - Learning Resource Services - University Archives and Special Collections [1394]
St. Cloud State University - Minnesota Real Estate Research Center [17621]
St. Cloud Visitors Guide and Area Map [50288]
St. Croix Valley Chamber of Commerce [52626]
"St. Elizabeth Fights for Share at St. Lukes" in Business Courier (Vol. 27, November 12, 2010, No. 28, pp. 1) [8681], [12855], [25634], [34424], [40315], [42156]
St. Francis Area Chamber of Commerce (SFACC) [52184]
St. Francis Xavier University - Coady International Institute [43337]
Ste. Genevieve Chamber of Commerce [54126]
St. George Area Chamber of Commerce (SGACC) [58674]
St. Germain Chamber of Commerce [59716]
St. Helena Chamber of Commerce (SHCC) [48947]
St. Ignace Chamber of Commerce [53428]
St. Ignace: Mackinac Area's Premier Vacation Guide [53429]
St. James Chamber of Commerce [54127]; [55330]
St. John Chamber of Commerce (SJCOC) [51715]
St. Johns Area Chamber of Commerce (SJACC) [53430]
St. Johns Regional Chamber of Commerce [47949]
St. Johns River Community College [50376]
St. Joseph Area Chamber of Commerce (SJACC) [54128]
St. Joseph Chamber of Commerce (SJCC) [53728]
St. Joseph Station [51762]
St. Joseph's University - Academy of Food Marketing [10022]
St. Joseph's University - Academy of Food Marketing - Campbell Library [19298]
St. Lawrence County Chamber of Commerce [55331]
St. Louis Bar and Grill [18227]
St. Louis Business Journal [54209]
St. Louis Community College - Institute for Continuing Education [54204]
St. Louis County Economic Council [54190]
St. Louis Enterprise Centers [54199]
St. Louis Genealogical Society Library [9558]
St. Louis Minority Business Council [54173]
St. Louis University - Smurfit-Stone Center for Entrepreneurship (SSCE) [47165]
St. Lucie County Chamber of Commerce [50289]
"St. Luke's Gets Shot in the Arm From Outpatient Services" in Saint Louis Business Journal (Vol. 31, August 19, 2011, No. 52, pp. 1) [34425], [44512]
St. Maries Chamber of Commerce [50797]
St. Martinville Chamber of Commerce [52495]
St. Marys Area Chamber of Commerce [57221]
St. Mary's County Chamber of Commerce (SMCCC) [52753]
St. Norbert Arts Centre Archives [1395], [6421], [14702], [14777]
St. Paul Area Chamber of Commerce (SPACC) [53729]
St. Peter Area Chamber of Commerce [53730]
St. Peters Chamber of Commerce [54129]
St. Petersburg Area Chamber of Commerce [50290]
"St. Rose Professor Builds Contractors and Micro-Doctors" in Business Review, Albany New York (Vol. 34, December 28, 2007, No. 39) [24544], [28333], [38402]
St. Tammany West Chamber of Commerce (STWCC) [52496]
St. Thomas - St. John Chamber of Commerce (STSJCC) [59872]
St. Vincent College Small Business Development Center [56913]
Saints Ventures [49311]
Salad Creations [18228]
"Salad Creations To Open 2nd Location" in Crain's Detroit Business (Vol. 24, March 3, 2008, No. 9, pp. 26) [17989], [23391], [32228]
Salado Chamber of Commerce [58422]
Saladworks LLC [18229]
Salamanca Area Chamber of Commerce [55332]
"Salary Hike for Managers Reflects Demand" in Farmer's Weekly (March 28, 2008, No. 320) [21679], [38403]
"Sale of Solo Cup Plant Pending" in Boston Business Journal (Vol. 29, June 17, 2011, No. 6, pp. 1) [17483], [25338], [39347], [44184]
Salem Area Chamber of Commerce [54130]
Salem Area Chamber of Commerce (SACC) [56286]; [56839]
Salem Chamber of Commerce [52956]
Salem Chamber of Commerce [51129]
Salem County Chamber of Commerce [54807]
Salem Industrial Directory [56287]
Salem SCORE [56695]
Salem Update [56288]
"Sales and the Absolute Power of Information" in Agency Sales Magazine (Vol. 39, July 2009, No. 7, pp. 16) [25635], [43593]
The Sales And Use Tax Seminar (Onsite) [21340]
Sales Bible [43594]
"Sales Communications in a Mobile World" in Business Communication Quarterly (December 2007, pp. 492) [3801], [18473], [22428], [35116], [43595]
Sales Directors Inc. [4547]
Sales and Exchange [59717]
The Sales Film [43742]
"Sales Force Expertise: A Competitive Advantage" in Agency Sales Magazine (Vol. 39, November 2009, No. 10, pp. 10) [25636], [26525], [43596]
"Sales at Furniture Showrooms Sink" in Puget Sound Business Journal (Vol. 29, October 10, 2008, No. 25, pp. 1) [10412], [10482], [17055], [27671]
"Sales Gave W&S Record '07" in Business Courier (Vol. 24, March 14, 2008, No. 49, pp. 1) [8682], [10748], [12856], [23392], [31792], [43597]
Sales and Marketing Success [16422]
"Sales of Pension Income Targeted by Senator" in Wall Street Journal Eastern Edition (November 21 , 2011, pp. C7) [12857], [21964], [33935], [45668]
The Sales Professionals: Building Your Clients' Confidence [43743]
Sales Systems Specialists [40643]
"Sales Tax Proposed to Revive KRM" in Business Journal-Milwaukee (Vol. 25, October 26, 2007, No. 4, pp. A1) [17812], [46346]
Sales in Turbulent Times [39604]
Sales and Use Tax 2012 Workshop (Onsite) [37734]
Salesforce.com Secrets of Success: Best Practices for Growth and Profitability [3609], [18983], [23393], [28855], [38404], [40316], [43598], [45201]
Salina Area Chamber of Commerce (SACC) [52185]
Salinas Area Chamber of Commerce [48949]
Salinas Valley Business Journal [48948]
Salinas Valley Chamber of Commerce [48949]
Saline Area Chamber of Commerce (SACC) [53431]
Saline Business Advocate [53432]
Saline Chamber Business Directory & Community Profile [53433]
Salisbury Area Chamber of Commerce (SACC) [52754]
Salisbury Chamber of Commerce [49756]
Salix Ventures [57812]
Sallisaw Chamber of Commerce [56579]
Salmon Area Chamber of Commerce [50799]
Salmon (Kurt) Assoc [43283]
Salmon Kurt Associates Inc. [43283]
Salmon River Chamber of Commerce [50798]
Salmon Valley Business Innovation Center [50819]
Salmon Valley Chamber of Commerce [50799]
Salon 2.0 - Salon and Spa Managment Software [10107]
Salon Today Magazine [10080]
Salsarita's Fresh Cantina [18230]
Salt Lake Chamber (SLACC) [58675]
Salt Lake Community College - Redwood Road Campus [58710]
Sam Houston State University Small Business Development Center [57867]
Sam Rosenbaum & Co. [42346]
Samford University - Institute of Genealogy and Historical Research (IGHR) [9572]
"Samll Fortunes" in Business Courier (Vol. 27, July 23, 2010, No. 12, pp. 1) [8683], [12858], [27672], [31793], [33936]
Sammy J. Peppers Restaurant & Lounge [18231]
Sample Employee Policy Handbook [57222]
"Samsung 'Holding Breath'" in Austin Business JournalInc. (Vol. 29, January 29, 2010, No. 47, pp. 1) [5769], [33325], [35117], [37477], [46347]
"Samsung's Metamorphosis" in Austin Business Journal (Vol. 31, May 20, 2011, No. 11, pp. 1) [3802], [4993], [23394], [25205], [35118], [35466], [41441]
San Angelo Chamber of Commerce (SACC) [58423]
San Anselmo Chamber of Commerce [48950]
San Antonio Hispanic Chamber of Commerce (SAHCC) [58424]
San Antonio Minority Business Development Enterprise - University of Texas at San Antonio, Downtown [58539]
San Antonio Small Business Development Center (SA SBDC) [57868]
San Antonio Women's Chamber of Commerce of Texas (SAWCC) [58425]
San Augustine County Chamber of Commerce [58426]
San Benito Area Chamber of Commerce [58427]
San Benito Chamber of Commerce [58427]
San Benito County Chamber of Commerce [48951]
San Bernardino Area Chamber of Commerce (SBACC) [48952]
San Bernardino Business [48953]
San Carlos Business [48954]
San Carlos Chamber of Commerce [48955]
San Clemente Chamber of Commerce [48956]
The San Clemente Current [48957]

3608 Small Business Sourcebook • 30th Edition

"Sears' Profit Result Puts Ball in Parent's Court" in Globe & Mail (February 3, 2006, pp. B4) [23400], [42163], [43174]

"Seasonal Franchises" in Franchising World (Vol. 42, August 2010, No. 8, pp. 50) [17990], [32230], [44114], [46352]

"The Seat-Of-The-Pants School of Marketing" in Brand-week (Vol. 49, April 21, 2008, No. 16, pp. 24) [2162], [2387], [24552], [25208], [40322], [42515], [42655], [44864]

Seattle International Motorcycle Show [14557]

Seattle JobBank: The Job Hunter's Guide to Washington [19183]

Seattle Metaphysical Library. [14829]

Seattle Small Business Development Center [59064]

Seattle Sutton's Franchise Corp. [18235]

Seaworthy [3870]

Sebago Lakes Region Chamber of Commerce (SLRCC) [52628]

Sebastian River Area Chamber of Commerce [50294]

Sebastopol Area Chamber of Commerce and Visitors Center [49011]

Sebastopol Area Chamber of Commerce [49011]

"SEC Doesn't Buy Biovail's Claims" in Barron's (Vol. 88, March 31, 2008, No. 13, pp. 20) [8691], [12869], [24013], [31804], [38414]

"SEC Extends Small Business Deadline for SOX Audit Requirement" in HRMagazine (Vol. 53, August 2008, No. 8, pp. 20) [141], [2311], [19666], [21422], [33942], [46353]

"SEC Report On Rating Agencies Falls Short" in Barron's (Vol. 88, July 14, 2008, No. 28, pp. 35) [8692], [12870], [26308], [26526], [27679], [31805], [33943], [45672]

"Secaucus-Based Freshpet is Barking Up the Right Tree" in Record (September 8, 2011) [10243], [15779], [19239]

"SECO Manufacturing" in Point of Beginning (Vol. , 2008, No. , pp.) [13617], [18475], [39352]

Second Amendment Foundation Library [10048]

Second Century Innovation and Ideas Corp [55495]

Second Chance Animal Center Library [1041], [1099]

"Second Chance Counselor" in Business Courier (Vol. 27, July 2, 2010, No. 9, pp. 1) [28335], [35468], [35920], [45994]

"A Second Chance to Make a Living" in The Business Journal-Milwaukee (Vol. 25, September 19, 2008, No. 52, pp. A1) [16551], [25339], [35469], [44220], [44865], [45673]

"A Second Chance at Road Dollars" in Orlando Business Journal (Vol. 26, February 5, 2010, No. 36, pp. 1) [2006], [5503], [33332], [33455]

The Second Cup Ltd. [9748]

"Second Cup?" in Canadian Business (Vol. 81, July 21, 2008, No. 11, pp. 50) [3612], [18986], [30152], [35124], [37107], [45204]

"The Second Most Fuel-Efficient Tractor of the Decade: John Deere 8320R" in Farm Industry News (November 10, 2011) [7303], [7662], [21681], [30787], [39353]

"Second to None" in Crain's Detroit Business (Vol. 26, January 18, 2010, No. 3, pp. 9) [23401], [33333], [35470]

Second Source, Healthcare Technology Management. [14220]

Second Source Imaging [14232]

The Secret of Exiting Your Business Under Your Terms! [1526], [12871], [25340], [32917], [42164], [44185], [46354]

"Secret Ingredient" in Entrepreneur (Vol. 35, November 2007, No. 11, pp. 172) [10056], [10072], [23402]

The Secret Language of Competitive Intelligence: How to See Through and Stay Ahead of Business Disruptions, Distortions, Rumors, and Smoke [25638], [30153]

"The Secret Life of a Serial CEO" in Inc. (January 2008, pp. 80-88) [2796], [25897], [30154]

"The Secret Strategy for Meaningful Sales Meetings" in Agency Sales Magazine (Vol. 39, December 2009, No. 11, pp. 40) [22436], [29155], [43601]

Secret of Training Dogs [15705]

Secrets of Copywriting Seminar: Fundamentals for Direct Marketing (Onsite) [39605]

The Secrets of Magic and Illusion [6151]

Secrets of Millionaire Moms [30155], [47370]

"The Secret's Out About Kansas City" in Women In Business (Vol. 61, August-September 2009, No. 4, pp. 26) [32918], [44722], [47371]

Secrets to Power Marketing [40323]

The Secrets of Spiritual Marketing: A Complete Guide for Natural Therapists [586], [14815], [40324]

Secrets of Telemarketing Scripts [19851]

"Secrets To Trade Show Success" in Women Entrepreneur (September 12, 2008) [20417], [22437], [23403], [32919], [43175], [44515], [46699], [47372]

Secrets of the Walleye Trail [1722]

Section for Women in Public Administration (SWPA) [42362]

"Secure Fortune: New Twist In Security: The Marketplace Is Going Digital" in Small Business Opportunities (November 2007) [18369], [32109]

"Secure Future" in Small Business Opportunities (November 2010) [18370], [47193]

The Secured Lender [13140]

"Securing a Fortune" in Small Business Opportunities (Fall 2010) [18371], [31011]

Securities and Exchange Commission - Atlanta Regional Office [60670]; [60671]

Securities and Exchange Commission - Boston Regional Office [60672]; [60673]

Securities and Exchange Commission - Chicago Regional Office [60674]; [60675]

Securities and Exchange Commission - Denver Regional Office [60676]; [60677]

Securities and Exchange Commission - Fort Worth Regional Office [60678]; [60679]

Securities and Exchange Commission - Los Angeles Regional Office [60680]; [60681]

Securities and Exchange Commission - Miami Regional Office [60682]; [60683]

Securities and Exchange Commission - New York Regional Office [60684]; [60685]

Securities and Exchange Commission (SEC) - Office of Small Business Policy - Small Business Ombudsman [60686]; [62169]

Securities and Exchange Commission - Office of Small Business Policy - Small Business Ombudsman [60687]

Securities and Exchange Commission - Philadelphia Regional Office [60688]; [60689]

Securities and Exchange Commission - Salt Lake Regional Office [60690]; [60691]

Securities and Exchange Commission - San Francisco Regional Office [60692]; [60693]

Securities Industry Association [11977]

Securities Industry and Financial Markets Association (SIFMA) [11977]

Securities Law Daily™ [8951], [13218], [14539]

Securities Regulation & Law Report™ [8952], [13219]

"Security Alert: Data Server" in Entrepreneur (Vol. 36, February 2008, No. 2, pp. 28) [14011], [18476], [25898], [35125], [40325]

Security Dynamics Technologies Inc. [19051]

Security Equipment Industry Association [18384]

Security Equipment Manufacturers Association [18384]

Security: For Buyers of Security Products, Systems, and Services [18516]

Security Hardware Distributors Association (SHDA) [13614]

Security Industry Association (SIA) [18384]

Security Letter [29296]

Security & Loss Prevention Associates Inc. [29311]

Security Management [18517]

"A Security Risk?" in Canadian Business (Vol. 80, October 22, 2007, No. 21, pp. 36) [12872], [18477], [24553], [31806], [42165]

Security Sales & Integration [3313], [18518]

Security Traders Association (STA) [11978]

Security World [18516]

Sedalia Area Chamber of Commerce [54132]

Sedalia Area Chamber of Commerce and Convention and Visitors' Bureau [54132]

Sedan Area Chamber of Commerce [52187]

Sedgwick County Zoo Library [7421]

"Sedo Keeps Trucking in Good Times and Bad" in Crain's Chicago Business (Vol. 31, April 28, 2008, No. 17, pp. 35) [11163], [20691], [23404], [36774], [42166]

Sedona-Oak Creek Canyon Chamber of Commerce (SOCCCC) [47953]

Sedro-Woolley Chamber of Commerce [59273]

See How They Grow: Farm Animals [3995]

See How They Grow: Forest Animals [3996]

See How They Grow: Insects and Spiders [3997]

See How They Grow: Pets [3998]

See How They Grow: Pond Animals [3999]

See How They Grow: Wild Animals [4000]

Seed Capital Partners [58567]

Seed Capital Partners/ SoftBank Capital [55455]

"Seed-Count Labeling" in Farm Industry News (October 20, 2010) [21682], [33944]

"Seed Funding" in Saint Louis Business Journal (Vol. 31, July 29, 2011, No. 49, pp. 1) [587], [40326], [47076]

Seed-Stage Venture Investing: The Ins and Outs for Entrepreneurs, Start-Ups, and Investors on Success-fully Starting a New Business [29392], [34723], [46967]

"Seeing Green in Going Green" in The Business Journal-Serving Greater Tampa Bay (Vol. 28, July 4, 2008, No. 28, pp. 1) [5504], [7663], [17487], [19113], [30788], [45674]

"Seeing the Light" in American Printer (Vol. 128, July 1, 2011, No. 7) [4511], [16399], [20797]

"SEEing an Opportunity; Golden's Eyewear Chain Has a National Vision" in Crain's Detroit Business (Vol. 24, January 7, 2008, No. 1) [20932], [23405], [30156]

Seek Information Service Library [11250]

"Seeking Local SBA Loan?" in Business Courier (Vol. 26, October 16, 2009, No. 25, pp. 1) [23406], [33334], [37487]

Segal Commercial Real Estate [17601]

Segal Co. [22074]

"Segmenting When It Matters" in Business Strategy Review (Vol. 21, Spring 2010, No. 1, pp. 46) [26527], [38415]

Seguin Area Chamber of Commerce (SACC) [58437]

Seguin-Guadalupe County Chamber of Commerce [58437]

Seidman School of Business [53476]

Seizure: European Journal of Epilepsy [34590]

Selby Venture Partners [49313]

Seldovia Chamber of Commerce [47815]

Select Community Funeral Homes Inc. [9343]

Select Sandwich Co. [18236]

SelectBooks Inc. [55534]

Selected Independent Funeral Homes [9327]

Self-Counsel Press Ltd. [59887]

"The Self-Destructive Habits of Good Companies, and How to Break Them" in Harvard Business Review (Vol. 85, July-August 2007, No. 7-8) [30157], [38416]

Self-Employed Tax Solutions: Quick, Simple, Money-Saving, Audit-Proof Tax and Recordkeeping Basics [142], [2312], [19667], [21423], [46355]

"Self-Employment in the United States" in Montly Labor Review (Vol. 133, September 2010, No. 9, pp. 17) [5505], [21683], [44516], [45675]

Self Employment Update [38608]

Self-Evaluation [34167]

Self Guided Tour of Deer Lodge Historic Buildings [54308]

Self-Motivation in Selling [8897], [13170], [43744]

The Self-Publishing Manual: How To Write, Print, and Sell Your Own Book [2163], [6523], [40327]

"A Self-Serving Opportunity" in Black Enterprise (Vol. 37, February 2007, No. 7, pp. 52) [20848]

Self Storage Association (SSA) [16644]

Self Storage Association Conference and Tradeshow [16658]

Self-Storage Now! [16657]

Self-Service Storage Association [16644]

"Sell: Going Zen" in Entrepreneur (Vol. 35, October 2007, No. 10, pp. 106) [40328], [43602]

Sell More of Anything to Anyone: Sales Tips for Individu-als, Business Owners and Sales Professionals [26528], [43603]

Sell More Books! Newsletter [2197], [2401]

Sell Your Business Your Way: Getting Out, Getting Rich, and Getting on with Your Life [30158], [44186]

Seller Direct, Inc. [3043]

"Sellers Face Excess Land Dilemma" in Crain's Cleveland Business (Vol. 28, November 12, 2007, No. 45, pp. 1) [5506], [17057], [17488]

Sellers, Feinberg & Associates L.L.C. [9301], [16633]

"Sellers Shift Gears" in Crain's Detroit Business (Vol. 25, June 22, 2009, No. 25, pp. 3) [14948], [18605], [30159], [32231], [39354]

Selling in the '90s [43745]

The Selling Advantage [43699]

Selling Christmas Decorations [6025]

Selling the Invisible: A Field Guide to Modern Marketing [20171], [20569], [24014], [34427], [40329], [43604], [44517]

"Selling a Job When There's Buyer's Remorse" in Contractor (Vol. 56, December 2009, No. 12, pp. 37) [863], [6900], [16268], [18706], [38417]

Selling to Major Accounts: A Strategic Approach (Onsite) [43358]

"Selling Michigan; R&D Pushed as Reason For Chinese To Locate In State" in Crain's Detroit Business (Vol. 24, January 14, 2008) [12873], [14949], [36775], [39355], [43954]

Selling Online: Canada's Bestselling Guide to Becoming a Successful E-Commerce Merchant [1527], [15299], [18478], [28863], [40330], [43176], [43605]

Selling on the Phone [19852]

Selling Power: Solutions for sales management [43700]

"Selling Pressures Rise in China" in Barron's (Vol. 88, March 10, 2008, No. 10, pp. M9) [8693], [12874], [27680], [31807], [33945], [36776]

Selling to Seniors [43701]

Selling Skills: Have I Got a Deal for You! [43746]

Selling: The Power of Confidence [43747]

"Selling With Strengths; Talent Trumps Training" in Gallup Management Journal (March 24, 2011) [28336], [43606]

MASTER INDEX Shelbyville
Master Index

"Selling Your Company" in Inc. (March 2008, pp. 78) **[18479]**, **[25899]**, **[44187]**
Selling to Zebras: How to Close 90 Percent of the Business You Pursue Faster, More Easily and More Profitably **[43607]**
Sellmeyer Engineering **[16760]**
Selma Business **[49012]**
Selma District Chamber of Commerce (SDCC) **[49013]**
SEMA News **[1579]**, **[39507]**
Seminole Chamber of Commerce **[56582]**
Seminole Chamber of Commerce Membership Directory and Visitor's Guide **[56583]**
Seminole Community College **[50378]**
Seminole County Regional Chamber of Commerce **[50295]**
Seminole County/Lake Mary Regional Chamber of Commerce [50295]
Seminole Technology Business Incubation Center **[50374]**
SEMO Communications Corp. **[20009]**
Semper Ventures **[49314]**
"Sen. Mark Warner Holds a Hearing on Government Contracting Modernization" in Political/Congressional Transcript Wire (July 20, 2010) **[33335]**, **[33946]**
"Senate Bill Would Eliminate MBT Surcharge in 2011" in Crain's Detroit Business (Vol. 24, April 7, 2008, No. 14, pp. 33) **[33947]**, **[45676]**, **[46356]**
"Senate OKs Funds for Promoting Tourism" in Crain's Detroit Business (Vol. 24, March 31, 2008, No. 13, pp. 6) **[20172]**, **[20570]**, **[28337]**, **[33948]**, **[40331]**, **[44866]**, **[45677]**
"Senate's Effort to Reform Immigration Policies Fizzles Out" in Hispanic Business (July-August 2007, pp. 62) **[33949]**, **[40913]**
"Senators Predict Online School Changes" in Puget Sound Business Journal (Vol. 29, September 19, 2008, No. 22, pp. 1) **[24015]**, **[28338]**, **[28864]**, **[33950]**, **[45678]**
Seneca Chamber of Commerce **[52188]**
Seneca County Chamber of Commerce **[55338]**
SENES Consultants Ltd. **[30886]**
Michael Senew & Associates **[10188]**
Senior Housing South **[314]**, **[15110]**
Senior Project Management (Onsite) (Canada) **[37735]**
Sense of the City **[1261]**
"Sense and Consensus" in Canadian Business (Vol. 81, October 13, 2008, No. 17, pp. 22) **[19842]**, **[31808]**, **[36777]**
"Sense of Discovery" in Business Journal Portland (Vol. 27, November 19, 2010, No. 38, pp. 1) **[3613]**, **[8694]**, **[12875]**, **[18987]**, **[23407]**, **[24016]**, **[37488]**, **[42167]**, **[45205]**
A Sense of Heritage: The Tryon Chamber of Commerce, 1991 **[55810]**
Sensitivity Skills in Working with Others (Onsite) **[22240]**
Sensor Technology **[35243]**, **[44070]**
"Sentiment Split on Financials" in Barron's (Vol. 88, March 24, 2008, No. 12, pp. M14) **[8695]**, **[12876]**, **[26309]**, **[27681]**, **[31809]**, **[37489]**
The Sentinel **[49014]**
Sentron Medical Inc. - Senmed Medical Ventures Library **[6729]**, **[14245]**, **[37177]**, **[47164]**
The SEO Manifesto: A Practical and Ethical Guide to Internet Marketing and Search Engine Optimization **[11863]**, **[21199]**, **[28865]**, **[30975]**
Sequel Venture Partners **[49620]**
Sequim-Dungeness Valley Chamber of Commerce **[59274]**
Sequoia Capital **[49315]**
SER Network Directory **[19164]**
Serial Number Reference Book for Metalworking Machinery [13708]
"Serial Starter" in Entrepreneur (Vol. 36, April 2008, No. 4, pp. 17) **[30160]**, **[44188]**, **[44776]**
"Serials Solutions Launches 360 Resource Manager Consortium Edition" in Information Today (Vol. 26, February 2009, No. 2, pp. 32) **[2164]**, **[3614]**, **[4727]**, **[18988]**, **[28866]**, **[37108]**, **[45206]**
"Serious Signal Flashing?" in Barron's (Vol. 88, July 7, 2008, No. 27, pp. 11) **[8696]**, **[12877]**, **[27682]**, **[31810]**
Serves You Right! **[26529]**, **[32920]**
The Service Contract Act (Onsite) **[46833]**
Service Corps of Retired Executives [32493], [37567]
Service Corps of Retired Executives-Chapter 6 **[51509]**
Service d'Entretien et de Reparation Automobiles du Canada [18580]
Service Excellence **[26608]**
"The Service Imperative" in Business Horizons (Vol. 51, January-February 2008, No. 1, pp. 39) **[28339]**, **[36778]**, **[37109]**, **[42874]**, **[43955]**, **[44518]**
Service One Janitorial **[2590]**
Service Quality Institute (SQI) **[26644]**
Service Sells/Phil Wexler **[26609]**
Service Specialists Association Annual Convention **[1585]**, **[1599]**, **[1632]**, **[14993]**, **[20719]**
Service Station Dealers of America/National Coalition of Petroleum Retailers and Allied Trades (SSDA-AT) **[18589]**
Service Station Dealers of America [18589]
Service Station Dealers of America and Allied Trades [18589]
Service-Tech Corporation **[2676]**
Service That Sells **[1792]**, **[26610]**, **[43748]**
"Service With a Smile..And Comfy Chairs" in Crain's Chicago Business (Vol. 31, April 28, 2008, No. 17, pp. 46) **[18606]**, **[25639]**, **[26530]**
Servicemaster of Canada Limited **[44623]**
ServiceMaster Residential and Commercial Services, L.P. **[6592]**
"Servicers Back National Effort" in Business First-Columbus (October 19, 2007, pp. A1) **[14491]**, **[33951]**
Services in Canada **[32921]**, **[44519]**
Services Forestiers Timmerlinn Inc. [4058]
Services Select Franchise Company, LLC **[3120]**
Services: The Magazine for the Building Service Contracting Industry **[2635]**, **[6567]**
"Serving Unfair Customers" in Business Horizons (Vol. 51, January-February 2008, No. 1, pp. 29) **[26531]**
Servpro **[6364]**, **[6593]**, **[20844]**
SES Newsletter **[7066]**, **[17698]**, **[30435]**
"A Set-Theoretic Approach to Organizational Configurations" in Academy of Management Review (October 2007, pp. 1180) **[38418]**, **[42875]**
"Seton Grows Heart Institute" in Austin Business Journal (Vol. 31, July 15, 2011, No. 19, pp. A1) **[23408]**, **[34428]**
Seton Hall University - Center for Public Service **[34687]**
"Setting Out on Your Own? Think Franchises" in Crain's Cleveland Business (Vol. 28, October 8, 2007, No. 40, pp. 20) **[32232]**, **[44867]**, **[45679]**
Setting the Table **[17991]**, **[30161]**
Setting the Table: The Transforming Power of Hospitality in Business **[30162]**, **[32922]**
"Setting Up Shop in a Political Hot Spot" in Harvard Business Review (Vol. 88, October 2010, No. 10, pp. 141) **[33952]**, **[36779]**
Setting Up a Telemarketing Program **[19853]**
Setting Up Your Ceramic Studio: Ideas and Plans from Working Artists **[5953]**, **[6088]**, **[6180]**
Settlement Music School - Blanche Wolf Kohn Library **[14705]**
Seven Days in the Art World **[1354]**, **[4512]**, **[5997]**
The Seven Principles of WOM and Buzz Marketing: Crossing the Tipping Point **[588]**, **[40332]**
"Seven Tips for Continuous Improvement" in American Printer (Vol. 128, July 1, 2011, No. 7) **[4513]**, **[16400]**, **[20798]**, **[39356]**
"Seven Ways to Fail Big" in Harvard Business Review (Vol. 86, September 2008, No. 9, pp. 82) **[2797]**, **[12878]**, **[32923]**, **[35126]**, **[44868]**
"Several Studio Projects in Production" in Crain's Detroit Business (Vol. 26, January 18, 2010, No. 3, pp. 21) **[7980]**, **[46357]**
Sevierville Chamber of Commerce **[57780]**
Sevierville Chamber Newsletter **[57781]**
Sevierville Group Tour Planner **[57782]**
Sevierville Marketing Plan **[57783]**
Sevin Rosen Management Co. / Sevin Rosen Funds **[58568]**
Sew News: Creating For You and Your Home **[4150]**, **[18738]**
Seward Area Chamber of Commerce **[54434]**
Seward Chamber of Commerce (SCC) **[47816]**
"Seward Restaurant Garners Accolades" in Alaska Business Monthly (Vol. 27, October 2011, No. 10, pp. 9) **[17992]**, **[19240]**
"Sewing Is a Life Skill; Teaching To Sew Is An Art" in Virginia-Pilot (August 31, 2010) **[6115]**, **[18731]**, **[28340]**
"Sewing Resurgence" in Northeast Mississippi Daily Journal (June 11, 2010) **[18732]**, **[45680]**
"Sewing Shoppe Is All His" in News & Observer (October 8, 2010) **[6116]**, **[18733]**
Sexual Harassment: A Reference Handbook **[26667]**
Sexual Harassment: Handling the Complaint **[26693]**
Sexual Harassment: Serious Business **[26694]**
Sexual Harassment in the Workplace. . .Identify. Stop. Prevent. **[26695]**
Seybold San Francisco Conference and Exposition **[6536]**
Seymour Chamber of Commerce (SCC) **[58438]**
"Seymour Schulich" in Canadian Business (Vol. 79, Winter 2006, No. 24, pp. 144) **[30163]**, **[45995]**
SF Camerawork Reference Library **[15892]**
Chris Shaff Consulting **[41644]**
Shafter Chamber of Commerce (SCC) **[49015]**
Shakamak Area Chamber of Commerce **[51717]**
Shake Hands with Your Computer **[4775]**
Shake's Frozen Custard **[10980]**
Shakespeare Composites & Electronics **[1319]**
Shakey's Pizza & Buffet **[18237]**
Shakopee Chamber of Commerce **[53734]**
Shakopee Valley Convention and Visitors Bureau [53734]
"Shaky on Free Trade" in Canadian Business (Vol. 81, December 24, 2007, No. 1, pp. 29) **[11164]**, **[24017]**, **[33953]**, **[36780]**
"A Shallow Pool" in Canadian Business (Vol. 81, Summer 2008, No. 9, pp. 44) **[8697]**, **[12879]**, **[14492]**, **[23409]**, **[27683]**, **[31811]**
Shamrock Chamber of Commerce (SCC) **[58439]**
Shane's Rib Shack **[18238]**
"Shanghai Butterfly" in Canadian Business (Vol. 80, March 12, 2007, No. 6, pp. 69) **[8698]**, **[12880]**, **[27684]**
Shanghai International Jewellery Fair **[13295]**
Shannon Staffing Inc. **[36064]**, **[40646]**, **[42559]**
Shape **[15990]**, **[21281]**
"Shape Up! Jamal Williams Develops KIDFIT App to Combat Childhood Obesity" in Black Enterprise (Vol. 41, August 2010, No. 1, pp. 62) **[15979]**, **[30164]**, **[34429]**
Share **[34591]**
"Shared Leadership In Teams: An Investigation of Antecedent Conditions and Performance" in Academy of Management Journal (Oct. 2007) **[29156]**, **[30165]**, **[38419]**
ShareOwner **[11979]**
SharePoint I (Onsite) **[30395]**
SharePoint II (Onsite) **[30396]**
SharePoint III (Onsite) **[30397]**
"Sharing the Micro Wealth" in Entrepreneur (Vol. 37, July 2009, No. 7, pp. 46) **[21200]**, **[28867]**, **[37490]**, **[44869]**
Sharing Savannah **[50611]**
"Shari's Berries Founder Shuts Last of Her Stores" in Sacramento Business Journal (Vol. 28, September 2, 2011, No. 27, pp. 1) **[3292]**, **[47373]**
Sharkey's Cuts For Kids, Franchising Co., LLC **[2591]**
Sharonville Chamber of Commerce **[56289]**
Richard Sharpe Associates P.C. **[1320]**
Sharpen Your Sales Presentation: Make It a Winner **[43749]**
Shattuck Chamber of Commerce **[56584]**
Irving Shaw and Associates **[26813]**
"Shaw Joins Green Institute Launch" in Home Textiles Today (Vol. 31, May 24, 2011, No. 13, pp. 4) **[7304]**, **[7664]**, **[10413]**, **[10483]**, **[30789]**
"Shaw, Telus Take Up Battle Positions" in Globe & Mail (January 1, 2006, pp. B1) **[11864]**, **[25640]**, **[44520]**
Shawano Country Chamber of Commerce (SACC) **[59722]**
Shawmut Capital Partners **[53063]**
Shawnee Area Chamber of Commerce (SACC) **[52189]**
Shawnee Chamber of Commerce [56524]
Shealy & Associates **[38807]**
"Shear Profit" in Crain's Cleveland Business (Vol. 28, October 29, 2007, No. 43, pp. 3) **[1021]**, **[21684]**, **[23410]**, **[46358]**
Sheboygan County Chamber of Commerce and Convention and Visitors Bureau **[59723]**
Sheboygan Falls Chamber Main Street **[59724]**
"Shedding Light on Innovation" in Rental Product News (Vol. 33, June 2011) **[17813]**, **[37110]**, **[39357]**
Shedworking: The Alternative Workplace Revolution **[5507]**, **[35618]**, **[45681]**
Sheet Metal and Air Conditioning Contractors' National Association (SMACNA) **[777]**
Sheet Metal and Air-Conditioning Contractors National Association Convention/Exhibition Forum **[897]**
Sheet Metal and Air Conditioning Contractors' National Association Inc. [777]
Sheet Metal Contractors National Association [777]
Sheet Music Magazine **[14753]**
"Sheets Energy Strips Unveils New Vending Machines" in Food and Beverage Close-Up (August 12, 2011) **[19342]**, **[19461]**, **[20869]**
"Sheets Makers Optimistic Amid Price, Delivery Issues" in Home Textiles Today (Vol. 31, May 24, 2011, No. 13, pp. 8) **[10414]**, **[10484]**, **[37207]**, **[43177]**
Shefield Gourmet **[20109]**
Shelburne Museum Research Library **[1157]**
Shelby Area Chamber of Commerce (SACC) **[54309]**
Shelby Chamber of Commerce **[56290]**
Shelby County Chamber of Commerce **[51966]**; **[58440]**
Shelby County Chamber of Commerce (SCCC) **[51718]**
Shelby Report of the Southeast **[10006]**
Shelby Report of the Southwest **[10007]**
Shelbyville Area Chamber of Commerce (SCC) **[51316]**

Small Business Sourcebook • 30th Edition 3613

Shelbyville-Bedford County Chamber of Commerce (SBCCC) **[57784]**
Sheldon Chamber and Community Development Corp. [51967]
Sheldon Chamber and Development Corp. (SCDC) **[51967]**
Shell Lake Chamber of Commerce (SLCC) **[59725]**
"Shell Profit Top $2 Billion as Oil Sands Output Surges" in Globe & Mail (January 26, 2006, pp. B6) **[23411]**, **[39358]**
"Shell Venture Aims at 'Oil Rocks" in Globe & Mail (March 22, 2006, pp. B1) **[24554]**, **[41350]**
Shelter Advertising Association [42584]
Sheltie Pacesetter **[1031]**
Shelton Journal **[59275]**
Shelton-Mason County Chamber of Commerce (SMCCC) **[59276]**
Shenandoah Chamber and Industry Association **[51968]**
Shenandoah Chamber of Commerce [51968]
Shenandoah County Library - Local History and Genealogy Collection **[9560]**
Shenango Valley Chamber of Commerce **[57226]**
Shenango Valley Chamber of Commerce Membership Directory and Buyer's Guide **[57227]**
Sherbrooke University - Centre de Recherche sur le Vieillissement [15143]
Sherbrooke University - Gerontology and Geriatrics Research Centre [15143]
Sherbrooke University - Research Centre on Aging **[15143]**
Sheridan County Chamber of Commerce **[54310]**; **[59844]**
"Shermag Plans Two Shutdowns, 300 More Layoffs" in Globe & Mail (February 13, 2007, pp. B5) **[24555]**, **[25209]**, **[39359]**
"Shermag Says Refinishing Not Complete" in Globe & Mail (February 14, 2006, pp. B3) **[24556]**, **[25210]**
Sherman Oaks Chamber NEWS **[49016]**
Sherman Oaks Chamber of Commerce [48623]
Sherpa Partners LLC **[53782]**
Sherwin-Williams Automotive Finishes Corporation Library **[15381]**, **[15408]**
"Sherwin-Williams Workers Forgo Travel for Virtual Trade Show" in Crain's Cleveland Business (Vol. 28, October 15, 2007, No. 41) **[11865]**, **[20418]**, **[35127]**, **[39360]**, **[46700]**
Sherwood Chamber of Commerce (SCC) **[48107]**; **[56841]**
Sherwood Chamber of Commerce Business and Community Directory **[56842]**
Sherwood Chamber of Commerce Newsletter **[56843]**
Shetland Properties Limited Partnership [51454]
Shhh! I'm Finding a Job: The Library and Your Self-Directed Job Search **[6993]**
Shiatsu Massage **[14152]**
Shiawassee Business Monthly **[53436]**
Shiawassee Regional Chamber of Commerce (SRCC) **[53437]**
SHIELD Security Systems **[18525]**
"Shifting Gears" in Business Journal-Serving Phoenix & the Valley of the Sun (Vol. 31, November 12, 2010, No. 10, pp. 1) **[1560]**, **[7305]**, **[7665]**, **[17718]**, **[27685]**, **[30790]**
Tom Shillock Consulting **[22538]**, **[40647]**, **[42560]**
The Shine Factory **[1610]**, **[3336]**
Shiner Chamber of Commerce **[58441]**
Shingle Springs Business and Professional Association Inc. [49017]
Shingle Springs/Cameron Park Chamber of Commerce **[49017]**
Shingle Springs/Cameron Park Chamber of Commerce Chamber News **[49018]**
"Ship Shape" in Hawaii Business (Vol. 53, January 2008, No. 7, pp. 46) **[41351]**, **[44521]**
"Shipbuilding & Defence" in Canadian Sailings (July 7, 2008) **[25641]**, **[39361]**, **[42168]**, **[43956]**
Shippensburg Area Chamber of Commerce (SACC) **[57228]**
Shippensburg University of Pennsylvania - Frehn Center for Management [2345]
Shippensburg University of Pennsylvania - Office of Extended Studies [2345]
Shippensburg University Small Business Development Center **[56915]**
"Shipping 2.0" in Entrepreneur (Vol. 36, April 2008, No. 4, pp. 54) **[11866]**, **[15347]**, **[15780]**, **[21201]**, **[26783]**, **[44522]**
"Shipwreck Floats Nickel's Boat" in Globe & Mail (January 24, 2007, pp. B1) **[8699]**, **[12881]**
"Shire Seeking New Digs for Headquarters" in Philadelphia Business Journal (Vol. 30, September 2, 2011, No. 29, pp. 1) **[6665]**, **[24767]**, **[36781]**, **[42876]**, **[43957]**, **[44723]**

Shoals Chamber of Commerce (SCC) **[47733]**
Shoals Entrepreneurial Center **[47765]**
Shoe Factory Buyer's Guide **[18766]**
Shoe Retailing Today **[18777]**
Shoe Service Institute of America (SSIA) **[18745]**
Shoeless Joe's Limited **[18239]**
Shoes-n-Feet **[18782]**
"Shoe's On Other Foot" in Business Courier (Vol. 24, November 30, 2008, No. 33, pp. 1) **[30166]**, **[39362]**, **[44870]**
"Shoestring-Budget Marketing" in Women Entrepreneur (January 5, 2009) **[589]**, **[11867]**, **[21202]**, **[22438]**, **[22627]**, **[23412]**, **[28868]**, **[40333]**, **[42516]**, **[42656]**, **[43608]**, **[45682]**
SHOOT Commercial Production and Postproduction Directory [7981]
Shoot Commercial Production Directory [7981]
The SHOOT Directory for Commercial Production and Postproduction **[7981]**
Shooting Federation of Prince Edward Island Library **[10049]**
The Shooting, Hunting, and Outdoor Trade Show (SHOT SHOW) **[1254]**, **[10040]**, **[19389]**
Shooting Industry **[1249]**, **[10035]**
Shooting Times **[1250]**
"Shop Around" in Houston Chronicle (December 7, 2010, pp. 3) **[1127]**, **[4267]**, **[6383]**, **[13278]**, **[18767]**, **[42169]**, **[47374]**
Shop Class as Soulcraft **[29157]**, **[32924]**
The Shop Rancho Retail Guide and Service Directory **[49019]**
ShopKeeper Publishing International Inc. [58609]
ShopKeeper Publishing - ShopKeeper Publishing International Inc. [58609]
ShopKeeper Software **[58609]**
Shoplifting Prevented **[43278]**
Shoppe Talk **[51319]**
"Shopped Out; Retailing Gloom" in The Economist (Vol. 390, January 3, 2009, No. 8612, pp. 26) **[11165]**, **[12882]**, **[23413]**, **[26310]**, **[27686]**, **[31812]**, **[36782]**, **[37491]**, **[43178]**
Shoppers Drug Mart **[6701]**
"Shoppers Targets an Upscale Move" in Globe & Mail (January 19, 2007, pp. B4) **[25211]**, **[43179]**
"Shoppes of Kenwood Files Chap. 11" in Business Courier (Vol. 26, December 18, 2009, No. 34, pp. 1) **[1528]**, **[12883]**, **[31813]**, **[43180]**
"Shopping Around for New Ideas" in Canadian Business (Vol. 79, July 17, 2006, No. 14-15, pp. 76) **[21966]**, **[24018]**, **[32925]**, **[33954]**, **[43181]**
Shopping Center world [17571]
Shopping and Dining Guide **[51318]**; **[51319]**
Shopping Guide **[54808]**
Shopping for Health **[15192]**
SHOPtalk | Engine Professional **[18622]**
Shoptalk **[51320]**
Shore Line **[51969]**; **[52755]**
Shore Lines **[56844]**
"Shore Total Office Liquidates Massive Supply of Bank Furniture and Used Furniture" in Internet Wire (June 21, 2010) **[5148]**, **[15251]**, **[41554]**
Shoreline **[58983]**
Shoreline Chamber of Commerce (SCC) **[59277]**
Shoreline General Contractors Inc. **[5669]**
Shoreline Venture Management, LLC **[49316]**
ShoreLines **[59278]**
Short Courses [9124], [16203]
Short Elliott Hendrickson Inc. (SEH) **[19554]**
"Short Sales,' A Sign of Housing Troubles, Start Popping Up" in The Business Review Albany (Vol. 35, April 11, 2008, No. 1, pp. 1) **[14493]**, **[17058]**, **[26311]**, **[27687]**, **[37492]**
Short Story Writers **[6830]**
"Shorts Story" in Barron's (Vol. 89, July 6, 2009, No. 27, pp. 16) **[8700]**, **[12884]**, **[24557]**, **[31814]**; **[8701]**, **[12885]**, **[24558]**, **[31815]**
Shotgun News: The World's Largest Gun Sales Publication **[10036]**
"Should the Fed Regulate Wall Street?" in Barron's (Vol. 88, March 24, 2008, No. 12, pp. M15) **[8702]**, **[12886]**, **[27688]**, **[31816]**, **[33336]**, **[33955]**
"Should I or Shouldn't I?" in Indoor Comfort Marketing (Vol. 70, February 2011, No. 2, pp. 30) **[7666]**, **[12887]**, **[30791]**, **[31817]**, **[40334]**, **[45683]**
"Should You Go Into Business With Your Spouse?" in Women Entrepreneur (September 1, 2008) **[24559]**, **[25212]**, **[31012]**, **[44777]**
"Should You Invest in the Long Tail?" in Harvard Business Review (Vol. 86, July-August 2008, No. 8, pp. 88) **[23414]**, **[40335]**, **[41221]**, **[43609]**
"Shout and Devour" in Tulsa World (November 7, 2009) **[5813]**, **[25642]**, **[32233]**, **[40336]**
"Show Dates" in Art Business News (Vol. 34, November 2007, No. 11, pp. 18) **[1355]**, **[4514]**, **[5998]**, **[20419]**, **[46701]**

Show Directory **[18826]**
Show Low Chamber of Commerce [47954]
Show Low Regional Chamber of Commerce **[47954]**
"Show Me the Love" in Canadian Business (Vol. 79, November 6, 2006, No. 22, pp. 77) **[590]**, **[9708]**, **[23415]**, **[40337]**
"Show and Tell" in Entrepreneur (Vol. 36, May 2008, No. 5, pp. 54) **[3803]**, **[7982]**, **[11868]**, **[26532]**, **[35128]**, **[40338]**, **[42657]**, **[44523]**
Show off Your Dog-Grooming Basics **[15795]**
Showcase International [13631]
Shred-It **[17736]**
Shreveport Chamber of Commerce [52468]
Shrimp Notes **[8988]**
Shriner-Midland Co. **[33092]**
Shutterbug **[15862]**, **[15916]**
SI Ventures **[50354]**
SIA Ski and Outdoor Sports Show Directory [18830]
SIA Ski, Snowboard and Outdoor Sports Show Directory [18830]
The SIA Snow Show **[18839]**
SIA Snow Sports Book **[18830]**
SIA Vegas [18839]
Sibley Chamber of Commerce (SCC) **[51970]**
Sibley Chamber of Commerce - Main Street [51970]
"Sick of Trends? You Should Be" in Brandweek (Vol. 49, April 21, 2008, No. 16, pp. 22) **[591]**, **[25900]**, **[40339]**, **[42517]**, **[45684]**
"A Side Project Threatens To Get Totally Out of Control and I Think, 'How Fun" in Inc. (October 2007, pp. 81-82) **[3615]**, **[18989]**, **[40340]**, **[41222]**, **[45207]**
Sidney Area Chamber of Commerce and Agriculture (SACCA) **[54311]**
Sidney Chamber of Commerce **[55339]**
Sidney Chamber of Commerce (SCC) **[51971]**
Sidney Chamber of Commerce [54311]
Siebrand-Wilton Associates Inc. **[22075]**, **[31002]**, **[36065]**, **[42347]**
SIECUS Report **[34592]**
"Siemens Boss on Big Scandals, Bullet-Proof Limos" in Globe & Mail (March 5, 2007, pp. B11) **[30167]**, **[38420]**
Sienna Ventures / Sienna Holdings Inc. **[49317]**
Sierra Club of Canada (SCC) **[7067]**
Sierra County Chamber of Commerce **[54986]**
Sierra County - Truth or Consequences Chamber of Commerce [54986]
Sierra Legal Defence Fund [7043]
Sierra Madre Chamber of Commerce **[49020]**
Sierra Ventures **[49318]**
Sierra Vista Tourism **[47955]**
Siesta Key Chamber of Commerce (SKCC) **[50296]**
SIGACT News **[4898]**
Sight Survey Professional 2009 **[19536]**
Sightlines **[34168]**
SIGIR Forum **[4738]**
Sigma Partners (Menlo Park) **[49319]**
Sign Association of Canada (SAC) **[361]**
Sign Biz, Inc. **[678]**, **[4555]**
"Sign of Progress" in Playthings (Vol. 106, October 1, 2008, No. 9, pp. 4) **[11166]**, **[18480]**, **[20265]**, **[24019]**, **[36783]**
"Sign, Sign, Everywhere a Sign: How I Did It: Richard Schaps" in Inc. (October 2007, pp. 128) **[592]**, **[18788]**, **[30168]**, **[40341]**, **[44189]**
"Sign of the Times: Temp-To-Perm Attorneys" in HRMagazine (Vol. 54, January 2009, No. 1, pp. 24) **[6974]**, **[7794]**, **[19165]**, **[20035]**, **[24020]**, **[35471]**, **[45685]**
"Sign Up To Grow Your Business, Generate Jobs" in Women Entrepreneur (November 25, 2008) **[23416]**, **[25213]**, **[27689]**, **[30169]**, **[35472]**, **[47375]**
Signal Graphics Business Centers **[18796]**
Signal Hill Chamber of Commerce **[49021]**
Signal Lake Management LLC **[49786]**
SIGNARAMA, Inc. **[18797]**
Signature Alert Security **[18526]**
SignCraft: The guide to profitable and creative sign production **[18793]**
Significant Earthquakes Database **[7392]**
Signpost **[52190]**
Signs Canada **[362]**
Signs First **[18798]**
Signs Now **[18799]**
Signs of the Times **[18794]**, **[40564]**
Signs of the Times Magazine--Buyers' Guide Issue **[18789]**
Signs of the Times Magazine--Sign Erection and Maintenance Directory Section **[18790]**
Signs of the Times Magazine--Sign Supply Distributors Directory Section **[18791]**
Signs of the Times & Screen Printing en Espanol **[16423]**
Signs by Tomorrow **[18800]**

MASTER INDEX Small
Master Index

SIGPLAN Notices **[4899]**
SIGSOFT Software Engineering Notes **[4900]**
Siguler Guff & Company **[55456]**
Sikeston Area Chamber of Commerce (SACC) **[54133]**
Silicon Alley Venture Partners LLC / SAVP **[55457]**
"Silicon Success: Solar Energy Shines for Dawn Alston Paige" in Black Enterprise (Vol. 38, October 2007, No. 3, pp. 46) **[19114]**
Silicon Valley Bancventures / Silicon Valley Bank (Menlo Park) **[49320]**
Silicon Valley Small Business Development Center at West Valley/Mission College **[48171]**
"Silicon Valley's Economic Recovery Picking Up Pace" in Globe & Mail (January 29, 2007, pp. B13) **[27690]**, **[35129]**
Siloam Springs Chamber of Commerce (SSCC) **[48108]**
Silos, Politics and Turf Wars: A Leadership Fable about Destroying the Barriers That Turn Colleagues Into Competitors **[25643]**, **[25901]**, **[29158]**, **[30170]**, **[38421]**
Silution Franchise Corp. **[4677]**, **[5056]**
Silver Burdett & Ginn - Editorial Library **[2231]**, **[14075]**
Silver City Chamber of Commerce [55658]
Silver City-Grant County Chamber of Commerce **[54987]**
"Silver Dollars" in Small Business Opportunities (September 2008) **[304]**, **[1431]**, **[15080]**, **[32234]**
"Silver Key Seeks Volunteer Drivers in Colorado Springs" in Colorado Springs Business Journal (October 21, 2011) **[9163]**, **[45996]**
Silver Lake Sand Dunes Area Chamber of Commerce **[53438]**
Silver Mine Subs **[18240]**
Silver River Marine Institute **[50383]**
Silver Spring Chamber of Commerce [52719]
"Silver Springs Creamery Opens Retail" in Bellingham Business Journal (Vol. March 2010, pp. 3) **[9972]**, **[10918]**, **[19241]**, **[43182]**
"Silver Standard Reports First Quarter 2007 Results" in Canadian Corporate News (May 14, 2007) **[8703]**, **[12888]**, **[31818]**
Silverdale Chamber of Commerce **[59279]**
"Silverdome Bidders Bring New Proposals" in Crain's Detroit Business (Vol. 24, March 17, 2008, No. 11, pp. 23) **[953]**, **[974]**, **[9403]**, **[10749]**, **[16552]**, **[17489]**, **[20420]**, **[44190]**, **[46702]**
"Silverpop Recognized for Email Marketing Innovations by Econsultancy" in Marketing Weekly News (January 23, 2010, pp. 124) **[11869]**, **[28869]**, **[40342]**
Silverton Area Chamber of Commerce (SACC) **[56845]**
Silverton Chamber of Commerce (SCC) **[49587]**
"The Silvery Moon Moves to Larger Space" in Bellingham Business Journal (Vol. March 2010, pp. 5) **[13279]**, **[23417]**, **[24768]**, **[44724]**
Simi Valley Chamber of Commerce **[49022]**
"Similac Introduces New Packaging" in Marketing to Women (Vol. 21, February 2008, No. 2, pp. 3) **[9973]**, **[40343]**, **[41223]**
Simmons College - Graduate School of Library and Information Science Library **[2232]**
"The Simon Cowell of Sales" in Inc. (March 2008, pp. 81-82) **[22439]**, **[43610]**
Simon Fraser University - Canadian Centre for Studies in Publishing (CCSP) **[2234]**
Simon Fraser University - Centre for Sustainable Community Development (CSCD) **[27944]**
Simon Fraser University - Community Economic Development Centre [27944]
"A Simple Old Reg that Needs Dusting Off" in Barron's (Vol. 88, June 30, 2008, No. 26, pp. 35) **[12889]**, **[21685]**, **[24021]**, **[33956]**, **[44524]**
A Simplified Guide to Small Business Tax Deductions **[46359]**
Simplified Incorporation Kit **[32926]**, **[43330]**
Simplified Technology Co. **[41518]**, **[41645]**
"Simplifying Social Media for Optimum Results" in Franchising World (Vol. 42, August 2010, No. 8, pp. 12) **[28870]**, **[32235]**, **[40344]**
"Simply Therapeutic" in Women In Business (Vol. 61, December 2009, No. 6, pp. 34) **[32927]**, **[41555]**
Simpsonville Area Chamber of Commerce **[57524]**
Simpsonville Membership Directory **[57525]**
Simsbury Chamber of Commerce (SCOC) **[49750]**
"Sinai Doctor Seeks FDA OK for Drug" in Baltimore Business Journal (Vol. 28, July 16, 2010, No. 10, pp. 1) **[6666]**, **[25644]**, **[34430]**, **[37111]**, **[41224]**
"Singapore Airlines' Balancing Act" in Harvard Business Review (Vol. 88, July-August 2010, No. 7-8, pp. 145) **[24917]**, **[31819]**, **[35130]**, **[37112]**
Single Audit Information Service **[188]**
"Single Most Important Problem" in Small Business Economic Trends (April 2008, pp. 18) **[27691]**, **[32928]**
"Single Most Important Problem" in Small Business Economic Trends (February 2008, pp. 18) **[27693]**, **[32930]**, **[45687]**
"Single Most Important Problem" in Small Business Economic Trends (January 2008, pp. 18) **[27694]**, **[32931]**, **[45688]**
"Single Most Important Problem" in Small Business Economic Trends (July 2010, pp. 18) **[33957]**, **[43612]**, **[45689]**, **[46361]**
"Single Most Important Problem" in Small Business Economic Trends (March 2008, pp. 18) **[27692]**, **[32929]**, **[45686]**
"Single Most Important Problem" in Small Business Economic Trends (September 2010, pp. 18) **[32932]**, **[43611]**, **[46360]**
Singles in the Suburbs Newsletter **[15440]**
Sins **[4159]**
Sinton Chamber of Commerce (SCC) **[58442]**
Sioux Center Chamber of Commerce (SCCC) **[51972]**
Sioux City Chamber of Commerce [51974]
Sioux Falls Area Chamber of Commerce (SFACC) **[57597]**
Sioux Falls Community Guide **[57598]**
Sioux Falls Small Business Development Center **[57555]**
Siouxland Business **[51973]**
Siouxland Chamber of Commerce (SCC) **[51974]**
Sir Speedy [5873], [16445]
Sir Speedy Inc. **[5873]**, **[16445]**
Sir Speedy Printing Centers [5873], [16445]
Sisters Area Chamber of Commerce **[56846]**
Sisters in Crime (SinC) **[6803]**
Sit-Up Shaped Cakes **[1793]**
Site Design Group Ltd. **[15264]**
Site Selection Magazine **[44750]**
"Sites Set" in Entrepreneur (Vol. 35, November 2007, No. 11, pp. 112) **[28871]**, **[40345]**, **[42170]**
SiteShapers **[3661]**, **[19052]**
"Siteworx Earns 4 Interactive Media Awards in Q1 of 2011" in Entertainment Close-Up (, 2011) **[21203]**, **[28872]**
"Sitting, Sitting, Sitting-Snapshots of Homes that Just Won't Sell" in Crain's Chicago Business (Vol. 31, April 21, 2008, No. 16) **[17059]**, **[17490]**
Situational Leadership II Workshop (Onsite) **[37736]**
Siver Insurance Consultants **[36258]**
"Six Great Stock Funds for the Long Haul" in Barron's (Vol. 89, July 13, 2009, No. 28, pp. L5) **[8704]**, **[12890]**, **[31820]**
"Six Leading Economists on What to Expect in the Year Ahead: David Wolf" in Canadian Business (Dec. 24, 2007) **[25645]**, **[27695]**, **[36784]**
"Six Leading Economists on What to Expect in the Year Ahead: Derek Holt; Housing" in Canadian Business (December 24, 2007) **[14494]**, **[17060]**, **[17491]**, **[24022]**, **[27696]**
"Six Leading Economists on What to Expect in the Year Ahead: Glen Hodgson; Canada in Depth" in Canadian Business (December 24, 2007) **[23418]**, **[27697]**
"Six Leading Economists on What to Expect in the Year Ahead: Peter Buchanan" in Canadian Business (December 24, 2007) **[23419]**, **[27698]**
"Six Sears Board Members to Resign in April" in Globe & Mail (March 1, 2006, pp. B1) **[38422]**, **[43183]**
Six SIGMA for Small Business **[143]**, **[21424]**, **[25341]**, **[31821]**, **[32933]**, **[35921]**, **[40346]**, **[41225]**, **[43613]**
The Six Sigma for Small and Medium Businesses: What You Need to Know Explained Simply **[30171]**, **[32934]**, **[39363]**
"Six Things You Can Do To Ride Out A Turbulent Market" in Hispanic Business (Vol. 30, March 2008, No. 3, pp. 20) **[8705]**, **[12891]**, **[31822]**, **[34431]**, **[36785]**
"Six Things You Can Do To Ride Out a Turbulent Market" in Hispanic Business (March 2008, pp. 20-21) **[12892]**, **[27699]**
"Six Tips To Maximize Networking Opportunities" in Women Entrepreneur (November 3, 2008) **[20421]**, **[22440]**, **[42171]**, **[43614]**, **[44871]**, **[46703]**, **[47376]**
"Sixty-Acre Vision for North Suburbs" in Business Courier (Vol. 24, April 4, 2008, No. 52, pp. 1) **[5508]**, **[16553]**, **[17492]**, **[24560]**, **[34432]**
Size of Craft/Hobby Industry **[6119]**
"Size Does Matter" in International Journal of Globalisation and Small Business (Vol. 4, September 21, 2010, No. 1, pp. 61) **[25646]**, **[29159]**, **[36786]**, **[37256]**, **[39364]**, **[42172]**
"Size Matters" in Entrepreneur (Vol. 36, April 2008, No. 4, pp. 44) **[22441]**, **[23420]**, **[30172]**, **[35473]**, **[38423]**
"Size Obsession" in Marketing to Women (Vol. 22, August 2009, No. 8, pp. 2) **[4268]**, **[40347]**
Sizzler USA Franchise, Inc. **[18241]**
Skagway Business Directory **[47817]**
Skagway Chamber of Commerce **[47818]**
Skamania County Chamber of Commerce **[59280]**
Skaneateles Area Chamber of Commerce **[55340]**
Skaneateles Community Directory **[55341]**
Skeet Shooting Review **[1251]**
SketchPad Graphic Design **[6546]**
SketchPad Publications [6546]
Ski **[18833]**
Ski Dazzle - Los Angeles Ski Show and Snowboard Expo **[18840]**
Ski Industries America [18827]
Ski Industries America--Trade Show Directory [18830]
Ski Industries Association [18827]
Ski, Snowboard, & Outdoor Sports Show [18839]
Skiatook Chamber of Commerce **[56585]**
Skiing: The Magazine of Winter Adventure **[18834]**
SkillSearch **[7010]**, **[7808]**
"A Skimmer's Guide to the Latest Business Books" in Inc. (Volume 32, December 2010, No. 10, pp. 34) **[32935]**
Skin Inc.: Professional Skin Care **[1909]**, **[2061]**, **[5904]**
The Skincare Market **[1905]**
Skinned Knuckles: A Journal of Car Restoration **[18623]**
"Skinner's No Drive-Thru CEO" in Crain's Chicago Business (Vol. 31, April 28, 2008, No. 17, pp. 1) **[12893]**, **[23421]**, **[24561]**, **[26533]**, **[30173]**, **[32236]**, **[38424]**, **[43615]**
"Skinny Jeans Sticking Around for Fall" in Charlotte Observer (February 5, 2007) **[4134]**, **[4269]**, **[45690]**
Sklar and Associates Inc. **[2969]**, **[3087]**, **[13883]**, **[24699]**, **[26098]**, **[38808]**, **[44957]**, **[45835]**
Skokie Chamber of Commerce (SCC) **[51321]**
Harvey C. Skoog **[22145]**, **[25363]**, **[25396]**, **[26099]**, **[32060]**, **[40648]**, **[44958]**, **[46457]**
Skowhegan Area Chamber of Commerce **[52629]**
Sky Valley Chamber of Commerce **[59281]**
Skyhawks **[19496]**
Skyline Ventures **[49321]**
Skyliner **[58443]**
"Skype Ltd. Acquired GroupMe" in Information Today (Vol. 28, October 2011, No. 9, pp. 12) **[3804]**, **[12894]**, **[25342]**, **[28873]**
"Skype on Steroids" in Inc. (Vol. 31, January-February 2009, No. 1, pp. 46) **[3616]**, **[3805]**, **[18990]**, **[45208]**
"The Skype's the Limit" in Canadian Business (Vol. 80, February 12, 2007, No. 4, pp. 70) **[12895]**, **[23422]**, **[35131]**, **[44525]**
"The Sky's the Limit" in Retail Merchandiser (Vol. 51, July-August 2011, No. 4, pp. 64) **[3293]**, **[37113]**, **[41226]**, **[43184]**
Slaton Chamber of Commerce **[58444]**
Slayton Area Chamber of Commerce (SACC) **[53735]**
"Sleeman Cuts Again as Cheap Suds Bite" in Globe & Mail (March 3, 2006, pp. B3) **[12896]**, **[24562]**, **[25214]**
Sleep **[34593]**
Sleep Inn **[10818]**
"Sleep It Off In a Silo B & B" in Chicago Tribune (December 14, 2008) **[1931]**, **[21686]**, **[24918]**
Sleepy Eye Area Chamber of Commerce (SEACC) **[53736]**
Sleepy Hollow Tarrytown Chamber of Commerce (SHCC) **[55342]**
"A Slice of Danish; Fixing Finance" in The Economist (Vol. 390, January 3, 2009, No. 8612, pp. 55) **[8706]**, **[12897]**, **[14495]**, **[26312]**, **[27700]**, **[31823]**, **[36787]**, **[37493]**
Slick Magazine **[56847]**
"Slick Science" in Canadian Business (Vol. 81, September 15, 2008, No. 14-15, pp. 55) **[7306]**, **[7667]**, **[30792]**, **[37114]**, **[41352]**, **[43958]**
Slidell City Map **[52497]**
Slidell Connection **[52498]**
"Slimmed-Down Supplier TI Automotive Relaunches" in Crain's Detroit Business (Vol. 26, January 11, 2010, No. 2, pp. 14) **[11167]**, **[24563]**, **[25215]**, **[26784]**, **[36788]**, **[39365]**, **[40348]**
"Slimmer Interiros Make Small Cars Seem Big" in Automotive News (Vol. 86, October 31, 2011, No. 6488, pp. 16) **[1561]**, **[14950]**, **[39366]**, **[45691]**
Slip Away to Branson **[54134]**
Slovenian Mutual Benefit Association [21849]
"Slow-Down Startups Hot" in Austin Business JournalInc. (Vol. 28, September 12, 2008, No. 26, pp. 1) **[29393]**, **[32427]**, **[33133]**
"Slow but Steady into the Future" in Barron's (Vol. 88, July 7, 2008, No. 27, pp. M) **[12898]**, **[18991]**, **[22442]**, **[25647]**, **[35132]**, **[42877]**, **[43959]**, **[44526]**, **[45209]**
"Sluggish Market Gives Hospitals the Financial Chills" in The Business Journal-Serving Greater Tampa Bay (Vol. 28, August 1, 2008) **[11425]**, **[27701]**, **[34433]**, **[36223]**
"S.M. Whitney Co. (1868-2010)" in Canadian Business (Vol. 83, October 12, 2010, No. 17, pp. 27) **[4270]**, **[18734]**, **[39367]**, **[44191]**
SMA Inc. [47993]
"The Small 300" in Canadian Business (Vol. 81, Summer 2008, No. 9, pp. 137) **[8707]**, **[12899]**, **[23423]**, **[31824]**, **[43616]**, **[45692]**

Small-Business MASTER INDEX

"*Small Biz Owners Are Tapping Into Health Savings Plans*" *in Small Business Opportunities (Fall 2007)* **[11426]**, **[21967]**, **[34434]**, **[36224]**
"*Small is Bountiful for Intuit*" *in Barron's (Vol. 90, September 13, 2010, No. 37, pp. 22)* **[144]**, **[3617]**, **[12900]**, **[18992]**, **[21425]**, **[45210]**
"*Small Budget, Big Impact*" *in Small Business Opportunities (Summer 2010)* **[28874]**, **[40349]**, **[43617]**
Small Business Access and Alternatives to Health Care: Congressional Hearing **[11427]**, **[34435]**, **[36225]**
Small Business Access to Health Care: Congressional Hearing **[24023]**, **[33958]**, **[34436]**
Small Business Accounting Systems **[21451]**
Small Business Administration **[53078]**
Small Business Administration Reference Library **[45840]**
The Small Business Advisor **[30355]**, **[44900]**
The Small Business Advocate **[34072]**
"*Small-Business Agenda: Increase Capital, Education, Tax Breaks*" *in Crain's Detroit Business (Vol. 24, March 17, 2008)* **[27702]**, **[28341]**, **[33337]**, **[44872]**, **[46362]**, **[47077]**
Small Business: An Entrepreneur's Business Plan **[24564]**, **[30174]**, **[32936]**
Small Business: An Entrepreneur's Plan **[30175]**, **[32937]**, **[46048]**
The Small Business Bible: Everything You Need to Know to Succeed in Your Small Business **[145]**, **[593]**, **[2313]**, **[21426]**, **[31825]**, **[32938]**, **[40350]**, **[42658]**
Small Business, Big Life: Five Steps to Creating a Great Life with Your Own Small Business **[25216]**, **[29160]**, **[29394]**, **[32428]**; **[30176]**, **[32939]**
Small Business in a Big World **[27911]**, **[44915]**
"*Small Business Capital Outlays*" *in Small Business Economic Trends (April 2008, pp. 16)* **[23424]**, **[31826]**
"*Small Business Capital Outlays*" *in Small Business Economic Trends (February 2008, pp. 16)* **[23426]**, **[31828]**, **[45694]**
"*Small Business Capital Outlays*" *in Small Business Economic Trends (January 2008, pp. 16)* **[23427]**, **[31829]**, **[45695]**
"*Small Business Capital Outlays*" *in Small Business Economic Trends (July 2010, pp. 16)* **[31831]**, **[45696]**
"*Small Business Capital Outlays*" *in Small Business Economic Trends (March 2008, pp. 16)* **[23425]**, **[31827]**, **[45693]**
"*Small Business Capital Outlays*" *in Small Business Economic Trends (September 2010, pp. 16)* **[31830]**
Small Business Cash Flow: Strategies for Making Your Business a Financial Success **[22123]**, **[23428]**, **[31832]**
Small Business Clustering Technology: Applications in Marketing, Management, Finance, and IT **[22124]**, **[27703]**, **[28875]**, **[31833]**, **[35133]**, **[38425]**, **[40351]**
"*Small Business Compensation*" *in Small Business Economic Trends (April 2008, pp. 10)* **[21968]**, **[32940]**, **[45697]**
"*Small Business Compensation*" *in Small Business Economic Trends (February 2008, pp. 10)* **[21970]**, **[32942]**, **[45699]**
"*Small Business Compensation*" *in Small Business Economic Trends (January 2008, pp. 10)* **[21971]**, **[32943]**, **[45700]**
"*Small Business Compensation*" *in Small Business Economic Trends (July 2010, pp. 10)* **[21972]**, **[25383]**, **[45701]**
"*Small Business Compensation*" *in Small Business Economic Trends (March 2008, pp. 10)* **[21969]**, **[32941]**, **[45698]**
"*Small Business Compensation*" *in Small Business Economic Trends (September 2010, pp. 10)* **[25382]**, **[25791]**
Small Business Council of America (SBCA) **[33477]**
Small Business Council of America--Alert **[46448]**
"*Small Business Credit Conditions*" *in Small Business Economic Trends (April 2008, pp. 12)* **[6207]**, **[6250]**, **[6326]**, **[26313]**, **[37494]**
"*Small Business Credit Conditions*" *in Small Business Economic Trends (February 2008, pp. 12)* **[6208]**, **[6251]**, **[6327]**, **[26314]**, **[37495]**
"*Small Business Credit Conditions*" *in Small Business Economic Trends (January 2008, pp. 12)* **[6209]**, **[6252]**, **[6328]**, **[26315]**, **[37496]**
"*Small Business Credit Conditions*" *in Small Business Economic Trends (July 2010, pp. 12)* **[6330]**, **[26317]**, **[37498]**, **[45702]**
"*Small Business Credit Conditions*" *in Small Business Economic Trends (September 2010, pp. 12)* **[6329]**, **[26316]**, **[37497]**
Small Business Desk Reference **[146]**, **[17853]**, **[21427]**, **[24024]**, **[24565]**, **[25343]**, **[25812]**, **[26534]**, **[30976]**, **[31834]**, **[32237]**, **[32944]**, **[36226]**, **[40352]**, **[42926]**, **[43618]**, **[44229]**, **[46363]**
Small Business Development Center at Manatee Community College - Sarasota [49894]
Small Business Development Center at Manatee Community College - Venice [49893]
Small Business Development Center Broward County **[49871]**
Small Business Development Center at Central Florida Development Council of Polk County **[49872]**
Small Business Development Center at Columbus State Community College **[55950]**
Small Business Development Center at Edison Community College **[55951]**
Small Business Development Center at Florida A&M University - Perry **[49873]**
Small Business Development Center at Florida A&M University - Tallahassee **[49874]**
Small Business Development Center at Florida Atlantic University - Boca Raton **[49875]**
Small Business Development Center at Florida Atlantic University - Downtown Campus **[49876]**
Small Business Development Center at Florida Atlantic University - Florida Keys Community College **[49877]**
Small Business Development Center at Florida Atlantic University - Miami-Dade County **[49878]**
Small Business Development Center at Florida Atlantic University - Port St. Lucie **[49879]**
Small Business Development Center at Florida Atlantic University - Treasure Coast **[49880]**
Small Business Development Center at Florida Gulf Coast University - Cape Coral **[49881]**
Small Business Development Center at Florida Gulf Coast University - Clewiston **[49882]**
Small Business Development Center at Florida Gulf Coast University - Fort Myers **[49883]**
Small Business Development Center at Florida Gulf Coast University - Immokalee **[49884]**
Small Business Development Center at Florida Gulf Coast University - Port Charlotte **[49885]**
Small Business Development Center at Gannon University **[56916]**
Small Business Development Center - Greater Sacramento **[48172]**
Small Business Development Center at Gulf Coast Community College **[49886]**
Small Business Development Center of Hampton Roads **[58816]**
Small Business Development Center of Hampton Roads - Eastern Shore **[58817]**
Small Business Development Center of Hampton Roads - Franklin **[58818]**
Small Business Development Center of Hampton Roads - Smithfield **[58819]**
Small Business Development Center of Hampton Roads - Suffolk **[58820]**
Small Business Development Center of Hampton Roads - Thomas Nelson **[58821]**
Small Business Development Center of Hampton Roads - Williamsburg **[58822]**
Small Business Development Center of the Heartland at South Florida Community College **[49887]**
Small Business Development Center at Indian River State College - Fort Pierce **[49888]**
Small Business Development Center at Indian River State College - Stuart **[49889]**
Small Business Development Center at James A. Rhodes State College **[55952]**
Small Business Development Center (Keene, New Hampshire) **[54535]**
Small Business Development Center at Kent State University Stark Campus **[55953]**
Small Business Development Center at Kent State University Tuscarawas Campus **[55954]**
Small Business Development Center at Lake County Economic Development Center **[55955]**
Small Business Development Center (Littleton, New Hampshire) **[54536]**
Small Business Development Center (Manchester, New Hampshire) **[54537]**
Small Business Development Center at Marietta **[55956]**
Small Business Development Center at Maumee Valley Planning Organization **[55957]**
Small Business Development Center Miami-Dade - Hialeah Gardens **[49890]**
Small Business Development Center (Nashua, New Hampshire) **[54538]**
Small Business Development Center at North Florida Community College **[49891]**
Small Business Development Center at Northern New Mexico College **[54907]**
Small Business Development Center at Ohio University **[55958]**
Small Business Development Center at Palm Beach Community College - Boca Raton **[49892]**
Small Business Development Center at Raritan Valley Community College **[54643]**
Small Business Development Center at St. Francis University **[56917]**
Small Business Development Center, St. Thomas Metro **[53538]**
Small Business Development Center - Seacoast **[54539]**
Small Business Development Center at Shasta College **[48173]**
Small Business Development Center - Southeast Missouri State University **[53938]**
Small Business Development Center at State College of Florida Manatee - Sarasota **[49894]**
Small Business Development Center at State College of Florida Manatee-Sarasota **[49893]**
Small Business Development Center - The College of New Jersey **[54644]**
Small Business Development Center at The Lorain County Chamber of Commerce **[55959]**, **[56291]**
Small Business Development Center at The OSU South Centers **[55960]**
Small Business Development Center at The University of Scranton **[56918]**
Small Business Development Center at The Urban League of Greater Cleveland **[55961]**
Small Business Development Center at Toledo Regional Chamber of Commerce **[55962]**, **[56292]**
Small Business Development Center at University of Central Florida - Clermont **[49895]**
Small Business Development Center at University of Central Florida - Kissimmee **[49896]**
Small Business Development Center at University of Central Florida - Melbourne **[49897]**
Small Business Development Center at University of Central Florida - Orlando **[49898]**
Small Business Development Center at University of Cincinnati **[55963]**
Small Business Development Center at University of North Florida - Gainesville **[49899]**
Small Business Development Center at University of North Florida - Jacksonville **[49900]**
Small Business Development Center at University of North Florida - Ocala/Marion County **[49901]**
Small Business Development Center at the University of Pittsburgh **[56919]**
Small Business Development Center at University of South Florida - Hillsborough County **[49902]**
Small Business Development Center at University of South Florida - St. Petersburg **[49903]**
Small Business Development Center at University of South Florida - Tampa **[49904]**
Small Business Development Center at University of West Florida - Fort Walton Beach **[49905]**
Small Business Development Center at University of West Florida - Pensacola **[49906]**
Small Business Development Center - UWSP Continuing Education - University of Wisconsin-Stevens Point **[59769]**
Small Business Development Center at Western Kentucky University **[52233]**
Small Business Development Center at Wright State University **[55964]**
Small Business Development Center at Youngstown State University **[55965]**
Small Business Development Center at Zane State College **[55966]**
Small Business Development Corp. of Orange County [48165]
Small Business for Dummies **[28876]**, **[32429]**
Small Business for Dummies, 3rd Ed. **[147]**, **[21428]**, **[22125]**, **[23429]**, **[29395]**, **[31835]**, **[32430]**, **[38426]**, **[39547]**
"*Small Business Earnings*" *in Small Business Economic Trends (April 2008, pp. 6)* **[23430]**, **[27704]**, **[45703]**
"*Small Business Earnings*" *in Small Business Economic Trends (February 2008, pp. 6)* **[23432]**, **[27706]**, **[31837]**
"*Small Business Earnings*" *in Small Business Economic Trends (January 2008, pp. 6)* **[23433]**, **[27707]**, **[31838]**
"*Small Business Earnings*" *in Small Business Economic Trends (July 2010, pp. 6)* **[23435]**, **[45704]**
"*Small Business Earnings*" *in Small Business Economic Trends (March 2008, pp. 6)* **[23431]**, **[27705]**, **[31836]**
"*Small Business Earnings*" *in Small Business Economic Trends (September 2010, pp. 6)* **[23434]**, **[27708]**, **[31839]**
"*Small Business Employment*" *in Small Business Economic Trends (April 2008, pp. 9)* **[35474]**, **[35922]**, **[45705]**
"*Small Business Employment*" *in Small Business Economic Trends (February 2008, pp. 9)* **[35476]**, **[35924]**, **[45707]**
"*Small Business Employment*" *in Small Business Economic Trends (January 2008, pp. 9)* **[35477]**, **[35925]**, **[45708]**

3616 Small Business Sourcebook • 30th Edition

"Small Business Employment" in Small Business Economic Trends (July 2010, pp. 9) [35479], [35927], [45709]
"Small Business Employment" in Small Business Economic Trends (March 2008, pp. 9) [35475], [35923], [45706]
"Small Business Employment" in Small Business Economic Trends (September 2010, pp. 9) [35478], [35926]
Small Business Entrepreneur: Launching a New Venture and Managing a Business on a Day-to-Day Basis [29396], [32431]
Small Business and Entrepreneurship [30177], [32945]
Small Business Exporters Association [11024]
Small Business Exporters Association of the United States (SBEA) [11024]
Small Business Focus [59859]
Small Business Guide/Business Start-up Checklist [47734]
The Small Business Guide to HSAs [33338], [34437], [45710]
Small Business: Innovation, Problems and Strategies [23436], [32946], [37115]
"Small Business Inventories" in Small Business Economic Trends (April 2008, pp. 14) [27709], [37208], [45711]
"Small Business Inventories" in Small Business Economic Trends (February 2008, pp. 14) [37210], [45713]
"Small Business Inventories" in Small Business Economic Trends (January 2008, pp. 14) [37211], [45714]
"Small Business Inventories" in Small Business Economic Trends (July 2010, pp. 14) [37213], [45715]
"Small Business Inventories" in Small Business Economic Trends (March 2008, pp. 14) [37209], [45712]
"Small Business Inventories" in Small Business Economic Trends (September 2010, pp. 15) [37212]
"Small Business: Just When Hopes Were High" in Business Week (January 8, 2007) [27710], [44873]
Small Business Legal Strategies [24025], [32947]
Small Business Legal Tool Kit [23671], [32432], [37116], [46364]
Small Business Legislative Council (SBLC) [33478], [45260]
Small Business Loan Program Kit [33339], [37499], [40812]
Small Business Management [22126], [24026], [28877], [29397], [30977], [37214], [37553], [46365]; [24027], [24566], [30178], [37500], [38427]
Small Business Management in Canada [30179], [38428]
Small-Business Management Guide: Advice from the Brass-Tacks Entrepreneur [30180], [38429]; [30181], [38430]
Small Business Management: Launching and Managing New Ventures [32433], [37554]
Small Business Marketing for Dummies [40353]
Small Business Opportunities: Money Making Ideas for Entrepreneurs [6181], [11220], [44901]
"Small Business Outlook" in Small Business Economic Trends (April 2008, pp. 4) [23437], [27711], [45716]
"Small Business Outlook" in Small Business Economic Trends (February 2008, pp. 4) [23439], [27713], [45718]
"Small Business Outlook" in Small Business Economic Trends (January 2008, pp. 4) [23440], [27714], [45719]
"Small Business Outlook" in Small Business Economic Trends (July 2009, pp. 4) [23441], [32948]
"Small Business Outlook" in Small Business Economic Trends (July 2010, pp. 4) [23443], [45720]
"Small Business Outlook" in Small Business Economic Trends (March 2008, pp. 4) [23438], [27712], [45717]
"Small Business Outlook" in Small Business Economic Trends (September 2010, pp. 4) [23442], [27715]
The Small Business Owner's Manual: Everything You Need to Know to Start Up and Run Your Business [148], [336], [4995], [8708], [21204], [21429], [23672], [24191], [26318], [32434], [35480], [37282], [38431], [39548], [41442], [41556], [43619]
"Small Business Prices" in Small Business Economic Trends (April 2008, pp. 8) [25792], [43620], [45721]
"Small Business Prices" in Small Business Economic Trends (February 2008, pp. 8) [25794], [43622], [45723]
"Small Business Prices" in Small Business Economic Trends (January 2008, pp. 8) [25795], [43623], [45724]
"Small Business Prices" in Small Business Economic Trends (July 2010, pp. 8) [23444], [25797], [45725]
"Small Business Prices" in Small Business Economic Trends (March 2008, pp. 8) [25793], [43621], [45722]
"Small Business Prices" in Small Business Economic Trends (September 2010, pp. 8) [25796], [27716]
Small Business Resource Center [33101]
"Small Business Sales" in Small Business Economic Trends (April 2008, pp. 7) [43185], [43624], [45726]
"Small Business Sales" in Small Business Economic Trends (February, pp. 7) [43187], [43626], [45728]
"Small Business Sales" in Small Business Economic Trends (January, pp. 7) [43188], [43627], [45729]
"Small Business Sales" in Small Business Economic Trends (July 2010, pp. 7) [23446], [27717], [43629], [45730]
"Small Business Sales" in Small Business Economic Trends (March 2008, pp. 7) [43186], [43625], [45727]
"Small Business Sales" in Small Business Economic Trends (September 2010, pp. 7) [23445], [43628]
The Small Business Savings Plan: 101 Tactics for Controlling Costs and Boosting the Bottom Line [22127], [31840]
Small Business Savvy [23447], [29398], [47194]
Small Business Sourcebook [23448], [32949]
The Small Business Start-Up Kit [21311], [29399], [32435], [33474], [46037], [46129]
The Small Business Start-Up Kit for California [32436], [46366]
Small Business Start-Up Workbook: A Step-by-Step Guide to Starting the Business You've Dreamed Of [29400], [32437], [38432], [40354]
Small Business Success [49384]
Small Business Survival Guide [149], [21430], [24028], [25402], [26319], [26535], [29401], [31112], [32438], [33475]; [32950]
Small Business Survival Guide: Starting, Protecting, and Securing Your Business for Long-Term Success [150], [21431], [24029], [25648], [26320], [30182], [32951], [46367]
Small Business Tax Deductions 2006 [19668], [46368]
Small Business Taxes 2006: Your Complete Guide to a Better Bottom Line [32952], [46369]
Small Business Taxes Made Easy: How to Increase Your Deductions, Reduce What You Owe, and Boost Your Profits [28878], [32953], [46370]
Small Business Taxes and Management [38609], [46449]
Small Business Tool Kit [29402], [37555], [42740]
Small Business Turnaround [23449], [32954]
"Small Business Unsure of Impact of New Tax Law" in Crain's Detroit Business (Vol. 23, October 15, 2007, No. 42, pp. 13) [44527], [46371]
"Small Businesses Benefiting from Movie-Struck Hub" in Boston Business Journal (Vol. 27, October 12, 2007, No. 37, pp. 1) [7983], [46372]
"Small Businesses Changing Their Health Plan Preferences" in Boston Business Journal (Vol. 29, June 24, 2011, No. 7, pp. 1) [11428], [21973], [34438], [36227]
"Small Businesses Get Creative to Retain Workers" in Crain's Detroit Business (Vol. 24, March 17, 2008, No. 11, pp. 21) [21974], [25649], [29161]
Small Businesses and Workplace Fatality Risk: An Exploratory Analysis [32955], [47476]
"Small, But Mighty" in Employee Benefit News (Vol. 25, November 1, 2011, No. 14, pp. 32) [11429], [21975], [25902], [27718], [33959], [34439], [36228]
"Small Changes Can Mean Big Energy Savings" in Crain's Cleveland Business (Vol. 28, November 5, 2007, No. 44, pp. 21) [17061], [17493], [30793], [45731]
"Small Dutch Islands Saba, Statia Content With Low-Key Niche" in Travel Weekly (Vol. 69, August 16, 2010, No. 33, pp. 22) [20173], [20571], [24919], [25650], [40355]
Small Engines [18631]
Small Farm News [38610]
"Small Firms Punch Ticket for Growth" in Houston Business Journal (Vol. 40, January 29, 2010, No. 38, pp. 1) [12901], [33960], [36789], [42173], [44528]
"Small Fish, Big Box Stores" in Hawaii Business (Vol. 53, November 2007, No. 5, pp. 55) [9023], [9974], [26536], [43189]
Small Giants: Companies that Choose to Be Great Instead of Big [32956]
Small Giants: Companies That Choose to Be Great Instead of Big [23450], [32957]
"Small Is Best, Says Housing Officials" in Business First Buffalo (November 16, 2007, pp. 1) [1432], [15081], [45997]
The Small-Mart Revolution: How Local Businesses Are Beating the Global Competition [25651], [36790]
Small and Medium-Sized Enterprises in Countries in Transition [32958], [36791]
Small & Minority Business - OSMB - Department of General Services - Office of Small Business and DVBE Services [49147]
"Small is the New Big in Autos" in Globe & Mail (February 16, 2006, pp. B3) [14951], [24567], [25217], [39368], [40356]
Small Press [2187], [6527], [15017], [15589]
Small Publishers Association of North America (SPAN) [2103], [6506]
Small Shop Tips and Techniques [3433]
Small Street [50612]
Small Street Journal [57229]
Small Talk [11474]
Small Time Operator: How to Start Your Own Business, Keep Your Books, Pay Your Taxes, and Stay Out of Trouble [24030], [32439], [46373]
"Small Wind Power Market to Double by 2015 at $634 Million" in Western Farm Press (September 30, 2011) [7307], [7668], [23451], [30794], [33340]
"Smaller Banks Could Face Tough 2008" in Austin Business JournalInc. (Vol. 28, January 2, 2009, No. 1, pp. 3) [8709], [27719], [45732]
Smallmouth Bass: America's Greatest Sportfish [1723]
Smart Access [4768]
SMART Body Shop Talk: Paint Tips [1596]
"Smart Businesses See Value, and Profit, in Promoting Women" in Crain's Chicago Business (Vol. 30, February 2007, No. 6, pp. 30) [32959], [42387], [42518]
"Smart Car Sales Take Big Hit in Recession" in Business Journal-Milwaukee (Vol. 28, December 10, 2010, No. 10, pp. A1) [7308], [7669], [14952], [25652], [30795], [39369], [43630]
Smart Customer Service [26585]
"Smart Investor's Shopping List: Coke, Walgreen, Drill Bits; A Conversation with Money Manager Paula Dorion-Gray" in Crain's Chicago Business [8710], [12902], [30183], [31841]
Smart Mail [9214]
"Smart Medicine" in Canadian Business (Vol. 80, February 26, 2007, No. 5, pp. 73) [8711], [12903], [43960]
Smart Start your Arizona Business [52649]
Smart Start your Arkansas Business [53803]
Smart Start your Colorado Business [49637]
Smart Start your Connecticut Business [52539]
Smart Start your Florida Business [53933]
Smart Start your Georgia Business [54530]
Smart Start your Hawaii Business [50727]
Smart Start your Illinois Business [51464]
Smart Start your Indiana Business [51772]
Smart Start your Iowa Business [52015]
Smart Start your Kentucky Business [52405]
Smart Start your Maryland Business [52799]
Smart Start your Massachusetts Business [53092]
Smart Start your Michigan Business [53526]
Smart Start your Missouri Business [54210]
Smart Start your New Hampshire Business [54634]
Smart Start your New Jersey Business [54885]
Smart Start your New Mexico Business [55009]
Smart Start your New York Business [55518]
Smart Start your North Carolina Business [55874]
Smart Start your Ohio Business [56419]
Smart Start your Oregon Business [56898]
Smart Start your Pennsylvania Business [57348]
Smart Start your South Carolina Business [57551]
Smart Start your Tennessee Business [57833]
Smart Start your Texas Business Guide [58602]
Smart Start your Virginia Business [59039]
Smart Start your Washington Business [59360]
Smart Start your Washington D.C. Business [52217]
Smart Start your Wisconsin Business [59789]
Smart Start Your California Business [54336]
Smart Tax Write-Offs, 5th Ed. [151], [19669], [21432], [35619], [46374]
Smart Ways to Work [38809], [46578]
"Smart Year-End Tax Moves" in Business Owner (Vol. 35, November-December 2011, No. 6, pp. 8) [152], [19670], [21433], [27720], [46375]
"A Smarter Kind of Taxes" in Canadian Business (Vol. 80, October 8, 2007, No. 20, pp. 203) [33961], [34440], [46376]
SMARTRISK [34169]
"Smarts Drive Sales" in Pet Product News (Vol. 64, December 2010, No. 12, pp. 1) [15734], [26537], [43190], [43631]
Smash Hit Subs [6492], [13344]
SMASHMOUTH [16040]
SME Cluster Development: A Dynamic View on Survival Clusters in Developing Countries [32960], [36792]
"The Smell of Fear: Is a Bottom Near?" in Barron's (Vol. 88, March 17, 2008, No. 11, pp. M3) [4271], [8712], [11430], [12904], [31842], [34441], [36229]
SMEs and New Technologies: Learning E-Business and Development [11870], [28879], [35134]
Ted Smith Associates (TSA) [36066]
Smith, Bridges & Associates [4548]
Smith Center Chamber of Commerce (SCCC) [52191]
S.B. Smith Consulting Group Inc. (SBS) [2970]
Smith County Chamber of Commerce [57785]
Smith, Dawson & Andrews [16629]

Small Business Sourcebook • 30th Edition 3617

Smith-Emery MASTER INDEX

Smith-Emery Co. **[5670]**
"Smith Fuels BNE Drive to Grow Job Market" in Business First Buffalo (November 2, 2007, pp. 1) **[23452]**
Smith Mountain Lake Chamber of Commerce/Partnership (SMLCC/P) **[58984]**
Smith, Turner & Reeves P.A. **[38810]**
Smith-Emery Company Inc. [5670]
John Smithkey, III, RN **[26711]**, **[47528]**
Paul Smith's College of Arts and Sciences - Joan Weill Adirondack Library **[5856]**, **[10835]**
Smithsonian Institute - Office of Equal Employment and Minority Affairs **[60694]**; **[60695]**
Smithsonian Institution - National Postal Museum Library **[4396]**
Smithsonian Institution - Smithsonian American Art Museum - National Portrait Gallery Library **[4583]**, **[15893]**
Smithsonian Institution - Smithsonian American Art Museum - Photograph Archives **[4584]**
Smithville Area Chamber of Commerce **[58445]**
Smithville - DeKalb County Chamber of Commerce **[57786]**
Smitty's **[18242]**
SMMA [41648]
Smocking Arts Guild of America (SAGA) **[5963]**
"Smoke Signals: Johnny Drake On What To Expect In a Fine Cigar" in Black Enterprise (Vol. 38, December 2007, No. 5, pp. 195) **[20090]**, **[30184]**, **[43191]**
Smoke in Your Eyes **[20108]**
Smokin' Donut Books **[57399]**
Smoking and Health Resource Library **[14301]**, **[16047]**
Smoky Mountain Coupon Book **[57787]**
Smoky Mountain Wedding Planner **[57788]**
Smoothie King Franchises, Inc. **[10260]**, **[10981]**
DW Smothers and Associates **[46093]**
Smugglers' Notch Area Chamber of Commerce (SNACC) **[58773]**
Smugglers Notch Area Vacation Guide **[58774]**
Smugglers Notch Chamber of Commerce [58773]
Smyth Fivenson Co. **[10189]**, **[30887]**
Snap Fitness Inc. **[16041]**
Snap-On Inc. **[10153]**
Snap-On Tools Of Canada Ltd. **[3318]**
Snap-on Tools Co. [10153]
Snap-on Tools Company LLC [10153]
Snap-on Tools Corp. [10153]
Snappy Tomato Pizza **[16192]**
"Snatching Talent: Local Law Firms Quietly Boost Poaching" in Boston Business Journal (Vol. 31, July 29, 2011, No. 27, pp. 3) **[24031]**, **[25653]**
"Sneak Preview: Alamo Revamp" in Austin Business JournalInc. (Vol. 28, December 12, 2008, No. 39, pp. 1) **[5509]**, **[14575]**, **[17494]**
Sneaker Wars: The Enemy Brothers Who Founded Adidas and Puma and the Family Feud that Forever Changed the Business of Sport **[18768]**, **[31113]**, **[39370]**
Snelling Staffing, LLC **[7005]**
Snip-Its **[2592]**
Snip N' Clip Haircut Shops **[10099]**
Snips Magazine **[894]**
SNL Bank DataSource [2745], [13220]
SNL DataSource [2745], [13220]
SNL Financial Banks & Thrifts Module **[2745]**, **[13220]**
SNL Financial North American Real Estate Module **[2746]**, **[13221]**
SNL Financial Services Daily **[13141]**
SNL Real Estate DataSource [2746], [13221]
SNL REIT DataSource [2746], [13221]
SNL REIT Weekly **[17572]**
Snohomish Chamber of Commerce **[59282]**
Snohomish County Tourist Bureau **[59283]**
Snoqualmie Valley Chamber of Commerce (SVCC) **[59284]**
Snow Hill Chamber of Commerce (SHCC) **[52756]**
"Snow Melt Systems Offer Practical Solutions" in Contractor (Vol. 56, October 2009, No. 10, pp. S6) **[7309]**, **[7670]**, **[20977]**, **[30796]**
Thomas J. Snow **[20490]**
The Snowball: Warren Buffett and the Business of Life **[12905]**, **[30185]**
Snowflake - Taylor Chamber of Commerce **[47956]**
Snowmass Village Resort Association **[49588]**
SnowSports Industries America (SIA) **[18827]**
Snyder Chamber of Commerce **[58446]**
So Smart **[4001]**
So, You Want to Be an Innkeeper **[1932]**, **[10750]**
So You Want to Be a Success at Selling? **[8898]**, **[13171]**, **[43750]**
"So You Want to Start a Business?" in Women Entrepreneur (August 5, 2008) **[24568]**, **[25218]**, **[44778]**, **[47377]**
So You Want to Start a Business? **[29403]**, **[32440]**, **[45733]**
Soap Lake Chamber of Commerce **[59285]**
Soaring Spirit: Tools & Teachings to Create Your Own Reality **[14824]**
Sobek Engineering **[21787]**
"Sobering Consequences" in The Business Journal-Milwaukee (Vol. 25, July 11, 2008, No. 42, pp. A1) **[13594]**, **[24769]**, **[27721]**, **[38433]**, **[39371]**, **[44725]**
"SoBran Partners with U.S. Navy" in Black Enterprise (Vol. 37, October 2006, No. 3, pp. 38) **[36085]**, **[42174]**, **[44529]**
Soccer Industry Council of America (SICA) **[19311]**
Social Development Canada and Human Resources and Skills Development Canada - Departmental Library - Career Library **[3407]**
Social Enterprise: Developing Sustainable Businesses **[27722]**, **[45734]**, **[45998]**
Social Enterprise in Europe **[30186]**, **[36793]**
Social Entrepreneurship **[27723]**, **[30187]**, **[45999]**
Social Entrepreneurship For Dummies **[30188]**, **[46000]**
Social Entrepreneurship: What Everyone Needs to Know **[30189]**, **[46001]**
"Social Intelligence and the Biology of Leadership" in Harvard Business Review (Vol. 86, September 2008, No. 9, pp. 74) **[29162]**, **[30190]**, **[32961]**, **[38434]**
The Social Media Bible: Tactics, Tools, and Strategies for Business Success **[594]**, **[22443]**, **[25654]**, **[26538]**, **[28880]**, **[29163]**, **[40357]**, **[43632]**, **[44530]**
"Social Media By the Numbers: Social-Media Marketing Is All the Rage" in Inc. (Vol. 33, November 2011, No. 9, pp. 70) **[28881]**, **[40358]**, **[45735]**
"Social Media: Communicate the Important Stuff" in Agency Sales Magazine (Vol. 39, November 2009, No. 10, pp. 52) **[11871]**, **[21205]**, **[22444]**, **[22628]**, **[40359]**
"Social Media, E-Mail Remain Challenging for Employees" in Workforce Management (Vol. 88, December 14, 2009, No. 13, pp. 4) **[11872]**, **[21206]**, **[22445]**, **[38435]**, **[40360]**
"Social Media Event Slated for March 25" in Bellingham Business Journal (Vol. February 2010, pp. 3) **[20422]**, **[28882]**, **[35135]**, **[46704]**
Social Media Marketing (Onsite) **[39606]**
Social Media Overview **[45855]**
"Social Networkers for Hire" in Black Enterprise (Vol. 40, December 2009, No. 5, pp. 56) **[11873]**, **[17993]**, **[21207]**, **[22446]**, **[28883]**, **[38436]**, **[40361]**, **[40813]**
"Social Networking Butterfly" in Entrepreneur (Vol. 37, September 2009, No. 9, pp. 48) **[21208]**, **[22447]**, **[30191]**
"Social Networking Site for Moms" in Marketing to Women (Vol. 21, March 2008, No. 3, pp. 3) **[11874]**, **[21209]**, **[22448]**, **[22629]**, **[35136]**, **[40362]**
"Social Networks in the Workplace" in Strategy & Leadership (Vol. 38, July-August 2010, No. 4, pp. 50-53) **[22449]**, **[28884]**, **[38437]**, **[40363]**, **[41443]**, **[45736]**
Social Venture Partners (SVP) **[7380]**
Social Work with Groups: A Journal of Community and Clinical Practice **[34594]**
Social Work in Health Care: A Quarterly Journal Adopted by the Society for Social Work Leadership in Health Care **[34595]**
Social Work in Public Health **[34596]**
Societe Canadienne de Cardiologie [34108]
Societe Canadienne de Nutrition [15153]
Societe canadienne de pediatrie [34121]
Societe canadienne de recherches cliniques [34125]
Societe Canadienne de Science de Laboratoire Medical [14265]
Societe Canadienne des Biologistes l'Environnement [7033]
Societe Canadienne des Infirmieres et Infirmiers en Gastoenterologie et Travailleurs Associes [10520]
Societe Canadienne des Relations Publiques [16578]
Societe Canadienne D'indexation [2]
Societe Canadienne d'Ophthalmologie [20915]
Societe Canadienne du Cancer [34107]
Societe Canadienne pour la Formation et le Perfectionnement [35653]
Societe Candienne de la Photographie Scientifique. [15887]
Societe Culinaire - Philanthropique **[5857]**
Societe de l'Energie solaire du Canada [7039]
Societe de Musique des Universites Canadiennes [14607]
Societe des designers graphiques du Canada [4447]
Societe d'Habitation du Quebec - Centre de Documentation **[5716]**
Societe de Genealogie de Quebec Library **[9561]**
Societe Planetaire pour l'Assainissement de l'Energie [30429]
Societe pour la nature et les parcs du Canada [7032]
Society for Accessible Travel and Hospitality Library **[20643]**
Society for Advancement of Management (SAM) **[37568]**, **[46484]**
Society of American Florists **[9097]**
Society for Applied Learning Technology (SALT) **[4758]**
Society for Business Ethics (SBE) **[30897]**
Society of Cable Telecommunications Engineers (SCTE) **[3160]**
Society for Calligraphy Library **[3228]**
Society for Calligraphy--Membership Directory **[3219]**
Society of Cleaning and Restoration Technicians (SCRT) **[20824]**
Society for Clinical and Medical Hair Removal (SCMHR) **[10053]**
Society of Collision Repair Specialists (SCRS) **[18590]**
Society of Corporate Secretaries and Governance Professionals **[20820]**
Society of Craft Designers Educational Seminar (SCD) **[6055]**, **[6161]**, **[46782]**
Society of Depreciation Professionals (SDP) **[52]**, **[21323]**
Society for Environmental Graphic Design (SEGD) **[4446]**
Society of Financial Service Professionals (SFSP) **[11301]**
Society of Financial Service Professionals--Society Page **[11475]**
Society for Foodservice Management (SFM) **[17873]**
Society for Automation in Business Education [4634], [4755]
Society for Automation in English and the Humanities [4634], [4755]
Society for Automation in Fine Arts [4634], [4755]
Society for Automation in Professional Education [4634], [4755]
Society for Automation in the Social Sciences [4634], [4755]
Society for Data Educators [4634], [4755]
Society for Educational Data Systems [4634], [4755]
Society for the Advancement of Women's Health Research [34172]
Society of Graphic Designers of Canada (GDC) **[4447]**
Society for Human Resource Management Exposition (SHRM) **[42726]**, **[46783]**
Society of Independent Gasoline Marketers of America (SIGMA) **[18591]**
Society of Inkwell Collectors Library **[1158]**
Society of Insurance Financial Management (SIFM) **[11302]**
Society of Insurance Research (SIR) **[11517]**
Society of Insurance Research Library **[11513]**
Society of International Business Fellows (SIBF) **[36311]**
Society of Management Accountants of Canada (CMA) **[53]**
Society of Manufacturing Engineers (SME) **[13693]**
Society of Manufacturing Engineers (NAMRI/SME) - North American Manufacturing Research Institution **[39535]**
Society for Nonprofit Organizations (SNPO) **[1459]**
Society of Authors' Representatives [13606]
Society of Cable Telecommunications Engineers Inc. [3160]
Society of Cable Television Engineers [3160]
Society of Cleaning Technicians [20824]
Society of Clinical and Medical Electrologists [10053]
Society of Competitive Intelligence Professionals [37231]
Society of Competitor Intelligence Professionals - Society of Competitive Intelligence Professionals [37231]
Society of Educational Programmers and Systems Analysts [4634], [4755]
Society of Environmental Graphic Designers [4446]
Society of Independent and Private School Data Education [4634], [4755]
Society of Industrial Engineers [37568], [46484]
Society of Insurance Accountants [11302]
Society of Logistics Engineers [16645]
Society of Magazine Photographers - American Society of Magazine Photographers - American Society of Magazine Publishers [15483], [15836]
Society of Magazine Writers [6772]
Society of Magazine Writers--Directory of Professional Writers [6816]
Society of Mortgage Consultants [14372]
Society of Professional Audio Recording Studios [17637]
Society of Real Estate Appraisers - American Institute of Real Estate Appraisers [1206]
Society of Technical Writers and Editors - Society of Technical Writers and Publishers - Technical Publishing Society [6804], [22152]
Society of Technical Writers and Publishers [6804], [22152]
Society of Translators and Interpreters of Canada [20468]
Society of Professional Accountants of Canada (SPAC) **[54]**, **[2262]**, **[19602]**
Society of Professional Audio Recording Services (SPARS) **[17637]**

3618 Small Business Sourcebook • 30th Edition

Southwest Colorado Small Business Development Center - Durango **[49429]**

Southwest Colorado Small Business Development Center - Pagosa **[49430]**

Southwest Exotic Plant Mapping Program (SWEMP) **[9838]**

Southwest Georgia Business Development Center **[50678]**

Southwest Health Center Medical Library **[6730]**, **[15133]**

Southwest Kansas SCORE **[52034]**

Southwest King County Chamber of Commerce (SWKCC) **[59288]**

Southwest Louisiana Economic Development Alliance **[52537]**

Southwest Louisiana Procurement Technical Assistance Center **[52523]**

Southwest Louisiana SCORE **[52423]**

Southwest Michigan Innovation Center **[53511]**

Southwest Minnesota State University - Southwest Minnesota Historical Center **[9573]**

Southwest Region University Transportation Center (SWUTC) **[19833]**

Southwest Small Business Development Center - Minnesota **[53539]**

Southwest Small Business Development Center - New Mexico **[54909]**

Southwest Valley Chamber of Commerce **[47957]**; **[58679]**

Southwest Virginia Small Business Development Center **[58824]**

Southwestern Auglaize County Chamber of Commerce **[56300]**

Southwestern College **[49374]**

Southwestern Colorado Small Business Development Center **[49431]**

Southwestern Financial Directory: 11th Fed, Dallas **[37502]**

Southwestern Illinois SCORE **[50883]**

Southwestern Indiana Small Business Development Center **[51482]**

Southwestern Michigan College - Workforce Education and Business Solutions **[53521]**

Southwestern Michigan Economic Growth Alliance, Inc. **[53512]**

Southwestern Oklahoma State University Small Business Development Center - Weatherford **[56436]**

Southwestern Oregon Community College **[56893]**

"Southwestern Resources Project Update" in Canadian Corporate News (May 14, 2007) **[41353]**, **[43963]**, **[44729]**

Southwestern Wisconsin Small Business Development Center (SWSBDC) **[59448]**

Southword **[50300]**

Miles F. Southworth, Consultant to the Graphic Arts **[4549]**

Souvenir Wholesale Distributors Association (SWDA) **[9594]**, **[9888]**

Souvenirs & Novelties Magazine--Buyer's Guide Issue [15032]

Souvenirs, Gifts & Novelties Magazine--Buyer's Guide Issue **[15032]**

Spa and Sauna [19548]

Spa Magazine **[20203]**, **[20609]**

Space Cowboys: Dysfunctional Superheroes II **[18837]**, **[19363]**

Space Management Programs Inc. **[5671]**, **[44755]**

"Space Shut Hot" in Canadian Business (Vol. 80, October 22, 2007, No. 21, pp. 28) **[40370]**, **[41227]**

Spacial Design **[41646]**

Spain-United States Chamber of Commerce **[36312]**

Sparking Innovation and Creativity (Onsite) **[29002]**

Sparkle Carpet Cleaning **[20845]**

Sparkle Wash **[16312]**

"The Spark's Back in Sanyo" in Barron's (Vol. 88, March 31, 2008, No. 13, pp. M9) **[8718]**, **[12914]**, **[23456]**, **[35140]**, **[39378]**

Sparks Chamber of Commerce **[54515]**

Sparks Community Chamber of Commerce [54515]

Sparkworks Media **[42561]**

Sparta Area Chamber of Commerce **[59727]**

Sparta - White County Chamber of Commerce **[57790]**

Spartanburg Area Chamber of Commerce **[57527]**

Spartanburg Small Business Development Center **[57411]**

Spartanburg Technical College - Industry and Business Training **[57550]**

"Speak Better: Five Tips for Polished Presentations" in Women Entrepreneur (September 19, 2008) **[9282]**, **[18566]**, **[20423]**, **[22452]**, **[23457]**, **[26786]**, **[30194]**, **[32963]**, **[40371]**, **[46705]**, **[47078]**, **[47379]**

Speak! Present! Influence! (Onsite) **[22241]**

"Speakers Address Authenticity, R&D Evolution" in Nation's Restaurant News (Vol. 45, October 24, 2011, No. 32, pp. 32) **[9164]**, **[17995]**, **[26543]**

Speakers' Bureau Listing **[49033]**

Speaking of Business **[58986]**

Speaking For Business **[52964]**

"Speaking In Tongues: Rosetta Stone's TOTALE Adds 'Social' To Language Learning" in Black Enterprise (Vol. 41, September 2010, No. 2) **[20482]**, **[36798]**, **[40914]**, **[45215]**

Speaking Skills for Professionals (Onsite) **[22242]**

Speaking of Success **[30371]**

Spearfish Area Chamber of Commerce **[57599]**

Spearfish Area Chamber of Commerce and Convention and Visitors Bureau [57599]

Spearfish Street Map **[57600]**

Spearman Chamber of Commerce (SCC) **[58456]**

Special Events **[50617]**

Special Events Guide **[49034]**

Special Events Resource **[49035]**

Special Investment Situations **[13142]**

Special Issues for Women Entrepreneurs **[47436]**

Special Libraries Association (SLA) **[2105]**, **[11228]**

Special Libraries Association Information Revolution **[2201]**, **[11245]**

"Special Sector" in Crain's Cleveland Business (Vol. 28, November 5, 2007, No. 44, pp. 3) **[24574]**, **[25656]**, **[39379]**

Specialized Carriers and Rigging Association (SC&RA) **[20666]**

Specialized Information Publishers Association (SIPA) **[15009]**

Specialized Moderator Skills for Qualitative Research Applications (Onsite) **[39607]**

Specialty Advertising Association [42586]

Specialty Advertising Association International [42586]

Specialty Advertising Association of Canada [39567]

Specialty Advertising Business [655]

Specialty Advertising Guild International [42586]

Specialty Advertising National Association [42586]

Specialty Automotive Magazine **[1580]**

Specialty Coffee Association of America (SCAA) **[4314]**, **[9693]**

Specialty Equipment Market Association (SEMA) **[1545]**

Specialty Graphic Imaging Association (SGIA) **[16351]**, **[18353]**

Specialty Graphic Imaging Association (SPTF) - Screen Printing Technical Foundation (SPTF) **[4448]**, **[16352]**, **[18354]**

The Specialty Shop: How to Create Your Own Unique and Profitable Retail Business **[1741]**, **[2349]**, **[4189]**, **[9592]**, **[9690]**, **[20227]**, **[42927]**

Specialty Tools and Fasteners Distributors Association (STAFDA) **[13694]**

"Spectre of Iran War Spooks Oil Markets" in Globe & Mail (March 28, 2007, pp. B1) **[8719]**, **[12915]**, **[27729]**, **[39380]**

The Spectrem Group Inc. **[14057]**

SPECTRUM **[7069]**, **[17700]**, **[30437]**

Spectrum **[189]**

Spectrum Equity Investors **[53066]**

Spectrum Health Consumer Library. [10265], [10328], [15222], [16050]

Spectrum Health Sciences Libraries **[1452]**

Spectrum Home Services **[13525]**

Speech Coach for Executives **[36067]**

"Speed Reader" in Crain's Chicago Business (Vol. 30, February 2007, No. 6, pp. 58) **[14955]**, **[30195]**

Speed Reading with Evelyn Wood Reading Dynamics (Onsite) **[28090]**

The Speed of Trust **[22453]**, **[30196]**

The SPEED of Trust: The One Thing That Changes Everything **[30197]**, **[30979]**, **[32964]**

"Speedway Explored Sale" in Business Courier (Vol. 24, October 12, 2008, No. 26, pp. 1) **[24035]**, **[44193]**

The Speedy Bee: The Beekeeper's Newspaper **[1951]**

Speedy Transmission Centers **[18661]**

"Spell It Out" in Entrepreneur (Vol. 36, April 2008, No. 4, pp. 123) **[4272]**, **[7849]**, **[22454]**, **[22630]**, **[35141]**, **[39381]**, **[40372]**

Spencer Area Association of Business and Industry Chamber of Commerce [51975]

Brenda Spencer **[1321]**

Spencer Chamber of Commerce **[51975]**

Spencer Chamber of Commerce [51698]

Spencer County Regional Chamber of Commerce **[51720]**

Spencer Trask Ventures, Inc. / Spencer Trask Securities **[55458]**

Spencer-Owen Chamber of Commerce [51698]

"Spend Wisely on Managing Your Hedgerows" in Farmer's Weekly (March 28, 2008, No. 320) **[21689]**, **[24575]**, **[38442]**

"Spending on Innovation Down Sharply in State" in Crain's Detroit Business (Vol. 24, March 10, 2008, No. 10, pp. 7) **[27730]**, **[44876]**, **[46382]**, **[47079]**

"Spending the Stimulus" in Crain's Cleveland Business (Vol. 30, June 29, 2009, No. 25, pp. 3) **[33343]**, **[39382]**

SPEX **[2198]**

Sphere Consulting Group L.L.C. **[237]**

Spherion **[20048]**

Spherix Inc. **[28965]**, **[47150]**

Lawrence G. Spielvogel Inc. **[907]**

"Spillover Effects" in Crain's Detroit Business (Vol. 24, October 6, 2008, No. 40, pp. 29) **[19463]**, **[19968]**, **[27731]**, **[43636]**

Spirit **[54137]**; **[54138]**

The Spirit **[48109]**

The Spirit of Entrepreneurship: Exploring the Essence of Entrepreneurship Through Personal Stories **[30198]**, **[32442]**

"The Spirit of a Man: Kedar Massenburg's Intoxicating Style of Conducting Business" in Black Enterprise (Vol. 38, March 2008) **[15980]**, **[19243]**, **[30199]**

Spirit of Math Schools **[28478]**

Spirit Music Inc. [16074]

Spirit of Payson **[47958]**

The Spirit of Tomball Texas **[58457]**

The Spiritual Entrepreneur **[29406]**, **[32443]**, **[46002]**

Spiro Area Chamber of Commerce **[56587]**

Splash Magazine **[980]**

A Splendid Exchange: How Trade Shaped the World **[11169]**, **[36799]**

Splendor on the Rim **[47959]**

Spokane Ag Expo **[21755]**

Spokane Falls Community College (SFCC) **[59356]**

Spokane Home and Garden Show **[9831]**

Spokane Regional Chamber of Commerce (SRCC) **[59289]**

Spokane Small Business Development Center **[59065]**

Spokesman **[52758]**; [5078]

"Sponsorship, Booths Available for Spring Business Showcase" in Bellingham Business Journal (Vol. February 2010, pp. 3) **[20424]**, **[26544]**, **[40373]**, **[42659]**, **[43637]**, **[46706]**

Spooner Area Chamber of Commerce (SACC) **[59728]**

Sport Clips **[10100]**

Sportball Systems Inc. **[16042]**

SportDiscus™ **[16048]**

Sporting Arms and Ammunitions Manufacturers Institute (SAAMI) **[10024]**

Sporting Goods and Activewear Buyers **[19343]**

Sporting Goods Buyers [19343]

Sporting Goods Dealer: The Voice of Team Dealers Since 1899 **[9677]**, **[18835]**, **[19354]**

Sporting Goods Manufacturers Association (SGMA) **[19312]**

Sports CustomWire® **[19499]**

Sports Experts 2000 Inc. **[43310]**

"A Sports Extravaganza - To Go" in Canadian Business (Vol. 79, June 19, 2006, No. 13, pp. 21) **[11876]**, **[19969]**, **[23458]**, **[35142]**, **[37117]**

Spotlight **[49036]**; **[54814]**; **[58458]**

Spotlight on Carthage **[54139]**

Spotlight on Dance **[6390]**

"Spotlight on Pensions" in Business Horizons (Vol. 51, March-April 2008, No. 2, pp. 105) **[153]**, **[12916]**, **[21434]**, **[21977]**, **[31848]**

"Spotlight on Principles-based Financial Reporting" in Business Horizons (September-October 2007, pp. 359) **[154]**, **[2314]**, **[19671]**, **[21435]**

"Spotlight; 'Classroom Focus' at Encyclopaedia Britannica" in Crain's Chicago Business (Vol. 34, October 24, 2011, No. 42, pp. 6) **[2166]**, **[28343]**, **[38443]**, **[40374]**

Spotlights **[2689]**, **[15361]**

Spray Venture Partners **[53067]**

Sprayglo Auto Refinishing & Body Repair **[1611]**, **[18662]**

"Spread Your Wings" in Canadian Business (Vol. 81, March 17, 2008, No. 4, pp. 31) **[8720]**, **[12917]**, **[21978]**, **[30200]**, **[31849]**, **[36095]**, **[44779]**, **[46968]**

Spring Art Fair/Novi **[6057]**

Spring Capital Partners, L.P. **[52776]**

Spring City Chamber of Commerce **[57791]**

Spring Crafts Festival/Fort Washington **[6061]**

Spring Crafts Festival/Gaithersburg **[6059]**

Spring Crafts Festival/Somerset **[6063]**

Spring Crafts Festival/Timonium **[6065]**

Spring Green Area Chamber of Commerce (SGACC) **[59729]**

Spring-Green Lawn Care Corp. **[13526]**

Spring Hill Chamber of Commerce **[57792]**

Spring Home & Patio Show **[9832]**

Spring Lake Area Chamber of Commerce (SLACC) **[55813]**

Spring Postage Stamp Mega Event **[4385]**

Spring River Area Chamber of Commerce **[48110]**

Spring Valley Area Chamber of Commerce (SVACC) **[56301]**

Spring Valley Chamber of Commerce (SVCC) [49037]
Springboro Chamber of Commerce [56302]
Springdale Chamber of Commerce (SCC) [48111]
Springerville-Eagar Regional Chamber of Commerce [47960]
Springfield Area Chamber of Commerce [54140]; [56849]
Springfield Area Chamber of Commerce (SACC) [53738]
Springfield Area Chamber of Commerce [56303]
Springfield Art Museum - Art Reference Library [4585], [15894]
Springfield Business Development Corporation (SBDC) [52808]
Springfield Business Incubator [53085]
Springfield Chamber of Commerce [49592]
Springfield Chamber of Commerce [58930]
Springfield-Clark County Chamber of Commerce (SACC) [56303]
Springfield College - Babson Library - Special Collections [16051]
Springfield Community Guide [58775]
Springfield Regional Chamber of Commerce [58776]
Springfield - Robertson County Chamber of Commerce [57793]
Springfield Scene [51325]
Springhill - North Webster Chamber of Commerce [52499]
Springhill-Cullen Chamber of Commerce [52499]
Springtown Area Chamber of Commerce (SACOC) [58459]
Springville Area Chamber of Commerce (SACC) [47736]
Springville Chamber of Commerce [49038]
"Sprinkler Advocates Beat Builders Again" in Contractor (Vol. 56, November 2009, No. 11, pp. 58) [16272], [45743]
"Sprint Tries to Wring Out Positives" in The Business Journal-Serving Metropolitan Kansas City (Vol. 26, August 8, 2008, No. 48) [3807], [8721], [12918], [23459], [31850], [44532]
Sprout Group (New York City) [55459]
Sprout Group (New York, New York) [47151]
Sprout Growth II L.P. [47151]
Squeegee Squad [44624]
"Squeeze Play" in Baltimore Business Journal (Vol. 28, September 3, 2010, No. 17, pp. 1) [19464], [33967]
S.R. One, Limited [57303]
SRDS International Media Guides: Newspapers Worldwide [4069]
SRIC-BI News [14028]
SRSU Rio Grande College Small Business Development Center [57871]
SS & C Technologies [8920], [13187]
SSE [6548]
SSM Partners [57813]
SSP [4674]
St. Charles Area Chamber of Commerce [51312]
St. Cloud Area Chamber of Commerce [50287]
St. Helens-Scappoose Chamber of Commerce [56848]
St. Louis Chamber [53272]
St. Louis University - Jefferson Smurfit Center for Entrepreneurial Studies [47165]
St. Simons Island Chamber of Commerce [50449]
Stable Value Association [11980]
Stable Value Investment Association (SVIA) [11980]
Stack's Rare Coin Company of New York - Technical Information Center [4397]
"Stadium Developers Seek a Win With the State" in The Business Journal-Serving Metropolitan Kansas City (Vol. 26, August 22, 2008) [17498], [19465], [24576], [25220], [27732], [46383]
Staff Association of the Organization of American States [19151]
"Staffing Firm Grows by Following Own Advice-Hire a Headhunter" in Crain's Detroit Business (Vol. 24, October 6, 2008, No. 40, pp. 1) [155], [2315], [8722], [19166], [21436], [23460], [24577], [31851], [35143], [35481], [38444]
"Staffing Firms are Picking Up the Pieces, Seeing Signs of Life" in Milwaukee Business Journal (Vol. 27, February 5, 2010, No. 19) [6975], [7795], [20692], [27733], [44533]
Staffing Industry Analysts [6946], [19189]
Stafford County Historical & Genealogical Society Library [9563]
Stage Equipment and Lighting Inc. [14583]
"Staging a Martini-and-GQ Lifestyle; Faux Possessions Play to Buyer's Aspirations" in Crain's Chicago Business (April 21, 2008) [11553], [17064], [17499], [25657], [45744]
"Stains Still Set After SBA Scrub" in Black Enterprise (March 2008) [32965], [33344], [33968]
"A Stalled Culture Change?" in Workforce Management (Vol. 88, December 14, 2009, No. 13, pp. 1) [29164], [38445], [39383], [46914]

Stalley Associates Inc. [38811], [42348]
Stamford Chamber of Commerce [49753]
Stamford Financial Consulting [55460]
Stamping Arts & Crafts [6143]
Stamps [4381]
"Stand-Up Guy" in Barron's (Vol. 88, July 7, 2008, No. 27, pp. L11) [8723], [12919], [31852]
"Standard-of-Living Gap With U.S. Closing" in Globe & Mail (March 27, 2007, pp. B3) [27734], [32966]
Standard Periodical Directory [4070], [15014], [15571]
Standard & Poor's (S&P) [55535]
Standard & Poor's Industry Surveys [648], [733], [1199], [1571], [1906], [2178], [2470], [3839], [4291], [4317], [4884], [5010], [5569], [5819], [6673], [9068], [9721], [9993], [10142], [10490], [10765], [11453], [13667], [13748], [14218], [14742], [14973], [15086], [17105], [17723], [18020], [19027], [20280], [20696]
Standard & Poor's The Outlook [13143]
Standard Rate & Data Service--Direct Mail List Rates & Data [13741]
Standard Trucking and Transportation Statistics [20712]
Standing Tall [46819]
Standish Press [53100]
Stanford University - Center for Research in Disease Prevention [46124]
Stanford University - Center for Information Technology (CIT) [11253]
Stanford University - Information Systems Laboratory (ISL) [5071]
Stanford University - Stanford Heart Disease Prevention Program [46124]
Stanford University - Stanford Prevention Research Center (SPRC) [46124]
Stanislaus County Industrial Directory [49039]
Stanley - Sawtooth Chamber of Commerce [50801]
Stanley Steemer Carpet Cleaner [20846]
Stanly County Chamber of Commerce (SCCC) [55814]
Stantec Consulting Services, Inc. Library [7733]
Stanton Chamber of Commerce [49040]
Stanton Chamber Directory [49041]
Stanwood Chamber of Commerce [59290]
Stanwood Chamber of Commerce Directory [59291]
"Staples Advantage Receives NJPA National Contract for Janitorial Supplies" in Professional Services Close-Up (April 22, 2011) [2629], [9283], [15281], [28344], [42179], [42388], [43193], [44534]
STAR Associates Inc. [36068]
"Star Power" in Small Business Opportunities (September 2008) [32967], [35482], [38446], [46915]
"Star Power Versus (Somewhat) Green Power" in Globe & Mail (January 18, 2007, pp. B2) [30800], [32968]
Star Spangled Beer: A Guide to America's New Micro-breweries and Brewpubs [2464]
"STAR TEC Incubator's Latest Resident Shows Promise" in The Business Journal-Serving Greater Tampa Bay (August 8, 2008) [18482], [23461], [35144], [36096], [39384], [41228], [43964]
Star Valley Chamber of Commerce (SVCCOM) [59845]
"Starbucks Drive-Throughs: Can the Cafe Keep Its Cool?" in Globe & Mail (January 6, 2006, pp. B7) [9710], [23462], [24578], [25221]
The Starbucks Experience [9711], [23463], [29165], [38447], [46003]
The Starbucks Experience: 5 Principles for Turing Ordinary into Extraordinary [9712], [23464]
"Starbucks' Wheel Strategy" in Puget Sound Business Journal (Vol. 29, October 3, 2008, No. 24, pp. 1) [9713], [24579]
The Starfish and the Spider [30201], [32969]
The Starfish and the Spider: The Unstoppable Power of Leaderless Organizations [25658], [30202], [32970], [38448]
Starke County Chamber of Commerce [51721]
Starke-Bradford County Chamber of Commerce [50243]
Starkville Area Chamber of Commerce [53904]
"The Stars Align: Trail Blazers, Headline Makers on 2007 List Set Example for Others" in Hispanic Business (October 2007, pp. 22) [30203], [38449], [40816], [47380]
"Stars Shine Downtown" in The Business Journal-Serving Metropolitan Kansas City (Vol. 26, August 29, 2008, No. 51, pp. 1) [14576], [16555], [27735]
Starsmore Center for Local History (SCLH) [9574]
"The Start of a Beautiful Friendship: Partnering with Your Customers on R&D" in Inc. (March 2008, pp. 37-38) [26545], [41229], [42180], [42879], [43965], [45745]
Start Business in California, 3E [29407], [32444]
"Start or Buy? It's a Tough Question for Eager Entrepreneurs" in Crain's Cleveland Business (Vol. 28, October 8, 2007, No. 40) [25344], [30204], [44877]
"Start Connecting Today" in Indoor Comfort Marketing (Vol. 70, May 2011, No. 5, pp. 34) [866], [7313], [7674], [30801], [40375], [45746]

"Start Filling Your Talent Gap - Now" in Business Strategy Review (Vol. 21, Spring 2010, No. 1, pp. 56) [29166], [35483], [35930], [38450]
"Start Moving Toward Advanced Fuels" in Indoor Comfort Marketing (Vol. 70, March 2011, No. 3, pp. 4) [7314], [7675], [30802], [40376]
Start and Run a Bookkeeping Business [7], [21312], [32445]
Start and Run a Delicatessen: Small Business Starters Series [6430], [17854], [24192], [42880], [44730]
Start, Run, and Grow a Successful Small Business, 2nd Edition [23465], [30205], [32446]
Start and Run a Home-Based Food Business [3456], [35581]
Start and Run a Profitable Bed and Breakfast [1934], [10752]
Start Small, Finish Big [23466], [32971]; [6431], [17855], [30206], [32110]
"Start Thinking About Carbon Assets - Now" in Harvard Business Review (Vol. 86, September 2008, No. 9, pp. 28) [7315], [7676], [30803]
Start Up and Business Plan Guides [54645]
Start-Up Guide [47961]
Start-Up Nation [27736], [36800]
"Start-Up Pointers" in Inside Business (Vol. 13, September-October 2011, No. 5, pp. Y3) [11216], [29408], [32447]
Start-ups That Work: Surprise Research on What Makes or Breaks a New Company [29409], [32448], [42881]
Start Your Own Blogging Business, Second Edition [8724], [22455], [28519], [40377], [42520], [42660]
Start Your Own Business on eBay, 2nd Edition [1485], [15300], [28520]
Start Your Own Business, Fifth Edition [29410], [32449]
Start Your Own Fashion Accessories Business [597], [4077], [4190], [7813], [35582], [40378], [42661]
Start Your Own Lawn Care Business: Your Step-by-Step Guide to Success [13362], [32450]
Start Your Own Lawn Care or Landscaping Business [13363], [13466]
Start Your Own Net Services Business [11599], [15301], [21025], [28521], [39549], [44230]
Start Your Own Tutoring and Test Prep Business: Your Step-by-Step Guide to Success [20730], [27965]
Start Your Own Wedding Consultant Business [2485], [32451]
STARTech Early Ventures [58569]
Starting an Ebay Business for Canadians for Dummies [1486], [11600], [15302], [28522]
Starting Green: An Ecopreneur's Guide to Starting a Green Business from Business Plans to Profits [7023], [7435], [24193], [25659], [29411], [30412], [32452]
Starting an iPhone Application Business for Dummies [3667], [21026], [28523], [29412], [40379]
Starting and Operating a Business in Alabama: A Step-by-Step Guide [47769]
Starting and Operating a Business in Alaska: A Step-by-Step Guide [47829]
Starting and Operating a Business in Arizona: A Step-by-Step Guide [47991]
Starting and Operating a Business in Arkansas: A Step-by-Step Guide [48131]
Starting and Operating a Business in California: A Step-by-Step Guide [49385]
Starting and Operating a Business in Colorado: A Step-by-Step Guide [49638]
Starting and Operating a Business in Connecticut: A Step-by-Step Guide [49798]
Starting and Operating a Business in Delaware: A Step-by-Step Guide [49838]
Starting and Operating a Business in District of Columbia: A Step-by-Step Guide [49859]
Starting and Operating a Business in Florida: A Step-by-Step Guide [50384]
Starting and Operating a Business in Georgia: A Step-by-Step Guide [50686]
Starting and Operating a Business in Hawaii: A Step-by-Step Guide [50728]
Starting and Operating a Business in Idaho: A Step-by-Step Guide [50829]
Starting and Operating a Business in Illinois: A Step-by-Step Guide [51465]
Starting and Operating a Business in Iowa: A Step-by-Step Guide [52016]
Starting and Running a Coaching Business [2749], [13756], [25813], [32453]
Starting and Running Your Own Horse Business [10593], [11431], [21485], [36230], [46384]
Starting a Small Business in Iowa [52017]
Starting a Successful Business in Canada [29413], [32454]
Starting Up On Your Own: How to Succeed as an Independent Consultant or Freelance [2750], [25814]

MASTER INDEX Still

Master Index

Starting a Yahoo! Business for Dummies **[11601]**, **[28524]**, **[40380]**, **[42928]**
Starting a Yahoo! Business For Dummies **[11602]**, **[21027]**, **[28525]**, **[40381]**
StartingUp Now Facilitator Guide **[28345]**, **[29414]**, **[32455]**
"Startup Aims to Cut Out Coupon Clipping" in The Business Journal-Serving Metropolitan Kansas City (Vol. 26, August 15, 2008, No. 49) **[4064]**, **[11603]**, **[21028]**, **[24194]**, **[24963]**, **[28526]**, **[34724]**, **[39550]**
"Startup on Cusp of Trend" in Austin Business JournalInc. (Vol. 29, January 8, 2010, No. 44, pp. 1) **[3622]**, **[18998]**, **[28887]**, **[35931]**, **[41230]**, **[45216]**, **[45747]**
"Startup Makes Attempt to 'Reform' Health Insurance" in Austin Business JournalInc. (Vol. 29, January 15, 2010, No. 45, pp. 1) **[11261]**, **[36100]**, **[42181]**, **[46051]**
"Startup to Serve Bar Scene" in Austin Business JournalInc. (Vol. 29, December 18, 2009, No. 41, pp. 1) **[1861]**, **[3808]**, **[17996]**, **[26321]**, **[28888]**, **[34725]**, **[41231]**
Stat Communications Ltd. **[59365]**
Stat Publishing [59365]
"The State of the Art in End-User Software Engineering" in ACM Computing Surveys (Vol. 43, Fall 2011, No. 3, pp. 21) **[3623]**, **[4651]**, **[4874]**, **[18999]**, **[45217]**
"State Aviation Fuel Tax Proposal Runs Into Turbulence" in Crain's Detroit Business (Vol. 25, June 15, 2009, No. 24, pp. 5) **[24924]**, **[46385]**
"State Barks At Servicers Over Reluctance To Back Compact" in Business First-Columbus (2007, pp.) **[14497]**, **[33969]**
State Board Report **[190]**
State Botanical Garden of Georgia Library **[9134]**, **[9874]**, **[13456]**
"State Budget Woes Hurt Many Vendors, Senior Services" in Sacramento Business Journal (Vol. 25, August 15, 2008, No. 24, pp. 1) **[305]**, **[21437]**, **[26322]**, **[27737]**, **[33345]**, **[34445]**, **[37503]**
"State Center Lease Deal High for Md." in Baltimore Business Journal (Vol. 28, August 6, 2010, No. 13, pp. 1) **[5513]**, **[17500]**, **[17814]**, **[42389]**, **[44731]**
State Chamber - Oklahoma's Association of Business and Industry **[56588]**
State of Connecticut Procurement Services - Purchasing Services Division **[49790]**
"State Democrats Push for Changes to Plant Security Law" in Chemical Week (Vol. 172, July 19, 2010, No. 17, pp. 8) **[18483]**, **[24036]**, **[33970]**, **[39385]**
"State Efforts to Boost Contract Efficiency Hurt Smaller Firms" in Boston Business Journal (Vol. 27, November 9, 2007, No. 41, pp. 1) **[3809]**, **[11877]**, **[33456]**, **[35145]**
"State Expects Increase of $50 Million from Film Bills; Come Back, Al Roker" in Crain's Detroit Business (March 24, 2008) **[7985]**, **[19970]**, **[21979]**, **[27738]**, **[33346]**, **[46386]**
"State of a Fair!" in Small Business Opportunities (March 2008) **[20425]**, **[46707]**
"State Fairgrounds Adding Year-Round Attractions" in Crain's Detroit Business (Vol. 24, February 18, 2008, No. 7, pp. 17) **[20426]**, **[46708]**
"State Film Business Tops $1.3 Billion" in The Business Journal-Portland (Vol. 25, August 22, 2008, No. 24, pp. 1) **[7986]**, **[23467]**, **[33971]**, **[44732]**, **[45748]**, **[46387]**
"State Fund That Aids New Companies Likely To Wither" in Crain's Detroit Business (Vol. 24, February 25, 2008, No. 8, pp. 16) **[37283]**, **[46969]**
State Health Care Regulatory Developments™ **[326]**, **[937]**, **[6706]**, **[14254]**, **[14302]**, **[15121]**, **[25399]**, **[47532]**
"State Investment Goes Sour" in Business Journal Portland (Vol. 26, December 4, 2009, No. 39, pp. 1) **[7316]**, **[7677]**, **[21690]**, **[30804]**, **[33347]**, **[37504]**
"State Lawmakers Should Try Raising Jobs, Not Taxes" in Crain's Chicago Business (Vol. 31, March 24, 2008, No. 12, pp. 20) **[25660]**, **[27739]**, **[33972]**, **[46388]**
"State of Play" in Canadian Business (Vol. 79, June 19, 2006, No. 13, pp. 25) **[8725]**, **[12920]**, **[23468]**, **[35146]**
"State Printing Plant on the Move" in Sacramento Business Journal (Vol. 25, August 29, 2008, No. 26, pp. 1) **[5514]**, **[17065]**, **[17501]**, **[24770]**, **[33973]**
"State Reaps $440M with Small-Biz Tax Crackdown" in Boston Business Journal (Vol. 27, October 19, 2007, No. 38, pp. 1) **[24037]**, **[46389]**
State & Regional Associations of the United States **[1464]**
"State Shock Prices Take Large Tumble" in The Business Journal-Milwaukee (Vol. 25, September 12, 2008, No. 51, pp. A1) **[8726]**, **[12921]**, **[23469]**, **[27740]**, **[31853]**, **[42182]**
"The State of the Stores" in Playthings (Vol. 106, November 1, 2008, No. 10, pp. 8) **[20266]**, **[27741]**, **[43194]**, **[45749]**
"State Targets Credit Fixers" in Business Journal-Portland (Vol. 24, October 12, 2007, No. 33, pp. 1) **[6210]**, **[6253]**, **[6331]**, **[14498]**, **[26323]**, **[33974]**
State Tax Notes® **[253]**, **[19732]**, **[24158]**, **[46467]**
State Tax Today® **[254]**, **[19733]**, **[24159]**, **[46468]**
State Telephone Regulation Report **[16316]**
"State Tourism Likely to Decline Two Percent this Year" in Crain's Detroit Business (Vol. 24, April 14, 2008, No. 15, pp. 6) **[20174]**, **[20572]**, **[27742]**
"State Unemployment Fraud Rising Sharply" in Sacramento Business Journal (Vol. 28, October 21, 2011, No. 34, pp. 1) **[24038]**, **[45750]**
"State of the Unions" in Canadian Business (Vol. 81, December 8, 2008, No. 21, pp. 23) **[40382]**, **[42183]**
State University of New York at Binghamton - Institute for Materials Research (IMR) **[44092]**
State University of New York at Buffalo - Center for Executive Development **[20221]**
State University of New York at Buffalo - Music Library **[14706]**
State University of New York at Buffalo - Research Institute on Addictions (RIA) **[46125]**
State University of New York at Buffalo - University Development Library **[9311]**
State University of New York College at Cortland Memorial Library **[16052]**
State University of New York College at Oneonta - Center for Economic and Community Development (CECD) **[27945]**
State University of New York at Plattsburgh - Economic Development and Technical Assistance **[55039]**
State University of New York at Stony Brook - Living Marine Resources Institute (LIMRI) **[9046]**
State University of New York at Buffalo - Research Institute on Alcoholism [46125]
"State VC Fund To Get At Least $7.5 Million" in Crain's Detroit Business (Vol. 24, February 25, 2008, No. 8, pp. 14) **[33975]**, **[37505]**, **[47080]**
"State Wants to Add Escape Clause to Leases" in Sacramento Business Journal (Vol. 28, October 14, 2011, No. 33, pp. 1) **[17066]**, **[17502]**, **[17815]**, **[25661]**, **[33976]**, **[37506]**
"State Weighs Tearing Down Hoan" in The Business Journal-Milwaukee (Vol. 25, August 22, 2008, No. 48, pp. A1) **[5515]**, **[24925]**
State Wildlife Laws Handbook **[7317]**
Staten Island Chamber of Commerce (SICC) **[55349]**
"State's Glass Ceiling Gets Higher" in Business Journal-Milwaukee (Vol. 25, October 5, 2007, No. 1, pp. A1) **[26546]**, **[38451]**, **[47381]**
States Organization for Boating Access (SOBA) **[3866]**
Statesboro-Bulloch Chamber of Commerce **[50618]**
Statistical Bulletin **[2449]**
"Statistical Data of Interest" in Business Owner (Vol. 35, July-August 2011, No. 4, pp. 7) **[19672]**, **[46390]**
Statistical Yearbook **[9014]**
Staubs Business Services (SBS) **[24700]**
Staunton Chamber of Commerce **[51326]**
Stay At Home **[10581]**
"Stay Calm, Bernanke Urges Markets" in Globe & Mail (March 1, 2007, pp. B1) **[8727]**, **[12922]**, **[27743]**, **[31854]**, **[32972]**
Stay Clean, Stay Safe **[1794]**
Stay Out of Court: The Small Business Owners Guide to Prevent or Resolve Disputes and Avoid Lawsuit Hell **[24039]**, **[33977]**
"Stay in School: Economy Got You Down?" in Canadian Business (Vol. 81, November 10, 2008, No. 19, pp. 98) **[27744]**, **[28346]**, **[38452]**
"Stay in Touch, Wherever You Roam: Smartphones for Overseas Travel" in Inc. (Volume 32, December 2010, No. 10, pp. 60) **[3810]**, **[24926]**, **[41445]**
"Staying Engaged" in Black Enterprise (Vol. 38, February 2008, No. 7, pp. 64) **[22456]**, **[30207]**, **[38453]**
"Staying Power" in Canadian Business (Vol. 79, November 6, 2006, No. 22, pp. 73) **[598]**, **[40383]**, **[42662]**, **[43195]**
Stayton Area Chamber of Commerce [56850]
Stayton - Sublimity Chamber of Commerce (SSCC) **[56850]**
"Steady Spending in Retail" in Business Week (September 22, 2008, No. 4100, pp. 13) **[23470]**, **[27745]**, **[43196]**
The Steak Escape **[18245]**
Steak N Shake **[18246]**
Steak-Out Charbroiled Delivery **[3483]**, **[18247]**
Steal These Ideas!: Marketing Secrets That Will Make You a Star **[40384]**, **[40963]**
Stealing MySpace: The Battle to Control the Most Popular Website in America **[7750]**, **[28889]**
Stealthmode Partners **[47987]**
Steam Brothers Professional Cleaning and Restoration **[20847]**
Steam Systems Maintenance, Safety & Optimization (Onsite) **[24997]**, **[28091]**
Steamatic, Inc. **[2677]**
Steamboat Springs Chamber Resort Association (SSCRA) **[49593]**
Stearns History Museum **[9575]**
Stearns Weaver Miller Weissler Alhadeff & Sitterson Library **[13245]**
Steel Recycling Institute (SRI) **[17701]**
Steel Valley Chamber of Commerce **[57236]**
Steelabor - Canadian Edition **[46820]**
Steeleader **[46821]**
"Steeling for Battle" in Crain's Chicago Business (Vol. 31, April 21, 2008, No. 16, pp. 3) **[11432]**, **[21980]**, **[36231]**, **[39386]**, **[46916]**
Steelville Chamber of Commerce **[54141]**
Steep-Slope Roofing Materials Guide **[18325]**
Steep Snow **[18838]**, **[19364]**
"Steering Toward Profitability" in Black Enterprise (Vol. 41, December 2010, No. 5, pp. 72) **[1562]**, **[14956]**, **[32238]**, **[39387]**, **[40817]**
Gary Steffy Lighting Design Inc. (GSLD) **[41647]**
Steilacoom Chamber of Commerce **[59292]**
Steinmann Facility Development Consultants (SFDC) **[5672]**
Steinmann, Grayson, Smylie [5672]
"Stelco Investors Told Their Stock Now Worthless" in Globe & Mail (January 23, 2006, pp. B4) **[8728]**, **[12923]**, **[24040]**, **[24580]**, **[25222]**, **[33978]**
"Stelco Seeks to Shave Its Fixed Costs" in Globe & Mail (March 8, 2007, pp. B1) **[24581]**, **[25223]**, **[27746]**
Stelle & Associates Inc. **[7381]**, **[16630]**
"The Stem Cell Revolution" in Canadian Business (Vol. 79, November 20, 2006, No. 23, pp. 31) **[12924]**, **[34446]**, **[43966]**
"Stent Cases at Md. Hospitals Falling" in Baltimore Business Journal (Vol. 28, November 12, 2010, No. 27, pp. 1) **[30980]**, **[34447]**
"A Step Up" in Black Enterprise (Vol. 38, January 2008, No. 6, pp. 53) **[38454]**, **[47382]**
"Step Up to Help Regionalism Step Forward" in Crain's Cleveland Business (Vol. 28, November 12, 2007, No. 45, pp. 10) **[27747]**, **[32973]**
Stephen M. Segal Inc. **[17601]**
Stephenville Chamber of Commerce **[58460]**
"Stepping Out" in Small Business Opportunities (Get Rich At Home 2010) **[18747]**, **[32111]**
"Stepping Up" in Baltimore Business Journal (Vol. 28, October 22, 2010, No. 24, pp. 1) **[18769]**, **[25224]**, **[25662]**, **[25798]**, **[41232]**
Stepping Up to Leadership (Canada) **[37737]**
Steps to Small Business Start-Up **[29415]**, **[32456]**
Sterile Preparations **[6641]**
Sterling Area Chamber of Commerce [51314]
Sterling Chamber of Commerce **[52192]**
Sterling Executive Counselors Inc. **[21789]**
Sterling Heights Area Chamber of Commerce (SHACC) **[53442]**
Sterling-Hoffman **[4906]**
Sterling Management Systems **[238]**
Sterling Optical **[20947]**
Sterling Partners **[52777]**
Sterling/Rock Falls Restaurant and Lodging Guide **[51327]**
Sternhill Partners **[58570]**
Stern's Management Review **[38836]**, **[45836]**
"Sterotaxis Needs $10 Million in 60 Days" in Saint Louis Business Journal (Vol. 32, October 7, 2011, No. 6, pp. 1) **[14212]**, **[37507]**
Stetson University - Roland and Sara George Investments Institute **[8972]**
"Steve Meginniss Helped Reinvent the Toothbrush. Can He Do the Same Thing for Wheels?" in Inc. (February 2008, pp. 32) **[30208]**, **[37118]**, **[39388]**, **[41233]**
Greg Stevens & Co. [9300], [16631]
Stevens, Reed, Curcio and Potholm **[9300]**, **[16631]**
Stevenson Real Estate Group Ltd. **[17602]**
Stewart County Chamber of Commerce (SCCC) **[57794]**
Stewart/Laurence Associates Inc. **[20010]**
The Sticking Point Solution: 9 Ways to Move Your Business from Stagnation to Stunning Growth in Tough Economic Times **[2798]**, **[13775]**, **[23471]**, **[25903]**, **[27748]**
"Sticking to Stories; Havey Ovshinksy Changes Method, Keeps the Mission" in Crain's Detroit Business (Vol. 24, March 31, 2008) **[7987]**, **[11878]**, **[21211]**, **[35147]**, **[40385]**
Stier Associates **[26712]**, **[29281]**, **[31148]**, **[36069]**
Stigler Kiamichi Technology Center - Incubator **[56645]**
"Stikemans' Ascent, Its Legacy, and Its Future" in Globe & Mail (January 29, 2007, pp. B2) **[24041]**, **[25225]**, **[25663]**, **[42184]**
"Still on the Block" in Entrepreneur (Vol. 35, November 2007, No. 11, pp. 22) **[30209]**, **[44733]**, **[46004]**

Small Business Sourcebook • 30th Edition 3623

"Still in the Jet Set" in Barron's (Vol. 89, July 13, 2009, No. 28, pp. 13) [24927], [44535]

"Still Looking Good" in Canadian Business (Vol. 80, March 26, 2007, No. 7, pp. 29) [17067], [17503], [23472]

"Still No Arena Financing Plan" in Sacramento Business Journal (Vol. 28, May 27, 2011, No. 13, pp. 1) [5516], [19466], [37508]

The Still River Fund [53068]

"Still Stretching" in Business Courier (Vol. 24, December 28, 2008, No. 37, pp. 1) [9975], [23473], [40818]

"Still Unprepared For Natural Disasters" in Black Enterprise (Vol. 38, January 2008, No. 6, pp. 28) [24582], [40819]

Stillman H. Publishers Inc. [2214], [6547], [15025], [23660], [38812]

Stillwater Chamber of Commerce [56589]

Stillwater Commerce [56590]

Stillwater Connection [56591]

Stillwater Consulting Group Inc. [239], [21471], [32061]

The Stillwater Group [239], [21471], [32061]

"Stimulating Fare at the SBA" in Barron's (Vol. 89, July 20, 2009, No. 29, pp. 12) [11879], [21212], [45751]

"Stimulus Effect Slow" in Baltimore Business Journal (Vol. 27, October 23, 2009, No. 24, pp. 1) [33348], [33457], [35484]

"Stimulus 'Loser' Won't Build Plant in Mass." in Boston Business Journal (Vol. 30, November 5, 2010, No. 41, pp. 1) [5517], [7318], [7678], [14957], [30805], [33349], [36801], [39389], [44734]

The Sting [1952]

"Stitching the City Together" in Business Courier (Vol. 24, February 8, 2008, No. 44, pp. 1) [27749], [30210]

"STMicroelectronics" in Canadian Electronics (Vol. 23, February 2008, No. 1, pp. 1) [5771], [12925], [35148], [42185]

STN Inc. [5054]

"Stock Analysts' Pans" in Canadian Business (Vol. 81, Summer 2008, No. 9, pp. 75) [8729], [12926], [31855]

"Stock Car Racing" in Canadian Business (Vol. 81, September 15, 2008, No. 14-15, pp. 29) [8730], [12927], [14958], [24042], [24583], [25226], [30806], [31856], [39390]

"Stock Delisting Could Hamper First Mariner" in Boston Business Journal (Vol. 29, July 29, 2011, No. 12, pp. 1) [8731], [12928], [31857], [42521], [42663]

The Stock Market [13172]

Stock Market Focus [13144]

Stock Market Game, The [11977]

Stockbridge Chamber of Commerce [52965]

"Stockerts Open Repair Business" in Dickinson Press (July 13, 2010) [1180], [31117], [44536]

"Stockgroup Completes US $4.5 Million Financing" in Canadian Corporate News (May 16, 2007) [8732], [12929], [25227], [42186]

Stockton Area Chamber of Commerce [54142]

Stockton Bates & Company P.C. [42349]

Stockton Bates L.L.P. [42349]

The Stoller Co. [22076]

"Stone Company Slated to Expand Here" in Austin Business JournalInc. (Vol. 28, September 12, 2008, No. 26, pp. 1) [1286], [5518], [23474]

Tavy Stone Fashion Library [4181], [4312], [5924]

Stone Harbor Chamber of Commerce [54815]

Stone Magazine [14115]

"Stone to Run Hickory Farmer's Market" in Charlotte Observer (January 31, 2007) [9976], [21691], [38455]

Stoneham Chamber of Commerce [52966]

"Stoneham Drilling Trust Announces Cash Distribution for May 2007" in Canadian Corporate News (May 16, 2007) [25228], [44537]

Stonewall Bulletin [58461]

Stonewall Chamber of Commerce (SCC) [58462]

Stony Brook Small Business Development Center [55031]

Stop Business Crime: Shoplifting & Employee Theft [29298]

"Stop the Innovation Wars" in Harvard Business Review (Vol. 88, July-August 2010, No. 7-8, pp. 76) [23475], [37119], [38456], [41234]

"Stop the Madness" in Hawaii Business (Vol. 53, October 2007, No. 4, pp. 10) [28347], [45752]

Stop 'N' Cash [37549]

"Stop Trying to Delight Your Customers" in Harvard Business Review (Vol. 88, July-August 2010, No. 7-8, pp. 116) [26547], [43638]

Stop Working: Start a Business, Globalize It, and Generate Enough Cash Flow to Get Out of the Rat Race [30211], [32457], [36802], [44194]

Storage Council [4687], [16642]

"StorageByMail Lets Customers Ship Away Their Clutter" in Inc. (Vol. 33, April 2011, No. 3, pp. 92) [9215], [16489]

Stores: The Magazine for Retail Decision Makers [4296], [21298]

Stork News [1673]

Storklink [39508]

Storm Lake Chamber of Commerce (SLCC) [51976]

"Storm Takes Toll On Area Businesses" in The Business Journal - Serving Phoenix and the Valley of the Sun (Vol. 28, September 5, 2008, No. 52, pp. 1) [43197], [45753]

Storm Water Management: How to Comply with Federal and State Regulations (Onsite) [33493]

Story City Chamber of Commerce [51977]

"The Story Of Diane Greene" in Barron's (Vol. 88, July 14, 2008, No. 28, pp. 31) [3624], [19000], [35149], [35485], [38457], [42187], [45218], [46917]

"Storytelling Star of Show for Scripps" in Business Courier (Vol. 26, November 13, 2009, No. 29, pp. 1) [3191], [15572], [19971], [28348], [29167]

Stoughton Chamber of Commerce [52967], [59730]

Stow-Munroe Falls Chamber of Commerce (SMFCC) [56304]

Stow-Munroe Falls Chamber of Commerce Member Business Directory [56305]

Stowe Area Association [58777]

Strack Hartmann L.L.C. [4550], [11486]

Strack Vaughan L.L.C. [4550], [11486]

Straight Talk About Small Business Success in New Jersey: How to Maximize the Growth, Cash Flow and Profitability of Your Small Business [23476], [32458]

Straightline Services Inc. [2971], [13884], [26100], [38813]

Stranger's Investment Advisor [2714]

Strasburg Chamber of Commerce (SCC) [58987]

Stratamar Inc. [28966], [40649], [41306]

Strategic Account Management Association - Resource Search Library [13906], [32081]

Strategic Agility and Resilience: Embracing Change to Drive Growth [37738]

Strategic Air Command Judo Association [14083]

Strategic and Competitive Intelligence Professionals (SCIP) [37231]

Strategic Computer Solutions Inc. [16761]

Strategic Decisions Group Information Center [38848]

Strategic Diversity Retention (Onsite) [37739]

Strategic Entrepreneurship [30212], [32974]

"Strategic Issue Management as Change Catalyst" in Strategy and Leadership (Vol. 39, September-October 2011, No. 5, pp. 20-29) [24584], [34448], [38458]

Strategic Job Search [3385]

Strategic Marketing: Concepts and Strategies (Onsite) [24206]

Strategic Partnerships: An Entrepreneur's Guide to Joint Ventures and Alliances [30213], [42188]

Strategic Planning (Onsite) (Canada) [29003]

Strategic Planning for Organizational Success (Onsite) [24207], [24998]

Strategic Press [57352]

"A Strategic Risk Approach to Knowledge Management" in Business Horizons (November-December 2007, pp. 523) [37257], [38459]

Strategic Sales Negotiations (Onsite) [43359]

Strategic S&T [44071]

Strategic Services on Unemployment and Workers' Compensation and the National Foundation for UC & WC [25369]

The Strategic Speed-Reading Advantage for Executives & Legal Professionals (Onsite) [46497]

Strategic Systems & Products Corp. [4674]

Strategies for Developing Effective Presentation Skills (Onsite) [22243]

Strategies of Effective Writing (Onsite) [22244]

Strategies for Growth in SMEs: The Role of Information and Information Systems [4728], [23477], [37258]

Strategies for Social Change L.L.C. [47152]

Strategies, Tactics and Results Associates Inc. [36068]

Strategizing, Disequilibrium, and Profit [24585], [32975]

Strategy [9076]

Strategy Execution: Getting it Done (Onsite) [39608]

"Strategy: Hurry Up and Wait" in Business Courier (Vol. 24, February 1, 2008, No. 43, pp. 50) [24586], [25229], [38460], [41235]

Stratford Area Chamber of Commerce [59731]

"Strathmore Receives Permit to Drill oca Honda Project in New Mexico" in Canadian Corporate News (May 14, 2007) [33979], [41354], [44115]

Straub Medical Research Institute [34678]

Straw Hat Pizza [16193]

Strawberry Shortcake Chat Group [4356], [20228]

Strawberry Shortcake Doll Club [4356], [20228]

Stream Trout Tactics [1724]

"Streaming Hot Currie" in Canadian Business (Vol. 80, April 23, 2007, No. 9, pp. 10) [32976], [35932]

Streamwood Chamber of Commerce (SCC) [51328]

Streator Area Chamber of Commerce and Industry (SACCI) [51329]

Street and Area Map [49042]

"Street Beaters: How the Top Stock Earners on Our List Pulled It Off" in Canadian Business (Vol. 80, Winter 2007, No. 24, pp. 135) [12930], [37120]

Street Corner [5827]

Street Fighters: The Last 72 Hours of Bears Stearns, the Toughest Firm on Wall Street [8733], [12931], [27750]

Streetsboro Area of Chamber of Commerce (SACC) [56306]

Streetwise Finance and Accounting for Entrepreneurs: Set Budgets, Manage Costs, Keep Your Business Profitable [156], [21438], [22128], [31858]

Streetwise Motivating and Rewarding Employees: New and Better Ways to Inspire Your People [29168], [38461]

Streetwise Small Business Book of Lists: Hundreds of Lists to Help You Reduce Costs, Increase Revenues, and Boost Your Profits! [157], [21439], [22129], [23478], [32977], [43639]

Streetwise Small Business Turnaround: Revitalizing Your Struggling or Stagnant Enterprise [23479], [25230]

"Strength In Numbers" in Black Enterprise (Vol. 38, January 2008, No. 6, pp. 53) [599], [14013], [40386]

Strengthening Your People Skills in the Workplace (Onsite) [22245]

Strengths Based Leadership [30214], [38462]

Strengthsfinder 2.0 [30215], [32978], [38463]

"Stress-Test Your Strategy: the 7 Questions to Ask" in Harvard Business Review (Vol. 88, November 2010, No. 11, pp. 92) [26548], [29169], [30216], [38464]

"Stressed Out: 7 Banks Rated 'At Risks" in Saint Louis Business Journal (Vol. 32, September 16, 2011, No. 3, pp. 1) [8734], [12932], [31859]

"Stretch Your Advertising Dollars" in Women Entrepreneur (January 27, 2009) [600], [11880], [22130], [27751], [40387]

"Stretch Your Last Dollar Or Invest It?" in Business Owner (Vol. 35, November-December 2011, No. 6, pp. 4) [12933], [31860]

"Strict Intersection Types for the Lambda Calculus" in ACM Computing Surveys (Vol. 43, Fall 2011, No. 3, pp. 20) [4652], [4875]

"Strictly Business" in Black Enterprise (Vol. 38, October 2007, No. 3, pp. 62) [3811], [24928], [41446]

Strictly Business [56307], [58988]

Strings Italian Cafe/Strings Italian Express [18248]

"Stronach Confirms Magna Eyeing Chrysler" in Globe & Mail (March 9, 2007, pp. B1) [32979], [39391]

"Stronger Corn? Take It Off Steroids, Make It All Female" in Farm Industry News (December 5, 2011) [21692], [41236], [42882], [43967]

Strongland Chamber of Commerce (SCC) [57237]

Strongsville Area Chamber of Commerce [56308]

Strongsville Chamber of Commerce (SCC) [56308]

Strongsville Chamber of Commerce News [56309]

Stroud Chamber of Commerce [56592]

Structured Query Language (SQL) I [45069]

Structured Query Language (SQL) II [45070]

Structuring Your Business [29416], [31861], [33980], [41704], [43317], [46038], [46130]

"Struggling Community Banks Find Little Help In Wall Street Bailout" in Crain's Detroit Business (Vol. 24, September 29, 2008) [8735], [12934], [14499], [27752], [31862], [33350], [37509], [45754]

"Struggling States Slashing Health Care For Poor" in Chicago Tribune (January 15, 2009) [11433], [27753], [33351], [34449], [36232]

STTAS [38803]

"Stuck With Two Mortgages; The Nightmare When Buyers Upgrade" in Crain's Chicago Business (Vol. 31, April 21, 2008, No. 16) [14500], [17068], [17504], [25664], [26324], [27754], [37510]

Student Business Incubator [52538]

Students In Free Enterprise [54200]

Students' and Visitors' Tabloid [55350]

Studies of Entrepreneurship, Business and Government in Hong Kong: The Economic Development of a Small Open Economy [27755], [30217], [33981], [36803]

"Studies Mixed on State's 2008 Retail Outlook" in Crain's Detroit Business (Vol. 24, March 24, 2008, No. 12, pp. 28) [27756], [43198]

Studio 6 [10819]

Studio City Business [49043]

Studio City Chamber of Commerce (SCCC) [49044]

Studio6Canada [10820]

"Study: Austin is Ready for a Pro Sports Team" in Austin Business JournalInc. (Vol. 29, December 25, 2009, No. 42, pp. 1) [19467]

"Study: Instant Messaging Can Benefit Workplaces" in HRMagazine (Vol. 53, August 2008, No. 8, pp. 20) [3812], [22457]

MASTER INDEX

Tap

Master Index

"*Swinging For the Fences" in Academy of Management Journal (October 2007, pp. 1055)* **[12950]**, **[21984]**, **[35937]**, **[38475]**
"*Swirling Debate" in Business Courier (Vol. 27, August 20, 2010, No. 16, pp. 1)* **[27774]**, **[42391]**
Swisher Hygiene Franchise Corp. **[2678]**
Swiss Days **[51723]**
Switch: How to Change Things When Change Is Hard **[29173]**, **[30225]**, **[38476]**
"*A Switch in the Kitchen" in Barron's (Vol. 88, March 24, 2008, No. 12, pp. 17)* **[1194]**, **[9979]**, **[10245]**, **[40400]**, **[45764]**
Switzerland of Ohio Chamber of Commerce [56231]
SWLA Business Directory **[52500]**
"*Swope: Breakup Won't Delay Job" in The Business Journal-Serving Metropolitan Kansas City (Vol. 26, August 22, 2008, No. 50, pp. 1)* **[5525]**, **[17510]**, **[42199]**
Swyrich Corporation **[9477]**
Sybase [49326]
Sybase Inc. **[49326]**
Sycamore Chamber of Commerce **[51334]**
Sydney Morning Herald Small Business Show **[33091]**
Sygenex [5055]
Sygenex Inc. **[5055]**
"*Sykes Group Targets GunnAllen" in The Business Journal-Serving Greater Tampa Bay (Vol. 28, September 5, 2008, No. 37, pp. 1)* **[8744]**, **[12951]**, **[23495]**, **[31870]**
"*Sykes Shift from GunnAllen to New Venture" in Tampa Bay Business Journal (Vol. 30, December 18, 2009, No. 52, pp. 1)* **[12952]**, **[24772]**, **[30226]**
Sylacauga Chamber of Commerce (SCC) **[47737]**
Sylvan Learning Center **[20748]**
Sylvania Area Chamber of Commerce (SACC) **[56313]**
"*Sylvie Collection Offers a Feminine Perspective and Voice in Male Dominated Bridal Industry" in Benzinga.com (October 29, 2011)* **[2523]**, **[13280]**, **[28892]**, **[40401]**, **[47385]**
"*Symantic Completes Acquisition of VeriSign's Security Business" in Internet Wire (August 9, 2010)* **[18486]**, **[25345]**, **[44198]**
"*Symbility Solutions Joins Motion Computing Partner Program" in Canadian Corporate News (May 14, 2007)* **[11436]**, **[35155]**, **[36235]**, **[40402]**, **[42200]**, **[46052]**
Symmes Maini & McKee Associates (SMMA) **[41648]**
Syndicat Canadien des Communications, de l'Energie et du Papier [46809]
Syndicat des Communications d'Amerique [6784], [46810]
Synergy Homecare **[10582]**
Synopsys [49327]
Synopsys Inc. **[49327]**
Syntaxis Inc. **[22539]**
"*Synthetic Drywall Rots Mechanical Parts" in Contractor (Vol. 56, December 2009, No. 12, pp. 50)* **[6903]**, **[15374]**, **[15398]**
Syosset Chamber of Commerce **[55353]**
Syracuse University - Center for Technology and Information Policy (CTIP) **[44093]**
Syracuse University - Program on the Analysis and Resolution of Conflicts (PARC) **[14181]**
Syracuse-Wawasee Chamber of Commerce (SWCC) **[51724]**
System-Built Advantage **[5612]**
"*A System for Continuous Organization Renewal" in Strategy & Leadership (Vol. 38, July-August 2010, No. 4, pp. 34-41)* **[38477]**
System4 **[2679]**
Systems Alternatives International Inc. [41520], [41649]
Systems Alternatives International L.L.C. (SAI) **[41520]**, **[41649]**
Systems and Computers in Japan **[44072]**
Systems Paving Franchising Inc. **[14127]**
Systems Service Enterprises Inc. (SSE) **[6548]**
Systems Thinking (Onsite) **[37743]**

T

T. Rowe Price Threshold Partnerships **[52778]**
"*T3 Grows, Recovers Well After Losing Dell" in Austin Business JournalInc. (Vol. 28, September 19, 2008, No. 27)* **[606]**, **[40403]**
T3-THE Commercial, Truck, Trailer, and Technology Expo and Annual NTEA Convention [20721]
TA Associates Inc. **[53070]**
TA Associates, Inc. (Menlo Park) **[49328]**
The Tab **[1252]**
"*Table Games Get a Leg Up" in Philadelphia Business Journal (Vol. 28, January 15, 2010, No. 48, pp. 1)* **[9404]**, **[23496]**
Table Rock Lake - Kimberling City Area Chamber of Commerce (TRLKCACC) **[54145]**
Table Rock Lake Vacation Guide **[54146]**
Table Rock Talk **[54147]**
Table Talk: The Savvy Girl's Alternative to Networking **[22460]**, **[22631]**, **[46534]**, **[47386]**
Table Time for Tots **[4003]**, **[28424]**
Tabletop Market **[10421]**
Tabloid of Services **[54313]**
"*Tabular Dreams" in Canadian Business (Vol. 80, February 12, 2007, No. 4, pp. 36)* **[35156]**, **[41243]**, **[43971]**
Taco Bell Canada **[18253]**
"*Taco Bell; David Ovens" in Advertising Age (Vol. 79, November 17, 2008, No. 43, pp. S2)* **[607]**, **[17998]**, **[23497]**, **[32241]**, **[40404]**, **[41244]**
Taco Del Mar **[18254]**
Taco John's International, Inc. **[18255]**
The Taco Maker **[18256]**
Taco Mayo **[18257]**
Taco Palace **[18258]**
Taco Time Canada Inc. **[18259]**
Tacoma Community College - Business and Industry Resource Center **[59357]**
Tacoma Dome Boat Show **[13969]**
Tacoma Home and Garden Show **[9833]**
Tacoma-Pierce County Business Directory **[59294]**
Tacoma-Pierce County Chamber of Commerce (TPCC) **[59295]**
Tacoma RV Show **[17684]**
Tacoma Small Business Development Center **[59066]**
TacoTime **[18260]**
Tactical Entrepreneur: The Entrepreneur's Game Plan **[21440]**, **[24594]**, **[30227]**, **[35938]**, **[40405]**, **[41448]**
The Tactix Group **[20627]**, **[40650]**, **[43770]**
Taft Chamber of Commerce [49050]
Taft District Chamber of Commerce **[49050]**
TAG International [12]
Tahlequah Area Chamber of Commerce and Tourism Council (TACC) **[56594]**
Tahlequah Area Chamber of Commerce [56594]
T'ai Chi: International Magazine of T'ai Chi Ch'uan **[14089]**
"*Taiwan Technology Initiatives Foster Growth" in Canadian Electronics (Vol. 23, February 2008, No. 1, pp. 28)* **[4997]**, **[5772]**, **[23498]**, **[30812]**, **[33982]**, **[35157]**, **[36812]**, **[39402]**
Take Action **[56314]**
Take Back Your Time: How to Regain Control of Work, Information and Technology **[38478]**, **[46535]**
"*Take Control of Your Company's Finances" in Green Industry Pro (Vol. 23, March 2011, No. 3, pp. 24)* **[9791]**, **[13399]**, **[13486]**, **[21441]**, **[31871]**
"*Take on an Elephant Without Getting Trampled" in Globe & Mail (March 17, 2007, pp. B3)* **[24049]**, **[25236]**
"*Take 'Em Out of the Ball Game" in Canadian Business (Vol. 79, November 20, 2006, No. 23, pp. 19)* **[24595]**, **[43209]**
Take Five **[49830]**; **[51335]**
"*Take a Flyer on Choice" in Canadian Business (Vol. 79, October 23, 2006, No. 21, pp. 163)* **[8745]**, **[12953]**
"*Take It to the Bank" in Barron's (Vol. 89, July 13, 2009, No. 28, pp. 20)* **[8746]**, **[12954]**, **[31872]**
Take It from the Top: The Business of Business Success **[33089]**
Take Off Pounds Sensibly (TOPS) **[21278]**
"*Take Out the Garbage" in Entrepreneur (Vol. 37, August 2009, No. 8, pp. 26)* **[26550]**, **[40406]**, **[43648]**
"*Take the Plunge" in Small Business Opportunities (July 2008)* **[30228]**, **[44780]**
"*Take the Right Approach to Concrete Polishing Rentals" in Rental Product News (Vol. 33, June 2011)* **[9065]**, **[17818]**, **[45765]**
"*Take This Job and Love It" in Green Industry Pro (Vol. 23, October 2011)* **[9792]**, **[13400]**, **[13487]**, **[26551]**, **[44543]**
Take Two . . . for Safety **[47509]**
"*Take the Wheel: the Pension Protection Act Doesn't Mean You Can Sit Back and Relax" in Black Enterprise (October 2007)* **[12955]**, **[21985]**, **[31873]**, **[33983]**, **[46395]**
"*Takeover Frenzy Stokes Steel Stocks" in Globe & Mail (February 7, 2006, pp. B1)* **[8747]**, **[12956]**, **[39403]**, **[42201]**
Taking Action: Substance Abuse in the Workplace **[46081]**
Taking Action 2: Frontline Against Drugs **[46082]**
Taking Care of Business **[48113]**; **[52258]**
"*Taking a Chance" in Baltimore Business Journal (Vol. 28, July 16, 2010, No. 10, pp. 1)* **[18487]**, **[23499]**, **[26552]**, **[30229]**, **[43649]**, **[44736]**
"*Taking Collections" in Investment Dealers' Digest (Vol. 75, October 9, 2009, No. 38, pp. 19)* **[6258]**, **[6336]**, **[8748]**, **[12957]**, **[23500]**, **[26330]**, **[27775]**, **[42202]**
"*Taking the 'Comprehensive' Out of Immigration Reform" in Hispanic Business (September 2007, pp. 8)* **[21693]**, **[33984]**, **[40915]**
"*Taking Full Advantage: What You Need To Know During Open-Enrollment Season" in Black Enterprise (Vol. 38, November 2007, No. 4)* **[11437]**, **[21986]**, **[36236]**
Taking on Greater Responsibility: Step-up Skills for Non-managers (Onsite) **[37744]**
"*Taking on Intel" in Canadian Business (Vol. 79, October 23, 2006, No. 21, pp. 27)* **[35158]**, **[39404]**, **[42203]**
"*Taking the Over-the-Counter Route to US" in Barron's (Vol. 88, July 7, 2008, No. 27, pp. 24)* **[8749]**, **[12958]**, **[24773]**, **[27776]**, **[31874]**, **[36813]**, **[42204]**
"*Taking a Pounding; Recession Fears Weigh Down Steakhouse Operator Morton's" in Crain's Chicago Business (March 31, 2008)* **[12959]**, **[17999]**, **[22131]**
"*Taking the Right Road" in Entrepreneur (Vol. 37, October 2009, No. 10, pp. 104)* **[10541]**, **[23501]**, **[30230]**, **[32242]**, **[34453]**
"*Taking the Steps Into the Clouds" in New Hampshire Business Review (Vol. 33, March 25, 2011, No. 6, pp. 19)* **[3627]**, **[4998]**, **[18488]**, **[19003]**, **[28893]**, **[35159]**, **[45221]**
"*Taking on the World" in Canadian Business (Vol. 79, November 20, 2006, No. 23, pp. 43)* **[30231]**, **[38479]**
"*Tale of a Gun" in Canadian Business (Vol. 80, February 26, 2007, No. 5, pp. 37)* **[35160]**, **[41245]**
"*Tale of the Tape: IPhone Vs. G1" in Advertising Age (Vol. 79, October 27, 2008, No. 40, pp. 6)* **[3813]**, **[11884]**, **[25671]**, **[35161]**
"*A Tale of Two Brothers" in Canadian Business (Vol. 80, March 26, 2007, No. 7, pp. 18)* **[30232]**, **[31120]**
The Talent Masters: Why Smart Leaders Put People Before Numbers **[30233]**, **[35939]**, **[38480]**
"*Talent Scout: How This Exec Finds and Develops Leaders Internally" in Black Enterprise (Vol. 38, November 2007, No. 4, pp. 63)* **[7796]**, **[30981]**
"*Talent Shows" in Canadian Business (Vol. 81, December 24, 2007, No. 1, pp. 14)* **[35488]**, **[35940]**, **[36814]**, **[40407]**, **[40916]**
"*Tales of the City" in Canadian Business (Vol. 81, December 8, 2008, No. 21, pp. 37)* **[11172]**, **[36815]**
Talihina Chamber of Commerce **[56595]**
"*Talisman CEO Touts Benefits of Going It Alone" in Globe & Mail (March 22, 2006, pp. B1)* **[24596]**, **[25237]**
Talk Show Contacts [19570]
Talk Show Producer Mailing List [19570]
Talk Show Selects [19570]
Talk Show Yearbook **[19570]**
Talk of the Towne **[54148]**
Talkeetna Chamber of Commerce **[47820]**
Tallahassee Area Chamber of Commerce [50144]
Tallahassee Chamber of Commerce [50144]
Tallmadge Chamber of Commerce **[56315]**
Tallwood Venture Capital **[49329]**
Tama Chamber of Commerce [51978]
Tama/Toledo Area Chamber of Commerce **[51978]**
TAMACC: The Voice of the Texas Hispanic Business Community **[58465]**
"*Tamara Vrooman" in Canadian Business (Vol. 80, November 19, 2007, No. 23, pp. 9)* **[8750]**, **[25672]**, **[47387]**
Tamayo Consulting Inc. **[24701]**, **[28451]**, **[29282]**, **[38814]**
Tampa Bay Beaches Chamber of Commerce **[50306]**
"*Tampa Bay's CMBS Exposure Looms Large" in Tampa Bay Business Journal (Vol. 30, December 4, 2009, No. 50, pp. 1)* **[6337]**, **[14506]**, **[26331]**
"*Tampa Condo Conversion Sells for $14.8 Million Less" in The Business Journal-Serving Greater Tampa Bay (Vol. 28, September 5, 2008)* **[17073]**, **[17511]**, **[27777]**, **[42205]**, **[44199]**
The Tan Sheet **[10255]**, **[15180]**, **[34073]**
"*Tanganyika Announces First Quarter 2007 Results" in Canadian Corporate News (May 14, 2007)* **[8751]**, **[12960]**, **[23502]**, **[31875]**
Tangram Press [58605]
TAN-MISSLARK - Nursery, Garden and Landscape Supply Show [9123], [9830], [16202]
Tanners' Council of America [13626]
Tanners Council of America Inc. [13626]
"*Tao of Downfall" in International Journal of Entrepreneurship and Small Business (Vol. 11, August 31, 2010, No. 2, pp. 121)* **[8752]**, **[12961]**, **[27778]**, **[30234]**, **[31876]**, **[33985]**, **[36816]**, **[40917]**
Taos County Chamber of Commerce **[54988]**
Taos County Vacation Guide **[54989]**
Tap Dancin' **[6412]**
"*Tap Into Food Truck Trend to Rev Up Sales, Build Buzz" in Nation's Restaurant News (Vol. 45, February 7, 2011, No. 3, pp. 18)* **[9166]**, **[18000]**, **[30235]**, **[40408]**, **[43650]**, **[45766]**
"*Tap the iPad and Mobile Internet Device Market" in Franchising World (Vol. 42, September 2010, No. 9, pp. 43)* **[3814]**, **[4999]**, **[26553]**, **[28894]**, **[32243]**, **[41449]**

Small Business Sourcebook • 30th Edition

3627

"The Tapestry of Life" in Women In Business (Vol. 61, December 2009, No. 6, pp. 8) [30236], [30813], [46007], [47388]

Tapioca Express Inc. [9749]

Tappahannock-Essex County Chamber of Commerce (TECC) [58990]

Tappin' across the Floor [6413]

Tappin' Rhythm [6414]

"Tapping the 'Well' in Wellness" in Pet Product News (Vol. 64, November 2010, No. 11, pp. 1) [1067], [10246], [15738], [26554], [43210], [45767]

Tarboro - Edgecombe Chamber of Commerce [55817]

Tarbutton Associates Inc. [10796], [32298]

Target [54437]

"Target Gets Exclusive with Ben & Jerry's" in Ice Cream Reporter (Vol. 23, July 20, 2010, No. 8, pp. 1) [10920], [43211]

Target Technology Center [52647]

Targets [43702]

Tarleton State University Small Business Development Center [57872]

Tarleton State University - Texas Institute for Applied Environmental Research (TIAER) [30891]

Tarpon Springs Chamber of Commerce (TSCC) [50307]

The Tarrance Group [16632]

Tarrant Small Business Development Center [57873]

Tarzana Chamber of Commerce (TOCC) [49051]

Task Force for Women in Public Administration [42362]

A Taste Above [19287]

"Tastee-Freez Celebrates 60th Anniversary" in Ice Cream Reporter (Vol. 23, July 20, 2010, No. 8, pp. 2) [10921], [30237], [37124], [42206]

"Tasti D-Lite Has Franchise Agreement for Australia" in Ice Cream Reporter (Vol. 23, November 20, 2010, No. 12, pp. 3) [10922], [32244], [36817], [42207]

Tastings - A Wine Experience [43311]

"The Tata Way" in Business Strategy Review (Vol. 21, Summer 2010, No. 2, pp. 14) [14961], [36818], [39405]

"Tata's Novi Unit Looks to Hire 200 Engineers" in Crain's Detroit Business (Vol. 26, January 18, 2010, No. 3, pp. 4) [35489], [41693]

"Tate & Lyle to Sell Redpath Division to American Sugar" in Globe & Mail (February 15, 2007, pp. B15) [25238], [39406], [42208]

Tattoo: The Magazine of Dermagraphics [19588]

Taunton Area Chamber of Commerce (TACC) [52969]

"Tauri Group Partner Joining Homeland Security and Defense" in Wireless News (December 15, 2009) [18489], [25905], [33986], [38481]

Tawas Area Chamber of Commerce [53447]

"Tax Abatement Changes Seen as Home Run for Cleveland Condo Market" in Crain's Cleveland Business (Vol. 30, June 15, 2009, No. 23) [5526], [17074], [17512], [46396]

Tax Centers of America [19725]

Tax Council-Alcoholic Beverage Industries [1829]

"Tax Credit Crunch" in Miami Daily Business Review (March 26, 2008) [5527], [12962], [17075], [33356], [46397]

"Tax Deal Yields Polaris Offices" in Business First-Columbus (October 26, 2007, pp. A1) [5528], [23503], [46398]

The Tax Directory® [255], [19734], [24160], [34093], [46469]

The Tax Executive [19696]

Tax Executives Institute (TEI) [19603], [46133]

Tax Executives Institute Inc. [19603], [46133]

Tax Executives Institute Library [19767]

Tax and Financial Planning for Real Estate [17577]

"Tax-Free Zones Need Shows; Out-of-State Shoppers Are Key To Success" in Crain's Detroit Business (Vol. 24, January 28, 2008, No. 4) [20428], [43212], [46399], [46710]

Tax Management Estates, Gifts, and Trusts Journal [7753]

Tax Management Memorandum [19735]

Tax Notes [19697]

Tax Notes International [19704]

Tax Notes Today [19697]

Tax Notes® Today [256], [19736]

TAX/PACK: Professional 1040 [264], [19742]

Tax Practice Bulletin [19698]

Tax Preparer [19743]

Tax Preparer: California Supplement [19744]

"Tax Reform Analysis: Reforms Equal Smaller 401(k)s" in Employee Benefit News (Vol. 25, December 1, 2011, No. 15, pp. 19) [21987], [31877], [33987], [46400]

Tax Savings Report [19699]

Tax Savvy for Small Business [19674], [46401]

Tax Savvy for Small Business: Year-Round Tax Strategies to Save You Money [24050], [46402]

Tax Season Update: Small Businesses and Their Owners [46451]

Tax Smarts for Small Business [19675], [46403]

"Tax Talk; Usual Election-Year Obstacles to Income Tax May Not Apply This Time" in Crain's Chicago Business (March 24, 2008) [33988], [45768], [46404]

"Tax Thriller in D.C." in Barron's (Vol. 90, August 30, 2010, No. 35, pp. 17) [33989], [46405]

"Taxes, Right-To-Work Top West Michigan Concerns" in Crain's Detroit Business (Vol. 24, September 22, 2008, No. 38, pp. 6) [33990], [45769], [46406], [46918]

Taxes--The Tax Magazine [191], [19700], [43333]

Taxi & Livery Management--Buyer's Guide Issue [19814]

Taxi and Livery Management [19819]

Taxicab, Limousine and Paratransit Association (TLPA) [19802]

Taxicab Management [19819]

Taxicab Management--Buyer's Guide Issue [19814]

Taxidermy by Video [19835]

Tax$imple [265], [19745]

"Taxing Position: Yoga Studios Hit for Back Sales Tax" in Puget Sound Business Journal (Vol. 29, August 29, 2008, No. 19, pp. 1) [15981], [46407]

"A Taxing Proposition" in Black Enterprise (Vol. 37, January 2007, No. 6, pp. 6) [11885], [21216], [46408]

"Taxis Are Set to Go Hybrid" in Philadelphia Business Journal (Vol. 30, September 16, 2011, No. 31, pp. 1) [7322], [7683], [13541], [19813], [30814], [45770]

The TaxLetter [19701]

TaxMama [54531]

"Taxpayer Says a Simple Thank-You Would Help" in Boston Business Journal (Vol. 27, November 16, 2007, No. 42, pp. 1) [46008], [46409]

"Taxpayers' Banks Share Even Higher" in Business Courier (Vol. 24, October 26, 2008, No. 28, pp. 1) [17513], [33357], [46410]

Taxpayers' Federation of Illinois (TFI) [19791]

TAXPRO Monthly [19702]

Taylor Business [58466]

Taylor Chamber of Commerce [58467]

Taylor Corporation [59019]

Bayard Taylor Memorial Library [1159]

Taylor Rental [17843]

Taylor Society [37568], [46484]

"Taylor Tests Land Grant Program" in Austin Business Journal (Vol. 31, June 3, 2011, No. 13, pp. 1) [5529], [30815], [33358], [35162], [39407], [44737]

Harold Taylor Time Consultants Inc. [46580]

Tazewell Area Chamber of Commerce (TACC) [58991]

TCBY [10984]

TCC Business News [49052]

TD Magazine [13307]

"TD Pares in U.S., Still Aims for Growth" in Globe & Mail (March 24, 2007, pp. B6) [25239], [31878]

TDL Group Corp. [9751]

"Tea for 33 Million" in Canadian Business (Vol. 80, March 12, 2007, No. 6, pp. 10) [23504], [24597], [25240]

Tea Association of the U.S.A. (TA) [9694]

"The Tea Bag Test" in Canadian Business (Vol. 79, October 23, 2006, No. 21, pp. 83) [23505], [30238], [38482]

Tea and Coffee Trade Journal [4319], [9723]

Tea Council of the United States of America (TC) [9695]

Teach Magazine: Education for Today and Tomorrow [28407]

"Teachable Moments: Worth Every Penny" in Pet Product News (Vol. 64, December 2010, No. 12, pp. 34) [15739], [20429], [26555], [28352], [43213], [43651], [46711]

Teacher Magazine [19844]

Teachers' Division of National Association of Cosmetology Schools [10059]

Teachers' Educational Council - National Association of Accredited Cosmetology Schools [10059]

Teachers' Educational Council - National Association of Cosmetology Schools [10059]

"Teachers, U.S. Fund Providence Made Moves On BCE Buyout" in Globe & Mail (April 10, 2007, pp. B17) [21988], [42209], [44544]

Teaching Exceptional Children [20738]

Teaching Kids How to Sail [13958]

Teague [4551]

Tealuxe, A Tea Bar & Cafe [9750]

"Team Bonding for Fun and Profit" in Women Entrepreneur (December 3, 2008) [22461], [25673], [29174], [38483]

Team Building [29221]

Team of Champions [29222]

Team Excellence [29223]

The TEAM FOCUS Group [38815]

"Team Implicit Coordination Processes: A Team Knowledge-based Approach" in Academy of Management Review (January 2008, pp. 163) [29175], [38484]

Team Leadership Effectiveness Program 'Team Top Gun' (Onsite) [37745]

The Team Line-Up [19355]

Team Player [29224]

Team Problem Solving [29287]

"A Team Sport" in Business Courier (Vol. 26, October 2, 2009, No. 23, pp. 1) [2053], [23506], [32245], [36819], [40409], [42524], [44545]

Teamlogic IT [4822]

The Teammate [54822]

"Teams Buy Into Screen Scene" in Business First Buffalo (October 5, 2007, pp. 1) [19469], [40410]

Teamwork [29197], [39509]

Teamwork, Leadership, Commitment [50620]

Teamwork for a Prosperous Community [59735]

Teaneck Chamber of Commerce [54823]

Teaneck Economic Development Corp. [54823]

"Teaneck Resident Chairs National Minority Business Group" in Record (January 5, 2011) [40820], [47389]

TECC Update [55818]

"The Tech 100" in Canadian Business (Vol. 81, July 21, 2008, No. 11, pp. 48) [12963], [23507], [35163], [42525], [43972]

"Tech Coalition Warns Takeover Spree is Nigh" in Globe & Mail (February 6, 2007, pp. B1) [35164], [43973]

"Tech Data Launches Unified Communications and Network Security Specialized Business Units" in Wireless News (October 22,2009) [4730], [5039], [18490], [35165]

"Tech Deal Couples Homegrown Firms" in The Business Journal-Serving Greater Tampa Bay (Vol. 28, July 4, 2008, No. 28, pp. 1) [3628], [19004], [25906], [26792], [38485], [42210], [45222]

Tech Directions--Annual Buyers' Guide: A Directory of Suppliers [13305]

Tech Directions--"Who's Got It?" Issue [13305]

TECH Fort Worth [58595]

"Tech Giving 2.0" in Boston Business Journal (Vol. 31, August 5, 2011, No. 28, pp. 1) [9284], [30239], [35166], [46009], [47082], [47594]

"Tech Godfather Steve Walker Winding Down Howard Venture Fund" in Baltimore Business Journal (Vol. 27, December 11, 2009, No. 31) [12964], [27779], [35167], [37513], [47083]

"Tech Investing: March's Long Road" in Canadian Business (Vol. 80, January 29, 2007, No. 3, pp. 67) [12965], [18491], [35168], [39408]

"Tech Tax Heroes Go from Political Neophytes to Savvy Fundraisers" in Baltimore Business Journal (Vol. 27, November 20, 2009, No. 28) [5000], [9285], [35169], [46411]

Tech-U-Fit Corporation Library [15270], [41654]

TechAmerica [44991]

TechColumbus [56405]

TechConnect (Onsite) [22248]

Techfarm Ventures / Techfund Capital [49330]

"TechLift Strives to Fill in Gaps in Entrepreneurial Support Efforts" in Crain's Cleveland Business (November 12, 2007) [27780], [30240], [35170], [36097], [47084]

Techni Graphic System, Inc. (pinpointer) [57735]

Technical Innovation Center [52794]

The Technical Management Program (Onsite) [37746]

Technical Project Management (Canada) [37747]

Technical Project Management (Onsite) [37748]

Technical Publishing Society [6804], [22152]

Technical Studies [44077]

Technical Valuation Society [1205]

Technical Writing: A Comprehensive Hands-On Introduction (Onsite) [22577], [28093]

Technical Writing (Onsite) [22249]

"Technically Speaking" in Black Enterprise (Vol. 38, February 2008, No. 7, pp. 64) [35171], [40411], [43652]

Techniques to Improve Your Writing: Practical G/T Business Writing [22646]

TechniScan Inc. [5675]

TechnoCap, Inc. [59963]

Technological Entrepreneurship [30241], [35172], [37125], [42885], [43974], [47085]

Technologies du Developpement Durable du Canada [26858]

Technology 2020 [57828]

Technology Centre of New Jersey [54877]

Technology Crossover Ventures [49331]

"Technology Drivers to Boost Your Bottom Line" in Franchising World (Vol. 42, August 2010, No. 8, pp. 15) [3815], [28895], [32246], [35173], [40412], [41246], [41450]

Technology Entrepreneur Center [54201]

Technology Funding [49332]

Technology Group Communications [20011]

Technology Management Associates Inc. [14059]

Technology Management Group Co. [2972], [26101], [44086]

Technology Partners [49333]

Texas Association of Nurserymen/Mississippi, Louisiana, and Arkansas Association of Nurserymen Regional Nursery and Garden Show [9123], [9830], [16202]

Texas Business Report [58474]

Texas Center for Policy Studies (TCPS) [7432]

Texas City - La Marque Chamber of Commerce (TCLMCC) [58475]

Texas City - La Marque Chamber Express [58476]

Texas City-La Marque Magazine [58477]

Texas Department of Economic Development [58599]

Texas Department of Economic Development and Tourism - Business Development Division [58540]

Texas Department of Economic Development and Tourism - Business Development Division - Advisory Council on Small Business Issues [57883]

Texas Discovery Gardens Horticulture Library [9875]

"Texas Fold 'Em" in Canadian Business (Vol. 79, October 9, 2006, No. 20, pp. 44) [11887], [21218], [33993], [35178]

Texas Forest Service - Texas Forest Products Laboratory Library [13682]

Texas Jurisprudence®, 3d, LawDesk® CD-ROM [24161]

Texas Music Educators Association Clinic/Convention [14664], [14761]

Texas Pharmacy Association Annual Meeting and Exhibit [6696]

Texas Physical Therapy Association Annual Conference [16090]

Texas Press Association Annual Midwinter Conference and Trade Show [22513]

Texas Press Association Trade Show and Texas Midwinter Convention [22513]

Texas Procurement Technical Assistance Center - Angelina College [58574]

Texas Procurement Technical Assistance Center - Cross Timbers Procurement Center [58575]

Texas Procurement Technical Assistance Center - Del Mar College - Workforce and Economic Development [58576]

Texas Procurement Technical Assistance Center - El Paso Community College - Contract Opportunities Center [58577]

Texas Procurement Technical Assistance Center - Midwestern State University - Wichita Falls Small Business Development Center (SBDC) [58578]

Texas Procurement Technical Assistance Center - Northwest Texas Regional Network - West Texas A&M University Small Business Development Center (SBDC) [58579]

Texas Procurement Technical Assistance Center - Pan Handle Regional Planning Commission [58580]

Texas Procurement Technical Assistance Center - San Antonio Procurement Outreach Program [58581]

Texas Procurement Technical Assistance Center - Texas Facilities Commission (TFC) [58582]

Texas Procurement Technical Assistance Center - Texas Information Procurement Service [58583]

Texas Procurement Technical Assistance Center - Texas Tech University [58584]

Texas Procurement Technical Assistance Center - Texas Tech University - Abilene Small Business Development Center [58585]

Texas Procurement Technical Assistance Center - Texas Tech University - Midland Small Business Development Center (SBDC) [58586]

Texas Procurement Technical Assistance Center - University of Houston - Small Business Development Center [58587]

Texas Procurement Technical Assistance Center - University of Texas - Permian Basin Small Business Development Center (SBDC) [58588]

Texas Procurement Technical Assistance Center - Valley Procurement Technical Assistance Center [58589]

Texas Public Policy Foundation (TPPF) [19792]

Texas Southern University - Robert James Terry Library - Business Library [33112]

"Texas State Poised for Boom" in Austin Business JournalInc. (Vol. 29, January 29, 2010, No. 47, pp. 1) [1287], [5531], [23513], [28354], [45772]

Texas State University-San Marcos - Edwards Aquifer Research and Data Center (EARDC) [21017]

Texas State University - San Marcos Small Business Development Center [57874]

Texas Tech University - Center for Communications Research (CCR) [20022]

Texas Tech University - Center for Health Care Leadership and Strategy [34690]

Texas Tech University - Center for Healthcare Innovation, Education and Research (CHIER) [34690]

Texas Tech University - Institute for Leadership Research (ILR) [34691]

Texas Tech University - Texas Wine Marketing Research Institute (TWMRI) [19300]

Texas Woman's University - F.W. and Bessie Dye Memorial Library [16098]

Textile Care Allied Trades Association (TCATA) [6739]

Textile Consultatnt Associates [10157]

"Thai Ice Cream Cremo Expanding to Middle East" in Ice Cream Reporter (Vol. 23, September 20, 2010, No. 10, pp. 3) [10923], [23514], [36821], [39413]

Thank God It's Monday! How to Create a Workplace You and Your Customers Love [26558], [29176], [41558]

"That Canadian Tire Couple Won't Be Annoying You Anymore" in Globe & Mail (March 10, 2006, pp. B3) [609], [40416]

"That Empty Feeling" in Crain's Cleveland Business (Vol. 28, October 15, 2007, No. 41, pp. 1) [5532], [17076], [17514], [27782]

"That Vision Thing" in Canadian Business (Vol. 80, December 25, 2006, No. 1, pp. 78) [25674], [27783], [46414]

"That's About It for Quantitative Easing" in Barron's (Vol. 89, July 20, 2009, No. 29, pp. M11) [8756], [12969], [27784], [31880]

That's Show Business: The Rules of Exhibiting [40570], [46735]

"That's the Spirit" in Entrepreneur (Vol. 36, March 2008, No. 3, pp. 78) [43655]

The American Institute of Certified Public Accountants [15]

The Beveridge Consulting Group Inc. [43760]

The Bond Market Association [11977]

The Bond Markets Association [11977]

The Broadcasting Cable Market Place [16707], [18336], [19915]

The Business Family Centre [47148]

The Canadian Appraiser [1220]

The Canadian Association of Financial Planners (CAFP) - Canadian Association of Insurance and Financial Advisors [8026]

The Canadian Direct Marketing Association [350]

The Canadian Importers Association [26846]

The Canadian Surveyor [19530]

The Carolina Craftsmen's Christmas Classic/Greensboro [6045]

The Carolina Craftsmen's Classic Arts & Crafts Festival-Columbia [6046]

The Carolina Craftsmen's Classic/Columbia [6046]

The Center for Association Leadership [1454]

The Computing Teacher [4765]

The Cooper Institute [16058]

The Cornell Hotel and Restaurant Administration Quarterly [10766], [18023]

The Costume Institute - Irene Lewisohn Costume Reference Library. [4176], [5941]

The Federal Tax Directory [255], [19734], [24160], [34093], [46469]

The Film Journal [14581]

The Food & Beverage Industry [9996], [19258]

The Food Institute. [1823], [3484], [5114], [6501], [9191], [10020], [18298], [19296]

The HeartMath System [40851]

The Herb Growing & Marketing Network [10360]

The Horseless Age [14975]

The HR Executive's Purchasing Resource [35814]

The Institute of Management Sciences [46480]

The Internet Society [11604], [15305]

The Investor Intelligence Group [13181]

The Journal of Laboratory and Clinical Medicine [14288]

The Journal of Long Term Home Health Care [10547], [34500]

The Kelsey Group Inc. [28960], [40582]

The Knitting Guild of America [5962]

The Laserdisk Professional [3651]

The Medicare Handbook [34368]

The Melting Pot Restaurants, Inc. [18183]

The MTM Association for Standards and Research [15242]

The Murdock Group Career Satisfaction Corp. [36054]

The National Center for Public Policy Research [2937], [26066], [42414]

The National Needlework Association [6098], [18719]

The National Writers Association [6798]

The Nature Conservancy - New Jersey Chapter [32328]

The New Food & Drug Packaging [4603]

The Ontario Land Surveyor Quarterly [19532]

The Pin Man [46794]

The Plain Language Group [22519]

The Plumbing & Mechanical Annual Directory [850]

The PMA [34507]

The Price-Pottenger Foundation, Weston A. Price Foundation, Santa Barbara Medical Research Foundation. [10267], [15227]

The PRIDE Institute Journal [10547], [34500]

The Production Makers Source of the Madison Avenue Handbook [7897]

The Progressive Fish-Culturist [9029]

The Quarter Horse Journal [19485]

The Recording Academy [17635]

The Savory Center [7430]

The Shannon Management Group [36064], [40646], [42559]

The SIA SnowSports Show [18839]

The Source Book [34216]

The Stanton Group [22059]

The Stranger Register: Investments and Strategies [2714]

The Television Yearbook [19991]

The Texas Financial Institutions Directory [37502]

The Visual Merchandising Show - Tradeshow and Seminars for Visual Merchandisers [21301]

The Voice [15819]

The Wholesaler--Guide to the Industry Issue [16282]

The Zig Ziglar Corp. [26647]

Theater Xtreme [43312]

Theatre Directory [14577]

Theatre Historical Society of America (THSA) [14592]

The Theatre Listing: A Directory of Professional Theatre in Canada [41356]

TheHomeMag [15604]

"Theme Park Sale has Vendor Upside" in Tampa Bay Business Journal (Vol. 29, October 23, 2009, No. 44, pp. 1) [975], [12970], [42214]

Therapeutic Massage for Sports and Fitness [14153]

Therapeutic Recreation Journal [34597]

There's a Business In Every Woman: A 7-Step Guide to Discovering, Starting, and Building the Business of Your Dreams [23515], [24602], [29421], [47195]

"There's More Upside in Germany" in Barron's (Vol. 90, September 6, 2010, No. 36, pp. M7) [8757], [12971], [14962], [27785], [36822], [39414]

There's Someplace Like Home: Developing an Adult Day Care Center in Your Church [285]

Thermopolis Chamber of Commerce [59848]

Thermopolis - Hot Springs Chamber of Commerce [59848]

"TheStree.com: Study Abroad" in Entrepreneur (Vol. 35, October 2007, No. 10, pp. 44) [12972], [31881], [36823]

"They Have Issues: New Black-Owned Investment Bank Nets $90 Million In Managed Issues" in Black Enterprise (Vol. 38, March 2008) [8758], [12973], [40821]

"They Like It Cold" in Business Journal Portland (Vol. 27, October 15, 2010, No. 33, pp. 1) [9980], [35179], [39415]

They Made America [4136], [7850], [30248], [32997], [47087]

TheYardSale.com [15362]

"They're Hopping Mad" in Canadian Business (Vol. 80, October 22, 2007, No. 21, pp. 20) [2465], [12974], [33994], [46415]

"They've Fallen, But They Can Get Up" in Barron's (Vol. 88, March 10, 2008, No. 10, pp. 43) [1434], [8759], [12975], [15082], [17077], [31882]

Thibodaux Chamber of Commerce (TCC) [52501]

Thibodaux Magazine [52502]

Thief River Falls Chamber of Commerce [53740]

Thimband-The Newsletter [28408]

The Thin Book of Naming Elephants: How to Surface Undiscussables for Greater Organizational Success [23516], [29177], [30249]

"Things Fall Apart" in Canadian Business (Vol. 80, October 8, 2007, No. 20, pp. 187) [5533], [27786], [33995]

"Things Really Clicking for Macy's Online" in Business Courier (Vol. 24, November 30, 2008, No. 33, pp. 1) [11888], [15349], [21219], [28899], [43214]

"Things Will Improve, or Not: a Chartered Financial Analyst Explains It All" in Canadian Business (Vol. 81, November 10, 2008) [12976], [27787], [36824]

"Think Again: What Makes a Leader?" in Business Strategy Review (Vol. 21, Autumn 2010, No. 3, pp. 64) [30250], [38492]

Think Big and Kick Ass in Business and Life [30251], [32998]

"Think Disruptive! How to Manage In a New Era of Innovation" in Strategy & Leadership (Vol. 38, July-August 2010, No. 4, pp. 5-10) [2799], [25907], [27788], [37126], [38493]

"Think the Oilsands Are an Environmental Disaster?" in Canadian Business (Vol. 83, October 12, 2010, No. 17, pp. 52) [7323], [7684], [30816]

"The Thinker" in Canadian Business (Vol. 81, March 31, 2008, No. 5, pp. 52) [28355], [30252], [32999], [38494], [44881]

Thinkertots [28479]

"Thinking Aloud" in Business Strategy Review (Vol. 21, Summer 2010, No. 2, pp. 47) [38495], [42887], [43976]

"Tiptoeing Beyond Treasuries" in Barron's (Vol. 88, March 31, 2008, No. 13, pp. M6) [8764], [12983], [27797], [31889]

Tipton Chamber of Commerce (TCC) [54149]

Tipton County Chamber of Commerce (TCCC) [51726]

Tipton County News and Views [51727]

Tire Association of North America [20069]

Tire Business [1590], [15002]

Tire Business: Your Number One information resource [20077]

Tire Industry Association (TIA) [20069]

Tire Retread Information Bureau [20070]

Tire Retread and Repair Information Bureau (TRIB) [20070]

Tire Retreading Institute [20069]

Tire Retreading/Repair Journal [20078]

Tire Review: Dedicated to Building your Business [20079]

Tire Review--Performance Tire and Custom Wheel Guide [1564]

Tire Review--Sourcebook & Directory Issue [20074]

Tire Review--Purchasing Directory Issue [20074]

Tire Review--Wheel Brand Profiles, Custom Wheel, and Tire Style Guide [1564]

Tire Review--Wheel Brand Profiles Issue [1564]

"Tired of PowerPoint? Try This Instead" in Harvard Business Review (Vol. 88, September 2010, No. 9, pp. 30) [18568], [22462], [41452]

"Titan to Become New York's Largest Provider of Phone Kiosk Advertising" in Marketing Weekly News (September 11, 2010, pp. 150) [614], [3818], [13331], [40427]

Titanium EBay: A Tactical Guide to Becoming a Millionaire PowerSeller [1530], [15350], [28902], [43657]

The Titens Consulting Group [31149]

"Title Creep: The Chief Revenue Officer" in Inc. (March 2008, pp. 28) [25800], [40428], [41251], [43658]

The Title Source™ III [2408]

Titusville Area Chamber of Commerce [50308]

Titusville Area Chamber of Commerce (TACC) [57242]

"TiVo, Domino's Team to Offer Pizza Ordering by DVR" in Advertising Age (Vol. 79, November 17, 2008, No. 43, pp. 48) [18003], [23523], [35184], [40429], [42220], [43659], [45776]

Tix Travel and Ticket Agency Inc. [20634]

TL Ventures / Radnor Venture Partners [57304]

TLA-Lighting Consultants Inc. [41650]

TLA Lighting Consultants, Inc. Library [6940]

"TLC's 'Jumping the Broom' Red Carpet Wedding Contest" in Benzinga.com (March 30, 2011) [2524]

TMA Issues Monitor [20094]

TMA Legislative Bulletin [20095]

TMA Tobacco Weekly [20096]

TMA Trademark Report [20097]

TMA World Alert [20098]

"TMC Development Closes $1.1 Million Real Estate Purchase" in Internet Wire (September 17, 2009) [5815], [17517], [23524], [33364], [37517], [44882]

TMNG Global [2919], [38763]

TMS Journal [14116]

TNG Canada Today [6805], [46824]

TNG Canada/CWA [6784], [46810]

TNNA Winter Trade Show [6066]

"To Be or Not To Be an S Corporation" in Modern Machine Shop (Vol. 84, September 2011, No. 4, pp. 38) [13713], [39422], [43332], [46419]

"To Be Seen Is to Be Successful" in Pet Product News (Vol. 64, December 2010, No. 12, pp. 12) [11006], [15740], [16599], [25677], [40430], [42666], [43216]

"To Blog, Or Not To Blog" in Canadian Business (Vol. 80, December 25, 2006, No. 1, pp. 15) [11892], [21222], [40431]

"To Build for the Future, Reach Beyond the Skies" in Canadian Business (Vol. 83, June 15, 2010. No. 10, pp. 11) [24932], [30261], [35185], [43979]

"To Catch Up, Colgate May Ratchet Up Its Ad Spending" in Advertising Age (Vol. 81, December 6, 2010, No. 43, pp. 1) [615], [2054], [15781], [40432]

"A 'To Do' List" in Plaything (Vol. 107, January 1, 2009, No. 1, pp. 9) [20269], [24055]

"To the Extreme" in Entrepreneur (Vol. 36, February 2008, No. 2, pp. 21) [19346], [19473]

"To Give and Receive: How to Pass On 401k Assets and Manage an Inheritance" in Black Enterprise (Vol. 38, October 2007, No. 3) [12984], [31890]

"To Help Maintain an Adequate Blood Supply During the Summer Months" in Ice Cream Reporter (Vol. 21, August 20, 2008, No. 9, pp. 8) [10924], [34456], [40433], [42221], [46012]

"To JM On Its 75th Anniversary" in Journal of Marketing (Vol. 75, July 2011, No. 4, pp. 129) [15577], [38502], [40434], [44552]

"To Keep Freight Rolling, Springfield Must Grease the Hub" in Crain's Chicago Business (Vol. 31, April 21, 2008, No. 16, pp. 22) [11176], [25678], [27798], [36830], [44553]

"To Live and Thrive in L.A." in Canadian Business (Vol. 81, October 13, 2008, No. 17, pp. 78) [1862], [18004], [30262], [47392]

"To Offshore Or Not To Offshore?" in Converting (Vol. 25, October 1, 2007, No. 10, pp. 10) [19527], [36831], [39423], [41694]

"To Sell or Not To Sell" in Inc. (December 2007, pp. 80) [12985], [31124], [44201]

"To Thine Own Self" in Entrepreneur (Vol. 35, November 2007, No. 11, pp. 50) [12986], [21991], [31891]

"To Win, Create What's Scarce" in Harvard Business Review (Vol. 88, November 2010, No. 11, pp. 46) [33003], [41252]

The Toastmaster [18573]

Tobacco Barometer: Cigarettes, Cigars, Smoking Tobacco, Chewing Tobacco and Snuff [20099]

Tobacco Industry Litigation Reporter [20100]

Tobacco International [20101]

Tobacco Merchants Association (TMA) [20086]

Tobacco Merchants Association of the U.S. - Howard S. Cullman Library [20115]

Tobacco Trade Barometer: Imports [20102]

Tobacconists' Association of America (TAA) [20087]

Tobbaco Valley Board of Commerce [54270]

Toca Family Publishing [50688]

Today's Business Choice [53449]

"Today's Business Sale Climate" in Business Owner (Vol. 35, September-October 2011, No. 5, pp. 10) [25347], [27799], [33365], [37518], [44202]

Today's Chamber [55358]

Today's Facility Manager: The Facility Decision Maker's Source for Products and Services [15255]

Today's Insurance Professionals [11476]

Today's Insurance Woman [11476]

Today's Window Fashions [21305]

"Toes for Business" in Hispanic Business (October 2007, pp. 10, 12) [6384], [23525], [47393]

"Tofutti Brands" in Ice Cream Reporter (Vol. 23, September 20, 2010, No. 10, pp. 6) [8765], [10925], [12987], [23526], [43660]

Together! [29225]

Together Inc. [46794]

Together We Can! [29226]

Togo's Eatery [6495]

Toilet Goods Association [1892], [2033], [5884]

The Toilet Paper Entrepreneur: The Tell-It-Like-It-Is Guide to Cleaning Up In Business, Even If You Are At the End of Your Roll [24197], [25909], [29423], [32461], [37284], [41705]

Tok Chamber of Commerce [47821]

Tokyo Stock Exchange Inc. (TSE) [55536]

Tole World: Creative Designs for Decorative Painting [6029]

Toledo Business Journal [56420]

Toledo Business and Technology Center [56406]

Toledo Chamber of Commerce [51978]

Toledo Profile Series [56318]

Toledo Regional Chamber of Commerce (TRCC) [56319]

Tolland County Chamber of Commerce [49755]

"Tom Gaglardi" in Canadian Business (Vol. 82, April 27, 2009, No. 7, pp. 56) [10754], [17079], [17518], [24606], [25679], [30263], [38503]

Tomahawk Chamber of Commerce [59736]

Tomatalk [59737]

Tomball Area Chamber of Commerce (TCC) [58479]

Tombstone Chamber of Commerce [47966]

TOMES Plus® System [24162], [34094]

Tomiki Aikido of the Americas (TAA) [14082]

Tompkins County Chamber of Commerce [55359]

Tompkinsville Area Chamber of Commerce [52387]

Tompkinsville - Monroe County Chamber of Commerce [52387]

Toms River - Ocean County Chamber of Commerce [54824]

"TomTom GO910: On the Road Again" in Black Enterprise (Vol. 37, January 2007, No. 6, pp. 52) [5001], [5774], [24933], [35186], [41253]

Tonasket Chamber of Commerce [59297]

"Tone-Deaf' Suitor or True Harasser: How to Tell" in HR Specialist (Vol. 8, September 2010, No. 9, pp. 1) [24056], [26669], [35944]

"A Tonic for Irrationality" in Barron's (Vol. 89, July 13, 2009, No. 28, pp. 12) [8766], [12988], [31892]

Tony Alessandra, Ph.D.: On Collaborative Selling [43754]

Tony Alessandra, Ph.D.: On Customer-Driven Service [26611]

"Tony Hawk Carves a New Niche" in Entrepreneur (Vol. 37, October 2009, No. 10, pp. 26) [954], [5775], [30264]

Tony Roma's, Famous for Ribs [18263]

Too Good to be Threw: The Complete Operations Manual for Resale and Consignment Shops [4277], [5149], [10486]

"Too Much Information?" in Black Enterprise (Vol. 37, December 2006, No. 5, pp. 59) [8767], [26332], [30265], [31893], [37519], [40435], [40822], [42667], [47394]

"Too Much Precaution About Biotech Corn" in Barron's (Vol. 88, March 17, 2008, No. 11, pp. 54) [8768], [11177], [12989], [21696], [30822], [31894], [35187], [36832]

"Too Much too Soon" in Barron's (Vol. 89, July 27, 2009, No. 30, pp. 33) [8769], [12990], [25680], [26333], [31895], [43217]

Tooele County Chamber of Commerce (TCCC) [58681]

Tooele County Chamber of Commerce and Tourism [58681]

"Tool-o-Rama" in Barron's (Vol. 90, September 6, 2010, No. 36) [8770], [12991], [28903]

"Tool Time" in Entrepreneur (Vol. 36, March 2008, No. 3, pp. 90) [20431], [25910], [28904], [37130], [41254], [46714]

Tooling & Production: The Manufacturing Magazine [13731]

Tooling, Manufacturing and Technologies Association (TMTA) [13695]

Tooling & Production: Providing Solutions for Metalworking Manufacturers [13731]

"Toolmakers' New Tack" in Crain's Detroit Business (Vol. 25, June 8, 2009,) [7328], [7689], [30823], [39424], [42222]

Tools & Techniques of Data Analysis (Onsite) [39610]

Tools and Techniques of Data Analysis (Onsite) [39611]

Toombs County Chamber of Commerce [50625]

Toombs-Montgomery Chamber of Commerce [50625]

Toot Your Horn [54150]

"Top 10 Retirement Mistakes and How to Avoid Them" in Canadian Business (Vol. 83, July 20, 2010, No. 11-12, pp. 39) [8771], [12992], [17080], [31896], [34457]

"Top 25 Graduate Programs" in Entrepreneur (Vol. 35, November 2007, No. 11, pp. 92) [27966], [29424], [32462]

"Top 25 Undergrad Programs" in Entrepreneur (Vol. 35, November 2007, No. 11, pp. 88) [27967], [29425], [32463]

"Top 49ers Alphabetical Listing with Five Years Rank and Revenue" in Alaska Business Monthly (Vol. 27, October 2011, No. 10, pp. 100) [23527], [33004]

"Top 50" in Entrepreneur (Vol. 35, November 2007, No. 11, pp. 38) [23528], [47395]

"Top 50 By 1-Year Return" in Canadian Business (Vol. 81, Summer 2008, No. 9, pp. 121) [8772], [12993], [23529], [31897], [44554]

"Top 50 By 5-Year Return" in Canadian Business (Vol. 81, Summer 2008, No. 9, pp. 123) [8773], [12994], [23530], [31898]

"Top 50 in the Capital Market" in Canadian Business (Vol. 81, Summer 2008, No. 9, pp. 117) [8774], [12995], [23531], [31899], [43980]

"Top 50 Exporters" in Hispanic Business (Vol. 30, July-August 2008, No. 7-8, pp. 42) [7690], [9981], [11178], [19119], [19244], [21697], [23532], [26794], [27800], [30824], [36833], [39425]

"Top 50 In Profits" in Canadian Business (Vol. 81, Summer 2008, No. 9, pp. 116) [8775], [12996], [23533], [24607], [25243], [27801], [31900], [42223]

"Top 50 In Total Revenue" in Canadian Business (Vol. 81, Summer 2008, No. 9, pp. 119) [8776], [11440], [12997], [23534], [31901], [36239]

"Top 100 Consolidate Gains" in Hispanic Business (Vol. 30, July-August 2008, No. 7-8, pp. 30) [5537], [23535], [27802], [34458], [35188], [40823], [44555]

The Top 100 List [14030]

"Top of the Class" in Entrepreneur (Vol. 35, November 2007, No. 11, pp. 82) [27968], [29426], [32464]

"Top Coffee Has Concord Ties" in Charlotte Observer (February 7, 2007) [9716], [18005]

"Top Design Award for Massey Ferguson 7624 Dyna-VT" in Farm Industry News (November 14, 2011) [21698], [25681], [39426]

"Top of the Food Chain" in Entrepreneur (Vol. 37, October 2009, No. 10, pp. 19) [19979], [44883], [47088]

"Top IPhone Apps" in Advertising Age (Vol. 79, December 15, 2008, No. 46, pp. 17) [3819], [22463], [24934], [32249], [35189]

"Top Law Firms Join Forces" in Business Journal Portland (Vol. 27, December 3, 2010, No. 40, pp. 1) [8777], [12998], [24057], [31902], [42224]

Top of the Line Fragrances [5916]

"Top Marks" in Canadian Business (Vol. 79, October 23, 2006, No. 21, pp. 143) [28358], [30266], [33005]

"The Top Mistakes of Social Media Marketing" in Agency Sales Magazine (Vol. 39, November 2009, No. 9, pp. 42) [616], [11893], [21223], [22464], [40436]

Top of Ohio Topics [56320]

Tying MASTER INDEX

Two Men and a Truck **[14600]**
Two Men and a Truck Canada **[14601]**
"Two Ways to Find New Customers" in Inc. (Vol. 31, January-February 2009, No. 1, pp. 41) **[3637]**, **[19013]**, **[28910]**, **[43667]**, **[45232]**
"Tying the Knot" in Entrepreneur (Vol. 36, April 2008, No. 4, pp. 48) **[42233]**, **[44885]**
Tyler Area Chamber of Commerce (TACC) **[58486]**
Tyler Chamber News **[58487]**
Tyler County Chamber of Commerce (TCCC) **[58488]**
Tyler Small Business Development Center **[57876]**
Type Directors Club (TDC) **[20756]**
"Types of Health Plans" in HRMagazine (Vol. 53, August 2008, No. 8, pp. 72) **[21994]**, **[34460]**, **[35947]**
Typographic Designers of Canada [4447]
Typography and Font Management (Onsite) **[45071]**
Tyrone Area Chamber of Commerce **[57248]**
Tyrone Chamber Tab **[57249]**

U

"U Overhauling Its Janitorial Program, but Custodians Taking Exception" in Saint Paul Pioneer Press (August 20, 2011) **[2630]**, **[28368]**, **[44567]**, **[46920]**
U-Save Car & Truck Rental **[17844]**
U-Start Business Incubator **[55497]**
"U-Swirl Added to SBA's Franchise Registry" in Ice Cream Reporter (Vol. 23, September 20, 2010, No. 10, pp. 1) **[10926]**, **[32252]**, **[33369]**, **[33460]**, **[37525]**
"U-Swirl To Open in Salt Lake City Metro Market" in Ice Cream Reporter (Vol. 23, November 20, 2010, No. 12, pp. 4) **[10927]**, **[23558]**, **[32253]**, **[42234]**
U-Wash Doggie **[15688]**
"UA, BP Test Unmanned Aircraft" in Alaska Business Monthly (Vol. 27, October 2011, No. 10, pp. 8) **[28369]**, **[42892]**, **[43983]**
"UA Turns Ann Arbor Green" in Contractor (Vol. 56, September 2009, No. 9, pp. 5) **[870]**, **[5542]**, **[7332]**, **[7696]**, **[19120]**, **[28370]**, **[30834]**
"UAlbany on the Hunt for New Brand" in Business Review, Albany New York (Vol. 34, October 5, 2007, No. 27, pp. 1) **[28371]**, **[40450]**, **[42669]**
UAMR Confidential Bulletin **[13918]**
UAW-Daimler Chrysler - Technology Training Center - Resource Library **[15008]**
UB Technology Incubator **[55498]**
CM Uberman Enterprises Inc. **[24957]**
"UBS Buys Out Canadian Partner" in Globe & Mail (January 20, 2006, pp. B1) **[8790]**, **[13016]**, **[42235]**
UBuildIt **[5696]**
Ubuntu!: An Aspiring Story About an African Tradition of Teamwork and Collaboration **[29178]**, **[30280]**, **[38518]**
"UC Lobbies for Big Chunk of New Funds" in Business Courier (Vol. 24, February 22, 2008, No. 46, pp. 1) **[33370]**, **[42893]**, **[43984]**
"UC May Expand into Old Ford Plant" in Business Courier (Vol. 26, December 25, 2009, No. 35, pp. 1) **[17820]**, **[24776]**, **[28372]**, **[39443]**, **[44738]**
UC Merced Small Business Development Center Regional Network **[48176]**
"UC's Goering Center to Get New Director" in Business Courier (Vol. 24, February 15, 2008, No. 45, pp. 3) **[23559]**, **[31128]**, **[38519]**
The Ugly Truth About Small Business: 50 Things That Can Go Wrong..and What You Can Do About It **[33017]**
UI Bulletin **[26862]**, **[46825]**
UIC Inc. [36259]
Ulrich's International Periodical Directory [4071], [15015], [15580]
Ulrich's Periodicals Directory: International Periodicals Information Since 1932 **[4071]**, **[15015]**, **[15580]**
"The Ultimate Business Tune-Up: For Times Like These" in Inc. (Vol. 31, January-February 2009, No. 1, pp. 70) **[23560]**, **[30281]**, **[33018]**
"Ultimate Business of the Week: McDougals Sewing Center" in Houston Chronicle (December 2, 2010) **[18737]**, **[31129]**
"The Ultimate Comfort System" in Contractor (Vol. 56, July 2009, No. 7, pp. 30) **[871]**, **[5543]**, **[30835]**
The Ultimate Competitive Advantage **[24611]**, **[25689]**, **[30282]**, **[38520]**
Ultimate Credit and Collection Handbook **[6340]**, **[26337]**
"The Ultimate Cure" in Conde Nast Portfolio (Vol. 2, June 2008, No. 6, pp. 110) **[23561]**, **[34461]**, **[38861]**, **[43783]**
The Ultimate Directory of Film Technicians: A Necrology of Dates and Places of Births and Deaths of More than 9,000 Producers, Directors, Screenwriters, Composers, Cinematographers. . . **[7898]**
Ultimate Guide to Buying or Selling Your Business **[24612]**, **[25348]**, **[32254]**, **[44203]**
The Ultimate Guide to Electronic Marketing for Small Business: Low-Cost/High Return Tools and Techniques That Really Work **[28911]**, **[40451]**, **[43668]**
Ultimate Guide to Project Management **[622]**, **[24066]**, **[33019]**, **[38521]**
"The Ultimate Home Shopping Network" in Austin Business JournalInc. (Vol. 28, October 17, 2008, No. 31, pp. A1) **[4138]**, **[4280]**, **[7851]**, **[35623]**
Ultimate Homebased Business Handbook: How to Start, Run, and Grow Your Own Profitable Business **[23562]**, **[35584]**
Ultimate Payroll **[15474]**
The Ultimate Sales Machine: Turbocharge Your Business With Relentless Focus on 12 Key Strategies **[43669]**
Ultimate Small Business Advisor **[24067]**, **[30283]**, **[33020]**, **[46429]**
Ultimate Small Business Marketing Guide **[40452]**
The Ultimate Small Business Marketing Toolkit: All the Tips, Forms, and Strategies You'll Ever Need! **[623]**, **[40453]**, **[43670]**
Ultimate Startup Directory: Expert Advice and 1,500 Great Startup Ideas **[13017]**, **[24068]**, **[29429]**, **[32468]**
The Ultimate Supervisor's Workshop (Onsite) **[37751]**
"The Ultimate Vending Machine" in Benzinga.com (August 15, 2011) **[1680]**, **[1773]**, **[20871]**
Ultimate Wealth Inc. **[40651]**
"Ultra Green Energy Services Opens NJ Biodiesel Transload Facility" in Indoor Comfort Marketing (Vol. 70, June 2011, No. 6, pp. 35) **[872]**, **[7333]**, **[7697]**, **[30836]**, **[40454]**, **[45785]**
"Ultra Low Sulfur Diesel: The Promise and the Reality" in Indoor Comfort Marketing (Vol. 70, July 2011, No. 7, pp. 22) **[873]**, **[7334]**, **[7698]**, **[30837]**, **[40455]**, **[45786]**
"UM-Dearborn to Launch Program for Entrepreneurs" in Crain's Detroit Business (Vol. 24, April 14, 2008, No. 15, pp. 7) **[27969]**, **[29430]**, **[41261]**, **[44783]**, **[46970]**
Umatilla Chamber of Commerce **[50313]**; **[56860]**
UMI InfoStore **[11251]**
"UMKC, Hospital Drill Down on Deal" in The Business Journal-Serving Metropolitan Kansas City (Vol. 26, July 18, 2008, No. 45, pp. 1) **[5544]**, **[14214]**, **[17524]**, **[23563]**, **[24613]**, **[25251]**, **[28373]**, **[42236]**
Umpqua Community College **[56894]**
"Unbound ID Raises $2 Million" in Austin Business JournalInc. (Vol. 28, December 12, 2008, No. 39, pp. 1) **[3638]**, **[18503]**, **[19014]**, **[45233]**, **[47090]**
"Unbreakable" in Canadian Business (Vol. 79, October 9, 2006, No. 20, pp. 111) **[19015]**, **[35201]**, **[41262]**
"Uncashed Checks: Retirement Plans in a Quandry" in Employee Benefit News (Vol. 25, December 1, 2011, No. 15, pp. 18) **[21995]**, **[31913]**, **[34016]**, **[35948]**
"Uncertain Labor Pool Troubles Businesses" in Business First-Columbus (October 19, 2007, pp. A1) **[35496]**, **[35949]**
Uncle Louie G, Inc. **[10261]**
"Uncle Volodya's Flagging Christmas Spirit; Russia" in The Economist (Vol. 390, January 3, 2009, No. 8612, pp. 22) **[11185]**, **[14966]**, **[27821]**, **[34017]**, **[36847]**, **[39444]**
"The Uncompromising Leader" in Harvard Business Review (Vol. 86, July-August 2008, No. 8, pp. 50) **[29179]**, **[33021]**, **[38522]**
Uncorked **[19261]**
Uncovering Fraud in Core Business Functions (Onsite) **[37752]**
"Uncovering Offshoring's Invisible Costs" in HRMagazine (Vol. 54, January 2009, No. 1, pp. 1) **[36848]**, **[40918]**, **[41696]**
Uncoverings: The Research Papers of the American Quilt Study Group **[1139]**, **[6145]**
"Under Armour Wants to Equip Athletes, Too" in Boston Business Journal (Vol. 29, July 8, 2011, No. 9, pp. 1) **[4281]**, **[19347]**, **[19474]**, **[37133]**, **[40456]**, **[41263]**
"Under Fire, Sabia Triggers Battle for BCE" in Globe & Mail (April 14, 2007, pp. B1) **[24069]**, **[25252]**, **[42237]**
"Under Pressure" in Canadian Business (Vol. 81, July 21, 2008, No. 11, pp. 18) **[33022]**, **[35497]**, **[38523]**
Undercar Digest **[18625]**
Undercar Digest--Buyer's Guide Issue: The Sourcebook **[1568]**, **[18609]**
Undercar Expo - Showpower- Transmission Expo **[1586]**
Underground Engineering Contractors' Association [5183]
Underhood Service **[1595]**, **[18626]**
Understanding Business Valuation **[25357]**, **[44916]**
Understanding Cats **[15796]**
"Understanding the Economy: People Worry That a Recession Is Coming" in Inc. (December 2007, pp. 103-104) **[13018]**, **[27822]**
Understanding EEOC, Part 1-3 **[36002]**, **[40934]**
Understanding Exporting in the Small and Micro Enterprise **[11186]**, **[36849]**, **[43671]**
"Understanding the Fed" in Black Enterprise (Vol. 38, December 2007, No. 5, pp. 66) **[13019]**, **[31914]**, **[34018]**
"Understanding Persuasive Online Sales Messages from eBay Auctions" in Business Communication Quarterly (December 2007, pp. 482) **[1532]**, **[5150]**, **[15352]**, **[22469]**, **[22632]**, **[28912]**, **[43672]**
Understanding Small Business **[24070]**, **[30284]**
Understanding & Troubleshooting Hydraulics (Onsite) **[25000]**, **[28095]**
Understanding and Troubleshooting Hydraulics (Onsite) **[2616]**
Understanding Workers Compensation: A Guide for Safety and Health Professionals **[21996]**
"Underworld Acquires Yukon Gold Property" in Canadian Corporate News (May 16, 2007) **[9451]**, **[41357]**, **[42238]**
Unemployment Insurance Reports with Social Security **[36253]**
"Unemployment Rates" in The Economist (Vol. 390, January 3, 2009, No. 8612, pp. 75) **[27823]**, **[33023]**, **[35498]**, **[36850]**
"Unemployment Tax Surge Could Hit Businesses Hard" in Orlando Business Journal (Vol. 26, January 1, 2010, No. 31, pp. 1) **[31915]**, **[46430]**
"Unexpected Guest" in Business Journal-Milwaukee (Vol. 28, November 19, 2010, No. 7, pp. A1) **[25349]**, **[39445]**
"Unfair Distraction of Employees" in Business Owner (Vol. 35, March-April 2011, No. 2, pp. 8) **[6341]**, **[24071]**, **[26338]**, **[35950]**
"An Unfair Knock on Nokia" in Barron's (Vol. 88, March 10, 2008, No. 10, pp. 36) **[8791]**, **[13020]**, **[23564]**, **[31916]**, **[37222]**, **[38524]**, **[39446]**
"Unfilled Hotels Go All Out for Business Meetings" in Crain's Detroit Business (Vol. 25, June 8, 2009, No. 23, pp. 9) **[10758]**, **[25690]**, **[25801]**, **[40457]**
Unicoi County Chamber of Commerce **[57797]**
"Unify Corp. Back in the Black, Poised to Grow" in Sacramento Business Journal (Vol. 25, August 29, 2008, No. 26, pp. 1) **[8792]**, **[13021]**, **[23565]**, **[25253]**, **[31917]**, **[38525]**
Uniglobe Travel International Limited Partnership **[20637]**
Uniglobe Travel, LLC (Irvine, California) **[20638]**
"Unilever Acquiring Danish Operations of Diplom-Is Ice Cream" in Ice Cream Reporter (Vol. 23, August 20, 2010, No. 9, pp. 1) **[10928]**, **[13022]**, **[42239]**
"Unilever Acquiring EVGA's Ice Cream Brands in Greece" in Ice Cream Reporter (Vol. 23, October 20, 2010, No. 11, pp. 1) **[10929]**, **[13023]**, **[26796]**, **[36851]**, **[39447]**, **[42240]**
Unilever Bestfoods - Library/Information Center **[9754]**
Unilever HPC NA Research Library **[5925]**
"Unilever to Sustainably Source All Paper and Board Packaging" in Ice Cream Reporter (Vol. 23, July 20, 2010, No. 8, pp. 1) **[7335]**, **[7699]**, **[10930]**, **[17720]**, **[30838]**
"Unilever's CMO Finally Gets Down To Business" in Advertising Age (Vol. 79, July 7, 2008, No. 26, pp. 11) **[24614]**, **[25254]**, **[38526]**, **[39448]**, **[40458]**
Uninterruptable Power Supply Systems for First Responders (In-House Training) **[6872]**
Uninterruptible Power Supply (UPS) Maintenance and Readiness (Onsite) **[25001]**, **[28096]**
Union Area Chamber of Commerce [54155]
Union of Canadian Transportation Employees (UCTE) **[46826]**
Union Chamber of Commerce (UCC) **[54155]**
Union Chamber of Commerce (UCCC) **[53906]**
Union City Chamber of Commerce **[49070]**
Union County Chamber of Commerce **[55820]**; **[56327]**; **[56861]**
Union County Chamber of Commerce (UCCC) **[51340]**; **[57529]**
Union County Chamber of Commerce and Development Board [57529]
Union County Economic Development Resource Directory **[55821]**
Union Electric Company. [47533]
"Union Ethics Training: Building the Legitimacy and Effectiveness of Organized Labor" in WorkingUSA (Vol. 11, September 2008, No. 3) **[30986]**, **[35951]**, **[46921]**
Union Grove Chamber of Commerce [59595]
"Union, Heal Thyself" in Canadian Business (Vol. 81, July 21, 2008, No. 11, pp. 9) **[24072]**, **[24615]**, **[33371]**, **[34019]**, **[39449]**, **[46922]**
Union Labor Report Weekly Newsletter **[46944]**
Union Parish Chamber of Commerce (UPCC) **[52503]**
Union Parish Community Guide **[52504]**
Union des Producteurs Agricoles **[46827]**
"Union Questions Patrick Cudahy Layoffs" in Business Journal-Milwaukee (Vol. 28, December 3, 2010, No. 9, pp. A1) **[24073]**, **[27824]**, **[34020]**, **[35499]**, **[35952]**, **[46923]**
Union Springs/Bullock County Chamber of Commerce **[47740]**
"The Union of Town and Gown" in Entrepreneur (Vol. 37, October 2009, No. 10, pp. 47) **[27825]**, **[36098]**, **[44886]**
Union Township Chamber of Commerce **[54828]**

3636 Small Business Sourcebook • 30th Edition

U.S MASTER INDEX

U.S. Department of Commerce - Center for Economic and Management Research - Michael F. Price College of Business - University of Oklahoma **[60786]**; **[60787]**
U.S. Department of Commerce - Center for Geographic Information and Analysis - Office of State Planning **[60788]**; **[60789]**
U.S. Department of Commerce - Center for Public Affairs Research - Nebraska State Data Center - University of Nebraska at Omaha **[60790]**; **[60791]**
U.S. Department of Commerce - Central Washington University - Department of Sociology - Applied Social Data Center **[60792]**; **[60793]**
U.S. Department of Commerce - Chicago Area Geographic Information Study - University of Illinois at Chicago **[60794]**; **[60795]**
U.S. Department of Commerce - Cleveland State University - Northern Ohio Data and Information Service - Maxine Goodman Levin College of Urban Affairs **[60796]**; **[60797]**
U.S. Department of Commerce - Colorado Department of Local Affairs - Division of Local Government **[60798]**; **[60799]**
U.S. Department of Commerce - Colorado State University - Agricultural and Resource Economics **[60800]**; **[60801]**
U.S. Department of Commerce - Colorado State University Libraries - Morgan Library **[60802]**; **[60803]**
U.S. Department of Commerce - Connecticut Department of Economic and Community Development - Research and Planning **[60804]**
U.S. Department of Commerce - Connecticut Department of Economic and Community Development - Research, Planning, and Information Systems **[60805]**
U.S. Department of Commerce - Connecticut Office of Policy and Management - Policy Development and Planning Division - Budget and Financial Management Division - Office of Finance **[60806]**; **[60807]**
U.S. Department of Commerce - Connecticut State Library - Government Information and References Services **[60808]**; **[60809]**
U.S. Department of Commerce - Cornell University (CISER) - Cornell Institute for Social and Economic Research Data Archive **[60810]**; **[60811]**
U.S. Department of Commerce - Delaware Economic Development Office (DEDO) **[60812]**; **[60813]**
U.S. Department of Commerce - Department of Administration - Demographic Services Center **[60814]**; **[60815]**
U.S. Department of Commerce - Department of Administration and Information - Economic Analysis Division **[60816]**; **[60817]**
U.S. Department of Commerce - Department of Commerce and Economic Opportunity - Springfield Office **[60818]**
U.S. Department of Commerce - Department of Employment Security - LMEA **[60819]**
U.S. Department of Commerce - Departmento de Educacion **[60820]**; **[60821]**
U.S. Department of Commerce - Economic Development Administration **[60822]**; **[60823]**
U.S. Department of Commerce - Employment Security Department - LMEA **[60824]**
U.S. Department of Commerce - Enoch Pratt Free Library - State Library Resource Center **[60825]**; **[60826]**
U.S. Department of Commerce - Florida Agency for Workforce Innovation - Labor Market Statistics - State Census Data Center **[60827]**
U.S. Department of Commerce - Florida Department of Commerce - Bureau of Economic Analysis **[60828]**
U.S. Department of Commerce - Florida Department of Economic Opportunity - Labor Market Information - Florida Census Data Center **[60829]**
U.S. Department of Commerce - Florida State University - Center for Demography and Population Health - College of Social Sciences **[60830]**; **[60831]**
U.S. Department of Commerce - Geographic Resources Center - University of Missouri--Columbia **[60832]**; **[60833]**
U.S. Department of Commerce - Georgia Department of Community Affairs - Office of Planning and Quality Growth **[60834]**
U.S. Department of Commerce - Georgia Department of Community Affairs, Office of Planning and Quality Growth **[60835]**
U.S. Department of Commerce - Georgia Institute of Technology - Georgia Tech Library - Government Information Department **[60836]**; **[60837]**
U.S. Department of Commerce - Georgia Office of Planning and Budget - Division of Operational Support and Development **[60838]**; **[60839]**
U.S. Department of Commerce - Governor's Office of Policy and Management **[60840]**; **[60841]**
U.S. Department of Commerce - Guam Department of Commerce **[60842]**; **[60843]**
U.S. Department of Commerce - Hawaii Department of Budget and Finance - Information and Communication Services Division **[60844]**; **[60845]**
U.S. Department of Commerce - Hawaii Department of Business, Economic Development, and Tourism - Hawaii State Data Center **[60846]**; **[60847]**
U.S. Department of Commerce - Headwaters Regional Development Commission **[60848]**; **[60849]**
U.S. Department of Commerce - Idaho Commission for Libraries **[60850]**; **[60851]**
U.S. Department of Commerce - Idaho Department of Commerce **[60852]**
U.S. Department of Commerce - Idaho State University - Business and Technology Center **[60853]**
U.S. Department of Commerce - Idaho State University - Center for Business Research and Services **[60854]**
U.S. Department of Commerce - Illinois Bureau of the Budget - Office of Management and Budget **[60855]**; **[60856]**
U.S. Department of Commerce - Illinois Department of Commerce and Economic Opportunity - Springfield Office **[60857]**
U.S. Department of Commerce - Illinois State University - Census and Data User Services - Applied Social Research Unit **[60858]**; **[60859]**
U.S. Department of Commerce - Indiana Business Research Center (IBRC) - Research at Indiana University **[60860]**; **[60861]**
U.S. Department of Commerce - Indiana Department of Workforce Development - Research and Analysis **[60862]**
U.S. Department of Commerce - Indiana Economic Development Corporation - Research Division and Technology **[60863]**
U.S. Department of Commerce - Indiana State Data Center - Indiana State Library **[60864]**; **[60865]**
U.S. Department of Commerce - Indiana University - Indiana Business Research Center **[60866]**; **[60867]**
U.S. Department of Commerce - Iowa Department of Education - Census Data Center **[60868]**; **[60869]**
U.S. Department of Commerce - Iowa State University - Iowa Community Indicators Program (ICIP) **[60870]**
U.S. Department of Commerce - Iowa State University - Regional Economics and Community Analysis Program (ReCAP) **[60871]**
U.S. Department of Commerce - Junta de Planificacion - Oficina del Censo **[60872]**; **[60873]**
U.S. Department of Commerce - Kansas Division of the Budget **[60874]**; **[60875]**
U.S. Department of Commerce - Kansas State University - Department of Sociology, Anthropology and Social Work - Kansas Population Center **[60876]**
U.S. Department of Commerce - Kentucky Department for Libraries and Archives - State Library Division **[60877]**; **[60878]**
U.S. Department of Commerce - L. William Seidman Research Institute - W.P. Carey School of Business **[60879]**; **[60880]**
U.S. Dept. of Commerce Library and Information Center **[23662]**
U.S. Department of Commerce - The Library of Michigan - Government Documents Service **[60881]**; **[60882]**
U.S. Department of Commerce - Library of Virginia - Collection Management Division **[60883]**
U.S. Department of Commerce - Library of Virginia - Records Management Division **[60884]**
U.S. Department of Commerce - Maine Department of Labor - Center for Workforce Research and Information **[60885]**; **[60886]**
U.S. Department of Commerce - Maine State Library **[60887]**; **[60888]**
U.S. Department of Commerce - Maine State Planning Office - Census Information Office **[60889]**
U.S. Department of Commerce - Maine State Planning Office - Census State Data Center **[60890]**
U.S. Department of Commerce - Maryland Department of Planning (MDP) **[60891]**
U.S. Department of Commerce - Massachusetts Institute for Social and Economic Research (MISER) **[60892]**; **[60893]**
U.S. Department of Commerce - Mayor's Office of Planning - Data Services Division **[60894]**; **[60895]**
U.S. Department of Commerce - Metropolitan Council Research - Metropolitan Council Data Center **[60896]**; **[60897]**
U.S. Department of Commerce - Metropolitan Washington Council of Governments **[60898]**; **[60899]**
U.S. Department of Commerce - Michigan Department of Technology, Management, and Budget - Center for Shared Solutions and Technology Partnerships - Michigan Information Center **[60900]**
U.S. Department of Commerce - Michigan Department of Technology, Management and Budget - Demographic Research and Statistics - Michigan Information Center **[60901]**
U.S. Department of Commerce - Minnesota Department of Administration - State Demographic Center **[60902]**; **[60903]**
U.S. Department of Commerce - Minnesota Department of Education - Education Resource Center **[60904]**
U.S. Department of Commerce - Minority Business Development Agency **[60906]**
U.S. Department of Commerce - Minority Business Development Agency (MBDA) **[60905]**, **[62172]**
U.S. Department of Commerce - Minority Business Development Agency - Atlanta Regional Office **[60907]**; **[60908]**
U.S. Department of Commerce - Minority Business Development Agency - Boston Regional Office **[60909]**
U.S. Department of Commerce - Minority Business Development Agency - California Native American Business Enterprise Center **[60910]**
U.S. Department of Commerce - Minority Business Development Agency - Chicago Regional Office **[60911]**; **[60912]**
U.S. Department of Commerce - Minority Business Development Agency - Dallas Regional Office **[60913]**; **[60914]**
U.S. Department of Commerce - Minority Business Development Agency District Office (Miami, Florida) - Atlanta Regional Enterprise Center - Miami (Florida) Business Center **[60916]**
U.S. Department of Commerce - Minority Business Development Agency District Office (Boston, Massachusetts) **[60915]**
U.S. Department of Commerce - Minority Business Development Agency District Office (Los Angeles, California) - Native American Business Enterprise Center **[60917]**
U.S. Department of Commerce - Minority Business Development Agency District Office (Philadelphia, Pennsylvania) - Philadelphia Regional Enterprise Center **[60918]**
U.S. Department of Commerce - Minority Business Development Agency - Miami Regional Enterprise Center **[60919]**
U.S. Department of Commerce - Minority Business Development Agency - New York Regional Office **[60920]**; **[60921]**
U.S. Department of Commerce - Minority Business Development Agency - Philadelphia Regional Enterprise Center **[60922]**
U.S. Department of Commerce - Minority Business Development Agency - San Francisco Regional Office **[60923]**; **[60924]**
U.S. Department of Commerce - Minority Business Development Agency - Washington DC, Regional Office **[60925]**
U.S. Department of Commerce - Minority Business Development Agency - Washington, DC, Regional Office **[60926]**
U.S. Department of Commerce - Mississippi Department of Economic and Community Development - Industry Resource Bureau - Mississippi Development Authority **[60927]**
U.S. Department of Commerce - Mississippi Development Authority **[53823]**, **[60928]**
U.S. Department of Commerce - Missouri Small Business and Technology Development Centers **[60929]**; **[60930]**
U.S. Department of Commerce - Missouri State Library - Library Development **[60931]**; **[60932]**
U.S. Department of Commerce - Missouri State Office of Administration **[60933]**; **[60934]**
U.S. Department of Commerce - Missouri State Office of Social and Economic Data Analysis - University of Missouri--Columbia **[60935]**; **[60936]**
U.S. Department of Commerce - Montana Department of Commerce - Census and Economic Information Center **[60937]**; **[60938]**
U.S. Department of Commerce - Montana Department of Labor and Industry - Research and Analysis Bureau - Employment Policy Division **[60939]**
U.S. Department of Commerce - Montana State Library - Digital Library Division **[60940]**; **[60941]**
U.S. Department of Commerce - Nebraska Department of Administrative Services - The Central Data Processing Division **[60942]**
U.S. Department of Commerce - Nebraska Department of Labor **[60943]**
U.S. Department of Commerce - Nebraska Department of Natural Resources **[60944]**; **[60945]**
U.S. Department of Commerce - Nebraska Governor's Policy Research and Energy Office **[60946]**

3638 Small Business Sourcebook • 30th Edition

U.S. Department of Commerce - University of Colorado at Boulder - Leeds School of Business - Business Research Division - Graduate School of Business Administration **[61106]**
U.S. Department of Commerce - University of Delaware - School of Public Policy and Administration **[61107]**; **[61108]**
U.S. Department of Commerce - University of Georgia Libraries - Government Documents Department **[61109]**; **[61110]**
U.S. Department of Commerce - University of Iowa - Iowa Social Science Research Center **[61111]**; **[61112]**
U.S. Department of Commerce - University of Kansas - Institute for Policy and Social Research **[61113]**; **[61114]**
U.S. Department of Commerce - University of Louisville - Department of Urban and Public Affairs - Urban Studies Institute **[61115]**
U.S. Department of Commerce - University of Louisville - School of Urban and Public Affairs - Urban Studies Institute **[61116]**
U.S. Department of Commerce - University of Maryland - Department of Computer Science **[61117]**; **[61118]**
U.S. Department of Commerce - University of Massachusetts at Amherst - Massachusetts Institute for Social and Economic Research **[61119]**; **[61120]**
U.S. Department of Commerce - The University of Mississippi - State Data Center of Mississippi - Center for Population Studies **[61121]**; **[61122]**
U.S. Department of Commerce - University of Missouri-Kansas City - Center for Economic Information **[61123]**; **[61124]**
U.S. Department of Commerce - University of Montana - Bureau of Business Administration **[61125]**
U.S. Department of Commerce - University of Montana - Bureau of Business and Economic Research **[61126]**
U.S. Department of Commerce - University of New Hampshire - Office of Biometrics **[61127]**; **[61128]**
U.S. Department of Commerce - University of New Mexico - Bureau of Business and Economic Research - Business and Industrial Data Center **[61129]**
U.S. Department of Commerce - University of New Mexico - Bureau of Business and Economic Research - Data Bank **[61130]**
U.S. Department of Commerce - University of North Carolina - Odum Institute for Research in Social Science **[61131]**; **[61132]**
U.S. Department of Commerce - University of North Dakota - Department of Geography **[61133]**; **[61134]**
U.S. Department of Commerce - University of Northern Colorado - Library Government Publics **[61135]**; **[61136]**
U.S. Department of Commerce - University of Northern Iowa - Center for Social and Behavioral Research **[61137]**; **[61138]**
U.S. Department of Commerce - University of Oregon Library - Document Center **[61139]**
U.S. Department of Commerce - University of Oregon Library - Documents Center **[61140]**
U.S. Department of Commerce - University of South Dakota - Beacom School of Business - Business Research Bureau **[61141]**
U.S. Department of Commerce - University of South Dakota - School of Business - Business Research Bureau **[61142]**
U.S. Department of Commerce - University of Southern Maine - Maine State Data Center - Center for Business and Economic Research **[61143]**; **[61144]**
U.S. Department of Commerce - University of Tennessee - Center for Business and Economic Research - College of Business Administration **[61145]**
U.S. Department of Commerce - University of Tennessee - College of Business Administration - Center for Business and Economic Research **[61146]**
U.S. Department of Commerce - University of Utah - Bureau of Economic and Business Research **[61147]**; **[61148]**
U.S. Department of Commerce - University of Vermont - Center for Rural Studies **[61149]**; **[61150]**
U.S. Department of Commerce - University of the Virgin Islands - Eastern Caribbean Center **[61151]**; **[61152]**
U.S. Department of Commerce - University of Virginia - Weldon Cooper Center for Public Service **[61153]**; **[61154]**
U.S. Department of Commerce - University of Washington (CSSCR) - Center for Social Science Computation and Research **[61155]**
U.S. Department of Commerce - University of Washington - CSSCR **[61156]**
U.S. Department of Commerce - University of Wisconsin - Madison - Applied Population Laboratory - Department of Community and Environmental Sociology **[61157]**
U.S. Department of Commerce - University of Wisconsin - Madison - Department of Community and Environmental Sociology - Applied Population Laboratory **[61158]**
U.S. Department of Commerce - University of Wyoming - Survey Research Center **[61159]**
U.S. Department of Commerce - University of Wyoming - Wyoming Survey and Analysis Center - Survey Research Center **[61160]**
U.S. Department of Commerce - Urban Information Center - University of Missouri--St. Louis **[61161]**; **[61162]**
U.S. Department of Commerce - Utah Governor's Office of Economic Development **[61163]**
U.S. Department of Commerce - Utah Governor's Office of Planning and Budget **[61164]**
U.S. Department of Commerce - Utah Office of Economic Development **[61165]**
U.S. Department of Commerce - Utah Office of Planning and Budget **[61166]**
U.S. Department of Commerce - Vermont Department of Libraries **[61167]**; **[61168]**
U.S. Department of Commerce - Vermont Department of Tourism and Marketing **[61169]**
U.S. Department of Commerce - Vermont Office of Policy Research and Coordination **[61170]**
U.S. Department of Commerce - Vermont Travel Department **[61171]**
U.S. Department of Commerce - Virgin Islands Department of Economic Development **[61172]**
U.S. Department of Commerce - Virgin Islands Economic Development Authority **[61173]**
U.S. Department of Commerce - Virginia Employment Commission **[61174]**; **[61175]**
U.S. Department of Commerce - Washington State Library - Federal Depository Program **[61176]**; **[61177]**
U.S. Department of Commerce - Washington State Office of Financial Management - Forecasting Division **[61178]**; **[61179]**; **[61180]**
U.S. Department of Commerce - Washington State University - School of Economics Sciences **[61181]**; **[61182]**
U.S. Department of Commerce - Wayne State University - Center for Urban Studies **[61183]**
U.S. Department of Commerce - Wayne State University - MIMIC/Center for Urban Studies **[61184]**
U.S. Department of Commerce - West Virginia Development Office - Research and Strategic Planning Division **[61185]**
U.S. Department of Commerce - West Virginia Development Office - Research and Strategic Planning Group **[61186]**
U.S. Department of Commerce - West Virginia State Library Commission - Reference Library **[61187]**; **[61188]**
U.S. Department of Commerce - West Virginia University Health Science Center - Office of Health Services Research **[61189]**
U.S. Department of Commerce - West Virginia University Health Sciences Center - Office of Health Services Research **[61190]**
U.S. Department of Commerce - Western Washington University - Demographic Research Laboratory - Department of Sociology **[61191]**; **[61192]**
U.S. Department of Commerce - Wichita State University - Center for Economic Development and Business Research **[61193]**; **[61194]**
U.S. Dept. of Defense - Central Repository for Military Working Dog Records Archives **[1042]**, **[15714]**
U.S. Department of Defense (DOD) - Office of Small Business Programs **[61310]**, **[62175]**
U.S. Department of Defense - Office of Small Business Programs **[61311]**
U.S. Department of Education - Assistant Secretary for Educational Research and Improvement - Small Business Innovation Research Program Coordinator **[61312]**; **[61313]**
U.S. Department of Education - Office for Civil Rights - Office of Small and Disadvantaged Business Utilization **[61314]**
U.S. Department of Education - Office of Small and Disadvantaged Business Utilization **[61315]**, **[62176]**; **[61316]**
U.S. Department of Energy - Alaska Power Administration **[61319]**; **[61320]**
U.S. Department of Energy - Albuquerque Operations Office **[61321]**
U.S. Department of Energy - Amarillo Field Office **[61322]**
U.S. Department of Energy - Argonne Area Office **[61323]**; **[61324]**
U.S. Department of Energy - Argonne National Laboratory (West) - Idaho Operations Office **[61325]**; **[61326]**
U.S. Department of Energy - Atlanta Support Office **[61327]**; **[61328]**
U.S. Department of Energy - Bettis Atomic Power Laboratory **[61329]**; **[61330]**
U.S. Department of Energy - Bonneville Power Administration **[61331]**; **[61332]**
U.S. Department of Energy - Boston Regional Office **[61333]**; **[61334]**
U.S. Department of Energy - Brookhaven Area Office **[61335]**
U.S. Department of Energy - Brookhaven National Laboratory **[61336]**
U.S. Department of Energy - Carlsbad Field Office **[61337]**
U.S. Department of Energy - Carlsbad Field Office - Waste Isolation Pilot Plant **[61338]**
U.S. Department of Energy - Chicago Operations Office **[61339]**; **[61340]**
U.S. Department of Energy - Chicago Regional Office **[61341]**; **[61342]**
U.S. Department of Energy - Denver Regional Office **[61343]**; **[61344]**
U.S. Department of Energy - Energy Efficiency and Renewable Energy - Golden Field Office **[61345]**; **[61346]**
U.S. Dept. of Energy - Energy Library **[19142]**
U.S. Department of Energy - Fermi National Accelerator Laboratory **[61347]**
U.S. Department of Energy - Fermi Site Office **[61348]**
U.S. Department of Energy, Headquarters (DOE) - Office of Small and Disadvantaged Business Utilization **[61349]**, **[62177]**
U.S. Department of Energy, Headquarters - Office of Small and Disadvantaged Business Utilization **[61350]**
U.S. Department of Energy - Idaho Operations Office **[61351]**; **[61352]**
U.S. Department of Energy - Kirtland Area Office **[61353]**
U.S. Department of Energy - Los Alamos Area Office **[61354]**; **[61355]**
U.S. Department of Energy (NETL-MGN) - National Energy Technology Laboratory **[61356]**; **[61357]**
U.S. Department of Energy - National Nuclear Security Administration Service Center **[61358]**
U.S. Department of Energy - National Renewable Energy Laboratory (NREL) **[19145]**
U.S. Department of Energy - Nevada Operations Office **[61359]**; **[61360]**
U.S. Department of Energy - Oak Ridge National Laboratory **[61361]**
U.S. Department of Energy - Oak Ridge Operations Office **[61362]**
U.S. Department of Energy - Office of Kansas City Site Operations **[61363]**; **[61364]**
U.S. Department of Energy - Philadelphia Regional Support Office **[61365]**; **[61366]**
U.S. Department of Energy - Pinellas Area Office **[61367]**; **[61368]**
U.S. Department of Energy - Pittsburgh Energy Technology Center **[61369]**; **[61370]**
U.S. Department of Energy - Pittsburgh Naval Reactors (PNR) **[61371]**; **[61372]**
U.S. Department of Energy - Princeton Area Office **[61373]**
U.S. Department of Energy - Princeton Plasma Physics Laboratory **[61374]**
U.S. Department of Energy - Richland Operations Office - Office of Organizational Effectiveness and Communications **[61375]**; **[61376]**
U.S. Department of Energy - Sandia National Laboratories **[61377]**
U.S. Department of Energy - Savannah River Operations Office **[61378]**; **[61379]**
U.S. Department of Energy - Schenectady Naval Reactors Office **[61380]**; **[61381]**
U.S. Department of Energy - Southeastern Power Administration **[61383]**
U.S. Department of Energy - SouthEastern Power Administration (SEPA) **[61382]**
U.S. Department of Energy - Southwestern Power Administration **[61384]**; **[61385]**
U.S. Department of Energy - Western Area Power Administration **[61386]**; **[61387]**
U.S. Department of Health and Human Services - Division of Grants and Contracts - Small Business Specialist **[61395]**
U.S. Department of Health and Human Services - Equal Employment Opportunity Office **[61396]**
U.S. Department of Health and Human Services - Office for Civil Rights - Equal Employment Opportunity/Affirmation Action Coordinator **[61397]**; **[61398]**
U.S. Department of Health and Human Services (HHS) - Office of Small and Disadvantaged Business Utilization **[61399]**, **[62178]**

3640 Small Business Sourcebook • 30th Edition

U.S. Fish and Wildlife Service - Business Utilization and Development Specialist - Division of Contracting and General Services **[61580]**; **[61581]**; **[61582]**; **[61583]**
U.S. Fish and Wildlife Service - Contracting & General Services Chief - Alaska Region **[61584]**; **[61585]**
U.S. Fish and Wildlife Service - Contracting & General Services Chief - Region 4 **[61586]**; **[61587]**
U.S. Fish and Wildlife Service - Contracting & General Services Officer - Region 2 **[61588]**; **[61589]**
U.S. Fish and Wildlife Service - Contracting Officer - Region 6 **[61590]**; **[61591]**
U.S. Fish and Wildlife Service - Contracting & Procurement Officer - Region 3 **[61592]**; **[61593]**
U.S. Fish and Wildlife Service - Policy, Management and Budget - Alaska Region **[61594]**; **[61595]**
U.S. Fish and Wildlife Service - Policy, Management and Budget - Great Lakes, Big Rivers Region **[61596]**
U.S. Fish and Wildlife Service - Policy, Management and Budget - Midwest Region **[61597]**
U.S. Fish and Wildlife Service - Policy, Management and Budget - Mountain Prairie Region **[61598]**; **[61599]**
U.S. Fish and Wildlife Service - Policy, Management and Budget - Northeast Regional Office **[61600]**; **[61601]**
U.S. Fish and Wildlife Service - Policy, Management and Budget - Pacific Region **[61602]**; **[61603]**
U.S. Fish and Wildlife Service - Policy, Management and Budget - Southeast Region **[61604]**; **[61605]**
U.S. Fish and Wildlife Service - Policy, Management and Budget - Southwest Region **[61606]**; **[61607]**
U.S. Fish and Wildlife Service - Procurement Assistant - Region 1 **[61608]**; **[61609]**
U.S. Food & Drug Administration - Center for Devices & Radiological Health Library HFZ-46 **[14341]**
U.S. Food and Drug Administration - Division of Contracts and Grants Management - Office of Management **[61422]**
U.S. Food and Drug Administration - Division of Contracts and Grants Management - Small and Disadvantaged Business Utilization Specialist **[61423]**
U.S. Food & Drug Administration osciences Library - CFSAN Branch Library **[5926]**, **[15231]**
U.S. Food and Drug Administration - Office of Acquisitions and Grants Services - Office of Regional Operations **[61424]**
U.S. Food and Drug Administration - Office of Acquisitions and Grants Services - Office of Small Disadvantaged Business Utilization Specialist **[61425]**
U.S. Food and Drug Administration - Office of Small Business, Scientific, and Trade Affairs **[61426]**; **[61427]**
U.S. General Services Administration (FAS) - Federal Acquisition Service - Office of Regional Services **[60302]**
U.S. General Services Administration - Great Lakes Region - Business Service Center **[60303]**
U.S. General Services Administration - Greater Southwest Region - Business Service Center **[60304]**
U.S. General Services Administration - The Heartland Region - Business Service Center **[60305]**
U.S. General Services Administration - Mid-Atlantic Region - Office of Business and Public Affairs **[60306]**
U.S. General Services Administration - National Capital Region - Business Services Center **[60307]**
U.S. General Services Administration - New England Region - Business Service Center **[60308]**
U.S. General Services Administration - Northeast and Caribbean Region - Business Service Center **[60309]**
U.S. General Services Administration - Northwest/Arctic Region - Business Service Center **[60310]**
U.S. General Services Administration - Office of Global Supply - Logistics Operations Ctr. **[60311]**
U.S. General Services Administration - Office of Management and Budget - Office of E-Government and Information Technology **[60312]**
U.S. General Services Administration (GSA) - Office of Small Business Utilization **[60313]**, **[62187]**
U.S. General Services Administration - Pacific Rim Region - Business Service Center **[60314]**
U.S. General Services Administration - Rocky Mountain Region - Business Service Center **[60315]**
U.S. General Services Administration - Southeast Sunbelt Region - Business Service Center **[60316]**
U.S. Geological Survey - Business Utilization and Development Specialist **[61610]**; **[61611]**; **[61612]**; **[61613]**
U.S. Geological Survey - Business Utilization and Development Specialist - Central Region **[61614]**; **[61615]**
United States Golf Association (USGA) **[9655]**, **[14360]**
United States Golf Association Library **[9686]**
United States Harness Writers' Association (USHWA) **[6806]**
U.S. Health Care Financing Administration - Equal Employment Opportunity Office **[61428]**
U.S. Health Resources Services Administration - Grants and Procurement Management Division - Contracts Policies and Operations **[61429]**
United States Hispanic Chamber of Commerce (USHCC) **[40692]**
U.S. Immigration and Naturalization Service - Human Resources and Administrative Services Division - Procurement Policy and Evaluation **[61633]**
U.S. International Trade Commission - National Library of International Trade **[11212]**
United States International Trade in Goods and Services **[36926]**
United States Judo Association (USJA) **[14083]**
The U.S. Kids' Foods Market **[9994]**
The U.S. Lawn and Garden Market, 5th Edition **[9798]**
United States Lawn Tennis Association [20060]
The U.S. Lighting Fixtures Industry **[6933]**
The U.S. Liquor Market **[13600]**
The U.S. Market for Bottled, Enhanced and Flavored Water - 3rd Edition **[20983]**
The U.S. Market for Pleasure Boats **[13947]**
The U.S. Market for Vitamin, Minerals, and Herbal Supplements **[14816]**
U.S. Marshals Service - Procurement Policy and Oversight Team **[61634]**; **[61635]**
United States Mexico Chamber of Commerce (USMCOC) **[36316]**
United States National Amateur Athletic Union Taekwondo Committee [14084]
U.S. National Arboretum Library **[9135]**, **[9876]**, **[13457]**
U.S. National Highway Traffic Safety Administration - Technical Information Services **[707]**, **[6616]**
U.S. National Institute for Occupational Safety and Health - Library C-21 **[47564]**
U.S. National Oceanic & Atmospheric Administration - Library and Information Services Division - Central Library **[9039]**
U.S. National Park Service - Blue Ridge Parkway Archives **[5718]**, **[13458]**
U.S. National Ski Hall of Fame and Museum - Roland Palmedo National Ski Library **[18843]**
U.S. News & World Report: Building Your Fortune **[8899]**
U.S. Nuclear Regulatory Commission - Office of Small and Disadvantaged Business Utilization/Civil Rights **[61809]**, **[62188]**; **[61810]**
U.S. Nuclear Regulatory Commission, Region 1 - King of Prussia Regional Office **[61811]**; **[61812]**
U.S. Nuclear Regulatory Commission, Region 2 - Atlanta Regional Office **[61813]**; **[61814]**
U.S. Nuclear Regulatory Commission, Region 3 - Lisle Regional Office **[61815]**; **[61816]**
U.S. Nuclear Regulatory Commission, Region 4 - Arlington Regional Office **[61817]**; **[61818]**
U.S. Office of Personnel Management - Office of Small and Disadvantaged Business Utilization - Contracting Division **[60636]**, **[62189]**
U.S. Pan Asian American Chamber of Commerce (USPAACC) **[36317]**
United States Pan Asian Chamber of Commerce [36317]
The U.S. Pasta Market **[19254]**
United States Patents Quarterly **[37153]**
"U.S. Playing Card Might Shuffle HQ" in Business Courier (Vol. 24, March 21, 2008, No. 50, pp. 1) **[24617]**, **[24777]**, **[39452]**, **[44739]**
United States Pony Clubs (USPC) **[10613]**
U.S. Postal Service - Administrative Operations - Information Technology Division **[61819]**; **[61820]**
U.S. Postal Service - Chicago Service Center **[61821]**; **[61822]**
U.S. Postal Service - Environmental and MRO Category Management Center **[61823]**
U.S. Postal Service - Environmental and MRO Category Management Centers **[61824]**
U.S. Postal Service - Field Operations - East **[61825]**; **[61826]**
U.S. Postal Service - Field Operations - South **[61827]**; **[61828]**
U.S. Postal Service - Field Operations - West **[61829]**; **[61830]**
U.S. Postal Service - General Counsel - Business Services **[61831]**; **[61832]**
U.S. Postal Service - Intelligent Mail **[61833]**
U.S. Postal Service - Intelligent Mail and Address Quality **[61834]**
U.S. Postal Service - Investigations and Security - Dangerous Mail Investigations and Homeland Security **[61835]**; **[61836]**
U.S. Postal Service - Memphis Purchasing Service Center **[61837]**; **[61838]**
U.S. Postal Service - Office of the Inspector General **[61839]**; **[61840]**
U.S. Postal Service - Office of Operations **[61841]**; **[61842]**
U.S. Postal Service - Office of Small and Disadvantaged Business Utilization **[61843]**, **[62190]**; **[61844]**
U.S. Postal Service - San Francisco Purchasing Service Center **[61845]**
U.S. Postal Service - United States Postal Inspection Service **[61846]**; **[61847]**
U.S. Postal Service - Windsor Purchasing Service Center E **[61848]**; **[61849]**
U.S. Printing Office - General Procurement Division - Office of Small and Disadvantaged Business Utilization **[61807]**; **[61808]**
United States Professional Lawn Tennis Association [20056]
United States Professional Tennis Association (USPTA) **[20056]**
United States Professional Tennis Association Convention **[19390]**, **[20066]**
United States Professional Tennis Association Inc. [20056]
United States Professional Tennis Registry [20054]
U.S. Public Health Service - Administrative Services Center - Small and Disadvantaged Business Utilization Specialist - Division of Acquisitions Management **[61430]**
U.S. Public Health Service - Division of Grants and Contracts - PHS Small Business Specialist **[61431]**
United States Racquet Stringers Association (USRSA) **[20057]**
United States Racquetball Association (USAR) **[15958]**, **[20058]**
"U.S. Recession Officially Over: Is Recovery Ever Going to Arrive?" in Montana Business Quarterly (Vol. 49, Spring 2011, No. 1, pp. 6) **[27827]**, **[45788]**
"U.S. Retailer Eyes 'Tween' Market" in Globe & Mail (January 30, 2007, pp. B1) **[23567]**, **[25256]**, **[40459]**, **[43228]**
U.S. Russia Business Council (USRBC) **[36318]**
"U.S. Savvy Helps Fuel TD's Fortunes" in Globe & Mail (February 23, 2007, pp. B1) **[23568]**, **[42244]**, **[43229]**, **[44568]**
U.S. SBA Office of Government Contracting for Maine and New Hampshire **[52644]**
United States Seamless **[3449]**
United States Ski Writers Association [6799], [15509]
U.S. Small Business Administration (SBA) **[49867]**
United States Small Business Administration **[54867]**
U.S. Small Business Administration - Albuquerque District Office **[61850]**; **[61851]**
U.S. Small Business Administration - Anchorage District Office **[61852]**; **[61853]**
U.S. Small Business Administration, Area 1 **[61854]**; **[61855]**
U.S. Small Business Administration, Area 3 **[61856]**
U.S. Small Business Administration, Area 6 **[61857]**
U.S. Small Business Administration - Arizona District Office **[61858]**
U.S. Small Business Administration - Arkansas District Office **[61859]**
U.S. Small Business Administration - Associate Deputy Administrator for Economic Development **[61860]**
U.S. Small Business Administration - Associate Deputy Administrator for Government Contracting and Minority Enterprise Development **[61861]**
U.S. Small Business Administration - Atlanta District Office **[61862]**; **[61863]**
U.S. Small Business Administration - Augusta District Office **[61864]**
U.S. Small Business Administration - Baltimore District Office **[61865]**; **[61866]**
U.S. Small Business Administration - Birmingham District Office **[61867]**; **[61868]**
U.S. Small Business Administration - Boise District Office **[61869]**; **[61870]**; **[61871]**
U.S. Small Business Administration - Boston District Office **[61872]**; **[61873]**; **[61874]**
U.S. Small Business Administration - Buffalo District Office **[61875]**; **[61876]**
U.S. Small Business Administration - Buffalo District Office - Rochester Branch Office **[61877]**
U.S. Small Business Administration - Business Information Center (Atlanta, Georgia) **[61878]**
U.S. Small Business Administration - Business Information Center (Boise, Idaho) **[61879]**
U.S. Small Business Administration - Business Information Center (Boston, Massachusetts) **[61880]**
U.S. Small Business Administration - Business Information Center (Chicago, Illinois) **[61881]**
U.S. Small Business Administration - Business Information Center (Denver, Colorado) **[61882]**
U.S. Small Business Administration - Business Information Center (East Randolph, Vermont) **[61883]**
U.S. Small Business Administration - Business Information Center (East Randolph, Vermonth) **[61884]**

Small Business Sourcebook • 30th Edition 3643

U.S. Small Business Administration - Business Information Center (Houston, Texas) **[61885]**
U.S. Small Business Administration - Business Information Center (Kansas City, Missouri) **[61886]**
U.S. Small Business Administration - Business Information Center (Los Angeles, California) **[61887]**
U.S. Small Business Administration - Business Information Center (Omaha, Nebraska) **[61888]**
U.S. Small Business Administration - Business Information Center (Providence, Rhode Island) **[61889]**
U.S. Small Business Administration - Business Information Center (St. Louis, Missouri) **[61890]**
U.S. Small Business Administration - Business Information Center (San Diego, California) **[61891]**
U.S. Small Business Administration - Business Information Center (Seattle, Washington) **[61892]**
U.S. Small Business Administration - Business Information Center (Warm Springs, Oregon) **[61893]**
U.S. Small Business Administration - Business Information Center (Washington, Distict of Columbia) **[61894]**
U.S. Small Business Administration - Casper District Office **[61895]**; **[61896]**
U.S. Small Business Administration - Cedar Rapids District Office **[61897]**; **[61898]**
U.S. Small Business Administration - Charleston Branch Office **[61899]**; **[61900]**
U.S. Small Business Administration - Charlotte District Office **[61901]**
U.S. Small Business Administration - Chicago District Office **[61902]**
U.S. Small Business Administration - Chicago Regional Office **[61903]**; **[61904]**
U.S. Small Business Administration - Clarksburg District Office **[61905]**; **[61906]**
U.S. Small Business Administration - Cleveland District Office **[61907]**; **[61908]**
U.S. Small Business Administration - Columbia District Office **[61909]**; **[61910]**
U.S. Small Business Administration - Columbus District Office **[61911]**; **[61912]**
U.S. Small Business Administration - Concord District Office **[61913]**
U.S. Small Business Administration - Confederated Tribes of the Grand Ronde Community - Business Information Center **[61914]**; **[61915]**
U.S. Small Business Administration - Connecticut District Office **[61916]**
U.S. Small Business Administration - Corpus Christi Branch Office **[61917]**
U.S. Small Business Administration - Dallas District Office **[61918]**
U.S. Small Business Administration - Dallas/Fort Worth District Office **[61919]**; **[61920]**; **[61921]**
U.S. Small Business Administration - Delaware Branch Office **[61922]**
U.S. Small Business Administration - Denver District Office **[61923]**; **[61924]**; **[61925]**
U.S. Small Business Administration - Des Moines District Office **[61926]**
U.S. Small Business Administration - Des Moines Office **[61927]**
U.S. Small Business Administration - Detroit District Office **[61928]**
U.S. Small Business Administration - Disaster Assistance Customer Service Center **[61929]**
U.S. Small Business Administration - Disaster Assistance Processing & Disbursement Center **[61930]**; **[61931]**
U.S. Small Business Administration - Disaster Field Offices - Field Operations Center - East **[61932]**
U.S. Small Business Administration - Disaster Field Offices - Field Operations Center - West **[61933]**; **[61934]**
U.S. Small Business Administration - Disaster Field Operations Center - East **[61935]**
U.S. Small Business Administration - Disaster Field Operations Center - West **[61936]**
U.S. Small Business Administration - Disaster Office - Customer Service Center **[61937]**
U.S. Small Business Administration - El Paso District Office **[61938]**; **[61939]**
U.S. Small Business Administration - Elmira Branch Office **[61940]**; **[61941]**
U.S. Small Business Administration - Fargo District Office **[61942]**; **[61943]**
U.S. Small Business Administration - Field Operations Center - West **[61944]**
U.S. Small Business Administration - Fresno District Office **[61945]**; **[61946]**
U.S. Small Business Administration - Georgia District Office **[61947]**
U.S. Small Business Administration - Gulfport Branch Office **[61948]**; **[61949]**
U.S. Small Business Administration - Harlingen District Office **[61950]**; **[61951]**
U.S. Small Business Administration - Hartford District Office **[61952]**
U.S. Small Business Administration - Hawaii District Office **[61953]**
U.S. Small Business Administration - Helena District Office **[61954]**
U.S. Small Business Administration - Honolulu District Office **[61955]**
U.S. Small Business Administration - Houston District Office **[61956]**; **[61957]**; **[61958]**
U.S. Small Business Administration - Indiana District Office **[61959]**
U.S. Small Business Administration - Indianapolis District Office **[61960]**
U.S. Small Business Administration - Jackson District Office **[61961]**; **[61962]**
U.S. Small Business Administration - Jacksonville District Office **[61963]**; **[61964]**
U.S. Small Business Administration - Kansas City District Office **[61965]**; **[61966]**; **[61967]**
U.S. Small Business Administration - Kentucky District Office **[61968]**
U.S. Small Business Administration - The Klamath Tribes - Business Information Center **[61969]**; **[61970]**
U.S. Small Business Administration - Las Vegas District Office **[61971]**
U.S. Small Business Administration - Little Rock District Office **[61972]**
U.S. Small Business Administration - Los Angeles District Office **[61973]**; **[61974]**; **[61975]**
U.S. Small Business Administration - Louisville District Office **[61976]**
U.S. Small Business Administration - Lower Rio Grande Valley District Office - Corpus Christi Branch Office **[61977]**
U.S. Small Business Administration - Lubbock District Office **[61978]**; **[61979]**
U.S. Small Business Administration - Madison District Office **[61980]**
U.S. Small Business Administration - Maine District Office **[61981]**
U.S. Small Business Administration - Marshall Post of Duty **[61982]**; **[61983]**
U.S. Small Business Administration - Melville Branch Office **[61984]**; **[61985]**
U.S. Small Business Administration - Miami District Office **[61986]**; **[61987]**
U.S. Small Business Administration - Michigan District Office **[61988]**
U.S. Small Business Administration - Minneapolis District Office **[61989]**
U.S. Small Business Administration - Minnesota District Office **[61990]**
U.S. Small Business Administration - Montana District Office **[61991]**
U.S. Small Business Administration - Montpelier District Office **[61992]**
U.S. Small Business Administration - Nashville District Office **[61993]**; **[61994]**; **[61995]**
U.S. Small Business Administration - Nebraska District Office **[61996]**
U.S. Small Business Administration - Nevada District Office **[61997]**
U.S. Small Business Administration - New Hampshire District Office - Concord District Office **[61998]**
U.S. Small Business Administration - New Jersey District Office **[61999]**
U.S. Small Business Administration - New York District Office **[62000]**; **[62001]**
U.S. Small Business Administration - Newark District Office **[62002]**
U.S. Small Business Administration - North Carolina District Office - Charlotte District Office **[62003]**
U.S. Small Business Administration - North Texas U.S. Export Assistance Center (Grapevine, Texas) **[62004]**; **[62005]**
U.S. Small Business Administration - Office of 8(a) Business Development **[62006]**; **[62007]**
U.S. Small Business Administration - Office of Advocacy **[62008]**; **[62009]**
U.S. Small Business Administration - Office of Advocacy - Research and Statistics - Office of Economic Research **[62010]**
U.S. Small Business Administration - Office of Business and Community Initiatives - Office of Entrepreneurial Development **[62011]**; **[62012]**
U.S. Small Business Administration - Office of Communications and Public Liaison **[62013]**; **[62014]**
U.S. Small Business Administration - Office of Financial Assistance - Office of Loan Programs **[62015]**; **[62016]**
U.S. Small Business Administration - Office of Government Contracting **[62017]**; **[62018]**
U.S. Small Business Administration - Office of the Inspector General **[62019]**; **[62020]**
U.S. Small Business Administration - Office of International Trade **[62021]**; **[62022]**
U.S. Small Business Administration - Office of Minority Enterprise Development - Division of 8(a) Program Certification and Eligibility **[62023]**; **[62024]**
U.S. Small Business Administration - Office of the National Ombudsman **[62025]**; **[62026]**
U.S. Small Business Administration - Office of Native American Affairs **[62027]**; **[62028]**
U.S. Small Business Administration (SBA) - Office of Small Business Development Centers **[62029]**, **[62191]**
U.S. Small Business Administration - Office of Small Business Development Centers **[62030]**
U.S. Small Business Administration - Office of Women's Business Ownership Entrepreneurial Development **[62031]**; **[62032]**
U.S. Small Business Administration - Oklahoma City District Office **[62033]**; **[62034]**
U.S. Small Business Administration - Omaha District Office **[62035]**; **[62036]**
U.S. Small Business Administration - Philadelphia District Office **[62037]**; **[62038]**
U.S. Small Business Administration - Phoenix District Office **[62039]**
U.S. Small Business Administration - Pittsburgh District Office **[62040]**; **[62041]**
U.S. Small Business Administration - Portland District Office **[62042]**; **[62043]**; **[62044]**
U.S. Small Business Administration - Providence District Office **[62045]**; **[62046]**
U.S. Small Business Administration - Puerto Rico and U.S. Virgin Islands District Office **[62047]**; **[62048]**
U.S. Small Business Administration, Region 1 **[62049]**; **[62050]**
U.S. Small Business Administration, Region 2 **[62051]**; **[62052]**
U.S. Small Business Administration, Region 3 **[62053]**; **[62054]**
U.S. Small Business Administration, Region 4 **[62055]**; **[62056]**
U.S. Small Business Administration, Region 5 **[62057]**; **[62058]**
U.S. Small Business Administration, Region 6 **[62059]**; **[62060]**
U.S. Small Business Administration, Region 7 **[62061]**; **[62062]**
U.S. Small Business Administration, Region 8 **[62063]**; **[62064]**
U.S. Small Business Administration, Region 9 **[62065]**; **[62066]**
U.S. Small Business Administration, Region 10 **[62067]**; **[62068]**
U.S. Small Business Administration - Research and Statistics - Office of Economic Research **[62069]**
U.S. Small Business Administration - Rhode Island District Office **[62070]**
U.S. Small Business Administration - Richmond District Office **[62071]**; **[62072]**
U.S. Small Business Administration - Rochester Office **[62073]**
U.S. Small Business Administration - Sacramento Branch Office **[62074]**; **[62075]**
U.S. Small Business Administration - St. Croix Post of Duty **[62076]**; **[62077]**
U.S. Small Business Administration - St. Louis District Office **[62078]**; **[62079]**; **[62080]**
U.S. Small Business Administration - St. Thomas Post of Duty **[62081]**; **[62082]**
U.S. Small Business Administration - Salt Lake City District Office **[62083]**; **[62084]**
U.S. Small Business Administration - San Antonio District Office **[62085]**; **[62086]**
U.S. Small Business Administration - San Diego District Office **[62087]**; **[62088]**; **[62089]**
U.S. Small Business Administration - San Francisco District Office **[62090]**; **[62091]**
U.S. Small Business Administration - Santa Ana District Office **[62092]**; **[62093]**
U.S. Small Business Administration - SBA/Greater El Paso Chamber of Commerce - Business Information Center **[62094]**; **[62095]**
U.S. Small Business Administration - SBA/NationsBank/MBDA/BellSouth/College of Charleston - Business Information Center **[62096]**; **[62097]**
U.S. Small Business Administration - SBA/NationsBank/MBDA - Business Information Center (Nashville, Tennessee) **[62098]**
U.S. Small Business Administration - Seattle District Office **[62099]**; **[62100]**; **[62101]**
U.S. Small Business Administration - Sioux Falls District Office **[62102]**
U.S. Small Business Administration - South Dakota District Office **[62103]**

3644 Small Business Sourcebook • 30th Edition

MASTER INDEX

University

Master Index

U.S. Small Business Administration - Space and Naval Warfare Systems **[62104]**; **[62105]**
U.S. Small Business Administration - Spokane Branch Office **[62106]**
U.S. Small Business Administration - Spokane Regional Chamber of Commerce - Business Information Center - Spokane Branch Office **[62107]**
U.S. Small Business Administration - Spokane, WA Branch Office **[62108]**; **[62109]**
U.S. Small Business Administration - Springfield, IL, Branch Office **[62110]**; **[62111]**
U.S. Small Business Administration - Springfield, MA, Branch Office **[62112]**; **[62113]**
U.S. Small Business Administration - Springfield, MO, Branch Office **[62114]**; **[62115]**
U.S. Small Business Administration - Sunbelt U.S. Export Assistance Center (Miami, Florida) **[62116]**
U.S. Small Business Administration - Syracuse District Office **[62117]**; **[62118]**
U.S. Small Business Administration - U.S. Export Assistance Center (Atlanta, Georgia) **[62119]**
U.S. Small Business Administration - U.S. Export Assistance Center (Baltimore, Maryland) **[62120]**; **[62121]**
U.S. Small Business Administration - U.S. Export Assistance Center (Boston, Massachusetts) **[62122]**; **[62123]**
U.S. Small Business Administration - U.S. Export Assistance Center (Chicago, Illinois) **[62124]**; **[62125]**
U.S. Small Business Administration - U.S. Export Assistance Center (Cleveland, Ohio) **[62126]**; **[62127]**
U.S. Small Business Administration - U.S. Export Assistance Center (Denver, Colorado) **[62128]**; **[62129]**
U.S. Small Business Administration - U.S. Export Assistance Center (Detroit, Michigan) **[62130]**; **[62131]**
U.S. Small Business Administration - U.S. Export Assistance Center (Miami, Florida) **[62132]**
U.S. Small Business Administration - U.S. Export Assistance Center (New York, New York) **[62133]**; **[62134]**
U.S. Small Business Administration - U.S. Export Assistance Center (Newport Beach, California) **[62135]**; **[62136]**
U.S. Small Business Administration - U.S. Export Assistance Center (Philadelphia, Pennsylvania) **[62137]**; **[62138]**
U.S. Small Business Administration - U.S. Export Assistance Center (St. Louis, Missouri) **[62139]**; **[62140]**
U.S. Small Business Administration - U.S. Export Assistance Center (Seattle, Washington) **[62141]**; **[62142]**
U.S. Small Business Administration - Vermont District Office **[62143]**
U.S. Small Business Administration - Washington DC, District Office **[62144]**
U.S. Small Business Administration - Washington, DC, District Office **[62145]**
U.S. Small Business Administration - Washington D.C. District Office - Associate Deputy Administrator for Economic Development **[62146]**
U.S. Small Business Administration - Washington D.C. District Office - Associate Deputy Administrator for Government Contracting and Minority Enterprise Development **[62147]**
U.S. Small Business Administration - Washington D.C. District Office - Business Information Center (Washington, District of Columbia) **[62148]**
U.S. Small Business Administration - West Palm Beach Post of Duty - South Florida District Office **[62149]**; **[62150]**
U.S. Small Business Administration - Wichita District Office **[62151]**; **[62152]**
U.S. Small Business Administration - Wilkes-Barre Branch Office **[62153]**; **[62154]**
U.S. Small Business Administration - Wilmington Branch Office **[62155]**
U.S. Small Business Administration - Wisconsin District Office **[62156]**
U.S. Small Business Administration - WVHTC Foundation - Business Information Center **[62157]**; **[62158]**
U.S. Social Security Administration - Office of Acquisitions and Grants - Small and Disadvantaged Business Utilization Specialist **[61432]**; **[61433]**
U.S. Source Book of R & D Spenders **[42895]**
United States Squash Racquets Association (USSRA) **[20059]**
The U.S. Tabletop Market **[10422]**
U.S. Taekwondo Union (USTU) **[14084]**
"U.S. Targets China's Exported Paper" in Globe & Mail (March 31, 2007, pp. B5) **[11187]**, **[36853]**
U.S. Tax Court Library **[282]**, **[19770]**
United States Taxes and Tax Policy **[27828]**, **[34022]**, **[46432]**
United States Tennis Association (USTA) **[20060]**
United States Tour Operators Association (USTOA) **[20135]**, **[20525]**
"U.S. Trade Body Clears Apple in Patent Case" in Wall Street Journal Eastern Edition (November 23 , 2011, pp. C1) **[5003]**, **[24075]**, **[36854]**, **[37134]**
U.S. Travel Association (TIAA) **[20526]**
U.S. Travel Data Center (USTDC) **[20527]**
U.S. Trout Farmers Association (USTFA) **[9015]**
U.S. Venture Partners **[49337]**
United States Veterinary Medical Association [1047]
United States Water Fitness Association **[15959]**
USWEEKLY [8954], [13223], [14541]
U.S. Weekly Statistics **[8954]**, **[13223]**, **[14541]**
"U.S. Widens Rocket Field" in Wall Street Journal Eastern Edition (October 17 , 2011, pp. B4) **[25692]**, **[33461]**, **[39453]**, **[42245]**
U.S.A. - Business and Industry Advisory Committee to the OECD (USA-BIAC) **[36319]**
U.S.A. Karate Federation (USAKF) **[14085]**
U.S.A. Toy Library Association (USA-TLA) **[3932]**, **[20230]**
United States-Italy Trade Directory [11180]
United Steelworkers of America - Canadian Branch (USWA) **[46829]**
United Typothetae of America [15511], [16350]
United Way 2-1-1 - Information & Referral Service **[331]**, **[15135]**
"UnitedHealthcare Resists Prognosis" in The Business Journal-Serving Metropolitan Kansas City (Vol. 26, August 29, 2008, No. 51) **[11442]**, **[34462]**, **[36241]**, **[46926]**
"United's Next Hurdle: Costly Repairs" in Crain's Chicago Business (Vol. 31, April 14, 2008, No. 15, pp. 1) **[34023]**, **[44569]**, **[47478]**
"Uniting Spring in OP Could Reduce Static" in Business Journal-Serving Metropolitan Kansas City (October 19, 2007) **[3824]**, **[42246]**, **[44740]**
Universal City-North Hollywood Chamber of Commerce **[49071]**
"Universal Energy Group Releases March 31, 2007 Financial Statements" in Canadian Corporate News (May 14, 2007) **[8793]**, **[13025]**, **[23569]**, **[31918]**, **[42247]**
Universal Gym Affiliates [15950]
"Universal Music Sues Grooveshark's Parent" in Wall Street Journal Eastern Edition (November 22 , 2011, pp. B5) **[14738]**, **[24076]**, **[28914]**, **[37135]**
Universal Payroll Company **[15465]**
Universite de Montreal - Bibliotheque de Kinesiologie **[16054]**
University of Akron **[56412]**
University of Akron - Fisher Institute for Professional Selling **[43779]**
University of Akron - Fisher Institute of Professional Selling - Sales Education Learning Library **[43778]**
University of Alabama - Alabama International Trade Center **[47613]**
University of Alabama at Birmingham - Lister Hill Center for Health Policy **[34693]**
University of Alabama - Environmental Institute **[10202]**
University of Alabama in Huntsville Small Business Development Center **[47607]**
University of Alabama Small Business Development Center **[47608]**
University of Alaska Anchorage **[61195]**
University at Albany, State University of New York - Institute for Informatics, Logics, and Security Studies (ILS) **[4926]**
University of Alberta - Devonian Botanic Garden Library **[9877]**, **[13459]**
University of Alberta - Institute for Public Economics (IPE) **[27947]**
University of Arizona - Arizona Center on Aging (ACOA) **[15144]**
University of Arizona - Center for Creative Photography Library **[15930]**
University of Arizona - Karsten Turfgrass Research Facility **[13531]**
University of Arizona - Native American Research and Training Center (NARTC) **[34694]**
University of Arkansas at Little Rock - Institute for Economic Advancement (IEA) **[19793]**
University at Albany, State University of New York - Institute of Programming and Logics [4926]
University of Baltimore - Merrick School of Business **[52797]**
"University Book Store Inc.: an Act of Independence" in Retail Merchandiser (Vol. 51, September-October 2011, No. 5, pp. 68) **[2169]**, **[2388]**, **[28374]**
University of British Columbia - Art, Architecture, and Planning Division **[4182]**
University of British Columbia - Botanical Garden **[16208]**
University of British Columbia - Bureau for Research on Applications of Information Technology (BRITE) **[36081]**
University of British Columbia - Centre for Operations Excellence (COE) **[38859]**
University of British Columbia - Fisheries Centre **[9047]**
University of British Columbia - Wine Research Centre (WRC) **[19301]**
University of British Columbia - W. Maurice Young Entrepreneurship and Venture Capital Research Centre **[30384]**
University of Calgary - Human Performance Laboratory (HPL) **[16114]**
University of Calgary - Vision and Aging Laboratory (VAL) **[20956]**
University of Calgary - World Tourism Education and Research Centre (WTERC) **[20222]**
University of California, Berkeley - The Bancroft Library - The Magnes Collection of Jewish Art and Life - Western Jewish Americana Archives - Western Jewish History Center **[9564]**
University of California, Berkeley - Berkeley Roundtable on International Economy (BRIE) **[35249]**
University of California, Berkeley - Botanical Garden - Myrtle R. Wolf Botanical & Horticultural Library **[9878]**
University of California, Berkeley - Center for Labor Research and Education **[34695]**
University of California, Berkeley - Fisher Center for Real Estate and Urban Economics (FCREUE) **[1179]**
University of California, Berkeley - Giannini Foundation of Agricultural Economics - Research Library **[21809]**
University of California, Berkeley - Institute of Governmental Studies (IGS) **[42437]**
University of California, Berkeley - Institute of Human Development - Harold E. Jones Child Study Center (CSC) **[4041]**
University of California, Berkeley - Marian Koshland Bioscience and Natural Resources Library **[15232]**
University of California, Berkeley - School of Public Health - Labor Occupational Health Program Library **[47565]**
University of California - California Institute for Energy and Environment (CIEE) **[915]**
University of California, Davis - Agricultural and Resource Economics Library **[21810]**
University of California, Davis - Air Quality Group **[931]**
University of California, Davis - Arboretum Library **[9879]**
University of California, Davis - Center for Companion Animal Health (CCAH) **[1106]**
University of California, Davis - Information Center for the Environment (ICE) **[30892]**
University of California, Davis - University Libraries - Special Collections **[1958]**, **[2483]**, **[19299]**
University of California, Davis - Veterinary Genetics Laboratory (VGL) **[1044]**
University of California, Irvine - Distributed Real-time Ever Available Microcomputing Laboratory (DREAM) **[4927]**
University of California, Los Angeles - Department of Education & Information Studies - Multimedia & Information Technology Lab **[11252]**
University of California, Los Angeles - Department of Special Collections **[4429]**
University of California, Los Angeles - Grunwald Center for the Graphic Arts **[4592]**
University of California, Los Angeles - Music Library **[14712]**
University of California, Los Angeles - Harold and Pauline Price Center for Entrepreneurial Studies **[30406]**
University of California, Los Angeles - Research Program in Takeovers and Corporate Restructuring **[25720]**
University of California, Los Angeles - Jules Stein Eye Institute (JSEI) **[20957]**
University of California, Los Angeles - UCLA Film and Television Archive - Research and Study Center **[20020]**
University of California, San Diego - The Arts Libraries **[1402]**
University of California, San Francisco - Center for AIDS Prevention Studies (CAPS) **[14308]**
University of California, San Francisco - Institute for Health Policy Studies **[34696]**
University of California, San Francisco - San Francisco Injury Center (SFIC) **[938]**
University of Central Florida - Florida Solar Energy Center (FSEC) **[19146]**
University of Central Florida - Dick Pope, Sr. Institute for Tourism Studies **[20223]**
University of Central Missouri - Small Business and Technology Development Center **[53941]**
University of Chicago - Center for Research in Security Prices (CRSP) **[8973]**
University of Cincinnati - College Conservatory of Music - Gorno Memorial Music Library **[6423]**, **[14713]**
University of Cincinnati - Design, Architecture, Art & Planning Library **[4183]**

Small Business Sourcebook • 30th Edition

3645

University City Science Center [57341]

University of Colorado at Boulder - Business Research Division [20224]

University of Colorado at Boulder - Center for Advanced Manufacturing and Packaging of Microwave, Optical and Digital Electronics (CAMPmode) [4620]

University of Colorado at Boulder - Environmental Program [7742]

University of Colorado at Boulder - Carl McGuire Center for International Studies [27948]

University of Colorado--Boulder - William M. White Business Library [44981]

University of Colorado at Denver - Center for Health Services Research [34697]

University of Connecticut - Center for International Community Health Studies (CICHS) [34698]

University of Connecticut - Connecticut Center for Economic Analysis (CCEA) [27949]

University of Connecticut - Institute for Teaching and Learning (ITL) [28500]

University of Connecticut Technology Incubation Program [49796]

"University Data Center Goes Off-Grid, Is Test Bed' in Contractor (Vol. 57, February 2010, No. 2, pp. 1) [874], [7336], [7700], [19121], [30839]

University of Delaware [61317]; [61318]

University of Delaware - Center for Molecular and Engineering Thermodynamics (CMET) [44094]

University of Delaware - Delaware Education Research and Development Center (DERDC) [28501]

University of Delaware - Halophyte Biotechnology Center [21830]

University of Delaware - Human Performance Laboratory [16115]

University of Delaware - Institute for Public Administration (IPA) [42438]

University of Denver - Penrose Library Special Collections and Archives [5858]

University District Business News [59303]

University of the District of Columbia - D.C. Water Resources Research Center Library [21005]

University Film Association [7894]

University Film Association--Membership Directory [7995]

University Film Producers Association [7894]

University Film and Video Association (UFVA) [7894]

University Film and Video Association--Membership Directory [7995]

University of Florida - Bergstrom Center for Real Estate Studies [17624]

University of Florida - Center for Exercise Science (CES) [16116]

University of Florida - Center for Nutritional Sciences [15238]

University of Florida - Database Systems Research Center [4750]

University of Florida - Hinkley Center for Solid and Hazardous Waste Management (FCSHWM) [10203]

University of Florida - Horse Research Center [10638]

University of Florida - Institute of Food and Agricultural Sciences (IFAS) [21831]

University of Florida - Institute of Food and Agricultural Sciences - Florida Medical Entomology Laboratory (FMEL) [15663]

University of Florida - Powell Center for Construction and Environment [30893]

University of Georgia - Center for Insurance Education and Research [11518]

University of Georgia - Center for Remote Sensing and Mapping Science (CRMS) [4928]

University of Georgia - Institute for Behavioral Research - Center for Family Research (CFR) [4042]

University of Georgia Small Business Development Center - Albany [50394]

University of Georgia Small Business Development Center - Athens [50395]

University of Georgia Small Business Development Center - Augusta [50396]

University of Georgia Small Business Development Center - Brunswick [50397]

University of Georgia Small Business Development Center - Columbus [50398]

University of Georgia Small Business Development Center - Dalton [50399]

University of Georgia Small Business Development Center - DeKalb [50400]

University of Georgia Small Business Development Center - Gainesville [50401]

University of Georgia Small Business Development Center - Gwinnett [50402]

University of Georgia Small Business Development Center - Macon [50403]

University of Georgia Small Business Development Center - Savannah [50404]

University of Georgia - Carl Vinson Institute of Government [42439]

University of Gloucestershire - Learning and Information Services - Park Learning Centre [38850]

University of Guam - Robert F. Kennedy Memorial Library - Instructional Media Division [3664], [4586]

University of Guelph - Arboretum [13463]

University of Guelph - Guelph Turfgrass Institute (GTI) [13532]

University of Hartford - Acoustics Laboratory [14794]

University of Hartford - Construction Institute [5725]

University of Hartford Entrepreneurial Center - Women's Business Center [49767]

University of Hartford - William H. Mortensen Library - Anne Bunce Cheney Art Collection [6080], [6177]

University of Hawaii - John A. Burns School of Medicine - Health Sciences Library [15233]

University of Hawaii at Manoa - Water Resources Research Center Library [21006]

University of Hawaii - Pacific Business Center Program [50695]

University of Hawaii at West O'ahu - Center for Labor Education and Research - CLEAR Labor Law Library [24173]

University of Houston - African American Studies Program (AAS) [40957]

University of Houston - Coastal Plains Small Business Development Center [57877]

University of Houston - Fort Bend Small Business Development Center [57878]

University of Houston - Victoria Small Business Development Center [57879]

University of Idaho - Aquaculture Research Institute (ARI) [9048]

University of Illinois at Chicago - Electronic Visualization Laboratory (EVL) [19063]

University of Illinois at Chicago - Institute for Health Research and Policy - Center for Health Services Research (CHSR) [34699]

University of Illinois - Health Systems Research (HSR) [34700]

University of Illinois at Urbana-Champaign - Applied Health Sciences Library [16055]

University of Illinois at Urbana-Champaign - Building Research Council [5726]

University of Illinois at Urbana-Champaign - Center for Reliable and High Performance Computing (CHRC) [5072]

University of Illinois at Urbana-Champaign - Communications Library [16635]

University of Illinois at Urbana-Champaign - Isaac Funk Family Library of Agricultural, Consumer and Environmental Sciences Library [21811]

University of Illinois at Urbana-Champaign - Office of Real Estate Research [17625]

University of Illinois at Urbana-Champaign - Technology Commercialization Laboratory (TCL) [35250]

University of Iowa - Center for Health Effects of Environmental Contamination (CHEEC) [10204]

University of Iowa Research Park - Business Incubation Program [52008]

University of Iowa - RSM McGladrey Institute of Accounting Education and Research [2346]

University of Iowa Small Business Development Center (Iowa City, Iowa) [51786]

University of Kentucky - Business & Economics Information Center [283], [13907], [21481], [27923], [32082], [40666]

University of Kentucky - Center on Drug and Alcohol Research (CDAR) [46126]

University of Kentucky - Center for Real Estate Studies (CRES) [17626]

University of Kentucky - Gluck Equine Research Center - John A. Morris Memorial Library [10634]

University of Kentucky - Horse Research Farm [10639]

University of Kentucky Office of Commercialization and Development - Advanced Science and Technology Commercialization Center [52399]

University of Kentucky Small Business Development Center (Elizabethtown, Iowa) [52235]

University of Louisville - Information Technology Resource Center (iTRC) [20969]

University of Louisville - Labor-Management Center (LMC) [46956]

University of Louisville - National Crime Prevention Institute (NCPI) [18528]

University of Maine at Machias [52648]

University of Manitoba - Manitoba Centre for Nursing and Health Research (MCNHR) [34701]

University of Manitoba - W.R. McQuade Laboratory [14134]

University of Mary Washington - Center for Historic Preservation (CHP) [1335]

University of Maryland at Baltimore - Center on Drugs and Public Policy (CDPP) [6733]

University of Maryland at College Park - Center on Aging [34702]

University of Maryland at College Park - Center for Global Business Education (CGBE) [36933]

University of Maryland at College Park - Center for International Economics [27950]

University of Maryland at College Park - Dingman Center for Entrepreneurship [43338]

University of Maryland at College Park - Institute for Advanced Computer Studies (UMIACS) [5073]

University of Maryland at College Park - Institute for Governmental Service and Research (IGSR) [42440]

University of Maryland at College Park - Institute for Systems Research (ISR) [5074]

University of Maryland at College Park - International Communications and Negotiations Simulations (ICONS) [36934]

University of Maryland, College Park Libraries - Hornbake Library - Library of American Broadcasting [16774]

University of Maryland - Crane Aquaculture Facility [9049]

University of Massachusetts at Amherst - Massachusetts Water Resources Research Center (WRRC) [21018]

University of Massachusetts at Boston - Gerontology Institute [15145]

University of Massachusetts at Lowell - Lydon Library [38851]

University of Massachusetts - Small Business Development Center [52802]

University of Memphis - Ecological Research Center (ERC) [9050]

University of Miami - Laboratory of Clinical and Applied Physiology [16117]

University of Michigan - Center for Ergonomics [47568]

University of Michigan - Center for National Truck and Bus Statistics (CNTBS) [20726]

University of Michigan - Collaboratory for Research on Electronic Work (CREW) [4793]

University of Michigan - Health Management Research Center (UM-HMRC) [34703]

University of Michigan - Information and Library Studies Library [11965]

University of Michigan - Kresge Hearing Research Institute (KHRI) [10354]

University of Michigan - Kresge Hearing Research Institute - Auditory Anatomy Laboratory [10355]

University of Michigan - Matthaei Botanical Gardens Library [9880]

University of Michigan - Office of Tax Policy Research (OTPR) [19794]

University of Michigan Tech Transfer - College of Engineering - Office of Technology Transfer - Industrial Development Division [53514]

University of Minnesota - Charles Babbage Institute for the History of Information Technology (CBI) [2693]

University of Minnesota - Business Library [4747]

University of Minnesota - Charles Babbage Institute - Center for the History of Information Technology [4748]

University of Minnesota - Children's Literature Research Collections [4430]

University of Minnesota, Crookston Library [10635]

University of Minnesota - Division of Health Policy and Management (HPM) [34704]

University of Minnesota, Duluth - Center for Community and Regional Research (CCRR) [42441]

University of Minnesota Duluth Center for Economic Development - Business Incubator [53792]

University of Minnesota - Eric Sevareid Journalism Library [4587]

University of Minnesota - Minnesota Landscape Arboretum - Andersen Horticultural Library [9881]

University of Minnesota, St. Paul - Magrath Library [21812]

University of Mississippi - Small Business Development Center (SBDC) [45847]

University of Mississippi Small Business Development Center (UMSBDC) [53820]

University of Missouri--Columbia - Frank Lee Martin Memorial Journalism Library [16636]

University of Missouri--Kansas City - Small Business and Technology Development Center [54174]

University of Missouri - Missouri Business Development Program [53942]

University of Missouri—St. Louis - Center for Business and Industrial Studies [41314]

University of Moncton - Centre for Acadians Studies [9576]

University of Montana - Montana Business Connections [54230]

University of Montreal - Health and Prevention Social Research Group [47569]

University of Texas Southwestern Medical Center at Dallas - Center for Human Nutrition [15239]
University of Texas—Houston Health Science Center - Cizik Eye Clinic [20958]
University of Texas—Pan American - Center for Entrepreneurship and Economic Development (CEED) [27953]
University of Toronto - Institute for the History and Philosophy of Science and Technology (IHPST) [44095]
University of Toronto - Institute for Policy Analysis (IPA) [19795]
University of Toronto - Ontario Institute for Studies in Education - Centre for Teacher Development (CTD) [28502]
University of Toronto - Ontario Institute for Studies in Education - International Centre for Educational Change (ICEC) [28503]
University of Tulsa - Mary K. Chapman Center for Communicative Disorders [10357]
University of Utah - Bureau of Economic and Business Research (BEBR) [27954]
University of Utah - Center for Public Policy and Administration (CPPA) [42444]
University of Utah - Human Performance Research Laboratory [16119]
University of Utah - Rocky Mountain Center for Occupational and Environmental Health (RMCOEH) [47570]
University of Vermont - McClure Musculoskeletal Research Center [16120]
University of the Virgin Islands Small Business Development Center [59869]
University of the Virgin Islands Small Business Development Center - St. Croix [59870]
University of the Virgin Islands Small Business Development Center - St. Thomas/St. John [59871]
University of Virginia - Olsson Center for Applied Ethics [46033]
University of Washington - Addictive Behaviors Research Center (ABRC) [46127]
University of Washington - Alcohol & Drug Abuse Institute Library [46116]
University of Washington Botanic Gardens - Elisabeth C. Miller Horticulture Library [9883]
University of Waterloo - Centre for Accounting Research and Education (CARE) [15478]
University of West Alabama Small Business Development Center [47611]
University of West Georgia - Richards College of Business [50682]
University of West Georgia Small Business Development Center [50405]
University of Wisconsin - Eau Claire Small Business Development Center [59449]
University of Wisconsin - Green Bay Small Business Development Center [59450]
University of Wisconsin - La Crosse Small Business Development Center [59451]
University of Wisconsin--Madison - Land Tenure Center Collection [21813]
University of Wisconsin--Madison - Ruth Ketterer Harris Library - Helen Louise Allen Textile Collection [5946]
University of Wisconsin - Madison Small Business Development Center [59452]
University of Wisconsin--Madison - Steenbock Memorial Library [21814]
University of Wisconsin - Milwaukee Small Business Development Center [59453]
University of Wisconsin - Oshkosh Small Business Development Center [59454]
University of Wisconsin - Parkside Small Business Development Center [59455]
University of Wisconsin - River Falls Small Business Development Center [59456]
University of Wisconsin - Stevens Point Small Business Development Center [59457]
University of Wisconsin--Stout - Library Learning Center [20219]
University of Wisconsin - Superior Small Business Development Center [59458]
University of Wisconsin - Whitewater Small Business Development Center [59459]
University of Wisconsin—Eau Claire - Eau Claire Area Research Center [9577]
University of Wisconsin—Green Bay - Area Research Center [9578]
University of Wisconsin—Madison - Center for Health System Research and Analysis (CHSRA) [34708]
University of Wisconsin—Madison - Hancock Agricultural Research Station [4062]
University of Wisconsin—Madison - Medical Instrumentation Laboratory [14247]

University of Wisconsin—Madison - Solar Energy Laboratory (SEL) [19149]
University of Wisconsin—Parkside - Archives and Area Research Center [9579]
University of Wisconsin—Superior - Northern Center for Community and Economic Development (NCCED) [27955]
University of Wisconsin—Whitewater - Wisconsin Innovation Service Center (WISC) [37179]
University of Wyoming - Wyoming State Veterinary Laboratory (WSVL) [1107]
"Univest Charter Switch Signals Banking Trend' in Philadelphia Business Journal (Vol. 30, September 2, 2011, No. 29, pp. 1) [27829], [31919], [34024], [45789]
"Univision" in Brandweek (Vol. 49, April 21, 2008, No. 16, pp. SR8) [624], [7996], [19985], [38527], [40460], [43673]
"'Unknown' Muted Grand Prix Impact' in Boston Business Journal (Vol. 29, September 9, 2011, No. 18, pp. 3) [10759], [13332], [18009], [19475]
"Unleashing the Power of Marketing' in Harvard Business Review (Vol. 88, October 2010, No. 10, pp. 90) [625], [40461], [41264], [43674]
"Unlicensed Utah Collection Agency Settles with Idaho Department of Finance" in Idaho Business Review, Boise (July 15, 2010) [6342], [24077], [26340], [34025], [37136]
Unlimited Future, Inc. [59444]
Unlimited Learning Publications [59877]
"Unlimited Priorities Strengthens Executive Team" in Entertainment Close-Up (November 1, 2011) [11898], [21229], [28915], [38528]
"Unmasking Manly Men" in Harvard Business Review (Vol. 86, July-August 2008, No. 8, pp. 20) [33024], [38529], [46927]
Uno Chicago Grill [6497]
The Unofficial Guide to Starting a Small Business [14014], [24198], [32469], [39551]
The Unorganized Salesperson [43755]
"Unpleasant Surprise" in Barron's (Vol. 88, March 24, 2008, No. 12, pp. 60) [8794], [13026], [18771], [24078], [31920]
"Unseen Injustice: Incivility as Modern Discrimination in Organizations" in Academy of Management Review (January 2008, pp. 55) [26670], [38530]
"Unwanted News for Hospitals" in Business Courier (Vol. 24, October 26, 2008, No. 28, pp. 1) [17525], [24079], [34463], [42248]
"Up Against the Ropes: A Professional Coach May Help" in Black Enterprise (Vol. 37, December 2006, No. 5, pp. 72) [13304], [25914], [28375]
"Up on the Farm" in Canadian Business (Vol. 81, October 27, 2008, No. 18, pp. 119) [21706], [34026]
Up Front [51341]
"Up In the Air" in The Business Journal-Serving Greater Tampa Bay (Vol. 28, July 18, 2008, No. 30, pp. 1) [976], [20186], [20583], [27830], [46433]
Up the Loyalty Ladder [26563], [43230], [43675]
"Up On The Farm" in Canadian Business (Vol. 81, March 31, 2008, No. 5, pp. 23) [11188], [21707], [27831], [36855]
Up and Running: Opening a Chiropractic Office [32470], [34098]
"Up To Code? Website Eases Compliance Burden for Entrepreneurs" in Black Enterprise (Vol. 38, March 2008, No. 8, pp. 48) [11899], [21230], [24080], [28916], [30286], [34027]
"Up, Up and Away" in Small Business Opportunities (November 2007) [6117], [13745], [31130]
UPDATE [1173], [27917]
UPdate [53453]
Update [1262]; [49072]; [49598]; [49757]; [50715]; [51342]; [51343]; [51344]; [51728]; [54156]; [54440]; [54622]; [54920]; [55364]; [55365]; [55822]; [56328]; [56598]; [57250]; [58993]
Update Magazine [53454]
Update Publicare Co. [49642]
"An Updated Ranking of Academic Journals in Economics" in Canadian Journal of Economics (Vol. 44, November 2011, No. 4, pp. 1525) [2170], [2389], [27832], [28376]
Upholstered Furniture Action Council (UFAC) [10455]
Upholstering a Dining Room Chair [20830]
W.E. Upjohn Institute for Employment Research [7013]
Upland Chamber of Commerce [49073]
UPMC Braddock Health Sciences Library [15137]
Upper Arlington Area Chamber of Commerce [56329]
Upper Bucks Chamber of Commerce [57251]
Upper Kennebec Valley Chamber of Commerce [52632]
Upper Midwest Electrical Expo [6914]
Upper Mississippi Harbor Guide [13944]
Upper Mon Valley SCORE [59386]

Upper Sandusky Area Chamber of Commerce (USACC) [56330]
Upper Tampa Bay Regional Chamber of Commerce [50314]
Upper Valley Bi-State Regional Chamber of Commerce (UVB-SRCC) [58780]
Upper Valley SCORE [54545]
Upper WestShore Chamber of Commerce [54288]
The UPS Store [4617], [16446]
The UPS Store / Mail Boxes Etc. [3121], [4618]
UPS Strategic Enterprise Fund [50658]
"The Upside of Fear and Loathing' in Barron's (Vol. 88, March 24, 2008, No. 12, pp. 11) [8795], [13027], [27833], [31921], [33025]
Upside Group Franchise Consulting Corp. [3046], [44218]
Upstart Guide to Owning and Managing a Bed and Breakfast [1935], [10760]
Upstarts! How GenY Entrepreneurs Are Rocking the World of Business and 8 Ways You Can Profit from Their Success [29431], [45790]
"Uptick in Clicks: Nordstrom's Online Sales Surging" in Puget Sound Business Journal (Vol. 29, August 22, 2008, No. 18, pp. 1) [4282], [15353], [23570], [28917], [43231]
Uptown Chamber of Commerce [51345]
Uptown Innovation Center [51763]
Uptown Shelby Association Inc. [1322]
"Uranerz Acquires Additional Uranium Property Adjoining Nichols Ranch" in Canadian Corporate News (May 14, 2007) [41358], [42249], [44116]
"Uranium Energy Corp Provides an Update on Its Goliad Operations" in Canadian Corporate News (May 16, 2007) [10167], [30840], [41359]
Urban Kitchen [18270]
Urban Land Magazine [44751]
Urban League of Greater New Orleans - Women's Business Resource Center [52515]
"Urban Tree Service" in New Hampshire Business Review (Vol. 33, March 25, 2011, No. 6, pp. 35) [13402], [22470], [40462]
Urban Ventures [57395]
Urbana - Champaign County Chamber of Commerce [56085]
Urbandale Buyers' Guide [51979]
Urbandale Chamber Annual Report [51980]
Urbandale Chamber of Commerce [51981]
Urbandale Restaurant Guide [51982]
"The Urge to Converge" in Canadian Business (Vol. 79, October 9, 2006, No. 20, pp. 41) [24618], [25257]
Urgent Communications: Technical Information for Paging, Trunking and Private Wireless Networks [3848], [40842]
Urner Barry's Meat and Poultry Directory [3142]
URS Library [928], [7737]
"US Airways Stock Up 5 Percent on Day Merger Try Ends" in Charlotte Observer (February 1, 2007) [13028], [42250]
U.S. and International Directory of Hotel, Restaurant, and Tourism Management Schools [20153]
US Aquatics Inc. [5680]
"US Cavalry Store" in Retail Merchandiser (Vol. 51, September-October 2011, No. 5, pp. 70) [26797], [33374], [43232]
U.S. Chapter, International Real Estate Federation [16783]
U.S. Department of Energy - National Renewable Energy Laboratory - Office of Education Programs [19145]
U.S. Department of Energy - Solar Energy Research Institute [19145]
U.S. Dressage Federation Inc. [10610]
U.S. Hispanic Chamber of Commerce [40692]
"US Hygiene Adds Bed Bug Fix to Its Line of Highly Effective Cleaning and Pest Control Products" in Benzinga.com (October 29, 2011) [15633], [41265]
U.S. Machine Tool Directory [13698]
US Market Access Center [49364]
The U.S. Market for Pet Supplies and Pet Care Products, 5th Edition [15786]
US Small Business Administration [50669]; [54868]
U.S. Telecommunications Suppliers Association [3674], [20962]
US Tobacco Trade Barometer: Exports [20103]
U.S. Trademark Association [36950], [55526]
U.S. Venetian Blind Association [2024], [11537]
US West Communications - Learning Systems/Employee Development Library [38853]
U.S.A. Directory of Machine Tools, Manufacturing Machinery and Related Products [13698]
USA Engage [26863]
U.S.A. Equestrian Association [10611]
USA Racquetball [15958], [20058]
USA Table Tennis Magazine [19356]

"The VC Shakeout" in Harvard Business Review (Vol. 88, July-August 2010, No. 7-8, pp. 21) [23575], [44204], [47097]

"VC Tax Almost Gone" in Business Journal-Portland (Vol. 24, November 23, 2007, No. 38, pp. 1) [46434], [47098]

Veenstra & Kimm Inc. [19555]

"Vegas in the D; Local Architects Collaborate On MGM Grand" in Crain's Detroit Business (Vol. 23, October 1, 2007, No. 40, pp. 1) [1290], [9407], [10761]

"A Vegas Sensation Inaugural Artexpo Las Vegas" in Art Business News (Vol. 34, November 2007, No. 11, pp. 1) [1356], [4523], [6000], [20438], [46721]

VEGASPEX - Las Vegas International Stamp, Coin, Antique Watch, Jewelry & Collectibles Expo [4420]

Vegetable Soup 1 [40935]

Vegetable Soup 2 [40936]

Vegetarian Journal [10304]

Vegetarian Journal's Foodservice Update [10305]

Vehicle Leasing Today [14984]

Vehicle Maintenance [18632]

Vehicle Tracking Solutions [5057]

VelociTel Inc. [32066]

Velocity Sports Performance [19497]

"Velvet Ice Cream" in Ice Cream Reporter (Vol. 21, July 20, 2008, No. 8, pp. 7) [10931], [25802]

"Velvet Ice Cream" in Ice Cream Reporter (Vol. 23, November 20, 2010, No. 12, pp. 7) [10932], [15438], [18010]

Venable LLP Library [7773]

Venango Area Chamber of Commerce (VACC) [57252]

Vencon Management Inc. (VMI) [42353]

Vencon Management, Inc. [55461]

The Vended Foods Market [20876]

Vending Times--Buyers Guide and Directory Issue [955], [4316], [20872]

Vending Times--International Buyers Guide and Directory Issue [955], [4316], [20872]

Venezuelan American Association of the United States (VAAUS) [36320]

Venezuelan Chamber of Commerce of the United States [36320]

Venice Area Chamber of Commerce [49078]

Venice Area Chamber of Commerce (VACC) [50316]

Venice Area Chamber of Commerce Newsletter [49079]

Venice Area Chamber of Commerce and Visitors Bureau [49078]

Venrock Associates [55462]

Venrock Associates (Palo Alto) [49339]

Ventana Capital Management, Inc. [49340]

Vente et Gestion [33102]

Ventura Business [49080]

Ventura Chamber Business Directory [49081]

Ventura Chamber of Commerce [49082]

Ventura College Small Business Development Center [48177]

Ventura County Industry Guide [49083]

"Ventura Police Install Electronic Kiosk to Access Services" in Ventura County Star (October 28, 2010) [13333], [44572]

The Venture Cafe [23576], [30292], [35204]

Venture Capital Fund of America, Inc. / VCFA Group [55463]

The Venture Capital Fund of New England [53072]

Venture Capital Journal [25354], [47114]

"Venture Capital's Capital Infusion: Federal Incentives Mean More Money for VC Firms" in Entrepreneur (August 2009) [33377], [44887], [47099]

"Venture Capital's Capital Infusion: Federal Incentives Mean More Money for VC Firms" in Entrepreneur (Vol. 37, August 2009) [33378], [44888], [47100]

Venture Financing: Raising Capital in Wisconsin [59791]

"Venture Gap" in Canadian Business (Vol. 81, March 17, 2008, No. 4, pp. 82) [11189], [13034], [27837], [44889], [46435], [47101]

Venture Investment Management Company LLC (VIMAC) [53073]

Venture Investors LLC [59776]

Venture Marketing Associates [3047]

Venture Marketing Associates L.L.C. [32299], [44961]

Venture Out Business Center [51764]

Venture Planning Associates Inc. [47154]

VenturEdge Corp. [24703], [32067], [37265], [38821]

Ventures [53074]

Ventures West Management, Inc. [59885]

Vera Institute of Justice, Inc. - Research Department [29313]

Verbit & Co. [32068], [36072], [38822], [41521]

"Verdict: Few Legal Jobs" in Boston Business Journal (Vol. 31, June 17, 2011, No. 21, pp. 1) [24082], [28381], [45796]

"VeriFone Announces Global Security Solutions Business" in Marketing Weekly News (October 3, 2009) [3825], [7338], [18506], [23577], [25915], [35205], [43233]

"Verizon Comes Calling With 500 Jobs" in Business First Columbus (Vol. 25, September 15, 2008, No. 4, pp. 1) [3826], [23578], [35503], [46436]

"Verizon Small Business Awards Give Companies a Technology Edge" in Hispanic Business (July-August 2009, pp. 32) [3827], [9105], [9717], [10073], [19587], [35206]

"Verizon, Union Dispute is a Vestige of the Past" in Philadelphia Business Journal (Vol. 30, August 26, 2011, No. 28, pp. 1) [3828], [46928]

"Verizon's Big Gamble Comes Down to the Wire" in Globe & Mail (February 3, 2007, pp. B1) [11902], [35207], [40466]

Verlo Mattress Factory Stores [10510]

Vermeer: Light, Love, and Silence [1415]

Vermilion Advantage-Chamber of Commerce Division (VACC) [51347]

Vermilion Chamber of Commerce (VCC) [56334]

Vermillion Area Chamber of Commerce and Development Company [57602]

Vermont Agency of Transportation, Policy and Planning Division Library [1655], [6617], [13556], [19832]

Vermont Business [58781]

Vermont Chamber of Commerce [58782]

Vermont Community and Technical Colleges Library [21815]

Vermont Connections [58783]

Vermont Small Business Development Center [58792]

Vermont Small Business Development Center, Addison County [58714]

Vermont Small Business Development Center, Bennington County [58715]

Vermont Small Business Development Center, Caledonia County [58716]

Vermont Small Business Development Center - Economic Development Department [58729]

Vermont Small Business Development Center, Franklin County [58717]

Vermont Small Business Development Center, Grand Isle County [58718]

Vermont Small Business Development Center, Lamoille County [58719]

Vermont Small Business Development Center - Lead Office (VTSBDC) [58720]

Vermont Small Business Development Center, Orange/Windsor Counties [58721]

Vermont Small Business Development Center, Rutland County [58722]

Vermont Small Business Development Center, Southern Windsor [58723]

Vermont Small Business Development Center, Washington County [58724]

Vermont Small Business Development Center, Windham County [58725]

Vermont State Chamber of Commerce [58782]

Vermont Women's Business Center - Central Vermont Community Action Council [58788]

Vernal Area Chamber of Commerce (VACC) [58683]

Vernal Directory [58684]

Vernal Small Business Development Center [58620]

Vernon Chamber of Commerce [49084]

Vernon Chamber of Commerce (VCC) [54829]; [58495]

"Vernon Revamp" in Business Courier (Vol. 26, October 9, 2009, No. 24, pp. 1) [1291], [5547], [10762], [17527], [23579], [34465], [40826]

Verona Area Chamber of Commerce [59739]

Versailles Area Chamber of Commerce (VACC) [54158]

Versar [30888]

Versar Inc. [30888]

"Versatile's Back" in Farm Industry News (Vol. 42, January 1, 2009, No. 1) [21708], [24620], [39455], [40467]

Vertex Consultants Inc. [14060]

The Vertical Group [54859]

Vertical Systems Analysis Inc. [1323]

"A Very Good Year for Beer" in Entrepreneur (Vol. 37, October 2009, No. 10, pp. 18) [13595], [21709]

The Vessel [58784]

Vestavia Hills Chamber of Commerce (VHCC) [47741]

Veterinary Clinics of North America: Equine Practice [1081]

Veterinary Infectious Disease Organization [1054]

VetLogic [1092]

VFDA Update [5822]

VHS Duplication Directory [8002]

Via Media Publishing Co. [55011]

Via Nova Consulting [2977], [13888], [26105], [38823], [41307], [42910]

Vickers Weekly Insider [32077]

Vickers Weekly Insider Report [13146]; [32077]

"Vicki Avril; Senior Vice-President of Tubular Division, Ipsco Inc." in Crain's Chicago Business (Vol. 31, May 5, 2008, No. 18) [36857], [38535], [39456], [42258], [46929]

Vicksburg-Warren County Chamber of Commerce (VWCCC) [53907]

Victor Chamber of Commerce [55367]

Victoria Chamber of Commerce [58496]

"Victoria Colligan; Co-Founder, Ladies Who Launch Inc., 38" in Crain's Cleveland Business (Vol. 28, November 19, 2007, No. 46) [30293], [32112], [36090], [44784], [47198]

Victorian Crafts Video Vol. 1 [6152]

Victorville Chamber of Commerce (VCC) [49085]

Victorville Chamber of Commerce Business Directory [49086]

Victory Lane Quick Oil Change [16684]

Victory Studios [20012]

Vidalia Chamber of Commerce [52505]

Vidalia-Lyons/Toombs County Chamber of Commerce [50625]

The Video Career Library [3386]

Video Duplication Directory [8002]

Video Presentations Inc. [42561]

Video Software Dealers Association [20880]

Video Source Book [20893]

Video Store [20895]

"Video Surveillance Enters Digital Era, Makes Giant Strides" in Arkansas Business (Vol. 26, September 28, 2009, No. 39, pp. 1) [3640], [7997], [18507], [19017], [35208], [45235], [45797]

Video Systems [8005]

Video Watchdog: The Perfectionist's Guide to Fantastic Video [20897]

Videography: The Magazine of Professional Video Production, Technology, and Applications [8008]

Videomaker Magazine [8009]

Videomasters Inc. [8017]

Videotex Industry Association [28529]

VIE Partners Inc. (VIE) [38824]

Vienna-Tysons Regional Chamber of Commerce (VTRCC) [58994]

Vietnamese American Chamber of Commerce [49087]

Vietnamese Chamber of Commerce [49087]

Vietnamese Chamber of Commerce in Orange County [49087]

The View [53908]; [54442]

"A View to a Killer Business Model" in Black Enterprise (Vol. 40, December 2009, No. 5, pp. 50) [7998], [11903], [21232], [28919], [40468], [40827]

View Point [59304]

View Points [54159]

"Viewing Ironman As Gold, R.I. Firm Buys Its Parent" in The Business Journal-Serving Greater Tampa Bay (Vol. 28, September 19, 2008) [19348], [19479], [24778], [37138], [42259]

Viewpoint [47742]; [59305]

Views [20484]

Viewtech Market Research & Analysis [40652]

Villa Enterprises [16195], [18271]

Villa Linda Mall [26809]

Villa Park Chamber of Commerce [51348]

Village [51349]

Village and Business [51350]

Village of Itasca Chamber of Commerce [51351]

Village of Mt. Zion Chamber of Commerce [51237]

The Village Voice [54516]

Village Voice [49088]; [49089]

Villages Chamber of Commerce [50317]

The Villages Chamber Connection [50318]

Villanova University - Falvey Memorial Library - Special Collections [1160], [2411]

Vincennes Area Chamber of Commerce [51657]

Vincennes University [2433]

The Vineyard - Real Estate, Shopping Center & Urban Development Information Center [14076]

Vinita Area Chamber of Commerce (VACC) [56599]

Vinod H. Dholakia-Architect P.C. [15266]

Vintage Stock [43313]

Vinton Area Chamber of Commerce [58995]

Vinton County Chamber of Commerce [56335]

Viola for Beginners [14654]

Violin for Beginners [14655]

VIP Books [59878]

"Virgin America Flies with V&S on Web" in ADWEEK (Vol. 51, July 12 2010, No. 27, pp. 31) [24946], [28920], [40469], [41268]

"Virgin Mobile has Big Plans for Year Two" in Globe & Mail (March 6, 2006, pp. B5) [23580], [24621], [25258], [35209], [44573]

"Virginia Albanese: President and CEO" in Inside Business (Vol. 13, September-October 2011, No. 5, pp. NC4) [9217], [38536], [47403]

Virginia All-Business Directory [58996]

Virginia Association of Chamber of Commerce Executives (VACCE) [58997]

Virginia Barbeque [18272]

Wage and Benefit Survey [57531]
Wage and Hour Law Compliance (Onsite) [46834]
Wages and Hours [25392]
Wahoo Chamber of Commerce and Economic Development [54443]
Wahoo Chamber of Commerce [54443]
Wahpeton Area Chamber of Commerce and CVB [55928]
Wahpeton Breckenridge Area Chamber of Commerce and Visitors Center [55928]
"Wait for the Call" in Canadian Business (Vol. 80, April 9, 2007, No. 8, pp. 74) [8806], [13044], [42534]
"Wait a Minute!" in Entrepreneur (Vol. 37, September 2009, No. 9, pp. 76) [13045], [22476], [27843], [44890], [47102]
"Waite, Cancer Survivor, Readies Sch'dy 'Big House' after Long Delay" in Business Review, Albany New York (October 26, 2007) [1865], [4401], [18011]
Wakarusa Chamber of Commerce [51733]
Wake Forest Chamber of Commerce [55831]
"Wake-Up Call" in Canadian Business (Vol. 80, October 8, 2007, No. 20, pp. 58) [11190], [27844], [36860], [40475]
Wake Up and Smell the Zeitgeist [23585], [30294], [33030], [38538]
Wakefield Chamber of Commerce [52979]
Wakulla County Chamber of Commerce [50329]
"Wal-Mart Doesn't Sell Council" in The Business Journal-Serving Metropolitan Kansas City (Vol. 26, July 4, 2008, No. 43, pp. 1) [10763], [20439], [43234], [46722]
"'Wal-Mart Effect' Feeds Grocer Price Wars" in Globe & Mail (March 15, 2007, pp. B14) [9984], [23586], [25803], [43235]
"Wal-Mart Expansion Plans Hit Roadblock" in Crain's Chicago Business (Vol. 31, March 24, 2008, No. 12, pp. 2) [21999], [23587], [43236], [46930]
"Wal-Mart Proposed for Timmerman Plaza" in Business Journal-Milwaukee (Vol. 28, December 31, 2010, No. 14, pp. A1) [5549], [23588], [43237]
"Wal-Mart Relaunches Private Brand, Reimagines Stores Layout" in Marketing to Women (Vol. 22, July 2009, No. 7, pp. 5) [24622], [25299], [40476], [43238]
"Wal-Mart Sharpens Focus on Roxbury" in Boston Business Journal (Vol. 31, July 8, 2011, No. 24, pp. 1) [35504], [40828], [43239], [44741], [46018]
"Wal-Mart Takes Expansion Up a Notch" in Globe & Mail (March 21, 2007, pp. B8) [23589], [43240]
Walcott Chamber of Commerce [51984]
The Walden Group [39527]
Walden International [49341]
Waldport Chamber of Commerce [56866]
Waldron Area Chamber of Commerce [48117]
Walgreen Performance Development Library [36080]
"Walgreen Takes Up Doctoring" in Crain's Chicago Business (Vol. 31, March 31, 2008, No. 13, pp. 18) [6668], [23590], [34467], [42264]
Walhalla Area Chamber of Commerce [55929]
Walk Softly [7072], [17703], [30438]
The Walk The Talk Co. [2980], [26107], [42733]
"Walk This Way" in Barron's (Vol. 90, August 23, 2010, No. 34, pp. 13) [13046], [18772], [23591], [39458]
Walk With Us [57799]
Walker Art Center - Staff Reference Library [4589], [15895]
Walker & Associates [13890]
Walker County Chamber of Commerce [50631]
"Walker Seeks More Business Participation" in Business Journal-Milwaukee (Vol. 28, December 10, 2010, No. 10, pp. A1) [24623], [25260], [27845], [33031], [33380], [34032], [35505], [35955], [42395]
Walker Ventures SBIC / Walker Ventures [52780]
Walkerton Area Chamber of Commerce (WACC) [51734]
Walkerton Chamber of Commerce [51734]
A Walking Tour of Historic Llano [58503]
The Wall Street Digest [13147]
"Wall Street Is No Friend to Radical Innovation" in Harvard Business Review (Vol. 88, July-August 2010, No. 7-8, pp. 28) [8807], [13047], [37139], [41272], [44575]
The Wall Street Journal. Complete Small Business Guidebook [23592], [24624], [30295], [33032], [35506], [37529], [38539], [40477], [41382], [41455], [47103]
Wall Street Services Inc. [47155]
Wall Street Week: An Investment Primer [13173]
Walla Walla Area Chamber of Commerce [59310]
Walla Walla Valley Chamber of Commerce (WWVCC) [59310]
Wallace Chamber of Commerce [50808]
Wallace Chamber of Commerce (WCC) [55832]
Wallcovering Manufacturers Association - Wallcovering Distributors Association - Wallpaper Wholesalers Association - National Wallpaper Wholesalers Association [15367], [15389]

Wallcoverings Association (WA) [15367], [15389]
Walled Lake Chamber of Commerce [53342]
Waller Area Chamber of Commerce (WACC) [58504]
Wallingford Chamber of Commerce (WCC) [59311]
Wallowa County Chamber of Commerce [56867]
Walls & Ceilings: Voice of the Industry since 1938 [14117]
"Walmart, Target Moving to Convenience Store Near You" in Hardware Retailing (Vol. 199, November 2010, No. 5, pp. 60) [5817], [23593], [43241]
Walnut Chamber of Commerce (WCC) [51355]
Walnut Creek Business Focus [49100]
Walnut Creek Chamber of Commerce [49101]
Walnut Creek Chamber Membership Directory [49102]
The Walnut Group [56370]
Walpole Chamber of Commerce [52980]
Walsh Bishop Associates (WBA) [15267]
Walt Disney World - Information Services Technical Resource Center. [4681], [4827], [4911], [5027], [36077]
Walter Sedovic Architects [1324]
Walterboro-Colleton Chamber of Commerce (WCCC) [57532]
Walthall County Chamber of Commerce [53911]
Waltham Map and Guide [52981]
Waltham West Suburban Chamber of Commerce (WWSCC) [52982]
Walther Cancer Institute, Inc. - Mary Margaret Walther Program for Cancer Care Research [34711]
Walton Area Chamber of Commerce [50330]
Walton County Chamber of Commerce [50632]
Walton County Chamber of Commerce (WCCC) [50331]
Wamego Area Chamber of Commerce (WCC) [52195]
"W&S to Trim Rich Retirement Plan" in Business Courier (Vol. 27, October 15, 2010, No. 24, pp. 1) [8808], [11444], [13048], [22000], [31929], [36243]
"Wannabe Buyers Take Their Own Sweet Time" in Crain's Chicago Business (Vol. 31, April 21, 2008, No. 16, pp. 50) [17088], [17529], [27846]
"Want a Facial With That Steak?" in Charlotte Observer (February 5, 2007) [2056], [5898], [14144], [18012], [47404]
"Want Leverage? Multi-Unit Franchisees Deliver Substantial Savings" in Franchising World (Vol. 42, October 2010, No. 10, pp. 39) [32259], [42265], [43242]
"Want People to Save? Force Them" in Harvard Business Review (Vol. 88, September 2010, No. 9, pp. 36) [8809], [13049], [31930], [34033], [36861]
"Want Some of This?" in Canadian Business (Vol. 80, April 9, 2007, No. 8, pp. 71) [8810], [13050], [27847]
"Want to Unleash the Next Best Seller? Think Like a Dog" in Advertising Age (Vol. 79, March 10, 2008, No. 10, pp. 14) [15782], [40478], [41273]
"Wanted: African American Professional for Hire" in Black Enterprise (Vol. 37, November 2006, No. 4, pp. 93) [7797], [35507], [35956], [38540], [40919]
"Wanted: Angels in the Country" in Austin Business JournalInc. (Vol. 28, July 18, 2008, No. 18, pp. 1) [34729], [37530], [41383], [42742], [43784], [46437], [47104]
Wapakoneta Area Chamber of Commerce (WACC) [56340]
"The War for Good Jobs; The World Will lBe Led with Economic Force" in Gallup Management Journal (September 7, 2011) [23594], [27848], [35508], [35957]
"The War for Talent" in Canadian Business (Vol. 80, January 29, 2007, No. 3, pp. 60) [35509], [38541], [45801]
"War Veteran Hit Payoff with Repair Business" in Tulsa World (July 28, 2010) [1195], [44576]
Warburg Pincus LLC [55464]
David L. Ward and Associates Inc. [46583]
Ward Mosaic Glass [46583]
Ward's Auto World [14985]
Ward's Business Directory of U.S. Private and Public Companies [33033], [36927]
Warehouse Distributors Association [16643]
Warehousing Education and Research Council (WERC) [16646], [16666]
Andy Warhol Museum - Archives Study Center [1405], [14719], [14782]
"Warm Floors Make Warm Homes" in Contractor (Vol. 56, October 2009, No. 10, pp. S18) [875], [7340], [7703], [19122], [30844]
Warman's Antiques & Collectibles Price Guide [1128]
Paul A. Warner Associates Inc. [14061]
"Warner Bros. Domestic Television Distribution" in Brand-week (Vol. 49, April 21, 2008, No. 16, pp. SR16) [628], [7999], [19987], [38542], [40479], [43680]
Warner Robins Area Chamber of Commerce [50633]
Warning Letter Bulletin [14235]

"Warning Lights Flashing for Air Canada: Carty's Back" in Globe & Mail (February 22, 2006, pp. B1) [25693], [40480], [44577]
Warren - Center Line - Sterling Heights Chamber of Commerce [53359]
Warren County Chamber of Business and Industry (WCCBI) [57257]
Warren County Chamber of Commerce [50634]
Warren County Community College Library Special Collections [44982]
Warren County Genealogical Society Library [9565]
Warren County Regional Chamber of Commerce [54831]
Warren/Forest Counties Economic Opportunity Council [57342]
Warren Hills County Regional Chamber of Commerce [54831]
Warrensburg Chamber of Commerce [55372]
Warrenton Area Chamber of Commerce [54161]
Warrick County Chamber of Commerce [51735]
The Warrior [14090]
Warsaw Area Chamber of Commerce [54162]
Warsaw Area Chamber of Commerce [55833]
Warsaw Chamber of Commerce (WCC) [55833]
Warsaw - Kosciusko County Chamber of Commerce [51736]
Warsaw-Richmond County Chamber of Commerce (WRCCC) [59002]
Warwick Valley Chamber of Commerce (WVCC) [55373]
"Wary Investors Turn to a Different Market for Strong Returns" in Boston Business Journal (Vol. 29, September 2, 2011, No. 17, pp. 1) [9985], [17530], [43243]
"Was Mandating Solar Power Water Heaters For New Homes Good Policy?" in Hawaii Business (Vol. 54, August 2008, No. 2, pp. 28) [5550], [7341], [7704], [17089], [17531], [19123], [30845], [34034], [46438]
Wasatch Business Connection [58686]
Wasatch Venture Corporation / EPIC Ventures [58695]
Wasco Chamber of Commerce and Agriculture [49103]
Wasco Chamber of Commerce [49103]
Waseca Area Chamber of Commerce [53754]
Wash-Word [3327]
Washburn Area Chamber of Commerce (WACC) [59746]
Washington Area Chamber of Commerce [54163]
Washington - Beaufort County Chamber of Commerce (WBCCC) [55834]
Washington Calligraphers Guild (WCG) [3217]
Washington Chamber of Commerce [51985]
Washington County Business Directory [52760]
Washington County Chamber of Commerce [50635]
Washington County Chamber of Commerce (WCCC) [50332]; [58505]; [59003]
Washington County Chamber of Commerce (WCCOC) [57258]
Washington County Historical & Genealogical Society Library [9566]
Washington County Magazine [58506]
Washington, DC, Metropolitan Area Procurement Center - Department of Transportation [49856]
Washington, D.C. Small Business Development Center at Howard University [49840]
Washington DC Women's Business Center [49848]
Washington Department of Commerce - International Trade & Economic Development Division [59072]
Washington Gift Show [4421], [9588], [9627]
Washington Minority Business Enterprise Center - Community Capital Development [59324]
Washington Procurement Technical Assistance Center - Columbia River Economic Development Council (CREDC) [59340]
Washington Procurement Technical Assistance Center - Community Capital Development [59341]
Washington Procurement Technical Assistance Center - Economic Development Association of Skagit County (EDASC) [59342]
Washington Procurement Technical Assistance Center - Northwest Economic Council [59343]
Washington Procurement Technical Assistance Center - The Northwest Native American Business Enterprise Center - NWNABEC [59344]
Washington Procurement Technical Assistance Center - Snohomish County Economic Development Council - PTAC [59345]
Washington Procurement Technical Assistance Center - Spokane Regional Chamber of Commerce [59346]
Washington Procurement Technical Assistance Center - William Factory - Tacoma-Pierce Small Business Incubator [59347]
Washington Procurement Technical Center - Grays Harbor Economic Development Council [59348]
Washington Research Council (WRC) [19797]
Washington Small Business Development Center - Lead Office (WSBDC) [59069]

Washington Sportsmen's Show [19391]

Washington State Department of Commerce - Business Development Division [59073]

Washington State Department of Natural Resources - Public Land Survey Office [19539]

Washington State Department of Revenue [59074]

Washington State Office of Minority and Women's Business Enterprises [59325]

Washington Tariff & Trade Letter [36907]

Washington Technical Assistance Center - Thurston County Economic Development Council [59349]

Washington Technology Center [59352]

Washington Technology Center (WTC) [35251]

Washington University - Center for Air Pollution Impact and Trend Analysis Library [929]

Washington University in St. Louis - Computer and Communications Research Center (CCRC) [5075]

Washington Weekly [13148]

Washington-Wilkes Chamber of Commerce [50636]

Washington Writer [6849]

Washngton DC Minority Business Enterprise Center [49849]

Washoe County Law Library [9421]

Waste Age: The Business Magazine for Waste Management Professionals [10172]

Waste Equipment Manufacturers Institute [10164]

Waste Equipment Manufacturers Institute--Directory [10168]

Waste Equipment Technology Association (WASTEC) [10164]

Waste Isolation Pilot Plant [61389]

"Waste Not" in *Entrepreneur* (Vol. 36, April 2008, No. 4, pp. 21) [9718], [10247], [30846], [44578]

Waste Recovery Report [17732]

WASTEC Product and Service Directory [10168]

Watch It! Inc. [15038], [43314]

Watch & Jewelry Review [13288]

"Watchful Eye: Entrepreneur Protects Clients and His Bottom Line" in *Black Enterprise* (Vol. 38, March 2008, No. 8, pp. 46) [18508], [22135], [23595], [30296], [31931]

"Water Company Eyeing Region for a New Plant" in *Charlotte Business Journal* (Vol. 25, December 10, 2010, No. 38, pp. 1) [20978], [35510], [44742]

Water Conditioning Association International [20972]

Water Conditioning Foundation [20972]

Water Conditioning & Purification [20987]

Water Conditioning & Purification--Buyers Guide Issue [20979]

"Water Conservation Helps GC's Building Attain LEED Gold Status" in *Contractor* (Vol. 56, September 2009, No. 9, pp. 5) [5551], [7342], [7705], [16278], [19124], [30847]

Water Depot [2423]

Water Desalination Report [20988]

"Water Distiller" in *Canadian Business* (Vol. 81, September 29, 2008, No. 16, pp. 52) [7343], [7706], [19125], [30848], [37140], [43988], [46019]

"Water Efficiency Bill Move Through Congress" in *Contractor* (Vol. 56, July 2009, No. 7, pp. 20) [876], [16279], [18713], [30849], [34035], [46439]

Water News [30439]

"Water Park, Convention Center Plan Matures" in *Austin Business JournalInc.* (Vol. 28, July 18, 2008, No. 18, pp. 1) [977], [5552]

Water Policy Report [7366], [20989], [30875], [34075]

Water Quality Association (WQA) [20972]

Water Quality Association--Membership Directory [20980]

Water Quality Research Journal of Canada [30440]

Water Resources Research Institute (WRRI). [21005]

Water Services Corp. [20993]

Water Ski Industry Association [19314]

Water Sports Industry Association (WSIA) [19314]

Water Supply Improvement Association [20970]

Water Technology [20990]

Water Treatment for Boilers, Chillers & Cooling Towers (Onsite) [25003], [28102]

"Water Treatment Play Zenon Goes to GE" in *Globe & Mail* (March 15, 2006, pp. B1) [42266], [44579]

"Water Works Spinoff Could Make Big Splash" in *Business Courier* (Vol. 24, October 19, 2008, No. 27, pp. 1) [13051], [25916], [27849], [33462]

Waterford Area Chamber of Commerce (WACC) [59747]

Waterfront Center [21833]

Waterloo-Cedar Falls Business Directory [51986]

Waterloo Chamber of Commerce [51356]

Waterloo Chamber of Commerce (WCC) [59748]

Waterloo Chamber of Commerce [51897]

WATERNET Bibliographic Database [2425], [20994]

"Watershed Solution" in *Business Courier* (Vol. 24, December 14, 2008, No. 35, pp. 1) [5553], [17532], [30850]

Watertown Area Chamber of Commerce [59749]

Watertown Area Chamber of Commerce (WACC) [57603]

Watertown - Belmont Chamber of Commerce (WBCC) [52983]

Watertown Small Business Development Center [57556]

Waterville Area Chamber of Commerce (WACC) [56341]

Waterville Chamber of Commerce [52196]

Waterville Valley Region Chamber of Commerce (WVRCC) [54624]

Watford City Area Chamber of Commerce [55930]

Watkins College of Art, Design, & Film Library [1406], [8022], [11594]

Watkins Glen Area Chamber of Commerce [55374]

Watonga Chamber of Commerce [56602]

Watseka Area Chamber of Commerce (WACC) [51357]

Scott M. Watson Inc. [41651]

Watsonville Area Chamber of Commerce [48861]

"Wattles Plugs Back Into State" in *Business Journal Portland* (Vol. 27, November 19, 2010, No. 38, pp. 1) [9986], [17533], [35512], [35958], [43245]

Waukegan Chamber of Commerce [51166]

Waukegan/Lake County [51166]

Waukegan-North Chicago Area Chamber of Commerce [51166]

Waukegan-North Chicago Chamber of Commerce [51166]

Waukesha Area Chamber of Commerce [59750]

Waukesha County Chamber of Commerce (WCCC) [59750]

Waukon Chamber of Commerce [51987]

Waunakee Area Chamber of Commerce [59751]

Waunakee/Westport Chamber of Commerce [59751]

Waupaca Area Association of Commerce [59752]

Waupaca Area Chamber of Commerce (WACC) [59752]

Waupaca Area Chamber of Commerce Newsline [59753]

Waupaca Area Chamber of Commerce Progress Report [59754]

Waupun Area Chamber of Commerce [59755]

Wausau/Marathon County Chamber of Commerce (WACC) [59756]

Wauseon Chamber of Commerce (WCC) [56342]

Wauseon Commerce Club [56342]

Waushara Area Chamber of Commerce (WACC) [59757]

The Wave [56343]

Wave [58507]

Waverly Area Development Group (WADG) [51988]

Waverly Chamber - Main Street [51988]

Waverly Chamber of Commerce [51988]

Waxahachie Chamber of Commerce (WCC) [58508]

"The Way I Work" in *Inc.* (March 2008, pp. 102-104, 106) [5130], [20188], [20585], [21235], [28922]

"The Way I Work: Kim Kleeman" in *Inc.* (October 2007, pp. 110-112, 114) [2171], [6524], [28383], [47405]

"The Way to the Market's Heart?" in *Canadian Business* (Vol. 80, March 26, 2007, No. 7, pp. 74) [8811], [13052], [43989]

"Way More Than Mowing" in *Green Industry Pro* (Vol. 23, September 2011) [9795], [13403], [13489], [25694], [44580]

The Way We'll Be: The Zogby Report on the Transformation of the American Dream [27850], [31932], [46020]

Wayne Chamber of Commerce (WCC) [53459]

Wayne County Chamber of Commerce [50637], [55835], [57259], [57800]

Wayne County Industrial [56344]

"Wayne, Oakland Counties Create Own 'Medical Corridor" in *Crain's Detroit Business* (Vol. 24, October 6, 2008, No. 40, pp. 8) [5554], [34468], [35513], [42267], [44891]

Wayne State College - Nebraska Business Development Center (NBDC) [40670]

Wayne State University [53522]

Waynesburg Chamber of Commerce [57260]

Waynesville Area Chamber of Commerce [56345]

Waynesville-St. Robert Area Chamber of Commerce [54164]

Waynoka Chamber of Commerce [56603]

WBusiness Books [49413]

WCC Community Guide [51361]

WDA: The RV Aftermarket Association [16643]

"We All Scream for Ice Cream" in *Crain's Chicago Business* (Vol. 31, April 28, 2008, No. 17, pp. 48) [21711], [23597], [31131], [39459]

"We Are Not a Marketing Company" in *Boston Business Journal* (Vol. 31, June 10, 2011, No. 20, pp. 1) [6669], [24779], [34469], [40481]

We Are Smarter Than Me: How to Unleash the Power of Crowds in Your Business [23598], [24625], [26565], [30298], [31933], [38543], [39460], [40482]

We Care Health Services Inc. [10586]

"We Do: Copreneurs Simultaneously Build Happy Marriages and Thriving Enterprises" in *Black Enterprise* (Vol. 38, February 2008) [31132], [40829]

"We Had to Won the Mistakes" in *Harvard Business Review* (Vol. 88, July-August 2010, No. 7-8, pp. 108) [9719], [11010], [16602], [24948], [26566], [36862], [42535], [42671]

"We Have a Budget, Too" in *Entrepreneur* (Vol. 37, October 2009, No. 10, pp. 89) [11445], [22001], [35959], [36244]

"We May Finally Find the Silver Lining" in *Crain's Detroit Business* (Vol. 24, April 7, 2008, No. 14, pp. 8) [8000], [11191], [27851]

We Mean Business [47973]

"We Move Forward as a Team" in *Women In Business* (Vol. 61, December 2009, No. 6, pp. 6) [22477], [29181], [33034]

We the People USA Inc. [3122]

We Toss'em, They're Awesome Pizza Factory [16197], [18273]

"We Were Strutting Our Stuff" in *Women In Business* (Vol. 63, Summer 2011, No. 2, pp. 10) [29182], [47406]

"A Weak Link Can Break the Chain of Good Service" in *Canadian Business* (Vol. 83, August 17, 2010, No. 13-14, pp. 11) [26567], [29183]

"Wealth and Jobs: the Broken Link" in *Harvard Business Review* (Vol. 88, November 2010, No. 11, pp. 44) [30299], [34036], [35514], [35960], [41274]

"The Wealth Portfolio" in *Canadian Business* (Vol. 79, Winter 2006, No. 24, pp. 146) [8812], [13053], [42268]

Wealth Without a Job: The Entrepreneur's Guide to Freedom and Security Beyond the 9 to 5 Lifestyle [30300]

"Wear More Hats" in *Canadian Business* (Vol. 80, March 12, 2007, No. 6, pp. 39) [23599], [30301], [38544]

The Weather Channel [3196], [15581], [19988], [30302]

Weatherford Area Chamber of Commerce (WACC) [56604]

Weatherford Chamber of Commerce (WCC) [58509]

Weatherford Chamber of Commerce [56604]

"Weathering the BlackBerry Storm" in *Hispanic Business* (January-February 2009, pp. 52) [3831], [35213], [41456]

"Weathering the Economic Storm" in *Playthings* (Vol. 107, January 1, 2009, No. 1, pp. 10) [20274], [24626], [27852], [37223]

Weathersby Guild [9368]

"Weaving a Stronger Fabric: Organizing a Global Sweat-Free Apparel Production Agreement" in *WorkingUSA* (Vol. 11, June 2008, No. 2) [3897], [4283], [34037], [36863], [39461], [43246], [46021], [46931]

"Web-Based Marketing Excites, Challenges Small Business Use" in *Colorado Springs Business Journal* (January 20, 2010) [629], [11909], [26800], [28923], [40483], [43681], [45802]

"Web-Based Solutions Streamline Operations" in *Contractor* (Vol. 56, December 2009, No. 12, pp. 28) [877], [11910], [16280], [21236], [38545]

"Web Biz Brulant Surfing for Acquisition Candidates" in *Crain's Cleveland Business* (Vol. 28, December 3, 2007, No. 48, pp. 6) [11911], [21237], [23600], [35214], [40484], [42269]

Web Design [30398]

Web Design with Adobe Dreamweaver and Photoshop (Onsite) [45073]

Web Design Business [21030], [35585]

"The Web Gets Real" in *Canadian Business* (Vol. 79, July 17, 2006, No. 14-15, pp. 19) [5040], [11912], [22478], [35215]

Web Graphics with Adobe Photoshop (Onsite) [45074]

Web Marketing: Design. Navigation. Analytics. Understanding the Big Picture (Onsite) [39612]

The Web Offset Press [16425]

"Web-Preneuring" in *Small Business Opportunities* (May 2008) [21238], [28924]

"Web to Print" in *American Printer* (Vol. 128, August 1, 2011, No. 8) [4524], [16412], [20806], [21239], [28925]

Web sett; www.wfcinc.com [10256]

"Web Sight: Do You See What I See?" in *Entrepreneur* (Vol. 35, October 2007, No. 10, pp. 58) [4139], [4284], [7852], [11913], [15354], [21240], [43247]

"Web Site Design, Content Can Boost Diversity" in *HR-Magazine* (Vol. 53, August 2008, No. 8, pp. 20) [21241], [35515], [35961], [40920]

"Web Site Focuses on Helping People Find Jobs, Internships with Area Businesses" in *Crain's Detroit Business* (Vol. 26, Jan. 4, 2010) [11914], [21242], [35516], [38546]

MASTER INDEX What

Master Index

West Suburban Chamber of Commerce (WSCC) **[59761]**
West Suburban Chamber of Commerce and Industry (WSCCI) **[51365]**
West Suburban Chamber of Commerce [51365]
West Texas A&M University Small Business Development Center **[57882]**
West Union Chamber of Commerce (WUCC) **[51992]**
West Valley-Taylorsville-Kearns Area Chamber of Commerce [58645]
West Virginia Chamber of Commerce **[59436]**
West Virginia Commercial L.L.C. **[17604]**
West Virginia Development Office - Business and Industrial Development Division **[59380]**
West Virginia Human Resources Journal **[59437]**
West Virginia International Auto Show **[14994]**
West Virginia Junior College Library **[3410]**
West Virginia Northern Community College Small Business Development Center **[59374]**
West Virginia Northern Community College (Wheeling) **[59446]**
West Virginia Procurement Technical Assistance Center **[59443]**
West Virginia Small Business Development Center - Lead Office (WVSBDC) **[59375]**
West Virginia University - College of Business and Economics - Bureau of Business and Economic Research **[27924]**
West Virginia University - Institute for Labor Studies and Research (ILSR) **[22095]**
West Virginia University - Institute of Occupational and Environmental Health (IOEH) **[47571]**
West Virginia University (Parkersburg) **[59447]**
West Virginia University Small Business Development Center **[59376]**
West Virginia University Small Business Development Center - Parkersburg **[59377]**
West Yellowstone Chamber of Commerce (WYCC) **[54319]**
West Yuma County Chamber of Commerce **[49605]**
Westar Capital (Costa Mesa) **[49343]**
WestCap Partners Inc. **[32070]**
Westchester Chamber of Commerce **[51366]**
Westchester County Business Journal **[55519]**
Westchester County Chamber of Commerce [55103]
Westchester Small Business Development Center **[55032]**
Western Arborists Inc. **[13436]**, **[13514]**
Western Association of Chamber Executives (WACE) **[49116]**
Western Association of Venture Capitalists--Directory of Members **[47106]**
Western Building Material Association (WBMA) **[13646]**
Western Business Services Ltd. **[2982]**, **[38827]**
Western Canada Conservation and Reclamation Association [30417]
Western Canada Wilderness Committee (WCWC) **[7073]**
Western Capital Financial Corporate [47156]
Western Capital Financial Services Inc. **[47156]**
Western Capital Holdings Inc. **[24706]**, **[32071]**, **[47157]**
Western Chester County Chamber of Commerce (WCCCC) **[57265]**
Western Colorado Business Development Corp. - Business Incubator Center **[49630]**
Western Connecticut State University - Ruth A. Haas Library **[14720]**
Western Douglas County Chamber of Commerce (WDCCC) **[54445]**
Western-English Industry Report **[43276]**
Western Fairs Association (WFA) **[5103]**
Western Floor Covering Association [9059]
Western Floors [9074], [20829]
The Western Flyer **[55838]**
Western Food Industry Expo **[10014]**
Western Food Service & Hospitality Expo Los Angeles **[10312]**, **[46789]**
Western Illinois Area Agency on Aging - Greta J. Brook Elderly Living and Learning Facility **[333]**, **[15139]**
Western Illinois University [51448]
Western Iowa Tech Small Business Development Center (Sioux City, Iowa) **[51788]**
Western Maryland Public Libraries - Regional Library **[1161]**, **[18672]**, **[21816]**
Western Michigan University - Center for the Study of Ethics in Society **[31008]**
Western Michigan University - Human Performance Institute (HPI) **[15271]**
Western Michigan University - Paper and Imaging **[18367]**
Western Monmouth Chamber of Commerce [54730]
Western New York Gift Show **[9589]**, **[9628]**
Western Pine Association - West Coast Lumbermen's Association [13648]
Western Red Cedar Lumber Association (WRCLA) **[13647]**
Western Region Hazardous Substance Research Center (WRHSRC) **[10206]**
Western Region Maryland Small Business Development Center **[52657]**
Western Regional Aquaculture Center (WRAC) **[9052]**
Western Research Institute (WRI) **[2021]**
Western Retail Lumbermen's Association [13646]
Western Rockingham Chamber of Commerce (WRCC) **[55839]**
Western Sizzlin [18275]
Western Sizzlin Corp. **[18275]**
Western Sizzlin Steak Franchises Inc. [18275]
Western State Psychiatric Center Library **[46118]**
Western States Advertising Agencies Association [42590]
Western States Investment Group **[49344]**
Western Technology Center - Burnes Flat Campus **[56668]**
Western Technology Investment **[49345]**
Western Vehicle Leasing Association [1620]
Western Veterinary Conference **[1088]**
Western View **[57266]**
Western Wholesale Druggists [6634]
Western Wholesale Pet Supply Association [1236], [15747]
"Western Wind Energy Corporation" in CNW Group (October 4, 2011) **[7344]**, **[7707]**, **[30851]**
Western Winter Sports Representatives Association (WWSRA) **[18828]**
Western Wood Moulding Producers - Wood Moulding and Millwork Producers - Wood Moulding and Millwork Producers Association [3414]
Western Wood Products Association (WWPA) **[13648]**
Western World Pet Supply Association [1236], [15747]
Western World Pet Supply Association Dealer Trade Show [15676], [15798]
Westerville Area Chamber of Commerce **[56348]**
Westfield Area Chamber of Commerce (WACC) **[54835]**
Westfield Chamber of Commerce **[59762]**
Westfield Chamber of Commerce (WCC) **[51738]**
"WestJet Gears Up for Domestic Dogfight" in Globe & Mail (May 1, 2007, pp. B6) **[25697]**, **[44584]**
"WestJet Hires a New CFO After Lengthy Search" in Globe & Mail (January 23, 2007, pp. B8) **[33035]**, **[38550]**
"WestJet Ponders Growth Plan Following Record Profit" in Globe & Mail (February 15, 2007, pp. B15) **[23605]**, **[25263]**, **[44585]**
Westlake Village Chamber of Commerce [48615]
Westland Chamber of Commerce **[53463]**
Westlife Consultants & Counsellors **[32072]**, **[38828]**, **[40653]**, **[42690]**, **[43771]**
Westminster Chamber of Commerce **[49117]**; **[57534]**
Westminster Choir College - Rider University - Talbott Library **[14721]**
The Westminster Kennel Club Dog Care Guide **[1034]**
Westmont Chamber of Commerce and Tourism Bureau **[51367]**
Westmoreland Chamber of Commerce (WCC) **[57267]**
Weston Area Chamber of Commerce (WACC) **[50336]**
Westport Chamber of Commerce [49761]
Westport-Grayland Chamber of Commerce **[59316]**
Westport/Weston Chamber of Commerce **[49761]**
Westridge Chamber of Commerce **[51368]**
WestWayne [40572]
Wethersfield Chamber of Commerce **[49762]**
Wetzel's Pretzels **[18276]**, **[19290]**
Wewoka Chamber of Commerce **[56606]**
Weyauwega Area Chamber of Commerce **[59763]**
"Weyerhaeuser's REIT Decision Shouldn't Scare Investors Away" in Barron's (Vol. 88, June 30, 2008, No. 26, pp. 18) **[8818]**, **[13061]**, **[17534]**, **[24629]**, **[25264]**, **[31940]**, **[38551]**, **[46443]**
Weyerhaeuser Company - Archives NP-190 **[13684]**
W.G. Grinders **[6498]**
A Whack on the Side of the Head **[25917]**, **[30309]**, **[38552]**
"Wham-O's Wisdom" in Playthings (Vol. 107, January 1, 2009, No. 1, pp. 13) **[20275]**, **[30310]**
Wharton Chamber of Commerce **[58517]**
Wharton Small Business Development Center (WSBDC) **[56921]**
"What 17th Century Pirates Can Teach Us About Job Design" in Harvard Business Review (Vol. 88, October 2010, No. 10, pp. 44) **[35964]**, **[38553]**
"What Are Canada's Industrial Polluters Doing to Reduce Emissions?" in Canadian Business (Vol. , pp.) **[7345]**, **[7708]**, **[30852]**
"What Are You, A Bank? You Probably Lend Your Customers More Money Than You Realize." in Inc. (November 2007, pp. 81) **[22136]**, **[26344]**
"What Are You Afraid Of?" in Entrepreneur (Vol. 37, July 2009, No. 7, pp. 79) **[27856]**, **[30311]**, **[44785]**, **[46539]**
"What Are You Doing Differently?" in Agency Sales Magazine (Vol. 39, December 2009, No. 11, pp. 3) **[24630]**, **[25265]**, **[43682]**
"What Are Your Party's Legislative Priorities for 2008?" in Hawaii Business (Vol. 53, January 2008, No. 7, pp. 22) **[24631]**, **[27857]**, **[33036]**, **[33382]**, **[34038]**, **[44892]**
"What Brain Science Tells Us About How to Excel" in Harvard Business Review (Vol. 88, December 2010, No. 12, pp. 123) **[26568]**, **[38554]**, **[46540]**
"What Businesses Can Do: Growing the Supply of Highly Skilled Graduates" in Canadian Business (Vol. 81, October 27, 2008, No. 18) **[28384]**, **[35518]**, **[35965]**
"What CEOs Will Admit Out of the Office" in Inc. (November 2007, pp. 30) **[30312]**, **[38555]**
"What Choice Did I Have?" in Entrepreneur (Vol. 37, October 2009, No. 10, pp. 88) **[11447]**, **[22002]**, **[34471]**, **[36246]**
"What City is the No. 1 Destination for Residents Moving From WNY?" in Business First Buffalo (October 26, 2007, pp. 1) **[24781]**
"What Dead Zone?" in Entrepreneur (Vol. 37, October 2009, No. 10, pp. 128) **[30313]**, **[32262]**, **[43252]**, **[44117]**
"What to Do in an Economic Upswing Before It's too Late" in Agency Sales Magazine (Vol. 39, November 2009, No. 10, pp. 36) **[27858]**, **[40494]**
"What Do Your ISO Procedures Say?" in Modern Machine Shop (Vol. 84, September 2011, No. 4, pp. 34) **[13716]**, **[34039]**, **[39465]**
"What Employees Worldwide Have in Common" in Gallup Management Journal (September 22, 2011) **[29184]**, **[35966]**, **[40921]**
"What Enforcement?" in Canadian Business (Vol. 81, December 24, 2007, No. 1, pp. 26) **[13062]**, **[24085]**, **[34040]**
"What Ever Happened to TGIF?" in Barron's (Vol. 88, March 10, 2008, No. 10, pp. M3) **[8819]**, **[13063]**, **[27859]**, **[31941]**
"What is the Future of Disk Drives, Death or Rebirth?" in ACM Computing Surveys (Vol. 43, Fall 2011, No. 3, pp. 23) **[4656]**, **[4733]**, **[4880]**, **[5004]**, **[45804]**
"What the Future Holds for Consumers" in Black Enterprise (Vol. 41, August 2010, No. 1, pp. 47) **[6345]**, **[18510]**, **[26345]**, **[28931]**, **[34041]**, **[43253]**, **[45805]**
What Got You Here Won't Get You There **[30314]**, **[38556]**
"What Happens in Vegas Could Happen in Baltimore, Too" in Boston Business Journal (Vol. 29, June 17, 2011, No. 6, pp. 1) **[5555]**, **[9408]**, **[17535]**, **[34042]**
What Has EX-IM Bank Done for Small Business Lately?: Congressional Hearing **[8820]**, **[11193]**
"What Has Sergey Wrought?" in Barron's (Vol. 89, July 13, 2009, No. 28, pp. 8) **[3642]**, **[8821]**, **[13064]**, **[19020]**, **[27860]**, **[29295]**, **[31942]**
"What Homes Do Retirees Want?" in Canadian Business (Vol. 79, July 17, 2006, No. 14-15, pp.) **[5556]**, **[17090]**, **[17536]**, **[24632]**, **[40495]**
What Is a Better Business Bureau **[49654]**
"What Is a Geothermal Heat Pump" in Indoor Comfort Marketing (Vol. 70, August 2011, No. 8, pp. 14) **[878]**, **[7346]**, **[7709]**, **[30853]**, **[45806]**
"What Is In Your Company Library?" in Modern Machine Shop (Vol. 84, October 2011, No. 5, pp. 60) **[13717]**, **[39466]**, **[41561]**
What Is Salesmanship? **[43756]**
What Is Telemarketing and How Do I Get Started? **[19857]**
"What It Takes to Be an Effective Leader" in Black Enterprise (Vol. 41, December 2010, No. 5, pp. 62) **[38557]**, **[40922]**
What to Know **[49118]**
What Losing Taught Me about Winning: The Ultimate Guide for Success in Small and Home-Based Business **[30315]**, **[33037]**, **[35624]**
"What Makes for an Effective, Production-Oriented VMC?" in Modern Machine Shop (Vol. 84, November 2011, No. 6, pp. 24) **[13718]**, **[25698]**, **[39467]**, **[41457]**
What Makes You Smile **[38829]**
What Men Don't Tell Woman about Business: Opening Up the Heavily Guarded Alpha Male Playbook **[22479]**, **[25699]**, **[30316]**, **[33038]**, **[47410]**
"What Moms Want" in Marketing to Women (Vol. 21, February 2008, No. 2, pp. 6) **[6566]**, **[10075]**, **[20587]**, **[40496]**, **[45807]**, **[46541]**
"What Most Banks Fail to See; New and Complex Financial Regulations Can be Daunting" in Gallup Management Journal (March 10, 2011) **[26569]**, **[31943]**, **[34043]**, **[40497]**
What No One Ever Tells You About Starting Your Own Business: Real-Life Start-Up Advice from 101 Successful Entrepreneurs **[24199]**, **[29433]**, **[32476]**, **[39552]**

Small Business Sourcebook • 30th Edition 3655

Whitehall Area Chamber of Commerce [56349]; [59764]
Whitehouse Area Chamber of Commerce [58519]
Whitesboro Area Chamber of Commerce (WCC) [58520]
Whitewater Area Chamber of Commerce (WACC) [59765]
Whiting - Robertsdale Chamber of Commerce [51739]
Whittier Area Chamber of Commerce (WACC) [49120]
C B Richard Ellis Whittier Partners (CBRE) [17605]
Who Does What? [38640]
"Who Gets the Last Laugh?' in Barron's (Vol. 88, March 31, 2008, No. 13, pp. 17) [8835], [13077], [18511], [31957], [36872], [39475]
Who Killed Service? [26613]
Who Makes It and Where Directory [20075]
"Who Produces for Whom in the World Economy?' in Canadian Journal of Economics (Vol. 44, November 2011, No. 4, pp. 1403) [11195], [36873]
Who Wants to Play God? [36003]
The Whole Child Learning Co. [28480]
Whole Foods: Informing and Educating Natural Products Retailers on Dietary Supplements, Herbs, HBC, Homeopathy, Foods [10256]
"The Whole Package' in Entrepreneur (Vol. 36, February 2008, No. 2, pp. 24) [21718], [25918], [30858], [39476], [47411]
Wholesale Commission Florists of America [9098]
Wholesale Drugs Magazine [6680]
Wholesale Florist and Florist Supplier Association (WF&FSA) [9098]
Wholesale Florist & Florist Supplier Association--Membership Directory [9107]
Wholesale Florists and Florist Suppliers of America [9098]
Wholesale Nursery Growers of America - American Association of Nurserymen - American Association of Nurserymen, Florists and Seedsmen [9758], [13345]
The Wholesaler--Directory of Manufacturers Representatives Issue [885], [16281]
The Wholesaler--'The Wholesaling 100' Issue [16282]
"Whopper; Russ Klein" in Advertising Age (Vol. 79, November 17, 2008, No. 43, pp. S10) [18016], [23616], [32266], [40509]
Who's Got Your Back [30324], [33046]
Who's Hiring: 5,000 Canadian Employers Indexed by Occupation [3347]
"Who's Next?' in Boston Business Journal (Vol. 27, November 16, 2007, No. 42, pp. 1) [24090], [35217], [42279], [44746]
Who's Who in Addison County [58785]
Who's Who in Alexandria Business [59004]
Who's Who in Association Management: Membership Directory & Buyer's Guide [1465]
Who's Who in Bristol County Business [57390]
Who's Who in Business [50337]; [56607]
Who's Who in the Capital Region [57268]
Who's Who in Chamber Membership [49121]
Who's Who Directory [47744]
Who's Who in Greater Cranston [57391]
Who's Who Greater Norwalk Business Directory [49763]
Who's Who in Grounds Management [3259]
Who's Who in Floor Covering Distribution [9064]
Who's Who in Professional Grounds Management Society [3259]
Who's Who in Screen Printing [18357]
Who's Who in the Media and Communications [365], [6815], [16581]
Who's Who of RV Dealers [17668]
Who's Who--Personal Care Products Council Membership Directory [5899]
Who's Who in Pine Bluff Business [48119]
Who's Who in SGIA [18357]
Who's Who in the Sumter Chamber [57535]
Who's Who--The CTFA Membership Directory [5899]
Who's Your City? How the Creative Economy is Making Where to Live the Most Important Decision of Your Life [27871], [36874], [44747]
Who's Your Gladys?: How to Turn Even the Most Difficult Customer into Your Biggest Fan [26571], [43685]
"Why Change?' in Canadian Business (Vol. 80, October 8, 2007, No. 20, pp. 9) [11196], [27872], [34051], [36875], [39477], [44587]
"Why Copyright Isn't Property' in Information Today (Vol. 26, February 2009, No. 2, pp. 18) [24091], [37147], [37262]
"Why Did We Ever Go Into HR?' in Harvard Business Review (Vol. 86, July-August 2008, No. 8, pp. 39) [29189], [33047], [35972], [38568]
"Why Entrepreneurs Matter More Than Innovators" in Gallup Management Journal (November 22, 2011) [30325], [35523], [37148], [41281]
"Why the Ethanol King Loves Driving his SUV' in Globe & Mail (January 29, 2007, pp. B17) [30859], [39478]
Why GM Matters: Inside the Race to Transform an American Icon [14967], [39479]

"Why HR Practices Are Not Evidence-Based' in Academy of Management Journal (Vol. 50, No. 5, October 2007, pp. 1033) [35973], [37263], [38569]
"Why Intel Should Dump Its Flash-Memory Business" in Barron's (Vol. 88, March 10, 2008, No. 10, pp. 35) [8836], [13078], [24637], [25268], [31958], [35218], [39480], [42280]
"Why Is It So Hard To Find Good People? The Problem Might Be You' in Inc. (Vol. 33, November 2011, No. 9, pp. 100) [30326], [35524], [35974]
"Why It Pays to be in the Boardroom" in Globe & Mail (January 16, 2006, pp. B1) [8837], [13079], [38570]
"Why LinkedIn is the Social Network that Will Never Die" in Advertising Age (Vol. 81, December 6, 2010, No. 43, pp. 2) [22484], [25701], [28935], [33048]
"Why-Max?' in Canadian Business (Vol. 81, July 22, 2008, No. 12-13, pp. 19) [3832], [11923], [21252], [25702], [35219], [44588]
"Why Men Still Get More Promotions Than Women' in Harvard Business Review (Vol. 88, September 2010, No. 9, pp. 80) [35975], [38571], [47412]
"Why Mumbai at 1PM is the Center of the Business World' in Harvard Business Review (Vol. 88, October 2010, No. 10, pp. 38) [22485], [22634], [36876], [46544]
"Why Nestle Should Sell Alcon" in Barron's (Vol. 88, March 17, 2008, No. 11, pp. M12) [21719], [25703], [39481], [42281]
"Why Oil Fell, and How It May Rise" in Globe & Mail (January 18, 2007, pp. B2) [33049], [44118]
"Why the Rally Should Keep Rolling..for Now" in Barron's (Vol. 89, July 27, 2009, No. 30, pp. M3) [8838], [13080], [27873], [31959], [34052]
"Why the Rout in Financials Isn't Over" in Barron's (Vol. 88, June 30, 2008, No. 26, pp. 23) [8839], [13081], [23617], [31960]
"Why Some Get Shaften By Google Pricing" in Advertising Age (Vol. 79, July 14, 2008, No. 7, pp. 3) [636], [8001], [11924], [21253], [28936], [35220], [40510]
Why Study Business?: Skills For the 21st Century [30372]
Why Value Diversity? [40937]
Why We Want You to be Rich: Two Men - One Message [30327], [41041]
"Why We'll Never Escape Facebook" in Canadian Business (Vol. 83, June 15, 2010, No. 10, pp. 28) [23618], [28937]
"Why WestJet's Culture Guru Chooses to Fly Under the Radar' in Globe & Mail (January 22, 2007, pp. B1) [8840], [13082]
"Why Women Blog and What They Read" in Marketing to Women (Vol. 22, July 2009, No. 7, pp. 8) [2172], [11925], [15375], [21254], [22486], [40511]
Why Work Sucks and How To Fix It [29190], [38572]
"Why You Aren't Buying Venezuelan Chocolate. " in Harvard Business Review (Vol. 88, December 2010, No. 12, pp. 25) [11197], [36877], [40512]
"Why You Need a New-Media 'Ringmaster'" in Harvard Business Review (Vol. 88, December 2010, No. 12, pp. 78) [637], [14015], [28938], [40513], [43686]
"Wi-Fi Finds Its Way Despite Nixed Plan for Free System" in Crain's Cleveland Business (Vol. 28, November 12, 2007, No. 45, pp. 3) [11926], [22487], [22635], [33463], [35221]
"Wi-Fi On Steroids: Will WiMAX Provide the Juice For Souped-Up Connections?' in Black Enterprise (November 2007) [11927], [28939], [35222]
Wichita Area Chamber of Commerce (WACC) [52200]
Wichita Falls Board of Commerce and Industry [58521]
Wichita Genealogical Society Library [9568]
Wichita State University - Center for Entrepreneurship [52215]
Wichita State University - College of Education Technology Center [52025]
Wichita Technology Corporation [52212]
Wickenburg Chamber of Commerce [47974]
Widener University Small Business Development Center [56922]
"Wielding a Big Ax" in Barron's (Vol. 89, July 13, 2009, No. 28, pp. 26) [6670], [8841], [13083], [31962]
Wienerschnitzel/Tastee-Freez [10986], [18279]
Donald Wigal [2215]
"The Wiki-Powered Workplace" in Workforce Management (Vol. 88, November 16, 2009, No. 12, pp. 8) [22488], [35223], [38573]
Wikinomics: How Mass Collaboration Changes Everything [11928], [28940]; [33050], [42282]
"Wikinomics: The Sequel" in Business Strategy Review (Vol. 21, Summer 2010, No. 2, pp. 64) [2173], [28941]; [2174], [27874], [28942], [42283], [45815]
Wilbur Sings the Classics [4004]
Wilburton Chamber of Commerce [56608]
Wild Bird Center [15806]

Wild Birds Unlimited Inc. [15807]
"Wild-Goose Chaser" in Entrepreneur (Vol. 37, September 2009, No. 9, pp. 96) [9673], [27875], [32267], [44589]
"The Wild West" in Canadian Business (Vol. 80, January 15, 2007, No. 2, pp. 57) [13084], [34053]
Wildomar Chamber of Commerce [49122]
John Wiley and Sons Information Center [2233]
Wilkes Chamber of Commerce [55840]
Wilkes University Small Business Development Center [56923]
Wilkinsburg Chamber of Commerce [57269]
"Will Call Center Servicing Solve Labor's Customer Satisfaction Problems?' in WorkingUSA (Vol. 11, September 2008, No. 3, pp. 383) [26572], [46933]
Will County Center for Economic Development (CED) [51372]
Will County Chamber of Commerce [51372]
"Will Focus on Business Continue?' in Baltimore Business Journal (Vol. 28, November 5, 2010, No. 26, pp. 1) [24092], [25704], [33051], [33386], [34054]
"Will the Force Be With Salesforce?' in Barron's (Vol. 88, March 24, 2008, No. 12, pp. 20) [3643], [8842], [11929], [13085], [19021], [21255], [25705], [31963], [45240]
"Will Home Buyers Pay for Green Features?' in Contractor (Vol. 56, October 2009, No. 10, pp. 70) [5560], [7349], [17094], [30860], [45816]
Will It Float [34174]
"Will mCommerce Make Black Friday Green?' in Retail Merchandiser (Vol. 51, September-October 2011, No. 5, pp. 8) [3833], [5005], [28943], [43257], [43687], [44119]
"Will Small Business be Stimulated' in Entrepreneur (Vol. 37, July 2009, No. 7, pp. 18) [27876], [33052], [33387], [45817]
"Will Work for Equity' in Inc. (March 2008, pp. 50, 52) [21848], [35224], [42284], [44590], [47108]
Will Work for Fun: 3 Simple Steps for Turning Any Hobby or Interest into Cash [5954], [6090]
"Will Workers Be Left To Build It Here?' in Boston Business Journal (Vol. 31, June 3, 2011, No. 19, pp. 1) [5561], [35976], [39482], [45818]
Willamette Management Associates Library [8966], [19771]
Willamette SCORE [56697]
Willapa Harbor Chamber of Commerce (RCC) [59318]
Willard Area Chamber of Commerce [56350]
Willcox Chamber of Commerce and Agriculture (WCCA) [47975]
"William Barr III; President, Co-Founder, Universal Windows Direct, 33' in Crain's Cleveland Business (November 19, 2007) [23619], [30328], [39483], [43688]
William Blades L.L.C. [40654], [43772]
William Blair Capital Partners [51424]
William Paterson University Small Business Development Center [54646]
Ralph E. Williams & Associates [21790]
Williams College - Center for Development Economics (CDE) [27956]
Williams College Center for Environmental Studies - Matt Cole Memorial Library [7427], [7738]
Williams College - Chapin Library [4590]
Williams Fresh Cafe Inc. [4326]
Williams-Grand Canyon Chamber of Commerce (WGCCC) [47976]
Horace Williams [40953]
"Williams-Sonoma Beats Expectations in Q1" in Home Textiles Today (Vol. 31, May 24, 2011, No. 13, pp. 2) [10416], [10487], [43258]
Williamsburg Area Chamber of Commerce [58932]
Williamsburg (Brooklyn) Minority Business Development Center - Opportunity Development Association (ODA) [55388]
Williamsburg Chamber of Commerce [51993]
Williamsburg County Chamber of Commerce [57536]
Williamsburg HomeTown Chamber of Commerce [57536]
Williamson County - Franklin Chamber of Commerce [57802]
Williamson County Magazine [57803]
Williamson Imagineering [37226]
Williamsport-Lycoming Chamber of Commerce [57270]
Williamston Area Chamber of Commerce [53466]
Williamstown Board of Trade [52987]
Williamstown Chamber of Commerce [52987]
Williston Area Chamber of Commerce [50338]
Williston Area Chamber of Commerce (WACC) [55933]
Williston Park Chamber of Commerce [55136]
Willits Chamber of Commerce (WCC) [49123]
Willkie Farr & Gallagher Library [7774]
Willmar Lakes Area Chamber of Commerce (WLACC) [53761]

Willoughby Area Chamber of Commerce (WACC) **[56351]**
Willow Chamber of Commerce **[47822]**
Willow Creek Chamber of Commerce **[49124]**
Willowbrook - Burr Ridge Chamber of Commerce and Industry **[51373]**
Willows Area Chamber of Commerce **[49125]**
Wills Point Chamber of Commerce **[58522]**
Willy Dog **[5112]**
Wilmette Chamber of Commerce (WCC) **[51374]**
Wilmette Chamber Headline News **[51375]**
Wilmington Board of Trade [49820]
Wilmington Business Directory **[52988]**
Wilmington Chamber of Commerce **[49126]**; **[51376]**; **[52989]**
Wilmington - Clinton County Chamber of Commerce (WCCCC) **[56352]**
Wilmington Minority Business Enterprise Office **[49832]**
Wilmington Small Business Development Center **[49807]**
Wilson Art Index [4556], [15269]
Wilson Business Periodicals Index [4073], [33097]
Wilson Chamber of Commerce (WCC) **[55841]**
Wilson Community College - Small Business Center **[55873]**
H.W. Wilson Co. **[55538]**
Steve Wilson and Co. **[29284]**
Wilson Humanities Full Text [6071]
Wilson Library Literature & Information Science Full Text [11249], [19197]
Wilsonville Chamber of Commerce **[56868]**
Wilsonville Community and Business Directory **[56869]**
Wilton Appreciation Series 100—Grades K-4 **[4005]**
Wilton Chamber of Commerce **[49764]**
Wilton Chamber of Commerce (WACC) **[51994]**
Wimberley Chamber of Commerce **[58523]**
Wimberley Chamber of Commerce and Visitor's Center **[58523]**
Wimpy's Diner Inc. **[18280]**
Win Government Contracts for Your Small Business **[33464]**
WIN Home Inspection **[2593]**
"The WIN Library" in Women In Business (Vol. 61, August-September 2009, No. 4, pp. 36) **[28390]**, **[44894]**, **[47413]**
Win-net-work **[51377]**
Win-Win Negotiations Training (Onsite) **[37754]**
"Winburn's Big Idea" in Business Courier (Vol. 27, October 8, 2010, No. 23, pp. 1) **[23620]**, **[25706]**, **[33388]**, **[34055]**, **[35525]**, **[35977]**
Winchester Area Chamber of Commerce **[51740]**
Winchester Chamber of Commerce (WCC) **[52990]**
Winchester-Clark County Chamber of Commerce **[52388]**
Wind Energy Weekly **[7367]**, **[19129]**, **[30876]**
"Wind Gets Knocked Out of Energy Farm Plan" in Buffalo News (September 28, 2011) **[7350]**, **[7712]**, **[30861]**
Wind Point Partners (Chicago) **[51425]**
"Wind Point Partners Closes Southfield HQ" in Crain's Detroit Business (Vol. 26, January 18, 2010, No. 3, pp. 18) **[8843]**, **[13086]**, **[31964]**
Windham Region Chamber of Commerce **[49674]**
Windom Area Chamber of Commerce and Visitors Bureau (WACCVB) **[53762]**
Windom Area Chamber of Commerce [53762]
Window Brigade **[2682]**
Window Covering Manufacturers Association (WCMA) **[2024]**, **[14253]**
Window and Door Manufacturers Association (WDMA) **[3416]**
Window Gang **[16313]**
Window Genie **[2683]**, **[16314]**
Window King **[2684]**
Window on Woodstock **[58786]**
Windows to a View: Chris Reis **[1371]**
Windows Vista: A Hands-On Introduction (Onsite) **[28103]**, **[45076]**
Windsor Area Chamber of Commerce **[54170]**
Windsor/Bertie County Chamber of Commerce **[55842]**
Windsor Chamber of Commerce (WCC) **[49606]**; **[49765]**
Windsor Chamber of Commerce Newsletter **[49607]**
Windsor Chamber of Commerce and Visitors Center (WCC) **[49127]**
Windsor Chamber of Commerce [49127]
Windsor County Area Chamber of Commerce **[55842]**
Windsor Locks Chamber of Commerce (WLCC) **[49766]**
Windsor Press Inc. **[57353]**
Windstar Wildlife Garden Weekly **[7368]**, **[34076]**
"Windstream Expands Business Service Into Monroe" in Marketing Weekly News (January 23, 2010, pp. 77) **[3058]**, **[18512]**, **[22489]**, **[23621]**
Windward Ventures (Thousand Oaks) **[49346]**
Wine & Spirits Buying Guide [19265]
The Wine Advocate **[19262]**

Wine and Spirits Wholesalers of America, Inc. [13569]
Wine Enthusiast Magazine **[19263]**
Wine Investment for Portfolio Diversification: How Investing in Wine Can Yield Greater Returns than Stocks and Bonds [13087], [19247], [31965]
Wine Lovers, Inc. **[19291]**
Wine News **[19264]**
Wine Not Custom Wineries **[19292]**
Wine On Line **[19295]**
"The Wine Spectator" in Business Courier (Vol. 27, November 26, 2010, No. 30, pp. 1) **[19248]**, **[26801]**, **[36878]**, **[43259]**
Wine & Spirits Magazine **[19265]**
Wine and Spirits Wholesalers of America **[13569]**
Wine and Spirits Wholesalers of America Convention and Exposition **[2477]**
Wines & Vines **[19266]**
WineStyles Inc. **[19293]**
Winfield Area Chamber of Commerce (WACC) **[52201]**
Winfield Area Chamber of Commerce [47745]
Winfield Chamber of Commerce (WCC) **[47745]**; **[51378]**
Winfield STUFF! **[51379]**
"Wing and a Prayer" in Canadian Business (Vol. 81, November 10, 2008, No. 19, pp. 70) **[27877]**, **[39484]**
Wing Zone **[18281]**
Wingate Partners, L.P. **[58573]**
Winger's Grill & Bar **[18282]**
Wings **[15516]**
Wings to Go **[18283]**
Wingstop **[18284]**
WinMDR--Medical Device Register on Disk **[14244]**
Winn Chamber of Commerce (WCC) **[52509]**
Winnemucca Nevada Small Business Development Center **[54464]**
Winner Area Chamber of Commerce (WACC) **[57604]**
"Winner: Caparo Group Plc" in Crain's Detroit Business (Vol. 24, March 24, 2008, No. 12, pp. 12) **[36879]**, **[38574]**, **[39485]**, **[42285]**
Winner Chamber of Commerce [57604]
"Winner Nonprofit, Hospitals" in Crain's Detroit Business (Vol. 25, June 22, 2009, No. 25, pp. E002) **[34473]**, **[46024]**
"Winner: Nonprofit, Human Services" in Crain's Detroit Business (Vol. 25, June 22, 2009, No. 25, pp. E002) **[23622]**, **[46025]**
"Winner: Private Company, $100M-$1B" in Crain's Detroit Business (Vol. 25, June 22, 2009, No. 25, pp. E004) **[6978]**, **[7799]**
"Winner: Private Company, Less Than $100M" in Crain's Detroit Business (Vol. 25, June 22, 2009, No. 25) **[21256]**, **[25919]**, **[26573]**, **[28944]**
Winner Take All: How Competitiveness Shapes the Fate of Nations **[11930]**, **[25707]**, **[28945]**, **[33053]**, **[34056]**, **[35225]**, **[36880]**, **[45819]**
Winner Takes All: Steve Wynn, Kirk Kerkorian, Gary Loveman, and the Race to Own Vegas **[9409]**, **[25708]**, **[30329]**
"The Winner's Circle" in Hispanic Business (Vol. 30, April 2008, No. 4, pp. 20) **[23623]**, **[36940]**, **[38575]**
"Winners and Losers" in Crain's Detroit Business (Vol. 25, June 22, 2009, No. 25, pp. 18) **[22004]**, **[27878]**, **[38576]**
Winnetka Chamber of Commerce (WCC) **[51380]**
Winning! **[30330]**, **[33054]**, **[9415]**
Winning Entrepreneurial Style **[38641]**
"Winning Gold" in The Business Journal-Milwaukee (Vol. 25, August 8, 2008, No. 46, pp. A1) **[7713]**, **[11198]**, **[19483]**, **[25269]**, **[25920]**, **[30862]**, **[36881]**
"Winning With Women" in Marketing to Women (Vol. 22, August 2009, No. 8, pp. 6) **[5778]**, **[40514]**
Winnsboro Area Chamber of Commerce **[58524]**
Winnsboro - Franklin Parish Chamber of Commerce (WFPCC) **[52510]**
Winnsboro-Franklin Chamber of Commerce [52510]
Winona Area Chamber of Commerce (WACC) **[53763]**
Winslow Chamber of Commerce **[47977]**
Winston Dillard Area Chamber of Commerce **[56870]**
Winston-Salem Chamber of Commerce **[55711]**
Steven Winter Associates, Inc. Library **[16576]**
Winter Harbor Chamber of Commerce [52627]
Winter Harbor/Couldsboro/Schoodic Peninsula Chamber of Commerce [52627]
Winter Haven Chamber of Commerce [50147]
The Winter Olympia Fine Art and Antiques Fair **[1142]**, **[1372]**, **[1416]**
Winter Park Chamber of Commerce **[50339]**
Winter Park-Fraser Valley Chamber of Commerce (WPFVCC) **[49608]**
Winters District Chamber of Commerce **[49128]**
Winters Guide to Provincetown **[52991]**
Winterset Area Chamber of Commerce **[51922]**
Winthrop Area Chamber of Commerce **[53764]**
Winthrop Chamber of Commerce **[52992]**; **[59319]**

Winthrop University - Small Business Development Center Library **[33128]**
Winthrop Washington Business Directory **[59320]**
Wireless **[3852]**
Wireless Business & Technology **[3850]**
Wireless Cellular / WMAX **[3851]**
Wireless Communications **[3840]**
"Wireless: Full Service" in Entrepreneur (Vol. 35, October 2007, No. 10, pp. 60) **[3834]**, **[11931]**, **[28946]**, **[35226]**, **[41458]**
"A Wireless Makes 8 Store-In-Store Kiosk Acquisitions" in Wireless News (October 16, 2010) **[1196]**, **[3835]**, **[5779]**, **[13334]**, **[42286]**, **[43260]**
"Wireless Provider's Star Grows $283 Million Brighter" in Hispanic Business (July-August 2007, pp. 60) **[3836]**, **[11932]**, **[23624]**, **[35227]**
Wireless Satellite & Broadcasting **[18343]**
Wireless Telecom **[3675]**
Wireless Toyz **[6945]**
Wireless Week **[5781]**, **[15593]**
Wirth Business Credit **[47160]**
"Wirtz Partners With California Liquor Wholesaler To Expand Reach" in Chicago Tribune (December 17, 2008) **[13597]**, **[19249]**, **[23625]**, **[26802]**, **[42287]**
Wisconsin Consumer Protection Office [59461]
Wisconsin Department of Agriculture, Trade and Consumer Protection (DATCP) **[59461]**
Wisconsin Department of Commerce - Bureau of Minority Business Development **[59770]**
Wisconsin Department of Commerce - Business Development Division **[59462]**
Wisconsin Department of Commerce - Entrepreneurs/ Start-ups **[59463]**
Wisconsin Department of Commerce - International Division **[59464]**
Wisconsin Department of Commerce - Women-Owned Business Enterprises **[59771]**
Wisconsin Department of Agriculture, Trade, and Consumer Protection - Marketing Div. [59461]
Wisconsin Financing Alternatives **[59792]**
Wisconsin HIV/STD/Hepatitis Information & Referral Center **[34642]**
Wisconsin Literacy Resource Network **[20754]**
Wisconsin Machine Tool Show [10150], [39515]
Wisconsin Manufacturers and Commerce (WMC) **[59766]**
Wisconsin Manufacturing & Technology Show **[10150]**, **[39515]**
Wisconsin Medical Directory **[34474]**
Wisconsin Minority Business Opportunity Center **[59772]**
Wisconsin Minority Business Resource Directory **[59793]**
Wisconsin Procurement Institute (WPI) - Regional PTAC **[59778]**
Wisconsin Procurement Technical Assistance Center - American Indian Chamber of Commerce of Wisconsin - Regional PTAC **[59779]**
Wisconsin Procurement Technical Assistance Center - Metropolitan Milwaukee Association of Commerce (MMAC) - Regional PTAC **[59780]**
Wisconsin Safety and Health Congress/Exposition **[47512]**
Wisconsin Small Business Development Center - Lead Office (WSBDC) **[59460]**
Wisconsin Solid Wastes Recycling Authority [60036]
Wisconsin Veterinary Medical Association Annual Convention **[1089]**
The Wisdom of Crowds: Why the Many Are Smarter Than the Few and How Collective Wisdom Shapes Business, Economies, Societies and Nations **[27879]**, **[33055]**
"Wisdom from the Mountaintops" in Canadian Business (Vol. 83, October 12, 2010, No. 17, pp. 91) **[24950]**, **[38577]**
Wise Counsel Press L.L.C. **[55539]**
Wise County Chamber of Commerce **[59005]**
"Wise Guy: Get In Good" in Entrepreneur (Vol. 35, October 2007, No. 10, pp. 46) **[22490]**, **[30331]**, **[42538]**
The Wisecracker **[50340]**
"With Algoma Steel Gone, Is Stelco Next?" in Globe & Mail (April 16, 2007, pp. B1) **[39486]**, **[42288]**
"With Building Plans in Flux, County Could Sell Key Site" in Crain's Cleveland Business (Vol. 28, October 8, 2007, No. 40, pp. 1) **[5562]**, **[17095]**, **[17541]**
"With the Indian Market, You Take the Good With the Bad" in Globe & Mail (March 23, 2007, pp. B11) **[13088]**, **[27880]**
"With Mine Approval, Crystallex's Value as Target Seen on Rise" in Globe & Mail (March 28, 2006, pp. B3) **[8844]**, **[13089]**, **[34057]**
"With New Listings, Business Brokers See Hope" in Business Courier (Vol. 27, September 3, 2010, No. 18, pp. 1) **[2705]**, **[25352]**, **[25805]**, **[27881]**, **[43689]**, **[44206]**

Xerox Corporation - Wilsonville Library [4923]
"Xerox Diverts Waste from Landfills" in Canadian
Electronics (Vol. 23, February 2008, No. 1, pp. 1)
[5863], [17722], [30864], [39489]
"Xerox's Former CEO On Why Succession Shouldn't Be
a Horse Race" in Harvard Business Review (Vol. 88,
October 2010, No. 10, pp. 47) [24640], [25710],
[38593]
(X)HTML and CSS I (Onsite) [30401]
(X)HTML and CSS II (Onsite) [30402]
(X)HTML and CSS III (Onsite) [30403]
XL Global Services Corporate Library [11515]
Xlibris Corp. [57354]
Xlibris Corporation [57354]
"XM Burning Through Cash to Catch Sirius" in Globe &
Mail (April 17, 2007, pp. B5) [641], [16736], [35233],
[40528]
"XM Mulls Betting the Bank in Competitive Game of
Subscriber Growth" in Globe & Mail (March 18, 2006,
pp. B3) [16737], [25711], [35234], [40529], [44594]
"XM and Sirius Satellite Radio Face Up to Their Losses
and Decide to Get Hitched" in Globe & Mail (February
20, 2007, pp. B17) [16738], [35235], [42291]
XML Development I (Onsite) [45078]
XML Development II (Onsite) [45079]
XML Development III (Onsite) [45080]
XML Web Services (Onsite) [22254], [45081]
Xpress [53767]
"Xstrata and CAW Get Tentative Deal" in Globe & Mail
(February 2, 2007, pp. B3) [14970], [39490], [46936]
"Xstrata's Takeover Bid Comes Up Short in
Shareholder's Eyes" in Globe & Mail (March 27, 2007,
pp. B16) [8850], [13096], [42292]
"Xtium Has Its Head in the Clouds" in Philadelphia Busi-
ness Journal (Vol. 30, September 23, 2011, No. 32, pp.
1) [4881], [5008], [5041], [11937], [28951], [44595],
[47111]

Y

"The Y Factor" in Entrepreneur (Vol. 35, November 2007,
No. 11, pp. 58) [32478], [34730], [46971]
Ya Gotta Wanna [29194], [30345], [33065]
Yachats Area Chamber of Commerce (YACC) [56873]
Yacht and Brokerage Show in Miami Beach [13970]
Yacht and Brokerage Show [13970]
Yacht Racing and Cruising [13952]
Yachting Magazine [13956]
Yachting: The Best of Today's Boats & Gear [13956]
Yadkin County Chamber of Commerce [55843]
Yadkin Valley Chamber of Commerce [55844]
"The Yahoo Family Tree" in Conde Nast Portfolio (Vol. 2,
June 2008, No. 6, pp. 34) [11938], [21260], [28952],
[35236], [42293]
"Yahoo! - Microsoft Pact: Alive Again?" in Barron's (Vol.
89, July 27, 2009, No. 30, pp. 8) [642], [8851],
[11939], [13097], [28953], [31975], [35237], [40530],
[42294]
Yakety Yak Wireless [3857]
Yakima County Development Associations - Washington
Procurement Technical Assistance Center [59350]
Yakima Small Business Development Center [59071]
Yakima Valley SCORE [59083]
Yale University - Arts Library - Special Collections
[2256], [3229], [20816]
Yale University - Arts of the Book Collection (Arts
Library). [2256], [3229], [20816]
Yale University - Drama Collection [5947]
The Yamamoto Forecast [13150]
"Yamana's Golden Boy" in Canadian Business (Vol. 80,
November 19, 2007, No. 23, pp. 49) [23637], [30346]
"Yamasaki Lays Off Last of U.S. Workers, to Vacate
World Headquarters in Troy" in Crain's Detroit Busi-
ness (Jan. 11, 2010) [17546], [27892]
"Yamasaki Lays Off Last of U.S. Workers, to Vacate
World Headquarters in Troy" in Crain's Detroit Busi-
ness (Vol. 26, January 11, 2010) [17547], [27893]
"Yammer Gets Serious" in Inc. (Volume 32, December
2010, No. 10, pp. 58) [3645], [19023], [22494],
[28954], [44596], [45242]
Yancey County/Burnsville Chamber of Commerce
[55845]
Yancey County Business Directory [55846]
William J. Yang & Associates [3091]
Yankee Tek Ventures [53075]
Yankton Area Chamber of Commerce (YACC) [57605]
Yankton Chamber News [57606]
Yankton Small Business Development Center [57557]
"Yao Ming Courts China's Wine Boom" in Wall Street
Journal Eastern Edition (November 28, 2011, pp. B4)
[19250], [36891], [45828]
Yard & Garden [13490]
Yard and Garden: Market Insights for Equipment Dealers
[9821]

The Yarmouth Chamber [52635]
Yarmouth Chamber of Commerce [52636]
"Yates Helps Turn Log Home Green" in Contractor (Vol.
56, December 2009, No. 12, pp. 40) [880], [7351],
[7714], [19126], [30865], [38594]
"Yates Helps Turn Log Home Green" in Contractor (Vol.
56, November 2009, No. 11, pp. 1) [881], [5563],
[30866]
"Yates Turns Log Home Green - Part Three" in Contrac-
tor (Vol. 57, January 2010, No. 1, pp. 5) [882], [7352],
[7715], [19127], [30867]
Yaya's Flame Broiled Chicken [18287]
Ybor City Chamber of Commerce [50341]
"A Year After Fiorina's Exit, Hurd Makes His Mark" in
Globe & Mail (February 8, 2006, pp. B9) [23638],
[24641], [25271]
"Year-End Tax Tips" in Hawaii Business (Vol. 53,
December 2007, No. 6, pp. 136) [11450], [19683],
[27894], [33066], [36249], [45829], [46445]
Year in Review [49928]
Yeast [44073]
The Yellow Balloon [10105]
Yellow Springs Chamber of Commerce [56355]
Yellville Area Chamber of Commerce [48120]
Yellville Chamber of Commerce [48120]
Yelm Area Chamber of Commerce [59322]
"Yes, No, and Somewhat Likely: Survey the World with
Web Polls" in Inc. (October 2007, pp. 58-59) [3646],
[19024], [19528], [40531], [40965], [42900], [45243]
Yeung's Lotus Express Franchise Corp. [18288]
YMCA Resident Camp Directory [3266]
Yoakum Area Chamber of Commerce (YACC) [58529]
Yoakum Chamber of Commerce [58529]
"YoCream" in Ice Cream Reporter (Vol. 23, September
20, 2010, No. 10, pp. 6) [8852], [10934], [13098],
[23639], [31976], [43692]
Yoga to Go with Misty Carey Volume 2: Strength [16011]
Yoga to Go with Misty Carey Volume 3: Health [16012]
Yogen Fruz [10987]
Yogi Bear's Jellystone Park Camp-Resorts [3274],
[10824]
"Yogun Fruz Adds First Location in Southern New York
State" in Ice Cream Reporter (Vol. 23, September 20,
2010, No. 10, pp. 2) [10248], [10296], [10935],
[23640], [32269]
Yogurt & Such Cafe [18289]
"Yogurtini" in Ice Cream Reporter (Vol. 23, September
20, 2010, No. 10, pp. 7) [10936], [23641]
Yonkers Chamber of Commerce [55384]
Yorba Linda Chamber of Commerce (YLCC) [49132]
York Area Chamber of Commerce [57271]
York County Chamber of Commerce [57271]
York County Regional Chamber of Commerce [57537]
York Economic Outlook [57272]
York Publishing Co. [56425]
York Small Business Development Center [55033]
York Technical College - Anne Springs Close Library
[41529]
York University - Centre for Research in Work and
Society [14175], [46952]
York University - Glendon Campus Counselling & Career
Centre [3411]
Yorktown Chamber of Commerce [58530]
Yorkville Area Chamber of Commerce [51384]
"You Are What They Click" in Entrepreneur (Vol. 37, July
2009, No. 7, pp. 43) [11940], [15358], [21261],
[28955], [35528]
"You Better Shop Around: Four Steps to Getting the Best
Deal On a Home Loan" in Black Enterprise (Vol. 40,
July 2010, No. 12, pp. 78) [14516], [17098], [37542]
You Can Do It Too: The 20 Essential Things Every Bud-
ding Entrepreneur Should Know [29435], [32479]
"You Can Rebuild It" in Entrepreneur (Vol. 37, July 2009,
No. 7, pp. 28) [26575], [27895], [30347], [40532]
"You Can't Beat Habit" in Entrepreneur (Vol. 37, July
2009, No. 7, pp. 61) [26576], [40533], [43693]
"You Can't Fix It If You Don't Face It!" in Indoor Comfort
Marketing (Vol. 70, June 2011, No. 6, pp. 14) [883],
[26577]
"You Have to Lead From Everywhere" in Harvard Busi-
ness Review (Vol. 88, November 2010, No. 11, pp. 76)
[38595], [42540], [42676]
"You Lost Me at Hello" in Entrepreneur (Vol. 35,
November 2007, No. 11, pp. 136) [643], [40534]
You Need to be a Little Bit Crazy: The Truth about Start-
ing and Growing Your Business [29436], [32480]
You Need To Be a Little Crazy [29437], [32481]
"You Won't Go Broke Filling Up On These Stocks" in
Barron's (Vol. 88, July 14, 2008, No. 28, pp. 38)
[8853], [13099], [17099], [17548], [23642], [31977],
[34061], [36892], [44597]
"Young Adult, Childless May Help Fuel Post-Recession
Rebound" in Pet Product News (Vol. 64, November
2010, No. 11, pp. 4) [15742], [27896], [40535],
[43265], [43694]

"Young Adults Choose to go Without Health Insurance" in
Business Review, Albany New York (Vol. 34, November
30, 2007, No. 35, pp. 1) [11451], [36250], [45830]
Young & Associates Inc. [14062], [44962]
Young Bucks: How to Raise a Future Millionaire [13100],
[30348], [31978], [47595]
Young Children: The Journal of the National Association
for the Education of Young Children [3951]
"Young Entrepreneur Gets Some Recognition and Some
Help for College" in Philadelphia Inquirer (August 30,
2010) [1533], [15359], [28399], [47596]
"Young Entrepreneur's Business Plan? An Ice Cream
Boat? Really Floats: Maine at Work" in Portland Press
Herald (August 9, 2010) [10838], [24642], [47597]
Young Entrepreneurs' Organization [44794], [47575]
"Young Giants" in Canadian Business (Vol. 79, August
14, 2006, No. 16-17, pp. 47) [30349], [36941],
[38596], [39491], [44598]
"Young-Kee Kim; Deputy Director, Fermi National Ac-
celerator Laboratory" in Crain's Chicago Business (Vol.
31, May 5, 2008, No. 18) [25712], [30350], [33389],
[35238], [38597], [43993]
Young Men's Business Association [51293]
"Young Millionaires" in Entrepreneur (Vol. 35, October
2007, No. 10, pp. 76) [24643], [30351], [47598]
Young Naturalists' Circle (YNC) [7076]
"Young People Speak Out On Credit Union Board
Involvement" in Credit Union Times (Vol. 21, July 14,
2010, No. 27, pp. 20) [8854], [13101], [31979]
Young Presidents' Organization (YPO) [47577]
Young Rembrandts - The Power Of Drawing [28481]
Young Women's Investment Association of New York -
Young Women's Financial Association of New York
[8034]
Youngstown Business Incubator [56407]
Youngstown SCORE [55985]
Youngstown/Warren Regional Chamber of Commerce
[56356]
Yountville Chamber of Commerce [49133]
"Your 2010 Windfall" in Small Business Opportunities
(July 2010) [8855], [13102], [31980]
"Your Annual Business Tune-Up" in Business Week
(December 28, 2006) [11941], [21262], [25272],
[30352]
Your Bay Area Business Connection [56874]
"Your Big Give" in Small Business Opportunities
(September 2008) [644], [23643], [40536], [42541],
[42677], [46028]
"Your Booming Business: How You Can Align Sales and
Marketing for Dynamic Growth" in Small Business Op-
portunities (Spring 2008) [2801], [23644], [24644],
[25922], [40537], [43695]
"Your Bottom Line: How To Bring In Dollars When Times
Are Tough" in Small Business Opportunities (November
2007) [22137], [27897], [40538]
Your Business [52995]
Your Business Connection [50642]; [57804]
Your Business Plan [56899]
Your Business, Your Future: How to Predict and Harness
Growth [23645], [30353]
Your Chamber Connection [54172]
Your Chamber at a Glance [52996]
Your Chamber Matters [57273]
Your Chamber News [53468]
Your Chamber Today [47824]
Your City Insider [49134]
Your Dog [1082], [15696]
"Your Exposure to Bear Stearns" in Barron's (Vol. 88,
March 17, 2008, No. 11, pp. 45) [8856], [13103],
[14517], [26352], [27898], [31981], [37543]
"Your First 100 Days on Your New Job" in Women In
Business (Vol. 63, Spring 2011, No. 1, pp. 28) [22495],
[29195], [35529], [35982], [38598]
Your First Business Plan: A Simple Question-and-Answer
Format Designed to Help You Write Your Own Plan
[23646], [23674], [32482]
Your First Year in Real Estate: Making the Transition
from Total Novice to Successful Professional [17100],
[17549], [25713], [28956], [40539]
Your Guide to Arranging Bank and Debt Financing for
Your Own Business in Canada [8857], [31982],
[37544]
Your Guide to Canadian Export Financing: Successful
Techniques for Financing Your Exports from Canada
[11200], [31983], [37545]
"Your Guide to Local Style Business" in Hawaii Business
(Vol. 53, December 2007, No. 6, pp. 36) [26578],
[27899], [33067], [44895], [45831]
Your Guide to Preparing a Plan to Raise Money for Your
Own Business [24645], [31984], [37546]
Your Idaho Business Plan [50731]
Your International Business Plan [56900]
Your Lawyer: An Owner's Manual [24097], [33068];
[24098]

CPSIA information can be obtained
at www.ICGtesting.com
Printed in the USA
FFOW040812140313
990FF